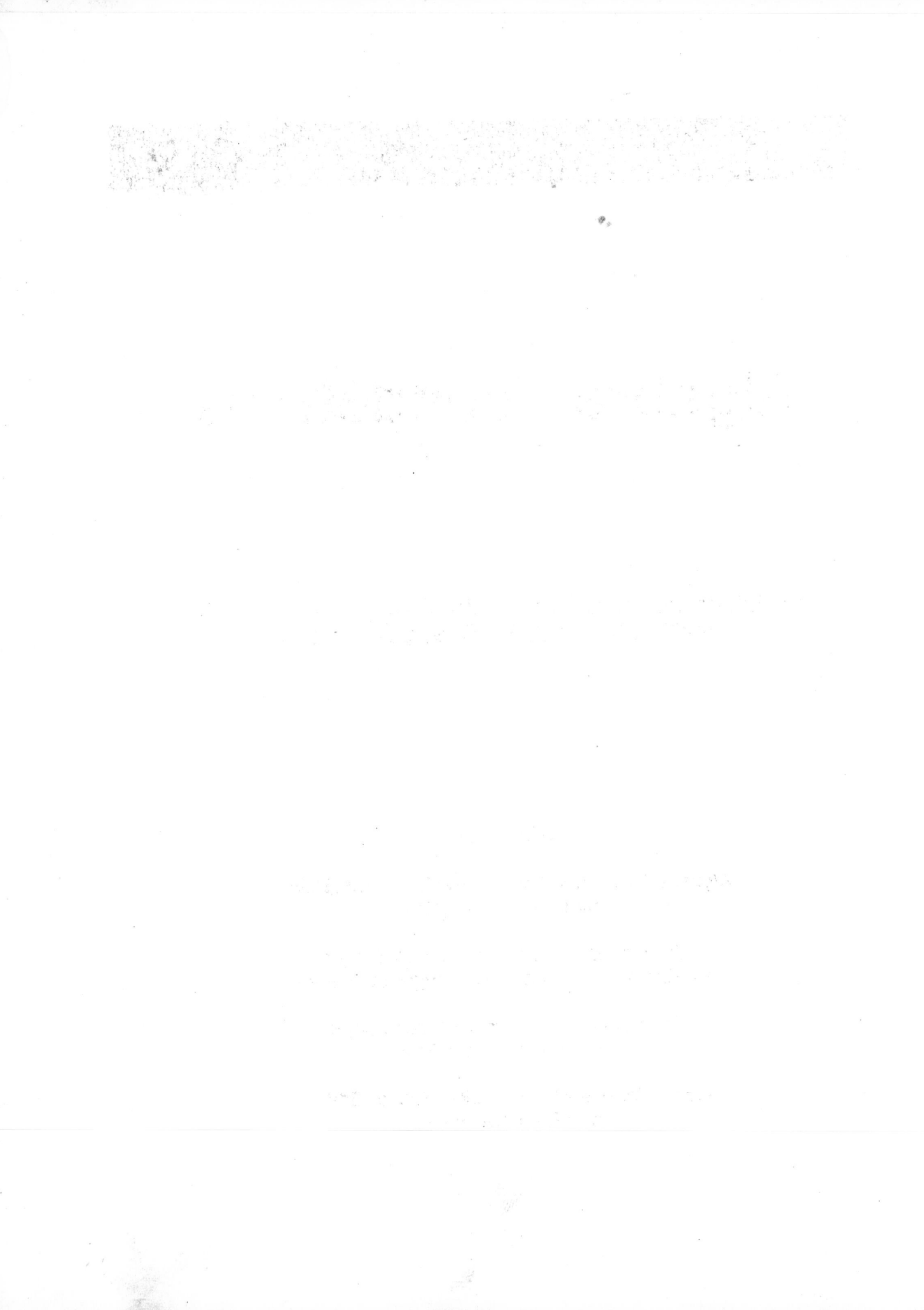

Contents

Taken from: *Basic College Mathematics,* Fourth Edition, by Elayn Martin-Gay

---

Taken from: *Basic College Mathematics,* Fourth Edition, by Elayn Martin-Gay

---

Taken from: *Basic College Mathematics,* Fourth Edition, by Elayn Martin-Gay

Taken from: *Basic College Mathematics,* Fourth Edition, by Elayn Martin-Gay

---

Taken from: *Basic College Mathematics,* Fourth Edition, by Elayn Martin-Gay

---

Taken from: *Basic College Mathematics,* Fourth Edition, by Elayn Martin-Gay

---

Taken from: *Basic College Mathematics,* Fourth Edition, by Elayn Martin-Gay

Taken from: *Introductory Algebra,* Fourth Edition, by Elayn Martin-Gay

Taken from: *Introductory Algebra,* Fourth Edition, by Elayn Martin-Gay

Taken from: *Introductory Algebra,* Fourth Edition, by Elayn Martin-Gay

Taken from: *Introductory Algebra,* Fourth Edition, by Elayn Martin-Gay and *Algebra: A Combined Approach,* Fourth Edition, by Elayn Martin-Gay

Taken from: *Introductory Algebra,* Fourth Edition, by Elayn Martin-Gay

Taken from: *Introductory Algebra,* Fourth Edition, by Elayn Martin-Gay

Taken from: *Introductory Algebra,* Fourth Edition, by Elayn Martin-Gay

---

Taken from: *Intermediate Algebra: A Graphing Approach,* Fourth Edition, by Elayn Martin-Gay and Margaret Greene

---

Taken from: *Intermediate Algebra: A Graphing Approach,* Fourth Edition, by Elayn Martin-Gay and Margaret Greene

---

Taken from: *Intermediate Algebra: A Graphing Approach,* Fourth Edition, by Elayn Martin-Gay and Margaret Greene

---

Taken from: *Intermediate Algebra: A Graphing Approach,* Fourth Edition, by Elayn Martin-Gay and Margaret Greene

Taken from: *Intermediate Algebra: A Graphing Approach,* Fourth Edition, by Elayn Martin-Gay and Margaret Greene

Taken from: *Intermediate Algebra: A Graphing Approach,* Fourth Edition, by Elayn Martin-Gay and Margaret Greene

The Whole Numbers

1

Whole numbers are the basic building blocks of mathematics. The whole numbers answer the question "How many?"

This chapter covers basic operations on whole numbers. Knowledge of these operations provides a good foundation on which to build further mathematical skills.

Sections

Check Your Progress

Alfred Nobel, 1833–1896, is probably best known for two major events in history. He was a Swedish chemist, engineer, weapons manufacturer, and the *inventor of dynamite*. In his later years, he became interested in peace and other social issues. In his will, he used his vast fortune to institute the *Nobel Prize*. These prizes are given in the fields of Physics, Chemistry, Literature, Physiology and Medicine, Economics, and Peace.

A person who receives the Nobel Prize earns a gold medal, such as the one shown. In Section 1.2, Example 13, we will see how whole numbers can be used to explore the countries of winners of the Nobel Prize.

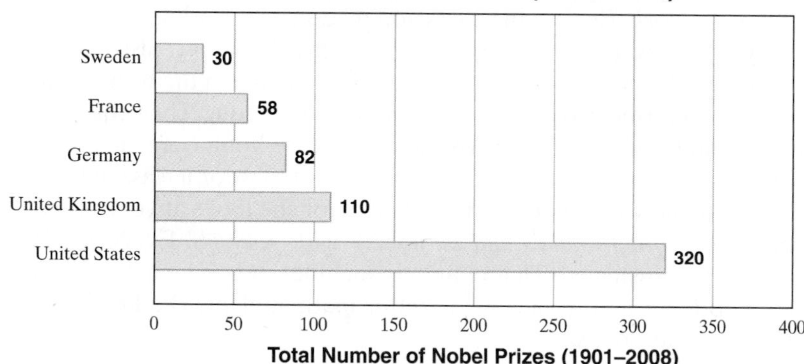

Source: Based on data from the official website of the Nobel Prize Committee

Objectives

A Get Ready for This Course.

B Understand Some General Tips for Success.

C Understand How to Use This Text.

D Get Help As Soon As You Need It.

E Learn How to Prepare for and Take an Exam.

F Develop Good Time Management.

1.1 TIPS FOR SUCCESS IN MATHEMATICS

Before reading this section, remember that your instructor is your best source of information. Please see your instructor for any additional help or information.

Objective A Getting Ready for This Course

Now that you have decided to take this course, remember that a *positive attitude* will make all the difference in the world. Your belief that you can succeed is just as important as your commitment to this course. Make sure you are ready for this course by having the time and positive attitude that it takes to succeed.

Next, make sure that you have scheduled your math course at a time that will give you the best chance for success. For example, if you are also working, you may want to check with your employer to make sure that your work hours will not conflict with your course schedule.

On the day of your first class period, double-check your schedule and allow yourself extra time to arrive on time in case of traffic problems or difficulty locating your classroom. Make sure that you bring at least your textbook, paper, and a writing instrument. Are you required to have a lab manual, graph paper, calculator, or some other supplies besides this text? If so, also bring this material with you.

Objective B General Tips for Success

Below are some general tips that will increase your chance for success in a mathematics class. Many of these tips will also help you in other courses you may be taking.

Exchange names and phone numbers or e-mail addresses with at least one other person in class. This contact person can be a great help if you miss an assignment or want to discuss math concepts or exercises that you find difficult.

Choose to attend all class periods. If possible, sit near the front of the classroom. This way, you will see and hear the presentation better. It may also be easier for you to participate in classroom activities.

MyMathLab® and MathXL®

If you are doing your homework online, you can work and re-work those exercises that you struggle with until you master them. Try working through all the assigned exercises twice before the due date.

Do your homework. You've probably heard the phrase "practice makes perfect" in relation to music and sports. It also applies to mathematics. You will find that the more time you spend solving mathematics exercises, the easier the process becomes. Be sure to schedule enough time to complete your assignments before the next due date assigned by your instructor.

MyMathLab® and MathXL®

If you are completing your homework online, it's important to work each exercise on paper before submitting the answer. That way, you can check your work and follow your steps to find and correct any mistakes.

Check your work. Review the steps you made while working a problem. Learn to check your answers in the original problems. You may also compare your answers with the "Answers to Selected Exercises" section in the back of the book. If you have made a mistake, try to figure out what went wrong. Then correct your mistake. If you can't find what went wrong, don't erase your work or throw it away. Bring your work to your instructor, a tutor in a math lab, or a classmate. It is easier for someone to find where you had trouble if he or she looks at your original work.

Learn from your mistakes and be patient with yourself. Everyone, even your instructor, makes mistakes. (That definitely includes me—Elayn Martin-Gay.) Use your errors to learn and to become a better math student. The key is finding and understanding your errors.

Was your mistake a careless one, or did you make it because you can't read your own math writing? If so, try to work more slowly or write more neatly and make a conscious effort to carefully check your work.

Did you make a mistake because you don't understand a concept? Take the time to review the concept or ask questions to better understand it.

Did you skip too many steps? Skipping steps or trying to do too many steps mentally may lead to preventable mistakes.

Know how to get help if you need it. It's all right to ask for help. In fact, it's a good idea to ask for help whenever there is something that you don't understand. Make sure you know when your instructor has office hours and how to find his or her office. Find out whether math tutoring services are available on your campus. Check on the hours, location, and requirements of the tutoring service.

Organize your class materials, including homework assignments, graded quizzes and tests, and notes from your class or lab. All of these items will make valuable references throughout your course and when studying for upcoming tests and the final exam. Make sure that you can locate these materials when you need them.

MyMathLab® and MathXL®

When assignments are turned in online, keep a hard copy of your complete written work. You will need to refer to your written work to be able to ask questions and to study for tests later.

Read your textbook before class. Reading a mathematics textbook is unlike reading a novel or a newspaper. Your pace will be much slower. It is helpful to have paper and a pencil with you when you read. Try to work out examples on your own as you encounter them in your text. You should also write down any questions that you want to ask in class. When you read a mathematics textbook, sometimes some of the information in a section will be unclear. But after you hear a lecture or watch a lecture video on that section, you will understand it much more easily than if you had not read your text beforehand.

Don't be afraid to ask questions. You are not the only person in class with questions. Other students are normally grateful that someone has spoken up.

Turn in assignments on time. This way you can be sure that you will not lose points for being late. Show every step of a problem and be neat and organized. Also be sure that you understand which problems are assigned for homework. If allowed, you can always double-check the assignment with another student in your class.

MyMathLab® and MathXL®

Be aware of assignments and due dates set by your instructor. Don't wait until the last minute to submit work online. Allow 6–8 hours before the deadline in case you have technology trouble.

Objective C Using This Text

There are many helpful resources that are available to you. It is important that you become familiar with and use these resources. They should increase your chances for success in this course.

- *Practice Exercises.* Each example in every section has a parallel Practice exercise. As you read a section, try each Practice exercise after you've finished the corresponding example. This "learn-by-doing" approach will help you grasp ideas before you move on to other concepts. Answers are at the bottom of the page.
- *Chapter Test Prep Videos.* These videos provide solutions to all of the Chapter Test exercises worked out by the author. This supplement is very helpful before a test or exam.
- *Interactive DVD Lecture Series.* Exercises marked with a are fully worked out by the author on the DVDs. The lecture series provides approximately 20 minutes of instruction per section.
- *Symbols at the Beginning of an Exercise Set.* If you need help with a particular section, the symbols listed at the beginning of each exercise set will remind you of the numerous supplements available.
- *Objectives.* The main section of exercises in each exercise set is referenced by an objective, such as A or B, and also an example(s). There is also often a section of exercises entitled "Mixed Practice," which is referenced by two or more objectives or sections. These are mixed exercises written to prepare you for your next exam. Use all of this referencing if you have trouble completing an assignment from the exercise set.
- *Icons (Symbols).* Make sure that you understand the meaning of the icons that are beside many exercises. tells you that the corresponding exercise may be viewed on the video segment that corresponds to that section. tells you that this exercise is a writing exercise in which you should answer in complete sentences. tells you that the exercise involves geometry.
- *Integrated Reviews.* Found in the middle of each chapter, these reviews offer you a chance to practice—in one place—the many concepts that you have learned separately over several sections.

MyMathLab®

In MyMathLab, you have access to the following video resources:

- Lecture Videos for each section
- Chapter Test Prep Videos

Use these videos provided by the author to prepare for class, review, and study for tests.

- *End of Chapter Opportunities.* There are many opportunities at the end of each chapter to help you understand the concepts of the chapter.

  Vocabulary Checks contain key vocabulary terms introduced in the chapter.

  Chapter Highlights contain chapter summaries and examples.

  Chapter Reviews contain review problems. The first part is organized section by section and the second part contains a set of mixed exercises.

  Chapter Tests are sample tests to help you prepare for an exam. The Chapter Test Prep Videos, found in this text, contain all the Chapter Test exercises worked by the author.

  Cumulative Reviews are reviews consisting of material from the beginning of the book to the end of that particular chapter.
- *Student Resources in Your Textbook.* You will find a **Student Resources** section at the back of this textbook. It contains the following to help you study and prepare for tests:

  Study Skill Builders contain study skills advice. To increase your chance for success in the course, read these study tips, and answer the questions.

  Bigger Picture—Study Guide Outline provides you with a study guide outline of the course, with examples.

  Practice Final provides you with a Practice Final Exam to help you prepare for your final. The video solutions to each question are provided in the Interactive DVD Lecture Series and within MyMathLab®.
- *Resources to Check Your Work.* The **Answers to Selected Exercises** section provides answers to all odd-numbered section exercises and all chapter test exercises. Use the **Selected Solutions** to see the worked out solution to every other odd exercise.

Helpful Hint

MyMathLab® and MathXL®

- Use the **Help Me Solve This** button to get step-by-step help for the exercise you are working. You will need to work an additional exercise of the same type before you can get credit for having worked it correctly.
- Use the **Video** button to view a video clip of the author working a similar exercise.

Objective D Getting Help

If you have trouble completing assignments or understanding the mathematics, get help as soon as you need it! This tip is presented as an objective on its own because it is so important. In mathematics, usually the material presented in one section builds on your understanding of the previous section. This means that if you don't understand the concepts covered during a class period, there is a good chance that you will not understand the concepts covered during the next class period. If this happens to you, get help as soon as you can.

Where can you get help? Many suggestions have been made in this section on where to get help, and now it is up to you to get it. Try your instructor, a tutoring center, or a math lab, or you may want to form a study group with fellow classmates. If you do decide to see your instructor or go to a tutoring center, make sure that you have a neat notebook and are ready with your questions.

Objective E Preparing for and Taking an Exam

Make sure that you allow yourself plenty of time to prepare for a test. If you think that you are a little "math anxious," it may be that you are not preparing for a test in a way that will ensure success. The way that you prepare for a test in mathematics is important. To prepare for a test:

MyMathLab® and MathXL®

Review your written work for previous assignments. Then, go back and re-work previous assignments. Open a previous assignment, and click **Similar Exercise** to generate new exercises. Re-work the exercises until you fully understand them and can work them without help features.

1. Review your previous homework assignments.
2. Review any notes from class and section-level quizzes you have taken. (If this is a final exam, also review chapter tests you have taken.)
3. Review concepts and definitions by reading the Chapter Highlights at the end of each chapter.
4. Practice working out exercises by completing the Chapter Review found at the end of each chapter. (If this is a final exam, go through a Cumulative Review. There is one found at the end of each chapter except Chapter 1. Choose the review found at the end of the latest chapter that you have covered in your course.) *Don't stop here!*

5. It is important that you place yourself in conditions similar to test conditions to find out how you will perform. In other words, as soon as you feel that you know the material, get a few blank sheets of paper and take a sample test. There is a Chapter Test available at the end of each chapter, or you can work selected problems from the Chapter Review. Your instructor may also provide you with a review sheet. During this sample test, do not use your notes or your textbook. Then check your sample test. If you are not satisfied with the results, study the areas that you are weak in and try again.
6. On the day of the test, allow yourself plenty of time to arrive at where you will be taking your exam.

When taking your test:

1. Read the directions on the test carefully.
2. Read each problem carefully as you take the test. Make sure that you answer the question asked.
3. Watch your time and pace yourself so that you can attempt each problem on your test.
4. If you have time, check your work and answers.
5. Do not turn your test in early. If you have extra time, spend it double-checking your work.

Objective F Managing Your Time

As a college student, you know the demands that classes, homework, work, and family place on your time. Some days you probably wonder how you'll ever get everything done. One key to managing your time is developing a schedule. Here are some hints for making a schedule:

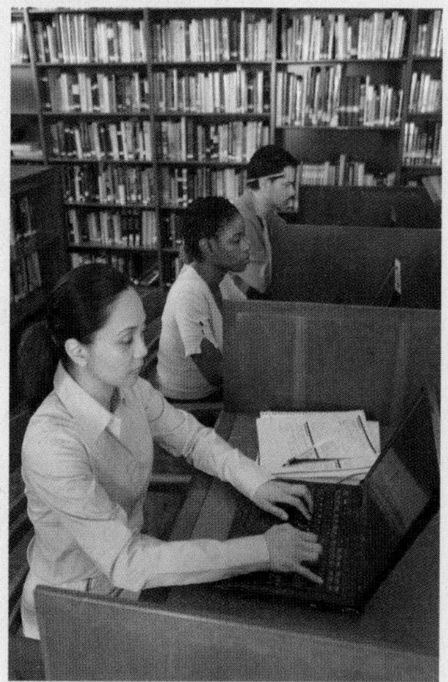

1. Make a list of all of your weekly commitments for the term. Include classes, work, regular meetings, extracurricular activities, etc. You may also find it helpful to list such things as laundry, regular workouts, grocery shopping, etc.
2. Next, estimate the time needed for each item on the list. Also make a note of how often you will need to do each item. Don't forget to include time estimates for the reading, studying, and homework you do outside of your classes. You may want to ask your instructor for help estimating the time needed.
3. In the exercise set that follows, you are asked to block out a typical week on the schedule grid given. Start with items with fixed time slots like classes and work.
4. Next, include the items on your list with flexible time slots. Think carefully about how best to schedule items such as study time.
5. Don't fill up every time slot on the schedule. Remember that you need to allow time for eating, sleeping, and relaxing! You should also allow a little extra time in case some items take longer than planned.
6. If you find that your weekly schedule is too full for you to handle, you may need to make some changes in your workload, classload, or in other areas of your life. You may want to talk to your advisor, manager or supervisor at work, or someone in your college's academic counseling center for help with such decisions.

1.1 Exercise Set

FOR EXTRA HELP

1. What is your instructor's name?

2. What are your instructor's office location and office hours?

3. What is the best way to contact your instructor?

4. Do you have the name and contact information of at least one other student in class?

5. Will your instructor allow you to use a calculator in this class?

6. Why is it important that you write step-by-step solutions to homework exercises and keep a hard copy of all work submitted?

7. Is there a tutoring service available on campus? If so, what are its hours? What services are available?

8. Have you attempted this course before? If so, write down ways that you might improve your chances of success during this second attempt.

9. List some steps that you can take if you begin having trouble understanding the material or completing an assignment. If you are completing your homework in MyMathLab® and MathXL®, list the resources you can use for help.

10. How many hours of studying does your instructor advise for each hour of instruction?

11. What does the ✎ icon in this text mean?

12. What does the icon in this text mean?

13. What does the △ icon in this text mean?

14. Search the minor columns in your text. What are Practice exercises?

15. When might be the best time to work a Practice exercise?

16. Where are the answers to Practice exercises?

17. What answers are contained in this text and where are they?

18. What solutions are contained in this text and where are they?

19. What and where are Integrated Reviews?

20. How many times is it suggested that you work through the homework exercises in MathXL® before the submission deadline?

21. How far in advance of the assigned due date is it suggested that homework be submitted online? Why?

22. Chapter Highlights are found at the end of each chapter. Find the Chapter 1 Highlights and explain how you might use it and how it might be helpful.

23. Chapter Reviews are found at the end of each chapter. Find the Chapter 1 Review and explain how you might use it and how it might be useful.

24. Chapter Tests are found at the end of each chapter. Find the Chapter 1 Test and explain how you might use it and how it might be helpful when preparing for an exam on Chapter 1. Include how the Chapter Test Prep Videos may help. If you are working in MyMathLab® and MathXL®, how can you use previous homework assignments to study?

25. Read or reread objective F and fill out the schedule grid on the next page.

	Monday	Tuesday	Wednesday	Thursday	Friday	Saturday	Sunday
4:00 a.m.							
5:00 a.m.							
6:00 a.m.							
7:00 a.m.							
8:00 a.m.							
9:00 a.m.							
10:00 a.m.							
11:00 a.m.							
12:00 p.m.							
1:00 p.m.							
2:00 p.m.							
3:00 p.m.							
4:00 p.m.							
5:00 p.m.							
6:00 p.m.							
7:00 p.m.							
8:00 p.m.							
9:00 p.m.							
10:00 p.m.							
11:00 p.m.							
Midnight							
1:00 a.m.							
2:00 a.m.							
3:00 a.m.							

Objectives

A **Find the Place Value of a Digit in a Whole Number.**

B **Write a Whole Number in Words and in Standard Form.**

C **Write a Whole Number in Expanded Form.**

D **Read Tables.**

1.2 PLACE VALUE, NAMES FOR NUMBERS, AND READING TABLES

The **digits** 0, 1, 2, 3, 4, 5, 6, 7, 8, and 9 can be used to write numbers. For example, the **whole numbers** are

0, 1, 2, 3, 4, 5, 6, 7, 8, 9, 10, 11, . . .

and the **natural numbers** are 1, 2, 3, 4, 5, 6, 7, 8, 9, 10, 11, . . .

The three dots (. . .) after the 11 mean that this list continues indefinitely. That is, there is no largest whole number. The smallest whole number is 0.

Objective A Finding the Place Value of a Digit in a Whole Number

The position of each digit in a number determines its **place value.** For example, the distance (in miles) between the planet Mercury and the planet Earth can be represented by the whole number 48,337,000. Below is a place-value chart for this whole number.

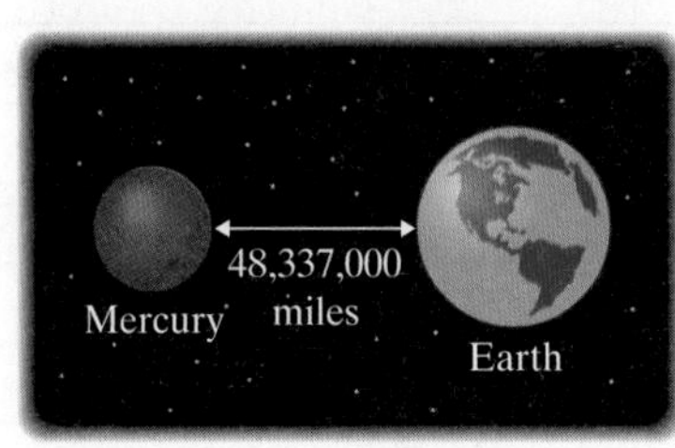

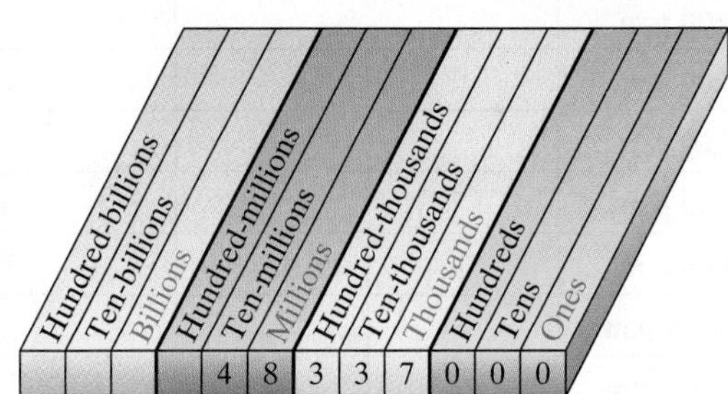

The two 3s in 48,337,000 represent different amounts because of their different placements. The place value of the 3 on the left is hundred-thousands. The place value of the 3 on the right is ten-thousands.

PRACTICE 1–3

Find the place value of the digit 8 in each whole number.

1. 38,760,005
2. 67,890
3. 481,922

Examples Find the place value of the digit 3 in each whole number.

1. 396,418 ↑ hundred-thousands
2. 93,192 ↑ thousands
3. 534,275,866 ↑ ten-millions

Work Practice 1–3

Objective B Writing a Whole Number in Words and in Standard Form

A whole number such as 1,083,664,500 is written in **standard form.** Notice that commas separate the digits into groups of three, starting from the right. Each group of three digits is called a **period.** The names of the first four periods are shown in red.

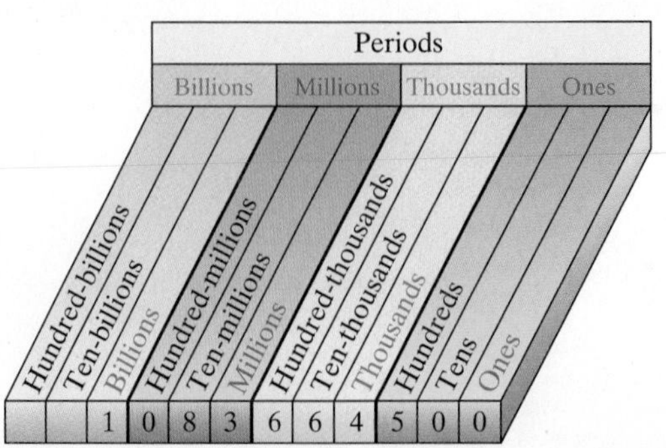

Answers
1. millions 2. hundreds
3. ten-thousands

Writing a Whole Number in Words

To write a whole number in words, write the number in each period followed by the name of the period. (The ones period is usually not written.) This same procedure can be used to read a whole number.

For example, we write 1,083,664,500 as

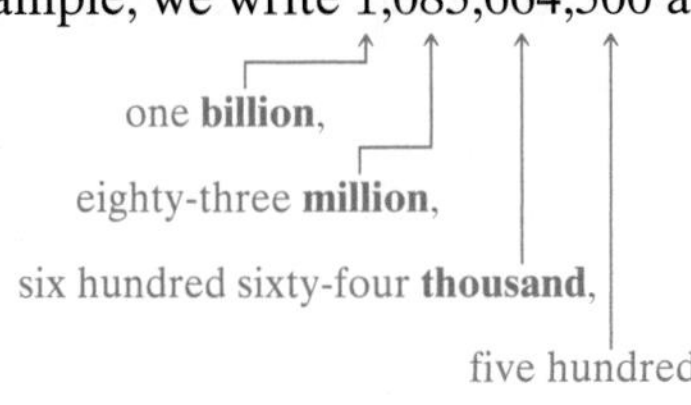

Helpful Hint Notice the commas after the name of each period.

Helpful Hint

The name of the ones period is not used when reading and writing whole numbers. For example,

9,265

is read as

"nine **thousand,** two hundred sixty-five."

Examples Write each number in words.

4. 85 eighty-five

5. 126 one hundred twenty-six

6. 27,034 twenty-seven thousand, thirty-four

Work Practice 4–6

Helpful Hint The word "and" is *not* used when reading and writing whole numbers. It is used when reading and writing mixed numbers and some decimal values, as shown later in this text.

PRACTICE 4–6

Write each number in words.

4. 67

5. 395

6. 12,804

Example 7 Write 106,052,447 in words.

Solution: 106,052,447 is written as

one hundred six **million**, fifty-two **thousand**, four hundred forty-seven

Work Practice 7

PRACTICE 7

Write 321,670,200 in words.

✓**Concept Check** True or false? When writing a check for $2600, the word name we write for the dollar amount of the check is "two thousand sixty." Explain your answer.

Writing a Whole Number in Standard Form

To write a whole number in standard form, write the number in each period, followed by a comma.

Answers

4. sixty-seven **5.** three hundred ninety-five **6.** twelve thousand, eight hundred four **7.** three hundred twenty-one million, six hundred seventy thousand, two hundred

✓ **Concept Check Answer**

false

PRACTICE 8–11

Write each number in standard form.

8. twenty-nine
9. seven hundred ten
10. twenty-six thousand, seventy-one
11. six million, five hundred seven

Examples Write each number in standard form.

8. sixty-one 61 **9.** eight hundred five 805

10. nine thousand, three hundred eighty-six

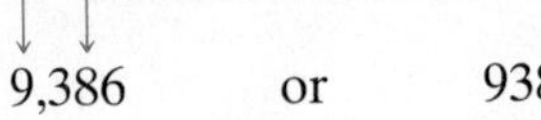

9,386 or 9386

11. two million, five hundred sixty-four thousand, three hundred fifty

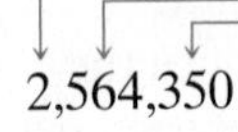

2,564,350

Work Practice 8–11

Helpful Hint

A comma may or may not be inserted in a four-digit number. For example, both

9,386 and 9386

are acceptable ways of writing nine thousand, three hundred eighty-six.

Objective C Writing a Whole Number in Expanded Form

The place value of a digit can be used to write a number in expanded form. The **expanded form** of a number shows each digit of the number with its place value. For example, 5672 is written in expanded form as

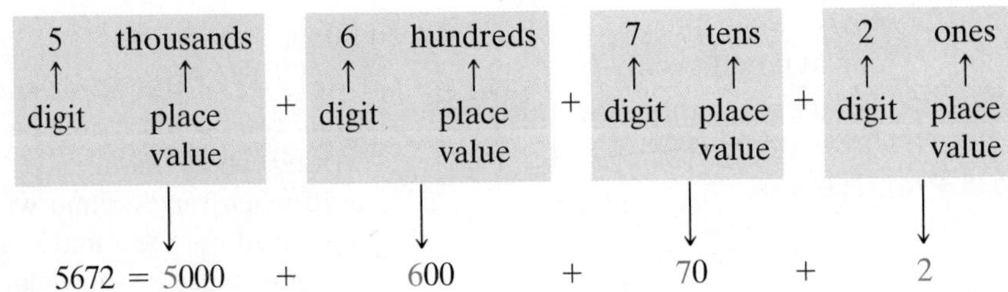

PRACTICE 12

Write 1,047,608 in expanded form.

Example 12 Write 2,706,449 in expanded form.

Solution: 2,000,000 + 700,000 + 6000 + 400 + 40 + 9

Work Practice 12

We can visualize whole numbers by points on a line. The line below is called a **number line.** This number line has equally spaced marks for each whole number. The arrow to the right simply means that the whole numbers continue indefinitely. In other words, there is no largest whole number.

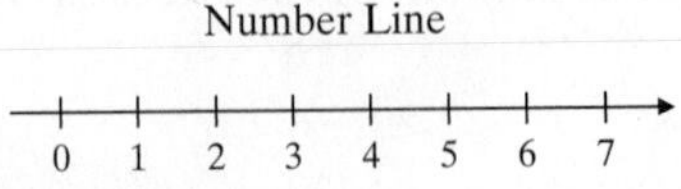

We will study number lines further in Section 1.5.

Answers

8. 29 9. 710
10. 26,071 11. 6,000,507
12. 1,000,000 + 40,000 + 7000 + 600 + 8

Objective D Reading Tables

Now that we know about place value and names for whole numbers, we introduce one way that whole numbers may be presented. **Tables** are often used to organize and display facts that involve numbers. The following table shows the ten countries with the most Nobel Prize winners since the inception of the Nobel Prize in 1901, and the categories of the prizes. The numbers for the Economics prize reflect the winners since 1969, when this category was established. (The numbers may seem large for two reasons: first, the annual Nobel Prize is often awarded to more than one individual, and second, several award winners hold dual citizenship, so they are counted in two countries.)

Countries with Most Nobel Prize Winners, 1901–2008

Country	Physics	Chemistry	Literature	Physiology and Medicine	Peace	Economics	Total
United States	88	59	11	96	22	44	320
United Kingdom	21	27	11	31	13	7	110
Germany	25	28	8	16	4	1	82
France	13	8	14	11	10	2	58
Sweden	4	4	8	7	5	2	30
Switzerland	3	6	2	6	4	0	21
Russia (USSR)	10	1	5	1	3	1	21
Austria	3	4	1	7	2	1	18
Italy	3	1	6	4	1	1	16
Netherlands	8	3	0	2	1	2	16
Japan	7	5	2	1	1	0	16

Source: Based on data from official website of the Nobel Prize Committee

For example, by reading from left to right along the row marked "United States," we find that the United States has 88 Physics, 59 Chemistry, 11 Literature, 96 Physiology and Medicine, 22 Peace, and 44 Economics Nobel Prize winners.

Example 13 Use the Nobel Prize Winner table to answer each question.

a. How many total Nobel Prize winners are from Sweden?

b. Which countries shown have fewer Nobel Prize winners than Austria?

Solution:

a. Find "Sweden" in the left column. Then read from left to right until the "Total" column is reached. We find that Sweden has 30 Nobel Prize winners.

b. Austria has 18 Nobel Prize winners. Italy, Netherlands, and Japan each has 16, so they have fewer Nobel Prize winners than Austria.

Work Practice 13

PRACTICE 13

Use the Nobel Prize Winner table to answer the following questions:

a. How many Nobel Prize winners in Literature come from France?

b. Which countries shown have more than 60 Nobel Prize winners?

Answers

13. a. 14 **b.** United States, United Kingdom, and Germany

Vocabulary and Readiness Check

Use the choices below to fill in each blank.

standard form	period	whole
expanded form	place value	words

1. The numbers 0, 1, 2, 3, 4, 5, 6, 7, 8, 9, 10, 11, 12, . . . are called ____________ numbers.
2. The number 1,286 is written in ____________.
3. The number "twenty-one" is written in ____________.
4. The number 900 + 60 + 5 is written in ____________.
5. In a whole number, each group of three digits is called a(n) ____________.
6. The ____________ of the digit 4 in the whole number 264 is ones.

1.2 Exercise Set

Objective A *Determine the place value of the digit 5 in each whole number. See Examples 1 through 3.*

1. 657 **2.** 905 **3.** 5423 **4.** 6527

5. 43,526,000 **6.** 79,050,000 **7.** 5,408,092 **8.** 51,682,700

Objective B *Write each whole number in words. See Examples 4 through 7.*

9. 354 **10.** 316 **11.** 8279 **12.** 5445

13. 26,990 **14.** 42,009 **15.** 2,388,000 **16.** 3,204,000

17. 24,350,185 **18.** 47,033,107

Write each number in the sentence in words. See Examples 4 through 7.

19. As of this writing, the population of Iceland is 304,367. (*Source:* The World Factbook)

20. Between 2000 and 2005, Brazil lost 13,382 acres of rainforest.

21. Due for completion in 2010, the Burj Dubai, in Dubai, United Arab Emirates, a hotel and office building, will be the tallest in the world at a height of more than 2600 feet. (*Source:* Council on Tall Buildings and Urban Habitat)

22. In a recent year, there were 99,769 patients in the United States waiting for an organ transplant. (*Source:* United Network for Organ Sharing)

23. Each day, UPS delivers an average of 15,800,000 packages worldwide. (*Source:* UPS)

24. Each year, 350,000,000 Americans visit a local carnival. (*Source:* Outdoor Amusement Business Association)

25. The highest point in Colorado is Mount Elbert, at an elevation of 14,433 feet. (*Source:* U.S. Geological Survey)

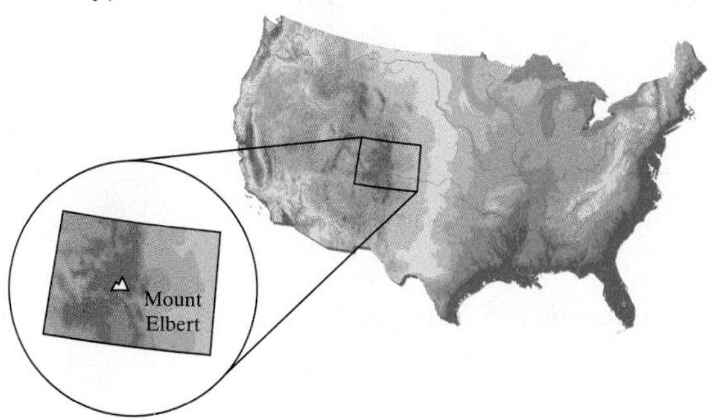

26. The highest point in Oregon is Mount Hood, at an elevation of 11,239 feet. (*Source:* U.S. Geological Survey)

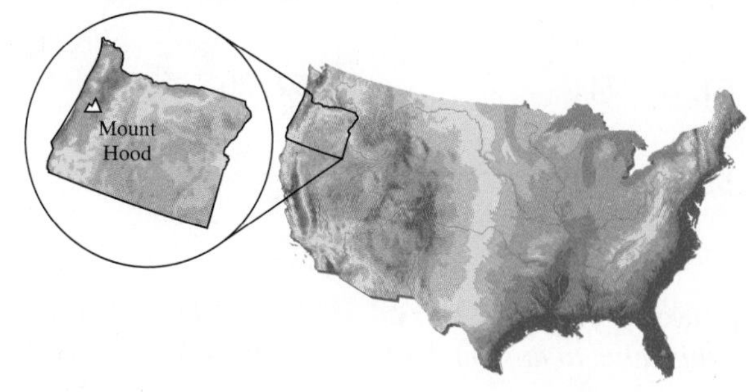

27. In a recent year, the Great Internet Mersenne Prime Search, a cooperative computing project, helped find a prime number that has nearly 13,000,000 digits. (*Source:* Science News)

28. The Goodyear blimp *Eagle* holds 202,700 cubic feet of helium. (*Source:* The Goodyear Tire & Rubber Company)

Write each whole number in standard form. See Examples 8 through 11.

29. Six thousand, five hundred eighty-seven

30. Four thousand, four hundred sixty-eight

31. Fifty-nine thousand, eight hundred

32. Seventy-three thousand, two

33. Thirteen million, six hundred one thousand, eleven

34. Sixteen million, four hundred five thousand, sixteen

35. Seven million, seventeen

36. Two million, twelve

37. Two hundred sixty thousand, nine hundred ninety-seven

38. Six hundred forty thousand, eight hundred eighty-one

Write the whole number in each sentence in standard form. See Examples 8 through 11.

39. The Mir Space Station orbits above Earth at an average altitude of three hundred ninety-five kilometers. (*Source:* Heavens Above)

40. The average distance between the surfaces of Earth and the Moon is about two hundred thirty-four thousand miles.

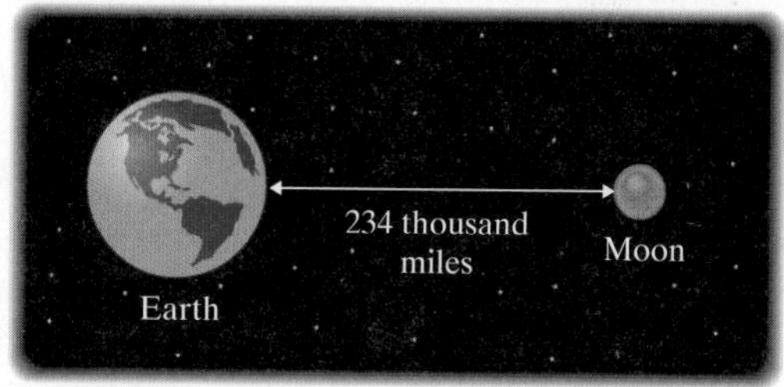

41. La Rinconada, Peru, is the highest town in the world. It is located sixteen thousand, seven hundred thirty-two feet above sea level. (*Source:* Russell Ash: *Top 10 of Everything*, 2009)

42. The world's tallest free-standing tower is the Guangzhou TV Tower in China. Its completed height is two thousand one feet tall. (*Source: The World Almanac*)

43. The Summit Entertainment film *The Twilight Saga: New Moon* set the U.S. and Canada record for opening day income when it took in approximately seventy-two million, seven hundred four thousand dollars in one day in 2009. (*Source:* wikipedia.org)

44. The Warner Brothers film *The Dark Knight* set the U.S. and Canada record for second-highest opening day income when it took in approximately sixty-seven million, one hundred sixty-five thousand dollars in one day in 2008. (*Source:* wikipedia.org)

45. As of 2009, there were one thousand, three hundred seventeen species classified as either threatened or endangered in the United States. (*Source:* U.S. Fish & Wildlife Service)

46. Morten Anderson, who played football for New Orleans, Atlanta, N.Y. Giants, Kansas City, and Minnesota between 1982 and 2007, holds the record for the most points scored in a career. Over his 25-year career he scored two thousand, five hundred forty-four points. (*Source:* NFL.com)

Objective C *Write each whole number in expanded form. See Example 12.*

47. 406 **48.** 789 **49.** 3470 **50.** 6040

51. 80,774 **52.** 20,215 **53.** 66,049 **54.** 99,032

55. 39,680,000 **56.** 47,703,029

Objectives B C D **Mixed Practice** *The table shows the six tallest mountains in New England and their elevations. Use this table to answer Exercises 57 through 62. See Example 13.*

Mountain (State)	Elevation (in feet)
Boott Spur (NH)	5492
Mt. Adams (NH)	5774
Mt. Clay (NH)	5532
Mt. Jefferson (NH)	5712
Mt. Sam Adams (NH)	5584
Mt. Washington (NH)	6288

Source: U.S. Geological Survey

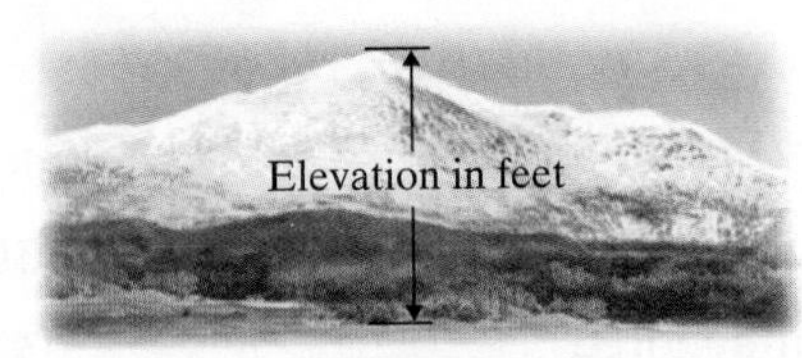

57. Write the elevation of Mt. Clay in standard form and then in words.

58. Write the elevation of Mt. Washington in standard form and then in words.

59. Write the height of Boott Spur in expanded form.

60. Write the height of Mt. Jefferson in expanded form.

61. Which mountain is the tallest in New England?

62. Which mountain is the second tallest in New England?

The table shows the top ten popular breeds of dogs in a recent year according to the American Kennel Club. Use this table to answer Exercises 63 through 68. See Example 13.

Top Ten American Kennel Club Registrations in 2007

Breed	Number of Registered Dogs	Average Dog Maximum Height (in inches)	Average Dog Maximum Weight (in pounds)
Beagle	39,384	15	30
Boxer	35,388	25	70
Bulldog	21,037	26	90
Dachshund	36,033	9	25
German shepherd dog	43,575	26	95
Golden retriever	42,962	24	80
Labrador retriever	123,760	25	75
Poodle (standard, miniature, and toy)	29,939	standard: 26	standard: 70
Shih Tzu	27,282	11	16
Yorkshire terrier	48,346	9	7

(*Source:* American Kennel Club)

63. Which breed has fewer dogs registered, Boxer or Dachshund?

64. Which breed has more dogs registered, Golden retriever or German shepherd dog?

65. Which breed has the most American Kennel Club registrations? Write the number of registrations for this breed in words.

66. Which of the listed breeds has the fewest registrations? Write the number of registered dogs for this breed in words.

67. What is the maximum weight of an average-size Dachshund?

68. What is the maximum height of an average-size standard poodle?

Concept Extensions

69. Write the largest four-digit number that can be made from the digits 1, 9, 8, and 6 if each digit must be used once. ____ ____ ____ ____

70. Write the largest five-digit number that can be made using the digits 5, 3, and 7 if each digit must be used at least once. ____ ____ ____ ____ ____.

Check to see whether each number written in standard form matches the number written in words. If not, correct the number in words. See the Concept Check in this section.

71.

60–8124/7233
1000613331 1401

DATE ________

PAY TO THE ORDER OF ________ $ 105.00

One Hundred Fifty and 00/100 ———— DOLLARS

FIRST STATE BANK
OF FARTHINGTON
FARTHINGTON, IL 64422

MEMO ________

⑆621497260⑆ 1000613331⑈ 1401

72.

60–8124/7233
1000613331 1402

DATE ________

PAY TO THE ORDER OF ________ $ 7030.00

Seven Thousand Thirty and 00/100 ———— DOLLARS

FIRST STATE BANK
OF FARTHINGTON
FARTHINGTON, IL 64422

MEMO ________

⑆621497260⑆ 1000613331⑈ 1402

73. If a number is given in words, describe the process used to write this number in standard form.

74. If a number is written in standard form, describe the process used to write this number in expanded form.

75. Called "Roadrunner" by its users, a computer built by IBM for Los Alamos National Laboratory topped the list of the 500 fastest computers, burning up the bytes at 1.026 petaflops, or more than 1000 trillion arithmetic operations per second. Look up "trillion" (in the American system) and use the definition to write this number in standard form. (*Source:* TechWorld)

76. A Hurricane Katrina victim was seeking \$3 quadrillion from the U.S. government. Look up "quadrillion" (in the American system) and write 3 quadrillion in standard form. (*Source:* Associated Press)

77. The Pro Football Hall of Fame was established on September 7, 1963, in this town. Use the information and the diagram to the right to find the name of the town.

- Alliance is east of Massillon.
- Dover is between Canton and New Philadelphia.
- Massillon is not next to Alliance.
- Canton is north of Dover.

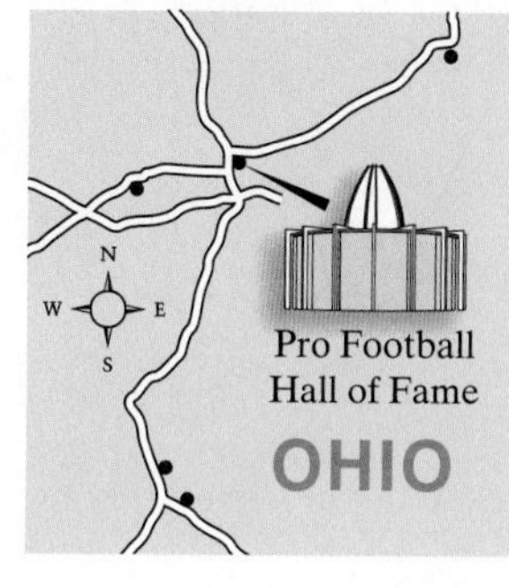

Objectives

A **Add Whole Numbers.**

B **Find the Perimeter of a Polygon.**

C **Solve Problems by Adding Whole Numbers.**

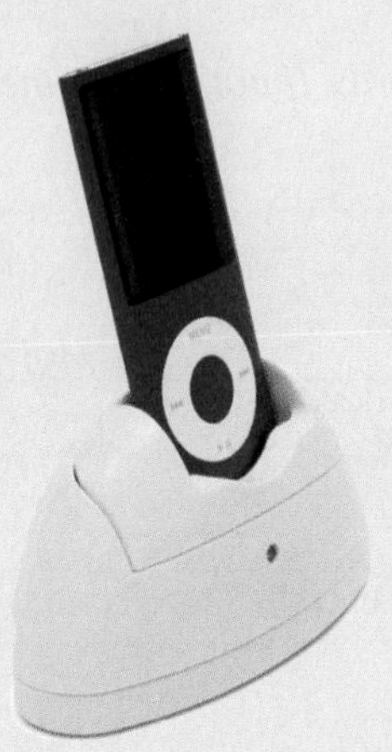

1.3 ADDING WHOLE NUMBERS AND PERIMETER

Objective A Adding Whole Numbers

According to ConsumerSearch, the iPod nano is the best overall MP3 player. (The newest nano also contains a video camera!)

Suppose that an electronics store received a shipment of two boxes of iPod nanos one day and an additional four boxes of iPod nanos the next day. The **total** shipment in the two days can be found by adding 2 and 4.

2 boxes of iPod nanos + 4 boxes of iPod nanos = 6 boxes of iPod nanos

The **sum** (or total) is 6 boxes of iPod nanos. Each of the numbers 2 and 4 is called an **addend,** and the process of finding the sum is called **addition.**

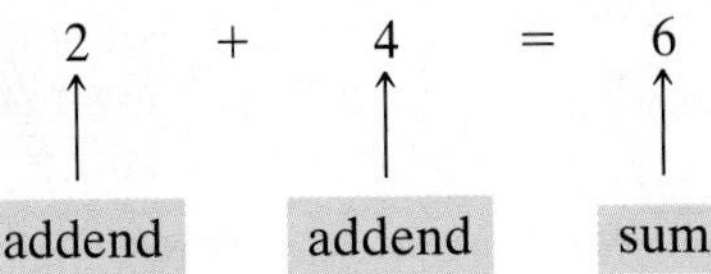

To add whole numbers, we add the digits in the ones place, then the tens place, then the hundreds place, and so on. For example, let's add 2236 + 160.

$$\begin{array}{r} 2236 \\ +160 \\ \hline 2396 \end{array}$$

Line up numbers vertically so that the place values correspond. Then add digits in corresponding place values, starting with the ones place.

- 6: sum of ones
- 9: sum of tens
- 3: sum of hundreds
- 2: sum of thousands

PRACTICE 1

Add: 7235 + 542

Example 1 Add: 23 + 136

Solution:

$$\begin{array}{r} 23 \\ +136 \\ \hline 159 \end{array}$$

Work Practice 1

When the sum of digits in corresponding place values is more than 9, **carrying** is necessary. For example, to add 365 + 89, add the ones-place digits first.

Carrying

$$\begin{array}{r} \overset{1}{3}65 \\ +\ 89 \\ \hline 4 \end{array}$$

5 ones + 9 ones = 14 ones or 1 ten + 4 ones

Write the 4 ones in the ones place and carry the 1 ten to the tens place.

Next, add the tens-place digits.

$$\begin{array}{r} \overset{1}{3}\overset{1}{6}5 \\ +\ 89 \\ \hline 54 \end{array}$$

1 ten + 6 tens + 8 tens = 15 tens or 1 hundred + 5 tens

Write the 5 tens in the tens place and carry the 1 hundred to the hundreds place.

Next, add the hundreds-place digits.

$$\begin{array}{r} \overset{1}{3}\overset{1}{6}5 \\ +\ 89 \\ \hline 454 \end{array}$$

1 hundred + 3 hundreds = 4 hundreds

Write the 4 hundreds in the hundreds place.

Answer

1. 7777

Example 2 Add: 34,285 + 149,761

Solution:

$$\begin{array}{r} \scriptstyle 1\,1\;\,1\;\;\;\;\; \\ 34{,}285 \\ +\,149{,}761 \\ \hline 184{,}046 \end{array}$$

Work Practice 2

PRACTICE 2

Add: 27,364 + 92,977

✓**Concept Check** What is wrong with the following computation?

$$\begin{array}{r} 394 \\ +\,283 \\ \hline 577 \end{array}$$

Before we continue adding whole numbers, let's review some properties of addition that you may have already discovered. The first property that we will review is the **addition property of 0.** This property reminds us that the sum of 0 and any number is that same number.

Addition Property of 0

The sum of 0 and any number is that number. For example,

$7 + 0 = 7$

$0 + 7 = 7$

Next, notice that we can add any two whole numbers in any order and the sum is the same. For example,

$4 + 5 = 9$ and $5 + 4 = 9$

We call this special property of addition the **commutative property of addition.**

Commutative Property of Addition

Changing the **order** of two addends does not change their sum. For example,

$2 + 3 = 5$ and $3 + 2 = 5$

Another property that can help us when adding numbers is the **associative property of addition.** This property states that when adding numbers, the grouping of the numbers can be changed without changing the sum. We use parentheses to group numbers. They indicate which numbers to add first. For example, let's use two different groupings to find the sum of 2 + 1 + 5.

$$\underbrace{(2 + 1)} + 5 = 3 + 5 = 8$$

Also,

$$2 + \underbrace{(1 + 5)} = 2 + 6 = 8$$

Both groupings give a sum of 8.

Answer

2. 120,341

✓ **Concept Check Answer**

forgot to carry 1 hundred to the hundreds place

Associative Property of Addition

Changing the **grouping** of addends does not change their sum. For example,

$$3 + \underbrace{(5 + 7)} = 3 + 12 = 15 \quad \text{and} \quad \underbrace{(3 + 5)} + 7 = 8 + 7 = 15$$

The commutative and associative properties tell us that we can add whole numbers using any order and grouping that we want.

When adding several numbers, it is often helpful to look for two or three numbers whose sum is 10, 20, and so on. Why? Adding multiples of 10 such as 10 and 20 is easier.

PRACTICE 3

Add: 11 + 7 + 8 + 9 + 13

Example 3 Add: 13 + 2 + 7 + 8 + 9

Solution:

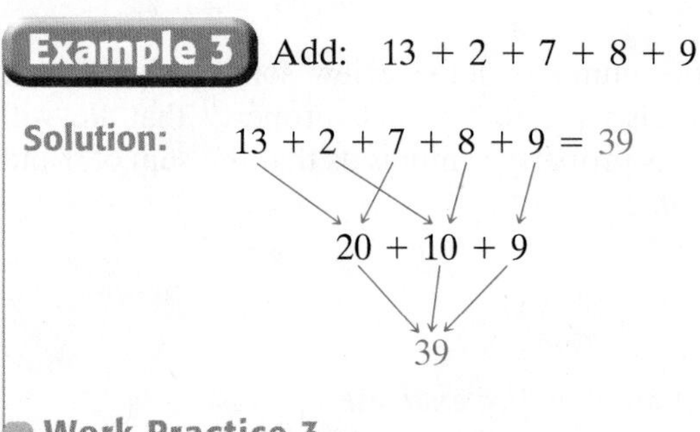

Work Practice 3

Feel free to use the process of Example 3 anytime when adding.

PRACTICE 4

Add: 19 + 5042 + 638 + 526

Example 4 Add: 1647 + 246 + 32 + 85

Solution:

$$\begin{array}{r} \scriptstyle 122 \\ 1647 \\ 246 \\ 32 \\ +\ \ 85 \\ \hline 2010 \end{array}$$

Work Practice 4

Objective B Finding the Perimeter of a Polygon

In geometry addition is used to find the perimeter of a polygon. A **polygon** can be described as a flat figure formed by line segments connected at their ends. (For more review, see Appendix A.3.) Geometric figures such as triangles, squares, and rectangles are called polygons.

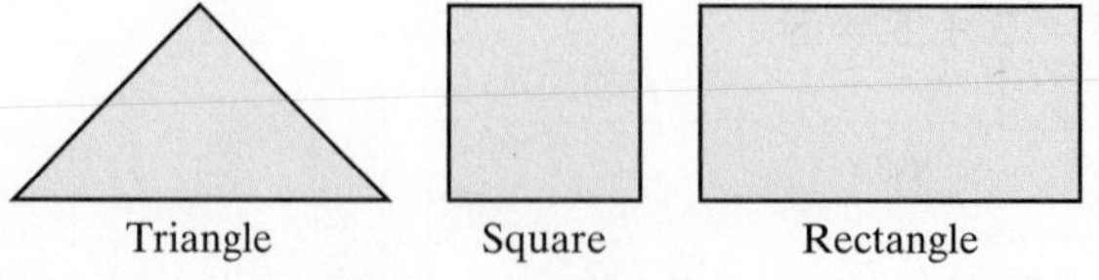

The **perimeter** of a polygon is the *distance around* the polygon. This means that the perimeter of a polygon is the sum of the lengths of its sides.

Answers
3. 48 **4.** 6225

Example 5 Find the perimeter of the polygon shown.

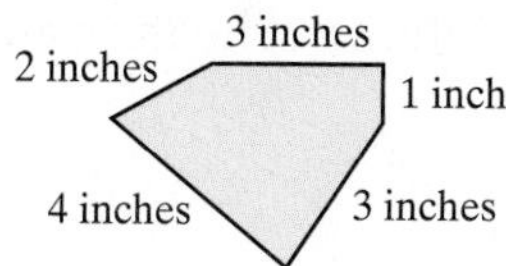

Solution: To find the perimeter (distance around), we add the lengths of the sides.

2 in. + 3 in. + 1 in. + 3 in. + 4 in. = 13 in.

The perimeter is 13 inches.

Work Practice 5

PRACTICE 5

Find the perimeter of the polygon shown. (A centimeter is a unit of length in the metric system.)

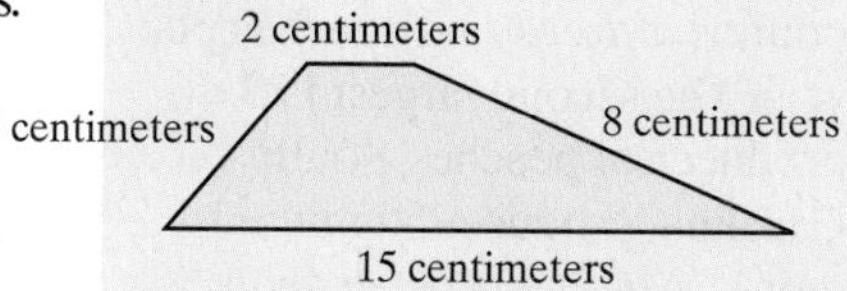

To make the addition appear simpler, we will often not include units with the addends. If you do this, make sure units are included in the final answer.

Example 6 Calculating the Perimeter of a Building

The largest commercial building in the world under one roof is the flower auction building of the cooperative VBA in Aalsmeer, Netherlands. The floor plan is a rectangle that measures 776 meters by 639 meters. Find the perimeter of this building. (A meter is a unit of length in the metric system.) (*Source: The Handy Science Answer Book,* Visible Ink Press)

Solution: Recall that opposite sides of a rectangle have the same length. To find the perimeter of this building, we add the lengths of the sides. The sum of the lengths of its sides is

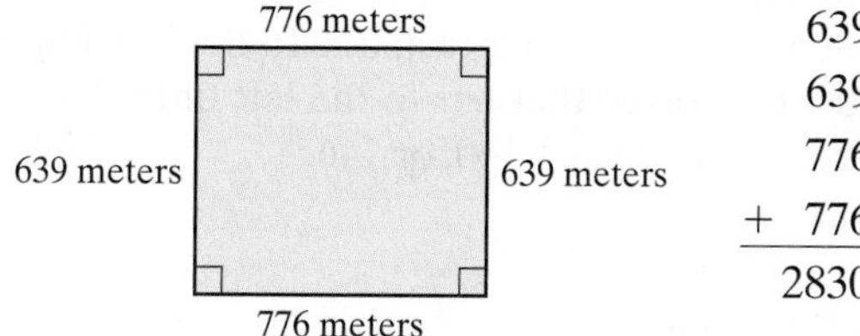

$$\begin{array}{r} 639 \\ 639 \\ 776 \\ +\ 776 \\ \hline 2830 \end{array}$$

The perimeter of the building is 2830 meters.

Work Practice 6

PRACTICE 6

A park is in the shape of a triangle. Each of the park's three sides is 647 feet. Find the perimeter of the park.

Objective C Solving Problems by Adding

Often, real-life problems occur that can be solved by adding. The first step in solving any word problem is to *understand* the problem by reading it carefully.

Descriptions of problems solved through addition *may* include any of these key words or phrases:

Addition		
Key Words or Phrases	**Examples**	**Symbols**
added to	5 added to 7	7 + 5
plus	0 plus 78	0 + 78
increased by	12 increased by 6	12 + 6
more than	11 more than 25	25 + 11
total	the total of 8 and 1	8 + 1
sum	the sum of 4 and 133	4 + 133

Answers

5. 30 cm **6.** 1941 ft

To solve a word problem that involves addition, we first use the facts given to write an addition statement. Then we write the corresponding solution of the real-life problem. It is sometimes helpful to write the statement in words (brief phrases) and then translate to numbers.

PRACTICE 7

Georgia produces 70 million pounds of freestone peaches per year. The second largest U.S. producer of peaches, South Carolina, produces 50 million more freestone peaches than Georgia. How much does South Carolina produce? (*Source:* farms.com)

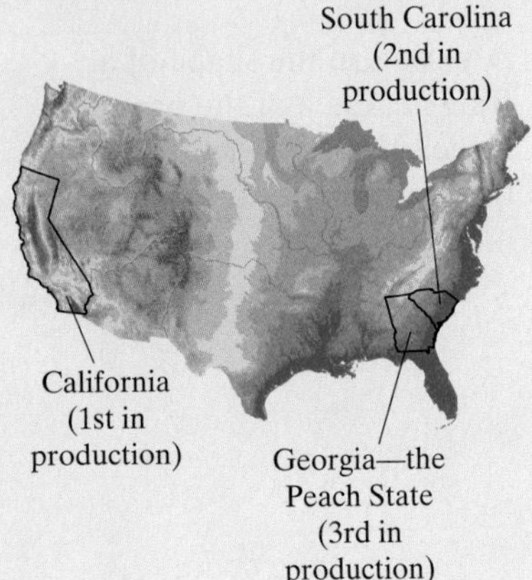

Example 7 Finding a Stadium Capacity

The Darrell K Royal Memorial Stadium, located in Austin, Texas, is the largest football stadium in the Big 12 Conference. Before 2009, it could seat 94,113 fans. Recently, the capacity of the stadium was increased by 4525 permanent bleacher seats. Find the new capacity of the home of the University of Texas Longhorns for the 2009 season. (*Source:* University of Texas Athletics)

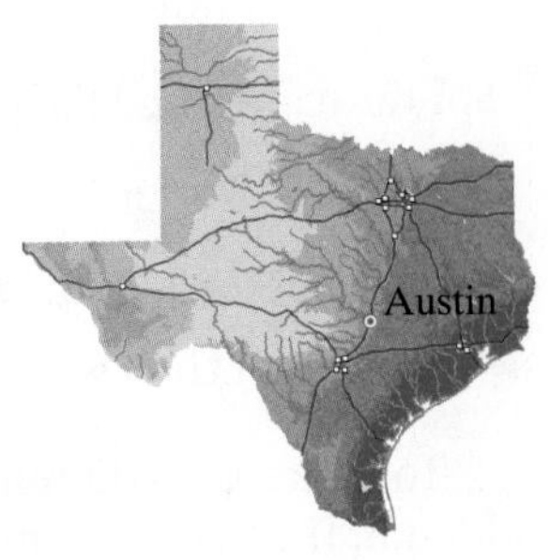

Solution: The key phrase here is "was increased by," which suggests that we add. To find the new capacity of the stadium, we add the increase, 4525, to the old capacity.

In Words		Translate to Numbers
Old capacity	⟶	94,113
+ increase	⟶	+ 4,525
New capacity	⟶	98,638

The number of seats in the stadium for the 2009 season was 98,638.

Work Practice 7

Graphs can be used to visualize data. The graph shown next is called a **bar graph.** For this bar graph, the height of each bar is labeled above the bar. To check this height, follow the top of each bar to the vertical line to the left. For example, the first bar is labeled 146. Follow the top of that bar to the left until the vertical line is reached, not quite halfway between 140 and 160, or 146.

PRACTICE 8

Use the graph in Example 8 to answer the following:

a. Which country shown has the fewest endangered species?

b. Find the total number of endangered species for Brazil, India, and Mexico.

Example 8 Reading a Bar Graph

In the following graph, each bar represents a country and the height of each bar represents the number of endangered species identified in that country.

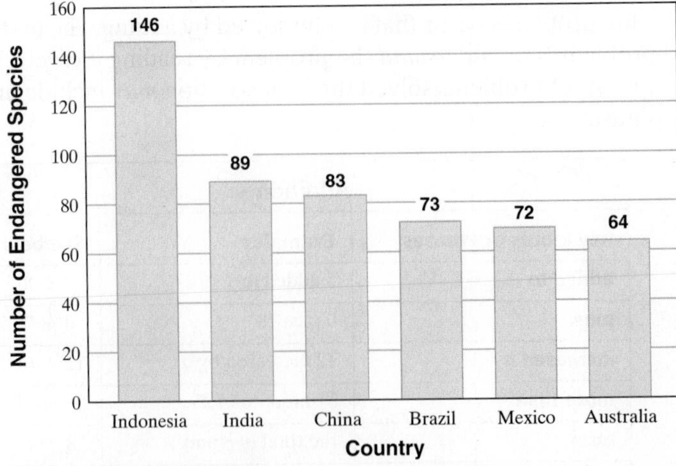

Source: The Top 10 of Everything, Russell Ash

Answer
7. 120 million lb
8. a. Australia **b.** 234

a. Which country shown has the greatest number of endangered species?
b. Find the total number of endangered species for Australia, China, and India.

Solution:

a. The country with the greatest number of endangered species corresponds to the tallest bar, which is Indonesia.
b. The key word here is "total." To find the total number of endangered species for Australia, China, and India, we add.

In Words		Translate to Numbers
Australia	→	64
China	→	83
India	→	+ 89
		Total 236

The total number of endangered species for Australia, China, and India is 236.

Work Practice 8

Calculator Explorations Adding Numbers

To add numbers on a calculator, find the keys marked [+] and [=] or [ENTER].

For example, to add 5 and 7 on a calculator, press the keys [5] [+] [7] [=] or [ENTER].

The display will read [12].
Thus, $5 + 7 = 12$.

To add 687, 981, and 49 on a calculator, press the keys [687] [+] [981] [+] [49] [=] or [ENTER].
The display will read [1717].

Thus, $687 + 981 + 49 = 1717$. (Although entering 687, for example, requires pressing more than one key, here numbers are grouped together for easier reading.)

Use a calculator to add.

1. $89 + 45$

2. $76 + 97$

3. $285 + 55$

4. $8773 + 652$

5.
$$\begin{array}{r} 985 \\ 1210 \\ 562 \\ +\ \ 77 \\ \hline \end{array}$$

6.
$$\begin{array}{r} 465 \\ 9888 \\ 620 \\ +1550 \\ \hline \end{array}$$

Vocabulary and Readiness Check

Use the choices below to fill in each blank. Some choices may be used more than once.

sum	order	addend	associative
perimeter	number	grouping	commutative

1. The sum of 0 and any number is the same ____________.
2. The sum of any number and 0 is the same ____________.
3. In 35 + 20 = 55, the number 55 is called the ____________ and 35 and 20 are each called a(n) ____________.
4. The distance around a polygon is called its ____________.
5. Since (3 + 1) + 20 = 3 + (1 + 20), we say that changing the ____________ in addition does not change the sum. This property is called the ____________ property of addition.
6. Since 7 + 10 = 10 + 7, we say that changing the ____________ in addition does not change the sum. This property is called the ____________ property of addition.

1.3 Exercise Set

FOR EXTRA HELP

MyMathLab

Objective A *Add. See Examples 1 through 4.*

1. $\begin{array}{r} 14 \\ +22 \\ \hline \end{array}$

2. $\begin{array}{r} 27 \\ +31 \\ \hline \end{array}$

3. $\begin{array}{r} 62 \\ +230 \\ \hline \end{array}$

4. $\begin{array}{r} 37 \\ +542 \\ \hline \end{array}$

5. $\begin{array}{r} 12 \\ 13 \\ +24 \\ \hline \end{array}$

6. $\begin{array}{r} 23 \\ 45 \\ +30 \\ \hline \end{array}$

7. $\begin{array}{r} 5267 \\ +\ \ 132 \\ \hline \end{array}$

8. $\begin{array}{r} 236 \\ +6243 \\ \hline \end{array}$

9. 53 + 64

10. 41 + 74

11. 22 + 490

12. 35 + 470

13. 22,781 + 186,297

14. 17,427 + 821,059

15. $\begin{array}{r} 8 \\ 9 \\ 2 \\ 5 \\ +1 \\ \hline \end{array}$

16. $\begin{array}{r} 3 \\ 5 \\ 8 \\ 5 \\ +7 \\ \hline \end{array}$

17. $\begin{array}{r} 6 \\ 21 \\ 14 \\ 9 \\ +12 \\ \hline \end{array}$

18. $\begin{array}{r} 12 \\ 4 \\ 8 \\ 26 \\ +10 \\ \hline \end{array}$

19. $\begin{array}{r} 81 \\ 17 \\ 23 \\ 79 \\ +12 \\ \hline \end{array}$

20. $\begin{array}{r} 64 \\ 28 \\ 56 \\ 25 \\ +32 \\ \hline \end{array}$

21. 62 + 18 + 14

22. 23 + 49 + 18

23. 40 + 800 + 70

24. 30 + 900 + 20

25. 7542 + 49 + 682

26. 1624 + 32 + 976

27. 24 + 9006 + 489 + 2407

28. 16 + 1056 + 748 + 7770

29. 627 + 628 + 629

30. 427 + 383 + 229

31. 6820 + 4271 + 5626

32. 6789 + 4321 + 5555

33. 507 + 593 + 10

34. 864 + 33 + 356

35. 4200 + 2107 + 2692

36. 5000 + 1400 + 3021

37. 49 + 628 + 5 762 + 29,462

38. 26 + 582 + 4 763 + 62,511

39. 121,742 + 57,279 + 26,586 + 426,782

40. 504,218 + 321,920 + 38,507 + 594,687

Objective B *Find the perimeter of each figure. See Examples 5 and 6.*

△ **41.**

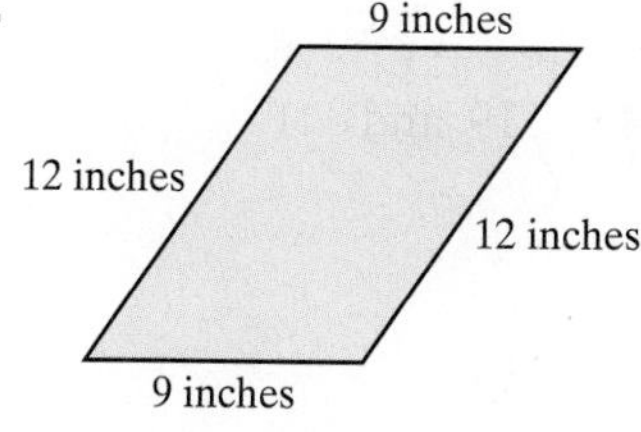

△ **42.**

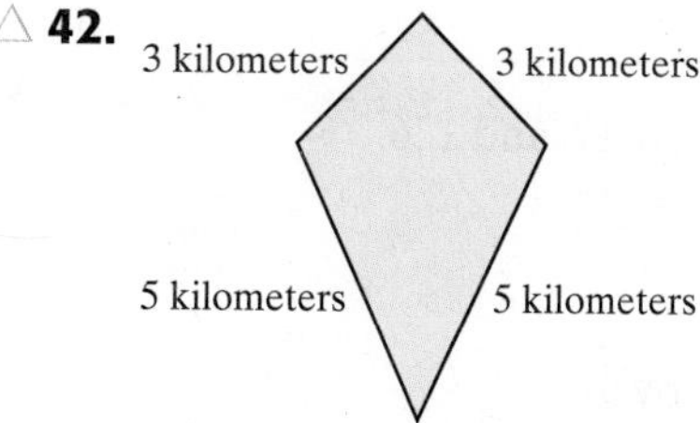

△ **43.**

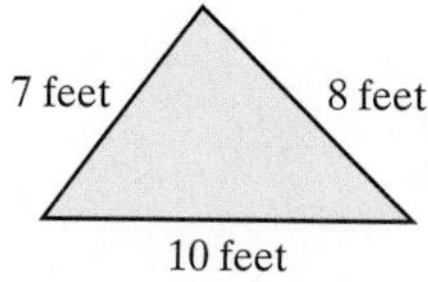

△ **44.**

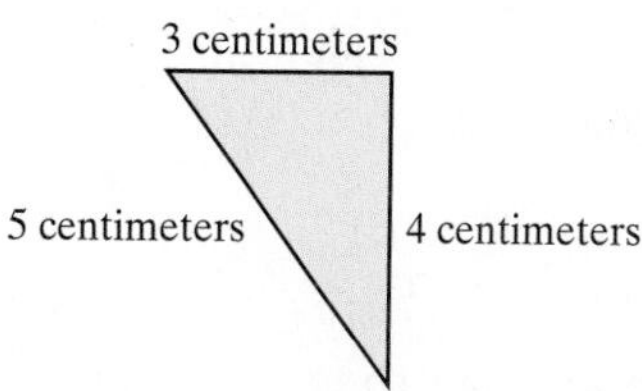

△ **45.**

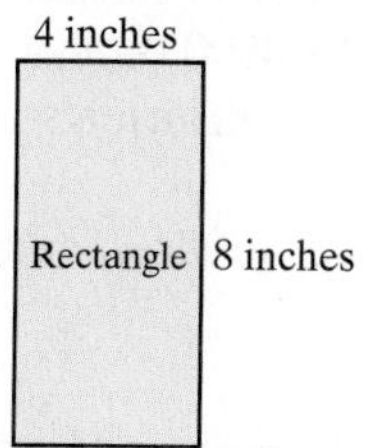

△ **46.**

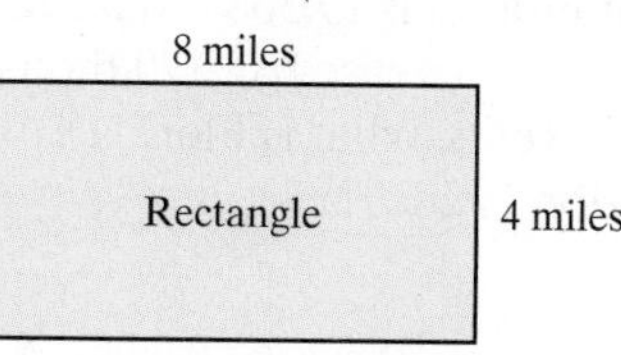

△ **47.**

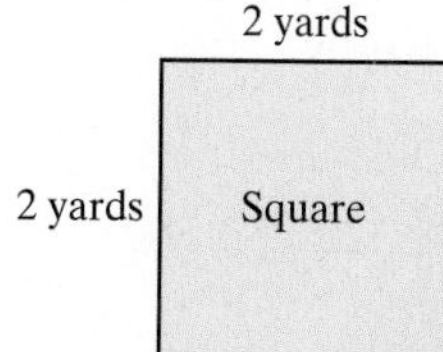

△ **48.**

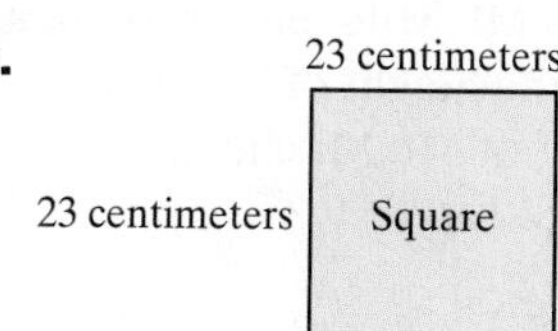

△ **49.**

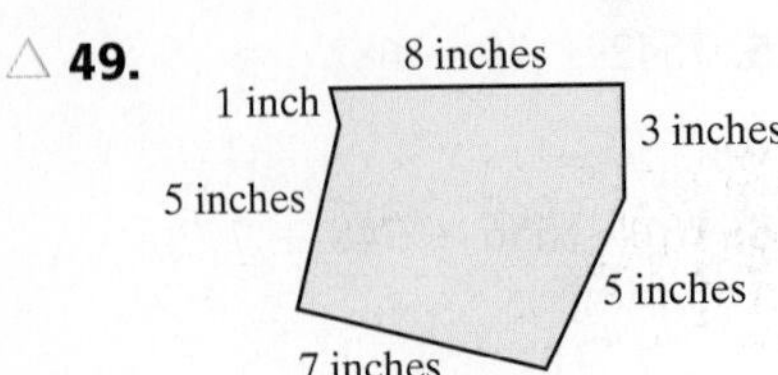

△ **50.**

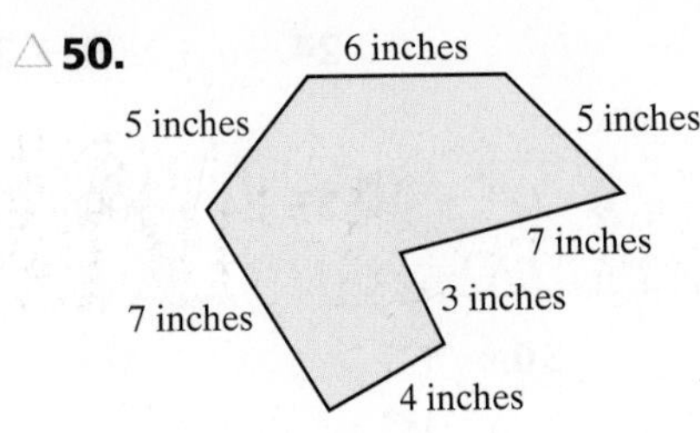

△ **51.**

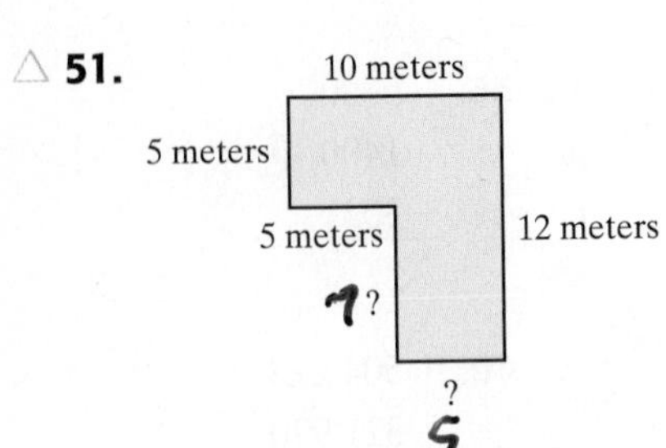

△ **52.**

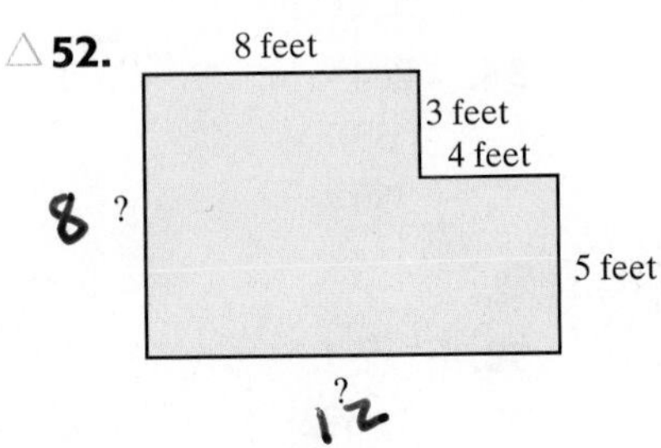

Objectives **A** **B** **C** **Mixed Practice–Translating** *Solve. See Examples 1 through 8.*

53. Find the sum of 297 and 1796.

54. Find the sum of 802 and 6487.

55. Find the total of 76, 39, 8, 17, and 126.

56. Find the total of 89, 45, 2, 19, and 341.

57. What is 452 increased by 92?

58. What is 712 increased by 38?

59. What is 2686 plus 686 plus 80?

60. What is 3565 plus 565 plus 70?

61. The population of Florida is 19,308 thousand in 2010. It is projected to increase by 3170 thousand during the next ten years. What is Florida's projected population in 2020?

62. The population of California is 39,136 thousand in 2010. It is projected to increase by 4990 thousand during the next ten years. What is California's projected population in 2020?

63. The highest point in South Carolina is Sassafras Mountain at 3560 feet above sea level. The highest point in North Carolina is Mt. Mitchell, whose peak is 3124 feet increased by the height of Sassafras Mountain. Find the height of Mt. Mitchell. (*Source:* U.S. Geological Survey)

64. The distance from Kansas City, Kansas, to Hays, Kansas, is 285 miles. Colby, Kansas, is 98 miles farther from Kansas City than Hays. Find the total distance from Kansas City to Colby.

△ **65.** Leo Callier is installing an invisible fence in his backyard. How many feet of wiring are needed to enclose the yard below?

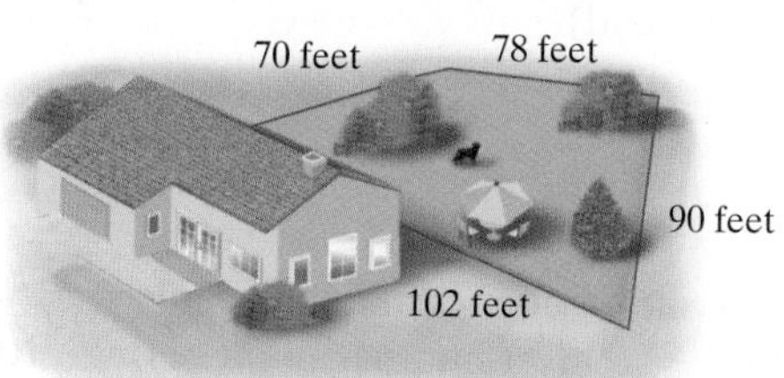

△ **66.** A homeowner is considering installing gutters around her home. Find the perimeter of her rectangular home.

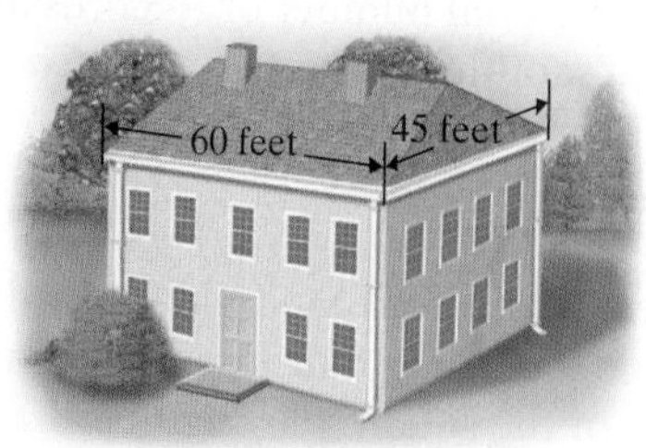

67. The highest waterfall in the United States is Yosemite Falls in Yosemite National Park in California. Yosemite Falls is made up of three sections, as shown in the graph. What is the total height of Yosemite Falls? (*Source:* U.S. Department of the Interior)

Highest U.S. Waterfalls

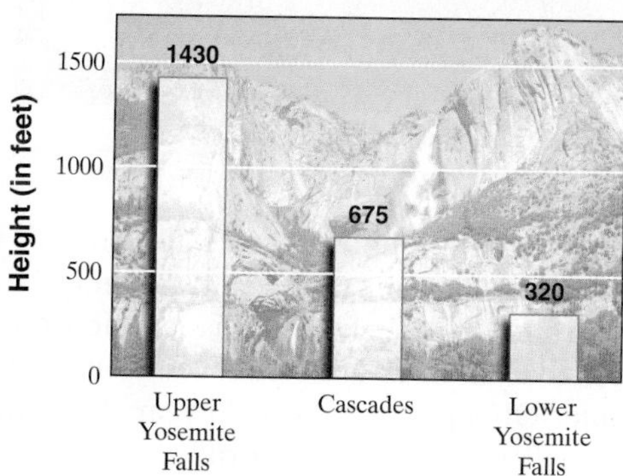

68. Jordan White, a nurse at Mercy Hospital, is recording fluid intake on a patient's medical chart. During his shift, the patient had the following types and amounts of intake measured in cubic centimeters (cc). What amount should Jordan record as the total fluid intake for this patient?

Oral	Intravenous	Blood
240	500	500
100	200	
355		

69. In 2008, Harley-Davidson sold 235,441 of its motorcycles domestically. In addition, 78,328 Harley-Davidson motorcycles were sold internationally. What was the total number of Harley-Davidson motorcycles sold in 2008? (*Source:* Harley-Davidson, Inc.)

70. Hank Aaron holds Major League Baseball's record for the most runs batted in over his career. He batted in 1305 runs from 1954 to 1965. He batted in another 992 runs from 1966 until he retired in 1976. How many total runs did Hank Aaron bat in during his career in professional baseball?

71. During one month in a recent year, the two top-selling automobiles in the United States were the Honda Accord and the Toyota Camry. There were 41,382 Accords and 44,064 Camrys sold that month. What was the total number of Accords and Camrys sold in that month? (*Source:* Toyota Corp. and Honda Corp.)

72. In a recent year, the country of New Zealand had 29,719,969 more sheep than people. If the human population of New Zealand in 2008 was 4,280,031, what was the sheep population? (*Source:* Statistics: New Zealand)

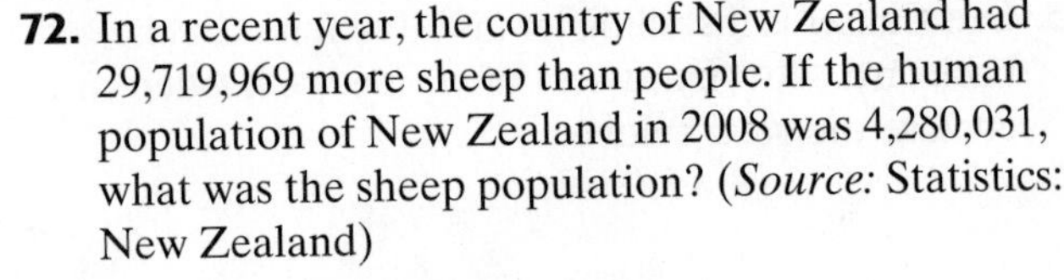

73. The largest permanent Monopoly board is made of granite and located in San Jose, California. Find the perimeter of the square playing board.

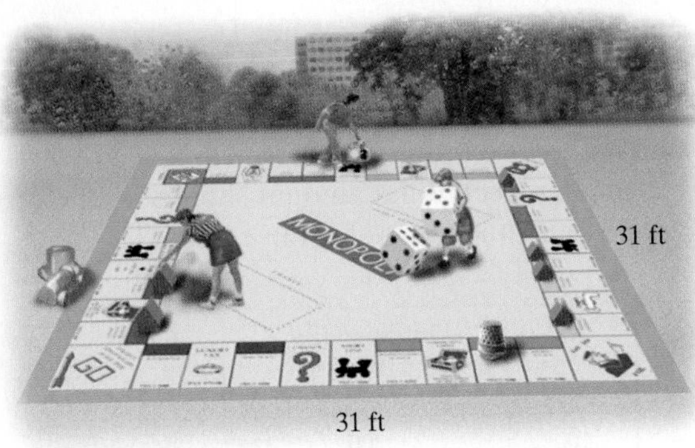

74. The smallest commercially available jigsaw puzzle (with the greatest number of pieces) is a 1000-piece puzzle manufactured in Spain. Find the perimeter of this rectangular-shaped puzzle.

75. In 2008, there were 2677 Gap Inc. (Gap, Banana Republic, Old Navy) stores located in the United States and 493 located outside the United States. How many Gap Inc. stores were located worldwide? (*Source:* Gap Inc.)

76. Wilma Rudolph, who won three gold medals in track and field events in the 1960 Summer Olympics, was born in 1940. Tirunesh Dibaba, who won two gold medals in track and field events but in the 2008 Summer Olympics, was born 45 years later. In what year was Tirunesh Dibaba born?

The table shows the number of Target stores in ten states. Use this table to answer Exercises 77 through 82.

The Top States for Target Stores in 2009

State	Number of Stores
Pennsylvania	53
California	236
Florida	124
Georgia	56
Illinois	85
New York	62
Michigan	60
Minnesota	73
Ohio	64
Texas	146

(*Source:* Target Corporation)

77. Which state has the most Target stores?

78. Which of the states listed in the table has the fewest Target stores?

79. What is the total number of Target stores located in the three states with the most Target stores?

80. How many Target stores are located in the ten states listed in the table?

81. Which pair of neighboring states has more Target stores combined, Florida and Georgia or Michigan and Ohio?

82. Target operates stores in 49 states. There are 739 Target stores located in the states not listed in the table. How many Target stores are in the United States?

83. The state of Delaware has 2029 miles of urban highways and 3865 miles of rural highways. Find the total highway mileage in Delaware. (*Source:* U.S. Federal Highway Administration)

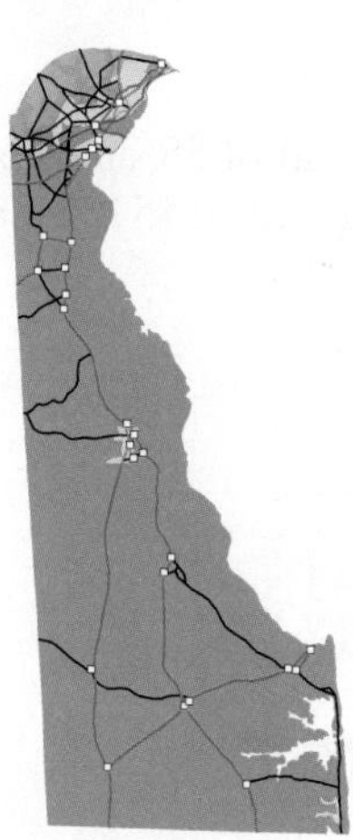

84. The state of Rhode Island has 5193 miles of urban highways and 1222 miles of rural highways. Find the total highway mileage in Rhode Island. (*Source:* U.S. Federal Highway Administration)

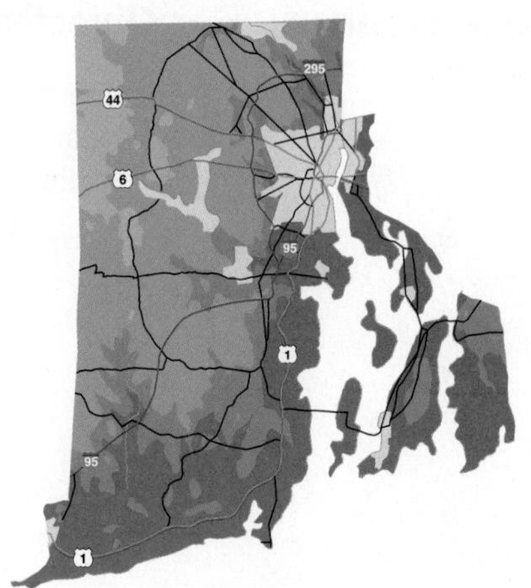

Concept Extensions

85. In your own words, explain the commutative property of addition.

86. In your own words, explain the associative property of addition.

87. Give any three whole numbers whose sum is 100.

88. Give any four whole numbers whose sum is 25.

89. Add: 56,468,980 + 1,236,785 + 986,768,000

90. Add: 78,962 + 129,968,350 + 36,462,880

Check each addition below. If it is incorrect, find the correct answer. See the Concept Check in this section.

91. $\begin{array}{r} 566 \\ 932 \\ +\ 871 \\ \hline 2369 \end{array}$

92. $\begin{array}{r} 773 \\ 659 \\ +\ 481 \\ \hline 1913 \end{array}$

93. $\begin{array}{r} 14 \\ 173 \\ 86 \\ +257 \\ \hline 520 \end{array}$

94. $\begin{array}{r} 19 \\ 214 \\ 49 \\ +651 \\ \hline 923 \end{array}$

Objectives

A Subtract Whole Numbers.

B Solve Problems by Subtracting Whole Numbers.

1.4 SUBTRACTING WHOLE NUMBERS

Objective A Subtracting Whole Numbers

If you have \$5 and someone gives you \$3, you have a total of \$8, since 5 + 3 = 8. Similarly, if you have \$8 and then someone borrows \$3, you have \$5 left. **Subtraction** is finding the **difference** of two numbers.

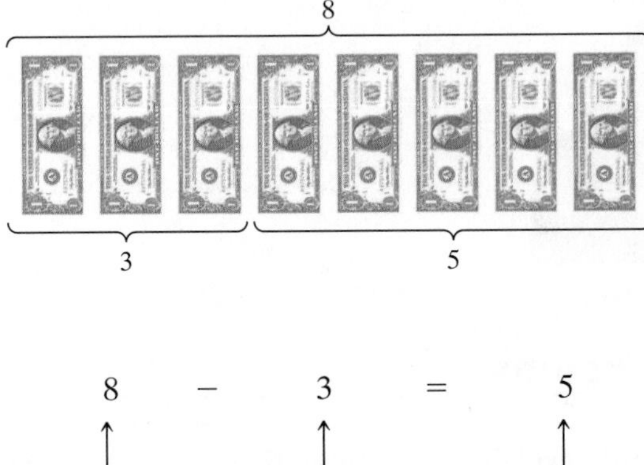

8 − 3 = 5

minuend ↑ subtrahend ↑ difference ↑

In this example, 8 is the **minuend,** and 3 is the **subtrahend.** The **difference** between these two numbers, 8 and 3, is 5.

Notice that addition and subtraction are very closely related. In fact, subtraction is defined in terms of addition.

8 − 3 = 5 because 5 + 3 = 8

This means that subtraction can be *checked* by addition, and we say that addition and subtraction are reverse operations.

PRACTICE 1

Subtract. Check each answer by adding.

a. 14 − 6

b. 20 − 8

c. 93 − 93

d. 42 − 0

Example 1 Subtract. Check each answer by adding.

a. 12 − 9 **b.** 22 − 7 **c.** 35 − 35 **d.** 70 − 0

Solution:

a. 12 − 9 = 3 because 3 + 9 = 12

b. 22 − 7 = 15 because 15 + 7 = 22

c. 35 − 35 = 0 because 0 + 35 = 35

d. 70 − 0 = 70 because 70 + 0 = 70

Work Practice 1

Look again at Examples 1(c) and 1(d).

1(c) 35 − 35 = 0 — 35 and 35: same number; 0: difference is 0

1(d) 70 − 0 = 70 — 70 − 0: a number minus 0; 70: difference is the same number

These two examples illustrate the subtraction properties of 0.

Answer

1. a. 8 **b.** 12 **c.** 0 **d.** 42

Subtraction Properties of 0

The difference of any number and that same number is 0. For example,

$11 - 11 = 0$

The difference of any number and 0 is that same number. For example,

$45 - 0 = 45$

To subtract whole numbers we subtract the digits in the ones place, then the tens place, then the hundreds place, and so on. When subtraction involves numbers of two or more digits, it is more convenient to subtract vertically. For example, to subtract $893 - 52$,

```
 893  ←— minuend
 −52  ←— subtrahend
 841  ←— difference
 ↑↑↑
 ││└ 3 − 2
 │└ 9 − 5
 8 − 0
```

Line up the numbers vertically so that the minuend is on top and the place values correspond. Subtract in corresponding place values, starting with the ones place.

To check, add.

```
  difference   or    841
+ subtrahend       +  52
  minuend            893  ←— Since this is the original minuend,
                             the problem checks.
```

Example 2 Subtract: $7826 - 505$. Check by adding.

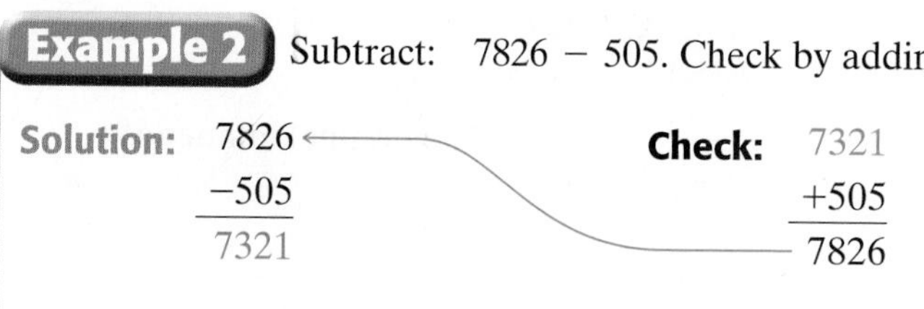

Work Practice 2

PRACTICE 2

Subtract. Check by adding.

a. $9143 - 122$

b. $978 - 851$

Subtracting by Borrowing

When subtracting vertically, if a digit in the second number (subtrahend) is larger than the corresponding digit in the first number (minuend), **borrowing** is necessary. For example, consider

```
  8[1]
− 6[3]
```

Since the 3 in the ones place of 63 is larger than the 1 in the ones place of 81, borrowing is necessary. We borrow 1 ten from the tens place and add it to the ones place.

Borrowing

```
                           7 11
 8   −  1   =  7    →      8̸ 1̸   ← 1 ten + 1 one = 11 ones
tens   ten   tens         − 6 3
```

Answer

2. a. 9021 **b.** 127

Now we subtract the ones-place digits and then the tens-place digits.

```
 7 11
 8 1  ←              Check:  18
−6 3                       +63
 1 8 ← 11 − 3 = 8           81  The original minuend.
 ↑
 └── 7 − 6 = 1
```

PRACTICE 3

Subtract. Check by adding.

a. 697 − 49

b. 326 − 245

c. 1234 − 822

Example 3 Subtract: 543 − 29. Check by adding.

Solution:

```
  3 13
 5 4 3 ←           Check:  514
  −2 9                     +29
 5 1 4                     543
```

Work Practice 3

Sometimes we may have to borrow from more than one place. For example, to subtract 7631 − 152, we first borrow from the tens place.

```
     2 11
 7 6 3 1
−  1 5 2
       9  ← 11 − 2 = 9
```

In the tens place, 5 is greater than 2, so we borrow again. This time we borrow from the hundreds place.

```
   ┌── 6 hundreds − 1 hundred = 5 hundreds
   ↓ 12 ←
   5 2 11  └── 1 hundred + 2 tens
 7 6 3 1 ←          or                  Check:  7479
−  1 5 2      10 tens + 2 tens = 12 tens        +152
 7 4 7 9                                        7631  The original minuend.
```

PRACTICE 4

Subtract. Check by adding.

a. 400 − 164

b. 1000 − 762

Example 4 Subtract: 900 − 174. Check by adding.

Solution: In the ones place, 4 is larger than 0, so we borrow from the tens place. But the tens place of 900 is 0, so to borrow from the tens place we must first borrow from the hundreds place.

```
 8 10
 9 0 0
−1 7 4
```

Now borrow from the tens place.

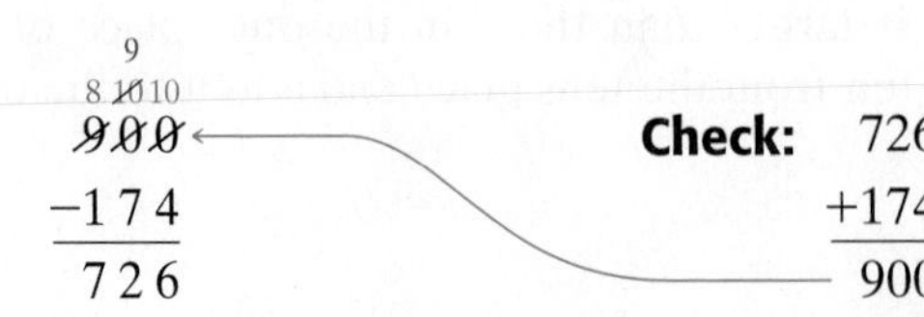

```
   9
 8 10 10
 9  0  0 ←          Check:  726
−1  7  4                   +174
 7  2  6                    900
```

Work Practice 4

Answers

3. a. 648 **b.** 81 **c.** 412

4. a. 236 **b.** 238

Objective B Solving Problems by Subtracting

Often, real-life problems occur that can be solved by subtracting. The first step in solving any word problem is to *understand* the problem by reading it carefully.

Descriptions of problems solved through subtraction *may* include any of these key words or phrases:

Subtraction

Key Words or Phrases	Examples	Symbols
subtract	subtract 5 from 8	8 − 5
difference	the difference of 10 and 2	10 − 2
less	17 less 3	17 − 3
less than	2 less than 20	20 − 2
take away	14 take away 9	14 − 9
decreased by	7 decreased by 5	7 − 5
subtracted from	9 subtracted from 12	12 − 9

Helpful Hint Be careful when solving applications that suggest subtraction. Although order *does not* matter when adding, order *does* matter when subtracting. For example, 20 − 15 and 15 − 20 do not simplify to the same number.

✓**Concept Check** In each of the following problems, identify which number is the minuend and which number is the subtrahend.

a. What is the result when 6 is subtracted from 40?

b. What is the difference of 15 and 8?

c. Find a number that is 15 fewer than 23.

To solve a word problem that involves subtraction, we first use the facts given to write a subtraction statement. Then we write the corresponding solution of the real-life problem. It is sometimes helpful to write the statement in words (brief phrases) and then translate to numbers.

Example 5 Finding the Radius of a Planet

The radius of Jupiter is 43,441 miles. The radius of Saturn is 7257 miles less than the radius of Jupiter. Find the radius of Saturn. (*Source:* National Space Science Data Center)

Solution:

In Words		Translate to Numbers
radius of Jupiter	⟶	43,441
− 7257	⟶	− 7257
radius of Saturn	⟶	36,184

The radius of Saturn is 36,184 miles.

Work Practice 5

PRACTICE 5

The radius of Uranus is 15,759 miles. The radius of Neptune is 458 miles less than the radius of Uranus. What is the radius of Neptune? (*Source:* National Space Science Data Center)

Helpful Hint Since subtraction and addition are reverse operations, don't forget that a subtraction problem can be checked by adding.

Answer

5. 15,301 miles

✓ **Concept Check Answers**

a. minuend: 40; subtrahend: 6

b. minuend: 15; subtrahend: 8

c. minuend: 23; subtrahend: 15

PRACTICE 6

During a sale, the price of a new suit is decreased by $47. If the original price was $92, find the sale price of the suit.

Example 6 Calculating Miles per Gallon

A subcompact car gets 42 miles per gallon of gas. A full-size car gets 17 miles per gallon of gas. Find the difference between the subcompact car miles per gallon and the full-size car miles per gallon.

Solution: **In Words** **Translate to Numbers**

In Words		Translate to Numbers
subcompact miles per gallon	→	$\overset{3}{\cancel{4}}\overset{12}{\cancel{2}}$
− full-size miles per gallon	→	−17
difference in miles per gallon		25

The difference in the subcompact car miles per gallon and the full-size car miles per gallon is 25 miles per gallon.

Work Practice 6

Helpful Hint

Once again, because subtraction and addition are reverse operations, don't forget that a subtraction problem can be checked by adding.

Calculator Explorations Subtracting Numbers

To subtract numbers on a calculator, find the keys marked [−] and [=] or [ENTER].

For example, to find 83 − 49 on a calculator, press the keys [83] [−] [49] [=] or [ENTER].

The display will read [34]. Thus, 83 − 49 = 34.

Use a calculator to subtract.

1. 865 − 95

2. 76 − 27

3. 147 − 38

4. 366 − 87

5. 9625 − 647

6. 10,711 − 8925

Answer

6. $45

Vocabulary and Readiness Check

Use the choices below to fill in each blank.

0	minuend	difference
number	subtrahend	

1. The difference of any number and that same number is ___________ .
2. The difference of any number and 0 is the same ___________ .
3. In $37 - 19 = 18$, the number 37 is the ___________ , and the number 19 is the ___________ .
4. In $37 - 19 = 18$, the number 18 is called the ___________ .

Find each difference.

5. $6 - 6$
6. $93 - 93$
7. $600 - 0$
8. $5 - 0$

1.4 Exercise Set

FOR EXTRA HELP MyMathLab

PRACTICE

WATCH

DOWNLOAD

READ

REVIEW

Objective A *Subtract. Check by adding. See Examples 1 and 2.*

1. $67 - 23$
2. $72 - 41$
3. $389 - 124$
4. $572 - 321$
5. $167 - 32$
6. $286 - 45$
7. $2677 - 423$
8. $5766 - 324$
9. $6998 - 1453$
10. $4912 - 2610$
11. $749 - 149$
12. $257 - 257$

Subtract. Check by adding. See Examples 1 through 4.

13. $62 - 37$
14. $55 - 29$
15. $70 - 25$
16. $80 - 37$
17. $938 - 792$
18. $436 - 275$
19. $922 - 634$
20. $674 - 299$
21. $600 - 432$
22. $300 - 149$
23. $142 - 36$
24. $773 - 29$
25. $923 - 476$
26. $813 - 227$
27. $6283 - 560$
28. $5349 - 720$
29. $533 - 29$
30. $724 - 16$
31. $200 - 111$
32. $300 - 211$
33. $1983 - 1904$
34. $1983 - 1914$
35. $56,422 - 16,508$
36. $76,652 - 29,498$

37. 50,000 − 17,289

38. 40,000 − 23,582

39. 7020 − 1979

40. 6050 − 1878

41. 51,111 − 19,898

42. 62,222 − 39,898

Objective B *Solve. See Examples 5 and 6.*

43. Subtract 5 from 9.

44. Subtract 9 from 21.

45. Find the difference of 41 and 21.

46. Find the difference of 16 and 5.

47. Subtract 56 from 63.

48. Subtract 41 from 59.

49. Find 108 less 36.

50. Find 25 less 12.

51. Find 12 subtracted from 100.

52. Find 86 subtracted from 90.

53. Professor Graham is reading a 503-page book. If she has just finished reading page 239, how many more pages must she read to finish the book?

54. When a couple began a trip, the odometer read 55,492. When the trip was over, the odometer read 59,320. How many miles did they drive on their trip?

55. In 2002, the hole in the Earth's ozone layer over Antarctica was about 22 million square kilometers in size. In 2008, the hole had grown to 25 million square kilometers. By how much did the hole grow from 2002 to 2008? (*Source:* U.S. Environmental Protection Agency EPA)

56. Bamboo can grow to 98 feet while Pacific giant kelp (a type of seaweed) can grow to 197 feet. How much taller is the kelp than the bamboo?

Bamboo

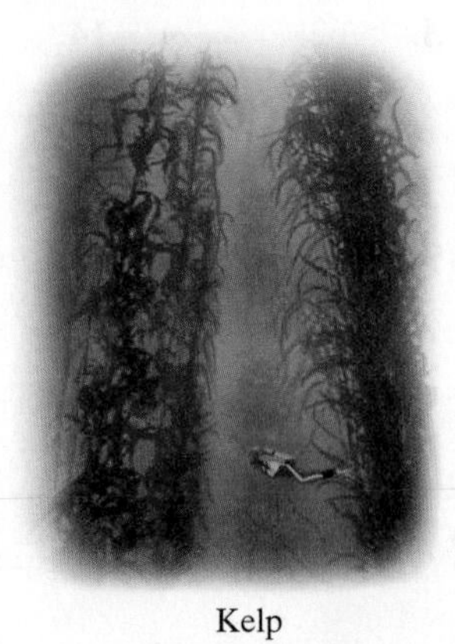

Kelp

A river basin is the geographic area drained by a river and its tributaries. The Mississippi River Basin is the third largest in the world and is divided into six sub-basins, whose areas are shown in the following bar graph. Use this graph for Exercises 57 through 60.

57. Find the total U.S. land area drained by the Upper Mississippi and Lower Mississippi sub-basins.

58. Find the total U.S. land area drained by the Ohio and Tennessee sub-basins.

59. How much more land is drained by the Missouri sub-basin than the Arkansas Red-White sub-basin?

60. How much more land is drained by the Upper Mississippi sub-basin than the Lower Mississippi sub-basin?

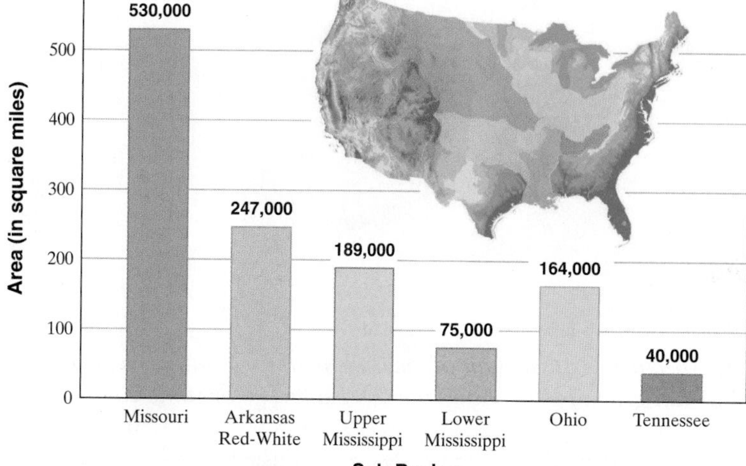

61. The peak of Mt. McKinley in Alaska is 20,320 feet above sea level. The peak of Long's Peak in Colorado is 14,255 feet above sea level. How much higher is the peak of Mt. McKinley than Long's Peak? (*Source:* U.S. Geological Survey)

62. On January 12, 1916, the city of Indianapolis, Indiana, had the greatest temperature change in a day. It dropped 58 degrees. If the high temperature was 68° Fahrenheit, what was the low temperature?

63. The Oroville Dam, on the Feather River, is the tallest dam in the United States at 754 feet. The Hoover Dam, on the Colorado River, is 726 feet high. How much taller is the Oroville Dam than the Hoover Dam? (*Source:* U.S. Bureau of Reclamation)

64. A new iPhone with 32 GB costs $299. Jocelyn Robinson has $713 in her savings account. How much will she have left in her savings account after she buys the iPhone? (*Source:* Apple, Inc.)

65. The distance from Kansas City to Denver is 645 miles. Hays, Kansas, lies on the road between the two and is 287 miles from Kansas City. What is the distance between Hays and Denver?

66. Pat Salanki's blood cholesterol level is 243. The doctor tells him it should be decreased to 185. How much of a decrease is this?

67. A new DVD player with remote control costs $295. A college student has $914 in her savings account. How much will she have left in her savings account after she buys the DVD player?

68. A stereo that regularly sells for $547 is discounted by $99 in a sale. What is the sale price?

69. The population of Oklahoma is projected to grow from 3648 thousand in 2009 to 4100 thousand in 2025. What is Oklahoma's projected population increase over this time?

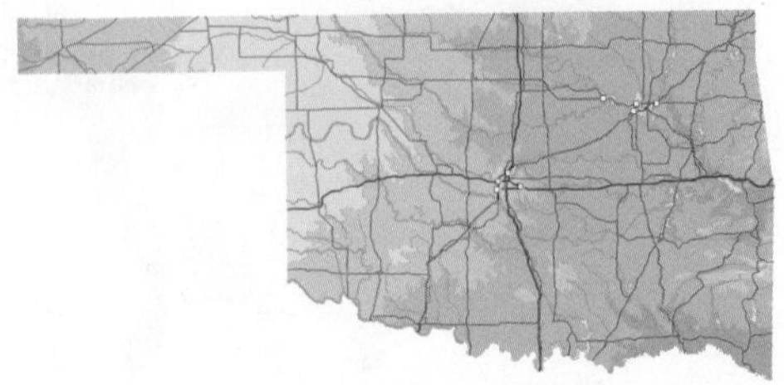

70. In 1996, the centennial of the Boston Marathon, the official number of participants was 38,708. In 2009, there were 12,322 fewer participants. How many official participants were there for the 2009 Boston Marathon?

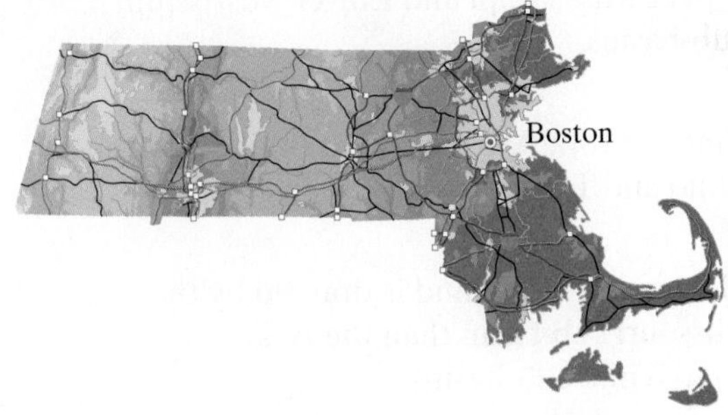

The decibel (dB) is a unit of measurement for sound. Every increase of 10 dB is a tenfold increase in sound intensity. The bar graph below shows the decibel levels for some common sounds. Use this graph for Exercises 71 through 74.

71. What is the dB rating for live rock music?

72. Which is the quietest of all the sounds shown in the graph?

73. How much louder is the sound of snoring than normal conversation?

74. What is the difference in sound intensity between live rock music and loud television?

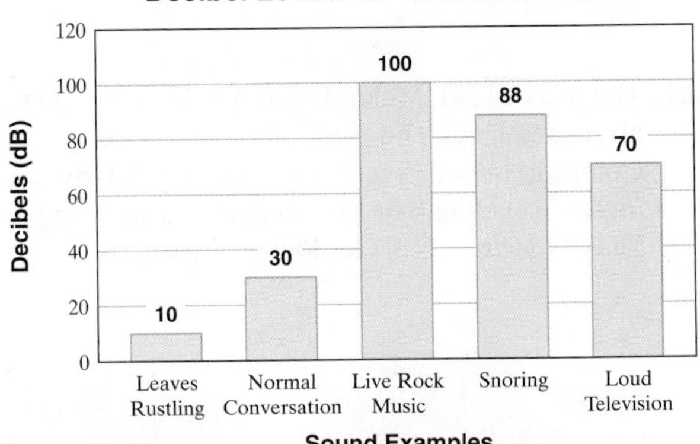

75. The 111th Congress has 539 senators and representatives. Of these, 219 were registered Boy Scouts at some time in their lives. How many members of the 111th Congress were never Boy Scouts? (*Source:* Boy Scouts of America, U.S. Senate)

76. In the United States, there were 23,729 tornadoes from 1990 through 2008. In all, 13,205 of these tornadoes occurred from 1990 through 2000. How many tornadoes occurred during the period after 2000? (*Source:* Storm Prediction Center, National Weather Service)

77. Until recently, the world's largest permanent maze was located in Ruurlo, Netherlands. This maze of beech hedges covers 94,080 square feet. A new hedge maze using hibiscus bushes at the Dole Plantation in Wahiawa, Hawaii, covers 100,000 square feet. How much larger is the Dole Plantation maze than the Ruurlo maze? (*Source: The Guinness Book of Records*)

78. There were only 25 California condors in the entire world in 1987. To date, the number has increased to an estimated 127 living in the wild. How much of an increase is this? (*Source:* California Department of Fish and Game)

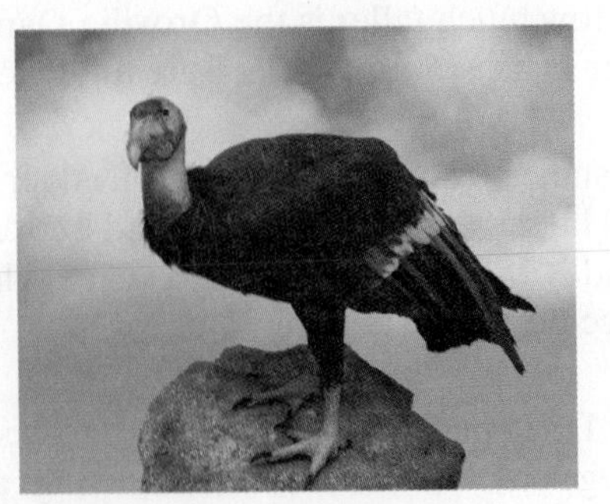

The bar graph shows the top five U.S. airports according to number of passengers arriving and departing in 2007. Use this graph to answer Exercises 79 through 82.

Source: Airports Council International

79. Which airport is the busiest?

80. Which airports have fewer than 70 million passengers per year?

81. How many more passengers per year does the Chicago O'Hare International Airport have than the Denver International Airport?

82. How many more passengers per year does the Hartsfield-Jackson Atlanta International Airport have than the Dallas/Ft. Worth International Airport?

Solve.

83. Two seniors, Jo Keen and Trudy Waterbury, were candidates for student government president. Who won the election if the votes were cast as follows? By how many votes did the winner win?

	Candidate	
Class	**Jo**	**Trudy**
Freshman	276	295
Sophomore	362	122
Junior	201	312
Senior	179	18

84. Two students submitted advertising budgets for a student government fund-raiser.

	Student A	**Student B**
Radio ads	\$600	\$300
Newspaper ads	\$200	\$400
Posters	\$150	\$240
Handbills	\$120	\$170

If \$1200 is available for advertising, how much excess would each budget have?

Mixed Practice (*Sections 1.3 and 1.4*) *Add or subtract as indicated.*

85. $\begin{array}{r} 986 \\ +\ 48 \\ \hline \end{array}$

86. $\begin{array}{r} 986 \\ -\ 48 \\ \hline \end{array}$

87. $76 - 67$

88. $80 + 93 + 17 + 9 + 2$

89. $\begin{array}{r} 9000 \\ -\ 482 \\ \hline \end{array}$

90. $\begin{array}{r} 10{,}000 \\ -\ 1786 \\ \hline \end{array}$

91. $\begin{array}{r} 10{,}962 \\ 4851 \\ +\ 7063 \\ \hline \end{array}$

92. $\begin{array}{r} 12{,}468 \\ 3211 \\ +\ 1988 \\ \hline \end{array}$

Concept Extensions

For each exercise, identify which number is the minuend and which number is the subtrahend. See the Concept Check in this section.

93. $\begin{array}{r} 48 \\ -\ 1 \\ \hline \end{array}$

94. $\begin{array}{r} 2863 \\ -\ 1904 \\ \hline \end{array}$

95. Subtract 7 from 70.

96. Find 86 decreased by 25.

Identify each answer as correct or incorrect. Use addition to check. If the answer is incorrect, then write the correct answer.

97.
```
  741
-  56
  675
```

98.
```
  478
-  89
  389
```

99.
```
  1029
-  888
   141
```

100.
```
  7615
-  547
  7168
```

Fill in the missing digits in each problem.

101.
```
  526_
- 2_85
  28_4
```

102.
```
  10,_4_
 -8 5_4
   _710
```

103. Is there a commutative property of subtraction? In other words, does order matter when subtracting? Why or why not?

104. Explain why the phrase "Subtract 7 from 10" translates to "10 − 7."

105. The local college library is having a Million Pages of Reading promotion. The freshmen have read a total of 289,462 pages; the sophomores have read a total of 369,477 pages; the juniors have read a total of 218,287 pages; and the seniors have read a total of 121,685 pages. Have they reached a goal of one million pages? If not, how many more pages need to be read?

1.5 ROUNDING AND ESTIMATING

Objectives

A Round Whole Numbers.

B Use Rounding to Estimate Sums and Differences.

C Solve Problems by Estimating.

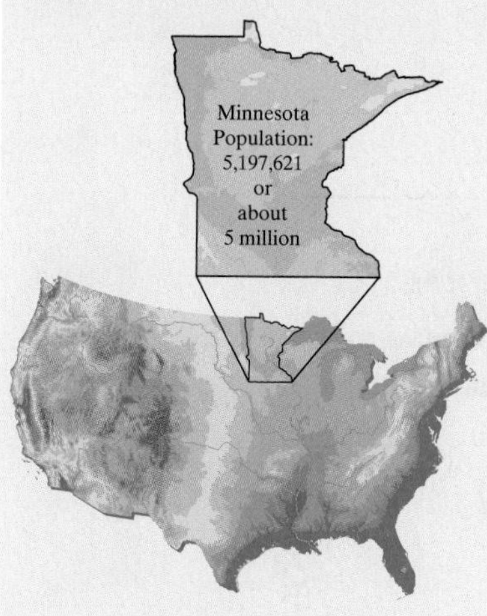

Objective A Rounding Whole Numbers

Rounding a whole number means approximating it. A rounded whole number is often easier to use, understand, and remember than the precise whole number. For example, instead of trying to remember the Minnesota state population as 5,197,621, it is much easier to remember it rounded to the nearest million: 5,000,000, or 5 million people. (*Source: World Almanac*)

Recall from Section 1.2 that the line below is called a number line. To **graph** a whole number on this number line, we darken the point representing the location of the whole number. For example, the number 4 is graphed below.

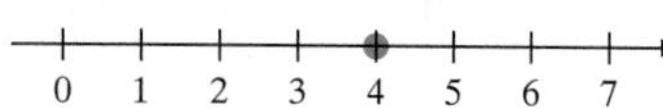

On the number line, the whole number 36 is closer to 40 than 30, so 36 rounded to the nearest ten is 40.

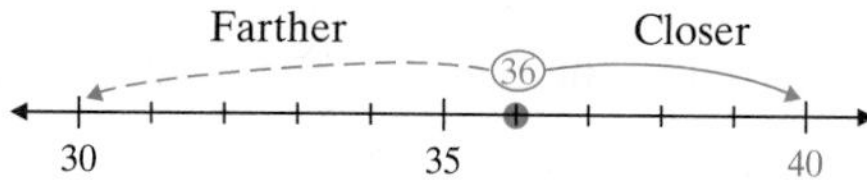

The whole number 52 is closer to 50 than 60, so 52 rounded to the nearest ten is 50.

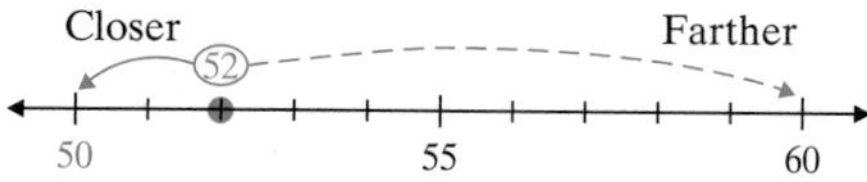

In trying to round 25 to the nearest ten, we see that 25 is halfway between 20 and 30. It is not closer to either number. In such a case, we round to the larger ten, that is, to 30.

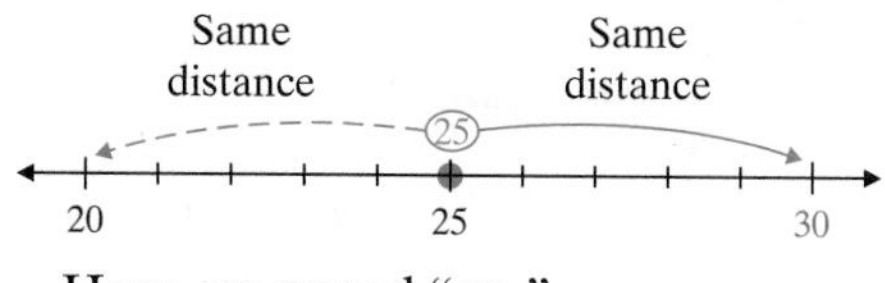

Here, we round "up."

To round a whole number without using a number line, follow these steps:

Rounding Whole Numbers to a Given Place Value

Step 1: Locate the digit to the right of the given place value.

Step 2: If this digit is 5 or greater, add 1 to the digit in the given place value and replace each digit to its right by 0.

Step 3: If this digit is less than 5, replace it and each digit to its right by 0.

PRACTICE 1

Round to the nearest ten.

a. 57

b. 641

c. 325

Example 1 Round 568 to the nearest ten.

Solution: 5 6(8) — tens place

The digit to the right of the tens place is the ones place, which is circled.

5 6(8) — Add 1. Replace with 0.

Since the circled digit is 5 or greater, add 1 to the 6 in the tens place and replace the digit to the right by 0.

We find that 568 rounded to the nearest ten is 570.

Work Practice 1

PRACTICE 2

Round to the nearest thousand.

a. 72,304

b. 9222

c. 671,800

Example 2 Round 278,362 to the nearest thousand.

Solution:

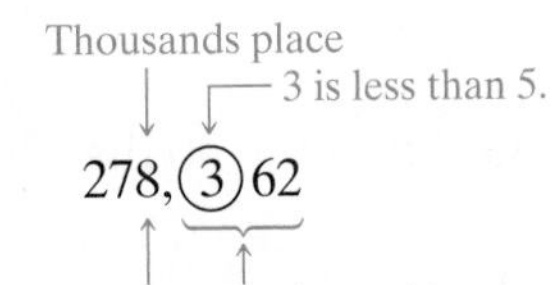
Thousands place
3 is less than 5.
278,(3)62
Do not add 1.
Replace with zeros.

The number 278,362 rounded to the nearest thousand is 278,000.

Work Practice 2

PRACTICE 3

Round to the nearest hundred.

a. 3474

b. 76,243

c. 978,965

Example 3 Round 248,982 to the nearest hundred.

Solution:

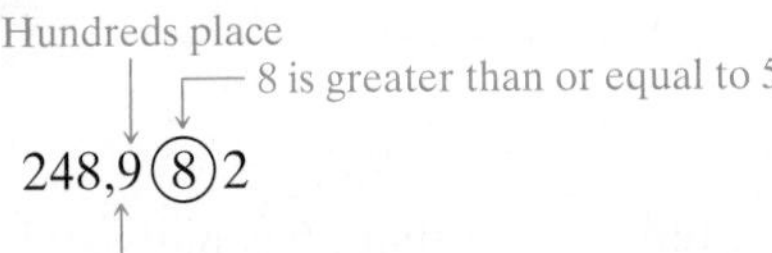
Hundreds place
8 is greater than or equal to 5.
248,9(8)2
Add 1.

$9 + 1 = 10$, so replace the digit 9 by 0 and carry 1 to the place value to the left.

2 4 8, 9 8 2 (8 + 1 above the 8, 0 above the 9) — Add 1. Replace with zeros.

The number 248,982 rounded to the nearest hundred is 249,000.

Work Practice 3

✓**Concept Check** Round each of the following numbers to the nearest *hundred*. Explain your reasoning.

a. 59 **b.** 29

Answers

1. a. 60 **b.** 640 **c.** 330

2. a. 72,000 **b.** 9000 **c.** 672,000

3. a. 3500 **b.** 76,200 **c.** 979,000

oncept Check Answers

b. 0

Objective B Estimating Sums and Differences

By rounding addends, minuends, and subtrahends, we can estimate sums and differences. An estimated sum or difference is appropriate when the exact number is not necessary. Also, an estimated sum or difference can help us determine if we made a mistake in calculating an exact amount. To estimate the sum below, round each number to the nearest hundred and then add.

768	rounds to	800
1952	rounds to	2000
225	rounds to	200
+ 149	rounds to	+ 100
		3100

The estimated sum is 3100, which is close to the **exact** sum of 3094.

Example 4 Round each number to the nearest hundred to find an estimated sum.

294
625
1071
+ 349

Solution:

Exact:		**Estimate:**
294	rounds to	300
625	rounds to	600
1071	rounds to	1100
+ 349	rounds to	+ 300
		2300

The estimated sum is 2300. (The exact sum is 2339.)

Work Practice 4

PRACTICE 4

Round each number to the nearest ten to find an estimated sum.

49
25
32
51
+ 98

Example 5 Round each number to the nearest hundred to find an estimated difference.

4725
− 2879

Solution:

Exact:		**Estimate:**
4725	rounds to	4700
−2879	rounds to	−2900
		1800

The estimated difference is 1800. (The exact difference is 1846.)

Work Practice 5

PRACTICE 5

Round each number to the nearest thousand to find an estimated difference.

3785
−2479

Objective C Solving Problems by Estimating

Making estimates is often the quickest way to solve real-life problems when solutions do not need to be exact.

Answers
4. 260 **5.** 2000

PRACTICE 6

Tasha Kilbey is trying to estimate how far it is from Gove, Kansas, to Hays, Kansas. Round each given distance on the map to the nearest ten to estimate the total distance.

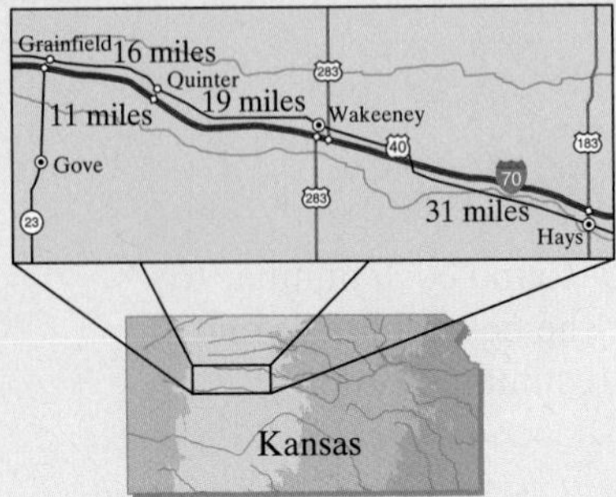

Example 6 Estimating Distances

A driver is trying to quickly estimate the distance from Temple, Texas, to Brenham, Texas. Round each distance given on the map to the nearest ten to estimate the total distance.

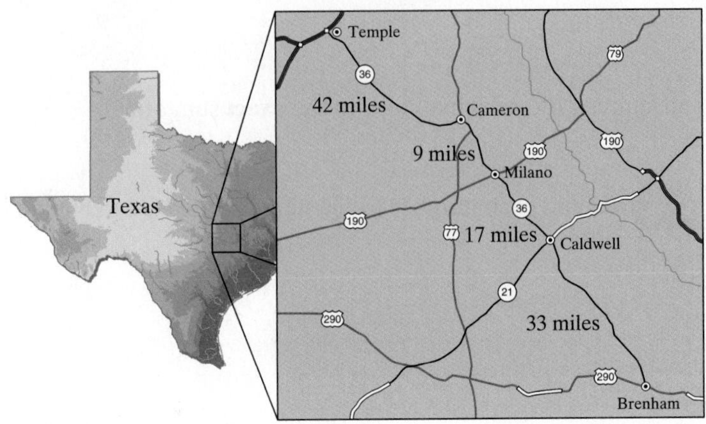

Solution:

Exact Distance:		Estimate:
42	rounds to	40
9	rounds to	10
17	rounds to	20
+33	rounds to	+30
		100

It is approximately 100 miles from Temple to Brenham. (The exact distance is 101 miles.)

Work Practice 6

PRACTICE 7

In a recent year, there were 48,445 reported cases of chicken pox, 6584 reported cases of mumps, and 15,632 reported cases of pertussis (whooping cough). Round each number to the nearest thousand to estimate the total number of cases reported for these preventable diseases. (*Source:* Centers for Disease Control and Prevention)

Example 7 Estimating Data

In three recent months, the numbers of tons of mail that went through Hartsfield-Jackson Atlanta International Airport were 635, 687, and 567. Round each number to the nearest hundred to estimate the tons of mail that passed through this airport.

Solution:

Exact Tons of Mail:		Estimate:
635	rounds to	600
687	rounds to	700
+567	rounds to	+600
		1900

The approximate tonnage of mail that moved through Atlanta's airport over this period was 1900 tons. (The exact tonnage was 1889 tons.)

Work Practice 7

vers

7. 71,000 total cases

Vocabulary and Readiness Check

Use the choices below to fill in each blank.

60	rounding	exact
70	estimate	graph

1. To __________ a number on a number line, darken the point representing the location of the number.
2. Another word for approximating a whole number is __________.
3. The number 65 rounded to the nearest ten is __________, but the number 61 rounded to the nearest ten is __________.
4. A(n) __________ number of products is 1265, but a(n) __________ is 1000.

1.5 Exercise Set

Objective A *Round each whole number to the given place. See Examples 1 through 3.*

1. 423 to the nearest ten

2. 273 to the nearest ten

3. 635 to the nearest ten

4. 846 to the nearest ten

5. 2791 to the nearest hundred

6. 8494 to the nearest hundred

7. 495 to the nearest ten

8. 898 to the nearest ten

9. 21,094 to the nearest thousand

10. 82,198 to the nearest thousand

11. 33,762 to the nearest thousand

12. 42,682 to the nearest ten-thousand

13. 328,495 to the nearest hundred

14. 179,406 to the nearest hundred

15. 36,499 to the nearest thousand

16. 96,501 to the nearest thousand

17. 39,994 to the nearest ten

18. 99,995 to the nearest ten

19. 29,834,235 to the nearest ten-million

20. 39,523,698 to the nearest million

Complete the table by estimating the given number to the given place value.

		Tens	Hundreds	Thousands
21.	5281			
22.	7619			
23.	9444			
24.	7777			
25.	14,876			
26.	85,049			

Round each number to the indicated place.

27. The University of California, Los Angeles, had 83,659 Alumni Association members in 2009. Round this number to the nearest thousand. (*Source:* UCLA)

28. In 2008, there were 11,565 Burger King restaurants. Round this number to the nearest hundred. (*Source:* Burger King Holdings, Inc.)

29. Kareem Abdul-Jabbar holds the NBA record for points scored, a total of 38,387 over his NBA career. Round this number to the nearest thousand. (*Source:* National Basketball Association)

30. It takes 60,149 days for Neptune to make a complete orbit around the Sun. Round this number to the nearest hundred. (*Source:* National Space Science Data Center)

31. In 2008, the most valuable brand in the world was Wal-Mart, having just overtaken the longtime leader, Coca-Cola. The estimated brand value of Wal-Mart was $42,570,000,000. Round this to the nearest billion. (*Source: Wall Street Journal*)

32. According to the 2009 Population Clock, the population of the United States was 305,747,409 in February 2009. Round this population figure to the nearest million. (*Source:* U.S. Census population clock)

33. The average salary for a Boston Red Sox baseball player during the 2009 season was $4,089,867. Round this average salary to the nearest hundred-thousand. (*Source:* ESPN)

34. In FY 2008, the Procter & Gamble Company had $83,503,000,000 in sales. Round this sales figure to the nearest billion. (*Source:* Procter & Gamble)

35. The United States currently has 262,700,000 cellular mobile phone users, while India has 296,886,000 users. Round each of the user numbers to the nearest million. (*Source:* Cellular Telecommunications Industry Association)

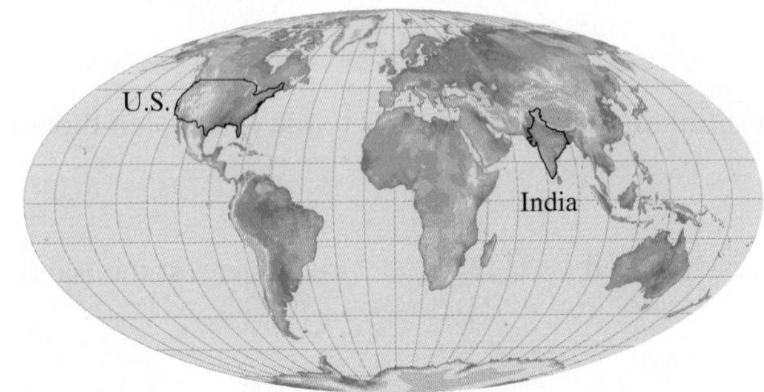

36. U.S. farms produced 2,933,888,000 bushels of soybeans in 2008. Round the soybean production figure to the nearest ten-million. (*Source:* U.S. Department of Agriculture)

Objective B *Estimate the sum or difference by rounding each number to the nearest ten. See Examples 4 and 5.*

37. $\begin{array}{r} 39 \\ 45 \\ 22 \\ +17 \\ \hline \end{array}$

38. $\begin{array}{r} 52 \\ 33 \\ 15 \\ +29 \\ \hline \end{array}$

39. $\begin{array}{r} 449 \\ -373 \\ \hline \end{array}$

40. $\begin{array}{r} 555 \\ -235 \\ \hline \end{array}$

Estimate the sum or difference by rounding each number to the nearest hundred. See Examples 4 and 5.

41. $\begin{array}{r} 1913 \\ 1886 \\ +1925 \\ \hline \end{array}$

42. $\begin{array}{r} 4050 \\ 3133 \\ +1220 \\ \hline \end{array}$

43. $\begin{array}{r} 1774 \\ -1492 \\ \hline \end{array}$

44. $\begin{array}{r} 1989 \\ -1870 \\ \hline \end{array}$

45. $\begin{array}{r} 3995 \\ 2549 \\ +4944 \\ \hline \end{array}$

46. $\begin{array}{r} 799 \\ 1655 \\ +271 \\ \hline \end{array}$

Three of the given calculator answers below are incorrect. Find them by estimating each sum.

47. 463 + 219 602

48. 522 + 785 1307

49. 229 + 443 + 606 1278

50. 542 + 789 + 198 2139

51. 7806 + 5150 12,956

52. 5233 + 4988 9011

Helpful Hint Estimation is useful to check for incorrect answers when using a calculator. For example, pressing a key too hard may result in a double digit, while pressing a key too softly may result in the digit not appearing in the display.

Objective C *Solve each problem by estimating. See Examples 6 and 7.*

53. An appliance store advertises three refrigerators on sale at $899, $1499, and $999. Round each cost to the nearest hundred to estimate the total cost.

54. Suppose you scored 89, 97, 100, 79, 75, and 82 on your biology tests. Round each score to the nearest ten to estimate your total score.

55. The distance from Kansas City to Boston is 1429 miles and from Kansas City to Chicago is 530 miles. Round each distance to the nearest hundred to estimate how much farther Boston is from Kansas City than Chicago is.

56. The Gonzales family took a trip and traveled 588, 689, 277, 143, 59, and 802 miles on six consecutive days. Round each distance to the nearest hundred to estimate the distance they traveled.

57. The peak of Mt. McKinley, in Alaska, is 20,320 feet above sea level. The top of Mt. Rainier, in Washington, is 14,410 feet above sea level. Round each height to the nearest thousand to estimate the difference in elevation of these two peaks. (*Source:* U.S. Geological Survey)

58. A student is pricing new car stereo systems. One system sells for $1895 and another system sells for $1524. Round each price to the nearest hundred dollars to estimate the difference in price of these systems.

59. In 2008, the population of Joliet, Illinois, was 142,702, and the population of Evanston, Illinois, was 75,543. Round each population to the nearest ten-thousand to estimate how much larger Joliet was than Evanston. (*Source:* U.S. Census Bureau)

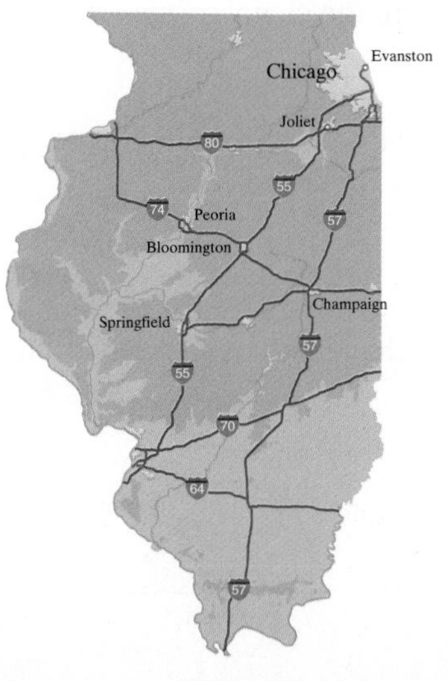

60. Round each distance given on the map to the nearest ten to estimate the total distance from North Platte, Nebraska, to Lincoln, Nebraska.

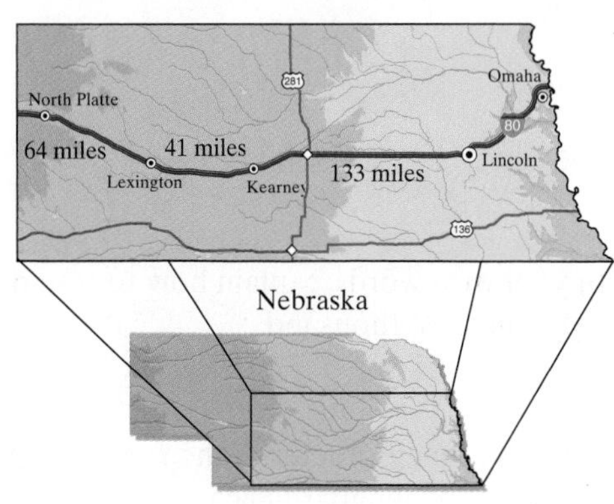

61. Head Start is a national program that provides developmental and social services for America's low-income preschool children ages three to five. Enrollment figures in Head Start programs showed an increase from 905,851 in 2004 to 908,412 in 2007. Round each number of children to the nearest thousand to estimate this increase. (*Source:* U.S. Department of Health and Human Services)

62. Enrollment figures at a local community college showed an increase from 49,713 credit hours in 2005 to 51,746 credit hours in 2006. Round each number to the nearest thousand to estimate the increase.

Mixed Practice (*Sections 1.2 and 1.5*) *The following table shows the top five leading U.S. television advertisers in 2007 and the amount of money spent that year on advertising. Complete this table. The first line is completed for you.* (*Source:* Television Bureau of Advertising)

	Advertiser	Amount Spent on Television Advertising in 2007 (in millions of dollars)	Amount Written in Standard Form	Standard Form Rounded to Nearest Ten-Million	Standard Form Rounded to Nearest Hundred-Million
	General Motors, Dealers	443	$443,000,000	$440,000,000	$400,000,000
63.	Chrysler-Cerberus	391			
64.	Ford, Dealers	364			
65.	AT & T Inc.	349			
66.	Toyota, Dealers	311			

Concept Extensions

67. Find one number that when rounded to the nearest hundred is 5700.

68. Find one number that when rounded to the nearest ten is 5700.

69. A number rounded to the nearest hundred is 8600.

a. Determine the smallest possible number.

b. Determine the largest possible number.

70. On August 23, 1989, it was estimated that 1,500,000 people joined hands in a human chain stretching 370 miles to protest the fiftieth anniversary of the pact that allowed what was then the Soviet Union to annex the Baltic nations in 1939. If the estimate of the number of people is to the nearest hundred-thousand, determine the largest possible number of people in the chain.

71. In your own words, explain how to round a number to the nearest thousand.

72. In your own words, explain how to round 9660 to the nearest thousand.

△ **73.** Estimate the perimeter of the rectangle by first rounding the length of each side to the nearest ten.

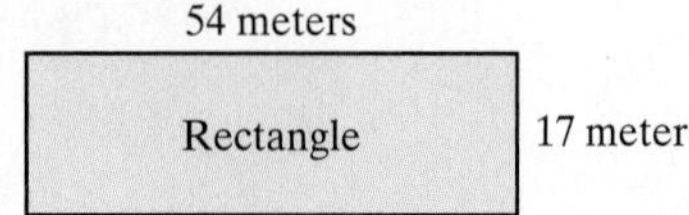

△ **74.** Estimate the perimeter of the triangle by first rounding the length of each side to the nearest hundred.

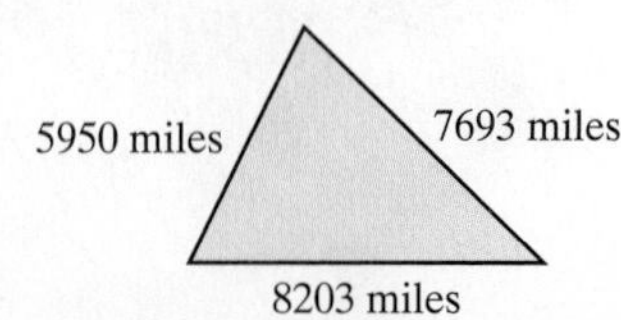

1.6 MULTIPLYING WHOLE NUMBERS AND AREA

Objectives

- **A** Use the Properties of Multiplication.
- **B** Multiply Whole Numbers.
- **C** Multiply by Whole Numbers Ending in Zero(s).
- **D** Find the Area of a Rectangle.
- **E** Solve Problems by Multiplying Whole Numbers.

Multiplication Shown as Repeated Addition Suppose that we wish to count the number of laptops provided in a computer class. The laptops are arranged in 5 rows, and each row has 6 laptops.

Adding 5 sixes gives the total number of laptops. We can write this as $6 + 6 + 6 + 6 + 6 = 30$ laptops. When each addend is the same, we refer to this as **repeated addition.**

Multiplication is repeated addition but with different notation.

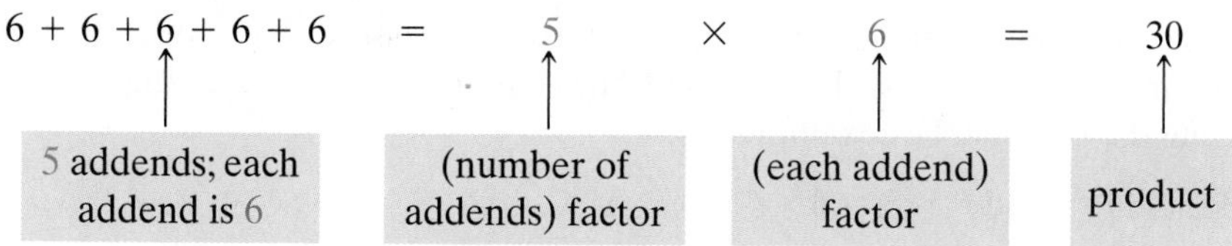

The × is called a **multiplication sign.** The numbers 5 and 6 are called **factors.** The number 30 is called the **product.** The notation 5 × 6 is read as "five times six." The symbols · and ( ) can also be used to indicate multiplication.

$$5 \times 6 = 30, \quad 5 \cdot 6 = 30, \quad (5)(6) = 30, \quad \text{and} \quad 5(6) = 30$$

✓Concept Check

a. Rewrite $5 + 5 + 5 + 5 + 5 + 5 + 5$ using multiplication.

b. Rewrite 3×16 as repeated addition. Is there more than one way to do this? If so, show all ways.

Objective A Using the Properties of Multiplication

As with addition, we memorize products of one-digit whole numbers and then use certain properties of multiplication to multiply larger numbers. (If necessary, review the multiplication of one-digit numbers in Appendix A.2)

Notice that when any number is multiplied by 0, the result is always 0. This is called the **multiplication property of 0.**

✓ Concept Check Answers

a. $7 \times 5 = 35$

b. $16 + 16 + 16 = 48$; yes, $3 + 3 + 3 + 3 + 3 + 3 + 3 + 3 + 3 + 3 + 3 + 3 + 3 + 3 + 3 + 3 = 48$

Multiplication Property of 0

The product of 0 and any number is 0. For example,

$5 \cdot 0 = 0$ and $0 \cdot 8 = 0$

Also notice in Appendix A.2 that when any number is multiplied by 1, the result is always the original number. We call this result the **multiplication property of 1.**

Multiplication Property of 1

The product of 1 and any number is that same number. For example,

$1 \cdot 9 = 9$ and $6 \cdot 1 = 6$

PRACTICE 1

Multiply.

a. 3×0
b. $4(1)$
c. $(0)(34)$
d. $1 \cdot 76$

Example 1 Multiply.

a. 6×1 **b.** $0(18)$ **c.** $1 \cdot 45$ **d.** $(75)(0)$

Solution:

a. $6 \times 1 = 6$ **b.** $0(18) = 0$
c. $1 \cdot 45 = 45$ **d.** $(75)(0) = 0$

Work Practice 1

Like addition, multiplication is commutative and associative. Notice that when multiplying two numbers, the order of these numbers can be changed without changing the product. For example,

$3 \cdot 5 = 15$ and $5 \cdot 3 = 15$

This property is the **commutative property of multiplication.**

Commutative Property of Multiplication

Changing the **order** of two factors does not change their product. For example,

$9 \cdot 2 = 18$ and $2 \cdot 9 = 18$

Another property that can help us when multiplying is the **associative property of multiplication.** This property states that when multiplying numbers, the grouping of the numbers can be changed without changing the product. For example,

$$(2 \cdot 3) \cdot 4 = 6 \cdot 4 = 24$$

Also,

$$2 \cdot (3 \cdot 4) = 2 \cdot 12 = 24$$

Both groupings give a product of 24.

Answers
1. a. 0 **b.** 4 **c.** 0 **d.** 76

Associative Property of Multiplication

Changing the **grouping** of factors does not change their product. From the previous page, we know that for example,

$(2 \cdot 3) \cdot 4 = 2 \cdot (3 \cdot 4)$

With these properties, along with the **distributive property,** we can find the product of any whole numbers. The distributive property says that multiplication **distributes** over addition. For example, notice that $3(2 + 5)$ simplifies to the same number as $3 \cdot 2 + 3 \cdot 5$.

$$3(2 + 5) = 3(7) = 21$$

$$3 \cdot 2 + 3 \cdot 5 = 6 + 15 = 21$$

Since $3(2 + 5)$ and $3 \cdot 2 + 3 \cdot 5$ both simplify to 21, then

$$3(2 + 5) = 3 \cdot 2 + 3 \cdot 5$$

Notice in $3(2 + 5) = 3 \cdot 2 + 3 \cdot 5$ that each number inside the parentheses is multiplied by 3.

Distributive Property

Multiplication distributes over addition. For example,

$$2(3 + 4) = 2 \cdot 3 + 2 \cdot 4$$

Example 2 Rewrite each using the distributive property.

a. $3(4 + 5)$ **b.** $10(6 + 8)$ **c.** $2(7 + 3)$

Solution: Using the distributive property, we have

a. $5(6 + 5) = 5 \cdot 6 + 5 \cdot 5$
b. $10(6 + 8) = 10 \cdot 6 + 10 \cdot 8$
c. $2(7 + 3) = 2 \cdot 7 + 2 \cdot 3$

Work Practice 2

PRACTICE 2

Rewrite each using the distributive property.

a. $5(2 + 3)$
b. $9(8 + 7)$
c. $3(6 + 1)$

Objective B Multiplying Whole Numbers

Let's use the distributive property to multiply 7(48). To do so, we begin by writing the expanded form of 48 (see Section 1.2) and then applying the distributive property.

$7(48) = 7(40 + 8)$ Write 48 in expanded form.
$= 7 \cdot 40 + 7 \cdot 8$ Apply the distributive property.
$= 280 + 56$ Multiply.
$= 336$ Add.

Answers

2. a. $5(2 + 3) = 5 \cdot 2 + 5 \cdot 3$
b. $9(8 + 7) = 9 \cdot 8 + 9 \cdot 7$
c. $3(6 + 1) = 3 \cdot 6 + 3 \cdot 1$

This is how we multiply whole numbers. When multiplying whole numbers, we will use the following notation.

First:

$$\begin{array}{r} {}^{5}\\ 48\\ \times 7\\ \hline 336 \end{array}$$

← 7·8 = 56 Write 6 in the ones place and carry 5 to the tens place.

Next:

$$\begin{array}{r} {}^{5}\\ 48\\ \times 7\\ \hline 336 \end{array}$$

7·4 + 5 = 28 + 5 = 33

The product of 48 and 7 is 336.

PRACTICE 3

Multiply.

a. $\begin{array}{r} 36\\ \times 4\\ \hline \end{array}$ b. $\begin{array}{r} 132\\ \times 9\\ \hline \end{array}$

Example 3 Multiply:

a. $\begin{array}{r} 25\\ \times 8\\ \hline \end{array}$ b. $\begin{array}{r} 246\\ \times 5\\ \hline \end{array}$

Solution:

a. $\begin{array}{r} {}^{4}\\ 25\\ \times 8\\ \hline 200 \end{array}$ b. $\begin{array}{r} {}^{2\,3}\\ 246\\ \times 5\\ \hline 1230 \end{array}$

Work Practice 3

To multiply larger whole numbers, use the following similar notation. Multiply 89 × 52.

Step 1

$$\begin{array}{r} {}^{1}\\ 89\\ \times 52\\ \hline 178 \end{array}$$

← Multiply 89 × 2.

Step 2

$$\begin{array}{r} {}^{4}\\ 89\\ \times 52\\ \hline 178\\ 4450\\ \hline \end{array}$$

← Multiply 89 × 50.

Step 3

$$\begin{array}{r} 89\\ \times 52\\ \hline 178\\ 4450\\ \hline 4628 \end{array}$$

Add.

The numbers 178 and 4450 are called **partial products.** The sum of the partial products, 4628, is the product of 89 and 52.

PRACTICE 4

Multiply.

a. $\begin{array}{r} 594\\ \times 72\\ \hline \end{array}$ b. $\begin{array}{r} 306\\ \times 81\\ \hline \end{array}$

Example 4 Multiply: 236 × 86

Solution:

$$\begin{array}{rl} 236 & \\ \times 86 & \\ \hline 1\,416 & \leftarrow 6(236)\\ 18\,880 & \leftarrow 80(236)\\ \hline 20{,}296 & \text{Add.} \end{array}$$

Work Practice 4

PRACTICE 5

Multiply.

a. $\begin{array}{r} 726\\ \times 142\\ \hline \end{array}$ b. $\begin{array}{r} 288\\ \times 4\\ \hline \end{array}$

Example 5 Multiply: 631 × 125

Solution:

$$\begin{array}{rl} 631 & \\ \times 125 & \\ \hline 3\,155 & \leftarrow 5(631)\\ 12\,620 & \leftarrow 20(631)\\ 63\,100 & \leftarrow 100(631)\\ \hline 78{,}875 & \text{Add.} \end{array}$$

Work Practice 5

Answers

3. a. 144 b. 1188
4. a. 42,768 b. 24,786
5. a. 103,092 b. 1152

✓Concept Check Find and explain the error in the following multiplication problem.

$$\begin{array}{r} 102 \\ \times\ 33 \\ \hline 306 \\ 306 \\ \hline 612 \end{array}$$

Objective C Multiplying by Whole Numbers Ending in Zero(s)

Interesting patterns occur when we multiply by a number that ends in zeros. To see these patterns, let's multiply a number, say 34, by 10, then 100, then 1000.

$34 \cdot 10 = 340$ (1 zero) — 1 zero attached to 34.

$34 \cdot 100 = 3400$ (2 zeros) — 2 zeros attached to 34.

$34 \cdot 1000 = 34{,}000$ (3 zeros) — 3 zeros attached to 34.

These patterns help us develop a shortcut for multiplying by whole numbers ending in zeros.

> To multiply by 10, 100, 1000, and so on,
> Form the product by attaching the number of zeros in that number to the other factor.
> For example, $41 \cdot 100 = 4100$. (2 zeros)

Examples Multiply.

6. $176 \cdot 1000 = 176{,}000$ Attach 3 zeros.
7. $2041 \cdot 100 = 204{,}100$ Attach 2 zeros.

Work Practice 6–7

PRACTICE 6–7

Multiply.

6. $75 \cdot 100$
7. $808 \cdot 1000$

We can use a similar format to multiply by any whole number ending in zeros. For example, since

$15 \cdot 500 = 15 \cdot 5 \cdot 100,$

we find the product by multiplying 15 and 5, then attaching two zeros to the product.

$$\begin{array}{r} \overset{2}{1}5 \\ \times 5 \\ \hline 75 \end{array} \qquad 15 \cdot 500 = 7500$$

Answers

6. 7500 7. 808,000

✓ Concept Check Answer

$$\begin{array}{r} 102 \\ \times\ 33 \\ \hline 306 \\ 3060 \\ \hline 3366 \end{array}$$

PRACTICE 8–9

Multiply.

8. $35 \cdot 3000$

9. $600 \cdot 600$

Examples Multiply.

8. $25 \cdot 9000 = 225{,}000$ Attach 3 zeros.

$$\begin{array}{r} \overset{4}{2}5 \\ \times 9 \\ \hline 225 \end{array}$$

9. $20 \cdot 7000 = 140{,}000$ Attach 4 zeros.

$2 \cdot 7$

Work Practice 8–9

Objective D Finding the Area of a Rectangle

A special application of multiplication is finding the **area** of a region. Area measures the amount of surface of a region. For example, we measure a plot of land or the living space of a home by its area. The figures below show two examples of units of area measure. (A centimeter is a unit of length in the metric system.)

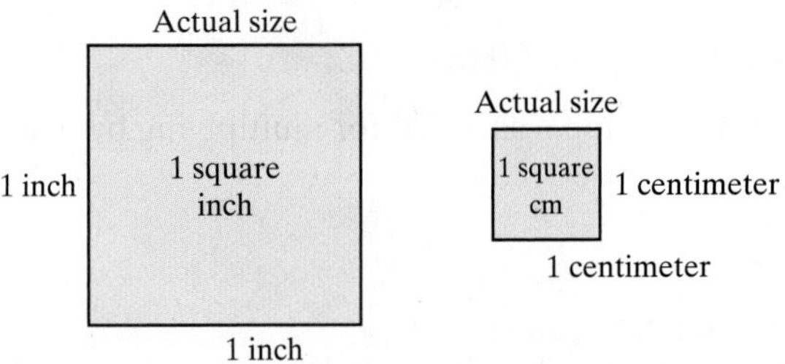

For example, to measure the area of a geometric figure such as the rectangle below, count the number of square units that cover the region.

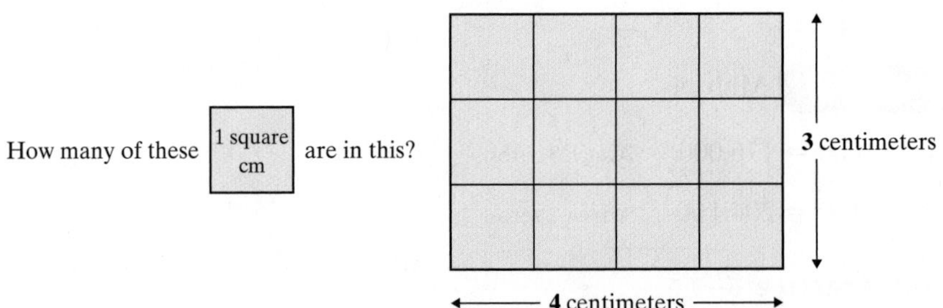

This rectangular region contains 12 square units, each 1 square centimeter. Thus, the area is 12 square centimeters. This total number of squares can be found by counting or by multiplying $4 \cdot 3$ (length · width).

$$\begin{aligned} \text{Area of a rectangle} &= \text{length} \cdot \text{width} \\ &= (4 \text{ centimeters})(3 \text{ centimeters}) \\ &= 12 \text{ square centimeters} \end{aligned}$$

In this section, we find the areas of rectangles only. In later sections, we will find the areas of other geometric regions.

Helpful Hint

Notice that area is measured in **square** units while perimeter is measured in units.

Answers

8. 105,000 **9.** 360,000

Example 10 Finding the Area of a State

The state of Colorado is in the shape of a rectangle whose length is 380 miles and whose width is 280 miles. Find its area.

Solution: The area of a rectangle is the product of its length and its width.

$$\begin{aligned} \text{Area} &= \text{length} \cdot \text{width} \\ &= (380 \text{ miles})(280 \text{ miles}) \\ &= 106{,}400 \text{ square miles} \end{aligned}$$

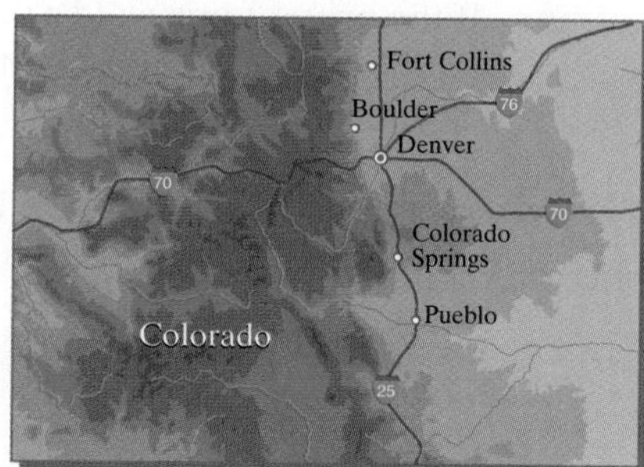

The area of Colorado is 106,400 square miles.

Work Practice 10

PRACTICE 10

The state of Wyoming is in the shape of a rectangle whose length is 360 miles and whose width is 280 miles. Find its area.

Objective E Solving Problems by Multiplying

There are several words or phrases that indicate the operation of multiplication. Some of these are as follows:

Multiplication		
Key Words or Phrases	**Examples**	**Symbols**
multiply	multiply 5 by 7	$5 \cdot 7$
product	the product of 3 and 2	$3 \cdot 2$
times	10 times 13	$10 \cdot 13$

Many key words or phrases describing real-life problems that suggest addition might be better solved by multiplication instead. For example, to find the **total** cost of 8 shirts, each selling for $27, we can either add

$$27 + 27 + 27 + 27 + 27 + 27 + 27 + 27$$

or we can multiply 8(27).

Example 11 Finding DVD Space

A digital video disc (DVD) can hold about 4800 megabytes (MB) of information. How many megabytes can 12 DVDs hold?

Solution: Twelve DVDs will hold 12×4800 megabytes.

In Words		**Translate to Numbers**
megabytes per disc	→	4800
× DVDs	→	× 12
		9600
		48000
total megabytes		57,600

Twelve DVDs will hold 57,600 megabytes.

Work Practice 11

PRACTICE 11

A particular computer printer can print 16 pages per minute in color. How many pages can it print in 45 minutes?

Answers

10. 100,800 sq mi **11.** 720 pages

PRACTICE 12

Ken Shimura purchased DVDs and CDs through a club. Each DVD was priced at $11 and each CD cost $9. Ken bought eight DVDs and five CDs. Find the total cost of the order.

Example 12 Budgeting Money

Suzanne Scarpulla and a friend plan to take their children to the Georgia Aquarium in Atlanta, the world's largest aquarium. The ticket price for each child is $22 and for each adult, $26. If five children and two adults plan to go, how much money is needed for admission? (*Source:* GeorgiaAquarium.org)

Solution: If the price of one child's ticket is $22, the price for 5 children is $5 \times 22 = \$110$. The price of one adult ticket is $26, so the price for two adults is $2 \times 26 = \$52$. The total cost is:

In Words		Translate to Numbers
price of 5 children	→	110
+ cost of 2 adults	→	+ 52
total cost		162

The total cost is $162.

Work Practice 12

PRACTICE 13

If an average page in a book contains 163 words, estimate, rounding each number to the nearest hundred, the total number of words contained on 391 pages.

Example 13 Estimating Word Count

The average page of a book contains 259 words. Estimate, rounding each number to the nearest hundred, the total number of words contained on 212 pages.

Solution: The exact number of words is 259×212. Estimate this product by rounding each factor to the nearest hundred.

$$\begin{array}{rlr} 259 & \text{rounds to} & 300 \\ \times 212 & \text{rounds to} & \times 200 \end{array}, \quad 300 \times 200 = 60{,}000$$

$$3 \cdot 2 = 6$$

There are approximately 60,000 words contained on 212 pages.

Work Practice 13

Calculator Explorations Multiplying Numbers

To multiply numbers on a calculator, find the keys marked [×] and [=] or [ENTER]. For example, to find $31 \cdot 66$ on a calculator, press the keys [31] [×] [66] [=] or [ENTER]. The display will read [2046]. Thus, $31 \cdot 66 = 2046$.

Use a calculator to multiply.

1. 72×48
2. 81×92
3. $163 \cdot 94$
4. $285 \cdot 144$
5. $983(277)$
6. $1562(843)$

Answers

12. $133 **13.** 80,000 words

Vocabulary and Readiness Check

Use the choices below to fill in each blank.

area	grouping	commutative	1	product	length
factor	order	associative	0	distributive	number

1. The product of 0 and any number is ____________.
2. The product of 1 and any number is the ____________.
3. In $8 \cdot 12 = 96$, the 96 is called the ____________ and 8 and 12 are each called a(n) ____________.
4. Since $9 \cdot 10 = 10 \cdot 9$, we say that changing the ____________ in multiplication does not change the product. This property is called the ____________ property of multiplication.
5. Since $(3 \cdot 4) \cdot 6 = 3 \cdot (4 \cdot 6)$, we say that changing the ____________ in multiplication does not change the product. This property is called the ____________ property of multiplication.
6. ____________ measures the amount of surface of a region.
7. Area of a rectangle = ____________ · width.
8. We know $9\,(10 + 8) = 9 \cdot 10 + 9 \cdot 8$ by the ____________ property.

1.6 Exercise Set

Objective A *Multiply. See Example 1.*

1. $1 \cdot 24$
2. $55 \cdot 1$
3. $0 \cdot 19$
4. $27 \cdot 0$
5. $8 \cdot 0 \cdot 9$
6. $7 \cdot 6 \cdot 0$
7. $87 \cdot 1$
8. $1 \cdot 41$

Use the distributive property to rewrite each expression. See Example 2.

9. $6(3 + 8)$
10. $5(8 + 2)$
11. $4(3 + 9)$
12. $6(1 + 4)$
13. $20(14 + 6)$
14. $12(12 + 3)$

Objective B *Multiply. See Example 3.*

15. 64×8
16. 79×3
17. 613×6
18. 638×5
19. 277×6
20. 882×2
21. 1074×6
22. 9021×3

Objectives A B Mixed Practice *Multiply. See Examples 1 through 5.*

23. 89×13
24. 91×72
25. 421×58
26. 526×23
27. 306×81
28. 708×21

29. (780)(20) **30.** (720)(80) **31.** (495)(13)(0) **32.** (593)(47)(0) **33.** (640)(1)(10)

34. (240)(1)(20) **35.** 1234×39 **36.** 1357×79 **37.** 609×234 **38.** 807×127

39. 8649×274 **40.** 1234×567 **41.** 589×110 **42.** 426×110 **43.** 1941×2035 **44.** 1876×1407

Objective C *Multiply. See Examples 6 through 9.*

45. 8×100 **46.** 6×100 **47.** 11×1000 **48.** 26×1000 **49.** $7406 \cdot 10$ **50.** $9054 \cdot 10$

51. $6 \cdot 4000$ **52.** $3 \cdot 9000$ **53.** $50 \cdot 900$ **54.** $70 \cdot 300$ **55.** $41 \cdot 80{,}000$ **56.** $27 \cdot 50{,}000$

Objective D **Mixed Practice (*Section 1.3*)** *Find the area and the perimeter of each rectangle. See Example 10.*

57.

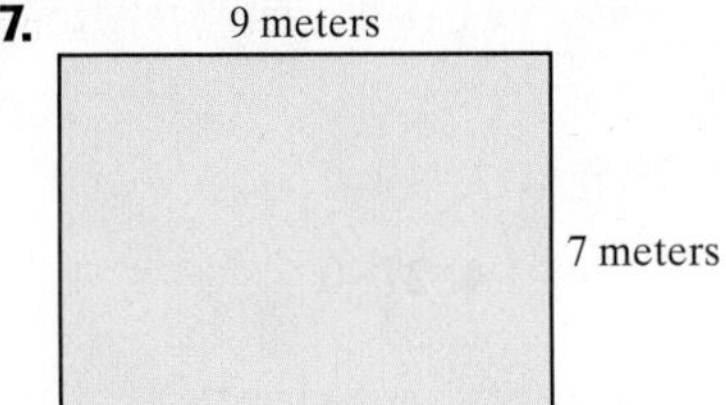

58.

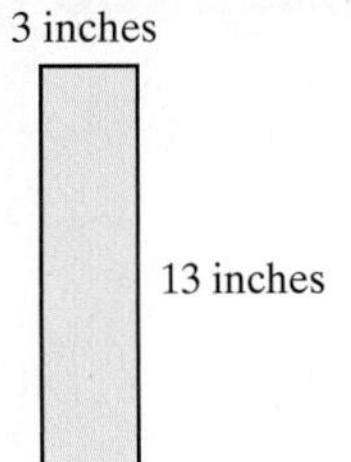

59.

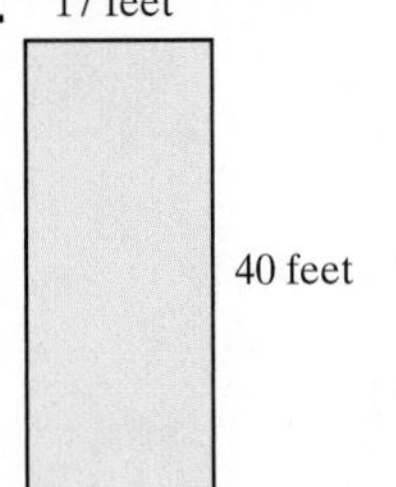

60.

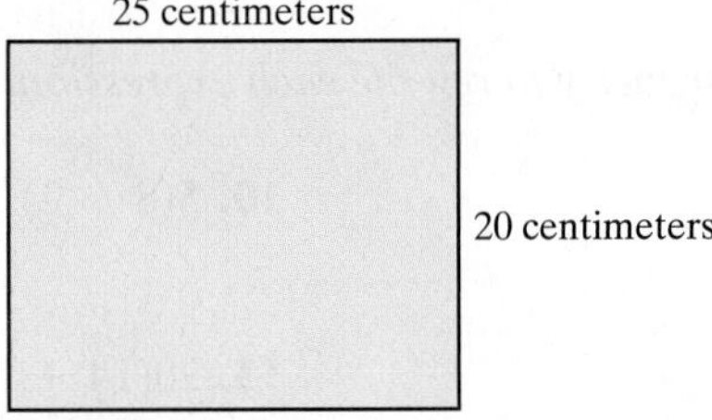

Objective E **Mixed Practice (*Section 1.5*)** *Estimate the products by rounding each factor to the nearest hundred. See Example 13.*

61. 576×354 **62.** 982×650 **63.** 604×451 **64.** 111×999

Without actually calculating, mentally round, multiply, and choose the best estimate.

65. $38 \times 42 =$
a. 16
b. 160
c. 1600
d. 16,000

66. $2872 \times 12 =$
a. 2872
b. 28,720
c. 287,200
d. 2,872,000

67. $612 \times 29 =$
a. 180
b. 1800
c. 18,000
d. 180,000

68. $706 \times 409 =$
a. 280
b. 2800
c. 28,000
d. 280,000

Objectives D E **Mixed Practice—Translating** *Solve. See Examples 10 through 13.*

69. Multiply 80 by 11.

70. Multiply 70 by 12.

71. Find the product of 6 and 700.

72. Find the product of 9 and 900.

73. Find 2 times 2240.

74. Find 3 times 3310.

75. One tablespoon of olive oil contains 125 calories. How many calories are in 3 tablespoons of olive oil? (*Source: Home and Garden Bulletin No. 72,* U.S. Department of Agriculture)

76. One ounce of hulled sunflower seeds contains 14 grams of fat. How many grams of fat are in 8 ounces of hulled sunflower seeds? (*Source: Home and Garden Bulletin No. 72,* U.S. Department of Agriculture)

77. The textbook for a course in biology costs $94. There are 35 students in the class. Find the total cost of the biology books for the class.

78. The seats in a large lecture hall are arranged in 14 rows with 34 seats in each row. Find how many seats are in this room.

79. Cabot Creamery is packing a pallet of 20-lb boxes of cheddar cheese to send to a local restaurant. There are five layers of boxes on the pallet, and each layer is four boxes wide by five boxes deep.

a. How many boxes are in one layer?
b. How many boxes are on the pallet?
c. What is the weight of the cheese on the pallet?

80. An apartment building has *three floors*. Each floor has five rows of apartments with four apartments in each row.

a. How many apartments are on 1 floor?
b. How many apartments are in the building?

△ **81.** A plot of land measures 80 feet by 110 feet. Find its area.

△ **82.** A house measures 45 feet by 60 feet. Find the floor area of the house.

△ **83.** The largest hotel lobby can be found at the Hyatt Regency in San Francisco, CA. It is in the shape of a rectangle that measures 350 feet by 160 feet. Find its area.

△ **84.** Recall from an earlier section that the largest commercial building in the world under one roof is the flower auction building of the cooperative VBA in Aalsmeer, Netherlands. The floor plan is a rectangle that measures 776 meters by 639 meters. Find the area of this building. (A meter is a unit of length in the metric system.) (*Source: The Handy Science Answer Book,* Visible Ink Press)

776 meters

639 meters

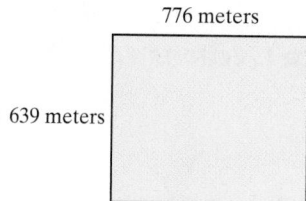

85. A pixel is a rectangular dot on a graphing calculator screen. If a graphing calculator screen contains 62 pixels in a row and 94 pixels in a column, find the total number of pixels on a screen.

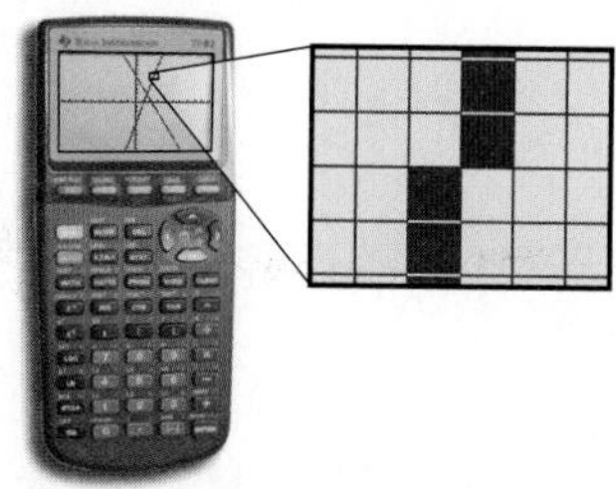

86. A certain compact disc (CD) can hold 700 megabytes (MB) of information. How many MBs can 17 discs hold?

87. A line of print on a computer contains 60 characters (letters, spaces, punctuation marks). Find how many characters there are in 35 lines.

88. An average cow eats 3 pounds of grain per day. Find how much grain a cow eats in a year. (Assume 365 days in 1 year.)

89. One ounce of Planters® Dry Roasted Peanuts has 160 calories. How many calories are in 8 ounces? (*Source:* RJR Nabisco, Inc.)

90. One ounce of Planters® Dry Roasted Peanuts has 13 grams of fat. How many grams of fat are in 16 ounces? (*Source:* RJR Nabisco, Inc.)

91. The Thespian club at a local community college is ordering T-shirts. T-shirts size S, M, or L cost $10 each and T-shirts size XL or XXL cost $12 each. Use the table below to find the total cost. (The first row is filled in for you.)

T-Shirt Size	Number of Shirts Ordered	Cost per Shirt	Cost per Size Ordered
S	4	$10	$40
M	6		
L	20		
XL	3		
XXL	3		

92. The student activities group at North Shore Community College is planning a trip to see the local minor league baseball team. Tickets cost $5 for students, $7 for nonstudents, and $2 for children under 12. Use the following table to find the total cost.

Person	Number of Persons	Cost per Person	Cost per Category
Student	24	$5	$120
Nonstudent	4		
Children under 12	5		

93. Celestial Seasonings of Boulder, Colorado, is a tea company that specializes in herbal teas, accounting for over $100,000,000 in herbal tea blend sales in the United States annually. Their plant in Boulder has bagging machines capable of bagging over 1000 bags of tea per minute. If the plant runs 24 hours a day, how many tea bags are produced in one day? (*Source:* Celestial Seasonings)

94. The number of "older" Americans (ages 65 and older) has increased twelvefold since 1900. If there were 3 million "older" Americans in 1900, how many were there in 2008? (*Source*: Administration on Aging, U.S. Census Bureau)

Mixed Practice (*Sections 1.3, 1.4, 1.6*) *Perform each indicated operation.*

95. $\begin{array}{r} 128 \\ +\ 7 \\ \hline \end{array}$

96. $\begin{array}{r} 126 \\ -\ 8 \\ \hline \end{array}$

97. $\begin{array}{r} 134 \\ \times\ 16 \\ \hline \end{array}$

98. $47 + 26 + 10 + 231 + 50$

99. Find the sum of 19 and 4.

100. Find the product of 19 and 4.

101. Find the difference of 19 and 4.

102. Find the total of 19 and 4.

Concept Extensions

Solve. See the first Concept Check in this section.

103. Rewrite $7 + 7 + 7 + 7$ using multiplication.

104. Rewrite $11 + 11 + 11 + 11 + 11 + 11$ using multiplication.

105. a. Rewrite $3 \cdot 5$ as repeated addition.
b. Explain why there is more than one way to do this.

106. a. Rewrite $4 \cdot 5$ as repeated addition.
b. Explain why there is more than one way to do this.

Find and explain the error in each multiplication problem. See the second Concept Check in this section.

107.
$$\begin{array}{r} 203 \\ \times\ 14 \\ \hline 812 \\ 203 \\ \hline 1015 \end{array}$$

108.
$$\begin{array}{r} 31 \\ \times\ 50 \\ \hline 155 \end{array}$$

Fill in the missing digits in each problem.

109.
$$\begin{array}{r} 4\_ \\ \times\ \_3 \\ \hline 126 \\ 3780 \\ \hline 3906 \end{array}$$

110.
$$\begin{array}{r} \_7 \\ \times\ 6\_ \\ \hline 171 \\ 3420 \\ \hline 3591 \end{array}$$

111. Explain how to multiply two 2-digit numbers using partial products.

112. In your own words, explain the meaning of the area of a rectangle and how this area is measured.

113. A window washer in New York City is bidding for a contract to wash the windows of a 23-story building. To write a bid, the number of windows in the building is needed. If there are 7 windows in each row of windows on 2 sides of the building and 4 windows per row on the other 2 sides of the building, find the total number of windows.

114. During the NBA's 2007–2008 regular season, Kobe Bryant of the Los Angeles Lakers scored 150 three-point field goals, 775 two-point field goals, and 623 free throws (worth one point each). How many points did Kobe Bryant score during the 2007–2008 regular season? (*Source:* NBA)

Objectives

A Divide Whole Numbers.

B Perform Long Division.

C Solve Problems That Require Dividing by Whole Numbers.

D Find the Average of a List of Numbers.

1.7 DIVIDING WHOLE NUMBERS

Suppose three people pooled their money and bought a raffle ticket at a local fund-raiser. Their ticket was the winner and they won a $75 cash prize. They then divided the prize into three equal parts so that each person received $25.

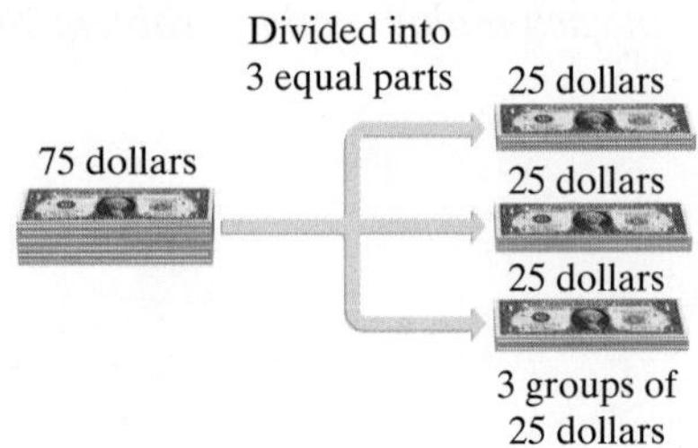

Objective A Dividing Whole Numbers

The process of separating a quantity into equal parts is called **division.** The division above can be symbolized by several notations.

$$3\overline{)75} = 25$$
(quotient: 25; dividend: 75; divisor: 3)

$$\frac{75}{3} = 25$$
(dividend: 75; divisor: 3; quotient: 25)

$$75 \div 3 = 25$$
(dividend: 75; divisor: 3; quotient: 25)

$$75/3 = 25$$
(dividend: 75; divisor: 3; quotient: 25)

(In the notation $\frac{75}{3}$, the bar separating 75 and 3 is called a **fraction bar.**) Just as subtraction is the reverse of addition, division is the reverse of multiplication. This means that division can be checked by multiplication.

$3\overline{)75}$ with quotient 25 because $25 \cdot 3 = 75$

Quotient · Divisor = Dividend

Since multiplication and division are related in this way, you can use your knowledge of multiplication facts (or study Appendix A.2) to review quotients of one-digit divisors if necessary.

Example 1 Find each quotient. Check by multiplying.

a. $42 \div 7$ **b.** $\frac{64}{8}$ **c.** $3\overline{)21}$

Solution:

a. $42 \div 7 = 6$ because $6 \cdot 7 = 42$

b. $\frac{64}{8} = 8$ because $8 \cdot 8 = 64$

c. $3\overline{)21}$ with quotient 7, because $7 \cdot 3 = 21$

Work Practice 1

PRACTICE 1

Find each quotient. Check by multiplying.

a. $9\overline{)72}$

b. $40 \div 5$

c. $\frac{24}{6}$

Example 2 Find each quotient. Check by multiplying.

a. $1\overline{)7}$ **b.** $12 \div 1$ **c.** $\frac{6}{6}$ **d.** $9 \div 9$ **e.** $\frac{20}{1}$ **f.** $18\overline{)18}$

Solution:

a. $1\overline{)7}$ with quotient 7, because $7 \cdot 1 = 7$

b. $12 \div 1 = 12$ because $12 \cdot 1 = 12$

c. $\frac{6}{6} = 1$ because $1 \cdot 6 = 6$

d. $9 \div 9 = 1$ because $1 \cdot 9 = 9$

e. $\frac{20}{1} = 20$ because $20 \cdot 1 = 20$

f. $18\overline{)18}$ with quotient 1, because $1 \cdot 18 = 18$

Work Practice 2

PRACTICE 2

Find each quotient. Check by multiplying.

a. $\frac{7}{7}$ **b.** $5 \div 1$

c. $1\overline{)11}$ **d.** $4 \div 1$

e. $\frac{10}{1}$ **f.** $21 \div 21$

Example 2 illustrates the important properties of division described next:

Division Properties of 1

The quotient of any number (except 0) and that same number is 1. For example,

$8 \div 8 = 1$ $\frac{5}{5} = 1$ $4\overline{)4}$ with quotient 1

The quotient of any number and 1 is that same number. For example,

$9 \div 1 = 9$ $\frac{6}{1} = 6$ $1\overline{)3}$ with quotient 3 $\frac{0}{1} = 0$

Example 3 Find each quotient. Check by multiplying.

a. $9\overline{)0}$ **b.** $0 \div 12$ **c.** $\frac{0}{5}$ **d.** $\frac{3}{0}$

Solution:

a. $9\overline{)0}$ with quotient 0, because $0 \cdot 9 = 0$ **b.** $0 \div 12 = 0$ because $0 \cdot 12 = 0$

c. $\frac{0}{5} = 0$ because $0 \cdot 5 = 0$

Continued on next page

PRACTICE 3

Find each quotient. Check by multiplying.

a. $\frac{0}{7}$ **b.** $8\overline{)0}$

c. $7 \div 0$ **d.** $0 \div 14$

Answers

1. a. 8 **b.** 8 **c.** 4 **2. a.** 1 **b.** 5 **c.** 11 **d.** 4 **e.** 10 **f.** 1 **3. a.** 0 **b.** 0 **c.** undefined **d.** 0

d. If $\frac{3}{0}$ = a *number*, then the *number* times 0 = 3. Recall from Section 1.6 that any number multiplied by 0 is 0 and not 3. We say, then, that $\frac{3}{0}$ is **undefined.**

Work Practice 3

Example 3 illustrates important division properties of 0.

Division Properties of 0

The quotient of 0 and any number (except 0) is 0. For example,

$$0 \div 9 = 0 \qquad \frac{0}{5} = 0 \qquad 14\overline{)0}^{\,0}$$

The quotient of any number and 0 is not a number. We say that

$$\frac{3}{0}, \quad 0\overline{)3}, \quad \text{and} \quad 3 \div 0$$

are **undefined.**

Objective B Performing Long Division

When dividends are larger, the quotient can be found by a process called **long division.** For example, let's divide 2541 by 3.

divisor → $3\overline{)2541}$
↑
dividend

We can't divide 3 into 2, so we try dividing 3 into the first two digits.

$$\begin{array}{r} 8 \\ 3\overline{)2541} \end{array}$$

25 ÷ 3 = 8 with 1 left, so our best estimate is 8. We place 8 over the 5 in 25.

Next, multiply 8 and 3 and subtract this product from 25. Make sure that this difference is less than the divisor.

$$\begin{array}{r} 8 \\ 3\overline{)2541} \\ -24 \\ \hline 1 \end{array}$$

8(3) = 24

25 − 24 = 1, and 1 is less than the divisor 3.

Bring down the next digit and go through the process again.

$$\begin{array}{r} 84 \\ 3\overline{)2541} \\ -24\downarrow \\ \hline 14 \\ -12 \\ \hline 2 \end{array}$$

14 ÷ 3 = 4 with 2 left

4(3) = 12

14 − 12 = 2

Once more, bring down the next digit and go through the process.

$$\begin{array}{r} 847 \\ 3\overline{)2541} \\ -24 \\ \hline 14 \\ -12\downarrow \\ \hline 21 \\ -21 \\ \hline 0 \end{array}$$

21 ÷ 3 = 7

7(3) = 21

21 − 21 = 0

The quotient is 847. To check, see that 847 × 3 = 2541.

Example 4 Divide: 3705 ÷ 5. Check by multiplying.

Solution:

```
   7        37 ÷ 5 = 7 with 2 left. Place this estimate, 7, over the 7 in 37.
5)3705
 -35↓       7(5) = 35
  20        37 − 35 = 2, and 2 is less than the divisor 5.
  ↑──────── Bring down the 0.

   74       20 ÷ 5 = 4
5)3705
 -35
  20
 -20↓       4(5) = 20
  05        20 − 20 = 0, and 0 is less than the divisor 5.
   ↑─────── Bring down the 5.

  741       5 ÷ 5 = 1
5)3705
 -35
  20
 -20↓
   5
  -5        1(5) = 5
   0        5 − 5 = 0
```

Check:

$$\begin{array}{r} 741 \\ \times \quad 5 \\ \hline 3705 \end{array}$$

Work Practice 4

PRACTICE 4

Divide. Check by multiplying.

a. 4908 ÷ 6

b. 2212 ÷ 4

c. 753 ÷ 3

Helpful Hint Since division and multiplication are reverse operations, don't forget that a division problem can be checked by multiplying.

Example 5 Divide and check: 1872 ÷ 9

Solution:

```
  208
9)1872
 -18↓      2(9) = 18
   07      18 − 18 = 0; bring down the 7.
  -0↓      0(9) = 0
   72      7 − 0 = 7; bring down the 2.
  -72      8(9) = 72
    0      72 − 72 = 0
```

Check: $208 \cdot 9 = 1872$

Work Practice 5

PRACTICE 5

Divide and check by multiplying.

a. 7)2128

b. 9)45,900

Answers

4. a. 818 **b.** 553 **c.** 251

5. a. 304 **b.** 5100

Naturally, quotients don't always "come out even." Making 4 rows out of 26 chairs, for example, isn't possible if each row is supposed to have exactly the same number of chairs. Each of 4 rows can have 6 chairs, but 2 chairs are still left over.

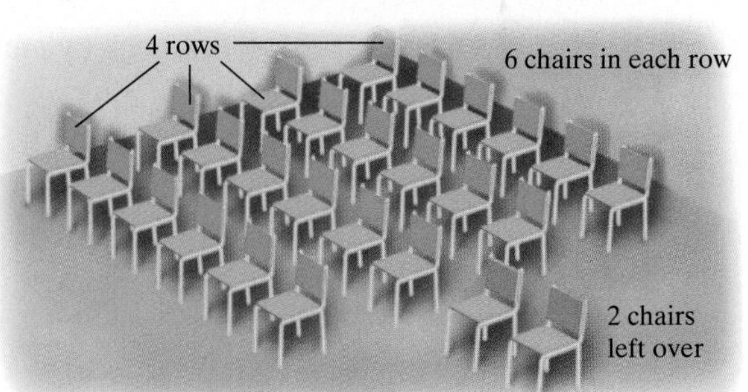

We signify "leftovers" or **remainders** in this way:

$$\begin{array}{r} 6 \text{ R } 2 \\ 4\overline{)26} \end{array}$$

The **whole number part of the quotient** is 6; the **remainder part of the quotient** is 2. Checking by multiplying,

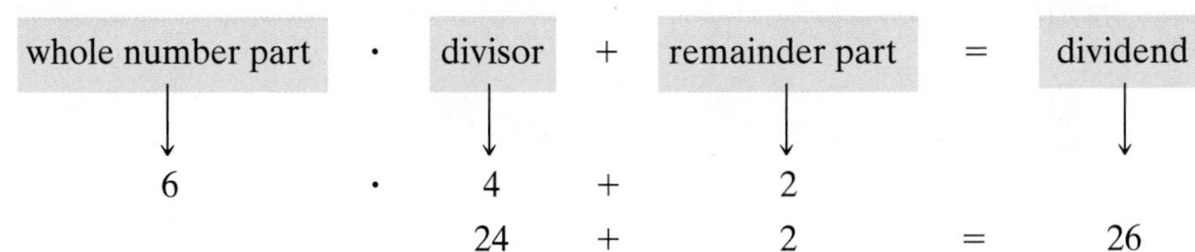

whole number part · divisor + remainder part = dividend
6 · 4 + 2
24 + 2 = 26

PRACTICE 6

Divide and check.

a. $4\overline{)939}$

b. $5\overline{)3287}$

Example 6 Divide and check: 2557 ÷ 7

Solution:

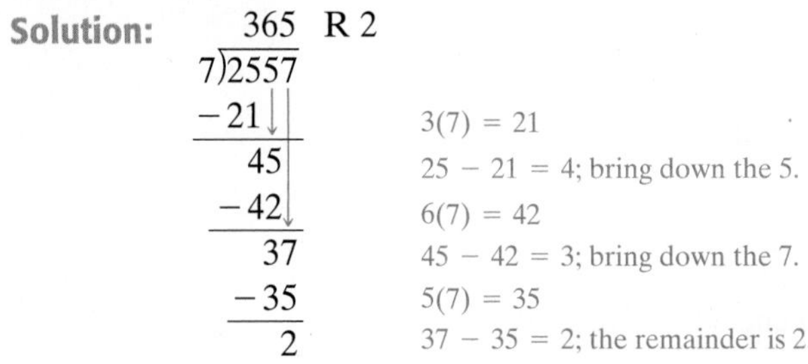

Check: 365 · 7 + 2 = 2557

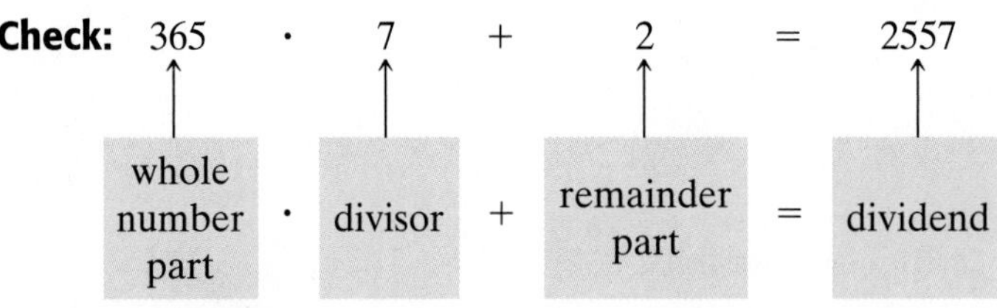

Work Practice 6

PRACTICE 7

Divide and check.

a. $9\overline{)81,605}$

b. $4\overline{)23,310}$

Example 7 Divide and check: 56,717 ÷ 8

Solution:

$$\begin{array}{r} 7089 \text{ R } 5 \\ 8\overline{)56717} \\ -56 \\ \hline 07 \\ -0 \\ \hline 71 \\ -64 \\ \hline 77 \\ -72 \\ \hline 5 \end{array}$$

7(8) = 56
Subtract and bring down the 7.
0(8) = 0
Subtract and bring down the 1.
8(8) = 64
Subtract and bring down the 7.
9(8) = 72
Subtract. The remainder is 5.

Answers

6. a. 234 R 3 **b.** 657 R 2

7. a. 9067 R 2 **b.** 5827 R 2

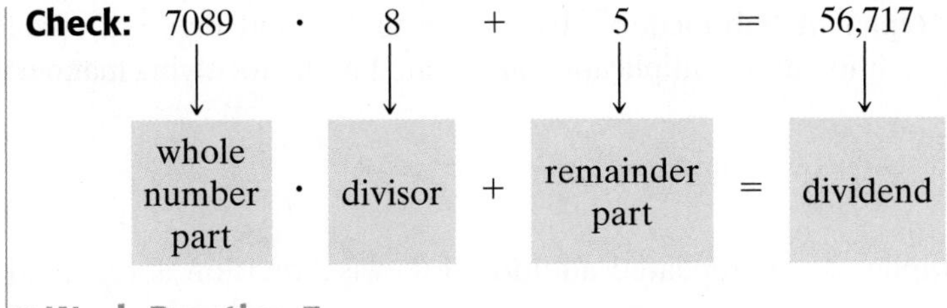
Check: 7089 · 8 + 5 = 56,717
whole number part · divisor + remainder part = dividend

Work Practice 7

When the divisor has more than one digit, the same pattern applies. For example, let's find 1358 ÷ 23.

```
     5        135 ÷ 23 = 5 with 20 left over. Our estimate is 5.
23)1358
  -115↓       5(23) = 115
    208       135 − 115 = 20. Bring down the 8.
```

Now we continue estimating.

```
     59 R 1   208 ÷ 23 = 9 with 1 left over.
23)1358
  -115
    208
   -207       9(23) = 207
      1       208 − 207 = 1. The remainder is 1.
```

To check, see that $59 \cdot 23 + 1 = 1358$.

Example 8 Divide: 6819 ÷ 17

Solution:

```
     401 R 2
17)6819
  -68↓        4(17) = 68
    01        Subtract and bring down the 1.
    -0↓       0(17) = 0
     19       Subtract and bring down the 9.
    -17       1(17) = 17
      2       Subtract. The reminder is 2.
```

To check, see that $401 \cdot 17 + 2 = 6819$.

Work Practice 8

PRACTICE 8

Divide: 8920 ÷ 17

Example 9 Divide: 51,600 ÷ 403

Solution:

```
      128 R 16
403)51600
   -403↓        1(403) = 403
    1130        Subtract and bring down the 0.
    -806↓       2(403) = 806
     3240       Subtract and bring down the 0.
    -3224       8(403) = 3224
       16       Subtract. The remainder is 16.
```

To check, see that $128 \cdot 403 + 16 = 51,600$.

Work Practice 9

PRACTICE 9

Divide: 33,282 ÷ 678

Answers

8. 524 R 12 **9.** 49 R 60

Division Shown as Repeated Subtraction To further understand division, recall from Section 1.6 that addition and multiplication are related in the following manner:

$$\underbrace{3 + 3 + 3 + 3}_{\text{4 addends; each addend is 3}} = 4 \times 3 = 12$$

In other words, multiplication is repeated addition. Likewise, division is repeated subtraction.

For example, let's find

$35 \div 8$

by repeated subtraction. Keep track of the number of times 8 is subtracted from 35. We are through when we can subtract no more because the difference is less than 8.

$35 \div 8$: Repeated Subtraction

$$\begin{array}{r} 35 \\ -8 \\ \hline 27 \\ -8 \\ \hline 19 \\ -8 \\ \hline 11 \\ -8 \\ \hline 3 \end{array}$$

35 − 8: 1 time
27 − 8: 2 times
19 − 8: 3 times
11 − 8: 4 times
3 ⟵ Remainder (We cannot subtract 8 again.)

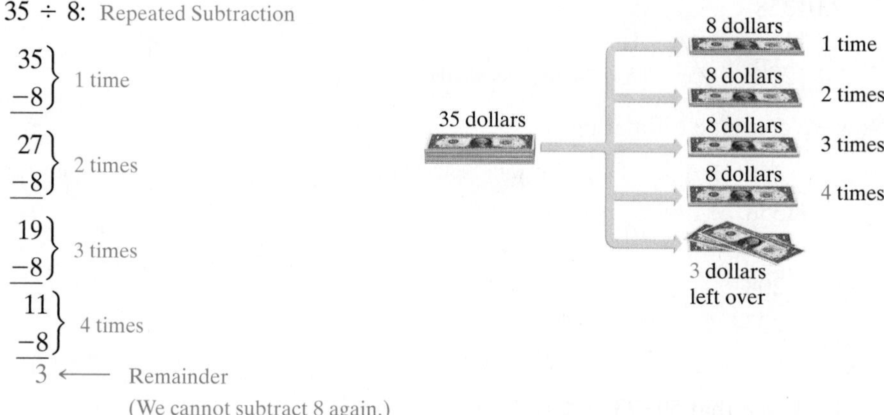

Thus, $35 \div 8 = 4 \text{ R } 3$.

To check, perform the same multiplication as usual, but finish by adding in the remainder.

whole number part of quotient	·	divisor	+	remainder	=	dividend
↓		↓		↓		↓
4	·	8	+	3	=	35

Objective C Solving Problems by Dividing

Below are some key words and phrases that may indicate the operation of division:

Division

Key Words or Phrases	Examples	Symbols
divide	divide 10 by 5	$10 \div 5$ or $\frac{10}{5}$
quotient	the quotient of 64 and 4	$64 \div 4$ or $\frac{64}{4}$
divided by	9 divided by 3	$9 \div 3$ or $\frac{9}{3}$
divided or shared equally among	$100 divided equally among five people	$100 \div 5$ or $\frac{100}{5}$
per	100 miles per 2 hours	$\frac{100 \text{ miles}}{2 \text{ hours}}$

✓**Concept Check** Which of the following is the correct way to represent "the quotient of 60 and 12"? Or are both correct? Explain your answer.

a. $12 \div 60$ **b.** $60 \div 12$

Example 10 Finding Shared Earnings

Three college students share a paper route to earn money for expenses. The total in their fund after expenses was \$2895. How much is each person's equal share?

Solution:

In words:	Each person's share	=	total money	÷	number of persons
	↓		↓		↓
Translate:	Each person's share	=	2895	÷	3

Then

$$\begin{array}{r} 965 \\ 3\overline{)2895} \\ -27 \\ \hline 19 \\ -18 \\ \hline 15 \\ -15 \\ \hline 0 \end{array}$$

Each person's share is \$965.

Work Practice 10

PRACTICE 10

Three students bought 171 blank CDs to share equally. How many CDs did each person get?

Example 11 Dividing Number of Downloads

As part of a promotion, an executive receives 238 cards, each good for one free song download. If she wants to share them evenly with 19 friends, how many download cards will each friend receive? How many will be left over?

Solution:

In words:	Number of cards for each person	=	number of cards	÷	number of friends
	↓		↓		↓
Translate:	Number of cards for each person	=	238	÷	19

$$\begin{array}{r} 12 \text{ R } 10 \\ 19\overline{)238} \\ -19 \\ \hline 48 \\ -38 \\ \hline 10 \end{array}$$

Each friend will receive 12 download cards. The cards cannot be divided equally among her friends since there is a nonzero remainder. There will be 10 download cards left over.

Work Practice 11

PRACTICE 11

Printers can be packed 12 to a box. If 532 printers are to be packed but only full boxes are shipped, how many full boxes will be shipped? How many printers are left over and not shipped?

Answers

10. 57 CDs

11. 44 full boxes; 4 printers left over

✓ **Concept Check Answers**

a. incorrect **b.** correct

Objective D Finding Averages

A special application of division (and addition) is finding the average of a list of numbers. The **average** of a list of numbers is the sum of the numbers divided by the *number* of numbers.

$$\text{average} = \frac{\text{sum of numbers}}{\textit{number} \text{ of numbers}}$$

PRACTICE 12

To compute a safe time to wait for reactions to occur after allergy shots are administered, a lab technician is given a list of elapsed times between administered shots and reactions. Find the average of the times 4 minutes, 7 minutes, 35 minutes, 16 minutes, 9 minutes, 3 minutes, and 52 minutes.

Example 12 Averaging Scores

A mathematics instructor is checking a simple program she wrote for averaging the scores of her students. To do so, she averages a student's scores of 75, 96, 81, and 88 by hand. Find this average score.

Solution: To find the average score, we find the sum of the student's scores and divide by 4, the number of scores.

$$\begin{array}{r} 75 \\ 96 \\ 81 \\ +88 \\ \hline 340 \end{array} \text{ sum} \qquad \text{average} = \frac{340}{4} = 85 \qquad \begin{array}{r} 85 \\ 4\overline{)340} \\ -32 \\ \hline 20 \\ -20 \\ \hline 0 \end{array}$$

The average score is 85.

Work Practice 12

Calculator Explorations Dividing Numbers

To divide numbers on a calculator, find the keys marked [÷] and [=] or [ENTER]. For example, to find 435 ÷ 5 on a calculator, press the keys [435] [÷] [5] [=] or [ENTER]. The display will read [87]. Thus, 435 ÷ 5 = 87.

Use a calculator to divide.

1. 848 ÷ 16

2. 564 ÷ 12

3. $95\overline{)5890}$

4. $27\overline{)1053}$

5. $\frac{32,886}{126}$

6. $\frac{143,088}{264}$

7. 0 ÷ 315

8. 315 ÷ 0

Answer

12. 18 minutes

Vocabulary and Readiness Check

Use the choices below to fill in each blank. Some choices may be used more than once.

1	number	divisor	dividend
0	undefined	average	quotient

1. In $90 \div 2 = 45$, the answer 45 is called the ____________, 90 is called the ____________, and 2 is called the ____________.

2. The quotient of any number and 1 is the same ____________.

3. The quotient of any number (except 0) and the same number is ____________.

4. The quotient of 0 and any number (except 0) is ____________.

5. The quotient of any number and 0 is ____________.

6. The ____________ of a list of numbers is the sum of the numbers divided by the ____________ of numbers.

1.7 Exercise Set

FOR EXTRA HELP

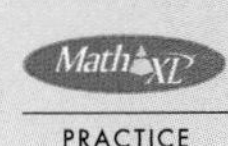

Objective **A** *Find each quotient. See Examples 1 through 3.*

1. $54 \div 9$ **2.** $72 \div 9$ **3.** $36 \div 3$ **4.** $24 \div 3$ **5.** $0 \div 8$

6. $0 \div 4$ **7.** $31 \div 1$ **8.** $38 \div 1$ **9.** $\frac{18}{18}$ **10.** $\frac{49}{49}$

11. $\frac{24}{3}$ **12.** $\frac{45}{9}$ **13.** $26 \div 0$ **14.** $\frac{12}{0}$ **15.** $26 \div 26$

16. $6 \div 6$ **17.** $0 \div 14$ **18.** $7 \div 0$ **19.** $18 \div 2$ **20.** $18 \div 3$

Objectives **A** **B** **Mixed Practice** *Divide and then check by multiplying. See Examples 1 through 5.*

21. $3\overline{)87}$ **22.** $5\overline{)85}$ **23.** $3\overline{)222}$ **24.** $8\overline{)640}$ **25.** $3\overline{)1014}$ **26.** $4\overline{)2104}$

27. $\frac{30}{0}$ **28.** $\frac{0}{30}$ **29.** $63 \div 7$ **30.** $56 \div 8$ **31.** $150 \div 6$ **32.** $121 \div 11$

Divide and then check by multiplying. See Examples 6 and 7.

33. $7\overline{)479}$ **34.** $7\overline{)426}$ **35.** $6\overline{)1421}$ **36.** $3\overline{)1240}$

37. $305 \div 8$ **38.** $167 \div 3$ **39.** $2286 \div 7$ **40.** $3333 \div 4$

Divide and then check by multiplying. See Examples 8 and 9.

41. $55\overline{)715}$
42. $23\overline{)736}$
43. $23\overline{)1127}$
44. $42\overline{)2016}$
45. $97\overline{)9417}$

46. $44\overline{)1938}$
47. $3146 \div 15$
48. $7354 \div 12$
49. $6578 \div 13$
50. $5670 \div 14$

51. $9299 \div 46$
52. $2505 \div 64$
53. $\frac{12{,}744}{236}$
54. $\frac{5781}{123}$
55. $\frac{10{,}297}{103}$

56. $\frac{23{,}092}{240}$
57. $20{,}619 \div 102$
58. $40{,}853 \div 203$
59. $244{,}989 \div 423$
60. $164{,}592 \div 543$

Divide. See Examples 1 through 9.

61. $7\overline{)119}$
62. $8\overline{)104}$
63. $7\overline{)3580}$
64. $5\overline{)3017}$

65. $40\overline{)85{,}312}$
66. $50\overline{)85{,}747}$
67. $142\overline{)863{,}360}$
68. $214\overline{)650{,}560}$

Objective C Translating *Solve. See Examples 10 and 11.*

69. Find the quotient of 117 and 5.

70. Find the quotient of 94 and 7.

71. Find 200 divided by 35.

72. Find 116 divided by 32.

73. Find the quotient of 62 and 3.

74. Find the quotient of 78 and 5.

75. Martin Thieme teaches American Sign Language classes for $65 per student for a 7-week session. He collects $2145 from the group of students. Find how many students are in the group.

76. Kathy Gomez teaches Spanish lessons for $85 per student for a 5-week session. From one group of students, she collects $4930. Find how many students are in the group.

77. The gravity of Jupiter is 318 times as strong as the gravity of Earth, so objects on Jupiter weigh 318 times as much as they weigh on Earth. If a person would weigh 52,470 pounds on Jupiter, find how much the person weighs on Earth.

78. Twenty-one people pooled their money and bought lottery tickets. One ticket won a prize of $5,292,000. Find how many dollars each person received.

79. An 18-hole golf course is 5580 yards long. If the distance to each hole is the same, find the distance between holes.

80. A truck hauls wheat to a storage granary. It carries a total of 5768 bushels of wheat in 14 trips. How much does the truck haul each trip if each trip it hauls the same amount?

81. There is a bridge over highway I-35 every three miles. The first bridge is at the beginning of a 265-mile stretch of highway. Find how many bridges there are over 265 miles of I-35.

82. The white stripes dividing the lanes on a highway are 25 feet long, and the spaces between them are 25 feet long. Let's call a "lane divider" a stripe followed by a space. Find how many whole "lane dividers" there are in 1 mile of highway. (A mile is 5280 feet.)

83. Ari Trainor is in the requisitions department of Central Electric Lighting Company. Light poles along a highway are placed 492 feet apart. The first light pole is at the beginning of a 1-mile strip. Find how many poles he should order for the 1-mile strip of highway. (A mile is 5280 feet.)

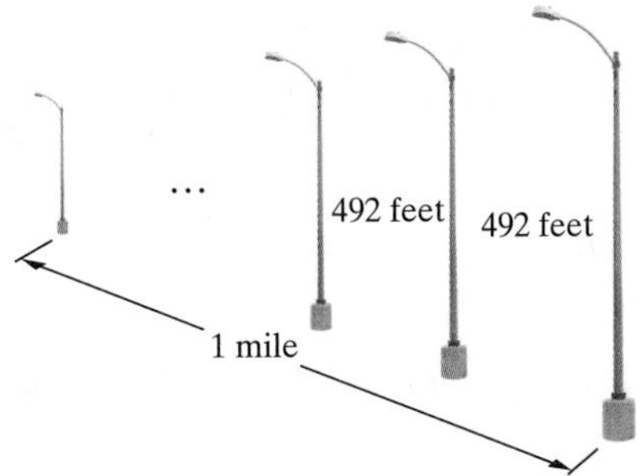

84. Professor Lopez has a piece of rope 185 feet long that she wants to cut into pieces for an experiment in her physics class. Each piece of rope is to be 8 feet long. Determine whether she has enough rope for her 22-student class. Determine the amount extra or the amount short.

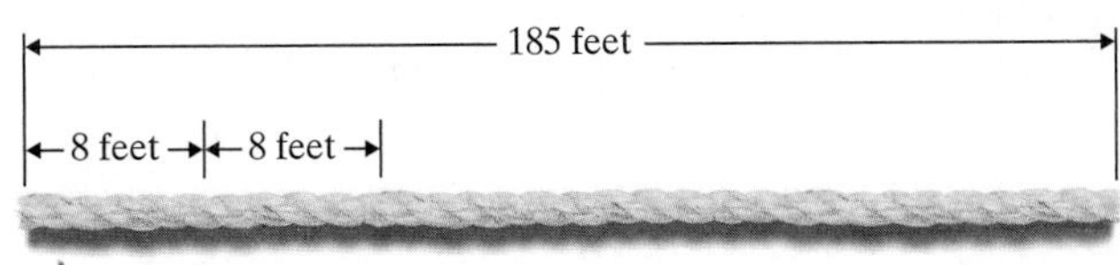

85. Broad Peak in Pakistan is the twelfth-tallest mountain in the world. Its elevation is 26,400 feet. A mile is 5280 feet. How many miles tall is Broad Peak? (*Source:* National Geographic Society)

86. DeAngelo Williams of the Carolina Panthers led the NFL in touchdowns during the 2008 football season, scoring a total of 120 points from touchdowns. If a touchdown is worth 6 points, how many touchdowns did Williams make during 2008? (*Source:* National Football League)

87. Find how many yards are in 1 mile. (A mile is 5280 feet; a yard is 3 feet.)

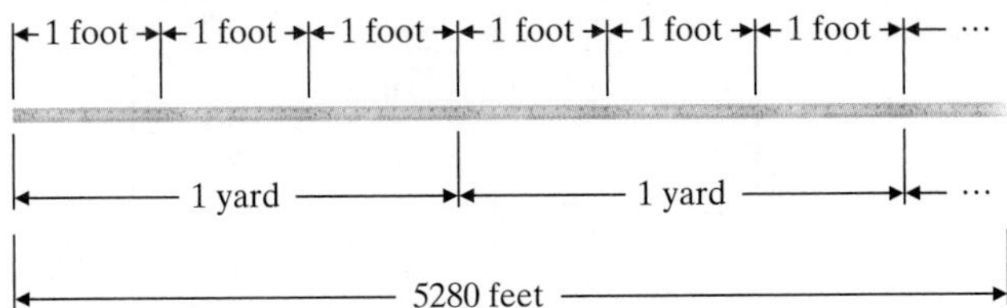

88. Find how many whole feet are in 1 rod. (A mile is 5280 feet; 1 mile is 320 rods.)

Objective D *Find the average of each list of numbers. See Example 12.*

89. 10, 24, 35, 22, 17, 12

90. 37, 26, 15, 29, 51, 22

91. 205, 972, 210, 161

92. 121, 200, 185, 176, 163

93. 86, 79, 81, 69, 80

94. 92, 96, 90, 85, 92, 79

The normal monthly temperature in degrees Fahrenheit for Salt Lake City, Utah, is given in the graph. Use this graph to answer Exercises 95 and 96. (Source: National Climatic Data Center)

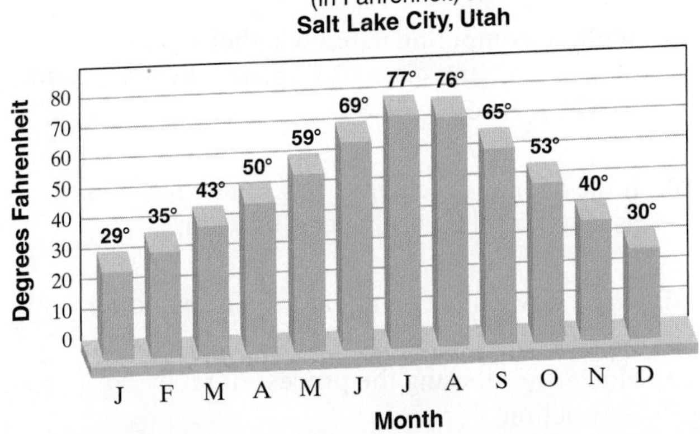

95. Find the average temperature for June, July, and August.

96. Find the average temperature for October, November, and December.

Mixed Practice (Sections 1.3, 1.4, 1.6, 1.7) *Perform each indicated operation. Watch the operation symbol.*

97. 82 + 463 + 29 + 8704

98. 23 + 407 + 92 + 7011

99. $\begin{array}{r} 546 \\ \times\ 28 \\ \hline \end{array}$

100. $\begin{array}{r} 712 \\ \times\ 54 \\ \hline \end{array}$

101. $\begin{array}{r} 722 \\ -\ 43 \\ \hline \end{array}$

102. $\begin{array}{r} 712 \\ -\ 54 \\ \hline \end{array}$

103. $\frac{45}{0}$

104. $\frac{0}{23}$

105. 228 ÷ 24

106. 304 ÷ 31

Concept Extensions

Match each word phrase to the correct translation. (Not all letter choices will be used.) See the Concept Check in this section.

107. The quotient of 40 and 8

108. The quotient of 200 and 20

109. 200 divided by 20

110. 40 divided by 8

a. 20 ÷ 200 **b.** 200 ÷ 20

c. 40 ÷ 8 **d.** 8 ÷ 40

The following table shows the top five countries with the most Nobel Prize winners through 2008. Use this table to answer Exercises 111 and 112. (Source: Nobel Prize Committee)

111. Find the average number of Nobel Prize winners for the countries shown.

112. Find the average number of Nobel Prize winners per category for Sweden.

Countries with the Most Nobel Prize Winners, 1901–2008

Country	Physics	Chemistry	Literature	Physiology and Medicine	Peace	Economics	Total
United States	88	59	11	96	22	44	320
United Kingdom	21	27	11	31	13	7	110
Germany	25	28	8	16	4	1	82
France	13	8	14	11	10	2	58
Sweden	4	4	8	7	5	2	30

In Example 12 in this section, we found that the average of 75, 96, 81, and 88 is 85. Use this information to answer Exercises 113 and 114.

113. If the number 75 is removed from the list of numbers, does the average increase or decrease? Explain why.

114. If the number 96 is removed from the list of numbers, does the average increase or decrease? Explain why.

115. Without computing it, tell whether the average of 126, 135, 198, 113 is 86. Explain why it is possible or why it is not.

116. Without computing it, tell whether the average of 38, 27, 58, and 43 is 17. Explain why it is possible or why it is not.

△ **117.** If the area of a rectangle is 60 square feet and its width is 5 feet, what is its length?

△ **118.** If the area of a rectangle is 84 square inches and its length is 21 inches, what is its width?

119. Write down any two numbers whose quotient is 25.

120. Write down any two numbers whose quotient is 1.

121. Find 26 ÷ 5 using the process of repeated subtraction.

122. Find 86 ÷ 10 using the process of repeated subtraction.

Integrated Review Sections 1.1–1.7

Operations on Whole Numbers

1. $\begin{array}{r} 23 \\ 46 \\ +79 \\ \hline \end{array}$

2. $\begin{array}{r} 7006 \\ -\ 451 \\ \hline \end{array}$

3. $\begin{array}{r} 36 \\ \times 45 \\ \hline \end{array}$

4. $8\overline{)4496}$

5. $1 \cdot 79$

6. $\dfrac{36}{0}$

7. $9 \div 1$

8. $9 \div 9$

9. $0 \cdot 13$

10. $7 \cdot 0 \cdot 8$

11. $0 \div 2$

12. $12 \div 4$

13. $4219 - 1786$

14. $1861 + 7965$

15. $5\overline{)1068}$

16. $\begin{array}{r} 1259 \\ \times\ \ 63 \\ \hline \end{array}$

17. $3 \cdot 9$

18. $45 \div 5$

19. $\begin{array}{r} 207 \\ -\ \ 69 \\ \hline \end{array}$

20. $\begin{array}{r} 207 \\ +\ \ 69 \\ \hline \end{array}$

21. $7\overline{)7695}$

22. $9\overline{)1000}$

23. $32\overline{)21{,}222}$

24. $65\overline{)70{,}000}$

25. $4000 - 2976$

26. $10{,}000 - 101$

27. $\begin{array}{r} 303 \\ \times 101 \\ \hline \end{array}$

28. $(475)(100)$

29. Find the total of 57 and 8.

30. Find the product of 57 and 8.

Answers

1. ______
2. ______
3. ______
4. ______
5. ______
6. ______
7. ______
8. ______
9. ______
10. ______
11. ______
12. ______
13. ______
14. ______
15. ______
16. ______
17. ______
18. ______
19. ______
20. ______
21. ______
22. ______
23. ______
24. ______
25. ______
26. ______
27. ______
28. ______
29. ______
30. ______

31. ______
32. ______
33. ______
34. ______
35. ______
36. ______
37. ______
38. ______
39. ______
40. ______
41. ______
42. ______
43. ______
44. ______
45. ______
46. ______

31. Find the quotient of 62 and 9.

32. Find the difference of 62 and 9.

33. Subtract 17 from 200.

34. Find the difference of 432 and 201.

Complete the table by rounding the given number to the given place value.

		Tens	Hundreds	Thousands
35.	9735			
36.	1429			
37.	20,801			
38.	432,198			

Find the perimeter and area of each figure.

△ **39.**

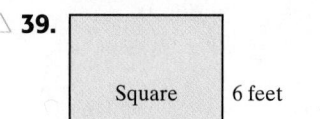

Square
6 feet

△ **40.**

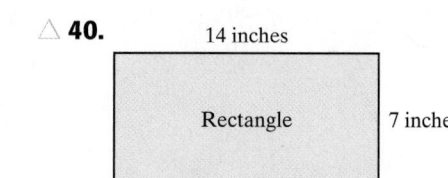

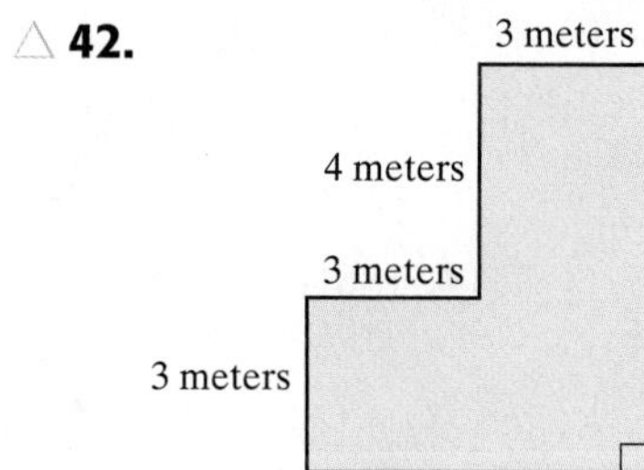

Find the perimeter of each figure.

△ **41.**

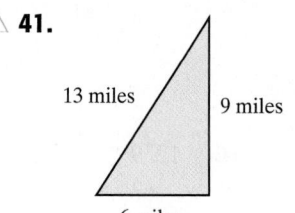

13 miles
9 miles
6 miles

△ **42.**

3 meters
4 meters
3 meters
3 meters

Find the average of each list of numbers.

43. 19, 15, 25, 37, 24

44. 108, 131, 98, 159

45. The Mackinac Bridge is a suspension bridge that connects the lower and upper peninsulas of Michigan across the Straits of Mackinac. Its total length is 26,372 feet. The Lake Pontchartrain Bridge is a twin concrete trestle bridge in Slidell, Louisiana. Its total length is 28,547 feet. Which bridge is longer and by how much? (*Sources:* Mackinac Bridge Authority and Federal Highway Administration, Bridge Division)

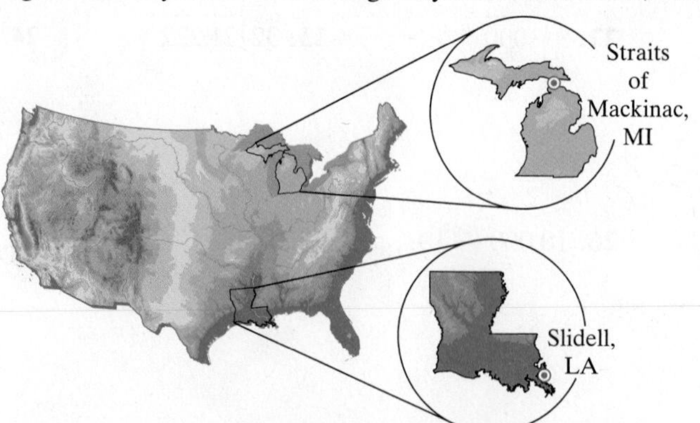

46. The average teenage male American consumes 2 quarts of carbonated soft drinks per day. On average, how many quarts of carbonated soft drinks would be consumed in a year? (Use 365 for the number of days.) (*Source:* American Beverage Association)

1.8 AN INTRODUCTION TO PROBLEM SOLVING

Objectives

A **Solve Problems by Adding, Subtracting, Multiplying, or Dividing Whole Numbers.**

B **Solve Problems That Require More Than One Operation.**

Objective A Solving Problems Involving Addition, Subtraction, Multiplication, or Division

In this section, we decide which operation to perform in order to solve a problem. Don't forget the key words and phrases that help indicate which operation to use. Some of these are listed below and were introduced earlier in the chapter. Also included are several words and phrases that translate to the symbol "=".

Addition (+)	Subtraction (−)	Multiplication (·)	Division (÷)	Equality (=)
sum	difference	product	quotient	equals
plus	minus	times	divide	is equal to
added to	subtract	multiply	shared equally	is/was
more than	less than	multiply by	among	yields
increased by	decreased by	of	divided by	
total	less	double/triple	divided into	

The following problem-solving steps may be helpful to you:

Problem-Solving Steps

1. UNDERSTAND the problem. Some ways of doing this are to read and reread the problem, construct a drawing, and look for key words to identify an operation.
2. TRANSLATE the problem. That is, write the problem in short form using words, and then translate to numbers and symbols.
3. SOLVE the problem. It is helpful to estimate the solution by rounding. Then carry out the indicated operation from step 2.
4. INTERPRET the results. *Check* the proposed solution in the stated problem and *state* your conclusions. Write your results with the correct units attached.

Example 1 Calculating the Length of a River

The Hudson River in New York State is 306 miles long. The Snake River in the northwestern United States is 732 miles longer than the Hudson River. How long is the Snake River? (*Source:* U.S. Department of the Interior)

Solution:

1. UNDERSTAND. Read and reread the problem, and then draw a picture. Notice that we are told that Snake River is 732 miles longer than the Hudson River. The phrase "longer than" means that we add.

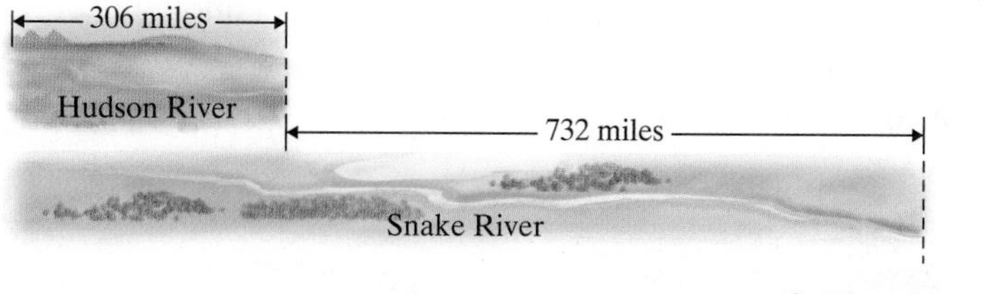

Continued on next page

PRACTICE 1

The Bank of America Building is the second-tallest building in San Francisco, California, at 779 feet. The tallest building in San Francisco is the Transamerica Pyramid, which is 74 feet taller than the Bank of America Building. How tall is the Transamerica Pyramid? (*Source: The World Almanac*)

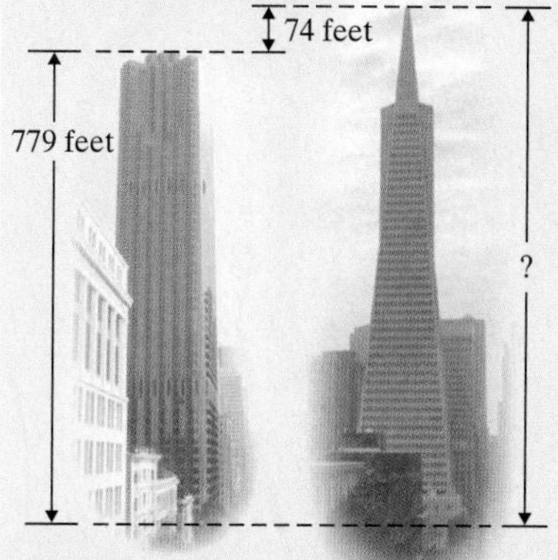

Answer
1. 853 ft

2. TRANSLATE.

In words:	Snake River	is	732 miles	longer than	the Hudson River
	↓	↓	↓	↓	↓
Translate:	Snake River	=	732	+	306

3. SOLVE: Let's see if our answer is reasonable by also estimating. We will estimate each addend to the nearest hundred.

732	rounds to	700	
+306	rounds to	300	
1038	exact	1000	estimate

4. INTERPRET. *Check* your work. The answer is reasonable since 1038 is close to our estimated answer of 1000. *State* your conclusion: The Snake River is 1038 miles long.

Work Practice 1

PRACTICE 2

Four friends bought a lottery ticket and won $65,000. If each person is to receive the same amount of money, how much does each person receive?

Example 2 Filling a Shipping Order

How many cases can be filled with 9900 cans of jalapeños if each case holds 48 cans? How many cans will be left over? Will there be enough cases to fill an order for 200 cases?

Solution:

1. UNDERSTAND. Read and reread the problem. Draw a picture to help visualize the situation.

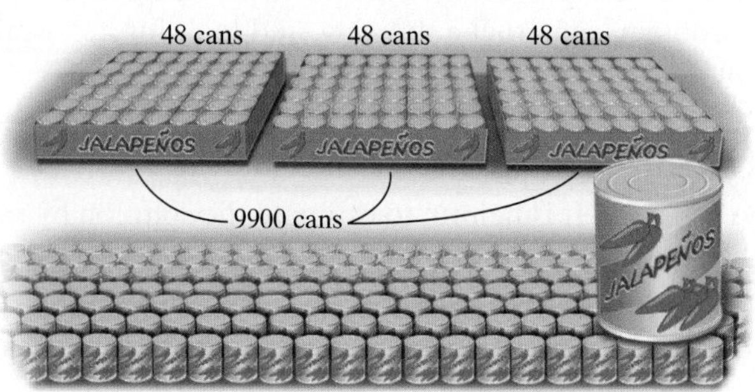

Since each case holds 48 cans, we want to know how many 48s there are in 9900. We find this by dividing.

2. TRANSLATE.

In words:	Number of cases	is	9900	divided by	48
	↓	↓	↓	↓	↓
Translate:	Number of cases	=	9900	÷	48

3. SOLVE: Let's estimate a reasonable solution before we actually divide. Since 9900 rounded to the nearest thousand is 10,000 and 48 rounded to the nearest ten is 50, $10{,}000 \div 50 = 200$. Now find the exact quotient.

$$\begin{array}{r} 206 \text{ R } 12 \\ 48\overline{)9900} \\ -96 \\ \hline 300 \\ -288 \\ \hline 12 \end{array}$$

Answer

2. $16,250

4. INTERPRET. *Check* your work. The answer is reasonable since 206 R 12 is close to our estimate of 200. *State* your conclusion: 206 cases will be filled, with 12 cans left over. There will be enough cases to fill an order for 200 cases.

Work Practice 2

Example 3 Calculating Budget Costs

The director of a learning lab at a local community college is working on next year's budget. Thirty-three new DVD players are needed at a cost of $187 each. What is the total cost of these DVD players?

Solution:

1. UNDERSTAND. Read and reread the problem, and then draw a diagram.

From the phrase "total cost," we might decide to solve this problem by adding. This would work, but repeated addition, or multiplication, would save time.

2. TRANSLATE.

In words:	Total cost	is	number of DVD players	times	cost of a DVD player
	↓	↓	↓	↓	↓
Translate:	Total cost	=	33	×	$187

3. SOLVE: Once again, let's estimate a reasonable solution.

$$\begin{array}{r} 187 \\ \times\ 33 \\ \hline 561 \\ 5610 \\ \hline 6171 \end{array} \text{ exact} \qquad \begin{array}{l} \text{rounds to} \\ \text{rounds to} \end{array} \qquad \begin{array}{r} 200 \\ \times\ 30 \\ \hline 6000 \end{array} \text{ estimate}$$

4. INTERPRET. *Check* your work. *State* your conclusion: The total cost of the DVD players is $6171.

Work Practice 3

PRACTICE 3

The director of the learning lab also needs to include in the budget a line for 425 blank CDs at a cost of $4 each. What is this total cost for the blank CDs?

Example 4 Calculating a Public School Teacher's Salary

In 2008, the average salary of a public school teacher in California was $64,424. For the same year, the average salary for a public school teacher in Iowa was $17,760 less than this. What was the average public school teacher's salary in Iowa? (*Source:* National Education Association)

Solution:

1. UNDERSTAND. Read and reread the problem. Notice that we are told that the Iowa salary is $17,760 less than the California salary. The phrase "less than" indicates subtraction.

Continued on next page

PRACTICE 4

In 2008, the average salary for a public school teacher in Alaska was $56,758. For the same year, the average salary for a public school teacher in Hawaii was $3358 less than this. What was the average public school teacher's salary in Hawaii? (*Source:* National Education Association)

Answers

3. $1700 4. $53,400

2. TRANSLATE. Remember that order matters when subtracting, so be careful when translating.

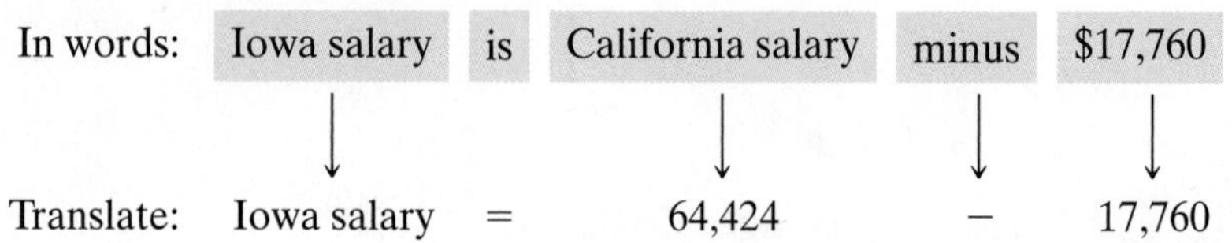

In words: Iowa salary is California salary minus $17,760
Translate: Iowa salary = 64,424 − 17,760

3. SOLVE. This time, instead of estimating, let's check by adding.

$$\begin{array}{r} 64{,}424 \\ -17{,}760 \\ \hline 46{,}664 \end{array} \qquad \textbf{Check:} \quad \begin{array}{r} 46{,}664 \\ +17{,}760 \\ \hline 64{,}424 \end{array}$$

4. INTERPRET. *Check* your work. The check is above. *State* your conclusion: The average Iowa teacher's salary in 2008 was $46,664.

Work Practice 4

Objective B Solving Problems That Require More Than One Operation

We must sometimes use more than one operation to solve a problem.

PRACTICE 5

A gardener is trying to decide how much fertilizer to buy for his yard. He knows that his lot is in the shape of a rectangle that measures 90 feet by 120 feet. He also knows that the floor of his house is in the shape of a rectangle that measures 45 feet by 65 feet. How much area of the lot is not covered by the house?

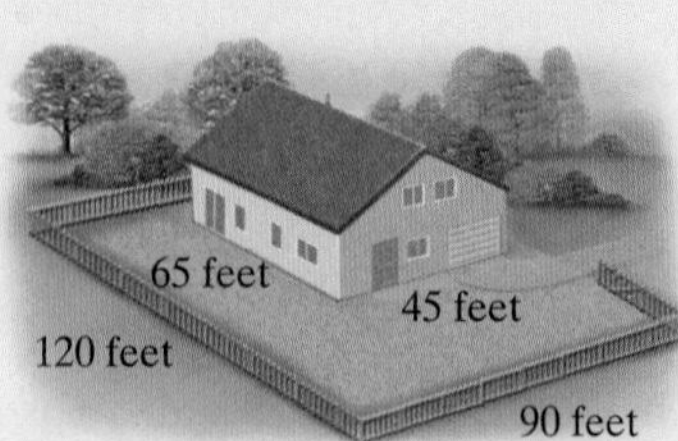

Answer
5. 7875 sq ft

Example 5 Planting a New Garden

A gardener bought enough plants to fill a rectangular garden with length 30 feet and width 20 feet. Because of shading problems from a nearby tree, the gardener changed the width of the garden to 15 feet. If the area is to remain the same, what is the new length of the garden?

Solution:

1. UNDERSTAND. Read and reread the problem. Then draw a picture to help visualize the problem.

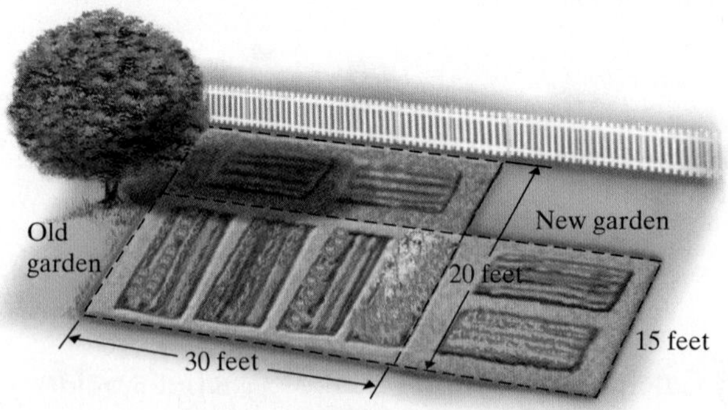

2. TRANSLATE. Since the area of the new garden is to be the same as the area of the old garden, let's find the area of the old garden. Recall that

$$\text{Area} = \text{length} \times \text{width} = 30 \text{ feet} \times 20 \text{ feet} = 600 \text{ square feet}$$

Since the area of the new garden is to be 600 square feet also, we need to see how many 15s there are in 600. This means division. In other words,

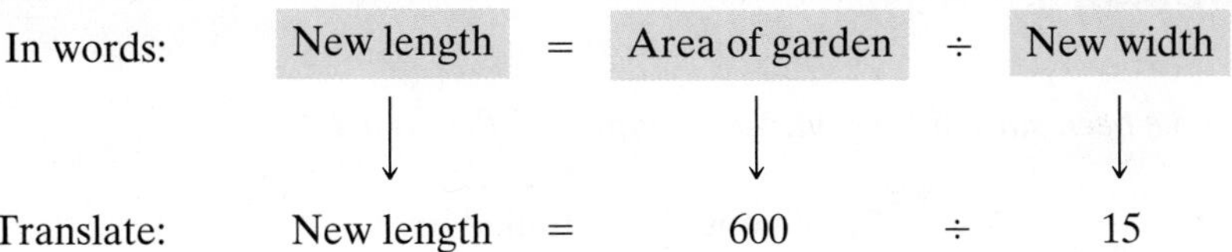

Translate: New length = 600 ÷ 15

3. SOLVE.

$$\begin{array}{r} 40 \\ 15\overline{)600} \\ \underline{-60} \\ 00 \end{array}$$

4. INTERPRET. *Check* your work. *State* your conclusion: The length of the new garden is 40 feet.

Work Practice 5

1.8 Exercise Set

FOR EXTRA HELP

Powered by CourseCompass and MathXL MyMathLab

PRACTICE

WATCH

DOWNLOAD

READ

REVIEW

Objective A *Solve. Exercises 1, 2, 11, and 12 have been started for you. See Examples 1 through 4.*

1. 41 increased by 8 is what number?
Start the Solution:
1. UNDERSTAND the problem. Reread it as many times as needed.
2. TRANSLATE into an equation. (Fill in the blanks below.)

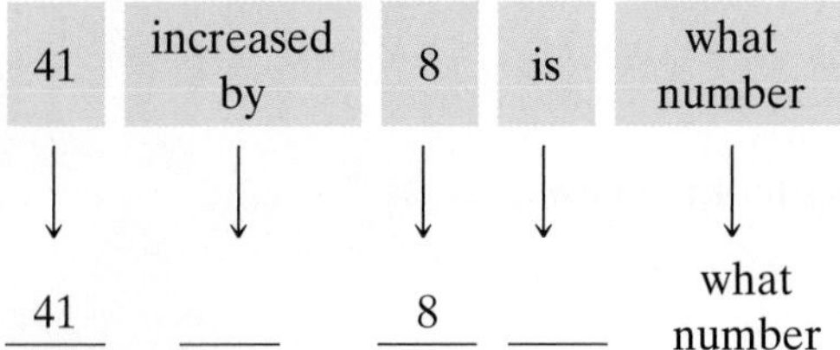

Finish with:
3. SOLVE
4. INTERPRET

2. What is 12 multiplied by 9?
Start the Solution:
1. UNDERSTAND the problem. Reread it as many times as needed.
2. TRANSLATE into an equation. (Fill in the blanks below.)

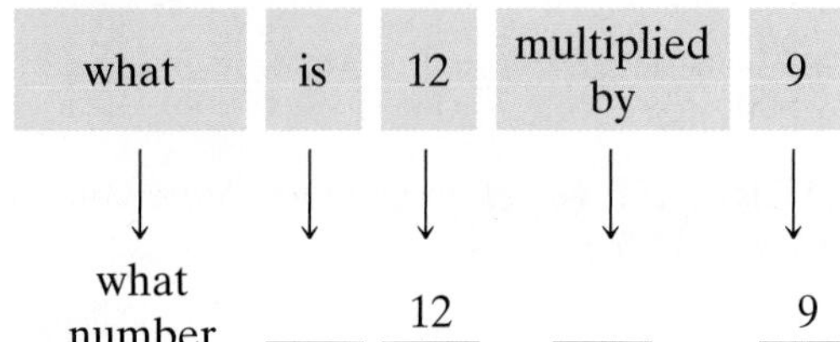

Finish with:
3. SOLVE
4. INTERPRET

3. What is the quotient of 1185 and 5?

4. 78 decreased by 12 is what number?

5. What is the total of 35 and 7?

6. What is the difference of 48 and 8?

7. 60 times 10 is what number?

8. 60 divided by 10 is what number?

△ **9.** A vacant lot in the shape of a rectangle measures 120 feet by 80 feet.

a. What is the perimeter of the lot?
b. What is the area of the lot?

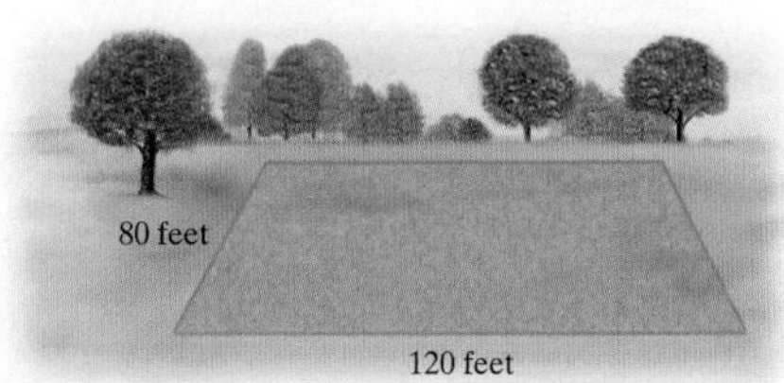

△ **10.** A parking lot in the shape of a rectangle measures 100 feet by 150 feet.

a. What is the perimeter of the lot?
b. What is the area of the parking lot?

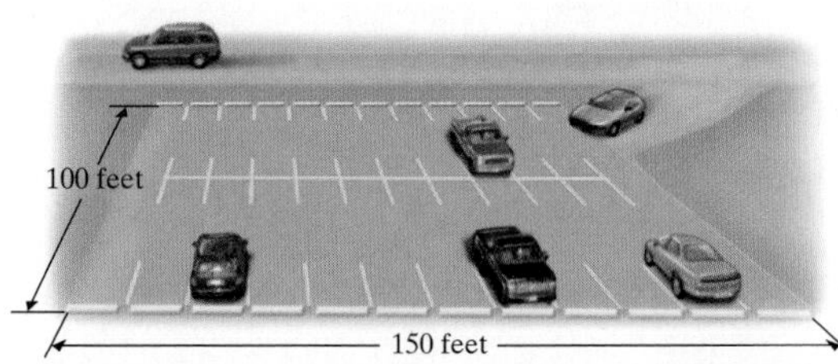

11. A family bought a house for \$185,700 and later sold the house for \$201,200. How much money did they make by selling the house?
Sart the Solution:
1. UNDERSTAND the problem. Reread it as many times as needed.
2. TRANSLATE into an equation. (Fill in the blanks below.)

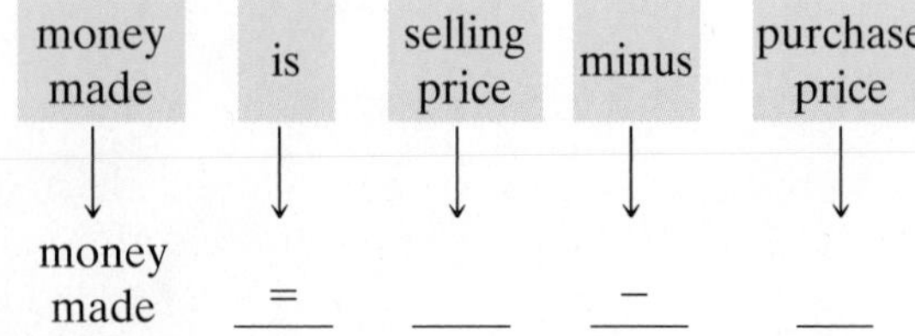

Finish with:
3. SOLVE
4. INTERPRET

12. Three people dream of equally sharing a \$147 million lottery. How much would each person receive if they have the winning ticket?
Start the solution:
1. UNDERSTAND the problem. Reread it as many times as needed.
2. TRANSLATE into an equation. (Fill in the blanks below.)

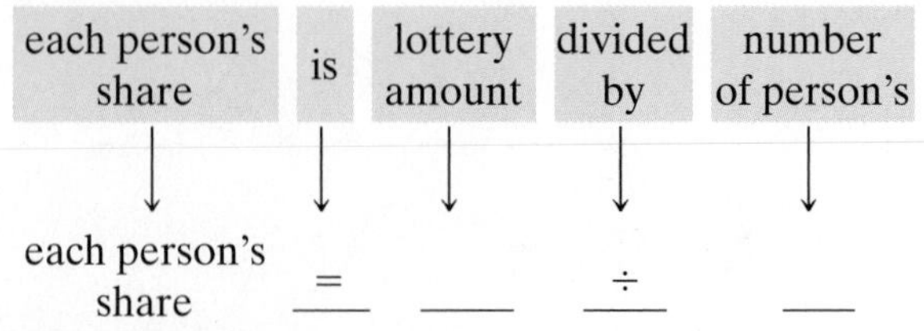

each person's share
is
lottery amount
divided by
number of person's
each person's share
=
____
÷
____

Finish with:
3. SOLVE
4. INTERPRET

13. There are 24 hours in a day. How many hours are in a week?

14. There are 60 minutes in an hour. How many minutes are in a day?

15. The Verrazano Narrows Bridge is the longest bridge in New York, measuring 4260 feet. The George Washington Bridge, also in New York, is 760 feet shorter than the Verrazano Narrows Bridge. Find the length of the George Washington Bridge.

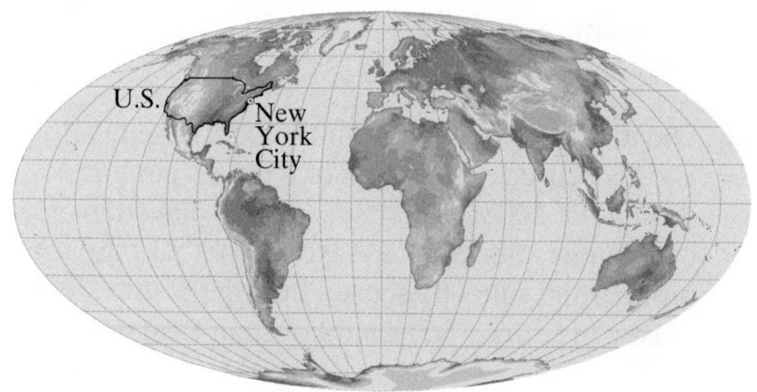

16. The Goodyear Tire & Rubber Company maintains a fleet of five blimps. The *Spirit of Goodyear* can hold 202,700 cubic feet of helium. Its smaller sister, the *Spirit of Europe,* can hold 132,700 fewer cubic feet of helium than *Spirit of Goodyear*. How much helium can *Spirit of Europe* hold? (*Source:* Goodyear Tire & Rubber Company)

17. Yellowstone National Park in Wyoming was the first national park in the United States. It was created in 1872. One of the more recent additions to the National Park System is Governors Island National Monument in New York. It was established in 2001. How much older is Yellowstone than Governors Island? (*Source:* National Park Service)

18. Razor scooters were introduced in 2000. Radio Flyer Wagons were first introduced 83 years earlier. In what year were Radio Flyer Wagons introduced? (*Source:* Toy Industry Association, Inc.)

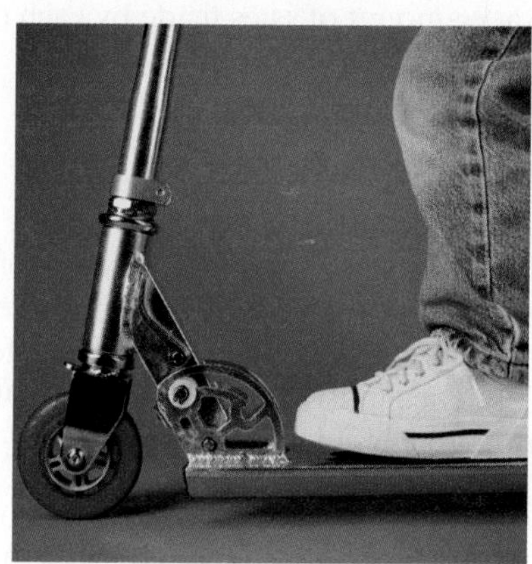

19. Since their introduction, the number of LEGO building bricks that have been sold is equivalent to the world's current population of approximately 6 billion people owning 52 LEGO bricks each. About how many LEGO bricks have been sold since their introduction? (*Source:* LEGO Company)

20. In 2010, the average weekly pay for a home health aide in the United States was about \$519. At this rate, how much will a home health aide earn working a 52-week year? (*Source:* Bureau of Labor Statistics)

21. The three most common city names in the United States are Fairview, Midway, and Riverside. There are 287 towns named Fairview, 252 named Midway, and 180 named Riverside. Find the total number of towns named Fairview, Midway, or Riverside.

22. In the game of Monopoly, a player must own all properties in a color group before building houses. The yellow color-group properties are Atlantic Avenue, Ventnor Avenue, and Marvin Gardens. These cost \$260, \$260, and \$280, respectively, when purchased from the bank. What total amount must a player pay to the bank before houses can be built on the yellow properties? (*Source:* Hasbro, Inc.)

23. In 2007, the average weekly pay for a correctional officer supervisor in the United States was $1080. If such a supervisor works 40 hours in one week, what is his or her hourly pay? (*Source:* Bureau of Labor Statistics)

24. In 2007, the average weekly pay for a bill collector was $600. If a bill collector works 40 hours in one week, what is his or her hourly pay? (*Source:* Bureau of Labor Statistics)

25. Three ounces of canned tuna in oil has 165 calories. How many calories does 1 ounce have? (*Source: Home and Garden Bulletin No. 72,* U.S. Department of Agriculture)

26. A whole cheesecake has 3360 calories. If the cheesecake is cut into 12 equal pieces, how many calories will each piece have? (*Source: Home and Garden Bulletin No. 72,* U.S. Department of Agriculture)

27. The average estimated 2008 U.S. population was 303,800,000. Between Memorial Day and Labor Day, 7 billion hot dogs are consumed. Approximately how many hot dogs were consumed per person between Memorial Day and Labor Day in 2008? Divide, but do not give the remainder part of the quotient. (*Source:* U.S. Census Bureau, National Hot Dog and Sausage Council)

28. David Akers, a kicker with the NFL's Philadelphia Eagles, scored an average of 9 points per game during the 2008 regular season. He played in a total of 16 games during the season. What was the total number of points he scored during the 2008 football season? (*Source:* National Football League)

29. Macy's, formerly the Federated Department Stores Company, operates 810 Macy's and 40 Bloomingdale's department stores around the country. In 2007, Macy's had sales of approximately $26,313,249,400. What is the average amount of sales made by each of the 850 stores? (*Source:* Macy's)

30. In 2008, approximately 2,132,000 pounds of mail were carried by mule train for delivery to the Havasupai Indians, on their reservation inside the Grand Canyon. If mail is delivered every one of the 52 weeks of the year, what was the average number of pounds of mail delivered to the Havasupai per week in 2008? (*Source:* United States Postal Service)

31. The Museum of Modern Art in New York welcomes 1,585,000 visitors per year. The Museum of Science in Boston receives 1,429,700 visitors per year. How many more people visit the Museum of Modern Art than the science museum? (*Source:* The Official Museum Directory)

32. In 2009, Target Corporation operated 1698 stores in the United States. Of these, 146 were in Texas. How many Target Stores were located in states other than Texas? (*Source:* Target Corporation)

33. The length of the southern boundary of the conterminous United States is 1933 miles. The length of the northern boundary of the conterminous United States is 2054 miles longer than this. What is the length of the northern boundary? (*Source:* U.S. Geological Survey)

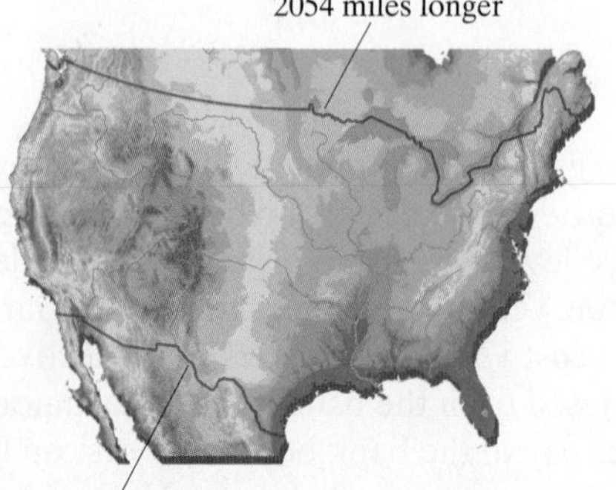

34. In humans, 14 muscles are required to smile. It takes 29 more muscles to frown. How many muscles does it take to frown?

35. An instructor at the University of New Orleans receives a paycheck every four weeks. Find how many paychecks he receives in a year. (A year has 52 weeks.)

36. A loan of $6240 is to be paid in 48 equal payments. How much is each payment?

Objective **B** *Solve. See Example 5.*

37. Find the total cost of 3 sweaters at $38 each and 5 shirts at $25 each.

38. Find the total cost of 10 computers at $2100 each and 7 boxes of diskettes at $12 each.

39. A college student has $950 in an account. She spends $205 from the account on books and then deposits $300 in the account. How much money is now in the account?

40. The temperature outside was 57°F (degrees Fahrenheit). During the next few hours, it decreased by 18 degrees and then increased by 23 degrees. Find the new temperature.

The table shows the menu from a concession stand at the county fair. Use this menu to answer Exercises 41 and 42.

41. A hungry college student is debating between the following two orders:

a. a hamburger, an order of onion rings, a candy bar, and a soda.
b. a hot dog, an apple, an order of french fries, and a soda.
Which order will be cheaper? By how much?

42. A family of four is debating between the following two orders:

a. 6 hot dogs, 4 orders of onion rings, and 4 sodas.
b. 4 hamburgers, 4 orders of french fries, 2 apples, and 4 sodas.
Will the family save any money by ordering (b) instead of (a)? If so, how much?

Corky's Concession Stand Menu

Item	Price
Hot dog	$3
Hamburger	$4
Soda	$1
Onion rings	$3
French fries	$2
Apple	$1
Candy bar	$2

Objectives **A B** **Mixed Practice** *Use the bar graph to answer Exercises 43 through 50. (Source: Miniwatts Marketing Group)*

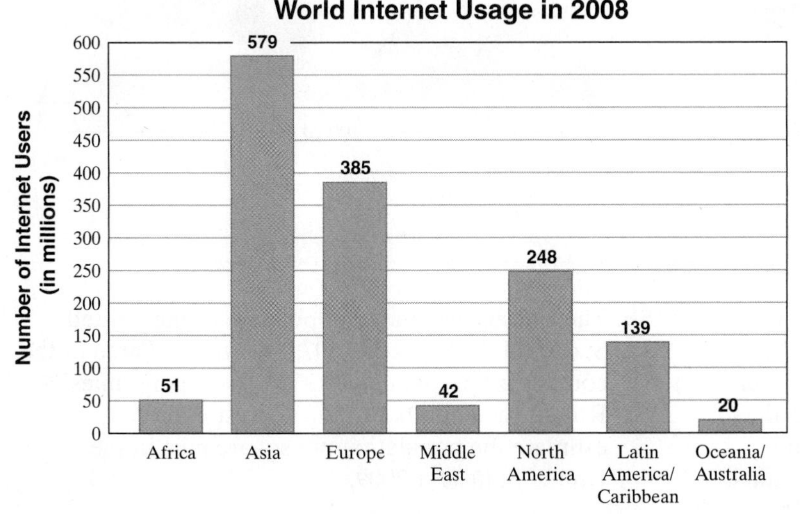

43. Which region of the world listed had the greatest number of Internet users in 2008?

44. Which region of the world listed had the fewest number of Internet users in 2008?

45. How many more Internet users (in millions) did the world region with the most Internet users have than the world region with the fewest Internet users?

46. How many more Internet users did Africa have than the Middle East in 2008?

47. How many more Internet users did North America have than Latin America/ Caribbean?

48. Which region of the world had more Internet users, Europe or North America? How many more Internet users did it have?

Find the average number of Internet users for the world regions listed in the graph on page 83.

49. The three world regions with the greatest number of Internet users.

50. The four world regions with the least number of Internet users.

Solve.

51. The learning lab at a local university is receiving new equipment. Twenty-two computers are purchased for $615 each and three printers for $408 each. Find the total cost for this equipment.

52. The washateria near the local community college is receiving new equipment. Thirty-six washers are purchased for $585 each and ten dryers are purchased for $388 each. Find the total cost for this equipment.

53. The American Heart Association recommends consuming no more than 2400 milligrams of salt per day. (This is about the amount in 1 teaspoon of salt.) How many milligrams of sodium is this in a week?

54. This semester a particular student pays $1750 for room and board, $709 for a meal ticket plan, and $2168 for tuition. What is her total bill?

△ **55.** The Meishs' yard is in the shape of a rectangle and measures 50 feet by 75 feet. In their yard, they have a rectangular swimming pool that measures 15 feet by 25 feet.

a. Find the area of the entire yard.
b. Find the area of the swimming pool.
c. Find the area of the yard that is not part of the swimming pool.

56. The community is planning to construct a rectangular-shaped playground within the local park. The park is in the shape of a square and measures 100 yards on each side. The playground is to measure 15 yards by 25 yards.

a. Find the area of the entire park.
b. Find the area of the playground.
c. Find the area of the park that is not part of the playground.

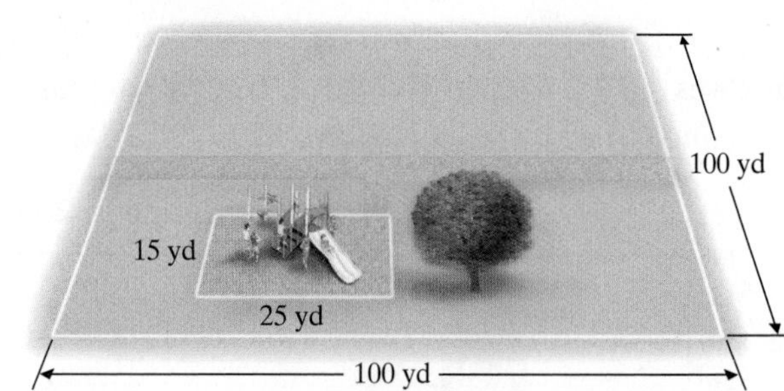

Concept Extensions

57. In 2008, the United States Postal Service issued approximately 149,100,000 money orders worth approximately $25,649,300,000. Round the number of money orders and the value of the money orders issued to the nearest ten-million to estimate the average value of each money order. (*Source:* United States Postal Service)

58. The average estimated population of the United States for 2009 was 307,607,800. The land area of the country is approximately 3,794,068 square miles. Round each number to the nearest million to estimate the population per square mile in the United States for 2009.

59. Write an application of your own that uses the term "bank account" and the numbers 1036 and 524.

1.9 EXPONENTS, SQUARE ROOTS, AND ORDER OF OPERATIONS

Objective A Using Exponential Notation

In the product $3 \cdot 3 \cdot 3 \cdot 3 \cdot 3$, notice that 3 is a factor several times. When this happens, we can use a shorthand notation, called an **exponent,** to write the repeated multiplication.

$\underbrace{3 \cdot 3 \cdot 3 \cdot 3 \cdot 3}_{\text{3 is a factor 5 times}}$ can be written as

3^5 (exponent: 5; base: 3) Read as "three to the fifth power."

This is called **exponential notation.** The **exponent,** 5, indicates how many times the **base,** 3, is a factor.

The table below shows examples of reading exponential notation in words.

Expression	In Words
5^2	"five to the second power" or "five squared"
5^3	"five to the third power" or "five cubed"
5^4	"five to the fourth power"

Usually, an exponent of 1 is not written, so when no exponent appears, we assume that the exponent is 1. For example, $2 = 2^1$ and $7 = 7^1$.

Examples Write using exponential notation.

1. $7 \cdot 7 \cdot 7 = 7^3$
2. $3 \cdot 3 = 3^2$
3. $6 \cdot 6 \cdot 6 \cdot 6 \cdot 6 = 6^5$
4. $3 \cdot 3 \cdot 3 \cdot 3 \cdot 17 \cdot 17 \cdot 17 = 3^4 \cdot 17^3$

Work Practice 1–4

Objective B Evaluating Exponential Expressions

To **evaluate** an exponential expression, we write the expression as a product and then find the value of the product.

Examples Evaluate.

5. $9^2 = 9 \cdot 9 = 81$
6. $6^1 = 6$
7. $3^4 = 3 \cdot 3 \cdot 3 \cdot 3 = 81$
8. $5 \cdot 6^2 = 5 \cdot 6 \cdot 6 = 180$

Work Practice 5–8

Objectives

- **A** Write Repeated Factors Using Exponential Notation.
- **B** Evaluate Expressions Containing Exponents.
- **C** Evaluate the Square Root of a Perfect Square.
- **D** Use the Order of Operations.
- **E** Find the Area of a Square.

PRACTICE 1–4

Write using exponential notation.

1. $8 \cdot 8 \cdot 8 \cdot 8$
2. $3 \cdot 3 \cdot 3$
3. $10 \cdot 10 \cdot 10 \cdot 10 \cdot 10$
4. $5 \cdot 5 \cdot 4 \cdot 4 \cdot 4 \cdot 4 \cdot 4 \cdot 4$

PRACTICE 5–8

Evaluate.

5. 4^2
6. 7^3
7. 11^1
8. $2 \cdot 3^2$

Answers

1. 8^4 2. 3^3 3. 10^5 4. $5^2 \cdot 4^6$
5. 16 6. 343 7. 11 8. 18

Example 8 illustrates an important property: An exponent applies only to its base. The exponent 2, in $5 \cdot 6^2$, applies only to its base, 6.

Helpful Hint

An exponent applies only to its base. For example, $4 \cdot 2^3$ means $4 \cdot 2 \cdot 2 \cdot 2$.

Helpful Hint

Don't forget that 2^4, for example, is *not* $2 \cdot 4$. The expression 2^4 means repeated multiplication of the same factor.

$$2^4 = 2 \cdot 2 \cdot 2 \cdot 2 = 16, \quad \text{whereas } 2 \cdot 4 = 8$$

✓ Concept Check Which of the following statements is correct?

a. 3^6 is the same as $6 \cdot 6 \cdot 6$.
b. "Eight to the fourth power" is the same as 8^4.
c. "Ten squared" is the same as 10^3.
d. 11^2 is the same as $11 \cdot 2$.

Objective C Evaluating Square Roots

A **square root** of a number is one of two identical factors of the number. For example,

$7 \cdot 7 = 49$, so a square root of 49 is 7.

We use this symbol $\sqrt{}$ (called a radical sign) for finding square roots. Since

$7 \cdot 7 = 49$, then $\sqrt{49} = 7$.

PRACTICE 9–11

Find each square root.

9. $\sqrt{100}$
10. $\sqrt{4}$
11. $\sqrt{1}$

Examples Find each square root.

9. $\sqrt{25} = 5$ because $5 \cdot 5 = 25$
10. $\sqrt{81} = 9$ because $9 \cdot 9 = 81$
11. $\sqrt{0} = 0$ because $0 \cdot 0 = 0$

Work Practice 9–11

Helpful Hint

Make sure you understand the difference between squaring a number and finding the square root of a number.

$9^2 = 9 \cdot 9 = 81 \quad \sqrt{9} = 3$ because $3 \cdot 3 = 9$

Not every square root simplifies to a whole number. We will study this more in a later chapter. In this section, we will find square roots of perfect squares only.

Answers

9. 10 **10.** 2 **11.** 1

✓ Concept Check Answer

b

Objective D Using the Order of Operations

Suppose that you are in charge of taking inventory at a local cell phone store. An employee has given you the number of a certain cell phone in stock as the expression

$6 + 2 \cdot 30$

To calculate the value of this expression, do you add first or multiply first? If you add first, the answer is 240. If you multiply first, the answer is 66.

Mathematical symbols wouldn't be very useful if two values were possible for one expression. Thus, mathematicians have agreed that, given a choice, we multiply first.

$$6 + 2 \cdot 30 = 6 + 60 \quad \text{Multiply.}$$
$$= 66 \quad \text{Add.}$$

This agreement is one of several **order of operations** agreements.

Order of Operations

1. Perform all operations within parentheses ( ), brackets [ ], or other grouping symbols such as fraction bars or square roots, starting with the innermost set.
2. Evaluate any expressions with exponents.
3. Multiply or divide in order from left to right.
4. Add or subtract in order from left to right.

Below we practice using order of operations to simplify expressions.

Example 12 Simplify: $2 \cdot 4 - 3 \div 3$

Solution: There are no parentheses and no exponents, so we start by multiplying and dividing, from left to right.

$$2 \cdot 4 - 3 \div 3 = 8 - 3 \div 3 \quad \text{Multiply.}$$
$$= 8 - 1 \quad \text{Divide.}$$
$$= 7 \quad \text{Subtract.}$$

Work Practice 12

PRACTICE 12

Simplify: $9 \cdot 3 - 8 \div 4$

Answer

12. 25

PRACTICE 13

Simplify: $48 \div 3 \cdot 2^2$

Example 13 Simplify: $4^2 \div 2 \cdot 4$

Solution: We start by evaluating 4^2.

$4^2 \div 2 \cdot 4 = 16 \div 2 \cdot 4$ Write 4^2 as 16.

Next we multiply or divide *in order* from left to right. Since division appears before multiplication from left to right, we divide first, then multiply.

$16 \div 2 \cdot 4 = 8 \cdot 4$ Divide.

$= 32$ Multiply.

Work Practice 13

PRACTICE 14

Simplify: $(10 - 7)^4 + 2 \cdot 3^2$

Example 14 Simplify: $(8 - 6)^2 + 2^3 \cdot 3$

Solution: $(8 - 6)^2 + 2^3 \cdot 3 = 2^2 + 2^3 \cdot 3$ Simplify inside parentheses.

$= 4 + 8 \cdot 3$ Write 2^2 as 4 and 2^3 as 8.

$= 4 + 24$ Multiply.

$= 28$ Add.

Work Practice 14

PRACTICE 15

Simplify:
$36 \div [20 - (4 \cdot 2)] + 4^3 - 6$

Example 15 Simplify: $4^3 + [3^2 - (10 \div 2)] - 7 \cdot 3$

Solution: Here we begin with the innermost set of parentheses.

$4^3 + [3^2 - (10 \div 2)] - 7 \cdot 3 = 4^3 + [3^2 - 5] - 7 \cdot 3$ Simplify inside parentheses.

$= 4^3 + [9 - 5] - 7 \cdot 3$ Write 3^2 as 9.

$= 4^3 + 4 - 7 \cdot 3$ Simplify inside brackets.

$= 64 + 4 - 7 \cdot 3$ Write 4^3 as 64.

$= 64 + 4 - 21$ Multiply.

$= 47$ Add and subtract from left to right.

Work Practice 15

PRACTICE 16

Simplify: $\dfrac{25 + 8 \cdot 2 - 3^3}{2(3 - 2)}$

Example 16 Simplify: $\dfrac{7 - 2 \cdot 3 + 3^2}{5(2 - 1)}$

Solution: Here, the fraction bar is like a grouping symbol. We simplify above and below the fraction bar separately.

$\dfrac{7 - 2 \cdot 3 + 3^2}{5(2 - 1)} = \dfrac{7 - 2 \cdot 3 + 9}{5(1)}$ Evaluate 3^2 and $(2 - 1)$.

$= \dfrac{7 - 6 + 9}{5}$ Multiply $2 \cdot 3$ in the numerator and multiply 5 and 1 in the denominator.

$= \dfrac{10}{5}$ Add and subtract from left to right.

$= 2$ Divide.

Work Practice 16

Answers
13. 64 **14.** 99 **15.** 61 **16.** 7

Example 17 Simplify: $64 \div \sqrt{64} \cdot 2 + 4$

Solution: $64 \div \sqrt{64} \cdot 2 + 4 = \underbrace{64 \div 8} \cdot 2 + 4$ Find the square root.

$= \underbrace{8 \cdot 2} + 4$ Divide.

$= 16 + 4$ Multiply.

$= 20$ Add.

Work Practice 17

PRACTICE 17

Simplify: $81 \div \sqrt{81} \cdot 5 + 7$

Objective E Finding the Area of a Square

Since a square is a special rectangle, we can find its area by finding the product of its length and its width.

Area of a rectangle = length · width

By recalling that each side of a square has the same measurement, we can use the following procedure to find its area:

Area of a square = length · width
= side · side
= $(\text{side})^2$

Square Side

Side

Helpful Hint

Recall from Section 1.6 that area is measured in **square** units while perimeter is measured in units.

Example 18 Find the area of a square whose side measures 4 inches.

Solution: Area of a square = $(\text{side})^2$
= $(4 \text{ inches})^2$
= 16 square inches

4 inches

The area of the square is 16 square inches.

Work Practice 18

PRACTICE 18

Find the area of a square whose side measures 12 centimeters.

Answers

17. 52 **18.** 144 sq cm

Calculator Explorations Exponents

To evaluate an exponent such as 4^7 on a calculator, find the keys marked $\boxed{y^x}$ or $\boxed{\wedge}$ and $\boxed{=}$ or $\boxed{\text{ENTER}}$. To evaluate 4^7, press the keys $\boxed{4}$ $\boxed{y^x}$ (or $\boxed{\wedge}$) $\boxed{7}$ $\boxed{=}$ or $\boxed{\text{ENTER}}$. The display will read $\boxed{16384}$. Thus, $4^7 = 16{,}384$.

Use a calculator to evaluate.

1. 4^6
2. 5^6
3. 5^5
4. 7^6
5. 2^{11}
6. 6^8

Order of Operations

To see whether your calculator has the order of operations built in, evaluate $5 + 2 \cdot 3$ by pressing the keys $\boxed{5}$ $\boxed{+}$ $\boxed{2}$ $\boxed{\times}$ $\boxed{3}$ $\boxed{=}$ or $\boxed{\text{ENTER}}$. If the display reads $\boxed{11}$, your calculator does have the order of operations built in. This means that most of the time, you can key in a problem exactly as it is written and the calculator will perform operations in the proper order. When evaluating an expression containing parentheses, key in the parentheses. (If an expression contains brackets, key in parentheses.) For example, to evaluate $2[25 - (8 + 4)] - 11$, press the keys $\boxed{2}$ $\boxed{\times}$ $\boxed{(}$ $\boxed{25}$ $\boxed{-}$ $\boxed{(}$ $\boxed{8}$ $\boxed{+}$ $\boxed{4}$ $\boxed{)}$ $\boxed{)}$ $\boxed{-}$ $\boxed{11}$ $\boxed{=}$ or $\boxed{\text{ENTER}}$.

The display will read $\boxed{15}$.

Use a calculator to evaluate.

7. $7^4 + 5^3$
8. $12^4 - 8^4$
9. $63 \cdot 75 - 43 \cdot 10$
10. $8 \cdot 22 + 7 \cdot 16$
11. $4(15 \div 3 + 2) - 10 \cdot 2$
12. $155 - 2(17 + 3) + 185$

Vocabulary and Readiness Check

Use the choices below to fill in each blank.

addition	multiplication	exponent	base
subtraction	division	square root	

1. In $2^5 = 32$, the 2 is called the ____________ and the 5 is called the ____________.
2. To simplify $8 + 2 \cdot 6$, which operation should be performed first? ____________
3. To simplify $(8 + 2) \cdot 6$, which operation should be performed first? ____________
4. To simplify $9(3 - 2) \div 3 + 6$, which operation should be performed first? ____________
5. To simplify $8 \div 2 \cdot 6$, which operation should be performed first? ____________
6. The ____________ of a whole number is one of two identical factors of the number.

1.9 Exercise Set

Objective **A** *Write using exponential notation. See Examples 1 through 4.*

1. $4 \cdot 4 \cdot 4$ **2.** $5 \cdot 5 \cdot 5 \cdot 5$ **3.** $7 \cdot 7 \cdot 7 \cdot 7 \cdot 7 \cdot 7$ **4.** $6 \cdot 6 \cdot 6 \cdot 6 \cdot 6 \cdot 6 \cdot 6$

5. $12 \cdot 12 \cdot 12$ **6.** $10 \cdot 10 \cdot 10$ **7.** $6 \cdot 6 \cdot 5 \cdot 5 \cdot 5$ **8.** $4 \cdot 4 \cdot 3 \cdot 3 \cdot 3$

9. $9 \cdot 8 \cdot 8$ **10.** $7 \cdot 4 \cdot 4 \cdot 4$ **11.** $3 \cdot 2 \cdot 2 \cdot 2 \cdot 2$ **12.** $4 \cdot 6 \cdot 6 \cdot 6 \cdot 6$

13. $3 \cdot 2 \cdot 2 \cdot 2 \cdot 2 \cdot 5 \cdot 5 \cdot 5 \cdot 5 \cdot 5$ **14.** $6 \cdot 6 \cdot 2 \cdot 9 \cdot 9 \cdot 9 \cdot 9$

Objective **B** *Evaluate. See Examples 5 through 8.*

15. 8^2 **16.** 6^2 **17.** 5^3 **18.** 6^3 **19.** 2^5 **20.** 3^5

21. 1^{10} **22.** 1^{12} **23.** 7^1 **24.** 8^1 **25.** 2^7 **26.** 5^4

27. 2^8 **28.** 3^3 **29.** 4^4 **30.** 4^3 **31.** 9^3 **32.** 8^3

33. 12^2 **34.** 11^2 **35.** 10^2 **36.** 10^3 **37.** 20^1 **38.** 14^1

39. 3^6 **40.** 4^5 **41.** $3 \cdot 2^6$ **42.** $5 \cdot 3^2$ **43.** $2 \cdot 3^4$ **44.** $2 \cdot 7^2$

Objective **C** *Find each square root. See Examples 9 through 11.*

45. $\sqrt{9}$ **46.** $\sqrt{36}$ **47.** $\sqrt{64}$ **48.** $\sqrt{121}$

49. $\sqrt{144}$ **50.** $\sqrt{0}$ **51.** $\sqrt{16}$ **52.** $\sqrt{169}$

Objective D *Simplify. See Examples 12 through 16. (This section does not contain square roots.)*

53. $15 + 3 \cdot 2$ **54.** $24 + 6 \cdot 3$ **55.** $14 \div 7 \cdot 2 + 3$ **56.** $100 \div 10 \cdot 5 + 4$

57. $32 \div 4 - 3$ **58.** $42 \div 7 - 6$ **59.** $13 + \frac{24}{8}$ **60.** $32 + \frac{8}{2}$

61. $6 \cdot 5 + 8 \cdot 2$ **62.** $3 \cdot 4 + 9 \cdot 1$ **63.** $\frac{5 + 12 \div 4}{1^7}$ **64.** $\frac{6 + 9 \div 3}{3^2}$

65. $(7 + 5^2) \div 4 \cdot 2^3$ **66.** $6^2 \cdot (10 - 8)$ **67.** $5^2 \cdot (10 - 8) + 2^3 + 5^2$

68. $5^3 \div (10 + 15) + 9^2 + 3^3$ **69.** $\frac{18 + 6}{2^4 - 2^2}$ **70.** $\frac{40 + 8}{5^2 - 3^2}$

71. $(3 + 5) \cdot (9 - 3)$ **72.** $(9 - 7) \cdot (12 + 18)$ **73.** $\frac{7(9 - 6) + 3}{3^2 - 3}$

74. $\frac{5(12 - 7) - 4}{5^2 - 18}$ **75.** $8 \div 0 + 37$ **76.** $18 - 7 \div 0$

77. $2^4 \cdot 4 - (25 \div 5)$ **78.** $2^3 \cdot 3 - (100 \div 10)$ **79.** $3^4 - [35 - (12 - 6)]$

80. $[40 - (8 - 2)] - 2^5$ **81.** $(7 \cdot 5) + [9 \div (3 \div 3)]$ **82.** $(18 \div 6) + [(3 + 5) \cdot 2]$

83. $8 \cdot [2^2 + (6 - 1) \cdot 2] - 50 \cdot 2$ **84.** $35 \div [3^2 + (9 - 7) - 2^2] + 10 \cdot 3$

85. $\frac{9^2 + 2^2 - 1^2}{8 \div 2 \cdot 3 \cdot 1 \div 3}$ **86.** $\frac{5^2 - 2^3 + 1^4}{10 \div 5 \cdot 4 \cdot 1 \div 4}$

Simplify. See Examples 12 through 17. (This section does contain square roots.)

87. $6 \cdot \sqrt{9} + 3 \cdot \sqrt{4}$ **88.** $3 \cdot \sqrt{25} + 2 \cdot \sqrt{81}$ **89.** $4 \cdot \sqrt{49} - 0 \div \sqrt{100}$

90. $7 \cdot \sqrt{36} - 0 \div \sqrt{64}$ **91.** $\frac{\sqrt{4} + 4^2}{5(20 - 16) - 3^2 - 5}$ **92.** $\frac{\sqrt{9} + 9^2}{3(10 - 6) - 2^2 - 1}$

93. $\sqrt{81} \div \sqrt{9} + 4^2 \cdot 2 - 10$ **94.** $\sqrt{100} \div \sqrt{4} + 3^3 \cdot 2 - 20$

95. $[\sqrt{225} \div (11 - 6) + 2^2] + (\sqrt{25} - \sqrt{1})^2$

96. $[\sqrt{169} \div (20 - 7) + 2^5] - (\sqrt{4} + \sqrt{9})^2$

97. $7^2 - \{18 - [40 \div (4 \cdot 2) + \sqrt{4}] + 5^2\}$

98. $29 - \{5 + 3[8 \cdot (10 - \sqrt{64})] - 50\}$

Objective **E** **Mixed Practice (*Sections 1.3, 1.6*)** *Find the area and perimeter of each square. See Example 15.*

99.

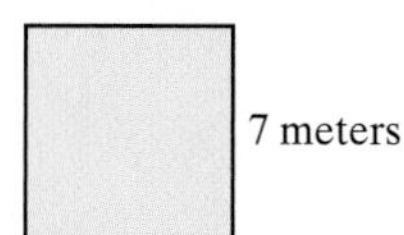

100.

9 centimeters

101.

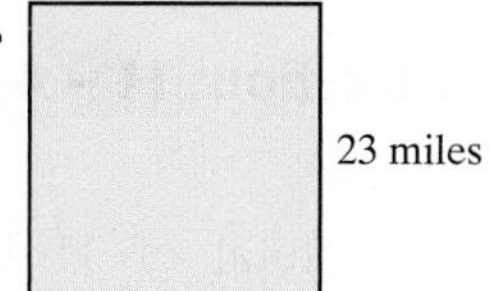

102.

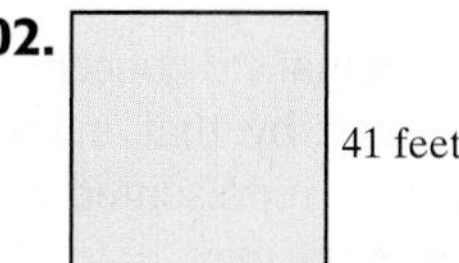

Concept Extensions

Answer the following true or false. See the Concept Check in this section.

103. "Six to the fifth power" is the same as 6^5.

104. "Seven squared" is the same as 7^2.

105. 2^5 is the same as $5 \cdot 5$.

106. 4^9 is the same as $4 \cdot 9$.

Insert grouping symbols (parentheses) so that each given expression evaluates to the given number.

107. $2 + 3 \cdot 6 - 2$; evaluates to 28

108. $2 + 3 \cdot 6 - 2$; evaluates to 20

109. $24 \div 3 \cdot 2 + 2 \cdot 5$; evaluates to 14

110. $24 \div 3 \cdot 2 + 2 \cdot 5$; evaluates to 15

111. A building contractor is bidding on a contract to install gutters on seven homes in a retirement community, all in the shape shown. To estimate the cost of materials, she needs to know the total perimeter of all seven homes. Find the total perimeter.

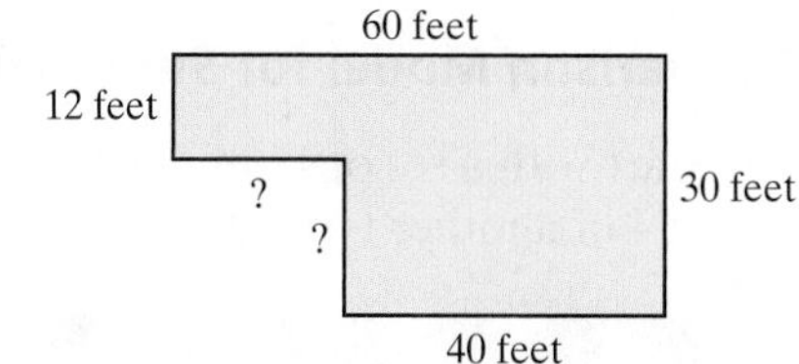

112. The building contractor from Exercise 111 plans to charge \$4 per foot for installing vinyl gutters. Find the total charge for the seven homes given the total perimeter answer to Exercise 111.

Simplify.

113. $(7 + 2^4)^5 - (3^5 - 2^4)^2$

114. $25^3 \cdot (45 - 7 \cdot 5) \cdot 5$

115. Write an expression that simplifies to 5. Use multiplication, division, addition, subtraction, and at least one set of parentheses. Explain the process you would use to simplify the expression.

116. Explain why $2 \cdot 3^2$ is not the same as $(2 \cdot 3)^2$.

Chapter 1 Group Activity

Modeling Subtraction of Whole Numbers

A mathematical concept can be represented or modeled in many different ways. For instance, subtraction can be represented by the following symbolic model:

$11 - 4$

The following verbal models can also represent subtraction of these same quantities:

"Four subtracted from eleven" or
"Eleven take away four"

Physical models can also represent mathematical concepts. In these models, a number is represented by that many objects. For example, the number 5 can be represented by five pennies, squares, paper clips, tiles, or bottle caps.

A physical representation of the number 5

Take-Away Model for Subtraction: 11 – 4

- Start with 11 objects.
- Take 4 objects away.
- How many objects remain?

Comparison Model for Subtraction: 11 – 4

- Start with a set of 11 of one type of object and a set of 4 of another type of object.

- Make as many pairs that include one object of each type as possible.

- How many more objects left are in the larger set?

Missing Addend Model for Subtraction: 11 – 4

- Start with 4 objects.
- Continue adding objects until a total of 11 is reached.
- How many more objects were needed to give a total of 11?

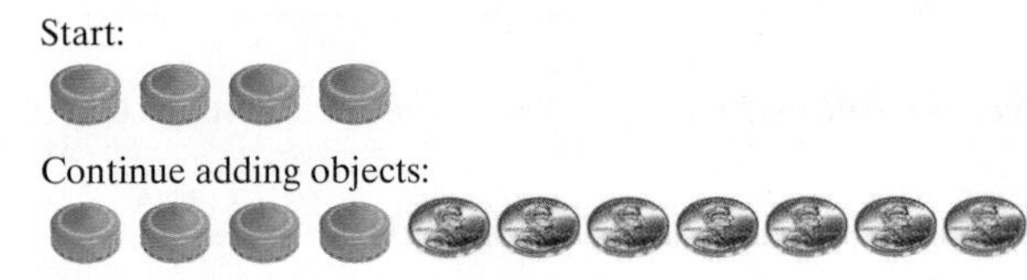

Group Activity

Use an appropriate physical model for subtraction to solve each of the following problems. Explain your reasoning for choosing each model.

1. Sneha has assembled 12 computer components so far this shift. If her quota is 20 components, how many more components must she assemble to reach her quota?

2. Yuko has 14 daffodil bulbs to plant in her yard. She planted 5 bulbs in the front yard. How many bulbs does she have left for planting in the backyard?

3. Todd is 19 years old and his sister Tanya is 13 years old. How much older is Todd than Tanya?

Chapter 1 Vocabulary Check

Fill in each blank with one of the words or phrases listed below.

difference	area	square root	addend	divisor	minuend
place value	factor	quotient	subtrahend	exponent	digits
sum	whole numbers	perimeter	dividend	average	product

1. The ______________ are 0, 1, 2, 3, . . .
2. The ______________ of a polygon is its distance around or the sum of the lengths of its sides.
3. The position of each digit in a number determines its ______________.
4. A(n) ______________ is a shorthand notation for repeated multiplication of the same factor.
5. To find the ______________ of a rectangle, multiply length times width.
6. A(n) ______________ of a number is one of two identical factors of the number.
7. The ______________ used to write numbers are 0, 1, 2, 3, 4, 5, 6, 7, 8, and 9.
8. The ______________ of a list of numbers is their sum divided by the number of numbers.

Use the facts below for Exercises 9 through 18.

$2 \cdot 3 = 6 \quad 4 + 17 = 21 \quad 20 - 9 = 11 \quad 5\overline{)35}$ with quotient 7

9. The 5 above is called the ______________.
10. The 35 above is called the ______________.
11. The 7 above is called the ______________.
12. The 3 above is called a(n) ______________.
13. The 6 above is called the ______________.
14. The 20 above is called the ______________.
15. The 9 above is called the ______________.
16. The 11 above is called the ______________.
17. The 4 above is called a(n) ______________.
18. The 21 above is called the ______________.

Helpful Hint Are you preparing for your test? Don't forget to take the Chapter 1 Test on page 106. Then check your answers at the back of the text and use the Chapter Test Prep Videos to see the fully worked-out solutions to any of the exercises you want to review.

1 Chapter Highlights

Definitions and Concepts	Examples
Section 1.2 Place Value, Names for Numbers, and Reading Tables	
The **whole numbers** are 0, 1, 2, 3, 4, 5, ...	0, 14, 968, 5,268,619
The position of each digit in a number determines its **place value.** A place-value chart is shown next with the names of the periods given. 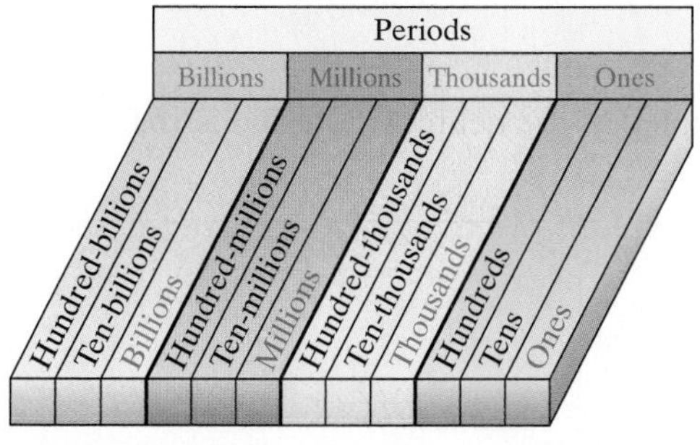	

(continued)

Definitions and Concepts	Examples
Section 1.2 Place Value, Names for Numbers, and Reading Tables (*continued*)	
To write a whole number in words, write the number in each period followed by the name of the period. (The name of the ones period is not included.)	9,078,651,002 is written as nine billion, seventy-eight million, six hundred fifty-one thousand, two.
To write a whole number in standard form, write the number in each period, followed by a comma.	Four million, seven hundred six thousand, twenty-eight is written as 4,706,028.
Section 1.3 Adding Whole Numbers and Perimeter	
To add whole numbers, add the digits in the ones place, then the tens place, then the hundreds place, and so on, carrying when necessary.	Find the sum: (carries: 2 1 1) 2689 ← addend 1735 ← addend + 662 ← addend 5086 ← sum
The **perimeter** of a polygon is its distance around or the sum of the lengths of its sides.	Find the perimeter of the polygon shown. 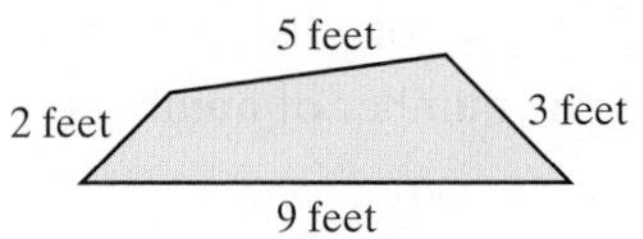 The perimeter is 5 feet + 3 feet + 9 feet + 2 feet = 19 feet.
Section 1.4 Subtracting Whole Numbers	
To subtract whole numbers, subtract the digits in the ones place, then the tens place, then the hundreds place, and so on, borrowing when necessary.	Subtract: (borrow: 8 15; 9 and 5 crossed out) 7954 ← minuend −5673 ← subtrahend 2281 ← difference
Section 1.5 Rounding and Estimating	
Rounding Whole Numbers to a Given Place Value **Step 1.** Locate the digit to the right of the given place value. **Step 2.** If this digit is 5 or greater, add 1 to the digit in the given place value and replace each digit to its right with 0. **Step 3.** If this digit is less than 5, replace it and each digit to its right with 0.	Round 15,721 to the nearest thousand. 15,(7)21 Add 1 (to the 5); Replace with zeros (721). Since the circled digit is 5 or greater, add 1 to the given place value and replace digits to its right with zeros. 15,721 rounded to the nearest thousand is 16,000.

Definitions and Concepts	Examples
Section 1.6 Multiplying Whole Numbers and Area	
To multiply 73 and 58, for example, multiply 73 and 8, then 73 and 50. The sum of these partial products is the product of 73 and 58. Use the notation to the right.	$\begin{array}{rl} 73 & \leftarrow \text{factor} \\ \times\ 58 & \leftarrow \text{factor} \\ \hline 584 & \leftarrow 73 \times 8 \\ 3650 & \leftarrow 73 \times 50 \\ \hline 4234 & \leftarrow \text{product} \end{array}$
To find the **area** of a rectangle, multiply length times width.	△ Find the area of the rectangle shown. 11 meters 7 meters area of rectangle = length · width = (11 meters)(7 meters) = 77 square meters
Section 1.7 Dividing Whole Numbers	
DIVISION PROPERTIES OF 0 The quotient of 0 and any number (except 0) is 0. The quotient of any number and 0 is not a number. We say that this quotient is undefined.	$\frac{0}{5} = 0$ $\frac{7}{0}$ is undefined
To divide larger whole numbers, use the process called **long division** as shown to the right.	$\begin{array}{rrl} & 507 \text{ R } 2 & \leftarrow \text{quotient and remainder} \\ \text{divisor} \rightarrow & 14\overline{)7100} & \leftarrow \text{dividend} \\ & -70 & 5(14) = 70 \\ \hline & 10 & \text{Subtract and bring down the 0.} \\ & -0 & 0(14) = 0 \\ \hline & 100 & \text{Subtract and bring down the 0.} \\ & -98 & 7(14) = 98 \\ \hline & 2 & \text{Subtract. The remainder is 2.} \end{array}$ To check, see that $507 \cdot 14 + 2 = 7100$.
The **average** of a list of numbers is $\text{average} = \frac{\text{sum of numbers}}{\textit{number} \text{ of numbers}}$	Find the average of 23, 35, and 38. $\text{average} = \frac{23 + 35 + 38}{3} = \frac{96}{3} = 32$

Definitions and Concepts	Examples

Section 1.8 An Introduction to Problem Solving

PROBLEM-SOLVING STEPS

Suppose that 225 tickets are sold for each performance of a play. How many tickets are sold for 5 performances?

1. UNDERSTAND the problem.

1. UNDERSTAND. Read and reread the problem. Since we want the number of tickets for 5 performances, we multiply.

2. TRANSLATE the problem.

2. TRANSLATE.

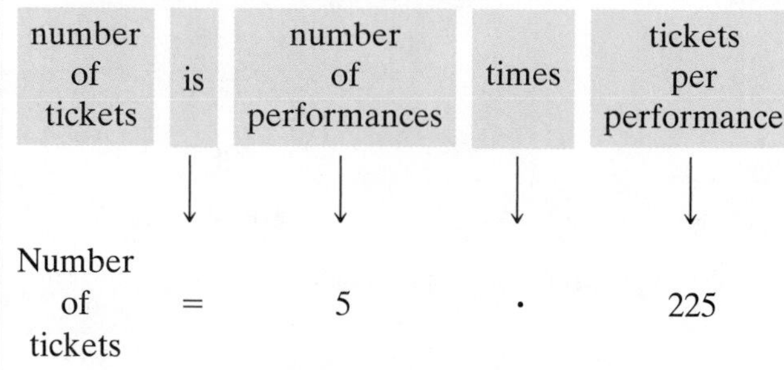

number of tickets
is
number of performances
times
tickets per performance

Number of tickets = 5 · 225

3. SOLVE the problem.

3. SOLVE: See if the answer is reasonable by also estimating.

$$\begin{array}{r} \scriptstyle{12} \\ 225 \\ \times \quad 5 \\ \hline 1125 \end{array} \text{ exact} \qquad \text{rounds to} \qquad \begin{array}{r} 200 \\ \times \quad 5 \\ \hline 1000 \end{array} \text{ estimate}$$

4. INTERPRET the results.

4. INTERPRET. **Check** your work. The product is reasonable since 1125 is close to our estimated answer of 1000, and **state** your conclusion: There are 1125 tickets sold for 5 performances.

Section 1.9 Exponents, Square Roots, and Order of Operations

An **exponent** is a shorthand notation for repeated multiplication of the same factor.

$$3^4 = \underbrace{3 \cdot 3 \cdot 3 \cdot 3}_{\text{4 factors of 3}} = 81$$

(base: 3; exponent: 4)

A **square root** of a number is one of two identical factors of the number.

$\sqrt{36} = 6$ because $6 \cdot 6 = 36$

$\sqrt{121} = 11$ because $11 \cdot 11 = 121$

$\sqrt{0} = 0$ because $0 \cdot 0 = 0$

ORDER OF OPERATIONS

1. Perform all operations within parentheses ( ), brackets [ ], or other grouping symbols such as square roots or fraction bars, starting with the innermost set.
2. Evaluate any expressions with exponents.
3. Multiply or divide in order from left to right.
4. Add or subtract in order from left to right.

Simplify: $\dfrac{5 + 3^2}{2(7 - 6)}$

Simplify above and below the fraction bar separately.

$\dfrac{5 + 3^2}{2(7 - 6)} = \dfrac{5 + 9}{2(1)}$ Evaluate 3^2 above the fraction bar. Subtract: $7 - 6$ below the fraction bar.

$= \dfrac{14}{2}$ Add. Multiply.

$= 7$ Divide.

The **area of a square** is $(\text{side})^2$.

Find the area of a square with side length 9 inches.

Area of the square $= (\text{side})^2$

$= (9 \text{ inches})^2$

$= 81$ square inches

Chapter 1 Review

(1.2) *Determine the place value of the digit 4 in each whole number.*

1. 7640

2. 46,200,120

Write each whole number in words.

3. 7640

4. 46,200,120

Write each whole number in expanded form.

5. 3158

6. 403,225,000

Write each whole number in standard form.

7. Eighty-one thousand, nine hundred

8. Six billion, three hundred four million

The following table shows the Internet use of world regions. Use this table to answer Exercises 9 through 12.

(*Source:* International Telecommunications Union)

Internet Use by World Regions			
World Region	**2000**	**2004**	**2008**
Africa	4,514,400	21,371,600	51,065,630
Asia	114,304,000	295,852,200	578,538,257
Europe	105,096,093	241,208,100	384,633,765
Middle East	3,284,800	28,917,600	41,939,200
North America	108,096,800	217,835,900	248,241,969
Latin America/ Caribbean	18,068,919	50,661,500	139,009,209
Oceania/ Australia	7,620,480	11,805,500	20,204,331

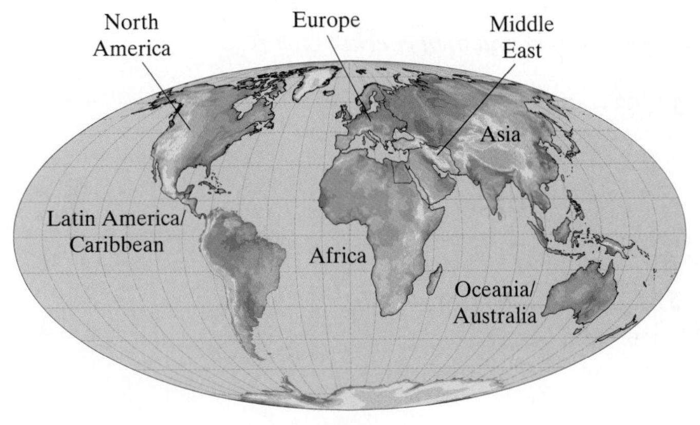

9. Find the number of Internet users in 2008 in Europe.

10. Find the number of Internet users in Oceania/Australia in 2004.

11. Which world region had the smallest number of Internet users in 2000?

12. Which world region had the greatest number of Internet users in 2008?

(1.3) *Add.*

13. $17 + 46$

14. $28 + 39$

15. $25 + 8 + 15$

16. $27 + 9 + 41$

17. $932 + 24$

18. $819 + 21$

19. $567 + 7383$

20. $463 + 6787$

21. $91 + 3623 + 497$

22. $82 + 1647 + 238$

Solve.

23. Find the sum of 86, 331, and 909.

24. Find the sum of 49, 529, and 308.

25. What is 26,481 increased by 865?

26. What is 38,556 increased by 744?

27. The distance from Chicago to New York City is 714 miles. The distance from New York City to New Delhi, India, is 7318 miles. Find the total distance from Chicago to New Delhi if traveling by air through New York City.

28. Susan Summerline earned salaries of \$62,589, \$65,340, and \$69,770 during the years 2002, 2003, and 2004, respectively. Find her total earnings during those three years.

Find the perimeter of each figure.

△ **29.**

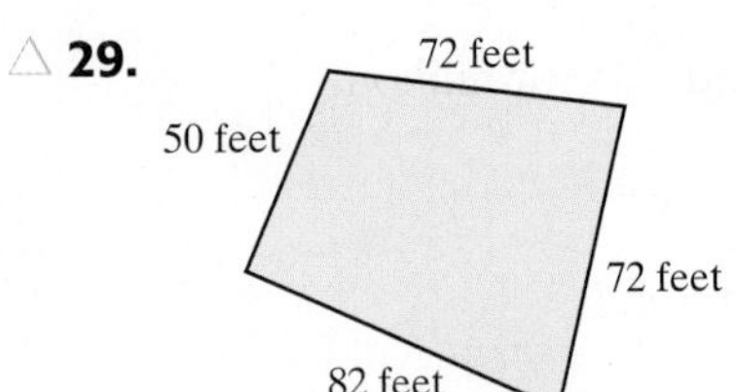

△ **30.** 11 kilometers 20 kilometers 35 kilometers

(1.4) *Subtract and then check.*

31. 93 − 79 **32.** 61 − 27 **33.** 462 − 397 **34.** 583 − 279 **35.** 4000 − 86 **36.** 8000 − 92

Solve.

37. Subtract 7965 from 25,862.

38. Subtract 4349 from 39,007.

39. Find the increase in population for San Antonio, Texas, from 2000 (population: 1,144,646) to 2007 (population: 1,328,984).

40. Find the decrease in population for Philadelphia, Pennsylvania, from 2000 (population: 1,517,550) to 2007 (population: 1,491,812).

41. Bob Roma is proofreading the Yellow Pages for his county. If he has finished 315 pages of the total 712 pages, how many pages does he have left to proofread?

42. Shelly Winters bought a new car listed at \$28,425. She received a discount of \$1599 and a factory rebate of \$1200. Find how much she paid for the car.

The following bar graph shows the monthly savings account balance for a freshman attending a local community college. Use this graph to answer Exercises 43 through 46.

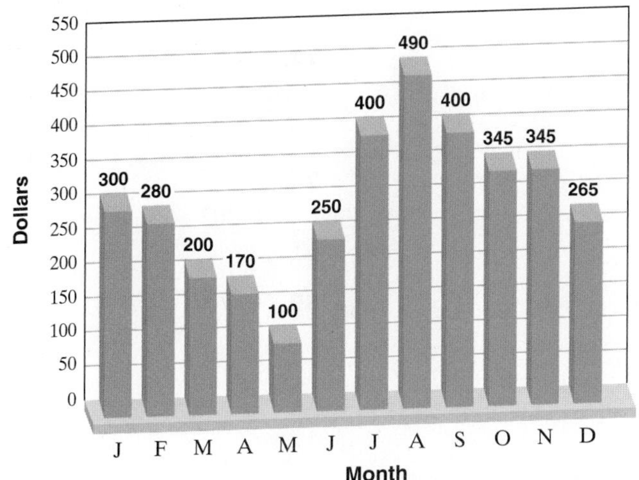

43. During what month was the balance the least?

44. During what month was the balance the greatest?

45. By how much did his balance decrease from February to April?

46. By how much did his balance increase from June to August?

(1.5) *Round to the given place.*

47. 93 to the nearest ten

48. 45 to the nearest ten

49. 467 to the nearest ten

50. 493 to the nearest hundred

51. 4832 to the nearest hundred

52. 57,534 to the nearest thousand

53. 49,683,712 to the nearest million

54. 768,542 to the nearest hundred-thousand

55. In 2008, 65,025,901 Americans voted for one of the major candidates for president. Round this number to the nearest million. (*Source:* CNN)

56. In 2007, there were 93,295 public elementary and secondary schools in the United States. Round this number to the nearest thousand. (*Source:* National Center for Educational Statistics)

Estimate the sum or difference by rounding each number to the nearest hundred.

57. $4892 + 647 + 1876$

58. $5925 - 1787$

59. A group of students took a week-long driving trip and traveled 628, 290, 172, 58, 508, 445, and 383 miles on seven consecutive days. Round each distance to the nearest hundred to estimate the distance they traveled.

60. According to the city population table, the 2007 population of Houston, Texas, was 2,208,180, and for San Diego, California, it was 1,336,865. Round each number to the nearest hundred-thousand and estimate how much larger Houston is than San Diego.

(1.6) *Multiply.*

61. $\begin{array}{r} 273 \\ \times \;\; 7 \\ \hline \end{array}$

62. $\begin{array}{r} 349 \\ \times \;\; 4 \\ \hline \end{array}$

63. $\begin{array}{r} 47 \\ \times 30 \\ \hline \end{array}$

64. $\begin{array}{r} 69 \\ \times 42 \\ \hline \end{array}$

65. 20(8)(5)

66. 25(9)(4)

67. $\begin{array}{r} 48 \\ \times 77 \\ \hline \end{array}$

68. $\begin{array}{r} 77 \\ \times 22 \\ \hline \end{array}$

69. $49 \cdot 49 \cdot 0$

70. $62 \cdot 88 \cdot 0$

71. $\begin{array}{r} 586 \\ \times 29 \\ \hline \end{array}$

72. $\begin{array}{r} 242 \\ \times 37 \\ \hline \end{array}$

73. $\begin{array}{r} 642 \\ \times 177 \\ \hline \end{array}$

74. $\begin{array}{r} 347 \\ \times 129 \\ \hline \end{array}$

75. $\begin{array}{r} 1026 \\ \times 401 \\ \hline \end{array}$

76. $\begin{array}{r} 2107 \\ \times 302 \\ \hline \end{array}$

77. $375 \cdot 1000$

78. $108 \cdot 1000$

79. $30 \cdot 400$

80. $50 \cdot 700$

81. $1700 \cdot 3000$

82. $1900 \cdot 4000$

Solve.

83. Find the product of 5 and 230.

84. Find the product of 6 and 820.

85. Multiply 9 and 12.

86. Multiply 8 and 14.

87. One ounce of Swiss cheese contains 8 grams of fat. How many grams of fat are in 3 ounces of Swiss cheese? (*Source: Home and Garden Bulletin No. 72,* U.S. Department of Agriculture)

88. The cost for a South Dakota resident to attend Black Hills State University full-time is \$6112 per semester. Determine the cost for 20 students to attend full-time. (*Source:* Black Hills State University)

Find the area of each rectangle.

△ **89.**

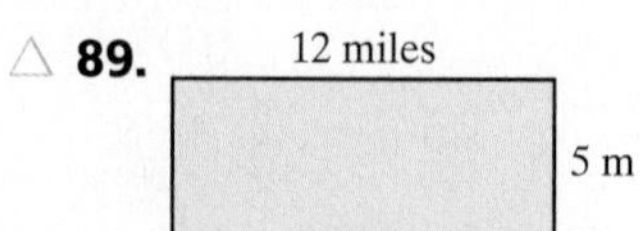

△ **90.**

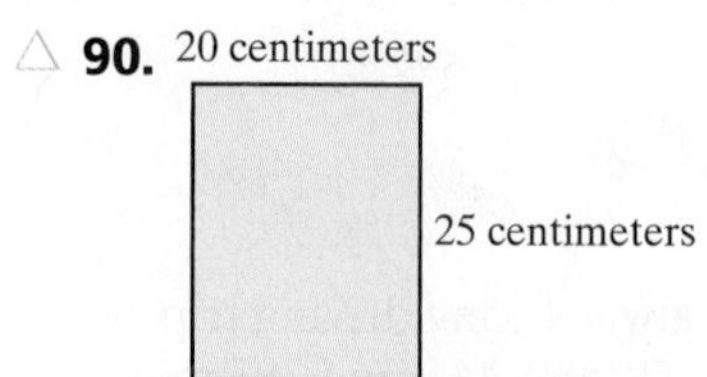

(1.7) *Divide and then check.*

91. $\frac{18}{6}$

92. $\frac{36}{9}$

93. $42 \div 7$

94. $35 \div 5$

95. $27 \div 5$

96. $18 \div 4$

97. $16 \div 0$

98. $0 \div 8$

99. $9 \div 9$

100. $10 \div 1$

101. $0 \div 668$

102. $918 \div 0$

103. $5\overline{)167}$

104. $8\overline{)159}$

105. $26\overline{)626}$

106. $19\overline{)680}$

107. $47\overline{)23{,}792}$

108. $53\overline{)48{,}111}$

109. $207\overline{)578{,}291}$

110. $306\overline{)615{,}732}$

Solve.

111. Find the quotient of 92 and 5.

112. Find the quotient of 86 and 4.

113. One foot is 12 inches. Find how many feet there are in 5496 inches.

114. One mile is 1760 yards. Find how many miles there are in 22,880 yards.

115. Find the average of the numbers 76, 49, 32, and 47.

116. Find the average of the numbers 23, 85, 62, and 66.

(1.8) *Solve.*

117. A box can hold 24 cans of corn. How many boxes can be filled with 648 cans of corn?

118. If a ticket to a movie costs \$6, how much do 32 tickets cost?

119. Aspirin was 100 years old in 1997 and was the first U.S. drug made in tablet form. Today, people take 11 billion tablets a year for heart disease prevention and 4 billion tablets a year for headaches. How many more tablets are taken a year for heart disease prevention? (*Source:* Bayer Market Research)

120. The cost to banks when a person uses an ATM (Automatic Teller Machine) is 27¢. The cost to banks when a person deposits a check with a teller is 48¢ more. How much is this cost?

121. A golf pro orders shirts for the company sponsoring a local charity golfing event. Shirts size large cost \$32 while shirts size extra-large cost \$38. If 15 large shirts and 11 extra-large shirts are ordered, find the cost.

122. Two rectangular pieces of land are purchased: one that measures 65 feet by 110 feet and one that measures 80 feet by 200 feet. Find the total area of land purchased. (*Hint:* Find the area of each rectangle, then add.)

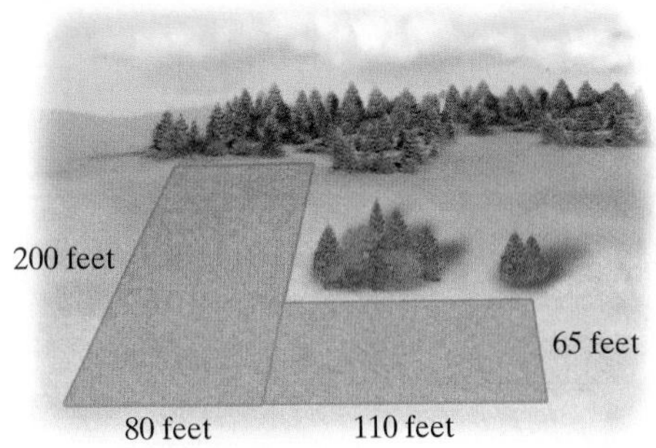

(1.9) *Simplify.*

123. 7^2

124. 5^3

125. $5 \cdot 3^2$

126. $4 \cdot 10^2$

127. $18 \div 3 + 7$

128. $12 - 8 \div 4$

129. $\dfrac{5(6^2 - 3)}{3^2 + 2}$

130. $\dfrac{7(16 - 8)}{2^3}$

131. $48 \div 8 \cdot 2$

132. $27 \div 9 \cdot 3$

133. $2 + 3[1^5 + (20 - 17) \cdot 3] + 5 \cdot 2$

134. $21 - [2^4 - (7 - 5) - 10] + 8 \cdot 2$

Simplify. (These exercises contain square roots.)

135. $\sqrt{81}$

136. $\sqrt{4}$

137. $\sqrt{1}$

138. $\sqrt{0}$

139. $4 \cdot \sqrt{25} - 2 \cdot 7$

140. $8 \cdot \sqrt{49} - 3 \cdot 9$

141. $(\sqrt{36} - \sqrt{16})^3 \cdot [10^2 \div (3 + 17)]$

142. $(\sqrt{49} - \sqrt{25})^3 \cdot [9^2 \div (2 + 7)]$

143. $\dfrac{5 \cdot 7 - 3 \cdot \sqrt{25}}{2(\sqrt{121} - 3^2)}$

144. $\dfrac{4 \cdot 8 - 1 \cdot \sqrt{121}}{3(\sqrt{81} - 2^3)}$

Find the area of each square.

△ **145.** A square with side length of 7 meters.

△ **146.**

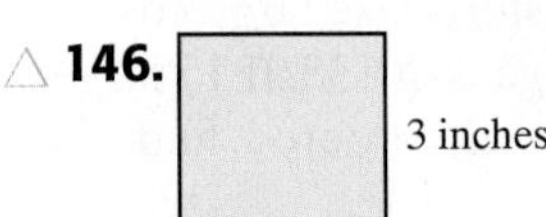

Mixed Review

Perform the indicated operations.

147. $375 - 68$

148. $729 - 47$

149. 723×3

150. 629×4

151. $264 + 39 + 598$

152. $593 + 52 + 766$

153. $13\overline{)5962}$

154. $18\overline{)4267}$

155. 1968×36

156. 5324×18

157. $2000 - 356$

158. $9000 - 519$

Round to the given place.

159. 736 to the nearest ten

160. 258,371 to the nearest thousand

161. 1999 to the nearest hundred

162. 44,499 to the nearest ten thousand

Write each whole number in words.

163. 36,911

164. 154,863

Write each whole number in standard form.

165. Seventy thousand, nine hundred forty-three

166. Forty-three thousand, four hundred one

Simplify.

167. 4^3

168. 5^3

169. $\sqrt{144}$

170. $\sqrt{100}$

171. $24 \div 4 \cdot 2$

172. $\sqrt{256} - 3 \cdot 5$

173. $\dfrac{8(7 - 4) - 10}{4^2 - 3^2}$

174. $\dfrac{(15 + \sqrt{9}) \cdot (8 - 5)}{2^3 + 1}$

Solve.

175. 36 divided by 9 is what number?

176. What is the product of 2 and 12?

177. 16 increased by 8 is what number?

178. 7 subtracted from 21 is what number?

The following table shows the average Major League Baseball salaries (rounded to the nearest thousand) for the five teams with the largest payrolls for 2008 and 2009. Use this table to answer Exercises 179 and 180. (Source: CBS Sports)

Team	2009 Average Salary	2008 Average Salary
NY Yankees	$7,748,000	$6,745,000
NY Mets	$4,849,000	$4,610,000
Chicago Cubs	$5,402,000	$4,392,000
Boston Red Sox	$4,090,000	$4,766,000
Detroit Tigers	$4,110,000	$4,623,000

179. How much less was the average salary for a Detroit Tiger in 2009 than in 2008?

180. The average salary for all teams in Major League Baseball for 2009 was $3,260,000. How much more was the average Yankee pay than the average pay across the major leagues?

181. A manufacturer of drinking glasses ships his delicate stock in special boxes that can hold 32 glasses. If 1714 glasses are manufactured, how many full boxes are filled? Are there any glasses left over?

182. A teacher orders 2 small white boards for $27 each and 8 boxes of dry erase pens for $4 each. What is her total bill before taxes?

Chapter 1 Test

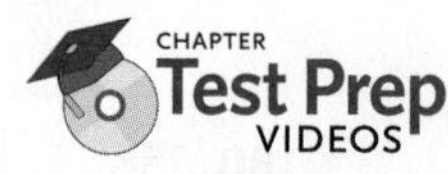

Step-by-step test solutions are found on the Chapter Test Prep Videos available via the Interactive DVD Lecture Series, in MyMathLab or on YouTube (search "MartinGayBasicMath" and click on "Channels").

Answers

1. ______
2. ______
3. ______
4. ______
5. ______
6. ______
7. ______
8. ______
9. ______
10. ______
11. ______
12. ______
13. ______
14. ______
15. ______
16. ______
17. ______
18. ______
19. ______

Simplify.

1. Write 82,426 in words.

2. Write "four hundred two thousand, five hundred fifty" in standard form.

3. $59 + 82$

4. $600 - 487$

5. $\begin{array}{r} 496 \\ \times\ 30 \\ \hline \end{array}$

6. $52{,}896 \div 69$

7. $2^3 \cdot 5^2$

8. $\sqrt{4} \cdot \sqrt{25}$

9. $0 \div 49$

10. $62 \div 0$

11. $(2^4 - 5) \cdot 3$

12. $16 + 9 \div 3 \cdot 4 - 7$

13. $\dfrac{64 \div 8 \cdot 2}{(\sqrt{9} - \sqrt{4})^2 + 1}$

14. $2[(6 - 4)^2 + (22 - 19)^2] + 10$

15. $5698 \cdot 1000$

16. $8000 \cdot 1400$

17. Round 52,369 to the nearest thousand.

Estimate each sum or difference by rounding each number to the nearest hundred.

18. $6289 + 5403 + 1957$

19. $4267 - 2738$

Solve.

20. Subtract 15 from 107.

21. Find the sum of 15 and 107.

22. Find the product of 15 and 107.

23. Find the quotient of 107 and 15.

24. Twenty-nine cans of Sherwin-Williams paint cost $493. How much was each can?

25. Jo McElory is looking at two new refrigerators for her apartment. One costs $599 and the other costs $725. How much more expensive is the higher-priced one?

26. One tablespoon of white granulated sugar contains 45 calories. How many calories are in 8 tablespoons of white granulated sugar? (*Source: Home and Garden Bulletin No. 72,* U.S. Department of Agriculture)

27. A small business owner recently ordered 16 digital cameras that cost $430 each and 5 printers that cost $205 each. Find the total cost for these items.

Find the perimeter and the area of each figure.

△ **28.** Square 5 centimeters

△ **29.** 20 yards Rectangle 10 yards

20. __________

21. __________

22. __________

23. __________

24. __________

25. __________

26. __________

27. __________

28. __________

29. __________

2

Multiplying and Dividing Fractions

Sections

Check Your Progress

Fractions are numbers, and like whole numbers, they can be added, subtracted, multiplied, and divided. Fractions are very useful and appear frequently in everyday language, in common phrases like "half an hour," "quarter of a pound," and "third of a cup." This chapter introduces the concept of fractions, presents some basic vocabulary, and demonstrates how to multiply and divide fractions.

What is a hoodoo? In the field of geology, a hoodoo is a tall, thin tower of sedimentary rock that is topped by a piece of harder stone. It is this less easily eroded stone that protects this tower.

The picture above shows hoodoos in Bryce Canyon. This park is known for its clear air and has a 7.4 magnitude night sky. This means that stargazers can see about 7500 stars with the naked eye while in most places fewer than 2000 can be seen.

The National Park Service (NPS) is charged with the enormous task of managing and protecting our national resources such as Bryce Canyon. In Section 2.3 and throughout Chapter 3, we will explore fractions relating to the various types of national parks and monuments that are protected by the NPS.

Overnight Stays at National Parks

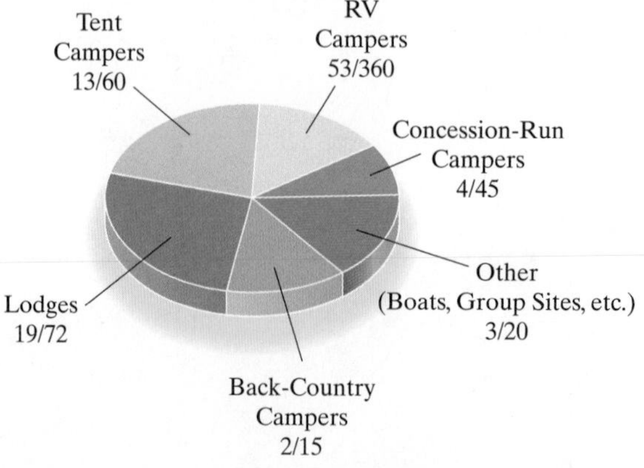

Source: National Park Service

2.1 INTRODUCTION TO FRACTIONS AND MIXED NUMBERS

Objectives

A Identify the Numerator and the Denominator of a Fraction and Review Division Properties for 0 and 1.

B Write a Fraction to Represent Parts of Figures or Real-Life Data.

C Identify Proper Fractions, Improper Fractions, and Mixed Numbers.

D Write Mixed Numbers as Improper Fractions.

E Write Improper Fractions as Mixed Numbers or Whole Numbers.

Objective A Identifying Numerators and Denominators and Reviewing Division Properties for 0 and 1

Whole numbers are used to count whole things or units, such as cars, horses, dollars, and people. To refer to a part of a whole, fractions can be used. Here are some examples of **fractions.** Study these examples for a moment.

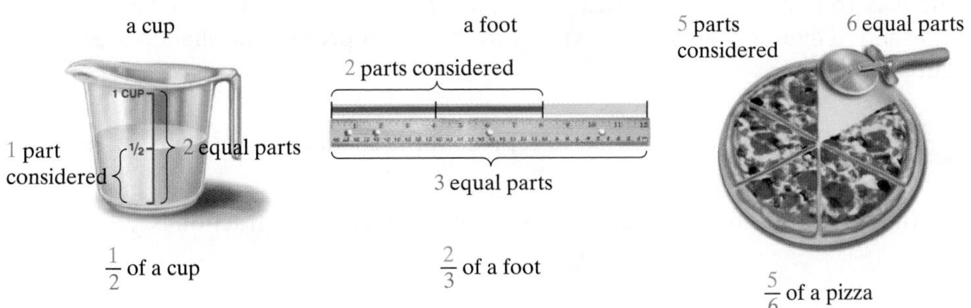

$\frac{1}{2}$ of a cup $\frac{2}{3}$ of a foot $\frac{5}{6}$ of a pizza

In a fraction, the top number is called the **numerator** and the bottom number is called the **denominator.** The bar between the numbers is called the **fraction bar.**

Names	Fraction	Meaning
numerator ⟶	5	⟵ number of parts being considered
denominator ⟶	6	⟵ number of equal parts in the whole

Examples Identify the numerator and the denominator of each fraction.

1. $\frac{3}{7}$ ← numerator, ← denominator

2. $\frac{13}{5}$ ← numerator, ← denominator

Work Practice 1–2

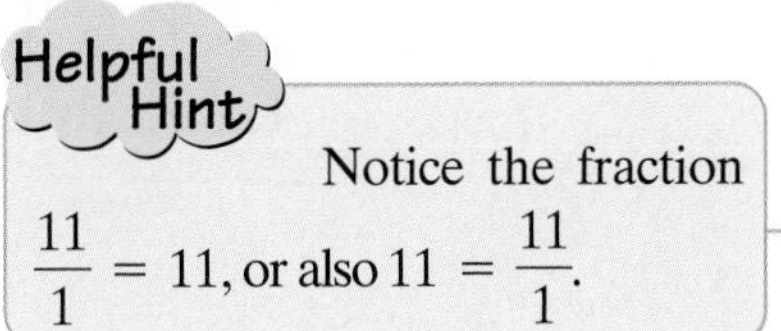

Notice the fraction $\frac{11}{1} = 11$, or also $11 = \frac{11}{1}$.

PRACTICE 1–2

Identify the numerator and the denominator of each fraction.

1. $\frac{9}{2}$ **2.** $\frac{10}{17}$

Before we continue further, don't forget from Section 1.7 that the fraction bar indicates division. Let's review some division properties for 1 and 0.

$\frac{9}{9} = 1$ because $1 \cdot 9 = 9$ $\frac{11}{1} = 11$ because $11 \cdot 1 = 11$

$\frac{0}{6} = 0$ because $0 \cdot 6 = 0$ $\frac{6}{0}$ *is undefined* because there is no number that when multiplied by 0 gives 6.

In general, we can say the following.

Let n be any whole number except 0.

$\frac{n}{n} = 1$ $\frac{0}{n} = 0$

$\frac{n}{1} = n$ $\frac{n}{0}$ is undefined.

Answers

1. numerator = 9, denominator = 2
2. numerator = 10, denominator = 17

PRACTICE 3–6

Simplify.

3. $\frac{0}{2}$ 4. $\frac{8}{8}$

5. $\frac{4}{0}$ 6. $\frac{20}{1}$

Examples Simplify.

3. $\frac{5}{5} = 1$ 4. $\frac{0}{7} = 0$ 5. $\frac{10}{1} = 10$ 6. $\frac{3}{0}$ is undefined

Work Practice 3–6

Objective B Writing Fractions to Represent Parts of Figures or Real-Life Data

One way to become familiar with the concept of fractions is to visualize fractions with shaded figures. We can then write a fraction to represent the shaded area of the figure.

PRACTICE 7–8

Write a fraction to represent the shaded part of each figure.

7.

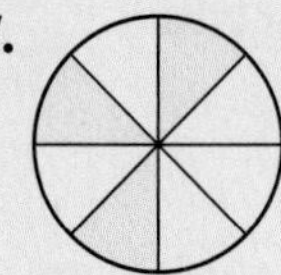

8.

Examples Write a fraction to represent the shaded part of each figure.

7. In this figure, 2 of the 5 equal parts are shaded. Thus, the fraction is $\frac{2}{5}$.

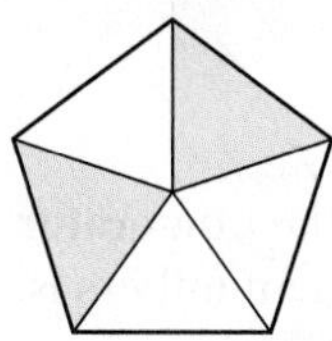

$\frac{2}{5}$ ← number of parts shaded / ← number of equal parts

8. In this figure, 3 of the 10 rectangles are shaded. Thus, the fraction is $\frac{3}{10}$.

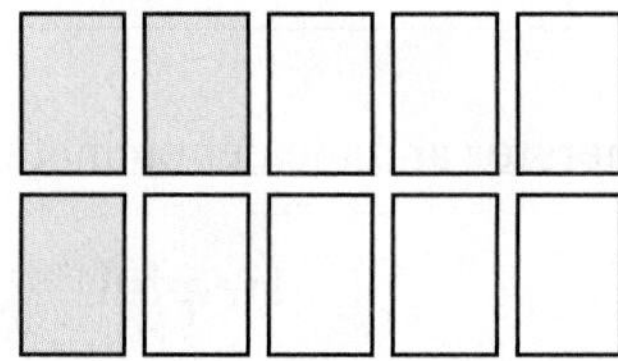

$\frac{3}{10}$ ← number of parts shaded / ← number of equal parts

Work Practice 7–8

PRACTICE 9–10

Write a fraction to represent the part of the whole shown.

9.

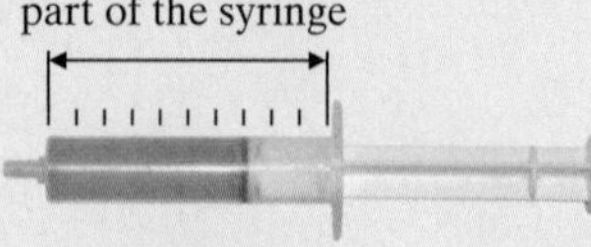

10.

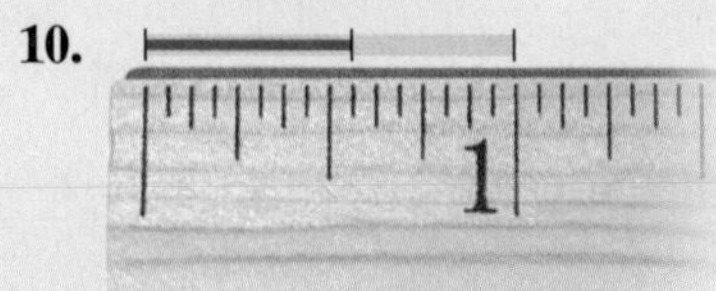

Examples Write a fraction to represent the shaded part of the diagram.

9.

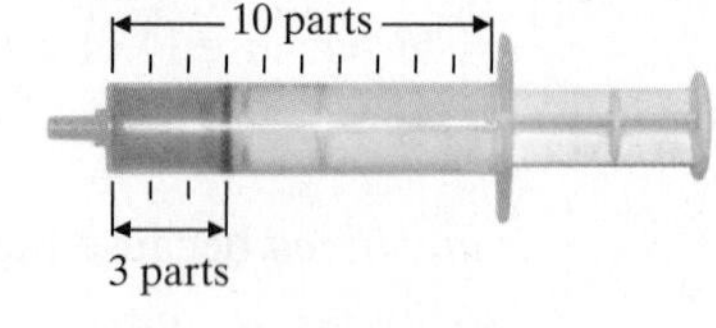

The fraction is $\frac{3}{10}$.

10.

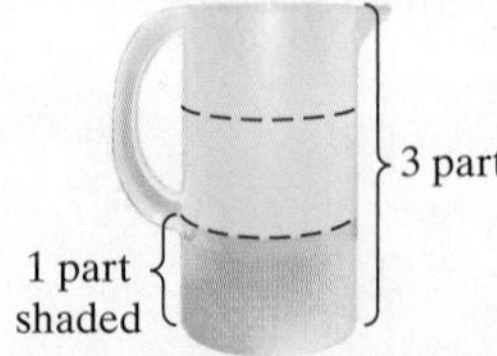

The fraction is $\frac{1}{3}$.

Work Practice 9–10

Answers

3. 0 4. 1 5. undefined 6. 20

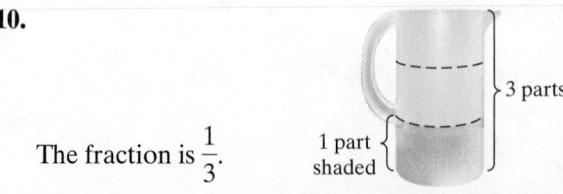

7. $\frac{3}{8}$ 8. $\frac{1}{6}$ 9. $\frac{7}{10}$ 10. $\frac{9}{16}$

Examples Draw a figure and then shade a part of it to represent each fraction.

11. $\frac{5}{6}$ of a figure

We will use a geometric figure such as a rectangle. Since the denominator is 6, we divide it into 6 equal parts. Then we shade 5 of the equal parts.

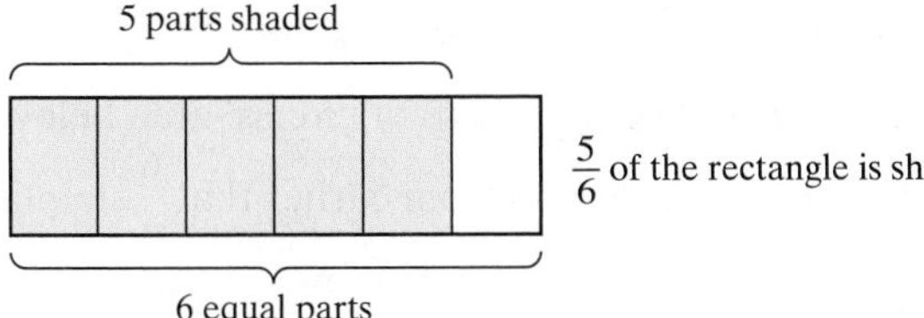

12. $\frac{3}{8}$ of a figure

If you'd like, our figure can consist of 8 triangles of the same size. We will shade 3 of the triangles.

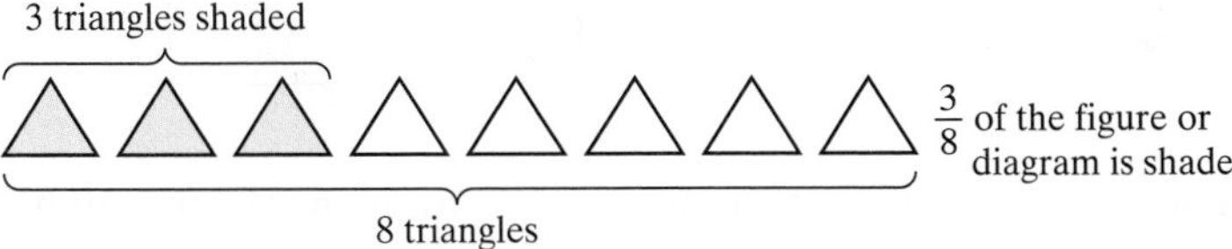

Work Practice 11–12

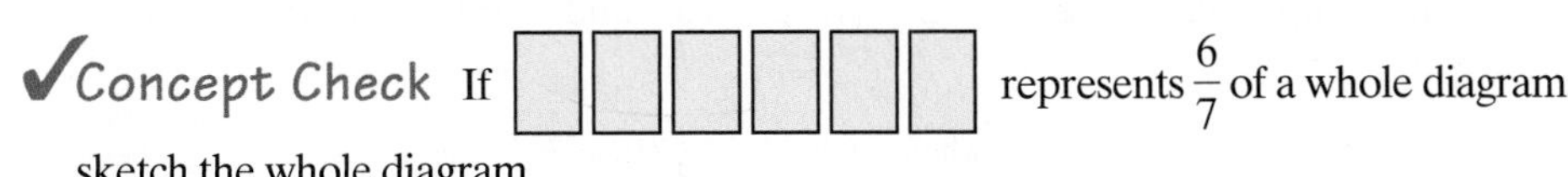

✓Concept Check If [six boxes] represents $\frac{6}{7}$ of a whole diagram, sketch the whole diagram.

PRACTICE 11–12

Draw and shade a part of a figure to represent each fraction.

11. $\frac{2}{3}$ of a figure

12. $\frac{7}{11}$ of a figure

Example 13 Writing Fractions from Real-Life Data

Of the eight planets in our solar system (Pluto is now a dwarf planet), three are closer to the Sun than Mars. What fraction of the planets are closer to the Sun than Mars?

Solution: The fraction of planets closer to the Sun than Mars is:

$\frac{3}{8}$ ← number of planets closer / ← number of planets in our solar system

Thus, $\frac{3}{8}$ of the planets in our solar system are closer to the Sun than Mars.

Work Practice 13

PRACTICE 13

Of the eight planets in our solar system, five are farther from the Sun than Earth is. What fraction of the planets are farther from the Sun than Earth is?

Answers

11. answers may vary; for example, ○○○

12. answers may vary; for example,

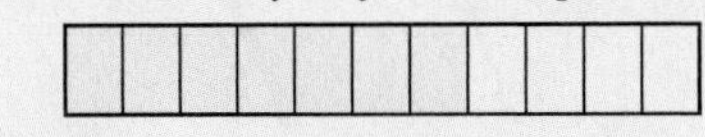

13. $\frac{5}{8}$

✓ Concept Check Answer

Objective C Identifying Proper Fractions, Improper Fractions, and Mixed Numbers

A **proper fraction** is a fraction whose numerator is less than its denominator. Proper fractions are less than 1. For example, the shaded portion of the triangle's area is represented by $\frac{2}{3}$.

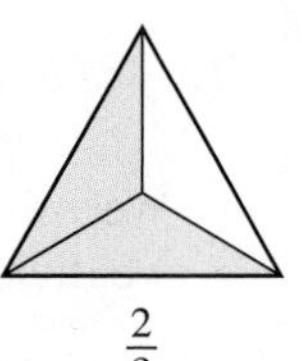

An **improper fraction** is a fraction whose numerator is greater than or equal to its denominator. Improper fractions are greater than or equal to 1. The shaded part of the group of circles' area below is $\frac{9}{4}$. The shaded part of the rectangle's area is $\frac{6}{6}$. (Recall from earlier that $\frac{6}{6}$ simplifies to 1 and notice that 1 whole figure or rectangle is shaded below.)

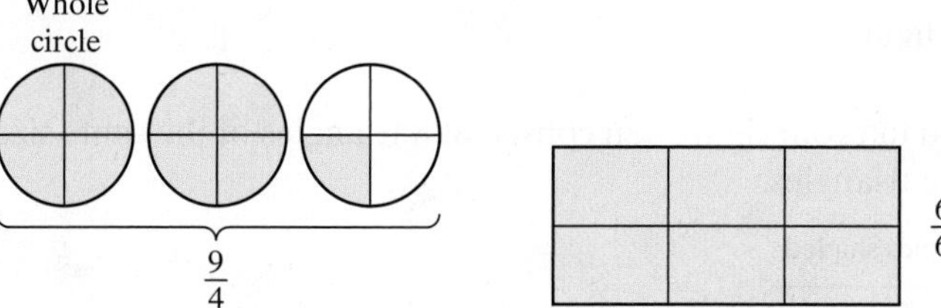

A **mixed number** contains a whole number and a fraction. Mixed numbers are greater than 1. Earlier, we wrote the shaded part of the group of circles below as the improper fraction $\frac{9}{4}$. Now let's write the shaded part as a mixed number. The shaded part of the group of circles' area is $2\frac{1}{4}$. (Read "two and one-fourth.")

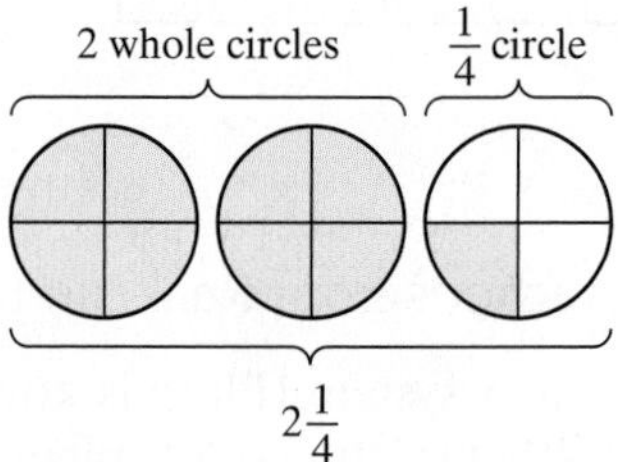

Helpful Hint

The mixed number $2\frac{1}{4}$ represents $2 + \frac{1}{4}$.

Example 14 Identify each number as a proper fraction, improper fraction, or mixed number.

a. $\frac{6}{7}$ is a proper fraction

b. $\frac{13}{12}$ is an improper fraction

c. $\frac{2}{2}$ is an improper fraction

d. $\frac{99}{101}$ is a proper fraction

e. $1\frac{7}{8}$ is a mixed number

f. $\frac{93}{74}$ is an improper fraction

Work Practice 14

PRACTICE 14

Identify each number as a proper fraction, improper fraction, or mixed number.

a. $\frac{5}{8}$ **b.** $\frac{7}{7}$

c. $\frac{14}{13}$ **d.** $\frac{13}{14}$

e. $5\frac{1}{4}$ **f.** $\frac{100}{49}$

Answers

14. a. proper fraction **b.** improper fraction **c.** improper fraction **d.** proper fraction **e.** mixed number **f.** improper fraction

Examples Represent the shaded part of each figure group's area as both an improper fraction and a mixed number.

15.

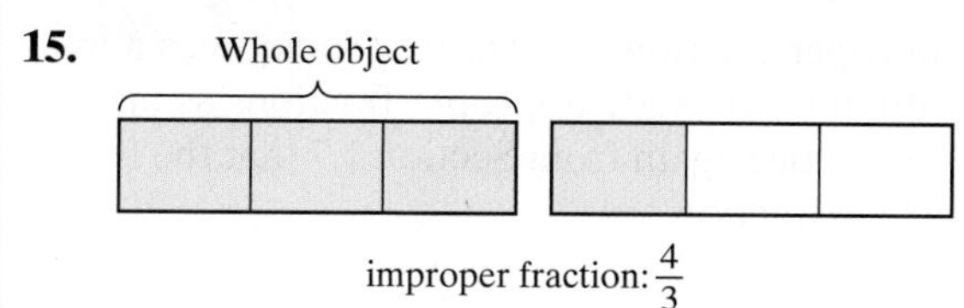

improper fraction: $\frac{4}{3}$

mixed number: $1\frac{1}{3}$

16.

improper fraction: $\frac{5}{2}$

mixed number: $2\frac{1}{2}$

Work Practice 15–16

PRACTICE 15–16

Represent the shaded part of each figure group as both an improper fraction and a mixed number.

15.

16.

✓**Concept Check** If you were to estimate $2\frac{1}{8}$ by a whole number, would you choose 2 or 3? Why?

Objective D Writing Mixed Numbers as Improper Fractions

Notice from Examples 15 and 16 that mixed numbers and improper fractions were both used to represent the shaded area of the figure groups. For example,

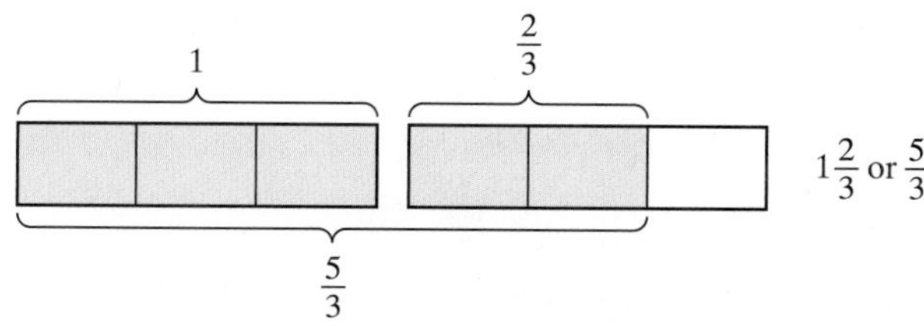

$1\frac{2}{3}$ or $\frac{5}{3}$

The following steps may be used to write a mixed number as an improper fraction:

Writing a Mixed Number as an Improper Fraction

To write a mixed number as an improper fraction:

Step 1: Multiply the denominator of the fraction by the whole number.

Step 2: Add the numerator of the fraction to the product from Step 1.

Step 3: Write the sum from Step 2 as the numerator of the improper fraction over the original denominator.

For example,

Step 1 Step 2

$$1\frac{2}{3} = \frac{3\cdot 1 + 2}{3} = \frac{3+2}{3} = \frac{5}{3}$$

Step 3

Example 17 Write each as an improper fraction.

a. $4\frac{2}{9} = \frac{9\cdot 4 + 2}{9} = \frac{36+2}{9} = \frac{38}{9}$

b. $1\frac{8}{11} = \frac{11\cdot 1 + 8}{11} = \frac{11+8}{11} = \frac{19}{11}$

Work Practice 17

PRACTICE 17

Write each as an improper fraction.

a. $2\frac{5}{7}$ **b.** $5\frac{1}{3}$

c. $9\frac{3}{10}$ **d.** $1\frac{1}{5}$

Answers

15. $\frac{8}{3}, 2\frac{2}{3}$ **16.** $\frac{5}{4}, 1\frac{1}{4}$

17. a. $\frac{19}{7}$ **b.** $\frac{16}{3}$ **c.** $\frac{93}{10}$ **d.** $\frac{6}{5}$

✓ **Concept Check Answer**

2; answers may vary

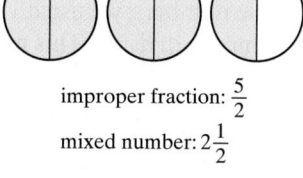

Objective E Writing Improper Fractions as Mixed Numbers or Whole Numbers

Just as there are times when an improper fraction is preferred, sometimes a mixed or a whole number better suits a situation. To write improper fractions as mixed or whole numbers, we use division. Recall once again from Section 1.7 that the fraction bar means division. This means that the fraction

$\frac{5}{3}$ (5 numerator, 3 denominator) means $3\overline{)5}$ (3 denominator, 5 numerator)

Writing an Improper Fraction as a Mixed Number or a Whole Number

To write an improper fraction as a mixed number or a whole number:

Step 1: Divide the denominator into the numerator.

Step 2: The whole number part of the mixed number is the quotient. The fraction part of the mixed number is the remainder over the original denominator.

$$\text{quotient}\frac{\text{remainder}}{\text{original denominator}}$$

For example,

Step 1: $\frac{5}{3}$: $3\overline{)5}$ gives quotient 1; $5 - 3 = 2$

Step 2: $\frac{5}{3} = 1\frac{2}{3}$ ← 2 is the remainder, 3 is the original denominator, 1 is the quotient

PRACTICE 18

Write each as a mixed number or a whole number.

a. $\frac{9}{5}$ b. $\frac{23}{9}$ c. $\frac{48}{4}$

d. $\frac{62}{13}$ e. $\frac{51}{7}$ f. $\frac{21}{20}$

Example 18 Write each as a mixed number or a whole number.

a. $\frac{30}{7}$ b. $\frac{16}{15}$ c. $\frac{84}{6}$

Solution:

a. $\frac{30}{7}$: $7\overline{)30}$ gives quotient 4; $30 - 28 = 2$. $\frac{30}{7} = 4\frac{2}{7}$

b. $\frac{16}{15}$: $15\overline{)16}$ gives quotient 1; $16 - 15 = 1$. $\frac{16}{15} = 1\frac{1}{15}$

c. $\frac{84}{6}$: $6\overline{)84}$ gives quotient 14; $8 - 6 = 2$, bring down 4: 24; $24 - 24 = 0$. $\frac{84}{6} = 14$ Since the remainder is 0, the result is the whole number 14.

Helpful Hint

When the remainder is 0, the improper fraction is a whole number. For example, $\frac{92}{4} = 23$.

$4\overline{)92}$ gives quotient 23; $9 - 8 = 1$, bring down 2: 12; $12 - 12 = 0$

Work Practice 18

Answers

18. a. $1\frac{4}{5}$ b. $2\frac{5}{9}$ c. 12 d. $4\frac{10}{13}$ e. $7\frac{2}{7}$ f. $1\frac{1}{20}$

Vocabulary and Readiness Check

Use the choices below to fill in each blank.

improper	fraction	proper	is undefined	mixed number	$= 0$
greater than or equal to 1	denominator	$= 1$	less than 1	numerator	

1. The number $\frac{17}{31}$ is called a(n) ______________. The number 31 is called its ______________ and 17 is called its ______________.

2. If we simplify each fraction, $\frac{9}{9}$ ______________, $\frac{0}{4}$ ______________, and we say $\frac{4}{0}$ ______________.

3. The fraction $\frac{8}{3}$ is called a(n) ______________ fraction, the fraction $\frac{3}{8}$ is called a(n) ______________ fraction, and $10\frac{3}{8}$ is called a(n) ______________.

4. The value of an improper fraction is always ______________, and the value of a proper fraction is always ______________.

2.1 Exercise Set

FOR EXTRA HELP MyMathLab

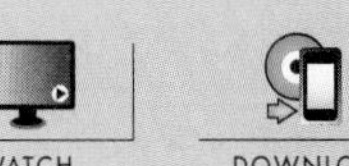

Objectives **A C** **Mixed Practice** *Identify the numerator and the denominator of each fraction and identify each fraction as proper or improper. See Examples 1, 2, and 14.*

1. $\frac{1}{2}$ **2.** $\frac{1}{4}$ **3.** $\frac{10}{3}$

4. $\frac{53}{21}$ **5.** $\frac{15}{15}$ **6.** $\frac{26}{26}$

Objective **A** *Simplify. See Examples 3 through 6.*

7. $\frac{21}{21}$ **8.** $\frac{14}{14}$ **9.** $\frac{5}{0}$ **10.** $\frac{1}{0}$ **11.** $\frac{13}{1}$ **12.** $\frac{14}{1}$

13. $\frac{0}{20}$ **14.** $\frac{0}{17}$ **15.** $\frac{10}{0}$ **16.** $\frac{0}{18}$ **17.** $\frac{16}{1}$ **18.** $\frac{18}{18}$

Objective **B** *Write a fraction to represent the shaded part of each. See Examples 7 through 10.*

19.

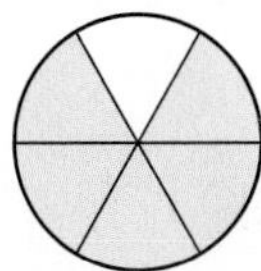

20.

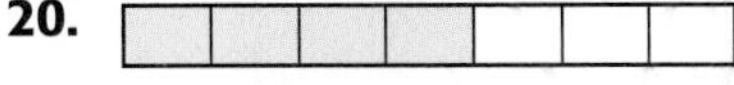

21.

22. 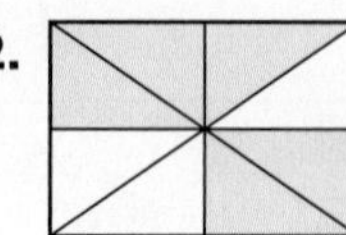

23.

24. 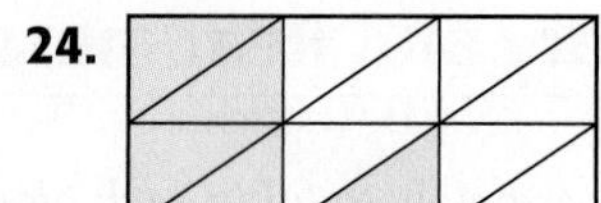

25. 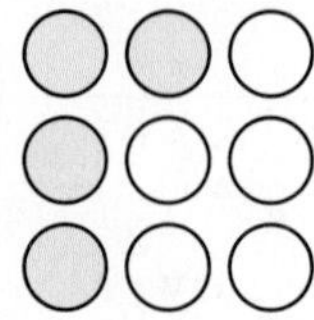

26. 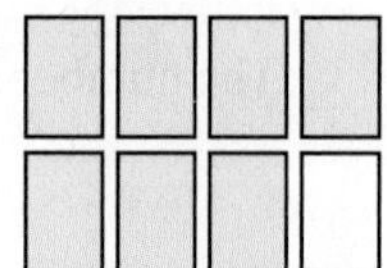

27. 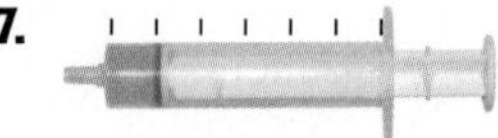

28. 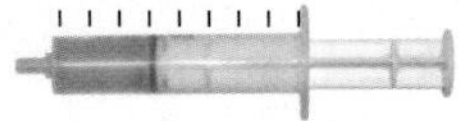

29. 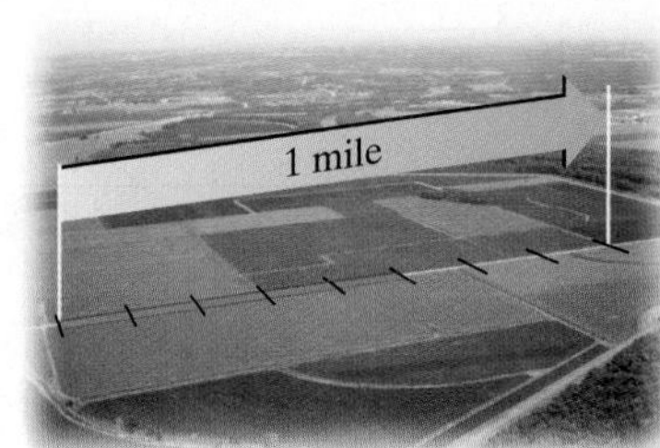

30. 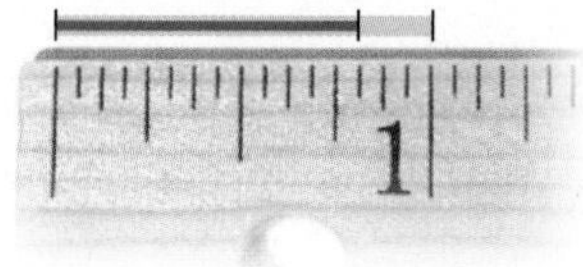

Draw and shade a part of a figure to represent each fraction. See Examples 11 and 12.

31. $\frac{1}{5}$ of a figure

32. $\frac{1}{16}$ of a figure

33. $\frac{7}{8}$ of a figure

34. $\frac{3}{5}$ of a figure

35. $\frac{6}{7}$ of a figure

36. $\frac{7}{9}$ of a figure

37. $\frac{4}{4}$ of a figure

38. $\frac{6}{6}$ of a figure

Write each fraction. See Example 13.

39. Of the 131 students at a small private school, 42 are freshmen. What fraction of the students are freshmen?

40. Of the 63 employees at a new biomedical engineering firm, 22 are men. What fraction of the employees are men?

41. Use Exercise 39 to answer a and b.

a. How many students are *not* freshmen?
b. What fraction of the students are *not* freshmen?

42. Use Exercise 40 to answer a and b.

a. How many of the employees are women?
b. What fraction of the employees are women?

43. As of the beginning of 2010, the United States has had 44 different presidents. A total of seven U.S. presidents were born in the state of Ohio, second only to the state of Virginia in producing U.S. presidents. What fraction of U.S. presidents were born in Ohio? (*Source: World Almanac and Book of Facts*)

44. Of the eight planets in our solar system, four have days that are longer than the 24-hour Earth day. What fraction of the planets have longer days than Earth has? (*Source:* National Space Science Data Center)

45. The Atlantic hurricane season of 2005 rewrote the record books. There were 28 tropical storms, 15 of which turned into hurricanes. What fraction of the 2005 Atlantic tropical storms escalated to hurricanes?

46. There are 12 inches in a foot. What fractional part of a foot does 5 inches represent?

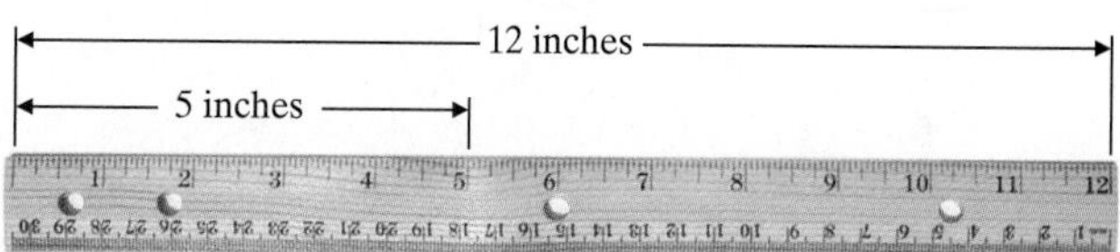

47. There are 31 days in the month of March. What fraction of the month does 11 days represent?

Mon.	Tue.	Wed.	Thu.	Fri.	Sat.	Sun.
					1	2
3	4	5	6	7	8	9
10	11	12	13	14	15	16
17	18	19	20	21	22	23
24	25	26	27	28	29	30
31						

48. There are 60 minutes in an hour. What fraction of an hour does 37 minutes represent?

49. In a basic college mathematics class containing 31 students, there are 18 freshmen, 10 sophomores, and 3 juniors. What fraction of the class is sophomores?

50. In a sports team with 20 children, there are 9 boys and 11 girls. What fraction of the team is boys?

51. Thirty-three out of the fifty total states in the United States contain federal Indian reservations.

a. What fraction of the states contain federal Indian reservations?
b. How many states do not contain federal Indian reservations?
c. What fraction of the states do not contain federal Indian reservations? (*Source:* Tiller Research, Inc., Albuquerque, NM)

52. Consumer fireworks are legal in 45 out of the 50 total states in the United States.

a. In what fraction of the states are consumer fireworks legal?
b. In how many states are consumer fireworks illegal?
c. In what fraction of the states are consumer fireworks illegal? (*Source:* United States Fireworks Safety Council)

53. A bag contains 50 red or blue marbles. If 21 marbles are blue,

a. What *fraction* of the marbles are blue?

b. How many marbles are red?

c. What *fraction* of the marbles are red?

54. An art dealer is taking inventory. His shop contains a total of 37 pieces, which are all sculptures, watercolor paintings, or oil paintings. If there are 15 watercolor paintings and 17 oil paintings, answer each question.

a. What fraction of the inventory is watercolor paintings?

b. What fraction of the inventory is oil paintings?

c. How many sculptures are there?

d. What fraction of the inventory is sculptures?

Objective C *Write the shaded area in each figure group as (a) an improper fraction and (b) a mixed number. See Examples 15 and 16.*

55.

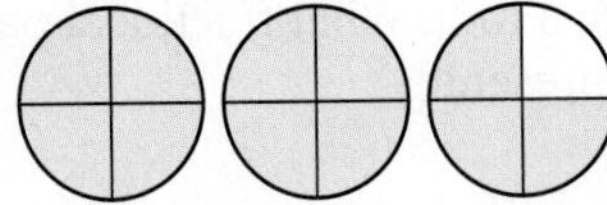

56.

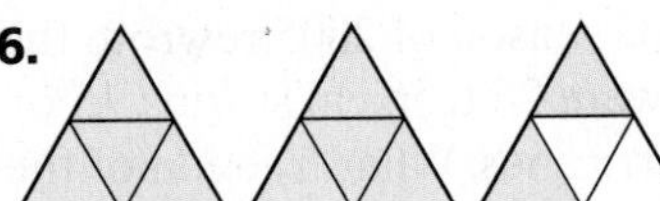

57.

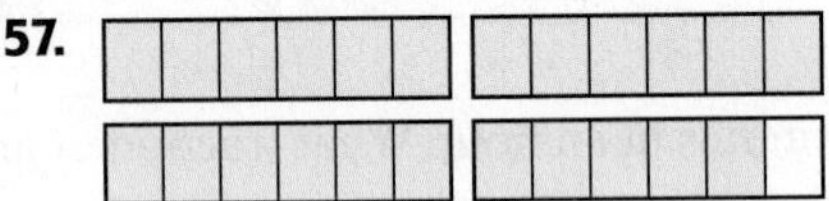

58.

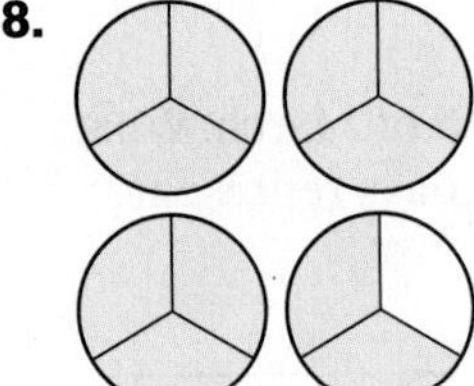

59.

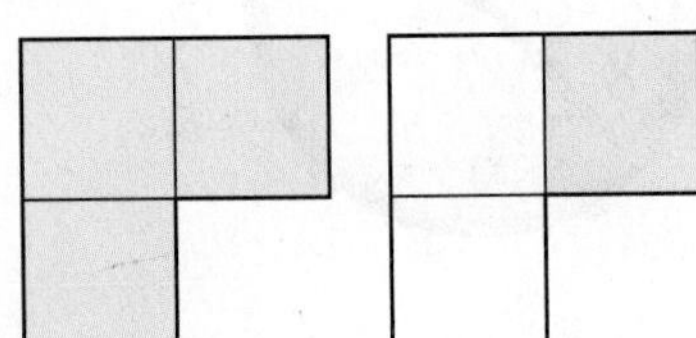

60.

61.

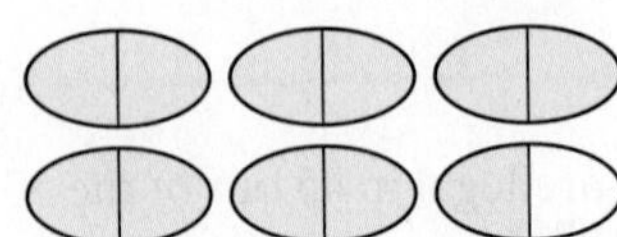

62.

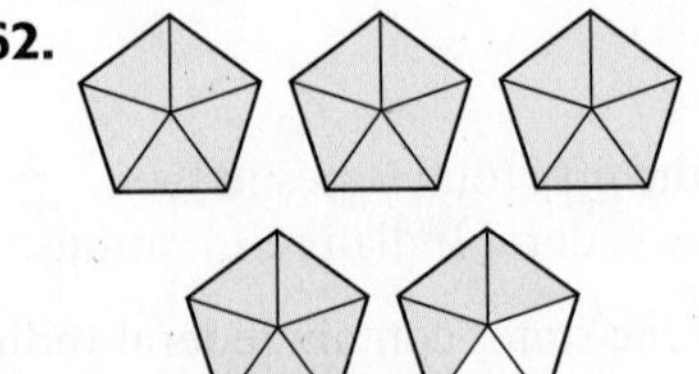

Objective D *Write each mixed number as an improper fraction. See Example 17.*

63. $2\frac{1}{3}$ **64.** $6\frac{3}{4}$ **65.** $3\frac{3}{5}$ **66.** $2\frac{5}{9}$ **67.** $6\frac{5}{8}$ **68.** $7\frac{3}{8}$

69. $2\frac{11}{15}$ **70.** $1\frac{13}{17}$ **71.** $11\frac{6}{7}$ **72.** $12\frac{2}{5}$ **73.** $6\frac{6}{13}$ **74.** $8\frac{9}{10}$

75. $4\frac{13}{24}$ **76.** $5\frac{17}{25}$ **77.** $17\frac{7}{12}$ **78.** $12\frac{7}{15}$ **79.** $9\frac{7}{20}$ **80.** $10\frac{14}{27}$

81. $2\frac{51}{107}$ **82.** $3\frac{27}{125}$ **83.** $166\frac{2}{3}$ **84.** $114\frac{2}{7}$

Objective E *Write each improper fraction as a mixed number or a whole number. See Example 18.*

85. $\frac{17}{5}$ **86.** $\frac{13}{7}$ **87.** $\frac{37}{8}$ **88.** $\frac{64}{9}$ **89.** $\frac{47}{15}$ **90.** $\frac{65}{12}$

91. $\frac{46}{21}$ **92.** $\frac{67}{17}$ **93.** $\frac{198}{6}$ **94.** $\frac{112}{7}$ **95.** $\frac{225}{15}$ **96.** $\frac{196}{14}$

97. $\frac{200}{3}$ **98.** $\frac{300}{7}$ **99.** $\frac{247}{23}$ **100.** $\frac{437}{53}$ **101.** $\frac{319}{18}$ **102.** $\frac{404}{21}$

103. $\frac{182}{175}$ **104.** $\frac{149}{143}$ **105.** $\frac{737}{112}$ **106.** $\frac{901}{123}$

Review

Simplify. See Section 1.9.

107. 3^2 **108.** 4^3 **109.** 5^3 **110.** 3^4

Write each using exponents.

111. $7 \cdot 7 \cdot 7 \cdot 7 \cdot 7$ **112.** $5 \cdot 5 \cdot 5 \cdot 5$ **113.** $2 \cdot 2 \cdot 2 \cdot 3$ **114.** $4 \cdot 4 \cdot 10 \cdot 10 \cdot 10$

Concept Extensions

Write each fraction.

115. In your own words, explain how to write an improper fraction as a mixed number.

116. In your own words, explain how to write a mixed number as an improper fraction.

Identify the larger fraction for each pair.

117. $\frac{1}{2}$ or $\frac{2}{3}$ (*Hint:* Represent each fraction by the shaded part of equivalent figures. Then compare the shaded areas.)

118. $\frac{7}{4}$ or $\frac{3}{5}$ (*Hint:* Identify each as a proper fraction or an improper fraction.)

Solve. See the first Concept Check in this section.

119. If ◯◯◯◯ represents $\frac{4}{9}$ of a whole diagram, sketch the whole diagram.

120. If △△ represents $\frac{1}{3}$ of a whole diagram, sketch the whole diagram.

121. The Gap Corporation owns stores with three different brand names, as shown on the bar graph. What fraction of the stores owned by The Gap Corporation are named "Banana Republic"?

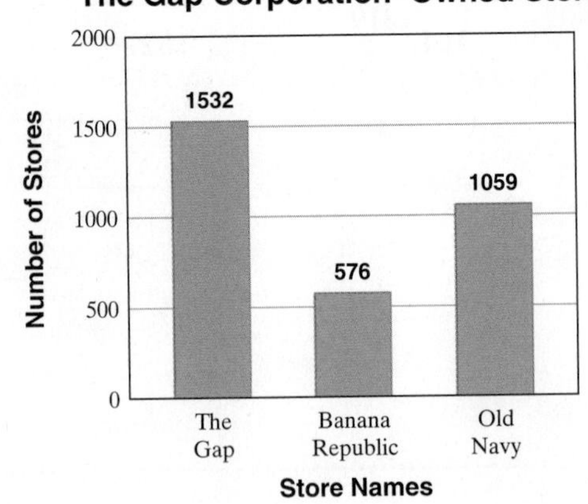

122. The Public Broadcasting Service (PBS) provides programming to the noncommercial public TV stations of the United States. The bar graph shows a breakdown of the public television licensees by type. Each licensee operates one or more PBS member TV stations. What fraction of the public television licensees are universities or colleges? (*Source:* The Public Broadcasting Service)

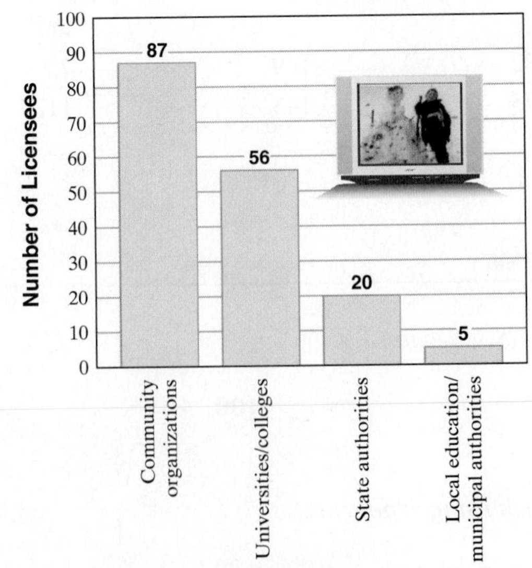

123. Habitat for Humanity is a nonprofit organization that helps provide affordable housing to families in need. Habitat for Humanity does its work of building and renovating houses through 1700 local affiliates in the United States and 550 international affiliates. What fraction of the total Habitat for Humanity affiliates are located in the United States? (*Hint:* First find the total number of affiliates.) (*Source:* Habitat for Humanity International)

124. The United States Marine Corps (USMC) has five principal training centers in California, three in North Carolina, two in South Carolina, one in Arizona, one in Hawaii, and one in Virginia. What fraction of the total USMC principal training centers are located in California? (*Hint:* First find the total number of USMC training centers.) (*Source:* U.S. Department of Defense)

Objectives

A Find the Factors of a Number.

B Identify Prime and Composite Numbers.

C Find the Prime Factorization of a Number.

2.2 FACTORS AND PRIME FACTORIZATION

To perform many operations with fractions, it is necessary to be able to factor a number. In this section, only the **natural numbers**—1, 2, 3, 4, 5, and so on—will be considered.

✓**Concept Check** How are the natural numbers and the whole numbers alike? How are they different?

Objective A Finding Factors of Numbers

Recall that when numbers are multiplied to form a product, each number is called a factor. Since $5 \cdot 9 = 45$, both 5 and 9 are **factors** of 45, and $5 \cdot 9$ is called a **factorization** of 45.

The two-number factorizations of 45 are

$1 \cdot 45 \quad 3 \cdot 15 \quad 5 \cdot 9$

Thus, we say that the factors of 45 are 1, 3, 5, 9, 15, and 45.

Helpful Hint

From our definition of factor above, notice that a **factor** of a number divides the number evenly (with a remainder of 0). For example,

$$1\overline{)45}^{\,45} \quad 3\overline{)45}^{\,15} \quad 5\overline{)45}^{\,9} \quad 9\overline{)45}^{\,5} \quad 15\overline{)45}^{\,3} \quad 45\overline{)45}^{\,1}$$

PRACTICE 1

Find all the factors of each number.

a. 15 **b.** 7 **c.** 24

Example 1 Find all the factors of 20.

Solution: First we write all the two-number factorizations of 20.

$1 \cdot 20 = 20$

$2 \cdot 10 = 20$

$4 \cdot 5 = 20$

The factors of 20 are 1, 2, 4, 5, 10, and 20.

Work Practice 1

Objective B Identifying Prime and Composite Numbers

Of all the ways to factor a number, one special way is called the **prime factorization.** To help us write prime factorizations, we first review prime and composite numbers.

Prime Numbers

A **prime number** is a natural number that has exactly two different factors, 1 and itself.

The first several prime numbers are

2, 3, 5, 7, 11, 13, 17

It would be helpful to memorize these.

If a natural number other than 1 is not a prime number, it is called a **composite number.**

Answers

1. a. 1, 3, 5, 15 **b.** 1, 7 **c.** 1, 2, 3, 4, 6, 8, 12, 24

✓ **Concept Check Answer**

answers may vary

Composite Numbers

A **composite number** is any natural number, other than 1, that is not prime.

Helpful Hint

The natural number 1 is neither prime nor composite.

Example 2 Determine whether each number is prime or composite. Explain your answers.

3, 9, 11, 17, 26

Solution: The number 3 is prime. Its only factors are 1 and 3 (itself).
The number 9 is composite. It has more than two factors: 1, 3, and 9.
The number 11 is prime. Its only factors are 1 and 11.
The number 17 is prime. Its only factors are 1 and 17.
The number 26 is composite. Its factors are 1, 2, 13, and 26.

Work Practice 2

PRACTICE 2

Determine whether each number is prime or composite. Explain your answers.

21, 13, 18, 29, 39

Objective C Finding Prime Factorizations

Now we are ready to find **prime factorizations** of numbers.

Prime Factorization

The **prime factorization** of a number is the factorization in which all the factors are prime numbers.

For example, the prime factorization of 12 is $2 \cdot 2 \cdot 3$ because

$$12 = \underbrace{2 \cdot 2 \cdot 3}$$

This product is 12 and each number is a prime number.

Every whole number greater than 1 has exactly one prime factorization.

Helpful Hint

Don't forget that multiplication is commutative, so $2 \cdot 2 \cdot 3$ can also be written as $2 \cdot 3 \cdot 2$ or $3 \cdot 2 \cdot 2$ or $2^2 \cdot 3$. Any one of these can be called *the prime factorization of* 12.

Example 3 Find the prime factorization of 45.

Solution: The first prime number, 2, does not divide 45 evenly (with a remainder of 0). The second prime number, 3, does, so we divide 45 by 3.

$$3\overline{)45}^{\;15}$$

Because 15 is not prime and 3 also divides 15 evenly, we divide by 3 again.

$$\begin{array}{r} 5 \\ 3\overline{)15} \\ 3\overline{)45} \end{array}$$

Continued on next page

PRACTICE 3

Find the prime factorization of 28.

Answers

2. 13, 29 are prime. 21, 18, and 39 are composite. **3.** $2 \cdot 2 \cdot 7$ or $2^2 \cdot 7$

The quotient, 5, is a prime number, so we are finished. The prime factorization of 45 is

$$45 = 3 \cdot 3 \cdot 5 \quad \text{or} \quad 45 = 3^2 \cdot 5,$$

using exponents.

Work Practice 3

There are a few quick **divisibility tests** to determine whether a number is divisible by the primes 2, 3, or 5. (A number is divisible by 2, for example, if 2 divides it evenly.)

Divisibility Tests

A whole number is divisible by:

- 2 if the last digit is 0, 2, 4, 6, or 8.

  ↓

  132 is divisible by 2 since the last digit is a 2.
- 3 if the sum of the digits is divisible by 3.

  144 is divisible by 3 since $1 + 4 + 4 = 9$ is divisible by 3.
- 5 if the last digit is 0 or 5.

  ↓

  1115 is divisible by 5 since the last digit is a 5.

Helpful Hint

Here are a few other divisibility tests you may find interesting. A whole number is divisible by:

- 4 if its last two digits are divisible by 4.

  1712 is divisible by 4.
- 6 if it's divisible by 2 and 3.

  9858 is divisible by 6.
- 9 if the sum of its digits is divisible by 9.

  5238 is divisible by 9 since $5 + 2 + 3 + 8 = 18$ is divisible by 9.

We will usually begin the division process with the smallest prime number factor of the given number. Since multiplication is commutative, this is not necessary. As long as the divisor is any prime number factor, this process works.

PRACTICE 4

Find the prime factorization of 120.

Example 4 Find the prime factorization of 180.

Solution: We divide 180 by 2 and continue dividing until the quotient is no longer divisible by 2. We then divide by the next largest prime number, 3, until the quotient is no longer divisible by 3. We continue this process until the quotient is a prime number.

$$\begin{array}{r} 5 \\ 3\overline{)\ 15} \\ 3\overline{)\ 45} \\ 2\overline{)\ 90} \\ 2\overline{)180} \end{array}$$

Answer

4. $2 \cdot 2 \cdot 2 \cdot 3 \cdot 5$ or $2^3 \cdot 3 \cdot 5$

Thus, the prime factorization of 180 is

$$180 = 2 \cdot 2 \cdot 3 \cdot 3 \cdot 5 \quad \text{or} \quad 180 = 2^2 \cdot 3^2 \cdot 5,$$

using exponents.

Work Practice 4

Example 5 Find the prime factorization of 945.

Solution: This number is not divisible by 2 but is divisible by 3. We will begin by dividing 945 by 3.

$$\begin{array}{r} 7 \\ 5\overline{)\ 35} \\ 3\overline{)105} \\ 3\overline{)315} \\ 3\overline{)945} \end{array}$$

Thus, the prime factorization of 945 is

$$945 = 3 \cdot 3 \cdot 3 \cdot 5 \cdot 7 \quad \text{or} \quad 945 = 3^3 \cdot 5 \cdot 7$$

Work Practice 5

PRACTICE 5

Find the prime factorization of 756.

Another way to find the prime factorization is to use a factor tree, as shown in the next example.

Example 6 Use a factor tree to find the prime factorization of 18.

Solution: We begin by writing 18 as a product of two natural numbers greater than 1, say $2 \cdot 9$.

```
 18
 / \
2 · 9
```

The number 2 is prime, but 9 is not. So we write 9 as $3 \cdot 3$.

```
 18
 / \
2 · 9
↓   ↓ ↘
2 · 3 · 3
```

Each factor is now prime, so the prime factorization is

$$18 = 2 \cdot 3 \cdot 3 \quad \text{or} \quad 18 = 2 \cdot 3^2,$$

using exponents.

Work Practice 6

PRACTICE 6

Use a factor tree to find the prime factorization of 45.

In this text, we will write the factorization of a number from the smallest factor to the largest factor.

Answers

5. $2 \cdot 2 \cdot 3 \cdot 3 \cdot 3 \cdot 7$ or $2^2 \cdot 3^3 \cdot 7$
6. $3 \cdot 3 \cdot 5$ or $3^2 \cdot 5$

PRACTICE 7

Use a factor tree to find the prime factorization of each number.

a. 30 **b.** 56 **c.** 72

Example 7 Use a factor tree to find the prime factorization of 80.

Solution: Write 80 as a product of two numbers. Continue this process until all factors are prime.

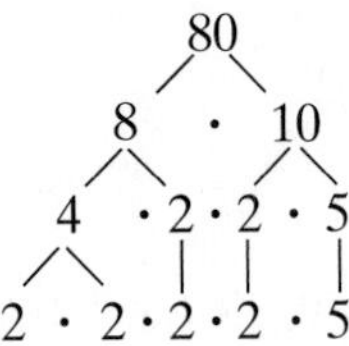

All factors are now prime, so the prime factorization of 80 is

$2 \cdot 2 \cdot 2 \cdot 2 \cdot 5$ or $2^4 \cdot 5$.

Work Practice 7

Helpful Hint

It makes no difference which factors you start with. The prime factorization of a number will be the same.

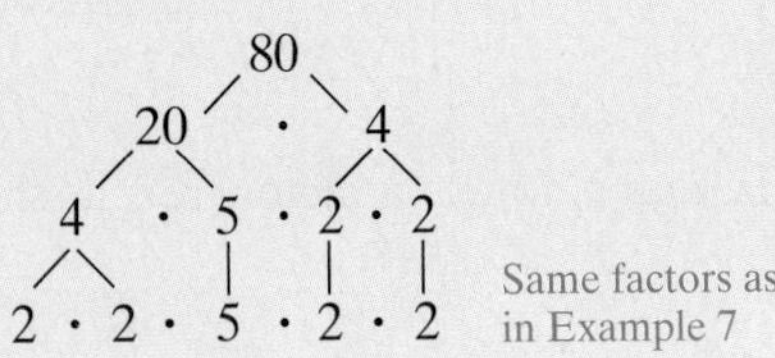
Same factors as in Example 7

✓Concept Check True or false? Two different numbers can have exactly the same prime factorization. Explain your answer.

PRACTICE 8

Use a factor tree to find the prime factorization of 117.

Example 8 Use a factor tree to find the prime factorization of 175.

Solution: We begin by writing 175 as a product of two numbers greater than 1, say $7 \cdot 25$.

175

$7 \cdot 25$

$7 \cdot 5 \cdot 5$

The prime factorization of 175 is

$175 = 5 \cdot 5 \cdot 7$ or $175 = 5^2 \cdot 7$

Work Practice 8

Answers

7. a. $2 \cdot 3 \cdot 5$ **b.** $2 \cdot 2 \cdot 2 \cdot 7$ or $2^3 \cdot 7$
c. $2 \cdot 2 \cdot 2 \cdot 3 \cdot 3$ or $2^3 \cdot 3^2$
8. $3 \cdot 3 \cdot 13$ or $3^2 \cdot 13$

✓ Concept Check Answer

false; answers may vary

Vocabulary and Readiness Check

Use the choices below to fill in each blank.

factor(s)	prime factorization	prime
natural	composite	

1. The number 40 equals $2 \cdot 2 \cdot 2 \cdot 5$. Since each factor is prime, we call $2 \cdot 2 \cdot 2 \cdot 5$ the ________________ of 40.
2. A natural number, other than 1, that is not prime is called a(n) ________________ number.
3. A natural number that has exactly two different factors, 1 and itself, is called a(n) ________________ number.
4. The numbers $1, 2, 3, 4, 5, \ldots$ are called the ________________ numbers.
5. Since $30 = 5 \cdot 6$, the numbers 5 and 6 are ________________ of 30.
6. Answer true or false: $5 \cdot 6$ is the prime factorization of 30. ________________

2.2 Exercise Set

FOR EXTRA HELP
MyMathLab
MathXL PRACTICE | WATCH | DOWNLOAD | READ | REVIEW

Objective A *List all the factors of each number. See Example 1.*

1. 8 **2.** 6 **3.** 25 **4.** 30 **5.** 4 **6.** 9

7. 18 **8.** 48 **9.** 29 **10.** 37 **11.** 80 **12.** 100

13. 12 **14.** 28 **15.** 34 **16.** 26

Objective B *Identify each number as prime or composite. See Example 2.*

17. 7 **18.** 5 **19.** 4 **20.** 10 **21.** 23 **22.** 13

23. 49 **24.** 45 **25.** 67 **26.** 89 **27.** 39 **28.** 21

29. 31 **30.** 27 **31.** 63 **32.** 51 **33.** 119 **34.** 147

Objective C *Find the prime factorization of each number. Write any repeated factors using exponents. See Examples 3 through 8.*

35. 32 **36.** 64 **37.** 15 **38.** 21 **39.** 40 **40.** 63

41. 36 **42.** 80 **43.** 39 **44.** 56 **45.** 60 **46.** 84

47. 110 **48.** 130 **49.** 85 **50.** 93 **51.** 128 **52.** 81

53. 154 **54.** 198 **55.** 300 **56.** 360 **57.** 240 **58.** 836

59. 828 **60.** 504 **61.** 882 **62.** 405 **63.** 637 **64.** 539

Objectives B C **Mixed Practice** *Find the prime factorization of each composite number. Write any repeated factors using exponents. Write prime if the number is prime.*

65. 33 **66.** 48 **67.** 98 **68.** 54 **69.** 67 **70.** 59

71. 459 **72.** 208 **73.** 97 **74.** 103 **75.** 700 **76.** 1000

Review

Round each whole number to the indicated place value. See Section 1.5.

77. 4267 hundreds **78.** 32,465 thousands **79.** 7,658,240 ten-thousands

80. 4,286,340 tens **81.** 19,764 thousands **82.** 10,292,876 millions

General Mills produces well-known brands such as Pillsbury, Cheerios, Yoplait, Häagen-Dazs, and many others. The bar graph below shows the number of patents that General Mills has been granted over a four-year period. Use this bar graph to answer the questions below. See Section 2.1. (*Source:* U.S. Patent Office)

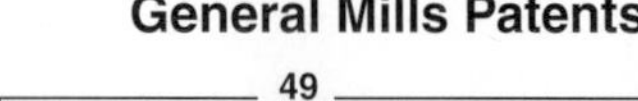

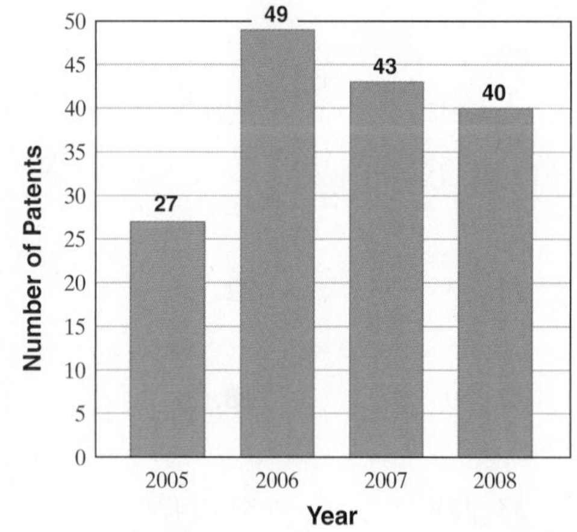

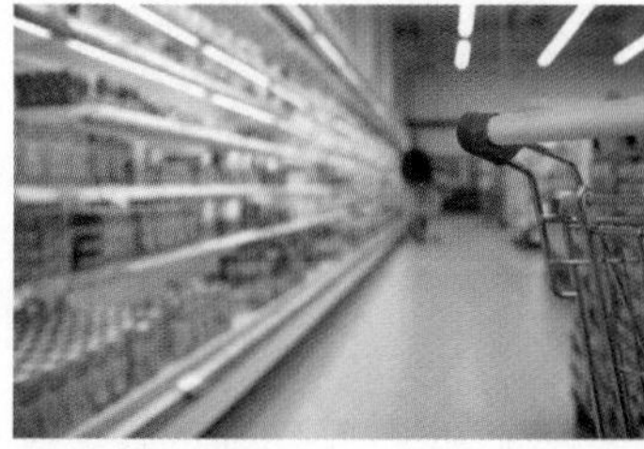

83. Find the total number of patents received by General Mills for the years shown.

84. How many fewer patents were granted in 2008 than in 2007?

85. What fraction of the patents were granted in 2005?

86. What fraction of the patents were granted in 2008?

Concept Extensions

Find the prime factorization of each number.

87. 34,020 **88.** 131,625

89. In your own words, define a prime number.

90. The number 2 is a prime number. All other even natural numbers are composite numbers. Explain why.

91. Why are we interested in the prime factorizations of nonzero whole numbers only?

92. Two students have different prime factorizations for the same number. Is this possible? Explain.

2.3 SIMPLEST FORM OF A FRACTION

Objectives

A Write a Fraction in Simplest Form or Lowest Terms.

B Determine Whether Two Fractions Are Equivalent.

C Solve Problems by Writing Fractions in Simplest Form.

Objective A Writing Fractions in Simplest Form

Fractions that represent the same portion of a whole are called **equivalent fractions.**

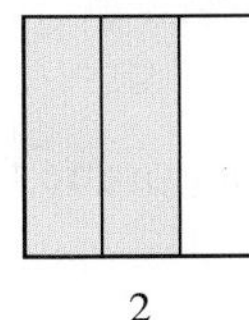

$\frac{2}{3}$

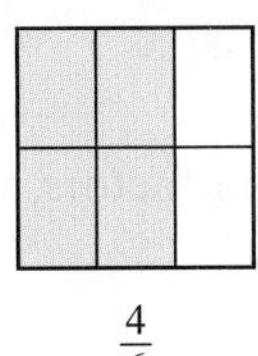

$\frac{4}{6}$

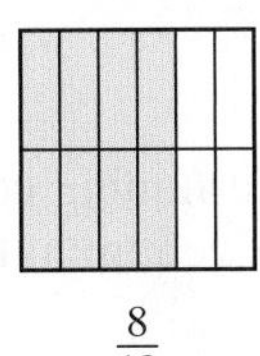

$\frac{8}{12}$

For example, $\frac{2}{3}, \frac{4}{6}$, and $\frac{8}{12}$ all represent the same shaded portion of the rectangle's area, so they are equivalent fractions.

$$\frac{2}{3} = \frac{4}{6} = \frac{8}{12}$$

There are many equivalent forms of a fraction. A special form of a fraction is called **simplest form.**

Simplest Form of a Fraction

A fraction is written in **simplest form** or **lowest terms** when the numerator and the denominator have no common factors other than 1.

For example, the fraction $\frac{2}{3}$ *is* in simplest form because 2 and 3 have no common factor other than 1. The fraction $\frac{4}{6}$ *is not* in simplest form because 4 and 6 both have a factor of 2. That is, 2 is a common factor of 4 and 6. The process of writing a fraction in simplest form is called **simplifying** the fraction.

To simplify $\frac{4}{6}$ and write it as $\frac{2}{3}$, let's first study a few properties. Recall from Section 2.1 that any nonzero whole number n divided by itself is 1.

Any nonzero number n divided by itself is 1.

$$\frac{5}{5} = 1, \frac{17}{17} = 1, \frac{24}{24} = 1, \text{ or, in general, } \frac{n}{n} = 1$$

Also, in general, if $\frac{a}{b}$ and $\frac{c}{d}$ are fractions (with b and d not 0), the following is true.

$$\frac{a \cdot c}{b \cdot d} = \frac{a}{b} \cdot \frac{c}{d}^{*}$$

These properties allow us to do the following:

$$\frac{4}{6} = \frac{2 \cdot 2}{2 \cdot 3} = \frac{2}{2} \cdot \frac{2}{3} = 1 \cdot \frac{2}{3} = \frac{2}{3}$$

(This is 1) When 1 is multiplied by a number, the result is the same number.

**Note:* We will study this concept further in the next section.

PRACTICE 1

Write in simplest form: $\frac{30}{45}$

Example 1 Write in simplest form: $\frac{12}{20}$

Solution: Notice that 12 and 20 have a common factor of 4.

$$\frac{12}{20} = \frac{4 \cdot 3}{4 \cdot 5} = \frac{4}{4} \cdot \frac{3}{5} = 1 \cdot \frac{3}{5} = \frac{3}{5}$$

Since 3 and 5 have no common factors (other than 1), $\frac{3}{5}$ is in simplest form.

Work Practice 1

If you have trouble finding common factors, write the prime factorization of the numerator and the denominator.

PRACTICE 2

Write in simplest form: $\frac{39}{51}$

Example 2 Write in simplest form: $\frac{42}{66}$

Solution: Let's write the prime factorizations of 42 and 66.

$$\frac{42}{66} = \frac{2 \cdot 3 \cdot 7}{2 \cdot 3 \cdot 11} = \frac{2}{2} \cdot \frac{3}{3} \cdot \frac{7}{11} = 1 \cdot 1 \cdot \frac{7}{11} = \frac{7}{11}$$

Work Practice 2

In the example above, you may have saved time by noticing that 42 and 66 have a common factor of 6.

$$\frac{42}{66} = \frac{6 \cdot 7}{6 \cdot 11} = \frac{6}{6} \cdot \frac{7}{11} = 1 \cdot \frac{7}{11} = \frac{7}{11}$$

Helpful Hint

Writing the prime factorizations of the numerator and the denominator is helpful in finding any common factors.

PRACTICE 3

Write in simplest form: $\frac{9}{50}$

Example 3 Write in simplest form: $\frac{10}{27}$

Solution:

$$\frac{10}{27} = \frac{2 \cdot 5}{3 \cdot 3 \cdot 3}$$ Prime factorizations of 10 and 27.

Since 10 and 27 have no common factors, $\frac{10}{27}$ is already in simplest form.

Work Practice 3

PRACTICE 4

Write in simplest form: $\frac{49}{112}$

Example 4 Write in simplest form: $\frac{30}{108}$

Solution:

$$\frac{30}{108} = \frac{2 \cdot 3 \cdot 5}{2 \cdot 2 \cdot 3 \cdot 3 \cdot 3} = \frac{2}{2} \cdot \frac{3}{3} \cdot \frac{5}{2 \cdot 3 \cdot 3} = 1 \cdot 1 \cdot \frac{5}{18} = \frac{5}{18}$$

Work Practice 4

We can use a shortcut procedure with common factors when simplifying.

$$\frac{4}{6} = \frac{\overset{1}{\cancel{2}} \cdot 2}{\underset{1}{\cancel{2}} \cdot 3} = \frac{1 \cdot 2}{1 \cdot 3} = \frac{2}{3}$$ Divide out the common factor of 2 in the numerator and denominator.

Answers

1. $\frac{2}{3}$ 2. $\frac{13}{17}$ 3. $\frac{9}{50}$ 4. $\frac{7}{16}$

This procedure is possible because dividing out a common factor in the numerator and denominator is the same as removing a factor of 1 in the product.

Writing a Fraction in Simplest Form

To write a fraction in simplest form, write the prime factorization of the numerator and the denominator and then divide both by all common factors.

Example 5 Write in simplest form: $\frac{72}{26}$

Solution:

$$\frac{72}{26} = \frac{\overset{1}{\cancel{2}} \cdot 2 \cdot 2 \cdot 3 \cdot 3}{\underset{1}{\cancel{2}} \cdot 13} = \frac{1 \cdot 2 \cdot 2 \cdot 3 \cdot 3}{1 \cdot 13} = \frac{36}{13},$$

which can also be written as

$$2\frac{10}{13}$$

Work Practice 5

PRACTICE 5

Write in simplest form: $\frac{64}{20}$

✓**Concept Check** Which is the correct way to simplify the fraction $\frac{15}{25}$? Or are both correct? Explain.

a. $\frac{15}{25} = \frac{3 \cdot \overset{1}{\cancel{5}}}{5 \cdot \underset{1}{\cancel{5}}} = \frac{3}{5}$ **b.** $\frac{1\overset{1}{\cancel{5}}}{2\underset{1}{\cancel{5}}} = \frac{11}{21}$

Example 6 Write in simplest form: $\frac{6}{60}$

Solution:

$$\frac{6}{60} = \frac{\overset{1}{\cancel{2}} \cdot \overset{1}{\cancel{3}}}{\underset{1}{\cancel{2}} \cdot 2 \cdot \underset{1}{\cancel{3}} \cdot 5} = \frac{1 \cdot 1}{1 \cdot 2 \cdot 1 \cdot 5} = \frac{1}{10}$$

Work Practice 6

PRACTICE 6

Write in simplest form: $\frac{8}{56}$

Helpful Hint

Be careful when all factors of the numerator or denominator are divided out. In Example 6, the numerator was $1 \cdot 1 = 1$, so the final result was $\frac{1}{10}$.

In the fraction of Example 6, $\frac{6}{60}$, you may have immediately noticed that the largest common factor of 6 and 60 is 6. If so, you may simply divide out that largest common factor.

$$\frac{6}{60} = \frac{\overset{1}{\cancel{6}}}{\underset{1}{\cancel{6}} \cdot 10} = \frac{1}{1 \cdot 10} = \frac{1}{10}$$ Divide out the common factor of 6.

Notice that the result, $\frac{1}{10}$, is in simplest form. If it were not, we would repeat the same procedure until the result was in simplest form.

Answers

5. $\frac{16}{5}$ or $3\frac{1}{5}$ **6.** $\frac{1}{7}$

✓ **Concept Check Answers**

a. correct **b.** incorrect

PRACTICE 7

Write in simplest form: $\frac{42}{48}$

Example 7 Write in simplest form: $\frac{45}{75}$

Solution: You may write the prime factorizations of 45 and 75 or you may notice that these two numbers have a common factor of 15.

$$\frac{45}{75} = \frac{3 \cdot \cancel{15}^{1}}{5 \cdot \cancel{15}_{1}} = \frac{3 \cdot 1}{5 \cdot 1} = \frac{3}{5}$$

The numerator and denominator of $\frac{3}{5}$ have no common factors other than 1, so $\frac{3}{5}$ is in simplest form.

Work Practice 7

Objective B Determining Whether Two Fractions Are Equivalent

Recall that two fractions are equivalent if they represent the same part of a whole. One way to determine whether two fractions are equivalent is to see whether they simplify to the same fraction.

PRACTICE 8

Determine whether $\frac{7}{9}$ and $\frac{21}{27}$ are equivalent.

Example 8 Determine whether $\frac{16}{40}$ and $\frac{10}{25}$ are equivalent.

Solution: Simplify each fraction.

$$\frac{16}{40} = \frac{\cancel{8}^{1} \cdot 2}{\cancel{8}_{1} \cdot 5} = \frac{1 \cdot 2}{1 \cdot 5} = \frac{2}{5}$$

$$\frac{10}{25} = \frac{2 \cdot \cancel{5}^{1}}{5 \cdot \cancel{5}_{1}} = \frac{2 \cdot 1}{5 \cdot 1} = \frac{2}{5}$$

Since these fractions are the same, $\frac{16}{40} = \frac{10}{25}$.

Work Practice 8

There is a shortcut method you may use to check or test whether two fractions are equivalent. In the example above, we learned that the fractions are equivalent, or

$$\frac{16}{40} = \frac{10}{25}$$

In this example above, we call $25 \cdot 16$ and $40 \cdot 10$ **cross products** because they are the products one obtains by multiplying across.

Cross Products

$$25 \cdot 16 \qquad \frac{16}{40} = \frac{10}{25} \qquad 40 \cdot 10$$

Notice that these cross products are equal

$$25 \cdot 16 = 400, \quad 40 \cdot 10 = 400$$

Answers

7. $\frac{7}{8}$ 8. equivalent

In general, this is true for equivalent fractions.

Equivalent Fractions

$8 \cdot 6$ $\quad$ $24 \cdot 2$

$$\frac{6}{24} \stackrel{?}{=} \frac{2}{8}$$

Since the cross products ($8 \cdot 6 = 48$ and $24 \cdot 2 = 48$) are equal, the fractions are equivalent.

Note: If the cross products are not equal, the fractions are not equivalent.

Example 9 Determine whether $\frac{8}{11}$ and $\frac{19}{26}$ are equivalent.

Solution: Let's check cross products.

$26 \cdot 8 = 208$ $\quad$ $\frac{8}{11} \stackrel{?}{=} \frac{19}{26}$ $\quad$ $11 \cdot 19 = 209$

Since $208 \neq 209$, then $\frac{8}{11} \neq \frac{19}{26}$.

"Not equal to" symbol.

Work Practice 9

PRACTICE 9

Determine whether $\frac{4}{13}$ and $\frac{5}{18}$ are equivalent.

Objective C Solving Problems by Writing Fractions in Simplest Form

Many real-life problems can be solved by writing fractions. To make the answers clearer, these fractions should be written in simplest form.

Example 10 Calculating Fraction of Parks in Wyoming State

There are currently 58 national parks in the United States. Two of these parks are located in the state of Wyoming. What fraction of the United States' national parks can be found in Wyoming? Write the fraction in simplest form. (*Source:* National Park Service)

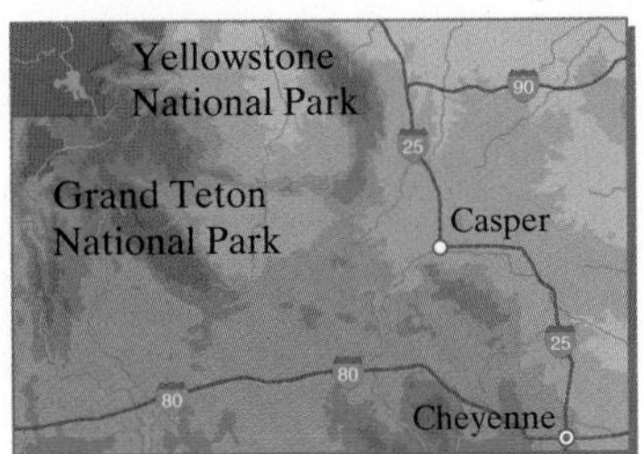

Solution: First we determine the fraction of parks found in Wyoming state.

$\frac{2}{58}$ ← national parks in Wyoming / ← total national parks

PRACTICE 10

There are six national parks (including historic) in Washington state. See Example 10 and determine what fraction of the United States' national parks are located in Washington. Write the fraction in simplest form.

Continued on next page

Answers

9. not equivalent **10.** $\frac{3}{29}$

Next we simplify the fraction.

$$\frac{2}{58} = \frac{\overset{1}{\cancel{2}}}{\underset{1}{\cancel{2}} \cdot 29} = \frac{1}{1 \cdot 29} = \frac{1}{29}$$

Thus, $\frac{1}{29}$ of the United States' national parks are in the state of Wyoming.

Work Practice 10

Calculator Explorations Simplifying Fractions

Scientific Calculator

Many calculators have a fraction key, such as [a b/c], that allows you to simplify a fraction on the calculator. For example, to simplify $\frac{324}{612}$, enter

[3] [2] [4] [a b/c] [6] [1] [2] [=]

The display will read

[9⌋17]

which represents $\frac{9}{17}$, the original fraction simplified.

Helpful Hint

The Calculator Explorations boxes in this chapter provide only an introduction to fraction keys on calculators. Any time you use a calculator, there are both advantages and limitations to its use. Never rely solely on your calculator. It is very important that you understand how to perform all operations on fractions by hand in order to progress through later topics. For further information, talk to your instructor.

Use your calculator to simplify each fraction.

1. $\frac{128}{224}$ **2.** $\frac{231}{396}$ **3.** $\frac{340}{459}$ **4.** $\frac{999}{1350}$

5. $\frac{810}{432}$ **6.** $\frac{315}{225}$ **7.** $\frac{243}{54}$ **8.** $\frac{689}{455}$

Vocabulary and Readiness Check

Use the choices below to fill in each blank.

0	cross products	equivalent
1	simplest form	n

1. In $\frac{11}{48}$, since 11 and 48 have no common factors other than 1, $\frac{11}{48}$ is in ________________.
2. Fractions that represent the same portion of a whole are called ________________ fractions.
3. In the statement $\frac{5}{12} = \frac{15}{36}$, $5 \cdot 36$ and $12 \cdot 15$ are called ________________.
4. The fraction $\frac{7}{7}$ simplifies to ________________.
5. The fraction $\frac{0}{7}$ simplifies to ________________.
6. The fraction $\frac{n}{1}$ simplifies to ________________.

2.3 Exercise Set

FOR EXTRA HELP

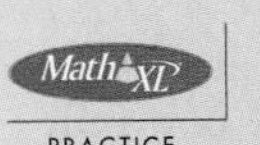

Objective A *Write each fraction in simplest form. See Examples 1 through 7.*

1. $\frac{3}{12}$ **2.** $\frac{5}{30}$ **3.** $\frac{4}{42}$ **4.** $\frac{9}{48}$

5. $\frac{14}{16}$ **6.** $\frac{22}{34}$ **7.** $\frac{20}{30}$ **8.** $\frac{70}{80}$

9. $\frac{35}{50}$ **10.** $\frac{25}{55}$ **11.** $\frac{63}{81}$ **12.** $\frac{21}{49}$

13. $\frac{24}{40}$ **14.** $\frac{36}{54}$ **15.** $\frac{27}{64}$ **16.** $\frac{32}{63}$

17. $\frac{25}{40}$ **18.** $\frac{36}{42}$ **19.** $\frac{40}{64}$ **20.** $\frac{28}{60}$

21. $\frac{56}{68}$ **22.** $\frac{39}{42}$ **23.** $\frac{36}{24}$ **24.** $\frac{60}{36}$

25. $\frac{90}{120}$ **26.** $\frac{60}{150}$ **27.** $\frac{70}{196}$ **28.** $\frac{98}{126}$

29. $\frac{66}{308}$ **30.** $\frac{65}{234}$ **31.** $\frac{55}{85}$ **32.** $\frac{78}{90}$

33. $\frac{75}{350}$ **34.** $\frac{72}{420}$ **35.** $\frac{189}{216}$ **36.** $\frac{144}{162}$

37. $\frac{288}{480}$ **38.** $\frac{135}{585}$ **39.** $\frac{224}{16}$ **40.** $\frac{270}{15}$

Objective B *Determine whether each pair of fractions is equivalent. See Examples 8 and 9.*

41. $\frac{3}{6}$ and $\frac{4}{8}$

42. $\frac{3}{9}$ and $\frac{2}{6}$

43. $\frac{7}{11}$ and $\frac{5}{8}$

44. $\frac{2}{5}$ and $\frac{4}{11}$

45. $\frac{10}{15}$ and $\frac{6}{9}$

46. $\frac{4}{10}$ and $\frac{6}{15}$

47. $\frac{3}{9}$ and $\frac{6}{18}$

48. $\frac{2}{8}$ and $\frac{7}{28}$

49. $\frac{10}{13}$ and $\frac{12}{15}$

50. $\frac{16}{20}$ and $\frac{9}{12}$

51. $\frac{8}{18}$ and $\frac{12}{24}$

52. $\frac{6}{21}$ and $\frac{14}{35}$

Objective C *Solve. Write each fraction in simplest form. See Example 10.*

53. A work shift for an employee at McDonald's consists of 8 hours. What fraction of the employee's work shift is represented by 2 hours?

54. Two thousand baseball caps were sold one year at the U.S. Open Golf Tournament. What fractional part of this total does 200 caps represent?

55. There are 5280 feet in a mile. What fraction of a mile is represented by 2640 feet?

56. There are 100 centimeters in 1 meter. What fraction of a meter is 20 centimeters?

57. Sixteen states in the United States have Ritz-Carlton hotels. (*Source:* Ritz-Carlton Hotel Company, LLC)

a. What fraction of states can claim at least one Ritz-Carlton hotel?

b. How many states do not have a Ritz-Carlton hotel?

c. Write the fraction of states without a Ritz-Carlton hotel.

58. There are 78 national monuments in the United States. Ten of these monuments are located in New Mexico. (*Source:* National Park Service)

a. What fraction of the national monuments in the United States can be found in New Mexico?

b. How many of the national monuments in the United States are found outside New Mexico?

c. Write the fraction of national monuments found in states other than New Mexico.

59. The outer wall of the Pentagon is 24 inches wide. Ten inches is concrete, 8 inches is brick, and 6 inches is limestone. What fraction of the wall is concrete? (*Source: USA Today*)

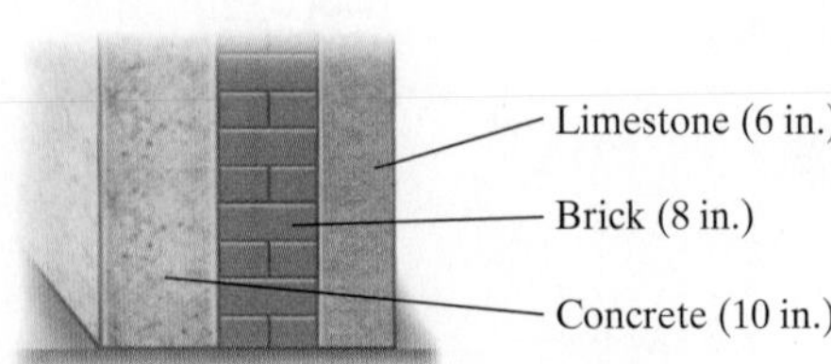

60. There are 35 students in a biology class. If 10 students made an A on the first test, what fraction of the students made an A?

61. Kroger Company operates stores under multiple banners in 32 states in the United States. (*Source:* Kroger Company)

a. How many states do not have a Kroger Company store?

b. What fraction of states do not have a Kroger company store?

62. Katy Biagini just bought a brand-new 2009 Toyota Camry hybrid for \$28,000. Her old car was traded in for \$12,000.

a. How much of her purchase price was not covered by her trade-in?

b. What fraction of the purchase price was not covered by the trade-in?

63. As of this writing, a total of 320 individuals from the United States are/have been astronauts. Of these, 22 were born in Texas. What fraction of U.S. astronauts were born in Texas? (*Source:* NASA)

64. Worldwide, Hallmark employs nearly 16,000 full-time employees. About 4200 employees work at the Hallmark headquarters in Kansas City, Missouri. What fraction of Hallmark employees work in Kansas City? (*Source:* Hallmark Cards, Inc.)

Review

Multiply. See Section 1.6.

65. 91×4

66. 73×8

67. 387×6

68. 562×9

69. 72×35

70. 238×26

Concept Extensions

 **71.** In your own words, define equivalent fractions.

 **72.** Given a fraction, say $\frac{3}{8}$, how many fractions are there that are equivalent to it? Explain your answer.

Write each fraction in simplest form.

73. $\frac{3975}{6625}$

74. $\frac{9506}{12{,}222}$

There are generally considered to be eight basic blood types. The table shows the number of people with the various blood types in a typical group of 100 blood donors. Use the table to answer Exercises 75 through 78. Write each answer in simplest form.

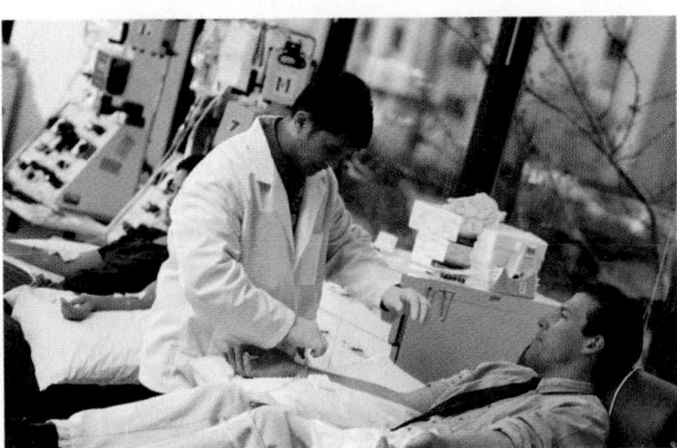

Distribution of Blood Types in Blood Donors

Blood Type	Number of People
O Rh-positive	37
O Rh-negative	7
A Rh-positive	36
A Rh-negative	6
B Rh-positive	9
B Rh-negative	1
AB Rh-positive	3
AB Rh-negative	1

(*Source:* American Red Cross Biomedical Services)

75. What fraction of blood donors have blood type A Rh-positive?

76. What fraction of blood donors have an O blood type?

77. What fraction of blood donors have an AB blood type?

78. What fraction of blood donors have a B blood type?

The following graph is called a circle graph or pie chart. Each sector (shaped like a piece of pie) shows the fraction of entering college freshmen who expect to major in each discipline shown. The whole circle represents the entire class of college freshmen. Use this graph to answer Exercises 79 through 82.

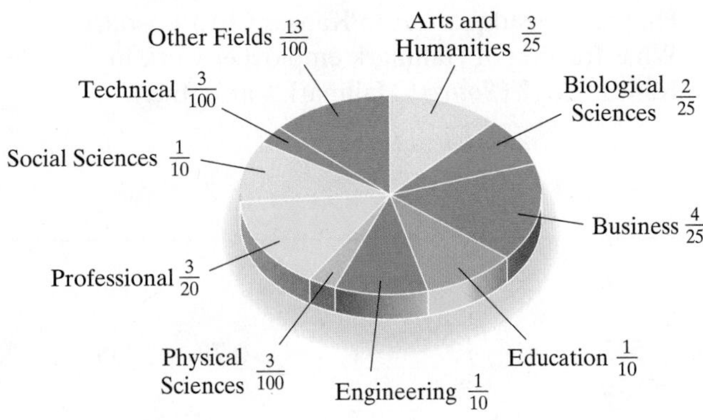

Source: The Higher Education Research Institute

79. What fraction of entering college freshmen plan to major in education?

80. What fraction of entering college freshmen plan to major in biological sciences?

81. Why is the Social Sciences sector the same size as the Engineering sector?

82. Why is the Physical Sciences sector smaller than the Business sector?

Use this circle graph to answer Exercises 83 through 86.

Areas Maintained by the National Park Service

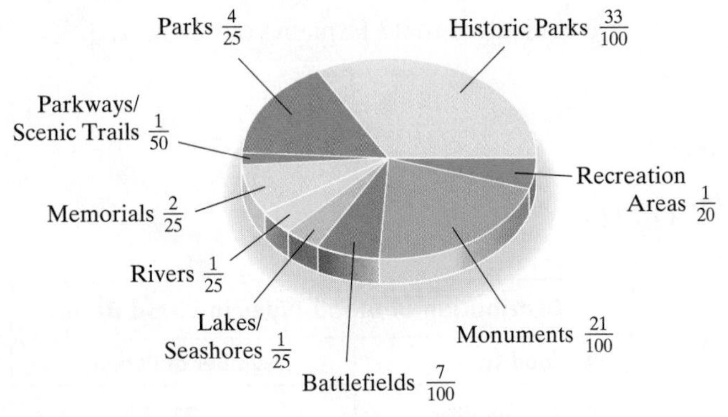

Source: National Park Service

83. What fraction of National Park Service areas are National Memorials?

84. What fraction of National Park Service areas are National Parks?

85. Why is the National Battlefields sector smaller than the National Monuments sector?

86. Why is the National Lakes/National Seashores sector the same size as the National Rivers sector?

Use the following numbers for Exercises 87 through 90.

8691 786 1235 2235 85 105 22 222 900 1470

87. List the numbers divisible by both 2 and 3.

88. List the numbers that are divisible by both 3 and 5.

89. The answers to Exercise 87 are also divisible by what number? Tell why.

90. The answers to Exercise 88 are also divisible by what number? Tell why.

Integrated Review Sections 2.1–2.3

Summary on Fractions, Mixed Numbers, and Factors

Use a fraction to represent the shaded area of each figure. If the fraction is improper, also write the fraction as a mixed number.

1. 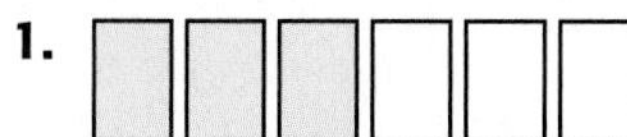

2. 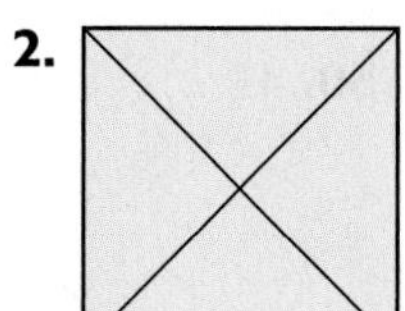 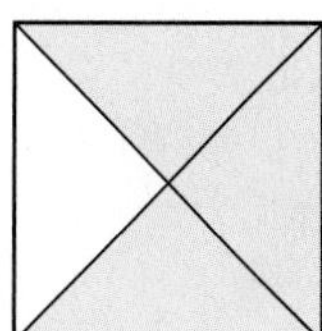

Solve.

3. In a survey, 73 people out of 85 get fewer than 8 hours of sleep each night. What fraction of people in the survey get fewer than 8 hours of sleep?

4. Sketch a diagram to represent $\frac{9}{13}$.

Simplify.

5. $\frac{11}{11}$ **6.** $\frac{17}{1}$ **7.** $\frac{0}{3}$ **8.** $\frac{7}{0}$

Write each mixed number as an improper fraction.

9. $3\frac{1}{8}$ **10.** $5\frac{3}{5}$ **11.** $9\frac{6}{7}$ **12.** $20\frac{1}{7}$

Write each improper fraction as a mixed number or a whole number.

13. $\frac{20}{7}$ **14.** $\frac{55}{11}$ **15.** $\frac{39}{8}$ **16.** $\frac{98}{11}$

List the factors of each number.

17. 35 **18.** 40

Determine whether each number is prime or composite.

19. 72 **20.** 13

Answers

1. _____
2. _____
3. _____
4. _____
5. _____
6. _____
7. _____
8. _____
9. _____
10. _____
11. _____
12. _____
13. _____
14. _____
15. _____
16. _____
17. _____
18. _____
19. _____
20. _____

21. ____
22. ____
23. ____
24. ____
25. ____
26. ____
27. ____
28. ____
29. ____
30. ____
31. ____
32. ____
33. ____
34. ____
35. ____
36. ____
37. ____
38. ____
39. ____
40. ____
41. ____
42. ____
43. a. b. c. ____
44. a. b. c. ____

Write the prime factorization of each composite number. Write prime if the number is prime. Write any repeated factors using exponents.

21. 65 **22.** 70 **23.** 96 **24.** 132

25. 252 **26.** 31 **27.** 315 **28.** 441

29. 286 **30.** 41

Write each fraction in simplest form.

31. $\frac{2}{14}$ **32.** $\frac{24}{20}$ **33.** $\frac{18}{38}$ **34.** $\frac{42}{110}$

35. $\frac{56}{60}$ **36.** $\frac{72}{80}$ **37.** $\frac{54}{135}$ **38.** $\frac{90}{240}$

39. $\frac{165}{210}$ **40.** $\frac{245}{385}$

Determine whether each pair of fractions is equivalent.

41. $\frac{7}{8}$ and $\frac{9}{10}$ **42.** $\frac{10}{12}$ and $\frac{15}{18}$

Solve. Write fraction answers in simplest form.

43. Of the 50 states, 2 states are not adjacent to any other states.
a. What fraction of the states are not adjacent to other states?
b. How many states are adjacent to other states?
c. What fraction of the states are adjacent to other states?

44. In a recent year, 475 films were released and rated. Of these, 165 were rated PG-13. (*Source:* Nash Information, LLC.)
a. What fraction were rated PG-13?
b. How many films were rated other than PG-13?
c. What fraction of films were rated other than PG-13?

2.4 MULTIPLYING FRACTIONS AND MIXED NUMBERS

Objective A Multiplying Fractions

Let's use a diagram to discover how fractions are multiplied. For example, to multiply $\frac{1}{2}$ and $\frac{3}{4}$, we find $\frac{1}{2}$ of $\frac{3}{4}$. To do this, we begin with a diagram showing $\frac{3}{4}$ of a rectangle's area shaded.

$\frac{3}{4}$ of the rectangle's area is shaded.

To find $\frac{1}{2}$ of $\frac{3}{4}$, we heavily shade $\frac{1}{2}$ of the part that is already shaded.

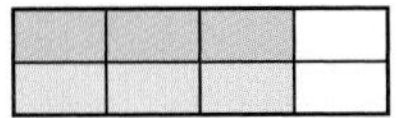

By counting smaller rectangles, we see that $\frac{3}{8}$ of the larger rectangle is now heavily shaded, so that

$\frac{1}{2}$ of $\frac{3}{4}$ is $\frac{3}{8}$, or $\frac{1}{2} \cdot \frac{3}{4} = \frac{3}{8}$ Notice that $\frac{1}{2} \cdot \frac{3}{4} = \frac{1 \cdot 3}{2 \cdot 4} = \frac{3}{8}$.

Multiplying Fractions

To multiply two fractions, multiply the numerators and multiply the denominators.

If a, b, c, and d represent positive whole numbers, we have

$$\frac{a}{b} \cdot \frac{c}{d} = \frac{a \cdot c}{b \cdot d}$$

Examples Multiply.

1. $\frac{2}{3} \cdot \frac{5}{11} = \frac{2 \cdot 5}{3 \cdot 11} = \frac{10}{33}$ Multiply numerators. Multiply denominators.

This fraction is in simplest form since 10 and 33 have no common factors other than 1.

2. $\frac{1}{4} \cdot \frac{1}{2} = \frac{1 \cdot 1}{4 \cdot 2} = \frac{1}{8}$ This fraction is in simplest form.

Work Practice 1–2

Objectives

A Multiply Fractions.

B Multiply Fractions and Mixed Numbers or Whole Numbers.

C Solve Problems by Multiplying Fractions.

PRACTICE 1–2

Multiply.

1. $\frac{3}{8} \cdot \frac{5}{7}$ **2.** $\frac{1}{3} \cdot \frac{1}{6}$

Answers

1. $\frac{15}{56}$ **2.** $\frac{1}{18}$

PRACTICE 3

Multiply and simplify: $\frac{6}{55} \cdot \frac{5}{8}$

Example 3 Multiply and simplify: $\frac{6}{7} \cdot \frac{14}{27}$

Solution:

$$\frac{6}{7} \cdot \frac{14}{27} = \frac{6 \cdot 14}{7 \cdot 27}$$

We can simplify by finding the prime factorizations and using our shortcut procedure of dividing out common factors in the numerator and denominator.

$$\frac{6 \cdot 14}{7 \cdot 27} = \frac{2 \cdot \overset{1}{\cancel{3}} \cdot 2 \cdot \overset{1}{\cancel{7}}}{\underset{1}{\cancel{7}} \cdot \underset{1}{\cancel{3}} \cdot 3 \cdot 3} = \frac{2 \cdot 2}{3 \cdot 3} = \frac{4}{9}$$

Work Practice 3

Helpful Hint

Remember that the shortcut procedure above is the same as removing factors of 1 in the product.

$$\frac{6 \cdot 14}{7 \cdot 27} = \frac{2 \cdot 3 \cdot 2 \cdot 7}{7 \cdot 3 \cdot 3 \cdot 3} = \frac{7}{7} \cdot \frac{3}{3} \cdot \frac{2 \cdot 2}{3 \cdot 3} = 1 \cdot 1 \cdot \frac{4}{9} = \frac{4}{9}$$

Helpful Hint

In simplifying a product, don't forget that it may be possible to identify common factors without actually writing the prime factorization. For example,

$$\frac{10}{11} \cdot \frac{1}{20} = \frac{10 \cdot 1}{11 \cdot 20} = \frac{\overset{1}{\cancel{10}} \cdot 1}{11 \cdot \underset{1}{\cancel{10}} \cdot 2} = \frac{1}{11 \cdot 2} = \frac{1}{22}$$

PRACTICE 4

Multiply and simplify: $\frac{4}{15} \cdot \frac{3}{8}$

Example 4 Multiply and simplify: $\frac{23}{32} \cdot \frac{4}{7}$

Solution: Notice that 4 and 32 have a common factor of 4.

$$\frac{23}{32} \cdot \frac{4}{7} = \frac{23 \cdot 4}{32 \cdot 7} = \frac{23 \cdot \overset{1}{\cancel{4}}}{\underset{1}{\cancel{4}} \cdot 8 \cdot 7} = \frac{23}{8 \cdot 7} = \frac{23}{56}$$

Work Practice 4

After multiplying two fractions, always check to see whether the product can be simplified.

PRACTICE 5–7

Multiply.

5. $\frac{2}{5} \cdot \frac{20}{7}$

6. $\frac{4}{11} \cdot \frac{33}{16}$

7. $\frac{1}{6} \cdot \frac{3}{10} \cdot \frac{25}{16}$

Examples Multiply.

5. $\frac{3}{4} \cdot \frac{8}{5} = \frac{3 \cdot 8}{4 \cdot 5} = \frac{3 \cdot \overset{1}{\cancel{4}} \cdot 2}{\underset{1}{\cancel{4}} \cdot 5} = \frac{6}{5}$

6. $\frac{6}{13} \cdot \frac{26}{30} = \frac{6 \cdot 26}{13 \cdot 30} = \frac{\overset{1}{\cancel{6}} \cdot \overset{1}{\cancel{13}} \cdot 2}{\underset{1}{\cancel{13}} \cdot \underset{1}{\cancel{6}} \cdot 5} = \frac{2}{5}$

7. $\frac{1}{3} \cdot \frac{2}{5} \cdot \frac{9}{16} = \frac{1 \cdot 2 \cdot 9}{3 \cdot 5 \cdot 16} = \frac{1 \cdot \overset{1}{\cancel{2}} \cdot \overset{1}{\cancel{3}} \cdot 3}{\underset{1}{\cancel{3}} \cdot 5 \cdot \underset{1}{\cancel{2}} \cdot 8} = \frac{3}{40}$

Work Practice 5–7

Answers

3. $\frac{3}{44}$ 4. $\frac{1}{10}$ 5. $\frac{8}{7}$ 6. $\frac{3}{4}$ 7. $\frac{5}{64}$

Objective B Multiplying Fractions and Mixed Numbers or Whole Numbers

When multiplying a fraction and a mixed or a whole number, remember that mixed and whole numbers can be written as fractions.

Multiplying Fractions and Mixed Numbers or Whole Numbers

To multiply with mixed numbers or whole numbers, first write any mixed or whole numbers as fractions and then multiply as usual.

Example 8 Multiply: $3\frac{1}{3} \cdot \frac{7}{8}$

Solution: The mixed number $3\frac{1}{3}$ can be written as the fraction $\frac{10}{3}$. Then,

$$3\frac{1}{3} \cdot \frac{7}{8} = \frac{10}{3} \cdot \frac{7}{8} = \frac{\overset{1}{\cancel{2}} \cdot 5 \cdot 7}{3 \cdot \underset{1}{\cancel{2}} \cdot 4} = \frac{35}{12} \text{ or } 2\frac{11}{12}$$

Work Practice 8

PRACTICE 8

Multiply and simplify: $2\frac{1}{2} \cdot \frac{8}{15}$

Don't forget that a whole number can be written as a fraction by writing the whole number over 1. For example,

$$20 = \frac{20}{1} \quad \text{and} \quad 7 = \frac{7}{1}$$

Example 9 Multiply.

$$\frac{3}{4} \cdot 20 = \frac{3}{4} \cdot \frac{20}{1} = \frac{3 \cdot 20}{4 \cdot 1} = \frac{3 \cdot \overset{1}{\cancel{4}} \cdot 5}{\underset{1}{\cancel{4}} \cdot 1} = \frac{15}{1} \text{ or } 15$$

Work Practice 9

PRACTICE 9

Multiply.

$\frac{2}{3} \cdot 18$

When both numbers to be multiplied are mixed or whole numbers, it is a good idea to estimate the product to see if your answer is reasonable. To do this, we first practice rounding mixed numbers to the nearest whole. If the fraction part of the mixed number is $\frac{1}{2}$ or greater, we round the whole number part up. If the fraction part of the mixed number is less than $\frac{1}{2}$, then we do not round the whole number part up. Study the table below for examples.

Mixed Number	Rounding
$5\frac{1}{4}$ — $\frac{1}{4}$ is less than $\frac{1}{2}$	Thus, $5\frac{1}{4}$ rounds to 5.
$3\frac{9}{16}$ ← 9 is greater than 8 → Half of 16 is 8.	Thus, $3\frac{7}{16}$ rounds to 4.
$1\frac{3}{7}$ ← 3 is less than $3\frac{1}{2}$. → Half of 7 is $3\frac{1}{2}$.	Thus, $1\frac{3}{7}$ rounds to 1.

Answers

8. $\frac{4}{3}$ or $1\frac{1}{3}$ **9.** 12

PRACTICE 10–11

Multiply.

10. $3\frac{1}{5} \cdot 2\frac{3}{4}$ **11.** $5 \cdot 3\frac{11}{15}$

Examples Multiply. Check by estimating.

10. $1\frac{2}{3} \cdot 2\frac{1}{4} = \frac{5}{3} \cdot \frac{9}{4} = \frac{5 \cdot 9}{3 \cdot 4} = \frac{5 \cdot \overset{1}{\cancel{3}} \cdot 3}{\underset{1}{\cancel{3}} \cdot 4} = \frac{15}{4}$ or $3\frac{3}{4}$ Exact

Let's check by estimating.

$1\frac{2}{3}$ rounds to 2, $2\frac{1}{4}$ rounds to 2, and $2 \cdot 2 = 4$ Estimate

The estimate is close to the exact value, so our answer is reasonable.

11. $7 \cdot 2\frac{11}{14} = \frac{7}{1} \cdot \frac{39}{14} = \frac{7 \cdot 39}{1 \cdot 14} = \frac{\overset{1}{\cancel{7}} \cdot 39}{1 \cdot 2 \cdot \underset{1}{\cancel{7}}} = \frac{39}{2}$ or $19\frac{1}{2}$ Exact

To estimate,

$2\frac{11}{14}$ rounds to 3 and $7 \cdot 3 = 21$. Estimate

The estimate is close to the exact value, so our answer is reasonable

Work Practice 10–11

Recall from Section 1.6 that 0 multiplied by any number is 0. This is true of fractions and mixed numbers also.

PRACTICE 12–13

Multiply.

12. $\frac{9}{11} \cdot 0$ **13.** $0 \cdot 4\frac{1}{8}$

Examples Multiply.

12. $0 \cdot \frac{3}{5} = 0$

13. $2\frac{3}{8} \cdot 0 = 0$

Work Practice 12–13

✓Concept Check

Find the error.

$2\frac{1}{4} \cdot \frac{1}{2} = 2\frac{1 \cdot 1}{4 \cdot 2} = 2\frac{1}{8}$

Objective C Solving Problems by Multiplying Fractions

To solve real-life problems that involve multiplying fractions, we use our four problem-solving steps from Chapter 1. In Example 14, a key word that implies multiplication is used. That key word is "**of**."

Helpful Hint

"of" usually translates to multiplication.

Answers

10. $\frac{44}{5}$ or $8\frac{4}{5}$ **11.** $\frac{56}{3}$ or $18\frac{2}{3}$
12. 0 **13.** 0

✓ Concept Check Answer

forgot to change mixed number to fraction

Example 14 Finding the Number of Roller Coasters in an Amusement Park

Cedar Point is an amusement park located in Sandusky, Ohio. Its collection of 68 rides is the largest in the world. Of the rides, $\frac{4}{17}$ are roller coasters. How many roller coasters are in Cedar Point's collection of rides? (*Source:* Wikipedia)

PRACTICE 14

Hershey Park is an amusement park in Hershey, Pennsylvania. Of its 60 rides, $\frac{1}{6}$ of them are roller coasters. How many roller coasters are in Hershey Park?

Solution:

1. UNDERSTAND the problem. To do so, read and reread the problem. We are told that $\frac{4}{17}$ of Cedar Point's rides are roller coasters. The word "of" here means multiplication.

2. TRANSLATE.

In words:	number of roller coasters	is	$\frac{4}{17}$	of	total rides at Cedar Point
	↓	↓	↓	↓	↓
Translate:	number of roller coasters	=	$\frac{4}{17}$	·	68

3. SOLVE: Before we solve, let's estimate a reasonable answer. The fraction $\frac{4}{17}$ is less than $\frac{1}{2}$ (draw a diagram, if needed), and $\frac{1}{2}$ of 68 rides is 34 rides, so the number of roller coasters should be less than 34.

$$\frac{4}{17} \cdot 68 = \frac{4}{17} \cdot \frac{68}{1} = \frac{4 \cdot 68}{17 \cdot 1} = \frac{4 \cdot \overset{1}{\cancel{17}} \cdot 4}{\underset{1}{\cancel{17}} \cdot 1} = \frac{16}{1} \text{ or } 16$$

4. INTERPRET. *Check* your work. From our estimate, our answer is reasonable. *State* your conclusion: The number of roller coasters at Cedar Point is 16.

Work Practice 14

Helpful Hint

To help visualize a fractional part of a whole number, look at the diagram below.

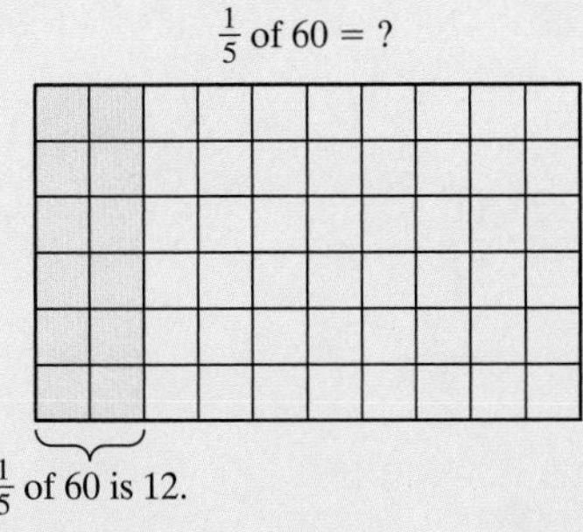

$\frac{1}{5}$ of 60 = ?
$\frac{1}{5}$ of 60 is 12.

Answer

14. 10 roller coasters

Vocabulary and Readiness Check

Use the choices below to fill in each blank. Not all choices will be used.

multiplication $\quad \dfrac{a \cdot d}{b \cdot c} \quad \dfrac{a \cdot c}{b \cdot d} \quad \dfrac{2 \cdot 2 \cdot 2}{7} \quad \dfrac{2}{7} \cdot \dfrac{2}{7} \cdot \dfrac{2}{7}$

division $\quad 0$

1. To multiply two fractions, we write $\dfrac{a}{b} \cdot \dfrac{c}{d} =$ ______________.

2. Using the definition of an exponent, the expression $\dfrac{2^3}{7} =$ ______________ while $\left(\dfrac{2}{7}\right)^3 =$ ______________.

3. The word "of" indicates ______________.

4. $\dfrac{1}{5} \cdot 0 =$ ______________.

2.4 Exercise Set

FOR EXTRA HELP

PRACTICE

WATCH

DOWNLOAD

READ

REVIEW

Objective A *Multiply. Write each answer in simplest form. See Examples 1 through 7 and 12.*

1. $\dfrac{1}{3} \cdot \dfrac{2}{5}$ **2.** $\dfrac{2}{3} \cdot \dfrac{4}{7}$ **3.** $\dfrac{6}{5} \cdot \dfrac{1}{7}$ **4.** $\dfrac{7}{3} \cdot \dfrac{1}{4}$ **5.** $\dfrac{3}{10} \cdot \dfrac{3}{8}$

6. $\dfrac{2}{5} \cdot \dfrac{7}{11}$ **7.** $\dfrac{2}{7} \cdot \dfrac{5}{8}$ **8.** $\dfrac{7}{8} \cdot \dfrac{2}{3}$ **9.** $\dfrac{16}{5} \cdot \dfrac{3}{4}$ **10.** $\dfrac{8}{3} \cdot \dfrac{5}{12}$

11. $\dfrac{5}{28} \cdot \dfrac{2}{25}$ **12.** $\dfrac{4}{35} \cdot \dfrac{5}{24}$ **13.** $0 \cdot \dfrac{8}{9}$ **14.** $\dfrac{11}{12} \cdot 0$ **15.** $\dfrac{1}{10} \cdot \dfrac{1}{11}$

16. $\dfrac{1}{9} \cdot \dfrac{1}{13}$ **17.** $\dfrac{18}{20} \cdot \dfrac{36}{99}$ **18.** $\dfrac{5}{32} \cdot \dfrac{64}{100}$ **19.** $\dfrac{3}{8} \cdot \dfrac{9}{10}$ **20.** $\dfrac{4}{5} \cdot \dfrac{8}{25}$

21. $\dfrac{11}{20} \cdot \dfrac{1}{7} \cdot \dfrac{5}{22}$ **22.** $\dfrac{27}{32} \cdot \dfrac{10}{13} \cdot \dfrac{16}{30}$ **23.** $\dfrac{1}{3} \cdot \dfrac{2}{7} \cdot \dfrac{1}{5}$ **24.** $\dfrac{3}{5} \cdot \dfrac{1}{2} \cdot \dfrac{3}{7}$ **25.** $\dfrac{9}{20} \cdot 0 \cdot \dfrac{4}{19}$

26. $\dfrac{8}{11} \cdot \dfrac{4}{7} \cdot 0$ **27.** $\dfrac{3}{14} \cdot \dfrac{6}{25} \cdot \dfrac{5}{27} \cdot \dfrac{7}{6}$ **28.** $\dfrac{7}{8} \cdot \dfrac{9}{20} \cdot \dfrac{12}{22} \cdot \dfrac{11}{14}$

Objective B *Round each mixed number to the nearest whole number. See the table at the bottom of page 143.*

29. $7\frac{7}{8}$ **30.** $11\frac{3}{4}$ **31.** $6\frac{1}{5}$ **32.** $4\frac{1}{9}$ **33.** $19\frac{11}{20}$ **34.** $18\frac{12}{22}$

Multiply. Write each answer in simplest form. For those exercises marked, find both an exact product and an estimated product. See Examples 8 through 11 and 13.

35. $12 \cdot \frac{1}{4}$ **36.** $\frac{2}{3} \cdot 6$ **37.** $\frac{5}{8} \cdot 4$ **38.** $10 \cdot \frac{7}{8}$ **39.** $1\frac{1}{4} \cdot \frac{4}{25}$

40. $\frac{3}{22} \cdot 3\frac{2}{3}$ **41.** $\frac{2}{5} \cdot 4\frac{1}{6}$ **42.** $2\frac{1}{9} \cdot \frac{6}{7}$ **43.** $\frac{2}{3} \cdot 1$ **44.** $1 \cdot \frac{5}{9}$

45. $2\frac{1}{5} \cdot 3\frac{1}{2}$
Exact:
Estimate:

46. $2\frac{1}{4} \cdot 7\frac{1}{8}$
Exact:
Estimate:

47. $3\frac{4}{5} \cdot 6\frac{2}{7}$
Exact:
Estimate:

48. $5\frac{5}{6} \cdot 7\frac{3}{5}$
Exact:
Estimate:

49. $5 \cdot 2\frac{1}{2}$

50. $6 \cdot 3\frac{1}{3}$ **51.** $1\frac{1}{5} \cdot 12\frac{1}{2}$ **52.** $1\frac{1}{6} \cdot 7\frac{1}{5}$ **53.** $\frac{3}{4} \cdot 16 \cdot \frac{1}{2}$ **54.** $\frac{7}{8} \cdot 24 \cdot \frac{1}{3}$

55. $\frac{3}{10} \cdot 15 \cdot 2\frac{1}{2}$ **56.** $\frac{11}{20} \cdot 12 \cdot 3\frac{1}{3}$ **57.** $3\frac{1}{2} \cdot 1\frac{3}{4} \cdot 2\frac{2}{3}$ **58.** $4\frac{1}{2} \cdot 2\frac{1}{9} \cdot 1\frac{1}{5}$

Objectives A B Mixed Practice *Multiply and simplify. See Examples 1 through 13.*

59. $\frac{1}{4} \cdot \frac{2}{15}$ **60.** $\frac{3}{8} \cdot \frac{5}{12}$ **61.** $\frac{19}{37} \cdot 0$ **62.** $0 \cdot \frac{3}{31}$ **63.** $2\frac{4}{5} \cdot 1\frac{1}{7}$

64. $3\frac{1}{5} \cdot 2\frac{11}{32}$ **65.** $\frac{3}{2} \cdot \frac{7}{3}$ **66.** $\frac{15}{2} \cdot \frac{3}{5}$ **67.** $\frac{6}{15} \cdot \frac{5}{16}$ **68.** $\frac{9}{20} \cdot \frac{10}{90}$

69. $\frac{7}{72} \cdot \frac{9}{49}$ **70.** $\frac{3}{80} \cdot \frac{2}{27}$ **71.** $20 \cdot \frac{11}{12}$ **72.** $30 \cdot \frac{8}{9}$ **73.** $9\frac{5}{7} \cdot 8\frac{1}{5} \cdot 0$

74. $4\frac{11}{13} \cdot 0 \cdot 12\frac{1}{13}$ **75.** $12\frac{4}{5} \cdot 6\frac{7}{8} \cdot \frac{26}{77}$ **76.** $14\frac{2}{5} \cdot 8\frac{1}{3} \cdot \frac{11}{16}$

Objective C *Solve. Write each answer in simplest form. For Exercises 77 through 80, recall that "of" translates to multiplication. See Example 14.*

77. Find $\frac{1}{4}$ of 200.

78. Find $\frac{1}{5}$ of 200.

79. Find $\frac{5}{6}$ of 24.

80. Find $\frac{5}{8}$ of 24.

Solve. For Exercises 81 and 82, the solutions have been started for you. See Example 14.

81. In the United States, $\frac{4}{25}$ of college freshmen major in business. A community college in Pennsylvania has a freshman enrollment of approximately 800 students. How many of these freshmen might we project are majoring in business?

Start the solution:

1. UNDERSTAND the problem. Reread it as many times as needed.
2. TRANSLATE into an equation. (Fill in the blank below.)

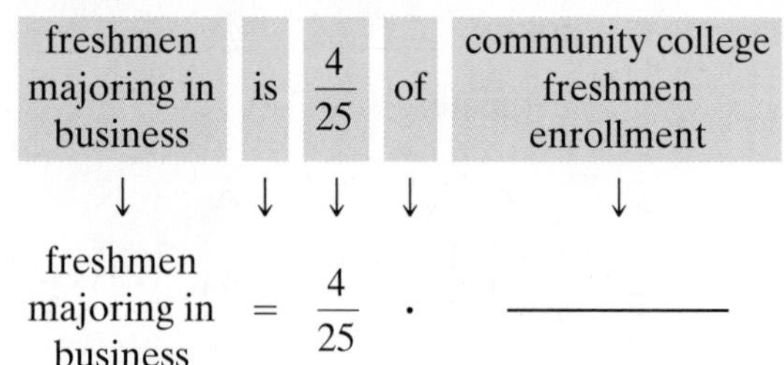

freshmen majoring in business $= \frac{4}{25} \cdot$ ________

Finish with:

3. SOLVE
4. INTERPRET

82. A patient was told that, at most, $\frac{1}{5}$ of his calories should come from fat. If his diet consists of 3000 calories a day, find the maximum number of calories that can come from fat.

Start the solution:

1. UNDERSTAND the problem. Reread it as many times as needed.
2. TRANSLATE into an equation. (Fill in the blank below.)

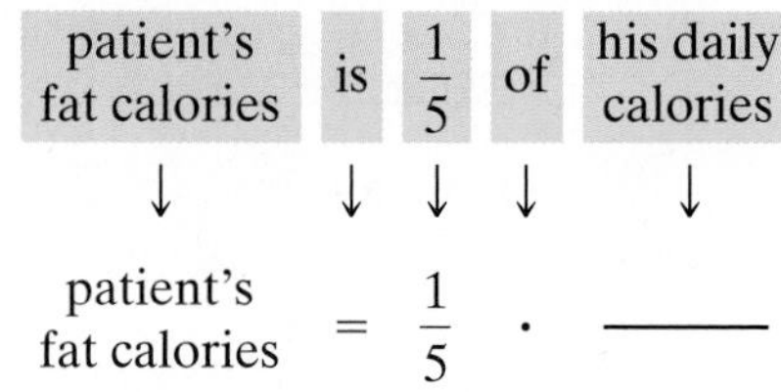

patient's fat calories $= \frac{1}{5} \cdot$ ______

Finish with:

3. SOLVE
4. INTERPRET

83. In a recent year, there were approximately 175 million moviegoers in the United States. Of these, about $\frac{7}{25}$ were ages 16–24. Find the approximate number of people ages 16–24 who attended the movies in that year. (*Source:* Motion Picture Association of America)

84. In a recent year, movie theater owners received a total of \$7660 million in movie admission tickets. About $\frac{7}{10}$ of this amount was for R-rated movies. Find the amount of money received from R-rated movies. (*Source:* Motion Picture Association of America)

85. The Oregon National Historic Trail is 2170 miles long. It begins in Independence, Missouri, and ends in Oregon City, Oregon. Manfred Coulon has hiked $\frac{2}{5}$ of the trail before. How many miles has he hiked? (*Source:* National Park Service)

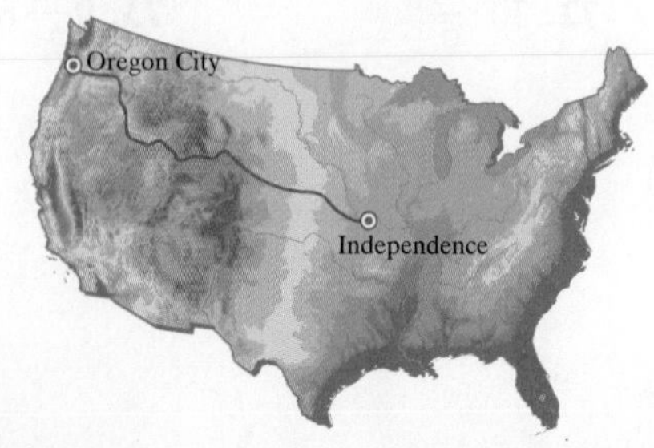

86. Each turn of a screw sinks it $\frac{3}{16}$ of an inch deeper into a piece of wood. Find how deep the screw is after 8 turns.

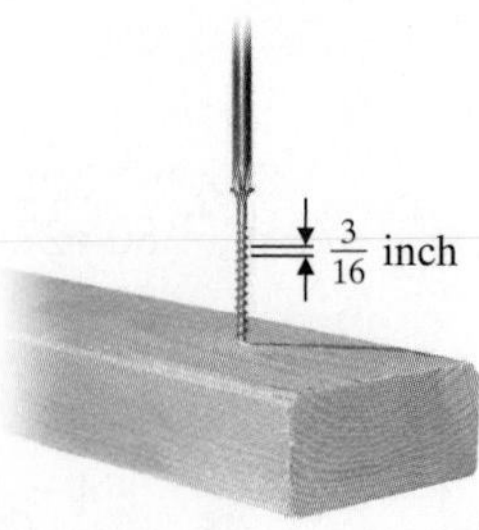

87. The radius of a circle is one-half of its diameter, as shown. If the diameter of a circle is $\frac{3}{8}$ of an inch, what is its radius?

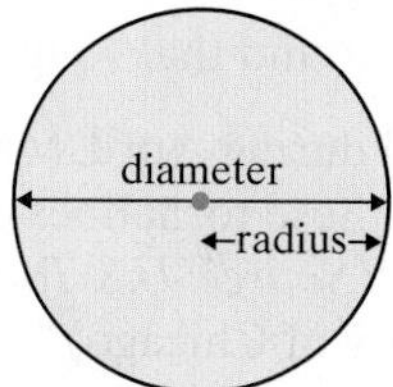

88. The diameter of a circle is twice its radius, as shown in the Exercise 87 illustration. If the radius of a circle is $\frac{7}{20}$ of a foot, what is its diameter?

89. A veterinarian's dipping vat holds 36 gallons of liquid. She normally fills it $\frac{5}{6}$ full of a medicated flea dip solution. Find how many gallons of solution are normally in the vat.

90. The plans for a deck call for $\frac{2}{5}$ of a 4-foot post to be underground. Find the length of the post that is to be buried.

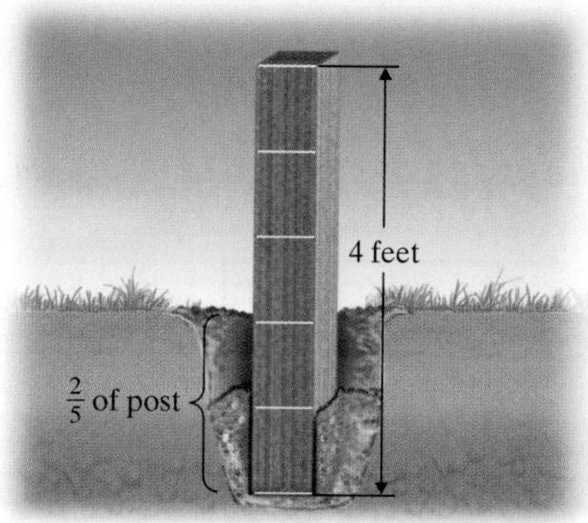

91. An estimate for the measure of an adult's wrist is $\frac{1}{4}$ of the waist size. If Jorge has a 34-inch waist, estimate the size of his wrist.

92. An estimate for an adult's waist measurement is found by multiplying the neck size (in inches) by 2. Jock's neck measures $\frac{36}{2}$ inches. Estimate his waist measurement.

93. A sidewalk is built 6 bricks wide by laying each brick side by side. How many inches wide is the sidewalk if each brick measures $3\frac{1}{4}$ inches wide?

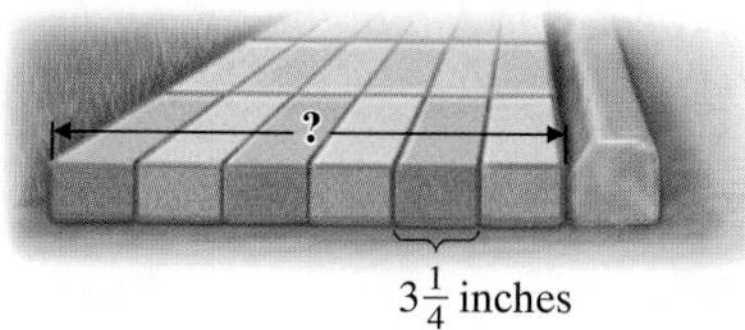

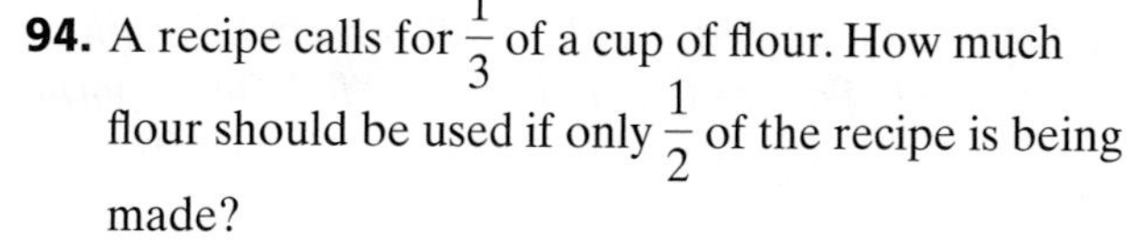

94. A recipe calls for $\frac{1}{3}$ of a cup of flour. How much flour should be used if only $\frac{1}{2}$ of the recipe is being made?

95. A Japanese company called Che-ez! manufactures a small digital camera, the SPYZ camera. The face of the camera measures $2\frac{9}{25}$ inches by $1\frac{13}{25}$ inches and is slightly bigger than a Zippo lighter. Find the area of the face of this camera. (Area = length · width)

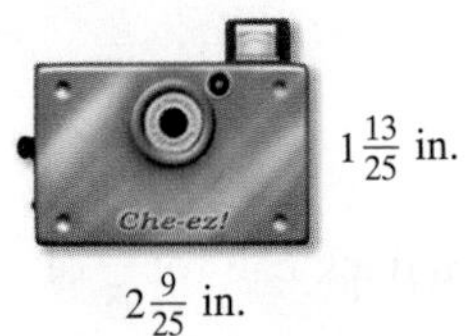

96. As part of his research, famous tornado expert Dr. T. Fujita studied approximately 31,050 tornadoes that occurred in the United States between 1916 and 1985. He found that roughly $\frac{7}{10}$ of these tornadoes occurred during April, May, June, and July. How many of these tornadoes occurred during these four months? (*Source: U.S. Tornadoes Part 1*, T. Fujita, University of Chicago)

Find the area of each rectangle. Recall that area = length · width.

△ **97.**

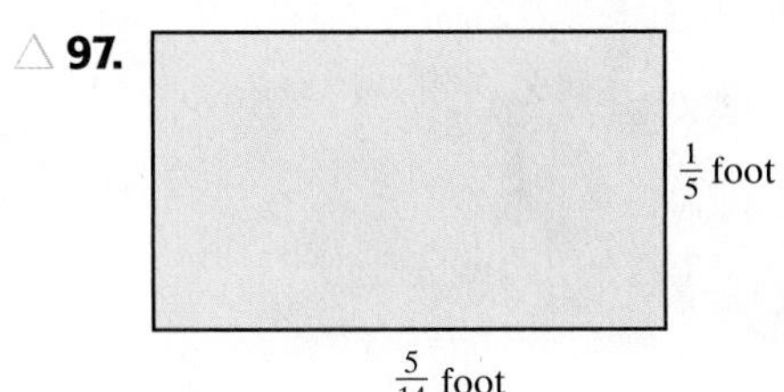

△ **98.**

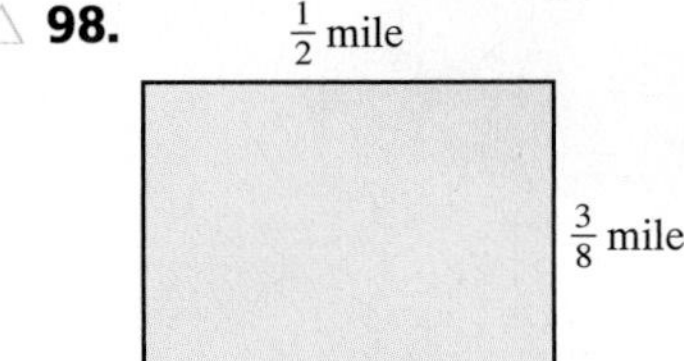

△ **99.**

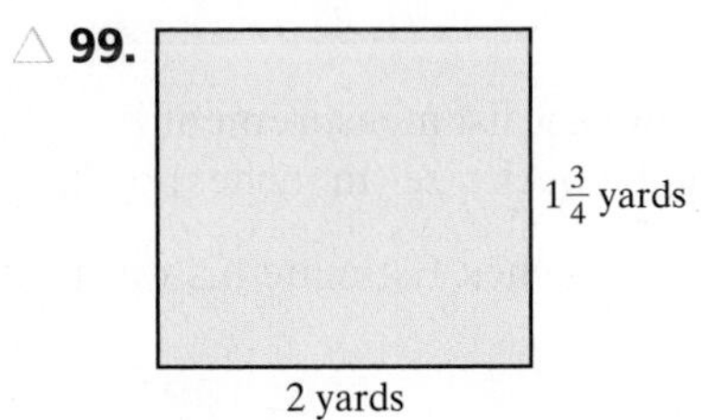

△ **100.**

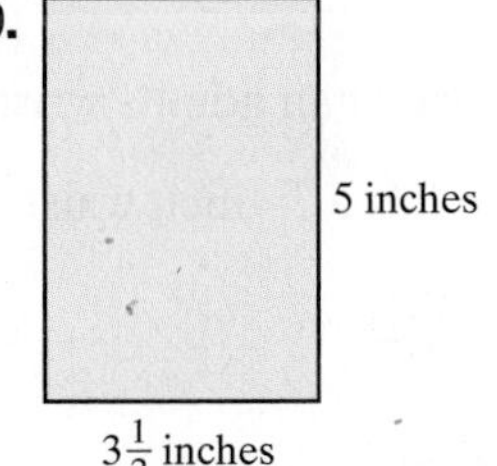

Recall that the following graph is called a **circle graph** *or* **pie chart**. *Each sector (shaped like a piece of pie) shows the fractional part of a car's total mileage that falls into a particular category. The whole circle represents a car's total mileage.*

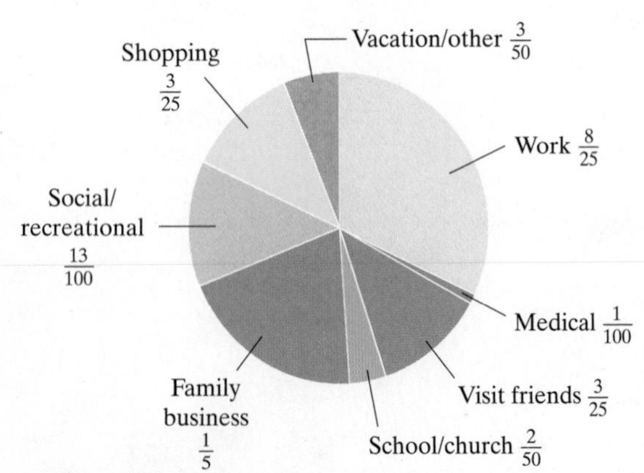

Source: The American Automobile Manufacturers Association and The National Automobile Dealers Association

In one year, a family drove 12,000 miles in the family car. Use the circle graph to determine how many of these miles might be expected to fall in the categories shown in Exercises 101 through 104.

101. Work

102. Shopping

103. Family business

104. Medical

Review

Divide. See Section 1.7.

105. $8\overline{)1648}$

106. $7\overline{)3920}$

107. $23\overline{)1300}$

108. $31\overline{)2500}$

Concept Extensions

109. In your own words, explain how to multiply
a. fractions
b. mixed numbers

110. In your own words, explain how to round a mixed number to the nearest whole number.

Find the error in each calculation. See the Concept Check in this section.

111. $3\frac{2}{3} \cdot 1\frac{1}{7} = 3\frac{2}{21}$

112. $5 \cdot 2\frac{1}{4} = 10\frac{1}{4}$

Choose the best estimate for each product.

113. $3\frac{1}{5} \cdot 4\frac{5}{8}$
a. 7
b. 15
c. 8
d. $12\frac{1}{8}$

114. $\frac{11}{12} \cdot 4\frac{1}{16}$
a. 16
b. 1
c. 4
d. 8

115. $9 \cdot \frac{10}{11}$
a. 9
b. 90
c. 99
d. 0

116. $7\frac{1}{4} \cdot 4\frac{1}{5}$
a. 40
b. $\frac{7}{5}$
c. 35
d. 28

117. If $\frac{3}{4}$ of 36 students on a first bus are girls and $\frac{2}{3}$ of the 30 students on a second bus are *boys*, how many students on the two buses are girls?

118. In 2008, there were approximately 14,120 commercial radio stations broadcasting in the United States. Of these, approximately $\frac{33}{625}$ were news/talk stations. How many radio stations were news/talk stations in 2008? (Round to the nearest whole.) (*Source:* Corporation for Public Broadcasting)

119. There were approximately $116\frac{4}{5}$ million households in the United States in 2009. About $\frac{3}{4}$ of these households had one or more credit cards. How many American households had one or more credit cards in 2009? (*Source:* Nilson report, April 2009)

120. Approximately $\frac{1}{8}$ of the U.S. population lives in the state of California. If the U.S. population is approximately 307,607,800, find the approximate population of California. (*Source:* U.S. Census Bureau)

2.5 DIVIDING FRACTIONS AND MIXED NUMBERS

Objectives

A Find the Reciprocal of a Fraction.

B Divide Fractions.

C Divide Fractions and Mixed Numbers or Whole Numbers.

D Solve Problems by Dividing Fractions.

Objective A Finding Reciprocals of Fractions

Before we can divide fractions, we need to know how to find the **reciprocal** of a fraction or whole number.

Reciprocal of a Fraction

Two numbers are **reciprocals** of each other if their product is 1. The reciprocal of the fraction $\frac{a}{b}$ is $\frac{b}{a}$ because $\frac{a}{b} \cdot \frac{b}{a} = \frac{a \cdot b}{b \cdot a} = 1$.

Finding the Reciprocal of a Fraction

To find the reciprocal of a fraction, interchange its numerator and denominator.

For example,

The reciprocal of $\frac{2}{5}$ is $\frac{5}{2}$ because $\frac{2}{5} \cdot \frac{5}{2} = \frac{10}{10} = 1$.

The reciprocal of 7, or $\frac{7}{1}$ is $\frac{1}{7}$ because $7 \cdot \frac{1}{7} = \frac{7}{1} \cdot \frac{1}{7} = \frac{7}{7} = 1$.

PRACTICE 1–4

Find the reciprocal of each number.

1. $\frac{4}{9}$
2. $\frac{15}{7}$
3. 9
4. $\frac{1}{8}$

Examples Find the reciprocal of each number.

1. The reciprocal of $\frac{5}{6}$ is $\frac{6}{5}$. $\quad \frac{5}{6} \cdot \frac{6}{5} = \frac{5 \cdot 6}{6 \cdot 5} = \frac{30}{30} = 1$
2. The reciprocal of $\frac{11}{8}$ is $\frac{8}{11}$. $\quad \frac{11}{8} \cdot \frac{8}{11} = \frac{11 \cdot 8}{8 \cdot 11} = \frac{88}{88} = 1$
3. The reciprocal of $\frac{1}{3}$ is $\frac{3}{1}$ or 3. $\quad \frac{1}{3} \cdot \frac{3}{1} = \frac{1 \cdot 3}{3 \cdot 1} = \frac{3}{3} = 1$
4. The reciprocal of 5, or $\frac{5}{1}$, is $\frac{1}{5}$. $\quad \frac{5}{1} \cdot \frac{1}{5} = \frac{5 \cdot 1}{1 \cdot 5} = \frac{5}{5} = 1$

Work Practice 1–4

Helpful Hint

Every number except 0 has a reciprocal. The number 0 has no reciprocal because there is no number that when multiplied by 0 gives a result of 1.

Objective B Dividing Fractions

Division of fractions has the same meaning as division of whole numbers. For example,

10 ÷ 5 means: How many 5s are there in 10?

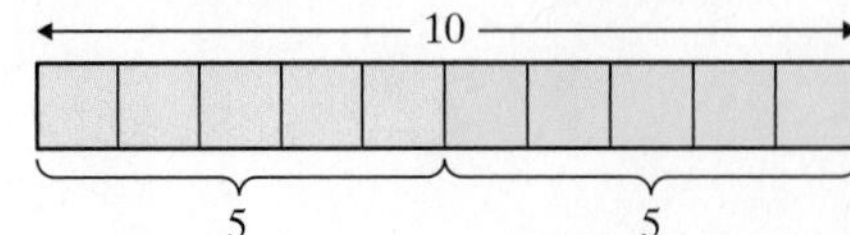

There are two 5s in 10, so 10 ÷ 5 = 2.

Answers

1. $\frac{9}{4}$ 2. $\frac{7}{15}$ 3. $\frac{1}{9}$ 4. 8

$\frac{3}{4} \div \frac{1}{8}$ means: How many $\frac{1}{8}$s are there in $\frac{3}{4}$?

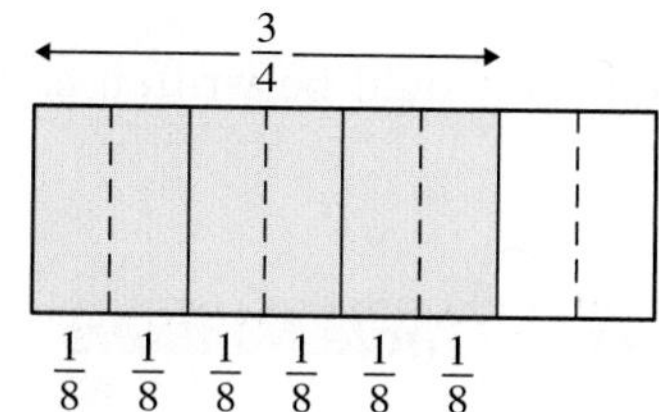

There are six $\frac{1}{8}$s in $\frac{3}{4}$, so $\frac{3}{4} \div \frac{1}{8} = 6$.

We use reciprocals to divide fractions.

Dividing Fractions

To divide two fractions, multiply the first fraction by the reciprocal of the second fraction.

If a, b, c, and d represent numbers, and b, c, and d are not 0, then

$$\frac{a}{b} \div \frac{c}{d} = \frac{a}{b} \cdot \frac{d}{c} = \frac{a \cdot d}{b \cdot c}$$

(reciprocal)

For example,

multiply by reciprocal

$$\frac{3}{4} \div \frac{1}{8} = \frac{3}{4} \cdot \frac{8}{1} = \frac{3 \cdot 8}{4 \cdot 1} = \frac{3 \cdot 2 \cdot \overset{1}{\cancel{4}}}{\underset{1}{\cancel{4}} \cdot 1} = \frac{6}{1} \text{ or } 6$$

Just as when you are multiplying fractions, always check to see whether your answer can be simplified when you divide fractions.

Examples Divide and simplify.

5. $\frac{7}{8} \div \frac{2}{9} = \frac{7}{8} \cdot \frac{9}{2} = \frac{7 \cdot 9}{8 \cdot 2} = \frac{63}{16}$

6. $\frac{5}{16} \div \frac{3}{4} = \frac{5}{16} \cdot \frac{4}{3} = \frac{5 \cdot 4}{16 \cdot 3} = \frac{5 \cdot \overset{1}{\cancel{4}}}{\underset{1}{\cancel{4}} \cdot 4 \cdot 3} = \frac{5}{12}$

7. $\frac{2}{5} \div \frac{1}{2} = \frac{2}{5} \cdot \frac{2}{1} = \frac{2 \cdot 2}{5 \cdot 1} = \frac{4}{5}$

Work Practice 5–7

PRACTICE 5–7

Divide and simplify.

5. $\frac{3}{2} \div \frac{14}{5}$ **6.** $\frac{8}{7} \div \frac{2}{9}$

7. $\frac{4}{9} \div \frac{1}{2}$

Helpful Hint

When dividing fractions, do *not* look for common factors to divide out until you rewrite the division as multiplication.

Do not try to divide out these two 2s.

$$\frac{1}{\mathbf{2}} \div \frac{\mathbf{2}}{3} = \frac{1}{2} \cdot \frac{3}{2} = \frac{3}{4}$$

Answers

5. $\frac{15}{28}$ **6.** $\frac{36}{7}$ **7.** $\frac{8}{9}$

Objective C Dividing Fractions and Mixed Numbers or Whole Numbers

Just as with multiplying, mixed or whole numbers should be written as fractions before you divide them.

Dividing Fractions and Mixed Numbers or Whole Numbers

To divide with a mixed number or a whole number, first write the mixed or whole number as a fraction and then divide as usual.

Examples Divide.

8. $\frac{3}{4} \div 5 = \frac{3}{4} \div \frac{5}{1} = \frac{3}{4} \cdot \frac{1}{5} = \frac{3 \cdot 1}{4 \cdot 5} = \frac{3}{20}$

9. $\frac{11}{18} \div 2\frac{5}{6} = \frac{11}{18} \div \frac{17}{6} = \frac{11}{18} \cdot \frac{6}{17} = \frac{11 \cdot 6}{18 \cdot 17} = \frac{11 \cdot \overset{1}{\cancel{6}}}{\underset{1}{\cancel{6}} \cdot 3 \cdot 17} = \frac{11}{51}$

10. $5\frac{2}{3} \div 2\frac{5}{9} = \frac{17}{3} \div \frac{23}{9} = \frac{17}{3} \cdot \frac{9}{23} = \frac{17 \cdot 9}{3 \cdot 23} = \frac{17 \cdot \overset{1}{\cancel{3}} \cdot 3}{\underset{1}{\cancel{3}} \cdot 23} = \frac{51}{23}$ or $2\frac{5}{23}$

Work Practice 8–10

PRACTICE 8–10

Divide.

8. $\frac{4}{9} \div 7$ **9.** $\frac{8}{15} \div 3\frac{4}{5}$

10. $3\frac{2}{7} \div 2\frac{3}{14}$

Recall from Section 1.7 that the quotient of 0 and any number (except 0) is 0. This is true of fractions and mixed numbers also. For example,

$$0 \div \frac{7}{8} = 0 \cdot \frac{8}{7} = 0$$ Recall that 0 multiplied by any number is 0.

Also recall from Section 1.7 that the quotient of any number and 0 is undefined. This is also true of fractions and mixed numbers. For example, to find $\frac{7}{8} \div 0$, or $\frac{7}{8} \div \frac{0}{1}$, we would need to find the reciprocal of 0 $\left(\text{or } \frac{0}{1}\right)$. As we mentioned in the helpful hint at the beginning of this section, 0 has no reciprocal because there is no number that when multiplied by 0 gives a result of 1. Thus,

$\frac{7}{8} \div 0$ is undefined.

Examples Divide.

11. $0 \div \frac{2}{21} = 0 \cdot \frac{21}{2} = 0$ **12.** $1\frac{3}{4} \div 0$ is undefined.

Work Practice 11–12

PRACTICE 11–12

Divide.

11. $\frac{14}{17} \div 0$ **12.** $0 \div 2\frac{1}{8}$

✓**Concept Check** Which of the following is the correct way to divide $\frac{2}{5}$ by $\frac{3}{4}$? Or are both correct? Explain.

a. $\frac{5}{2} \cdot \frac{3}{4}$ **b.** $\frac{2}{5} \cdot \frac{4}{3}$

Answers

8. $\frac{4}{63}$ **9.** $\frac{8}{57}$ **10.** $\frac{46}{31}$ or $1\frac{15}{31}$ **11.** undefined **12.** 0

✓ **Concept Check Answers**

a. incorrect **b.** correct

Objective D Solving Problems by Dividing Fractions

To solve real-life problems that involve dividing fractions, we continue to use our four problem-solving steps.

Example 13 Calculating Manufacturing Materials Needed

In a manufacturing process, a metal-cutting machine cuts strips $1\frac{3}{5}$ inches wide from a piece of metal stock. How many such strips can be cut from a 48-inch piece of stock?

Solution:

1. UNDERSTAND the problem. To do so, read and reread the problem. Then draw a diagram:

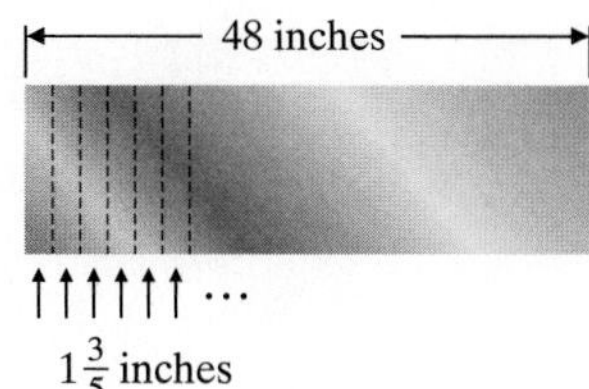

We want to know how many $1\frac{3}{5}$s there are in 48.

2. TRANSLATE.

In words:	Number of strips	is	48	divided by	$1\frac{3}{5}$
	↓	↓	↓	↓	↓
Translate:	Number of strips	=	48	÷	$1\frac{3}{5}$

3. SOLVE: Let's estimate a reasonable answer. The mixed number $1\frac{3}{5}$ rounds to 2 and $48 \div 2 = 24$.

$$48 \div 1\frac{3}{5} = 48 \div \frac{8}{5} = \frac{48}{1} \cdot \frac{5}{8} = \frac{48 \cdot 5}{1 \cdot 8} = \frac{\overset{1}{\cancel{8}} \cdot 6 \cdot 5}{1 \cdot \underset{1}{\cancel{8}}} = \frac{30}{1} \text{ or } 30$$

4. INTERPRET. *Check* your work. Since the exact answer of 30 is close to our estimate of 24, our answer is reasonable. *State* your conclusion: Thirty strips can be cut from the 48-inch piece of stock.

Work Practice 13

PRACTICE 13

A designer of clothing designs an outfit that requires $2\frac{1}{7}$ yards of material. How many outfits can be made from a 30-yard bolt of material?

Answer

13. 14 outfits

Vocabulary and Readiness Check

Use the choices below to fill in each blank. Not all choices will be used.

multiplication	$\frac{a \cdot d}{b \cdot c}$	$\frac{a \cdot c}{b \cdot d}$
division	0	reciprocals

1. Two numbers are ____________ of each other if their product is 1.
2. Every number has a reciprocal except ____________.
3. To divide two fractions, we write $\frac{a}{b} \div \frac{c}{d} =$ ____________.
4. The word "per" usually indicates ____________.

2.5 Exercise Set

FOR EXTRA HELP

MyMathLab

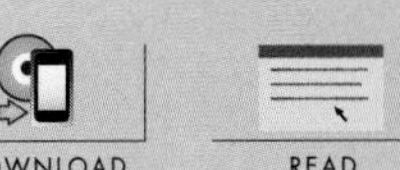

Objective A *Find the reciprocal of each number. See Examples 1 through 4.*

1. $\frac{4}{7}$ **2.** $\frac{9}{10}$ **3.** $\frac{1}{11}$ **4.** $\frac{1}{20}$

5. 15 **6.** 13 **7.** $\frac{12}{7}$ **8.** $\frac{10}{3}$

Objective B *Divide. Write each answer in simplest form. See Examples 5 through 7 and 11 and 12.*

9. $\frac{2}{3} \div \frac{5}{6}$ **10.** $\frac{5}{8} \div \frac{2}{3}$ **11.** $\frac{8}{9} \div \frac{1}{2}$ **12.** $\frac{10}{11} \div \frac{4}{5}$ **13.** $\frac{3}{7} \div \frac{5}{6}$

14. $\frac{16}{27} \div \frac{8}{15}$ **15.** $\frac{3}{5} \div \frac{4}{5}$ **16.** $\frac{11}{16} \div \frac{13}{16}$ **17.** $\frac{1}{10} \div \frac{10}{1}$ **18.** $\frac{3}{13} \div \frac{13}{3}$

19. $\frac{7}{9} \div \frac{7}{3}$ **20.** $\frac{6}{11} \div \frac{6}{5}$ **21.** $\frac{5}{8} \div \frac{3}{8}$ **22.** $\frac{7}{8} \div \frac{5}{6}$ **23.** $\frac{7}{45} \div \frac{4}{25}$

24. $\frac{14}{52} \div \frac{1}{13}$ **25.** $\frac{2}{37} \div \frac{1}{7}$ **26.** $\frac{100}{158} \div \frac{10}{79}$ **27.** $\frac{3}{25} \div \frac{27}{40}$ **28.** $\frac{6}{15} \div \frac{7}{10}$

29. $\frac{11}{12} \div \frac{11}{12}$ **30.** $\frac{7}{13} \div \frac{7}{13}$ **31.** $\frac{8}{13} \div 0$ **32.** $0 \div \frac{4}{11}$ **33.** $0 \div \frac{7}{8}$

34. $\frac{2}{3} \div 0$ **35.** $\frac{25}{126} \div \frac{125}{441}$ **36.** $\frac{65}{495} \div \frac{26}{231}$

Objective C *Divide. Write each answer in simplest form. See Examples 8 through 11.*

37. $\frac{2}{3} \div 4$ **38.** $\frac{5}{6} \div 10$ **39.** $8 \div \frac{3}{5}$ **40.** $7 \div \frac{2}{11}$ **41.** $2\frac{1}{2} \div \frac{1}{2}$

42. $4\frac{2}{3} \div \frac{2}{5}$ **43.** $\frac{5}{12} \div 2\frac{1}{3}$ **44.** $\frac{4}{15} \div 2\frac{1}{2}$ **45.** $3\frac{3}{7} \div 3\frac{1}{3}$ **46.** $2\frac{5}{6} \div 4\frac{6}{7}$

47. $1\frac{4}{9} \div 2\frac{5}{6}$ **48.** $3\frac{1}{10} \div 2\frac{1}{5}$ **49.** $0 \div 15\frac{4}{7}$ **50.** $\frac{33}{50} \div 1$ **51.** $1 \div \frac{13}{17}$

52. $0 \div 7\frac{9}{10}$ **53.** $1 \div \frac{18}{35}$ **54.** $\frac{17}{75} \div 1$ **55.** $10\frac{5}{9} \div 16\frac{2}{3}$ **56.** $20\frac{5}{6} \div 137\frac{1}{2}$

Objectives B C **Mixed Practice** *Divide. Write each answer in simplest form. See Examples 5 through 12.*

57. $\frac{6}{15} \div \frac{12}{5}$ **58.** $\frac{4}{15} \div \frac{8}{3}$ **59.** $\frac{11}{20} \div \frac{3}{11}$ **60.** $\frac{9}{20} \div \frac{2}{9}$

61. $12 \div \frac{1}{8}$ **62.** $9 \div \frac{1}{6}$ **63.** $\frac{3}{7} \div \frac{4}{7}$ **64.** $\frac{3}{8} \div \frac{5}{8}$

65. $2\frac{3}{8} \div 0$ **66.** $20\frac{1}{5} \div 0$ **67.** $\frac{11}{85} \div \frac{7}{5}$ **68.** $\frac{13}{84} \div \frac{3}{16}$

69. $4\frac{5}{11} \div 1\frac{2}{5}$ **70.** $8\frac{2}{7} \div 3\frac{1}{7}$ **71.** $\frac{27}{100} \div \frac{3}{20}$ **72.** $\frac{25}{128} \div \frac{5}{32}$

Objective D *Solve. For Exercises 73 and 74, the solutions have been started for you. Write each answer in simplest form. See Example 13.*

73. A heart attack patient in rehabilitation walked on a treadmill $12\frac{3}{4}$ miles over 4 days. How many miles is this per day?

Start the solution:

1. UNDERSTAND the problem. Reread it as many times as needed.
2. TRANSLATE into an equation. (Fill in the blanks.)

miles per day	is	total miles	divided by	number of days
↓	↓	↓	↓	↓
miles per day	=	____	÷	____

Finish with:

3. SOLVE and
4. INTERPRET

74. A local restaurant is selling hamburgers from a booth on Memorial Day. A total of $27\frac{3}{4}$ pounds of hamburger have been ordered. How many quarter-pound hamburgers can this make?

Start the solution:

1. UNDERSTAND the problem. Reread it as many times as needed.
2. TRANSLATE into an equation. (Fill in the blanks.)

how many quarter-pound hamburgers	is	total pounds of hamburger	divided by	a quarter-pound
↓	↓	↓	↓	↓
how many quarter-pound hamburgers	=	____	÷	____

Finish with:

3. SOLVE and
4. INTERPRET

75. A patient is to take $3\frac{1}{3}$ tablespoons of medicine per day in 4 equally divided doses. How much medicine is to be taken in each dose?

76. If there are $13\frac{1}{3}$ grams of fat in 4 ounces of lean hamburger meat, how many grams of fat are in an ounce?

77. The record for rainfall during a 24-hour period in Alaska is $15\frac{1}{5}$ inches. This record was set in Angoon, Alaska, in October 1982. How much rain fell per hour on average? (*Source:* National Climatic Data Center)

78. An order for 125 custom-made candle stands was placed with Mr. Levi, the manager of Just For You, Inc. The worker assigned to the job can produce $2\frac{3}{5}$ candle stands per hour. Using this worker, how many work hours will be required to complete the order?

79. At this writing, the average price of aluminum is $98\frac{1}{2}$¢ per pound. During that time, a family received 1379¢ for aluminum cans that they sold for recycling at a scrap metal center. Assuming that they received the average price, how many pounds of aluminum cans did they recycle? (*Source:* London Metal Exchange)

80. Yoko's Fine Jewelry paid $450 for a $\frac{3}{4}$-carat gem. At this price, what is the cost of one carat?

△ **81.** The area of the rectangle below is 12 square meters. If its width is $2\frac{4}{7}$ meters, find its length.

Rectangle $2\frac{4}{7}$ meters

△ **82.** The perimeter of the square below is $23\frac{1}{2}$ feet. Find the length of each side.

Square

Mixed Practice (Sections 2.4, 2.5)

Perform the indicated operation.

83. $\frac{2}{5} \cdot \frac{4}{7}$

84. $\frac{2}{5} \div \frac{4}{7}$

85. $2\frac{2}{3} \div 1\frac{1}{16}$

86. $2\frac{2}{3} \cdot 1\frac{1}{16}$

87. $5\frac{1}{7} \cdot \frac{2}{9} \cdot \frac{14}{15}$

88. $8\frac{1}{6} \cdot \frac{3}{7} \cdot \frac{18}{25}$

89. $\frac{11}{20} \div \frac{20}{11}$

90. $2\frac{1}{5} \div 1\frac{7}{10}$

Review

Perform each indicated operation. See Sections 1.3 and 1.4.

91. $27 + 76 + 98$

92. $811 + 42 + 69$

93. $968 - 772$

94. $882 - 773$

95. $2000 - 431$

96. $500 - 92$

Concept Extensions

A student asked you to find the error in the work below. Find the error and correct it. See the Concept Check in this section.

97. $20\frac{2}{3} \div 10\frac{1}{2} = 2\frac{1}{3}$

98. $6\frac{1}{4} \div \frac{1}{2} = 3\frac{1}{8}$

Choose the best estimate for each quotient.

99. $20\frac{1}{4} \div \frac{5}{6}$

a. 5 **b.** $5\frac{1}{8}$ **c.** 20 **d.** 10

100. $\frac{11}{12} \div 16\frac{1}{5}$

a. $\frac{1}{16}$ **b.** 4 **c.** 8 **d.** 16

101. $12\frac{2}{13} \div 3\frac{7}{8}$

a. 4 **b.** 9 **c.** 36 **d.** 3

102. $10\frac{1}{4} \div 2\frac{1}{16}$

a. 8 **b.** 5 **c.** 20 **d.** 12

Simplify.

103. $\frac{42}{25} \cdot \frac{125}{36} \div \frac{7}{6}$

104. $\left(\frac{8}{13} \cdot \frac{39}{16} \cdot \frac{8}{9}\right)^2 \div \frac{1}{2}$

105. The FedEx Express air fleet includes 252 Cessnas. These Cessnas make up $\frac{42}{109}$ of the FedEx fleet. How many aircraft make up the entire FedEx Express air fleet? (*Source:* FedEx Corporation)

106. One-third of all native flowering plant species in the United States are at risk of becoming extinct. That translates into 5144 at-risk flowering plant species. Based on this data, how many flowering plant species are native to the United States overall? (*Source:* The Nature Conservancy) (*Hint:* How many $\frac{1}{3}$s are in 5144?)

107. In your own words, describe how to find the reciprocal of a number.

108. In your own words, describe how to divide fractions.

Chapter 2 Group Activity

Blood and Blood Donation (Sections 2.1, 2.2, 2.3)

Blood is the workhorse of the body. It carries to the body's tissues everything they need, from nutrients to antibodies to heat. Blood also carries away waste products like carbon dioxide. Blood contains three types of cells—red blood cells, white blood cells, and platelets—suspended in clear, watery fluid called plasma. Blood is $\frac{11}{20}$ plasma, and plasma itself is $\frac{9}{10}$ water. In the average healthy adult human, blood accounts for $\frac{1}{11}$ of a person's body weight.

Roughly every 2 seconds someone in the United States needs blood. Although only $\frac{1}{20}$ of eligible donors donate blood, the American Red Cross is still able to collect nearly 6 million volunteer donations of blood each year. This volume makes Red Cross Biomedical Services the largest blood supplier for blood transfusions in the United States.

Group Activity

Contact your local Red Cross Blood Service office. Find out how many people donated blood in your area in the past two months. Ask whether it is possible to get a breakdown of the blood donations by blood type. (For more on blood types, see Exercises 75 through 78 in Section 2.3.)

1. Research the population of the area served by your local Red Cross Blood Service office. Write the fraction of the local population who gave blood in the past two months.
2. Use the breakdown by blood type to write the fraction of donors giving each type of blood.

Chapter 2 Vocabulary Check

Fill in each blank with one of the words or phrases listed below.

mixed number	equivalent	0	undefined
composite number	improper fraction	simplest form	prime factorization
prime number	proper fraction	numerator	denominator
reciprocals	cross products		

1. Two numbers are ______________ of each other if their product is 1.
2. A(n) ______________ is a natural number greater than 1 that is not prime.
3. Fractions that represent the same portion of a whole are called ______________ fractions.
4. A(n) ______________ is a fraction whose numerator is greater than or equal to its denominator.
5. A(n) ______________ is a natural number greater than 1 whose only factors are 1 and itself.
6. A fraction is in ______________ when the numerator and the denominator have no factors in common other than 1.
7. A(n) ______________ is one whose numerator is less than its denominator.
8. A(n) ______________ contains a whole number part and a fraction part.
9. In the fraction $\frac{7}{9}$, the 7 is called the ______________ and the 9 is called the ______________.
10. The ______________ of a number is the factorization in which all the factors are prime numbers.
11. The fraction $\frac{3}{0}$ is ______________.
12. The fraction $\frac{0}{5}$ = ______________.
13. In $\frac{a}{b} = \frac{c}{d}$, $a \cdot d$ and $b \cdot c$ are called ______________.

Helpful Hint Are you preparing for your test? Don't forget to take the Chapter 2 Test on page 168. Then check your answers at the back of the text and use the Chapter Test Prep Videos to see the fully worked-out solutions to any of the exercises you want to review.

2 Chapter Highlights

Definitions and Concepts	Examples
Section 2.1 Introduction to Fractions and Mixed Numbers	
A **fraction** is of the form. $\frac{\text{numerator}}{\text{denominator}}$ ← number of parts being considered / ← number of equal parts in the whole	Write a fraction to represent the shaded part of the figure. $\frac{3}{8}$ ← number of parts shaded / ← number of equal parts

(*continued*)

Definitions and Concepts	Examples
Section 2.1 Introduction to Fractions and Mixed Numbers (*continued*)	
A fraction is called a **proper fraction** if its numerator is less than its denominator.	$\frac{1}{3}, \frac{2}{5}, \frac{7}{8}, \frac{100}{101}$
A fraction is called an **improper fraction** if its numerator is greater than or equal to its denominator.	$\frac{5}{4}, \frac{2}{2}, \frac{9}{7}, \frac{101}{100}$
A **mixed number** contains a whole number and a fraction.	$1\frac{1}{2}, 5\frac{7}{8}, 25\frac{9}{10}$
TO WRITE A MIXED NUMBER AS AN IMPROPER FRACTION **1.** Multiply the denominator of the fraction by the whole number. **2.** Add the numerator of the fraction to the product from step 1. **3.** Write this sum from step 2 as the numerator of the improper fraction over the original denominator.	$5\frac{2}{7} = \frac{7 \cdot 5 + 2}{7} = \frac{35 + 2}{7} = \frac{37}{7}$
TO WRITE AN IMPROPER FRACTION AS A MIXED NUMBER OR A WHOLE NUMBER **1.** Divide the denominator into the numerator. **2.** The whole number part of the mixed number is the quotient. The fraction is the remainder over the original denominator. $\text{quotient}\frac{\text{remainder}}{\text{original denominator}}$	$\frac{17}{3} = 5\frac{2}{3}$ $3\overline{)17}$ quotient 5, -15, remainder 2
Section 2.2 Factors and Prime Factorization	
A **prime number** is a natural number that has exactly two different factors, 1 and itself.	2, 3, 5, 7, 11, 13, 17, . . .
A **composite number** is any natural number other than 1 that is not prime.	4, 6, 8, 9, 10, 12, 14, 15, 16, . . .
The prime factorization of a number is the factorization in which all the factors are prime numbers.	Write the prime factorization of 60. $60 = 6 \cdot 10$ $= 2 \cdot 3 \cdot 2 \cdot 5$ or $2^2 \cdot 3 \cdot 5$
Section 2.3 Simplest Form of a Fraction	
Fractions that represent the same portion of a whole are called **equivalent fractions.**	$\frac{3}{4} = \frac{12}{16}$
A fraction is in **simplest form** or **lowest terms** when the numerator and the denominator have no common factors other than 1.	The fraction $\frac{2}{3}$ is in simplest form.

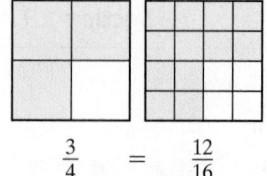

Definitions and Concepts	Examples
Section 2.3 Simplest Form of a Fraction (*continued*)	
To write a fraction in simplest form, write the prime factorizations of the numerator and the denominator and then divide both by all common factors.	Write in simplest form: $\frac{30}{36}$ $\frac{30}{36} = \frac{2\cdot 3\cdot 5}{2\cdot 2\cdot 3\cdot 3} = \frac{2}{2}\cdot\frac{3}{3}\cdot\frac{5}{2\cdot 3} = 1\cdot 1\cdot\frac{5}{6} = \frac{5}{6}$ or $\frac{30}{36} = \frac{\overset{1}{\cancel{2}}\cdot\overset{1}{\cancel{3}}\cdot 5}{\underset{1}{\cancel{2}}\cdot 2\cdot\underset{1}{\cancel{3}}\cdot 3} = \frac{5}{6}$
Two fractions are equivalent if	Determine whether $\frac{7}{8}$ and $\frac{21}{24}$ are equivalent.
Method 1. They simplify to the same fraction.	**Method 1.** $\frac{7}{8}$ is in simplest form; $\frac{21}{24} = \frac{\overset{1}{\cancel{3}}\cdot 7}{\underset{1}{\cancel{3}}\cdot 8} = \frac{7}{8}$ Since both simplify to $\frac{7}{8}$, then $\frac{7}{8} = \frac{21}{24}$.
Method 2. Their cross products are equal.	**Method 2.** $24\cdot 7 = 168$ $\quad \frac{7}{8} = \frac{21}{24} \quad$ $8\cdot 21 = 168$ Since $168 = 168$, $\frac{7}{8} = \frac{21}{24}$
Section 2.4 Multiplying Fractions and Mixed Numbers	
To multiply two fractions, multiply the numerators and multiply the denominators.	Multiply. $\frac{7}{8}\cdot\frac{3}{5} = \frac{7\cdot 3}{8\cdot 5} = \frac{21}{40}$ $\frac{3}{4}\cdot\frac{1}{6} = \frac{3\cdot 1}{4\cdot 6} = \frac{\overset{1}{\cancel{3}}\cdot 1}{4\cdot\underset{1}{\cancel{3}}\cdot 2} = \frac{1}{8}$
To multiply with mixed numbers or whole numbers, first write any mixed or whole numbers as fractions and then multiply as usual.	$2\frac{1}{3}\cdot\frac{1}{9} = \frac{7}{3}\cdot\frac{1}{9} = \frac{7\cdot 1}{3\cdot 9} = \frac{7}{27}$
Section 2.5 Dividing Fractions and Mixed Numbers	
To find the **reciprocal** of a fraction, interchange its numerator and denominator.	The reciprocal of $\frac{3}{5}$ is $\frac{5}{3}$.
To divide two fractions, multiply the first fraction by the reciprocal of the second fraction.	Divide. $\frac{3}{10} \div \frac{7}{9} = \frac{3}{10}\cdot\frac{9}{7} = \frac{3\cdot 9}{10\cdot 7} = \frac{27}{70}$
To divide with mixed numbers or whole numbers, first write any mixed or whole numbers as fractions and then divide as usual.	$2\frac{5}{8} \div 3\frac{7}{16} = \frac{21}{8} \div \frac{55}{16} = \frac{21}{8}\cdot\frac{16}{55} = \frac{21\cdot 16}{8\cdot 55}$ $= \frac{21\cdot 2\cdot\overset{1}{\cancel{8}}}{\underset{1}{\cancel{8}}\cdot 55} = \frac{42}{55}$

Chapter 2 Review

(2.1) *Determine whether each number is an improper fraction, a proper fraction, or a mixed number.*

1. $\frac{11}{23}$ **2.** $\frac{9}{8}$ **3.** $\frac{1}{2}$ **4.** $2\frac{1}{4}$

Write a fraction to represent the shaded area.

5. 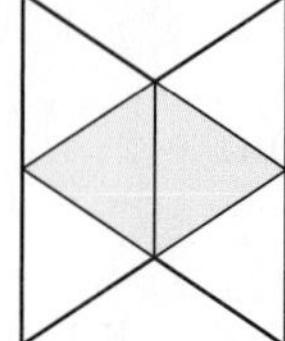

6. 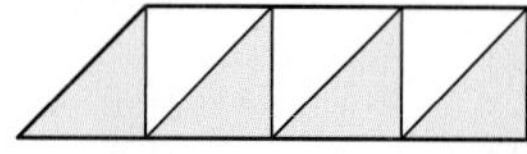

7. 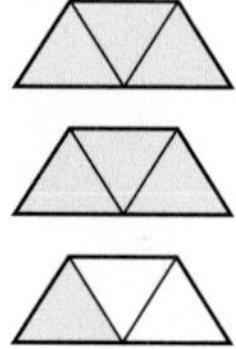

8. 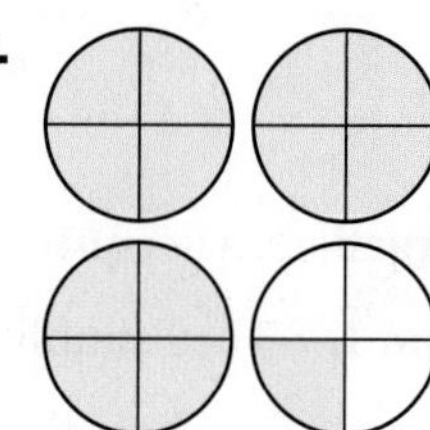

9. A basketball player made 11 free throws out of 12 during a game. What fraction of free throws did the player make?

10. A new car lot contained 23 blue cars out of a total of 131 cars.

a. How many cars on the lot are not blue?
b. What fraction of cars on the lot are not blue?

Write each improper fraction as a mixed number or a whole number.

11. $\frac{15}{4}$ **12.** $\frac{275}{6}$ **13.** $\frac{39}{13}$ **14.** $\frac{60}{12}$

Write each mixed number as an improper fraction.

15. $1\frac{1}{5}$ **16.** $1\frac{1}{21}$ **17.** $2\frac{8}{9}$ **18.** $3\frac{11}{12}$

(2.2) *Identify each number as prime or composite.*

19. 51 **20.** 17

List all factors of each number.

21. 42 **22.** 20

Find the prime factorization of each number.

23. 68 **24.** 90 **25.** 785 **26.** 255

(2.3) *Write each fraction in simplest form.*

27. $\frac{12}{28}$

28. $\frac{15}{27}$

29. $\frac{25}{75}$

30. $\frac{36}{72}$

31. $\frac{29}{32}$

32. $\frac{18}{23}$

33. $\frac{48}{6}$

34. $\frac{54}{9}$

Solve.

35. There are 12 inches in a foot. What fractional part of a foot does 8 inches represent?

12 inches = 1 foot

8 inches

36. Six out of 15 cars are white. What fraction of the cars are *not* white?

Determine whether each two fractions are equivalent.

37. $\frac{10}{34}$ and $\frac{4}{14}$

38. $\frac{30}{50}$ and $\frac{9}{15}$

(2.4) *Multiply. Write each answer in simplest form. Estimate where noted.*

39. $\frac{3}{5} \cdot \frac{1}{2}$

40. $\frac{6}{7} \cdot \frac{5}{12}$

41. $\frac{24}{5} \cdot \frac{15}{8}$

42. $\frac{27}{21} \cdot \frac{7}{18}$

43. $5 \cdot \frac{7}{8}$

44. $6 \cdot \frac{5}{12}$

45. $\frac{39}{3} \cdot \frac{7}{13} \cdot \frac{5}{21}$

46. $\frac{42}{5} \cdot \frac{15}{6} \cdot \frac{7}{9}$

47. $1\frac{5}{8} \cdot 3\frac{1}{5}$

Exact:

Estimate:

48. $3\frac{6}{11} \cdot 1\frac{7}{13}$

Exact:

Estimate:

49. $\frac{3}{4} \cdot 8 \cdot 4\frac{1}{8}$

50. $2\frac{1}{9} \cdot 3 \cdot \frac{1}{38}$

51. There are $7\frac{1}{3}$ grams of fat in each ounce of hamburger. How many grams of fat are in a 5-ounce hamburger patty?

52. An art teacher needs 45 pieces of PVC piping for an art project. If each piece needs to be $\frac{3}{4}$ inch long, find the total length of piping she needs.

△ **53.** Find the area of each rectangle.

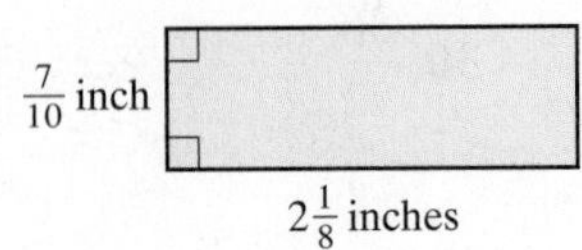

△ **54.**

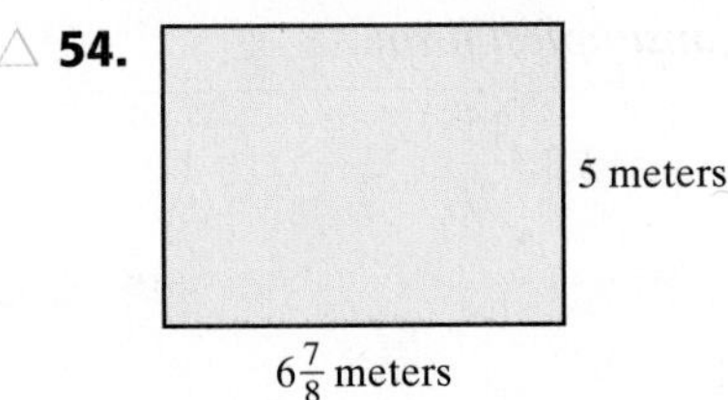

(2.5) *Find the reciprocal of each number.*

55. 7

56. $\frac{1}{8}$

57. $\frac{14}{23}$

58. $\frac{17}{5}$

Divide. Write each answer in simplest form.

59. $\frac{3}{4} \div \frac{3}{8}$

60. $\frac{21}{4} \div \frac{7}{5}$

61. $\frac{5}{3} \div 2$

62. $5 \div \frac{15}{8}$

63. $6\frac{3}{4} \div 1\frac{2}{7}$

64. $5\frac{1}{2} \div 2\frac{1}{11}$

65. A truck traveled 341 miles on $15\frac{1}{2}$ gallons of gas. How many miles might we expect the truck to travel on 1 gallon of gas?

66. Herman Heltznutt walks 5 days a week for a total distance of $5\frac{1}{4}$ miles per week. If he walks the same distance each day, find the distance he walks each day.

Mixed Review

Determine whether each number is an improper fraction, a proper fraction, or a mixed number.

67. $\frac{0}{3}$

68. $\frac{12}{12}$

69. $5\frac{6}{7}$

70. $\frac{13}{9}$

Write each improper fraction as a mixed number or a whole number. Write each mixed number as an improper fraction.

71. $\frac{125}{4}$

72. $\frac{54}{9}$

73. $5\frac{10}{17}$

74. $7\frac{5}{6}$

Identify each number as prime or composite.

75. 27

76. 23

Find the prime factorization of each number.

77. 180

78. 98

Write each fraction in simplest form.

79. $\frac{45}{50}$

80. $\frac{30}{42}$

81. $\frac{140}{150}$

82. $\frac{84}{140}$

Multiply or divide as indicated. Write each answer in simplest form. Estimate where noted.

83. $\frac{7}{8} \cdot \frac{2}{3}$

84. $\frac{6}{15} \cdot \frac{5}{8}$

85. $\frac{18}{5} \div \frac{2}{5}$

86. $\frac{9}{2} \div \frac{1}{3}$

87. $4\frac{1}{6} \cdot 2\frac{2}{5}$

Exact:

Estimate:

88. $5\frac{2}{3} \cdot 2\frac{1}{4}$

Exact:

Estimate:

89. $\frac{7}{2} \div 1\frac{1}{2}$

90. $1\frac{3}{5} \div \frac{1}{4}$

△ **91.** A slab of natural granite is purchased and a rectangle with length $7\frac{4}{11}$ feet and width $5\frac{1}{2}$ feet is cut from it. Find the area of the rectangle.

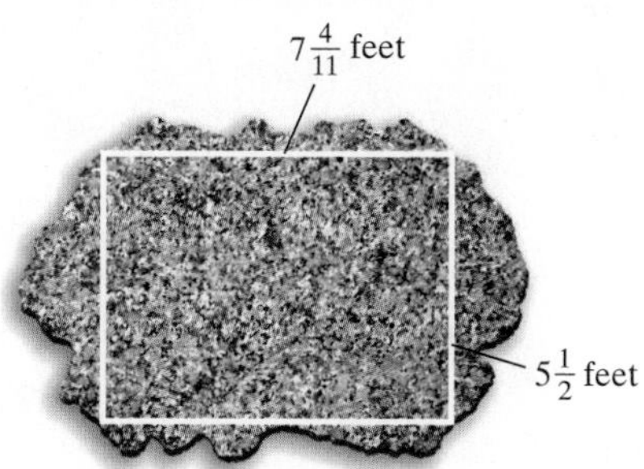

92. An area of Mississippi received $23\frac{1}{2}$ inches of rain in $30\frac{1}{2}$ hours. How many inches per 1 hour is this?

Chapter 2 Test

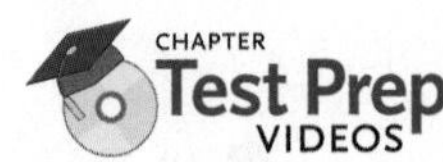

Step-by-step test solutions are found on the Chapter Test Prep Videos available via the Interactive DVD Lecture Series, in MyMathLab or on YouTube (search "MartinGayBasicMath" and click on "Channels").

Answers

1. ______
2. ______
3. ______
4. ______
5. ______
6. ______
7. ______
8. ______
9. ______
10. ______
11. ______
12. ______

Write a fraction to represent the shaded area.

1. 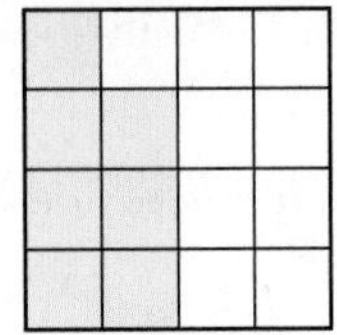

2. 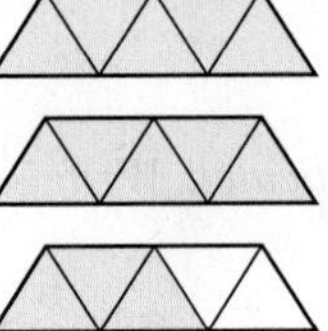

Write each mixed number as an improper fraction.

3. $7\frac{2}{3}$

4. $3\frac{6}{11}$

Write each improper fraction as a mixed number or a whole number.

5. $\frac{23}{5}$

6. $\frac{75}{4}$

Write each fraction in simplest form.

7. $\frac{24}{210}$

8. $\frac{42}{70}$

Determine whether these fractions are equivalent.

9. $\frac{5}{7}$ and $\frac{8}{11}$

10. $\frac{6}{27}$ and $\frac{14}{63}$

Find the prime factorization of each number.

11. 84

12. 495

Perform each indicated operation. Write each answer in simplest form.

13. $\frac{4}{4} \div \frac{3}{4}$

14. $\frac{4}{3} \cdot \frac{4}{4}$

15. $2 \cdot \frac{1}{8}$

16. $\frac{2}{3} \cdot \frac{8}{15}$

17. $8 \div \frac{1}{2}$

18. $13\frac{1}{2} \div 3$

19. $\frac{3}{8} \cdot \frac{16}{6} \cdot \frac{4}{11}$

20. $5\frac{1}{4} \div \frac{7}{12}$

21. $\frac{16}{3} \div \frac{3}{12}$

22. $3\frac{1}{3} \cdot 6\frac{3}{4}$

23. $12 \div 3\frac{1}{3}$

24. $\frac{14}{5} \cdot \frac{25}{21} \cdot 2$

△ **25.** Find the area of the figure.

$\frac{2}{3}$ mile

$1\frac{8}{9}$ miles

26. During a 258-mile trip, a car used $10\frac{3}{4}$ gallons of gas. How many miles would we expect the car to travel on 1 gallon of gas?

27. How many square yards of artificial turf are necessary to cover a football field, *not* including the end zones and the sidelines? (*Hint:* A football field measures $100 \times 53\frac{1}{3}$ yards.)

28. Prior to an oil spill, the stock in an oil company sold for \$120 per share. As a result of the liability that the company incurred from the spill, the price per share fell to $\frac{3}{4}$ of the price before the spill. What did the stock sell for after the spill?

13. ______
14. ______
15. ______
16. ______
17. ______
18. ______
19. ______
20. ______
21. ______
22. ______
23. ______
24. ______
25. ______
26. ______
27. ______
28. ______

Answers

1. ______

2. ______

3. ______

4. ______

5. ______

6. ______

7. ______

8. ______

9. ______

10. ______

11. ______

12. ______

13. a. ______

b. ______

Cumulative Review Chapters 1–2

1. Find the place value of the digit 3 in the whole number 396,418.

2. Write 2036 in words.

3. Write the number, eight hundred five, in standard form.

4. Add: $7 + 6 + 10 + 3 + 5$

5. Add: $34{,}285 + 149{,}761$

6. Find the average of 56, 18, and 43.

△ **7.** Find the perimeter of the polygon shown.

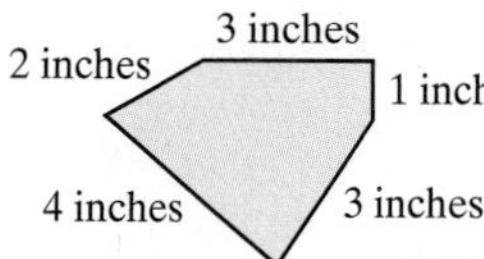

8. Subtract 8 from 25.

9. The Darrell K. Royal Memorial Stadium, located in Austin, Texas, is the largest football stadium in the Big 12 Conference. Before 2009, it could seat 94,113 fans. Recently, the capacity of the stadium was increased by 4525 permanent bleacher seats. Find the new capacity of the home of the University of Texas Longhorns for the 2009 season. (*Source:* University of Texas Athletics)

10. Find $\sqrt{25}$.

11. Subtract: $7826 - 505$
Check by adding.

12. Find 8^2.

13. In the following graph, each bar represents a country and the height of each bar represents the number of endangered species identified in that country.

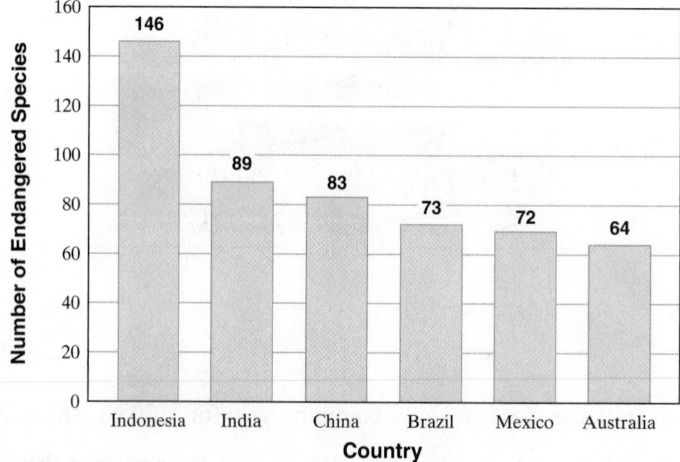

Source: The Top 10 of Everything, Russell Ash

a. Which country shown has the greatest number of endangered species?

b. Find the total number of endangered species for Australia, China, and India.

14. Find 205 ÷ 8.

15. Round 568 to the nearest ten.

16. Round 2366 to the nearest hundred.

17. Round each number to the nearest hundred to find an estimated difference.

$$\begin{array}{r} 4725 \\ -2879 \\ \hline \end{array}$$

18. Round each number to the nearest ten to find an estimated sum.
38 + 43 + 126 + 92

19. Multiply.

a. 6 × 1 **b.** 0(18)
c. 1 · 45 **d.** (75)(0)

20. Simplify: 30 ÷ 3 · 2

21. Rewrite each using the distributive property.

a. 3(4 + 5) **b.** 10(6 + 8)
c. 2(7 + 3)

22. Multiply: 12 × 15

23. Find each quotient. Check by multiplying.

a. $9\overline{)0}$ **b.** 0 ÷ 12
c. $\frac{0}{5}$ **d.** $\frac{3}{0}$

24. Find the area.

7 miles | Rectangle | 22 miles

25. Divide and check: 1872 ÷ 9

26. Subtract: 5000 − 986

27. As part of a promotion, an executive receives 238 cards, each good for one free song download. If she wants to share them evenly with 19 friends, how many download cards will each friend receive? How many will be left over?

28. Find the product of 9 and 7.

29. A gardener bought enough plants to fill a rectangular garden with length 30 feet and width 20 feet. Because of shading problems from a nearby tree, the gardener changed the width of the garden to 15 feet. If the area is to remain the same, what is the new length of the garden?

30. Find the sum of 9 and 7.

14. ________
15. ________
16. ________
17. ________
18. ________
19. a. ________
b. ________
c. ________
d. ________
20. ________
21. a. ________
b. ________
c. ________
22. ________
23. a. ________
b. ________
c. ________
d. ________
24. ________
25. ________
26. ________
27. ________
28. ________
29. ________
30. ________

31. ______
32. ______
33. ______
34. ______
35. ______
36. ______
37. ______
38. ______
39. a. ______
b. ______
40. ______
41. ______
42. ______
43. ______
44. ______
45. ______
46. ______
47. ______
48. ______
49. ______
50. ______

Write using exponential notation.

31. $7 \cdot 7 \cdot 7$

32. $7 \cdot 7 \cdot 7 \cdot 7$

33. $3 \cdot 3 \cdot 3 \cdot 3 \cdot 17 \cdot 17 \cdot 17$

34. $2 \cdot 2 \cdot 3 \cdot 3 \cdot 3 \cdot 3$

35. Simplify: $2 \cdot 4 - 3 \div 3$

36. Simplify: $8 \cdot \sqrt{100} - 4^2 \cdot 5$

37. Write a fraction to represent the shaded part of the figure.

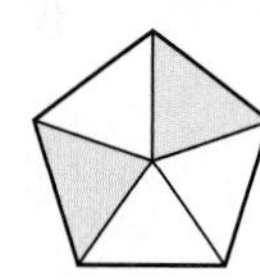

38. Write the prime factorization of 156.

39. Write each as an improper fraction.

a. $4\frac{2}{9}$ **b.** $1\frac{8}{11}$

40. Write $7\frac{4}{5}$ as an improper fraction.

41. Find all the factors of 20.

42. Determine whether $\frac{8}{20}$ and $\frac{14}{35}$ are equivalent.

43. Write in simplest form: $\frac{42}{66}$

44. Write in simplest form: $\frac{70}{105}$

45. Multiply: $3\frac{1}{3} \cdot \frac{7}{8}$

46. Multiply: $\frac{2}{3} \cdot 4$

47. Find the reciprocal of $\frac{1}{3}$.

48. Find the reciprocal of 9.

49. Divide and simplify: $\frac{5}{16} \div \frac{3}{4}$

50. Divide: $1\frac{1}{10} \div 5\frac{3}{5}$

Adding and Subtracting Fractions

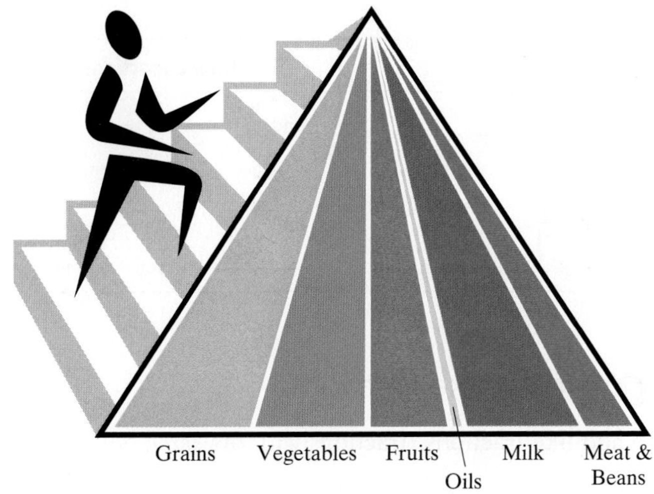

Steps to a Healthier You

Sections

Check Your Progress

Having learned what fractions are and how to multiply and divide them in Chapter 2, we are ready to continue our study of fractions. In this chapter, we learn how to add and subtract fractions and mixed numbers. We then conclude this chapter with solving problems using fractions.

The United States Department of Agriculture (USDA) has a new MyPyramid diagram that embraces the idea of a personal approach to healthy eating and exercise. The colored widths in the diagram above suggest a general guide as to how much one should eat from each food group.

While your age, weight, and level of physical activity affect your personal needs, the pyramid shows the fraction of the servings of various food groups that a healthy diet requires. The circle graph below is just one example of a healthy college student's requirements. For example, in the circle graph below, 3/24 of daily servings come from the milk category, and so on. In Section 3.1, Exercises 49–52, we use fractions to help us understand the healthy eating illustrated in this circle graph.

An Example of Daily Healthy Eating

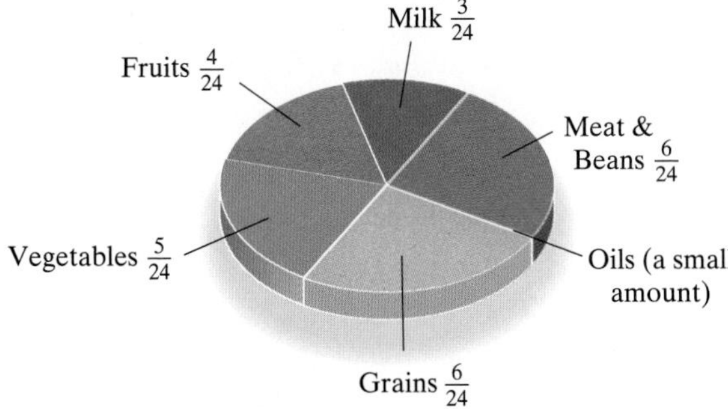

Objectives

A Add Like Fractions.

B Subtract Like Fractions.

C Solve Problems by Adding or Subtracting Like Fractions.

3.1 ADDING AND SUBTRACTING LIKE FRACTIONS

Fractions with the same denominator are called **like fractions.** Fractions that have different denominators are called **unlike fractions.**

Like Fractions	Unlike Fractions
$\frac{2}{5}$ and $\frac{3}{5}$ — same denominator	$\frac{2}{5}$ and $\frac{3}{4}$ — different denominators
$\frac{5}{21}, \frac{16}{21}$, and $\frac{7}{21}$ — same denominator	$\frac{5}{7}$ and $\frac{5}{9}$ — different denominators

Objective A Adding Like Fractions

To see how we add like fractions (fractions with the same denominator), study the figures below:

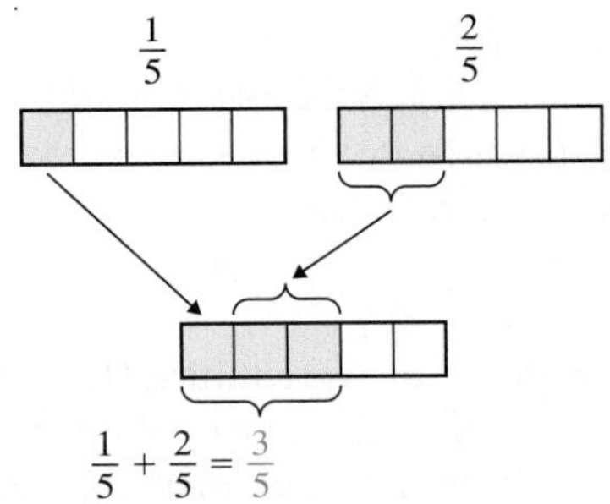

Adding Like Fractions (Fractions with the Same Denominator)

To add like fractions, add the numerators and write the sum over the common denominator.

If a, b, and c represent nonzero whole numbers, we have

$$\frac{a}{c}+\frac{b}{c}=\frac{a+b}{c}$$

For example,

$$\frac{1}{4}+\frac{2}{4}=\frac{1+2}{4}=\frac{3}{4}$$

← Add the numerators.
← Keep the denominator.

Helpful Hint

As usual, don't forget to write all answers in simplest form.

Examples Add and simplify.

1. $\frac{2}{7} + \frac{3}{7} = \frac{2+3}{7} = \frac{5}{7}$ ⟵ Add the numerators. ⟵ Keep the common denominator.

2. $\frac{3}{16} + \frac{7}{16} = \frac{3+7}{16} = \frac{10}{16} = \frac{\overset{1}{\cancel{2}} \cdot 5}{\underset{1}{\cancel{2}} \cdot 8} = \frac{5}{8}$

3. $\frac{7}{13} + \frac{6}{13} + \frac{3}{13} = \frac{7+6+3}{13} = \frac{16}{13}$ or $1\frac{3}{13}$

Work Practice 1–3

PRACTICE 1–3

Add and simplify.

1. $\frac{5}{9} + \frac{2}{9}$

2. $\frac{5}{8} + \frac{1}{8}$

3. $\frac{10}{11} + \frac{1}{11} + \frac{7}{11}$

✓**Concept Check** Find and correct the error in the following:

$\frac{1}{5} + \frac{1}{5} = \frac{2}{10}$ (crossed out)

Objective B Subtracting Like Fractions

To see how we subtract like fractions (fractions with the same denominator), study the following figure:

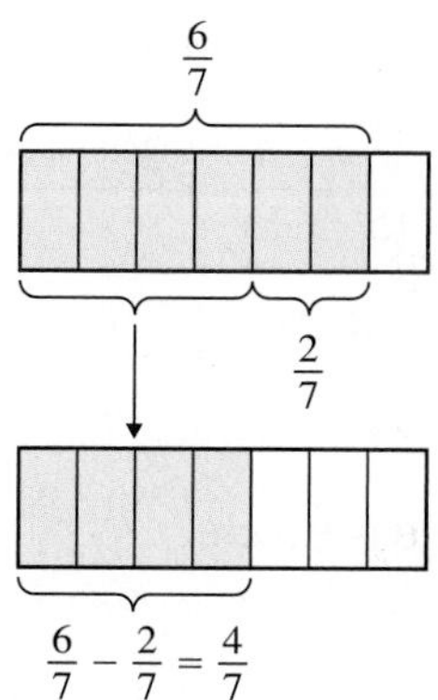

Subtracting Like Fractions (Fractions with the Same Denominator)

To subtract like fractions, subtract the numerators and write the difference over the common denominator.

If a, b, and c represent nonzero whole numbers, then

$$\frac{a}{c} - \frac{b}{c} = \frac{a-b}{c}$$

For example,

$\frac{4}{5} - \frac{2}{5} = \frac{4-2}{5} = \frac{2}{5}$ ⟵ Subtract the numerators. ⟵ Keep the denominator.

Examples Subtract and simplify.

4. $\frac{8}{9} - \frac{1}{9} = \frac{8-1}{9} = \frac{7}{9}$ ⟵ Subtract the numerators. ⟵ Keep the common denominator.

5. $\frac{7}{8} - \frac{5}{8} = \frac{7-5}{8} = \frac{2}{8} = \frac{\overset{1}{\cancel{2}}}{\underset{1}{\cancel{2}} \cdot 4} = \frac{1}{4}$

Work Practice 4–5

PRACTICE 4–5

Subtract and simplify.

4. $\frac{7}{12} - \frac{2}{12}$ 5. $\frac{9}{10} - \frac{1}{10}$

Answers

1. $\frac{7}{9}$ 2. $\frac{3}{4}$ 3. $\frac{18}{11}$ or $1\frac{7}{11}$ 4. $\frac{5}{12}$ 5. $\frac{4}{5}$

✓ **Concept Check Answer**

We don't add denominators together; correct solution: $\frac{1}{5} + \frac{1}{5} = \frac{2}{5}$.

Objective C Solving Problems by Adding or Subtracting Like Fractions

Many real-life problems involve finding the perimeters of square or rectangular areas such as pastures, swimming pools, and so on. We can use our knowledge of adding fractions to find perimeters.

PRACTICE 6

Find the perimeter of the square.

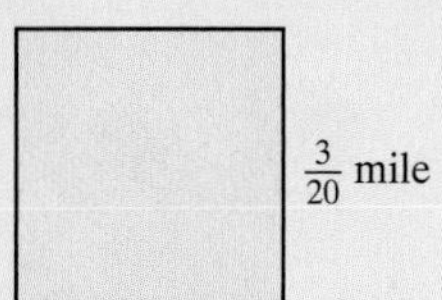

Example 6 Find the perimeter of the rectangle.

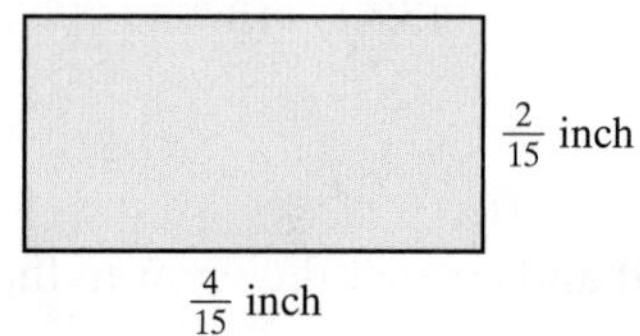

Solution: Recall that perimeter means distance around and that opposite sides of a rectangle are the same length.

$\frac{4}{15}$ inch

$\frac{2}{15}$ inch $\frac{2}{15}$ inch

$\frac{4}{15}$ inch

$$\text{Perimeter} = \frac{2}{15} + \frac{4}{15} + \frac{2}{15} + \frac{4}{15} = \frac{2+4+2+4}{15}$$

$$= \frac{12}{15} = \frac{\overset{1}{\cancel{3}} \cdot 4}{\underset{1}{\cancel{3}} \cdot 5} = \frac{4}{5}$$

The perimeter of the rectangle is $\frac{4}{5}$ inch.

Work Practice 6

We can combine our skills in adding and subtracting fractions with our four problem-solving steps from Chapter 1 to solve many kinds of real-life problems.

PRACTICE 7

If a piano student practices the piano $\frac{3}{8}$ of an hour in the morning and $\frac{1}{8}$ of an hour in the evening, how long did she practice that day?

Example 7 Total Amount of an Ingredient in a Recipe

A recipe calls for $\frac{1}{3}$ of a cup of honey at the beginning and $\frac{2}{3}$ of a cup of honey later. How much total honey is needed to make the recipe?

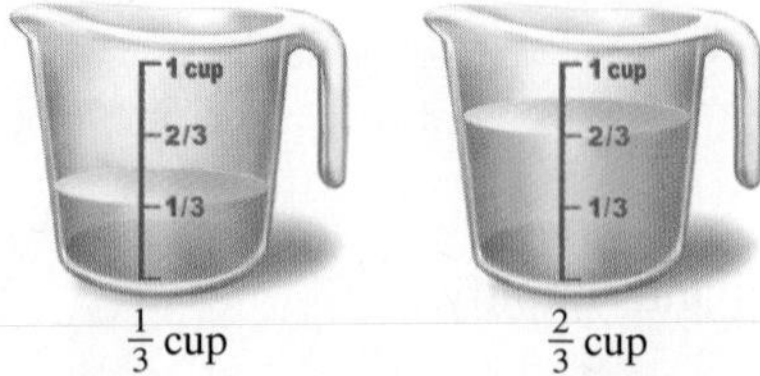

Solution:

1. UNDERSTAND the problem. To do so, read and reread the problem. Since we are finding total honey, we add.

Answers

6. $\frac{3}{5}$ mi 7. $\frac{1}{2}$ hr

2. TRANSLATE.

In words:	total honey	is	honey at the beginning	added to	honey later
	↓	↓	↓	↓	↓
Translate:	total honey	=	$\frac{1}{3}$	+	$\frac{2}{3}$

3. SOLVE: $\frac{1}{3} + \frac{2}{3} = \frac{1+2}{3} = \frac{\overset{1}{\cancel{3}}}{\underset{1}{\cancel{3}}} = 1$

4. INTERPRET. *Check* your work. *State* your conclusion: The total honey needed for the recipe is 1 cup.

Work Practice 7

Example 8 Calculating Distance

The distance from home to the World Gym is $\frac{7}{8}$ of a mile and from home to the post office is $\frac{3}{8}$ of a mile. How much farther is it from home to the World Gym than from home to the post office?

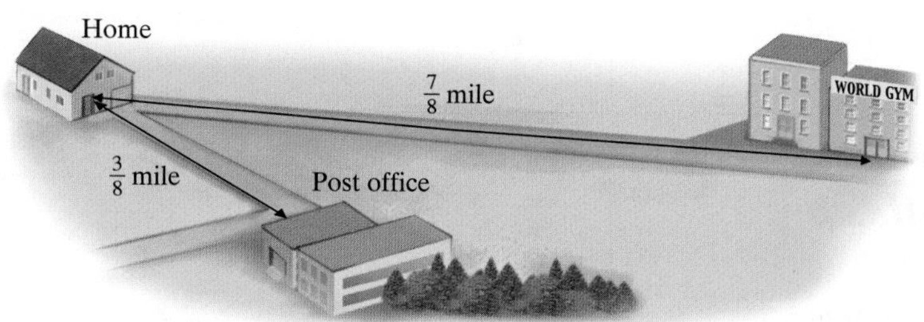

Solution:

1. UNDERSTAND. Read and reread the problem. The phrase "How much farther" tells us to subtract distances.
2. TRANSLATE.

In words:	distance farther	is	home to World Gym distance	minus	home to post office distance
	↓	↓	↓	↓	↓
Translate:	distance farther	=	$\frac{7}{8}$	−	$\frac{3}{8}$

3. SOLVE: $\frac{7}{8} - \frac{3}{8} = \frac{7-3}{8} = \frac{4}{8} = \frac{\overset{1}{\cancel{4}}}{2 \cdot \underset{1}{\cancel{4}}} = \frac{1}{2}$

4. INTERPRET. *Check* your work. *State* your conclusion: The distance from home to the World Gym is $\frac{1}{2}$ mile farther than from home to the post office.

Work Practice 8

PRACTICE 8

A jogger ran $\frac{13}{4}$ miles on Monday and $\frac{7}{4}$ miles on Wednesday. How much farther did he run on Monday than on Wednesday?

Answer

8. $\frac{3}{2}$ or $1\frac{1}{2}$ mi

Vocabulary and Readiness Check

Use the choices below to fill in each blank. Not all choices will be used.

perimeter | like | $\frac{a-c}{b}$ | $\frac{a+c}{b}$

equivalent | unlike

1. The fractions $\frac{9}{11}$ and $\frac{13}{11}$ are called ________ fractions while $\frac{3}{4}$ and $\frac{1}{3}$ are called ________ fractions.

2. $\frac{a}{b}+\frac{c}{b}=$ ________.

3. $\frac{a}{b}-\frac{c}{b}=$ ________.

4. The distance around a figure is called its ________.

State whether the fractions in each list are like or unlike fractions.

5. $\frac{7}{8}, \frac{7}{10}$ **6.** $\frac{2}{3}, \frac{4}{9}$ **7.** $\frac{9}{10}, \frac{1}{10}$ **8.** $\frac{8}{11}, \frac{2}{11}$

9. $\frac{2}{31}, \frac{30}{31}, \frac{19}{31}$ **10.** $\frac{3}{10}, \frac{3}{11}, \frac{3}{13}$ **11.** $\frac{5}{12}, \frac{7}{12}, \frac{12}{11}$ **12.** $\frac{1}{5}, \frac{2}{5}, \frac{4}{5}$

3.1 Exercise Set

FOR EXTRA HELP MyMathLab

Objective A *Add and simplify. See Examples 1 through 3.*

1. $\frac{1}{7}+\frac{2}{7}$ **2.** $\frac{9}{17}+\frac{2}{17}$ **3.** $\frac{1}{10}+\frac{1}{10}$ **4.** $\frac{1}{4}+\frac{1}{4}$

5. $\frac{2}{9}+\frac{4}{9}$ **6.** $\frac{3}{10}+\frac{2}{10}$ **7.** $\frac{6}{20}+\frac{1}{20}$ **8.** $\frac{2}{8}+\frac{3}{8}$

9. $\frac{3}{14}+\frac{4}{14}$ **10.** $\frac{5}{24}+\frac{7}{24}$ **11.** $\frac{10}{11}+\frac{3}{11}$ **12.** $\frac{13}{17}+\frac{9}{17}$

13. $\frac{4}{13}+\frac{2}{13}+\frac{1}{13}$ **14.** $\frac{5}{11}+\frac{1}{11}+\frac{2}{11}$ **15.** $\frac{7}{18}+\frac{3}{18}+\frac{2}{18}$ **16.** $\frac{7}{15}+\frac{4}{15}+\frac{1}{15}$

Objective B *Subtract and simplify. See Examples 4 and 5.*

17. $\frac{10}{11} - \frac{4}{11}$
18. $\frac{9}{13} - \frac{5}{13}$
19. $\frac{4}{5} - \frac{1}{5}$
20. $\frac{7}{8} - \frac{4}{8}$

21. $\frac{7}{4} - \frac{3}{4}$
22. $\frac{18}{5} - \frac{3}{5}$
23. $\frac{7}{8} - \frac{1}{8}$
24. $\frac{5}{6} - \frac{1}{6}$

25. $\frac{25}{12} - \frac{15}{12}$
26. $\frac{30}{20} - \frac{15}{20}$
27. $\frac{11}{10} - \frac{3}{10}$
28. $\frac{14}{15} - \frac{4}{15}$

29. $\frac{86}{90} - \frac{85}{90}$
30. $\frac{74}{80} - \frac{73}{80}$
31. $\frac{27}{33} - \frac{8}{33}$
32. $\frac{37}{45} - \frac{18}{45}$

Objectives A B **Mixed Practice** *Perform the indicated operation. See Examples 1 through 5.*

33. $\frac{8}{21} + \frac{5}{21}$
34. $\frac{7}{37} + \frac{9}{37}$
35. $\frac{99}{100} - \frac{9}{100}$
36. $\frac{85}{200} - \frac{15}{200}$

37. $\frac{13}{28} - \frac{13}{28}$
38. $\frac{15}{26} - \frac{15}{26}$
39. $\frac{3}{16} + \frac{7}{16} + \frac{2}{16}$
40. $\frac{5}{18} + \frac{1}{18} + \frac{6}{18}$

Objective C *Find the perimeter of each figure. (Hint: Recall that perimeter means distance around.) See Example 6.*

41.

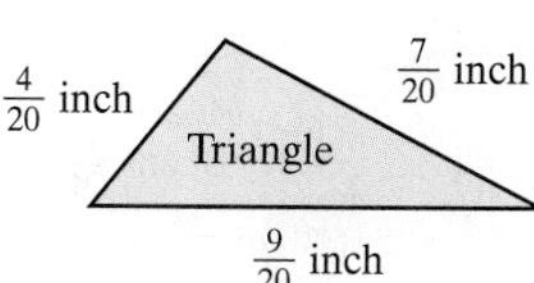

42.

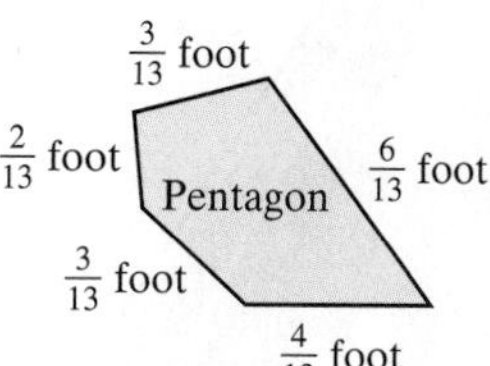

43.

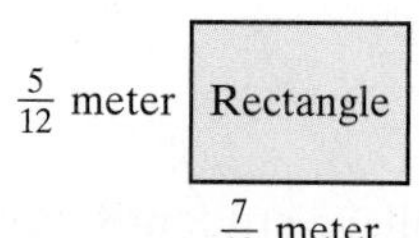

44.

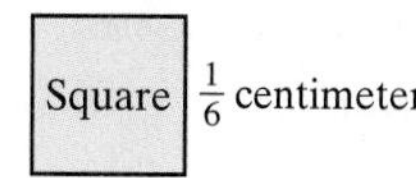

Solve. For Exercises 45 and 46, the solutions have been started for you. Write each answer in simplest form. See Examples 7 and 8.

45. A railroad inspector must inspect $\frac{19}{20}$ of a mile of railroad track. If she has already inspected $\frac{5}{20}$ of a mile, how much more does she need to inspect?

Start the solution:

1. UNDERSTAND the problem. Reread it as many times as needed.
2. TRANSLATE into an equation. (Fill in the blanks.)

distance left to inspect	is	distance needed to inspect	minus	distance already inspected
↓	↓	↓	↓	↓
distance left to inspect	=	______	−	______

Finish with:

3. SOLVE. and
4. INTERPRET.

46. Scott Davis has run $\frac{11}{8}$ miles already and plans to complete $\frac{16}{8}$ miles. To do this, how much farther must he run?

Start the solution:

1. UNDERSTAND the problem. Reread it as many times as needed.
2. TRANSLATE into an equation. (Fill in the blanks.)

distance left to run	is	distance planned to run	minus	distance already run
↓	↓	↓	↓	↓
distance left to run	=	______	−	______

Finish with:

3. SOLVE. and
4. INTERPRET.

47. Emil Vasquez, a bodybuilder, worked out $\frac{7}{8}$ of an hour one morning before school and $\frac{5}{8}$ of an hour that evening. How long did he work out that day?

48. A recipe for Heavenly Hash cake calls for $\frac{3}{4}$ cup of sugar and later $\frac{1}{4}$ cup of sugar. How much sugar is needed to make the recipe?

The Chapter Opener pyramid shows the servings of various foods that a healthy diet requires. While your age, weight, and level of physical activity may change your personal needs, the circle graph below is just one example of an average healthy college student's requirements. Use this graph for Exercises 49–52. Write your answers in simplest form. (Source: United States Department of Agriculture—mypyramid.gov)

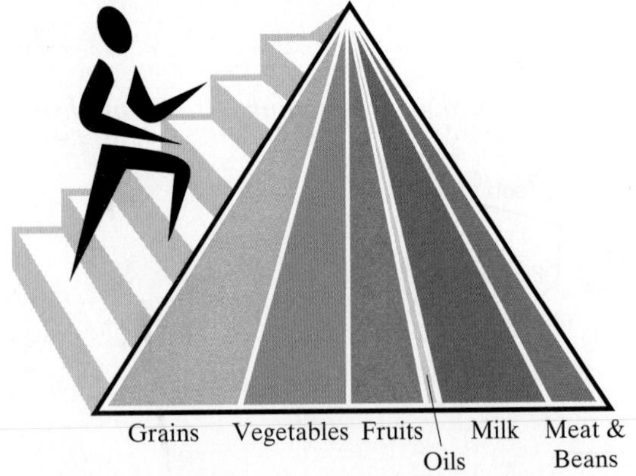

Steps to a Healthier You

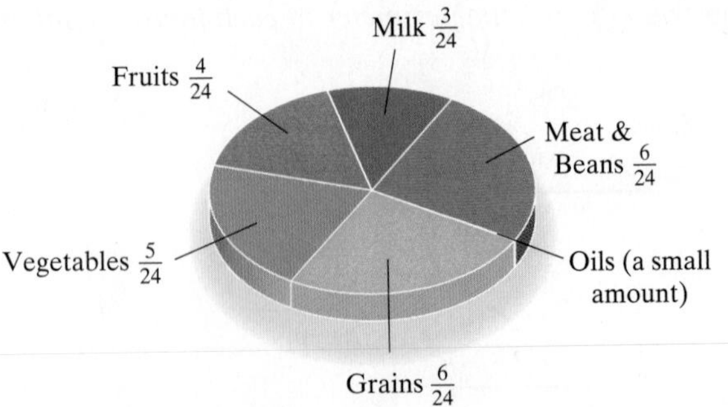

49. Find the fractional part of a college student's daily servings that should come from vegetables and fruit.

50. Find the fractional part of a college student's daily servings that should come from grains and milk.

51. How much greater is the fractional part of a college student's daily servings that comes from grains than from fruit?

52. How much greater is the fractional part of a college student's daily servings that comes from vegetables than from fruit?

Solve.

53. According to a recent poll, approximately $\frac{6}{100}$ of teenagers who have cell phones do social networking tasks every day. Approximately $\frac{7}{100}$ of teenagers with cell phones do social networking tasks once a week to several times a week. What fractions of teenagers with cell phones do social networking tasks at least once a week? (*Source:* Harris Interactive Polls)

54. In a recent survey, $\frac{55}{100}$ of people said that visiting family and friends would be their pleasure trip of choice while $\frac{29}{100}$ of people surveyed said that going to a beach resort would be their pleasure trip of choice. What fraction of people surveyed said visiting family and friends or going to a beach resort? (*Source:* American Express)

55. In 2009, the fraction of states in the United States with maximum interstate highway speed limits up to and including 70 mph was $\frac{19}{25}$. The fraction of states with 70 mph speed limits was $\frac{9}{25}$. What fraction of states had speed limits that were less than 70 mph? (*Source:* Insurance Institute for Highway Safety)

56. When people take aspirin, $\frac{31}{50}$ of the time it is used to treat some type of pain. Approximately $\frac{7}{50}$ of all aspirin use is for treating headaches. What fraction of aspirin use is for treating pain other than headaches? (*Source:* Bayer Market Research)

The map of the world below shows the fraction of the world's surface land area taken up by each continent. In other words, the continent of Africa makes up $\frac{20}{100}$ of the land in the world. Use this map for Exercises 57 through 60.

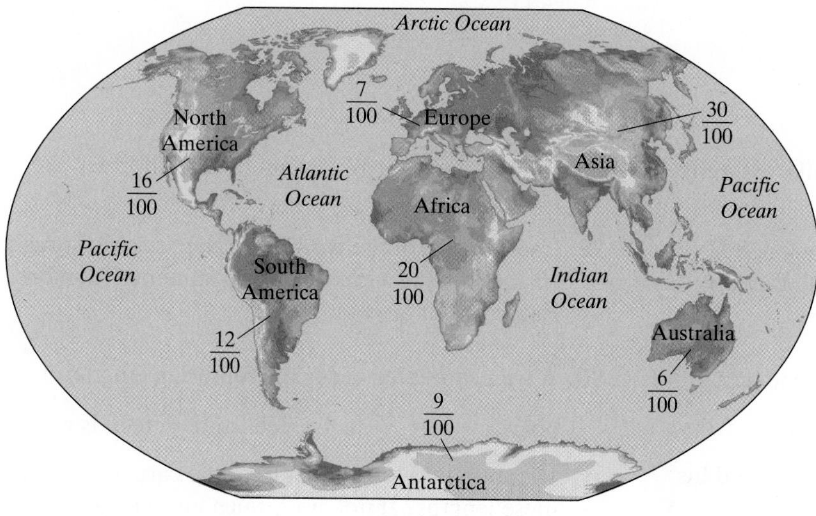

57. Find the fractional part of the world's land area within the continents of North America and South America.

58. Find the fractional part of the world's land area within the continents of Asia and Africa.

59. How much greater is the fractional part of the continent of Antarctica than the fractional part of the continent of Europe?

60. How much greater is the fractional part of the continent of Asia than the continent of Australia?

The theater industry is shifting toward theaters with multiple screens. Use the circle graph to answer Exercises 61 and 62. Write fraction answers in simplest form.

Fraction of U.S. Screens by Theater Type

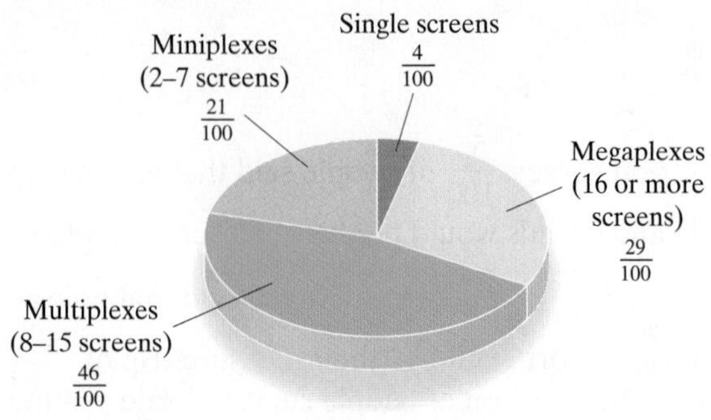

Source: Motion Picture Association of America

61. What fraction of U.S. theaters are single screens or miniplexes?

62. What fraction of U.S. theaters are multiplexes or megaplexes?

Review

Write the prime factorization of each number. See Section 2.2.

63. 10 **64.** 12 **65.** 8 **66.** 20 **67.** 55 **68.** 28

Concept Extensions

Perform each indicated operation.

69. $\frac{3}{8} + \frac{7}{8} - \frac{5}{8}$ **70.** $\frac{12}{20} - \frac{1}{20} - \frac{3}{20}$ **71.** $\frac{4}{11} + \frac{5}{11} - \frac{3}{11} + \frac{2}{11}$ **72.** $\frac{9}{12} + \frac{1}{12} - \frac{3}{12} - \frac{5}{12}$

Find and correct the error. See the Concept Check in this section.

73. $\frac{2}{7} + \frac{9}{7} = \frac{11}{14}$

74. $\frac{3}{4} - \frac{1}{4} = \frac{2}{8} = \frac{1}{4}$

Solve. Write each answer in simplest form.

75. In your own words, explain how to add like fractions.

76. In your own words, explain how to subtract like fractions.

77. Use the food pyramid for Exercises 49 through 52 and find the sum of all the daily servings' fractions. Explain your answer.

78. Use the map of the world for Exercises 57 through 60 and find the sum of all the continents' fractions. Explain your answer.

79. Mike Cannon jogged $\frac{3}{8}$ of a mile from home and then rested. Then he continued jogging farther from home for another $\frac{3}{8}$ of a mile until he discovered his watch had fallen off. He walked back along the same path for $\frac{4}{8}$ of a mile until he found his watch. Find how far he was from his home.

80. A trim carpenter needs the following lengths of boards: $\frac{5}{4}$ feet, $\frac{15}{4}$ feet, $\frac{9}{4}$ feet, and $\frac{13}{4}$ feet. Is a 10-foot board long enough for the carpenter to cut these lengths? If not, how much more length is needed?

3.2 LEAST COMMON MULTIPLE

Objectives

A Find the Least Common Multiple (LCM) Using Multiples.

B Find the LCM Using Prime Factorization.

C Write Equivalent Fractions.

Objective A Finding the Least Common Multiple Using Multiples

A multiple of a number is the product of that number and a natural number. For example, multiples of 5 are

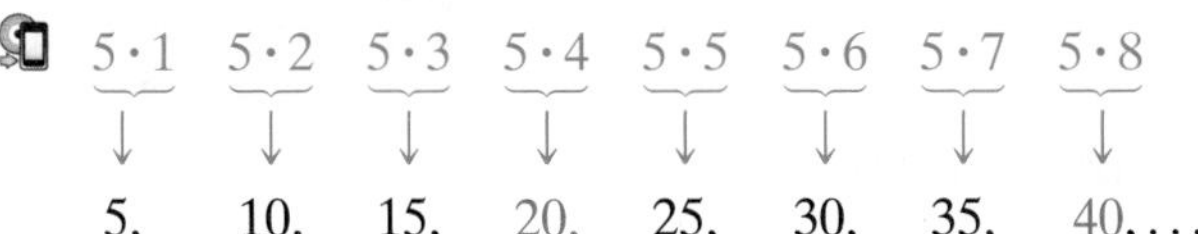

$$\underbrace{5\cdot 1}_{5},\ \underbrace{5\cdot 2}_{10},\ \underbrace{5\cdot 3}_{15},\ \underbrace{5\cdot 4}_{20},\ \underbrace{5\cdot 5}_{25},\ \underbrace{5\cdot 6}_{30},\ \underbrace{5\cdot 7}_{35},\ \underbrace{5\cdot 8}_{40},\ldots$$

Multiples of 4 are

4, 8, 12, 16, 20, 24, 28, 32, 36, 40, 44, . . .

Common multiples of both 4 and 5 are numbers that are found in both lists above. If we study the lists of multiples and extend them we have

Common multiples of 4 and 5: 20, 40, 60, 80, . . .

We call the smallest number in the list of common multiples the **least common multiple (LCM).** From the list of common multiples of 4 and 5, we see that the LCM of 4 and 5 is 20.

Example 1 Find the LCM of 6 and 8.

Solution: Multiples of 6: 6, 12, 18, (24), 30, 36, 42, (48), . . .

Multiples of 8: 8, 16, (24), 32, 40, (48), 56, . . .

The common multiples are 24, 48, ... The least common multiple (LCM) is 24.

Work Practice 1

PRACTICE 1

Find the LCM of 15 and 50.

Listing all the multiples of every number in a list can be cumbersome and tedious. We can condense the procedure shown in Example 1 with the following steps:

Method 1: Finding the LCM of a List of Numbers Using Multiples of the Largest Number

Step 1: Write the multiples of the largest number (starting with the number itself) until a multiple common to all numbers in the list is found.

Step 2: The multiple found in Step 1 is the LCM.

Example 2 Find the LCM of 9 and 12.

Solution: We write the multiples of 12 until we find a number that is also a multiple of 9.

$12\cdot 1 = 12$ Not a multiple of 9.

$12\cdot 2 = 24$ Not a multiple of 9.

$12\cdot 3 = 36$ A multiple of 9.

The LCM of 9 and 12 is 36.

Work Practice 2

PRACTICE 2

Find the LCM of 8 and 10.

Answers

1. 150 **2.** 40

PRACTICE 3

Find the LCM of 8 and 16.

Example 3 Find the LCM of 7 and 14.

Solution: We write the multiples of 14 until we find one that is also a multiple of 7.

$14 \cdot 1 = 14$ A multiple of 7

The LCM of 7 and 14 is 14.

Work Practice 3

PRACTICE 4

Find the LCM of 25 and 30.

Example 4 Find the LCM of 12 and 20.

Solution: We write the multiples of 20 until we find one that is also a multiple of 12.

$20 \cdot 1 = 20$ Not a multiple of 12

$20 \cdot 2 = 40$ Not a multiple of 12

$20 \cdot 3 = 60$ A multiple of 12

The LCM of 12 and 20 is 60.

Work Practice 4

Objective B Finding the LCM Using Prime Factorization

Method 1 for finding multiples works fine for smaller numbers, but may get tedious for larger numbers. A second method that uses prime factorization may be easier to use for larger numbers.

For example, to find the LCM of 270 and 84, let's look at the prime factorization of each.

$$270 = 2 \cdot 3 \cdot 3 \cdot 3 \cdot 5$$
$$84 = 2 \cdot 2 \cdot 3 \cdot 7$$

Recall that the LCM must be a multiple of both 270 and 84. Thus, to build the LCM, we will circle the greatest number of factors for each different prime number. The LCM is the product of the circled factors.

Prime Number Factors

270 =	2 ·	(3 · 3 · 3) ·	(5)	
84 =	(2 · 2) ·	3 ·		(7)

Circle the greatest number of factors for each different prime number.

$$\text{LCM} = 2 \cdot 2 \cdot 3 \cdot 3 \cdot 3 \cdot 5 \cdot 7 = 3780$$

The number 3780 is the smallest number that both 270 and 84 divide into evenly.

This method 2 is summarized below:

Method 2: Finding the LCM of a List of Numbers Using Prime Factorization

Step 1: Write the prime factorization of each number.

Step 2: For each different prime factor in step 1, circle the greatest number of times that factor occurs in any one factorization.

Step 3: The LCM is the product of the circled factors.

Answers

3. 16 **4.** 150

Example 5 Find the LCM of 72 and 60.

Solution: First we write the prime factorization of each number.

$72 = 2 \cdot 2 \cdot 2 \cdot 3 \cdot 3$

$60 = 2 \cdot 2 \cdot 3 \cdot 5$

For the prime factors shown, we circle the greatest number of prime factors found in either factorization.

$72 = \textcircled{2 \cdot 2 \cdot 2} \cdot \textcircled{3 \cdot 3}$

$60 = 2 \cdot 2 \cdot 3 \cdot \textcircled{5}$

The LCM is the product of the circled factors.

$\text{LCM} = 2 \cdot 2 \cdot 2 \cdot 3 \cdot 3 \cdot 5 = 360$

The LCM is 360.

Work Practice 5

PRACTICE 5

Find the LCM of 40 and 108.

Helpful Hint

If you prefer working with exponents, circle the factor with the greatest exponent. Example 5:

$72 = \textcircled{2^3} \cdot \textcircled{3^2}$

$60 = 2^2 \cdot 3 \cdot \textcircled{5}$

$\text{LCD} = 2^3 \cdot 3^2 \cdot 5 = 360$

Helpful Hint

If the number of factors of a prime number are equal, circle either one, but not both. For example,

$12 = \textcircled{2 \cdot 2} \cdot \textcircled{3}$

$15 = 3 \cdot \textcircled{5}$

Circle either 3 but not both.

The LCM is $2 \cdot 2 \cdot 3 \cdot 5 = 60$.

Example 6 Find the LCM of 15, 18, and 54.

Solution: $15 = 3 \cdot \textcircled{5}$

$18 = \textcircled{2} \cdot 3 \cdot 3$

$54 = 2 \cdot \textcircled{3 \cdot 3 \cdot 3}$

The LCM is $2 \cdot 3 \cdot 3 \cdot 3 \cdot 5$ or 270.

Work Practice 6

PRACTICE 6

Find the LCM of 20, 24, and 45.

Example 7 Find the LCM of 11 and 33.

Solution: $11 = \textcircled{11}$

$33 = \textcircled{3} \cdot 11$

It makes no difference which 11 is circled.

The LCM is $3 \cdot 11$ or 33.

Work Practice 7

PRACTICE 7

Find the LCM of 7 and 21.

Answers

5. 1080 **6.** 360 **7.** 21

Objective C Writing Equivalent Fractions

To add or subtract unlike fractions in the next section, we first write equivalent fractions with the LCM as the denominator. Recall from Section 2.3 that fractions that represent the same portion of a whole are called "equivalent fractions."

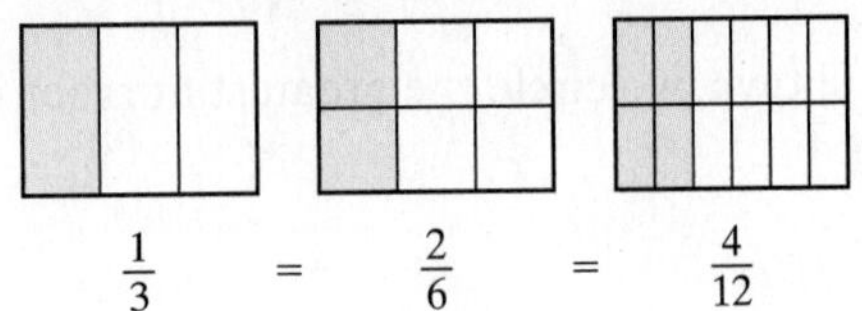

$$\frac{1}{3} = \frac{2}{6} = \frac{4}{12}$$

To write $\frac{1}{3}$ as an equivalent fraction with a denominator of 12, we multiply by 1 in the form of $\frac{4}{4}$.

$$\frac{1}{3} = \frac{1}{3} \cdot 1 = \frac{1}{3} \cdot \frac{4}{4} = \frac{1 \cdot 4}{3 \cdot 4} = \frac{4}{12}$$

$\frac{4}{4} = 1$

So $\frac{1}{3} = \frac{4}{12}$.

> To write an equivalent fraction,
>
> $$\frac{a}{b} = \frac{a}{b} \cdot \frac{c}{c} = \frac{a \cdot c}{b \cdot c}$$
>
> where a, b, and c are nonzero numbers.

✓Concept Check Which of the following is not equivalent to $\frac{3}{4}$?

a. $\frac{6}{8}$ **b.** $\frac{18}{24}$ **c.** $\frac{9}{14}$ **d.** $\frac{30}{40}$

PRACTICE 8

Write an equivalent fraction with the indicated denominator:

$\frac{7}{8} = \frac{}{56}$

Example 8 Write an equivalent fraction with the indicated denominator.

$$\frac{3}{4} = \frac{}{20}$$

Solution: In the denominators, since $4 \cdot 5 = 20$, we will multiply by 1 in the form of $\frac{5}{5}$.

$$\frac{3}{4} = \frac{3}{4} \cdot \frac{5}{5} = \frac{3 \cdot 5}{4 \cdot 5} = \frac{15}{20}$$

Thus, $\frac{3}{4} = \frac{15}{20}$.

Work Practice 8

Answer

8. $\frac{49}{56}$

✓ Concept Check Answer

c

Helpful Hint

To check Example 8, write $\frac{15}{20}$ in simplest form.

$$\frac{15}{20} = \frac{3 \cdot \overset{1}{\cancel{5}}}{4 \cdot \underset{1}{\cancel{5}}} = \frac{3}{4}, \text{ the original fraction.}$$

If the original fraction is in lowest terms, we can check our work by writing the new equivalent fraction in simplest form. This form should be the original fraction.

✓Concept Check True or false? When the fraction $\frac{2}{9}$ is rewritten as an equivalent fraction with 27 as the denominator, the result is $\frac{2}{27}$.

Example 9 Write an equivalent fraction with the indicated denominator.

$$\frac{1}{2} = \frac{}{24}$$

Solution: Since $2 \cdot 12 = 24$, we multiply by 1 in the form of $\frac{12}{12}$.

$$\frac{1}{2} = \frac{1}{2} \cdot \frac{12}{12} = \frac{1 \cdot 12}{2 \cdot 12} = \frac{12}{24}$$

Thus, $\frac{1}{2} = \frac{12}{24}$.

Work Practice 9

PRACTICE 9

Write an equivalent fraction with the indicated denominator.

$$\frac{3}{5} = \frac{}{15}$$

Example 10 Write an equivalent fraction with the given denominator.

$$3 = \frac{}{7}$$

Solution: Recall that $3 = \frac{3}{1}$. Since $1 \cdot 7 = 7$, multiply by 1 in the form $\frac{7}{7}$.

$$\frac{3}{1} = \frac{3}{1} \cdot \frac{7}{7} = \frac{3 \cdot 7}{1 \cdot 7} = \frac{21}{7}$$

Work Practice 10

PRACTICE 10

Write an equivalent fraction with the given denominator.

$$4 = \frac{}{6}$$

Answers

9. $\frac{9}{15}$ **10.** $\frac{24}{6}$

✓ Concept Check Answer

false; the correct result would be $\frac{6}{27}$

Vocabulary and Readiness Check

Use the choices below to fill in each blank.

least common multiple (LCM) multiple equivalent

1. Fractions that represent the same portion of a whole are called ______________ fractions.
2. The smallest positive number that is a multiple of all numbers in a list is called the ______________.
3. A(n) ______________ of a number is the product of that number and a natural number.

3.2 Exercise Set

FOR EXTRA HELP

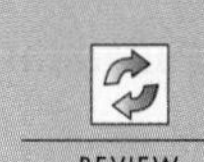

Objectives **A** **B** **Mixed Practice** *Find the LCM of each list of numbers. See Examples 1 through 7.*

1. 3, 4 **2.** 4, 6 **3.** 9, 15 **4.** 15, 20 **5.** 12, 18 **6.** 10, 15

7. 24, 36 **8.** 42, 70 **9.** 18, 21 **10.** 24, 45 **11.** 15, 25 **12.** 21, 14

13. 8, 24 **14.** 15, 90 **15.** 6, 7 **16.** 13, 8 **17.** 8, 6, 27 **18.** 6, 25, 10

19. 25, 15, 6 **20.** 4, 14, 20 **21.** 34, 68 **22.** 25, 175 **23.** 84, 294 **24.** 48, 54

25. 30, 36, 50 **26.** 21, 28, 42 **27.** 50, 72, 120 **28.** 70, 98, 100 **29.** 11, 33, 121 **30.** 10, 15, 100

31. 4, 6, 10, 15 **32.** 25, 3, 15, 10

Objective **C** *Write each fraction or whole number as an equivalent fraction with the given denominator. See Examples 8 through 10.*

33. $\frac{4}{7} = \frac{}{35}$ **34.** $\frac{3}{5} = \frac{}{20}$ **35.** $\frac{2}{3} = \frac{}{21}$ **36.** $6 = \frac{}{10}$ **37.** $5 = \frac{}{3}$

38. $\frac{9}{10} = \frac{}{70}$ **39.** $\frac{1}{2} = \frac{}{30}$ **40.** $\frac{1}{3} = \frac{}{30}$ **41.** $\frac{10}{7} = \frac{}{21}$ **42.** $\frac{5}{3} = \frac{}{21}$

43. $\frac{3}{4} = \frac{}{28}$ **44.** $\frac{4}{5} = \frac{}{45}$ **45.** $\frac{2}{3} = \frac{}{45}$ **46.** $\frac{2}{3} = \frac{}{75}$ **47.** $\frac{4}{9} = \frac{}{81}$

48. $\frac{5}{11} = \frac{}{88}$ **49.** $\frac{15}{13} = \frac{}{78}$ **50.** $\frac{9}{7} = \frac{}{84}$ **51.** $\frac{14}{17} = \frac{}{68}$ **52.** $\frac{19}{21} = \frac{}{126}$

The table shows the fraction of goods sold online by type of goods in a recent year. Use this table to answer Exercises 53 through 56.

53. Complete the table by writing each fraction as an equivalent fraction with a denominator of 100.

54. Which of these types of goods has the largest fraction sold online?

55. Which of these types of goods has the smallest fraction sold online?

56. Which of the types of goods has **more than** $\frac{3}{5}$ of the goods sold online? (*Hint:* write $\frac{3}{5}$ as an equivalent fraction with a denominator of 100.)

Type of Goods	Fraction of All Goods That Are Sold Online	Equivalent Fraction with a Denominator of 100
books and magazines	$\frac{27}{50}$	
clothing and accessories	$\frac{1}{2}$	
computer hardware	$\frac{23}{50}$	
computer software	$\frac{1}{2}$	
drugs, health and beauty aids	$\frac{3}{20}$	
electronics and appliances	$\frac{13}{20}$	
food, beer, and wine	$\frac{9}{20}$	
home furnishings	$\frac{13}{25}$	
music and videos	$\frac{3}{5}$	
office equipment and supplies	$\frac{61}{100}$	
sporting goods	$\frac{12}{25}$	
toys, hobbies, and games	$\frac{1}{2}$	

(*Source:* Fedstats.gov)

Review

Add or subtract as indicated. See Section 3.1.

57. $\frac{7}{10} - \frac{2}{10}$ **58.** $\frac{8}{13} - \frac{3}{13}$ **59.** $\frac{1}{5} + \frac{1}{5}$ **60.** $\frac{1}{8} + \frac{3}{8}$

61. $\frac{23}{18} - \frac{15}{18}$ **62.** $\frac{36}{30} - \frac{12}{30}$ **63.** $\frac{2}{9} + \frac{1}{9} + \frac{6}{9}$ **64.** $\frac{2}{12} + \frac{7}{12} + \frac{3}{12}$

Concept Extensions

Write each fraction as an equivalent fraction with the indicated denominator.

65. $\frac{37}{165} = \frac{\quad}{3630}$

66. $\frac{108}{215} = \frac{\quad}{4085}$

67. In your own words, explain how to find the LCM of two numbers.

68. In your own words, explain how to write a fraction as an equivalent fraction with a given denominator.

Solve. See the Concept Checks in this section.

69. Which of the following are equivalent to $\frac{2}{3}$?

a. $\frac{10}{15}$ **b.** $\frac{40}{60}$

c. $\frac{16}{20}$ **d.** $\frac{200}{300}$

70. True or False? When the fraction $\frac{7}{12}$ is rewritten with a denominator of 48, the result is $\frac{11}{48}$. If false, give the correct fraction.

3.3 ADDING AND SUBTRACTING UNLIKE FRACTIONS

Objectives

A Add Unlike Fractions.

B Subtract Unlike Fractions.

C Solve Problems by Adding or Subtracting Unlike Fractions.

Objective A Adding Unlike Fractions

In this section we add and subtract fractions with unlike denominators. To add or subtract these unlike fractions, we first write the fractions as equivalent fractions with a common denominator and then add or subtract the like fractions. The common denominator that we use is the least common multiple (LCM) of the denominators. This denominator is called the **least common denominator (LCD).**

To begin, let's add the unlike fractions $\frac{3}{4} + \frac{1}{6}$. The LCM of denominators 4 and 6 is 12. This means that the number 12 is also the LCD. So we write each fraction as an equivalent fraction with a denominator of 12, then add as usual. This addition process is shown next and also illustrated by figures.

Add: $\frac{3}{4} + \frac{1}{6}$	**The LCD is 12.**
Figures	**Algebra**
$\frac{3}{4} + \frac{1}{6}$ $\frac{9}{12} + \frac{2}{12}$ $\frac{9}{12} + \frac{2}{12} = \frac{11}{12}$	$\frac{3}{4} = \frac{3}{4} \cdot \frac{3}{3} = \frac{9}{12}$ and $\frac{1}{6} = \frac{1}{6} \cdot \frac{2}{2} = \frac{2}{12}$ Remember $\frac{3}{3} = 1$ and $\frac{2}{2} = 1$. Now we can add just as we did in Section 3.1. $\frac{3}{4} + \frac{1}{6} = \frac{9}{12} + \frac{2}{12} = \frac{11}{12}$
Thus, the sum is $\frac{11}{12}$.	

Adding or Subtracting Unlike Fractions

Step 1: Find the LCM of the denominators of the fractions. This number is the least common denominator (LCD).

Step 2: Write each fraction as an equivalent fraction whose denominator is the LCD.

Step 3: Add or subtract the like fractions.

Step 4: Write the sum or difference in simplest form.

PRACTICE 1

Add: $\frac{1}{6} + \frac{5}{18}$

Example 1 Add: $\frac{2}{5} + \frac{4}{15}$

Solution:

Step 1: The LCM of the denominators 5 and 15 is 15. Thus, the LCD is 15. In later examples, we shall simply say, for example, that the LCD of 5 and 15 is 15.

Step 2: $\frac{2}{5} = \frac{2}{5} \cdot \frac{3}{3} = \frac{6}{15}, \quad \frac{4}{15} = \frac{4}{15}$ ⟵ This fraction already has a denominator of 15.

↑ Multiply by 1 in the form $\frac{3}{3}$

Step 3: $\frac{2}{5} + \frac{4}{15} = \frac{6}{15} + \frac{4}{15} = \frac{10}{15}$

Step 4: Write in simplest form.

$$\frac{10}{15} = \frac{2 \cdot \overset{1}{\cancel{5}}}{3 \cdot \underset{1}{\cancel{5}}} = \frac{2}{3}$$

Work Practice 1

PRACTICE 2

Add: $\frac{5}{6} + \frac{2}{9}$

Example 2 Add: $\frac{11}{15} + \frac{3}{10}$

Solution:

Step 1: The LCD of 15 and 10 is 30.

Step 2: $\frac{11}{15} = \frac{11}{15} \cdot \frac{2}{2} = \frac{22}{30} \qquad \frac{3}{10} = \frac{3}{10} \cdot \frac{3}{3} = \frac{9}{30}$

Step 3: $\frac{11}{15} + \frac{3}{10} = \frac{22}{30} + \frac{9}{30} = \frac{31}{30}$

Step 4: $\frac{31}{30}$ is in simplest form. We can write the sum as $\frac{31}{30}$ or $1\frac{1}{30}$.

Work Practice 2

PRACTICE 3

Add: $\frac{2}{5} + \frac{4}{9}$

Example 3 Add: $\frac{2}{3} + \frac{1}{7}$

Solution: The LCD of 3 and 7 is 21.

$$\frac{2}{3} + \frac{1}{7} = \frac{2}{3} \cdot \frac{7}{7} + \frac{1}{7} \cdot \frac{3}{3}$$

$$= \frac{14}{21} + \frac{3}{21}$$

$$= \frac{17}{21} \quad \text{Simplest form.}$$

Work Practice 3

Answers

1. $\frac{4}{9}$ **2.** $\frac{19}{18}$ or $1\frac{1}{18}$ **3.** $\frac{38}{45}$

Example 4 Add: $\frac{1}{2} + \frac{2}{3} + \frac{5}{6}$

Solution: The LCD of 2, 3, and 6 is 6.

$$\frac{1}{2} + \frac{2}{3} + \frac{5}{6} = \frac{1}{2}\cdot\frac{3}{3} + \frac{2}{3}\cdot\frac{2}{2} + \frac{5}{6}$$
$$= \frac{3}{6} + \frac{4}{6} + \frac{5}{6}$$
$$= \frac{12}{6} = 2$$

Work Practice 4

PRACTICE 4

Add: $\frac{1}{4} + \frac{4}{5} + \frac{9}{10}$

✓**Concept Check** Find and correct the error in the following:

$$\frac{2}{9} + \frac{4}{11} = \frac{6}{20} = \frac{3}{10}$$

Objective B Subtracting Unlike Fractions

As indicated in the box on page 191, we follow the same steps when subtracting unlike fractions as when adding them.

Example 5 Subtract: $\frac{2}{5} - \frac{3}{20}$

Solution:

Step 1: The LCD of 5 and 20 is 20.

Step 2: $\frac{2}{5} = \frac{2}{5}\cdot\frac{4}{4} = \frac{8}{20}$ $\quad \frac{3}{20} = \frac{3}{20}$ ⟵ The fraction already has a denominator of 20.

Step 3: $\frac{2}{5} - \frac{3}{20} = \frac{8}{20} - \frac{3}{20} = \frac{5}{20}$

Step 4: Write in simplest form.

$$\frac{5}{20} = \frac{\overset{1}{\cancel{5}}}{\underset{1}{\cancel{5}}\cdot 4} = \frac{1}{4}$$

Work Practice 5

PRACTICE 5

Subtract: $\frac{7}{12} - \frac{5}{24}$

Example 6 Subtract: $\frac{10}{11} - \frac{2}{3}$

Solution:

Step 1: The LCD of 11 and 3 is 33.

Step 2: $\frac{10}{11} = \frac{10}{11}\cdot\frac{3}{3} = \frac{30}{33}$ $\quad \frac{2}{3} = \frac{2}{3}\cdot\frac{11}{11} = \frac{22}{33}$

Step 3: $\frac{10}{11} - \frac{2}{3} = \frac{30}{33} - \frac{22}{33} = \frac{8}{33}$

Step 4: $\frac{8}{33}$ is in simplest form.

Work Practice 6

PRACTICE 6

Subtract: $\frac{9}{10} - \frac{3}{7}$

Answers

4. $\frac{39}{20}$ or $1\frac{19}{20}$ **5.** $\frac{3}{8}$ **6.** $\frac{33}{70}$

✓ **Concept Check Answer**

When adding unlike fractions, we don't add the denominators. Correct solution:

$$\frac{2}{9} + \frac{4}{11} = \frac{22}{99} + \frac{36}{99} = \frac{58}{99}$$

PRACTICE 7

Subtract: $\frac{7}{8} - \frac{5}{6}$

Example 7 Subtract: $\frac{11}{12} - \frac{2}{9}$

Solution: The LCD of 12 and 9 is 36.

$$\frac{11}{12} - \frac{2}{9} = \frac{11}{12} \cdot \frac{3}{3} - \frac{2}{9} \cdot \frac{4}{4} = \frac{33}{36} - \frac{8}{36} = \frac{25}{36}$$

Work Practice 7

✓**Concept Check** Find and correct the error in the following:

$$\frac{11}{12} - \frac{3}{4} = \frac{8}{8} = 1$$

Objective C Solving Problems by Adding or Subtracting Unlike Fractions

Very often, real-world problems involve adding or subtracting unlike fractions.

PRACTICE 8

To repair her sidewalk, a homeowner must pour small amounts of cement in three different locations. She needs $\frac{3}{5}$ of a cubic yard, $\frac{2}{10}$ of a cubic yard, and $\frac{2}{15}$ of a cubic yard for these locations. Find the total amount of cement the homeowner needs.

Example 8 Finding Total Weight

A freight truck has $\frac{1}{4}$ ton of computers, $\frac{1}{3}$ ton of televisions, and $\frac{3}{8}$ ton of small appliances. Find the total weight of its load.

Solution:

1. UNDERSTAND. Read and reread the problem. The phrase "total weight" tells us to add.
2. TRANSLATE.

In words:	total weight	is	weight of computers	plus	weight of televisions	plus	weight of appliances
	↓	↓	↓	↓	↓	↓	↓
Translate:	total weight	=	$\frac{1}{4}$	+	$\frac{1}{3}$	+	$\frac{3}{8}$

3. SOLVE: The LCD is 24.

$$\frac{1}{4} + \frac{1}{3} + \frac{3}{8} = \frac{1}{4} \cdot \frac{6}{6} + \frac{1}{3} \cdot \frac{8}{8} + \frac{3}{8} \cdot \frac{3}{3} = \frac{6}{24} + \frac{8}{24} + \frac{9}{24} = \frac{23}{24}$$

4. INTERPRET. *Check* the solution. *State* your conclusion: The total weight of the truck's load is $\frac{23}{24}$ ton.

Work Practice 8

Answers

7. $\frac{1}{24}$ 8. $\frac{14}{15}$ cu yd

✓ **Concept Check Answer**

Correct solution:

$\frac{11}{12} - \frac{3}{4} = \frac{11}{12} - \frac{9}{12} = \frac{2}{12} = \frac{1}{6}$

Example 9 Calculating Flight Time

A flight from Tucson to Phoenix, Arizona, requires $\frac{5}{12}$ of an hour. If the plane has been flying $\frac{1}{4}$ of an hour, find how much time remains before landing.

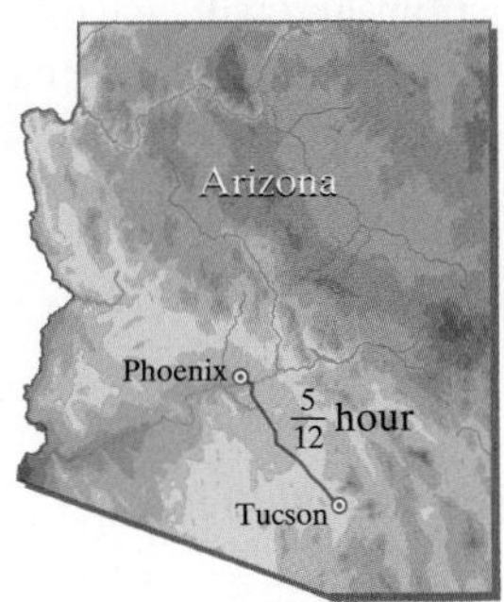

Solution:

1. UNDERSTAND. Read and reread the problem. The phrase "how much time remains" tells us to subtract.
2. TRANSLATE.

In words:	time remaining	is	flight time from Tucson of Phoenix	minus	flight time already passed
	↓	↓	↓	↓	↓
Translate:	time remaining	=	$\frac{5}{12}$	−	$\frac{1}{4}$

3. SOLVE: The LCD is 12.

$$\frac{5}{12} - \frac{1}{4} = \frac{5}{12} - \frac{1}{4}\cdot\frac{3}{3}$$
$$= \frac{5}{12} - \frac{3}{12}$$
$$= \frac{2}{12}$$
$$= \frac{\overset{1}{\cancel{2}}}{\underset{1}{\cancel{2}}\cdot 6}$$
$$= \frac{1}{6}$$

4. INTERPRET. *Check* the solution. *State* your conclusion: The flight time remaining is $\frac{1}{6}$ of an hour.

Work Practice 9

PRACTICE 9

Find the difference in length of two boards if one board is $\frac{4}{5}$ of a foot long and the other is $\frac{2}{3}$ of a foot long.

Answer

9. $\frac{2}{15}$ ft

Calculator Explorations Performing Operations on Fractions

Scientific Calculator

Many calculators have a fraction key, such as [a b/c], that allows you to enter fractions and perform operations on them, and then it gives the result as a fraction. If your calculator has a fraction key, use it to calculate

$$\frac{3}{5} + \frac{4}{7}$$

Enter the keystrokes

[3] [a b/c] [5] [+] [4] [a b/c] [7] [=]

The display should read [1_6 35], which represents the mixed number $1\frac{6}{35}$. Let's write the result as a fraction. To convert from mixed number notation to fractional notation, press

[2nd] [d/c]

The display now reads [41 35], which represents $\frac{41}{35}$, the sum in fractional notation.

Graphing Calculator

Graphing calculators also allow you to perform operations on fractions and will give exact fractional results. The fraction option on a graphing calculator may be found under the [MATH] menu. To perform the addition to the left, try the keystrokes.

[3] [÷] [5] [+] [4] [÷] [7] [MATH] [ENTER]

[ENTER]

The display should read

[3/5 + 4/7 ▶Frac 41/35]

Use a calculator to add the following fractions. Give each sum as a fraction.

1. $\frac{1}{16} + \frac{2}{5}$

2. $\frac{3}{20} + \frac{2}{25}$

3. $\frac{4}{9} + \frac{7}{8}$

4. $\frac{9}{11} + \frac{5}{12}$

5. $\frac{10}{17} + \frac{12}{19}$

6. $\frac{14}{31} + \frac{15}{21}$

Vocabulary and Readiness Check

Use the choices below to fill in each blank. Any numerical answers are not listed.

least common denominator   equivalent

1. To add or subtract unlike fractions, we first write the fractions as ______________________ fractions with a common denominator. The common denominator we use is called the ______________________.

2. The LCD for $\frac{5}{8}$ and $\frac{1}{6}$ is ______________________.

3. $\frac{5}{8} + \frac{1}{6} = \frac{5}{8} \cdot \frac{3}{3} + \frac{1}{6} \cdot \frac{4}{4} = \frac{\quad}{\_\_} + \frac{\quad}{\_\_} = \frac{\quad}{\_\_}$.

4. $\frac{5}{8} - \frac{1}{6} = \frac{5}{8} \cdot \frac{3}{3} - \frac{1}{6} \cdot \frac{4}{4} = \frac{\quad}{\_\_} - \frac{\quad}{\_\_} = \frac{\quad}{\_\_}$.

3.3 Exercise Set

FOR EXTRA HELP

PRACTICE

WATCH

DOWNLOAD

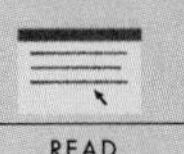
READ

REVIEW

Objective A *Add and simplify. See Examples 1 through 4.*

1. $\frac{2}{3} + \frac{1}{6}$

2. $\frac{5}{6} + \frac{1}{12}$

3. $\frac{1}{2} + \frac{1}{3}$

4. $\frac{2}{3} + \frac{1}{4}$

5. $\frac{2}{11} + \frac{2}{33}$

6. $\frac{5}{9} + \frac{1}{3}$

7. $\frac{3}{14} + \frac{3}{7}$

8. $\frac{2}{5} + \frac{2}{15}$

9. $\frac{11}{35} + \frac{2}{7}$

10. $\frac{4}{5} + \frac{3}{40}$

11. $\frac{8}{25} + \frac{7}{35}$

12. $\frac{5}{14} + \frac{10}{21}$

13. $\frac{7}{15} + \frac{5}{12}$

14. $\frac{5}{8} + \frac{3}{20}$

15. $\frac{2}{28} + \frac{2}{21}$

16. $\frac{6}{25} + \frac{7}{35}$

17. $\frac{9}{44} + \frac{17}{36}$

18. $\frac{2}{33} + \frac{2}{21}$

19. $\frac{5}{11} + \frac{3}{13}$

20. $\frac{3}{7} + \frac{9}{17}$

21. $\frac{1}{3} + \frac{1}{9} + \frac{1}{27}$

22. $\frac{1}{4} + \frac{1}{16} + \frac{1}{64}$

23. $\frac{5}{7} + \frac{1}{8} + \frac{1}{2}$

24. $\frac{10}{13} + \frac{7}{10} + \frac{1}{5}$

25. $\frac{5}{36} + \frac{3}{4} + \frac{1}{6}$

26. $\frac{7}{18} + \frac{2}{9} + \frac{5}{6}$

27. $\frac{13}{20} + \frac{3}{5} + \frac{1}{3}$

28. $\frac{2}{7} + \frac{13}{28} + \frac{2}{5}$

Objective B *Subtract and simplify. See Examples 5 through 7.*

29. $\frac{7}{8} - \frac{3}{16}$

30. $\frac{5}{13} - \frac{3}{26}$

31. $\frac{5}{6} - \frac{3}{7}$

32. $\frac{3}{4} - \frac{1}{7}$

33. $\frac{5}{7} - \frac{1}{8}$

34. $\frac{10}{13} - \frac{7}{10}$

35. $\frac{9}{11} - \frac{4}{9}$

36. $\frac{7}{18} - \frac{2}{9}$

37. $\frac{11}{35} - \frac{2}{7}$

38. $\frac{2}{5} - \frac{3}{25}$

39. $\frac{5}{12} - \frac{1}{9}$

40. $\frac{7}{12} - \frac{5}{18}$

41. $\frac{7}{15} - \frac{5}{12}$

42. $\frac{5}{8} - \frac{3}{20}$

43. $\frac{3}{28} - \frac{2}{21}$

44. $\frac{6}{25} - \frac{7}{35}$

45. $\frac{1}{100} - \frac{1}{1000}$

46. $\frac{1}{50} - \frac{1}{500}$

47. $\frac{21}{44} - \frac{11}{36}$

48. $\frac{7}{18} - \frac{2}{45}$

Objectives A B **Mixed Practice** *Perform the indicated operation. See Examples 1 through 7.*

49. $\frac{5}{12} + \frac{1}{9}$

50. $\frac{7}{12} + \frac{5}{18}$

51. $\frac{17}{35} - \frac{2}{7}$

52. $\frac{13}{24} - \frac{1}{6}$

53. $\frac{9}{28} - \frac{3}{40}$

54. $\frac{10}{26} - \frac{3}{8}$

55. $\frac{2}{3} + \frac{4}{45} + \frac{4}{5}$

56. $\frac{3}{16} + \frac{1}{4} + \frac{1}{16}$

Objective C *Find the perimeter of each geometric figure. (Hint: Recall that perimeter means distance around.)*

57.

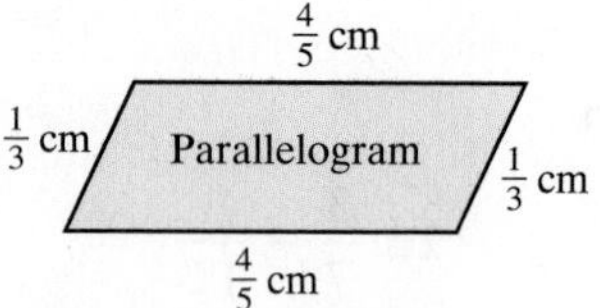

58.

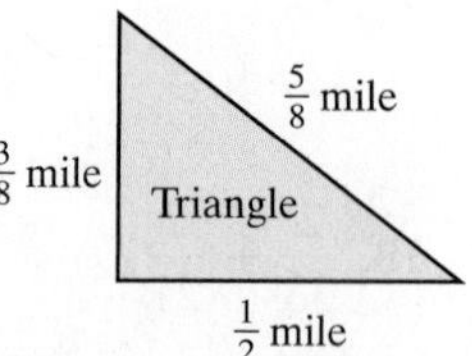

59.

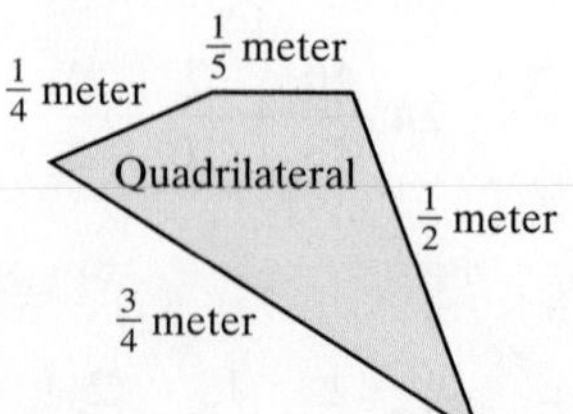

60.

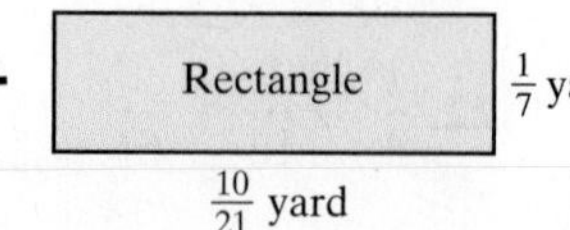

Solve. For Exercises 61 and 62, the solutions have been started for you. See Examples 8 and 9.

61. The slowest mammal is the three-toed sloth from South America. The sloth has an average ground speed of $\frac{1}{10}$ mph. In the trees, it can accelerate to $\frac{17}{100}$ mph. How much faster can a sloth travel in the trees? (*Source: The Guinness Book of World Records*)

Start the solution:

1. UNDERSTAND the problem. Reread it as many times as needed.
2. TRANSLATE into an equation. (Fill in the blanks.)

how much faster sloth travels in trees	is	sloth speed in trees	minus	sloth speed on ground
↓	↓	↓	↓	↓
how much faster sloth travels in trees	=	______	−	______

Finish with:

3. SOLVE. and
4. INTERPRET.

62. Killer bees have been known to chase people for up to $\frac{1}{4}$ of a mile, while domestic European honeybees will normally chase a person for no more than 100 feet, or $\frac{5}{264}$ of a mile. How much farther will a killer bee chase a person than a domestic honeybee? (*Source:* Coachella Valley Mosquito & Vector Control District)

Start the solution:

1. UNDERSTAND the problem. Reread it as many times as needed.
2. TRANSLATE into an equation. (Fill in the blanks.)

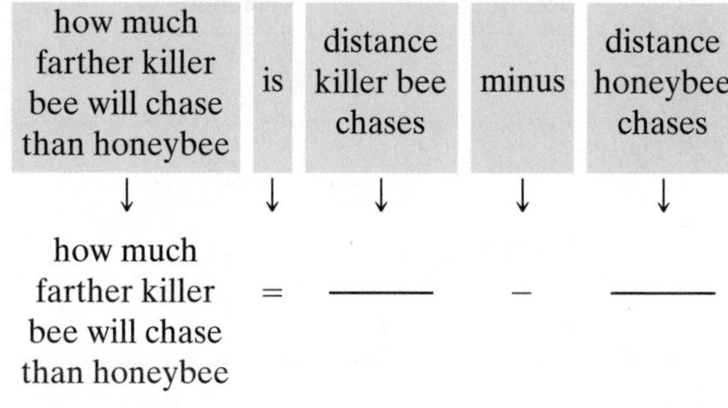

how much farther killer bee will chase than honeybee
is
distance killer bee chases
minus
distance honeybee chases
how much farther killer bee will chase than honeybee
=
−

Finish with

3. SOLVE. and
4. INTERPRET.

63. Find the inner diameter of the washer. (*Hint:* Use the outer diameter and subtract the washer widths.)

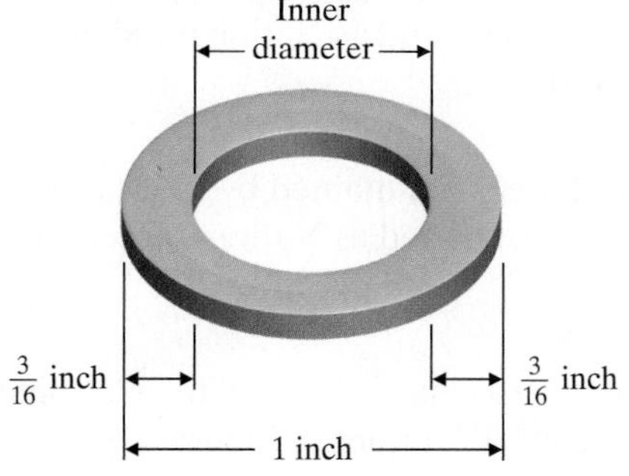

64. Find the inner diameter of the tubing. (See the hint for Exercise 63.)

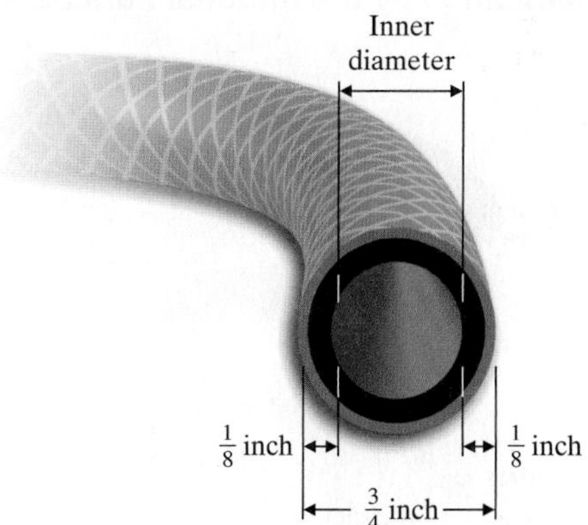

65. Given the following diagram, find its total length. (*Hint:* Find the sum of the partial lengths.)

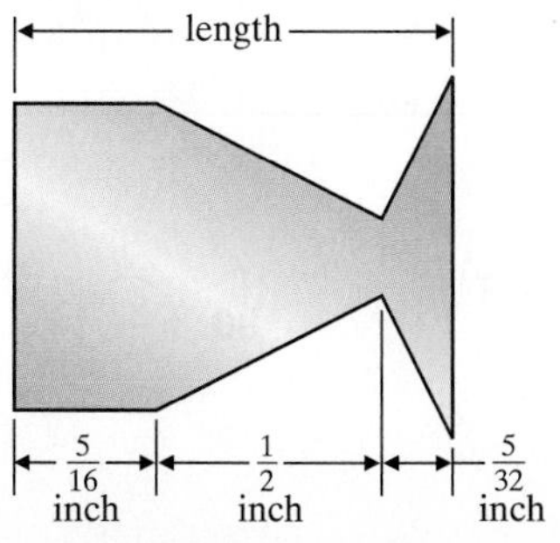

66. Given the following diagram, find its total width. (*Hint:* Find the sum of the partial widths.)

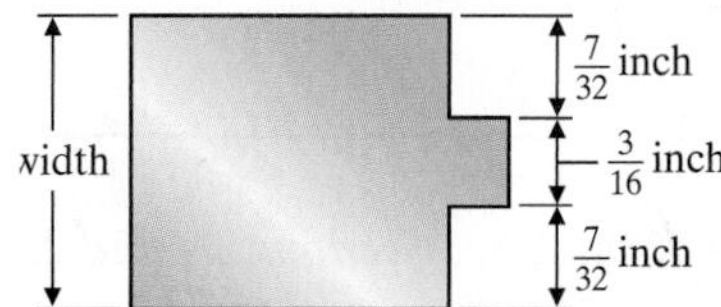

67. Together, Thin Mints and Samoas account for $\frac{11}{25}$ of the Girl Scout cookies sold each year. Thin Mints alone account for $\frac{1}{4}$ of all Girl Scout cookie sales. What fraction of Girl Scout cookies sold are Samoas? (*Source:* Girl Scouts of the United States of America)

68. About $\frac{13}{20}$ of American students ages 10 to 17 name math, science, or art as their favorite subject in school. Art is the favorite subject for about $\frac{4}{25}$ of the American students ages 10 to 17. For what fraction of students this age is math or science their favorite subject? (*Source:* Peter D. Hart Research Associates for the National Science Foundation)

The table below shows the fraction of the Earth's water area taken up by each ocean. Use this table for Exercises 69 and 70.

Fraction of Earth's Water Area per Ocean

Ocean	Fraction
Arctic	$\frac{1}{25}$
Atlantic	$\frac{13}{50}$
Pacific	$\frac{1}{2}$
Indian	$\frac{1}{5}$

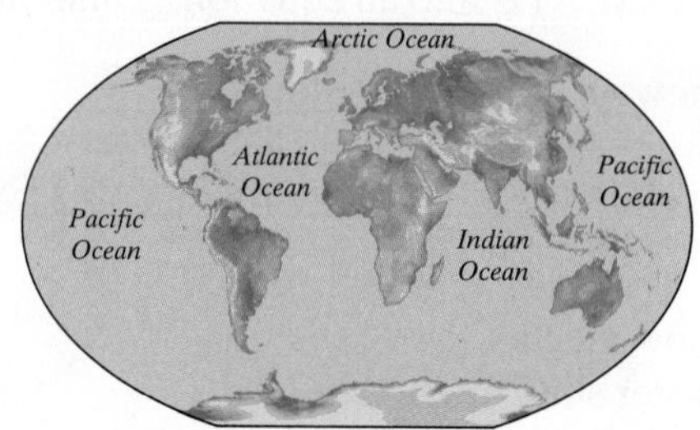

69. What fraction of the world's water surface area is accounted for by the Pacific and Atlantic Oceans?

70. What fraction of the world's water surface area is accounted for by the Arctic and Indian Oceans?

We first viewed this circle graph in Section 2.3. In this section we study it further. Use it to answer Exercises 71 through 74.

Areas Maintained by the National Park Service

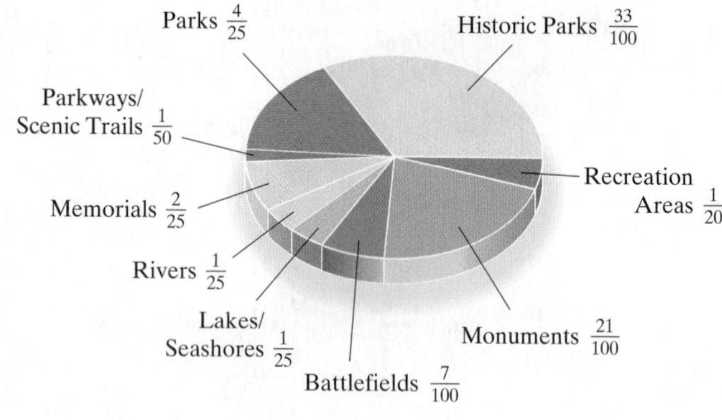

Source: National Park Service

71. What fraction of areas maintained by the National Park Service are designated as National Lakes or National Seashores?

72. What fraction of areas maintained by the National Park Service are designated as National Recreation Areas?

73. What fraction of areas maintained by the National Park Service are NOT National Monuments?

74. What fraction of areas maintained by the National Park Service are NOT National Parkways or Scenic Trails?

Review

Multiply or divide as indicated. See Sections 2.4 and 2.5.

75. $1\frac{1}{2} \cdot 3\frac{1}{3}$

76. $2\frac{5}{6} \div 5$

77. $4 \div 7\frac{1}{4}$

78. $4\frac{3}{4} \cdot 5\frac{1}{5}$

79. $3 \cdot 2\frac{1}{9}$

80. $6\frac{2}{7} \cdot 14$

Concept Extensions

For Exercises 81 and 82 below, do the following:

a. *Draw three rectangles of the same size and represent each fraction in the sum or difference, one fraction per rectangle, by shading.*

b. *Using these rectangles as estimates, determine whether there is an error in the sum or difference.*

c. *If there is an error, correctly calculate the sum or difference.*

See the Concept Checks in this section.

81. $\frac{3}{5} + \frac{4}{5} \stackrel{?}{=} \frac{7}{10}$

82. $\frac{3}{4} - \frac{5}{8} \stackrel{?}{=} \frac{2}{4}$

Subtract from left to right.

83. $\frac{2}{3} - \frac{1}{4} - \frac{2}{540}$

84. $\frac{9}{10} - \frac{7}{200} - \frac{1}{3}$

Perform each indicated operation.

85. $\frac{30}{55} + \frac{1000}{1760}$

86. $\frac{19}{26} - \frac{968}{1352}$

87. In your own words, describe how to add or subtract two fractions with different denominators.

88. Find the sum of the fractions in the circle graph on page 200. Did the sum surprise you? Why or why not?

Answers

1. ______

2. ______

3. ______

4. ______

5. ______

6. ______

7. ______

8. ______

9. ______

10. ______

11. ______

12. ______

13. ______

14. ______

15. ______

16. ______

17. ______

18. ______

19. ______

20. ______

21. ______

Integrated Review Sections 3.1–3.3

Operations on Fractions and Mixed Numbers

Find the LCM of each list of numbers.

1. 5, 6

2. 3, 7

3. 2, 14

4. 5, 25

5. 4, 20, 25

6. 6, 18, 30

Write each fraction as an equivalent fraction with the indicated denominator.

7. $\frac{3}{8} = \frac{}{24}$

8. $\frac{7}{9} = \frac{}{36}$

9. $\frac{1}{4} = \frac{}{40}$

10. $\frac{2}{5} = \frac{}{30}$

11. $\frac{11}{15} = \frac{}{75}$

12. $\frac{5}{6} = \frac{}{48}$

Add or subtract as indicated. Simplify if necessary.

13. $\frac{3}{8} + \frac{1}{8}$

14. $\frac{7}{10} - \frac{3}{10}$

15. $\frac{17}{24} - \frac{3}{24}$

16. $\frac{4}{15} + \frac{9}{15}$

17. $\frac{1}{4} + \frac{1}{2}$

18. $\frac{1}{3} - \frac{1}{5}$

19. $\frac{7}{9} - \frac{2}{5}$

20. $\frac{3}{10} + \frac{2}{25}$

21. $\frac{7}{8} + \frac{1}{20}$

22. $\frac{5}{12} - \frac{2}{18}$

23. $\frac{1}{11} - \frac{1}{11}$

24. $\frac{3}{17} - \frac{2}{17}$

25. $\frac{9}{11} - \frac{2}{3}$

26. $\frac{1}{6} - \frac{1}{7}$

27. $\frac{2}{9} + \frac{1}{18}$

28. $\frac{4}{13} + \frac{2}{26}$

29. $\frac{2}{9} + \frac{1}{18} + \frac{1}{3}$

30. $\frac{3}{10} + \frac{1}{5} + \frac{6}{25}$

Mixed Practice (*Sections 2.4, 2.5, 3.1, 3.2, 3.3*) *Perform the indicated operation.*

31. $\frac{9}{10} + \frac{2}{3}$

32. $\frac{9}{10} - \frac{2}{3}$

33. $\frac{9}{10} \cdot \frac{2}{3}$

34. $\frac{9}{10} \div \frac{2}{3}$

35. $\frac{21}{25} - \frac{3}{70}$

36. $\frac{21}{25} + \frac{3}{70}$

37. $\frac{21}{25} \div \frac{3}{70}$

38. $\frac{21}{25} \cdot \frac{3}{70}$

39. $3\frac{7}{8} \cdot 2\frac{2}{3}$

40. $3\frac{7}{8} \div 2\frac{2}{3}$

41. $\frac{2}{9} + \frac{5}{27} + \frac{1}{2}$

42. $\frac{3}{8} + \frac{11}{16} + \frac{2}{3}$

43. $11\frac{7}{10} \div 3\frac{3}{100}$

44. $7\frac{1}{4} \cdot 3\frac{1}{5}$

45. $\frac{14}{15} - \frac{4}{27}$

46. $\frac{9}{14} - \frac{11}{32}$

22. _____
23. _____
24. _____
25. _____
26. _____
27. _____
28. _____
29. _____
30. _____
31. _____
32. _____
33. _____
34. _____
35. _____
36. _____
37. _____
38. _____
39. _____
40. _____
41. _____
42. _____
43. _____
44. _____
45. _____
46. _____

Objectives

A Add Mixed Numbers.

B Subtract Mixed Numbers.

C Solve Problems by Adding or Subtracting Mixed Numbers.

3.4 ADDING AND SUBTRACTING MIXED NUMBERS

Objective A Adding Mixed Numbers

Recall that a mixed number has a whole number part and a fraction part.

$$2\frac{3}{8} \text{ means } 2 + \frac{3}{8}$$

(whole number: 2; fraction: $\frac{3}{8}$)

✓Concept Check Which of the following are equivalent to 7?

a. $6\frac{5}{5}$ **b.** $6\frac{7}{7}$ **c.** $5\frac{8}{4}$

d. $6\frac{17}{17}$ **e.** all of these

Adding or Subtracting Mixed Numbers

To add or subtract mixed numbers, add or subtract the fraction parts and then add or subtract the whole number parts.

For example,

$$\begin{array}{r} 2\frac{2}{7} \\ +6\frac{3}{7} \\ \hline 8\frac{5}{7} \end{array}$$

← Add the fractions; then add the whole numbers

PRACTICE 1

Add: $4\frac{2}{5} + 5\frac{1}{6}$

Example 1 Add: $2\frac{1}{3} + 5\frac{3}{8}$. Check by estimating.

Solution: The LCD of 3 and 8 is 24.

$$\begin{array}{rcl} 2\frac{1\cdot 8}{3\cdot 8} & = & 2\frac{8}{24} \\ +5\frac{3\cdot 3}{8\cdot 3} & = & 5\frac{9}{24} \\ \hline & & 7\frac{17}{24} \end{array}$$

← Add the fractions

Add the whole numbers

To check by estimating, we round as usual. The fraction $2\frac{1}{3}$ rounds to 2, $5\frac{3}{8}$ rounds to 5, and $2 + 5 = 7$, our estimate.

Our exact answer is close to 7, so our answer is reasonable.

Work Practice 1

Answer

1. $9\frac{17}{30}$

✓ Concept Check Answer

e

Helpful Hint

When adding or subtracting mixed numbers and whole numbers, it is a good idea to estimate to see if your answer is reasonable.

For the rest of this section, we leave most of the checking by estimating to you.

Example 2 Add: $3\frac{4}{5} + 1\frac{4}{15}$

Solution: The LCD of 5 and 15 is 15.

$$3\frac{4}{5} = 3\frac{12}{15}$$

$$+1\frac{4}{15} = 1\frac{4}{15}$$ Add the fractions; then add the whole numbers.

$$4\frac{16}{15}$$ Notice that the fraction part is improper.

Since $\frac{16}{15}$ is $1\frac{1}{15}$ we can write the sum as

$$4\frac{16}{15} = 4 + 1\frac{1}{15} = 5\frac{1}{15}$$

Work Practice 2

PRACTICE 2

Add: $2\frac{5}{14} + 5\frac{6}{7}$

✓Concept Check Explain how you could estimate the following sum: $5\frac{1}{9} + 14\frac{10}{11}$.

Example 3 Add: $1\frac{4}{5} + 4 + 2\frac{1}{2}$

Solution: The LCD of 5 and 2 is 10.

$$1\frac{4}{5} = 1\frac{8}{10}$$

$$4 = 4$$

$$+2\frac{1}{2} = 2\frac{5}{10}$$

$$7\frac{13}{10} = 7 + 1\frac{3}{10} = 8\frac{3}{10}$$

Work Practice 3

PRACTICE 3

Add: $10 + 2\frac{6}{7} + 3\frac{1}{5}$

Answers

2. $8\frac{3}{14}$ **3.** $16\frac{2}{35}$

✓ Concept Check Answer

Round each mixed number to the nearest whole number and add. $5\frac{1}{9}$ rounds to 5 and $14\frac{10}{11}$ rounds to 15, and the estimated sum is $5 + 15 = 20$.

Objective B Subtracting Mixed Numbers

PRACTICE 4

Subtract: $29\frac{7}{9} - 13\frac{5}{18}$

Example 4 Subtract: $9\frac{3}{7} - 5\frac{2}{21}$. Check by estimating.

Solution: The LCD of 7 and 21 is 21.

$$\begin{array}{rcl} 9\frac{3}{7} & = & 9\frac{9}{21} \quad \leftarrow \text{The LCD of 7 and 21 is 21.} \\ -5\frac{2}{21} & = & -5\frac{2}{21} \\ \hline & & 4\frac{7}{21} \quad \leftarrow \text{Subtract the fractions.} \end{array}$$

↑ Subtract the whole numbers.

Then $4\frac{7}{21}$ simplifies to $4\frac{1}{3}$. The difference is $4\frac{1}{3}$.

To check, $9\frac{3}{7}$ rounds to 9, $5\frac{2}{21}$ rounds to 5, and $9 - 5 = 4$, our estimate.

Our exact answer is close to 4, so our answer is reasonable.

Work Practice 4

When subtracting mixed numbers, borrowing may be needed, as shown in the next example.

PRACTICE 5

Subtract: $9\frac{7}{15} - 5\frac{3}{5}$

Example 5 Subtract: $7\frac{3}{14} - 3\frac{6}{7}$

Solution: The LCD of 7 and 14 is 14.

$$\begin{array}{rcl} 7\frac{3}{14} & = & 7\frac{3}{14} \\ -3\frac{6}{7} & = & -3\frac{12}{14} \\ \hline \end{array}$$

Notice that we cannot subtract $\frac{12}{14}$ from $\frac{3}{14}$, so we borrow from the whole number 7.

borrow 1 from 7

$$7\frac{3}{14} = 6 + 1\frac{3}{14} = 6 + \frac{17}{14} \text{ or } 6\frac{17}{14}$$

Now subtract.

$$\begin{array}{rcccl} 7\frac{3}{14} & = & 7\frac{3}{14} & = & 6\frac{17}{14} \\ -3\frac{6}{7} & = & -3\frac{12}{14} & = & -3\frac{12}{14} \\ \hline & & & & 3\frac{5}{14} \quad \leftarrow \text{Subtract the fractions.} \end{array}$$

↑ Subtract the whole numbers.

Work Practice 5

✓Concept Check In the subtraction problem $5\frac{1}{4} - 3\frac{3}{4}$, $5\frac{1}{4}$ must be rewritten because $\frac{3}{4}$ cannot be subtracted from $\frac{1}{4}$. Why is it incorrect to rewrite $5\frac{1}{4}$ as $5\frac{5}{4}$?

Answers

4. $16\frac{1}{2}$ **5.** $3\frac{13}{15}$

✓ Concept Check Answer

Rewrite $5\frac{1}{4}$ as $4\frac{5}{4}$ by borrowing from the 5.

Example 6 Subtract: $12 - 8\frac{3}{7}$

Solution:

$$\begin{array}{rcl} 12 & = & 11\frac{7}{7} \quad \text{Borrow 1 from 12 and write it as } \frac{7}{7}. \\ -8\frac{3}{7} & = & -8\frac{3}{7} \\ \hline & & 3\frac{4}{7} \leftarrow \text{Subtract the fractions.} \end{array}$$

↑ Subtract the whole numbers.

Work Practice 6

PRACTICE 6

Subtract: $25 - 10\frac{2}{9}$

Objective C Solving Problems by Adding or Subtracting Mixed Numbers

Now that we know how to add and subtract mixed numbers, we can solve real-life problems.

Example 7 Calculating Total Weight

Two packages of ground round are purchased. One package weighs $2\frac{3}{8}$ pounds and the other $1\frac{4}{5}$ pounds. What is the combined weight of the ground round?

Solution:

1. UNDERSTAND. Read and reread the problem. The phrase "combined weight" tells us to add.
2. TRANSLATE.

In words:	combined weight	is	weight of one package	plus	weight of second package
	↓	↓	↓	↓	↓
Translate:	combined weight	=	$2\frac{3}{8}$	+	$1\frac{4}{5}$

3. SOLVE: Before we solve, let's estimate. The fraction $2\frac{3}{8}$ rounds to 2, $1\frac{4}{5}$ rounds to 2, and $2 + 2 = 4$. The combined weight should be close to 4.

$$\begin{array}{rcl} 2\frac{3}{8} & = & 2\frac{15}{40} \\ +1\frac{4}{5} & = & 1\frac{32}{40} \\ \hline & & 3\frac{47}{40} = 4\frac{7}{40} \end{array}$$

4. INTERPRET. *Check* your work. Our estimate of 4 tells us that the exact answer of $4\frac{7}{40}$ is reasonable. *State* your conclusion: The combined weight of the ground round is $4\frac{7}{40}$ pounds.

Work Practice 7

PRACTICE 7

Two rainbow trout weigh $2\frac{1}{2}$ pounds and $3\frac{2}{3}$ pounds. What is the total weight of the two trout?

Answers

6. $14\frac{7}{9}$ **7.** $6\frac{1}{6}$ lb

PRACTICE 8

The measurement around the trunk of a tree just below shoulder height is called its girth. The largest known American beech tree in the United States has a girth of $23\frac{1}{4}$ feet. The largest known sugar maple tree in the United States has a girth of $19\frac{5}{12}$ feet. How much larger is the girth of the largest known American beech tree than the girth of the largest known sugar maple tree? (*Source: American Forests*)

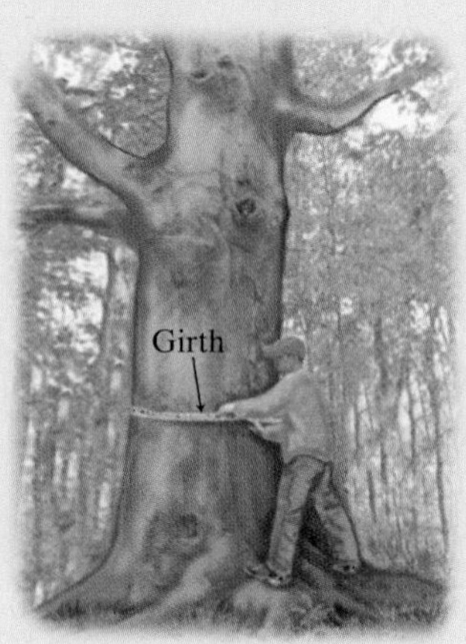

Answer

8. $3\frac{5}{6}$ ft

Example 8 Finding Legal Lobster Size

Lobster fishermen must measure the upper body shells of the lobsters they catch. Lobsters that are too small are thrown back into the ocean. Each state has its own size standard for lobsters to help control the breeding stock. Massachusetts divided its waters into four Lobster Conservation Management Areas, with a different minimum lobster size permitted in each area. In the off-shore area, the legal lobster size increased from $3\frac{13}{32}$ inches in 2006 to $3\frac{1}{2}$ inches in 2008. How much of an increase was this? (*Source:* Massachusetts Division of Marine Fisheries)

Solution:

1. UNDERSTAND. Read and reread the problem carefully. The word "increase" found in the problem might make you think that we add to solve the problem. But the phrase "how much of an increase" tells us to subtract to find the increase.
2. TRANSLATE.

In words:	increase	is	new lobster size	minus	old lobster size
	↓	↓	↓	↓	↓
Translate:	increase	=	$3\frac{1}{2}$	−	$3\frac{13}{32}$

3. SOLVE. Before we solve, let's estimate. The fraction $3\frac{1}{2}$ can be rounded to 4, $3\frac{13}{32}$ can be rounded to 3, and $4 - 3 = 1$. The increase is not 1, but will be smaller since we rounded $3\frac{1}{2}$ up more than we rounded $3\frac{13}{32}$ down.

$$\begin{array}{rcr} 3\frac{1}{2} & = & 3\frac{16}{32} \\ -\,3\frac{13}{32} & = & 3\frac{13}{32} \\ \hline & & \frac{3}{32} \end{array}$$

4. INTERPRET. *Check* your work. Our estimate tells us that the exact increase of $\frac{3}{32}$ is reasonable. *State* your conclusion: The increase in lobster size is $\frac{3}{32}$ of an inch.

Work Practice 8

Vocabulary and Readiness Check

Use the choices below to fill in each blank.

round	fraction	whole number
improper	mixed number	

1. The number $5\frac{3}{4}$ is called a(n) ________________.

2. For $5\frac{3}{4}$, the 5 is called the ________________ part and $\frac{3}{4}$ is called the ________________ part.

3. To estimate operations on mixed numbers, we ________________ mixed numbers to the nearest whole number.

4. The mixed number $2\frac{5}{8}$ written as a(n) ________________ fraction is $\frac{21}{8}$.

Choose the best estimate for each sum or difference.

5. $3\frac{7}{8} + 2\frac{1}{5}$

a. 6 **b.** 5 **c.** 1 **d.** 2

6. $3\frac{7}{8} - 2\frac{1}{5}$

a. 6 **b.** 5 **c.** 1 **d.** 2

7. $8\frac{1}{3} - 1\frac{1}{2}$

a. 4 **b.** 10 **c.** 6 **d.** 16

8. $8\frac{1}{3} + 1\frac{1}{2}$

a. 4 **b.** 10 **c.** 6 **d.** 16

3.4 Exercise Set

FOR EXTRA HELP

MyMathLab

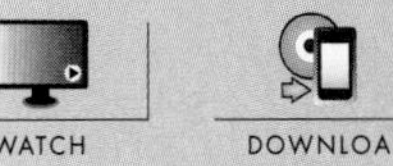

Objective A *Add. For those exercises marked, find an exact sum and an estimated sum. See Examples 1 through 3.*

1. $4\frac{7}{10} + 2\frac{1}{10}$

Exact:

Estimate:

2. $7\frac{4}{9} + 3\frac{2}{9}$

Exact:

Estimate:

3. $10\frac{3}{14} + 3\frac{4}{7}$

Exact:

Estimate:

4. $12\frac{5}{12} + 4\frac{1}{6}$

Exact:

Estimate:

5. $9\frac{1}{5} + 8\frac{2}{25}$

6. $6\frac{2}{13} + 8\frac{7}{26}$

7. $3\frac{1}{2} + 4\frac{1}{8}$

8. $9\frac{3}{4} + 2\frac{1}{8}$

9. $1\frac{5}{6} + 5\frac{3}{8}$

10. $2\frac{5}{12} + 1\frac{5}{8}$

11. $\begin{array}{r} 8\frac{2}{5} \\ +11\frac{2}{3} \\ \hline \end{array}$

12. $\begin{array}{r} 7\frac{3}{7} \\ +3\frac{3}{5} \\ \hline \end{array}$

13. $\begin{array}{r} 11\frac{3}{5} \\ +7\frac{2}{5} \\ \hline \end{array}$

14. $\begin{array}{r} 19\frac{7}{9} \\ +\ 8\frac{2}{9} \\ \hline \end{array}$

15. $\begin{array}{r} 40\frac{9}{10} \\ +15\frac{8}{27} \\ \hline \end{array}$

16. $\begin{array}{r} 102\frac{5}{8} \\ +\ 96\frac{21}{25} \\ \hline \end{array}$

17. $\begin{array}{r} 3\frac{5}{8} \\ 2\frac{1}{6} \\ +7\frac{3}{4} \\ \hline \end{array}$

18. $\begin{array}{r} 4\frac{1}{3} \\ 9\frac{2}{5} \\ +3\frac{1}{6} \\ \hline \end{array}$

19. $\begin{array}{r} 12\frac{3}{14} \\ 10 \\ +25\frac{5}{12} \\ \hline \end{array}$

20. $\begin{array}{r} 8\frac{2}{9} \\ 32 \\ +\ 9\frac{10}{21} \\ \hline \end{array}$

Objective B *Subtract. For those exercises marked, find an exact difference and an estimated difference. See Examples 4 through 6.*

21. $\begin{array}{r} 4\frac{7}{10} \\ -2\frac{1}{10} \\ \hline \end{array}$

Exact:

Estimate:

22. $\begin{array}{r} 7\frac{4}{9} \\ -3\frac{2}{9} \\ \hline \end{array}$

Exact:

Estimate:

23. $\begin{array}{r} 10\frac{13}{14} \\ -\ 3\frac{4}{7} \\ \hline \end{array}$

Exact:

Estimate:

24. $\begin{array}{r} 12\frac{5}{12} \\ -\ 4\frac{1}{6} \\ \hline \end{array}$

Exact:

Estimate:

25. $\begin{array}{r} 9\frac{1}{5} \\ -8\frac{6}{25} \\ \hline \end{array}$

26. $\begin{array}{r} 5\frac{2}{13} \\ -4\frac{7}{26} \\ \hline \end{array}$

27. $5\frac{2}{3} - 3\frac{1}{5}$

28. $\begin{array}{r} 23\frac{3}{5} \\ -\ 8\frac{8}{15} \\ \hline \end{array}$

29. $\begin{array}{r} 15\frac{4}{7} \\ -\ 9\frac{11}{14} \\ \hline \end{array}$

30. $5\frac{3}{8} - 2\frac{13}{20}$

31. $47\frac{4}{18} - 23\frac{19}{24}$

32. $6\frac{1}{6} - 5\frac{11}{14}$

33. $\begin{array}{r} 10 \\ -\ 8\frac{1}{5} \\ \hline \end{array}$

34. $\begin{array}{r} 23 \\ -17\frac{3}{4} \\ \hline \end{array}$

35. $\begin{array}{r} 11\frac{3}{5} \\ -\ 9\frac{11}{15} \\ \hline \end{array}$

36. $\begin{array}{r} 9\frac{1}{10} \\ -7\frac{2}{5} \\ \hline \end{array}$

37. $\begin{array}{r} 6 \\ -2\frac{4}{9} \\ \hline \end{array}$

38. $\begin{array}{r} 8 \\ -1\frac{7}{10} \\ \hline \end{array}$

39. $\begin{array}{r} 63\frac{1}{6} \\ -47\frac{5}{12} \\ \hline \end{array}$

40. $\begin{array}{r} 86\frac{2}{15} \\ -27\frac{3}{10} \\ \hline \end{array}$

Objectives **A** **B** **Mixed Practice** *Perform the indicated operation. See Examples 1 through 6.*

41. $15\frac{1}{6} + 13\frac{5}{12}$

42. $21\frac{3}{10} + 11\frac{3}{5}$

43. $22\frac{7}{8} - 7$

44. $27\frac{3}{21} - 9$

45. $5\frac{8}{9} + 2\frac{1}{9}$

46. $12\frac{13}{16} + 7\frac{3}{16}$

47. $33\frac{11}{20} - 15\frac{19}{30}$

48. $54\frac{7}{30} - 38\frac{29}{50}$

Objective **C** *Solve. For Exercises 49 and 50, the solutions have been started for you. Write each answer in simplest form. See Examples 7 and 8.*

49. To prevent intruding birds, birdhouses built for Eastern Bluebirds should have an entrance hole measuring $1\frac{1}{2}$ inches in diameter. Entrance holes in birdhouses for Mountain Bluebirds should measure $1\frac{9}{16}$ inches in diameter. How much wider should entrance holes for Mountain Bluebirds be than for Eastern Bluebirds? (*Source:* North American Bluebird Society)

Start the solution:

1. UNDERSTAND the problem. Reread it as many times as needed.
2. TRANSLATE into an equation. (Fill in the blanks.)

how much wider	is	larger entrance hole	minus	smaller entrance hole
↓	↓	↓	↓	↓
how much wider	=	______	−	______

Finish with:

3. SOLVE and
4. INTERPRET

50. If the total weight allowable without overweight charges is 50 pounds and the traveler's luggage weighs $60\frac{5}{8}$ pounds, on how many pounds will the traveler's overweight charges be based?

Start the solution:

1. UNDERSTAND the problem. Reread it as many times as needed.
2. TRANSLATE into an equation. (Fill in the blanks.)

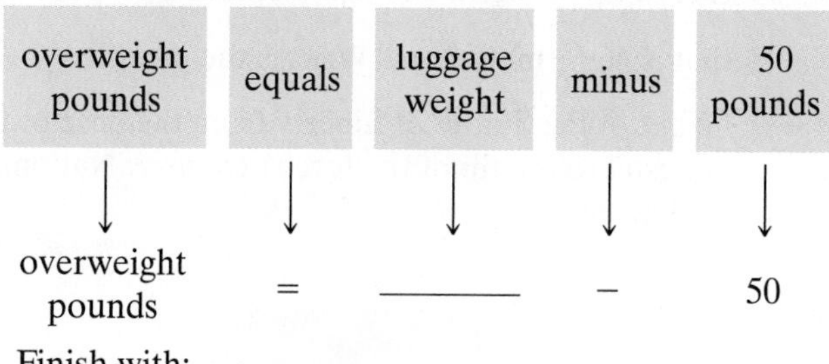

overweight pounds	equals	luggage weight	minus	50 pounds
↓	↓	↓	↓	↓
overweight pounds	=	______	−	50

Finish with:

3. SOLVE and
4. INTERPRET

51. Charlotte Dowlin has $15\frac{2}{3}$ feet of plastic pipe. She cuts off a $2\frac{1}{2}$-foot length and then a $3\frac{1}{4}$-foot length. If she now needs a 10-foot piece of pipe, will the remaining piece do? If not, by how much will the piece be short?

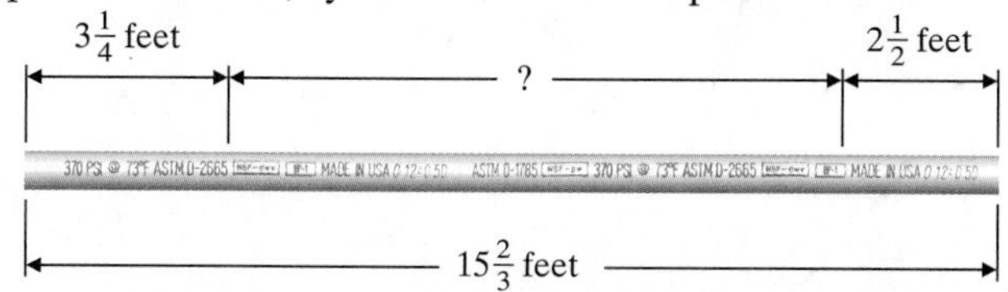

52. A trim carpenter cuts a board $3\frac{3}{8}$ feet long from one 6 feet long. How long is the remaining piece?

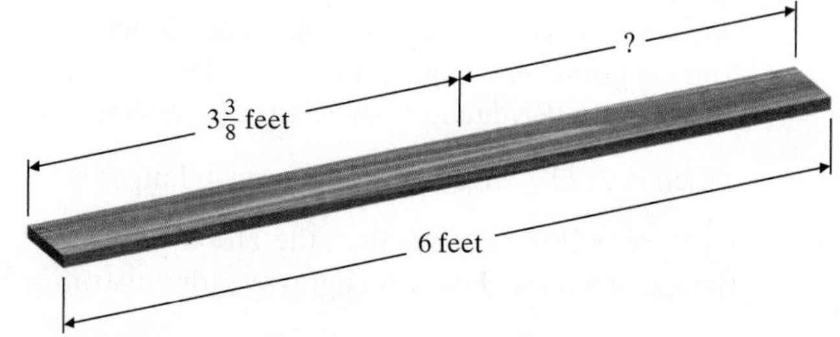

53. If Tucson's average annual rainfall is $11\frac{1}{4}$ inches and Yuma's is $3\frac{3}{5}$ inches, how much more rain, on average, does Tucson get than Yuma?

54. A pair of crutches needs adjustment. One crutch is 43 inches and the other is $41\frac{5}{8}$ inches. Find how much the short crutch should be lengthened to make both crutches the same length.

55. On four consecutive days, a concert pianist practiced for $2\frac{1}{2}$ hours, $1\frac{2}{3}$ hours, $2\frac{1}{4}$ hours, and $3\frac{5}{6}$ hours. Find his total practice time.

56. A tennis coach was preparing her team for a tennis tournament and enforced this practice schedule: Monday, $2\frac{1}{2}$ hours; Tuesday, $2\frac{2}{3}$ hours; Wednesday, $1\frac{3}{4}$ hours; and Thursday, $1\frac{9}{16}$ hours. How long did the team practice that week before Friday's tournament?

57. Jerald Divis, a tax consultant, takes $3\frac{1}{2}$ hours to prepare a personal tax return and $5\frac{7}{8}$ hours to prepare a small business return. How much longer does it take him to prepare the small business return?

58. Jessica Callac takes $2\frac{3}{4}$ hours to clean her room. Her brother Matthew takes $1\frac{1}{3}$ hours to clean his room. If they start at the same time, how long does Matthew have to wait for Jessica to finish?

59. Located on an island in New York City's harbor, the Statue of Liberty is one of the largest statues in the world. The copper figure is $46\frac{1}{20}$ meters tall from feet to tip of torch. The figure stands on a pedestal that is $46\frac{47}{50}$ meters tall. What is the overall height of the Statue of Liberty from the base of the pedestal to the tip of the torch? (*Source:* National Park Service)

60. The record for largest rainbow trout ever caught is $42\frac{1}{8}$ pounds and was set in Alaska in 1970. The record for largest tiger trout ever caught is $20\frac{13}{16}$ pounds and was set in Michigan in 1978. How much more did the record-setting rainbow trout weigh than the record-setting tiger trout? (*Source:* International Game Fish Association)

61. The longest floating pontoon bridge in the United States is the Evergreen Point Bridge in Seattle, Washington. It is 2526 yards long. The second-longest pontoon bridge in the United States is the Hood Canal Bridge in Point Gamble, Washington, which is $2173\frac{2}{3}$ yards long. How much longer is the Evergreen Point Bridge than the Hood Canal Bridge? (*Source:* Federal Highway Administration)

62. What is the difference between interest rates of $11\frac{1}{2}$ percent and $9\frac{3}{4}$ percent?

The following table lists some upcoming total eclipses of the Sun that will be visible in North America. The duration of each eclipse is listed in the table. Use the table to answer Exercises 63 through 66.

Total Solar Eclipses Visible from North America	
Date of Eclipse	**Duration (in Minutes)**
August 21, 2017	$2\frac{2}{3}$
April 8, 2024	$4\frac{7}{15}$
August 12, 2026	$2\frac{3}{10}$
(*Source:* NASA/Goddard Space Flight Center)	

63. What is the total duration for the three eclipses?

64. What is the total duration for the two eclipses occuring in even-numbered years?

65. How much longer will the April 8, 2024, eclipse be than the August 21, 2017, eclipse?

66. How much longer will the August 21, 2017, eclipse be than the August 12, 2026, eclipse?

Find the perimeter of each figure.

△ **67.**

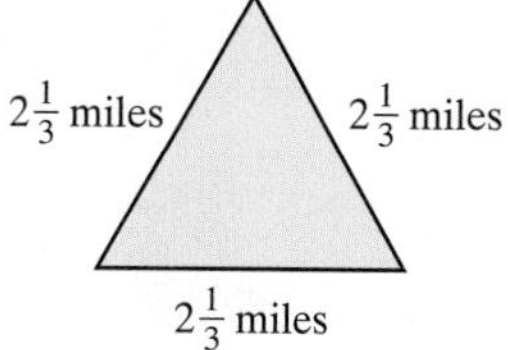

△ **68.**

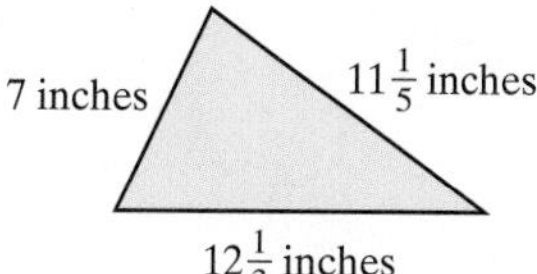

△ **69.**

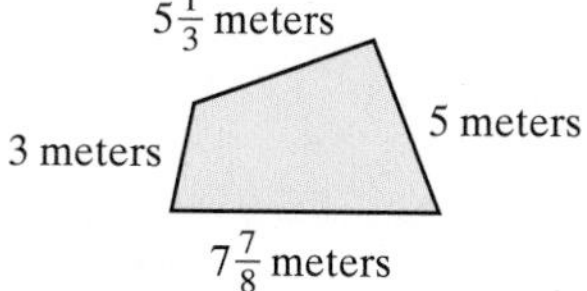

△ **70.**

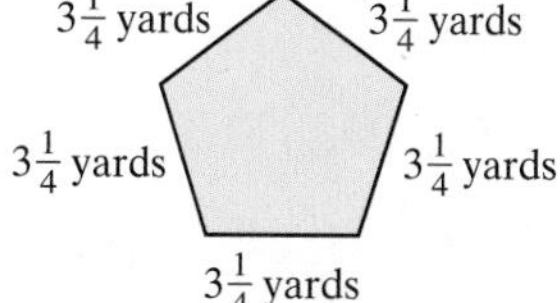

Review

Evaluate each expression. See Section 1.9.

71. 2^3

72. 3^2

73. 5^2

74. 2^5

75. $20 \div 10 \cdot 2$

76. $36 - 5 \cdot 6 + 10$

77. $2 + 3(8 \cdot 7 - 1)$

78. $2(10 - 2 \cdot 5) + 13$

Simplify. Write any mixed number whose fraction part is not a proper fraction in simplest form. See Section 2.1.

79. $3\frac{5}{5}$

80. $10\frac{8}{7}$

81. $9\frac{10}{16}$

82. $6\frac{7}{14}$

Concept Extensions

Solve. See the Concept Checks in this section.

83. Which of the following are equivalent to 10?

a. $9\frac{5}{5}$ **b.** $9\frac{100}{100}$ **c.** $6\frac{44}{11}$ **d.** $8\frac{13}{13}$

84. Which of the following are equivalent to $7\frac{3}{4}$?

a. $6\frac{7}{4}$ **b.** $5\frac{11}{4}$ **c.** $7\frac{12}{16}$ **d.** all of them

Solve.

85. Explain in your own words why $9\frac{13}{9}$ is equal to $10\frac{4}{9}$.

86. In your own words, explain

a. when to borrow when subtracting mixed numbers, and

b. how to borrow when subtracting mixed numbers.

87. Carmen's Candy Clutch is famous for its "Nutstuff," a special blend of nuts and candy. A Supreme box of Nutstuff has $2\frac{1}{4}$ pounds of nuts and $3\frac{1}{2}$ pounds of candy. A Deluxe box has $1\frac{3}{8}$ pounds of nuts and $4\frac{1}{4}$ pounds of candy. Which box is heavier and by how much?

88. Willie Cassidie purchased three Supreme boxes and two Deluxe boxes of Nutstuff from Carmen's Candy Clutch. (See Exercise 87.) What is the total weight of his purchase?

3.5 ORDER, EXPONENTS, AND THE ORDER OF OPERATIONS

Objectives

A Compare Fractions.

B Evaluate Fractions Raised to Powers.

C Review Operations on Fractions.

D Use the Order of Operations.

Objective A Comparing Fractions

Recall that whole numbers can be shown on a number line using equally spaced distances.

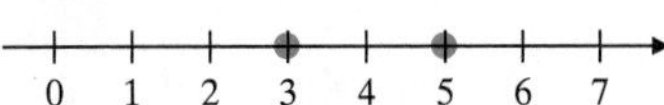

From the number line, we can see the order of numbers. For example, we can see that 3 is less than 5 because 3 is to the left of 5.

For any two numbers on a number line, the number to the left is always the smaller number, and the number to the right is always the larger number.

We use the **inequality symbols** $<$ or $>$ to write the order of numbers.

Inequality Symbols

$<$ means *is less than.*

$>$ means *is greater than.*

For example,

3 is less than 5 or 5 is greater than 3

$3 < 5$ $\qquad$ $5 > 3$

We can compare fractions the same way. To see fractions on a number line, divide the spaces between whole numbers into equal parts.

For example, let's compare $\frac{2}{5}$ and $\frac{4}{5}$.

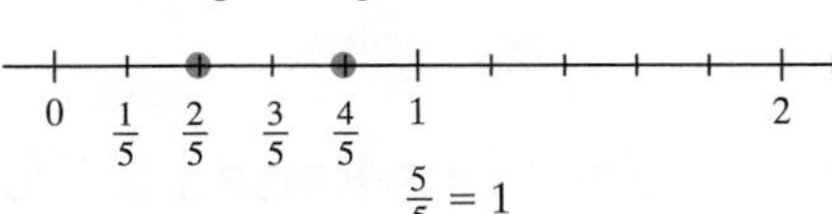

Since $\frac{4}{5}$ is to the right of $\frac{2}{5}$,

$\frac{2}{5} < \frac{4}{5}$ Notice that $2 < 4$ also.

Comparing Fractions

To determine which of two fractions is greater,

Step 1: Write the fractions as like fractions.

Step 2: The fraction with the greater numerator is the greater fraction.

Example 1 Insert $<$ or $>$ to form a true statement.

$\frac{3}{10} \quad \frac{2}{7}$

Solution:

Step 1: The LCD of 10 and 7 is 70.

$\frac{3}{10} = \frac{3}{10} \cdot \frac{7}{7} = \frac{21}{70}; \qquad \frac{2}{7} = \frac{2}{7} \cdot \frac{10}{10} = \frac{20}{70}$

Continued on next page

PRACTICE 1

Insert $<$ or $>$ to form a true statement.

$\frac{8}{9} \quad \frac{10}{11}$

Answer

1. $<$

Step 2: Since $21 > 20$, then $\frac{21}{70} > \frac{20}{70}$ or

$\frac{3}{10} > \frac{2}{7}$

Work Practice 1

PRACTICE 2

Insert < or > to form a true statement.

$\frac{3}{5} \quad \frac{2}{9}$

Example 2 Insert < or > to form a true statement.

$\frac{9}{10} \quad \frac{11}{12}$

Solution:

Step 1: The LCD of 10 and 12 is 60.

$$\frac{9}{10} = \frac{9}{10}\cdot\frac{6}{6} = \frac{54}{60} \qquad \frac{11}{12} = \frac{11}{12}\cdot\frac{5}{5} = \frac{55}{60}$$

Step 2: Since $54 < 55$, then $\frac{54}{60} < \frac{55}{60}$ or

$\frac{9}{10} < \frac{11}{12}$

Work Practice 2

Helpful Hint

If we think of < and > as arrowheads, a true statement is always formed when the arrow points to the smaller number.

$\frac{2}{3} > \frac{1}{3}$ — points to smaller number

$\frac{5}{6} < \frac{7}{6}$ — points to smaller number

Objective B Evaluating Fractions Raised to Powers

Recall from Section 1.9 that exponents indicate repeated multiplication.

$$5^3 = \underbrace{5\cdot5\cdot5}_{\text{3 factors of 5}} = 125$$

(exponent: 3; base: 5)

Exponents mean the same when the base is a fraction. For example,

$$\left(\frac{1}{3}\right)^4 = \underbrace{\frac{1}{3}\cdot\frac{1}{3}\cdot\frac{1}{3}\cdot\frac{1}{3}}_{\text{4 factors of }\frac{1}{3}} = \frac{1}{81}$$

(base: $\frac{1}{3}$)

PRACTICE 3–5

Evaluate each expression.

3. $\left(\frac{1}{5}\right)^2$ **4.** $\left(\frac{2}{3}\right)^3$

5. $\left(\frac{1}{4}\right)^2\left(\frac{2}{3}\right)^3$

Examples Evaluate each expression.

3. $\left(\frac{1}{4}\right)^2 = \frac{1}{4}\cdot\frac{1}{4} = \frac{1}{16}$

4. $\left(\frac{3}{5}\right)^3 = \frac{3}{5}\cdot\frac{3}{5}\cdot\frac{3}{5} = \frac{27}{125}$

5. $\left(\frac{1}{6}\right)^2\cdot\left(\frac{3}{4}\right)^3 = \left(\frac{1}{6}\cdot\frac{1}{6}\right)\cdot\left(\frac{3}{4}\cdot\frac{3}{4}\cdot\frac{3}{4}\right) = \frac{1\cdot1\cdot\cancel{3}^{1}\cdot\cancel{3}^{1}\cdot3}{2\cdot\cancel{3}_{1}\cdot2\cdot\cancel{3}_{1}\cdot4\cdot4\cdot4} = \frac{3}{256}$

Work Practice 3–5

Answers

2. > **3.** $\frac{1}{25}$ **4.** $\frac{8}{27}$ **5.** $\frac{1}{54}$

Objective C Reviewing Operations on Fractions

To get ready to use the order of operations with fractions, let's first review the operations on fractions that we have learned.

Review of Operations on Fractions

Operation	Procedure	Example
Multiply	Multiply the numerators and multiply the denominators.	$\frac{5}{9}\cdot\frac{1}{2}=\frac{5\cdot 1}{9\cdot 2}=\frac{5}{18}$
Divide	Multiply the first fraction by the reciprocal of the second fraction.	$\frac{2}{3}\div\frac{11}{13}=\frac{2}{3}\cdot\frac{13}{11}=\frac{2\cdot 13}{3\cdot 11}=\frac{26}{33}$
Add or Subtract	1. Write each fraction as an equivalent fraction whose denominator is the LCD 2. Add or subtract numerators and write the result over the common denominator.	$\frac{3}{4}+\frac{1}{8}=\frac{3}{4}\cdot\frac{2}{2}+\frac{1}{8}=\frac{6}{8}+\frac{1}{8}=\frac{7}{8}$

Examples Perform each indicated operation.

6. $\frac{1}{2}\div\frac{8}{7}=\frac{1}{2}\cdot\frac{7}{8}=\frac{1\cdot 7}{2\cdot 8}=\frac{7}{16}$ To divide: multiply by the reciprocal.

7. $\frac{6}{35}+\frac{3}{7}=\frac{6}{35}+\frac{3}{7}\cdot\frac{5}{5}=\frac{6}{35}+\frac{15}{35}=\frac{21}{35}$ To add: need the LCD. The LCD is 35.

$=\frac{\overset{1}{\cancel{7}}\cdot 3}{\underset{1}{\cancel{7}}\cdot 5}=\frac{3}{5}$

8. $\frac{2}{9}\cdot\frac{3}{11}=\frac{2\cdot 3}{9\cdot 11}=\frac{2\cdot\overset{1}{\cancel{3}}}{\underset{1}{\cancel{3}}\cdot 3\cdot 11}=\frac{2}{33}$ To multiply: multiply numerators and multiply denominators.

9. $\frac{6}{7}-\frac{1}{3}=\frac{6}{7}\cdot\frac{3}{3}-\frac{1}{3}\cdot\frac{7}{7}=\frac{18}{21}-\frac{7}{21}=\frac{11}{21}$ To subtract: need the LCD. The LCD is 21.

Work Practice 6–9

PRACTICE 6–9

Perform each indicated operation.

6. $\frac{3}{7}\div\frac{10}{11}$ 7. $\frac{4}{15}+\frac{2}{5}$

8. $\frac{2}{3}\cdot\frac{9}{10}$ 9. $\frac{11}{12}-\frac{2}{5}$

Objective D Using the Order of Operations

The order of operations that we use on whole numbers applies to expressions containing fractions and mixed numbers also.

Order of Operations

1. Perform all operations within parentheses ( ), brackets [ ], or other grouping symbols such as square roots or fraction bars, starting with the innermost set.
2. Evaluate any expressions with exponents.
3. Multiply or divide in order from left to right.
4. Add or subtract in order from left to right.

Answers

6. $\frac{33}{70}$ 7. $\frac{2}{3}$ 8. $\frac{3}{5}$ 9. $\frac{31}{60}$

PRACTICE 10

Simplify: $\frac{2}{9} \div \frac{4}{7} \cdot \frac{3}{10}$

Example 10 Simplify: $\frac{1}{5} \div \frac{2}{3} \cdot \frac{4}{5}$

Solution: Multiply or divide *in order* from left to right. We divide first.

$$\frac{1}{5} \div \frac{2}{3} \cdot \frac{4}{5} = \underbrace{\frac{1}{5} \cdot \frac{3}{2}}_{\uparrow} \cdot \frac{4}{5} \quad \text{To divide, multiply by the reciprocal.}$$

$$= \frac{3}{10} \cdot \frac{4}{5}$$

$$= \frac{3 \cdot 4}{10 \cdot 5} \quad \text{Multiply.}$$

$$= \frac{3 \cdot 2 \cdot \overset{1}{\cancel{2}}}{\underset{1}{\cancel{2}} \cdot 5 \cdot 5} \quad \text{Simplify.}$$

$$= \frac{6}{25} \quad \text{Simplify.}$$

Work Practice 10

PRACTICE 11

Simplify: $\left(\frac{2}{5}\right)^2 \div \left(\frac{3}{5} - \frac{11}{25}\right)$

Example 11 Simplify: $\left(\frac{2}{3}\right)^2 \div \left(\frac{8}{27} + \frac{2}{3}\right)$

Solution: Start within the right set of parentheses. We add.

$$\left(\frac{2}{3}\right)^2 \div \left(\frac{8}{27} + \frac{2}{3}\right) = \left(\frac{2}{3}\right)^2 \div \left(\frac{8}{27} + \frac{18}{27}\right) \quad \text{The LCD is 27. Write } \frac{2}{3} \text{ as } \frac{18}{27}.$$

$$= \left(\frac{2}{3}\right)^2 \div \frac{26}{27} \quad \text{Simplify inside the parentheses.}$$

$$= \frac{4}{9} \div \frac{26}{27} \quad \text{Write } \left(\frac{2}{3}\right)^2 \text{ as } \frac{4}{9}.$$

$$= \frac{4}{9} \cdot \frac{27}{26}$$

$$= \frac{\overset{1}{\cancel{2}} \cdot 2 \cdot 3 \cdot \overset{1}{\cancel{9}}}{\underset{1}{\cancel{9}} \cdot \underset{1}{\cancel{2}} \cdot 13}$$

$$= \frac{6}{13}$$

Work Practice 11

✓**Concept Check** What should be done first to simplify $3\left[\left(\frac{1}{4}\right)^2 + \frac{3}{2}\left(\frac{6}{7} - \frac{1}{3}\right)\right]$?

Recall from Section 1.7 that the average of a list of numbers is their sum divided by the number of numbers in the list.

PRACTICE 12

Find the average of $\frac{1}{2}, \frac{3}{8}$, and $\frac{7}{24}$.

Example 12 Find the average of $\frac{1}{3}, \frac{2}{5}$, and $\frac{2}{9}$.

Solution: The average is their sum, divided by 3.

$$\left(\frac{1}{3} + \frac{2}{5} + \frac{2}{9}\right) \div 3 = \left(\frac{15}{45} + \frac{18}{45} + \frac{10}{45}\right) \div 3 \quad \text{The LCD is 45.}$$

$$= \frac{43}{45} \div 3 \quad \text{Add.}$$

$$= \frac{43}{45} \cdot \frac{1}{3}$$

$$= \frac{43}{135} \quad \text{Multiply.}$$

Work Practice 12

Answers

10. $\frac{7}{60}$ **11.** 1 **12.** $\frac{7}{18}$

✓ **Concept Check Answer**

$\frac{6}{7} - \frac{1}{3}$

Vocabulary and Readiness Check

Use the choices below to fill in each blank. Not all choices will be used.

addition	multiplication	evaluate the exponential expression
subtraction	division	

1. To simplify $\frac{1}{2} + \frac{2}{3} \cdot \frac{7}{8}$, which operation do we perform first? ____________________

2. To simplify $\frac{1}{2} \div \frac{2}{3} \cdot \frac{7}{8}$, which operation do we perform first? ____________________

3. To simplify $\frac{7}{8} \cdot \left(\frac{1}{2} - \frac{2}{3}\right)$, which operation do we perform first? ____________________

4. To simplify $9 - \left(\frac{3}{4}\right)^2$, which operation do we perform first? ____________________

3.5 Exercise Set

FOR EXTRA HELP

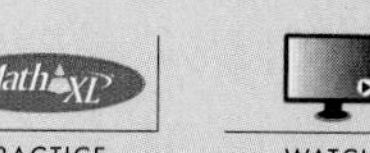

READ

Objective A *Insert $<$ or $>$ to form a true statement. See Examples 1 and 2.*

1. $\frac{7}{9} \quad \frac{6}{9}$

2. $\frac{12}{17} \quad \frac{13}{17}$

3. $\frac{3}{3} \quad \frac{5}{3}$

4. $\frac{3}{23} \quad \frac{4}{23}$

5. $\frac{9}{42} \quad \frac{5}{21}$

6. $\frac{17}{32} \quad \frac{5}{16}$

7. $\frac{9}{8} \quad \frac{17}{16}$

8. $\frac{3}{8} \quad \frac{14}{40}$

9. $\frac{3}{4} \quad \frac{2}{3}$

10. $\frac{2}{5} \quad \frac{1}{3}$

11. $\frac{3}{5} \quad \frac{9}{14}$

12. $\frac{3}{10} \quad \frac{7}{25}$

13. $\frac{1}{10} \quad \frac{1}{11}$

14. $\frac{1}{13} \quad \frac{1}{14}$

15. $\frac{27}{100} \quad \frac{7}{25}$

16. $\frac{37}{120} \quad \frac{9}{30}$

Objective B *Evaluate each expression. See Examples 3 through 5.*

17. $\left(\frac{1}{2}\right)^4$

18. $\left(\frac{1}{7}\right)^2$

19. $\left(\frac{2}{5}\right)^3$

20. $\left(\frac{3}{4}\right)^3$

21. $\left(\frac{4}{7}\right)^3$

22. $\left(\frac{2}{3}\right)^4$

23. $\left(\frac{2}{9}\right)^2$

24. $\left(\frac{7}{11}\right)^2$

25. $\left(\frac{3}{4}\right)^2 \cdot \left(\frac{2}{3}\right)^3$ 26. $\left(\frac{1}{6}\right)^2 \cdot \left(\frac{9}{10}\right)^2$ 27. $\frac{9}{10}\left(\frac{2}{5}\right)^2$ 28. $\frac{7}{11}\left(\frac{3}{10}\right)^2$

Objective C *Perform each indicated operation. See Examples 6 through 9.*

29. $\frac{2}{15} + \frac{3}{5}$ 30. $\frac{5}{12} + \frac{5}{6}$ 31. $\frac{3}{7} \cdot \frac{1}{5}$ 32. $\frac{9}{10} \div \frac{2}{3}$ 33. $1 - \frac{4}{9}$

34. $5 - \frac{2}{3}$ 35. $4\frac{2}{9} + 5\frac{9}{11}$ 36. $7\frac{3}{7} + 6\frac{3}{5}$ 37. $\frac{5}{6} - \frac{3}{4}$ 38. $\frac{7}{10} - \frac{3}{25}$

39. $\frac{6}{11} \div \frac{2}{3}$ 40. $\frac{3}{8} \cdot \frac{1}{11}$ 41. $0 \cdot \frac{9}{10}$ 42. $\frac{5}{6} \cdot 0$ 43. $0 \div \frac{9}{10}$

44. $\frac{5}{6} \div 0$ 45. $\frac{20}{35} \cdot \frac{7}{10}$ 46. $\frac{18}{25} \div \frac{3}{5}$ 47. $\frac{4}{7} - \frac{6}{11}$ 48. $\frac{11}{20} + \frac{7}{15}$

Objective D *Use the order of operations to simplify each expression. See Examples 10 and 11.*

49. $\frac{1}{5} + \frac{1}{3} \cdot \frac{1}{4}$ 50. $\frac{1}{2} + \frac{1}{6} \cdot \frac{1}{3}$ 51. $\frac{5}{6} \div \frac{1}{3} \cdot \frac{1}{4}$ 52. $\frac{7}{8} \div \frac{1}{4} \cdot \frac{1}{7}$

53. $\frac{1}{5} \cdot \left(2\frac{5}{6} - \frac{1}{3}\right)$ 54. $\frac{4}{7} \cdot \left(6 - 2\frac{1}{2}\right)$ 55. $2 \cdot \left(\frac{1}{4} + \frac{1}{5}\right) + 2$ 56. $\frac{2}{5} \cdot \left(5 - \frac{1}{2}\right) - 1$

57. $\left(\frac{3}{4}\right)^2 \div \left(\frac{3}{4} - \frac{1}{12}\right)$ 58. $\left(\frac{8}{9}\right)^2 \div \left(2 - \frac{2}{3}\right)$ 59. $\left(\frac{2}{3} - \frac{5}{9}\right)^2$ 60. $\left(1 - \frac{2}{5}\right)^3$

61. $\frac{5}{9} \cdot \frac{1}{2} + \frac{2}{3} \cdot \frac{5}{6}$ 62. $\frac{7}{10} \cdot \frac{1}{2} + \frac{3}{4} \cdot \frac{3}{5}$ 63. $\frac{27}{16} \cdot \left(\frac{2}{3}\right)^2 - \frac{3}{20}$ 64. $\frac{64}{27} \cdot \left(\frac{3}{4}\right)^2 - \frac{7}{10}$

65. $\frac{3}{13} \div \frac{9}{26} - \frac{7}{24} \cdot \frac{8}{14}$

66. $\frac{5}{11} \div \frac{15}{77} - \frac{7}{10} \cdot \frac{5}{14}$

67. $\frac{3}{14} + \frac{10}{21} \div \left(\frac{3}{7}\right)\left(\frac{9}{4}\right)$

68. $\frac{11}{15} + \frac{7}{9} \div \left(\frac{14}{3}\right)\left(\frac{2}{3}\right)$

69. $\left(\frac{3}{4} + \frac{1}{8}\right)^2 - \left(\frac{1}{2} + \frac{1}{8}\right)$

70. $\left(\frac{1}{6} + \frac{1}{3}\right)^3 + \left(\frac{2}{5} \cdot \frac{3}{4}\right)^2$

Find the average of each list of numbers. See Example 12.

71. $\frac{5}{6}$ and $\frac{2}{3}$

72. $\frac{1}{2}$ and $\frac{4}{7}$

73. $\frac{1}{5}, \frac{3}{10},$ and $\frac{3}{20}$

74. $\frac{1}{3}, \frac{1}{4},$ and $\frac{1}{6}$

Objectives C D **Mixed Practice**

75. The average fraction of online sales of computer hardware is $\frac{23}{50}$, of computer software is $\frac{1}{2}$, and of music and videos is $\frac{3}{5}$. Find the average of these fractions.

76. The average fraction of online sales of sporting goods is $\frac{12}{25}$, of toys and hobbies and games is $\frac{1}{2}$, and of computer hardware is $\frac{23}{50}$. Find the average of these fractions.

Review

Identify each key word with the operation it most likely translates to. After each word, write A for addition, S for subtraction, M for multiplication, and D for division. See Sections 1.3, 1.4, 1.6, and 1.7.

77. increased by

78. sum

79. triple

80. product

81. subtracted from

82. decreased by

83. quotient

84. divided by

85. times

86. difference

87. total

88. more than

Concept Extensions

Solve.

89. Calculate $\frac{2^3}{3}$ and $\left(\frac{2}{3}\right)^3$. Do both of these expressions simplify to the same number? Explain why or why not.

90. Calculate $\left(\frac{1}{2}\right)^2 \cdot \left(\frac{3}{4}\right)^2$ and $\left(\frac{1}{2} \cdot \frac{3}{4}\right)^2$. Do both of these expressions simplify to the same number? Explain why or why not.

Each expression contains one addition, one subtraction, one multiplication, and one division. Write the operations in the order that they should be performed. Do not actually simplify. See the Concept Check in this section.

91. $[9 + 3(4 - 2)] \div \frac{10}{21}$

92. $[30 - 4(3 + 2)] \div \frac{5}{2}$

93. $\frac{1}{3} \div \left(\frac{2}{3}\right)\left(\frac{4}{5}\right) - \frac{1}{4} + \frac{1}{2}$

94. $\left(\frac{5}{6} - \frac{1}{3}\right) \cdot \frac{1}{3} + \frac{1}{2} \div \frac{9}{8}$

Solve.

95. In 2008, about $\frac{114}{250}$ of the total weight of mail delivered by the United States Postal Service was first-class mail. That same year, about $\frac{49}{100}$ of the total weight of mail delivered by the United States Postal Service was standard mail. Which of these two categories account for a greater portion of the mail handled by weight? (*Source:* U.S. Postal Service)

96. The National Park System (NPS) in the United States includes a wide variety of park types. National military parks account for $\frac{3}{128}$ of all NPS parks, and $\frac{1}{24}$ of NPS parks are classified as national preserves. Which category, national military park or national preserve, is bigger? (*Source:* National Park Service)

97. As of this writing, there are several hundred individuals who are or have been United States astronauts. Of these, $\frac{11}{160}$ were born in Texas, while $\frac{5}{64}$ were born in New York. Which state is the birthplace of the greater number of astronauts, Texas or New York? (*Source:* NASA)

98. Approximately $\frac{7}{10}$ of U.S. adults have a savings account. About $\frac{11}{25}$ of U.S. adults have a non-interest-bearing checking account. Which type of banking service, savings account or non-interest-bearing checking account, do adults in the United States use more? (*Source:* Scarborough Research/ US Data.com, Inc.)

3.6 FRACTIONS AND PROBLEM SOLVING

Objective

A **Solve Problems by Performing Operations on Fractions or Mixed Numbers.**

Objective A Solving Problems Containing Fractions or Mixed Numbers

Now that we know how to add, subtract, multiply, and divide fractions and mixed numbers, we can solve problems containing these numbers.

Don't forget the key words and phrases listed below that help indicate which operation to use. Also included are several words and phrases that translate to the symbol "=".

Addition (+)	Subtraction (−)	Multiplication (·)	Division (÷)	Equality (=)
sum	difference	product	quotient	equals
plus	minus	times	divide	is equal to
added to	subtract	multiply	shared equally	is/was
more than	less than	multiply by	among	yields
increased by	decreased by	of	divided by	
total	less	double/triple	divided into	

Recall the following problem-solving steps introduced in Section 1.8. They may be helpful to you:

Problem-Solving Steps

1. UNDERSTAND the problem. Some ways of doing this are to read and reread the problem, construct a drawing, and look for key words to identify an operation.
2. TRANSLATE the problem. That is, write the problem in short form using words, and then translate to numbers and symbols.
3. SOLVE the problem. It is helpful to estimate the solution by rounding. Then carry out the indicated operation from step 2.
4. INTERPRET the results. *Check* the proposed solution in the stated problem and *state* your conclusions. Write your results with the correct units attached.

In the first example, we find the volume of a box. Volume measures the space enclosed by a region and is measured in cubic units. We study volume further in a later chapter.

Volume of a box = length · width · height

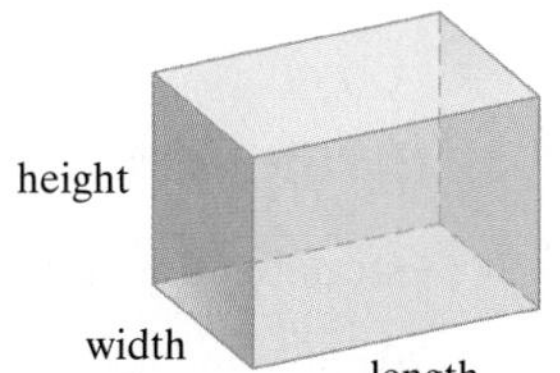

Helpful Hint

Remember:

Perimeter measures the distance around a figure. It is measured in **units.**

Perimeter

Area measures the amount of surface of a figure. It is measured in **square units.**

Area

Volume measures the amount of space enclosed by a region. It is measured in **cubic units.**

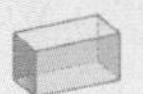
Volume

PRACTICE 1

Find the volume of a box that measures $4\frac{1}{3}$ feet by $1\frac{1}{2}$ feet by $3\frac{1}{3}$ feet.

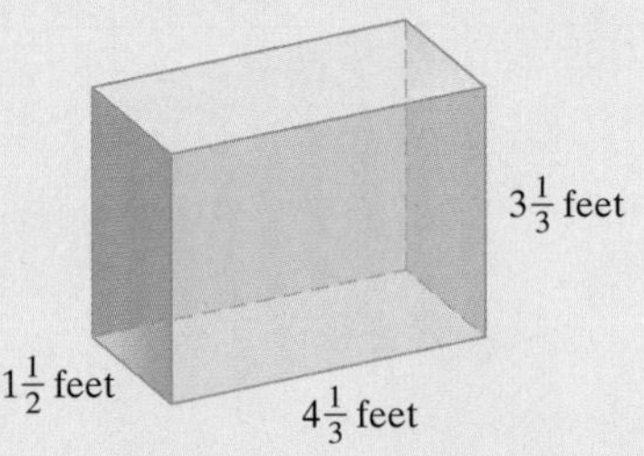

Example 1 Finding Volume of a Camcorder Box

Sony recently produced a small camcorder. It measures 5 inches by $2\frac{1}{2}$ inches by $1\frac{3}{4}$ inches and can store 30 minutes of moving images. Find the volume of a box with these dimensions. (*Source: Guinness World Records*)

Solution:

1. UNDERSTAND. Read and reread the problem. The phrase "volume of a box" tells us what to do. The volume of a box is the product of its length, width, and height. Since we are multiplying, it makes no difference which measurement we call length, width, or height.
2. TRANSLATE.

In words:	volume of a box	is	length	·	width	·	height
	↓	↓	↓		↓		↓
Translate:	volume of a box	=	5 in.	·	$2\frac{1}{2}$ in.	·	$1\frac{3}{4}$ in.

3. SOLVE: Before we multiply, let's estimate by rounding each dimension to a whole number. The number 5 rounds to 5, $2\frac{1}{2}$ rounds to 3, and $1\frac{3}{4}$ rounds to 2, so our estimate is $5 \cdot 3 \cdot 2$ or 30 cubic inches.

$$5\text{ in.} \cdot 2\frac{1}{2}\text{ in.} \cdot 1\frac{3}{4}\text{ in.} = \frac{5}{1} \cdot \frac{5}{2} \cdot \frac{7}{4} \quad \text{cubic inches}$$
$$= \frac{5 \cdot 5 \cdot 7}{1 \cdot 2 \cdot 4} \quad \text{cubic inches}$$
$$= \frac{175}{8} \text{ or } 21\frac{7}{8} \quad \text{cubic inches}$$

4. INTERPRET. *Check* your work. The exact answer is somewhat close to our estimate. If you'd like, round $2\frac{1}{2}$ down to 2, and our estimate is $5 \cdot 2 \cdot 2$ or 20 cubic inches. This estimate is also appropriate and closer to our exact answer, so it is reasonable. *State* your conclusion: The volume of a box that measures 5 inches by $2\frac{1}{2}$ inches by $1\frac{3}{4}$ inches is $21\frac{7}{8}$ cubic inches.

Work Practice 1

Answer

1. $21\frac{2}{3}$ cu ft

Example 2 Finding Unknown Length

Given the following diagram, find its total length.

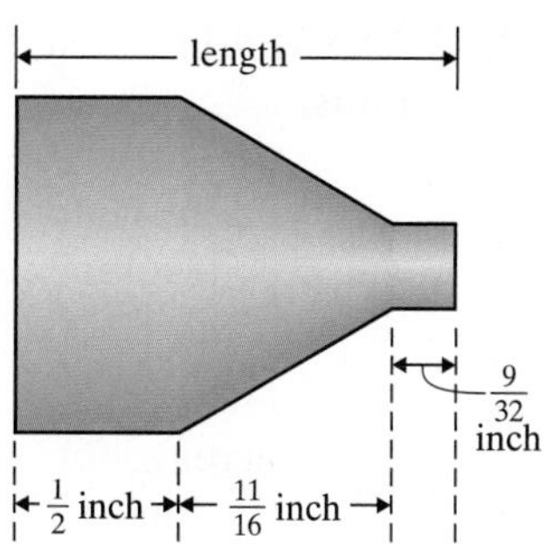

Solution:

1. UNDERSTAND. Read and reread the problem. Then study the diagram. The phrase "total length" tells us to add.
2. TRANSLATE. It makes no difference which length we call first, second, or third length.

In word:	total length	is	first length	+	second length	+	third length
	↓	↓	↓		↓		↓
Translate:	total length	=	$\frac{1}{2}$ in.	+	$\frac{11}{16}$ in.	+	$\frac{9}{32}$ in.

3. SOLVE:

$$\frac{1}{2} + \frac{11}{16} + \frac{9}{32} = \frac{1 \cdot 16}{2 \cdot 16} + \frac{11 \cdot 2}{16 \cdot 2} + \frac{9}{32}$$
$$= \frac{16}{32} + \frac{22}{32} + \frac{9}{32}$$
$$= \frac{47}{32} \text{ or } 1\frac{15}{32}$$

4. INTERPRET. *Check* your work. *State* your conclusion: The total length is $1\frac{15}{32}$ inches.

Work Practice 2

PRACTICE 2

Given the following diagram, find its total width.

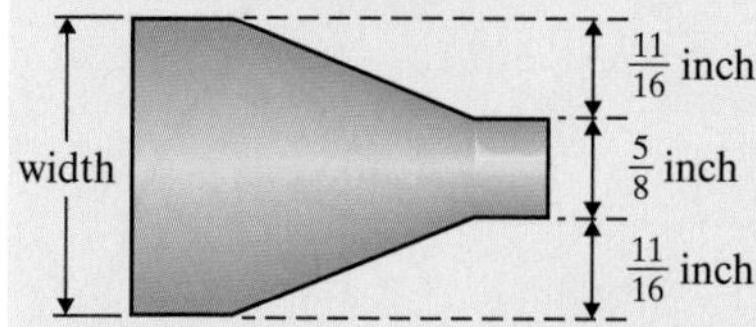

Many problems require more than one operation to solve, as shown in the next application.

Example 3 Acreage for Single-Family Home Lots

A contractor is considering buying land to develop a subdivision for single-family homes. Suppose she buys 44 acres and calculates that $4\frac{1}{4}$ acres of this land will be used for roads and a retention pond. How many $\frac{3}{4}$-acre lots can she sell using the rest of the acreage?

Solution:

1a. UNDERSTAND. Read and reread the problem. The phrase "using the rest of the acreage" tells is that initially we are to subtract.

Continued on next page

PRACTICE 3

Suppose that 25 acres of land are purchased, but because of roads and wetlands concerns, $6\frac{2}{3}$ acres cannot be developed into lots. How many $\frac{5}{6}$-acre lots can the rest of the land be divided into?

Answers

2. 2 in. 3. 22 lots

2a. TRANSLATE. First, let's calculate the amount of acreage that can be used for lots.

In words:	acreage for lots	is	total acreage	minus	acreage for roads and a pond
	↓	↓	↓	↓	↓
Translate:	acreage for lots	=	44	−	$4\frac{1}{4}$

3a. SOLVE:

$$\begin{array}{rcr} 44 & = & 43\frac{4}{4} \\ -\;4\frac{1}{4} & = & -\;4\frac{1}{4} \\ \hline & & 39\frac{3}{4} \end{array}$$

1b. UNDERSTAND. Now that we know $39\frac{3}{4}$ acres can be used for lots, we calculate how many $\frac{3}{4}$ acres are in $39\frac{3}{4}$. This means that we divide.

2b. TRANSLATE.

In words:	number of $\frac{3}{4}$-acre lots	is	acreage for lots	divided by	size of each lot
	↓	↓	↓	↓	↓
Translate:	number of $\frac{3}{4}$-acre lots	=	$39\frac{3}{4}$	÷	$\frac{3}{4}$

3b. SOLVE:

$$39\frac{3}{4} \div \frac{3}{4} = \frac{159}{4} \cdot \frac{4}{3} = \frac{\overset{53}{\cancel{159}} \cdot \overset{1}{\cancel{4}}}{\underset{1}{\cancel{4}} \cdot \underset{1}{\cancel{3}}} = \frac{53}{1} \text{ or } 53$$

4. INTERPRET. *Check* your work. *State* your conclusion: The contractor can sell 53 $\frac{3}{4}$-acre lots.

Work Practice 3

3.6 Exercise Set

FOR EXTRA HELP

MyMathLab

PRACTICE

WATCH

DOWNLOAD

READ

REVIEW

To prepare for problem-solving, translate each phrase to an expression. Do not simplify the expression.

1. The sum of $\frac{1}{2}$ and $\frac{1}{3}$.

2. The product of $\frac{1}{2}$ and $\frac{1}{3}$.

3. The quotient of 20 and $6\frac{2}{5}$.

4. The difference of 20 and $6\frac{2}{5}$.

5. Subtract $\frac{5}{8}$ from $\frac{15}{16}$.

6. The total of $\frac{15}{36}$ and $\frac{18}{30}$.

7. $\frac{21}{68}$ increased by $\frac{7}{34}$.

8. $\frac{21}{68}$ decreased by $\frac{7}{34}$.

9. The product of $8\frac{1}{3}$ and $\frac{7}{9}$.

10. $37\frac{1}{2}$ divided by $9\frac{1}{2}$.

Objective A *Solve. Write any improper-fraction answers as mixed numbers. For Exercises 11 and 12, the solutions have been started for you. Write each answer in simplest form. See Examples 1 through 3.*

11. A recipe for brownies calls for $1\frac{2}{3}$ cups of sugar. If you are doubling the recipe, how much sugar do you need?

Start the solution:

1. UNDERSTAND the problem. Reread it as many times as needed.

2. TRANSLATE into an equation. (Fill in the blanks below.)

sugar needed	is	double	recipe amount of sugar
↓	↓	↓	↓
sugar needed	=	2 ·*	____

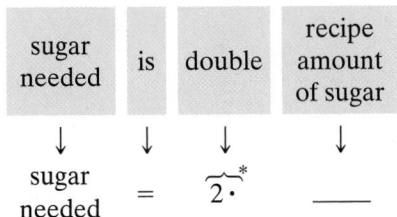

Finish with:

3. SOLVE

4. INTERPRET

*Note: Another way to double a number is to add the number to the same number.

12. A nacho recipe calls for $\frac{1}{3}$ cup cheddar cheese and $\frac{1}{2}$ cup jalapeño cheese. Find the total amount of cheese in the recipe.

Start the solution:

1. UNDERSTAND the problem. Reread it as many times as needed.

2. TRANSLATE into an equation. (Fill in the blanks below.)

total cheese	is	how much cheddar	added to	how much jalapeño cheese
↓	↓	↓	↓	↓
total cheese	=	____	+	____

Finish with:

3. SOLVE

4. INTERPRET

13. A decorative wall in a garden is to be built using bricks that are $2\frac{3}{4}$ inches wide and mortar joints that are $\frac{1}{2}$ inch wide. Use the diagram to find the height of the wall.

14. Suppose that the contractor building the wall in Exercise 13 decides that he wants one more layer of bricks with a mortar joint below and above that layer. Find the new height of the wall.

15. Doug and Claudia Scaggs recently drove $290\frac{1}{4}$ miles on $13\frac{1}{2}$ gallons of gas. Calculate how many miles per gallon they get in their vehicle.

16. A contractor is using 18 acres of his land to sell $\frac{3}{4}$-acre lots. How many lots can he sell?

17. The life expectancy of a circulating coin is 30 years. The life expectancy of a circulating dollar bill is only $\frac{1}{20}$ as long. Find the life expectancy of circulating paper money. (*Source:* The U.S. Mint)

18. The Indian head one-cent coin of 1859–1864 was made of copper and nickel only. If $\frac{3}{25}$ of the coin was nickel, what part of the whole coin was copper? (*Source:* The U.S. Mint)

19. The Gauge Act of 1846 set the standard gauge for U.S. railroads at $56\frac{1}{2}$ inches. (See figure.) If the standard gauge in Spain is $65\frac{9}{10}$ inches, how much wider is Spain's standard gauge than the U.S. standard gauge? (*Source:* San Diego Railroad Museum)

20. The standard railroad track gauge (see figure) in Spain is $65\frac{9}{10}$ inches, while in neighboring Portugal it is $65\frac{11}{20}$ inches. Which gauge is wider and by how much? (*Source:* San Diego Railroad Museum)

21. Mark Nguyen is a tailor making costumes for a play. He needs enough material for 1 large shirt that requires $1\frac{1}{2}$ yards of material and 5 small shirts that each require $\frac{3}{4}$ yard of material. He finds a 5-yard remnant of material on sale. Is 5 yards of material enough to make all 6 shirts? If not, how much more material does he need?

22. A beanbag manufacturer makes a large beanbag requiring $4\frac{1}{3}$ yards of vinyl fabric and a smaller size requiring $3\frac{1}{4}$ yards. A 100-yard roll of fabric is to be used to make 12 large beanbags. How many smaller beanbags can be made from the remaining piece?

23. A plumber has a 10-foot piece of PVC pipe. How many $\frac{9}{5}$-foot pieces can be cut from the 10-foot piece?

24. A carpenter has a 12-foot board to be used to make windowsills. If each sill requires $2\frac{5}{16}$ feet, how many sills can be made from the 12-foot board?

25. Suppose that the cross section of a piece of pipe looks like the diagram shown. Find the total outer diameter.

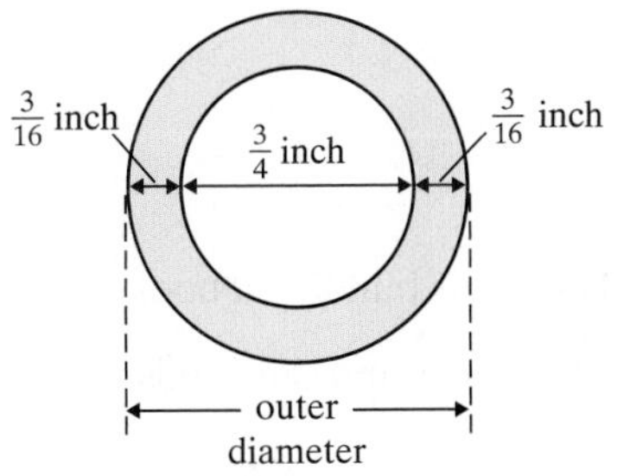

26. Suppose that the cross section of a piece of pipe looks like the diagram shown. Find the total inner diameter.

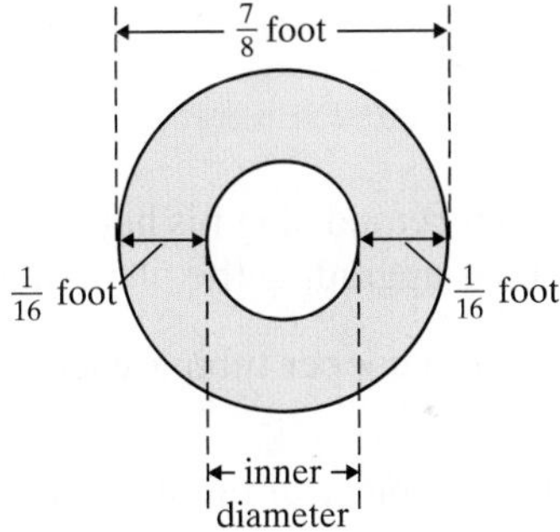

27. A recipe for chocolate chip cookies calls for $2\frac{1}{2}$ cups of flour. If you are making $1\frac{1}{2}$ recipes, how many cups of flour are needed?

28. A recipe for a homemade cleaning solution calls for $1\frac{3}{4}$ cups of vinegar. If you are tripling the recipe, how much vinegar is needed?

△ **29.** The Polaroid Pop Shot, the world's first disposable instant camera, can take color photographs measuring $4\frac{1}{2}$ inches by $2\frac{1}{2}$ inches. Find the area of a photograph. (*Source: Guinness World Records*)

△ **30.** A model for a proposed computer chip measures $\frac{3}{4}$ inch by $1\frac{1}{4}$ inches. Find its area.

31. A total solar eclipse on July 11, 2010, will last $5\frac{1}{3}$ minutes and can be viewed from the South Pacific, Easter Island, Chile, and Argentina. The next total solar eclipse on November 13, 2012, will last $4\frac{1}{30}$ minutes and can be viewed in the South Pacific and Australia. How much longer is the 2010 eclipse? (*Source:* NASA/Goddard Space Flight Center)

32. The pole vault record for the 1908 Summer Olympics was $12\frac{1}{6}$ feet. The record for the 2008 Summer Olympics was a little over $19\frac{1}{2}$ feet. Find the difference in the heights. (*Source:* International Olympic Committee)

△ **33.** A small cell phone measures $3\frac{1}{5}$ inches by $1\frac{7}{10}$ inches by 1 inch. Find the volume of a box with those dimensions. (*Source: Guinness World Records*)

△ **34.** Early cell phones were large and heavy. One early model measured approximately 8 inches by $2\frac{1}{2}$ inches by $2\frac{1}{2}$ inches. Find the volume of a box with those dimensions.

35. A stack of $\frac{5}{8}$-inch-wide sheetrock has a height of $41\frac{7}{8}$ inches. How many sheets of sheetrock are in the stack?

36. A stack of $\frac{5}{4}$-inch-thick books has a height of $28\frac{3}{4}$ inches. How many books are in the stack?

37. William Arcencio is remodeling his home. In order to save money, he is upgrading the plumbing himself. He needs 12 pieces of copper tubing, each $\frac{3}{4}$ of a foot long.

a. If he has a 10-foot piece of tubing, will that be enough?

b. How much more does he need or how much tubing will he have left over?

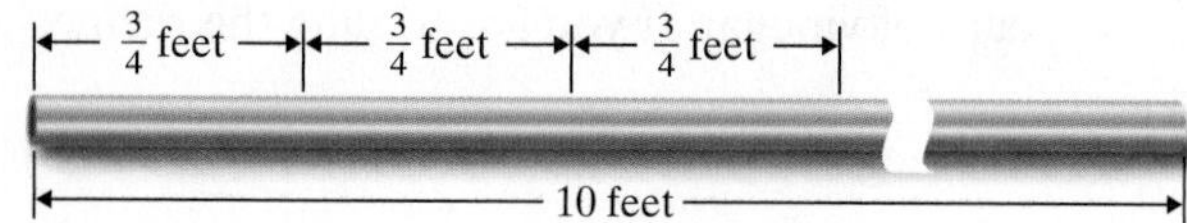

38. Trishelle Dallam is building a bookcase. Each shelf will be $2\frac{3}{8}$ feet long, and she needs wood for 7 shelves.

a. How many shelves can she cut from an 8-foot board?

b. Based on your answer for part a, how many 8-foot boards will she need?

Recall that the average of a list of numbers is their sum divided by the number of numbers in the list. Use this procedure for Exercises 39 and 40.

39. A female lion had 4 cubs. They weighed $2\frac{1}{8}$, $2\frac{7}{8}$, $3\frac{1}{4}$, and $3\frac{1}{2}$ pounds. What is the average cub weight?

40. Three brook trout were caught, tagged, and then released. They weighed $1\frac{1}{2}$, $1\frac{3}{8}$, and $1\frac{7}{8}$ pounds. Find their average weight.

Find the area and perimeter of each figure.

△ **41.**

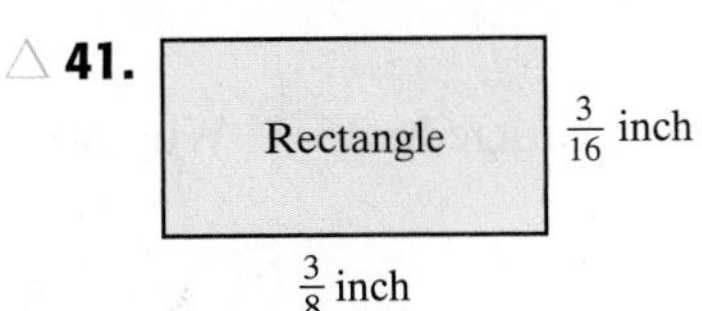

△ **42.**

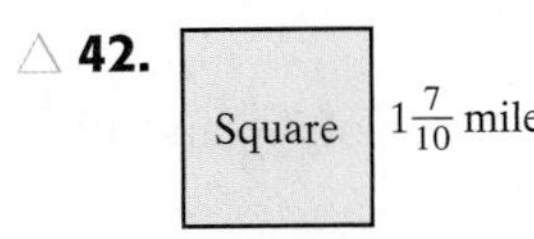

△ **43.**

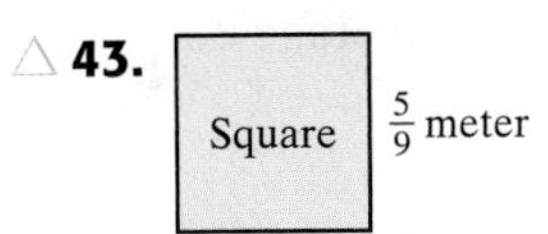

△ **44.**

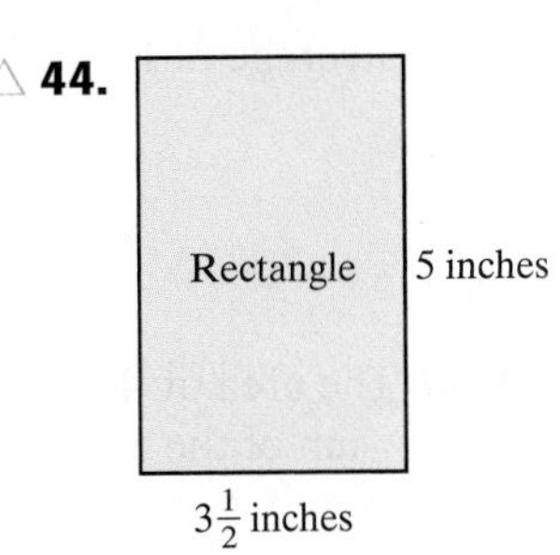

For Exercises 45 through 48, see the diagram. (Source: www.usflag.org)

45. The length of the U.S. flag is $1\frac{9}{10}$ its width. If a flag is being designed with a width of $2\frac{1}{2}$ feet, find its length.

46. The width of the Union portion of the U.S. flag is $\frac{7}{13}$ of the width of the flag. If a flag is being designed with a width of $2\frac{1}{2}$ feet, find the width of the Union portion.

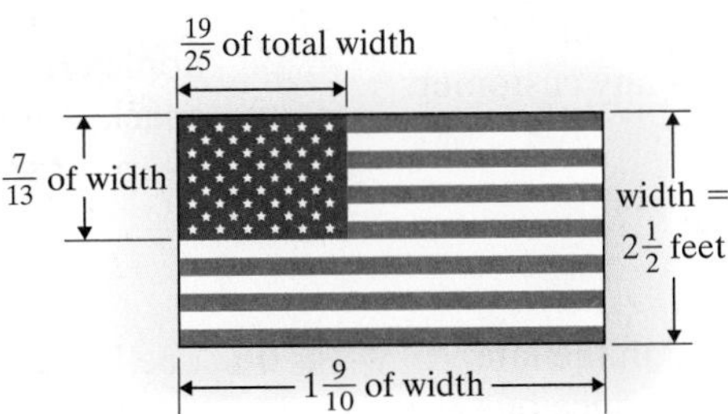

47. There are 13 stripes of equal width in the flag. If the width of a flag is $2\frac{1}{2}$ feet, find the width of each stripe.

48. The length of the Union portion of the flag is $\frac{19}{25}$ of the total width. If the width of a flag is $2\frac{1}{2}$ feet, find the length of the Union portion.

Review

Simplify. See Section 1.9.

49. $\sqrt{9}$

50. $\sqrt{4}$

51. 9^2

52. 4^2

53. $8 \div 4 \cdot 2$

54. $20 \div 5 \cdot 2$

55. $3^2 - 2^2 + 5^2$

56. $8^2 - 6^2 + 7^2$

57. $5 + 3[14 - (12 \div 3)]$

58. $7 + 2[20 - (35 \div 5)]$

Concept Extensions

59. Suppose you are finding the average of $7\frac{1}{9}$ and $12\frac{19}{20}$. Can the average be $1\frac{1}{2}$? Can the average be $15\frac{1}{2}$? Why or why not?

60. Suppose that you are finding the average of $1\frac{3}{4}$, $1\frac{1}{8}$, and $1\frac{9}{10}$. Can the average be $2\frac{1}{4}$? Can the average be $\frac{15}{16}$? Why or why not?

The figure shown is for Exercises 61 and 62.

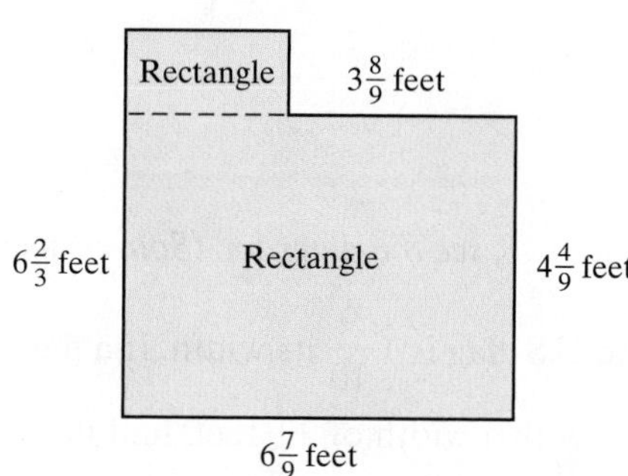

61. Find the area of the figure. (*Hint:* The area of the figure can be found by finding the sum of the areas of the rectangles shown in the figure.)

62. Find the perimeter of the figure.

63. On a particular day, 240 customers ate lunch at a local restaurant. If $\frac{3}{10}$ of them ordered a \$7 lunch, $\frac{5}{12}$ of them ordered a \$5 lunch, and the remaining customers ordered a \$9 lunch, how many customers ordered a \$9 lunch?

64. Scott purchased a case of 24 apples. He used $\frac{1}{3}$ of them to make an apple pie, $\frac{1}{4}$ of them to make apple crisp, and kept the rest for after-school snacks for his children. How many apples did Scott keep for snacks?

65. Coins were practically made by hand in the late 1700s. Back then, it took 3 years to produce our nation's first million coins. Today, it takes only $\frac{11}{13,140}$ as long to produce the same amount. Calculate how long it takes today in hours to produce one million coins. (*Hint:* First convert 3 years to equivalent hours.) (*Source:* The U.S. Mint)

66. The largest suitcase measures $13\frac{1}{3}$ feet by $8\frac{3}{4}$ feet by $4\frac{4}{25}$ feet. Find its volume. (*Source: Guinness World Records*)

Chapter 3 Group Activity

Sections 3.1–3.6

This activity may be completed by working in groups or individually.

Lobsters are normally classified by weight. Use the weight classification table to answer the questions in this activity.

Classification of Lobsters

Class	Weight (in Pounds)
Chicken	1 to $1\frac{1}{8}$
Quarter	$1\frac{1}{4}$
Half	$1\frac{1}{2}$ to $1\frac{3}{4}$
Select	$1\frac{3}{4}$ to $2\frac{1}{2}$
Large select	$2\frac{1}{2}$ to $3\frac{1}{2}$
Jumbo	Over $3\frac{1}{2}$

(*Source:* The Maine Lobster Promotion Council)

1. A lobster fisher has kept four lobsters from a lobster trap. Classify each lobster if they have the following weights:

a. $1\frac{7}{8}$ pounds

b. $1\frac{9}{16}$ pounds

c. $2\frac{3}{4}$ pounds

d. $2\frac{3}{8}$ pounds

2. A recipe requires 5 pounds of lobster. Using the minimum weight for each class, decide whether a chicken, half, and select lobster will be enough for the recipe, and explain your reasoning. If not, suggest a better choice of lobsters to meet the recipe requirements.

3. A lobster market customer has selected two chickens, a select, and a large select. What is the most that these four lobsters could weigh? What is the least that these four lobsters could weigh?

4. A lobster market customer wishes to buy four quarters. If lobsters sell for \$7 per pound, how much will the customer owe for her purchase?

5. Why do you think there is no classification for lobsters weighing under 1 pound?

Chapter 3 Vocabulary Check

Fill in each blank with one of the words or phrases listed below.

equivalent	least common multiple	exponent	unlike
mixed number	$<$ $>$	least common denominator	like

1. Fractions that have the same denominator are called ______________ fractions.
2. The ______________ is the smallest number that is a multiple of all numbers in a list of numbers.
3. ______________ fractions represent the same portion of a whole.
4. A ______________ has a whole number part and a fraction part.
5. The symbol ______________ means is greater than.
6. The symbol ______________ means is less than.
7. The LCM of the denominators in a list of fractions is called the ______________.
8. Fractions that have different denominators are called ______________ fractions.
9. A shorthand notation for repeated multiplication of the same factor is a(n) ______________.

Helpful Hint Are you preparing for your test? Don't forget to take the Chapter 3 Test on page 242. Then check your answers at the back of the text and use the Chapter Test Prep Videos to see the fully worked-out solutions to any of the exercises you want to review.

3 Chapter Highlights

Definitions and Concepts	Examples
Section 3.1 Adding and Subtracting Like Fractions	
Fractions that have the same denominator are called **like fractions.**	$\frac{1}{3}$ and $\frac{2}{3}$; $\frac{5}{7}$ and $\frac{6}{7}$
To add or subtract like fractions, combine the numerators and place the sum or difference over the common denominator.	$\frac{2}{7}+\frac{3}{7}=\frac{5}{7}$ ← Add the numerators. ← Keep the common denominator. $\frac{7}{8}-\frac{4}{8}=\frac{3}{8}$ ← Subtract the numerators. ← Keep the common denominator.
Section 3.2 Least Common Multiple	
The **least common multiple (LCM)** is the smallest number that is a multiple of all numbers in a list of numbers.	The LCM of 2 and 6 is 6 because 6 is the smallest number that is a multiple of both 2 and 6.
Method 1 for Finding the LCM of a List of Numbers Using Multiples **Step 1:** Write the multiples of the largest number (starting with the number itself) until a multiple common to all numbers in the list is found. **Step 2:** The multiple found in step 1 is the LCM.	Find the LCM of 4 and 6 using Method 1. $6\cdot 1=6$ Not a multiple of 4 $6\cdot 2=12$ A multiple of 4 The LCM is 12.

Definitions and Concepts	Examples
Section 3.2 Least Common Multiple (*continued*)	
METHOD 2 FOR FINDING THE LCM OF A LIST OF NUMBERS USING PRIME FACTORIZATION **Step 1:** Write the prime factorization of each number. **Step 2:** For each different prime factor in step 1, circle the greatest number of times that factor occurs in any one factorization. **Step 3:** The LCM is the product of the circled factors.	Find the LCM of 6 and 20 using Method 2. $6 = 2 \cdot \textcircled{3}$ $20 = \textcircled{2 \cdot 2} \cdot \textcircled{5}$ The LCM is $2 \cdot 2 \cdot 3 \cdot 5 = 60$
Equivalent fractions represent the same portion of a whole.	Write an equivalent fraction with the indicated denominator. $\frac{2}{8} = \frac{}{16}$ $\frac{2 \cdot 2}{8 \cdot 2} = \frac{4}{16}$
Section 3.3 Adding and Subtracting Unlike Fractions	
TO ADD OR SUBTRACT FRACTIONS WITH UNLIKE DENOMINATORS	Add: $\frac{3}{20} + \frac{2}{5}$
Step 1: Find the LCD.	**Step 1:** The LCD of 20 and 5 is 20.
Step 2: Write each fraction as an equivalent fraction whose denominator is the LCD.	**Step 2:** $\frac{3}{20} = \frac{3}{20}$; $\frac{2}{5} = \frac{2}{5} \cdot \frac{4}{4} = \frac{8}{20}$
Step 3: Add or subtract the like fractions.	**Step 3:** $\frac{3}{20} + \frac{2}{5} = \frac{3}{20} + \frac{8}{20} = \frac{11}{20}$
Step 4: Write the sum or difference in simplest form.	**Step 4:** $\frac{11}{20}$ is in simplest form.
Section 3.4 Adding and Subtracting Mixed Numbers	
To add or subtract with mixed numbers, add or subtract the fractions and then add or subtract the whole numbers.	Add: $2\frac{1}{2} + 5\frac{7}{8}$ $2\frac{1}{2} = 2\frac{4}{8}$ $+5\frac{7}{8} = 5\frac{7}{8}$ $7\frac{11}{8} = 7 + 1\frac{3}{8} = 8\frac{3}{8}$
Section 3.5 Order, Exponents, and the Order of Operations	
To compare like fractions, compare the numerators. The order of the fractions is the same as the order of the numerators.	Compare $\frac{3}{10}$ and $\frac{4}{10}$. $\frac{3}{10} < \frac{4}{10}$ since $3 < 4$

(*continued*)

Definitions and Concepts	Examples

Section 3.5 Order, Exponents, and the Order of Operations (*continued*)

To compare unlike fractions, first write the fractions as like fractions. Then the fraction with the greater numerator is the greater fraction.

Compare $\frac{2}{5}$ and $\frac{3}{7}$.

$$\frac{2}{5} = \frac{2}{5} \cdot \frac{7}{7} = \frac{14}{35} \qquad \frac{3}{7} = \frac{3}{7} \cdot \frac{5}{5} = \frac{15}{35}$$

Since $14 < 15$, then

$$\frac{14}{35} < \frac{15}{35} \quad \text{or} \quad \frac{2}{5} < \frac{3}{7}$$

Exponents mean repeated multiplication whether the base is a whole number or a fraction.

$$\left(\frac{1}{2}\right)^3 = \frac{1}{2} \cdot \frac{1}{2} \cdot \frac{1}{2} = \frac{1}{8}$$

ORDER OF OPERATIONS

1. Perform all operations within parentheses ( ), brackets [ ], or other grouping symbols such as square roots or fraction bars.
2. Evaluate any expressions with exponents.
3. Multiply or divide in order from left to right.
4. Add or subtract in order from left to right.

Perform each indicated operation.

$$\frac{1}{2} + \frac{2}{3} \cdot \frac{1}{5} = \frac{1}{2} + \frac{2}{15} \qquad \text{Multiply.}$$

$$= \frac{1}{2} \cdot \frac{15}{15} + \frac{2}{15} \cdot \frac{2}{2} \qquad \text{The LCD is 30.}$$

$$= \frac{15}{30} + \frac{4}{30}$$

$$= \frac{19}{30} \qquad \text{Add.}$$

Section 3.6 Fractions and Problem Solving

PROBLEM-SOLVING STEPS

1. UNDERSTAND the problem.
2. TRANSLATE the problem.
3. SOLVE the problem.
4. INTERPRET the results.

A stack of $\frac{3}{4}$-inch plywood has a height of $50\frac{1}{4}$ inches. How many sheets of plywood are in the stack?

1. UNDERSTAND. Read and reread the problem. We want to know how many $\frac{3}{4}$'s are in $50\frac{1}{4}$, so we divide.
2. TRANSLATE.

number of sheets in stack	is	height of stack	÷	height of a sheet
number of sheets in stack	=	$50\frac{1}{4}$	÷	$\frac{3}{4}$

3. SOLVE. $50\frac{1}{4} \div \frac{3}{4} = \frac{201}{4} \cdot \frac{4}{3}$

$$= \frac{\overset{67}{\cancel{201}} \cdot \overset{1}{\cancel{4}}}{\underset{1}{\cancel{4}} \cdot \underset{1}{\cancel{3}}}$$

$$= 67$$

4. INTERPRET. *Check* your work and *state* your conclusion: There are 67 sheets of plywood in the stack.

Chapter 3 Review

(3.1) *Add or subtract as indicated. Simplify your answers.*

1. $\frac{7}{11} + \frac{3}{11}$

2. $\frac{4}{50} + \frac{2}{50}$

3. $\frac{11}{15} - \frac{1}{15}$

4. $\frac{4}{21} - \frac{1}{21}$

5. $\frac{4}{15} + \frac{3}{15} + \frac{2}{15}$

6. $\frac{3}{20} + \frac{7}{20} + \frac{2}{20}$

7. $\frac{1}{12} + \frac{11}{12}$

8. $\frac{3}{4} + \frac{1}{4}$

9. $\frac{11}{25} + \frac{6}{25} + \frac{2}{25}$

10. $\frac{4}{21} + \frac{1}{21} + \frac{11}{21}$

Solve.

11. One evening Mark Alorenzo did $\frac{3}{8}$ of his homework before supper, another $\frac{2}{8}$ of it while his children did their homework, and $\frac{1}{8}$ after his children went to bed. What part of his homework did he do that evening?

△ **12.** The Simpsons will be fencing in their land, which is in the shape of a rectangle. In order to do this, they need to find its perimeter. Find the perimeter of their land.

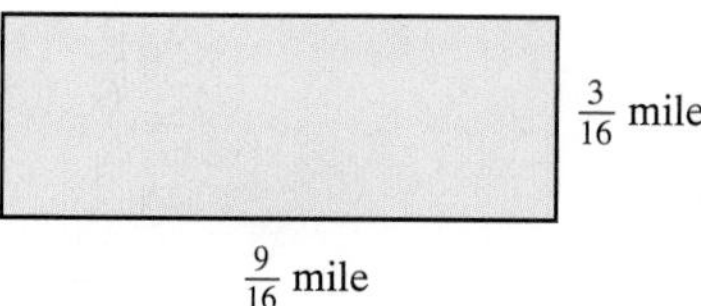

(3.2) *Find the LCM of each list of numbers.*

13. 5, 11

14. 20, 30

15. 20, 24

16. 16, 5

17. 12, 21, 63

18. 6, 8, 18

Write each fraction as an equivalent fraction with the given denominator.

19. $\frac{7}{8} = \frac{}{64}$

20. $\frac{2}{3} = \frac{}{30}$

21. $\frac{7}{11} = \frac{}{33}$

22. $\frac{10}{13} = \frac{}{26}$

23. $\frac{4}{15} = \frac{}{60}$

24. $\frac{5}{12} = \frac{}{60}$

(3.3) *Add or subtract as indicated. Simplify your answers.*

25. $\frac{7}{18} + \frac{2}{9}$

26. $\frac{4}{15} + \frac{1}{5}$

27. $\frac{4}{13} - \frac{1}{26}$

28. $\frac{7}{12} - \frac{1}{9}$

29. $\frac{1}{3} + \frac{9}{14}$

30. $\frac{7}{18} + \frac{5}{24}$

31. $\frac{11}{15} - \frac{4}{9}$

32. $\frac{9}{14} - \frac{3}{35}$

Find the perimeter of each figure.

△ **33.**

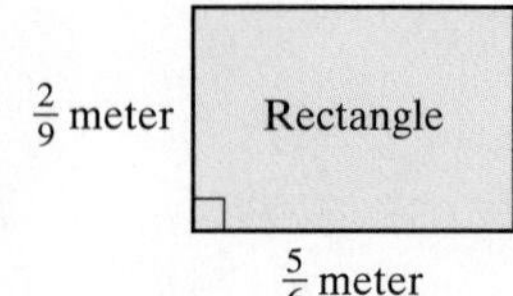

△ **34.** $\frac{1}{5}$ foot, $\frac{3}{5}$ foot, $\frac{7}{10}$ foot

35. Find the difference in length of two scarves if one scarf is $\frac{5}{12}$ of a yard long and the other is $\frac{2}{3}$ of a yard long.

36. Truman Kalzote cleaned $\frac{3}{5}$ of his house yesterday and $\frac{1}{10}$ of it today. How much of the house has been cleaned?

(3.4) *Add or subtract as indicated. Simplify your answers.*

37. $31\frac{2}{7} + 14\frac{10}{21}$

38. $24\frac{4}{5} + 35\frac{1}{5}$

39. $69\frac{5}{22} - 36\frac{7}{11}$

40. $36\frac{3}{20} - 32\frac{5}{6}$

41. $\begin{array}{r} 29\frac{2}{9} \\ 27\frac{7}{18} \\ +54\frac{2}{3} \\ \hline \end{array}$

42. $\begin{array}{r} 7\frac{3}{8} \\ 9\frac{5}{6} \\ +3\frac{1}{12} \\ \hline \end{array}$

43. $\begin{array}{r} 9\frac{3}{5} \\ -4\frac{1}{7} \\ \hline \end{array}$

44. $\begin{array}{r} 8\frac{3}{11} \\ -5\frac{1}{5} \\ \hline \end{array}$

Solve.

45. The average annual snowfall at a certain ski resort is $62\frac{3}{10}$ inches. Last year it had $54\frac{1}{2}$ inches. How many inches below average was last year's snowfall?

46. Dinah's homemade canned peaches contain $15\frac{3}{5}$ ounces per can. A can of Amy's brand contains $15\frac{5}{8}$ ounces per can. Amy's brand weighs how much more than Dinah's?

△ **47.** Find the perimeter of a sheet of shelf paper needed to fit exactly a square drawer $1\frac{1}{4}$ feet long on each side.

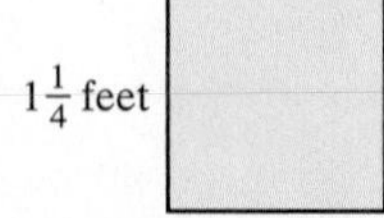

△ **48.** Find the perimeter of a rectangular sheet of gift wrap that is $2\frac{1}{4}$ feet by $3\frac{1}{3}$ feet.

(3.5) *Insert < or > to form a true statement.*

49. $\frac{5}{11} \quad \frac{6}{11}$

50. $\frac{4}{35} \quad \frac{3}{35}$

51. $\frac{5}{14} \quad \frac{16}{42}$

52. $\frac{6}{35} \quad \frac{17}{105}$

53. $\frac{7}{8} \quad \frac{6}{7}$

54. $\frac{7}{10} \quad \frac{2}{3}$

Evaluate each expression. Use the order of operations to simplify.

55. $\left(\frac{3}{7}\right)^2$

56. $\left(\frac{4}{5}\right)^3$

57. $\left(\frac{1}{2}\right)^4 \cdot \left(\frac{3}{5}\right)^2$

58. $\left(\frac{1}{3}\right)^2 \cdot \left(\frac{9}{10}\right)^2$

59. $\frac{5}{13} \div \frac{1}{2} \cdot \frac{4}{5}$

60. $\frac{8}{11} \div \frac{1}{3} \cdot \frac{11}{12}$

61. $\left(\frac{6}{7} - \frac{3}{14}\right)^2$

62. $\left(\frac{1}{3}\right)^2 - \frac{2}{27}$

63. $\frac{8}{9} - \frac{1}{8} \div \frac{3}{4}$

64. $\frac{9}{10} - \frac{1}{9} \div \frac{2}{3}$

65. $\frac{2}{7} \cdot \left(\frac{1}{5} + \frac{3}{10}\right)$

66. $\frac{9}{10} \div \left(\frac{1}{5} + \frac{1}{20}\right)$

67. $\left(\frac{3}{4} + \frac{1}{2}\right) \div \left(\frac{4}{9} + \frac{1}{3}\right)$

68. $\left(\frac{3}{8} - \frac{1}{16}\right) \div \left(\frac{1}{2} - \frac{1}{8}\right)$

69. $\frac{6}{7} \cdot \frac{5}{2} - \frac{3}{4} \cdot \frac{1}{2}$

70. $\frac{9}{10} \cdot \frac{1}{3} - \frac{2}{5} \cdot \frac{1}{11}$

Find the average of each list of fractions.

71. $\frac{2}{3}, \frac{5}{6}, \frac{1}{9}$

72. $\frac{4}{5}, \frac{9}{10}, \frac{3}{20}$

(3.6)

73. Saturn has 28 moons. The planet Uranus has only $\frac{3}{4}$ as many. Find the number of moons for Uranus. (*Source:* NASA)

74. James Hardaway just bought $5\frac{7}{8}$ acres of land adjacent to the $9\frac{3}{4}$ acres he already owned. How much land does he now own?

Find the unknown measurements.

△ **75.**

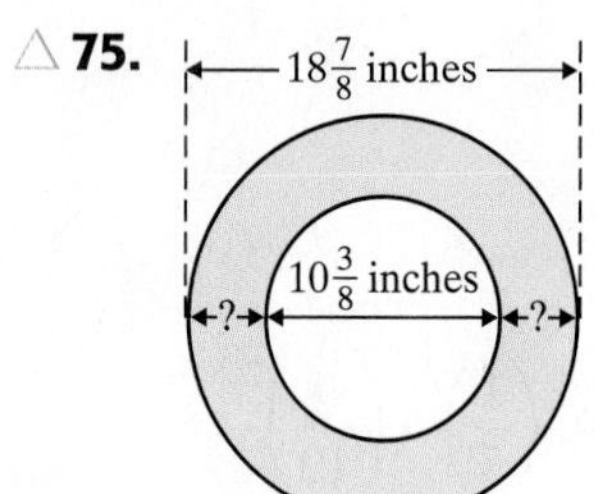

△ **76.**

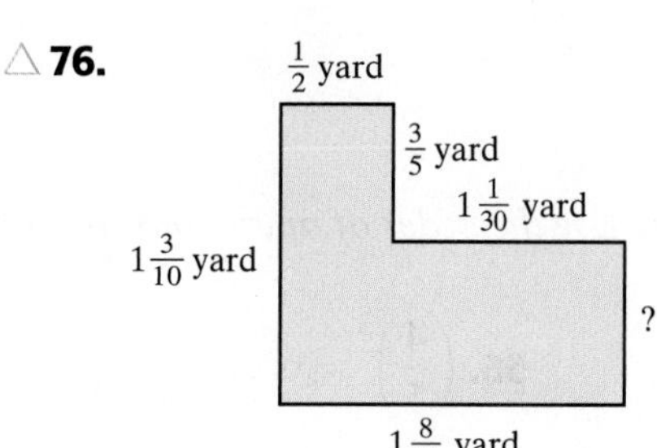

Find the perimeter and area of each rectangle. Attach the proper units to each. Remember that perimeter is measured in units and area is measured in square units.

△ **77.**

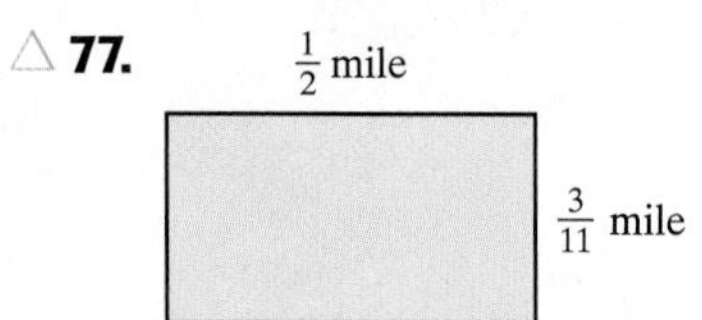

△ **78.**

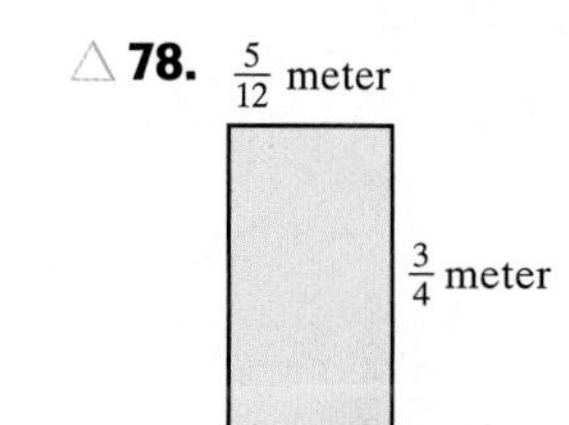

Mixed Review

Find the LCM of each list of numbers.

79. 15, 30, 45

80. 6, 15, 20

Write each fraction as an equivalent fraction with the given denominator.

81. $\frac{5}{6} = \frac{}{48}$

82. $\frac{7}{8} = \frac{}{72}$

Add or subtract as indicated. Simplify your answers.

83. $\frac{5}{12} - \frac{3}{12}$

84. $\frac{3}{10} - \frac{1}{10}$

85. $\frac{2}{3} + \frac{1}{4}$

86. $\frac{5}{11} + \frac{2}{55}$

87. $\begin{array}{r} 7\frac{3}{4} \\ +5\frac{2}{3} \\ \hline \end{array}$

88. $\begin{array}{r} 2\frac{7}{8} \\ +9\frac{1}{2} \\ \hline \end{array}$

89. $\begin{array}{r} 12\frac{3}{5} \\ -9\frac{1}{7} \\ \hline \end{array}$

90. $\begin{array}{r} 32\frac{10}{21} \\ -24\frac{3}{7} \\ \hline \end{array}$

Evaluate each expression. Use the order of operations to simplify.

91. $\frac{2}{5} + \left(\frac{2}{5}\right)^2 - \frac{3}{25}$

92. $\frac{1}{4} + \left(\frac{1}{2}\right)^2 - \frac{3}{8}$

93. $\left(\frac{5}{6} - \frac{3}{4}\right)^2$

94. $\left(2 - \frac{2}{3}\right)^3$

95. $\frac{2}{3} \div \left(\frac{3}{5} + \frac{5}{3}\right)$

96. $\frac{3}{8} \cdot \left(\frac{2}{3} - \frac{4}{9}\right)$

Insert < *or* > *to form a true statement.*

97. $\frac{3}{14} \quad \frac{2}{3}$

98. $\frac{7}{23} \quad \frac{3}{16}$

Solve.

99. Gregor Krowsky studied math for $\frac{3}{8}$ of an hour and geography for $\frac{1}{8}$ of an hour. How long did he study?

100. Two packages to be mailed weigh $3\frac{3}{4}$ pounds and $2\frac{3}{5}$ pounds. Find their combined weight.

101. A ribbon $5\frac{1}{2}$ yards long is cut from a reel of ribbon with 50 yards on it. Find the length of the piece remaining on the reel.

102. Linda Taneff has a board that is $10\frac{2}{3}$ feet in length. She plans to cut it into 5 equal lengths to use for a bookshelf. Find the length of each piece.

103. A recipe for pico de gallo calls for $1\frac{1}{2}$ tablespoons of cilantro. Five recipes will be made for a charity event. How much cilantro is needed?

104. Beryl Goldstein mixed $\frac{5}{8}$ of a gallon of water with $\frac{1}{8}$ of a gallon of punch concentrate. Then she and her friends drank $\frac{3}{8}$ of a gallon of the punch. How much of the punch was left?

Chapter 3 Test

Step-by-step test solutions are found on the Chapter Test Prep Videos available via the Interactive DVD Lecture Series, in MyMathLab or on YouTube (search "MartinGayBasicMath" and click on "Channels").

Answers

1. ________
2. ________
3. ________
4. ________
5. ________
6. ________
7. ________
8. ________
9. ________
10. ________
11. ________
12. ________
13. ________
14. ________
15. ________
16. ________
17. ________
18. ________
19. ________

1. Find the LCM of 4 and 15.

2. Find the LCM of 8, 9, and 12.

Insert $<$ or $>$ to form a true statement.

3. $\frac{5}{6} \quad \frac{26}{30}$

4. $\frac{7}{8} \quad \frac{8}{9}$

Perform each indicated operation. Simplify your answers.

5. $\frac{7}{9} + \frac{1}{9}$

6. $\frac{8}{15} - \frac{2}{15}$

7. $\frac{9}{10} + \frac{2}{5}$

8. $\frac{1}{6} + \frac{3}{14}$

9. $\frac{7}{8} - \frac{1}{3}$

10. $\frac{17}{21} - \frac{1}{7}$

11. $\frac{9}{20} + \frac{2}{3}$

12. $\frac{16}{25} - \frac{1}{2}$

13. $\frac{11}{12} + \frac{3}{8} + \frac{5}{24}$

14. $\begin{array}{r} 3\frac{7}{8} \\ 7\frac{2}{5} \\ +2\frac{3}{4} \\ \hline \end{array}$

15. $\begin{array}{r} 8\frac{2}{9} \\ 12 \\ +10\frac{1}{15} \\ \hline \end{array}$

16. $\begin{array}{r} 5\frac{1}{6} \\ -3\frac{7}{8} \\ \hline \end{array}$

17. $\begin{array}{r} 19 \\ -\ 2\frac{3}{11} \\ \hline \end{array}$

18. $\frac{2}{7} \cdot \left(6 - \frac{1}{6}\right)$

19. $\left(\frac{2}{3}\right)^4$

20. $\frac{1}{2} \div \frac{2}{3} \cdot \frac{3}{4}$

21. $\left(\frac{4}{5}\right)^2 + \left(\frac{1}{2}\right)^3$

22. $\left(\frac{3}{4}\right)^2 \div \left(\frac{2}{3} + \frac{5}{6}\right)$

23. Find the average of $\frac{5}{6}$, $\frac{4}{3}$, and $\frac{7}{12}$.

Solve.

24. A carpenter cuts a piece $2\frac{3}{4}$ feet long from a cedar plank that is $6\frac{1}{2}$ feet long. How long is the remaining piece?

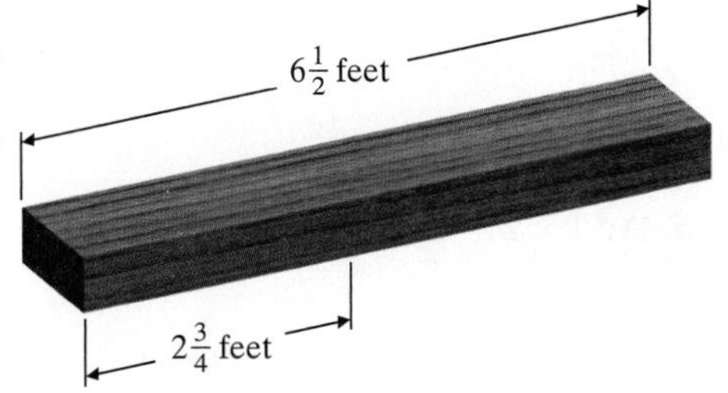

25. A small airplane used $58\frac{3}{4}$ gallons of fuel on a $7\frac{1}{2}$-hour trip. How many gallons of fuel were used for each hour?

The circle graph below shows us how the average consumer spends money. For example, $\frac{7}{50}$ of your spending goes for food. Use this information for Exercises 26 through 28.

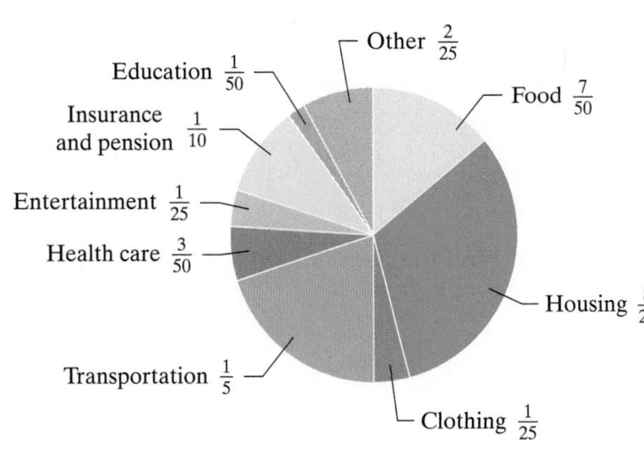

26. What fraction of spending goes for housing and food combined?

27. What fraction of spending goes for education, transportation, and clothing?

28. Suppose your family spent \$47,000 on the items in the graph. How much might we expect was spent on health care?

Find the perimeter of each figure. For Exercise 29, find the area also.

△ **29.**

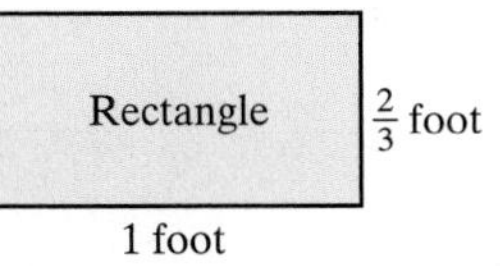

△ **30.**

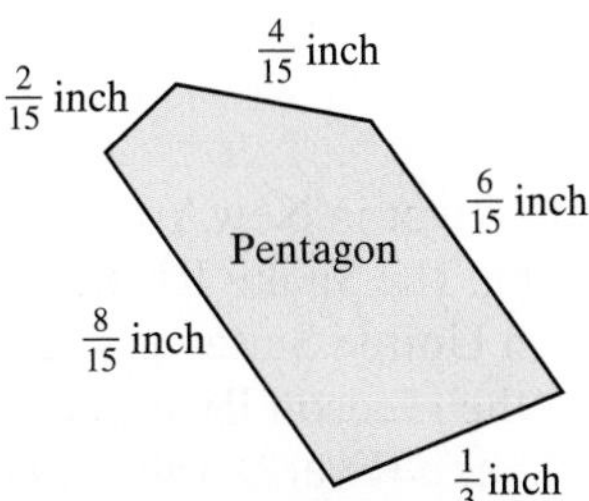

20. ______

21. ______

22. ______

23. ______

24. ______

25. ______

26. ______

27. ______

28. ______

29. ______

30. ______

Answers

1. ______

2. ______

3. ______

4. ______

5. ______

6. ______

7. ______

8. ______

9. ______

10. ______

11. ______

12. ______

13. a. ______

b. ______

c. ______

d. ______

e. ______

f. ______

14. ______

15. ______

16. ______

Cumulative Review Chapters 1–3

Write each number in words.

1. 85

2. 107

3. 126

4. 5026

5. Add: $23 + 136$

6. Find the perimeter.

3 in.
7 in.
9 in.

7. Subtract: $543 - 29$. Then check by adding.

8. Divide: $3268 \div 27$

9. Round 278,362 to the nearest thousand.

10. Find all the factors of 30.

11. Multiply: 236×86

12. Multiply: $236 \times 86 \times 0$

13. Find each quotient and then check the answer by multiplying.

a. $1\overline{)7}$

b. $12 \div 1$

c. $\frac{6}{6}$

d. $9 \div 9$

e. $\frac{20}{1}$

f. $18\overline{)18}$

14. Find the average of 25, 17, 19, and 39.

15. The Hudson River in New York State is 306 miles long. The Snake River, in the northwestern United States, is 732 miles longer than the Hudson River. How long is the Snake River? (*Source:* U.S. Department of the Interior)

16. Evaluate: $\sqrt{121}$

Evaluate.

17. 9^2 **18.** 5^3 **19.** 3^4 **20.** 10^3

Write the shaded part of each diagram as an improper fraction and a mixed number.

21. 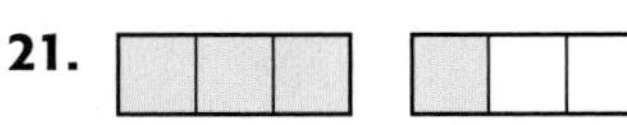

22. 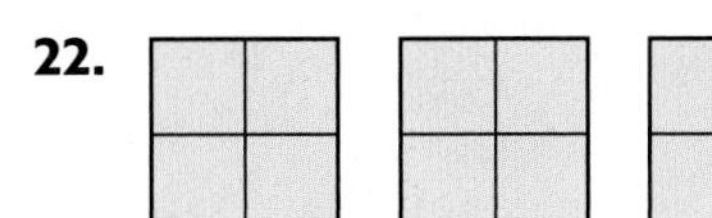 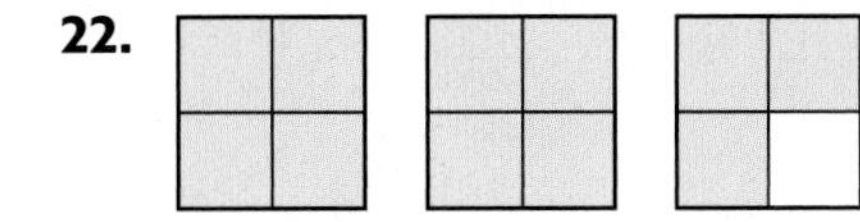

23. 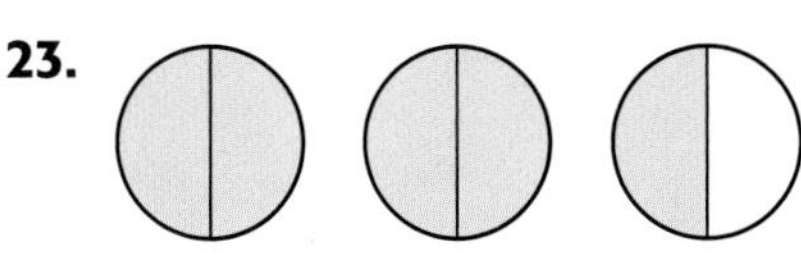

24. 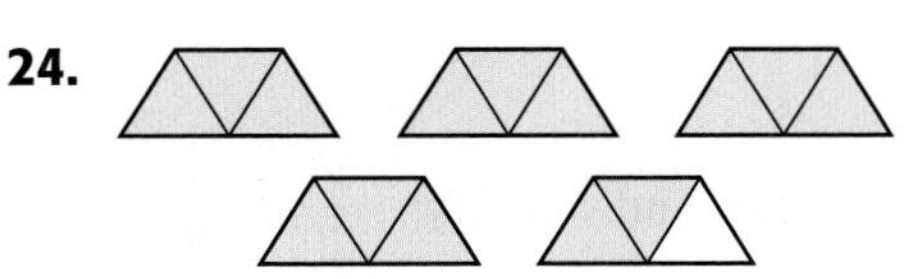

25. Of the numbers 3, 9, 11, 17, 26, which are prime and which are composite?

26. Simplify: $\dfrac{6^2 + 4 \cdot 4 + 2^3}{37 - 5^2}$

27. Find the prime factorization of 180.

28. Find the difference of 87 and 25.

29. Write $\dfrac{72}{26}$ in simplest form.

30. Write $9\dfrac{7}{8}$ as an improper fraction.

31. Determine whether $\dfrac{16}{40}$ and $\dfrac{10}{25}$ are equivalent.

32. Insert < or > to form a true statement. $\dfrac{4}{7} \quad \dfrac{5}{9}$

Multiply.

33. $\dfrac{2}{3} \cdot \dfrac{5}{11}$ **34.** $2\dfrac{5}{8} \cdot \dfrac{4}{7}$

35. $\dfrac{1}{4} \cdot \dfrac{1}{2}$ **36.** $7 \cdot 5\dfrac{2}{7}$

17. ______
18. ______
19. ______
20. ______
21. ______
22. ______
23. ______
24. ______
25. ______
26. ______
27. ______
28. ______
29. ______
30. ______
31. ______
32. ______
33. ______
34. ______
35. ______
36. ______

37. ______
38. ______
39. ______
40. ______
41. ______
42. ______
43. ______
44. ______
45. ______
46. ______
47. ______
48. ______
49. ______
50. ______

Divide.

37. $\frac{11}{18} \div 2\frac{5}{6}$

38. $\frac{15}{19} \div \frac{3}{5}$

39. $5\frac{2}{3} \div 2\frac{5}{9}$

40. $\frac{8}{11} \div \frac{1}{22}$

41. Add and simplify: $\frac{3}{16} + \frac{7}{16}$

42. Subtract and simplify: $\frac{11}{20} - \frac{7}{20}$

43. Find the LCM of 6 and 8.

44. Find the LCM of 7 and 5.

45. Add: $\frac{1}{2} + \frac{2}{3} + \frac{5}{6}$

46. Evaluate: $\left(\frac{5}{9}\right)^2$

47. Subtract: $9\frac{3}{7} - 5\frac{2}{21}$

48. Subtract: $\frac{31}{100} - \frac{5}{25}$

49. Simplify: $\left(\frac{2}{3}\right)^2 \div \left(\frac{8}{27} + \frac{2}{3}\right)$

50. $\frac{1}{10} \div \frac{7}{8} \cdot \frac{2}{5}$

4 Decimals

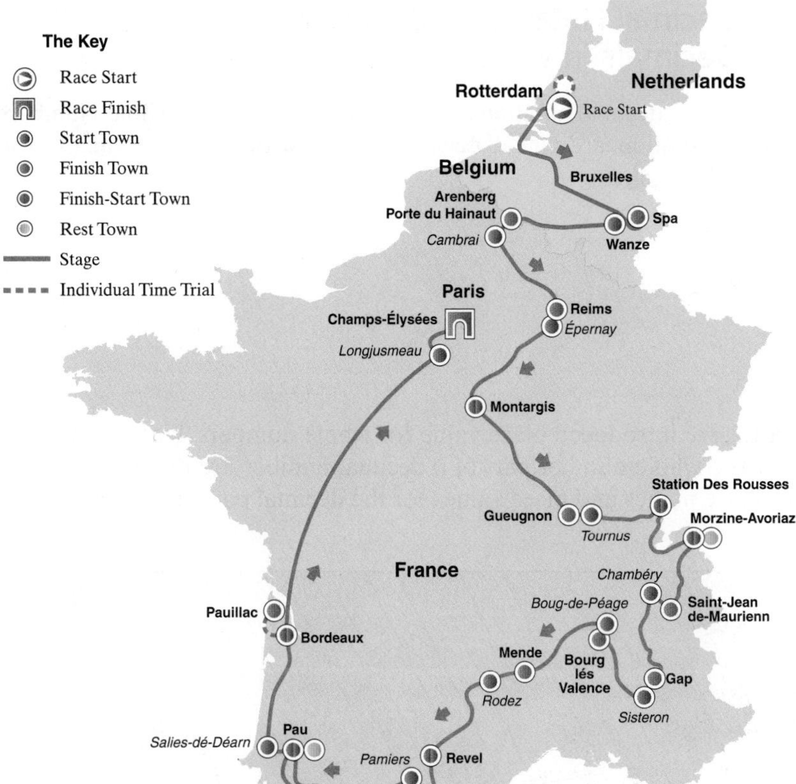

Sections

Check Your Progress

Decimal numbers represent parts of a whole, just like fractions. In this chapter, we learn to perform arithmetic operations using decimals and to analyze the relationship between fractions and decimals. We also learn how decimals are used in the real world.

Believe it or not, the Tour de France started as a publicity stunt for a French newspaper in 1903. It has grown to become the most prestigious bicycle race in the world. This race is an annual event covering around 3500 kilometers throughout France and bordering countries. It is a "Grand Tour," which means that it is raced in 21 day-long stages over 23 days.

The unmatched success of Lance Armstrong, who won seven consecutive Tours de France from 1999 through 2005, has guaranteed this sport a place in American sports lore.

In Section 4.2, Exercises 69 through 72, we will explore the average speeds of recent Tour de France winners.

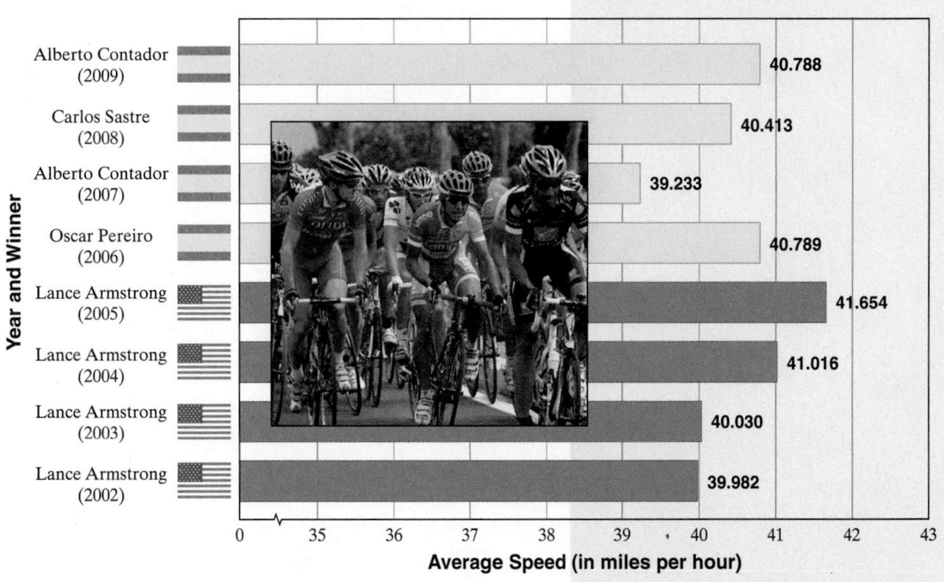

Objectives

A **Know the Meaning of Place Value for a Decimal Number, and Write Decimals in Words.**

B **Write Decimals in Standard Form.**

C **Write Decimals as Fractions.**

D **Write Fractions as Decimals.**

4.1 INTRODUCTION TO DECIMALS

Objective A Decimal Notation and Writing Decimals in Words

Like fractional notation, decimal notation is used to denote a part of a whole. Numbers written in decimal notation are called **decimal numbers,** or simply **decimals.** The decimal 17.758 has three parts.

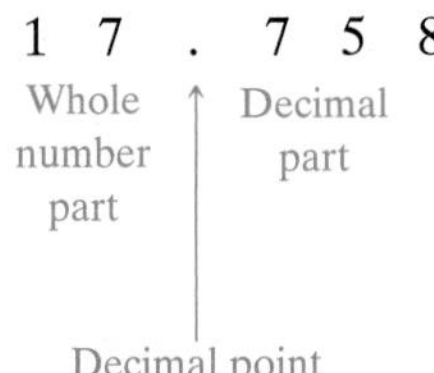

In Section 1.2, we introduced place value for whole numbers. Place names and place values for the whole number part of a decimal number are exactly the same, as shown next. Place names and place values for the decimal part are also shown.

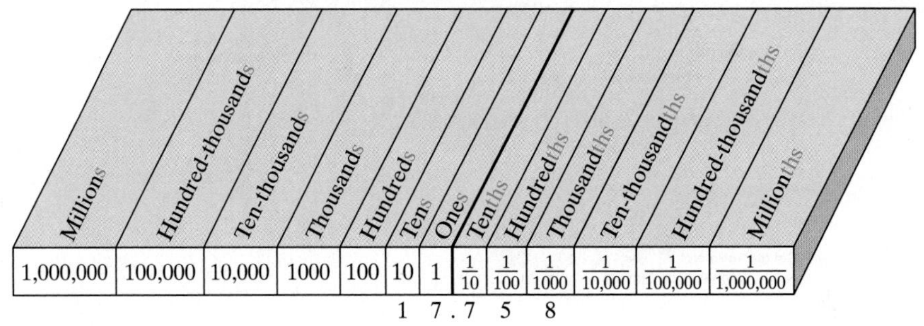

Helpful Hint Notice that place values to the left of the decimal point end in "s." Place values to the right of the decimal point end in "ths."

Notice that the value of each place is $\frac{1}{10}$ of the value of the place to its left. For example,

$$1 \cdot \frac{1}{10} = \frac{1}{10}$$

↑ ones ↑ tenths

$$\frac{1}{10} \cdot \frac{1}{10} = \frac{1}{100}$$

↑ tenths ↑ hundredths

The decimal number 17.758 means

1 ten	+	7 ones	+	7 tenths	+	5 hundredths	+	8 thousandths
or $1 \cdot 10$	+	$7 \cdot 1$	+	$7 \cdot \frac{1}{10}$	+	$5 \cdot \frac{1}{100}$	+	$8 \cdot \frac{1}{1000}$
or 10	+	7	+	$\frac{7}{10}$	+	$\frac{5}{100}$	+	$\frac{8}{1000}$

Writing (or Reading) a Decimal in Words

Step 1: Write the whole number part in words.

Step 2: Write "and" for the decimal point.

Step 3: Write the decimal part in words as though it were a whole number, followed by the place value of the last digit.

Example 1 Write the decimal 1.3 in words.

Solution: one and three tenths

Work Practice 1

PRACTICE 1

Write the decimal 8.7 in words.

Example 2

Write the decimal in the following sentence in words: The Golden Jubilee Diamond is a 545.67-carat cut diamond. (*Source: The Guinness Book of Records*)

Solution: five hundred forty-five and sixty-seven hundredths

Work Practice 2

PRACTICE 2

Write the decimal 97.28 in words.

Example 3 Write the decimal 19.5023 in words.

Solution: nineteen and five thousand, twenty-three ten-thousandths

Work Practice 3

PRACTICE 3

Write the decimal 302.105 in words.

Example 4

Write the decimal in the following sentence in words: The oldest known fragments of the Earth's crust are zircon crystals; they were discovered in Australia and are thought to be 4.276 billion years old. (*Source: The Guinness Book of Records*)

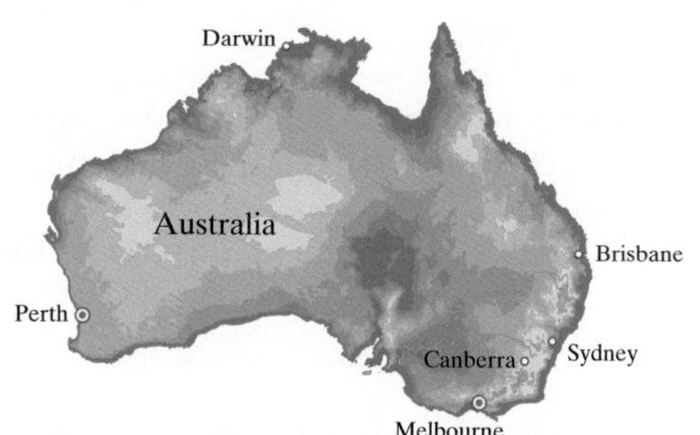

Solution: four and two hundred seventy-six thousandths

Work Practice 4

PRACTICE 4

Write the decimal 72.1085 in words.

Suppose that you are paying $368.42 for an automotive repair job at Jake's Body Shop by writing a check. Checks are usually written using the following format.

Elayn Martin-Gay 60–8124/7233 1000613331 1403

DATE (Current date)

PAY TO THE ORDER OF Jake's Body Shop $ 368.42

Three hundred sixty-eight and 42/100 —— DOLLARS

FIRST STATE BANK OF FARTHINGTON FARTHINGTON, IL 64422

MEMO Elayn Martin-Gay

⑆621497260⑆ 1000613331⑈ 1403

Answers

1. eight and seven tenths **2.** ninety-seven and twenty-eight hundredths **3.** three hundred two and one hundred five thousandths **4.** seventy-two and one thousand eighty-five ten-thousandths

PRACTICE 5

Fill in the check to CLECO (Central Louisiana Electric Company) to pay for your monthly electric bill of $207.40.

Your Preprinted Name 60-8124/7233 1406
Your Preprinted Address 1000613331
DATE
PAY TO THE ORDER OF $
DOLLARS
FIRST STATE BANK OF FARTHINGTON FARTHINGTON, IL 64422
MEMO
⑆621497260⑆ 1000613331⑈ 1406

Fill in the check to Camelot Music to pay for your purchase of $92.98.

Solution:

Your Preprinted Name 60-8124/7233 1404
Your Preprinted Address 1000613331
DATE (Current date)
PAY TO THE ORDER OF Camelot Music $ 92.98
Ninety-two and 98/100 DOLLARS
FIRST STATE BANK OF FARTHINGTON FARTHINGTON, IL 64422
MEMO (Your signature)
⑆621497260⑆ 1000613331⑈ 1404

Work Practice 5

Objective B Writing Decimals in Standard Form

A decimal written in words can be written in standard form by reversing the preceding procedure.

PRACTICE 6–7

Write each decimal in standard form.

6. Three hundred and ninety-six hundredths
7. Thirty-nine and forty-two thousandths

Examples Write each decimal in standard form.

6. Forty-eight and twenty-six hundredths is

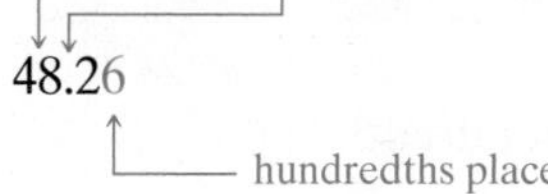

7. Six and ninety-five thousandths is

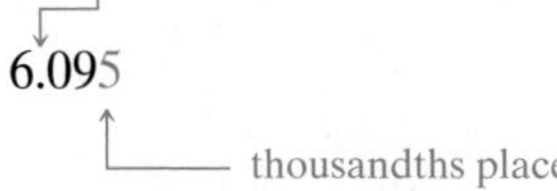

Work Practice 6–7

Helpful Hint

When converting a decimal from words to decimal notation, make sure the last digit is in the correct place by inserting 0s if necessary. For example,

Two and thirty-eight thousandths is 2.038 (thousandths place)

Objective C Writing Decimals as Fractions

Once you master reading and writing decimals, writing a decimal as a fraction follows naturally.

Decimal	In Words	Fraction
0.7	seven tenths	$\frac{7}{10}$
0.51	fifty-one hundredths	$\frac{51}{100}$
0.009	nine thousandths	$\frac{9}{1000}$
0.05	five hundredths	$\frac{5}{100} = \frac{1}{20}$

Answers
5. CLECO; 207.40; Two hundred seven and $\frac{40}{100}$ 6. 300.96 7. 39.042

Notice that the number of decimal places in a decimal number is the same as the number of zeros in the denominator of the equivalent fraction. We can use this fact to write decimals as fractions.

$$0.51 = \frac{51}{100} \qquad 0.009 = \frac{9}{1000}$$

2 decimal places — 2 zeros; 3 decimal places — 3 zeros

Example 8 Write 0.43 as a fraction.

Solution: $0.43 = \dfrac{43}{100}$

2 decimal places — 2 zeros

Work Practice 8

PRACTICE 8

Write 0.037 as a fraction.

Example 9 Write 5.7 as a mixed number.

Solution: $5.7 = 5\dfrac{7}{10}$

1 decimal place — 1 zero

Work Practice 9

PRACTICE 9

Write 14.97 as a mixed number.

Examples Write each decimal as a fraction or a mixed number. Write your answer in simplest form.

10. $0.125 = \dfrac{125}{1000} = \dfrac{\overset{1}{\cancel{125}}}{8 \cdot \underset{1}{\cancel{125}}} = \dfrac{1}{8}$

11. $23.5 = 23\dfrac{5}{10} = 23\dfrac{\overset{1}{\cancel{5}}}{2 \cdot \underset{1}{\cancel{5}}} = 23\dfrac{1}{2 \cdot 1} = 23\dfrac{1}{2}$

12. $105.083 = 105\dfrac{83}{1000}$

Work Practice 10–12

PRACTICE 10–12

Write each decimal as a fraction or mixed number. Write your answer in simplest form.

10. 0.12

11. 57.8

12. 209.986

Objective D Writing Fractions as Decimals

If the denominator of a fraction is a power of 10, we can write it as a decimal by reversing the procedure above.

Examples Write each fraction as a decimal.

13. $\dfrac{8}{10} = 0.8$ — 1 zero, 1 decimal place

14. $\dfrac{87}{10} = 8.7$ — 1 zero, 1 decimal place

15. $\dfrac{18}{1000} = 0.018$ — 3 zeros, 3 decimal places

16. $\dfrac{507}{100} = 5.07$ — 2 zeros, 2 decimal places

Work Practice 13–16

PRACTICE 13–16

Write each fraction as a decimal.

13. $\dfrac{58}{100}$ **14.** $\dfrac{59}{100}$

15. $\dfrac{6}{1000}$ **16.** $\dfrac{172}{10}$

Answers

8. $\dfrac{37}{1000}$ **9.** $14\dfrac{97}{100}$ **10.** $\dfrac{3}{25}$ **11.** $57\dfrac{4}{5}$ **12.** $209\dfrac{493}{500}$ **13.** 0.58 **14.** 0.59 **15.** 0.006 **16.** 17.2

Vocabulary and Readiness Check

Use the choices below to fill in each blank.

words	decimals	and
tens	tenths	standard form

1. The number "twenty and eight hundredths" is written in ______________ and "20.08" is written in ______________.
2. Like fractions, ______________ are used to denote parts of a whole.
3. When writing a decimal number in words, the decimal point is written as ______________.
4. The place value ______________ is to the right of the decimal point while ______________ is to the left of the decimal point.

Determine the place value for the digit 7 in each number.

5. 70
6. 700
7. 0.7
8. 0.07

4.1 Exercise Set

FOR EXTRA HELP

PRACTICE

WATCH

DOWNLOAD

READ

REVIEW

Objective A *Write each decimal number in words. See Examples 1 through 4.*

1. 6.52

2. 7.59

3. 16.23

4. 47.65

5. 0.205

6. 0.495

7. 167.009

8. 233.056

9. 200.005

10. 5000.02

11. 105.6

12. 410.30

13. The Akashi Kaikyo Bridge, between Kobe and Awaji-Shima, Japan, is approximately 2.43 miles long.

14. The English Channel Tunnel is 31.04 miles long. (*Source:* *Railway Directory & Year Book*)

15. Mercury makes a complete orbit of the Sun every 87.97 days. (*Source:* National Space Science Data Center)

16. Saturn makes a complete orbit of the Sun every 29.48 years. (*Source:* National Space Science Data Center)

17. The total number of television households within the United States for the 2008–2009 season was 114.5 million. (*Source:* Nielsen Media Research)

18. In 2009, it took the United States Postal Service an average of 3.9 days to deliver a book rate parcel. (*Source:* USPS)

Fill in each check for the described purchase. See Example 5.

19. Your monthly car loan of $321.42 to R. W. Financial.

Your Preprinted Name
Your Preprinted Address
60–8124/7233
1000613331
1407
DATE
PAY TO THE ORDER OF $
DOLLARS
FIRST STATE BANK
OF FARTHINGTON
FARTHINGTON, IL 64422
MEMO
⑆621497260⑆ 1000613331⑈ 1407

20. Your part of the monthly apartment rent, which is $213.70. You pay this to Amanda Dupre.

Your Preprinted Name
Your Preprinted Address
60–8124/7233
1000613331
1408
DATE
PAY TO THE ORDER OF $
DOLLARS
FIRST STATE BANK
OF FARTHINGTON
FARTHINGTON, IL 64422
MEMO
⑆621497260⑆ 1000613331⑈ 1408

21. Your cell phone bill of $59.68 to Bell South.

Your Preprinted Name
Your Preprinted Address
60–8124/7233
1000613331
1409
DATE
PAY TO THE ORDER OF $
DOLLARS
FIRST STATE BANK
OF FARTHINGTON
FARTHINGTON, IL 64422
MEMO
⑆621497260⑆ 1000613331⑈ 1409

22. Your grocery bill of $87.49 to Albertsons.

Your Preprinted Name
Your Preprinted Address
60–8124/7233
1000613331
1410
DATE
PAY TO THE ORDER OF $
DOLLARS
FIRST STATE BANK
OF FARTHINGTON
FARTHINGTON, IL 64422
MEMO
⑆621497260⑆ 1000613331⑈ 1410

Objective **B** *Write each decimal number in standard form. See Examples 6 and 7.*

23. Six and five tenths

24. Three and nine tenths

25. Nine and eight hundredths

26. Twelve and six hundredths

27. Seven hundred five and six hundred twenty-five thousandths

28. Eight hundred four and three hundred ninety-nine thousandths

29. Forty-six ten-thousandths

30. Thirty-eight ten-thousandths

31. The record rainfall amount for a 24-hour period in Alabama is thirty-two and fifty-two hundredths inches. This record was set at Dauphin Island Sea Lab in 1997. (*Source:* National Climatic Data Center)

32. In June, 2009, MySpace.com blogs had a twelve and sixty-four hundredths market share, the most of any blog or personal website. (*Source:* Marketingcharts.com)

33. The average IndyCar burns one and three-tenths gallons of fuel per lap at the Indianapolis Motor Speedway. (*Source:* INDY500.com)

34. Dario Franchitti posted the fastest lap speed in the 2009 Indianapolis 500 of two hundred twenty-two and forty-four thousandths miles per hour on lap 187. (*Source:* INDY500.com)

Objective C *Write each decimal as a fraction or a mixed number. Write your answer in simplest form. See Examples 8 through 12.*

35. 0.3 **36.** 0.9 **37.** 0.27 **38.** 0.39 **39.** 0.8

40. 0.4 **41.** 0.15 **42.** 0.64 **43.** 5.47 **44.** 6.3

45. 0.048 **46.** 0.082 **47.** 7.008 **48.** 9.005 **49.** 15.802

50. 11.406 **51.** 0.3005 **52.** 0.2006 **53.** 487.32 **54.** 298.62

Objective D *Write each fraction as a decimal. See Examples 13 through 16.*

55. $\frac{6}{10}$ **56.** $\frac{3}{10}$ **57.** $\frac{45}{100}$ **58.** $\frac{75}{100}$

59. $\frac{37}{10}$ **60.** $\frac{28}{10}$ **61.** $\frac{268}{1000}$ **62.** $\frac{709}{1000}$

63. $\frac{9}{100}$ **64.** $\frac{7}{100}$ **65.** $\frac{4026}{1000}$ **66.** $\frac{3601}{1000}$

67. $\frac{28}{1000}$ **68.** $\frac{63}{1000}$ **69.** $\frac{563}{10}$ **70.** $\frac{206}{10}$

Objectives A B C D **Mixed Practice** *Fill in the chart. The first row is completed for you. See Examples 1 through 16.*

	Decimal Number in Standard Form	In Words	Fraction
	0.37	thirty-seven hundredths	$\frac{37}{100}$
71.			$\frac{43}{100}$
72.			$\frac{89}{100}$
73.		eight tenths	
74.		five tenths	
75.	0.077		
76.	0.019		

Review

Round 47,261 to the indicated place value. See Section 1.5.

77. tens

78. hundreds

79. thousands

80. ten-thousands

Concept Extensions

81. In your own words, describe how to write a decimal as a fraction or a mixed number.

82. In your own words, describe how to write a fraction as a decimal.

83. Write 0.00026849576 in words.

84. Write 0.00026849576 as a fraction. Do not simplify the resulting fraction.

85. Write $17\frac{268}{1000}$ as a decimal.

86. Write $7\frac{12}{100}$ as a decimal.

Objectives

A **Compare Decimals.**

B **Round a Decimal Number to a Given Place Value.**

4.2 ORDER AND ROUNDING

Objective A Comparing Decimals

One way to compare decimals is to compare their graphs on a number line. Recall from Section 3.5 that for any two numbers on a number line, the number to the left is smaller and the number to the right is larger. The decimals 0.5 and 0.8 are graphed as follows:

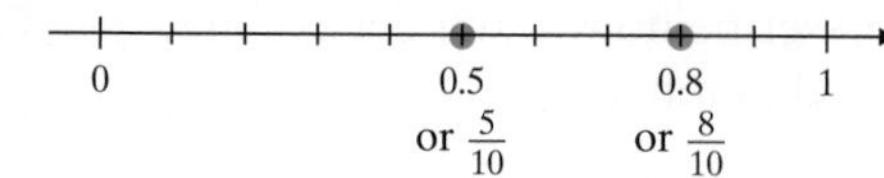

Comparing decimals by comparing their graphs on a number line can be time consuming. Another way to compare the size of decimals is to compare digits in corresponding places.

Comparing Two Decimals

Compare digits in the same places from left to right. When two digits are not equal, the number with the larger digit is the larger decimal. If necessary, insert 0s after the last digit to the right of the decimal point to continue comparing.

Compare hundredths-place digits

28.253   28.263

↑   ↑

5   <   6

so 28.253   <   28.263

Before we continue, let's take a moment and convince ourselves that inserting a zero after the last digit to the right of a decimal point does not change the value of the number.

For example, let's show that

$0.7 = 0.70$

If we write 0.7 as a fraction, we have

$$0.7 = \frac{7}{10}$$

Let's now multiply by 1. Recall that multiplying a number by 1 does not change the value of the number.

$$0.7 = \frac{7}{10} = \frac{7}{10} \cdot 1 = \frac{7}{10} \cdot \frac{10}{10} = \frac{7 \cdot 10}{10 \cdot 10} = \frac{70}{100} = 0.70$$

Thus $0.7 = 0.70$ and so on.

Helpful Hint

For any decimal, inserting 0s after the last digit to the right of the decimal point does not change the value of the number.

$7.6 = 7.60 = 7.600$, and so on

When a whole number is written as a decimal, the decimal point is placed to the right of the ones digit.

$25 = 25.0 = 25.00$, and so on

Example 1 Insert <, >, or = to form a true statement.

0.378 0.368

Solution:

0.378 0.368 The tenths places are the same.

0.378 0.368 The hundredths places are different.

Since 7 > 6, then 0.378 > 0.368.

Work Practice 1

PRACTICE 1

Insert <, >, or = to form a true statement.

13.208 13.281

Example 2 Insert <, >, or = to form a true statement.

0.052 0.236

Solution: 0.052 < 0.236 0 is smaller than 2 in the tenths place.

Work Practice 2

PRACTICE 2

Insert <, >, or = to form a true statement.

0.124 0.086

Example 3 Insert <, >, or = to form a true statement.

0.52 0.063

Solution: 0.52 > 0.063 0 is smaller than 5 in the tenths place.

Work Practice 3

PRACTICE 3

Insert <, >, or = to form a true statement.

0.61 0.076

Example 4 Write the decimals in order from smallest to largest.

7.035, 8.12, 7.03, 7.1

Solution: By comparing the ones digits, the decimal 8.12 is the largest number. To write the rest of the decimals in order, we compare digits to the right of the decimal point. We will insert zeros to help us compare.

7.035 7.030 7.100

Helpful Hint

You may also immediately notice that 7.1 is larger than both 7.035 and 7.03.

By comparing digits to the right of the decimal point, we can now arrange the decimals from smallest to largest.

7.030, 7.035, 7.100, 8.12 or
7.03, 7.035, 7.1, 8.12

Work Practice 4

PRACTICE 4

Write the decimals in order from smallest to largest.

14.605, 14.65, 13.9, 14.006

Objective B Rounding Decimals

We **round the decimal part** of a decimal number in nearly the same way as we round whole numbers. The only difference is that we delete digits to the right of the rounding place, instead of replacing these digits by 0s. For example,

24.954 rounded to the nearest hundredth is 24.95

hundredths place

Answers

1. < 2. > 3. >
4. 13.9, 14.006, 14.605, 14.65

Rounding Decimals to a Place Value to the Right of the Decimal Point

Step 1: Locate the digit to the right of the given place value.

Step 2: If this digit is 5 or greater, add 1 to the digit in the given place value and delete all digits to its right. If this digit is less than 5, delete all digits to the right of the given place value.

PRACTICE 5

Round 123.7814 to the nearest thousandth.

Example 5 Round 736.2359 to the nearest tenth.

Solution:

Step 1: We locate the digit to the right of the tenths place.

736.2③59 (tenths place: 2; digit to the right: ③)

Step 2: Since the digit to the right is less than 5, we delete it and all digits to its right.

Thus, 736.2359 rounded to the nearest tenth is 736.2.

Work Practice 5

PRACTICE 6

Round 123.7817 to the nearest tenth.

Example 6 Round 736.2359 to the nearest hundredth.

Solution:

Step 1: We locate the digit to the right of the hundredths place.

736.23⑤9 (hundredths place: 3; digit to the right: ⑤)

Step 2: Since the digit to the right is 5, we add 1 to the digit in the hundredths place and delete all digits to the right of the hundredths place.

736.23⑤9 (Add 1. — to 3; Delete these digits. — ⑤9)

Thus, 736.2359 rounded to the nearest hundredth is 736.24.

Work Practice 6

Rounding often occurs with money amounts. Since there are 100 cents in a dollar, each cent is $\frac{1}{100}$ of a dollar. This means that if we want to round to the nearest cent, we round to the nearest hundredth of a dollar.

PRACTICE 7

In Sandersville, the price of a gallon of premium gasoline is \$3.1589. Round this to the nearest cent.

Example 7 The price of a gallon of premium gasoline in Cross City is currently \$3.1779. Round this to the nearest cent.

Solution:

\$3.17⑦9 (hundredths place: 7; 7 is greater than 5; Add 1. — to hundredths digit; Delete these digits. — ⑦9)

Since the digit to the right is greater than 5, we add 1 to the hundredths digit and delete all digits to the right of the hundredths digit.

Thus, \$3.1779 rounded to the nearest cent is \$3.18.

Work Practice 7

Answers

5. 123.781 **6.** 123.8 **7.** \$3.16

Example 8 Round \$0.098 to the nearest cent.

Solution:

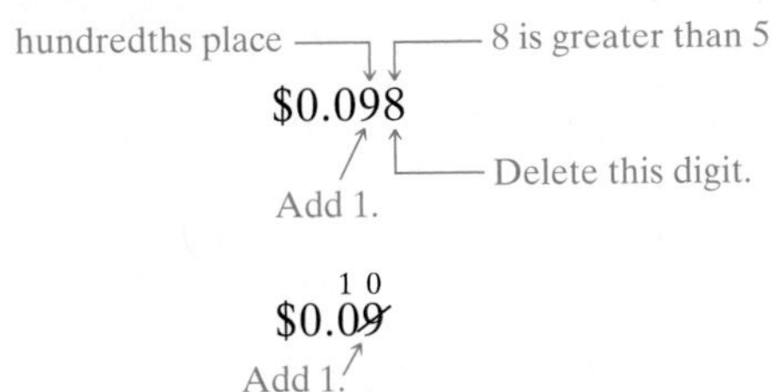

$9 + 1 = 10$, so replace the digit 9 by 0 and carry the 1 to the place value to the left. Thus, \$0.098 rounded to the nearest cent is \$0.10.

Work Practice 8

PRACTICE 8

Round \$1.095 to the nearest cent.

✓**Concept Check** 1756.0894 rounded to the nearest ten is

a. 1756.1 **b.** 1760.0894
c. 1760 **d.** 1750

Example 9 Determining State Taxable Income

A high school teacher's taxable income is \$41,567.72. The tax tables in the teacher's state use amounts to the nearest dollar. Round the teacher's income to the nearest whole dollar.

Solution: Rounding to the nearest whole dollar means rounding to the ones place.

ones place → 7 is greater than 5
\$41,567.72
Add 1. Delete these digits.

Thus, the teacher's income rounded to the nearest dollar is \$41,568.

Work Practice 9

PRACTICE 9

Water bills in Gotham City are always rounded to the nearest dollar. Round a water bill of \$24.62 to the nearest dollar.

In Section 4.4, we will introduce a formula for the distance around a circle. The distance around a circle is given the special name **circumference.**

The symbol π is the Greek letter pi, pronounced "pie." We use π to denote the following constant:

$$\pi = \frac{\text{circumference of a circle}}{\text{diameter of a circle}}$$

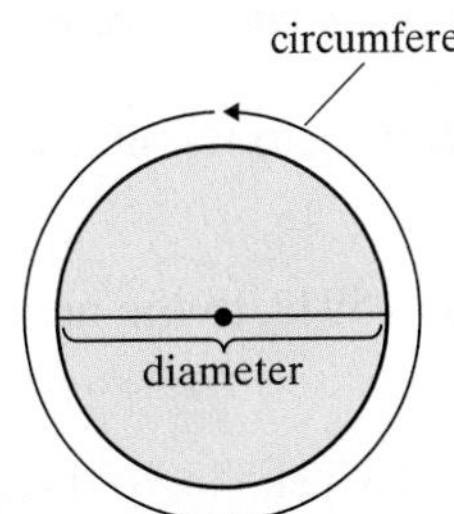

The value π is an **irrational number.** This means if we try to write it as a decimal, it neither ends nor repeats in a pattern.

Example 10 $\pi \approx 3.14159265$. Round π to the nearest hundredth.

Solution:

hundredths place → 1 is less than 5.
3.14159265
Delete these digits.

Thus, 3.14159265 rounded to the nearest hundredth is 3.14. In other words, $\pi \approx 3.14$.

Work Practice 10

PRACTICE 10

$\pi \approx 3.14159265$. Round π to the nearest ten-thousandth.

Answers
8. \$1.10 **9.** \$25
10. $\pi \approx 3.1416$

✓ **Concept Check Answer**
c

Vocabulary and Readiness Check

Use the choices below to fill in each blank. Some choices may be used more than once or not at all.

before	7.0	diameter
after	0.7	circumference

1. Another name for the distance around a circle is its ____________.
2. $\pi = \dfrac{\text{\_\_\_\_\_\_\_\_ of a circle}}{\text{\_\_\_\_\_\_\_\_ of a circle}}$
3. The decimal point in a whole number is ____________ the last digit.
4. The whole number 7 = ____________.

4.2 Exercise Set

FOR EXTRA HELP

MyMathLab

Objective A *Insert <, >, or = to form a true statement. See Examples 1 through 3.*

1. 0.15 0.16

2. 0.12 0.15

3. 0.57 0.54

4. 0.59 0.52

5. 0.098 0.1

6. 0.0756 0.2

7. 0.54900 0.549

8. 0.98400 0.984

9. 167.908 167.980

10. 519.3405 519.3054

11. 420,000 0.000042

12. 0.000987 987,000

Write the decimals in order from smallest to largest. See Example 4.

13. 0.006, 0.06, 0.0061

14. 0.082, 0.008, 0.080

15. 0.042, 0.36, 0.03

16. 0.21, 0.056, 0.065

17. 1.1, 1.16, 1.01, 1.09

18. 3.6, 3.069, 3.09, 3.06

19. 21.001, 20.905, 21.03, 21.12

20. 36.050, 35.72, 35.702, 35.072

Objective B *Round each decimal to the given place value. See Examples 5 through 10.*

21. 0.57, to the nearest tenth

22. 0.54, to the nearest tenth

23. 0.234, to the nearest hundredth

24. 0.452, to the nearest hundredth

25. 0.5942, to the nearest thousandth

26. 63.4523, to the nearest thousandth

27. 98,207.23, to the nearest ten

28. 68,934.543, to the nearest ten

29. 12.342, to the nearest tenth

30. 42.9878, to the nearest thousandth

31. 17.667, to the nearest hundredth

32. 0.766, to the nearest hundredth

33. 0.501, to the nearest tenth

34. 0.602, to the nearest tenth

35. 0.1295, to the nearest thousandth

36. 0.8295, to the nearest thousandth

37. 3829.34, to the nearest ten

38. 4520.876, to the nearest hundred

Round each monetary amount to the nearest cent or dollar as indicated. See Examples 7 through 9.

39. \$0.067, to the nearest cent

40. \$0.025, to the nearest cent

41. \$42,650.14, to the nearest dollar

42. \$768.45, to the nearest dollar

43. \$26.95, to the nearest dollar

44. \$14,769.52, to the nearest dollar

45. \$0.1992, to the nearest cent

46. \$0.7633, to the nearest cent

Round each number to the given place value. See Examples 5 through 10.

47. The Apple MacBook Air, at its thinnest point, measures 0.4064 cm. Round this number to the nearest tenth. (*Source:* Apple, Inc.)

48. A large tropical cockroach of the family Dictyoptera is the fastest-moving insect. This insect was clocked at a speed of 3.36 miles per hour. Round this number to the nearest tenth. (*Source:* University of California, Berkeley)

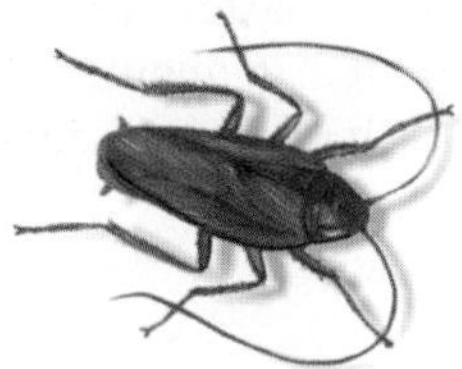

49. During the 2009 Boston Marathon, Ernst Van Dyk of South Africa was the first wheelchair competitor to cross the finish line. His time was 1.5581 hours. Round this time to the nearest hundredth. (*Source:* Boston Athletic Association)

50. The population density of the state of Louisiana is 102.5794 people per square mile. Round this population density to the nearest tenth. (*Source:* U.S. Census Bureau)

51. A used biology textbook is priced at \$47.89. Round this price to the nearest dollar.

52. A used office desk is advertised at \$49.95 by Drawley's Office Furniture. Round this price to the nearest dollar.

53. Lindsey Vonn of the United States won the gold medal for the women's downhill in the 2010 Winter Olympics. Her winning time was 1.736 minutes. Round this time to the nearest hundredth of a minute. (*Source:* International Olympic Committee)

54. The population density of the state of Arkansas is 54.444 people per square mile. Round this population density to the nearest tenth. (*Source:* U.S. Census Bureau)

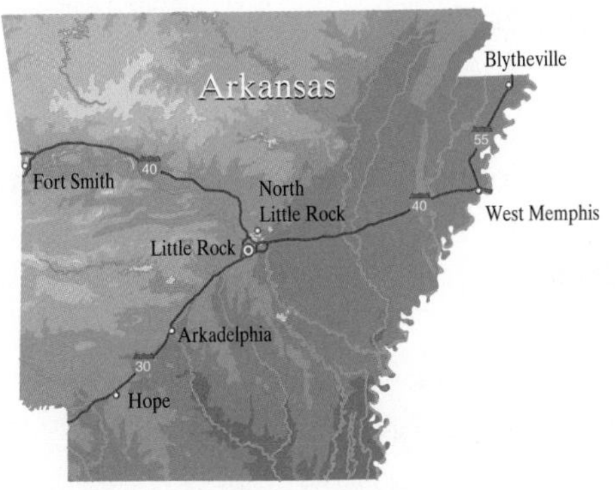

55. The length of a day on Mars is 24.6229 hours. Round this figure to the nearest thousandth. (*Source:* National Space Science Data Center)

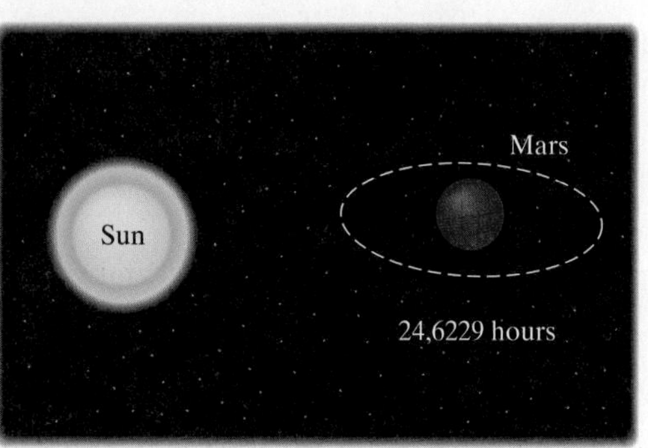

56. Venus makes a complete orbit around the Sun every 224.695 days. Round this figure to the nearest whole day. (*Source:* National Space Science Data Center)

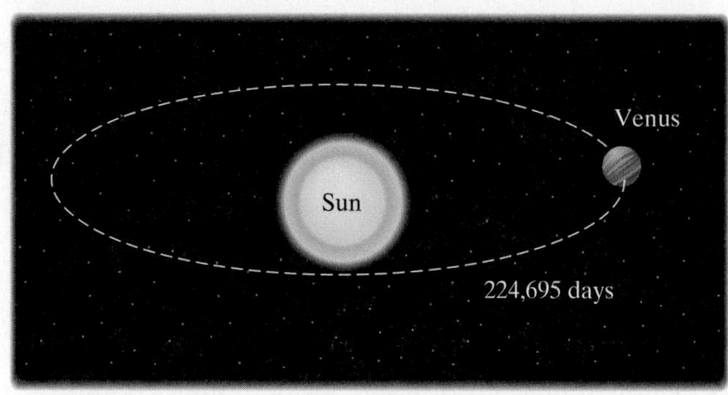

57. Millennium Force is a roller coaster at Cedar Point, an amusement park in Sandusky, Ohio. At the time of its debut, Millennium Force was the world's tallest and fastest roller coaster. A ride on the Millennium Force lasts about 2.75 minutes. Round this figure to the nearest tenth. (*Source:* Cedar Fair, L.P.)

58. During the 2008 NFL season, the average length of an Oakland Raiders' punt was 48.78 yards. Round this figure to the nearest whole yard. (*Source:* National Football League)

Review

Perform each indicated operation. See Sections 1.3 and 1.4.

59. $3452 + 2314$

60. $8945 + 4536$

61. $94 - 23$

62. $82 - 47$

63. $482 - 239$

64. $4002 - 3897$

Concept Extensions

Solve. See the Concept Check in this section.

65. 2849.1738 rounded to the nearest hundred is
   a. 2849.17
   b. 2800
   c. 2850
   d. 2849.174

66. 146.059 rounded to the nearest ten is
   a. 146.0
   b. 146.1
   c. 140
   d. 150

67. 2849.1738 rounded to the nearest hundredth is
   a. 2849.17
   b. 2800
   c. 2850
   d. 2849.174

68. 146.059 rounded to the nearest tenth is
   a. 146.0
   b. 146.1
   c. 140
   d. 150

Mixed Practice (Sections 4.1, 4.2) *The table gives the average speed, in kilometers per hour, for the winners of the Tour de France for each of the years listed. Use the table to answer Exercises 69 through 72.* (*Source:* letour.fr/us)

Year	Cyclist/Nationality	Average Speed (in kph)
2002	Lance Armstrong/USA	39.982
2003	Lance Armstrong/USA	40.030
2004	Lance Armstrong/USA	41.016
2005	Lance Armstrong/USA	41.654
2006	Oscar Pereiro/Spain	40.789
2007	Alberto Contador/Spain	39.233
2008	Carlos Sastre/Spain	40.413
2009	Alberto Contador/Spain	40.788

69. What is the fastest average speed on the list? Write this speed as a mixed number. Which cyclist achieved this average speed?

70. What is the slowest average speed on the list? Write this speed as a mixed number. Which cyclist achieved this speed?

71. Make a list of the average winning speeds in order from fastest to slowest for the years 2006 through 2009.

72. Make a list of the average winning speeds in order from fastest to slowest for the years 2002 through 2005.

73. Write a 5-digit number that rounds to 1.7.

74. Write a 4-digit number that rounds to 26.3.

75. Write a decimal number that is greater than 8 but less than 9.

76. Write a decimal number that is greater than 48.1, but less than 48.2.

77. Which number(s) rounds to 0.26?
0.26559 0.26499 0.25786 0.25186

78. Which number(s) rounds to 0.06?
0.0612 0.066 0.0586 0.0506

Write these numbers from smallest to largest.

79. 0.9
0.1038
0.10299
0.1037

80. 0.01
0.0839
0.09
0.1

81. The all-time top six movies* (those that earned the most money in the United States) along with the approximate amount of money they have earned are listed in the table. Estimate the total amount of money that these movies have earned by first rounding each earning to the nearest hundred million. (*Source:* The Internet Movie Database)

Top All-Time American Movies

Movie	Gross Domestic Earnings
Avatar (2009)	$737.6 million
Titanic (1997)	$600.8 million
The Dark Knight (2008)	$533.3 million
Star Wars: A New Hope (1977)	$460.9 million
Shrek 2 (2004)	$436.5 million
E.T. (1982)	$434.9 million

*Note: Many of these movies are still earning substantial amounts of money.

82. In a recent year, American manufacturers shipped approximately 27.5 million music videos to retailers. The value of these shipments was approximately $484.9 million. Estimate the value of an individual music video by rounding 484.9 and 27.5 to the nearest ten, then dividing. (*Source:* Recording Industry Association of America)

Objectives

A Add Decimals.

B Subtract Decimals.

C Estimate When Adding or Subtracting Decimals.

D Solve Problems That Involve Adding or Subtracting Decimals.

4.3 ADDING AND SUBTRACTING DECIMALS

Objective A Adding Decimals

Adding decimals is similar to adding whole numbers. We add digits in corresponding place values from right to left, carrying if necessary. To make sure that digits in corresponding place values are added, we line up the decimal points vertically.

Adding or Subtracting Decimals

Step 1: Write the decimals so that the decimal points line up vertically.

Step 2: Add or subtract as with whole numbers.

Step 3: Place the decimal point in the sum or difference so that it lines up vertically with the decimal points in the problem.

In this section, we will insert zeros in decimal numbers so that place value digits line up neatly. For instance, see Example 1.

PRACTICE 1

Add.

a. 15.52 + 2.371

b. 20.06 + 17.612

c. 0.125 + 122.8

Example 1 Add: 23.85 + 1.604

Solution: First we line up the decimal points vertically.

```
  23.850   Insert one 0 so that digits line up neatly.
+  1.604
     ↑
line up decimal points
```

Then we add the digits from right to left as for whole numbers.

```
   1
  23.850
+  1.604
  25.454
    ↑— Place the decimal point in the sum so that all decimal points line up.
```

Work Practice 1

Helpful Hint

Recall that 0's may be placed after the last digit to the right of the decimal point without changing the value of the decimal. This may be used to help line up place values when adding decimals.

```
   3.2    becomes      3.200   Insert two 0s.
  15.567              15.567
+  0.11             +  0.110   Insert one 0.
                      18.877   Add.
```

Answers

1. a. 17.891 **b.** 37.672 **c.** 122.925

Example 2 Add: 763.7651 + 22.001 + 43.89

Solution: First we line up the decimal points.

```
  1 1 1
 763.7651
  22.0010   Insert one 0.
+ 43.8900   Insert two 0s.
 829.6561   Add.
```

Work Practice 2

PRACTICE 2

Add.

a. 34.567 + 129.43 + 2.8903

b. 11.21 + 46.013 + 362.526

Helpful Hint

Don't forget that the decimal point in a whole number is after the last digit.

Example 3 Add: 45 + 2.06

Solution:

```
  45.00   Insert a decimal point and two 0s.
+  2.06   Line up decimal points.
  47.06   Add.
```

Work Practice 3

PRACTICE 3

Add: 26.072 + 119

✓**Concept Check** What is wrong with the following calculation of the sum of 7.03, 2.008, 19.16, and 3.1415?

```
  7.03
  2.008
  19.16
+3.1415
 3.6042
```

Objective B Subtracting Decimals

Subtracting decimals is similar to subtracting whole numbers. We line up digits and subtract from right to left, borrowing when needed.

Example 4 Subtract: 35.218 − 23.65. Check your answer.

Solution: First we line up the decimal points.

```
  4 1111
 35.218
-23.650   Insert one 0.
 11.568   Subtract.
```

Recall that we can check a subtraction problem by adding.

```
  1 1
 11.568   Difference
+23.650   Subtrahend
 35.218   Minuend
```

Work Practice 4

PRACTICE 4

Subtract. Check your answers.

a. 82.75 − 15.9

b. 126.032 − 95.71

Answers

2. a. 166.8873 **b.** 419.749

3. 145.072 **4. a.** 66.85 **b.** 30.322

✓ **Concept Check Answer**

The decimal points and places are not lined up properly.

PRACTICE 5

Subtract. Check your answers.

a. 5.8 − 3.92

b. 9.72 − 4.068

Example 5 Subtract: 3.5 − 0.068. Check your answer.

Solution:

	9 4 10 10 3.500	Insert two 0s.
	− 0.0 6 8	Line up decimal points.
	3.4 3 2	Subtract.

Check:

3.432	Difference
+ 0.068	Subtrahend
3.500	Minuend

Work Practice 5

PRACTICE 6

Subtract. Check your answers.

a. 53 − 29.31

b. 120 − 68.22

Example 6 Subtract: 85 − 17.31. Check your answer.

Solution:

9
7 14 10 10
85.00
−1 7.3 1
6 7.6 9

Check:

67.69	Difference
+17.31	Subtrahend
85.00	Minuend

Work Practice 6

Objective C Estimating When Adding or Subtracting Decimals

To help avoid errors, we can also estimate to see if our answer is reasonable when adding or subtracting decimals. Although only one estimate is needed per operation, we show two to show variety.

PRACTICE 7

Add or subtract as indicated. Then estimate to see if the answer is reasonable by rounding the given numbers and adding or subtracting the rounded numbers.

a. 48.1 + 326.97

b. 18.09 − 0.746

Example 7 Add or subtract as indicated. Then estimate to see if the answer is reasonable by rounding the given numbers and adding or subtracting the rounded numbers.

a. 27.6 + 519.25

Solution:

Exact		Estimate 1		Estimate 2
1 27.60	rounds to	30		30
+ 519.25	rounds to	+500	or	+520
546.85		530		550

Since the exact answer is close to either estimate, it is reasonable. (In the first estimate, each number is rounded to the place value of the leftmost digit. In the second estimate, each number is rounded to the nearest ten.)

b. 11.01 − 0.862

Solution:

Exact		Estimate 1		Estimate 2
0 9 10 10 11.010	rounds to	10		11
− 0.8 6 2	rounds to	− 1	or	− 1
1 0.1 4 8		9		10

In the first estimate, we rounded the first number to the nearest ten and the second number to the nearest one. In the second estimate, we rounded both numbers to the nearest one. Both estimates show us that our answer is reasonable.

Work Practice 7

Helpful Hint Remember that estimates are for our convenience to quickly check the reasonableness of an answer.

Answers

5. a. 1.88 **b.** 5.652

6. a. 23.69 **b.** 51.78

7. a. 375.07 **b.** 17.344

✓**Concept Check** Why shouldn't the sum 21.98 + 42.36 be estimated as 30 + 50 = 80?

Objective D Solving Problems by Adding or Subtracting Decimals

Decimals are very common in real-life problems.

Example 8 Calculating the Cost of Owning an Automobile

Find the total monthly cost of owning and operating a certain automobile given the expenses shown.

Monthly car payment:	\$256.63
Monthly insurance cost:	\$47.52
Average gasoline bill per month:	\$95.33

Solution:

1. UNDERSTAND. Read and reread the problem. The phrase "total monthly cost" tells us to add.
2. TRANSLATE.

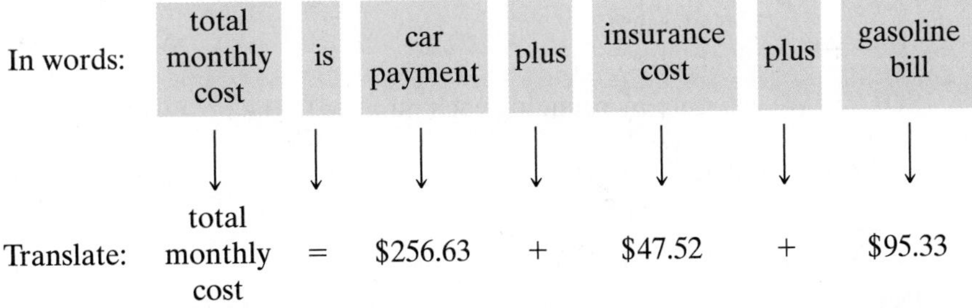
In words:
total monthly cost
is
car payment
plus
insurance cost
plus
gasoline bill
Translate:
total monthly cost
=
\$256.63
+
\$47.52
+
\$95.33

3. SOLVE: Let's also estimate by rounding each number to the nearest ten.

256.63	rounds to	260
47.52	rounds to	50
+ 95.33	rounds to	100
\$399.48 Exact.		410 Estimate.

4. INTERPRET. *Check* your work. Since our estimate is close to our exact answer, our answer is reasonable. *State* your conclusion: The total monthly cost is \$399.48.

Work Practice 8

PRACTICE 8

Find the total monthly cost of owning and operating a certain automobile given the expenses shown.

Monthly car payment:	\$536.52
Monthly insurance cost:	\$52.68
Average gasoline bill per month:	\$87.50

The next bar graph has horizontal bars. To visualize the value represented by a bar, see how far it extends to the right. The value of each bar is labeled and we will study bar graphs further in a later chapter.

Example 9 Comparing Average Heights

The bar graph shows the current average heights for adults in various countries. How much greater is the average height in Denmark than the average height in the United States?

Continued on next page

Answer

8. \$676.70

✓ **Concept Check Answer**

Each number is rounded incorrectly. The estimate is too high.

PRACTICE 9

Use the bar graph in Example 9. How much greater is the average height in the Netherlands than the average height in Israel?

Average Adult Height

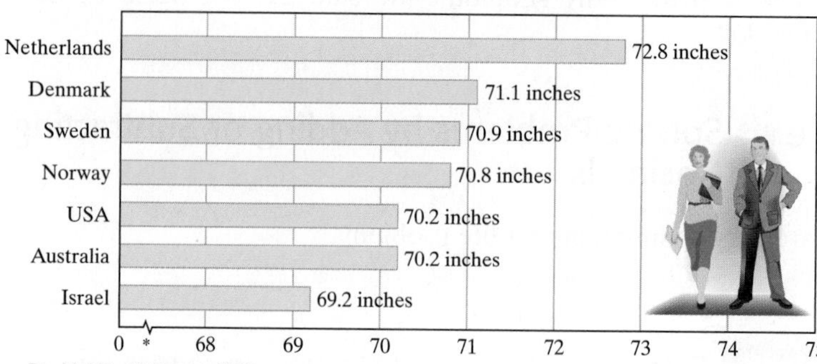

Source: Disabled World, October 2008

* The -\/- means that some numbers are purposefully missing on the axis.

Solution:

1. UNDERSTAND. Read and reread the problem. Since we want to know "how much greater," we subtract.
2. TRANSLATE.

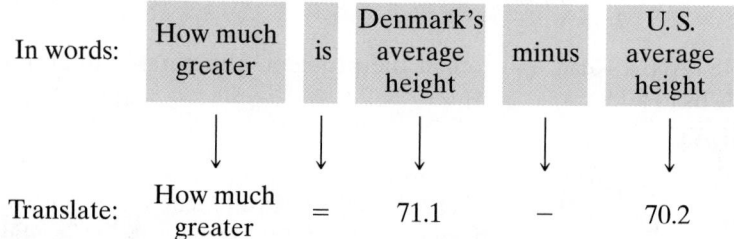

In words:	How much greater	is	Denmark's average height	minus	U. S. average height
	↓	↓	↓	↓	↓
Translate:	How much greater	=	71.1	−	70.2

3. SOLVE: We estimate by rounding each number to the nearest whole.

$7\cancel{1}.\cancel{1}$ (0 11)	rounds to	71	
-70.2	rounds to	-70	
0.9	Exact.	1	Estimate.

4. INTERPRET. *Check* your work. Since our estimate is close to our exact answer, 0.9 inches is reasonable. *State* your conclusion: The average height in Denmark is 0.9 inch greater than the average U.S. height.

Work Practice 9

Answer

9. 3.6 in.

Calculator Explorations

Entering Decimal Numbers

To enter a decimal number, find the key marked [·]. To enter the number 2.56, for example, press the keys [2] [·] [5] [6].

The display will read [2.56].

Operations on Decimal Numbers

Operations on decimal numbers are performed in the same way as operations on whole or signed numbers. For example, to find 8.625 − 4.29, press the keys [8.625] [−] [4.29] [=] or [ENTER].

The display will read [4.335]. (Although entering 8.625, for example, requires pressing more than one key, we group numbers together here for easier reading.)

Use a calculator to perform each indicated operation.

1. 315.782 + 12.96

2. 29.68 + 85.902

3. 6.249 − 1.0076

4. 5.238 − 0.682

5.
$$\begin{array}{r} 12.555 \\ 224.987 \\ 5.2 \\ +622.65 \\ \hline \end{array}$$

6.
$$\begin{array}{r} 47.006 \\ 0.17 \\ 313.259 \\ +139.088 \\ \hline \end{array}$$

Vocabulary and Readiness Check

Use the choices below to fill in each blank. Not all choices will be used.

minuend	vertically	first	true	37.0	horizontally
difference	subtrahend	last	false	0.37	

1. The number 37 equals __________.
2. The decimal point in a whole number is positioned after the __________ digit.
3. In 89.2 − 14.9 = 74.3, the number 74.3 is called the __________, 89.2 is the __________, and 14.9 is the __________.
4. To add or subtract decimals, we line up the decimal points __________.
5. True or false: The number 5.6 is closer to 5 than 6 on a number line. __________.
6. True or false: The number 10.48 is closer to 10 than 11 on a number line. __________.

4.3 Exercise Set

FOR EXTRA HELP MyMathLab

Objectives A C Mixed Practice *Add. See Examples 1 through 3, and 7. For those exercises marked, also estimate to see if the answer is reasonable.*

1. 1.3 + 2.2 **2.** 2.5 + 4.1 **3.** 5.7 + 1.13 **4.** 2.31 + 6.4 **5.** 0.003 + 0.091

6. 0.004 + 0.085 **7.** 19.23 + 602.782 **8.** 47.14 + 409.567 **9.** 490 + 93.09 **10.** 600 + 83.0062

11. 234.89 + 230.67
Exact: Estimate:

12. 734.89 + 640.56
Exact: Estimate:

13. 100.009 + 6.08 + 9.034
Exact: Estimate:

14. 200.89 + 7.49 + 62.83
Exact: Estimate:

15. 24.6 + 2.39 + 0.0678

16. 32.4 + 1.58 + 0.0934

17. Find the sum of 45.023, 3.006, and 8.403

18. Find the sum of 65.0028, 5.0903, and 6.9003

Objectives B C Mixed Practice *Subtract and check. See Examples 4 through 7. For those exercises marked, also estimate to see if the answer is reasonable.*

19. 8.8 − 2.3 **20.** 7.6 − 2.1 **21.** 18 − 2.7 **22.** 28 − 3.3

23. 654.9 − 56.67

24. 863.23 − 39.453

25. 5.9 − 4.07
Exact:
Estimate:

26. 6.4 − 3.04
Exact:
Estimate:

27. 923.5 − 61.9

28. 845.93 − 45.8

29. 500.34 − 123.45

30. 600.74 − 463.98

31. $\begin{array}{r} 1000 \\ -\ 123.4 \\ \hline \end{array}$

Exact:

Estimate:

32. $\begin{array}{r} 2000 \\ -\ 327.47 \\ \hline \end{array}$

Exact:

Estimate:

33. 200 − 5.6

34. 800 − 8.9

35. 3 − 0.0012

36. 7 − 0.097

37. Subtract 6.7 from 23.

38. Subtract 9.2 from 45.

Objectives **A B Mixed Practice** *Perform the indicated operation. See Examples 1 through 6.*

39. 86.05 + 1.978

40. 95.07 + 4.216

41. 86.05 − 1.978

42. 95.07 − 4.216

43. Add 150 and 93.17.

44. Add 250 and 86.07.

45. 150 − 93.17

46. 250 − 86.07

47. Subtract 8.94 from 12.1.

48. Subtract 6.73 from 20.2.

Objective **D** *Solve. For Exercises 49 and 50, the solutions have been started for you. See Examples 8 and 9.*

49. Ann-Margaret Tober bought a book for $32.48. If she paid with two $20 bills, what was her change?

Start the solution:

1. UNDERSTAND the problem. Reread it as many times as needed.
2. TRANSLATE into an equation. (Fill in the blank.)

change	is	two $20 bills	minus	cost of book
↓	↓	↓	↓	↓
change	=	40	−	____

Finish with

3. SOLVE and 4. INTERPRET

50. Phillip Guillot bought a car part for $18.26. If he paid with two $10 bills, what was his change?

Start the solution:

1. UNDERSTAND the problem. Reread it as many times as needed.
2. TRANSLATE into an equation. (Fill in the blank.)

change	is	two $10 bills	minus	cost of car part
↓	↓	↓	↓	↓
change	=	20	−	____

Finish with

3. SOLVE and 4. INTERPRET

51. Find the total monthly cost of owning and maintaining a car given the information shown.

Monthly car payment:	$275.36
Monthly insurance cost:	$ 83.00
Average cost of gasoline per month:	$ 81.60
Average maintenance cost per month:	$ 14.75

52. Find the total monthly cost of owning and maintaining a car given the information shown.

Monthly car payment:	$306.42
Monthly insurance cost:	$ 53.50
Average cost of gasoline per month:	$123.00
Average maintenance cost per month:	$ 23.50

53. Gasoline was $2.839 per gallon one week and $2.979 per gallon the next. By how much did the price change?

54. A pair of eyeglasses costs a total of $347.89. The frames of the glasses are $97.23. How much do the lenses of the eyeglasses cost?

55. Find the perimeter.

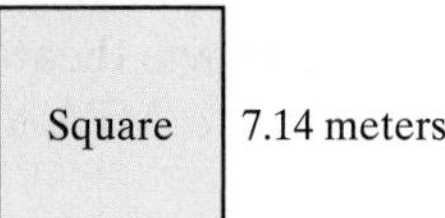

56. Find the perimeter.

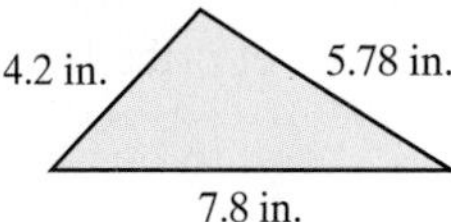

The iPod nano is a miniature version of Apple Computer's popular iPod audio player. The nano was first introduced in 2005 with a storage capacity of 16 gigabytes. (This is about 4000 3-minute or 3-megabyte songs.)

57. The top face of the iPod nano measures 3.6 inches by 1.5 inches. Find the perimeter of the rectangular face.

58. The face of the larger Apple iPod measures 4.1 inches by 2.4 inches. Find the perimeter of this rectangular face.

59. The long-term mean average U.S. temperature (the average of all U.S. average temperatures) is 52.85 degrees Fahrenheit. The average temperature in 1998, the warmest annual average, was 55.08 degrees Fahrenheit. How much warmer was the average U.S. temperature in 1998 than the mean of all U.S. average temperatures?

60. In 2008, the U.S. minimum wage was \$6.65 per hour. One year later, in 2009, the U.S. minimum wage was raised to \$7.25 per hour. How much of an increase was this? (*Source:* U.S. Department of Labor)

61. The average wind speed at the weather station on Mt. Washington in New Hampshire is 35.2 miles per hour. The highest speed ever recorded at the station is 321.0 miles per hour. How much faster is the highest speed than the average wind speed? (*Source:* National Climatic Data Center)

62. The average annual rainfall in Omaha, Nebraska, is 30.22 inches. The average annual rainfall in New Orleans, Louisiana, is 61.88 inches. On average, how much more rain does New Orleans receive annually than Omaha? (*Source:* National Climatic Data Center)

63. Andy Green still holds the record for one-mile land speed. This record was 129.567 miles per hour faster than a previous record of 633.468 set in 1983. What was Green's record-setting speed? (*Source:* United States Auto Club; this record was made in October 1997)

64. It costs \$4.90 to send a 2-pound package locally via parcel post at a U.S. Post Office. To send the same package as Express Mail, it costs \$16.30. How much more does it cost to send a package as Express Mail? (*Source:* USPS)

65. The Apple iPhone was a revolutionary touch screen phone when it was introduced in 2007. It measured 4.5 inches by 2.4 inches. Find the perimeter of this phone. (*Source: New York Times*)

66. The Google phone, G1, which was introduced in October 2008 to rival the Apple iPhone, measures 4.6 inches by 2.16 inches. Find the perimeter of the phone. (*Source: New York Times*)

67. The average U.S. movie theater ticket price in 2009 was \$7.50. In 2008, it was \$7.18. Find the increase in average movie theater ticket price from 2008 to 2009. (*Source:* MPAA)

68. The average U.S. movie theater ticket price in 2000 was \$5.39. For 2010, it is predicted to be \$7.80. Find the increase in average movie theater ticket price for this 10-year period. (*Source:* MPAA and Internet)

This bar graph shows the predicted increase in the total number of text messaging users in the United States. Use this graph for Exercises 69 and 70. (Source: CellSigns, Inc.) Note: Some of these values are projections.

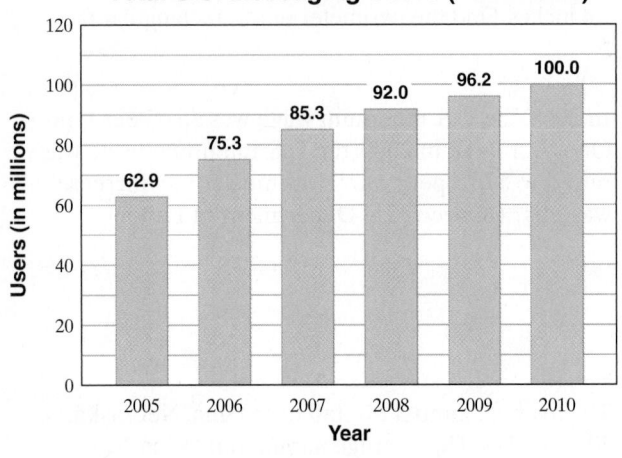

Total U.S. Messaging Users (in millions)

Year	2005	2006	2007	2008	2009	2010
Users (in millions)	62.9	75.3	85.3	92.0	96.2	100.0

69. Find the increase in U.S. messaging users from 2005 to 2006.

70. Find the increase in U.S. messaging users from 2007 to 2009.

71. The snowiest city in the United States is Blue Canyon, California, which receives an average of 111.6 more inches of snow than the second snowiest city. The second snowiest city in the United States is Marquette, Michigan. Marquette receives an average of 129.2 inches of snow annually. How much snow does Blue Canyon receive on average each year? (*Source:* National Climatic Data Center)

72. The driest city in the world is Aswan, Egypt, which receives an average of only 0.02 inch of rain per year. Yuma, Arizona, is the driest city in the United States. Yuma receives an average of 2.63 more inches of rain each year than Aswan. What is the average annual rainfall in Yuma? (*Source:* National Climatic Data Center)

△ **73.** A landscape architect is planning a border for a flower garden shaped like a triangle. The sides of the garden measure 12.4 feet, 29.34 feet, and 25.7 feet. Find the amount of border material needed.

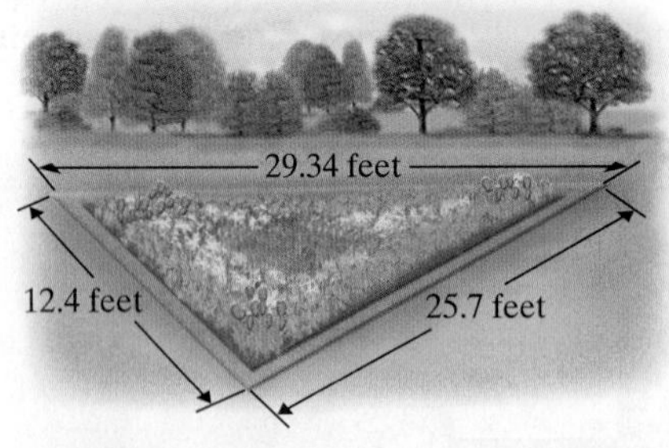

△ **74.** A contractor purchased enough railing to completely enclose the newly built deck shown below. Find the amount of railing purchased.

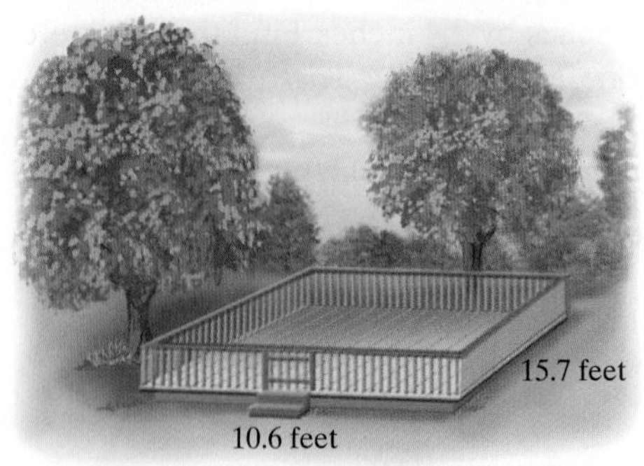

The table shows the average retail price of a gallon of gasoline (all grades and formulations) in the United States in May of each of the years shown. Use this table to answer Exercises 75 and 76. (*Source:* Energy Information Administration)

Year	Gasoline Price (dollars per gallon)
2005	2.338
2006	2.752
2007	3.176
2008	3.813
2009	2.314

75. How much more was the average cost of a gallon of gasoline in 2008 than in 2005?

76. How much less was the average cost of a gallon of gasoline in 2009 than in 2007?

The following table shows spaceflight information for astronaut James A. Lovell. Use this table to answer Exercises 77 and 78.

Spaceflights of James A. Lovell		
Year	Mission	Duration (in hours)
1965	Gemini 6	330.583
1966	Gemini 12	94.567
1968	Apollo 8	147.0
1970	Apollo 13	142.9

(*Source:* NASA)

77. Find the total time spent in spaceflight by astronaut James A. Lovell.

78. Find the total time James A. Lovell spent in spaceflight on all Apollo missions.

The bar graph shows the top five chocolate-consuming nations in the world. Use this table to answer Exercises 79 through 84.

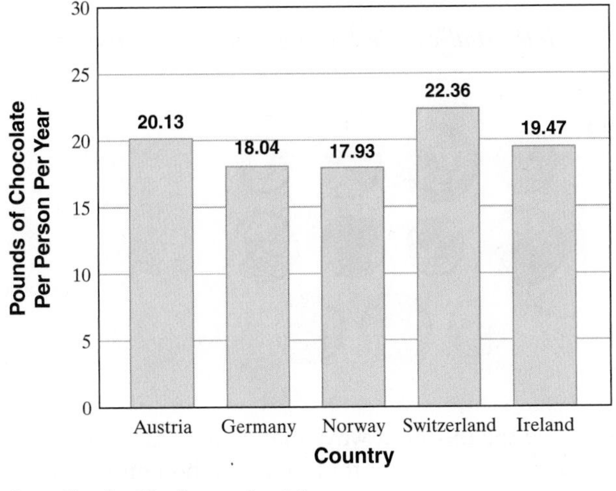

Source: Chocolate Manufacturers Association

79. Which country in the table has the greatest chocolate consumption per person?

80. Which country in the table has the least chocolate consumption per person?

81. How much more is the greatest chocolate consumption than the least chocolate consumption shown in the table?

82. How much more chocolate does the average Austrian consume than the average German?

83. Make a new chart listing the countries and their corresponding chocolate consumptions in order from greatest to least.

84. Find the sum of the five bar heights shown in the graph. What type of company might be interested in this sum?

Review

Multiply. See Sections 1.6 and 3.5.

85. $23 \cdot 2$

86. $46 \cdot 3$

87. $43 \cdot 90$

88. $30 \cdot 32$

89. $\left(\frac{2}{3}\right)^2$

90. $\left(\frac{1}{5}\right)^3$

Concept Extensions

A friend asks you to check his calculations for Exercises 91 and 92. Are they correct? If not, explain your friend's errors and correct the calculations. See the first Concept Check in this section.

91.
$$\begin{array}{r} \overset{1}{9.2} \\ \overset{1}{8}.63 \\ +\,4.005 \\ \hline 4.960 \end{array}$$

92.
$$\begin{array}{r} \overset{8999}{\cancel{900.0}} \\ -\ 96.4 \\ \hline 803.5 \end{array}$$

Find the unknown length in each figure.

 **93.**

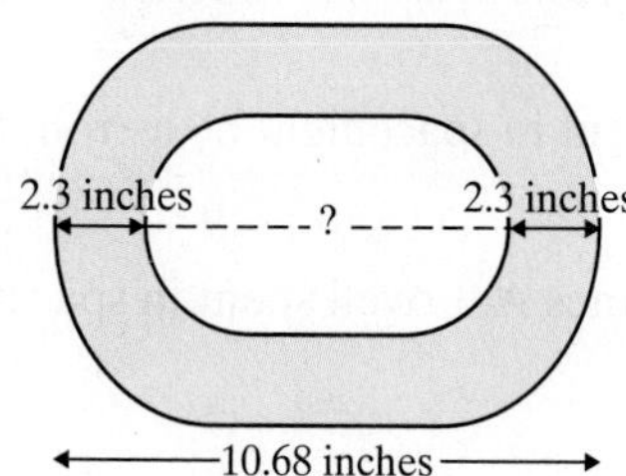

△ **94.**

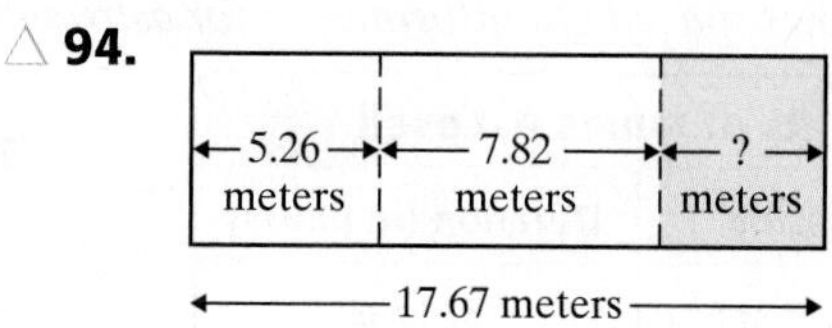

Let's review the values of these common U.S. coins in order to answer the following exercises.

Penny Nickel Dime Quarter

$0.01 $0.05 $0.10 $0.25

For Exercises 95 and 96, write the value of each group of coins. To do so, it is usually easiest to start with the coin(s) of greatest value and end with the coin(s) of least value.

95.

96.

97. Name the different ways that coins can have a value of $0.17 given that you may use no more than 10 coins.

98. Name the different ways that coin(s) can have a value of $0.25 given that there are no pennies.

99. Why shouldn't the sum

$$82.95 + 51.26$$

be estimated as $90 + 60 = 150$?
See the second Concept Check in this section.

100. Laser beams can be used to measure the distance to the moon. One measurement showed the distance to the moon to be 256,435.235 miles. A later measurement showed that the distance is 256,436.012 miles. Find how much farther away the moon is in the second measurement as compared to the first.

101. Explain how adding or subtracting decimals is similar to adding or subtracting whole numbers.

102. Explain how adding or subtracting decimals is different from adding or subtracting whole numbers.

4.4 MULTIPLYING DECIMALS AND CIRCUMFERENCE OF A CIRCLE

Objectives

A Multiply Decimals.

B Estimate When Multiplying Decimals.

C Multiply by Powers of 10.

D Find the Circumference of a Circle.

E Solve Problems by Multiplying Decimals.

Objective A Multiplying Decimals

Multiplying decimals is similar to multiplying whole numbers. The only difference is that we place a decimal point in the product. To discover where a decimal point is placed in the product, let's multiply 0.6 × 0.03. We first write each decimal as an equivalent fraction and then multiply.

$$\underset{\substack{\uparrow \\ \text{1 decimal} \\ \text{place}}}{0.6} \times \underset{\substack{\uparrow \\ \text{2 decimal} \\ \text{places}}}{0.03} = \frac{6}{10} \times \frac{3}{100} = \frac{18}{1000} = \underset{\substack{\uparrow \\ \text{3 decimal} \\ \text{places}}}{0.018}$$

Notice that 1 + 2 = 3, the number of decimal places in the product. Now let's multiply 0.03 × 0.002.

$$\underset{\substack{\uparrow \\ \text{2 decimal} \\ \text{places}}}{0.03} \times \underset{\substack{\uparrow \\ \text{3 decimal} \\ \text{places}}}{0.002} = \frac{3}{100} \times \frac{2}{1000} = \frac{6}{100{,}000} = \underset{\substack{\uparrow \\ \text{5 decimal} \\ \text{places}}}{0.00006}$$

Again, we see that 2 + 3 = 5, the number of decimal places in the product.

Instead of writing decimals as fractions each time we want to multiply, we notice a pattern from these examples and state a rule that we can use:

Multiplying Decimals

Step 1: Multiply the decimals as though they are whole numbers.

Step 2: The decimal point in the product is placed so that the number of decimal places in the product is equal to the *sum* of the number of decimal places in the factors.

Example 1 Multiply: 23.6 × 0.78

Solution:

```
   23.6   1 decimal place
 × 0.78   2 decimal places
   1888
  16520
 18.408   Since 1 + 2 = 3, insert the
          decimal point in the product so
          that there are 3 decimal places.
```

Work Practice 1

PRACTICE 1

Multiply: 45.9 × 0.42

Example 2 Multiply: 0.283 × 0.3

Solution:

```
  0.283   3 decimal places
 ×  0.3   1 decimal place
 0.0849   Since 3 + 1 = 4, insert the
          decimal point in the product so
          that there are 4 decimal places.
```

Insert one 0 since the product must have 4 decimal places.

Work Practice 2

PRACTICE 2

Multiply: 0.112 × 0.6

Answers

1. 19.278 2. 0.0672

PRACTICE 3

Multiply: 0.0721×48

Example 3 Multiply: 0.0531×16

Solution:

```
   0.0531   4 decimal places
 ×     16   0 decimal places
   ------
     3186
     5310
   ------
   0.8496   4 decimal places (4 + 0 = 4)
```

Work Practice 3

✓**Concept Check** True or false? The number of decimal places in the product of 0.261 and 0.78 is 6. Explain.

Objective B Estimating When Multiplying Decimals

Just as for addition and subtraction, we can estimate when multiplying decimals to check the reasonableness of our answer.

PRACTICE 4

Multiply: 30.26×2.98. Then estimate to see whether the answer is reasonable.

Example 4 Multiply: 28.06×1.95. Then estimate to see whether the answer is reasonable by rounding each factor, then multiplying the rounded numbers.

Solution:

Exact:	Estimate 1	Estimate 2
28.06	28 Rounded to ones	30 Rounded to tens
× 1.95	× 2	× 2
14030	56	60
252540		
280600		
54.7170		

The answer 54.7170 is reasonable.

Work Practice 4

As shown in Example 4, estimated results will vary depending on what estimates are used. Notice that estimating results is a good way to see whether the decimal point has been correctly placed.

Objective C Multiplying by Powers of 10

There are some patterns that occur when we multiply a number by a power of 10 such as 10, 100, 1000, 10,000, and so on.

$23.6951 \times 10 = 236.951$ (1 zero) — Move the decimal point *1 place* to the *right*.

$23.6951 \times 100 = 2369.51$ (2 zeros) — Move the decimal point *2 places* to the *right*.

$23.6951 \times 100{,}000 = 2{,}369{,}510.$ (5 zeros) — Move the decimal point *5 places* to the *right* (insert a 0).

Answers

3. 3.4608 **4.** 90.1748

✓ **Concept Check Answer**

false: 3 decimal places and 2 decimal places means 5 decimal places in the product

Notice that we move the decimal point the same number of places as there are zeros in the power of 10.

Multiplying Decimals by Powers of 10 such as 10, 100, 1000, 10,000...

Move the decimal point to the *right* the same number of places as there are *zeros* in the power of 10.

Examples Multiply.

5. $7.68 \times 10 = 76.8$ 7.68

6. $23.702 \times 100 = 2370.2$ 23.702

7. $76.3 \times 1000 = 76{,}300$ 76.300

Work Practice 5–7

PRACTICE 5–7

Multiply.

5. 23.7×10

6. 203.004×100

7. 1.15×1000

There are also powers of 10 that are less than 1. The decimals 0.1, 0.01, 0.001, 0.0001, and so on are examples of powers of 10 less than 1. Notice the pattern when we multiply by these powers of 10:

$569.2 \times 0.1 = 56.92$ Move the decimal point *1 place* to the *left*.
(1 decimal place)

$569.2 \times 0.01 = 5.692$ Move the decimal point *2 places* to the *left*.
(2 decimal places)

$569.2 \times 0.0001 = 0.05692$ Move the decimal point *4 places* to the *left* (insert one 0).
(4 decimal places)

Multiplying Decimals by Powers of 10 such as 0.1, 0.01, 0.001, 0.0001...

Move the decimal point to the *left* the same number of places as there are *decimal places* in the power of 10.

Examples Multiply.

8. $42.1 \times 0.1 = 4.21$ 42.1

9. $76{,}805 \times 0.01 = 768.05$ 76,805.

10. $9.2 \times 0.001 = 0.0092$ 0009.2

Work Practice 8–10

PRACTICE 8–10

Multiply.

8. 7.62×0.1

9. 1.9×0.01

10. 7682×0.001

Many times we see large numbers written, for example, in the form 451.8 million rather than in the longer standard notation. The next example shows us how to interpret these numbers.

Answers

5. 237 **6.** 20,300.4 **7.** 1150
8. 0.762 **9.** 0.019 **10.** 7.682

PRACTICE 11

In 2015, the population of the United States is projected to be 321.2 million. Write this number in standard notation. (*Source:* United Nations Population Division)

Example 11 In 2050, the population of the United States is projected to be 451.8 million. Write this number in standard notation. (*Source:* U.S. Census Bureau)

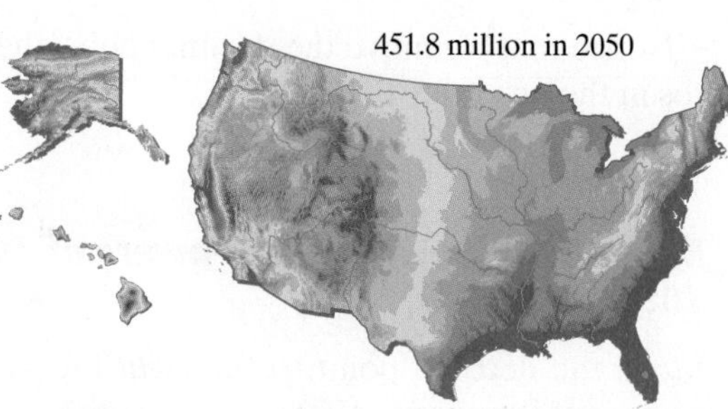

Solution: 451.8 million $= 451.8 \times 1$ million

$= 451.8 \times 1{,}000{,}000 = 451{,}800{,}000$

Work Practice 11

Objective D Finding the Circumference of a Circle

Recall from Section 1.3 that the distance around a polygon is called its perimeter. The distance around a circle is given the special name **circumference,** and this distance depends on the radius or the diameter of the circle.

Circumference of a Circle

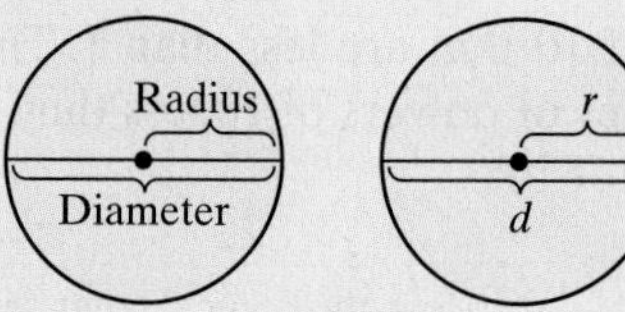

Circumference $= 2 \cdot \pi \cdot$ **radius** or Circumference $= \pi \cdot$ **diameter**

In Section 4.2, we learned about the symbol π as the Greek letter pi, pronounced "pie." It is a constant between 3 and 4.

Approximations for π

Two common approximations for π are:

$\pi \approx 3.14$ (a decimal approximation) or $\pi \approx \frac{22}{7}$ (a fraction approximation)

PRACTICE 12

Find the circumference of a circle whose radius is 11 meters. Then use the approximation 3.14 for π to approximate this circumference.

Example 12 Circumference of a Circle

Find the circumference of a circle whose radius is 5 inches. Then use the approximation 3.14 for π to approximate the circumference.

Solution: Circumference $= 2 \cdot \pi \cdot$ radius

$= 2 \cdot \pi \cdot 5$ inches

$= 10\pi$ inches

5 inches

Next, we replace π with the approximation 3.14.

Circumference $= 10\pi$ inches

("is approximately") → $\approx 10(3.14)$ inches

$= 31.4$ inches

The *exact* circumference or distance around the circle is 10π inches, which is *approximately* 31.4 inches.

Work Practice 12

Answers

11. 321,200,000 **12.** 22π m; 69.08 m

Objective E Solving Problems by Multiplying Decimals

The solutions to many real-life problems are found by multiplying decimals. We continue using our four problem-solving steps to solve such problems.

Example 13 Finding the Total Cost of Materials for a Job

A college student is hired to paint a billboard with paint costing $2.49 per quart. If the job requires 3 quarts of paint, what is the total cost of the paint?

Solution:

1. UNDERSTAND. Read and reread the problem. The phrase "total cost" might make us think addition, but since this problem requires repeated addition, let's multiply.
2. TRANSLATE.

In words:	Total cost	is	cost per quart of paint	times	number of quarts
	↓	↓	↓	↓	↓
Translate:	Total cost	=	2.49	×	3

3. SOLVE. We can estimate to check our calculations. The number 2.49 rounds to 2 and $2 \times 3 = 6$.

$$\begin{array}{r} \overset{1\,2}{2.49} \\ \times \quad 3 \\ \hline 7.47 \end{array}$$

4. INTERPRET. *Check* your work. Since 7.47 is close to our estimate of 6, our answer is reasonable. *State* your conclusion: The total cost of the paint is $7.47.

Work Practice 13

PRACTICE 13

A biology major is fertilizing her garden. She uses 5.6 ounces of fertilizer per square yard. The garden measures 60.5 square yards. How much fertilizer does she need?

Answer

13. 338.8 oz

Vocabulary and Readiness Check

Use the choices below to fill in each blank.

circumference	left	sum	zeros
decimal places	right	product	factor

1. When multiplying decimals, the number of decimal places in the product is equal to the ____________ of the number of decimal places in the factors.
2. In $8.6 \times 5 = 43$, the number 43 is called the ____________, while 8.6 and 5 are each called a(n) ____________.
3. When multiplying a decimal number by powers of 10, such as 10, 100, 1000, and so on, we move the decimal point in the number to the ____________ the same number of places as there are ____________ in the power of 10.
4. When multiplying a decimal number by powers of 10, such as 0.1, 0.01, and so on, we move the decimal point in the number to the ____________ the same number of places as there are ____________ in the power of 10.
5. The distance around a circle is called its ____________.

Do not multiply. Just give the number of decimal places in the product. See the Concept Check in this section.

6. $\begin{array}{r} 0.46 \\ \times\ 0.81 \\ \hline \end{array}$ **7.** $\begin{array}{r} 57.9 \\ \times\ 0.36 \\ \hline \end{array}$ **8.** $\begin{array}{r} 0.428 \\ \times\ 0.2 \\ \hline \end{array}$ **9.** $\begin{array}{r} 0.0073 \\ \times\ 21 \\ \hline \end{array}$ **10.** $\begin{array}{r} 0.028 \\ \times\ 1.36 \\ \hline \end{array}$ **11.** $\begin{array}{r} 5.1296 \\ \times\ 7.3987 \\ \hline \end{array}$

4.4 Exercise Set

FOR EXTRA HELP

MyMathLab

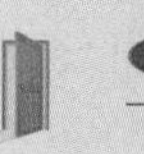

Objectives A B Mixed Practice *Multiply. See Examples 1 through 4. For those exercises marked, also estimate to see if the answer is reasonable.*

1. $\begin{array}{r} 0.2 \\ \times 0.6 \\ \hline \end{array}$ **2.** $\begin{array}{r} 0.7 \\ \times 0.9 \\ \hline \end{array}$ **3.** $\begin{array}{r} 1.2 \\ \times 0.5 \\ \hline \end{array}$ **4.** $\begin{array}{r} 6.8 \\ \times 0.3 \\ \hline \end{array}$

5. 0.26×5

6. 0.19×6

7. 5.3×4.2
Exact:
Estimate:

8. 6.2×3.8
Exact:
Estimate:

9. $\begin{array}{r} 0.576 \\ \times\ 0.7 \\ \hline \end{array}$ **10.** $\begin{array}{r} 0.971 \\ \times\ 0.5 \\ \hline \end{array}$

11. $\begin{array}{r} 1.0047 \\ \times\ 8.2 \\ \hline \end{array}$
Exact: Estimate:

12. $\begin{array}{r} 2.0005 \\ \times\ 5.5 \\ \hline \end{array}$
Exact: Estimate:

13. $\begin{array}{r} 490.2 \\ \times 0.023 \\ \hline \end{array}$ **14.** $\begin{array}{r} 300.9 \\ \times 0.032 \\ \hline \end{array}$

15. Multiply 16.003 and 5.31

16. Multiply 31.006 and 3.71

Objective C *Multiply. See Examples 5 through 10.*

17. 6.5×10

18. 7.2×100

19. 6.5×0.1

20. 4.7×0.1

21. 7.2×0.01

22. 0.06×0.01

23. 7.093×100

24. 0.5×100

25. 6.046×1000

26. 9.1×1000

27. 37.62×0.001

28. 14.3×0.001

Objectives **A B C Mixed Practice** *Multiply. See Examples 1 through 10.*

29. 0.123×0.4

30. 0.216×0.3

31. 0.123×100

32. 0.216×100

33. 8.6×0.15

34. 0.42×5.7

35. 9.6×0.01

36. 5.7×0.01

37. 562.3×0.001

38. 993.5×0.001

39. $\begin{array}{r} 5.62 \\ \times\ 7.7 \\ \hline \end{array}$

40. $\begin{array}{r} 8.03 \\ \times\ 5.5 \\ \hline \end{array}$

Write each number in standard notation. See Example 11.

41. The storage silos at the main Hershey chocolate factory in Hershey, Pennsylvania, can hold enough cocoa beans to make 5.5 billion Hershey's milk chocolate bars. (*Source:* Hershey Foods Corporation)

42. The total forecasted amount of money spent in the United States on online advertising in 2010 is \$26.1 billion. (*Source:* ClickZ)

43. The Blue Streak is the oldest roller coaster at Cedar Point, an amusement park in Sandusky, Ohio. Since 1964, it has given more than 49.8 million rides. (*Source:* Cedar Fair, L.P.)

44. About 45.6 million American households own at least one dog. (*Source:* American Pet Products Association)

45. The most-visited national park in the United States in the Blue Ridge Parkway in Viriginia and North Carolina. An estimated 314 thousand people visit the park each week. (*Source:* National Park Service)

46. In a recent year, approximately 21.4 thousand vessels passed through the Suez Canal. (*Source:* suezcanal.gov)

Objective **D** *Find the circumference of each circle. Then use the approximation 3.14 for π and approximate each circumference. See Example 12.*

47.

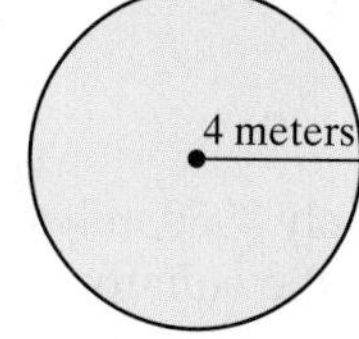

48.

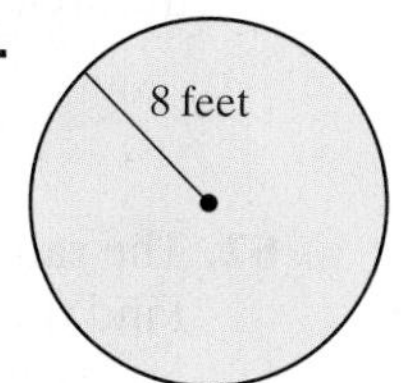

49.

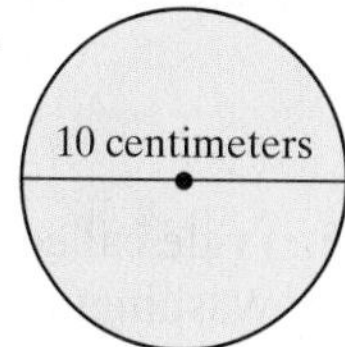

50.

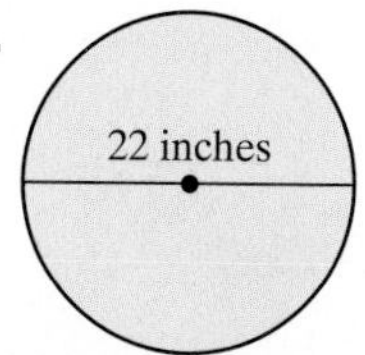

51.

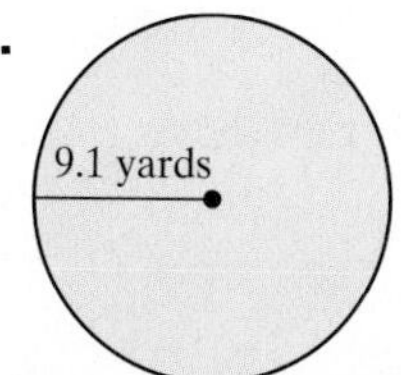

52.

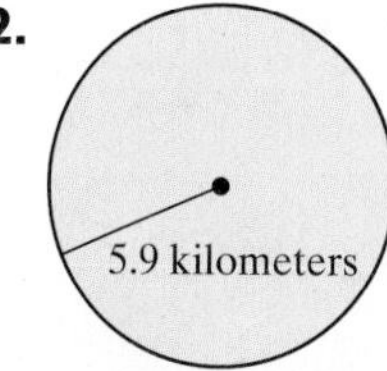

Objectives D E Mixed Practice *Solve. For Exercises 53 and 54, the solutions have been started for you. See Examples 12 and 13. For circumference applications, find the exact circumference and then use 3.14 for π to approximate the circumference.*

53. An electrician for Central Power and Light worked 40 hours last week. Calculate his pay before taxes for last week if his hourly wage is $17.88.

Start the solution:

1. UNDERSTAND the problem. Reread it as many times as needed.
2. TRANSLATE into an equation. (Fill in the blanks.)

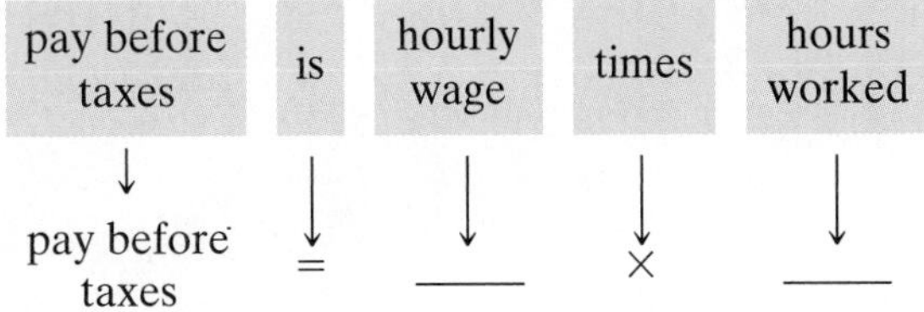

Finish with:

3. SOLVE and 4. INTERPRET.

54. An assembly line worker worked 20 hours last week. Her hourly rate is $19.52 per hour. Calculate her pay before taxes.

Start the solution:

1. UNDERSTAND the problem. Reread it as many times as needed.
2. TRANSLATE into an equation. (Fill in the blanks.)

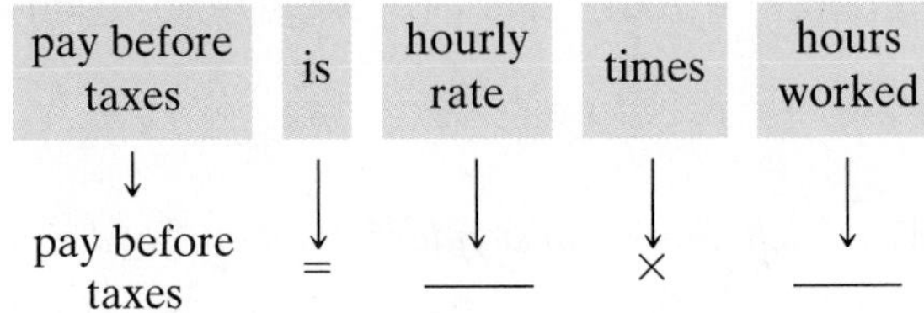

Finish with:

3. SOLVE and 4. INTERPRET.

55. Under certain conditions, the average cost of driving a medium sedan in 2009 was $0.54 per mile. How much would it have cost to drive a car 8750 miles in 2009? (*Source:* American Automobile Association)

56. At the beginning of 2010, a U.S. airline passenger paid $0.1433, on average, to fly 1 mile. Use this number to calculate the cost to fly from Atlanta, Georgia, to Minneapolis, Minnesota, a distance of 905 miles. Round to the nearest cent. (*Source:* Air Transport Association of America)

57. A 1-ounce serving of cream cheese contains 6.2 grams of saturated fat. How much saturated fat is in 4 ounces of cream cheese? (*Source: Home and Garden Bulletin No. 72;* U.S. Department of Agriculture)

58. A 3.5-ounce serving of lobster meat contains 0.1 gram of saturated fat. How much saturated fat do 3 servings of lobster meat contain? (*Source:* The National Institute of Health)

△ **59.** Recall that the face of the Apple iPhone (see Section 4.3) measures 4.5 inches by 2.4 inches. Find the area of the face of the Apple iPhone.

△ **60.** Recall that the face of the Google G1 phone (see Section 4.3) measures 4.6 inches by 2.16 inches. Find the area of the face of the Google G1 phone.

△ **61.** In 1893, the first ride called a Ferris wheel was constructed by Washington Gale Ferris. Its diameter was 250 feet. Find its circumference. Give an exact answer and an approximation using 3.14 for π. (*Source: The Handy Science Answer Book,* Visible Ink Press, 1994)

△ **62.** The radius of Earth is approximately 3950 miles. Find the distance around Earth at the equator. Give an exact answer and an approximation using 3.14 for π. (*Hint:* Find the circumference of a circle with radius 3950 miles.)

63. The London Eye, built for the Millennium celebration in London, resembles a gigantic ferris wheel with a diameter of 135 meters. If Adam Hawn rides the Eye for one revolution, find how far he travels. Give an exact answer and an approximation using 3.14 for π. (*Source:* Londoneye.com)

64. The world's longest suspension bridge is the Akashi Kaikyo Bridge in Japan. This bridge has two circular caissons, which are underwater foundations. If the diameter of a caisson is 80 meters, find its circumference. Give an exact answer and an approximation using 3.14 for π. (*Source: Scientific American;* How Things Work Today)

65. A meter is a unit of length in the metric system that is approximately equal to 39.37 inches. Sophia Wagner is 1.65 meters tall. Find her approximate height in inches.

66. The doorway to a room is 2.15 meters tall. Approximate this height in inches. (*Hint:* See Exercise 65.)

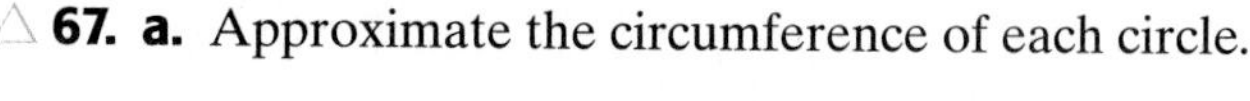

67. a. Approximate the circumference of each circle.

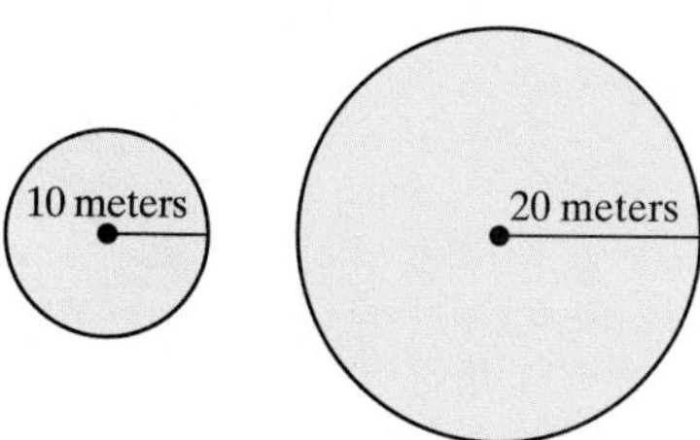

b. If the radius of a circle is doubled, is its corresponding circumference doubled?

68. a. Approximate the circumference of each circle.

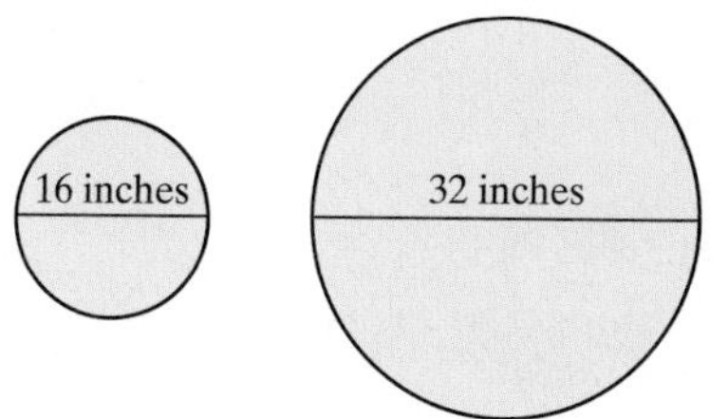

b. If the diameter of a circle is doubled, is its corresponding circumference doubled?

69. Recall that the top face of the Apple iPod nano (see Section 4.3) measures 3.6 inches by 1.5 inches. Find the area of the face of the iPod nano.

70. Recall that the face of the regular Apple iPod (see Section 4.3) measures 4.1 inches by 2.4 inches. Find the area of the face of this iPod.

Review

Divide. See Sections 1.7 and 2.5.

71. $130 \div 5$

72. $486 \div 27$

73. $2016 \div 56$

74. $1863 \div 69$

75. $2920 \div 365$

76. $2916 \div 6$

77. $\frac{24}{7} \div \frac{8}{21}$

78. $\frac{162}{25} \div \frac{9}{75}$

Concept Extensions

Mixed Practice (*Sections 4.3, 4.4*) *Perform the indicated operations.*

79. $3.6 + 0.04$

80. $7.2 + 0.14 + 98.6$

81. $3.6 - 0.04$

82. $100 - 48.6$

83. 0.221×0.5

84. 3.6×0.04

85. Find how far radio waves travel in 20.6 seconds. (Radio waves travel at a speed of $1.86 \times 100{,}000$ miles per second.)

86. If it takes radio waves approximately 8.3 minutes to travel from the Sun to the Earth, find approximately how far it is from the Sun to the Earth. (*Hint:* See Exercise 85.)

87. In your own words, explain how to find the number of decimal places in a product of decimal numbers.

88. In your own words, explain how to multiply by a power of 10.

89. Write down two decimal numbers whose product will contain 5 decimal places. Without multiplying, explain how you know your answer is correct.

90. Explain the process for multiplying a decimal number by a power of 10.

Integrated Review Sections 4.1–4.4

Operations on Decimals

Perform the indicated operations.

1. $1.6 + 0.97$

2. $3.2 + 0.85$

3. $9.8 - 0.9$

4. $10.2 - 6.7$

5. $\begin{array}{r} 0.8 \\ \times 0.2 \\ \hline \end{array}$

6. $\begin{array}{r} 0.6 \\ \times 0.4 \\ \hline \end{array}$

7. $8 + 2.16 + 0.9$

8. $6 + 3.12 + 0.6$

9. $\begin{array}{r} 9.6 \\ \times 0.5 \\ \hline \end{array}$

10. $\begin{array}{r} 8.7 \\ \times 0.7 \\ \hline \end{array}$

11. $\begin{array}{r} 123.6 \\ -\ 48.04 \\ \hline \end{array}$

12. $\begin{array}{r} 325.2 \\ -\ 36.08 \\ \hline \end{array}$

13. $25 + 0.026$

14. $0.125 + 44$

15. $100 - 17.3$

16. $300 - 26.1$

17. 2.8×100

18. 1.6×1000

19. $\begin{array}{r} 96.21 \\ 7.028 \\ +121.7 \\ \hline \end{array}$

20. $\begin{array}{r} 0.268 \\ 1.93 \\ +142.881 \\ \hline \end{array}$

21. Find the product of 1.2 and 5.

22. Find the sum of 1.2 and 5.

23. $\begin{array}{r} 12.004 \\ \times \quad 2.3 \\ \hline \end{array}$

24. $\begin{array}{r} 28.006 \\ \times \quad 5.2 \\ \hline \end{array}$

25. Subtract 4.6 from 10.

26. Subtract 0.26 from 18.

Answers

1. ______
2. ______
3. ______
4. ______
5. ______
6. ______
7. ______
8. ______
9. ______
10. ______
11. ______
12. ______
13. ______
14. ______
15. ______
16. ______
17. ______
18. ______
19. ______
20. ______
21. ______
22. ______
23. ______
24. ______
25. ______
26. ______

27. $\begin{array}{r} 268.19 \\ +\,146.25 \\ \hline \end{array}$

28. $\begin{array}{r} 860.18 \\ +\,434.85 \\ \hline \end{array}$

29. $160 - 43.19$

30. $120 - 101.21$

31. 15.62×10

32. $15.62 + 10$

33. $15.62 - 10$

34. 117.26×2.6

35. $117.26 - 2.6$

36. $117.26 + 2.6$

37. 0.0072×0.06

38. 0.0025×0.03

39. $0.0072 + 0.06$

40. $0.03 - 0.0025$

41. 0.862×1000

42. 2.93×0.01

43. Estimate the distance in miles between Garden City, Kansas, and Wichita, Kansas, by rounding each given distance to the nearest ten.

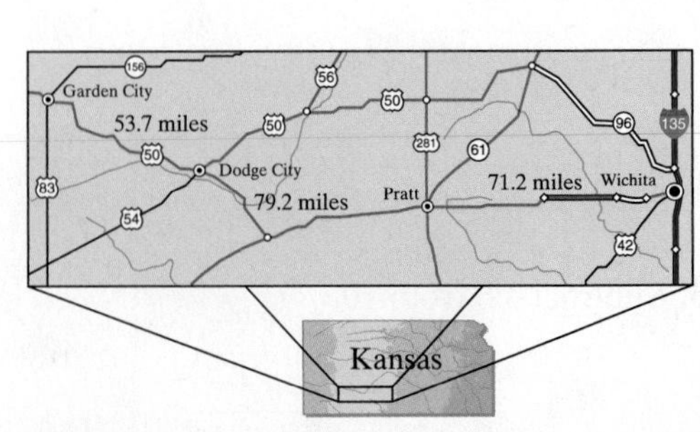

27. ______

28. ______

29. ______

30. ______

31. ______

32. ______

33. ______

34. ______

35. ______

36. ______

37. ______

38. ______

39. ______

40. ______

41. ______

42. ______

43. ______

4.5 DIVIDING DECIMALS AND ORDER OF OPERATIONS

Objective A Dividing Decimals

Dividing decimal numbers is similar to dividing whole numbers. The only difference is that we place a decimal point in the quotient. If the divisor is a whole number, we place the decimal point in the quotient directly above the decimal point in the dividend, and then divide as with whole numbers. Recall that division can be checked by multiplication.

Dividing by a Whole Number

Step 1: Place the decimal point in the quotient directly above the decimal point in the dividend.

Step 2: Divide as with whole numbers.

Example 1 Divide: 270.2 ÷ 7. Check your answer.

Solution: We divide as usual. The decimal point in the quotient is directly above the decimal point in the dividend.

```
           ┌ Write the decimal point.
           ↓
         38.6 ← quotient
divisor → 7)270.2 ← dividend
         −21
          60
         −56
          42
         −42
           0
```

Check:

```
     64
   38.6 ← quotient
 ×    7 ← divisor
  270.2 ← dividend
```

The quotient is 38.6.

Work Practice 1

Example 2 Divide: $32\overline{)8.32}$

Solution: We divide as usual. The decimal point in the quotient is directly above the decimal point in the dividend.

```
             0.26   ← quotient
divisor ↦ 32)8.32   ← dividend
            −64
             192
            −192
               0
```

Check:

```
  0.26   quotient
 × 32    divisor
    52
  7 80
  8.32   dividend
```

Work Practice 2

Sometimes to continue dividing we need to insert zeros after the last digit in the dividend.

Objectives

A Divide Decimals.

B Estimate When Dividing Decimals.

C Divide Decimals by Powers of 10.

D Solve Problems by Dividing Decimals.

E Review Order of Operations to Simplify Expressions Containing Decimals.

PRACTICE 1

Divide: 370.4 ÷ 8. Check your answer.

PRACTICE 2

Divide: $48\overline{)34.08}$. Check your answer.

Answers

1. 46.3 **2.** 0.71

PRACTICE 3

Divide and check.

a. $0.4 \div 8$

b. $13.62 \div 12$

Example 3 Divide and check: $0.5 \div 4$.

Solution:

$$\begin{array}{r} 0.125 \\ 4\overline{)0.500} \\ -4 \\ \hline 10 \\ -8 \\ \hline 20 \\ -20 \\ \hline 0 \end{array}$$

Insert two 0s to continue dividing.

Check:

$$\begin{array}{r} \overset{1\,2}{0.125} \\ \times\quad 4 \\ \hline 0.500 \end{array}$$

Work Practice 3

If the divisor is not a whole number, before we divide we need to move the decimal point to the right until the divisor is a whole number.

$1.5\overline{)64.85}$

divisor ↑ ↑ dividend

To understand how this works, let's rewrite

$1.5\overline{)64.85}$ as $\frac{64.85}{1.5}$

and then multiply by 1 in the form of $\frac{10}{10}$. We use the form $\frac{10}{10}$ so that the denominator (divisor) becomes a whole number.

$$\frac{64.85}{1.5} = \frac{64.85}{1.5} \cdot 1 = \frac{64.85}{1.5} \cdot \frac{10}{10} = \frac{64.85 \cdot 10}{1.5 \cdot 10} = \frac{648.5}{15},$$

which can be written as $15.\overline{)648.5}$. Notice that

$1.5\overline{)64.85}$ is equivalent to $15.\overline{)648.5}$

The decimal points in the dividend and the divisor were both moved one place to the right, and the divisor is now a whole number. This procedure is summarized next:

Dividing by a Decimal

Step 1: Move the decimal point in the divisor to the right until the divisor is a whole number.

Step 2: Move the decimal point in the dividend to the right the *same number of places* as the decimal point was moved in Step 1.

Step 3: Divide. Place the decimal point in the quotient directly over the moved decimal point in the dividend.

Answers

3. a. 0.05 **b.** 1.135

Example 4 Divide: $10.764 \div 2.3$

Solution: We move the decimal points in the divisor and the dividend one place to the right so that the divisor is a whole number.

$$2.3\overline{)10.764} \quad \text{becomes} \quad \begin{array}{r} 4.68 \\ 23.\overline{)107.64} \\ -92 \\ \hline 15\,6 \\ -13\,8 \\ \hline 1\,84 \\ -1\,84 \\ \hline 0 \end{array}$$

Work Practice 4

PRACTICE 4

Divide: $166.88 \div 5.6$

Example 5 Divide: $5.264 \div 0.32$

Solution:

$$0.32\overline{)5.264} \quad \text{becomes} \quad \begin{array}{r} 16.45 \\ 32.\overline{)526.40} \\ -32 \\ \hline 206 \\ -192 \\ \hline 14\,4 \\ -12\,8 \\ \hline 1\,60 \\ -1\,60 \\ \hline 0 \end{array} \quad \text{Insert one 0.}$$

Work Practice 5

PRACTICE 5

Divide: $1.976 \div 0.16$

✓**Concept Check** Is it always true that the number of decimal places in a quotient equals the sum of the decimal places in the dividend and divisor?

Example 6 Divide: $17.5 \div 0.48$. Round the quotient to the nearest hundredth.

Solution: First we move the decimal points in the divisor and the dividend two places. Then we divide and round the quotient to the nearest hundredth.

hundredths place

$$\begin{array}{r} 36.458 \\ 48.\overline{)1750.000} \\ -144 \\ \hline 310 \\ -288 \\ \hline 22\,0 \\ -19\,2 \\ \hline 2\,80 \\ -2\,40 \\ \hline 400 \\ -384 \\ \hline 16 \end{array} \approx 36.46$$

"is approximately"

When rounding to the nearest hundredth, carry the division process out to one more decimal place, the thousandths place.

Work Practice 6

PRACTICE 6

Divide $23.4 \div 0.57$. Round the quotient to the nearest hundredth.

Answers

4. 29.8 **5.** 12.35 **6.** 41.05

✓ **Concept Check Answer**

no

Objective B Estimating When Dividing Decimals

Just as for addition, subtraction, and multiplication of decimals, we can estimate when dividing decimals to check the reasonableness of our answer.

PRACTICE 7

Divide: 713.7 ÷ 91.5. Then estimate to see whether the proposed answer is reasonable.

Example 7 Divide: 272.356 ÷ 28.4. Then estimate to see whether the proposed result is reasonable.

Solution:

Exact:

$$\begin{array}{r} 9.59 \\ 284.\overline{)2723.56} \\ -2556 \\ \hline 167\ 5 \\ -142\ 0 \\ \hline 25\ 56 \\ -25\ 56 \\ \hline 0 \end{array}$$

Estimate 1

$$\begin{array}{r} 9 \\ 30\overline{)270} \end{array}$$

or

Estimate 2

$$\begin{array}{r} 10 \\ 30\overline{)300} \end{array}$$

The estimate is 9 or 10, so 9.59 is reasonable.

Work Practice 7

✓**Concept Check** If a quotient is to be rounded to the nearest thousandth, to what place should the division be carried out? (Assume that the division carries out to your answer.)

Objective C Dividing Decimals by Powers of 10

As with multiplication, there are patterns that occur when we divide decimals by powers of 10 such as 10, 100, 1000, and so on.

$\frac{569.2}{10} = 56.92$ (1 zero) Move the decimal point *1 place* to the *left*.

$\frac{569.2}{10{,}000} = 0.05692$ (4 zeros) Move the decimal point *4 places* to the *left*.

This pattern suggests the following rule:

Dividing Decimals by Powers of 10 such as 10, 100, or 1000

Move the decimal point of the dividend to the *left* the same number of places as there are *zeros* in the power of 10.

PRACTICE 8–9

Divide.

8. $\frac{128.3}{1000}$ **9.** $\frac{0.56}{10}$

Examples Divide.

8. $\frac{786.1}{1000} = 0.7861$ (3 zeros) Move the decimal point *3 places* to the *left*.

9. $\frac{0.12}{10} = 0.012$ (1 zero) Move the decimal point *1 place* to the *left*.

Work Practice 8–9

Answers

7. 7.8 **8.** 0.1283 **9.** 0.056

✓ **Concept Check Answer**

ten-thousandths place

Objective D Solving Problems by Dividing Decimals

Many real-life problems involve dividing decimals.

Example 10 Calculating Materials Needed for a Job

A gallon of paint covers a 250-square-foot area. If Betty Adkins wishes to paint a wall that measures 1450 square feet, how many gallons of paint does she need? If she can buy only gallon containers of paint, how many gallon containers does she need?

Solution:

1. UNDERSTAND. Read and reread the problem. We need to know how many 250s are in 1450, so we divide.
2. TRANSLATE.

In words:	number of gallons	is	square feet	divided by	square feet per gallon
	↓	↓	↓	↓	↓
Translate:	number of gallons	=	1450	÷	250

3. SOLVE. Let's see if our answer is reasonable by estimating. The dividend 1450 rounds to 1500 and divisor 250 rounds to 300. Then $1500 \div 300 = 5$.

$$\begin{array}{r} 5.8 \\ 250\overline{)1450.0} \\ -1250 \\ \hline 200\ 0 \\ -200\ 0 \\ \hline 0 \end{array}$$

4. INTERPRET. *Check* your work. Since our estimate is close to our answer of 5, our answer is reasonable. *State* your conclusion: Betty needs 5.8 gallons of paint. If she can buy only gallon containers of paint, she needs 6 gallon containers of paint to complete the job.

Work Practice 10

PRACTICE 10

A bag of fertilizer covers 1250 square feet of lawn. Tim Parker's lawn measures 14,800 square feet. How many bags of fertilizer does he need? If he can buy only whole bags of fertilizer, how many whole bags does he need?

Objective E Simplifying Expressions with Decimals

In the remaining examples, we will review the order of operations by simplifying expressions that contain decimals.

Order of Operations

1. Perform all operations within parentheses ( ), brackets [ ], or other grouping symbols such as square roots or fraction bars, starting with the innermost set.
2. Evaluate any expressions with exponents.
3. Multiply or divide in order from left to right.
4. Add or subtract in order from left to right.

Answer

10. 11.84 bags; 12 bags

PRACTICE 11

Simplify: $897.8 \div 100 \times 10$

Example 11 Simplify: $723.6 \div 1000 \times 10$

Solution: Multiply or divide in order from left to right.

$$723.6 \div 1000 \times 10 = 0.7236 \times 10 \quad \text{Divide.}$$
$$= 7.236 \quad \text{Multiply.}$$

Work Practice 11

PRACTICE 12

Simplify: $8.69(3.2 - 1.8)$

Example 12 Simplify: $0.5(8.6 - 1.2)$

Solution: According to the order of operations, we simplify inside the parentheses first.

$$0.5(8.6 - 1.2) = 0.5(7.4) \quad \text{Subtract.}$$
$$= 3.7 \quad \text{Multiply.}$$

Work Practice 12

PRACTICE 13

Simplify: $\dfrac{20.06 - (1.2)^2 \div 10}{0.02}$

Example 13 Simplify: $\dfrac{5.68 + (0.9)^2 \div 100}{0.2}$

Solution: First we simplify the numerator of the fraction. Then we divide.

$$\frac{5.68 + (0.9)^2 \div 100}{0.2} = \frac{5.68 + 0.81 \div 100}{0.2} \quad \text{Simplify } (0.9)^2.$$
$$= \frac{5.68 + 0.0081}{0.2} \quad \text{Divide.}$$
$$= \frac{5.6881}{0.2} \quad \text{Add.}$$
$$= 28.4405 \quad \text{Divide.}$$

Work Practice 13

Answers
11. 89.78 **12.** 12.166 **13.** 995.8

Calculator Explorations

Calculator errors can easily be made by pressing an incorrect key or by not pressing a correct key hard enough. Estimation is a valuable tool that can be used to check calculator results.

Example Use estimation to determine whether the calculator result is reasonable or not. (For example, a result that is not reasonable can occur if proper keys are not pressed.)

Simplify: $82.064 \div 23$

Calculator display: 35.68

Solution: Round each number to the nearest 10. Since $80 \div 20 = 4$, the calculator display 35.68 is not reasonable.

Use estimation to determine whether each result is reasonable or not.

1. 102.62×41.8 Result: 428.9516
2. $174.835 \div 47.9$ Result: 3.65
3. $1025.68 - 125.42$ Result: 900.26
4. $562.781 + 2.96$ Result: 858.781

Vocabulary and Readiness Check

Use the choices below to fill in each blank. Some choices may be used more than once, and some not used at all.

dividend	divisor	quotient	true
zeros	left	right	false

1. In $6.5 \div 5 = 1.3$, the number 1.3 is called the ____________, 5 is the ____________, and 6.5 is the ____________.
2. To check a division exercise, we can perform the following multiplication: quotient · ____________ = ____________.
3. To divide a decimal number by a power of 10, such as 10, 100, 1000, and so on, we move the decimal point in the number to the ____________ the same number of places as there are ____________ in the power of 10.
4. True or false: If $1.058 \div 0.46 = 2.3$, then $2.3 \times 0.46 = 1.058$ ____________.

Recall properties of division and simplify.

5. $\frac{5.9}{1}$ **6.** $\frac{0.7}{0.7}$ **7.** $\frac{0}{9.86}$ **8.** $\frac{2.36}{0}$

9. $\frac{7.261}{7.261}$ **10.** $\frac{8.25}{1}$ **11.** $\frac{11.1}{0}$ **12.** $\frac{0}{89.96}$

4.5 Exercise Set

FOR EXTRA HELP

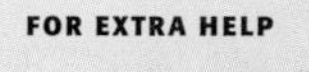

Objectives A B Mixed Practice *Divide. See Examples 1 through 5 and 7. For those exercises marked, also estimate to see if the answer is reasonable.*

1. $3\overline{)13.8}$ **2.** $2\overline{)11.8}$ **3.** $5\overline{)0.47}$ **4.** $6\overline{)0.51}$ **5.** $0.06\overline{)18}$

6. $0.04\overline{)20}$ **7.** $0.82\overline{)4.756}$ **8.** $0.92\overline{)3.312}$ **9.** $5.5\overline{)36.3}$ Exact: Estimate: **10.** $2.2\overline{)21.78}$ Exact: Estimate:

11. $6.195 \div 15$ **12.** $8.823 \div 17$ **13.** $0.54 \div 12$ **14.** $1.35 \div 18$ **15.** Divide 4.2 by 0.6.

16. Divide 3.6 by 0.9. **17.** $0.27\overline{)1.296}$ **18.** $0.34\overline{)2.176}$ **19.** $0.02\overline{)42}$ **20.** $0.03\overline{)24}$

21. $0.6\overline{)18}$ **22.** $0.4\overline{)20}$ **23.** $0.005\overline{)35}$ **24.** $0.0007\overline{)35}$ **25.** $7.2\overline{)70.56}$ Exact: Estimate:

26. $6.3\overline{)54.18}$ Exact: Estimate: **27.** $5.4\overline{)51.84}$ **28.** $7.7\overline{)33.88}$ **29.** $\frac{1.215}{0.027}$ **30.** $\frac{3.213}{0.051}$

31. $0.25\overline{)13.648}$ **32.** $0.75\overline{)49.866}$ **33.** $3.78\overline{)0.02079}$ **34.** $2.96\overline{)0.01332}$

Divide. Round the quotients as indicated. See Example 6.

35. Divide 429.34 by 2.4 and round the quotient to the nearest whole number.

36. Divide 54.8 by 2.6 and round the quotient to the nearest whole number.

37. Divide 0.549 by 0.023 and round the quotient to the nearest hundredth.

38. Divide 0.0453 by 0.98 and round the quotient to the nearest thousandth.

39. Divide 45.23 by 0.4 and round the quotient to the nearest tenth.

40. Divide 83.32 by 0.6 and round the quotient to the nearest tenth.

Objective C *Divide. See Examples 8 and 9.*

41. $\frac{54.982}{100}$ **42.** $\frac{342.54}{100}$ **43.** $\frac{26.87}{10}$ **44.** $\frac{13.49}{10}$ **45.** $\frac{12.9}{1000}$ **46.** $\frac{0.27}{1000}$

Objectives A C Mixed Practice *Divide. See Examples 1, 5, 8, and 9.*

47. $7\overline{)88.2}$ **48.** $9\overline{)130.5}$ **49.** $\frac{13.1}{10}$ **50.** $\frac{17.7}{10}$

51. $6.8\overline{)83.13}$ **52.** $4.8\overline{)123.72}$ **53.** $\frac{456.25}{10{,}000}$ **54.** $\frac{986.11}{10{,}000}$

Objective D *Solve. For Exercises 55 and 56, the solutions have been started for you. See Example 10.*

△ **55.** Josef Jones is painting the walls of a room. The walls have a total area of 546 square feet. A quart of paint covers 52 square feet. If he must buy paint in whole quarts, how many quarts does he need?

Start the solution:

1. UNDERSTAND the problem. Reread it as many times as needed.
2. TRANSLATE into an equation. (Fill in the blanks.)

number of quarts	is	square feet	divided by	square feet per quart
↓	↓	↓	↓	↓
number of quarts	=	____	÷	____

3. SOLVE. Don't forget to round up your quotient.
4. INTERPRET.

56. A shipping box can hold 36 books. If 486 books must be shipped, how many boxes are needed?

Start the solution:

1. UNDERSTAND the problem. Reread it as many times as needed.
2. TRANSLATE into an equation. (Fill in the blanks.)

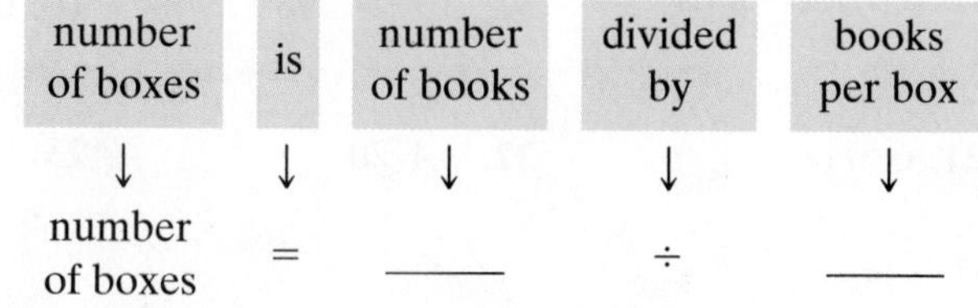

3. SOLVE. Don't forget to round up your quotient.
4. INTERPRET.

△ **57.** A pound of fertilizer covers 39 square feet of lawn. Vivian Bulgakov's lawn measures 7883.5 square feet. How much fertilizer, to the nearest tenth of a pound, does she need to buy?

58. A page of a book contains about 1.5 kilobytes of information. If a computer disk can hold 740 kilobytes of information, how many pages of a book can be stored on one computer disk? Round to the nearest tenth of a page.

59. There are approximately 39.37 inches in 1 meter. How many meters, to the nearest tenth of a meter, are there in 200 inches?

←1 meter→
←≈39.37 inches→

60. There are 2.54 centimeters in 1 inch. How many inches are there in 50 centimeters? Round to the nearest tenth.

← 1 inch →
← 2.54 cm →

61. In the United States, an average child will wear down 730 crayons by his or her tenth birthday. Find the number of boxes of 64 crayons this is equivalent to. Round to the nearest tenth. (*Source:* Binney & Smith Inc.)

62. During a recent year, American farmers received an average of \$47.20 per hundred pounds of turkey. What was the average price per pound for turkeys? Round to the nearest cent. (*Source:* National Agricultural Statistics Service)

A child is to receive a dose of 0.5 teaspoon of cough medicine every 4 hours. If the bottle contains 4 fluid ounces, answer Exercises 63 through 66.

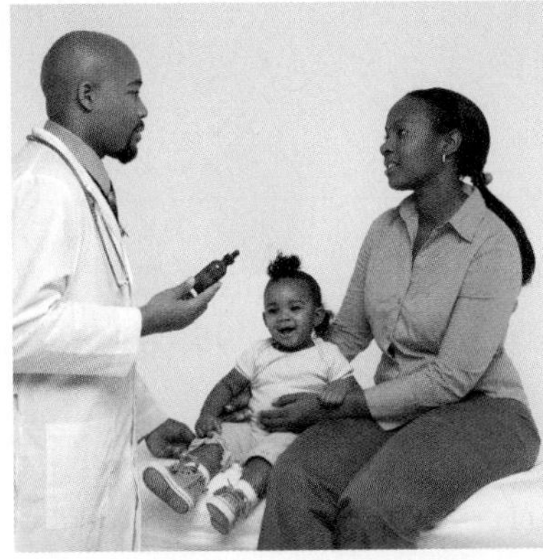

63. A fluid ounce equals 6 teaspoons. How many teaspoons are in 4 fluid ounces?

64. The bottle of medicine contains how many doses for the child? (*Hint:* See Exercise 63.)

65. If the child takes a dose every four hours, how many days will the medicine last?

66. If the child takes a dose every six hours, how many days will the medicine last?

67. Americans ages 18–22 drive, on average, 12,900 miles per year. About how many miles each week is that? Round to the nearest tenth. (*Note:* There are 52 weeks in a year.) (*Source:* U.S. Department of Energy)

68. Drake Saucier was interested in the gas mileage on his "new" used car. He filled the tank, drove 423.8 miles, and filled the tank again. When he refilled the tank, it took 19.35 gallons of gas. Calculate the miles per gallon for Drake's car. Round to the nearest tenth.

69. During the 24 hours of the Le Mans endurance auto race in 2009, the winning team of Marc Gene, Alexander Wurz, and David Brabham drove a total of 3230.4 miles in 24 hours. What was their average speed in miles per hour? (*Source:* Automobile Club de l'Ouest)

70. In 2008, Ethiopian runner Tirunesh Dibaba set a new world record for the women's 5000-meter event. Her time for the event was 851.15 seconds. What was her average speed in meters per second? Round to the nearest tenth. (*Source: USA Today*)

71. Candace Parker of the Los Angeles Sparks was the WNBA's Rookie of the Year for 2008. She scored a total of 610 points in the 33 games she played in the 2008 regular season. What was the average number of points she scored per game? Round to the nearest hundredth. (*Source:* Women's National Basketball Association)

72. During the 2008 National Football League regular season, the New Orleans Saints was the top-scoring team with a total of 463 points throughout the season. The Saints played 16 games. What was the average number of points the team scored per game? Round to the nearest hundredth. (*Source:* National Football League)

Objective **E** *Simplify each expression. See Examples 11 through 13.*

73. $0.7(6 - 2.5)$

74. $1.4(2 - 1.8)$

75. $\dfrac{0.29 + 1.69}{3}$

76. $\dfrac{1.697 - 0.29}{0.7}$

77. $30.03 + 5.1 \times 9.9$

78. $60 - 6.02 \times 8.97$

79. $7.8 - 4.83 \div 2.1 + 9.2$

80. $90 - 62.1 \div 2.7 + 8.6$

81. $93.07 \div 10 \times 100$

82. $35.04 \div 100 \times 10$

83. $\dfrac{7.8 + 1.1 \times 100 - 3.6}{0.2}$

84. $\dfrac{9.6 - 7.8 \div 10 + 1.2}{0.02}$

85. $5(20.6 - 2.06) - (0.8)^2$

86. $(10.6 - 9.8)^2 \div 0.01 + 8.6$

87. $6 \div 0.1 + 8.9 \times 10 - 4.6$

88. $8 \div 10 + 7.6 \times 0.1 - (0.1)^2$

Review

Write each decimal as a fraction. See Section 4.1.

89. 0.9

90. 0.7

91. 0.05

92. 0.08

Concept Extensions

Mixed Practice (*Sections 4.3, 4.4, 4.5*) *Perform the indicated operation.*

93. $1.278 \div 0.3$

94. 1.278×0.3

95. $1.278 + 0.3$

96. $1.278 - 0.3$

97. $\begin{array}{r} 8.6 \\ \times\ 3.1 \\ \hline \end{array}$

98. $7.2 + 0.05 + 49.1$

99. $\begin{array}{r} 1000 \\ -\ 95.71 \\ \hline \end{array}$

100. $\dfrac{87.2}{10{,}000}$

Choose the best estimate.

101. 8.62×41.7
a. 36
b. 32
c. 360
d. 3.6

102. $1.437 + 20.69$
a. 34
b. 22
c. 3.4
d. 2.2

103. $78.6 \div 97$
a. 7.86
b. 0.786
c. 786
d. 7860

104. $302.729 - 28.697$
a. 270
b. 20
c. 27
d. 300

Recall from Section 1.7 that the average of a list of numbers is their total divided by how many numbers there are in the list. Use this procedure to find the average of the test scores listed in Exercises 105 and 106. If necessary, round to the nearest tenth.

105. 86, 78, 91, 87

106. 56, 75, 80

△ **107.** The area of a rectangle is 38.7 square feet. If its width is 4.5 feet, find its length.

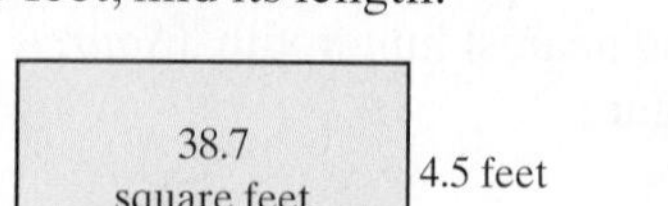

△ **108.** The perimeter of a square is 180.8 centimeters. Find the length of a side.

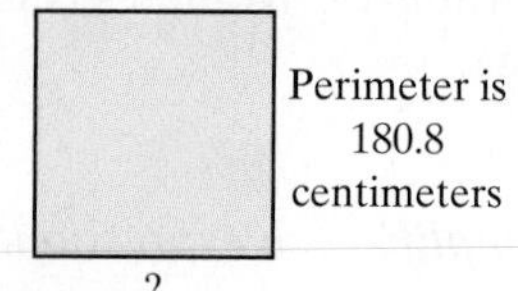

109. When dividing decimals, describe the process you use to place the decimal point in the quotient.

110. In your own words, describe how to quickly divide a number by a power of 10 such as 10, 100, 1000, etc.

To convert wind speeds in miles per hour to knots, divide by 1.15. Use this information and the Saffir-Simpson Hurricane Intensity chart below to answer Exercises 111 and 112. Round to the nearest tenth.

Saffir-Simpson Hurricane Intensity Scale

Category	Wind Speed	Barometric Pressure [inches of mercury (Hg)]	Storm Surge	Damage Potential
1 (Weak)	75–95 mph	≥28.94 in.	4–5 ft	Minimal damage to vegetation
2 (Moderate)	96–110 mph	28.50–28.93 in.	6–8 ft	Moderate damage to houses
3 (Strong)	111–130 mph	27.91–28.49 in.	9–12 ft	Extensive damage to small buildings
4 (Very Strong)	131–155 mph	27.17–27.90 in.	13–18 ft	Extreme structural damage
5 (Devastating)	>155 mph	<27.17 in.	>18 ft	Catastrophic building failures possible

111. The chart gives wind speeds in miles per hour. What is the range of wind speeds for a Category 1 hurricane in knots?

112. What is the range of wind speeds for a Category 4 hurricane in knots?

113. A rancher is building a horse corral that's shaped like a rectangle with dimensions of 24.28 meters by 15.675 meters. He plans to make a four-wire fence; that is, he will string four wires around the corral. How much wire will he need?

114. A college student signed up for a new credit card that guarantees her no interest charges on transferred balances for a year. She transferred over a $2523.86 balance from her old credit card. Her minimum payment is $185.35 per month. If she only pays the minimum, will she pay off her balance before interest charges start again?

Objectives

A **Write Fractions as Decimals.**

B **Compare Fractions and Decimals.**

C **Solve Area Problems Containing Fractions and Decimals.**

4.6 FRACTIONS AND DECIMALS

Objective A Writing Fractions as Decimals

To write a fraction as a decimal, we interpret the fraction bar to mean division and find the quotient.

Writing Fractions as Decimals

To write a fraction as a decimal, divide the numerator by the denominator.

PRACTICE 1

a. Write $\frac{2}{5}$ as a decimal.

b. Write $\frac{9}{40}$ as a decimal.

Example 1 Write $\frac{1}{4}$ as a decimal.

Solution: $\frac{1}{4} = 1 \div 4$

$$\begin{array}{r} 0.25 \\ 4\overline{)1.00} \\ -\ 8 \\ \hline 20 \\ -20 \\ \hline 0 \end{array}$$

Thus, $\frac{1}{4}$ written as a decimal is 0.25.

Work Practice 1

PRACTICE 2

a. Write $\frac{5}{6}$ as a decimal.

b. Write $\frac{2}{9}$ as a decimal.

Example 2 Write $\frac{2}{3}$ as a decimal.

Solution:

$$\begin{array}{rl} 0.666\ldots & \\ 3\overline{)2.000} & \text{This pattern will continue because } \frac{2}{3} = 0.6666\ldots \\ -1\,8 & \\ \hline 20 & \text{Remainder is 2, then 0 is brought down.} \\ -18 & \\ \hline 20 & \text{Remainder is 2, then 0 is brought down.} \\ -18 & \\ \hline 2 & \text{Remainder is 2.} \end{array}$$

Notice the digit 2 keeps occurring as the remainder. This will continue so that the digit 6 will keep repeating in the quotient. We place a bar over the digit 6 to indicate that it repeats.

$$\frac{2}{3} = 0.666\ldots = 0.\overline{6}$$

We can also write a decimal approximation for $\frac{2}{3}$. For example, $\frac{2}{3}$ rounded to the nearest hundredth is 0.67. This can be written as $\frac{2}{3} \approx 0.67$.

Work Practice 2

Answers

1. a. 0.4 **b.** 0.225

2. a. $0.8\overline{3}$ **b.** $0.\overline{2}$

Example 3 Write $\frac{22}{7}$ as a decimal. (The fraction $\frac{22}{7}$ is an approximation for π.) Round to the nearest hundredth.

Solution:

$$\begin{array}{r} 3.142 \\ 7\overline{)22.000} \\ -21 \\ \hline 1\,0 \\ -7 \\ \hline 30 \\ -28 \\ \hline 20 \\ -14 \\ \hline 6 \end{array} \approx 3.14$$

Carry the division out to the thousandths place.

The fraction $\frac{22}{7}$ in decimal form is approximately 3.14. Thus, $\pi \approx \frac{22}{7}$ (a fraction approximation for π) and $\pi \approx 3.14$ (a decimal approximation for π).

Work Practice 3

PRACTICE 3

Write $\frac{28}{13}$ as a decimal. Round to the nearest thousandth.

Example 4 Write $2\frac{3}{16}$ as a decimal.

Solution:

Option 1. Write the fractional part only as a decimal.

$$\frac{3}{16} \longrightarrow \begin{array}{r} 0.1875 \\ 16\overline{)3.0000} \\ -1\,6 \\ \hline 1\,40 \\ -1\,28 \\ \hline 120 \\ -112 \\ \hline 80 \\ -80 \\ \hline 0 \end{array}$$

Thus $2\frac{3}{16} = 2.1875$

Option 2. Write $2\frac{3}{16}$ as an improper fraction, and divide.

$$2\frac{3}{16} = \frac{35}{16} \longrightarrow \begin{array}{r} 2.1875 \\ 16\overline{)35.0000} \\ -32 \\ \hline 3\,0 \\ -1\,6 \\ \hline 1\,40 \\ -1\,28 \\ \hline 120 \\ -112 \\ \hline 80 \\ -80 \\ \hline 0 \end{array}$$

Thus $2\frac{3}{16} = 2.1875$

Work Practice 4

PRACTICE 4

Write $3\frac{5}{16}$ as a decimal.

Some fractions may be written as decimals using our knowledge of decimals. From Section 4.1, we know that if the denominator of a fraction is 10, 100, 1000, or so on, we can immediately write the fraction as a decimal. For example,

$$\frac{4}{10} = 0.4, \quad \frac{12}{100} = 0.12, \text{ and so on.}$$

Answers
3. 2.154 **4.** 3.3125

PRACTICE 5

Write $\frac{3}{5}$ as a decimal.

Example 5 Write $\frac{4}{5}$ as a decimal.

Solution: Let's write $\frac{4}{5}$ as an equivalent fraction with a denominator of 10.

$$\frac{4}{5} = \frac{4}{5} \cdot \frac{2}{2} = \frac{8}{10} = 0.8$$

Work Practice 5

PRACTICE 6

Write $\frac{3}{50}$ as a decimal.

Example 6 Write $\frac{1}{25}$ as a decimal.

Solution: $\frac{1}{25} = \frac{1}{25} \cdot \frac{4}{4} = \frac{4}{100} = 0.04$

Work Practice 6

✓**Concept Check** Suppose you are writing the fraction $\frac{9}{16}$ as a decimal. How do you know you have made a mistake if your answer is 1.735?

Objective B Comparing Fractions and Decimals

Now we can compare decimals and fractions by writing fractions as equivalent decimals.

PRACTICE 7

Insert <, >, or = to form a true statement.

$\frac{1}{5}$ 0.25

Example 7 Insert <, >, or = to form a true statement.

$\frac{1}{8}$ 0.12

Solution: First we write $\frac{1}{8}$ as an equivalent decimal. Then we compare decimal places.

$$\begin{array}{r} 0.125 \\ 8\overline{)1.000} \\ -8 \\ \hline 20 \\ -16 \\ \hline 40 \\ -40 \\ \hline 0 \end{array}$$

Original numbers	$\frac{1}{8}$	0.12
Decimals	0.125	0.120
Compare	0.125 > 0.12	

Thus, $\frac{1}{8} > 0.12$

Work Practice 7

PRACTICE 8

Insert <, >, or = to form a true statement.

a. $\frac{1}{2}$ 0.54 **b.** $0.\overline{4}$ $\frac{4}{9}$

c. $\frac{5}{7}$ 0.72

Example 8 Insert <, >, or = to form a true statement.

$0.\overline{7}$ $\frac{7}{9}$

Solution: We write $\frac{7}{9}$ as a decimal and then compare.

$$\begin{array}{r} 0.77\ldots = 0.\overline{7} \\ 9\overline{)7.00} \\ -6\,3 \\ \hline 70 \\ -63 \\ \hline 7 \end{array}$$

Original numbers	$0.\overline{7}$	$\frac{7}{9}$
Decimals	$0.\overline{7}$	$0.\overline{7}$
Compare	$0.\overline{7} = 0.\overline{7}$	

Thus, $0.\overline{7} = \frac{7}{9}$

Work Practice 8

Answers

5. 0.6 **6.** 0.06 **7.** <
8. a. < **b.** = **c.** <

✓**Concept Check Answer**

$\frac{9}{16}$ is less than 1 while 1.735 is greater than 1.

Example 9 Write the numbers in order from smallest to largest.

$\frac{9}{20}, \frac{4}{9}, 0.456$

Solution:

Original numbers	$\frac{9}{20}$	$\frac{4}{9}$	0.456
Decimals	0.450	0.444...	0.456
Compare in order	2nd	1st	3rd

Written in order, we have

1st 2nd 3rd
↓ ↓ ↓
$\frac{4}{9}, \frac{9}{20}, 0.456$

Work Practice 9

PRACTICE 9

Write the numbers in order from smallest to largest.

a. $\frac{1}{3}, 0.302, \frac{3}{8}$ **b.** $1.26, 1\frac{1}{4}, 1\frac{2}{5}$

c. $0.4, 0.41, \frac{5}{7}$

Objective C Solving Area Problems Containing Fractions and Decimals

Sometimes real-life problems contain both fractions and decimals. In this section, we solve such problems concerning area. In the next example, we review the area of a triangle. This concept will be studied more in depth in a later chapter.

Example 10 The area of a triangle is Area $= \frac{1}{2} \cdot \text{base} \cdot \text{height}$. Find the area of the triangle shown.

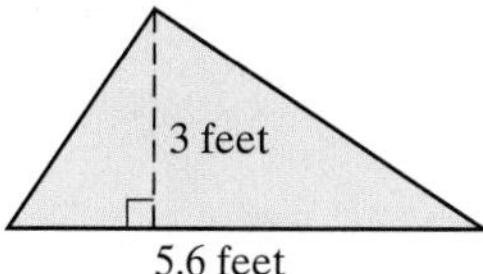

Solution:

$$\begin{aligned} \text{Area} &= \frac{1}{2} \cdot \text{base} \cdot \text{height} \\ &= \frac{1}{2} \cdot 5.6 \cdot 3 \\ &= 0.5 \cdot 5.6 \cdot 3 \quad \text{Write } \frac{1}{2} \text{ as the decimal 0.5.} \\ &= 8.4 \end{aligned}$$

The area of the triangle is 8.4 square feet.

Work Practice 10

PRACTICE 10

Find the area of the triangle.

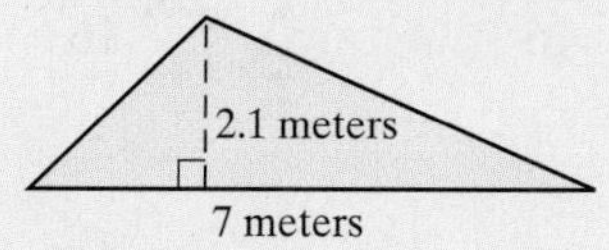

Answers

9. a. $0.302, \frac{1}{3}, \frac{3}{8}$ **b.** $1\frac{1}{4}, 1.26, 1\frac{2}{5}$ **c.** $0.4, 0.41, \frac{5}{7}$ **10.** 7.35 sq m

Vocabulary and Readiness Check

Answer each exercise "true" or "false."

1. The number $0.\overline{5}$ means 0.555.
2. To write $\frac{9}{19}$ as a decimal, perform the division $9\overline{)19}$.
3. $(1.2)^2$ means (1.2)(1.2) or 1.44.
4. To simplify $8.6(9.6 - 4.8)$, we first subtract.

4.6 Exercise Set

FOR EXTRA HELP

MyMathLab

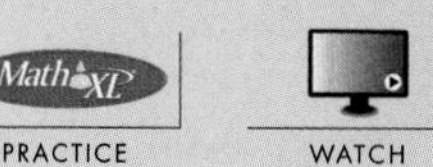

PRACTICE WATCH DOWNLOAD READ REVIEW

Objective A *Write each number as a decimal. See Examples 1 through 6.*

1. $\frac{1}{5}$ **2.** $\frac{1}{20}$ **3.** $\frac{17}{25}$ **4.** $\frac{13}{25}$ **5.** $\frac{3}{4}$ **6.** $\frac{3}{8}$

7. $\frac{2}{25}$ **8.** $\frac{3}{25}$ **9.** $\frac{6}{5}$ **10.** $\frac{5}{4}$ **11.** $\frac{11}{12}$ **12.** $\frac{5}{12}$

13. $\frac{17}{40}$ **14.** $\frac{19}{25}$ **15.** $\frac{9}{20}$ **16.** $\frac{31}{40}$ **17.** $\frac{1}{3}$ **18.** $\frac{7}{9}$

19. $\frac{7}{16}$ **20.** $\frac{9}{16}$ **21.** $\frac{7}{11}$ **22.** $\frac{9}{11}$ **23.** $5\frac{17}{20}$ **24.** $4\frac{7}{8}$

25. $\frac{78}{125}$ **26.** $\frac{159}{375}$

Round each number as indicated.

27. Round your decimal answer to Exercise 17 to the nearest hundredth.

28. Round your decimal answer to Exercise 18 to the nearest hundredth.

29. Round your decimal answer to Exercise 19 to the nearest hundredth.

30. Round your decimal answer to Exercise 20 to the nearest hundredth.

31. Round your decimal answer to Exercise 21 to the nearest tenth.

32. Round your decimal answer to Exercise 22 to the nearest tenth.

Write each fraction as a decimal. If necessary, round to the nearest hundredth.

33. Of the U.S. mountains that are over 14,000 feet in elevation, $\frac{56}{91}$ are located in Colorado. (*Source:* U.S. Geological Survey)

34. About $\frac{21}{50}$ of all blood donors have type A blood. (*Source:* American Red Cross Biomedical Services)

35. The United States contains the greatest fraction of people who use the Internet, with about $\frac{71}{97}$ people using it. (*Source:* UCLA Center for Communication Policy)

36. By 2008, $\frac{39}{62}$ of all individuals who had flown in space were citizens of the United States. (*Source:* World Spaceflight)

37. When first launched, the Hubble Space Telescope's primary mirror was out of shape on the edges by $\frac{1}{50}$ of a human hair. This very small defect made it difficult to focus on faint objects being viewed. Because the HST was in low Earth orbit, it was serviced by a shuttle and the defect was corrected.

38. The two mirrors currently in use in the Hubble Space Telescope were ground so that they do not deviate from a perfect curve by more than $\frac{1}{800{,}000}$ of an inch. Do not round this number.

Objective **B** *Insert <, >, or = to form a true statement. See Examples 7 and 8.*

39. 0.562 0.569

40. 0.983 0.988

41. 0.215 $\frac{43}{200}$

42. $\frac{29}{40}$ 0.725

43. $\frac{9}{100}$ 0.0932

44. $\frac{1}{200}$ 0.00563

45. $0.\overline{6}$ $\frac{5}{6}$

46. $0.\overline{1}$ $\frac{2}{17}$

47. $\frac{51}{91}$ $0.56\overline{4}$

48. $0.58\overline{3}$ $\frac{6}{11}$

49. $\frac{1}{9}$ 0.1

50. 0.6 $\frac{2}{3}$

51. 1.38 $\frac{18}{13}$

52. 0.372 $\frac{22}{59}$

53. 7.123 $\frac{456}{64}$

54. 12.713 $\frac{89}{7}$

Write the numbers in order from smallest to largest. See Example 9.

55. 0.34, 0.35, 0.32

56. 0.47, 0.42, 0.40

57. 0.49, 0.491, 0.498

58. 0.72, 0.727, 0.728

59. $\frac{3}{4}$, 0.78, 0.73

60. $\frac{2}{5}$, 0.49, 0.42

61. $\frac{4}{7}$, 0.453, 0.412

62. $\frac{6}{9}$, 0.663, 0.668

63. 5.23, $\frac{42}{8}$, 5.34

64. 7.56, $\frac{67}{9}$, 7.562

65. $\frac{12}{5}$, 2.37, $\frac{17}{8}$

66. $\frac{29}{16}$, 1.75, $\frac{59}{32}$

Objective C *Find the area of each triangle or rectangle. See Example 10.*

△ **67.**

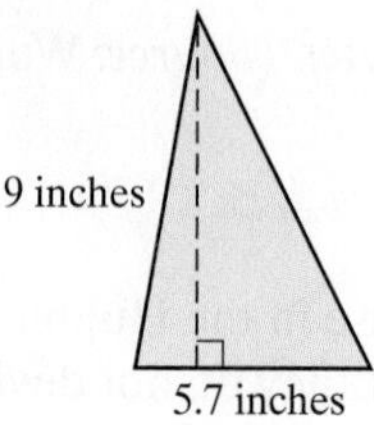

△ **68.**

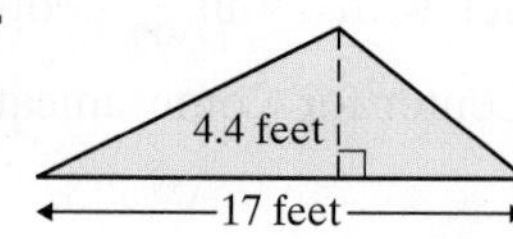

△ **69.**

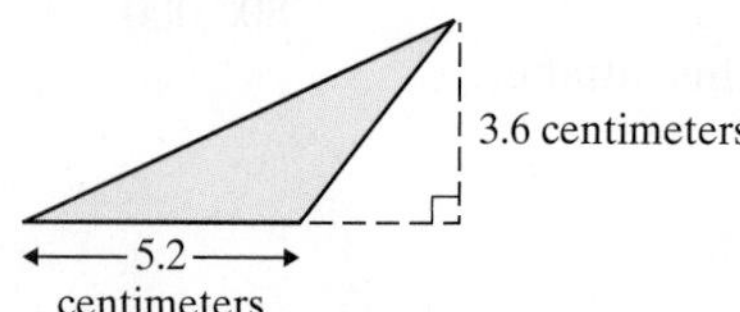

△ **70.**

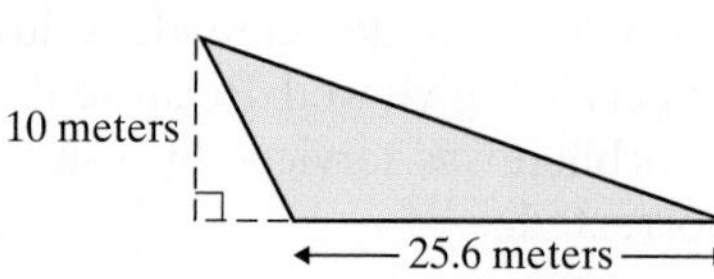

△ **71.**

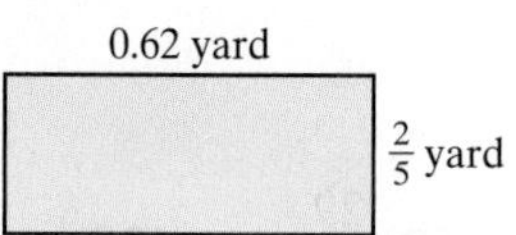

△ **72.**

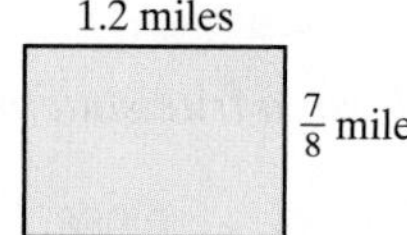

Review

Simplify. See Sections 1.9 and 3.5.

73. 2^3

74. 5^4

75. $6^2 \cdot 2$

76. $4 \cdot 3^4$

77. $\left(\frac{1}{3}\right)^4$

78. $\left(\frac{4}{5}\right)^3$

79. $\left(\frac{3}{5}\right)^2$

80. $\left(\frac{7}{2}\right)^2$

81. $\left(\frac{2}{5}\right)\left(\frac{5}{2}\right)^2$

82. $\left(\frac{2}{3}\right)^2\left(\frac{3}{2}\right)^3$

Concept Extensions

Without calculating, describe each number as < 1, $= 1$, *or* > 1. *See the Concept Check in this section.*

83. 1.0

84. 1.0000

85. 1.00001

86. $\frac{101}{99}$

87. $\frac{99}{100}$

88. $\frac{99}{99}$

In 2009, there were 13,750 commercial radio stations in the United States. The most popular formats are listed in the table along with their counts. Use this graph to answer Exercises 89–92.

89. Write the fraction of radio stations with a country music format as a decimal. Round to the nearest thousandth.

90. Write the fraction of radio stations with a news/talk format as a decimal. Round to the nearest hundredth.

91. Estimate, by rounding each number in the table to the nearest hundred, the total number of stations with the top six formats in 2009.

92. Use your estimate from Exercise 91 to write the fraction of radio stations accounted for by the top six formats as a decimal. Round to the nearest hundredth.

Top Commercial Radio Station Formats in 2009

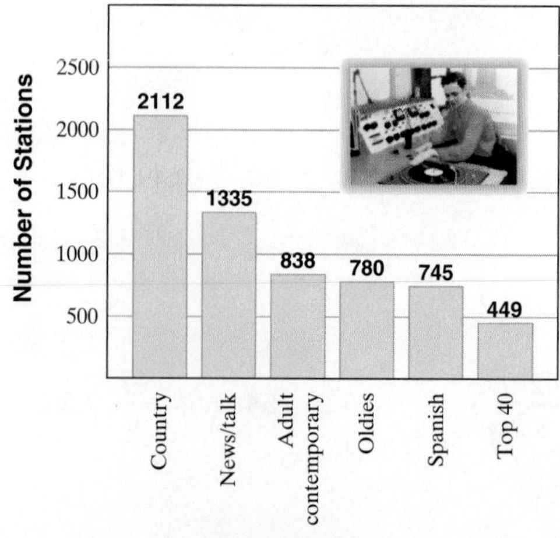

Format (Total stations: 13,750)

93. Describe two ways to determine the larger of two fractions.

94. Describe two ways to write fractions as decimals.

95. Describe two ways to write mixed numbers as decimals.

96. Do you prefer performing operations on decimals or fractions? Why?

Find the value of each expression. Give the result as a decimal.

97. $(9.6)(5) - \frac{3}{4}$

98. $2(7.8) - \frac{1}{5}$

99. $\left(\frac{1}{10}\right)^2 + (1.6)(2.1)$

100. $8.25 - \left(\frac{1}{2}\right)^2$

101. $\frac{3}{8}(5.9 - 4.7)$

102. $\frac{1}{4}(9.6 + 5.2)$

Chapter 4 Group Activity

Maintaining a Checking Account (Sections 4.1, 4.2, 4.3, 4.4)

This activity may be completed by working in groups or individually.

A checking account is a convenient way of handling money and paying bills. To open a checking account, the bank or savings and loan association requires a customer to make a deposit. Then the customer receives a checkbook that contains checks, deposit slips, and a register for recording checks written and deposits made. It is important to record all payments and deposits that affect the account. It is also important to keep the checkbook balance current by subtracting checks written and adding deposits made.

About once a month checking customers receive a statement from the bank listing all activity that the account has had in the last month. The statement lists a beginning balance, all checks and deposits, any service charges made against the account, and an ending balance. Because it may take several days for checks that a customer has written to clear the banking system, the check register may list checks that do not appear on the monthly bank statement. These checks are called **outstanding checks.** Deposits that are recorded in the check register but do not appear on the statement are called **deposits in transit.** Because of these differences, it is important to balance, or reconcile, the checkbook against the monthly statement. The steps for doing so are listed below.

Balancing or Reconciling a Checkbook

Step 1: Place a check mark in the checkbook register next to each check and deposit listed on the monthly bank statement. Any entries in the register without a check mark are outstanding checks or deposits in transit.

Step 2: Find the ending checkbook register balance and add to it any outstanding checks and any interest paid on the account.

Step 3: From the total in Step 2, subtract any deposits in transit and any service charges.

Step 4: Compare the amount found in Step 3 with the ending balance listed on the bank statement. If they are the same, the checkbook balances with the bank statement. Be sure to update the check register with service charges and interest.

Step 5: If the checkbook does not balance, recheck the balancing process. Next, make sure that the running checkbook register balance was calculated correctly. Finally, compare the checkbook register with the statement to make sure that each check was recorded for the correct amount.

For the checkbook register and monthly bank statement given:

a. *update the checkbook register* **b.** *list the outstanding checks and deposits in transit*

c. *balance the checkbook—be sure to update the register with any interest or service fees*

Checkbook Register

#	Date	Description	Payment	✓	Deposit	Balance 425.86
114	4/1	Market Basket	30.27			
115	4/3	May's Texaco	8.50			
	4/4	Cash at ATM	50.00			
116	4/6	UNO Bookstore	121.38			
	4/7	Deposit			100.00	
117	4/9	MasterCard	84.16			
118	4/10	Blockbuster	6.12			
119	4/12	Kroger	18.72			
120	4/14	Parking sticker	18.50			
	4/15	Direct deposit			294.36	
121	4/20	Rent	395.00			
122	4/25	Student fees	20.00			
	4/28	Deposit			75.00	

First National Bank Monthly Statement 4/30

BEGINNING BALANCE:		425.86
Date	Number	Amount
CHECKS AND ATM WITHDRAWALS		
4/3	114	30.27
4/4	ATM	50.00
4/11	117	84.16
4/13	115	8.50
4/15	119	18.72
4/22	121	395.00
DEPOSITS		
4/7		100.00
4/15	Direct deposit	294.36
SERVICE CHARGES		
Low balance fee		7.50
INTEREST		
Credited 4/30		1.15
ENDING BALANCE:		227.22

Chapter 4 Vocabulary Check

Fill in each blank with one of the choices listed below. Some choices may be used more than once or not at all.

vertically	decimal	and	right triangle	diameter
standard form	product	quotient	circumference	difference
sum	denominator	numerator		

1. Like fractional notation, ________________ notation is used to denote a part of a whole.
2. To write fractions as decimals, divide the ________________ by the ________________.
3. To add or subtract decimals, write the decimals so that the decimal points line up ________________.
4. When writing decimals in words, write " ________________ " for the decimal point.
5. When multiplying decimals, the decimal point in the product is placed so that the number of decimal places in the product is equal to the ________________ of the number of decimal places in the factors.
6. The distance around a circle is called the ________________.
7. When 2 million is written as 2,000,000, we say it is written in ________________.
8. $\pi = \dfrac{\text{\_\_\_\_\_\_\_\_\_\_ of a circle}}{\text{\_\_\_\_\_\_\_\_\_\_ of the same circle}}$
9. In $3.4 - 2 = 1.4$, the number 1.4 is called the ________________.
10. In $3.4 \div 2 = 1.7$, the 1.7 is called the ________________.
11. In $3.4 \times 2 = 6.8$, the 6.8 is called the ________________.
12. In $3.4 + 2 = 5.4$, the 5.4 is called the ________________.

Helpful Hint Are you preparing for your test? Don't forget to take the Chapter 4 Test on page 314. Then check your answers at the back of the text and use the Chapter Test Prep Videos to see the fully worked-out solutions to any of the exercises you want to review.

4 Chapter Highlights

Definitions and Concepts	Examples

Section 4.1 Introduction to Decimals

PLACE-VALUE CHART

____	____	4	.	2	6	5	____	____
hundreds	tens	ones	↑	tenths	hundredths	thousandths	ten-thousandths	hundred-thousandths
100	10	1	decimal point	$\frac{1}{10}$	$\frac{1}{100}$	$\frac{1}{1000}$	$\frac{1}{10,000}$	$\frac{1}{100,000}$

4.265 means

$$4\cdot 1 + 2\cdot\frac{1}{10} + 6\cdot\frac{1}{100} + 5\cdot\frac{1}{1000}$$

or

$$4 + \frac{2}{10} + \frac{6}{100} + \frac{5}{1000}$$

(continued)

Definitions and Concepts	Examples
Section 4.1 Introduction to Decimals (*continued*)	
WRITING (OR READING) A DECIMAL IN WORDS **Step 1:** Write the whole number part in words. **Step 2:** Write "and" for the decimal point. **Step 3:** Write the decimal part in words as though it were a whole number, followed by the place value of the last digit.	Write 3.08 in words. Three and eight hundredths
A decimal written in words can be written in standard form by reversing the above procedure.	Write "four and twenty-one thousandths" in standard form. 4.021
Section 4.2 Order and Rounding	
To **compare decimals,** compare digits in the same place from left to right. When two digits are not equal, the number with the larger digit is the larger decimal.	3.0261 > 3.0186 because ↑ ↑ 2 > 1
TO ROUND DECIMALS TO A PLACE VALUE TO THE RIGHT OF THE DECIMAL POINT **Step 1:** Locate the digit to the right of the given place value. **Step 2:** If this digit is 5 or greater, add 1 to the digit in the given place value and delete all digits to its right. If this digit is less than 5, delete all digits to the right of the given place value.	Round 86.1256 to the nearest hundredth. hundredths place **Step 1:** 86.12(5)6 digit to the right **Step 2:** Since the digit to the right is 5 or greater, we add 1 to the digit in the hundredths place and delete all digits to its right. 86.1256 rounded to the nearest hundredth is 86.13.
Section 4.3 Adding and Subtracting Decimals	
TO ADD OR SUBTRACT DECIMALS **Step 1:** Write the decimals so that the decimal points line up vertically. **Step 2:** Add or subtract as with whole numbers. **Step 3:** Place the decimal point in the sum or difference so that it lines up vertically with the decimal points in the problem.	Add: $4.6 + 0.28$ 4.60 +0.28 4.88 Subtract: $2.8 - 1.04$ 7 10 2.80 − 1.04 1.76
Section 4.4 Multiplying Decimals and Circumference of a Circle	
TO MULTIPLY DECIMALS **Step 1:** Multiply the decimals as though they are whole numbers. **Step 2:** The decimal point in the product is placed so that the number of decimal places in the product is equal to the *sum* of the number of decimal places in the factors.	Multiply: 1.48×5.9 1.48 ← 2 decimal places × 5.9 ← 1 decimal place 1332 7400 8.732 ← 3 decimal places
The **circumference** of a circle is the distance around the circe. 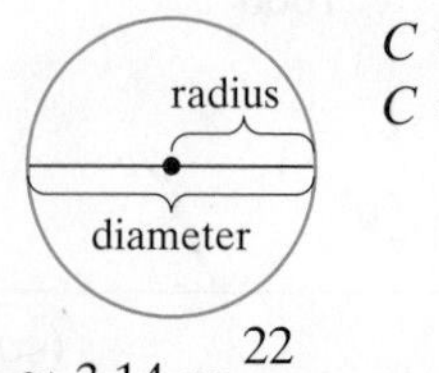 $C = 2 \cdot \pi \cdot \text{radius}$ or $C = \pi \cdot \text{diameter}$, where $\pi \approx 3.14$ or $\frac{22}{7}$.	Find the exact circumference of a circle with radius 5 miles and an approximation by using 3.14 for π. $C = 2 \cdot \pi \cdot \text{radius}$ $= 2 \cdot \pi \cdot 5$ $= 10\pi$ $\approx 10(3.14)$ $= 31.4$ The circumference is exactly 10π miles and *approximately* 31.4 miles.

Definitions and Concepts	Examples
Section 4.5 Dividing Decimals and Order of Operations	
To Divide Decimals **Step 1:** If the divisor is not a whole number, move the decimal point in the divisor to the right until the divisor is a whole number. **Step 2:** Move the decimal point in the dividend to the right the *same number of places* as the decimal point was moved in step 1. **Step 3:** Divide. The decimal point in the quotient is directly over the moved decimal point in the dividend.	Divide: $1.118 \div 2.6$ $2.6\overline{)1.118}$ = 0.43 -104 78 -78 0
Order of Operations 1. Perform all operations within parentheses ( ), brackets [ ], or grouping symbols such as square roots or fraction bars. 2. Evaluate any expressions with exponents. 3. Multiply or divide in order from left to right. 4. Add or subtract in order from left to right.	Simplify. $1.9(12.8 - 4.1) = 1.9(8.7)$ Subtract. $= 16.53$ Multiply.
Section 4.6 Fractions and Decimals	
To **write fractions as decimals,** divide the numerator by the denominator.	Write $\frac{3}{8}$ as a decimal. $8\overline{)3.000}$ = 0.375 -24 60 -56 40 -40 0

Chapter 4 Review

(4.1) *Determine the place value of the digit 4 in each decimal.*

1. 23.45

2. 0.000345

Write each decimal in words.

3. 0.45

4. 0.00345

5. 109.23

6. 46.007

Write each decimal in standard form.

7. Two and fifteen hundredths

8. Five hundred three and one hundred two thousandths

Write the decimal as a fraction or a mixed number. Write your answer in simplest form.

9. 0.16

10. 12.023

11. 1.0045

12. 25.25

Write each fraction as a decimal.

13. $\frac{9}{10}$

14. $\frac{25}{100}$

15. $\frac{45}{1000}$

16. $\frac{261}{10}$

(4.2) *Insert $<$, $>$, or $=$ to make a true statement.*

17. 0.49 0.43

18. 0.973 0.9730

Write the decimals in order from smallest to largest.

19. 8.6, 8.09, 0.92

20. 0.09, 0.1, 0.091

Round each decimal to the given place value.

21. 0.623, nearest tenth

22. 0.9384, nearest hundredth

Round each money amount to the nearest cent.

23. \$0.259

24. \$12.461

Solve.

25. In a recent year, engaged couples in the United States spent an average of \$31,304.35 on their wedding. Round this number to the nearest whole dollar.

26. A certain kind of chocolate candy bar contains 10.75 teaspoons of sugar. Write this number as a mixed number.

(4.3) *Add or subtract as indicated.*

27. 2.4 + 7.12

28. 3.9 − 1.2

29. 6.4 + 0.88

30. 19.02 + 6.98 + 0.007

31. 892.1 − 432.4

32. 100.342 − 0.064

33. Subtract 34.98 from 100.

34. Subtract 10.02 from 200.

35. Find the total distance between Grove City and Jerome.

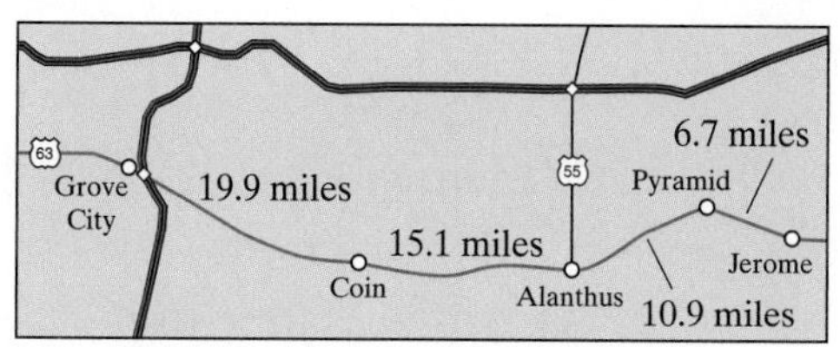

36. The price of oil was $49.02 per barrel on October 23. It was $51.46 on October 24. Find by how much the price of oil increased from the 23rd to the 24th.

△ **37.** Find the perimeter.

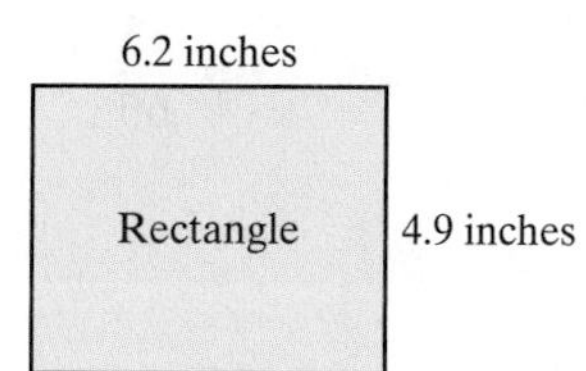

△ **38.** Find the perimeter.

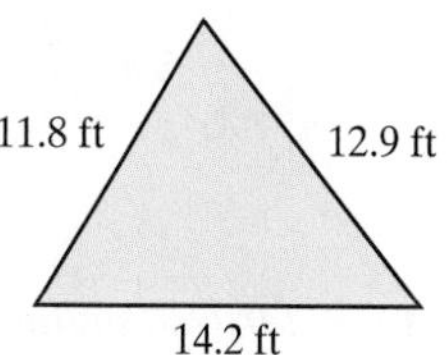

(4.4) *Multiply.*

39. $\begin{array}{r} 3.7 \\ \times\ 5 \\ \hline \end{array}$

40. $\begin{array}{r} 9.1 \\ \times\ 6 \\ \hline \end{array}$

41. 7.2 × 10

42. 9.345 × 1000

43. $\begin{array}{r} 4.02 \\ \times\ 2.3 \\ \hline \end{array}$

44. $\begin{array}{r} 39.02 \\ \times\ 87.3 \\ \hline \end{array}$

Solve.

△ **45.** Find the exact circumference of the circle. Then use the approximation 3.14 for π and approximate the circumference.

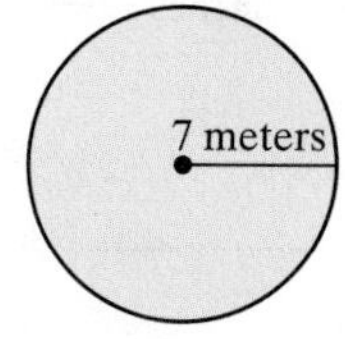

46. A kilometer is approximately 0.625 mile. It is 102 kilometers from Hays to Colby. Write 102 kilometers in miles to the nearest tenth of a mile.

Write each number in standard notation.

47. Saturn is a distance of about 887 million miles from the Sun.

48. The tail of a comet can be over 600 thousand miles long.

(4.5) *Divide. Round the quotient to the nearest thousandth if necessary.*

49. $3\overline{)0.2631}$

50. $20\overline{)316.5}$

51. 21 ÷ 0.3

52. 0.0063 ÷ 0.03

53. $0.34\overline{)2.74}$

54. $19.8\overline{)601.92}$

55. $\frac{2.67}{100}$

56. $\frac{93}{10}$

57. There are approximately 3.28 feet in 1 meter. Find how many meters are in 24 feet to the nearest tenth of a meter.

1 meter

≈3.28 feet

58. George Strait pays $69.71 per month to pay back a loan of $3136.95. In how many months will the loan be paid off?

Simplify each expression.

59. $7.6 \times 1.9 + 2.5$

60. $(2.3)^2 - 1.4$

61. $\frac{7 + 0.74}{0.06}$

62. $\frac{(1.5)^2 + 0.5}{0.05}$

63. $0.9(6.5 - 5.6)$

64. $0.0726 \div 10 \times 1000$

(4.6) *Write each fraction as a decimal. Round to the nearest thousandth if necessary.*

65. $\frac{4}{5}$

66. $\frac{12}{13}$

67. $2\frac{1}{3}$

68. $\frac{13}{60}$

Insert <, >, or = to make a true statement.

69. 0.392 0.3920

70. $0.\overline{4}$ $\frac{4}{9}$

71. 0.293 $\frac{5}{17}$

72. $\frac{4}{7}$ 0.625

Write the numbers in order from smallest to largest.

73. $0.839, \frac{17}{20}, 0.837$

74. $\frac{18}{11}, 1.63, \frac{19}{12}$

Find each area.

75.

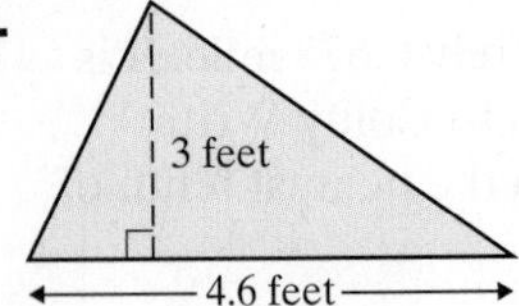

76.

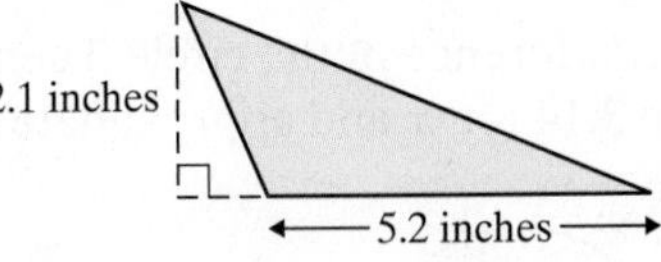

Mixed Review

77. Write 200.0032 in words.

78. Write sixteen thousand twenty-five and fourteen thousandths in standard form.

79. Write 0.00231 as a fraction or a mixed number.

80. Write the numbers $\frac{6}{7}, \frac{8}{9}$, 0.75 in order from smallest to largest.

Write each fraction as a decimal. Round to the nearest thousandth, if necessary.

81. $\frac{7}{100}$

82. $\frac{9}{80}$ (Do not round.)

83. $\frac{8935}{175}$

Insert <, >, or = to make a true statement.

84. 402.00032 402.000032

85. 0.230505 0.23505

86. $\frac{6}{11}$ 0.55

Round each decimal to the given place value.

87. 42.895, nearest hundredth

88. 16.34925, nearest thousandth

Round each money amount to the nearest dollar.

89. \$123.46

90. \$3645.52

Add or subtract as indicated.

91. $4.9 - 3.2$

92. $5.23 - 2.74$

93. $200.49 + 16.82 + 103.002$

94. $0.00236 + 100.45 + 48.29$

Multiply or divide as indicated. Round to the nearest thousandth, if necessary.

95. $\begin{array}{r} 2.54 \\ \times\ 3.2 \\ \hline \end{array}$

96. $\begin{array}{r} 3.45 \\ \times\ 2.1 \\ \hline \end{array}$

97. $0.005\overline{)24.5}$

98. $2.3\overline{)54.98}$

Solve.

△ **99.** Tomaso is going to fertilize his lawn, a rectangle that measures 77.3 feet by 115.9 feet. Approximate the area of the lawn by rounding each measurement to the nearest ten feet.

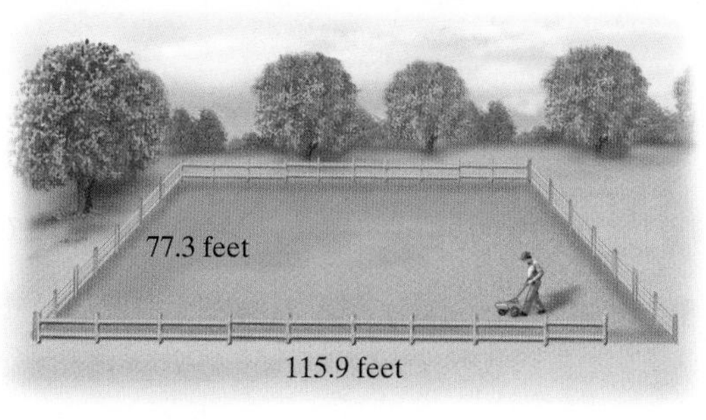

100. Estimate the cost of the items to see whether the groceries can be purchased with a \$5 bill.

Simplify each expression.

101. $\frac{(3.2)^2}{100}$

102. $(2.6 + 1.4)(4.5 - 3.6)$

Chapter 4 Test

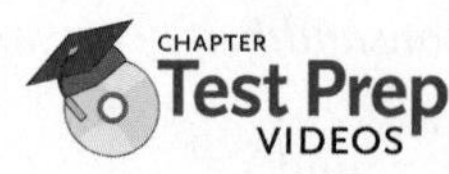

Step-by-step test solutions are found on the Chapter Test Prep Videos available via the Interactive DVD Lecture Series, in MyMathLab or on YouTube (search "MartinGayBasicMath" and click on "Channels").

Answers

1. ______

2. ______

3. ______

4. ______

5. ______

6. ______

7. ______

8. ______

9. ______

10. ______

11. ______

12. ______

13. ______

14. ______

15. ______

16. ______

17. ______

Write the decimal as indicated.

1. 45.092, in words

2. Three thousand and fifty-nine thousandths, in standard form

Round the decimal to the indicated place value.

3. 34.8923, nearest tenth

4. 0.8623, nearest thousandth

5. Insert <, >, or = to make a true statement. 25.0909 25.9090

6. Write the numbers in order from smallest to largest. $\frac{4}{9}$ 0.454 0.445

Write the decimal as a fraction or a mixed number in simplest form.

7. 0.345

8. 24.73

Write the fraction or mixed number as a decimal. If necessary, round to the nearest thousandth.

9. $\frac{13}{20}$

10. $5\frac{8}{9}$

11. $\frac{16}{17}$

Perform the indicated operations. Round the result to the nearest thousandth if necessary.

12. 2.893 + 4.2 + 10.49

13. Subtract 8.6 from 20.

14. $\begin{array}{r} 10.2 \\ \times\ 4.3 \\ \hline \end{array}$

15. $0.23\overline{)12.88}$

16. $\begin{array}{r} 0.165 \\ \times\ 0.47 \\ \hline \end{array}$

17. $7\overline{)46.71}$

18. 126.9×100

19. $\dfrac{47.3}{10}$

18. ______________

20. $0.3[1.57 - (0.6)^2]$

21. $\dfrac{0.23 + 1.63}{0.3}$

19. ______________

22. At its farthest, Pluto is 4,583 million miles from the Sun. Write this number using standard notation.

20. 

△ **23.** Find the area.

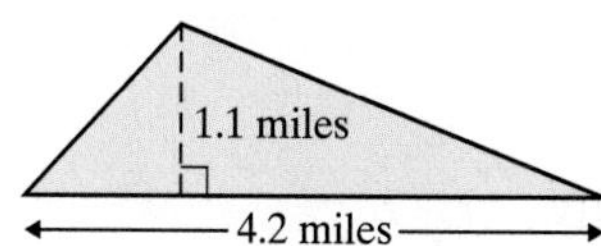

△ **24.** Find the exact circumference of the circle. Then use the approximation 3.14 for π and approximate the circumference.

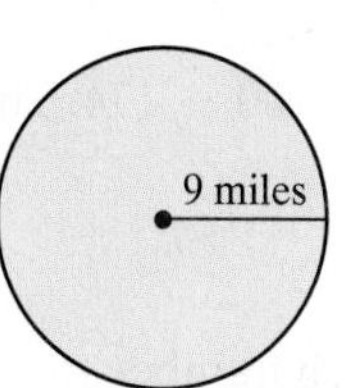

21. ______________

22. ______________

23. ______________

25. Vivian Thomas is going to put insecticide on her lawn to control grubworms. The lawn is a rectangle that measures 123.8 feet by 80 feet. The amount of insecticide required is 0.02 ounces per square foot.

a. Find the area of her lawn.

b. Find how much insecticide Vivian needs to purchase.

24. ______________

25. a. ______________

26. Find the total distance from Bayette to Center City.

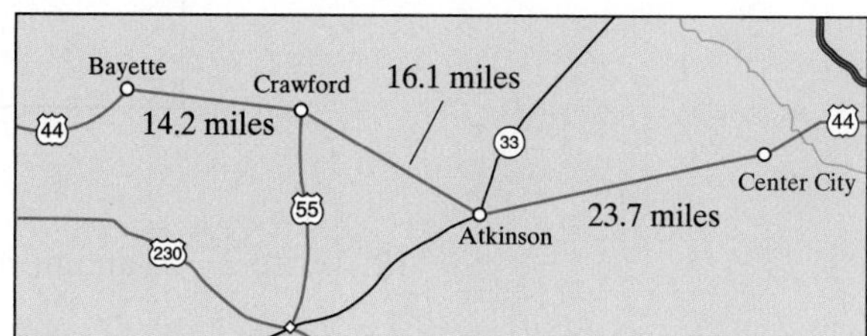

b. ______________

26. ______________

Answers

1. ______

2. ______

3. ______

4. ______

5. ______

6. ______

7. ______

8. ______

9. ______

10. ______

11. ______

12. ______

13. ______

14. ______

15. ______

16. ______

17. ______

18. ______

Cumulative Review Chapters 1–4

1. Write 106,052,447 in words.

2. Write two hundred seventy-six thousand, four in standard form.

3. The Darrell K. Royal Memorial Stadium, located in Austin, Texas, is the largest football stadium in the Big 12 Conference. Before 2009, it could seat 94,113 fans. Recently, the capacity of the stadium was increased by 4525 permanent bleacher seats. Find the new capacity of the home of the University of Texas Longhorns for the 2009 season. (*Source:* University of Texas Athletics)

4. There are 12 fluid ounces of soda in a can. How many fluid ounces of soda are in a case (24 cans) of soda?

5. Subtract: $900 - 174$. Then check by adding.

6. Simplify: $5^2 \cdot 2^3$

7. Round each number to the nearest hundred to find an estimated sum.

$$\begin{array}{r} 294 \\ 625 \\ 1071 \\ +\ 349 \\ \hline \end{array}$$

8. Simplify: $7 \cdot \sqrt{144}$

9. A digital video disc (DVD) can hold about 4800 megabytes (MB) of information. How many megabytes can 12 DVDs hold?

10. Find the perimeter and area of the square.

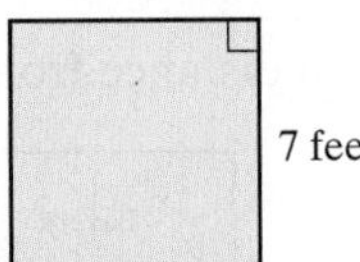

11. Divide: $6819 \div 17$

12. Write $2\frac{5}{8}$ as an improper fraction.

13. Simplify: $4^3 + [3^2 - (10 \div 2)] - 7 \cdot 3$

14. Write $\frac{64}{5}$ as a mixed number.

15. Identify the numerator and the denominator: $\frac{3}{7}$

16. Simplify: $24 \div 8 \cdot 3$

17. Write $\frac{6}{60}$ in simplest form.

18. Simplify: $(8 - 5)^2 + (10 - 8)^3$

19. Multiply: $\frac{3}{4} \cdot 20$

20. Simplify: $1 + 2[30 \div (7 - 2)]$

21. Divide: $\frac{7}{8} \div \frac{2}{9}$

22. Find the average of 117, 125, and 142.

23. Multiply: $1\frac{2}{3} \cdot 2\frac{1}{4}$

24. A total of $324 is paid for 36 tickets to the Audubon Zoo. How much did each ticket cost?

25. Divide: $\frac{3}{4} \div 5$

26. Simplify: $\left(\frac{3}{4} \div \frac{1}{2}\right) \cdot \frac{9}{10}$

Simplify.

27. $\frac{8}{9} - \frac{1}{9}$

28. $\frac{4}{15} + \frac{2}{15}$

29. $\frac{7}{8} - \frac{5}{8}$

30. $\frac{1}{20} + \frac{3}{20} + \frac{4}{20}$

Write an equivalent fraction with the indicated denominator.

31. $\frac{3}{4} = \frac{}{20}$

32. $\frac{7}{9} = \frac{}{45}$

Perform the indicated operations.

33. $\frac{2}{15} + \frac{3}{10}$

34. $\frac{7}{30} - \frac{2}{9}$

35. Two packages of ground round are purchased. One package weighs $2\frac{3}{8}$ pounds and the other $1\frac{4}{5}$ pounds. What is the combined weight of the ground round?

36. A color cartridge for a business printer weights $2\frac{5}{16}$ pounds. How much do 12 cartridges weigh?

19. ________

20. ________

21. ________

22. ________

23. ________

24. ________

25. ________

26. ________

27. ________

28. ________

29. ________

30. ________

31. ________

32. ________

33. ________

34. ________

35. ________

36. ________

37. ______
38. ______
39. ______
40. ______
41. ______
42. ______
43. ______
44. ______
45. ______
46. ______
47. ______
48. ______
49. ______
50. ______

Evaluate each expression.

37. $\left(\frac{1}{4}\right)^2$

38. $\left(\frac{7}{11}\right)^2$

39. $\left(\frac{1}{6}\right)^2 \cdot \left(\frac{3}{4}\right)^3$

40. $\left(\frac{1}{2}\right)^3 \cdot \left(\frac{4}{9}\right)^2$

41. Write 0.43 as a fraction.

42. Write $\frac{3}{4}$ as a decimal.

43. Insert $<$, $>$, or $=$ to form a true statement.

0.378   0.368

44. Write "five and six hundredths" in standard form.

45. Subtract: $35.218 - 23.65$

Check your answer.

46. Add: $75.1 + 0.229$

Multiply.

47. 23.702×100

48. 1.7×0.07

49. $76{,}805 \times 0.01$

50. Divide: $0.1157 \div 0.013$

Ratio and Proportion

5

Sections

Check Your Progress

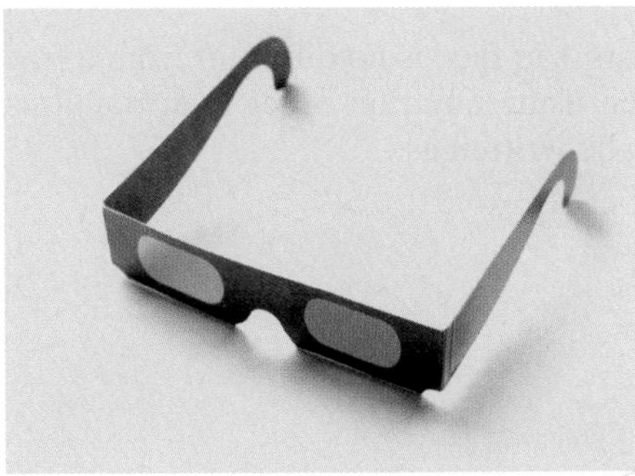

3-D glasses, used to view early 3-D films.

Polarized glasses are the standard for theatrical releases and theme park attractions.

Note: 3-D viewing systems that do not require viewing glasses are currently being tested and manufactured.

Having studied fractions in Chapters 2 and 3, we are ready to explore the useful notations of ratio and proportion. Ratio is another name for quotient and is usually written in fraction form. A proportion is an equation with two equal ratios.

A 3-D (three-dimensional) film is a film that enhances the illusion of depth perception. Believe it or not, 3-D films have existed in some form since 1890, but because of high cost and lack of a standardized format, these films are only now starting to be widely shown and produced. Although there was a decline in the total number of films released in 2009, there were 20 films released with digital 3-D versions.

In Section 5.1, Exercise 47, we calculate the ratio of 3-D to non–3-D films.

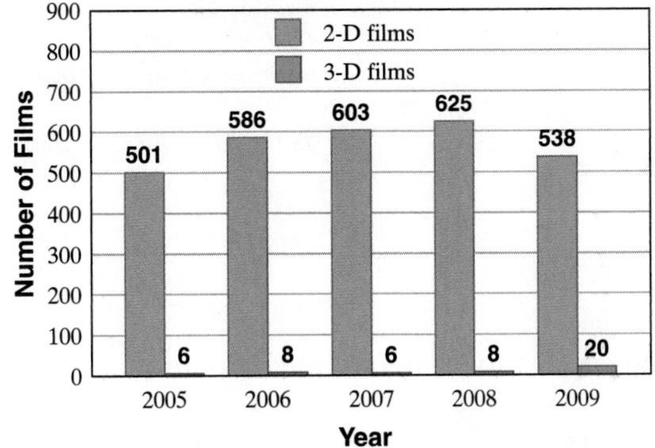

Source: Motion Picture Association of America

Objectives

A **Write Ratios as Fractions.**

B **Write Ratios in Simplest Form.**

5.1 RATIOS

Objective A Writing Ratios as Fractions

A **ratio** is the quotient of two quantities. A ratio, in fact, is no different from a fraction, except that a ratio is sometimes written using notation other than fractional notation. For example, the ratio of 1 to 2 can be written as

$$1 \text{ to } 2 \quad \text{or} \quad \frac{1}{2} \quad \text{or} \quad 1:2$$

$\frac{1}{2}$ ← fractional notation; $1:2$ ← colon notation

These ratios are all read as, "the ratio of 1 to 2."

✓**Concept Check** How should each ratio be read aloud?

a. $\frac{8}{5}$ **b.** $\frac{5}{8}$

In this section, we write ratios using fractional notation. If the fraction happens to be an improper fraction, do not write the fraction as a mixed number. Why? The mixed number form is not a ratio or quotient of two quantities.

Writing a Ratio as a Fraction

The order of the quantities is important when writing ratios. To write a ratio as a fraction, write the *first number* of the ratio as the *numerator* of the fraction and the *second number* as the *denominator*.

Helpful Hint

The ratio of 6 to 11 is $\frac{6}{11}$, *not* $\frac{11}{6}$.

Example 1 Write the ratio of 12 to 17 using fractional notation.

Solution: The ratio is $\frac{12}{17}$.

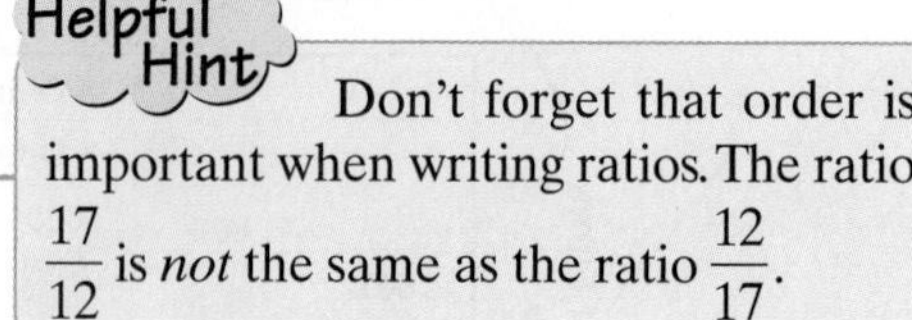

Helpful Hint Don't forget that order is important when writing ratios. The ratio $\frac{17}{12}$ is *not* the same as the ratio $\frac{12}{17}$.

Work Practice 1

PRACTICE 1

Write the ratio of 20 to 23 using fractional notation.

Examples Write each ratio using fractional notation.

2. The ratio of 2.6 to 3.1 is $\frac{2.6}{3.1}$.

3. The ratio of $1\frac{1}{2}$ to $7\frac{3}{4}$ is $\frac{1\frac{1}{2}}{7\frac{3}{4}}$.

Work Practice 2–3

PRACTICE 2–3

Write each ratio using fractional notation.

2. The ratio of 10.3 to 15.1

3. The ratio of $3\frac{1}{3}$ to $12\frac{1}{5}$

Answers

1. $\frac{20}{23}$ **2.** $\frac{10.3}{15.1}$ **3.** $\frac{3\frac{1}{3}}{12\frac{1}{5}}$

✓ **Concept Check Answers**

a. "the ratio of eight to five"

b. "the ratio of five to eight"

Objective B Writing Ratios in Simplest Form

To simplify a ratio, we just write the fraction in simplest form. Common factors as well as common units can be divided out.

Example 4 Write the ratio of \$15 to \$10 as a fraction in simplest form.

Solution:

$$\frac{\$15}{\$10} = \frac{15}{10} = \frac{3 \cdot \cancel{5}^{1}}{2 \cdot \cancel{5}_{1}} = \frac{3}{2}$$

Work Practice 4

PRACTICE 4

Write the ratio of \$8 to \$6 as a fraction in simplest form.

Helpful Hint

In the example above, although $\frac{3}{2} = 1\frac{1}{2}$, a ratio is a quotient of *two* quantities. For that reason, ratios are not written as mixed numbers.

If a ratio contains decimal numbers or mixed numbers, we simplify by writing the ratio as a ratio of whole numbers.

Example 5 Write the ratio of 2.6 to 3.1 as a fraction in simplest form.

Solution: The ratio in fraction form is

$$\frac{2.6}{3.1}$$

Now let's clear the ratio of decimals.

$$\frac{2.6}{3.1} = \frac{2.6}{3.1} \cdot 1 = \frac{2.6}{3.1} \cdot \frac{10}{10} = \frac{2.6 \cdot 10}{3.1 \cdot 10} = \frac{26}{31} \quad \text{Simplest form}$$

Work Practice 5

PRACTICE 5

Write the ratio of 3.9 to 8.8 as a fraction in simplest form.

Example 6 Write the ratio of $1\frac{1}{5}$ to $2\frac{7}{10}$ as a fraction in simplest form.

Solution: The ratio in fraction form is $\dfrac{1\frac{1}{5}}{2\frac{7}{10}}$.

To simplify, remember that the fraction bar means division.

$$\frac{1\frac{1}{5}}{2\frac{7}{10}} = 1\frac{1}{5} \div 2\frac{7}{10} = \frac{6}{5} \div \frac{27}{10} = \frac{6}{5} \cdot \frac{10}{27} = \frac{6 \cdot 10}{5 \cdot 27} = \frac{2 \cdot \cancel{3}^{1} \cdot 2 \cdot \cancel{5}^{1}}{\cancel{5}_{1} \cdot \cancel{3}_{1} \cdot 3 \cdot 3} = \frac{4}{9} \quad \text{Simplest form.}$$

Work Practice 6

PRACTICE 6

Write the ratio of $2\frac{2}{3}$ to $1\frac{13}{15}$ as a fraction in simplest form.

Answers

4. $\frac{4}{3}$ **5.** $\frac{39}{88}$ **6.** $\frac{10}{7}$

PRACTICE 7

Use the circle graph for Example 7 to write the ratio of work miles to total miles as a fraction in simplest form.

Example 7 Writing a Ratio from a Circle Graph

The circle graph at the right shows the part of a car's total mileage that falls into a particular category. Write the ratio of family business miles to total miles as a fraction in simplest form.

Work 4800 miles
Medical 150 miles
Vacation/ other 900 miles
Visit friends 1800 miles
Shopping 1800 miles
School/ church 600 miles
Social/ recreational 1950 miles
Family business 3000 miles

Total yearly mileage: 15,000

Sources: The American Automobile Manufacturers Association and The National Automobile Dealers Association.

Solution:

$$\frac{\text{family business miles}}{\text{total miles}} = \frac{3000 \text{ miles}}{15{,}000 \text{ miles}} = \frac{3000}{15{,}000} = \frac{\overset{1}{\cancel{3000}}}{5 \cdot \underset{1}{\cancel{3000}}} = \frac{1}{5}$$

Work Practice 7

△ **PRACTICE 8**

Given the triangle shown:

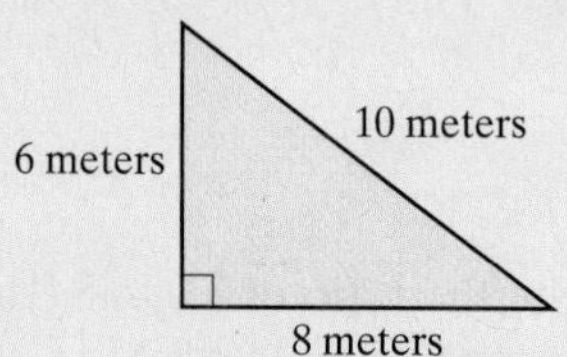

a. Find the ratio of the length of the shortest side to the length of the longest side.

b. Find the ratio of the length of the longest side to the perimeter of the triangle.

△ **Example 8** Given the rectangle shown:

a. Find the ratio of its width to its length.

b. Find the ratio of its length to its perimeter.

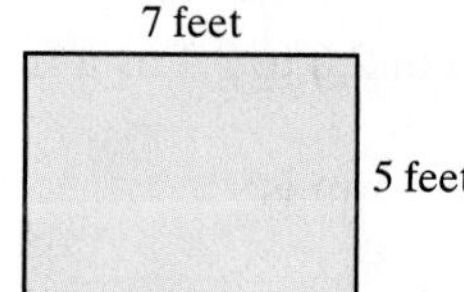

Solution:

a. The ratio of its width to its length is

$$\frac{\text{width}}{\text{length}} = \frac{5 \cancel{\text{ feet}}}{7 \cancel{\text{ feet}}} = \frac{5}{7}$$

b. Recall that the perimeter of the rectangle is the distance around the rectangle: $7 + 5 + 7 + 5 = 24$ feet. The ratio of its length to its perimeter is

$$\frac{\text{length}}{\text{perimeter}} = \frac{7 \cancel{\text{ feet}}}{24 \cancel{\text{ feet}}} = \frac{7}{24}$$

Work Practice 8

✓**Concept Check** Explain why the answer $\frac{7}{5}$ would be incorrect for part **a** of Example 8.

Answers

7. $\frac{8}{25}$ **8. a.** $\frac{3}{5}$ **b.** $\frac{5}{12}$

✓ **Concept Check Answer**

$\frac{7}{5}$ would be the ratio of the rectangle's length to its width.

Vocabulary and Readiness Check

Answer each statement true or false.

1. The quotient of two quantities is called a ratio. ________
2. The ratio $\frac{7}{5}$ means the same as the ratio $\frac{5}{7}$. ________
3. The ratio $\frac{7.2}{8.1}$ is in simplest form. ________
4. The ratio $\frac{10 \text{ feet}}{30 \text{ feet}}$ is in simplest form. ________
5. The ratio $\frac{9}{10}$ is in simplest form. ________
6. The ratio 2 to 5 equals $\frac{5}{2}$ in fractional notation. ________
7. The ratio 30 : 41 equals $\frac{30}{41}$ in fractional notation. ________
8. The ratio 15 to 45 equals $\frac{3}{1}$ in fractional notation. ________

5.1 Exercise Set

FOR EXTRA HELP MyMathLab

Objective A *Write each ratio using fractional notation. Do not simplify. See Examples 1 through 3.*

1. 11 to 14 **2.** 7 to 12 **3.** 23 to 10 **4.** 14 to 5 **5.** 151 to 201 **6.** 673 to 1000

7. 2.8 to 7.6 **8.** 3.9 to 4.2 **9.** 5 to $7\frac{1}{2}$ **10.** $5\frac{3}{4}$ to 3 **11.** $3\frac{3}{4}$ to $1\frac{2}{3}$ **12.** $2\frac{2}{5}$ to $6\frac{1}{2}$

Objectives A B Mixed Practice *Write each ratio as a ratio of whole numbers using fractional notation. Write the fraction in simplest form. See Examples 1 through 6.*

13. 16 to 24 **14.** 25 to 150 **15.** 7.7 to 10 **16.** 8.1 to 10

17. 4.63 to 8.21 **18.** 9.61 to 7.62 **19.** 9 inches to 12 inches **20.** 14 centimeters to 20 centimeters

21. 10 hours to 24 hours **22.** 18 quarts to 30 quarts **23.** \$32 to \$100 **24.** \$46 to \$102

25. 24 days to 14 days

26. 80 miles to 120 miles

27. 32,000 bytes to 46,000 bytes

28. 600 copies to 150 copies

29. 8 inches to 20 inches

30. 9 yards to 2 yards

31. $3\frac{1}{2}$ to $12\frac{1}{4}$

32. $3\frac{1}{3}$ to $4\frac{1}{6}$

33. $7\frac{3}{5}$ hours to $1\frac{9}{10}$ hours

34. $25\frac{1}{2}$ days to $2\frac{5}{6}$ days

Write the ratio described in each exercise as a fraction in simplest form. See Examples 7 and 8.

35.

Average Weight of Mature Whales	
Blue Whale	**Fin Whale**
145 tons	50 tons

Use the table to find the ratio of the weight of an average mature Fin Whale to the weight of an average mature Blue Whale.

36.

Countries with Small Land Areas	
Tuvalu	**San Marino**
10 sq mi	24 sq mi

(*Source: World Almanac*)

Use the table to find the ratio of the land area of Tuvalu to the land area of San Marino.

37. The mural *Independence and the Opening of the West,* painted by Thomas Hart Benton on the wall of the lobby of the Harry Truman Presidential Library in Independence, Missouri, occupies a space that measures 32 feet wide by 19 feet high. Find the ratio of the width to the perimeter of this mural.

38. More than one billion people per year see Wyland's Whaling Wall murals throughout the United States, Canada, Japan, Australia, New Zealand, and Europe. The mural on the Marketplace Design Center in Philadelphia, *East Coast Humpbacks*, measures 125 feet long by 130 feet high. Find the ratio of the height to the perimeter of this mural.

△ **39.** Find the ratio of the width of a regulation size basketball court to its perimeter.

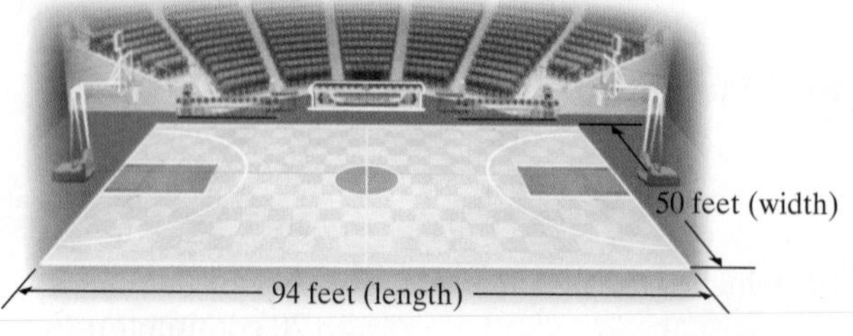

△ **40.** Find the ratio of the width to the perimeter shown of the swimming pool.

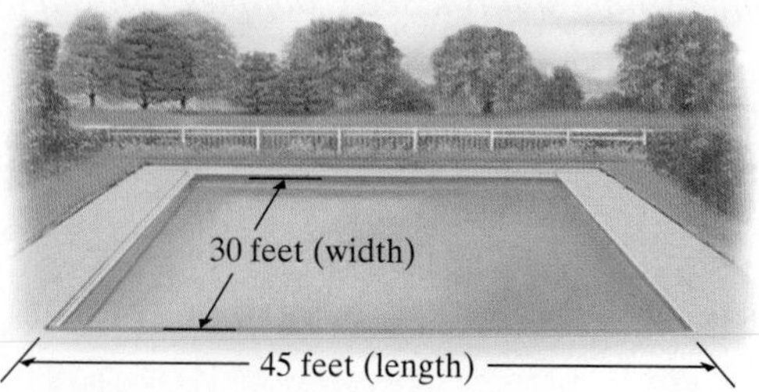

At the Hidalgo County School Board meeting one night, there were 125 women and 100 men present.

41. Find the ratio of women to men.

42. Find the ratio of men to the total number of people present.

Blood contains three types of cells: red blood cells, white blood cells, and platelets. For approximately every 600 red blood cells in healthy humans, there are 40 platelets and 1 white blood cell. Use this information for Exercises 43 and 44. (Source: American Red Cross Biomedical Services)

43. Write the ratio of red blood cells to platelet cells.

44. Write the ratio of white blood cells to red blood cells.

△ **45.** Find the ratio of the longest side to the perimeter of the right-triangular-shaped billboard.

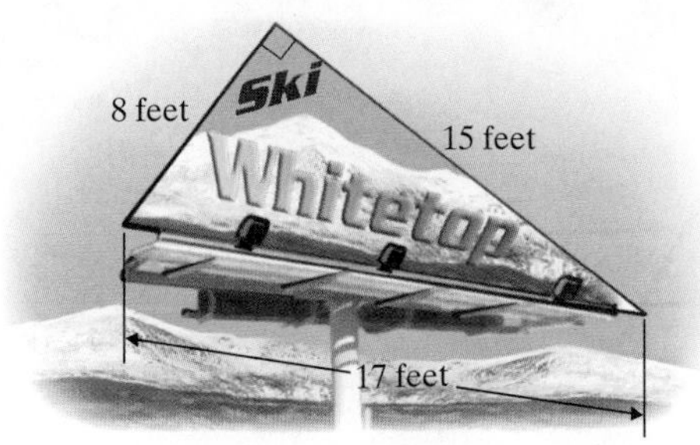

△ **46.** Find the ratio of the base to the perimeter of the triangular mainsail.

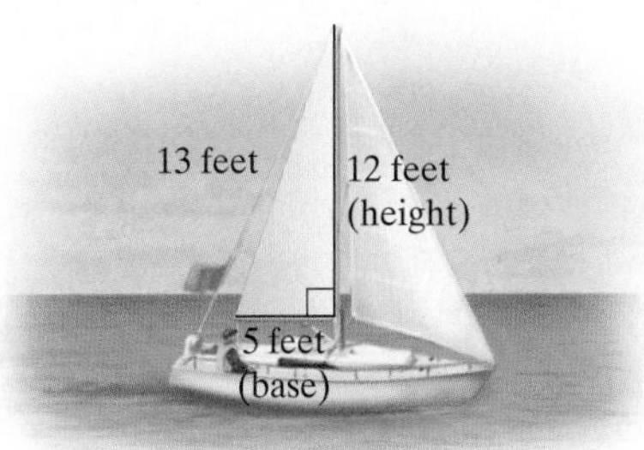

In 2009, 558 films by U.S. production companies were released. Use this information for Exercises 47 and 48.

47. In 2009, 20 digital 3-D films were released by U.S. production companies. Find the ratio of digital films to total films for 2009.

48. In 2009, 400 independent films were released by U.S. production compaines. Find the ratio of independent films to total films for 2009.

49. Of the U.S. mountains that are over 14,000 feet in elevation, 57 are located in Colorado and 19 are located in Alaska. Find the ratio of the number of mountains over 14,000 feet found in Alaska to the number of mountains over 14,000 feet found in Colorado. (*Source:* U.S. Geological Survey)

50. Citizens of the United States eat an average of 25 pints of ice cream per year. Residents of the New England states eat an average of 39 pints of ice cream per year. Find the ratio of the amount of ice cream eaten by New Englanders to the amount eaten by the average U.S. citizen. (*Source:* International Dairy Foods Association)

51. At the Summer Olympics in Beijing, China, a total of 302 gold medals were awarded, and Australian athletes won a total of 14 gold medals. Find the ratio of gold medals won by the Australian athletes to the total gold medals awarded. (*Source:* International Olympic Committee)

52. For the 2009 Boston Marathon, 13,545 males and 9298 females completed the race. Find the ratio of female finishers to male finishers. (*Source:* Boston Athletic Association)

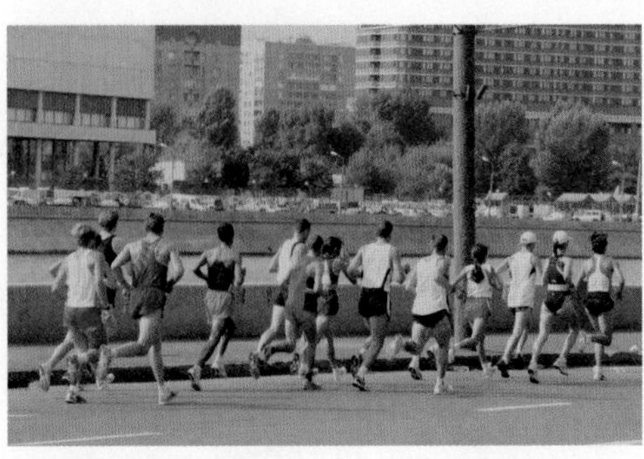

53. As of 2009, Target stores operate in 49 states. Find the ratio of states without Target stores to states with Target stores. (*Source:* Target Corporation)

54. Four states in the United States officially designate themselves as "commonwealths": Kentucky, Massachusetts, Pennsylvania, and Virginia. Find the ratio of states that are designated as commonwealths to the states that are not designed as commonwealths.

Review

Divide. See Section 4.5.

55. $9\overline{)20.7}$ **56.** $7\overline{)60.2}$ **57.** $3.7\overline{)0.555}$ **58.** $4.6\overline{)1.15}$

Concept Extensions

Solve. See the Concept Checks in this section. Write how each should be read as a ratio.

59. $\frac{7}{9}$ **60.** $\frac{12}{5}$ **61.** 30 : 1 **62.** 5 to 4

63. Is the ratio $\frac{11}{15}$ the same as the ratio of $\frac{15}{11}$? Explain your answer.

64. Explain why the ratio $\frac{40}{17}$ is incorrect for Exercise 45.

Decide whether each value is a ratio written as a fraction in simplest form. If not, write it as a fraction in simplest form.

65. $\frac{\$3}{\$2}$

66. $\frac{7.1}{4.3}$

67. $\frac{1 \text{ foot}}{30 \text{ inches}}$

68. $\frac{2\frac{1}{10}}{3\frac{3}{14}}$

69. $4\frac{1}{2}$

70. $\frac{12 \text{ inches}}{2 \text{ feet}}$

71. A grocer will refuse a shipment of tomatoes if the ratio of bruised tomatoes to the total batch is at least 1 to 10. A sample is found to contain 3 bruised tomatoes and 33 good tomatoes. Determine whether the shipment should be refused.

72. A panty hose manufacturing machine will be repaired if the ratio of defective panty hose to good panty hose is at least 1 to 20. A quality control engineer found 10 defective panty hose in a batch of 200. Determine whether the machine should be repaired.

73. In 2009, 30 states had primary seat belt laws. These laws allow law enforcement officers to ticket a driver for not wearing a seat belt, even if no other traffic offense has occurred. The remaining states had secondary seat belt laws, where a ticket for not wearing a seat belt may be issued only when there is another citable traffic infraction. (*Source:* Governors Highway Safety Association)

a. Find the ratio of states with primary seat belt laws to total U.S. states.

b. Find the ratio of states with primary seat belt laws to states with secondary seat belt laws.

c. Are your ratios for **a** and **b** the same? Explain why or why not.

Objectives

A **Write Rates as Fractions.**

B **Find Unit Rates.**

C **Find Unit Prices.**

5.2 RATES

Objective A Writing Rates as Fractions

A special type of ratio is a rate. **Rates** are used to compare *different* kinds of quantities. For example, suppose that a recreational runner can run 3 miles in 33 minutes. If we write this rate as a fraction, we have

$$\frac{3 \text{ miles}}{33 \text{ minutes}} = \frac{1 \text{ mile}}{11 \text{ minutes}} \quad \text{In simplest form}$$

Helpful Hint

When comparing quantities with different units, write the units as part of the comparison. They do not divide out.

Same Units: $\frac{3 \cancel{\text{inches}}}{12 \cancel{\text{inches}}} = \frac{1}{4}$

Different Units: $\frac{2 \text{ miles}}{20 \text{ minutes}} = \frac{1 \text{ mile}}{10 \text{ minutes}}$ Units are still written.

PRACTICE 1

Write the rate as a fraction in simplest form: 12 commercials every 45 minutes

Example 1 Write the rate as a fraction in simplest form: 10 nails every 6 feet

Solution:

$$\frac{10 \text{ nails}}{6 \text{ feet}} = \frac{5 \text{ nails}}{3 \text{ feet}}$$

Work Practice 1

PRACTICE 2–3

Write each rate as a fraction in simplest form.

2. \$1680 for 8 weeks
3. 236 miles on 12 gallons of gasoline

Examples Write each rate as a fraction in simplest form.

2. \$2160 for 12 weeks is $\frac{2160 \text{ dollars}}{12 \text{ weeks}} = \frac{180 \text{ dollars}}{1 \text{ week}}$
3. 360 miles on 16 gallons of gasoline is $\frac{360 \text{ miles}}{16 \text{ gallons}} = \frac{45 \text{ miles}}{2 \text{ gallons}}$

Work Practice 2–3

✓**Concept Check** True or false? $\frac{16 \text{ gallons}}{4 \text{ gallons}}$ is a rate. Explain.

Objective B Finding Unit Rates

A **unit rate** is a rate with a denominator of 1. A familiar example of a unit rate is 55 mph, read as "55 **miles per hour.**" This means 55 miles per 1 hour or

$$\frac{55 \text{ miles}}{1 \text{ hour}} \quad \text{Denominator of 1}$$

Helpful Hint

In this context, the word "per" translates to division.

Answers

1. $\frac{4 \text{ commercials}}{15 \text{ min}}$ 2. $\frac{\$210}{1 \text{ wk}}$ 3. $\frac{59 \text{ mi}}{3 \text{ gal}}$

✓ **Concept Check Answer**

false; a rate compares different kinds of quantities

Writing a Rate as a Unit Rate

To write a rate as a unit rate, divide the numerator of the rate by the denominator.

Example 4 Write as a unit rate: $31,500 every 7 months

Solution:

$$\frac{31{,}500 \text{ dollars}}{7 \text{ months}} \qquad 7\overline{)31{,}500} = 4{,}500$$

The unit rate is

$$\frac{4500 \text{ dollars}}{1 \text{ month}} \text{ or } 4500 \text{ dollars/month}$$ Read as, "4500 dollars per month."

Work Practice 4

PRACTICE 4

Write as a unit rate: 3200 feet every 8 seconds

Example 5 Write as a unit rate: 337.5 miles every 15 gallons of gas

Solution:

$$\frac{337.5 \text{ miles}}{15 \text{ gallons}} \qquad 15\overline{)337.5} = 22.5$$

The unit rate is

$$\frac{22.5 \text{ miles}}{1 \text{ gallon}} \text{ or } 22.5 \text{ miles/gallon}$$ Read as, "22.5 miles per gallon."

Work Practice 5

PRACTICE 5

Write as a unit rate: 78 bushels of fruit from 12 trees

Objective C Finding Unit Prices

Rates are used extensively in sports, business, medicine, and science. One of the most common uses of rates is in consumer economics. When a unit rate is "money per item," it is also called a **unit price.**

$$\text{unit price} = \frac{\text{price}}{\text{number of units}}$$

Answers

4. $\frac{400 \text{ ft}}{1 \text{ sec}}$ or 400 ft/sec

5. $\frac{6.5 \text{ bushels}}{1 \text{ tree}}$ or 6.5 bushels/tree

PRACTICE 6

An automobile rental agency charges $170 for 5 days for a certain model car. What is the unit price in dollars per day?

Example 6 Finding Unit Price

A store charges $3.36 for a 16-ounce jar of picante sauce. What is the unit price in dollars per ounce?

Solution:

$$\text{unit price} = \frac{\text{price}}{\text{number of units}} = \frac{\$3.36}{16 \text{ ounces}} = \frac{\$0.21}{1 \text{ ounce}} \text{ or } \$0.21 \text{ per ounce}$$

Work Practice 6

PRACTICE 7

Approximate each unit price to decide which is the better buy for a bag of nacho chips:
11 ounces for $2.32 or
16 ounces for $3.59.

Example 7 Finding the Best Buy

Approximate each unit price to decide which is the better buy: 4 bars of soap for $0.99 or 5 bars of soap for $1.19.

Solution:

$$\text{unit price} = \frac{\text{price}}{\text{no. of units}} = \frac{\$0.99}{4 \text{ bars}} \approx \$0.25 \text{ per bar of soap} \qquad 4\overline{)0.990} = 0.247 \approx 0.25$$

("is approximately")

$$\text{unit price} = \frac{\text{price}}{\text{no. of units}} = \frac{\$1.19}{5 \text{ bars}} \approx \$0.24 \text{ per bar of soap} \qquad 5\overline{)1.190} = 0.238 \approx 0.24$$

Thus, the 5-bar package is the better buy.

Work Practice 7

Answers
6. $34 per day
7. 11-oz bag

Vocabulary and Readiness Check

Use the choices below to fill in each blank. Not all choices will be used.

rate division unit price unit

numerator different denominator

1. A rate with a denominator of 1 is called a(n) ____________ rate.
2. When a rate is written as money per item, a unit rate is called a(n) ____________.
3. The word *per* translates to "____________."
4. Rates are used to compare ____________ types of quantities.
5. To write a rate as a unit rate, divide the ____________ of the rate by the ____________.

5.2 Exercise Set

FOR EXTRA HELP

PRACTICE

WATCH

DOWNLOAD

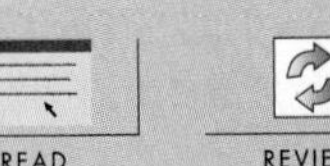
READ

REVIEW

Objective A *Write each rate as a fraction in simplest form. See Examples 1 through 3.*

1. 5 shrubs every 15 feet

2. 14 lab tables for 28 students

3. 15 returns for 100 sales

4. 8 phone lines for 36 employees

5. 6 laser printers for 28 computers

6. 4 inches of rain in 18 hours

7. 18 gallons of pesticide for 4 acres of crops

8. 150 graduate students for 8 advisors

9. 6 flight attendants for 200 passengers

10. 240 pounds of grass seed for 9 lawns

11. 355 calories in a 10-fluid-ounce chocolate milkshake (*Source: Home and Garden Bulletin No. 72,* U.S. Department of Agriculture)

12. 160 calories in an 8-fluid-ounce serving of cream of tomato soup (*Source: Home and Garden Bulletin No. 72,* U.S. Department of Agriculture)

Objective B *Write each rate as a unit rate. See Examples 4 and 5.*

13. 330 calories in a 3-ounce serving

14. 275 miles in 11 hours

15. 375 riders in 5 subway cars

16. 18 signs in 6 blocks

17. A hummingbird moves its wings at a rate of 5400 wingbeats a minute. Write this rate in wingbeats per second.

18. A bat moves its wings at a rate of 1200 wingbeats a minute. Write this rate in wingbeats per second.

19. $1,000,000 lottery winnings paid over 20 years

20. 400,000 library books for 8000 students

21. The state of Delaware has 450,500 registered voters for two senators. (*Source:* The Delaware Liberal Census)

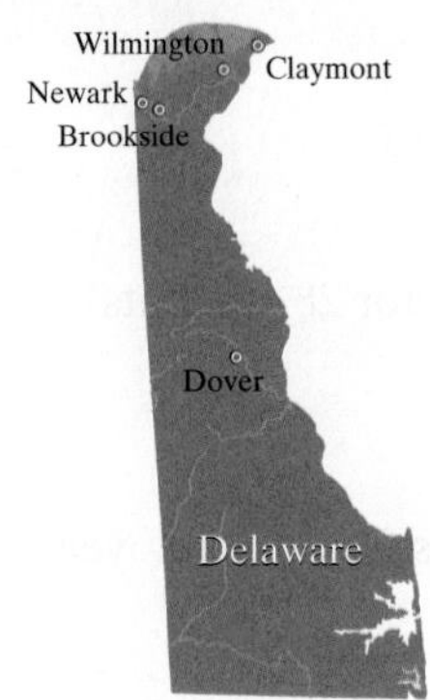

22. The 2010 projected population of Louisiana is approximately 4,684,800 residents for 64 parishes. (*Note:* Louisiana is the only U.S. state with parishes instead of counties.) (*Source:* U.S. Bureau of the Census)

23. 12,000 good assembly-line products to 40 defective products

24. 5,000,000 lottery tickets for 4 lottery winners

25. The combined salary for the 20 highest-paid players of the 2008 World Series Champion Philadelphia Phillies was approximately $87,800,000. (*Source:* Major League Baseball)

26. The top-grossing concert tour was the 2005–2007 Rolling Stones *A Bigger Bang* tour, which grossed $558 million for 150 shows worldwide. (*Source:* Pollstar)

27. Doug Mehrens uses more crayons annually than anyone else in the world. The Phoenix-based artist goes through about 24,000 a year, many of them melted, to complete his contemporary art works. If he works on his art every day, determine how many crayons Doug Mehrens uses each day. Round your answer to the nearest whole crayon. (*Note:* use 1 year = 365 days) (*Source:* Crayola, LLC)

28. 12,000,000 tons of dust and dirt are trapped by the 25,000,000 acres of lawns in the United States each year. (*Source:* Professional Lawn Care Association of America)

29. On average in a recent year, it cost each passenger about \$700 to travel 5000 miles internationally by plane. (*Source:* Air Transport Association of America)

30. The National Zoo in Washington, D.C., has an annual budget of \$28,595,000 for its 475 different species. (*Source:* Smithsonian Institution)

31. On average, it costs \$1,495,000 to build 25 Habitat for Humanity houses in the United States. (*Source:* Habitat for Humanity International)

32. In 2009, the number of movie admissions (tickets) sold was about 1419 million for 330 million people in the U.S. and Canada. Find the number of tickets sold per person. (*Source:* MPAA)

Find each unit rate.

33. The record number of tornadoes in the U.S. for one 24-hour period is 148. Write this as a unit rate of tornadoes per hour rounded to the nearest tenth.

34. Sammy Joe Wingfield from Arlington, Texas, is the fastest bricklayer on record. On May 20, 1994, he laid 1048 bricks in 60 minutes. Find his unit rate of bricks per minute rounded to the nearest tenth. (*Source: The Guinness Book of Records*)

35. Charlie Catlett can assemble 250 computer boards in an 8-hour shift while Suellen Catlett can assemble 402 computer boards in a 12-hour shift.

a. Find the unit rate of Charlie.
b. Find the unit rate of Suellen.
c. Who can assemble computer boards faster, Charlie or Suellen?

36. Jerry Stein laid 713 bricks in 46 minutes while his associate, Bobby Burns, laid 396 bricks in 30 minutes.

a. Find the unit rate of Jerry.
b. Find the unit rate of Bobby.
c. Who is the faster bricklayer?

For Exercises 37 and 38, round the rates to the nearest tenth.

37. One student drove 400 miles in his car on 14.5 gallons of gasoline. His sister drove 270 miles in her truck on 9.25 gallons of gasoline.

a. Find the unit rate of the car.
b. Find the unit rate of the truck.
c. Which vehicle gets better gas mileage?

38. Charlotte Leal is a grocery scanner who can scan an average of 100 items in 3.5 minutes while her cousin Leo can scan 148 items in 5.5 minutes.

a. Find the unit rate of Charlotte.
b. Find the unit rate of Leo.
c. Who is the faster scanner?

Objective **C** *Find each unit price. See Example 6.*

39. \$57.50 for 5 DVDs

40. \$0.87 for 3 apples

41. \$1.19 for 7 bananas

42. \$73.50 for 6 lawn chairs

Find each unit price and decide which is the better buy. Round to three decimal places. Assume that we are comparing different sizes of the same brand. See Examples 6 and 7.

43. Crackers:
\$1.19 for 8 ounces
\$1.59 for 12 ounces

44. Pickles:
\$1.89 for 32 ounces
\$0.89 for 18 ounces

45. Frozen orange juice:
\$1.69 for 16 ounces
\$0.69 for 6 ounces

46. Eggs:
\$0.69 for a dozen
\$2.10 for a flat $\left(2\frac{1}{2}\text{ dozen}\right)$

47. Soy sauce:
12 ounces for \$2.29
8 ounces for \$1.49

48. Shampoo:
20 ounces for \$1.89
32 ounces for \$3.19

49. Napkins:
100 for \$0.59
180 for \$0.93

50. Crackers:
20 ounces for \$2.39
8 ounces for \$0.99

Review

Multiply or divide as indicated. See Sections 4.4 and 4.5.

51. $\begin{array}{r} 1.7 \\ \times\ 6 \\ \hline \end{array}$

52. $\begin{array}{r} 2.3 \\ \times\ 9 \\ \hline \end{array}$

53. $\begin{array}{r} 3.7 \\ \times\ 1.2 \\ \hline \end{array}$

54. $\begin{array}{r} 6.6 \\ \times\ 2.5 \\ \hline \end{array}$

55. $2.3\overline{)4.37}$

56. $3.5\overline{)22.75}$

Concept Extensions

Fill in the table to calculate miles per gallon.

	Beginning Odometer Reading	Ending Odometer Reading	Miles Driven	Gallons of Gas Used	Miles per Gallon (round to the nearest tenth)
57.	29,286	29,543		13.4	
58.	16,543	16,895		15.8	
59.	79,895	80,242		16.1	
60.	31,623	32,056		11.9	

Find each unit rate.

61. The longest stairway is the service stairway for the Niesenbahn Cable railway near Spiez, Switzerland. It has 11,674 steps and rises to a height of 7759 feet. Find the unit rate of steps per foot rounded to the nearest tenth of a step. (*Source: Guinness World Records*)

62. In the United States, the total number of students enrolled in public schools is 49,610,000. There are 97,300 public schools. Write a unit rate in students per school. Round to the nearest whole. (*Source:* National Center for Education Statistics)

63. In your own words, define the phrase "unit rate."

64. In your own words, define the phrase "unit price."

65. Should the rate $\frac{3 \text{ lights}}{2 \text{ feet}}$ be written as $\frac{3}{2}$? Explain why or why not.

66. Find an item in the grocery store and calculate its unit price.

Answers

1. ______

2. ______

3. ______

4. ______

5. ______

6. ______

7. ______

8. ______

9. ______

10. ______

11. ______

12. ______

13. a. ______

b. ______

14. ______

Integrated Review Sections 5.1–5.2

Ratio and Rate

Write each ratio as a ratio of whole numbers using fractional notation. Write the fraction in simplest form.

1. 18 to 20

2. 36 to 100

3. 8.6 to 10

4. 1.6 to 4.6

5. \$8.65 to \$6.95

6. 7.2 ounces to 8.4 ounces

7. $3\frac{1}{2}$ to 13

8. $1\frac{2}{3}$ to $2\frac{3}{4}$

9. 8 inches to 12 inches

10. 3 hours to 24 hours

Find the ratio described in each problem.

11. In 2009, a full college professor earned \$108.7 thousand, while an associate professor earned \$76.1 thousand. Find the ratio of full professor salary to associate professor salary. (*Source*: American Association of University Professors)

12. The New York Yankees are a dynastic powerhouse. They have won 26 out of the 104 Major League Baseball World Series played through 2008. (*Source*: Major League Baseball)

13. The circle graph below shows how the top 25 movies of 2009 were rated. Use this graph to answer the questions.

a. How many top 25 movies were rated PG-13?

b. Find the ratio of top 25 R-rated movies to PG-rated movies for 2009.

Top 25 Movies of 2009

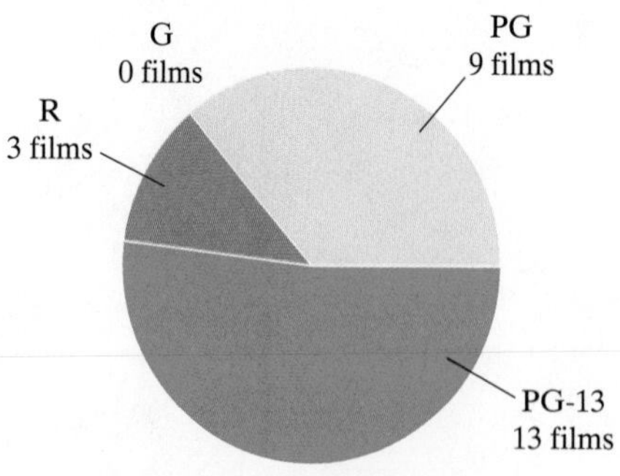

Source: MPAA
Note: There were no G-rated films in the top 25 for 2009

14. Find the ratio of the width to the length of the sign below.

Write each rate as a fraction in simplest form.

15. 5 offices for every 20 graduate assistants

16. 6 lights every 15 feet

17. 100 U.S. senators for 50 states

18. 5 teachers for every 140 students

19. 64 computers every 100 households

20. 45 students for every 10 computers

Write each rate as a unit rate.

21. 165 miles in 3 hours

22. 560 feet in 4 seconds

23. 63 employees for 3 fax lines

24. 85 phone calls for 5 teenagers

25. 115 miles every 5 gallons

26. 112 teachers for 7 computers

27. 7524 books for 1254 college students

28. 2002 pounds for 13 adults

Write each unit price, rounded to the nearest hundredths, and decide which is the better buy.

29. Dog food:
$2.16 for 8 pounds
$4.99 for 18 pounds

30. Paper plates:
$1.98 for 100
$8.99 for 500
(Round to the nearest thousandths.)

31. Microwave popcorn:
3 packs for $2.39
8 packs for $5.99

32. AA batteries:
4 for $3.69
10 for $9.89

15. ______
16. ______
17. ______
18. ______
19. ______
20. ______
21. ______
22. ______
23. ______
24. ______
25. ______
26. ______
27. ______
28. ______
29. ______
30. ______
31. ______
32. ______

Objectives

A Write Sentences as Proportions.

B Determine Whether Proportions Are True.

C Find an Unknown Number in a Proportion.

5.3 PROPORTIONS

Objective A Writing Proportions

A **proportion** is a statement that two ratios or rates are equal. For example,

$$\frac{5}{6} = \frac{10}{12}$$

is a proportion. We can read this as, "5 is to 6 as 10 is to 12."

Example 1 Write each sentence as a proportion.

a. 12 diamonds is to 15 rubies as 4 diamonds is to 5 rubies.

b. 5 hits is to 9 at bats as 20 hits is to 36 at bats.

Solution:

a. $\begin{array}{rcccl} \text{diamonds} & \rightarrow & \frac{12}{15} = \frac{4}{5} & \leftarrow & \text{diamonds} \\ \text{rubies} & \rightarrow & & \leftarrow & \text{rubies} \end{array}$

b. $\begin{array}{rcccl} \text{hits} & \rightarrow & \frac{5}{9} = \frac{20}{36} & \leftarrow & \text{hits} \\ \text{at bats} & \rightarrow & & \leftarrow & \text{at bats} \end{array}$

Work Practice 1

PRACTICE 1

Write each sentence as a proportion.

a. 24 right is to 6 wrong as 4 right is to 1 wrong.

b. 32 Cubs fans is to 18 Mets fans as 16 Cubs fans is to 9 Mets fans.

Helpful Hint

Notice in the above examples of proportions that the numerators contain the same units and the denominators contain the same units. In this text, proportions will be written so that this is the case.

Objective B Determining Whether Proportions Are True

Like other mathematical statements, a proportion may be either true or false. A proportion is true if its ratios are equal. Since ratios are fractions, one way to determine whether a proportion is true is to write both fractions in simplest form and compare them.

Another way is to compare cross products as we did in Section 2.3.

Note: In the box below, we are using letters to represent numbers. We later call these letters *variables*.

Using Cross Products to Determine Whether Proportions Are True or False

Cross products

$$a \cdot d \qquad \frac{a}{b} = \frac{c}{d} \qquad b \cdot c$$

If cross products are *equal,* the proportion is *true.*

If cross products are *not equal,* the proportion is *false.*

Answers

1. a. $\frac{24}{6} = \frac{4}{1}$ **b.** $\frac{32}{18} = \frac{16}{9}$

Example 2 Is $\frac{2}{3} = \frac{4}{6}$ a true proportion?

Solution:

Cross products

$2 \cdot 6$ $\quad$ $3 \cdot 4$

$$\frac{2}{3} = \frac{4}{6}$$

$2 \cdot 6 \stackrel{?}{=} 3 \cdot 4$ Are cross products equal?

$12 = 12$ Equal, so proportion is true.

Since the cross products are equal, the proportion is true.

Work Practice 2

PRACTICE 2

Is $\frac{3}{6} = \frac{4}{8}$ a true proportion?

Example 3 Is $\frac{4.1}{7} = \frac{2.9}{5}$ a true proportion?

Solution:

Cross products

$4.1 \cdot 5$ $\quad$ $7 \cdot 2.9$

$$\frac{4.1}{7} = \frac{2.9}{5}$$

$4.1 \cdot 5 \stackrel{?}{=} 7 \cdot 2.9$ Are cross products equal?

$20.5 \neq 20.3$ Not equal, so proportion is false.

Since the cross products are not equal, $\frac{4.1}{7} \neq \frac{2.9}{5}$. The proportion is false.

Work Practice 3

PRACTICE 3

Is $\frac{3.6}{6} = \frac{5.4}{8}$ a true proportion?

Example 4 Is $\dfrac{1\frac{1}{6}}{10\frac{1}{2}} = \dfrac{\frac{1}{2}}{4\frac{1}{2}}$ a true proportion?

Solution:

$$\frac{1\frac{1}{6}}{10\frac{1}{2}} = \frac{\frac{1}{2}}{4\frac{1}{2}}$$

$1\frac{1}{6} \cdot 4\frac{1}{2} \stackrel{?}{=} 10\frac{1}{2} \cdot \frac{1}{2}$ Are cross products equal?

$\frac{7}{6} \cdot \frac{9}{2} \stackrel{?}{=} \frac{21}{2} \cdot \frac{1}{2}$ Write mixed numbers as improper fractions.

$\frac{21}{4} = \frac{21}{4}$ Equal, so proportion is true.

Since the cross products are equal, the proportion is true.

Work Practice 4

PRACTICE 4

Is $\dfrac{4\frac{1}{5}}{2\frac{1}{3}} = \dfrac{3\frac{3}{10}}{1\frac{5}{6}}$ a true proportion?

Answers

2. yes **3.** no **4.** yes

✓**Concept Check** Think about cross products and write the true proportion $\frac{5}{8} = \frac{10}{16}$ in two other ways so that each result is also a true proportion.

(*Note:* There are no units attached in this proportion.)

Objective C Finding Unknown Numbers in Proportions

When one number of a proportion is unknown, we can use cross products to find the unknown number. For example, to find the unknown number n in the proportion $\frac{n}{30} = \frac{2}{3}$, we first find the cross products.

$n \cdot 3$ $\quad \frac{n}{30} = \frac{2}{3} \quad$ $30 \cdot 2$ Find the cross products.

If the proportion is true, then cross products are equal.

$n \cdot 3 = 30 \cdot 2$ Set the cross products equal to each other.

$n \cdot 3 = 60$ Write $2 \cdot 30$ as 60.

To find the unknown number n, we ask ourselves, "What number times 3 is 60?" The number is 20 and can be found by dividing 60 by 3.

$n = \frac{60}{3}$ Divide 60 by the number multiplied by n.

$n = 20$ Simplify.

Thus, the unknown number is 20.

Check: To *check,* let's replace n with this value, 20, and verify that a true proportion results.

$\frac{20}{30} \stackrel{?}{=} \frac{2}{3}$ ← Replace n with 20.

$\frac{20}{30} \stackrel{?}{=} \frac{2}{3}$

$3 \cdot 20 \stackrel{?}{=} 2 \cdot 30$

$60 = 60$ Cross products are equal.

Finding an Unknown Value n in a Proportion

Step 1: Set the cross products equal to each other.

Step 2: Divide the number not multiplied by n by the number multiplied by n.

✓ **Concept Check Answer**

possible answers: $\frac{8}{5} = \frac{16}{10}$ and $\frac{5}{10} = \frac{8}{16}$

Example 5 Find the value of the unknown number n.

$$\frac{51}{34} = \frac{3}{n}$$

Solution:

Step 1:

$$\frac{51}{34} = \frac{3}{n}$$

$51 \cdot n = 34 \cdot 3$ Set cross products equal.

$51 \cdot n = 102$ Multiply.

Step 2:

$n = \frac{102}{51}$ Divide 102 by 51, the number multiplied by n.

$n = 2$ Simplify.

Check: $\frac{34}{51} \stackrel{?}{=} \frac{2}{3}$ Replace n with its value, 2.

$$\frac{51}{34} \stackrel{?}{=} \frac{3}{2}$$

$51 \cdot 2 \stackrel{?}{=} 34 \cdot 3$ Cross products are equal,

$102 = 102$ so the proportion is true.

Work Practice 5

PRACTICE 5

Find the value of the unknown number n.

$$\frac{15}{2} = \frac{60}{n}$$

Example 6 Find the unknown number n.

$$\frac{7}{n} = \frac{6}{5}$$

Solution:

Step 1:

$$\frac{7}{n} = \frac{6}{5}$$

$7 \cdot 5 = n \cdot 6$ Set the cross products equal to each other.

$35 = n \cdot 6$ Multiply.

Step 2:

$\frac{35}{6} = n$ Divide 35 by 6, the number multiplied by n.

$5\frac{5}{6} = n$

Check: Check to see that $5\frac{5}{6}$ is the unknown number.

Work Practice 6

PRACTICE 6

Find the unknown number n.

$$\frac{8}{n} = \frac{5}{9}$$

Answers

5. $n = 8$

6. $n = 14\frac{2}{5}$

PRACTICE 7

Find the unknown number n.

$$\frac{n}{6} = \frac{0.7}{1.2}$$

Example 7 Find the unknown number n.

$$\frac{n}{3} = \frac{0.8}{1.5}$$

Solution:

Step 1:

$$\frac{n}{3} = \frac{0.8}{1.5}$$

$n \cdot 1.5 = 3 \cdot 0.8$ Set the cross products equal to each other.

$n \cdot 1.5 = 2.4$ Multiply.

Step 2:

$n = \frac{2.4}{1.5}$ Divide 2.4 by 1.5, the number multiplied by n.

$n = 1.6$ Simplify.

Check: Check to see that 1.6 is the unknown number.

Work Practice 7

PRACTICE 8

Find the unknown number n.

$$\frac{n}{4\frac{1}{3}} = \frac{4\frac{1}{2}}{1\frac{3}{4}}$$

Example 8 Find the unknown number n.

$$\frac{1\frac{2}{3}}{3\frac{1}{4}} = \frac{n}{2\frac{3}{5}}$$

Solution:

Step 1:

$$\frac{1\frac{2}{3}}{3\frac{1}{4}} = \frac{n}{2\frac{3}{5}}$$

$1\frac{2}{3} \cdot 2\frac{3}{5} = 3\frac{1}{4} \cdot n$ Set the cross products equal to each other.

$\frac{13}{3} = 3\frac{1}{4} \cdot n$ Multiply. $1\frac{2}{3} \cdot 2\frac{3}{5} = \frac{5}{3} \cdot \frac{13}{5} = \frac{\overset{1}{\cancel{5}} \cdot 13}{3 \cdot \underset{1}{\cancel{5}}} = \frac{13}{3}$

$\frac{13}{3} = \frac{13}{4} \cdot n$ Write $3\frac{1}{4}$ as $\frac{13}{4}$.

Step 2:

$\frac{13}{3} \div \frac{13}{4} = n$ Divide $\frac{13}{3}$ by $\frac{13}{4}$, the number multiplied by n.

or

$n = \frac{13}{3} \cdot \frac{4}{13} = \frac{4}{3}$ or $1\frac{1}{3}$ Divide by multiplying by the reciprocal.

Check: Check to see that $1\frac{1}{3}$ is the unknown number.

Work Practice 8

Answers

7. $n = 3.5$

8. $n = 11\frac{1}{7}$

Vocabulary and Readiness Check

Use the words and phrases below to fill in each blank.

ratio	cross products	true
false	proportion	

1. $\frac{4.2}{8.4} = \frac{1}{2}$ is called a ____________ while $\frac{7}{8}$ is called a(n) ____________.

2. In $\frac{a}{b} = \frac{c}{d}$, $a \cdot d$ and $b \cdot c$ are called ____________.

3. In a proportion, if cross products are equal, the proportion is ____________.

4. In a proportion, if cross products are not equal, the proportion is ____________.

Use cross products and mentally determine whether each proportion is true or false.

5. $\frac{2}{1} = \frac{6}{3}$ **6.** $\frac{3}{1} = \frac{15}{5}$ **7.** $\frac{1}{2} = \frac{3}{5}$ **8.** $\frac{2}{11} = \frac{1}{5}$ **9.** $\frac{2}{3} = \frac{40}{60}$ **10.** $\frac{3}{4} = \frac{6}{8}$

5.3 Exercise Set

FOR EXTRA HELP

MyMathLab

Objective A *Write each sentence as a proportion. See Example 1.*

1. 10 diamonds is to 6 opals as 5 diamonds is to 3 opals.

2. 8 books is to 6 courses as 4 books is to 3 courses.

3. 3 printers is to 12 computers as 1 printer is to 4 computers.

4. 4 hit songs is to 16 releases as 1 hit song is to 4 releases.

5. 6 eagles is to 58 sparrows as 3 eagles is to 29 sparrows.

6. 12 errors is to 8 pages as 1.5 errors is to 1 page.

7. $2\frac{1}{4}$ cups of flour is to 24 cookies as $6\frac{3}{4}$ cups of flour is to 72 cookies.

8. $1\frac{1}{2}$ cups milk is to 10 bagels as $\frac{3}{4}$ cup milk is to 5 bagels.

9. 22 vanilla wafers is to 1 cup of cookie crumbs as 55 vanilla wafers is to 2.5 cups of cookie crumbs. (*Source:* Based on data from *Family Circle* magazine)

10. 1 cup of instant rice is to 1.5 cups cooked rice as 1.5 cups of instant rice is to 2.25 cups of cooked rice. (*Source:* Based on data from *Family Circle* magazine)

Objective **B** *Determine whether each proportion is a true proportion. See Examples 2 through 4.*

11. $\frac{15}{9} = \frac{5}{3}$ **12.** $\frac{8}{6} = \frac{20}{15}$ **13.** $\frac{8}{6} = \frac{9}{7}$ **14.** $\frac{7}{12} = \frac{4}{7}$ **15.** $\frac{9}{36} = \frac{2}{8}$ **16.** $\frac{8}{24} = \frac{3}{9}$

17. $\frac{5}{8} = \frac{625}{1000}$ **18.** $\frac{30}{50} = \frac{600}{1000}$ **19.** $\frac{0.8}{0.3} = \frac{0.2}{0.6}$ **20.** $\frac{0.7}{0.4} = \frac{0.3}{0.1}$ **21.** $\frac{8}{10} = \frac{5.6}{0.7}$ **22.** $\frac{4.2}{8.4} = \frac{5}{10}$

23. $\frac{\frac{3}{4}}{\frac{4}{3}} = \frac{\frac{1}{2}}{\frac{8}{9}}$ **24.** $\frac{\frac{2}{5}}{\frac{2}{7}} = \frac{\frac{1}{10}}{\frac{1}{3}}$ **25.** $\frac{2\frac{2}{5}}{\frac{2}{3}} = \frac{1\frac{1}{9}}{\frac{1}{4}}$ **26.** $\frac{5\frac{5}{8}}{\frac{5}{3}} = \frac{4\frac{1}{2}}{1\frac{1}{5}}$ **27.** $\frac{\frac{4}{5}}{6} = \frac{\frac{6}{5}}{9}$ **28.** $\frac{\frac{6}{7}}{3} = \frac{\frac{10}{7}}{5}$

Objectives **A** **B** **Mixed Practice—Translating** *Write each sentence as a proportion. Then determine whether the proportion is a true proportion. See Examples 1 through 4.*

29. eight is to twelve as four is to six

30. six is to eight as nine is to twelve

31. five is to two as thirteen is to five

32. four is to three as seven is to five

33. one and eight tenths is to two as four and five tenths is to five

34. fifteen hundredths is to three as thirty-five hundredths is to seven

35. two thirds is to one fifth as two fifths is to one ninth

36. ten elevenths is to three fourths as one fourth is to one half

Objectives **C** *For each proportion, find the unknown number n. See Examples 5 through 8.*

37. $\frac{n}{5} = \frac{6}{10}$ **38.** $\frac{n}{3} = \frac{12}{9}$ **39.** $\frac{18}{54} = \frac{3}{n}$ **40.** $\frac{25}{100} = \frac{7}{n}$

41. $\frac{n}{8} = \frac{50}{100}$ **42.** $\frac{n}{21} = \frac{12}{18}$ **43.** $\frac{8}{15} = \frac{n}{6}$ **44.** $\frac{12}{10} = \frac{n}{16}$

45. $\frac{24}{n} = \frac{60}{96}$

46. $\frac{26}{n} = \frac{28}{49}$

47. $\frac{3.5}{12.5} = \frac{7}{n}$

48. $\frac{0.2}{0.7} = \frac{8}{n}$

49. $\frac{0.05}{12} = \frac{n}{0.6}$

50. $\frac{7.8}{13} = \frac{n}{2.6}$

51. $\frac{8}{\frac{1}{3}} = \frac{24}{n}$

52. $\frac{12}{\frac{3}{4}} = \frac{48}{n}$

53. $\frac{\frac{1}{3}}{\frac{3}{8}} = \frac{\frac{2}{5}}{n}$

54. $\frac{\frac{7}{9}}{\frac{8}{27}} = \frac{\frac{1}{4}}{n}$

55. $\frac{12}{n} = \frac{\frac{2}{3}}{\frac{6}{9}}$

56. $\frac{24}{n} = \frac{\frac{8}{15}}{\frac{5}{9}}$

57. $\frac{n}{1\frac{1}{5}} = \frac{4\frac{1}{6}}{6\frac{2}{3}}$

58. $\frac{n}{3\frac{1}{8}} = \frac{7\frac{3}{5}}{2\frac{3}{8}}$

59. $\frac{25}{n} = \frac{3}{\frac{7}{30}}$

60. $\frac{9}{n} = \frac{5}{\frac{11}{15}}$

Review

Insert < or > to form a true statement. See Sections 3.5 and 4.2.

61. 8.01 8.1

62. 7.26 7.026

63. $2\frac{1}{2}$ $2\frac{1}{3}$

64. $9\frac{1}{5}$ $9\frac{1}{4}$

65. $5\frac{1}{3}$ $6\frac{2}{3}$

66. $1\frac{1}{2}$ $2\frac{1}{2}$

Concept Extensions

Use the numbers in each proportion to write two other true proportions. See the Concept Check in this section.

67. $\frac{9}{15} = \frac{3}{5}$

68. $\frac{1}{4} = \frac{5}{20}$

69. $\frac{6}{18} = \frac{1}{3}$

70. $\frac{2}{7} = \frac{4}{14}$

71. If the proportion $\frac{a}{b} = \frac{c}{d}$ is a true proportion, write two other true proportions using the same letters.

72. Write a true proportion.

73. Explain the difference between a ratio and a proportion.

74. Explain how to find the unknown number in a proportion such as $\frac{n}{18} = \frac{12}{8}$.

For each proportion, find the unknown number n. For Exercises 75 through 80, round your answer to the given place value.

75. $\frac{3.2}{0.3} = \frac{n}{1.4}$

Round to the nearest tenth.

76. $\frac{1.8}{n} = \frac{2.5}{8.4}$

Round to the nearest tenth.

77. $\frac{n}{5.2} = \frac{0.08}{6}$

Round to the nearest hundredth.

78. $\frac{4.25}{6.03} = \frac{5}{n}$

Round to the nearest hundredth.

79. $\frac{43}{17} = \frac{8}{n}$

Round to the nearest thousandth.

80. $\frac{n}{12} = \frac{18}{7}$

Round to the nearest hundredth.

81. $\frac{n}{7} = \frac{0}{8}$

82. $\frac{0}{2} = \frac{n}{3.5}$

83. $\frac{n}{1150} = \frac{588}{483}$

84. $\frac{585}{n} = \frac{117}{474}$

85. $\frac{222}{1515} = \frac{37}{n}$

86. $\frac{1425}{1062} = \frac{n}{177}$

5.4 PROPORTIONS AND PROBLEM SOLVING

Objective

A **Solve Problems by Writing Proportions.**

Objective A Solving Problems by Writing Proportions

Writing proportions is a powerful tool for solving problems in almost every field, including business, chemistry, biology, health sciences, and engineering, as well as in daily life. Given a specified ratio (or rate) of two quantities, a proportion can be used to determine an unknown quantity.

In this section, we use the same problem-solving steps that we have used earlier in this text.

Example 1 Determining Distances from a Map

On a chamber of commerce map of Abita Springs, 5 miles corresponds to 2 inches. How many miles correspond to 7 inches?

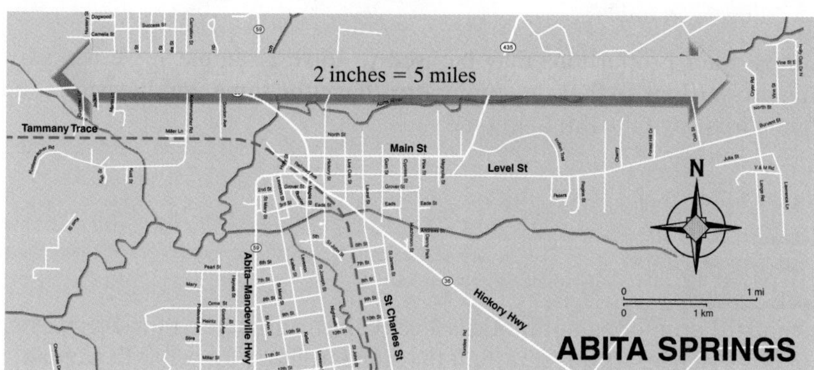

Solution:

1. UNDERSTAND. Read and reread the problem. You may want to draw a diagram.

between 15 and 20 miles

15 miles (above the first three columns); 20 miles (above all four columns)

5 miles	5 miles	5 miles	5 miles	= a little over 15 miles
2 inches	2 inches	2 inches	2 inches	= 7 inches

6 inches (below the first three columns); 8 inches (below all four columns)

7 inches

From the diagram we can see that a reasonable solution should be between 15 and 20 miles.

2. TRANSLATE. We will let n represent our unknown number. Since 5 miles corresponds to 2 inches as n miles corresponds to 7 inches, we have the proportion

$$\begin{array}{lcccl} \text{miles} & \rightarrow & \dfrac{5}{2} = \dfrac{n}{7} & \leftarrow & \text{miles} \\ \text{inches} & \rightarrow & & \leftarrow & \text{inches} \end{array}$$

3. SOLVE: In earlier sections, we estimated to obtain a reasonable answer. Notice we did this in Step 1 above.

$$\frac{5}{2} = \frac{n}{7}$$

Continued on next page

PRACTICE 1

On an architect's blueprint, 1 inch corresponds to 4 feet. How long is a wall represented by a $4\frac{1}{4}$-inch line on the blueprint?

Answer

1. 17 ft

$$5 \cdot 7 = 2 \cdot n \quad \text{Set the cross products equal to each other.}$$
$$35 = 2 \cdot n \quad \text{Multiply.}$$
$$\frac{35}{2} = n \quad \text{Divide 35 by 2, the number multiplied by } n.$$
$$n = 17\frac{1}{2} \text{ or } 17.5 \quad \text{Simplify.}$$

4. INTERPRET. *Check* your work. This result is reasonable since it is between 15 and 20 miles. *State* your conclusion: 7 inches corresponds to 17.5 miles.

Work Practice 1

Helpful Hint

We can also solve Example 1 by writing the proportion

$$\frac{2 \text{ inches}}{5 \text{ miles}} = \frac{7 \text{ inches}}{n \text{ miles}}$$

Although other proportions may be used to solve Example 1, we will solve by writing proportions so that the numerators have the same unit measures and the denominators have the same unit measures.

PRACTICE 2

An auto mechanic recommends that 3 ounces of isopropyl alcohol be mixed with a tankful of gas (14 gallons) to increase the octane of the gasoline for better engine performance. At this rate, how many gallons of gas can be treated with a 16-ounce bottle of alcohol?

Example 2 Finding Medicine Dosage

The standard dose of an antibiotic is 4 cc (cubic centimeters) for every 25 pounds (lb) of body weight. At this rate, find the standard dose for a 140-lb woman.

Solution:

1. UNDERSTAND. Read and reread the problem. You may want to draw a diagram to estimate a reasonable solution.

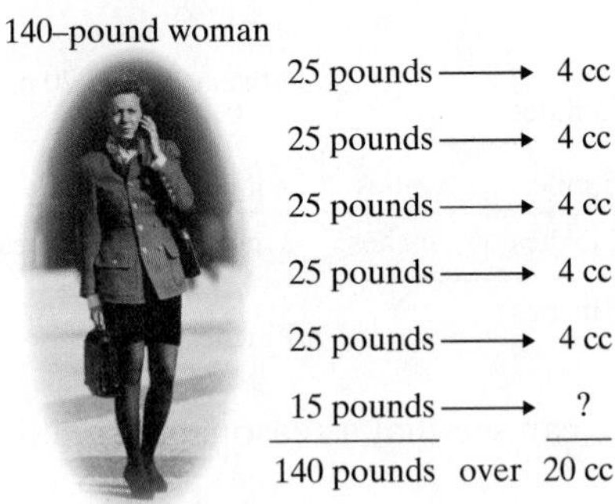

From the diagram, we can see that a reasonable solution is a little over 20 cc.

2. TRANSLATE. We will let n represent the unknown number. From the problem, we know that 4 cc is to 25 pounds as n cc is to 140 pounds, or

$$\begin{array}{rcl} \text{cubic centimeters} \rightarrow & \dfrac{4}{25} = \dfrac{n}{140} & \leftarrow \text{cubic centimeters} \\ \text{pounds} \rightarrow & & \leftarrow \text{pounds} \end{array}$$

3. SOLVE:

$$\frac{4}{25} = \frac{n}{140}$$

Answer

2. $74\frac{2}{3}$ or $74.\overline{6}$ gal

$4 \cdot 140 = 25 \cdot n$ Set the cross products equal to each other.

$560 = 25 \cdot n$ Multiply.

$\frac{560}{25} = n$ Divide 560 by 25, the number multiplied by n.

$n = 22\frac{2}{5}$ or 22.4 Simplify.

4. INTERPRET. *Check* your work. This result is reasonable since it is a little over 20 cc. *State* your conclusion: The standard dose for a 140-lb woman is 22.4 cc.

Work Practice 2

Example 3 Calculating Supplies Needed to Fertilize a Lawn

A 50-pound bag of fertilizer covers 2400 square feet of lawn. How many bags of fertilizer are needed to cover a town square containing 15,360 square feet of lawn? Round the answer up to the nearest whole bag.

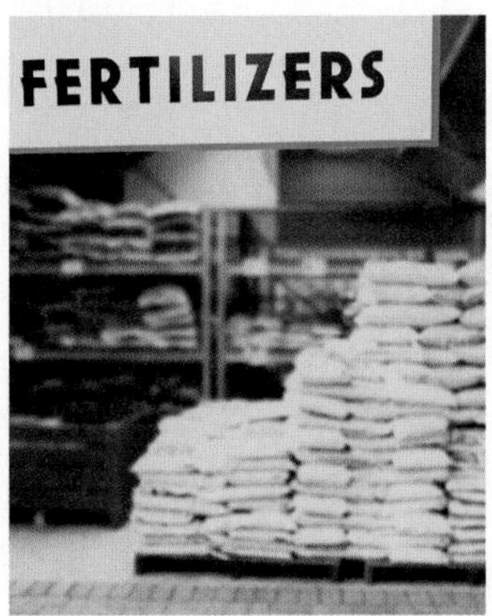

PRACTICE 3

If a gallon of paint covers 400 square feet, how many gallons are needed to paint a retaining wall that is 260 feet long and 4 feet high? Round the answer up to the nearest whole gallon.

Solution:

1. UNDERSTAND. Read and reread the problem. Draw a picture.

Since one bag covers 2400 square feet, let's see how many 2400's there are in 15,360. We will estimate. The number 15,360 rounded to the nearest thousand is 15,000 and 2400 rounded to the nearest thousand is 2000. Then

$15{,}000 \div 2000 = 7\frac{1}{2}$ or 7.5.

2. TRANSLATE. We'll let n represent the unknown number. From the problem, we know that 1 bag is to 2400 square feet as n bags is to 15,360 square feet.

$$\begin{array}{lcccl} \text{bags} & \rightarrow & \frac{1}{2400} = \frac{n}{15{,}360} & \leftarrow & \text{bags} \\ \text{square feet} & \rightarrow & & \leftarrow & \text{square feet} \end{array}$$

Continued on next page

Answer

3. 3 gal

3. SOLVE:

$$\frac{1}{2400} = \frac{n}{15{,}360}$$

$1 \cdot 15{,}360 = 2400 \cdot n$	Set the cross products equal to each other.
$15{,}360 = 2400 \cdot n$	Multiply.
$\frac{15{,}360}{2400} = n$	Divide 15,360 by 2400, the number multiplied by n.
$n = 6.4$	Simplify.

4. INTERPRET. *Check* that replacing n with 6.4 makes the proportion true. Is the answer reasonable? Yes, since it's close to $7\frac{1}{2}$ or 7.5. Since we must buy whole bags of fertilizer, 7 bags are needed. *State* your conclusion: To cover 15,360 square feet of lawn, 7 bags are needed.

Work Practice 3

✓Concept Check You are told that 12 ounces of ground coffee will brew enough coffee to serve 20 people. How could you estimate how much ground coffee will be needed to serve 95 people?

✓ Concept Check Answer

Find how much will be needed for 100 people (20×5) by multiplying 12 ounces by 5, which is 60 ounces.

5.4 Exercise Set

FOR EXTRA HELP

MyMathLab

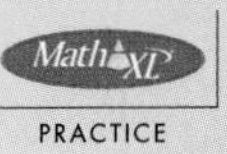
PRACTICE

WATCH

DOWNLOAD

READ

REVIEW

Objective **A** *Solve. For Exercises 1 and 2, the solutions have been started for you. See Examples 1 through 3.*
An NBA basketball player averages 45 baskets for every 100 attempts.

1. If he attempted 800 field goals, how many field goals did he make?

Start the solution:

1. UNDERSTAND the problem. Reread it as many times as needed. Let's let

x = how many field goals he made

2. TRANSLATE into an equation.

baskets (field goals) → / attempts → $\frac{45}{100} = \frac{x}{800}$ ← baskets (field goals) / ← attempts

3. SOLVE the equation. Set cross products equal to each other and solve.

$$\frac{45}{100} \times \frac{x}{800}$$

After SOLVING, then **4.** INTERPRET.

2. If he made 225 baskets, how many did he attempt?

Start the solution:

1. UNDERSTAND the problem. Reread it as many times as needed. Let's let

x = how many baskets attempted

2. TRANSLATE into an equation.

baskets → / attempts → $\frac{45}{100} = \frac{225}{x}$ ← baskets / ← attempts

3. SOLVE the equation. Set cross products equal to each other and solve.

$$\frac{45}{100} \times \frac{225}{x}$$

After SOLVING, then **4.** INTERPRET.

It takes a word processor 30 minutes to word process and spell check 4 pages.

3. Find how long it takes her to word process and spell check 22 pages.

4. Find how many pages she can word process and spell check in 4.5 hours.

University Law School accepts 2 out of every 7 applicants.

5. If the school accepted 180 students, find how many applications they received.

6. If the school accepted 150 students, find how many applications they received.

On an architect's blueprint, 1 inch corresponds to 8 feet.

7. Find the length of a wall represented by a line $2\frac{7}{8}$ inches long on the blueprint.

8. Find the length of a wall represented by a line $5\frac{1}{4}$ inches long on the blueprint.

A human-factors expert recommends that there be at least 9 square feet of floor space in a college classroom for every student in the class.

△ **9.** Find the minimum floor space that 30 students require.

△ **10.** Due to a lack of space, a university converts a 21-by-15-foot conference room into a classroom. Find the maximum number of students the room can accommodate.

A Honda Civic Hybrid car averages 627 miles on a 12.3-gallon tank of gas.

11. Manuel Lopez is planning a 1250-mile vacation trip in his Honda Civic Hybrid. Find how many gallons of gas he can expect to burn. Round to the nearest gallon.

12. Ramona Hatch has enough money to put 6.9 gallons of gas in her Honda Civic Hybrid. She is planning on driving home from college for the weekend. If her home is 290 miles away, should she make it home before she runs out of gas?

The scale on an Italian map states that 1 centimeter corresponds to 30 kilometers.

13. Find how far apart Milan and Rome are if their corresponding points on the map are 15 centimeters apart.

14. On the map, a small Italian village is located 0.4 centimeter from the Mediterranean Sea. Find the actual distance.

A bag of Scott fertilizer covers 3000 square feet of lawn.

△ **15.** Find how many bags of fertilizer should be purchased to cover a rectangular lawn 260 feet by 180 feet.

△ **16.** Find how many bags of fertilizer should be purchased to cover a square lawn measuring 160 feet on each side.

A Cubs baseball player gets 3 hits every 8 times at bat.

17. If this Cubs player comes up to bat 40 times in the World Series, find how many hits he would be expected to get.

18. At this rate, if he got 12 hits, find how many times he batted.

A survey reveals that 2 out of 3 people prefer Coke to Pepsi.

19. In a room of 40 people, how many people are likely to prefer Coke? Round the answer to the nearest person.

20. In a college class of 36 students, find how many students are likely to prefer Pepsi.

A self-tanning lotion advertises that a 3-oz bottle will provide four applications.

21. Jen Haddad found a great deal on a 14-oz bottle of the self-tanning lotion she had been using. Based on the advertising claims, how many applications of the self-tanner should Jen expect? Round down to the smaller whole number.

22. The Community College thespians need fake tans for a play they are doing. If the play has a cast of 35, how many ounces of self-tanning lotion should the cast purchase? Round up to the next whole number of ounces.

The school's computer lab goes through 5 reams of printer paper every 3 weeks.

23. Find out how long a case of printer paper is likely to last (a case of paper holds 8 reams of paper). Round to the nearest week.

24. How many cases of printer paper should be purchased to last the entire semester of 15 weeks? Round up to the next case.

A recipe for pancakes calls for 2 cups flour and $1\frac{1}{2}$ *cups milk to make a serving for four people.*

25. Ming has plenty of flour, but only 4 cups milk. How many servings can he make?

26. The swim team has a weekly breakfast after early practice. How much flour will it take to make pancakes for 18 swimmers?

27. In the Seattle Space Needle, the elevators whisk you to the revolving restaurant at a speed of 800 feet in 60 seconds. If the revolving restaurant is 500 feet up, how long will it take you to reach the restaurant by elevator? (*Source:* Seattle Space Needle)

28. A 16-oz grande Tazo Black Iced Tea at Starbucks has 80 calories. How many calories are there in a 24-oz venti Tazo Black Iced Tea? (*Source:* Starbucks Coffee Company)

29. Mosquitos are annoying insects. To eliminate mosquito larvae, a certain granular substance can be applied to standing water in a ratio of 1 tsp per 25 sq ft of standing water.

a. At this rate, find how many teaspoons of granules must be used for 450 square feet.

b. If 3 tsp = 1 tbsp, how many tablespoons of granules must be used?

30. Another type of mosquito control is liquid, where 3 oz of pesticide is mixed with 100 oz of water. This mixture is sprayed on roadsides to control mosquito breeding grounds hidden by tall grass.

a. If one mixture of water with this pesticide can treat 150 feet of roadway, how many ounces of pesticide are needed to treat one mile? (*Hint:* 1 mile = 5280 feet)

b. If 8 liquid ounces equals one cup, write your answer to part **a** in cups. Round to the nearest cup.

31. The daily supply of oxygen for one person is provided by 625 square feet of lawn. A total of 3750 square feet of lawn would provide the daily supply of oxygen for how many people? (*Source:* Professional Lawn Care Association of America)

32. In a recent year, approximately $16 billion of the $40 billion Americans spent on their pets was spent on pet food. Petsmart had $4,672,656 in net sales that year. How much of Petsmart's net sales would you expect to have been spent on pet food? (*Source:* American Pet Products Manufacturers Association and Petsmart)

33. A student would like to estimate the height of the Statue of Liberty in New York City's harbor. The length of the Statue of Liberty's right arm is 42 feet. The student's right arm is 2 feet long and her height is $5\frac{1}{3}$ feet. Use this information to estimate the height of the Statue of Liberty. How close is your estimate to the statue's actual height of 111 feet, 1 inch from heel to top of head? (*Source:* National Park Service)

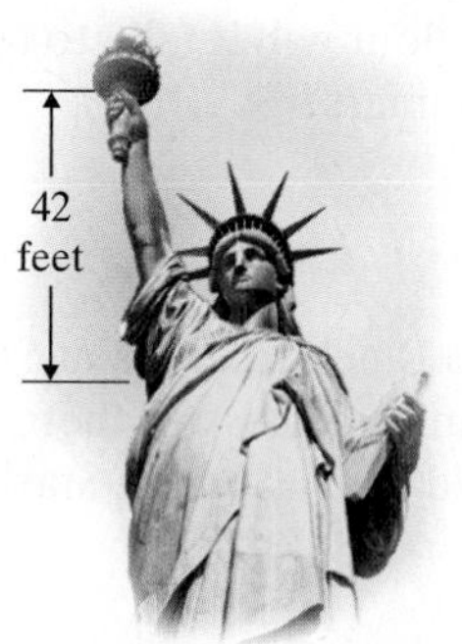

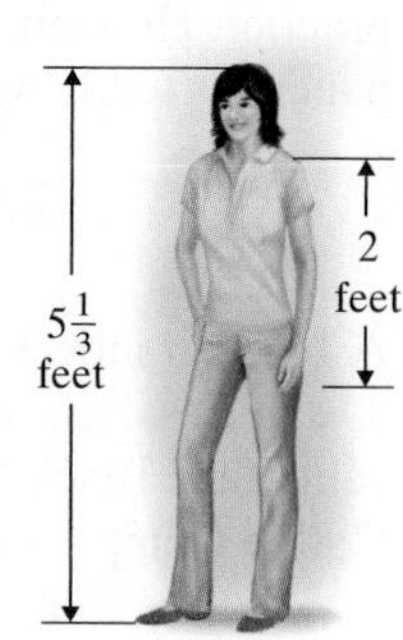

34. The length of the Statue of Liberty's index finger is 8 feet while the height to the top of the head is about 111 feet. Suppose your measurements are proportionally the same as this statue and your height is 5 feet.

a. Use this information to find the proposed length of your index finger. Give an exact measurement and then a decimal rounded to the nearest hundredth.

b. Measure your index finger and write it as a decimal in feet rounded to the nearest hundredth. How close is the length of your index finger to the answer to part **a**? Explain why.

35. There are 72 milligrams of cholesterol in a 3.5-ounce serving of lobster. How much cholesterol is in 5 ounces of lobster? Round to the nearest tenth of a milligram. (*Source:* The National Institute of Health)

36. There are 76 milligrams of cholesterol in a 3-ounce serving of skinless chicken. How much cholesterol is in 8 ounces of chicken? (*Source:* USDA)

37. Trump World Tower in New York City is 881 feet tall and contains 72 stories. The Empire State Building contains 102 stories. If the Empire State Building has the same number of feet per floor as the Trump World Tower, approximate its height rounded to the nearest foot. (*Source:* skyscrapers.com)

38. In 2009, in the United States, approximately 178 million of the 250 million cars and light trucks in service had driver-side airbags. In a parking lot containing 750 cars and light trucks, how many would be expected to have driver-side air bags? (*Source:* Insurance Institute for Highway Safety)

39. Medication is prescribed in 7 out of every 10 hospital emergency room visits that involve an injury. If a large urban hospital had 620 emergency room visits involving an injury in the past month, how many of these visits would you expect included a prescription for medication? (*Source:* National Center for Health Statistics)

40. Currently in the American population of people aged 65 years old and older, there are 145 women for every 100 men. In a nursing home with 280 male residents over the age of 65, how many female residents over the age of 65 would be expected? (*Source:* U.S. Bureau of the Census)

41. One out of three American adults has worked in the restaurant industry at some point during his or her life. In an office of 84 workers, how many of these people would you expect to have worked in the restaurant industry at some point? (*Source:* National Restaurant Association)

42. One pound of firmly packed brown sugar yields $2\frac{1}{4}$ cups. How many pounds of brown sugar will be required in a recipe that calls for 6 cups of firmly packed brown sugar? (*Source:* Based on data from *Family Circle* magazine)

When making homemade ice cream in a hand-cranked freezer, the tub containing the ice cream mix is surrounded by a brine (water/salt) solution. To freeze the ice cream mix rapidly so that smooth and creamy ice cream results, the brine solution should combine crushed ice and rock salt in a ratio of 5 to 1. Use this information for Exercises 43 and 44. (*Source:* White Mountain Freezers, The Rival Company)

43. A small ice cream freezer requires 12 cups of crushed ice. How much rock salt should be mixed with the ice to create the necessary brine solution?

44. A large ice cream freezer requires $18\frac{3}{4}$ cups of crushed ice. How much rock salt will be needed to create the necessary brine solution?

45. The gas/oil ratio for a certain chainsaw is 50 to 1.

a. How much oil (in gallons) should be mixed with 5 gallons of gasoline?

b. If 1 gallon equals 128 fluid ounces, write the answer to part **a** in fluid ounces. Round to the nearest whole ounce.

46. The gas/oil ratio for a certain tractor mower is 20 to 1.

a. How much oil (in gallons) should be mixed with 10 gallons of gas?

b. If 1 gallon equals 4 quarts, write the answer to part **a** in quarts.

47. The adult daily dosage for a certain medicine is 150 mg (milligrams) of medicine for every 20 pounds of body weight.

a. At this rate, find the daily dose for a man who weighs 275 pounds.

b. If the man is to receive 500 mg of this medicine every 8 hours, is he receiving the proper dosage?

48. The adult daily dosage for a certain medicine is 80 mg (milligrams) for every 25 pounds of body weight.

a. At this rate, find the daily dose for a woman who weighs 190 pounds.

b. If she is to receive this medicine every 6 hours, find the amount to be given every 6 hours.

Review

Find the prime factorization of each number. See Section 2.2.

49. 15 **50.** 21 **51.** 20 **52.** 24

53. 200 **54.** 300 **55.** 32 **56.** 81

Concept Extensions

As we have seen earlier, proportions are often used in medicine dosage calculations. The exercises below have to do with liquid drug preparations, where the weight of the drug is contained in a volume of solution. The description of mg and ml below will help. We will study metric units further in Chapter 7.

mg means milligrams (A paper clip weighs about a gram. A milligram is about the weight of $\frac{1}{1000}$ *of a paper clip.)*

ml means milliliter (A liter is about a quart. A milliliter is about the amount of liquid in $\frac{1}{1000}$ *of a quart.)*

One way to solve the applications below is to set up the proportion $\frac{\text{mg}}{\text{ml}} = \frac{\text{mg}}{\text{ml}}$.

A solution strength of 15 mg of medicine in 1 ml of solution is available.

57. If a patient needs 12 mg of medicine, how many ml do you administer?

58. If a patient needs 33 mg of medicine, how many ml do you administer?

A solution strength of 8 mg of medicine in 1 ml of solution is available.

59. If a patient needs 10 mg of medicine, how many ml do you administer?

60. If a patient needs 6 mg of medicine, how many ml do you administer?

Estimate the following. See the Concept Check in this section.

61. It takes 1.5 cups of milk to make 11 muffins. Estimate the amount of milk needed to make 8 dozen muffins. Explain your calculation.

62. A favorite chocolate chip recipe calls for $2\frac{1}{2}$ cups of flour to make 2 dozen cookies. Estimate the amount of flour needed to make 50 cookies. Explain your calculation.

A board such as the one pictured below will balance if the following proportion is true:

$$\frac{\text{first weight}}{\text{second distance}} = \frac{\text{second weight}}{\text{first distance}}$$

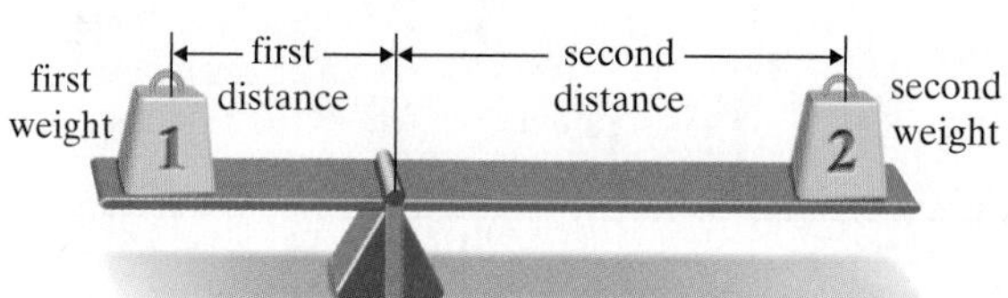

Use this proportion to solve Exercises 63 and 64.

63. Find the distance n that will allow the board to balance.

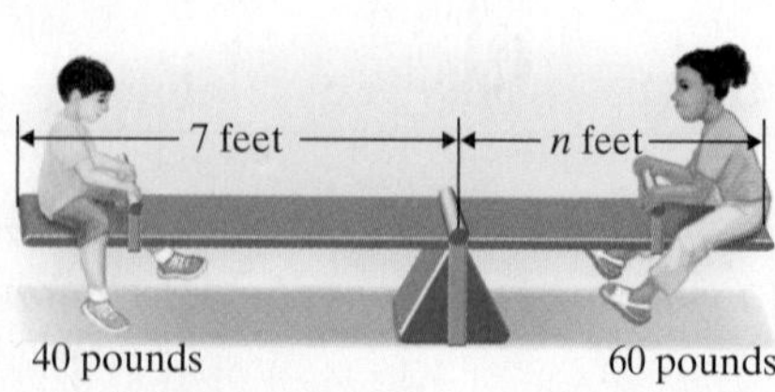

64. Find the length n needed to lift the weight below.

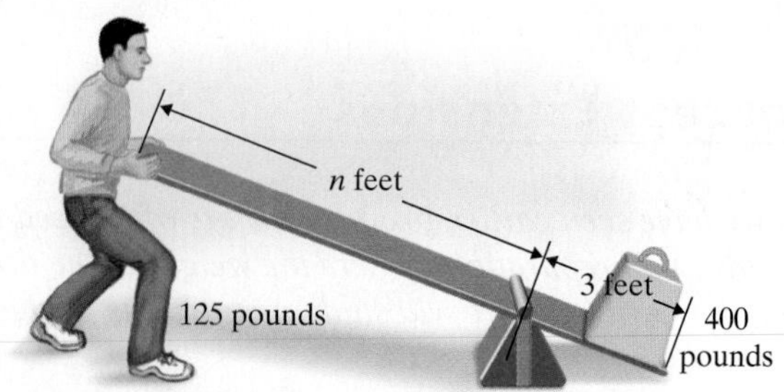

65. Describe a situation in which writing a proportion might solve a problem related to driving a car.

Chapter 5 Group Activity

Sections 5.1–5.4 Consumer Price Index

Do you remember when the regular price of a candy bar was 5¢, 10¢, or 25¢? It is certainly difficult to find a candy bar for that price these days. The reason is inflation: the tendency for the price of a given product to increase over time. Businesses and government agencies use the Consumer Price Index (CPI) to track inflation. The CPI measures the change in prices over time of basic consumer goods and services.

The CPI is very useful for comparing the prices of fixed items in various years. For instance, suppose an insurance company customer submits a claim for the theft of a fishing boat purchased in 1975. Because the customer's policy includes replacement cost coverage, the insurance company must calculate how much it would cost to replace the boat at the time of the theft. (Let's assume the theft took place in February 2010.) The customer has a receipt for the boat showing that it cost \$598 in 1975. The insurance company can use the following proportion to calculate the replacement cost:

$$\frac{\text{price in earlier year}}{\text{price in later year}} = \frac{\text{CPI value in earlier year}}{\text{CPI value in later year}}$$

The CPI value is 53.8 for 1975. In February 2010, the CPI value is 216.9. The insurance company would then use the following proportion for this situation. (We will let n represent the unknown price in February 2010.)

$$\frac{\text{price in 1975}}{\text{price in 2010}} = \frac{\text{CPI value in 1975}}{\text{CPI value in Feb. 2010}}$$

$$\frac{598}{n} = \frac{53.8}{216.9}$$

$$53.8 \cdot n = 598(216.9)$$

$$53.8 \cdot n = 129{,}706.2$$

$$\frac{53.8 \cdot n}{53.8} = \frac{129{,}706.2}{53.8}$$

$$n \approx 2411$$

The replacement cost of the fishing boat at February 2010 prices is \$2411.

Critical Thinking

1. What trends do you see in the CPI values in the table? Do you think these trends make sense? Explain.
2. A piece of jewelry cost \$800 in 1985. What is its 2005 replacement value?
3. In 2000, the cost of a loaf of bread was about \$1.89. What would an equivalent loaf of bread cost in 1950?
4. Suppose a couple purchased a house for \$12,000 in 1940. At what price could they have been expected to sell the house in 1990?
5. An original Ford Model T cost about \$850 in 1915. What is the equivalent cost of a Model T in 2008 dollars?

Consumer Price Index

Year	CPI
1915	10.1
1920	20.0
1925	17.5
1930	16.7
1935	13.7
1940	14.0
1945	18.0
1950	24.1
1955	26.8
1960	29.6
1965	31.5
1970	38.8
1975	53.8
1980	82.4
1985	107.6
1990	130.7
1995	152.4
2000	172.2
2005	195.3
2006	201.6
2007	207.3
2008	215.3
2009	214.5

(*Source:* Bureau of Labor Statistics, U.S. Department of Labor)

Chapter 5 Vocabulary Check

Fill in each blank with one of the words or phrases listed below.

not equal	equal	cross products	rate
unit rate	ratio	unit price	proportion

1. A(n) _______________ is the quotient of two numbers. It can be written as a fraction, using a colon, or using the word *to*.

2. $\frac{x}{2} = \frac{7}{16}$ is an example of a(n) _______________.

3. A(n) _______________ is a rate with a denominator of 1.

4. A(n) _______________ is a "money per item" unit rate.

5. A(n) _______________ is used to compare different kinds of quantities.

6. In the proportion $\frac{x}{2} = \frac{7}{16}$, $x \cdot 16$ and $2 \cdot 7$ are called _______________.

7. If cross products are _______________, the proportion is true.

8. If cross products are _______________, the proportion is false.

Helpful Hint Are you preparing for your test? Don't forget to take the Chapter 5 Test on page 365. Then check your answers at the back of the text and use the Chapter Test Prep Videos to see the fully worked-out solutions to any of the exercises you want to review.

5 Chapter Highlights

Definitions and Concepts	Examples
Section 5.1 Ratios	
A **ratio** is the quotient of two quantities.	The ratio of 3 to 4 can be written as $\frac{3}{4}$ (fraction notation) or $3:4$ (colon notation)
Section 5.2 Rates	
Rates are used to compare different kinds of quantities.	Write the rate 12 spikes every 8 inches as a fraction in simplest form. $\frac{12 \text{ spikes}}{8 \text{ inches}} = \frac{3 \text{ spikes}}{2 \text{ inches}}$
A **unit rate** is a rate with a denominator of 1.	Write as a unit rate: 117 miles on 5 gallons of gas $\frac{117 \text{ miles}}{5 \text{ gallons}} = \frac{23.4 \text{ miles}}{1 \text{ gallon}}$ or 23.4 miles per gallon or 23.4 miles/gallon
A **unit price** is a "money per item" unit rate.	Write as a unit price: \$5.88 for 42 ounces of detergent $\frac{\$5.88}{42 \text{ ounces}} = \frac{\$0.14}{1 \text{ ounce}} = \$0.14$ per ounce

Definitions and Concepts	Examples
Section 5.3 Proportions	
A **proportion** is a statement that two ratios or rates are equal.	$\frac{1}{2} = \frac{4}{8}$ is a proportion.
USING CROSS PRODUCTS TO DETERMINE WHETHER PROPORTIONS ARE TRUE OR FALSE 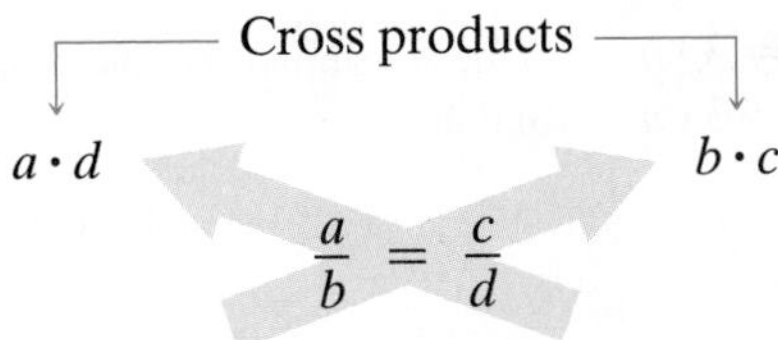 If cross products are equal, the proportion is true. If $ad = bc$, then the proportion is true. If cross products are not equal, the proportion is false. If $ad \neq bc$, then the proportion is false.	Is $\frac{6}{10} = \frac{9}{15}$ a true proportion? Cross products: $6 \cdot 15$ and $10 \cdot 9$ for $\frac{6}{10} = \frac{9}{15}$ $6 \cdot 15 \stackrel{?}{=} 10 \cdot 9$ Are cross products equal? $90 = 90$ Since cross products are equal, the proportion is a true proportion.
FINDING AN UNKNOWN VALUE n IN A PROPORTION **Step 1:** Set the cross products equal to each other.	Find n: $\frac{n}{7} = \frac{5}{8}$ **Step 1:** $\frac{n}{7} = \frac{5}{8}$ $n \cdot 8 = 7 \cdot 5$ Set the cross products equal to each other. $n \cdot 8 = 35$ Multiply.
Step 2: Divide the number not multiplied by n by the number multiplied by n.	**Step 2:** $n = \frac{35}{8}$ Divide 35 by 8, the number multiplied by n. $n = 4\frac{3}{8}$
Section 5.4 Proportions and Problem Solving	
Given a specified ratio (or rate) of two quantities, a proportion can be used to determine an unknown quantity.	On a map, 50 miles corresponds to 3 inches. How many miles correspond to 10 inches? **1.** UNDERSTAND. Read and reread the problem. **2.** TRANSLATE. We let n represent the unknown number. We are given that 50 miles is to 3 inches as n miles is to 10 inches. miles → $\frac{50}{3} = \frac{n}{10}$ ← miles inches → ← inches

(continued)

Definitions and Concepts	Examples
Section 5.4 Proportions and Problem Solving (*continued*)	
	3. SOLVE: $\frac{50}{3} = \frac{n}{10}$ $50 \cdot 10 = 3 \cdot n$ Set the cross products equal to each other. $500 = 3 \cdot n$ Multiply. $\frac{500}{3} = n$ Divide 500 by 3, the number multiplied by n. $n = 166\frac{2}{3}$ **4.** INTERPRET. *Check* your work. *State* your conclusion: On the map, $166\frac{2}{3}$ miles corresponds to 10 inches.

Chapter 5 Review

(5.1) *Write each ratio as a fraction in simplest form.*

1. 23 to 37

2. 14 to 51

3. 6000 people to 4800 people

4. \$121 to \$143

5. 3.5 centimeters to 7.5 centimeters

6. 4.25 yards to 8.75 yards

7. $2\frac{1}{4}$ to $4\frac{3}{8}$

8. $3\frac{1}{2}$ to $2\frac{7}{10}$

The circle graph below shows how the top 25 movies (or films) of 2009 were rated. Use this graph to answer the questions.

Top 25 Movies of 2009

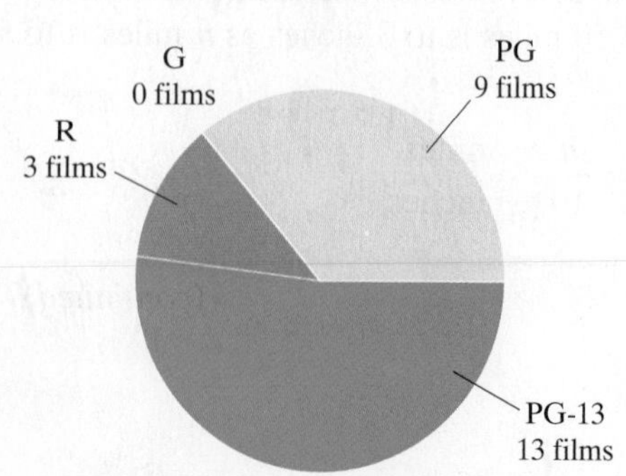

Source: MPAA
Note: There were no G-rated films in the top 25 for 2009

9. a. How many top 25 movies were rated PG?

b. Find the ratio of top 25 PG-rated movies to total movies for that year.

10. a. How many top 25 movies were rated R?

b. Find the ratio of top 25 R-rated movies to total movies for that year.

(5.2) *Write each rate as a fraction in simplest form.*

11. 8 stillborn births to 1000 live births

12. 6 professors for 20 graduate research assistants

13. 15 word processing pages printed in 6 minutes

14. 8 computers assembled in 6 hours

Write each rate as a unit rate.

15. 468 miles in 9 hours

16. 180 feet in 12 seconds

17. \$27.84 for 4 CDs

18. 8 gallons of pesticide for 6 acres of crops

19. \$234 for books for 5 college courses

20. 104 bushels of fruit from 8 trees

Find each unit price and decide which is the better buy. Round to 3 decimal places. Assume that we are comparing different sizes of the same brand.

21. Taco sauce: 8 ounces for \$0.99 or 12 ounces for \$1.69

22. Peanut butter: 18 ounces for \$1.49 or 28 ounces for \$2.39

23. 2% milk: \$0.59 for 16 ounces, \$1.69 for 64 ounces, or \$2.29 for 1 gallon (1 gallon = 128 fluid ounces)

24. Coca-Cola: \$0.59 for 12 ounces, \$0.79 for 16 ounces, or \$1.19 for 32 ounces

(5.3) *Write each sentence as a proportion.*

25. 20 men is to 14 women as 10 men is to 7 women.

26. 50 tries is to 4 successes as 25 tries is to 2 successes.

27. 16 sandwiches is to 8 players as 2 sandwiches is to 1 player.

28. 12 tires is to 3 cars as 4 tires is to 1 car.

Determine whether each proportion is true.

29. $\frac{21}{8} = \frac{14}{6}$ **30.** $\frac{3}{5} = \frac{60}{100}$ **31.** $\frac{3.75}{3} = \frac{7.5}{6}$ **32.** $\frac{3.1}{6.2} = \frac{0.8}{0.16}$

Find the unknown number n in each proportion.

33. $\frac{n}{6} = \frac{15}{18}$ **34.** $\frac{n}{9} = \frac{5}{3}$ **35.** $\frac{4}{13} = \frac{10}{n}$ **36.** $\frac{8}{5} = \frac{9}{n}$

37. $\frac{\frac{8}{3}}{2} = \frac{n}{6}$ **38.** $\frac{\frac{9}{2}}{2} = \frac{n}{\frac{3}{2}}$ **39.** $\frac{\frac{27}{9}}{4} = \frac{n}{5}$ **40.** $\frac{\frac{6}{5}}{2} = \frac{n}{3}$

41. $\frac{0.4}{n} = \frac{2}{4.7}$ **42.** $\frac{7.2}{n} = \frac{6}{0.3}$ **43.** $\frac{n}{4\frac{1}{2}} = \frac{2\frac{1}{10}}{8\frac{2}{5}}$ **44.** $\frac{n}{4\frac{2}{7}} = \frac{3\frac{1}{9}}{9\frac{1}{3}}$

(5.4) *Solve.*

The ratio of a quarterback's completed passes to attempted passes is 3 to 7.

45. If he attempts 32 passes, find how many passes he completed. Round to the nearest whole pass.

46. If he completed 15 passes, find how many passes he attempted.

One bag of pesticide covers 4000 square feet of garden.

△ **47.** Find how many bags of pesticide should be purchased to cover a rectangular garden that is 180 feet by 175 feet.

△ **48.** Find how many bags of pesticide should be purchased to cover a square garden that is 250 feet on each side.

An owner of a Ford Escort can drive 420 miles on 11 gallons of gas.

49. If Tom Aloiso runs out of gas in an Escort and AAA comes to his rescue with $1\frac{1}{2}$ gallons of gas, determine whether Tom can then drive to a gas station 65 miles away.

50. Find how many gallons of gas Tom can expect to burn on a 3000-mile trip. Round to the nearest gallon.

Yearly homeowner property taxes are figured at a rate of $1.15 tax for every $100 of house value.

51. If a homeowner pays $627.90 in property taxes, find the value of his home.

52. Find the property taxes on a townhouse valued at $89,000.

On an architect's blueprint, 1 inch = 12 feet.

53. Find the length of a wall represented by a $3\frac{3}{8}$-inch line on the blueprint.

54. If an exterior wall is 99 feet long, find how long the blueprint measurement should be.

Mixed Review

Write each ratio as a fraction in simplest form.

55. 15 to 25

56. 16 to 36

57. 14 feet to 28 feet

58. 25 feet to 60 feet

59. 3 pints to 81 pints

60. 6 pints to 48 pints

Write each rate as a fraction in simplest form.

61. 2 teachers for 18 students

62. 6 nurses for 24 patients

Write each rate as a unit rate.

63. 24 cups for 6 people

64. 18 toys for 3 children

65. 136 miles in 4 hours

66. 12 gallons of milk from 6 cows

Find each unit price and decide which is the better buy. Round to 3 decimal places. Assume that we are comparing different sizes of the same brand.

67. cold medicine:
$4.94 for 4 oz,
$9.98 for 8 oz

68. juice:
12 oz for $0.65,
64 oz for $2.98

Write each sentence as a proportion.

69. 2 cups of cookie dough is to 30 cookies as 4 cups of cookie dough is to 60 cookies

70. 5 nickels is to 3 dollars as 20 nickels is to 12 dollars

Determine whether each proportion is a true proportion.

71. $\frac{3}{4} = \frac{87}{116}$

72. $\frac{2}{3} = \frac{4}{9}$

Find the unknown number n in each proportion.

73. $\frac{3}{n} = \frac{15}{8}$

74. $\frac{6}{n} = \frac{30}{24}$

75. $\frac{42}{5} = \frac{n}{10}$

76. $\frac{5}{4} = \frac{n}{20}$

Solve. The monthly loan payment for a car is \$39.75 for each \$1500 borrowed.

77. Find the monthly payment for a \$23,000 car loan.

78. Find the monthly payment for an \$18,000 car loan.

An investment of \$1,200 yields \$152 each year.

79. At the same rate, how much will an investment of \$1350 yield in one year?

80. At the same rate, how much will an investment of \$750 yield in one year?

Chapter 5 Test

Step-by-step test solutions are found on the Chapter Test Prep Videos available via the Interactive DVD Lecture Series, in MyMathLab or on YouTube (search "MartinGayBasicMath" and click on "Channels").

Write each ratio or rate as a fraction in simplest form.

1. \$75 to \$10

2. 4500 trees to 6500 trees

3. 28 men to every 4 women

4. 9 inches of rain in 30 days

5. 8.6 to 10

6. $5\frac{7}{8}$ to $9\frac{3}{4}$

7. The world's largest yacht, the Al Salamah, measures in at 456 feet. A Boeing 787-8 Dreamliner measures 186 feet long. Find the ratio of the Al Salamah to the length of a 787-8. (*Source: Power & Motoryacht* magazine)

Find each unit rate.

8. 650 kilometers in 8 hours

9. 8 inches of rain in 12 hours

10. 140 students for 5 teachers

11. QRI0 (Quest for Curiosity) is the world's first bipedal robot capable of running (moving with both legs off the ground at the same time) at a rate of 108 inches each 12 seconds. (*Source*: *Guinness World Records*)

Find each unit price and decide which is the better buy.

12. Steak sauce:
8 ounces for \$1.19
12 ounces for \$1.89

13. Jelly:
\$1.49 for 16 ounces
\$2.39 for 24 ounces

Determine whether each proportion is true.

14. $\frac{28}{16} = \frac{14}{8}$

15. $\frac{3.6}{2.2} = \frac{1.9}{1.2}$

16. Write the sentence as a proportion.
25 computers is to 600 students as 1 computer is to 24 students.

Answers

1. ______
2. ______
3. ______
4. ______
5. ______
6. ______
7. ______
8. ______
9. ______
10. ______
11. ______
12. ______
13. ______
14. ______
15. ______
16. ______

17. ______
18. ______
19. ______
20. ______
21. ______
22. ______
23. ______
24. ______
25. ______
26. ______

Find the unknown number n in each proportion.

17. $\frac{n}{3} = \frac{15}{9}$

18. $\frac{8}{n} = \frac{11}{6}$

19. $\frac{\frac{15}{12}}{\frac{3}{7}} = \frac{n}{\frac{4}{5}}$

20. $\frac{1.5}{5} = \frac{2.4}{n}$

21. $\frac{n}{2\frac{5}{8}} = \frac{1\frac{1}{6}}{3\frac{1}{2}}$

Solve.

22. On an architect's drawing, 2 inches corresponds to 9 feet. Find the length of a home represented by a line that is 11 inches long.

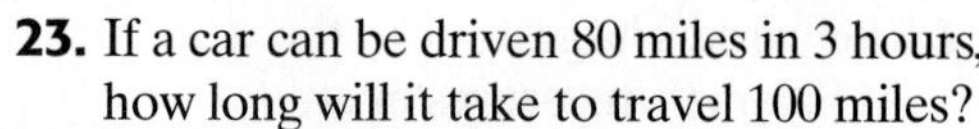

23. If a car can be driven 80 miles in 3 hours, how long will it take to travel 100 miles?

24. The standard dose of medicine for a dog is 10 grams for every 15 pounds of body weight. What is the standard dose for a dog that weighs 80 pounds?

25. Jerome Grant worked 6 hours and packed 86 cartons of books. At this rate, how many cartons can he pack in 8 hours?

26. Currently 27 out of every 50 American adults drink coffee every day. In a town with a population of 7900 adults, how many of these adults would you expect to drink coffee every day? (*Source:* National Coffee Association)

Cumulative Review Chapters 1–5

1. Subtract. Check each answer by adding.
   a. $12 - 9$
   b. $22 - 7$
   c. $35 - 35$
   d. $70 - 0$

2. Multiply
   a. $20 \cdot 0$
   b. $20 \cdot 1$
   c. $0 \cdot 20$
   d. $1 \cdot 20$

3. Round 248,982 to the nearest hundred.

4. Round 248,982 to the nearest thousand.

5. Multiply:
   a. $\begin{array}{r} 25 \\ \times\ 8 \\ \hline \end{array}$
   b. $\begin{array}{r} 246 \\ \times\ 5 \\ \hline \end{array}$

6. Divide: $10{,}468 \div 28$

7. The director of a learning lab at a local community college is working on next year's budget. Thirty-three new DVD players are needed at a cost of $187 each. What is the total cost of these DVD players?

8. A study is being conducted for erecting soundproof walls along the interstate of a metropolitan area. The following feet of walls are part of the proposal. Find their total: 4800 feet, 3270 feet, 2761 feet, 5760 feet.

9. Find the prime factorization of 45.

10. Find $\sqrt{64}$.

11. Write $\frac{12}{20}$ in simplest form.

12. Find $9^2 \cdot \sqrt{9}$.

Multiply.

13. $\frac{3}{4} \cdot \frac{8}{5}$

14. $3\frac{3}{8} \cdot 4\frac{5}{9}$

15. $\frac{6}{13} \cdot \frac{26}{30}$

16. $\frac{2}{11} \cdot \frac{5}{8} \cdot \frac{22}{27}$

Perform the indicated operation and simplify.

17. $\frac{2}{7} + \frac{3}{7}$

18. $\frac{26}{30} - \frac{7}{30}$

Answers

1. a. ______
   b. ______
   c. ______
   d. ______

2. a. b. ______
   c. d. ______

3. ______

4. ______

5. a. ______
   b. ______

6. ______

7. ______

8. ______

9. ______

10. ______

11. ______

12. ______

13. ______

14. ______

15. ______

16. ______

17. ______

18. ______

19. ______

20. ______

21. ______

22. ______

23. ______

24. ______

25. ______

26. ______

27. ______

28. ______

29. ______

30. ______

31. ______

32. ______

33. ______

34. ______

35. ______

36. ______

37. ______

19. $\frac{7}{13} + \frac{6}{13} + \frac{3}{13}$

20. $\frac{7}{10} - \frac{3}{10} + \frac{4}{10}$

21. Find the LCM of 9 and 12.

22. Add: $\frac{17}{25} + \frac{3}{10}$

23. Write an equivalent fraction with the indicated denominator. $\frac{1}{2} = \frac{}{24}$

24. Determine whether these fractions are equivalent.
$\frac{10}{55}, \frac{6}{33}$

25. Subtract: $\frac{10}{11} - \frac{2}{3}$

26. Subtract: $17\frac{5}{24} - 9\frac{5}{9}$

27. A flight from Tucson to Phoenix, Arizona, requires $\frac{5}{12}$ of an hour. If the plane has been flying $\frac{1}{4}$ of an hour, find how much time remains before landing.

28. Simplify: $80 \div 8 \cdot 2 + 7$

29. Add: $2\frac{1}{3} + 5\frac{3}{8}$

30. Find the average of $\frac{3}{5}, \frac{4}{9}$, and $\frac{11}{15}$.

31. Insert $<$ or $>$ to form a true statement.
$\frac{3}{10} \quad \frac{2}{7}$

32. Multiply: $28{,}000 \times 500$

33. Write the decimal 1.3 in words.

34. Write "seventy-five thousandths" in standard form.

35. Round 736.2359 to the nearest tenth.

36. Round 736.2359 to the nearest thousandth.

37. Add: $23.85 + 1.604$

38. Subtract: $700 - 18.76$

39. Multiply: 0.283×0.3

40. Write $\frac{3}{8}$ as a decimal.

41. Divide and check: $0.5 \div 4$

42. Write 7.9 as an improper fraction.

43. Simplify: $0.5(8.6 - 1.2)$

44. Find the unknown number n.

$$\frac{n}{4} = \frac{12}{16}$$

45. Write the numbers in order from smallest to largest.

$$\frac{9}{20}, \frac{4}{9}, 0.456$$

46. Write the rate as a unit rate.
700 meters in 5 seconds

Write each ratio using fractional notation. Simplify Exercises 48 and 50 only.

47. The ratio of 2.6 to 3.1

48. The ratio of 7 to 21

49. The ratio of $1\frac{1}{2}$ to $7\frac{3}{4}$

50. The ratio of 900 to 9000

38. ____
39. ____
40. ____
41. ____
42. ____
43. ____
44. ____
45. ____
46. ____
47. ____
48. ____
49. ____
50. ____

6

Percent

Sections

Check Your Progress

This chapter is devoted to percent, a concept used virtually every day in ordinary and business life. Understanding percent and using it efficiently depend on understanding ratios because a percent is a ratio whose denominator is 100. We present techniques to write percents as fractions and as decimals and then solve problems relating to sales tax, commission, discounts, interest, and other real-life situations that use percents.

The number of U.S. households using cell phones only has been increasing while households using landlines only has been decreasing. In the latter part of 2008, the percent of households using cell phones only surpassed the percent using landlines only.

In Section 6.1, Exercises 27 and 28, we learn the percent of U.S. households using cell phones only and landlines only, and we convert these percents to decimals.

Cell-Phone-Only Users by State

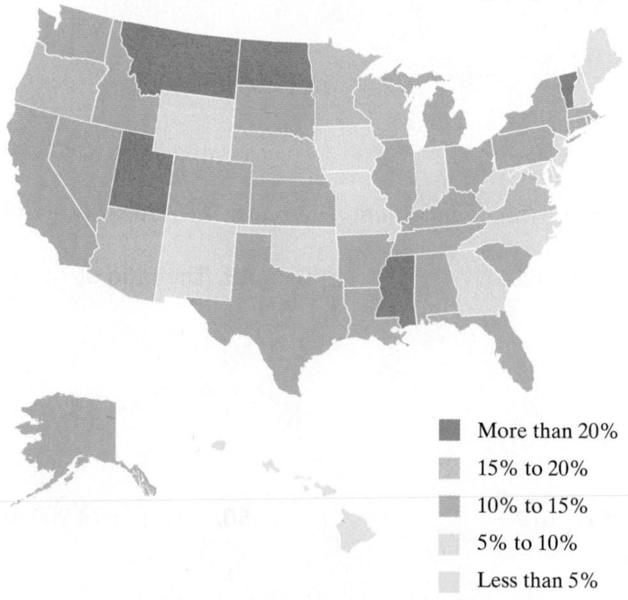

6.1 INTRODUCTION TO PERCENT

Objectives

A Understand Percent.

B Write Percents as Decimals.

C Write Decimals as Percents.

Objective A Understanding Percent

The word **percent** comes from the Latin phrase *per centum*, which means **"per 100."** For example, 53% (percent) means 53 per 100. In the square below, 53 of the 100 squares are shaded. Thus, 53% of the figure is shaded.

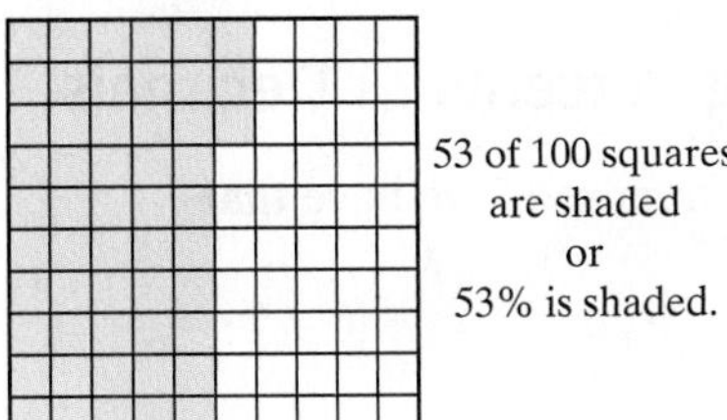

53 of 100 squares are shaded or 53% is shaded.

Since 53% means 53 per 100, 53% is the ratio of 53 to 100, or $\frac{53}{100}$.

$$53\% = \frac{53}{100}$$

Also,

$$7\% = \frac{7}{100} \quad \text{7 parts per 100 parts}$$

$$73\% = \frac{73}{100} \quad \text{73 parts per 100 parts}$$

$$109\% = \frac{109}{100} \quad \text{109 parts per 100 parts}$$

Percent

Percent means **per one hundred.** The "%" symbol is used to denote percent.

Percent is used in a variety of everyday situations. For example,

- 77.6% of the U.S. population uses the Internet.
- The store is having a 25%-off sale.
- 78% of us trust our local fire department.
- The enrollment in community colleges is predicted to increase 1.3% each year.
- The South is the home of 49% of all frequent paintball participants.

Example 1 Silver (gray) has been the most popular color for cars in the United States the past nine years.

Out of 100 people, 25 people drive silver cars. What percent of people drive silver cars? (*Source: U.S. News & World Report*)

Solution: Since 25 people out of 100 drive silver cars, the fraction is $\frac{25}{100}$. Then

$$\frac{25}{100} = 25\%$$

Work Practice 1

PRACTICE 1

Of 100 students in a club, 23 are freshmen. What percent of the students are freshmen?

Answer

1. 23%

PRACTICE 2

29 out of 100 executives are in their forties. What percent of executives are in their forties?

Example 2 46 out of every 100 college students live at home. What percent of students live at home? (*Source:* Independent Insurance Agents of America)

Solution:

$$\frac{46}{100} = 46\%$$

Work Practice 2

Objective B Writing Percents as Decimals

Since percent means "per hundred," we have that

$$1\% = \frac{1}{100} = 0.01$$

In other words, the percent symbol means "per hundred" or, equivalently, "$\frac{1}{100}$" or "0.01." Thus

$$87\% = 87 \times \frac{1}{100} = \frac{87}{100}$$

or

$$87\% = 87 \times (0.01) = 0.87$$

Results are the same.

Of course, we know that the end results are the same, that is,

$$\frac{87}{100} = 0.87$$

The above gives us two options for converting percents. We can replace the percent symbol, %, by $\frac{1}{100}$ or 0.01 and then multiply.

For consistency, when we

- convert from a percent to a *decimal,* we will drop the % symbol and multiply by 0.01 (this section).
- convert from a percent to a *fraction,* we will drop the % symbol and multiply by $\frac{1}{100}$ (next section).

Thus, to write 53.% as a decimal,

$$53\% = 53(0.01) = 0.53$$ Replace the percent symbol with 0.01. Then multiply.

Writing a Percent as a Decimal

Replace the percent symbol with its decimal equivalent, 0.01; then multiply.

$$43\% = 43(0.01) = 0.43$$

Helpful Hint

If it helps, think of writing a percent as a decimal by

Percent → | Remove the % symbol and move decimal point 2 places to the left | → Decimal

Answer

2. 29%

Example 3 Write 23% as a decimal.

Solution:

$23\% = 23(0.01)$ Replace the percent symbol with 0.01.

$= 0.23$ Multiply.

Work Practice 3

Examples Write each percent as a decimal.

4. $4.6\% = 4.6(0.01) = 0.046$ Replace the percent symbol with 0.01. Then multiply.

5. $190\% = 190(0.01) = 1.90$ or 1.9

6. $0.74\% = 0.74(0.01) = 0.0074$

7. $100\% = 100(0.01) = 1.00$ or 1

Helpful Hint
We just learned that 100% = 1

Work Practice 4–7

✓**Concept Check** Why is it incorrect to write the percent 0.033% as 3.3 in decimal form?

Objective C Writing Decimals as Percents

To write a decimal as a percent, we use the result of Example 7 above. In this example, we found that $1 = 100\%$.

$0.38 = 0.38(1) = 0.38(100\%) = 38\%$

Notice that the result is

$0.38 = 0.38(100\%) = 38.\%$ Multiply by 1 in the form of 100%.

Writing a Decimal as a Percent

Multiply by 1 in the form of 100%.

$0.27 = 0.27(100\%) = 27.\%$

Helpful Hint

If it helps, think of writing a decimal as a percent by reversing the steps in the Helpful Hint on the previous page.

Percent ← | Move the decimal point 2 places to the right and attach a % symbol. | ← Decimal

PRACTICE 3

Write 89% as a decimal.

PRACTICE 4–7

Write each percent as a decimal.

4. 2.7% **5.** 150%

6. 0.69% **7.** 800%

Answers

3. 0.89 **4.** 0.027 **5.** 1.5
6. 0.0069 **7.** 8.00 or 8

✓ **Concept Check Answer**

To write a percent as a decimal, the decimal point should be moved two places to the left, not to the right. So the correct answer is 0.00033.

PRACTICE 8

Write 0.19 as a percent.

Example 8 Write 0.65 as a percent.

Solution:

$$0.65 = 0.65(100\%) = 65.\% \quad \text{Multiply by 100\%.}$$
$$= 65\%$$

Work Practice 8

PRACTICE 9–11

Write each decimal as a percent.

9. 1.75 **10.** 0.044 **11.** 0.7

Examples Write each decimal as a percent.

9. $1.25 = 1.25(100\%) = 125.\%$ or 125%

10. $0.012 = 0.012(100\%) = 001.2\%$ or 1.2%

11. $0.6 = 0.6(100\%) = 060.\%$ or 60%

Helpful Hint A zero was inserted as a placeholder.

Work Practice 9–11

✓**Concept Check** Why is it incorrect to write the decimal 0.0345 as 34.5% in percent form?

Answers

8. 19% **9.** 175% **10.** 4.4% **11.** 70%

✓ **Concept Check Answer**

To change a decimal to a percent, multiply by 100%, or move the decimal point *only* two places to the right. So the correct answer is 3.45%.

Vocabulary and Readiness Check

Use the choices below to fill in each blank. Some choices may be used more than once, some not at all.

$\frac{1}{100}$ 0.01 100% percent

1. ______________ means "per hundred."
2. ______________ = 1.
3. The % symbol is read as ______________.
4. To write a decimal as a *percent*, multiply by 1 in the form of ______________.
5. To write a percent as a *decimal,* drop the % symbol and multiply by ______________.

6.1 Exercise Set

Objective A *Solve. See Examples 1 and 2.*

1. In a survey of 100 college students, 96 use the Internet. What percent use the Internet?

2. A basketball player makes 81 out of 100 attempted free throws. What percent of free throws are made?

3. Michigan leads the United States in tart cherry production, producing 75 out of every 100 tart cherries each year.

a. What percent of tart cherries are produced in Michigan?

b. What percent of tart cherries are *not* produced in Michigan? (*Source:* Cherry Marketing Institute)

4. The United States is the world's second-largest producer of apples. Twenty-five out of every 100 apples harvested in the United States are exported (shipped to other countries). (*Source:* U.S. Apple Association)

a. What percent of U.S.–grown apples are exported?

b. What percent of U.S.–grown apples are not exported?

One hundred adults were asked to name their favorite sport, and the results are shown in the circle graph.

5. What sport was preferred by most adults? What percent preferred this sport?

6. What sport was preferred by the least number of adults? What percent preferred this sport?

7. What percent of adults preferred football or soccer?

8. What percent of adults preferred basketball or baseball?

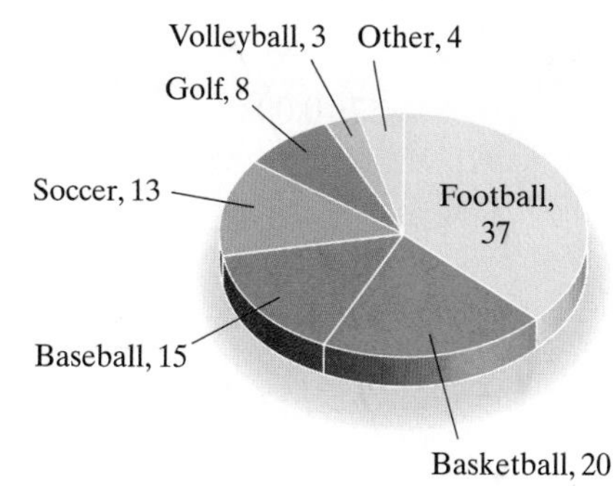

Objective B *Write each percent as a decimal. See Examples 3 through 7.*

9. 41%

10. 62%

11. 6%

12. 3%

13. 100%

14. 136%

15. 73.6%

16. 45.7%

17. 2.8%
18. 1.4%
19. 0.6%
20. 0.9%

21. 300%
22. 500%
23. 32.58%
24. 72.18%

Write each percent as a decimal. See Examples 3 through 7.

25. People take aspirin for a variety of reasons. The most common use of aspirin is to prevent heart disease, accounting for 38% of all aspirin use. (*Source:* Bayer Market Research)

26. Japan exports 73.2% of all motorcycles manufactured there. (*Source:* Japan Automobile Manufacturers Association)

27. In the United States recently, 20.2% of households had no landlines, just cell phones. (*Source:* CTIA—The Wireless Association)

28. In the United States recently, 17.4% of households had no cell phones, just landlines. (*Source:* CTIA—The Wireless Association)

29. Women make up 46.5% of the total U.S. labor force. (*Source:* U.S. Department of Labor)

30. In 2008, 57.4% of the paper used in the United States was recovered for recycling. (*Source:* American Forest & Paper Association)

Objective **C** *Write each decimal as a percent. See Examples 8 through 11.*

31. 0.98
32. 0.75
33. 3.1
34. 4.8
35. 29

36. 56
37. 0.003
38. 0.006
39. 0.22
40. 0.45

41. 5.3
42. 1.6
43. 0.056
44. 0.027
45. 0.3328

46. 0.1115
47. 3
48. 5
49. 0.7
50. 0.8

Write each decimal as a percent. See Examples 8 through 11.

51. About 0.68 of homes with televisions were tuned into Super Bowl XLIV.

52. The cost of an item for sale is 0.7 of the sale price.

53. In the 2009 Tour de France, 0.039 of the riders participating were Americans. (*Source:* Versus.com)

54. In the second quarter of 2009, retail sales of new Harley-Davidson motorcycles were down about 0.301. (*Source:* Harley-Davidson)

55. Nearly 0.093 of people in the United States are affected by pollen allergies. (*Source:* National Institute of Allergy and Infectious Diseases)

56. According to the 2000 census, 0.491 of the American population is male. (*Source:* U.S. Census Bureau)

Review

Write each fraction as a decimal. See Section 4.6.

57. $\frac{1}{4}$ **58.** $\frac{3}{5}$ **59.** $\frac{13}{20}$ **60.** $\frac{11}{40}$ **61.** $\frac{9}{10}$ **62.** $\frac{7}{10}$

Concept Extensions

Solve. See the Concept Checks in this section.

63. Which of the following are correct?

a. $6.5\% = 0.65$ **b.** $7.8\% = 0.078$

c. $120\% = 0.12$ **d.** $0.35\% = 0.0035$

64. Which of the following are correct?

a. $0.231 = 23.1\%$ **b.** $5.12 = 0.0512\%$

c. $3.2 = 320\%$ **d.** $0.0175 = 0.175\%$

Recall that 1 = 100%. This means that 1 whole is 100%. Use this for Exercises 65 through 66. (Source: Some Body by Dr. Pete Rowen)

65. The four blood types are A, B, O, and AB. (Each blood type can also be further classified as Rh-positive or Rh-negative depending upon whether your blood contains protein or not.) Given the percent blood types for the United States below, calculate the percent of U.S. population with AB blood type.

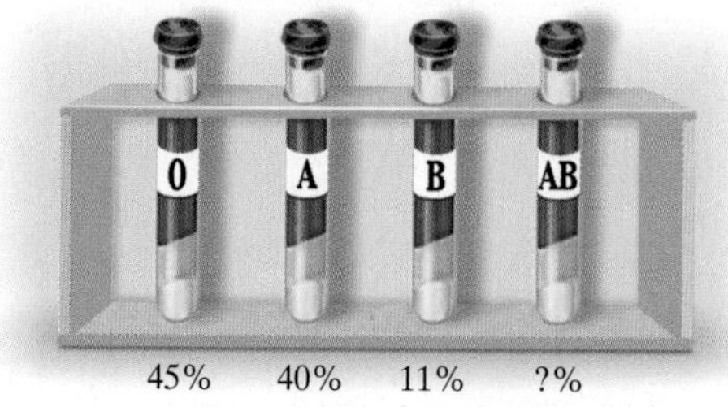

66. The top four components of bone are below. Find the missing percent.

1. Minerals—45%

2. Living tissue—30%

3. Water—20%

4. Other—?

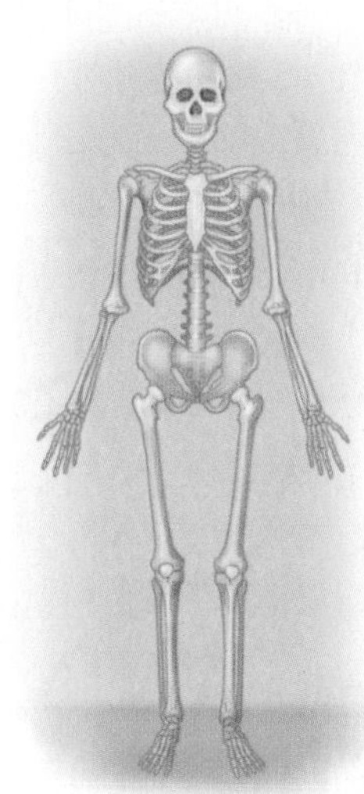

The bar graph shows the predicted fastest-growing occupations. Use the graph for Exercises 67 through 70. (Source: Bureau of Labor Statistics)

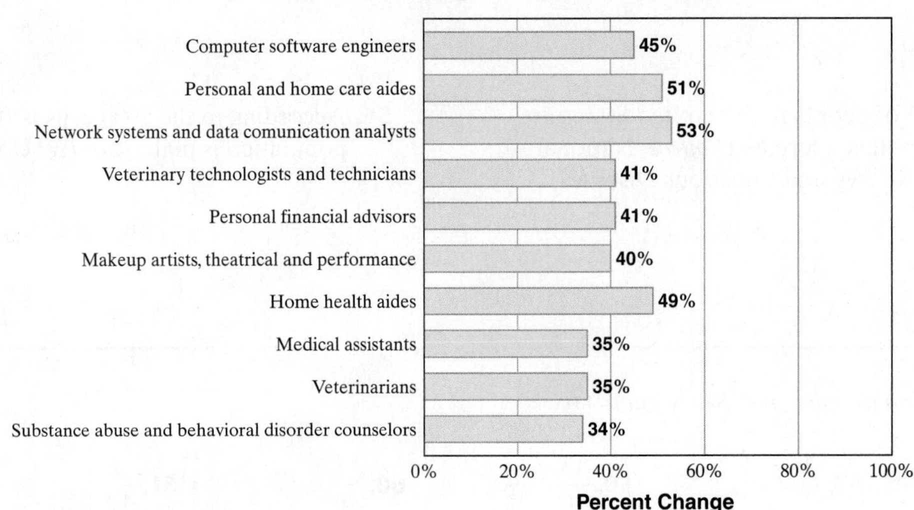

67. What occupation is predicted to be the fastest growing?

68. What occupation is predicted to be the second fastest growing?

69. Write the percent change for veterinarians as a decimal.

70. Write the percent change for makeup artists as a decimal.

71. In your own words, explain how to write a percent as a decimal.

72. In your own words, explain how to write a decimal as a percent.

6.2 PERCENTS AND FRACTIONS

Objective A Writing Percents as Fractions

Recall from Section 6.1 that percent means per hundred. Thus

$$1\% = \frac{1}{100} = 0.01$$

For example,

$$87\% = 87 \times \frac{1}{100} = \frac{87}{100} \quad \text{Writing 87\% as a fraction.}$$

or

$$87\% = 87 \times 0.01 = 0.87 \quad \text{Writing 87\% as a decimal.}$$

In this section we are writing percents as fractions, so we do the following.

> ***Writing a Percent as a Fraction***
>
> Replace the percent symbol with its fraction equivalent, $\frac{1}{100}$; then multiply. Don't forget to simplify the fraction if possible.
>
> $$7\% = 7 \cdot \frac{1}{100} = \frac{7}{100}$$

Examples Write each percent as a fraction or mixed number in simplest form.

1. $40\% = 40 \cdot \frac{1}{100} = \frac{40}{100} = \frac{2 \cdot \cancel{20}}{5 \cdot \cancel{20}} = \frac{2}{5}$

2. $1.9\% = 1.9 \cdot \frac{1}{100} = \frac{1.9}{100}$. We don't want the numerator of the fraction to contain a decimal, so we multiply by 1 in the form of $\frac{10}{10}$.

   $= \frac{1.9}{100} \cdot \frac{10}{10} = \frac{1.9 \cdot 10}{100 \cdot 10} = \frac{19}{1000}$

3. $125\% = 125 \cdot \frac{1}{100} = \frac{125}{100} = \frac{5 \cdot \cancel{25}}{4 \cdot \cancel{25}} = \frac{5}{4}$ or $1\frac{1}{4}$

4. $33\frac{1}{3}\% = 33\frac{1}{3} \cdot \frac{1}{100} = \frac{100}{3} \cdot \frac{1}{100} = \frac{\cancel{100} \cdot 1}{3 \cdot \cancel{100}} = \frac{1}{3}$

   ($33\frac{1}{3}$ → Write as an improper fraction.)

5. $100\% = 100 \cdot \frac{1}{100} = \frac{100}{100} = 1$

Helpful Hint Just as in the previous section, we confirm that 100% = 1

Work Practice 1–5

Objectives

A Write Percents as Fractions.

B Write Fractions as Percents.

C Convert Percents, Decimals, and Fractions.

PRACTICE 1–5

Write each percent as a fraction or mixed number in simplest form.

1. 25%
2. 2.3%
3. 225%
4. $66\frac{2}{3}\%$
5. 8%

Answers

1. $\frac{1}{4}$ 2. $\frac{23}{1000}$ 3. $\frac{9}{4}$ or $2\frac{1}{4}$ 4. $\frac{2}{3}$ 5. $\frac{2}{25}$

Objective B Writing Fractions as Percents

Recall that to write a percent as a fraction, we replace the percent symbol by its fraction equivalent, $\frac{1}{100}$. We reverse these steps to write a fraction as a percent.

Writing a Fraction as a Percent

Multiply by 1 in the form of 100%.

$$\frac{1}{8} = \frac{1}{8} \cdot 100\% = \frac{1}{8} \cdot \frac{100}{1}\% = \frac{100}{8}\% = 12\frac{1}{2}\% \quad \text{or} \quad 12.5\%$$

Helpful Hint

From Example 5, we know that

100% = 1

Recall that when we multiply a number by 1, we are not changing the value of that number. This means that when we multiply a number by 100%, we are not changing its value but rather writing the number as an equivalent percent.

PRACTICE 6–8

Write each fraction or mixed number as a percent.

6. $\frac{1}{2}$ **7.** $\frac{7}{40}$ **8.** $2\frac{1}{4}$

Examples Write each fraction or mixed number as a percent.

6. $\frac{9}{20} = \frac{9}{20} \cdot 100\% = \frac{9}{20} \cdot \frac{100}{1}\% = \frac{900}{20}\% = 45\%$

7. $\frac{2}{3} = \frac{2}{3} \cdot 100\% = \frac{2}{3} \cdot \frac{100}{1}\% = \frac{200}{3}\% = 66\frac{2}{3}\%$

8. $1\frac{1}{2} = \frac{3}{2} \cdot 100\% = \frac{3}{2} \cdot \frac{100}{1}\% = \frac{300}{2}\% = 150\%$

Helpful Hint

$\frac{200}{3} = 66.\overline{6}$. Thus, another way to write $\frac{200}{3}\%$ is $66.\overline{6}\%$.

Work Practice 6–8

✓**Concept Check** Which digit in the percent 76.4582% represents

a. A tenth percent?
b. A thousandth percent?
c. A hundredth percent?
d. A whole percent?

Answers

6. 50% **7.** $17\frac{1}{2}\%$ **8.** 225%

✓ **Concept Check Answers**

a. 4 **b.** 8 **c.** 5 **d.** 6

Example 9 Write $\frac{1}{12}$ as a percent. Round to the nearest hundredth percent.

Solution:

$$\frac{1}{12} = \frac{1}{12} \cdot 100\% = \frac{1}{12} \cdot \frac{100}{1}\% = \frac{100}{12}\% \approx 8.33\%$$

("approximately")

$$\begin{array}{r} 8.333 \approx 8.33 \\ 12\overline{)100.000} \\ \underline{-96} \\ 4\,0 \\ \underline{-3\,6} \\ 40 \\ \underline{-36} \\ 40 \\ \underline{-36} \\ 4 \end{array}$$

Thus, $\frac{1}{12}$ is approximately 8.33%.

Work Practice 9

PRACTICE 9

Write $\frac{3}{17}$ as a percent. Round to the nearest hundredth percent.

Objective C Converting Percents, Decimals, and Fractions

Let's summarize what we have learned so far about percents, decimals, and fractions:

Summary of Converting Percents, Decimals, and Fractions

- *To write a percent as a decimal,* replace the % symbol with its decimal equivalent, 0.01; then multiply.
- *To write a percent as a fraction,* replace the % symbol with its fraction equivalent, $\frac{1}{100}$; then multiply.
- *To write a decimal or fraction as a percent,* multiply by 100%.

If we let p represent a number, below we summarize using symbols.

Write a percent as a decimal:	Write a percent as a fraction:	Write a number as a percent:
$p\% = p(0.01)$	$p\% = p \cdot \frac{1}{100}$	$p = p \cdot 100\%$

Answer

9. 17.65%

PRACTICE 10

A family decides to spend no more than 22.5% of its monthly income on rent. Write 22.5% as a decimal and as a fraction.

Example 10 36.4% of automobile thefts in the continental United States occur in the South. Write this percent as a decimal and as a fraction. (*Source:* National Insurance Crime Bureau)

Solution:

As a decimal: $36.4\% = 36.4(0.01) = 0.364$

As a fraction: $36.4\% = 36.4 \cdot \frac{1}{100} = \frac{36.4}{100} = \frac{36.4}{100} \cdot \frac{10}{10} = \frac{364}{1000} = \frac{\overset{1}{\cancel{4}} \cdot 91}{\underset{1}{\cancel{4}} \cdot 250} = \frac{91}{250}$

Thus, 36.4% written as a decimal is 0.364, and written as a fraction is $\frac{91}{250}$.

Work Practice 10

PRACTICE 11

Provincetown's budget for waste disposal increased by $1\frac{1}{4}$ times over the budget from last year. What percent increase is this?

Example 11 An advertisement for a stereo system reads "$\frac{1}{4}$ off." What percent off is this?

Solution: Write $\frac{1}{4}$ as a percent.

$$\frac{1}{4} = \frac{1}{4} \cdot 100\% = \frac{1}{4} \cdot \frac{100}{1}\% = \frac{100}{4}\% = 25\%$$

Thus, "$\frac{1}{4}$ off" is the same as "25% off."

Work Practice 11

Note: It is helpful to know a few basic percent conversions. Appendix A.4 contains a handy reference of percent, decimal, and fraction equivalencies.

Also, Appendix A.5 shows how to find common percents of a number.

Answers

10. $0.225, \frac{9}{40}$ **11.** 125%

Vocabulary and Readiness Check

Use the choices below to fill in each blank. Some choices may be used more than once.

$\frac{1}{100}$ 100% percent

1. ________ means "per hundred."

2. ________ = 1.

3. To write a decimal or a fraction as a *percent*, multiply by 1 in the form of ________.

4. To write a percent as a *fraction*, drop the % symbol and multiply by ________.

Write each fraction as a percent.

5. $\frac{13}{100}$ 6. $\frac{92}{100}$ 7. $\frac{87}{100}$ 8. $\frac{71}{100}$ 9. $\frac{1}{100}$ 10. $\frac{2}{100}$

6.2 Exercise Set

FOR EXTRA HELP

PRACTICE

WATCH

DOWNLOAD

READ

REVIEW

Objective A *Write each percent as a fraction or mixed number in simplest form. See Examples 1 through 5.*

1. 12% **2.** 24% **3.** 4% **4.** 2% **5.** 4.5%

6. 7.5% **7.** 175% **8.** 250% **9.** 73% **10.** 86%

11. 12.5% **12.** 62.5% **13.** 6.25% **14.** 3.75% **15.** 6%

16. 16% **17.** $10\frac{1}{3}\%$ **18.** $7\frac{3}{4}\%$ **19.** $22\frac{3}{8}\%$ **20.** $15\frac{5}{8}\%$

Objective B *Write each fraction or mixed number as a percent. See Examples 6 through 8.*

21. $\frac{3}{4}$ **22.** $\frac{1}{4}$ **23.** $\frac{7}{10}$ **24.** $\frac{3}{10}$ **25.** $\frac{2}{5}$ **26.** $\frac{4}{5}$

27. $\frac{59}{100}$ **28.** $\frac{83}{100}$ **29.** $\frac{17}{50}$ **30.** $\frac{47}{50}$ **31.** $\frac{3}{8}$ **32.** $\frac{5}{8}$

33. $\frac{5}{16}$ **34.** $\frac{7}{16}$ **35.** $1\frac{3}{5}$ **36.** $1\frac{3}{4}$ **37.** $\frac{7}{9}$ **38.** $\frac{1}{3}$

39. $\frac{13}{20}$ **40.** $\frac{3}{20}$ **41.** $2\frac{1}{2}$ **42.** $2\frac{1}{5}$ **43.** $1\frac{9}{10}$ **44.** $2\frac{7}{10}$

Write each fraction as a percent. Round to the nearest hundredth percent. See Example 9.

45. $\frac{7}{11}$ **46.** $\frac{5}{12}$ **47.** $\frac{4}{15}$ **48.** $\frac{10}{11}$

49. $\frac{1}{7}$ **50.** $\frac{1}{9}$ **51.** $\frac{11}{12}$ **52.** $\frac{5}{6}$

Objective **C** *Complete each table. See Examples 10 and 11.*

53.

Percent	Decimal	Fraction
35%		
		$\frac{1}{5}$
	0.5	
70%		
		$\frac{3}{8}$

54.

Percent	Decimal	Fraction
60%		
		$\frac{2}{5}$
	0.25	
12.5%		
		$\frac{5}{8}$
		$\frac{7}{50}$

55.

Percent	Decimal	Fraction
40%		
	0.235	
		$\frac{4}{5}$
$33\frac{1}{3}\%$		
		$\frac{7}{8}$
7.5%		

56.

Percent	Decimal	Fraction
	0.525	
		$\frac{3}{4}$
$66\frac{2}{3}\%$		
		$\frac{5}{6}$
100%		

57.

Percent	Decimal	Fraction
200%		
	2.8	
705%		
		$4\frac{27}{50}$

58.

Percent	Decimal	Fraction
800%		
	3.2	
608%		
		$9\frac{13}{50}$

Solve. See Examples 10 and 11.

59. China produces 26.2% of the world's aluminum products. Write this percent as a decimal and a fraction. (*Source:* U.S. Geological Survey, *Minerals Yearbook*)

60. In 2008, 46.5% of all veterinarians in private practice were female. Write this percent as a decimal and a fraction. (*Source:* American Veterinary Medical Association)

61. At this writing, 23% of Americans surveyed are in favor of abolishing the penny. Write this percent as a decimal and a fraction.

62. One version of the quarter is made of an alloy of copper, nickel, and strengthening impurities. About 8% is nickel. Write this percent as a decimal and a fraction. (*Source:* Gallup)

63. Mali has a very young population. It is estimated that $\frac{483}{1000}$ of its population is under the age of 12. Write this fraction as a percent. (*Source:* The Top 10 of Everything, 2009)

64. In 2008, approximately $\frac{2}{5}$ of the total money that Americans spent on their pets was spent on pet food. Write this fraction as a percent. (*Source:* American Pet Products Manufacturers Association)

65. The sales tax in Slidell, Louisiana, is 8.75%. Write this percent as a decimal.

66. A real estate agent receives a commission of 3% of the sale price of a house. Write this percent as a decimal.

67. Canada produces $\frac{1}{4}$ of the uranium produced in the world. Write this fraction as a percent. (*Source:* World Nuclear Association)

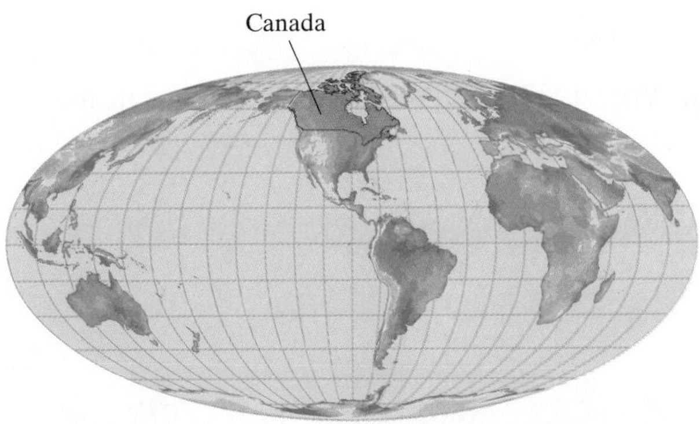

68. In 2008, the U.S. Postal Service handled $\frac{23}{50}$ of the world's card and letter mail volume. Write this decimal as a percent. (*Source:* U.S. Postal Service)

In Exercises 69 through 74, write the percent from the circle graph as a decimal and a fraction.

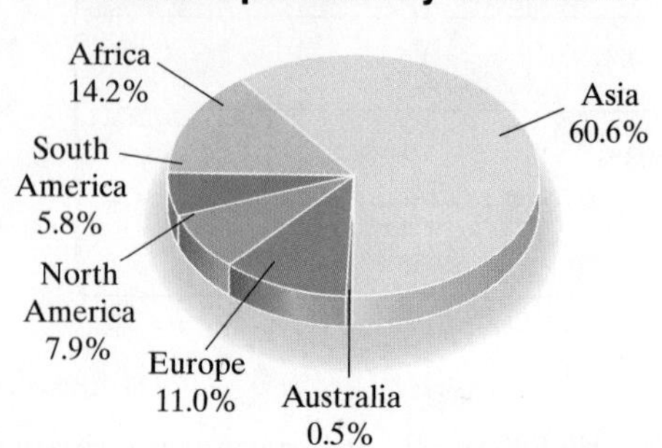

69. Australia: 0.5%

70. Europe: 11%

71. Africa: 14.2%

72. Asia: 60.6%

73. North America: 7.9%

74. South America: 5.8%

Review

Find the value of n. See Section 5.3.

75. $3 \cdot n = 45$

76. $7 \cdot n = 48$

77. $8 \cdot n = 80$

78. $2 \cdot n = 16$

79. $6 \cdot n = 72$

80. $5 \cdot n = 35$

Concept Extensions

Solve. See the Concept Check in this section.

81. Given the percent 52.8647%, round as indicated.

a. Round to a tenth of a percent.
b. Round to a hundredth of a percent.

82. Given the percent 0.5269%, round as indicated.

a. Round to a tenth of a percent.
b. Round to a hundredth of a percent.

83. Write 1.07835 as a percent rounded to the nearest tenth of a percent.

84. Write 1.25348 as a percent rounded to the nearest tenth of a percent.

85. Write 0.65794 as a percent rounded to the nearest hundredth of a percent.

86. Write 0.92571 as a percent rounded to the nearest hundredth of a percent.

87. Write 0.7682 as a percent rounded to the nearest percent.

88. Write 0.2371 as a percent rounded to the nearest percent.

What percent of the figure is shaded?

89.

90. 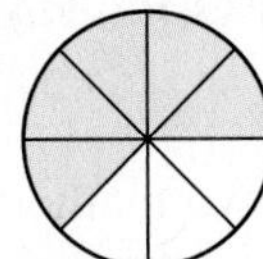

91. 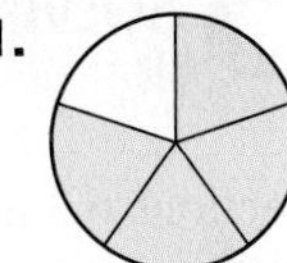

92. 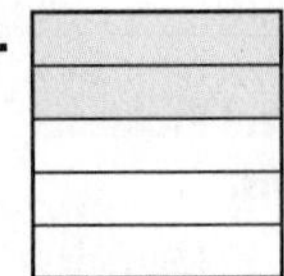

Fill in the blanks.

93. A fraction written as a percent is greater than 100% when the numerator is __________ than the denominator. (greater/less)

94. A decimal written as a percent is less than 100% when the decimal is _______ than 1. (greater/less)

95. In your own words, explain how to write a percent as a fraction.

96. In your own words, explain how to write a fraction as a decimal.

Write each fraction as a decimal and then write each decimal as a percent. Round the decimal to three decimal places (nearest thousandth) and the percent to the nearest tenth of a percent.

97. $\frac{21}{79}$

98. $\frac{56}{102}$

99. $\frac{850}{736}$

100. $\frac{506}{248}$

Objectives

A **Write Percent Problems as Equations.**

B **Solve Percent Problems**

6.3 SOLVING PERCENT PROBLEMS USING EQUATIONS

Note: Sections 6.3 and 6.4 introduce two methods for solving percent problems. It is not necessary that you study both sections. You may want to check with your instructor for further advice.

Throughout this text, we have written mathematical statements such as $3 + 10 = 13$, or area $=$ length $\cdot$ width. These statements are called "equations." An **equation** is a mathematical statement that contains an equal sign. To solve percent problems in this section, we translate the problems into such mathematical statements, or equations.

Objective A Writing Percent Problems as Equations

Recognizing key words in a percent problem is helpful in writing the problem as an equation. Three key words in the statement of a percent problem and their meanings are as follows:

of means **multiplication** $(\cdot)$
is means **equals** $(=)$
what (or some equivalent) means **the unknown number**

In our examples, we let the letter n stand for the unknown number.

Helpful Hint

Any letter of the alphabet can be used to represent the unknown number. In this section, we mostly use the letter n.

PRACTICE 1

Translate: 6 is what percent of 24?

Example 1 Translate to an equation.

5 is what percent of 20?

Solution: 5 is what percent of 20?

$$5 = n \cdot 20$$

Work Practice 1

Helpful Hint

Remember that an equation is simply a mathematical statement that contains an equal sign $(=)$.

$5 = n \cdot 20$
↑
equal sign

PRACTICE 2

Translate: 1.8 is 20% of what number?

Example 2 Translate to an equation.

1.2 is 30% of what number?

Solution: 1.2 is 30% of what number?

$$1.2 = 30\% \cdot n$$

Work Practice 2

Answers
1. $6 = n \cdot 24$ **2.** $1.8 = 20\% \cdot n$

Example 3 Translate to an equation.

What number is 25% of 0.008?

Solution: What number is 25% of 0.008?

$$n = 25\% \cdot 0.008$$

Work Practice 3

PRACTICE 3

Translate: What number is 40% of 3.6?

Examples Translate each of the following to an equation:

4. 38% of 200 is what number?

$$38\% \cdot 200 = n$$

5. 40% of what number is 80?

$$40\% \cdot n = 80$$

6. What percent of 85 is 34?

$$n \cdot 85 = 34$$

Work Practice 4–6

PRACTICE 4–6

Translate each to an equation.

4. 42% of 50 is what number?

5. 15% of what number is 9?

6. What percent of 150 is 90?

✓**Concept Check** In the equation $2 \cdot n = 10$, what step should be taken to solve the equation for n?

Objective B Solving Percent Problems

You may have noticed by now that each percent problem has contained three numbers—in our examples, two are known and one is unknown. Each of these numbers is given a special name.

15% of 60 is 9

15% percent	·	60 base	=	9 amount

We call this equation the **percent equation.**

Percent Equation

percent · base = amount

Helpful Hint

Notice that the percent equation given above is a true statement. To see this, simplify the left side as shown:

$15\% \cdot 60 = 9$

$0.15 \cdot 60 = 9$ Write 15% as 0.15.

$9 = 9$ Multiply.

The statement $9 = 9$ is true.

Answers

3. $n = 40\% \cdot 3.6$ **4.** $42\% \cdot 50 = n$ **5.** $15\% \cdot n = 9$ **6.** $n \cdot 150 = 90$

✓ **Concept Check Answers**

If $2 \cdot n = 10$, then $n = \frac{10}{2}$, or $n = 5$.

After a percent problem has been written as a percent equation, we can use the equation to find the unknown number. This is called **solving** the equation.

PRACTICE 7

What number is 20% of 85?

Example 7 Solving Percent Equation for the Amount

What number is 35% of 40?

Solution:

$n = 35\% \cdot 40$	Translate to an equation.
$n = 0.35 \cdot 40$	Write 35% as 0.35.
$n = 14$	Multiply $0.35 \cdot 40 = 14$.

Thus, 14 is 35% of 40.

Is this reasonable? To see, round 35% to 40%. Then 40% of 40 or 0.40(40) is 16. Our result is reasonable since 16 is close to 14.

Work Practice 7

Helpful Hint

When solving a percent equation, write the percent as a decimal (or fraction).

PRACTICE 8

90% of 150 is what number?

Example 8 Solving Percent Equation for the Amount

85% of 300 is what number?

Solution:

$85\% \cdot 300 = n$	Translate to an equation.
$0.85 \cdot 300 = n$	Write 85% as 0.85.
$255 = n$	Multiply $0.85 \cdot 300 = 255$.

Thus, 85% of 300 is 255.

Is this result reasonable? To see, round 85% to 90%. Then 90% of 300 or $0.90(300) = 270$, which is close to 255.

Work Practice 8

PRACTICE 9

15% of what number is 1.2?

Example 9 Solving Percent Equation for the Base

12% of what number is 0.6?

Solution:

$12\% \cdot n = 0.6$	Translate to an equation.
$0.12 \cdot n = 0.6$	Write 12% as 0.12.

Recall from Section 5.3 that if "0.12 times some number is 0.6," then the number is 0.6 divided by 0.12.

$n = \frac{0.6}{0.12}$ Divide 0.6 by 0.12, the number multiplied by n.

$n = 5$

Thus, 12% of 5 is 0.6.

Is this reasonable? To see, round 12% to 10%. Then 10% of 5 or $0.10(5) = 0.5$, which is close to 0.6.

Work Practice 9

Answers

7. 17 **8.** 135 **9.** 8

Example 10 Solving Percent Equation for the Base

13 is $6\frac{1}{2}\%$ of what number?

Solution:

$$13 = 6\frac{1}{2}\% \cdot n \quad \text{Translate to an equation.}$$

$$13 = 0.065 \cdot n \quad 6\frac{1}{2}\% = 6.5\% = 0.065.$$

$$\frac{13}{0.065} = n \quad \text{Divide 13 by 0.065, the number multiplied by } n.$$

$$200 = n$$

Thus, 13 is $6\frac{1}{2}\%$ of 200.

Check to see if this result is reasonable.

Work Practice 10

PRACTICE 10

27 is $4\frac{1}{2}\%$ of what number?

Example 11 Solving Percent Equation for the Percent

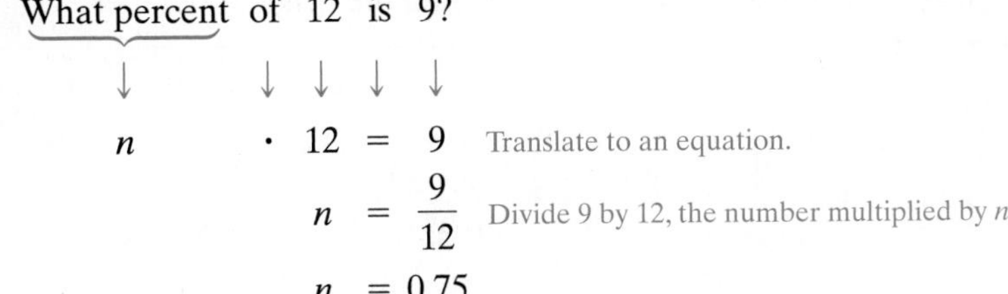

What percent of 12 is 9?

Solution:

$$n \cdot 12 = 9 \quad \text{Translate to an equation.}$$

$$n = \frac{9}{12} \quad \text{Divide 9 by 12, the number multiplied by } n.$$

$$n = 0.75$$

Next, since we are looking for percent, we write 0.75 as a percent.

$n = 75\%$

So, 75% of 12 is 9.

To check, see that $75\% \cdot 12 = 9$.

Work Practice 11

PRACTICE 11

What percent of 80 is 8?

Helpful Hint

If your unknown in the percent equation is the percent, don't forget to convert your answer to a percent.

Example 12 Solving Percent Equation for the Percent

78 is what percent of 65?

Solution:

$$78 = n \cdot 65 \quad \text{Translate to an equation.}$$

$$\frac{78}{65} = n \quad \text{Divide 78 by 65, the number multiplied by } n.$$

$$1.2 = n$$

$$120\% = n \quad \text{Write 1.2 as a percent.}$$

So, 78 is 120% of 65.

Check this result.

Work Practice 12

PRACTICE 12

35 is what percent of 25?

Answers

10. 600 **11.** 10% **12.** 140%

✓Concept Check Consider these problems.

1. 75% of 50 =
a. 50 **b.** a number greater than 50 **c.** a number less than 50

2. 40% of a number is 10. Is the number
a. 10? **b.** less than 10? **c.** greater than 10?

3. 800 is 120% of what number? Is the number
a. 800? **b.** less than 800? **c.** greater than 800?

Helpful Hint

Use the following to see if your answers are reasonable.

(100%) of a number = the number

$\left(\begin{array}{c}\text{a percent}\\ \text{greater than}\\ 100\%\end{array}\right)$ of a number = a number greater than the original number

$\left(\begin{array}{c}\text{a percent}\\ \text{less than } 100\%\end{array}\right)$ of a number = a number less than the original number

✓ Concept Check Answers
1. c **2.** c **3.** b

Vocabulary and Readiness Check

Use the choices below to fill in each blank.

percent	amount	of	less
base	the number	is	greater

1. The word ______________ translates to " =".
2. The word ______________ usually translates to "multiplication."
3. In the statement "10% of 90 is 9," the number 9 is called the ______________, 90 is called the ______________, and 10 is called the ______________.
4. 100% of a number = ______________.
5. Any "percent greater than 100%" of "a number" = "a number ______________ than the original number."
6. Any "percent less than 100%" of "a number" = "a number ______________ than the original number."

Identify the percent, the base, and the amount in each equation. Recall that percent · base = amount.

7. $42\% \cdot 50 = 21$

8. $30\% \cdot 65 = 19.5$

9. $107.5 = 125\% \cdot 86$

10. $99 = 110\% \cdot 90$

6.3 Exercise Set

FOR EXTRA HELP

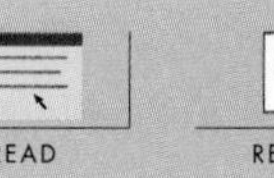

MathXL PRACTICE REVIEW

Objective A Translating *Translate each to an equation. Do not solve. See Examples 1 through 6.*

1. 18% of 81 is what number?

2. 36% of 72 is what number?

3. 20% of what number is 105?

4. 40% of what number is 6?

5. 0.6 is 40% of what number?

6. 0.7 is 20% of what number?

7. What percent of 80 is 3.8?

8. 9.2 is what percent of 92?

9. What number is 9% of 43?

10. What number is 25% of 55?

11. What percent of 250 is 150?

12. What percent of 375 is 300?

Objective B *Solve. See Examples 7 and 8.*

13. 10% of 35 is what number?

14. 25% of 68 is what number?

15. What number is 14% of 205?

16. What number is 18% of 425?

Solve. See Examples 9 and 10.

17. 1.2 is 12% of what number?

18. 0.22 is 44% of what number?

19. $8\frac{1}{2}\%$ of what number is 51?

20. $4\frac{1}{2}\%$ of what number is 45?

Solve. See Examples 11 and 12.

21. What percent of 80 is 88?

22. What percent of 40 is 60?

23. 17 is what percent of 50?

24. 48 is what percent of 50?

Objectives **A** **B** **Mixed Practice** *Solve. See Examples 1 through 12.*

25. 0.1 is 10% of what number?

26. 0.5 is 5% of what number?

27. 150% of 430 is what number?

28. 300% of 56 is what number?

29. 82.5 is $16\frac{1}{2}\%$ of what number?

30. 7.2 is $6\frac{1}{4}\%$ of what number?

31. 2.58 is what percent of 50?

32. 2.64 is what percent of 25?

33. What number is 42% of 60?

34. What number is 36% of 80?

35. What percent of 184 is 64.4?

36. What percent of 120 is 76.8?

37. 120% of what number is 42?

38. 160% of what number is 40?

39. 2.4% of 26 is what number?

40. 4.8% of 32 is what number?

41. What percent of 600 is 3?

42. What percent of 500 is 2?

43. 6.67 is 4.6% of what number?

44. 9.75 is 7.5% of what number?

45. 1575 is what percent of 2500?

46. 2520 is what percent of 3500?

47. 2 is what percent of 50?

48. 2 is what percent of 40?

Review

Find the value of n in each proportion. See Section 5.3.

49. $\frac{27}{n} = \frac{9}{10}$

50. $\frac{35}{n} = \frac{7}{5}$

51. $\frac{n}{5} = \frac{8}{11}$

52. $\frac{n}{3} = \frac{6}{13}$

Write each phrase as a proportion.

53. 17 is to 12 as n is to 20

54. 20 is to 25 as n is to 10

55. 8 is to 9 as 14 is to n

56. 5 is to 6 as 15 is to n

Concept Extensions

For each equation, determine the next step taken to find the value of n. See the first Concept Check in this section.

57. $5 \cdot n = 32$

a. $n = 5 \cdot 32$ **b.** $n = \frac{5}{32}$ **c.** $n = \frac{32}{5}$ **d.** none of these

58. $n = 0.7 \cdot 12$

a. $n = 8.4$ **b.** $n = \frac{12}{0.7}$ **c.** $n = \frac{0.7}{12}$ **d.** none of these

59. $0.06 = n \cdot 7$

a. $n = 0.06 \cdot 7$ **b.** $n = \frac{0.06}{7}$ **c.** $n = \frac{7}{0.06}$ **d.** none of these

60. $0.01 = n \cdot 8$

a. $n = 0.01 \cdot 8$ **b.** $n = \frac{8}{0.01}$ **c.** $n = \frac{0.01}{8}$ **d.** none of these

61. Write a word statement for the equation $20\% \cdot n = 18.6$. Use the phrase "some number" for "n".

62. Write a word statement for the equation $n = 33\frac{1}{3}\% \cdot 24$. Use the phrase "some number" for "n".

For each exercise, determine whether the percent, n, is (a) 100%, (b) greater than 100%, or (c) less than 100%. See the last Concept Check in this section.

63. $n\%$ of 20 is 30

64. $n\%$ of 98 is 98

65. $n\%$ of 120 is 85

66. $n\%$ of 35 is 50

For each exercise, determine whether the number, n, is (a) equal to 45, (b) greater than 45, or (c) less than 45.

67. 55% of 45 is n

68. 230% of 45 is n

69. 100% of 45 is n

70. 30% of n is 45

71. 100% of n is 45

72. 180% of n is 45

73. In your own words, explain how to solve a percent equation.

74. Write a percent problem that uses the percent 50%.

Solve.

75. 1.5% of 45,775 is what number?

76. What percent of 75,528 is 27,945.36?

77. 22,113 is 180% of what number?

Objectives

A **Write Percent Problems as Proportions.**

B **Solve Percent Problems.**

6.4 SOLVING PERCENT PROBLEMS USING PROPORTIONS

There is more than one method that can be used to solve percent problems. (See the note at the beginning of Section 6.3.) In the last section, we used the percent equation. In this section, we will use proportions.

Objective A Writing Percent Problems as Proportions

To understand the proportion method, recall that 70% means the ratio of 70 to 100, or $\frac{70}{100}$.

$$70\% = \frac{70}{100} = \frac{7}{10}$$

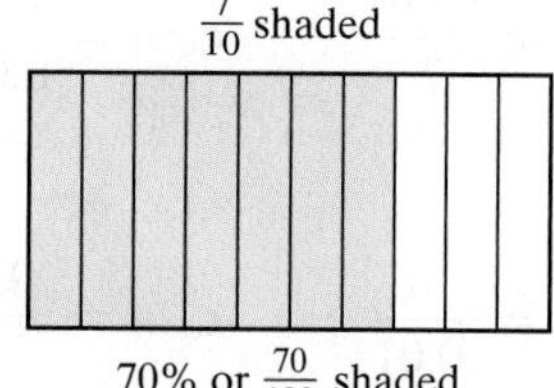

Since the ratio $\frac{70}{100}$ is equal to the ratio $\frac{7}{10}$, we have the proportion

$$\frac{7}{10} = \frac{70}{100}.$$

We call this proportion the "percent proportion." In general, we can name the parts of this proportion as follows:

Percent Proportion

$$\frac{\text{amount}}{\text{base}} = \frac{\text{percent}}{100} \quad \leftarrow \text{always } 100$$

or

$$\begin{matrix}\text{amount} \rightarrow \\ \text{base} \rightarrow\end{matrix} \frac{a}{b} = \frac{p}{100} \leftarrow \text{percent}$$

When we translate percent problems to proportions, the **percent,** p, can be identified by looking for the symbol % or the word *percent.* The **base,** b, usually follows the word *of.* The **amount,** a, is the part compared to the whole.

Helpful Hint

Part of Proportion	How It's Identified
Percent	% or percent
Base	Appears after *of*
Amount	Part compared to whole

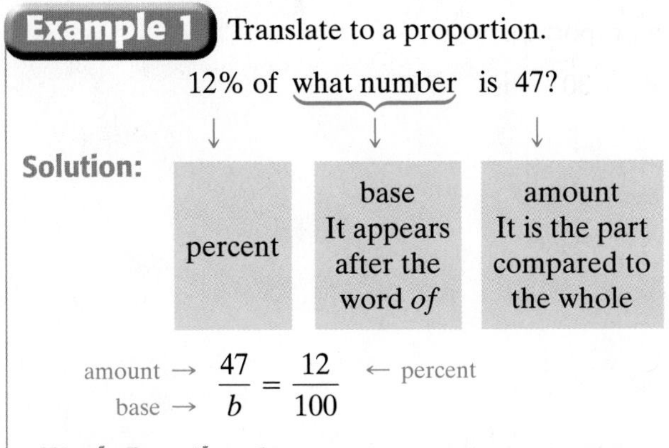

Example 1
Translate to a proportion.
12% of what number is 47?
Solution:
percent
base
It appears after the word *of*
amount
It is the part compared to the whole

amount → $\frac{47}{b} = \frac{12}{100}$ ← percent
base →

Work Practice 1

PRACTICE 1

Translate to a proportion.
15% of what number is 55?

Example 2 Translate to a proportion.

101 is what percent of 200?

Solution:

amount It is the part compared to the whole	percent	base It appears after the word *of*

amount → $\frac{101}{200} = \frac{p}{100}$ ← percent
base →

Work Practice 2

PRACTICE 2

Translate to a proportion.
35 is what percent of 70?

Example 3 Translate to a proportion.

What number is 90% of 45?

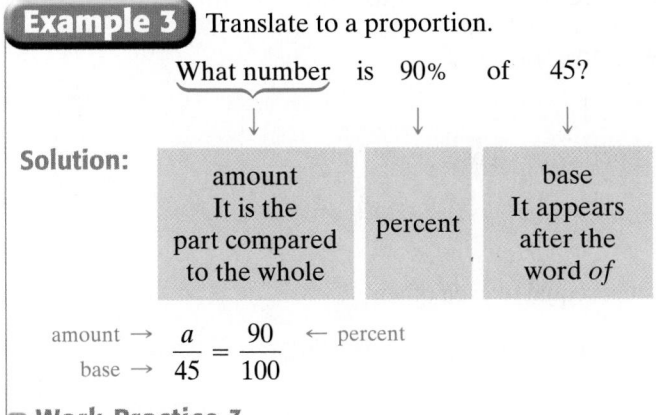

Solution:

amount It is the part compared to the whole	percent	base It appears after the word *of*

amount → $\frac{a}{45} = \frac{90}{100}$ ← percent
base →

Work Practice 3

PRACTICE 3

Translate to a proportion. What number is 25% of 68?

Example 4 Translate to a proportion.

238 is 40% of what number?

Solution: amount percent base

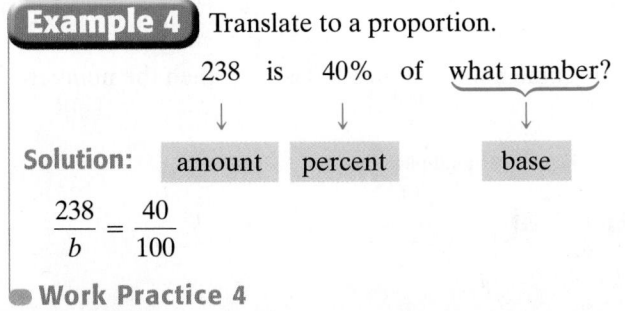

$$\frac{238}{b} = \frac{40}{100}$$

Work Practice 4

PRACTICE 4

Translate to a proportion.
520 is 65% of what number?

Answers

1. $\frac{55}{b} = \frac{15}{100}$ 2. $\frac{35}{70} = \frac{p}{100}$ 3. $\frac{a}{68} = \frac{25}{100}$ 4. $\frac{520}{b} = \frac{65}{100}$

PRACTICE 5

Translate to a proportion. What percent of 50 is 65?

Example 5 Translate to a proportion.

What percent of 30 is 75?

Solution: What percent → percent; 30 → base; 75 → amount

$$\frac{75}{30} = \frac{p}{100}$$

Work Practice 5

PRACTICE 6

Translate to a proportion. 36% of 80 is what number?

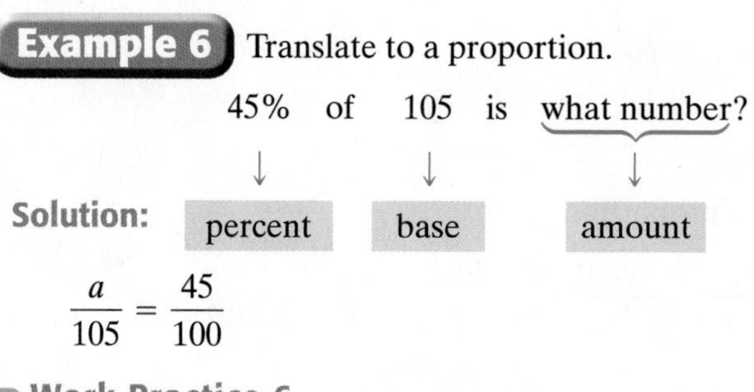

Example 6 Translate to a proportion.

45% of 105 is what number?

Solution: 45% → percent; 105 → base; what number → amount

$$\frac{a}{105} = \frac{45}{100}$$

Work Practice 6

Objective B Solving Percent Problems

The proportions that we have written in this section contain three values that can change: the percent, the base, and the amount. If any two of these values are known, we can find the third (the unknown value). To do this, we write a percent proportion and find the unknown value as we did in Section 5.3.

PRACTICE 7

What number is 8% of 120?

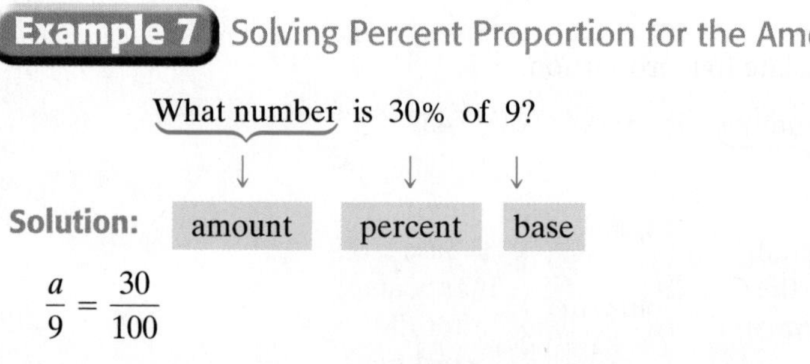

Example 7 Solving Percent Proportion for the Amount

What number is 30% of 9?

Solution: What number → amount; 30% → percent; 9 → base

$$\frac{a}{9} = \frac{30}{100}$$

To solve, we set cross products equal to each other.

$$\frac{a}{9} = \frac{30}{100}$$

$a \cdot 100 = 9 \cdot 30$ Set cross products equal.

$a \cdot 100 = 270$ Multiply.

Recall from Section 5.3 that if "some number times 100 is 270," then the number is 270 divided by 100.

$a = \frac{270}{100}$ Divide 270 by 100, the number multiplied by *a*.

$a = 2.7$ Simplify.

Thus, 2.7 is 30% of 9.

Work Practice 7

Helpful Hint

The proportion in Example 7 contains the ratio $\frac{30}{100}$. A ratio in a proportion may be simplified before solving the proportion. The unknown number in both $\frac{a}{9} = \frac{30}{100}$ and $\frac{a}{9} = \frac{3}{10}$ is 2.7

Answers

5. $\frac{65}{50} = \frac{p}{100}$ **6.** $\frac{a}{80} = \frac{36}{100}$

7. 9.6

✓**Concept Check** Consider the statement: "78 is what percent of 350?"

Which part of the percent proportion is unknown?

a. the amount **b.** the base **c.** the percent

Consider another statement: "14 is 10% of some number."
Which part of the percent proportion is unknown?

a. the amount **b.** the base **c.** the percent

Example 8 Solving Percent Proportion for the Base

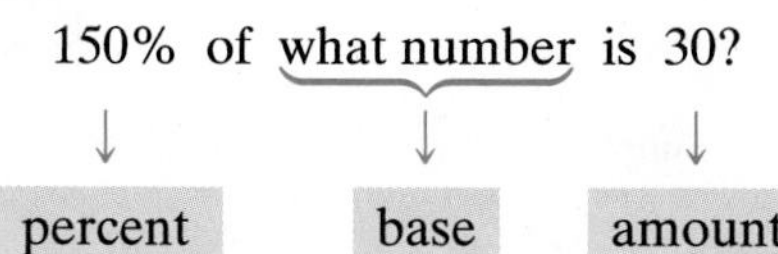

Solution:

$$\frac{30}{b} = \frac{150}{100} \quad \text{Write the proportion.}$$

$$\frac{30}{b} = \frac{3}{2} \quad \text{Write } \frac{150}{100} \text{ as } \frac{3}{2}.$$

$$30 \cdot 2 = b \cdot 3 \quad \text{Set cross products equal.}$$

$$60 = b \cdot 3 \quad \text{Multiply.}$$

$$\frac{60}{3} = b \quad \text{Divide 60 by 3, the number multiplied by } b.$$

$$20 = b \quad \text{Simplify.}$$

Thus, 150% of 20 is 30.

Work Practice 8

PRACTICE 8

75% of what number is 60?

✓**Concept Check** When solving a percent problem by using a proportion, describe how you can check the result.

Example 9 Solving Percent Proportion for the Base

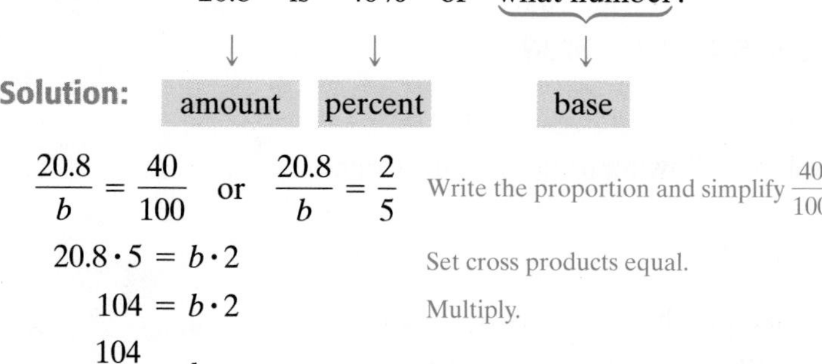

Solution:

$$\frac{20.8}{b} = \frac{40}{100} \text{ or } \frac{20.8}{b} = \frac{2}{5} \quad \text{Write the proportion and simplify } \frac{40}{100}.$$

$$20.8 \cdot 5 = b \cdot 2 \quad \text{Set cross products equal.}$$

$$104 = b \cdot 2 \quad \text{Multiply.}$$

$$\frac{104}{2} = b \quad \text{Divide 104 by 2, the number multiplied by } b.$$

$$52 = b \quad \text{Simplify.}$$

So, 20.8 is 40% of 52.

Work Practice 9

PRACTICE 9

15.2 is 5% of what number?

Answers

8. 80 **9.** 304

✓ **Concept Check Answers**

c, b; by putting the result into the proportion and checking that the proportion is true

PRACTICE 10

What percent of 40 is 6?

Example 10 Solving Percent Proportion for the Percent

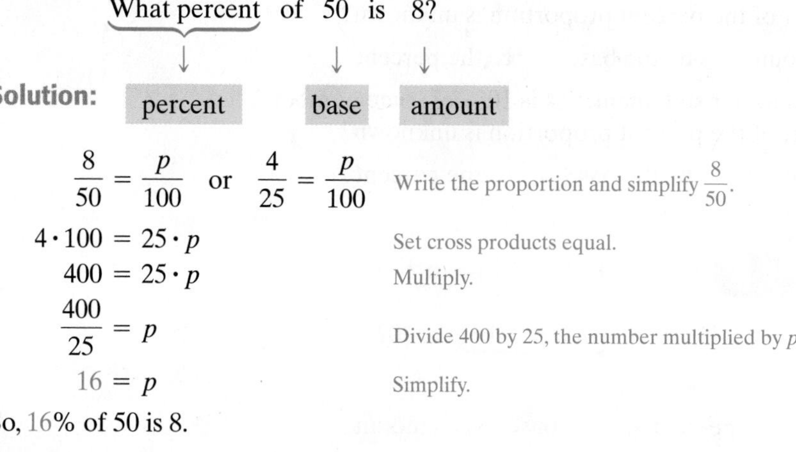

What percent of 50 is 8?

Solution: percent → What percent; base → 50; amount → 8

$$\frac{8}{50} = \frac{p}{100} \quad \text{or} \quad \frac{4}{25} = \frac{p}{100}$$ Write the proportion and simplify $\frac{8}{50}$.

$4 \cdot 100 = 25 \cdot p$ Set cross products equal.

$400 = 25 \cdot p$ Multiply.

$\frac{400}{25} = p$ Divide 400 by 25, the number multiplied by p.

$16 = p$ Simplify.

So, 16% of 50 is 8.

Work Practice 10

Helpful Hint

Recall from our percent proportion that this number already is a percent. Just keep the number as is and attach a % symbol.

PRACTICE 11

336 is what percent of 160?

Example 11 Solving Percent Proportion for the Percent

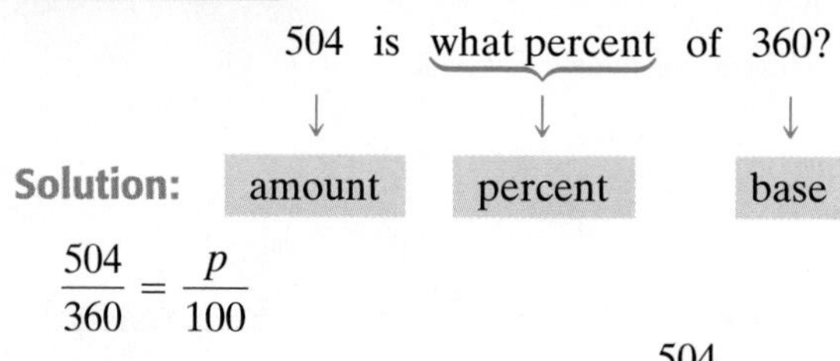

504 is what percent of 360?

Solution: amount → 504; percent → what percent; base → 360

$$\frac{504}{360} = \frac{p}{100}$$

Let's choose not to simplify the ratio $\frac{504}{360}$.

$504 \cdot 100 = 360 \cdot p$ Set cross products equal.

$50{,}400 = 360 \cdot p$ Multiply.

$\frac{50{,}400}{360} = p$ Divide 50,400 by 360, the number multiplied by p.

$140 = p$ Simplify.

Notice that by choosing not to simplify $\frac{504}{360}$, we had larger numbers in our equation.

Either way, we find that 504 is 140% of 360.

Work Practice 11

You may have noticed the following while working examples.

Helpful Hint

Use the following to see whether your answers are reasonable.

100% of a number = the number

(a percent greater than 100%) of a number = a number larger than the original number

(a percent less than 100%) of a number = a number less than the original number

Answers

10. 15% **11.** 210%

Vocabulary and Readiness Check

Use the choices below to fill in each blank. These choices will be used more than once.

amount base percent

1. When translating the statement "20% of 15 is 3" to a proportion, the number 3 is called the ______________, 15 is the ______________, and 20 is the ______________.
2. In the question "50% of what number is 28?", which part of the percent proportion is unknown? ______________
3. In the question "What number is 25% of 200?", which part of the percent proportion is unknown? ______________
4. In the question "38 is what percent of 380?", which part of the percent proportion is unknown? ______________

Identify the amount, the base, and the percent in each equation. Recall that $\frac{\text{amount}}{\text{base}} = \frac{\text{percent}}{100}$.

5. $\frac{12.6}{42} = \frac{30}{100}$
6. $\frac{201}{300} = \frac{67}{100}$
7. $\frac{20}{100} = \frac{102}{510}$
8. $\frac{40}{100} = \frac{248}{620}$

6.4 Exercise Set

Objective A Translating *Translate each to a proportion. Do not solve. See Examples 1 through 6.*

1. 98% of 45 is what number?
2. 92% of 30 is what number?
3. What number is 4% of 150?
4. What number is 7% of 175?
5. 14.3 is 26% of what number?
6. 1.2 is 47% of what number?
7. 35% of what number is 84?
8. 85% of what number is 520?
9. What percent of 400 is 70?
10. What percent of 900 is 216?
11. 8.2 is what percent of 82?
12. 9.6 is what percent of 96?

Objective B *Solve. See Example 7.*

13. 40% of 65 is what number?
14. 25% of 84 is what number?
15. What number is 18% of 105?
16. What number is 60% of 29?

Solve. See Examples 8 and 9.

17. 15% of what number is 90?
18. 55% of what number is 55?
19. 7.8 is 78% of what number?
20. 1.1 is 44% of what number?

Solve. See Examples 10 and 11.

21. What percent of 35 is 42?

22. What percent of 98 is 147?

23. 14 is what percent of 50?

24. 24 is what percent of 50?

Objectives **A** **B** **Mixed Practice** *Solve. See Examples 1 through 11.*

25. 3.7 is 10% of what number?

26. 7.4 is 5% of what number?

27. 2.4% of 70 is what number?

28. 2.5% of 90 is what number?

29. 160 is 16% of what number?

30. 30 is 6% of what number?

31. 394.8 is what percent of 188?

32. 550.4 is what percent of 172?

33. What number is 89% of 62?

34. What number is 53% of 130?

35. What percent of 6 is 2.7?

36. What percent of 5 is 1.6?

37. 140% of what number is 105?

38. 170% of what number is 221?

39. 1.8% of 48 is what number?

40. 7.8% of 24 is what number?

41. What percent of 800 is 4?

42. What percent of 500 is 3?

43. 3.5 is 2.5% of what number?

44. 9.18 is 6.8% of what number?

45. 20% of 48 is what number?

46. 75% of 14 is what number?

47. 2486 is what percent of 2200?

48. 9310 is what percent of 3800?

Review

Add or subtract the fractions. See Sections 3.1, 3.3, and 3.4.

49. $\frac{11}{16} + \frac{3}{16}$

50. $\frac{5}{8} - \frac{7}{12}$

51. $3\frac{1}{2} - \frac{11}{30}$

52. $2\frac{2}{3} + 4\frac{1}{2}$

Add or subtract the decimals. See Section 4.3.

53. $\begin{array}{r} 0.41 \\ +0.29 \\ \hline \end{array}$

54. $\begin{array}{r} 10.78 \\ 4.3 \\ +\ 0.21 \\ \hline \end{array}$

55. $\begin{array}{r} 2.38 \\ -0.19 \\ \hline \end{array}$

56. $\begin{array}{r} 16.37 \\ -\ 2.61 \\ \hline \end{array}$

Concept Extensions

57. Write a word statement for the proportion $\frac{x}{28} = \frac{25}{100}$. Use the phrase "what number" for "x."

58. Write a percent statement that translates to $\frac{16}{80} = \frac{20}{100}$.

Suppose you have finished solving four percent problems using proportions that you set up correctly. Check each answer to see if each makes the proportion a true proportion. If any proportion is not true, solve it to find the correct solution. See the Concept Checks in this section.

59. $\frac{a}{64} = \frac{25}{100}$
Is the amount equal to 17?

60. $\frac{520}{b} = \frac{65}{100}$
Is the base equal to 800?

61. $\frac{p}{100} = \frac{13}{52}$
Is the percent equal to 25 (25%)?

62. $\frac{36}{12} = \frac{p}{100}$
Is the percent equal to 50 (50%)?

63. In your own words, describe how to identify the percent, the base, and the amount in a percent problem.

64. In your own words, explain how to use a proportion to solve a percent problem.

Solve. Round to the nearest tenth, if necessary.

65. What number is 22.3% of 53,862?

66. What percent of 110,736 is 88,542?

67. 8652 is 119% of what number?

Answers

1. ______
2. ______
3. ______
4. ______
5. ______
6. ______
7. ______
8. ______
9. ______
10. ______
11. ______
12. ______
13. ______
14. ______
15. ______
16. ______
17. ______
18. ______
19. ______
20. ______
21. ______
22. ______
23. ______
24. ______

Integrated Review Sections 6.1–6.4

Percent and Percent Problems

Write each number as a percent.

1. 0.12 **2.** 0.68 **3.** $\frac{1}{8}$ **4.** $\frac{5}{2}$

5. 5.2 **6.** 8 **7.** $\frac{3}{50}$ **8.** $\frac{11}{25}$

9. $7\frac{1}{2}$ **10.** $3\frac{1}{4}$ **11.** 0.03 **12.** 0.05

Write each percent as a decimal.

13. 65% **14.** 31% **15.** 8% **16.** 7%

17. 142% **18.** 400% **19.** 2.9% **20.** 6.6%

Write each percent as a decimal and as a fraction or mixed number in simplest form. (If necessary when writing as a decimal, round to the nearest thousandth.)

21. 3% **22.** 5% **23.** 5.25% **24.** 12.75%

25. 38%

26. 45%

27. $12\frac{1}{3}\%$

28. $16\frac{2}{3}\%$

25. ____________

26. ____________

27. ____________

28. ____________

29. ____________

30. ____________

31. ____________

32. ____________

33. ____________

34. ____________

35. ____________

36. ____________

37. ____________

38. ____________

39. ____________

40. ____________

Solve each percent problem.

29. 12% of 70 is what number?

30. 36 is 36% of what number?

31. 212.5 is 85% of what number?

32. 66 is what percent of 55?

33. 23.8 is what percent of 85?

34. 38% of 200 is what number?

35. What number is 25% of 44?

36. What percent of 99 is 128.7?

37. What percent of 250 is 215?

38. What number is 45% of 84?

39. 42% of what number is 63?

40. 95% of what number is 58.9?

Objectives

A **Solve Applications Involving Percent.**

B **Find Percent Increase and Percent Decrease.**

6.5 APPLICATIONS OF PERCENT

Objective A Solving Applications Involving Percent

Percent is used in a variety of everyday situations. The next examples show just a few ways that percent occurs in real-life settings. (Each of these examples shows two ways of solving these problems. If you studied Section 6.3 only, see *Method 1.* If you studied Section 6.4 only, see *Method 2.*)

The first example has to do with the Appalachian Trail, a hiking trail conceived by a forester in 1921 and diagrammed to the right.

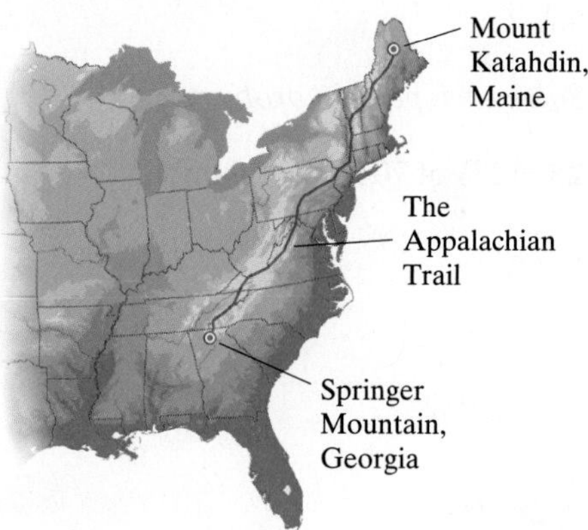

PRACTICE 1

If the total mileage of the Appalachian Trail is 2174, use the circle graph to determine the number of miles in the state of Virginia.

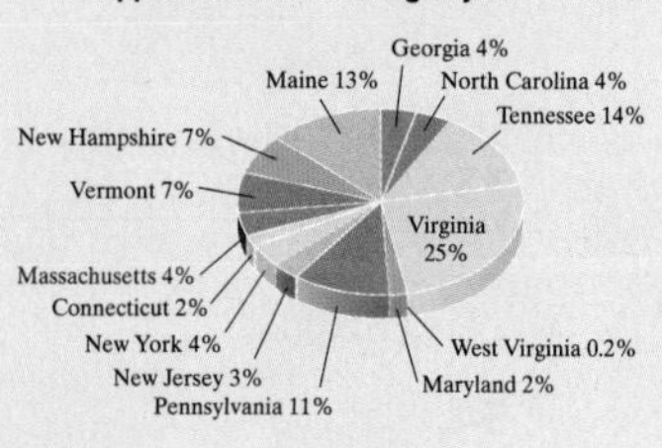

Example 1 The circle graph in the margin shows the Appalachian Trail mileage by state. If the total mileage of the trail is 2174, use the circle graph to determine the number of miles in the state of New York. Round to the nearest whole mile.

Solution: *Method 1.* First, we state the problem in words.

In words: What number is 4% of 2174?

Translate: $n = 4\% \cdot 2174$

To solve for n, we find $4\% \cdot 2174$.

$n = 0.04 \cdot 2174$ Write 4% as a decimal.

$n = 86.96$ Multiply.

$n \approx 87$ Round to the nearest whole.

Rounded to the nearest whole mile, we have that approximately 87 miles of the Appalachian Trail are in New York state.

Method 2. State the problem in words; then translate.

In words: What number (amount) is 4% (percent) of 2174 (base)?

Translate: $\frac{a}{2174} = \frac{4}{100}$ (amount → a, base → 2174, 4 ← percent)

Next, we solve for a.

$a \cdot 100 = 2174 \cdot 4$ Set cross products equal.

$a \cdot 100 = 8696$ Multiply.

$\frac{a \cdot 100}{100} = \frac{8696}{100}$ Divide both sides by 100.

$a = 86.96$ Simplify.

$a \approx 87$ Round to the nearest whole.

Rounded to the nearest whole mile, we have that approximately 87 miles of the Appalachian Trail are in New York state.

Work Practice 1

Answer

1. 543.5 mi

Example 2 Finding Percent of Nursing Schools with Increases in Enrollment

There is a worldwide shortage of nurses, with numbers of nurses projected to be 20% below requirements by 2020. Until 2001, there has also been a continual decline in enrollment in nursing schools. That has recently changed.

In 2003, 2178 of the total 2593 nursing schools in the United States had an increase in applications or enrollment. What percent of nursing schools had an increase? Round to the nearest whole percent. (*Source:* CNN and *Nurse Week*)

Solution: *Method 1.* First, we state the problem in words.

In words: 2178 is what percent of 2593?

Translate: $2178 = n \cdot 2593$

Next, solve for n.

$\frac{2178}{2593} = n$ Divide 2178 by 2593, the number multiplied by n.

$0.84 \approx n$ Divide and round to the nearest hundredth.

$84\% \approx n$ Write as a percent.

In 2003, about 84% of nursing schools had an increase in applications or enrollment.

Method 2.

In words: 2178 is what percent of 2593?

2178 → amount; what percent → percent; 2593 → base

Translate: $\frac{\text{amount} \rightarrow 2178}{\text{base} \rightarrow 2593} = \frac{p}{100} \leftarrow \text{percent}$

Next, solve for p.

$2178 \cdot 100 = 2593 \cdot p$ Set cross products equal.

$217{,}800 = 2593 \cdot p$ Multiply.

$\frac{217{,}800}{2593} = p$ Divide 217,800 by 2593, the number multiplied by p.

$84 \approx p$

In 2003, about 84% of nursing schools had an increase in applications or enrollment.

Work Practice 2

Example 3 Finding the Base Number of Absences

Mr. Buccaran, the principal at Slidell High School, counted 31 freshmen absent during a particular day. If this is 4% of the total number of freshmen, how many freshmen are there at Slidell High School?

Solution: *Method 1.* First we state the problem in words; then we translate.

In words: 31 is 4% of what number?

Translate: $31 = 4\% \cdot n$

Continued on next page

PRACTICE 2

In Florida, about 34,000 new nurses were recently needed and hired. If there are now 130,000 nurses, what percent of new nurses were needed in Florida? Round to the nearest whole percent. (*Source*: *St. Petersburg Times* and *The Registered Nurse Population*)

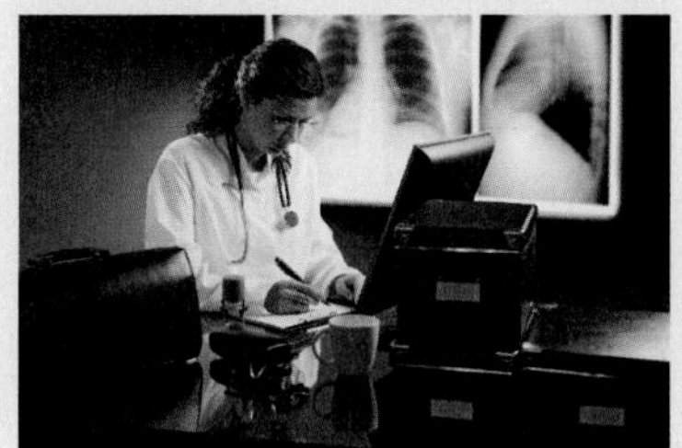

PRACTICE 3

The freshmen class of 775 students is 31% of all students at Euclid University. How many students go to Euclid University?

Answers

2. 26% **3.** 2500

Next, we solve for n.

$$31 = 0.04 \cdot n \quad \text{Write 4\% as a decimal.}$$

$$\frac{31}{0.04} = n \quad \text{Divide 31 by 0.04, the number multiplied by } n.$$

$$775 = n \quad \text{Simplify.}$$

There are 775 freshmen at Slidell High School.

Method 2. First we state the problem in words; then we translate.

In words: 31 is 4% of what number?

31 ↓ amount; 4% ↓ percent; what number ↓ base

Translate: amount → $\frac{31}{b} = \frac{4}{100}$ ← percent; base → b

Next, we solve for b.

$$31 \cdot 100 = b \cdot 4 \quad \text{Set cross products equal.}$$

$$3100 = b \cdot 4 \quad \text{Multiply.}$$

$$\frac{3100}{4} = b \quad \text{Divide 3100 by 4, the number multiplied by } b.$$

$$775 = b \quad \text{Simplify.}$$

There are 775 freshmen at Slidell High School.

Work Practice 3

PRACTICE 4

From 2000 to 2007, the number of registered vehicles on the road in the United States increased by 3%. In 2000, the number of vehicles on the road was 240 million.

a. Find the increase in the number of vehicles on the road in 2007.

b. Find the total number of registered vehicles on the road in 2007.

(*Source:* Federal Highway Administration)

Answers

4. a. 7.2 million **b.** 247.2 million

Example 4 Finding the Base Increase in Licensed Drivers

From 2000 to 2007, the number of licensed drivers on the road in the United States increased by 6.5%. In 2000, there were 190 million licensed drivers on the road.

a. Find the increase in licensed drivers from 2000 to 2007.

b. Find the number of licensed drivers on the road in 2007.

(*Source:* Federal Highway Administration)

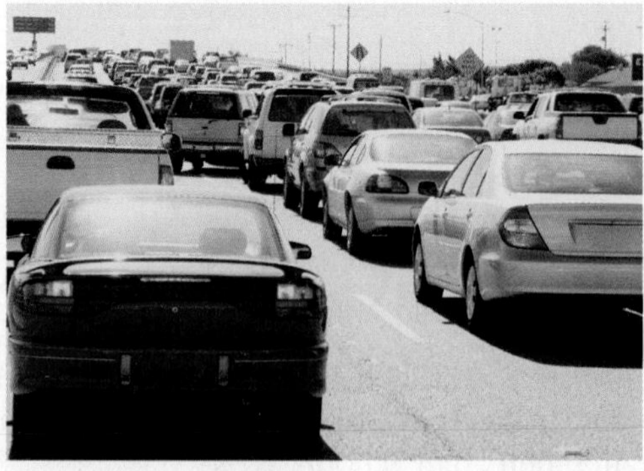

Solution: *Method 1.* First we find the increase in licensed drivers.

In words: What number is 6.5% of 190?

Translate: $n = 6.5\% \cdot 190$

Next, we solve for n.

$n = 0.065 \cdot 190$ Write 6.5 as a decimal.

$n = 12.35$ Multiply.

a. The increase in licensed drivers was 12.35 million.

b. This means that the number of licensed drivers in 2007 was

$$\begin{array}{c}\text{Number of}\\\text{licensed drivers}\\\text{in 2007}\end{array} = \begin{array}{c}\text{Number of}\\\text{licensed drivers}\\\text{in 2000}\end{array} + \begin{array}{c}\text{Increase}\\\text{in number of}\\\text{licensed drivers}\end{array}$$

$$= 190 \text{ million} + 12.35 \text{ million}$$

$$= 202.35 \text{ million}$$

Method 2. First we find the increase in licensed drivers.

In words: What number is 6.5% of 190?

What number ↓ amount; 6.5% ↓ percent; 190 ↓ base

Translate: $\dfrac{a}{190} = \dfrac{6.5}{100}$ (amount → a, base → 190, 6.5 ← percent)

Next, we solve for a.

$a \cdot 100 = 190 \cdot 6.5$ Set cross products equal.

$a \cdot 100 = 1235$ Multiply.

$\dfrac{a \cdot 100}{100} = \dfrac{1235}{100}$ Divide both sides by 100.

$a = 12.35$ Simplify.

a. The increase in licensed drivers was 12.35 million.

b. This means that the number of licensed drivers in 2007 was

$$\begin{array}{c}\text{Number of}\\\text{licensed drivers}\\\text{in 2007}\end{array} = \begin{array}{c}\text{Number of}\\\text{licensed drivers}\\\text{in 2000}\end{array} + \begin{array}{c}\text{Increase}\\\text{in number of}\\\text{licensed drivers}\end{array}$$

$$= 190 \text{ million} + 12.35 \text{ million}$$

$$= 202.35 \text{ million}$$

Work Practice 4

Objective B Finding Percent Increase and Percent Decrease

We often use percents to show how much an amount has increased or decreased.

Suppose that the population of a town is 10,000 people and then it increases by 2000 people. The **percent of increase** is

$$\frac{2000}{10{,}000} = 0.2 = 20\%$$

(amount of increase → 2000, original amount → 10,000)

In general, we have the following.

Percent of Increase

$$\text{percent of increase} = \frac{\text{amount of increase}}{\text{original amount}}$$

Then write the quotient as a percent.

PRACTICE 5

The number of people attending the local play, *Peter Pan,* increased from 285 on Friday to 333 on Saturday. Find the percent increase in attendance. Round to the nearest tenth percent.

Example 5 Finding Percent Increase

The number of applications for a mathematics scholarship at Yale increased from 34 to 45 in one year. What is the percent increase? Round to the nearest whole percent.

Solution: First we find the amount of increase by subtracting the original number of applicants from the new number of applicants.

amount of increase $= 45 - 34 = 11$

The amount of increase is 11 applicants. To find the percent of increase,

$$\text{percent of increase} = \frac{\text{amount of increase}}{\text{original amount}} = \frac{11}{34} \approx 0.32 = 32\%$$

Helpful Hint Make sure that this number is the original number and not the new number.

The number of applications increased by about 32%.

Work Practice 5

✓**Concept Check** A student is calculating the percent increase in enrollment from 180 students one year to 200 students the next year. Explain what is wrong with the following calculations:

$$\text{Amount of increase} = 200 - 180 = 20$$

$$\text{Percent of increase} = \frac{20}{200} = 0.1 = 10\%$$

Suppose that your income was $300 a week and then it decreased by $30. The **percent of decrease** is

$$\frac{\text{amount of decrease} \rightarrow \$30}{\text{original amount} \rightarrow \$300} = 0.1 = 10\%$$

Percent of Decrease

$$\text{percent of decrease} = \frac{\text{amount of decrease}}{\text{original amount}}$$

Then write the quotient as a percent.

PRACTICE 6

A town with a population of 20,200 in 1995 decreased to 18,483 in 2005. What was the percent decrease?

Example 6 Finding Percent Decrease

In response to a decrease in sales, a company with 1500 employees reduces the number of employees to 1230. What is the percent decrease?

Solution: First we find the amount of decrease by subtracting 1230 from 1500.

amount of decrease $= 1500 - 1230 = 270$

The amount of decrease is 270. To find the percent of decrease,

$$\text{percent of decrease} = \frac{\text{amount of decrease}}{\text{original amount}} = \frac{270}{1500} = 0.18 = 18\%$$

The number of employees decreased by 18%.

Work Practice 6

✓**Concept Check** An ice cream stand sold 6000 ice cream cones last summer. This year the same stand sold 5400 cones. Was there a 10% increase, a 10% decrease, or neither? Explain.

Answers

5. 16.8% **6.** 8.5%

✓ **Concept Check Answers**

To find the percent of increase, you have to divide the amount of increase (20) by the original amount (180); 10% decrease.

6.5 Exercise Set

Objective A *Solve. For Exercises 1 and 2, the solutions have been started for you. See Examples 1 through 4. If necessary, round percents to the nearest tenth and all other answers to the nearest whole.*

1. An inspector found 24 defective bolts during an inspection. If this is 1.5% of the total number of bolts inspected, how many bolts were inspected?

Start the solution:

1. UNDERSTAND the problem. Reread it as many times as needed.

Go to Method 1 or Method 2.

Method 1.

2. TRANSLATE into an equation. (Fill in the boxes.)

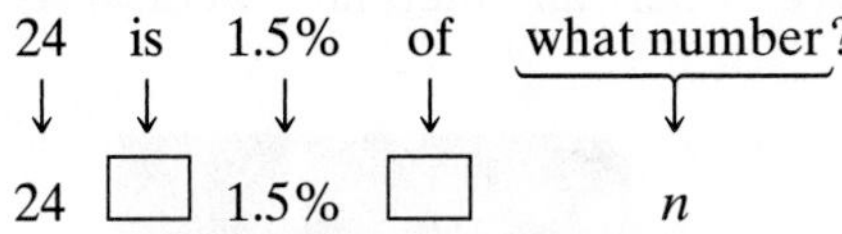

3. SOLVE for n. (See Example 3, Method 1, for help.)

4. INTERPRET. The total number of bolts inspected was ________.

Method 2.

2. TRANSLATE into a proportion. (Fill in the blanks with "amount" or "base.")

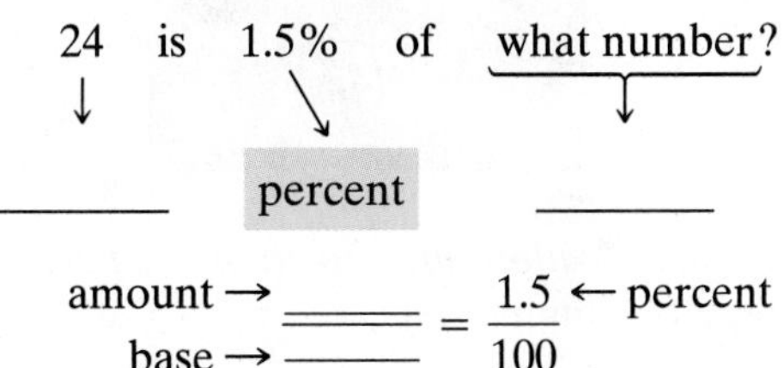

3. SOLVE the proportion. (See Example 3, Method 2, for help.)

4. INTERPRET. The total number of bolts inspected was ________.

2. A day care worker found 28 children absent one day during an epidemic of chicken pox. If this was 35% of the total number of children attending the day care center, how many children attend this day care center?

Start the solution:

1. UNDERSTAND the problem. Reread it as many times as needed.

Go to Method 1 or Method 2.

Method 1.

2. TRANSLATE into an equation. (Fill in the boxes.)

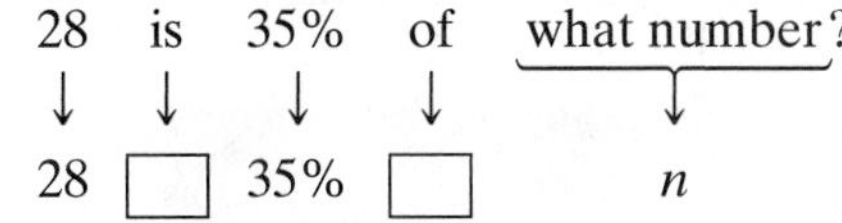

3. SOLVE for n. (See Example 3, Method 1, for help.)

4. INTERPRET. The total number of children attending the day care center was ________.

Method 2.

2. TRANSLATE into a proportion. (Fill in the blanks with "amount" or "base.")

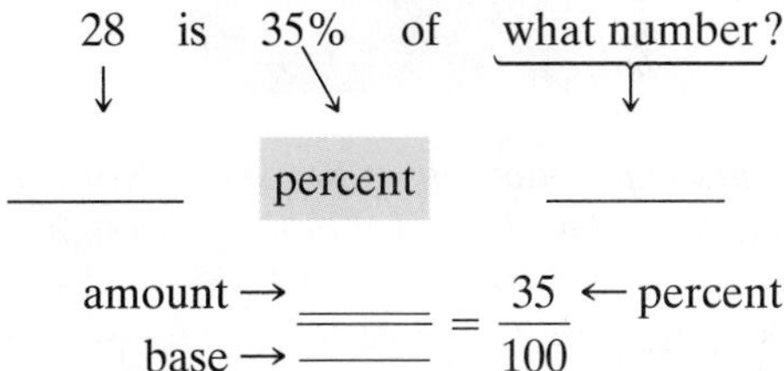

3. SOLVE the proportion. (See Example 3, Method 2, for help.)

4. INTERPRET. The total number of children attending the day care center was ________.

3. The Total Gym® provides weight resistance through adjustments of incline. The minimum weight resistance is 4% of the weight of the person using the Total Gym. Find the minimum weight resistance possible for a 220-pound man. (*Source:* Total Gym)

4. The maximum weight resistance for the Total Gym is 60% of the weight of the person using it. Find the maximum weight resistance possible for a 220-pound man. (See Exercise 3 if needed.)

5. A student's cost for last semester at her community college was \$2700. She spent \$378 of that on books. What percent of last semester's college costs was spent on books?

6. Pierre Sampeau belongs to his local food cooperative, where he receives a percentage of what he spends each year as a dividend. He spent \$3850 last year at the food cooperative store and received a dividend of \$154. What percent of his total spending at the food cooperative did he receive as a dividend?

7. In a recent year, approximately 32% of films were rated R. If 725 films were rated, how many were rated R? (*Source:* Motion Picture Association of America)

8. In a recent year, approximately 8% of films were rated PG. If 725 films were rated, how many were rated PG? (*Source:* Motion Picture Association of America)

9. Approximately 160,650 of America's 945,000 restaurants are pizza restaurants. Determine the percent of restaurants in America that are pizza restaurants. (*Source:* Pizza Marketplace, National Restaurant Association)

10. Of the 58,200 veterinarians in private practice in the United States, approximately 27,354 are female. Determine the percent of female veterinarians in private practice in the United States. (*Source:* American Veterinary Medical Association)

11. A furniture company currently produces 6200 chairs per month. If production decreases by 8%, find the decrease and the new number of chairs produced each month.

12. The enrollment at a local college decreased by 5% over last year's enrollment of 7640. Find the decrease in enrollment and the current enrollment.

13. From 2006 to 2016, the number of people employed as physician assistants in the United States is expected to increase by 27%. The number of people employed as physician assistants in 2006 was 66,000. Find the predicted number of physician assistants in 2016. (*Source:* Bureau of Labor Statistics)

14. From 2001 to 2007, the number of households owning dogs increased by 13.5%. The number of households owning dogs in 2001 was 37,900,000. Find the number of households owning dogs in 2007. (*Source:* American Veterinary Medical Association)

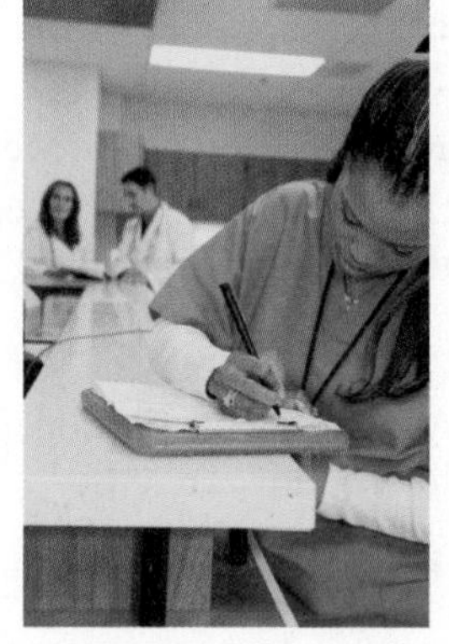

Let's look at the populations of two states, North Dakota and Louisiana. Their locations are shown on the partial U.S. map below. Round each answer to the nearest thousand. (*Source:* U.S. Dept. of Commerce)

15. In 2000, the population of North Dakota was approximately 642 thousand. If the population decreased by 0.8% between 2000 and 2009, find the population of North Dakota in 2009.

16. In 2000, the population in Louisiana was approximately 4470 thousand. If the population increased about 0.5% between 2000 and 2009, find the population of Louisiana in 2009.

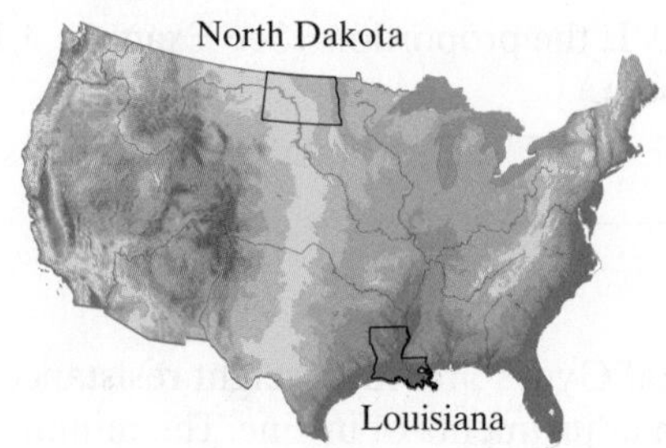

A popular extreme sport is snowboarding. Ski trails are marked with difficulty levels of easy ●, intermediate ■, difficult ◆, expert ◆◆, and other variations. Use this information for Exercises 17 and 18. Round each percent to the nearest whole. See Example 2.

17. At Keystone ski area in Colorado, approximately 41 of the 135 total ski runs are rated intermediate. What percent of the runs are intermediate?

18. At Telluride ski area in Colorado, about 28 of the 115 total ski runs are rated easy. What percent of the runs are easy?

For each food described, find the percent of total calories from fat. If necessary, round to the nearest tenth percent. See Example 2.

19. Ranch dressing serving size of 2 tablespoons

	Calories
Total	40
From fat	20

20. Unsweetened cocoa powder serving size of 1 tablespoon

	Calories
Total	20
From fat	5

21.

Nutrition Facts
Serving Size 1 pouch (20g)
Servings Per Container 6

Amount Per Serving	
Calories	80
Calories from fat	10
	% Daily Value*
Total Fat 1g	**2%**
Sodium 45mg	**2%**
Total Carbohydrate 17g	**6%**
Sugars 9g	
Protein 0g	
Vitamin C	25%

Not a significant source of saturated fat, cholesterol, dietary fiber, vitamin A, calcium and iron.

*Percent Daily Values are based on a 2,000 calorie diet.

Artificial Fruit Snacks

22.

Nutrition Facts
Serving Size $\frac{1}{4}$ cup (33g)
Servings Per Container About 9

Amount Per Serving	
Calories 190 **Calories from Fat** 130	
	% Daily Value
Total Fat 16g	**24%**
Saturated Fat 3g	**16%**
Cholesterol 0mg	**0%**
Sodium 135mg	**6%**
Total Carbohydrate 9g	**3%**
Dietary Fiber 1g	**5%**
Sugars 2g	
Protein 5g	

Vitamin A 0% • Vitamin C 0%
Calcium 0% • Iron 8%

Peanut Mixture

23.

Nutrition Facts
Serving Size 18 crackers (29g)
Servings Per Container About 9

Amount Per Serving	
Calories 120 **Calories from Fat** 35	
	% Daily Value*
Total Fat 4g	**6%**
Saturated Fat 0.5g	**3%**
Polyunsaturated Fat 0g	
Monounsaturated Fat 1.5g	
Cholesterol 0mg	**0%**
Sodium 220mg	**9%**
Total Carbohydrate 21g	**7%**
Dietary Fiber 2g	**7%**
Sugars 3g	
Protein 2g	

Vitamin A 0% • Vitamin C 0%
Calcium 2% • Iron 4%
Phosphorus 10%

Snack Crackers

24.

Nutrition Facts
Serving Size 28 crackers (31g)
Servings Per Container About 6

Amount Per Serving	
Calories 130 **Calories from Fat** 35	
	% Daily Value*
Total Fat 4g	**6%**
Saturated Fat 2g	**10%**
Polyunsaturated Fat 1g	
Monounsaturated Fat 1g	
Cholesterol 0mg	**0%**
Sodium 470mg	**20%**
Total Carbohydrate 23g	**8%**
Dietary Fiber 1g	**4%**
Sugars 4g	
Protein 2g	

Vitamin A 0% • Vitamin C 0%
Calcium 0% • Iron 2%

Snack Crackers

Solve. If necessary, round money amounts to the nearest cent and all other amounts to the nearest tenth. See Examples 1 through 4.

25. A family paid $26,250 as a down payment for a home. If this represents 15% of the price of the home, find the price of the home.

26. A banker learned that $842.40 is withheld from his monthly check for taxes and insurance. If this represents 18% of his total pay, find the total pay.

27. An owner of a repair service company estimates that for every 40 hours a repairperson is on the job, he can bill for only 78% of the hours. The remaining hours, the repairperson is idle or driving to or from a job. Determine the number of hours per 40-hour week the owner can bill for a repairperson.

28. A manufacturer of electronic components expects 1.04% of its products to be defective. Determine the number of defective components expected in a batch of 28,350 components. Round to the nearest whole component.

29. A car manufacturer announced that next year the price of a certain model of car will increase by 4.5%. This year the price is $19,286. Find the increase in price and the new price.

30. A union contract calls for a 6.5% salary increase for all employees. Determine the increase and the new salary that a worker currently making $58,500 under this contract can expect.

A popular extreme sport is artificial wall climbing. The photo shown is an artificial climbing wall. Exercises 31 and 32 are about the Footsloggers Climbing Tower in Boone, North Carolina.

31. A climber is resting at a height of 21 feet while on the Footsloggers Climbing Tower. If this is 60% of the tower's total height, find the height of the tower.

32. A group plans to climb the Footsloggers Climbing Tower at the group rate, once they save enough money. Thus far, $126 has been saved. If this is 70% of the total amount needed for the group, find the total price.

33. Tuition for an Ohio resident at the Columbus campus of Ohio State University was $4761 in 2001. The tuition increased by 82.3% during the period from 2001 to 2009. Find the increase, and the tuition for the 2009–2010 school year. Round the increase to the nearest whole dollar. (*Source:* Ohio State University)

34. The population of Americans aged 65 and older was 38 million in 2007. That population is projected to increase by 90% by 2030. Find the increase and the projected 2030 population. (*Source:* Bureau of the Census)

35. From 2008–2009 to 2017–2018, the number of associate degrees awarded is projected to increase by 5.7%. If the number of associate degrees awarded in 2008–2009 is 731,000, find the increase and the projected number of associate degrees awarded in the 2017–2018 school year. (*Source:* National Center for Education Statistics)

36. From 2008–2009 to 2017–2018, the number of bachelor degrees awarded is projected to increase by 8%. If the number of bachelor degrees awarded in 2008–2009 was 1,603,000, find the increase and the projected number of bachelor degrees awarded in the 2017–2018 school year. (*Source:* National Center for Education Statistics)

Objective B *Find the amount of increase and the percent increase. See Example 5.*

	Original Amount	New Amount	Amount of Increase	Percent Increase
37.	50	80		
38.	8	12		
39.	65	117		
40.	68	170		

Find the amount of decrease and the percent decrease. See Example 6.

	Original Amount	New Amount	Amount of Decrease	Percent Decrease
41.	8	6		
42.	25	20		
43.	160	40		
44.	200	162		

Solve. Round percents to the nearest tenth, if necessary. See Examples 5 and 6.

45. There are 150 calories in a cup of whole milk and only 84 in a cup of skim milk. In switching to skim milk, find the percent decrease in number of calories per cup.

46. In reaction to a slow economy, the number of employees at a soup company decreased from 530 to 477. What was the percent decrease in the number of employees?

47. The number of cable TV systems recently decreased from 10,845 to 10,700. Find the percent decrease.

48. Before taking a typing course, Geoffry Landers could type 32 words per minute. By the end of the course, he was able to type 76 words per minute. Find the percent increase.

49. In 1940, the average size of a privately owned farm in the United States was 174 acres. In a recent year, the average size of a privately owned farm in the United States had increased to 449 acres. What is this percent increase? (*Source:* National Agricultural Statistics Service)

50. In 2003, 5.5 million digital television sets were sold in the United States. By 2007, this number had increased to 27.1 million. What was the percent increase? Round to the nearest percent. (*Source:* Motion Picture Association of America)

51. When music CDs were first introduced in 1983, the average suggested list price was \$21.50. By 2007, the average suggested list price was \$14.88. What was the percent decrease in the average suggested list price for music CDs from 1983 to 2007? (*Source:* Recording Industry Association of America)

52. In 1994, there were 784 deaths from boating accidents in the United States. By 2008, the number of deaths from boating accidents had decreased to 655. What was the percent decrease? (*Source:* U.S. Coast Guard)

53. In 2006, there were 3570 thousand elementary and secondary teachers employed in the United States. This number is expected to increase to 3769 thousand teachers in 2012. What is the percent increase? (*Source:* National Center for Education Statistics)

54. In 2006, approximately 500,000 correctional officers were employed in the United States. By 2016, this number is expected to increase to 580,000 correctional officers. What is the percent increase? (*Source:* Bureau of Labor Statistics)

55. In a recent 10-year period, the number of indoor cinema sites in the United States decreased from 6903 to 5545. What is this percent decrease? (*Source:* National Association of Theater Owners)

56. As the largest health care occupation, registered nurses held about 2.5 million jobs in 2006. The number of registered nurses is expected to be 3.075 million by 2016. What is the percent increase? (*Source:* Bureau of Labor Statistics)

57. In 2006, approximately 504,000 computer systems analysts were employed in the United States. By 2016, this is expected to increase to 650,000. What is the percent increase? (*Source:* Bureau of Labor Statistics)

58. In 1999, there were 10.9 million total restaurant employees in the United States. By 2019, this number is expected to increase to 14.8 million. What is the percent increase? (*Source:* National Restaurant Association)

59. The number of cell phone tower sites in the United States was 178,025 in 2005. By 2010, the number of cell sites had increased to 247,081. What is the percent increase? Round to the nearest percent. (*Source:* CTIA—The Wireless Association)

60. The population of Tokyo is expected to decrease from 127,400 thousand in 2005 to 99,900 thousand in 2050. Find the percent decrease. (*Source:* International Programs Center, Bureau of the Census, U.S. Dept. of Commerce)

Review

Perform each indicated operation. See Sections 4.3 and 4.4.

61. $\begin{array}{r} 0.12 \\ \times\ 38 \\ \hline \end{array}$

62. $\begin{array}{r} 42 \\ \times\ 0.7 \\ \hline \end{array}$

63. $9.20 + 1.98$

64. $46 + 7.89$

65. $78 - 19.46$

66. $64.80 - 10.72$

Concept Extensions

67. If a number is increased by 100%, how does the increased number compare with the original number? Explain your answer.

68. In your own words, explain what is wrong with the following statement. "Last year we had 80 students attend. This year we have a 50% increase or a total of 160 students attending."

Explain what errors were made by each student when solving percent of increase or decrease problems and then correct the errors. See the Concept Checks in this section.

The population of a certain rural town was 150 in 1980, 180 in 1990, and 150 in 2000.

69. Find the percent of increase in population from 1980 to 1990.

Miranda's solution: Percent of increase $= \frac{30}{180} = 0.1\overline{6} \approx 16.7\%$

70. Find the percent of decrease in population from 1990 to 2000.

Jeremy's solution: Percent of decrease $= \frac{30}{150} = 0.20 = 20\%$

71. The percent of increase from 1980 to 1990 is the same as the percent of decrease from 1990 to 2000. True or false.

Chris's answer: True because they had the same amount of increase as the amount of decrease.

6.6 PERCENT AND PROBLEM SOLVING: SALES TAX, COMMISSION, AND DISCOUNT

Objectives

Ⓐ Calculate Sales Tax and Total Price.

Ⓑ Calculate Commissions.

Ⓒ Calculate Discount and Sale Price.

Objective Ⓐ Calculating Sales Tax and Total Price

Percents are frequently used in the retail trade. For example, most states charge a tax on certain items when purchased. This tax is called a **sales tax,** and retail stores collect it for the state. Sales tax is almost always stated as a percent of the purchase price.

A 9% sales tax rate on a purchase of a $10 calculator gives a sales tax of

sales tax = 9% of $10 = 0.09 · $10.00 = $0.90

The total price to the customer would be

purchase price	plus	sales tax	
↓	↓	↓	
$10.00	+	$0.90	= $10.90

This example suggests the following equations:

Sales Tax and Total Price

sales tax = tax rate · purchase price

total price = purchase price + sales tax

In this section we round dollar amounts to the nearest cent.

Example 1 Finding Sales Tax and Purchase Price

Find the sales tax and the total price on the purchase of an $85.50 atlas in a city where the sales tax rate is 7.5%.

Solution: The purchase price is $85.50 and the tax rate is 7.5%.

sales tax = tax rate · purchase price

sales tax = 7.5% · $85.50

= 0.075 · $85.5 Write 7.5% as a decimal.

≈ $6.41 Rounded to the nearest cent

Thus, the sales tax is $6.41. Next find the total price.

total price = purchase price + sales tax

total price = $85.50 + $6.41

= $91.91

The sales tax on $85.50 is $6.41, and the total price is $91.91.

Work Practice 1

PRACTICE 1

If the sales tax rate is 8.5%, what is the sales tax and the total amount due on a $59.90 Goodgrip tire? (Round the sales tax to the nearest cent.)

Answer

1. tax: $5.09; total: $64.99

✓**Concept Check** The purchase price of a textbook is \$50 and sales tax is 10%. If you are told by the cashier that the total price is \$75, how can you tell that a mistake has been made?

PRACTICE 2

The sales tax on an \$18,500 automobile is \$1665. Find the sales tax rate.

Example 2 Finding a Sales Tax Rate

The sales tax on a \$406 Sony flat-screen digital 27-inch television is \$34.51. Find the sales tax rate.

Solution: Let r represent the unknown sales tax rate. Then

$$\text{sales tax} = \text{tax rate} \cdot \text{purchase price}$$

$$\$34.51 = r \cdot \$406$$

$$\frac{34.51}{406} = \frac{r \cdot 406}{406} \quad \text{Divide both sides by 406.}$$

$$0.085 = r \quad \text{Simplify.}$$

$$8.5\% = r \quad \text{Write 0.085 as a percent.}$$

The sales tax rate is 8.5%.

Work Practice 2

Objective B Calculating Commissions

A **wage** is payment for performing work. Hourly wage, commissions, and salary are some of the ways wages can be paid. Many people who work in sales are paid a commission. An employee who is paid a **commission** is paid a percent of his or her total sales.

Commission

commission = commission rate · sales

PRACTICE 3

A sales representative for Office Product Copiers sold \$47,632 worth of copy equipment and supplies last month. What is his commission for the month if he is paid a commission of 6.6% of his total sales for the month?

Example 3 Finding the Amount of Commission

Sherry Souter, a real estate broker for Wealth Investments, sold a house for \$214,000 last week. If her commission is 1.5% of the selling price of the home, find the amount of her commission.

Solution:

$$\text{commission} = \text{commission rate} \cdot \text{sales}$$

$$\text{commission} = 1.5\% \cdot \$214{,}000$$

$$= 0.015 \cdot \$214{,}000 \quad \text{Write 1.5\% as 0.015.}$$

$$= \$3210 \quad \text{Multiply.}$$

Answers

2. 9% **3.** \$3143.71

✓ **Concept Check Answer**

Since $10\% = \frac{1}{10}$, the sales tax is $\frac{\$50}{10} = \$5$. The total price should have been \$55.

Her commission on the house is \$3210.

Work Practice 3

Example 4 Finding a Commission Rate

A salesperson earned \$1560 for selling \$13,000 worth of electronics equipment. Find the commission rate.

Solution: Let r stand for the unknown commission rate. Then

commission = commission rate · sales

$$\$1560 = r \cdot \$13{,}000$$

$$\frac{1560}{13{,}000} = r \quad \text{Divide 1560 by 13,000, the number multiplied by } r.$$

$$0.12 = r \quad \text{Simplify.}$$

$$12\% = r \quad \text{Write 0.12 as a percent.}$$

The commission rate is 12%.

Work Practice 4

PRACTICE 4

A salesperson earns \$645 for selling \$4300 worth of appliances. Find the commission rate.

Objective C Calculating Discount and Sale Price

Suppose that an item that normally sells for \$40 is on sale for 25% off. This means that the **original price** of \$40 is reduced, or **discounted,** by 25% of \$40, or \$10. The **discount rate** is 25%, the **amount of discount** is \$10, and the **sale price** is \$40 − \$10, or \$30. Study the diagram below to visualize these terms.

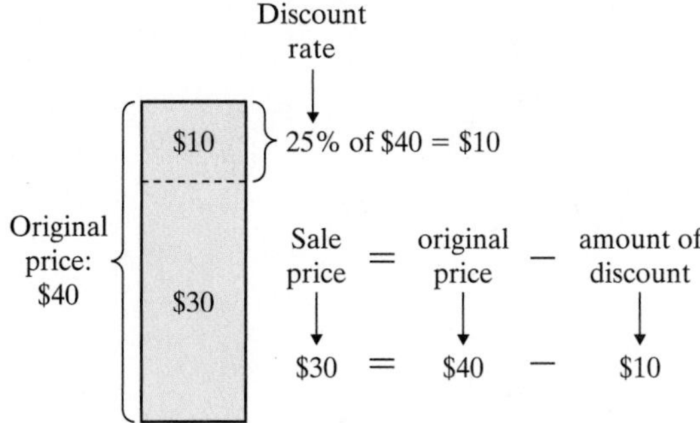

To calculate discounts and sale prices, we can use the following equations:

Discount and Sale Price

amount of discount = discount rate · original price

sale price = original price − amount of discount

Answer

4. 15%

PRACTICE 5

A discontinued washer and dryer combo is advertised on sale for 35% off the regular price of $700. Find the amount of discount and the sale price.

Example 5 Finding a Discount and a Sale Price

An electric rice cooker that normally sells for $65 is on sale for 25% off. What is the amount of discount and what is the sale price?

Solution: First we find the amount of discount, or simply the discount.

amount of discount	=	discount rate	·	original price
↓		↓		↓
amount of discount	=	25%	·	$65

= 0.25 · $65 Write 25% as 0.25.

= $16.25 Multiply.

The discount is $16.25. Next, find the sale price.

sale price	=	original price	–	discount
↓		↓		↓
sale price	=	$65	–	$16.25

= $48.75 Subtract.

The sale price is $48.75.

Work Practice 5

Answer

5. $245; $455

Vocabulary and Readiness Check

Use the choices below to fill in each blank. Some choices may be used more than once.

amount of discount   sale price   sales tax

commission   total price

1. ____________ = tax rate · purchase price.
2. ____________ = purchase price + sales tax.
3. ____________ = commission rates · sales.
4. ____________ = discount rate · original rate.
5. ____________ = original price − amount of discount.
6. sale price = original price − ____________

6.6 Exercise Set

Objective A *Solve. See Examples 1 and 2.*

1. What is the sales tax on a jacket priced at $150 if the sales tax rate is 5%?

2. If the sales tax rate is 6%, find the sales tax on a microwave oven priced at $188.

3. The purchase price of a camcorder is $799. What is the total price if the sales tax rate is 7.5%?

4. A stereo system has a purchase price of $426. What is the total price if the sales tax rate is 8%?

5. A new large-screen television has a purchase price of $4790. If the sales tax on this purchase is $335.30, find the sales tax rate.

6. The sales tax on the purchase of a $6800 used car is $374. Find the sales tax rate.

7. The sales tax on a table saw is $10.20.

a. What is the purchase price of the table saw (before tax) if the sales tax rate is 8.5%? (*Hint:* Use the sales tax equation and insert the replacement values.)

b. Find the total price of the table saw.

8. The sales tax on a one-half-carat diamond ring is $76.

a. Find the purchase price of the ring (before tax) if the sales tax rate is 9.5%. (See the hint for Exercise 7a.)

b. Find the total price of the ring.

9. A gold and diamond bracelet sells for $1800. Find the sales tax and the total price if the sales tax rate is 6.5%.

10. The purchase price of a personal computer is $1890. If the sales tax rate is 8%, what is the sales tax and the total price?

11. The sales tax on the purchase of a futon is $24.25. If the tax rate is 5%, find the purchase price of the futon.

12. The sales tax on the purchase of a TV-DVD combination is $32.85. If the tax rate is 9%, find the purchase price of the TV-DVD.

13. The sales tax is $98.70 on a stereo sound system purchase of $1645. Find the sales tax rate.

14. The sales tax is $103.50 on a necklace purchase of $1150. Find the sales tax rate.

15. A cell phone costs $210, a battery recharger costs $15, and batteries cost $5. What is the sales tax and total price for purchasing these items if the sales tax rate is 7%?

16. Ms. Warner bought a blouse for $35, a skirt for $55, and a blazer for $95. Find the sales tax and the total price she paid, given a sales tax rate of 6.5%.

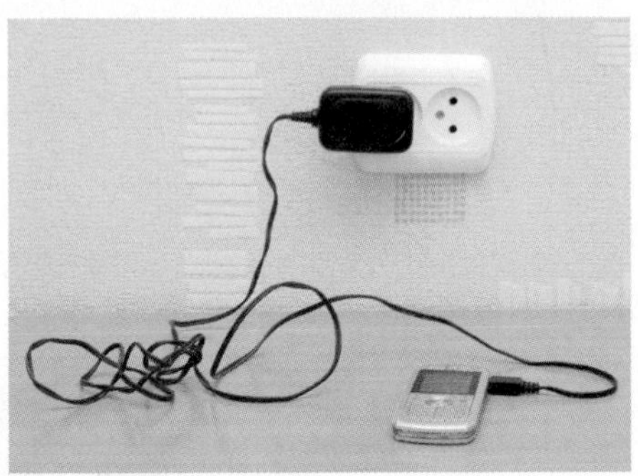

Objective **B** *Solve. See Examples 3 and 4.*

17. A sales representative for a large furniture warehouse is paid a commission rate of 4%. Find her commission if she sold $1,329,401 worth of furniture last year.

18. Rosie Davis-Smith is a beauty consultant for a home cosmetic business. She is paid a commission rate of 12.8%. Find her commission if she sold $1638 in cosmetics last month.

19. A salesperson earned a commission of $1380.40 for selling $9860 worth of paper products. Find the commission rate.

20. A salesperson earned a commission of $3575 for selling $32,500 worth of books to various bookstores. Find the commission rate.

21. How much commission will Jack Pruet make on the sale of a $325,900 house if he receives 1.5% of the selling price?

22. Frankie Lopez sold $9638 of jewelry this week. Find her commission for the week if she receives a commission rate of 5.6%.

23. A real estate agent earned a commission of $5565 for selling a house. If his rate is 3%, find the selling price of the house. (*Hint:* Use the commission equation and insert the replacement values.)

24. A salesperson earned $1750 for selling fertilizer. If her commission rate is 7%, find the selling price of the fertilizer. (See the hint for Exercise 23.)

Objective **C** *Find the amount of discount and the sale price. See Example 5.*

	Original Price	Discount Rate	Amount of Discount	Sale Price
25.	$89	10%		
26.	$74	20%		
27.	$196.50	50%		
28.	$110.60	40%		
29.	$410	35%		
30.	$370	25%		
31.	$21,700	15%		
32.	$17,800	12%		

33. A $300 fax machine is on sale for 15% off. Find the amount of discount and the sale price.

34. A $4295 designer dress is on sale for 30% off. Find the amount of discount and the sale price.

Objectives **A** **B** **Mixed Practice** *Complete each table.*

	Purchase Price	Tax Rate	Sales Tax	Total Price
35.	$305	9%		
36.	$243	8%		
37.	$56	5.5%		
38.	$65	8.4%		

	Sale	Commission Rate	Commission
39.	$235,800	3%	
40.	$195,450	5%	
41.	$17,900		$1432
42.	$25,600		$2304

Review

Multiply. See Sections 4.4 and 4.6.

43. $2000 \cdot \frac{3}{10} \cdot 2$

44. $500 \cdot \frac{2}{25} \cdot 3$

45. $400 \cdot \frac{3}{100} \cdot 11$

46. $1000 \cdot \frac{1}{20} \cdot 5$

47. $600 \cdot 0.04 \cdot \frac{2}{3}$

48. $6000 \cdot 0.06 \cdot \frac{3}{4}$

Concept Extensions

Solve. See the Concept Check in this section.

49. Your purchase price is $68 and the sales tax rate is 9.5%. Round each amount and use the rounded amounts to estimate the total price. Choose the best estimate.

a. $105 **b.** $58 **c.** $93 **d.** $77

50. Your purchase price is $200 and the tax rate is 10%. Choose the best estimate of the total price.

a. $190 **b.** $210 **c.** $220 **d.** $300

Tipping

One very useful application of percent is mentally calculating a tip. Recall that to find 10% of a number, simply move the decimal point one place to the left. To find 20% of a number, just double 10% of the number. To find 15% of a number, find 10% and then add to that number half of the 10% amount. Mentally fill in the chart below. To do so, start by rounding the bill amount to the nearest dollar.

Tipping Chart

	Bill Amount	10%	15%	20%
51.	$40.21			
52.	$15.89			
53.	$72.17			
54.	$9.33			

55. Suppose that the original price of a shirt is $50. Which is better, a 60% discount or a discount of 30% followed by a discount of 35% of the reduced price? Explain your answer.

56. Which is better, a 30% discount followed by an additional 25% off or a 20% discount followed by an additional 40% off? To see, suppose an item costs $100 and calculate each discounted price. Explain your answer.

57. A diamond necklace sells for $24,966. If the tax rate is 7.5%, find the total price.

58. A house recently sold for $562,560. The commission rate on the sale is 5.5%. If the real estate agent is to receive 60% of the commission, find the amount received by the agent.

Objectives

A Calculate Simple Interest.

B Calculate Compound Interest.

C Calculate Monthly Payments.

6.7 PERCENT AND PROBLEM SOLVING: INTEREST

Objective A Calculating Simple Interest

Interest is money charged for using other people's money. When you borrow money, you pay interest. When you loan or invest money, you earn interest. The money borrowed, loaned, or invested is called the **principal amount,** or simply **principal.** Interest is normally stated in terms of a percent of the principal for a given period of time. The **interest rate** is the percent used in computing the interest. Unless stated otherwise, *the rate is understood to be per year.* When the interest is computed on the original principal, it is called **simple interest.** Simple interest is calculated using the following equation:

Simple Interest

Simple Interest = Principal · Rate · Time

$$I = P \cdot R \cdot T$$

where the rate is understood to be per year and time is in years.

PRACTICE 1

Find the simple interest after 5 years on $875 at an interest rate of 7%.

Example 1 Finding Simple Interest

Find the simple interest after 2 years on $500 at an interest rate of 12%.

Solution: In this example, $P = \$500$, $R = 12\%$, and $T = 2$ years. Replace the variables with values in the formula $I = PRT$.

$I = P \cdot R \cdot T$

$I = \$500 \cdot 12\% \cdot 2$ Let $P = \$500$, $R = 12\%$, and $T = 2$.

$= \$500 \cdot (0.12) \cdot 2$ Write 12% as a decimal.

$= \$120$ Multiply.

The simple interest is $120.

Work Practice 1

If time is not given in years, we need to convert the given time to years.

PRACTICE 2

A student borrowed $1500 for 9 months on her credit card at a simple interest rate of 20%. How much interest did she pay?

Example 2 Finding Simple Interest

Ivan Borski borrowed $2400 at 10% simple interest for 8 months to buy a used Toyota Corolla. Find the simple interest he paid.

Solution: Since there are 12 months in a year, we first find what part of a year 8 months is.

$$8 \text{ months} = \frac{8}{12} \text{ year} = \frac{2}{3} \text{ year}$$

Now we find the simple interest.

simple interest	=	principal	·	rate	·	time
↓		↓		↓		↓
simple interest	=	$2400	·	10%	·	$\frac{2}{3}$

Answers
1. $306.25 **2.** $225

$$= \$2400 \cdot 0.10 \cdot \frac{2}{3}$$
$$= \$160$$

The interest on Ivan's loan is \$160.

Work Practice 2

✓Concept Check Suppose in Example 2 you had obtained an answer of \$16,000. How would you know that you had made a mistake in this problem?

When money is borrowed, the borrower pays the original amount borrowed, or the principal, as well as the interest. When money is invested, the investor receives the original amount invested, or the principal, as well as the interest. In either case, the **total amount** is the sum of the principal and the interest.

Finding the Total Amount of a Loan or Investment

total amount (paid or received) = principal + interest

Example 3 Finding the Total Amount of an Investment

An accountant invested \$2000 at a simple interest rate of 10% for 2 years. What total amount of money will she have from her investment in 2 years?

Solution: First we find her interest.

$I = P \cdot R \cdot T$
$= \$2000 \cdot (0.10) \cdot 2$ Let $P = \$2000$, $R = 10\%$ or 0.10, and $T = 2$.
$= \$400$

The interest is \$400.

Next, we add the interest to the principal.

total amount	=	principal	+	interest
↓		↓		↓
total amount	=	\$2000	+	\$400
	=	\$2400		

After 2 years, she will have a total amount of \$2400.

Work Practice 3

PRACTICE 3

If \$2100 is borrowed at a simple interest rate of 13% for 6 months, find the total amount paid.

✓Concept Check Which investment would earn more interest: an amount of money invested at 8% interest for 2 years, or the same amount of money invested at 8% for 3 years? Explain.

Objective B Calculating Compound Interest

Recall that simple interest depends on the original principal only. Another type of interest is compound interest. **Compound interest** is computed on not only the principal, but also on the interest already earned in previous compounding periods. Compound interest is used more often than simple interest.

Let's see how compound interest differs from simple interest. Suppose that \$2000 is invested at 7% interest **compounded annually** for 3 years. This means that

Answer

3. \$2236.50

✓ Concept Check Answers

\$16,000 is too much interest;

8% for 3 years. Since the interest rate is the same, the longer you keep the money invested, the more interest you earn.

interest is added to the principal at the end of each year and that next year's interest is computed on this new amount. In this section, we round dollar amounts to the nearest cent.

	Amount at Beginning of Year	Principal	·	Rate	·	Time	= Interest	Amount at End of Year
1st year	\$2000	\$2000	·	0.07	·	1	= \$140	\$2000 + 140 = \$2140
2nd year	\$2140	\$2140	·	0.07	·	1	= \$149.80	\$2140 + 149.80 = \$2289.80
3rd year	\$2289.80	\$2289.80	·	0.07	·	1	= \$160.29	\$2289.80 + 160.29 = \$2450.09

The compound interest earned can be found by

total amount	−	original principal	=	compound interest
↓		↓		↓
\$2450.09	−	\$2000	=	\$450.09

The simple interest earned would have been

principal	·	rate	·	time	=	interest
↓		↓		↓		↓
\$2000	·	0.07	·	3	=	\$420

Since compound interest earns "interest on interest," compound interest earns more than simple interest.

Computing compound interest using the method above can be tedious. We can use a calculator and the compound interest formula below to compute compound interest more quickly.

Compound Interest Formula

The total amount A in an account is given by

$$A = P\left(1 + \frac{r}{n}\right)^{n \cdot t}$$

where P is the principal, r is the interest rate written as a decimal, t is the length of time in years, and n is the number of times compounded per year.

PRACTICE 4

\$3000 is invested at 4% interest compounded annually. Find the total amount after 6 years.

Example 4 \$1800 is invested at 2% interest compounded annually. Find the total amount after 3 years.

Solution: "Compounded annually" means 1 time a year, so $n = 1$. Also, $P = \$1800$, $r = 2\% = 0.02$, and $t = 3$ years.

$$A = P\left(1 + \frac{r}{n}\right)^{n \cdot t}$$

$$= 1800\left(1 + \frac{0.02}{1}\right)^{1 \cdot 3}$$

$$= 1800(1.02)^3$$

$$\approx 1910.17 \quad \text{Round to 2 decimal places.}$$

Helpful Hint Remember order of operations. **First** evaluate $(1.02)^3$, then multiply by 1800.

The total amount at the end of 3 years is \$1910.17.

Work Practice 4

Answer

4. \$3795.96

Example 5 Finding Total Amount Received from an Investment

\$4000 is invested at 5.3% compounded quarterly for 10 years. Find the total amount at the end of 10 years.

Solution: "Compounded quarterly" means 4 times a year, so

$n = 4$. Also, $P = \$4000$, $r = 5.3\% = 0.053$, and $t = 10$ years.

$$\begin{aligned} A &= P\left(1 + \frac{r}{n}\right)^{n \cdot t} \\ &= 4000\left(1 + \frac{0.053}{4}\right)^{4 \cdot 10} \\ &= 4000(1.01325)^{40} \\ &\approx 6772.12 \end{aligned}$$

The total amount after 10 years is \$6772.12.

Work Practice 5

PRACTICE 5

\$5500 is invested at $6\frac{1}{4}\%$ compounded *daily* for 5 years. Find the total amount at the end of 5 years. (Use 1 year = 365 days.)

Note: Part of the compound interest formula, $\left(1 + \frac{r}{n}\right)^{n \cdot t}$, is called the **compound interest factor.** Appendix A.7 contains a table of various calculated compound interest factors. Another way to calculate the total amount, A, in the compound interest formula is to multiply the principal, P, by the appropriate compound interest factor found in Appendix A.7.

The Calculator Explorations box on page 428 shows how compound interest factors are calculated.

Objective C Calculating a Monthly Payment

We conclude this section with a method to find the monthly payment on a loan.

Finding the Monthly Payment of a Loan

$$\text{monthly payment} = \frac{\text{principal} + \text{interest}}{\text{total number of payments}}$$

Example 6 Finding a Monthly Payment

Find the monthly payment on a \$2000 loan for 2 years. The interest on the 2-year loan is \$435.88.

Solution: First we determine the total number of monthly payments. The loan is for 2 years. Since there are 12 months per year, the number of payments is $2 \cdot 12$, or 24. Now we calculate the monthly payment.

$$\text{monthly payment} = \frac{\text{principal} + \text{interest}}{\text{total number of payments}}$$

$$\text{monthly payment} = \frac{\$2000 + \$435.88}{24}$$

$$\approx \$101.50$$

The monthly payment is about \$101.50.

Work Practice 6

PRACTICE 6

Find the monthly payment on a \$3000 3-year loan if the interest on the loan is \$1123.58.

Answers

5. \$7517.41

6. \$114.54

Calculator Explorations Compound Interest Factor

A compound interest factor may be found by using your calculator and evaluating the formula

$$\textbf{compound interest factor} = \left(1 + \frac{r}{n}\right)^{n \cdot t}$$

where r is the interest rate, t is the time in years, and n is the number of times compounded per year. For example, the compound interest factor for 10 years at 8% compounded semiannually is 2.19112. Let's find this factor by evaluating the compound interest factor formula when $r = 8\%$ or 0.08, $t = 10$, and $n = 2$ (compounded semiannually means 2 times per year). Thus,

$$\text{compound interest factor} = \left(1 + \frac{0.08}{2}\right)^{2 \cdot 10}$$

or $\left(1 + \frac{0.08}{2}\right)^{20}$

To evaluate, press the keys

(1 + 0.08 ÷ 2) y^x or ∧ 20 = or ENTER. The display will read 2.1911231.

Rounded to 5 decimal places, this is 2.19112.

Find the compound interest factors. Use the table in Appendix A.7 to check your answers.

1. 5 years, 9%, compounded quarterly
2. 15 years, 14%, compounded daily
3. 20 years, 11%, compounded annually
4. 1 year, 7%, compounded semiannually
5. Find the total amount after 4 years when \$500 is invested at 6% compounded quarterly. (Multiply the appropriate compound interest factor by \$500.)
6. Find the total amount for 19 years when \$2500 is invested at 5% compounded daily.

Vocabulary and Readiness Check

Use the choices below to fill in each blank. Choices may be used more than once.

total amount   simple   principal amount   compound

1. To calculate ______________ interest, use $I = P \cdot R \cdot T$.
2. To calculate ______________ interest, use $A = P\left(1 + \frac{r}{n}\right)^{n \cdot t}$.
3. ______________ interest is computed not only on the original principal, but also on interest already earned in previous compounding periods.
4. When interest is computed on the original principal only, it is called ______________ interest.
5. ______________ (paid or received) = principal + interest.
6. The ______________ is the money borrowed, loaned, or invested.

6.7 Exercise Set

FOR EXTRA HELP MyMathLab — PRACTICE — WATCH — DOWNLOAD — READ — REVIEW

Objective A *Find the simple interest. See Examples 1 and 2.*

	Principal	Rate	Time
1.	\$200	8%	2 years
3.	\$160	11.5%	4 years
5.	\$5000	10%	$1\frac{1}{2}$ years
7.	\$375	18%	6 months
9.	\$2500	16%	21 months

	Principal	Rate	Time
2.	\$800	9%	3 years
4.	\$950	12.5%	5 years
6.	\$1500	14%	$2\frac{1}{4}$ years
8.	\$775	15%	8 months
10.	\$1000	10%	18 months

Solve. See Examples 1 through 3.

11. A company borrows \$162,500 for 5 years at a simple interest rate of 12.5%. Find the interest paid on the loan and the total amount paid back.

12. \$265,000 is borrowed to buy a house. If the simple interest rate on the 30-year loan is 8.25%, find the interest paid on the loan and the total amount paid back.

13. A money market fund advertises a simple interest rate of 9%. Find the total amount received on an investment of \$5000 for 15 months.

14. The Real Service Company takes out a 270-day (9-month) short-term, simple interest loan of \$4500 to finance the purchase of some new equipment. If the interest rate is 14%, find the total amount that the company pays back.

15. Marsha borrows \$8500 and agrees to pay it back in 4 years. If the simple interest rate is 17%, find the total amount she pays back.

16. An 18-year-old is given a high school graduation gift of \$2000. If this money is invested at 8% simple interest for 5 years, find the total amount.

Objective B *Find the total amount in each compound interest account. See Examples 4 and 5.*

17. \$6150 is compounded semiannually at a rate of 14% for 15 years.

18. \$2060 is compounded annually at a rate of 15% for 10 years.

19. \$1560 is compounded daily at a rate of 8% for 5 years.

20. \$1450 is compounded quarterly at a rate of 10% for 15 years.

21. \$10,000 is compounded semiannually at a rate of 9% for 20 years.

22. \$3500 is compounded daily at a rate of 8% for 10 years.

23. \$2675 is compounded annually at a rate of 9% for 1 year.

24. \$6375 is compounded semiannually at a rate of 10% for 1 year.

25. \$2000 is compounded annually at a rate of 8% for 5 years.

26. \$2000 is compounded semiannually at a rate of 8% for 5 years.

27. \$2000 is compounded quarterly at a rate of 8% for 5 years.

28. \$2000 is compounded daily at a rate of 8% for 5 years.

Objective C *Solve. See Example 6.*

29. A college student borrows \$1500 for 6 months to pay for a semester of school. If the interest is \$61.88, find the monthly payment.

30. Jim Tillman borrows \$1800 for 9 months. If the interest is \$148.90, find his monthly payment.

31. \$20,000 is borrowed for 4 years. If the interest on the loan is \$10,588.70, find the monthly payment.

32. \$105,000 is borrowed for 15 years. If the interest on the loan is \$181,125, find the monthly payment.

Review

Find the perimeter of each figure. See Section 1.3.

△ **33.** Rectangle 6 yards 10 yards

△ **34.**

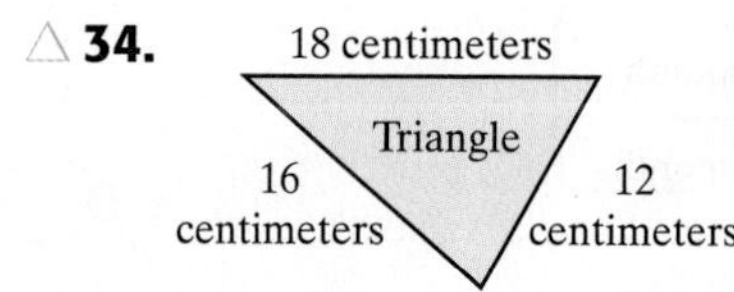

△ **35.** Regular pentagon— All sides are same length 7 meters

△ **36.**

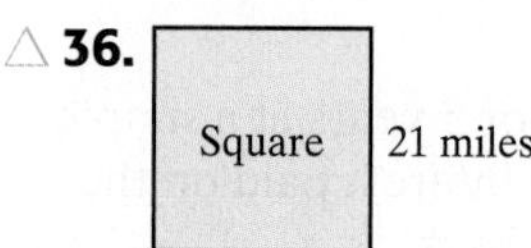

Concept Extensions

37. Explain how to look up a compound interest factor in the compound interest table.

38. Explain how to find the amount of interest in a compounded account.

39. Compare the following accounts: Account 1: \$1000 is invested for 10 years at a simple interest rate of 6%. Account 2: \$1000 is compounded semiannually at a rate of 6% for 10 years. Discuss how the interest is computed for each account. Determine which account earns more interest. Why?

Chapter 6 Group Activity

Fastest-Growing Occupations

According to U.S. Bureau of Labor Statistics projections, the careers listed below are the top ten fastest-growing jobs ranked by expected percent increase through the year 2016. (*Source:* Bureau of Labor Statistics)

	Occupation	Employment in 2006	Percent Change	Expected Employment in 2016
1	Network systems and data communication analysts	262,000	53.4%	
2	Personal and home care aides	767,000	50.6%	
3	Home health aides	787,000	48.7%	
4	Computer software engineers	507,000	44.6%	
5	Veterinary technologists and technicians	71,000	41.0%	
6	Personal financial advisors	176,000	41.0%	
7	Makeup artists, theatrical and performance	2000	39.8%	
8	Medical assistants	417,000	35.4%	
9	Veterinarians	62,000	35.0%	
10	Substance abuse and behavioral disorder counselors	83,000	34.3%	

What do most of these fast-growing occupations have in common? They require knowledge of math! For some careers, such as home health aides, personal financial advisors, and computer engineers, the ways math is used on the job may be obvious. For other occupations, the use of math may not be quite as apparent. However, tasks common to many jobs—filling in a time sheet, writing up an expense or mileage report, planning a budget, figuring a bill, ordering supplies, and even making a work schedule—all require math.

This activity may be completed by working in groups or individually.

1. List the top five occupations by order of employment figures for 2006.
2. Using the 2006 employment figures and the percent increase from 2006 to 2016, find the expected 2016 employment figures for each occupation listed in the table. Round to the nearest thousand.
3. List the top five occupations by order of employment figures for 2016. Did the order change at all from 2006? Explain.

Chapter 6 Vocabulary Check

Fill in each blank with one of the words or phrases listed below. Some words may be used more than once.

percent	sales tax	is	0.01	$\frac{1}{100}$	amount of discount	percent of decrease	total price
base	of	amount	100%	compound interest	percent of increase	sale price	commission

1. In a mathematical statement, ________________ usually means "multiplication."
2. In a mathematical statement, ________________ means "equals."
3. ________________ means "per hundred."
4. ________________ is computed not only on the principal, but also on interest already earned in previous compounding periods.
5. In the percent proportion, $\frac{\text{\_\_\_\_\_\_\_\_\_\_}}{\text{\_\_\_\_\_\_\_\_\_\_}} = \frac{\text{percent}}{100}$.
6. To write a decimal or fraction as a percent, multiply by ________________.
7. The decimal equivalent of the % symbol is ________________.
8. The fraction equivalent of the % symbol is ________________.
9. The percent equation is ________________ · percent = ________________.
10. ________________ $= \frac{\text{amount of decrease}}{\text{original amount}}$.
11. ________________ $= \frac{\text{amount of increase}}{\text{original amount}}$.
12. ________________ = tax rate · purchase price.
13. ________________ = purchase price + sales tax.
14. ________________ = commission rate · sales.
15. ________________ = discount rate · original price.
16. ________________ = original price − amount of discount.

Helpful Hint Are you preparing for your test? Don't forget to take the Chapter 6 Test on page 439. Then check your answers at the back of the text and use the Chapter Test Prep Videos to see the fully worked-out solutions to any of the exercises you want to review.

6 Chapter Highlights

Definitions and Concepts	Examples
Section 6.1 Introduction to Percent	
Percent means "per hundred." The % symbol denotes percent.	$51\% = \frac{51}{100}$ 51 per 100 $7\% = \frac{7}{100}$ 7 per 100
To write a percent as a decimal, replace the % symbol with its decimal equivalent, 0.01, and multiply. **To write a decimal as a percent,** multiply by 100%.	$32\% = 32(0.01) = 0.32$ $0.08 = 0.08(100\%) = 08.\% = 8\%$
Section 6.2 Percents and Fractions	
To write a percent as a fraction, replace the % symbol with its fraction equivalent, $\frac{1}{100}$, and multiply.	$25\% = \frac{25}{100} = \frac{\cancel{25}^{1}}{4 \cdot \cancel{25}_{1}} = \frac{1}{4}$
To write a fraction as a percent, multiply by 100%.	$\frac{1}{6} = \frac{1}{6} \cdot 100\% = \frac{1}{6} \cdot \frac{100}{1}\% = \frac{100}{6}\% = 16\frac{2}{3}\%$

Definitions and Concepts	Examples

Section 6.3 Solving Percent Problems Using Equations

Three key words in the statement of a percent problem are

of, which means **multiplication** ($\cdot$)

is, which means **equals** (=)

what (or some equivalent word or phrase), which stands for **the unknown number**

Solve:

6 is 12% of what number?

$$6 = 12\% \cdot n$$

$$6 = 0.12 \cdot n \quad \text{Write 12\% as a decimal.}$$

$$\frac{6}{0.12} = n \quad \text{Divide 6 by 0.12, the number multiplied by } n.$$

$$50 = n$$

Thus, 6 is 12% of 50.

Section 6.4 Solving Percent Problems Using Proportions

PERCENT PROPORTION

$$\frac{\text{amount}}{\text{base}} = \frac{\text{percent}}{100} \leftarrow \text{always 100}$$

or

$$\text{amount} \rightarrow \frac{a}{b} = \frac{p}{100} \leftarrow \text{percent}, \quad \text{base} \rightarrow b$$

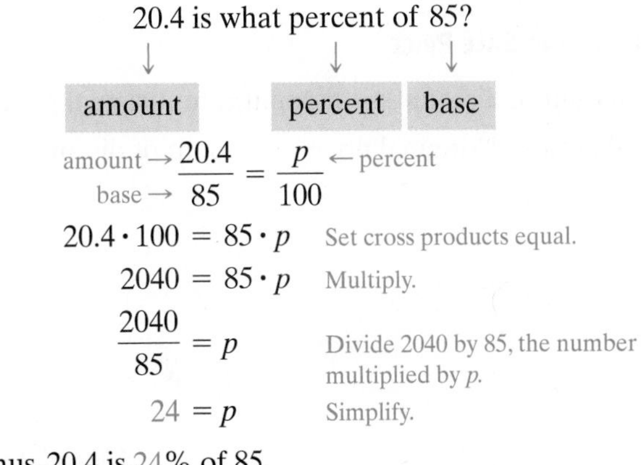

Solve:

20.4 is what percent of 85?

amount — percent — base

$$\text{amount} \rightarrow \frac{20.4}{85} = \frac{p}{100} \leftarrow \text{percent}, \quad \text{base} \rightarrow 85$$

$$20.4 \cdot 100 = 85 \cdot p \quad \text{Set cross products equal.}$$

$$2040 = 85 \cdot p \quad \text{Multiply.}$$

$$\frac{2040}{85} = p \quad \text{Divide 2040 by 85, the number multiplied by } p.$$

$$24 = p \quad \text{Simplify.}$$

Thus, 20.4 is 24% of 85.

Section 6.5 Applications of Percent

PERCENT OF INCREASE

$$\text{percent of increase} = \frac{\text{amount of increase}}{\text{original amount}}$$

PERCENT OF DECREASE

$$\text{percent of decrease} = \frac{\text{amount of decrease}}{\text{original amount}}$$

A town with a population of 16,480 decreased to 13,870 over a 12-year period. Find the percent decrease. Round to the nearest whole percent.

$$\text{amount of decrease} = 16{,}480 - 13{,}870 = 2610$$

$$\text{percent of decrease} = \frac{\text{amount of decrease}}{\text{original amount}} = \frac{2610}{16{,}480} \approx 0.16 = 16\%$$

The town's population decreased by 16%.

Section 6.6 Percent and Problem Solving: Sales Tax, Commission, and Discount

SALES TAX AND TOTAL PRICE

$$\text{sales tax} = \text{sales tax rate} \cdot \text{purchase price}$$

$$\text{total price} = \text{purchase price} + \text{sales tax}$$

Find the sales tax and the total price of a purchase of \$42 if the sales tax rate is 9%.

sales tax = sales tax rate · purchase price

$$\text{sales tax} = 9\% \cdot \$42 = 0.09 \cdot \$42 = \$3.78$$

(continued)

Definitions and Concepts	Examples
Section 6.6 Percent and Problem Solving: Sales Tax, Commission, and Discount (*continued*)	
	The total price is total price = purchase price + sales tax ↓ ↓ ↓ total price = \$42 + \$3.78 = \$45.78
COMMISSION commission = commission rate · total sales	A salesperson earns a commission of 3%. Find the commission from sales of \$12,500 worth of appliances. commission = commission rate · sales ↓ ↓ ↓ commission = 3% · \$12,500 = 0.03 · 12,500 = \$375
DISCOUNT AND SALE PRICE amount of discount = discount rate · original price sale price = original price − amount of discount	A suit is priced at \$320 and is on sale today for 25% off. What is the sale price? amount of discount = discount rate · original price ↓ ↓ ↓ amount of discount = 25% · \$320 = 0.25 · 320 = \$80 sale price = original price − amount of discount ↓ ↓ ↓ sale price = \$320 − \$80 = \$240 The sale price is \$240.
Section 6.7 Percent and Problem Solving: Interest	
SIMPLE INTEREST interest = principal · rate · time where the rate is understood to be per year.	Find the simple interest after 3 years on \$800 at an interest rate of 5%. interest = principal · rate · time ↓ ↓ ↓ ↓ interest = \$800 · 5% · 3 = \$800 · 0.05 · 3 Write 5% as 0.05. = \$120 Multiply. The interest is \$120.
Compound interest is computed not only on the principal, but also on interest already earned in previous compounding periods. (See Appendix A7 for various compound interest factors.) $A = P\left(1 + \frac{r}{n}\right)^{n \cdot t}$ where n is the number of times compounded per year.	\$800 is invested at 5% compounded quarterly for 10 years. Find the total amount at the end of 10 years. $A = \$800\left(1 + \frac{0.05}{4}\right)^{4 \cdot 10}$ $= \$800(1.0125)^{40}$ $\approx \$1314.90$

Chapter 6 Review

(6.1) *Solve.*

1. In a survey of 100 adults, 37 preferred pepperoni on their pizzas. What percent preferred pepperoni?

2. A basketball player made 77 out of 100 attempted free throws. What percent of free throws was made?

Write each percent as a decimal.

3. 83%

4. 75%

5. 73.5%

6. 1.5%

7. 125%

8. 145%

9. 0.5%

10. 0.7%

11. 200%

12. 400%

13. 26.25%

14. 85.34%

Write each decimal as a percent.

15. 2.6

16. 1.02

17. 0.35

18. 0.055

19. 0.725

20. 0.252

21. 0.076

22. 0.085

23. 0.71

24. 0.65

25. 4

26. 9

(6.2) *Write each percent as a fraction or mixed number in simplest form.*

27. 1%

28. 10%

29. 25%

30. 8.5%

31. 10.2%

32. $16\frac{2}{3}\%$

33. $33\frac{1}{3}\%$

34. 110%

Write each fraction or mixed number as a percent.

35. $\frac{1}{5}$

36. $\frac{7}{10}$

37. $\frac{5}{6}$

38. $\frac{3}{5}$

39. $1\frac{1}{4}$

40. $1\frac{2}{3}$

41. $\frac{1}{16}$

42. $\frac{5}{8}$

(6.3) *Translate each to an equation and solve.*

43. 1250 is 1.25% of what number?

44. What number is $33\frac{1}{3}\%$ of 24,000?

45. 124.2 is what percent of 540?

46. 22.9 is 20% of what number?

47. What number is 40% of 7500?

48. 693 is what percent of 462?

(6.4) *Translate each to a proportion and solve.*

49. 104.5 is 25% of what number?

50. 16.5 is 5.5% of what number?

51. What number is 36% of 180?

52. 63 is what percent of 35?

53. 93.5 is what percent of 85?

54. What number is 33% of 500?

(6.5) *Solve.*

55. In a survey of 2000 people, it was found that 1320 have a microwave oven. Find the percent of people who own microwaves.

56. Of the 12,360 freshmen entering County College, 2000 are enrolled in basic college mathematics. Find the percent of entering freshmen who are enrolled in basic college mathematics. Round to the nearest whole percent.

57. The number of violent crimes in a city decreased from 675 to 534. Find the percent decrease. Round to the nearest tenth of a percent.

58. The current charge for dumping waste in a local landfill is $16 per cubic foot. To cover new environmental costs, the charge will increase to $33 per cubic foot. Find the percent increase.

59. This year the fund drive for a charity collected $215,000. Next year, a 4% decrease is expected. Find how much is expected to be collected in next year's drive.

60. A local union negotiated a new contract that increases the hourly pay 15% over last year's pay. The old hourly rate was $11.50. Find the new hourly rate rounded to the nearest cent.

(6.6) *Solve.*

61. If the sales tax rate is 5.5%, what is the total amount charged for a $250 coat?

62. Find the sales tax paid on a $25.50 purchase if the sales tax rate is 4.5%.

63. Russ James is a sales representative for a chemical company and is paid a commission rate of 5% on all sales. Find his commission if he sold $100,000 worth of chemicals last month.

64. Carol Sell is a sales clerk in a clothing store. She receives a commission of 7.5% on all sales. Find her commission for the week if her sales for the week were $4005. Round to the nearest cent.

65. A $3000 mink coat is on sale for 30% off. Find the discount and the sale price.

66. A $90 calculator is on sale for 10% off. Find the discount and the sale price.

(6.7) *Solve.*

67. Find the simple interest due on $4000 loaned for 4 months at 12% interest.

68. Find the simple interest due on $6500 loaned for 3 months at 20%.

69. Find the total amount in an account if $5500 is compounded annually at 12% for 15 years.

70. Find the total amount in an account if $6000 is compounded semiannually at 11% for 10 years.

71. Find the compound interest earned if $100 is compounded quarterly at 12% for 5 years.

72. Find the compound interest earned if $1000 is compounded quarterly at 18% for 20 years.

Mixed Review

Write each percent as a decimal.

73. 3.8%

74. 24.5%

75. 0.9%

Write each decimal as a percent.

76. 0.54

77. 95.2

78. 0.3

Write each percent as a fraction or mixed number in simplest form.

79. 47%

80. $6\frac{2}{5}\%$

81. 5.6%

Write each fraction or mixed number as a percent.

82. $\frac{3}{8}$

83. $\frac{2}{13}$

84. $\frac{6}{5}$

Translate each into an equation and solve.

85. 43 is 16% of what number?

86. 27.5 is what percent of 25?

87. What number is 36% of 1968?

88. 67 is what percent of 50?

Translate each into a proportion and solve.

89. 75 is what percent of 25?

90. What number is 16% of 240?

91. 28 is 5% of what number?

92. 52 is what percent of 16?

Solve.

93. The total number of cans in a soft drink machine is 300. If 78 soft drinks have been sold, find the percent of soft drink cans that have been sold.

94. A home valued at $96,950 last year has lost 7% of its value this year. Find the loss in value.

95. A dinette set sells for $568.00. If the sales tax rate is 8.75%, find the purchase price of the dinette set.

96. The original price of a video game is $23.00. It is on sale for 15% off. What is the amount of the discount?

97. A candy salesman makes a commission of $1.60 from each case of candy he sells. If a case of candy costs $12.80, what is his rate of commission?

98. Find the total amount due on a 6-month loan of $1400 at a simple interest rate of 13%.

99. $8,800 is invested at 8% interest compounded quarterly. Find the total amount after 9 years.

100. Find the total amount due on a loan of $5,500 for 9 years at 12.5% simple interest.

Chapter 6 Test

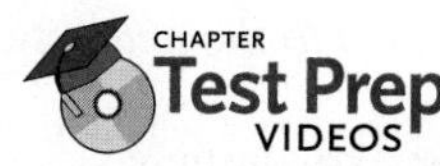

Step-by-step test solutions are found on the Chapter Test Prep Videos available via the Interactive DVD Lecture Series, in MyMathLab or on YouTube (search "MartinGayBasicMath" and click on "Channels").

Write each percent as a decimal.

1. 85% **2.** 500% **3.** 0.8%

Write each decimal as a percent.

4. 0.056 **5.** 6.1 **6.** 0.39

Write each percent as a fraction or mixed number in simplest form.

7. 120% **8.** 38.5% **9.** 0.2%

Write each fraction or mixed number as a percent.

10. $\frac{11}{20}$ **11.** $\frac{3}{8}$ **12.** $1\frac{5}{9}$

Solve.

13. What number is 42% of 80?

14. 0.6% of what number is 7.5?

15. 567 is what percent of 756?

Answers

1. __________
2. __________
3. __________
4. __________
5. __________
6. __________
7. __________
8. __________
9. __________
10. __________
11. __________
12. __________
13. __________
14. __________
15. __________

16. ______________

17. ______________

18. ______________

19. ______________

20. ______________

21. ______________

22. ______________

23. ______________

24. ______________

25. ______________

Solve. Round all dollar amounts to the nearest cent.

16. An alloy is 12% copper. How much copper is contained in 320 pounds of this alloy?

17. A farmer in Nebraska estimates that 20% of his potential crop, or \$11,350, has been lost to a hard freeze. Find the total value of his potential crop.

18. If the local sales tax rate is 1.25%, find the total amount charged for a stereo system priced at \$354.

19. A town's population increased from 25,200 to 26,460. Find the percent increase.

20. A \$120 framed picture is on sale for 15% off. Find the discount and the sale price.

21. Randy Nguyen is paid a commission rate of 4% on all sales. Find Randy's commission if his sales were \$9875.

22. A sales tax of \$1.53 is added to an item's price of \$152.99. Find the sales tax rate. Round to the nearest whole percent.

23. Find the simple interest earned on \$2000 saved for $3\frac{1}{2}$ years at an interest rate of 9.25%.

24. \$1365 is compounded annually at 8%. Find the total amount in the account after 5 years.

25. A couple borrowed \$400 from a bank at 13.5% simple interest for 6 months for car repairs. Find the total amount due the bank at the end of the 6-month period.

Cumulative Review Chapters 1–6

1. How many cases can be filled with 9900 cans of jalapeños if each case holds 48 cans? How many cans will be left over? Will there be enough cases to fill an order for 200 cases?

2. Multiply: 409×76

3. Write each fraction as a mixed number or a whole number.

   a. $\frac{30}{7}$ **b.** $\frac{16}{15}$ **c.** $\frac{84}{6}$

4. Write each mixed number as an improper fraction.

   a. $2\frac{5}{7}$ **b.** $10\frac{1}{10}$ **c.** $5\frac{3}{8}$

5. Use a factor tree to find the prime factorization of 80.

6. Find the area of the rectangle.

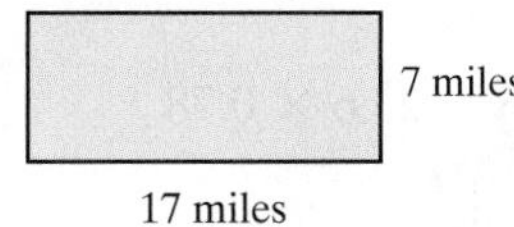

7. Write $\frac{10}{27}$ in simplest form.

8. Find the average of 28, 34, and 70.

9. Multiply and simplify: $\frac{23}{32} \cdot \frac{4}{7}$

10. Round 76,498 to the nearest ten.

11. Find the reciprocal of $\frac{11}{8}$.

12. Write the shaded part of the figure as an improper fraction and as a mixed number.

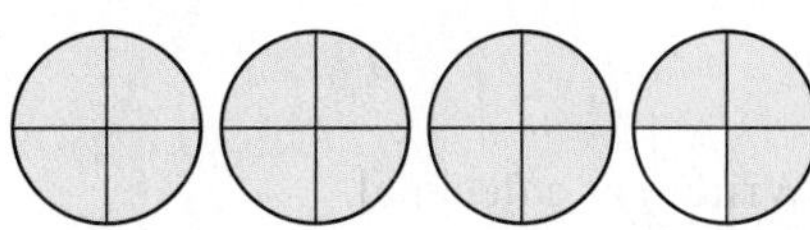

△ 13. Find the perimeter of the rectangle.

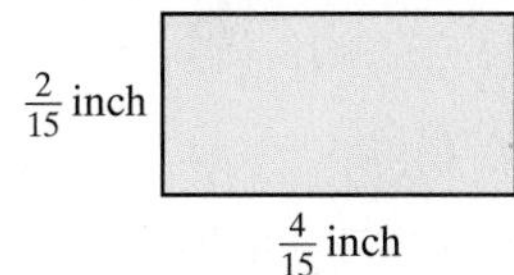

14. Find $2 \cdot 5^2$

15. Find the LCM of 12 and 20.

16. Subtract $\frac{7}{9}$ from $\frac{10}{9}$.

17. Add: $\frac{2}{5} + \frac{4}{15}$

18. Find $\frac{2}{3}$ of 510.

19. Subtract: $7\frac{3}{14} - 3\frac{6}{7}$

20. Simplify: $9 \cdot \sqrt{25} - 6 \cdot \sqrt{4}$

Perform each indicated operation.

21. $\frac{1}{2} \div \frac{8}{7}$

22. $20\frac{4}{5} + 12\frac{7}{8}$

Answers

1. ______
2. ______
3. a. ______
   b. ______
   c. ______
4. a. ______
   b. ______
   c. ______
5. ______
6. ______
7. ______
8. ______
9. ______
10. ______
11. ______
12. ______
13. ______
14. ______
15. ______
16. ______
17. ______
18. ______
19. ______
20. ______
21. ______
22. ______

23. ______
24. ______
25. ______
26. ______
27. ______
28. ______
29. ______
30. ______
31. ______
32. ______
33. ______
34. ______
35. ______
36. ______
37. ______
38. ______
39. ______
40. ______
41. ______
42. ______
43. ______
44. ______
45. ______
46. ______
47. ______
48. a. ______
b. ______
c. ______
49. ______
50. ______

23. $\frac{2}{9} \cdot \frac{3}{11}$

24. $1\frac{7}{8} \cdot 3\frac{2}{5}$

Write each fraction as a decimal.

25. $\frac{8}{10}$

26. $\frac{9}{100}$

27. $\frac{87}{10}$

28. $\frac{48}{10{,}000}$

29. The price of a gallon of premium gasoline in Cross City is currently \$3.1779. Round this to the nearest cent.

30. Subtract: $38 - 10.06$

31. Add: $763.7651 + 22.001 + 43.89$

32. 12.483×100

33. Multiply: 23.6×0.78

34. 76.3×1000

Divide.

35. $\frac{786.1}{1000}$

36. $0.5\overline{)0.638}$

37. $\frac{0.12}{10}$

38. $0.23\overline{)11.6495}$

39. Simplify: $723.6 \div 1000 \times 10$

40. Simplify: $\frac{3.19 - 0.707}{13}$

41. Write $\frac{1}{4}$ as a decimal.

42. Write $\frac{5}{9}$ as a decimal. Give an exact answer and a three-decimal-place approximation.

Write the following rates as fractions in simplest form.

43. 10 nails every 6 feet

44. 115 miles every 5 gallons

45. Is $\frac{4.1}{7} = \frac{2.9}{5}$ a true proportion?

46. Find each unit rate and decide on the better buy.
\$0.93 for 18 flour tortillas
\$1.40 for 24 flour tortillas

47. On a chamber of commerce map of Abita Springs, 5 miles corresponds to 2 inches. How many miles correspond to 7 inches?

48. Write each percent as a decimal.
a. 7% **b.** 200% **c.** 0.5%

49. Translate to an equation: What number is 25% of 0.008?

50. Write $\frac{3}{8}$ as a percent.

Measurement

7

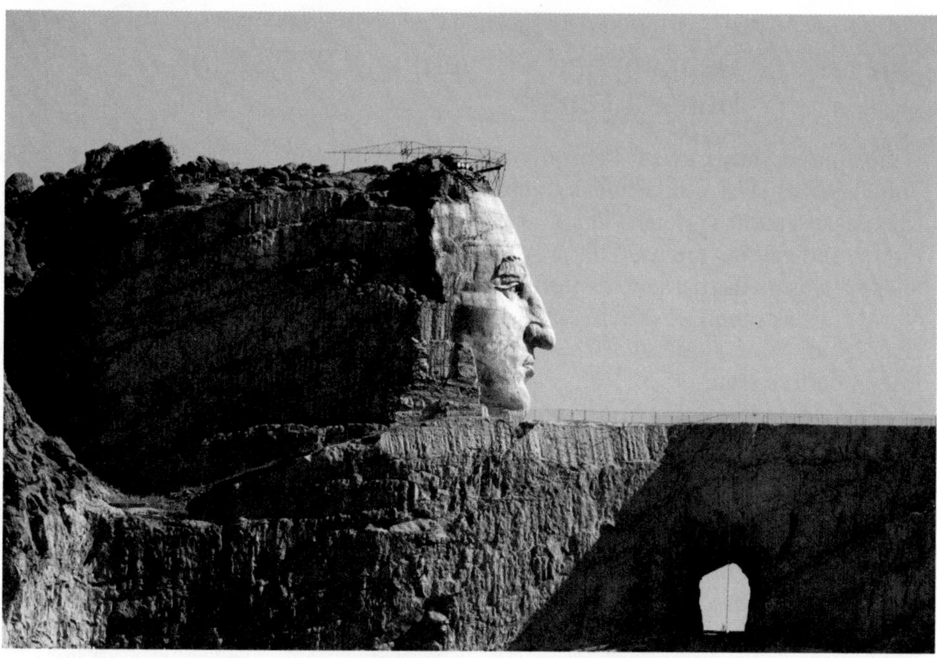

The use of measurements is common in everyday life. A sales representative records the number of miles she has driven when she submits her travel expense report. A respiratory therapist measures the volume of air exhaled by a patient. A measurement is necessary in each case.

Sections

Check Your Progress

Mt. Rushmore, an American icon honoring four U.S. presidents, was carved out of the rock of South Dakota. Did you know that there is another massive sculpture being carved into the Black Hills, about 8 miles from Mt. Rushmore? This sculpture, of Lakota leader Crazy Horse, was officially started on June 3, 1948. Once completed, the sculpture will be a 563-foot-high carving of Crazy Horse astride his horse. Currently, the face of Crazy Horse is complete and work is proceeding on the horse's head.

To compare the dimensions of these two sculptures, each U.S. president's head is 60 feet in height, while the head of Crazy Horse has a height of 87.5 feet. In fact, all heads on Mt. Rushmore will fit in Crazy Horse's head.

In Section 7.1, Exercises 83 and 84, we will explore measurements of the Crazy Horse memorial.

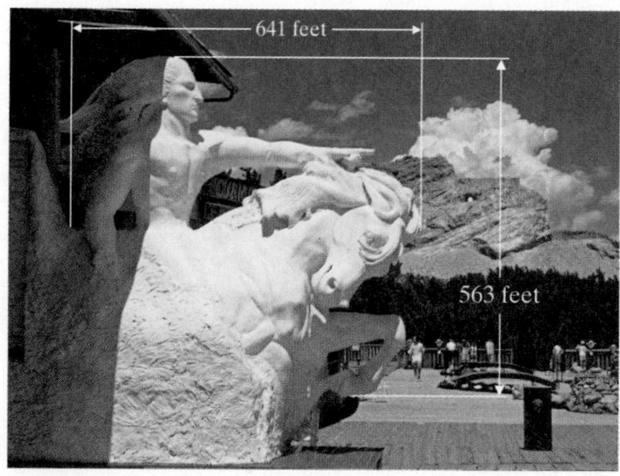

Objectives

A Define U.S. Units of Length and Convert from One Unit to Another.

B Use Mixed U.S. Units of Length.

C Perform Arithmetic Operations on U.S. Units of Length.

D Define Metric Units of Length and Convert from One Unit to Another.

E Perform Arithmetic Operations on Metric Units of Length.

7.1 LENGTH: U.S. AND METRIC SYSTEMS OF MEASUREMENT

Objective A Defining and Converting U.S. System Units of Length

In the United States, two systems of measurement are commonly used. They are the **United States (U.S.), or English, measurement system** and the **metric system.** The U.S. measurement system is familiar to most Americans. Units such as feet, miles, ounces, and gallons are used. However, the metric system is also commonly used in fields such as medicine, sports, international marketing, and certain physical sciences. We are accustomed to buying 2-liter bottles of soft drinks, watching televised coverage of the 100-meter dash at the Olympic Games, or taking a 200-milligram dose of pain reliever.

The U.S. system of measurement uses the **inch, foot, yard,** and **mile** to measure **length.** The following is a summary of equivalencies between units of length:

U.S. Units of Length

12 inches (in.) = 1 foot (ft)
3 feet = 1 yard (yd)
36 inches = 1 yard
5280 feet = 1 mile (mi)

To convert from one unit of length to another, we will use **unit fractions.** We define a unit fraction to be a fraction that is equivalent to 1. Examples of unit fractions are as follows:

Unit Fractions

$$\frac{12\text{ in.}}{1\text{ ft}} = 1 \text{ or } \frac{1\text{ ft}}{12\text{ in.}} = 1 \text{ (since 12 in. = 1 ft)}$$

$$\frac{3\text{ ft}}{1\text{ yd}} = 1 \text{ or } \frac{1\text{ yd}}{3\text{ ft}} = 1 \text{ (since 3 ft = 1 yd)}$$

$$\frac{5280\text{ ft}}{1\text{ mi}} = 1 \text{ or } \frac{1\text{ mi}}{5280\text{ ft}} = 1 \text{ (since 5280 ft = 1 mi)}$$

Remember that multiplying a number by 1 does not change the value of the number.

PRACTICE 1

Convert 6 feet to inches.

Example 1 Convert 8 feet to inches.

Solution: We multiply 8 feet by a unit fraction that uses the equality 12 inches = 1 foot. The unit fraction should be in the form $\frac{\text{units to convert to}}{\text{original units}}$ or, in this case, $\frac{12\text{ inches}}{1\text{ foot}}$. We do this so that like units will divide out to 1, as shown.

$$8\text{ ft} = \frac{8\text{ ft}}{1} \cdot 1$$

$$= \frac{8\text{ }\cancel{\text{ft}}}{1} \cdot \frac{12\text{ in.}}{1\text{ }\cancel{\text{ft}}} \quad \text{Multiply by 1 in the form of } \frac{12\text{ in.}}{1\text{ ft}}.$$

$$= 8 \cdot 12\text{ in.}$$

$$= 96\text{ in.} \quad \text{Multiply.}$$

Answer
1. 72 in.

Thus, 8 ft = 96 in., as shown in the diagram:

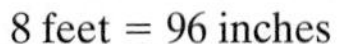

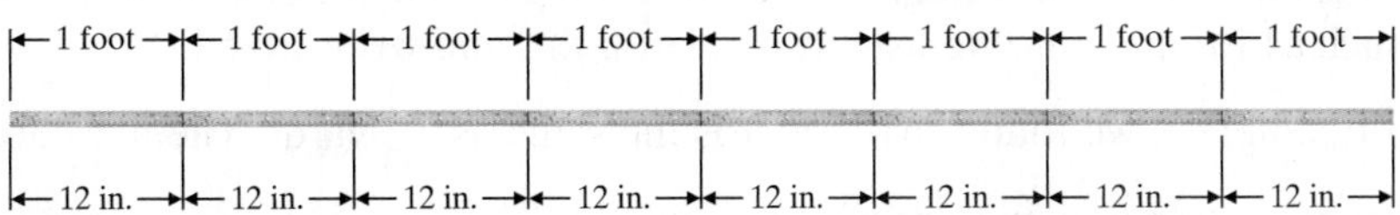

Work Practice 1

Example 2 Convert 7 feet to yards.

Solution: We multiply by a unit fraction that compares 1 yard to 3 feet.

$$7 \text{ ft} = \frac{7 \text{ ft}}{1} \cdot 1$$

$$= \frac{7 \cancel{\text{ft}}}{1} \cdot \frac{1 \text{ yd}}{3 \cancel{\text{ft}}} \quad \begin{array}{l} \leftarrow \text{Units to convert to} \\ \leftarrow \text{Original units} \end{array}$$

$$= \frac{7}{3} \text{ yd}$$

$$= 2\frac{1}{3} \text{ yd} \qquad \text{Divide.}$$

Thus, 7 ft = $2\frac{1}{3}$ yd, as shown in the diagram.

7 feet = $2\frac{1}{3}$ yards

1 foot | 1 foot | 1 foot | 1 foot | 1 foot | 1 foot | 1 foot

1 yard | 1 yard | $\frac{1}{3}$ yard

Work Practice 2

PRACTICE 2

Convert 8 yards to feet.

Helpful Hint When converting from one unit to another, select a unit fraction with the properties below:

$$\frac{\text{units you are converting to}}{\text{original units}}$$

By using this unit fraction, the original units will divide out, as wanted.

Example 3 Finding the Length of a Pelican's Bill

The Australian pelican has the longest bill, measuring from 13 to 18.5 inches long. The pelican in the photo has a 15-inch bill. Convert 15 inches to feet, using decimals in your final answer.

Solution:

$$15 \text{ in.} = \frac{15 \cancel{\text{in.}}}{1} \cdot \frac{1 \text{ ft}}{12 \cancel{\text{in.}}} \quad \begin{array}{l} \leftarrow \text{Units to convert to} \\ \leftarrow \text{Original units} \end{array}$$

$$= \frac{15}{12} \text{ ft}$$

$$= \frac{5}{4} \text{ ft} \qquad \text{Simplify } \frac{15}{12}.$$

$$= 1.25 \text{ ft} \qquad \text{Divide.}$$

Thus, 15 in. = 1.25 ft, as shown in the diagram.

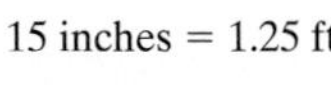

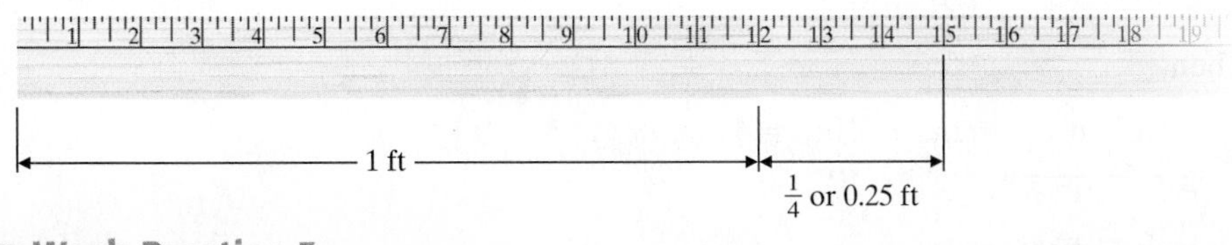

Work Practice 3

PRACTICE 3

Suppose the pelican's bill (in the photo) measures 18 inches. Convert 18 inches to feet, using decimals.

Answers

2. 24 ft **3.** 1.5 ft

Objective B Using Mixed U.S. System Units of Length

Sometimes it is more meaningful to express a measurement of length with mixed units such as 1 ft and 5 in. We usually condense this and write 1 ft 5 in.

In Example 2, we found that 7 feet is the same as $2\frac{1}{3}$ yards. The measurement can also be written as a mixture of yards and feet. That is,

7 ft = ____ yd ____ ft

Because 3 ft = 1 yd, we divide 3 into 7 to see how many whole yards are in 7 feet. The quotient is the number of yards, and the remainder is the number of feet.

$$\begin{array}{r} 2 \text{ yd } 1 \text{ ft} \\ 3\overline{)7} \\ -6 \\ \hline 1 \end{array}$$

Thus, 7 ft = 2 yd 1 ft, as seen in the diagram:

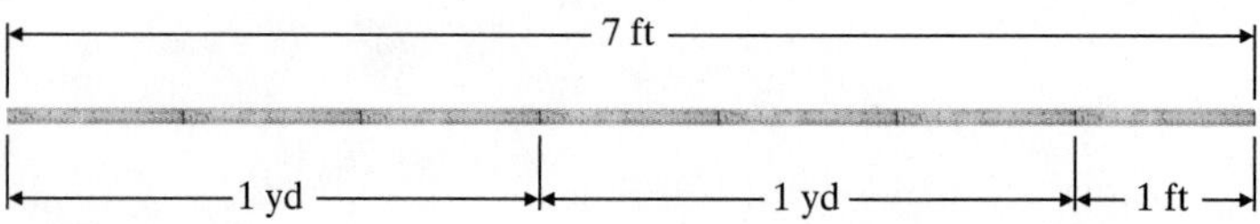

PRACTICE 4

Convert: 68 in. = ______ ft ______ in.

Example 4 Convert: 134 in. = ________ ft ________ in.

Solution: Because 12 in. = 1 ft, we divide 12 into 134. The quotient is the number of feet. The remainder is the number of inches. To see why we divide 12 into 134, notice that

$$134 \text{ in.} = \frac{134 \cancel{\text{in.}}}{1} \cdot \frac{1 \text{ ft}}{12 \cancel{\text{in.}}} = \frac{134}{12} \text{ ft}$$

$$\begin{array}{r} 11 \text{ ft } 2 \text{ in.} \\ 12\overline{)134} \\ -12 \\ \hline 14 \\ -12 \\ \hline 2 \end{array}$$

Thus, 134 in. = 11 ft 2 in.

Work Practice 4

PRACTICE 5

Convert 5 yards 2 feet to feet.

Example 5 Convert 3 feet 7 inches to inches.

Solution: First, we convert 3 feet to inches. Then we add 7 inches.

$$3 \text{ ft} = \frac{3 \cancel{\text{ft}}}{1} \cdot \frac{12 \text{ in.}}{1 \cancel{\text{ft}}} = 36 \text{ in.}$$

Then

3 ft 7 in. = 36 in. + 7 in. = 43 in.

Work Practice 5

Answers

4. 5 ft 8 in. **5.** 17 ft

Objective C Performing Operations on U.S. System Units of Length

Finding sums or differences of measurements often involves converting units, as shown in the next example. Just remember that, as usual, only like units can be added or subtracted.

Example 6 Add 3 ft 2 in. and 5 ft 11 in.

Solution: To add, we line up the similar units.

$$\begin{array}{r} 3\text{ ft } \ 2\text{ in.} \\ +\ 5\text{ ft } 11\text{ in.} \\ \hline 8\text{ ft } 13\text{ in.} \end{array}$$

Since 13 inches is the same as 1 ft 1 in., we have

$$\begin{aligned} 8\text{ ft } 13\text{ in.} &= 8\text{ ft} + 1\text{ ft } 1\text{ in.} \\ &= 9\text{ ft } 1\text{ in.} \end{aligned}$$

Work Practice 6

PRACTICE 6

Add 4 ft 8 in. to 8 ft 11 in.

✓**Concept Check** How could you estimate the following sum?

$$\begin{array}{r} 7\text{ yd } \ 4\text{ in.} \\ +\ 3\text{ yd } 27\text{ in.} \\ \hline \end{array}$$

Example 7 Multiply 8 ft 9 in. by 3.

Solution: By the distributive property, we multiply 8 ft by 3 and 9 in. by 3.

$$\begin{array}{r} 8\text{ ft } \ 9\text{ in.} \\ \times \qquad 3 \\ \hline 24\text{ ft } 27\text{ in.} \end{array}$$

Since 27 in. is the same as 2 ft 3 in., we simplify the product as

$$\begin{aligned} 24\text{ ft } 27\text{ in.} &= 24\text{ ft} + 2\text{ ft } 3\text{ in.} \\ &= 26\text{ ft } 3\text{ in.} \end{aligned}$$

We divide in a similar manner as above.

Work Practice 7

PRACTICE 7

Multiply 4 ft 7 in. by 4.

Example 8 Finding the Length of a Piece of Rope

A rope of length 6 yd 1 ft has 2 yd 2 ft cut from one end. Find the length of the remaining rope.

Solution: Subtract 2 yd 2 ft from 6 yd 1 ft.

$$\begin{array}{rcr} \text{beginning length} & \rightarrow & 6\text{ yd } 1\text{ ft} \\ -\quad \text{amount cut} & \rightarrow & -\ 2\text{ yd } 2\text{ ft} \\ \hline \text{remaining length} & & \end{array}$$

We cannot subtract 2 ft from 1 ft, so we borrow 1 yd from the 6 yd. One yard is converted to 3 ft and combined with the 1 ft already there.

Continued on next page

PRACTICE 8

A carpenter cuts 1 ft 9 in. from a board of length 5 ft 8 in. Find the remaining length of the board.

Answers

6. 13 ft 7 in. **7.** 18 ft 4 in. **8.** 3 ft 11 in.

✓ **Concept Check Answer**

round each to the nearest yard: 7 yd + 4 yd = 11 yd

Borrow 1 yd = 3 ft

5 yd + (1 yd) (3 ft)

~~6 yd~~ 1 ft	=	5 yd 4 ft
− 2 yd 2 ft	=	− 2 yd 2 ft
		3 yd 2 ft

The remaining rope is 3 yd 2 ft long.

Work Practice 8

Objective D Defining and Converting Metric System Units of Length

The basic unit of length in the metric system is the **meter.** A meter is slightly longer than a yard. It is approximately 39.37 inches long. Recall that a yard is 36 inches long.

1 yard = 36 inches

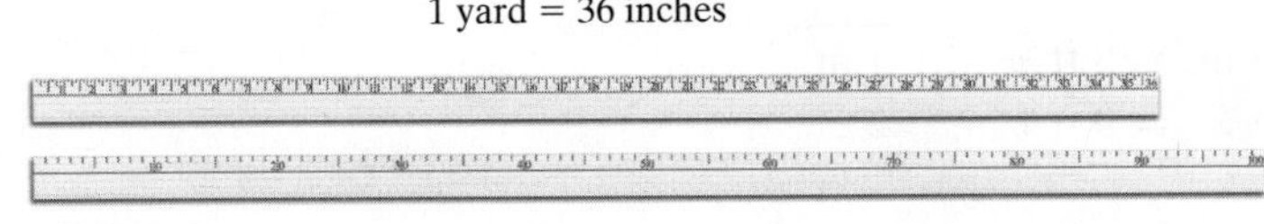

1 meter ≈ 39.37 inches

All units of length in the metric system are based on the meter. The following is a summary of the prefixes used in the metric system. Also shown are equivalencies between units of length. Like the decimal system, the metric system uses powers of 10 to define units.

Metric Units of Length
1 **kilo**meter (km) = 1000 meters (m)
1 **hecto**meter (hm) = 100 m
1 **deka**meter (dam) = 10 m
1 meter (m) = 1 m
1 **deci**meter (dm) = 1/10 m or 0.1 m
1 **centi**meter (cm) = 1/100 m or 0.01 m
1 **milli**meter (mm) = 1/1000 m or 0.001 m

The figure below will help you with decimeters, centimeters, and millimeters.

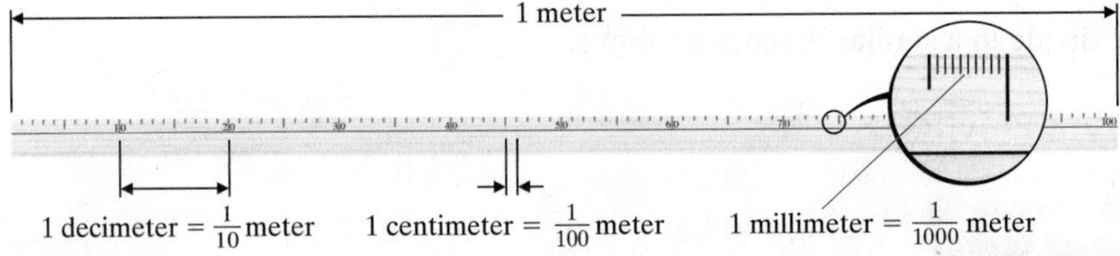

1 decimeter = $\frac{1}{10}$ meter 1 centimeter = $\frac{1}{100}$ meter 1 millimeter = $\frac{1}{1000}$ meter

Helpful Hint

Study the figure above for other equivalencies between metric units of length.

10 decimeters = 1 meter 10 millimeters = 1 centimeter
100 centimeters = 1 meter 10 centimeters = 1 decimeter
1000 millimeters = 1 meter

These same prefixes are used in the metric system for mass and capacity. The most commonly used measurements of length in the metric system are the **meter, millimeter, centimeter,** and **kilometer.**

✓Concept Check Is this statement reasonable? "The screen of a home television set has a 30-meter diagonal." Why or why not?

Being comfortable with the metric units of length means gaining a "feeling" for metric lengths, just as you have a "feeling" for the lengths of an inch, a foot, and a mile. To help you accomplish this, study the following examples:

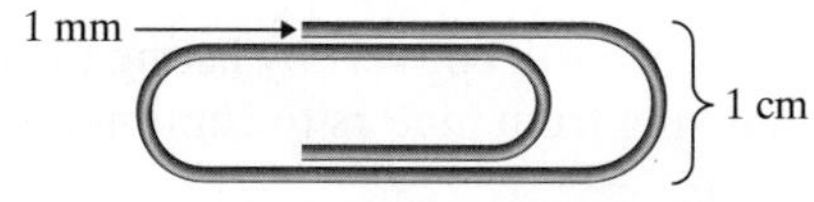

A millimeter is about the thickness of a large paper clip.

A centimeter is about the width of a large paper clip.

A meter is slightly longer than a yard.

A kilometer is about two-thirds of a mile.

The width of this book is approximately 21.5 centimeters.

The distance between New York City and Philadelphia is about 160 kilometers.

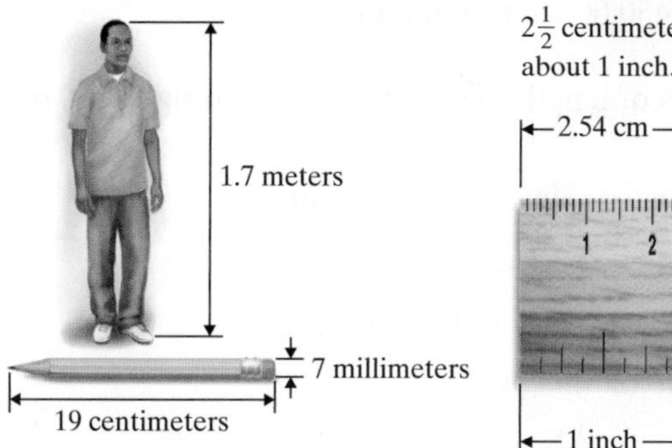

$2\frac{1}{2}$ centimeters is about 1 inch.

2.54 cm

1 inch

As with the U.S. system of measurement, unit fractions may be used to convert from one unit of length to another. For example, let's convert 1200 meters to kilometers. To do so, we will multiply by 1 in the form of the unit fraction

$$\frac{1\text{ km}}{1000\text{ m}} \quad \begin{matrix}\leftarrow \text{Units to convert to} \\ \leftarrow \text{Original units}\end{matrix}$$

$$1200\text{ m} = \frac{1200\text{ m}}{1} \cdot 1 = \frac{1200\text{ m}}{1} \cdot \overbrace{\frac{1\text{ km}}{1000\text{ m}}}^{\text{Unit fraction}} = \frac{1200\text{ km}}{1000} = 1.2\text{ km}$$

The metric system does, however, have a distinct advantage over the U.S. system of measurement: the ease of converting from one unit of length to another. Since all units of length are powers of 10 of the meter, converting from one unit of length to another is as simple as moving the decimal point. Listing units of length in order from largest to smallest helps to keep track of how many places to move the decimal point when converting.

Let's again convert 1200 meters to kilometers. This time, to convert from meters to kilometers, we move along the chart shown, 3 units to the left, from meters to kilometers. This means that we move the decimal point 3 places to the left.

km hm dam **m** dm cm mm

3 units to the left

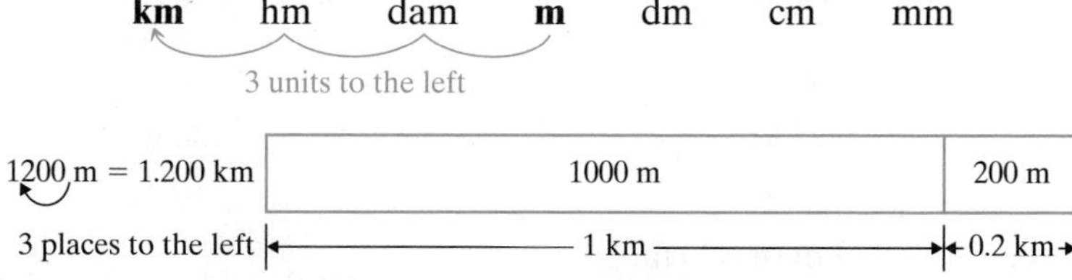

Thus, 1200 m = 1.2 km, as shown in the diagram.

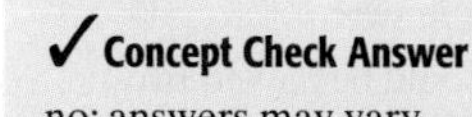

✓ Concept Check Answer

no; answers may vary

PRACTICE 9

Convert 2.5 m to millimeters.

Example 9 Convert 2.3 m to centimeters.

Solution: First we will convert by using a unit fraction.

$$2.3 \text{ m} = \frac{2.3 \cancel{\text{m}}}{1} \cdot \overbrace{\frac{100 \text{ cm}}{1 \cancel{\text{m}}}}^{\text{Unit fraction}} = 230 \text{ cm}$$

Now we will convert by listing the units of length in order from left to right and moving from meters to centimeters.

km hm dam m dm cm mm

2 units to the right (m → cm)

2.30 m = 230. cm

2 places to the right

With either method, we get 230 cm.

Work Practice 9

PRACTICE 10

Convert 3500 m to kilometers.

Example 10 Convert 450,000 mm to meters.

Solution: We list the units of length in order from left to right and move from millimeters to meters.

km hm dam m dm cm mm

3 units to the left (mm → m)

Thus, move the decimal point 3 places to the left.

450,000 mm = 450.000 m or 450 m

Work Practice 10

✓**Concept Check** What is wrong with the following conversion of 150 cm to meters?

~~150.00 cm = 15,000 m~~

Objective E Performing Operations on Metric System Units of Length

To add, subtract, multiply, or divide with metric measurements of length, we write all numbers using the same unit of length and then add, subtract, multiply, or divide as with decimals.

PRACTICE 11

Subtract 640 m from 2.1 km.

Example 11 Subtract 430 m from 1.3 km.

Solution: First we convert both measurements to kilometers or both to meters.

430 m = 0.43 km or 1.3 km = 1300 m

```
  1.30 km        1300 m
- 0.43 km      -  430 m
---------      --------
  0.87 km         870 m
```

The difference is 0.87 km or 870 m.

Work Practice 11

Answers

9. 2500 mm **10.** 3.5 km **11.** 1.46 km or 1460 m

✓ **Concept Check Answer**

decimal point should be moved two places to the left: 1.5 m

Example 12 Multiply 5.7 mm by 4.

Solution: Here we simply multiply the two numbers. Note that the unit of measurement remains the same.

$$\begin{array}{r} 5.7 \text{ mm} \\ \times \quad 4 \\ \hline 22.8 \text{ mm} \end{array}$$

Work Practice 12

PRACTICE 12

Multiply 18.3 hm by 5.

Example 13 Finding a Person's Height

Fritz Martinson was 1.2 meters tall on his last birthday. Since then, he has grown 14 centimeters. Find his current height in meters.

Solution:

original height	→	1.20 m	
+ height grown	→	+ 0.14 m	(Since 14 cm = 0.14 m)
current height		1.34 m	

Fritz is now 1.34 meters tall.

Work Practice 13

PRACTICE 13

A child was 55 centimeters at birth. Her adult height was 1.72 meters. Find how much she grew from birth to adult height.

Example 14 Finding a Crocodile's Length

A newly hatched Nile crocodile averages 26 centimeters in length. This type of crocodile normally grows 4.74 meters to reach its adult length. What is the adult length of this type of crocodile?

Solution:

original length	→	0.26 m	(since 26 cm = 0.26 m)
+ length grown	→	+ 4.74 m	
adult length		5.00 m	

The adult length is 5 meters.

Work Practice 14

PRACTICE 14

Doris Blackwell is knitting a scarf that is currently 0.8 meter long. If she knits an additional 45 centimeters, how long will the scarf be?

Answers

12. 91.5 hm **13.** 117 cm or 1.17 m
14. 125 cm or 1.25 m

Vocabulary and Readiness Check

Use the choices below to fill in each blank. Some choices may be used more than once.

inches yard unit fraction

feet meter

1. The basic unit of length in the metric system is the ______________.
2. The expression $\frac{1 \text{ foot}}{12 \text{ inches}}$ is an example of a(n) ______________.
3. A meter is slightly longer than a(n) ______________.
4. One foot equals 12 ______________.
5. One yard equals 3 ______________.
6. One yard equals 36 ______________.
7. One mile equals 5280 ______________.
8. One foot equals $\frac{1}{3}$ ______________.

7.1 Exercise Set

FOR EXTRA HELP

PRACTICE

WATCH

DOWNLOAD

READ

REVIEW

Objective A *Convert each measurement as indicated. See Examples 1 through 3.*

1. 60 in. to feet

2. 84 in. to feet

3. 12 yd to feet

4. 18 yd to feet

5. 42,240 ft to miles

6. 36,960 ft to miles

7. $8\frac{1}{2}$ ft to inches

8. $12\frac{1}{2}$ ft to inches

9. 10 ft to yards

10. 25 ft to yards

11. 6.4 mi to feet

12. 3.8 mi to feet

13. 162 in. to yd (Write answer as a decimal.)

14. 7216 yd to mi (Write answer as a decimal.)

15. 3 in. to ft (Write answer as a decimal.)

16. 129 in. to ft (Write answer as a decimal.)

Objective B *Convert each measurement as indicated. See Examples 4 and 5.*

17. 40 ft = _____ yd _____ ft

18. 100 ft = _____ yd _____ ft

19. 85 in. = _____ ft _____ in.

20. 47 in. = _____ ft _____ in.

21. 10,000 ft = _____ mi _____ ft

22. 25,000 ft = _____ mi _____ ft

23. 5 ft 2 in. = _____ in.

24. 4 ft 11 in. = _____ in.

25. 8 yd 2 ft = _____ ft

26. 4 yd 1 ft = _____ ft

27. 2 yd 1 ft = _____ in.

28. 1 yd 2 ft = _____ in.

Objective C *Perform each indicated operation. Simplify the result if possible. See Examples 6 through 8.*

29. 3 ft 10 in. + 7 ft 4 in.

30. 12 ft 7 in. + 9 ft 11 in.

31. 12 yd 2 ft + 9 yd 2 ft

32. 16 yd 2 ft + 8 yd 2 ft

33. 22 ft 8 in. − 16 ft 3 in.

34. 15 ft 5 in. − 8 ft 2 in.

35. 18 ft 3 in. − 10 ft 9 in.

36. 14 ft 8 in. − 3 ft 11 in.

37. 28 ft 8 in. ÷ 2

38. 34 ft 6 in. ÷ 2

39. 16 yd 2 ft × 5

40. 15 yd 1 ft × 8

Objective D *Convert as indicated. See Examples 9 and 10.*

41. 60 m to centimeters

42. 46 m to centimeters

43. 40 mm to centimeters

44. 14 mm to centimeters

45. 500 m to kilometers

46. 400 m to kilometers

47. 1700 mm to meters

48. 6400 mm to meters

49. 1500 cm to meters

50. 6400 cm to meters

51. 0.42 km to centimeters

52. 0.95 km to centimeters

53. 7 km to meters

54. 5 km to meters

55. 8.3 cm to millimeters

56. 4.6 cm to millimeters

57. 20.1 mm to decimeters

58. 140.2 mm to decimeters

59. 0.04 m to millimeters

60. 0.2 m to millimeters

Objective E *Perform each indicated operation. Remember to insert units when writing your answers. See Examples 11 through 14.*

61. 8.6 m + 0.34 m

62. 14.1 cm + 3.96 cm

63. 2.9 m + 40 mm

64. 30 cm + 8.9 m

65. 24.8 mm − 1.19 cm

66. 45.3 m − 2.16 dam

67. 15 km − 2360 m

68. 14 cm − 15 mm

69. 18.3 m × 3

70. 14.1 m × 4

71. 6.2 km ÷ 4

72. 9.6 m ÷ 5

Objectives A C D E Mixed Practice *Solve. Remember to insert units when writing your answers. For Exercises 73 through 82, complete the charts. See Examples 1 through 14.*

		Yards	Feet	Inches
73.	Chrysler Building in New York City		1046	
74.	4-story building			792
75.	Python length		35	
76.	Ostrich height			108

Complete the chart.

		Meters	Millimeters	Kilometers	Centimeters
77.	Length of elephant	5			
78.	Height of grizzly bear	3			
79.	Tennis ball diameter				6.5
80.	Golf ball diameter				4.6
81.	Distance from London to Paris			342	
82.	Distance from Houston to Dallas			396	

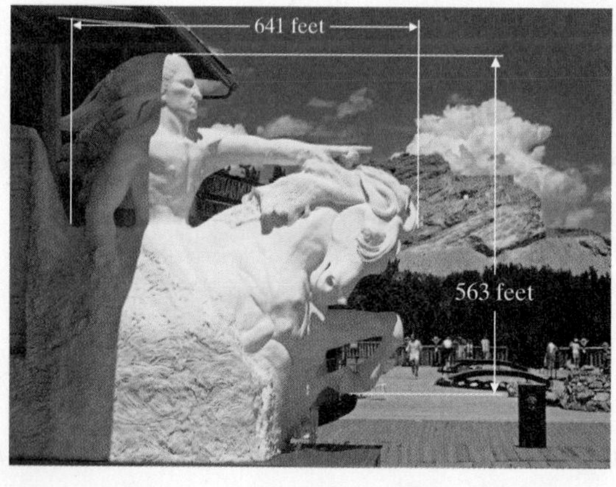

83. The total width of the Crazy Horse carving is 641 feet. Convert this width to

a. yards

b. inches

84. The total height of the Crazy Horse carving is 563 feet. Convert this height to

a. yards

b. inches

85. The National Zoo maintains a small patch of bamboo, which it grows as a food supply for its pandas. Two weeks ago, the bamboo was 6 ft 10 in. tall. Since then, the bamboo has grown 3 ft 8 in. How tall is the bamboo now?

86. While exploring in the Marianas Trench, a submarine probe was lowered to a point 1 mile 1400 feet below the ocean's surface. Later it was lowered an additional 1 mile 4000 feet below this point. How far was the probe below the surface of the Pacific?

87. At its deepest point, the Grand Canyon of the Colorado River in Arizona is about 6000 ft. The Grand Canyon of the Yellowstone River, which is in Yellowstone National Park in Wyoming, is at most 900 feet deep. How much deeper is the Grand Canyon of the Colorado River than the Grand Canyon of the Yellowstone River? (*Source:* National Park Service)

88. The Black Canyon of the Gunnison River is only 1150 ft wide at its narrowest point. At its narrowest, the Grand Canyon of the Yellowstone is $\frac{1}{2}$ mile wide. Find the difference in width between the Grand Canyon of the Yellowstone and the Black Canyon of the Gunnison. (*Note:* Notice that the dimensions are different.) (*Source:* National Park Service)

89. The tallest man in the world is recorded as Robert Pershing Wadlow of Alton, Illinois. Born in 1918, he measured 8 ft 11 in. at his tallest. The shortest man in the world is Gul Mohammed of India, who measures 22.5 in. How many times taller than Gul is Robert? Round to one decimal place. (*Source: Guinness World Records*)

90. A 3.4-m rope is attached to a 5.8-m rope. However, when the ropes are tied, 8 cm of length is lost to form the knot. What is the length of the tied ropes?

91. The length of one of the Statue of Liberty's hands is 16 ft 5 in. One of the statue's eyes is 2 ft 6 in. across. How much longer is a hand than the width of an eye? (*Source:* National Park Service)

92. The width of the Statue of Liberty's head from ear to ear is 10 ft. The height of the statue's head from chin to cranium is 17 ft 3 in. How much taller is the statue's head than its width? (*Source:* National Park Service)

93. The ice on a pond is 5.33 cm thick. For safe skating, the owner of the pond insists that it must be 80 mm thick. How much thicker must the ice be before skating is allowed?

94. The sediment on the bottom of the Towamencin Creek is normally 14 cm thick, but the recent flood washed away 22 mm of sediment. How thick is it now?

95. The Amana Corporation stacks up its microwave ovens in a distribution warehouse. Each stack is 1 ft 9 in. wide. How far from the wall would 9 of these stacks extend?

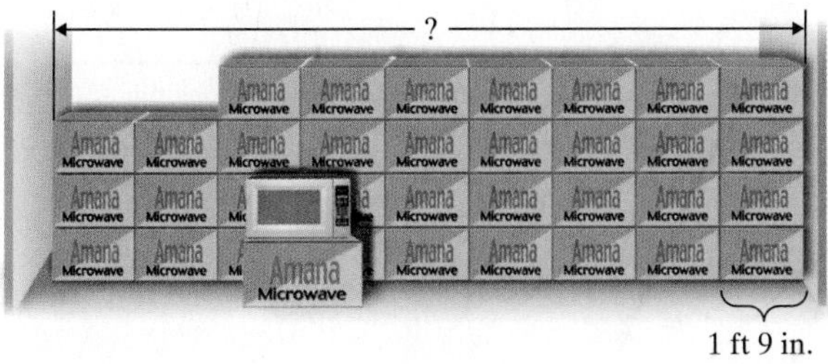

96. The highway commission is installing concrete sound barriers along a highway. Each barrier is 1 yd 2 ft long. Find the total length of 25 barriers placed end to end.

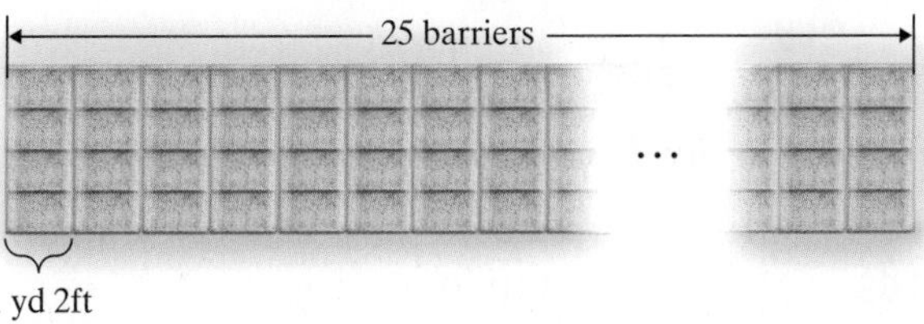

97. A carpenter needs to cut a board into thirds. If the board is 9 ft 3 in. long originally, how long will each cut piece be?

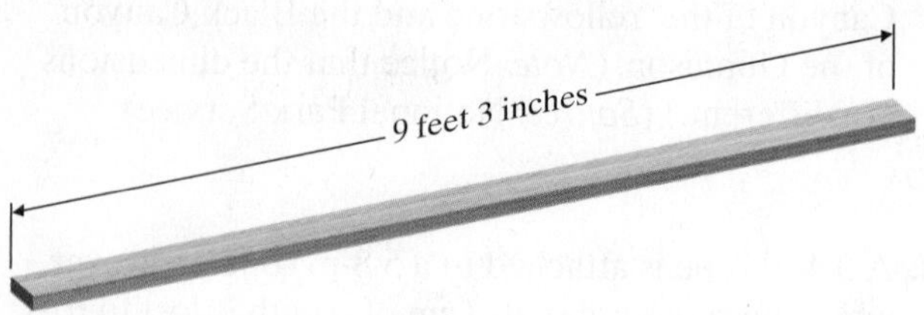

98. A wall is erected exactly halfway between two buildings that are 192 ft 8 in. apart. If the wall is 8 in. wide, how far is it from the wall to either of the buildings?

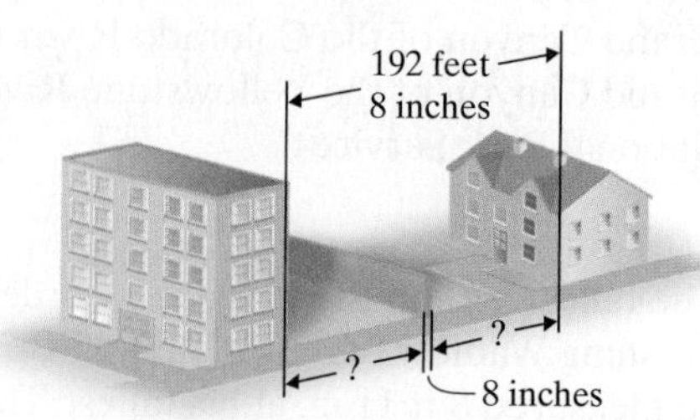

99. An art class is learning how to make kites. The two sticks used for each kite have lengths of 1 m and 65 cm. What total length of wood must be ordered for the sticks if 25 kites are to be built?

100. The total pages of a hardbound economics text are 3.1 cm thick. The front and back covers are each 2 mm thick. How high would a stack of 10 of these texts be?

101. A logging firm needs to cut a 67-m-long redwood log into 20 equal pieces before loading it onto a truck for shipment. How long will each piece be?

102. An 18.3-m-tall flagpole is mounted on a 65-cm-high pedestal. How far is the top of the flagpole from the ground?

103. A 2.15-m-long sash cord has become frayed at both ends so that 1 cm is trimmed from each end. How long is the remaining cord?

104. A 112.5-foot-tall dead pine tree is removed by starting at the top and cutting off 9-foot-long sections. How many whole sections are removed?

105. The longest truck in the world is operated by Gould Transport in Australia, and is the 182-ft Road Train. How many *yards* long are 2 of these trucks? (*Source: Guinness World Records*)

106. Three hundred fifty thousand people daily see the large Coca-Cola sign in the Tokyo Ginza shopping district. It is in the shape of a rectangle whose length is 31 yards and whose width is 49 feet. Find the area of the sign in square feet. (*Source:* Coca-Cola Company) (*Hint:* Recall that the area of a rectangle is the product length times width.)

107. A floor tile is 22.86 cm wide. How many tiles in a row are needed to cross a room 3.429 m wide?

△ **108.** A standard postcard is 1.6 times longer than it is wide. If it is 9.9 cm wide, what is its length?

Review

Write each decimal as a fraction and each fraction as a decimal. See Section 4.6.

109. 0.21 **110.** 0.86 **111.** $\frac{13}{100}$ **112.** $\frac{47}{100}$ **113.** $\frac{1}{4}$ **114.** $\frac{3}{20}$

Concept Extensions

Determine whether the measurement in each statement is reasonable.

115. The width of a twin-size bed is 20 meters.

116. A window measures 1 meter by 0.5 meter.

117. A drinking glass is made of glass 2 millimeters thick.

118. A paper clip is 4 kilometers long.

119. The distance across the Colorado River is 50 kilometers.

120. A model's hair is 30 centimeters long.

Estimate each sum or difference. See the first Concept Check in this section.

121.

$$\begin{array}{r} 5 \text{ yd} \;\; 2 \text{ in.} \\ +\; 7 \text{ yd} \; 30 \text{ in.} \\ \hline \end{array}$$

122.

$$\begin{array}{r} 45 \text{ ft} \;\; 1 \text{ in.} \\ -\; 10 \text{ ft} \; 11 \text{ in.} \\ \hline \end{array}$$

123. Using a unit other than the foot, write a length that is equivalent to 4 feet. (*Hint:* There are many possibilities.)

124. Using a unit other than the meter, write a length that is equivalent to 7 meters. (*Hint:* There are many possibilities.)

125. To convert from meters to centimeters, the decimal point is moved two places to the right. Explain how this relates to the fact that the prefix *centi* means $\frac{1}{100}$.

126. Explain why conversions in the metric system are easier to make than conversions in the U.S. system of measurement.

127. An advertisement sign outside Fenway Park in Boston measures 18.3 m by 18.3 m. What is the area of this sign?

Objectives

A Define U.S. Units of Weight and Convert from One Unit to Another.

B Perform Arithmetic Operations on U.S. Units of Weight.

C Define Metric Units of Mass and Convert from One Unit to Another.

D Perform Arithmetic Operations on Metric Units of Mass.

7.2 WEIGHT AND MASS: U.S. AND METRIC SYSTEMS OF MEASUREMENT

Objective A Defining and Converting U.S. System Units of Weight

Whenever we talk about how heavy an object is, we are concerned with the object's **weight.** We discuss weight when we refer to a 12-ounce box of Rice Krispies, a 15-pound tabby cat, or a barge hauling 24 tons of garbage.

12 ounces

15 pounds

24 tons of garbage

The most common units of weight in the U.S. measurement system are the **ounce,** the **pound,** and the **ton.** The following is a summary of equivalencies between units of weight:

U.S. Units of Weight	***Unit Fractions***
16 ounces (oz) = 1 pound (lb)	$\frac{16\text{ oz}}{1\text{ lb}} = \frac{1\text{ lb}}{16\text{ oz}} = 1$
2000 pounds = 1 ton	$\frac{2000\text{ lb}}{1\text{ ton}} = \frac{1\text{ ton}}{2000\text{ lb}} = 1$

✓**Concept Check** If you were describing the weight of a fully loaded semitrailer, which type of unit would you use: ounce, pound, or ton? Why?

Unit fractions that equal 1 are used to convert between units of weight in the U.S. system. When converting using unit fractions, recall that the numerator of a unit fraction should contain the units we are converting to and the denominator should contain the original units.

PRACTICE 1

Convert 6500 pounds to tons.

Example 1 Convert 9000 pounds to tons.

Solution: We multiply 9000 lb by a unit fraction that uses the equality 2000 pounds = 1 ton.

Remember, the unit fraction should be $\frac{\text{units to convert to}}{\text{original units}}$ or $\frac{1\text{ ton}}{2000\text{ lb}}$.

Answer

1. $3\frac{1}{4}$ tons

✓ **Concept Check Answer**

ton

$$9000 \text{ lb} = \frac{9000 \text{ lb}}{1} \cdot 1 = \frac{9000 \not{\text{lb}}}{1} \cdot \frac{1 \text{ ton}}{2000 \not{\text{lb}}} = \frac{9000 \text{ tons}}{2000} = \frac{9}{2} \text{ tons or } 4\frac{1}{2} \text{ tons}$$

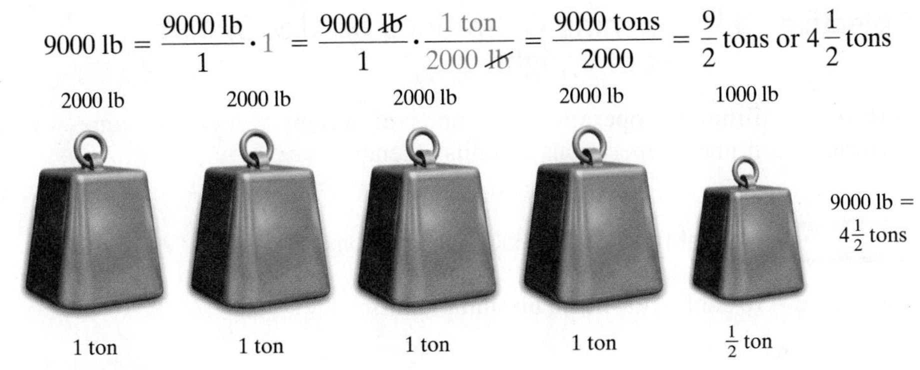

Work Practice 1

Example 2 Convert 3 pounds to ounces.

Solution: We multiply by the unit fraction $\frac{16 \text{ oz}}{1 \text{ lb}}$ to convert from pounds to ounces.

$$3 \text{ lb} = \frac{3 \text{ lb}}{1} \cdot 1 = \frac{3 \not{\text{lb}}}{1} \cdot \frac{16 \text{ oz}}{1 \not{\text{lb}}} = 3 \cdot 16 \text{ oz} = 48 \text{ oz}$$

Work Practice 2

PRACTICE 2

Convert 72 ounces to pounds.

As with length, it is sometimes useful to simplify a measurement of weight by writing it in terms of mixed units.

Example 3 Convert: 33 ounces = _____ lb _____ oz

Solution: Because 16 oz = 1 lb, divide 16 into 33 to see how many pounds are in 33 ounces. The quotient is the number of pounds, and the remainder is the number of ounces. To see why we divide 16 into 33, notice that

$$33 \text{ oz} = 33 \not{\text{oz}} \cdot \frac{1 \text{ lb}}{16 \not{\text{oz}}} = \frac{33}{16} \text{ lb}$$

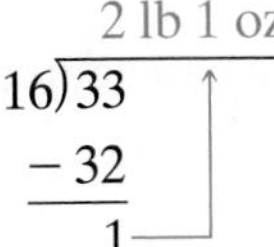

$$\begin{array}{r} 2 \text{ lb } 1 \text{ oz} \\ 16\overline{)33} \\ -32 \\ \hline 1 \end{array}$$

Thus, 33 ounces is the same as 2 lb 1 oz

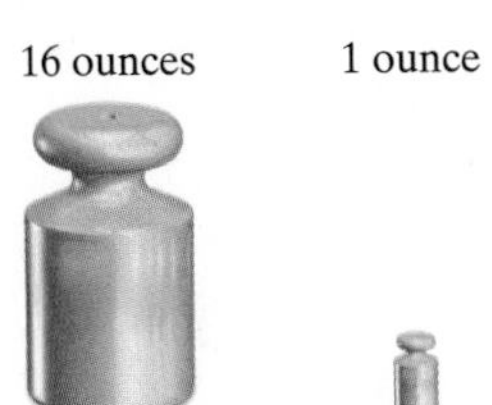

Work Practice 3

PRACTICE 3

Convert:

47 ounces = _____ lb _____ oz

Answers

2. $4\frac{1}{2}$ lb **3.** 2 lb 15 oz

Objective B Performing Operations on U.S. System Units of Weight

Performing arithmetic operations on units of weight works the same way as performing arithmetic operations on units of length.

PRACTICE 4

Subtract 5 tons 1200 lb from 8 tons 100 lb.

Example 4 Subtract 3 tons 1350 lb from 8 tons 1000 lb.

Solution: To subtract, we line up similar units.

$$\begin{array}{r} 8 \text{ tons } 1000 \text{ lb} \\ -3 \text{ tons } 1350 \text{ lb} \\ \hline \end{array}$$

Since we cannot subtract 1350 lb from 1000 lb, we borrow 1 ton from the 8 tons. To do so, we write 1 ton as 2000 lb and combine it with the 1000 lb.

7 tons + (1 ton) 2000 lb

$$\begin{array}{r} \not{8} \text{ tons } 1000 \text{ lb} \\ -3 \text{ tons } 1350 \text{ lb} \\ \hline \end{array} \quad = \quad \begin{array}{r} 7 \text{ tons } 3000 \text{ lb} \\ -3 \text{ tons } 1350 \text{ lb} \\ \hline 4 \text{ tons } 1650 \text{ lb} \end{array}$$

To check, see that the sum of 4 tons 1650 lb and 3 tons 1350 lb is 8 tons 1000 lb.

Work Practice 4

PRACTICE 5

Divide 5 lb 8 oz by 4.

Example 5 Divide 9 lb 6 oz by 2.

Solution: We divide each of the units by 2.

$$\begin{array}{rll} & 4 \text{ lb} & 11 \text{ oz} \\ 2) & 9 \text{ lb} & 6 \text{ oz} \\ & -8 & \\ & 1 \text{ lb} = & 16 \text{ oz} \\ & & 22 \text{ oz} \end{array}$$

Divide 2 into 22 oz to get 11 oz.

To check, multiply 4 pounds 11 ounces by 2. The result is 9 pounds 6 ounces.

Work Practice 5

PRACTICE 6

A 5-lb 14-oz batch of cookies is packed into a 6-oz container before it is mailed. Find the total weight.

Example 6 Finding the Weight of a Child

Bryan weighed 8 lb 8 oz at birth. By the time he was 1 year old, he had gained 11 lb 14 oz. Find his weight at age 1 year.

Solution:

$$\begin{array}{rcr} \text{birth weight} & \rightarrow & 8 \text{ lb } \ 8 \text{ oz} \\ + \text{ weight gained} & \rightarrow & + 11 \text{ lb } 14 \text{ oz} \\ \hline \text{total weight} & \rightarrow & 19 \text{ lb } 22 \text{ oz} \end{array}$$

Since 22 oz equals 1 lb 6 oz,

$$\begin{aligned} 19 \text{ lb } 22 \text{ oz} &= 19 \text{ lb} + 1 \text{ lb } 6 \text{ oz} \\ &= 20 \text{ lb } 6 \text{ oz} \end{aligned}$$

Bryan weighed 20 lb 6 oz on his first birthday.

Work Practice 6

Answers

4. 2 tons 900 lb 5. 1 lb 6 oz
6. 6 lb 4 oz

Objective C Defining and Converting Metric System Units of Mass

In scientific and technical areas, a careful distinction is made between **weight** and **mass. Weight** is really a measure of the pull of gravity. The farther from Earth an object gets, the less it weighs. However, **mass** is a measure of the amount of substance in the object and does not change. Astronauts orbiting Earth weigh much less than they weigh on Earth, but they have the same mass in orbit as they do on Earth. Here on Earth, weight and mass are the same, so either term may be used.

The basic unit of mass in the metric system is the **gram.** It is defined as the mass of water contained in a cube 1 centimeter (cm) on each side.

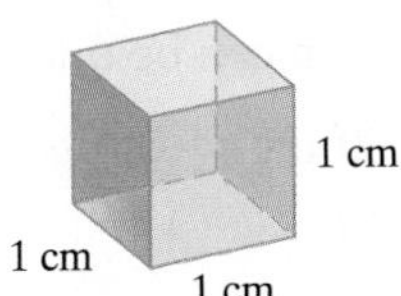

The following examples may help you get a feeling for metric masses:

A tablet contains 200 milligrams of ibuprofen.

A large paper clip weighs approximately 1 gram.

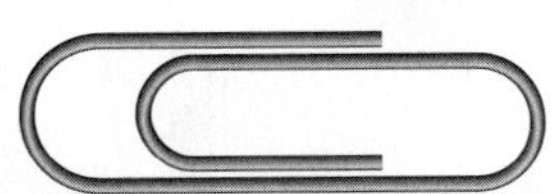

A box of crackers weighs 453 grams.

A kilogram is slightly over 2 pounds. An adult woman may weigh 60 kilograms.

The prefixes for units of mass in the metric system are the same as for units of length, as shown in the following table:

Metric Units of Mass
1 **kilo**gram (kg) = 1000 grams (g)
1 **hecto**gram (hg) = 100 g
1 **deka**gram (dag) = 10 g
1 gram (g) = 1 g
1 **deci**gram (dg) = 1/10 g or 0.1 g
1 **centi**gram (cg) = 1/100 g or 0.01 g
1 **milli**gram (mg) = 1/1000 g or 0.001 g

✓**Concept Check** True or false? A decigram is larger than a dekagram. Explain.

The **milligram,** the **gram,** and the **kilogram** are the three most commonly used units of mass in the metric system.

As with lengths, all units of mass are powers of 10 of the gram, so converting from one unit of mass to another only involves moving the decimal point. To convert

✓ **Concept Check Answer**

false

from one unit of mass to another in the metric system, list the units of mass in order from largest to smallest.

Let's convert 4300 milligrams to grams. To convert from milligrams to grams, we move along the list 3 units to the left.

kg hg dag **g** dg cg **mg**

3 units to the left

This means that we move the decimal point 3 places to the left to convert from milligrams to grams.

4300 mg = 4.3 g

Don't forget, the same conversion can be done with unit fractions.

$$4300 \text{ mg} = \frac{4300 \text{ mg}}{1} \cdot 1 = \frac{4300 \cancel{\text{mg}}}{1} \cdot \frac{0.001 \text{ g}}{1 \cancel{\text{mg}}}$$

$$= 4300 \cdot 0.001 \text{ g}$$

$$= 4.3 \text{ g}$$ To multiply by 0.001, move the decimal point 3 places to the left.

To see that this is reasonable, study the diagram:

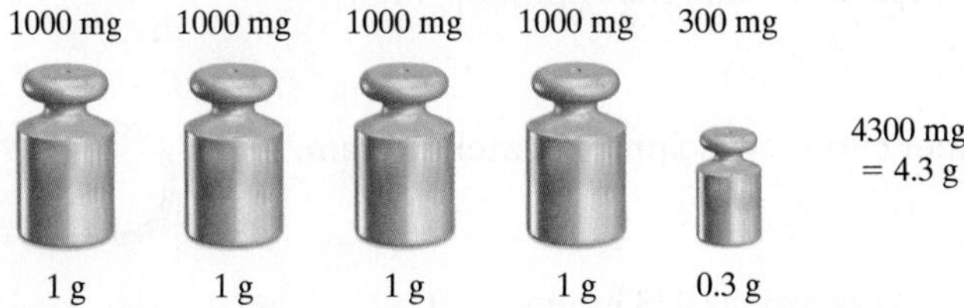

Thus, 4300 mg = 4.3 g

PRACTICE 7

Convert 3.41 g to milligrams.

Example 7 Convert 3.2 kg to grams.

Solution: First we convert by using a unit fraction.

$$3.2 \text{ kg} = 3.2 \text{ kg} \cdot 1 = 3.2 \cancel{\text{kg}} \cdot \overbrace{\frac{1000 \text{ g}}{1 \cancel{\text{kg}}}}^{\text{Unit fraction}} = 3200 \text{ g}$$

Now let's list the units of mass in order from left to right and move from kilograms to grams.

kg hg dag g dg cg mg

3 units to the right

3.200 kg = 3200. g

3 places to the right

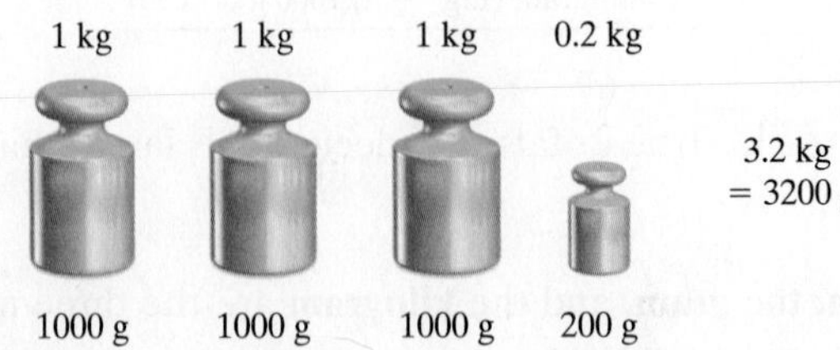

Work Practice 7

Answer

7. 3410 mg

Example 8 Convert 2.35 cg to grams.

Solution: We list the units of mass in a chart and move from centigrams to grams.

kg hg dag g dg cg mg

2 units to the left

02.35 cg = 0.0235 g

2 places to the left

Work Practice 8

PRACTICE 8

Convert 56.2 cg to grams.

Objective D Performing Operations on Metric System Units of Mass

Arithmetic operations can be performed with metric units of mass just as we performed operations with metric units of length. We convert each number to the same unit of mass and add, subtract, multiply, or divide as with decimals.

Example 9 Subtract 5.4 dg from 1.6 g.

Solution: We convert both numbers to decigrams or to grams before subtracting.

5.4 dg = 0.54 g   or   1.6 g = 16 dg

$$\begin{array}{r} 1.60\text{ g} \\ -\ 0.54\text{ g} \\ \hline 1.06\text{ g} \end{array} \qquad \begin{array}{r} 16.0\text{ dg} \\ -\ 5.4\text{ dg} \\ \hline 10.6\text{ dg} \end{array}$$

The difference is 1.06 g or 10.6 dg.

Work Practice 9

PRACTICE 9

Subtract 3.1 dg from 2.5 g.

Example 10 Calculating Allowable Weight in an Elevator

An elevator has a weight limit of 1400 kg. A sign posted in the elevator indicates that the maximum capacity of the elevator is 17 persons. What is the average allowable weight for each passenger, rounded to the nearest kilogram?

Solution: To solve, notice that the total weight of 1400 kilograms ÷ 17 = average weight.

$$\begin{array}{r} 82.3\text{ kg} \approx 82\text{ kg} \\ 17\overline{)\,1400.0\text{ kg}} \\ -136 \\ \hline 40 \\ -34 \\ \hline 60 \\ -51 \\ \hline 9 \end{array}$$

Each passenger can weigh an average of 82 kg. (Recall that a kilogram is slightly over 2 pounds, so 82 kilograms is over 164 pounds.)

Work Practice 10

PRACTICE 10

Twenty-four bags of cement weigh a total of 550 kg. Find the average weight of 1 bag, rounded to the nearest kilogram.

Answers

8. 0.562 g **9.** 2.19 g or 21.9 dg
10. 23 kg

Vocabulary and Readiness Check

Use the choices below to fill in each blank.

mass weight gram

1. ___________ is a measure of the amount of substance in an object. This measure does not change.
2. ___________ is the measure of the pull of gravity.
3. The basic unit of mass in the metric system is the ___________.

Fill in these blanks with the correct number. Choices for these blanks are not shown in the list of terms above.

4. One pound equals ___________ ounces.
5. One ton equals ___________ pounds.

Convert without pencil or paper.

6. 3 tons to pounds
7. 32 ounces to pounds
8. 3 pounds to ounces
9. 4000 pounds to tons
10. 1 ton to pounds

7.2 Exercise Set

FOR EXTRA HELP

MyMathLab

Objective A *Convert as indicated. See Examples 1 through 3.*

1. 2 pounds to ounces

2. 5 pounds to ounces

3. 5 tons to pounds

4. 7 tons to pounds

5. 18,000 pounds to tons

6. 28,000 pounds to tons

7. 60 ounces to pounds

8. 90 ounces to pounds

9. 3500 pounds to tons

10. 11,000 pounds to tons

11. 12.75 pounds to ounces

12. 9.5 pounds to ounces

13. 4.9 tons to pounds

14. 8.3 tons to pounds

15. $4\frac{3}{4}$ pounds to ounces

16. $9\frac{1}{8}$ pounds to ounces

17. 2950 pounds to the nearest tenth of a ton

18. 51 ounces to the nearest tenth of a pound

19. $\frac{4}{5}$ oz to pounds

20. $\frac{1}{4}$ oz to pounds

21. $5\frac{3}{4}$ lb to ounces

22. $2\frac{1}{4}$ lb to ounces

23. 10 lb 1 oz to ounces

24. 7 lb 6 oz to ounces

25. 89 oz = _____ lb _____ oz

26. 100 oz = _____ lb _____ oz

Objective B *Perform each indicated operation. See Examples 4 through 6.*

27. 34 lb 12 oz + 18 lb 14 oz

28. 6 lb 10 oz + 10 lb 8 oz

29. 3 tons 1820 lb + 4 tons 930 lb

30. 1 ton 1140 lb + 5 tons 1200 lb

31. 5 tons 1050 lb − 2 tons 875 lb

32. 4 tons 850 lb − 1 ton 260 lb

33. 12 lb 4 oz − 3 lb 9 oz

34. 45 lb 6 oz − 26 lb 10 oz

35. 5 lb 3 oz × 6

36. 2 lb 5 oz × 5

37. 6 tons 1500 lb ÷ 5

38. 5 tons 400 lb ÷ 4

Objective C *Convert as indicated. See Examples 7 and 8.*

39. 500 g to kilograms

40. 820 g to kilograms

41. 4 g to milligrams

42. 9 g to milligrams

43. 25 kg to grams

44. 18 kg to grams

45. 48 mg to grams

46. 112 mg to grams

47. 6.3 g to kilograms

48. 4.9 g to kilograms

49. 15.14 g to milligrams

50. 16.23 g to milligrams

51. 6.25 kg to grams

52. 3.16 kg to grams

53. 35 hg to centigrams

54. 4.26 cg to dekagrams

Objective D *Perform each indicated operation. Remember to insert units when writing your answers. See Examples 9 and 10.*

55. 3.8 mg + 9.7 mg

56. 41.6 g + 9.8 g

57. 205 mg + 5.61 g

58. 2.1 g + 153 mg

59. 9 g − 7150 mg

60. 6.13 g − 418 mg

61. 1.61 kg − 250 g

62. 4 kg − 2410 g

63. 5.2 kg × 2.6

64. 4.8 kg × 9.3

65. 17 kg ÷ 8

66. 8.25 g ÷ 6

Objectives A B C D Mixed Practice *Solve. Remember to insert units when writing your answers. For Exercises 67 through 74, complete the chart. See Examples 1 through 10.*

	Object	Tons	Pounds	Ounces
67.	Statue of Liberty—weight of copper sheeting	100		
68.	Statue of Liberty—weight of steel	125		
69.	A 12-inch cube of osmium (heaviest metal)		1345	
70.	A 12-inch cube of lithium (lightest metal)		32	

	Object	Grams	Kilograms	Milligrams	Centigrams
71.	Capsule of amoxicillin (antibiotic)			500	
72.	Tablet of Topamax (epilepsy and migraine uses)			25	
73.	A six-year-old boy		21		
74.	A golf ball	45			

75. A can of 7-Up weighs 336 grams. Find the weight in kilograms of 24 cans.

76. Guy Green normally weighs 73 kg, but he lost 2800 grams after being sick with the flu. Find Guy's new weight.

77. Sudafed is a decongestant that comes in two strengths. Regular strength contains 60 mg of medication. Extra strength contains 0.09 g of medication. How much extra medication is in the extra-strength tablet?

78. A small can of Planters sunflower seeds weighs 177 g. If each can contains 6 servings, find the weight of one serving.

79. Doris Johnson has two open containers of Uncle Ben's rice. If she combines 1 lb 10 oz from one container with 3 lb 14 oz from the other container, how much total rice does she have?

80. Dru Mizel maintains the records of the amount of coal delivered to his department in the steel mill. In January, 3 tons 1500 lb were delivered. In February, 2 tons 1200 lb were delivered. Find the total amount delivered in these two months.

81. Carla Hamtini was amazed when she grew a 28-lb 10-oz zucchini in her garden, but later she learned that the heaviest zucchini ever grown weighed 64 lb 8 oz in Llanharry, Wales, by B. Lavery in 1990. How far below the record weight was Carla's zucchini? (*Source: Guinness World Records*)

82. The heaviest baby born in good health weighed an incredible 22 lb 8 oz. He was born in Italy in September 1955. How much heavier is this than a 7-lb 12-oz baby? (*Source: Guinness World Records*)

83. The smallest baby born in good health weighed only 8.6 ounces, less than a can of soda. She was born in Chicago in December 2004. How much lighter was she than an average baby, who weighs about 7 lb 8 ounces?

84. A large bottle of Hire's Root Beer weighs 1900 grams. If a carton contains 6 large bottles of root beer, find the weight in kilograms of 5 cartons.

85. Three milligrams of preservatives are added to a 0.5-kg box of dried fruit. How many milligrams of preservatives are in 3 cartons of dried fruit if each carton contains 16 boxes?

86. One box of Swiss Miss Cocoa Mix weighs 0.385 kg, but 39 grams of this weight is the packaging. Find the actual weight of the cocoa in 8 boxes.

87. A carton of 12 boxes of Quaker Oats Oatmeal weighs 6.432 kg. Each box includes 26 grams of packaging material. What is the actual weight of the oatmeal in the carton?

88. The supermarket prepares hamburger in 85-gram market packages. When Leo Gonzalas gets home, he divides the package in half before refrigerating the meat. How much will each package weigh?

89. The Shop 'n Bag supermarket chain ships hamburger meat by placing 10 packages of hamburger in a box, with each package weighing 3 lb 4 oz. How much will 4 boxes of hamburger weigh?

90. The Quaker Oats Company ships its 1-lb 2-oz boxes of oatmeal in cartons containing 12 boxes of oatmeal. How much will 3 such cartons weigh?

91. A carton of Del Monte Pineapple weighs 55 lb 4 oz, but 2 lb 8 oz of this weight is due to packaging. Find the actual weight of the pineapple in 4 cartons.

92. The Hormel Corporation ships cartons of canned ham weighing 43 lb 2 oz each. Of this weight, 3 lb 4 oz is due to packaging. Find the actual weight of the ham found in 3 cartons.

Review

Write each fraction as a decimal. See Section 4.6.

93. $\frac{4}{25}$

94. $\frac{3}{5}$

95. $\frac{7}{8}$

96. $\frac{3}{16}$

Concept Extensions

Determine whether the measurement in each statement is reasonable.

97. The doctor prescribed a pill containing 2 kg of medication.

98. A full-grown cat weighs approximately 15 g.

99. A bag of flour weighs 4.5 kg.

100. A staple weighs 15 mg.

101. A professor weighs less than 150 g.

102. A car weighs 2000 mg.

103. Use a unit other than centigram and write a mass that is equivalent to 25 centigrams. (*Hint:* There are many possibilities.)

104. Use a unit other than pound and write a weight that is equivalent to 4000 pounds. (*Hint:* There are many possibilities.)

True or false? See the second Concept Check in this section.

105. A kilogram is larger than a gram.

106. A decigram is larger than a milligram.

107. Why is the decimal point moved to the right when grams are converted to milligrams?

108. To change 8 pounds to ounces, multiply by 16. Why is this the correct procedure?

Objectives

A **Define U.S. Units of Capacity and Convert from One Unit to Another.**

B **Perform Arithmetic Operations on U.S. Units of Capacity.**

C **Define Metric Units of Capacity and Convert from One Unit to Another.**

D **Perform Arithmetic Operations on Metric Units of Capacity.**

7.3 CAPACITY: U.S. AND METRIC SYSTEMS OF MEASUREMENT

Objective A Defining and Converting U.S. System Units of Capacity

Units of **capacity** are generally used to measure liquids. The number of gallons of gasoline needed to fill a gas tank in a car, the number of cups of water needed in a bread recipe, and the number of quarts of milk sold each day at a supermarket are all examples of using units of capacity. The following summary shows equivalencies between units of capacity:

U.S. Units of Capacity

8 fluid ounces (fl oz) = 1 cup (c)

2 cups = 1 pint (pt)

2 pints = 1 quart (qt)

4 quarts = 1 gallon (gal)

Just as with units of length and weight, we can form unit fractions to convert between different units of capacity. For instance,

$$\frac{2\text{ c}}{1\text{ pt}} = \frac{1\text{ pt}}{2\text{ c}} = 1 \quad \text{and} \quad \frac{2\text{ pt}}{1\text{ qt}} = \frac{1\text{ qt}}{2\text{ pt}} = 1$$

PRACTICE 1

Convert 43 pints to quarts.

Example 1 Convert 9 quarts to gallons.

Solution: We multiply by the unit fraction $\frac{1\text{ gal}}{4\text{ qt}}$.

$$\begin{aligned} 9\text{ qt} &= \frac{9\text{ qt}}{1} \cdot 1 \\ &= \frac{9\text{ qt}}{1} \cdot \frac{1\text{ gal}}{4\text{ qt}} \\ &= \frac{9\text{ gal}}{4} \\ &= 2\frac{1}{4}\text{ gal} \end{aligned}$$

Thus, 9 quarts is the same as $2\frac{1}{4}$ gallons, as shown in the diagram:

Work Practice 1

Answer

1. $21\frac{1}{2}$ qt

Example 2 Convert 14 cups to quarts.

Solution: Our equivalency table contains no direct conversion from cups to quarts. However, from this table we know that

$$1\text{ qt} = 2\text{ pt} = \frac{2\text{ pt}}{1}\cdot 1 = \frac{2\text{ pt}}{1}\cdot\frac{2\text{ c}}{1\text{ pt}} = 4\text{ c}$$

so 1 qt = 4 c. Now we have the unit fraction $\frac{1\text{ qt}}{4\text{ c}}$. Thus,

$$14\text{ c} = \frac{14\text{ c}}{1}\cdot 1 = \frac{14\not{c}}{1}\cdot\frac{1\text{ qt}}{4\not{c}} = \frac{14\text{ qt}}{4} = \frac{7}{2}\text{qt} \quad\text{or}\quad 3\frac{1}{2}\text{qt}$$

1 quart + 1 quart + 1 quart + $\frac{1}{2}$ quart

14 cups $= 3\frac{1}{2}$ qt

Work Practice 2

PRACTICE 2

Convert 26 quarts to cups.

✓**Concept Check** If 50 cups is converted to quarts, will the equivalent number of quarts be less than or greater than 50? Explain.

Objective B Performing Operations on U.S. System Units of Capacity

As is true of units of length and weight, units of capacity can be added, subtracted, multiplied, and divided.

Example 3 Subtract 3 qt from 4 gal 2 qt.

Solution: To subtract, we line up similar units.

$$\begin{array}{r} 4\text{ gal }2\text{ qt} \\ -\quad 3\text{ qt} \\ \hline \end{array}$$

We cannot subtract 3 qt from 2 qt. We need to borrow 1 gallon from the 4 gallons, convert it to 4 quarts, and then combine it with the 2 quarts.

3 gal + (1 gal) 4 qt

$$\begin{array}{r} 4\text{ gal }2\text{ qt} \\ -\quad 3\text{ qt} \\ \hline \end{array} = \begin{array}{r} 3\text{ gal }6\text{ qt} \\ -\quad 3\text{ qt} \\ \hline 3\text{ gal }3\text{ qt} \end{array}$$

To check, see that the sum of 3 gal 3 qt and 3 qt is 4 gal 2 qt.

Work Practice 3

PRACTICE 3

Subtract 2 qt from 1 gal 1 qt.

Example 4 Divide 3 gal 2 qt by 2.

Solution: We divide each unit of capacity by 2.

$$\begin{array}{l} \quad\ 1\text{ gal}\quad 3\text{ qt} \\ 2\overline{)3\text{ gal}\quad 2\text{ qt}} \\ \ \ \underline{-2} \\ \quad\ 1\text{ gal} = 4\text{ qt} \\ \qquad\qquad\ \ 6\text{ qt} \end{array}$$

Convert 1 gallon to 4 qt and add to 2 qt before continuing.
6 qt ÷ 2 = 3 qt

Work Practice 4

PRACTICE 4

Divide 6 gal 3 qt by 2.

Answers

2. 104 c **3.** 3 qt **4.** 3 gal 1 qt 1 pt

✓ **Concept Check Answer**

less than 50

PRACTICE 5

A large oil drum contains 15 gal 3 qt of oil. How much will be in the drum if an additional 4 gal 3 qt of oil is poured into it?

Example 5 Finding the Amount of Water in an Aquarium

An aquarium contains 6 gal 3 qt of water. If 2 gal 2 qt of water is added, what is the total amount of water in the aquarium?

Solution:

beginning water	→	6 gal 3 qt
+ water added	→	+ 2 gal 2 qt
total water	→	8 gal 5 qt

Since 5 qt = 1 gal 1 qt, we have

$$\overbrace{8 \text{ gal}}^{8 \text{ gal}} \quad \overbrace{5 \text{ qt}}^{5 \text{ qt}}$$
$$= 8 \text{ gal} + 1 \text{ gal } 1 \text{ qt}$$
$$= 9 \text{ gal } 1 \text{ qt}$$

The total amount of water is 9 gal 1 qt.

Work Practice 5

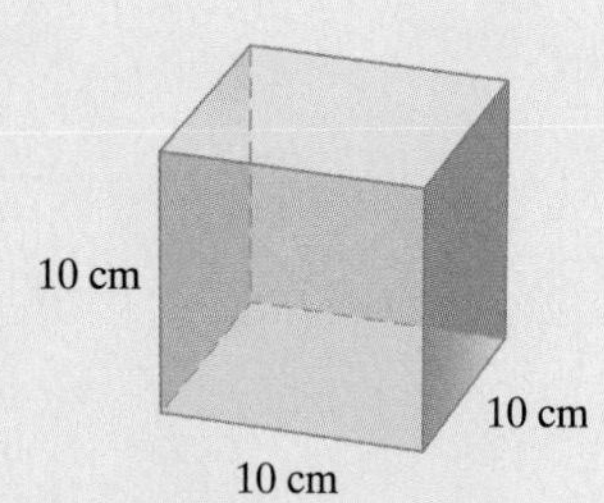

Objective C Defining and Converting Metric System Units of Capacity

Thus far, we know that the basic unit of length in the metric system is the meter and that the basic unit of mass in the metric system is the gram. What is the basic unit of capacity? The **liter.** By definition, a **liter** is the capacity or volume of a cube measuring 10 centimeters on each side.

The following examples may help you get a feeling for metric capacities:

One liter of liquid is slightly more than one quart.
Many soft drinks are packaged in 2-liter bottles.

The metric system was designed to be a consistent system. Once again, the prefixes for metric units of capacity are the same as for metric units of length and mass, as summarized in the following table:

2 liters

Metric Units of Capacity
1 **kilo**liter (kl) = 1000 liters (L)
1 **hecto**liter (hl) = 100 L
1 **deka**liter (dal) = 10 L
1 liter (L) = 1 L
1 **deci**liter (dl) = 1/10 L or 0.1 L
1 **centi**liter (cl) = 1/100 L or 0.01 L
1 **milli**liter (ml) = 1/1000 L or 0.001 L

The **milliliter** and the **liter** are the two most commonly used metric units of capacity.

Converting from one unit of capacity to another involves multiplying by powers of 10 or moving the decimal point to the left or to the right. Listing units of capacity in order from largest to smallest helps to keep track of how many places to move the decimal point when converting.

Let's convert 2.6 liters to milliliters. To convert from liters to milliliters, we move along the chart 3 units to the right.

kl hl dal **L** dl cl **ml**

3 units to the right

Answer

5. 20 gal 2 qt

This means that we move the decimal point 3 places to the right to convert from liters to milliliters.

$$2.600 \text{ L} = 2600. \text{ ml}$$

This same conversion can be done with unit fractions.

$$\begin{aligned} 2.6 \text{ L} &= \frac{2.6 \text{ L}}{1} \cdot 1 \\ &= \frac{2.6 \cancel{\text{L}}}{1} \cdot \frac{1000 \text{ ml}}{1 \cancel{\text{L}}} \\ &= 2.6 \cdot 1000 \text{ ml} \\ &= 2600 \text{ ml} \end{aligned}$$

To multiply by 1000, move the decimal point 3 places to the right.

To visualize the result, study the diagram below:

Thus, 2.6 L = 2600 ml.

Example 6 Convert 3210 ml to liters.

Solution: Let's use the unit fraction method first.

$$3210 \text{ ml} = \frac{3210 \text{ ml}}{1} \cdot 1 = 3210 \cancel{\text{ml}} \cdot \overbrace{\frac{1 \text{ L}}{1000 \cancel{\text{ml}}}}^{\text{Unit fraction}} = 3.21 \text{ L}$$

Now let's list the unit measures in order from left to right and move from milliliters to liters.

kl hl dal L dl cl ml

3 units to the left

3210 ml = 3.210 L, the same results as before and shown below in the diagram.

3 places to the left

Work Practice 6

PRACTICE 6

Convert 2100 ml to liters.

Answer

6. 2.1 L

PRACTICE 7

Convert 2.13 dal to liters.

Example 7 Convert 0.185 dl to milliliters.

Solution: We list the unit measures in order from left to right and move from deciliters to milliliters.

kl hl dal L dl cl ml

2 units to the right

0.185 dl = 18.5 ml

2 places to the right

Work Practice 7

Objective D Performing Operations on Metric System Units of Capacity

As was true for length and weight, arithmetic operations involving metric units of capacity can also be performed. Make sure that the metric units of capacity are the same before adding or subtracting.

PRACTICE 8

Add 1250 ml to 2.9 L.

Example 8 Add 2400 ml to 8.9 L.

Solution: We must convert both to liters or both to milliliters before adding the capacities together.

2400 ml = 2.4 L or 8.9 L = 8900 ml

$$\begin{array}{r} 2.4\text{ L} \\ +\ 8.9\text{ L} \\ \hline 11.3\text{ L} \end{array} \qquad \begin{array}{r} 2400\text{ ml} \\ +\ 8900\text{ ml} \\ \hline 11{,}300\text{ ml} \end{array}$$

The total is 11.3 L or 11,300 ml. They both represent the same capacity.

Work Practice 8

✓**Concept Check** How could you estimate the following operation? Subtract 950 ml from 7.5 L.

PRACTICE 9

If 28.6 L of water can be pumped every minute, how much water can be pumped in 85 minutes?

Example 9 Finding the Amount of Medication a Person Has Received

A patient hooked up to an IV unit in the hospital is to receive 12.5 ml of medication every hour. How much medication does the patient receive in 3.5 hours?

Solution: We multiply 12.5 ml by 3.5.

$$\begin{array}{rcr} \text{medication per hour} & \rightarrow & 12.5\text{ ml} \\ \times\quad\text{hours} & \rightarrow & \times\ 3.5 \\ \hline \text{total medication} & & 625 \\ & & 3750 \\ \hline & & 43.75\text{ ml} \end{array}$$

The patient receives 43.75 ml of medication.

Work Practice 9

Answers

7. 21.3 L **8.** 4150 ml or 4.15 L
9. 2431 L

✓ **Concept Check Answer**

950 ml = 0.95 L; round 0.95 to 1;
7.5 − 1 = 6.5 L

Vocabulary and Readiness Check

Use the choices below to fill in each blank. Some choices may be used more than once.

cups	pints	liter
quarts	fluid ounces	capacity

1. Units of ____________ are generally used to measure liquids.
2. The basic unit of capacity in the metric system is the ____________.
3. One cup equals 8 ____________.
4. One quart equals 2 ____________.
5. One pint equals 2 ____________.
6. One quart equals 4 ____________.
7. One gallon equals 4 ____________.

Convert as indicated without pencil or paper or calculator.

8. 2 c to pints **9.** 4 c to pints **10.** 4 qt to gallons **11.** 8 qt to gallons **12.** 2 pt to quarts

13. 6 pt to quarts **14.** 8 fl oz to cups **15.** 24 fl oz to cups **16.** 3 pt to cups

7.3 Exercise Set

FOR EXTRA HELP

Objective A *Convert each measurement as indicated. See Examples 1 and 2.*

1. 32 fluid ounces to cups **2.** 16 quarts to gallons **3.** 8 quarts to pints **4.** 9 pints to quarts

5. 14 quarts to gallons **6.** 11 cups to pints **7.** 80 fluid ounces to pints **8.** 18 pints to gallons

9. 2 quarts to cups **10.** 3 pints to fluid ounces **11.** 120 fluid ounces to quarts **12.** 20 cups to gallons

13. 42 cups to quarts **14.** 7 quarts to cups **15.** $4\frac{1}{2}$ pints to cups **16.** $6\frac{1}{2}$ gallons to quarts

17. 5 gal 3 qt to quarts **18.** 4 gal 1 qt to quarts **19.** $\frac{1}{2}$ cup to pints **20.** $\frac{1}{2}$ pint to quarts

21. 58 qt = _____ gal _____ qt **22.** 70 qt = _____ gal _____ qt

23. 39 pt = _____ gal _____ qt _____ pt **24.** 29 pt = _____ gal _____ qt _____ pt

25. $2\frac{3}{4}$ gallons to pints **26.** $3\frac{1}{4}$ quarts to cups

Objective **B** *Perform each indicated operation. See Examples 3 through 5.*

27. 5 gal 3 qt + 7 gal 3 qt

28. 2 gal 2 qt + 9 gal 3 qt

29. 1 c 5 fl oz + 2 c 7 fl oz

30. 2 c 3 fl oz + 2 c 6 fl oz

31. 3 gal − 1 gal 3 qt

32. 2 pt − 1 pt 1 c

33. 3 gal 1 qt − 1 qt 1 pt

34. 3 qt 1 c − 1 c 4 fl oz

35. 8 gal 2 qt × 2

36. 6 gal 1 pt × 2

37. 9 gal 2 qt ÷ 2

38. 5 gal 6 fl oz ÷ 2

Objective **C** *Convert as indicated. See Examples 6 and 7.*

39. 5 L to milliliters

40. 8 L to milliliters

41. 0.16 L to kiloliters

42. 0.127 L to kiloliters

43. 5600 ml to liters

44. 1500 ml to liters

45. 3.2 L to centiliters

46. 1.7 L to centiliters

47. 410 L to kiloliters

48. 250 L to kiloliters

49. 64 ml to liters

50. 39 ml to liters

51. 0.16 kl to liters

52. 0.48 kl to liters

53. 3.6 L to milliliters

54. 1.9 L to milliliters

Objective **D** *Perform each indicated operation. Remember to insert units when writing your answers. See Examples 8 and 9.*

55. 3.4 L + 15.9 L

56. 18.5 L + 4.6 L

57. 2700 ml + 1.8 L

58. 4.6 L + 1600 ml

59. 8.6 L − 190 ml

60. 4.8 L − 283 ml

61. 17,500 ml − 0.9 L

62. 6850 ml − 0.3 L

63. 480 ml × 8

64. 290 ml × 6

65. 81.2 L ÷ 0.5

66. 5.4 L ÷ 3.6

Objectives **A B C D** **Mixed Practice** *Solve. Remember to insert units when writing your answers. For Exercises 67 through 70, complete the chart. See Examples 1 through 9.*

	Capacity	Cups	Gallons	Quarts	Pints
67.	An average-size bath of water		21		
68.	A dairy cow's daily milk yield				38
69.	Your kidneys filter about this amount of blood every minute	4			
70.	The amount of water needed in a punch recipe	2			

71. Mike Schaferkotter drank 410 ml of Mountain Dew from a 2-liter bottle. How much Mountain Dew remains in the bottle?

72. The Werners' Volvo has a 54.5-L gas tank. Only 3.8 liters of gasoline still remain in the tank. How much is needed to fill it?

73. Margie Phitts added 354 ml of Prestone dry gas to the 18.6 L of gasoline in her car's tank. Find the total amount of gasoline in the tank.

74. Chris Peckaitis wishes to share a 2-L bottle of Coca-Cola equally with 7 of his friends. How much will each person get?

75. A garden tool engine requires a 30-to-1 gas-to-oil mixture. This means that $\frac{1}{30}$ of a gallon of oil should be mixed with 1 gallon of gas. Convert $\frac{1}{30}$ gallon to fluid ounces. Round to the nearest tenth.

76. Henning's Supermarket sells homemade soup in 1 qt 1 pt containers. How much soup is contained in three such containers?

77. Can 5 pt 1 c of fruit punch and 2 pt 1 c of ginger ale be poured into a 1-gal container without it overflowing?

78. Three cups of prepared Jell-O are poured into 6 dessert dishes. How many fluid ounces of Jell-O are in each dish?

79. Stanley Fisher paid $14 to fill his car with 44.3 liters of gasoline. Find the price per liter of gasoline to the nearest thousandth of a dollar.

80. A student carelessly misread the scale on a cylinder in the chemistry lab and added 40 cl of water to a mixture instead of 40 ml. Find the excess amount of water.

Review

Write each fraction in simplest form. See Section 2.3.

81. $\frac{20}{25}$ **82.** $\frac{75}{100}$ **83.** $\frac{27}{45}$ **84.** $\frac{56}{60}$ **85.** $\frac{72}{80}$ **86.** $\frac{18}{20}$

Concept Extensions

Determine whether the measurement in each statement is reasonable.

87. Clair took a dose of 2 L of cough medicine to cure her cough.

88. John drank 250 ml of milk for lunch.

89. Jeannie likes to relax in a tub filled with 3000 ml of hot water.

90. Sarah pumped 20 L of gasoline into her car yesterday.

Solve. See the Concept Checks in this section.

91. If 70 pints are converted to gallons, will the equivalent number of gallons be less than or greater than 70? Explain why.

92. If 30 gallons are converted to quarts, will the equivalent number of quarts be less than or greater than 30? Explain why.

93. Explain how to estimate the following operation: Add 986 ml to 6.9 L.

94. Explain how to borrow in order to subtract 1 gal 2 qt from 3 gal 1 qt.

95. Find the number of fluid ounces in 1 gallon.

96. Find the number of fluid ounces in 1.5 gallons.

A cubic centimeter (cc) is the amount of space that a volume of 1 ml occupies. Because of this, we will say that 1 cc = 1 ml.

A common syringe is one with a capacity of 3 cc. Use the diagram and give the measurement indicated by each arrow.

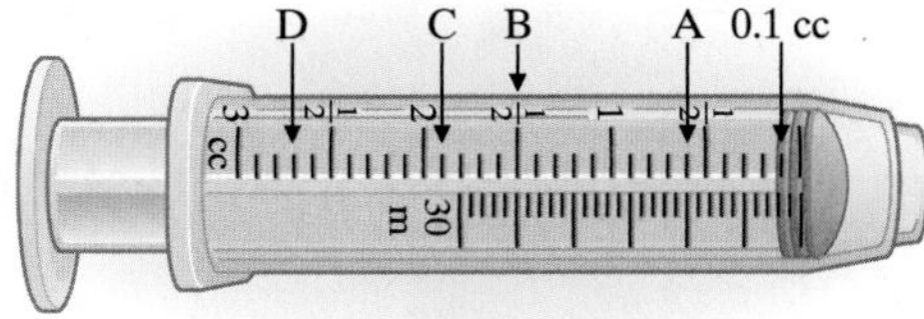

97. B **98.** A **99.** D **100.** C

In order to measure small dosages, such as for insulin, u-100 syringes are used. For these syringes, 1 cc has been divided into 100 equal units (u). Use the diagram and give the measurement indicated by each arrow in units (u) and then in cubic centimeters. Use 100 u = 1 cc.

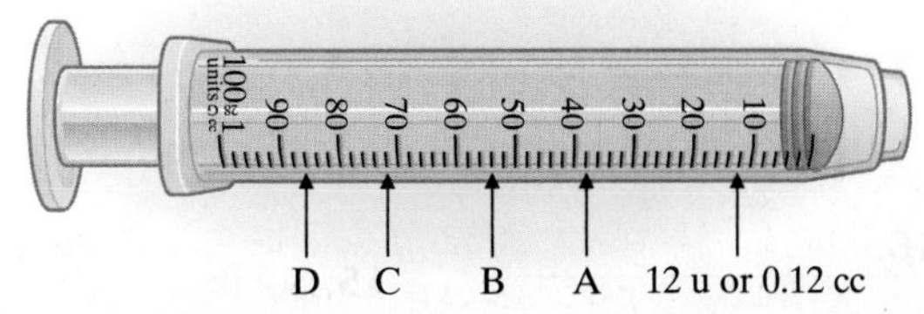

101. B **102.** A

103. D **104.** C

Answers

1. ______

2. ______

3. ______

4. ______

5. ______

6. ______

7. ______

8. ______

9. ______

10. ______

11. ______

12. ______

13. ______

14. ______

15. ______

16. ______

Integrated Review Sections 7.1–7.3

Length, Weight, and Capacity

Convert each measurement as indicated.

Length

1. 36 in. = _____ ft

2. 10,560 ft = _____ mi

3. 20 ft = _____ yd

4. $6\frac{1}{3}$ yd = _____ ft

5. 2.1 mi = _____ ft

6. 3.2 ft = _____ in.

7. 30 m = _____ cm

8. 24 mm = _____ cm

9. 2000 mm = _____ m

10. 1800 cm = _____ m

11. 7.2 cm = _____ mm

12. 600 m = _____ km

Weight or Mass

13. $7\frac{1}{2}$ tons = _____ lb

14. 11,000 lb = _____ tons

15. 8.5 lb = _____ oz

16. 72 oz = _____ lb

17. 104 oz = _____ lb

18. 5 lb = _____ oz

19. 28 kg = _____ g

20. 1400 mg = _____ g

21. 5.6 g = _____ kg

22. 6 kg = _____ g

23. 670 mg = _____ g

24. 3.6 g = _____ kg

Capacity

25. 6 qt = _____ pt

26. 5 pt = _____ qt

27. 14 qt = _____ gal

28. 17 c = _____ pt

29. $3\frac{1}{2}$ pt = _____ c

30. 26 qt = _____ gal

31. 7 L = _____ ml

32. 350 L = _____ kl

33. 47 ml = _____ L

34. 0.97 kl = _____ L

35. 0.126 kl = _____ L

36. 75 ml = _____ L

37. $\frac{1}{2}$ c = _____ fl oz

38. $\frac{3}{4}$ gal = _____ c

17. ______________

18. ______________

19. ______________

20. ______________

21. ______________

22. ______________

23. ______________

24. ______________

25. ______________

26. ______________

27. ______________

28. ______________

29. ______________

30. ______________

31. ______________

32. ______________

33. ______________

34. ______________

35. ______________

36. ______________

37. ______________

38. ______________

Objective

A **Convert Between the U.S. and Metric Systems.**

7.4 CONVERSIONS BETWEEN THE U.S. AND METRIC SYSTEMS

Objective A Converting Between the U.S. and Metric Systems

The metric system probably had its beginnings in France in the 1600s, but it was the Metric Act of 1866 that made the use of this system legal (but not mandatory) in the United States. Other laws have followed that allow for a slow, but deliberate, transfer to the modernized metric system. In April 2001, for example, the U.S. Stock Exchanges completed their change to decimal trading instead of fractions. By the end of 2009, all products sold in Europe (with some exceptions) were required to have only metric units on their labels. (*Source:* U.S. Metric Association and National Institute of Standards and Technology)

You may be surprised at the number of everyday items we use that are already manufactured in metric units. We easily recognize 1L and 2L soda bottles, but what about the following?

Pencil leads (0.5 mm or 0.7 mm)
Camera film (35 mm)
Sporting events (5-km or 10-km races)
Medicines (500-mg capsules)
Labels on retail goods (dual-labeled since 1994)

Since the United States has not completely converted to the metric system, we need to practice converting from one system to the other. Below is a table of mostly approximate conversions.

Length: 1 yard / 1 meter

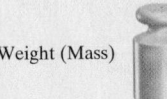

Capacity: 1 quart / 1 liter

Weight (Mass): 1 pound / 1 kilogram

Length:

Metric	U.S. System
1 m	≈ 1.09 yd
1 m	≈ 3.28 ft
1 km	≈ 0.62 mi
2.54 cm	= 1 in.
0.30 m	≈ 1 ft
1.61 km	≈ 1 mi

Capacity:

Metric	U.S. System
1 L	≈ 1.06 qt
1 L	≈ 0.26 gal
3.79 L	≈ 1 gal
0.95 L	≈ 1 qt
29.57 ml	≈ 1 fl oz

Weight (mass):

Metric	U.S. System
1 kg	≈ 2.20 lb
1 g	≈ 0.04 oz
0.45 kg	≈ 1 lb
28.35 g	≈ 1 oz

There are many ways to perform these metric-to-U.S. conversions. We will do so by using unit fractions.

PRACTICE 1

The center hole of a standard-sized compact disc is 1.5 centimeters in diameter. Convert this length to inches. Round the result to 2 decimal places.

Example 1 Compact Discs

Standard-sized compact discs are 12 centimeters in diameter. Convert this length to inches. Round the result to two decimal places. (*Source:* usByte.com)

Solution: From our length conversion table, we know that 2.54 cm = 1 in. This fact gives us two unit fractions: $\frac{2.54\text{ cm}}{1\text{ in.}}$ and $\frac{1\text{ in.}}{2.54\text{ cm}}$. We use the unit fraction with cm in the denominator so that these units divide out.

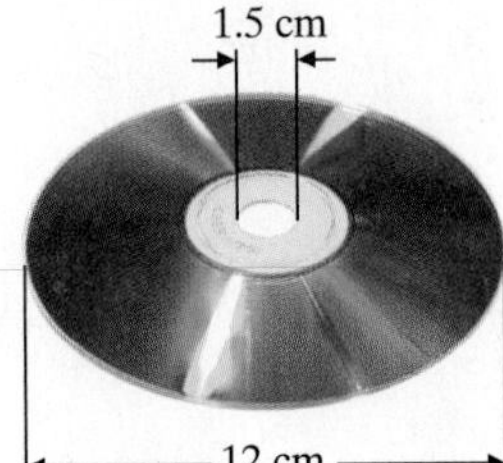

$$12\text{ cm} = \frac{12\text{ cm}}{1}\cdot 1 = \frac{12\text{ }\cancel{\text{cm}}}{1}\cdot\overbrace{\frac{1\text{ in.}}{2.54\text{ }\cancel{\text{cm}}}}^{\text{Unit fraction}}\begin{array}{l}\leftarrow\text{Units to convert to}\\ \leftarrow\text{Original units}\end{array}$$

$$= \frac{12\text{ in.}}{2.54}$$

$$\approx 4.72\text{ in.}\quad\text{Divide.}$$

Answer
1. 0.59 in.

Thus, the diameter of a standard compact disc is exactly 12 cm or approximately 4.72 inches. For a dimension this size, you can use a ruler to check. Another method is to approximate. Our result, 4.72 in., is close to 5 inches. Since 1 in. is about 2.5 cm, then 5 in. is about 5(2.5 cm) = 12.5 cm, which is close to 12 cm.

Work Practice 1

Example 2 Liver

The liver is your largest internal organ. It weighs about 3.5 pounds in a grown man. Convert this weight to kilograms. Round to the nearest tenth. (*Source: Some Body!* by Dr. Pete Rowan)

Solution: $3.5 \text{ lb} \approx \frac{3.5 \text{ lb}}{1} \cdot \overbrace{\frac{0.45 \text{ kg}}{1 \text{ lb}}}^{\text{Unit fraction}} = 3.5(0.45 \text{ kg}) \approx 1.6 \text{ kg}$

Thus 3.5 pounds are approximately 1.6 kilograms. From the table of conversions, we know that 1 kg ≈ 2.2 lb. So that means 0.5 kg ≈ 1.1 lb and after adding, we have 1.5 kg ≈ 3.3 lb. Our result is reasonable.

Work Practice 2

PRACTICE 2

A full-grown human heart weighs about 8 ounces. Convert this weight to grams. If necessary, round your result to the nearest tenth of a gram.

Example 3 Postage Stamp

Australia converted to the metric system in 1973. In that year, four postage stamps were issued to publicize this conversion. One such stamp is shown. Let's check the mathematics on the stamp by converting 7 fluid ounces to milliliters. Round to the nearest hundred.

Solution: $7 \text{ fl oz} \approx \frac{7 \text{ fl oz}}{1} \cdot \overbrace{\frac{29.57 \text{ ml}}{1 \text{ fl oz}}}^{\text{Unit fraction}} = 7(29.57 \text{ ml}) = 206.99 \text{ ml}$

Rounded to the nearest hundred, 7 fl oz ≈ 200 ml.

Work Practice 3

PRACTICE 3

Convert 237 ml to fluid ounces. Round to the nearest whole fluid ounce.

Answers

2. 226.8 g **3.** 8 fl oz

7.4 Exercise Set

Note: Because approximations are used, your answers may vary slightly from the answers given in the back of the book.

Objective A *Convert as indicated. If necessary, round answers to two decimal places. See Examples 1 through 3.*

1. 756 milliliters to fluid ounces

2. 18 liters to quarts

3. 86 inches to centimeters

4. 86 miles to kilometers

5. 1000 grams to ounces

6. 100 kilograms to pounds

7. 93 kilometers to miles

8. 9.8 meters to feet

9. 14.5 liters to gallons

10. 150 milliliters to fluid ounces

11. 30 pounds to kilograms

12. 15 ounces to grams

Fill in the chart. Give exact answers or round to 1 decimal place. See Examples 1 through 3.

		Meters	Yards	Centimeters	Feet	Inches
13.	The height of a woman				5	
14.	Statue of Liberty length of nose	1.37				
15.	Leaning Tower of Pisa		60			
16.	Blue whale		36			

Solve. If necessary, round answers to two decimal places. See Examples 1 through 3.

17. The balance beam for female gymnasts is 10 centimeters wide. Convert this width to inches.

18. In men's gymnastics, the rings are 250 centimeters from the floor. Convert this height to inches, then to feet.

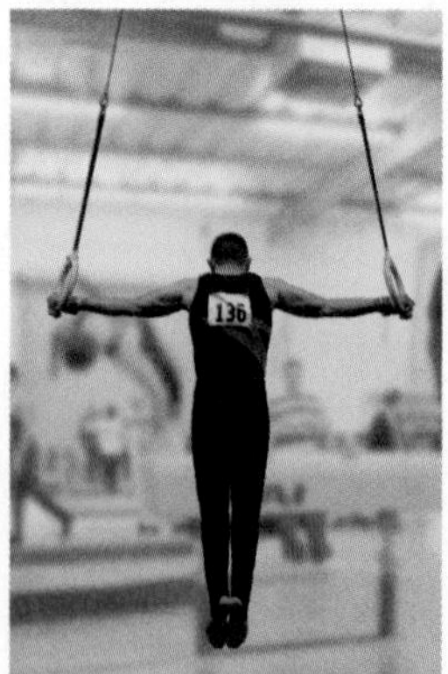

19. In many states, the maximum speed limit for recreational vehicles is 50 miles per hour. Convert this to kilometers per hour.

20. In some states, the speed limit is 70 miles per hour. Convert this to kilometers per hour.

21. Ibuprofen comes in 200-milligram tablets. Convert this to ounces. (Round your answer to this exercise to 3 decimal places.)

22. Vitamin C tablets come in 500-milligram caplets. Convert this to ounces.

23. A stone is a unit in the British customary system. Use the conversion 14 pounds = 1 stone to check the equivalencies in this 1973 Australian stamp. Is 100 kilograms approximately 15 stone 10 pounds?

24. Convert 5 feet 11 inches to centimeters and check the conversion on this 1973 Australian stamp. Is it correct?

25. The Monarch butterfly migrates annually between the northern United States and central Mexico. The trip is about 4500 km long. Convert this to miles.

26. There is a species of African termite that builds nests up to 18 ft high. Convert this to meters.

27. A $3\frac{1}{2}$-inch diskette is not really $3\frac{1}{2}$ inches. To find its actual width, convert this measurement to centimeters, then to millimeters. Round the result to the nearest ten.

28. The average two-year-old is 84 centimeters tall. Convert this to feet and inches.

29. For an average adult, the weight of the right lung is greater than the weight of the left lung. If the right lung weighs 1.5 pounds and the left lung weighs 1.25 pounds, find the difference in grams. (*Source: Some Body!*)

30. The skin of an average adult weighs 9 pounds and is the heaviest organ. Find the weight in grams. (*Source: Some Body!*)

31. A fast sneeze has been clocked at about 167 kilometers per hour. Convert this to miles per hour. Round to the nearest whole.

32. A Boeing 747 has a cruising speed of about 980 kilometers per hour. Convert this to miles per hour. Round to the nearest whole.

33. The General Sherman giant sequoia tree has a diameter of about 8 meters at its base. Convert this to feet. (*Source: Fantastic Book of Comparisons*)

34. The largest crater on the near side of the moon is Billy Crater. It has a diameter of 303 kilometers. Convert this to miles. (*Source: Fantastic Book of Comparisons*)

35. The total length of the track on a CD is about 4.5 kilometers. Convert this to miles. Round to the nearest whole mile.

36. The distance between Mackinaw City, Michigan, and Cheyenne, Wyoming, is 2079 kilometers. Convert this to miles. Round to the nearest whole mile.

37. A doctor orders a dosage of 5 ml of medicine every 4 hours for 1 week. How many fluid ounces of medicine should be purchased? Round up to the next whole fluid ounce.

38. A doctor orders a dosage of 12 ml of medicine every 6 hours for 10 days. How many fluid ounces of medicine should be purchased? Round up to the next whole fluid ounce.

Without actually converting, choose the most reasonable answer.

39. This math book has a height of about _____.

a. 28 mm **b.** 28 cm
c. 28 m **d.** 28 km

40. A mile is _____ a kilometer.

a. shorter than **b.** longer than
c. the same length as

41. A liter has _____ capacity than a quart.

a. less **b.** greater
c. the same

42. A foot is _____ a meter.

a. shorter than **b.** longer than
c. the same length as

43. A kilogram weighs _____ a pound.

a. the same as **b.** less than
c. greater than

44. A football field is 100 yards, which is about _____.

a. 9 m **b.** 90 m
c. 900 m **d.** 9000 m

45. An $8\frac{1}{2}$-ounce glass of water has a capacity of about _____.

a. 250 L **b.** 25 L
c. 2.5 L **d.** 250 ml

46. A 5-gallon gasoline can has a capacity of about _____.

a. 19 L **b.** 1.9 L
c. 19 ml **d.** 1.9 ml

47. The weight of an average man is about _____.

a. 700 kg **b.** 7 kg
c. 0.7 kg **d.** 70 kg

48. The weight of a pill is about _____.

a. 200 kg **b.** 20 kg
c. 2 kg **d.** 200 mg

Review

Perform the indicated operations. See Section 1.9.

49. $6 \cdot 4 + 5 \div 1$

50. $10 \div 2 + 9(8)$

51. $\frac{10 + 8}{10 - 8}$

52. $\frac{14 + 1}{5(3)}$

53. $3 + 5(19 - 17) - 8$

54. $1 + 4(19 - 9) + 5$

55. $3[(1 + 5) \cdot (8 - 6)]$

56. $5[(18 - 8) - 9]$

Concept Extensions

Body surface area (BSA) is often used to calculate dosages for some drugs. BSA is calculated in square meters using a person's weight and height.

$$\text{BSA} = \sqrt{\frac{(\text{weight in kg}) \times (\text{height in cm})}{3600}}$$

For Exercises 57 through 62, calculate the BSA for each person. Round to the nearest hundredth. You will need to use the square root key on your calculator.

57. An adult whose height is 182 cm and weight is 90 kg.

58. An adult whose height is 157 cm and weight is 63 kg.

59. A child whose height is 40 in. and weight is 50 kg. (*Hint:* Don't forget to first convert inches to centimeters)

60. A child whose height is 26 in. and weight is 13 kg.

61. An adult whose height is 60 in. and weight is 150 lb.

62. An adult whose height is 69 in. and weight is 172 lb.

Solve.

63. Suppose the adult from Exercise 57 is to receive a drug that has a recommended dosage range of 10–12 mg per sq meter. Find the dosage range for the adult.

64. Suppose the child from Exercise 60 is to receive a drug that has a recommended dosage of 30 mg per sq meter. Find the dosage for the child.

65. A handball court is a rectangle that measures 20 meters by 40 meters. Find its area in square meters and square feet.

66. A backpack measures 16 inches by 13 inches by 5 inches. Find the volume of a box with these dimensions. Find the volume in cubic inches and cubic centimeters. Round the cubic centimeters to the nearest whole cubic centimeter.

Objectives

A **Convert Temperatures from Degrees Celsius to Degrees Fahrenheit.**

B **Convert Temperatures from Degrees Fahrenheit to Degrees Celsius.**

7.5 TEMPERATURE: U.S. AND METRIC SYSTEMS OF MEASUREMENT

When Gabriel Fahrenheit and Anders Celsius independently established units for temperature scales, each based his unit on the heat of water the moment it boils compared to the moment it freezes. One degree Celsius is 1/100 of the difference in heat. One degree Fahrenheit is 1/180 of the difference in heat. Celsius arbitrarily labeled the temperature at the freezing point at 0°C, making the boiling point 100°C; Fahrenheit labeled the freezing point 32°F, making the boiling point 212°F. Water boils at 212°F and 100°C.

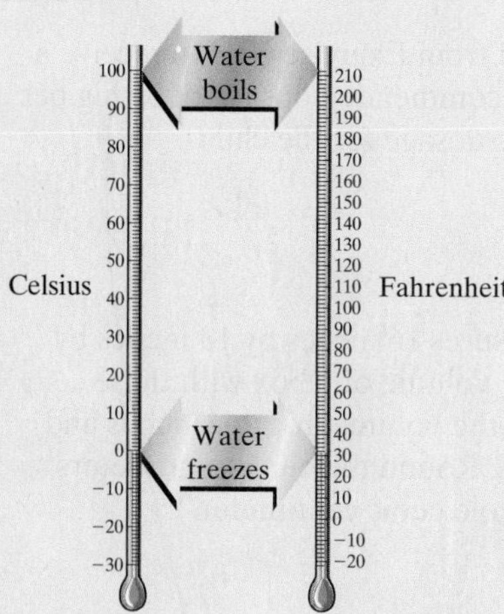

By comparing the two scales in the figure, we see that a 20°C day is as warm as a 68°F day. Similarly, a sweltering 104°F day in the Mojave Desert corresponds to a 40°C day.

✓Concept Check Which of the following statements is correct? Explain.

a. 6°C is below the freezing point of water.

b. 6°F is below the freezing point of water.

Objective A Converting Degrees Celsius to Degrees Fahrenheit

To convert from Celsius temperatures to Fahrenheit temperatures, we can use either of the equations in the box below.

Converting Celsius to Fahrenheit

$$F = \frac{9}{5} \cdot C + 32 \quad \text{or} \quad F = 1.8 \cdot C + 32$$

(To convert to Fahrenheit temperature, multiply the Celsius temperature by $\frac{9}{5}$ or 1.8, and then add 32.)

In these equations, we use the symbol F to represent degrees Fahrenheit and the symbol C to represent degrees Celsius.

PRACTICE 1

Convert 50°C to degrees Fahrenheit.

Example 1 Convert 15°C to degrees Fahrenheit.

Solution:

$$\begin{aligned} F &= \frac{9}{5} \cdot C + 32 \\ &= \frac{9}{5} \cdot 15 + 32 && \text{Replace C with 15.} \\ &= 27 + 32 && \text{Simplify.} \\ &= 59 && \text{Add.} \end{aligned}$$

Thus, 15°C is equivalent to 59°F.

Work Practice 1

PRACTICE 2

Convert 18°C to degrees Fahrenheit.

Example 2 Convert 29°C to degrees Fahrenheit.

Solution:

$$\begin{aligned} F &= 1.8 \cdot C + 32 \\ &= 1.8 \cdot 29 + 32 && \text{Replace C with 29.} \\ &= 52.2 + 32 && \text{Multiply 1.8 by 29.} \\ &= 84.2 && \text{Add.} \end{aligned}$$

Therefore, 29°C is the same as 84.2°F.

Work Practice 2

Answers

1. 122°F **2.** 64.4°F

✓ Concept Check Answer

b

Objective B Converting Degrees Fahrenheit to Degrees Celsius

To convert from Fahrenheit temperatures to Celsius temperatures, see the box below. The symbol C represents degrees Celsius and the symbol F represents degrees Fahrenheit.

Converting Fahrenheit to Celsius

$$C = \frac{5}{9}(F - 32)$$

(To convert to Celsius temperature, subtract 32 from the Fahrenheit temperature, and then multiply by $\frac{5}{9}$.)

Example 3 Convert 59°F to degrees Celsius.

Solution: We evaluate the formula $C = \frac{5}{9}(F - 32)$ when F is 59.

$C = \frac{5}{9}(F - 32)$

$= \frac{5}{9} \cdot (59 - 32)$ Replace F with 59.

$= \frac{5}{9} \cdot (27)$ Subtract inside parentheses.

$= 15$ Multiply.

Therefore, 59°F is the same temperature as 15°C.

Work Practice 3

(Compare the results of Examples 1 and 3.)

Example 4 Convert 114°F to degrees Celsius. If necessary, round to the nearest tenth of a degree.

Solution: $C = \frac{5}{9}(F - 32)$

$= \frac{5}{9}(114 - 32)$ Replace F with 114.

$= \frac{5}{9} \cdot (82)$ Subtract inside parentheses.

≈ 45.6 Multiply.

Therefore, 114°F is approximately 45.6°C.

Work Practice 4

PRACTICE 3

Convert 68°F to degrees Celsius.

PRACTICE 4

Convert 113°F to degrees Celsius. If necessary, round to the nearest tenth of a degree.

Answers

3. 20°C **4.** 45°C

PRACTICE 5

During a bout with the flu, Albert's temperature reaches 102.8°F. What is his temperature measured in degrees Celsius? Round to the nearest tenth of a degree.

Example 5 Body Temperature

Normal body temperature is 98.6°F. What is this temperature in degrees Celsius?

Solution: We evaluate the formula $C = \frac{5}{9}(F - 32)$ when F is 98.6.

$$C = \frac{5}{9}(F - 32)$$

$$= \frac{5}{9}(98.6 - 32) \quad \text{Replace F with 98.6.}$$

$$= \frac{5}{9} \cdot (66.6) \quad \text{Subtract inside parentheses.}$$

$$= 37 \quad \text{Multiply.}$$

Therefore, normal body temperature is 37°C.

Work Practice 5

✓**Concept Check** Clarissa must convert 40°F to degrees Celsius. What is wrong with her work shown below?

$F = 1.8 \cdot C + 32$
$F = 1.8 \cdot 40 + 32$
$F = 72 + 32$
$F = 104$

Answer

5. 39.3°C

✓ **Concept Check Answer**

She used the conversion for Celsius to Fahrenheit instead of Fahrenheit to Celsius.

7.5 Exercise Set

Objectives A B Mixed Practice *Convert as indicated. When necessary, round to the nearest tenth of a degree. See Examples 1 through 5.*

1. 41°F to degrees Celsius

2. 68°F to degrees Celsius

3. 104°F to degrees Celsius

4. 77°F to degrees Celsius

5. 60°C to degrees Fahrenheit

6. 80°C to degrees Fahrenheit

7. 115°C to degrees Fahrenheit

8. 35°C to degrees Fahrenheit

9. 62°F to degrees Celsius

10. 182°F to degrees Celsius

11. 142.1°F to degrees Celsius

12. 43.4°F to degrees Celsius

13. 92°C to degrees Fahrenheit

14. 75°C to degrees Fahrenheit

15. 16.3°C to degrees Fahrenheit

16. 48.6°C to degrees Fahrenheit

17. The hottest temperature ever recorded in New Mexico was 122°F. Convert this temperature to degrees Celsius. (*Source:* National Climatic Data Center)

18. The hottest temperature ever recorded in Rhode Island was 104°F. Convert this temperature to degrees Celsius. (*Source:* National Climatic Data Center)

19. A weather forecaster in Caracas predicts a high temperature of 27°C. Find this measurement in degrees Fahrenheit.

20. While driving to work, Alan Olda notices a temperature of 22°C flash on the local bank's temperature display. Find the corresponding temperature in degrees Fahrenheit.

21. Water boils at 212°F. Find this temperature in degrees Celsius.

22. Water freezes at 0°C. Find this temperature in degrees Fahrenheit.

23. Najib Tan is running a fever of 100.2°F. Find his temperature as it would be shown on a Celsius thermometer.

24. William Saylor generally has a subnormal temperature of 98.2°F. Find what this temperature would be on a Celsius thermometer.

25. In a European cookbook, a recipe requires the ingredients for caramels to be heated to 118°C, but the cook has access only to a Fahrenheit thermometer. Find the temperature in degrees Fahrenheit that should be used to make the caramels.

26. The ingredients for divinity should be heated to 127°C, but the candy thermometer that Myung Kim has is calibrated to degrees Fahrenheit. Find how hot he should heat the ingredients.

27. The surface temperature of Venus can reach 864°F. Find this temperature in degrees Celsius.

28. The temperature of Earth's core is estimated to be 4000°C. Find the corresponding temperature in degrees Fahrenheit.

29. At Mack Trucks' headquarters, the room temperature is to be set at 70°F, but the thermostat is calibrated in degrees Celsius. Find the temperature to be set.

30. The computer room at Merck, Sharp, and Dohm is normally cooled to 66°F. Find the corresponding temperature in degrees Celsius.

Review

Find the perimeter of each figure. Recall that the perimeter of a figure is the distance around the figure. See Section 1.3.

△ **31.**

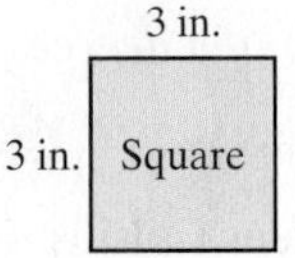

△ **32.**

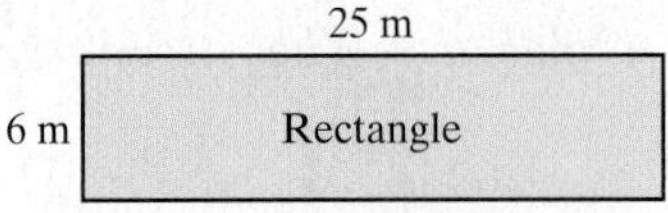

△ **33.**

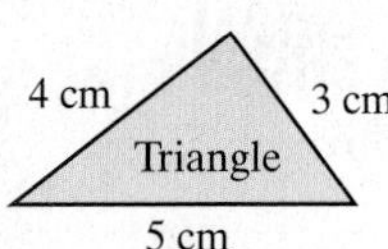

△ **34.**

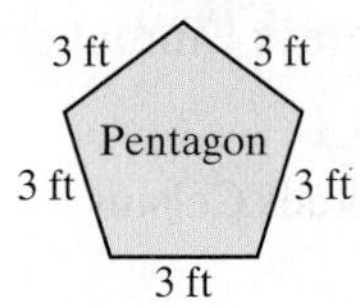

△ **35.**

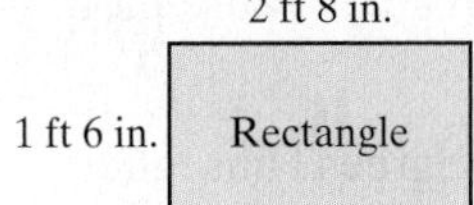

△ **36.**

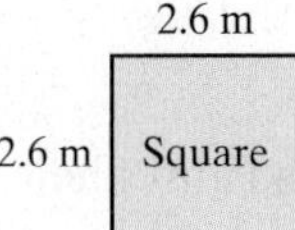

Concept Extensions

Solve. See the first Concept Check in this section. True or False.

37. 10°F is above the freezing point of water.

38. 10°C is above the freezing point of water.

39. 102°C is above the boiling point of water.

40. 102°F is above the boiling point of water.

41. On July 19, 1996, at the Naka Fusion Research Establishment in Nakamachi, Ibaraki, Japan, the highest temperature produced in a laboratory was achieved. This temperature was approximately 936,000,000°F. Convert this temperature to degrees Celsius. (*Note:* This is almost 30 times the temperature at the center of the sun.) (*Source: Guinness Book of Records*)

42. The hottest-burning substance known is carbon subnitride. Its flame at one atmospheric pressure reaches 9010°F. Convert this temperature to degrees Celsius. (*Source: Guinness Book of Records*)

Determine whether the measurement in each statement is reasonable by answering yes or no.

43. A 72°F room feels comfortable.

44. Water heated to 110°F will boil.

45. Josiah has a fever if a thermometer shows his temperature to be 40°F.

46. An air temperature of 20°F on a Vermont ski slope can be expected in the winter.

47. When the temperature is 30°C outside, an overcoat is needed.

48. An air-conditioned room at 60°C feels quite chilly.

49. Barbara has a fever when a thermometer records her temperature at 40°C.

50. Water cooled to 32°C will freeze.

51. In your own words, describe how to convert from degrees Celsius to degrees Fahrenheit.

52. In your own words, describe how to convert from degrees Fahrenheit to degrees Celsius.

Chapter 7 Group Activity

Speeds

Section 7.1

A speed measures how far something travels in a given unit of time. You already learned in Section 5.2 that the speed 55 miles per hour is a rate that can be written as $\frac{55 \text{ miles}}{1 \text{ hour}}$. Just as there are different units of measurement for length or distance, there are different units of measurement for speed as well. It is also possible to perform unit conversions on speeds. Before we learn about converting speeds, we will review units of time. The following is a summary of equivalencies between various units of time.

Units of Time	Unit Fractions
60 seconds (s) = 1 minute (min)	$\frac{60 \text{ s}}{1 \text{ min}} = \frac{1 \text{ min}}{60 \text{ s}} = 1$
60 minutes = 1 hour (h)	$\frac{60 \text{ min}}{1 \text{ h}} = \frac{1 \text{ h}}{60 \text{ min}} = 1$
3600 seconds = 1 hour	$\frac{3600 \text{ s}}{1 \text{ h}} = \frac{1 \text{ h}}{3600 \text{ s}}$

Here are some common speeds.

Speeds

Miles per hour (mph)
Miles per minute (mi/min)
Miles per second (mi/s)
Feet per second (ft/s)
Feet per minute (ft/min)
Kilometers per hour (kmph or km/h)
Kilometers per second (kmps or km/s)
Meters per second (m/s)
Knots

To convert from one speed to another, unit fractions may be used. To convert from mph to ft/s first write the original speed as a unit rate. Then multiply by a unit fraction that relates miles to feet and by a unit fraction that relates hours to seconds. The unit fractions should be written so that like units will divide out. For example, to convert 55 mph to ft/s:

$$\begin{aligned} 55 \text{ mph} &= \frac{55 \text{ miles}}{1 \text{ hour}} = \frac{55 \cancel{\text{miles}}}{1 \cancel{\text{hour}}} \cdot \frac{5280 \text{ ft}}{1 \cancel{\text{mile}}} \cdot \frac{1 \cancel{\text{hour}}}{3600 \text{ s}} \\ &= \frac{55 \cdot 5280 \text{ ft}}{3600 \text{ s}} \\ &= \frac{290{,}400 \text{ ft}}{3600 \text{ s}} \\ &= 80\frac{2}{3} \text{ ft/s} \end{aligned}$$

Group Activity

1. Research the current world land speed record. Convert the speed from mph to feet per second.
2. Research the current world water speed record. Convert from mph to knots.
3. Research and then describe the Beaufort Wind Scale, its origins, and how it is used. Give the scale keyed to both miles per hour and knots. Why would both measures be useful?

Helpful Hint

A **knot** is 1 nautical mile per hour and is a measure of speed used for ships.

1 nautical mile (nmi) ≈ 1.15 miles (mi)

1 nautical mile (nmi) ≈ 6076.12 feet (ft)

Chapter 7 Vocabulary Check

Fill in each blank with one of the words or phrases listed below.

mass	unit fractions	gram	energy	weight
meter	liter	calorie	British Thermal Unit	

1. ________________ is a measure of the pull of gravity.
2. ________________ is a measure of the amount of substance in an object. This measure does not change.
3. The basic unit of length in the metric system is the ________________.
4. To convert from one unit of length to another, ________________ may be used.
5. A(n) ________________ is the basic unit of mass in the metric system.
6. ________________ is the capacity to do work.
7. In the U.S. system of measurement, a(n) ________________ is the amount of heat required to raise the temperature of 1 pound of water 1 degree Fahrenheit.
8. The ________________ is the basic unit of capacity in the metric system.
9. In the metric system, a(n) ________________ is the amount of heat required to raise the temperature of 1 kilogram of water 1 degree Celsius.

Helpful Hint Are you preparing for your test? Don't forget to take the Chapter 7 Test on page 503. Then check your answers at the back of the text and use the Chapter Test Prep Videos to see the fully worked-out solutions to any of the exercises you want to review.

7 Chapter Highlights

Definitions and Concepts	Examples

Section 7.1 Length: U.S. and Metric Systems of Measurement

Definitions and Concepts

To convert from one unit of length to another, multiply by a **unit fraction** in the form

$$\frac{\text{units to convert to}}{\text{original units}}.$$

LENGTH: U.S. SYSTEM OF MEASUREMENT

12 inches (in.) = 1 foot (ft)

3 feet = 1 yard (yd)

5280 feet = 1 mile (mi)

The basic unit of length in the metric system is the **meter.** A meter is slightly longer than a yard.

LENGTH: METRIC SYSTEM OF MEASUREMENT

Metric Unit of Length
1 **kilo**meter (km) = 1000 meters (m)
1 **hecto**meter (hm) = 100 m
1 **deka**meter (dam) = 10 m
1 meter (m) = 1 m
1 **deci**meter (dm) = 1/10 m or 0.1 m
1 **centi**meter (cm) = 1/100 m or 0.01 m
1 **milli**meter (mm) = 1/1000 m or 0.001 m

Examples

$$\frac{12 \text{ inches}}{1 \text{ foot}}, \frac{1 \text{ foot}}{12 \text{ inches}}, \frac{3 \text{ feet}}{1 \text{ yard}}$$

Convert 6 feet to inches.

$$\begin{aligned} 6 \text{ ft} &= \frac{6 \text{ ft}}{1} \cdot 1 \\ &= \frac{6 \cancel{\text{ft}}}{1} \cdot \frac{12 \text{ in.}}{1 \cancel{\text{ft}}} \quad \begin{matrix} \leftarrow \text{units to convert to} \\ \leftarrow \text{original units} \end{matrix} \\ &= 6 \cdot 12 \text{ in.} \\ &= 72 \text{ in.} \end{aligned}$$

Convert 3650 centimeters to meters.

$$\begin{aligned} 3650 \text{ cm} &= 3650 \text{ cm} \cdot 1 \\ &= \frac{3650 \cancel{\text{cm}}}{1} \cdot \frac{0.01 \text{ m}}{1 \cancel{\text{cm}}} = 36.5 \text{ m} \end{aligned}$$

or

km hm dam m dm cm mm

2 units to the left

3650 cm = 36.5 m

2 places to the left

Definitions and Concepts	Examples

Section 7.2 Weight and Mass: U.S. and Metric Systems of Measurement

Weight is really a measure of the pull of gravity. **Mass** is a measure of the amount of substance in an object and does not change.

WEIGHT: U.S. SYSTEM OF MEASUREMENT

16 ounces (oz) = 1 pound (1b)

2000 pounds = 1 ton

Convert 5 pounds to ounces.

$$5 \text{ lb} = 5 \text{ lb} \cdot 1 = \frac{5 \cancel{\text{lb}}}{1} \cdot \frac{16 \text{ oz}}{1 \cancel{\text{lb}}} = 80 \text{ oz}$$

A **gram** is the basic unit of mass in the metric system. It is the mass of water contained in a cube 1 centimeter on each side. A paper clip weighs about 1 gram.

MASS: METRIC SYSTEM OF MEASUREMENT

Metric Unit of Mass
1 kilogram (kg) = 1000 grams (g)
1 hectogram (hg) = 100 g
1 dekagram (dag) = 10 g
1 gram (g) = 1 g
1 decigram (dg) = 1/10 g or 0.1 g
1 centigram (cg) = 1/100 g or 0.01 g
1 milligram (mg) = 1/1000 g or 0.001 g

Convert 260 grams to kilograms.

$$260 \text{ g} = \frac{260 \text{ g}}{1} \cdot 1 = \frac{260 \cancel{\text{g}}}{1} \cdot \frac{1 \text{ kg}}{1000 \cancel{\text{g}}} = 0.26 \text{ kg}$$

or

kg hg dag g dg cg mg

3 units to the left

260 g = 0.260 kg

3 places to the left

Section 7.3 Capacity: U.S. and Metric Systems of Measurement

CAPACITY: U.S. SYSTEM OF MEASUREMENT

8 fluid ounces (fl oz) = 1 cup (c)

2 cups = 1 pint (pt)

2 pints = 1 quart (qt)

4 quarts = 1 gallon (gal)

Convert 5 pints to gallons.

1 gal = 4 qt = 8 pt

$$5 \text{ pt} = 5 \text{ pt} \cdot 1 = \frac{5 \cancel{\text{pt}}}{1} \cdot \frac{1 \text{ gal}}{8 \cancel{\text{pt}}} = \frac{5}{8} \text{ gal}$$

The **liter** is the basic unit of capacity in the metric system. It is the capacity or volume of a cube measuring 10 centimeters on each side. A liter of liquid is slightly more than 1 quart.

CAPACITY: METRIC SYSTEM OF MEASUREMENT

Metric Unit of Capacity
1 kiloliter (kl) = 1000 liters (L)
1 hectoliter (hl) = 100 L
1 dekaliter (dal) = 10 L
1 liter (L) = 1 L
1 deciliter (dl) = 1/10 L or 0.1 L
1 centiliter (cl) = 1/100 L or 0.01 L
1 milliliter (ml) = 1/1000 L or 0.001 L

Convert 1.5 liters to milliliters.

$$1.5 \text{ L} = \frac{1.5 \text{ L}}{1} \cdot 1 = \frac{1.5 \cancel{\text{L}}}{1} \cdot \frac{1000 \text{ ml}}{1 \cancel{\text{L}}} = 1500 \text{ ml}$$

or

kl hl dal L dl cl ml

3 units to the right

1.500 L = 1500 ml

3 places to the right

Definitions and Concepts	Examples
Section 7.4 Conversions Between the U.S. and Metric Systems	
To convert between systems, use approximate unit fractions from Section 7.4.	Convert 7 feet to meters. $7\text{ ft} \approx \frac{7\text{ ft}}{1} \cdot \frac{0.30\text{ m}}{1\text{ ft}} = 2.1\text{ m}$ Convert 8 liters to quarts. $8\text{ L} \approx \frac{8\text{ L}}{1} \cdot \frac{1.06\text{ qt}}{1\text{ L}} = 8.48\text{ qt}$ Convert 363 grams to ounces. $363\text{ g} \approx \frac{363\text{ g}}{1} \cdot \frac{0.04\text{ oz}}{1\text{ g}} = 14.52\text{ oz}$
Section 7.5 Temperature: U.S. and Metric Systems of Measurement	
TO CONVERT FROM CELSIUS TEMPERATURE TO FAHRENHEIT TEMPERATURE $F = \frac{9}{5} \cdot C + 32$ or $F = 1.8 \cdot C + 32$	Convert 35°C to degrees Fahrenheit. $F = \frac{9}{5} \cdot 35 + 32 = 63 + 32 = 95$ 35°C = 95°F
TO CONVERT FROM FAHRENHEIT TEMPERATURE TO CELSIUS TEMPERATURE $C = \frac{5}{9} \cdot (F - 32)$	Convert 50°F to degrees Celsius. $C = \frac{5}{9} \cdot (50 - 32) = \frac{5}{9} \cdot 18 = 10$ 50°F = 10°C

Chapter 7 Review

(7.1) *Convert.*

1. 108 in. to feet

2. 72 ft to yards

3. 1.5 mi to feet

4. $\frac{1}{2}$ yd to inches

5. 52 ft = _____yd _____ft

6. _____ft _____in.

7. 42 m to centimeters

8. 82 cm to millimeters

9. 12.18 mm to meters

10. 2.31 m to kilometers

Perform each indicated operation.

11. 4 yd 2 ft + 16 yd 2 ft

12. 12 ft 1 in. − 4 ft 8 in.

13. 8 ft 3 in. × 5

14. 7 ft 4 in. ÷ 2

15. 8 cm + 15 mm

16. 4 m − 126 cm

17. 8.62 m × 4

18. 19.6 km ÷ 8

Solve.

19. A bolt of cloth contains 333 yd 1 ft of cotton ticking. Find the amount of material that remains after 163 yd 2 ft is removed from the bolt.

20. The local ambulance corps plans to award 20 framed certificates of valor to some of its outstanding members. If each frame requires 6 ft 4 in. of framing material, how much material is needed for all the frames?

21. The trip from Philadelphia to Washington, D.C., is 217 km each way. Four friends agree to share the driving equally. How far must each drive on this round-trip vacation?

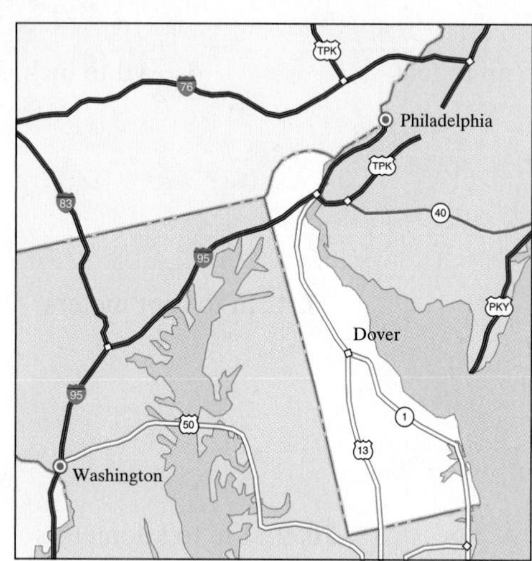

△ **22.** The college has ordered that NO SMOKING signs be placed above the doorway of each classroom. Each sign is 0.8 m long and 30 cm wide. Find the area of each sign. (*Hint:* Recall that the area of a rectangle = width · length.)

0.8 meter

NO SMOKING

30 centimeters

(7.2) *Convert.*

23. 66 oz to pounds

24. 2.3 tons to pounds

25. 52 oz = _____lb _____oz.

26. 10,300 lb = _____tons _____lb

27. 27 mg to grams

28. 40 kg to grams

29. 2.1 hg to dekagrams

30. 0.03 mg to decigrams

Perform each indicated operation.

31. 6 lb 5 oz − 2 lb 12 oz

32. 5 tons 1600 lb + 4 tons 1200 lb

33. 6 tons 2250 lb ÷ 3

34. 8 lb 6 oz × 4

35. 4.3 mg × 5

36. 4.8 kg − 4200 g

Solve.

37. Donshay Berry ordered 1 lb 12 oz of soft-center candies and 2 lb 8 oz of chewy-center candies for his party. Find the total weight of the candy ordered.

38. Four local townships jointly purchase 38 tons 300 lb of cinders to spread on their roads during an ice storm. Determine the weight of the cinders each township receives if they share the purchase equally.

39. Linda Holden ordered 8.3 kg of whole wheat flour from the health-food store, but she received 450 g less. How much flour did she actually receive?

40. Eight friends spent a weekend in the Poconos tapping maple trees and preparing 9.3 kg of maple syrup. Find the weight each friend receives if they share the syrup equally.

(7.3) *Convert.*

41. 16 pints to quarts

42. 40 fluid ounces to cups

43. 3 qt 1 pt to pints

44. 18 quarts to cups

45. 9 pt = _____ qt _____pt

46. 15 qt = _____gal _____ qt

47. 3.8 L to milliliters

48. 4.2 ml to deciliters

49. 14 hl to kiloliters

50. 30.6 L to centiliters

Perform each indicated operation.

51. 1 qt 1 pt + 3 qt 1 pt

52. 3 gal 2 qt × 2

53. 0.946 L − 210 ml

54. 6.1 L + 9400 ml

Solve.

55. Carlos Perez prepares 4 gal 2 qt of iced tea for a block party. During the first 30 minutes of the party, 1 gal 3 qt of the tea is consumed. How much iced tea remains?

56. A recipe for soup stock calls for 1 c 4 fl oz of beef broth. How much should be used if the recipe is cut in half?

57. Each bottle of Kiwi liquid shoe polish holds 85 ml of the polish. Find the number of liters of shoe polish contained in 8 boxes if each box contains 16 bottles.

58. Ivan Miller wants to pour three separate containers of saline solution into a single vat with a capacity of 10 liters. Will 6 liters of solution in the first container combined with 1300 milliliters in the second container and 2.6 liters in the third container fit into the larger vat?

(7.4) *Note: Because approximations are used in this section, your answers may vary slightly from the answers given in the back of the book.*

Convert as indicated. If necessary, round to two decimal places.

59. 7 meters to feet

60. 11.5 yards to meters

61. 17.5 liters to gallons

62. 7.8 liters to quarts

63. 15 ounces to grams

64. 23 pounds to kilograms

65. A 100-meter dash is being held today. How many yards is this?

66. If a person weighs 82 kilograms, how many pounds is this?

67. How many quarts are contained in a 3-liter bottle of cola?

68. A compact disc is 1.2 mm thick. Find the height (in inches) of 50 discs.

(7.5) *Convert. Round to the nearest tenth of a degree, if necessary.*

69. 245°C to degrees Fahrenheit

70. 160°C to degrees Fahrenheit

71. 42°C to degrees Fahrenheit

72. 93.2°F to degrees Celsius

73. 41.3°F to degrees Celsius

74. 80°F to degrees Celsius

Solve. Round to the nearest tenth of a degree, if necessary.

75. A sharp dip in the jet stream caused the temperature in New Orleans to drop to 35°F. Find the corresponding temperature in degrees Celsius.

76. The recipe for meat loaf calls for a 165°C oven. Find the setting used if the oven has a Fahrenheit thermometer.

Mixed Review

Convert the following.

85. 2.5 mi to feet

86. 6.25 ft to inches

87. 23,760 ft to miles

88. 129 in. to feet

89. 8200 lb = _____ tons _____ lb

90. 4300 lb = _____ tons _____ lb

91. 5 m to centimeters

92. 286 mm to kilometers

93. 1400 mg to grams

94. 240 mg to grams

95. 6.75 gallons to quarts

96. 5.25 gallons to quarts

97. 8.5 pints to cups

98. 6.25 pints to cups

99. 86°C to degrees Fahrenheit

100. 15°C to degrees Fahrenheit

101. 51.8°F to degrees Celsius

102. 82.4°F to degrees Celsius

Perform the indicated operations and simplify.

103. 9.3 km − 183 m

104. 8.6 km − 247 m

105. 7.4 L + 6500 ml

106. 35 L + 700 ml

107. 9.3 g − 1200 mg

108. 3.4 g − 1800 mg

109. 6.3 kg × 8

110. 3.2 kg × 4

111. 3 gal 1 qt + 4 gal 2 qt

112. 6 gal 1 qt + 2 gal 1 qt

113. 4100 mm − 3 dm

114. 6300 mm − 5 dm

115. 4.5 tons ÷ 2

116. 6.75 tons ÷ 3

Chapter 7 Test

Step-by-step test solutions are found on the Chapter Test Prep Videos available via the Interactive DVD Lecture Series, in MyMathLab or on YouTube (search "MartinGayBasicMath" and click on "Channels").

Answers

1. ______
2. ______
3. ______
4. ______
5. ______
6. ______
7. ______
8. ______
9. ______
10. ______
11. ______
12. ______
13. ______
14. ______
15. ______
16. ______
17. ______
18. ______
19. ______
20. ______
21. ______
22. ______

Convert.

1. 280 in. = _____ ft _____ in.

2. $2\frac{1}{2}$ gal to quarts

3. 30 oz to pounds

4. 2.8 tons to pounds

5. 38 pt to gallons

6. 40 mg to grams

7. 2.4 kg to grams

8. 3.6 cm to millimeters

9. 4.3 dg to grams

10. 0.83 L to milliliters

Perform each indicated operation.

11. 3 qt 1 pt + 2 qt 1 pt

12. 8 lb 6 oz − 4 lb 9 oz

13. 2 ft 9 in. × 3

14. 5 gal 2 qt ÷ 2

15. 8 cm − 14 mm

16. 1.8 km + 456 m

Convert. Round to the nearest tenth of a degree, if necessary.

17. 84°F to degrees Celsius

18. 12.6°C to degrees Fahrenheit

19. The sugar maples in front of Bette MacMillan's house are 8.4 meters tall. Because they interfere with the phone lines, the telephone company plans to remove the top third of the trees. How tall will the maples be after they are shortened?

20. A total of 15 gal 1 qt of oil has been removed from a 20-gallon drum. How much oil still remains in the container?

21. The engineer in charge of bridge construction said that the span of a certain bridge would be 88 m. But the actual construction required it to be 340 cm longer. Find the span of the bridge, in meters.

22. If 2 ft 9 in. of material is used to manufacture one scarf, how much material is needed for 6 scarves?

23. The Vietnam Veterans Memorial, inscribed with the names of 58,226 deceased and missing U.S. soldiers from the Vietnam War, is located on the National Mall in Washington, D.C. This memorial is formed from two straight sections of wall that meet at an angle at the center of the monument. Each wall is 246 ft 9 in. long. What is the total length of the Vietnam Veterans Memorial's wall? (*Source:* National Park Service)

24. Each panel making up the wall of the Vietnam Veterans Memorial is 101.6 cm wide. There are a total of 148 panels making up the wall. What is the total length of the wall in meters? (*Source:* National Park Service)

25. The hottest temperature ever recorded was 136°F in El Azizia, Libya, on September 13, 1922. Convert this temperature to degrees Celsius. Round your answer to the nearest tenth of a degree. (*Source:* National Climatic Data Center)

26. The doctors are quite concerned about Lucia Gillespie, who is running a 41°C fever. Find Lucia's temperature in degrees Fahrenheit.

27. The largest ice cream sundae ever made in the United States was assembled in Anaheim, California, in 1985. This giant sundae used 4667 gallons of ice cream. How many pints of ice cream were used?

28. A piece of candy weighs 5 grams. How many ounces is this?

29. A 5-kilometer race is being held today. How many miles is this?

30. A 5-gallon container holds how many liters?

23. ______

24. ______

25. ______

26. ______

27. ______

28. ______

29. ______

30. ______

Answers

1. ____

2. ____

3. ____

4. ____

5. ____

6. ____

7. ____

8. ____

9. ____

10. ____

11. ____

12. ____

13. ____

14. ____

15. ____

16. ____

17. ____

18. ____

19. ____

20. ____

21. ____

22. ____

Cumulative Review Chapters 1–7

1. Add: $1647 + 246 + 32 + 85$

2. Subtract: $2000 - 469$

3. Find the prime factorization of 945.

4. Find the area of the rectangle.

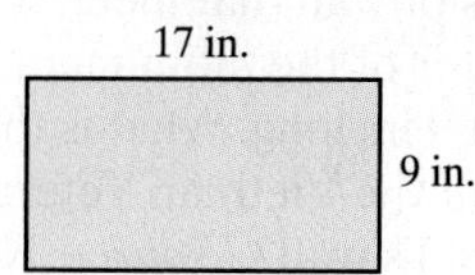

5. Find the LCM of 11 and 33.

6. Subtract: $\frac{8}{21} - \frac{2}{9}$

7. Add: $3\frac{4}{5} + 1\frac{4}{15}$

8. Multiply: $2\frac{1}{2} \cdot 4\frac{2}{15}$

Write each decimal as a fraction or mixed number in simplest form.

9. 0.125

10. 1.2

11. 105.083

12. Evaluate: $\left(\frac{2}{3}\right)^3$

13. Insert $<$, $>$, or $=$ to form a true statement.

0.052 0.236

14. Evaluate: $30 \div 6 \cdot 5$

15. Subtract $85 - 17.31$. Check your answer.

16. Add: $27.9 + 8.07 + 103.261$

Multiply.

17. 42.1×0.1

18. 186.04×1000

19. 9.2×0.001

20. Find the average of 6.8, 9.7, and 0.9.

21. Divide: $8.32 \div 32$. Check your answer.

22. Add: $\frac{3}{10} + \frac{3}{4}$

23. Write $2\frac{3}{16}$ as a decimal.

24. Round 7.2846 to the nearest tenth.

25. Write $\frac{2}{3}$ as a decimal.

26. Simplify: $\frac{0.12 + 0.96}{0.5}$

27. Write the ratio of 12 to 17 using fractional notation.

28. Write the ratio of $2\frac{2}{3}$ to $5\frac{1}{9}$ as a ratio of whole numbers using fractional notation.

29. Write "337.5 miles every 15 gallons of gas" as a unit rate.

30. A square is 9 inches by 9 inches. Find the ratio of a side to its perimeter.

31. Find the unknown number n. $\frac{7}{n} = \frac{6}{5}$

32. A recipe that makes 2 piecrusts calls for 3 cups of flour. How much flour is needed to make 5 piecrusts?

△ **33.** A 50-pound bag of fertilizer covers 2400 square feet of lawn. How many bags of fertilizer are needed to cover a town square containing 15,360 square feet of lawn? Round the answer up to the nearest whole bag.

34. Write 23% as a fraction.

35. Write 23% as a decimal.

36. Write $\frac{7}{8}$ as a percent.

37. Write $\frac{1}{12}$ as a percent. Round to the nearest hundredth percent.

38. 108 is what percent of 450?

39. What number is 35% of 40?

40. Convert 4 gallons to pints.

41. Translate to a proportion. What percent of 30 is 75?

42. Convert 8.6 meters to centimeters.

43. In response to a decrease in sales, a company with 1500 employees reduces the number of employees to 1230. What is the percent decrease?

44. Convert 13,000 pounds to tons.

23. ____________
24. ____________
25. ____________
26. ____________
27. ____________
28. ____________
29. ____________
30. ____________
31. ____________
32. ____________
33. ____________
34. ____________
35. ____________
36. ____________
37. ____________
38. ____________
39. ____________
40. ____________
41. ____________
42. ____________
43. ____________
44. ____________

45. ____________

46. ____________

47. ____________

48. ____________

49. ____________

50. ____________

45. An electric rice cooker that normally sells for \$65 is on sale for 25% off. What is the amount of discount and what is the sale price?

46. Convert $3\frac{1}{4}$ pounds to ounces.

47. Find the simple interest after 2 years on \$500 at an interest rate of 12%.

48. The number of faculty at a local community college was recently increased from 240 to 276. What is the percent increase?

49. Convert 9000 pounds to tons.

50. Convert 25° Celsius to degrees Fahrenheit.

Real Numbers and Introduction to Algebra

8

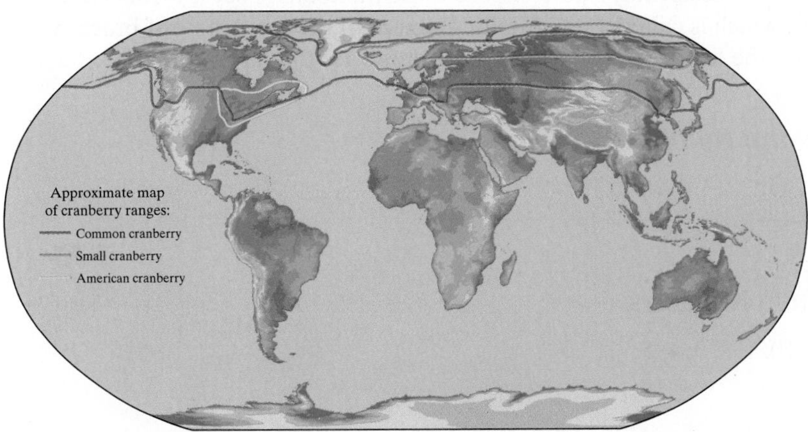

In this chapter, we begin with a review of the basic symbols—the language—of mathematics. We then introduce algebra by using a variable in place of a number. From there, we translate phrases to algebraic expressions and sentences to equations. This is the beginning of problem solving, which we formally study in Chapter 9.

Sections

Check Your Progress

The cranberry is one of only three fruits that are native to North America (the other two are the blueberry and the Concord grape). Native Americans pounded cranberries into paste, which they mixed with dried meat to create pemmican. American and Canadian sailors took cranberries on long sea voyages to combat scurvy, because of their high vitamin C content. Cranberries received their common name from "crane berry" because colonists thought the flower resembled the head, neck, and beak of the crane.

Americans consume 400 million pounds annually, 20% of them during Thanksgiving week. They are available in many forms: fresh, jellied, dried, or in juice. They are high in antioxidants and beneficial to the health of gums and teeth. In Exercises 81–84, Section 8.1, you will explore information about cranberry crops from the top five cranberry-producing states. (*Source:* Cape Cod Cranberry Growers Association)

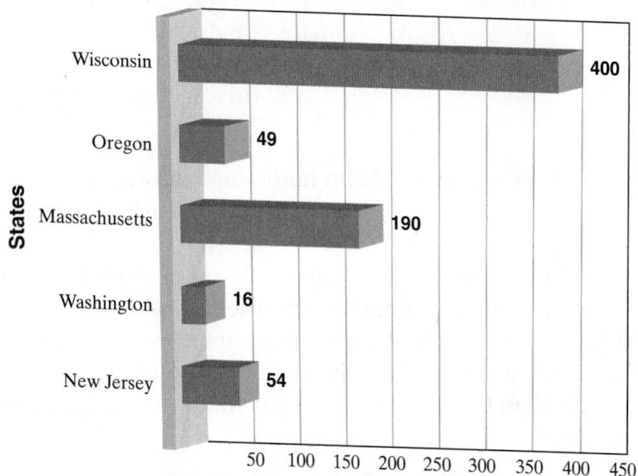

Source: National Agricultural Statistics Service

Objectives

A **Define the Meaning of the Symbols $=, \neq, <, >, \leq$, and $\geq$.**

B **Translate Sentences into Mathematical Statements.**

C **Identify Integers, Rational Numbers, Irrational Numbers, and Real Numbers.**

D **Find the Absolute Value of a Real Number.**

8.1 SYMBOLS AND SETS OF NUMBERS

We begin with a review of the set of natural numbers and the set of whole numbers and how we use symbols to compare these numbers. A **set** is a collection of objects, each of which is called a **member** or **element** of the set. A pair of brace symbols { } encloses the list of elements and is translated as "the set of" or "the set containing."

Natural Numbers

$\{1, 2, 3, 4, 5, 6, \ldots\}$

Whole Numbers

$\{0, 1, 2, 3, 4, 5, 6, \ldots\}$

Helpful Hint

The three dots (an ellipsis) at the end of the list of elements of a set means that the list continues in the same manner indefinitely.

Objective A Equality and Inequality Symbols

Picturing natural numbers and whole numbers on a number line helps us to see the order of the numbers. Symbols can be used to describe in writing the order of two quantities. We will use equality symbols and inequality symbols to compare quantities.

Below is a review of these symbols. The letters *a* and *b* are used to represent quantities. Letters such as *a* and *b* that are used to represent numbers or quantities are called **variables.**

Equality and Inequality Symbols

		Meaning
Equality symbol:	$a = b$	*a* is equal to *b*.
Inequality symbols:	$a \neq b$	*a* is not equal to *b*.
	$a < b$	*a* is less than *b*.
	$a > b$	*a* is greater than *b*.
	$a \leq b$	*a* is less than or equal to *b*.
	$a \geq b$	*a* is greater than or equal to *b*.

These symbols may be used to form **mathematical statements** such as

$$2 = 2 \quad \text{and} \quad 2 \neq 6$$

Recall that on a number line, we see that a number **to the right of** another number is **larger.** Similarly, a number **to the left of** another number is **smaller.** For example, 3 is to the left of 5 on the number line, which means that 3 is less than 5, or $3 < 5$. Similarly, 2 is to the right of 0 on the number line, which means that 2 is greater than 0, or $2 > 0$. Since 0 is to the left of 2, we can also say that 0 is less than 2, or $0 < 2$.

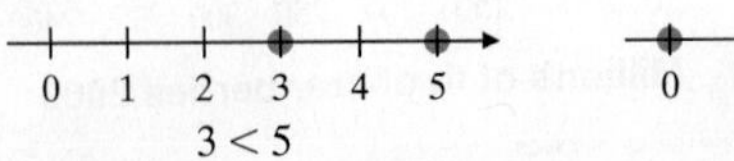

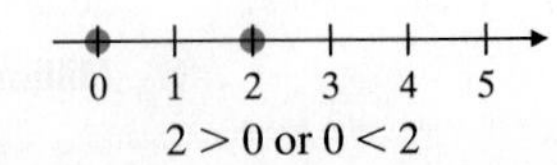

Helpful Hint

Recall that $2 > 0$ has exactly the same meaning as $0 < 2$. Switching the order of the numbers and reversing the direction of the inequality symbol does not change the meaning of the statement.

$6 > 4$ has the same meaning as $4 < 6$.

Also notice that when the statement is true, the inequality arrow points to the smaller number.

Our discussion above can be generalized in the order property below.

Order Property for Real Numbers

For any two real numbers a and b, a is less than b if a is to the left of b on a number line.

$a < b$ or also $b > a$

Examples Determine whether each statement is true or false.

1. $2 < 3$ True. Since 2 is to the left of 3 on a number line
2. $72 < 27$ False. 72 is to the right of 27 on a number line, so $72 > 27$.
3. $8 \geq 8$ True. Since $8 = 8$ is true
4. $8 \leq 8$ True. Since $8 = 8$ is true
5. $23 \leq 0$ False. Since neither $23 < 0$ nor $23 = 0$ is true
6. $0 \leq 23$ True. Since $0 < 23$ is true

Work Practice 1–6

PRACTICE 1–6

Determine whether each statement is true or false.

1. $8 < 6$
2. $100 > 10$
3. $21 \leq 21$
4. $21 \geq 21$
5. $0 \geq 5$
6. $25 \geq 22$

If either $3 < 3$ or $3 = 3$ is true, then $3 \leq 3$ is true.

Objective B Translating Sentences into Mathematical Statements

Now, let's use the symbols discussed above to translate sentences into mathematical statements.

Example 7 Translate each sentence into a mathematical statement.

a. Nine is less than or equal to eleven.
b. Eight is greater than one.
c. Three is not equal to four.

Solution:

a. nine → 9; is less than or equal to → $\leq$; eleven → 11

b. eight → 8; is greater than → $>$; one → 1

c. three → 3; is not equal to → $\neq$; four → 4

Work Practice 7

PRACTICE 7

Translate each sentence into a mathematical statement.

a. Fourteen is greater than or equal to fourteen.
b. Zero is less than five.
c. Nine is not equal to ten.

Answers

1. false 2. true 3. true 4. true 5. false 6. true 7. a. $14 \geq 14$ b. $0 < 5$ c. $9 \neq 10$

Objective C Identifying Common Sets of Numbers

Whole numbers are not sufficient to describe many situations in the real world. For example, quantities smaller than zero must sometimes be represented, such as temperatures less than 0 degrees.

Recall that we can place numbers less than zero on a number line as follows: Numbers less than 0 are to the left of 0 and are labeled $-1, -2, -3$, and so on. The numbers we have labeled on the number line below are called the set of **integers.**

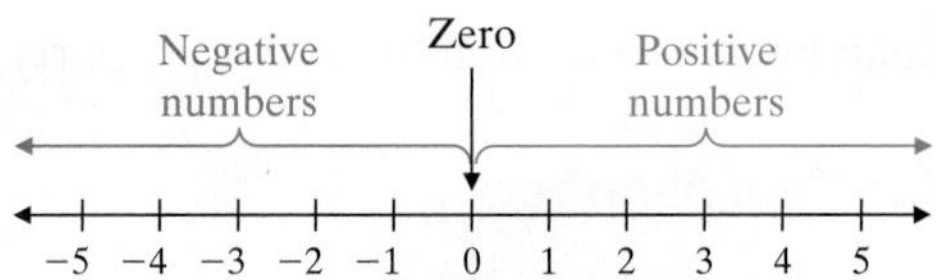

Integers to the left of 0 are called **negative integers;** integers to the right of 0 are called **positive integers.** The integer 0 is neither positive nor negative.

Integers

$\{\ldots, -3, -2, -1, 0, 1, 2, 3, \ldots\}$

Helpful Hint

A $-$ sign, such as the one in -2, tells us that the number is to the left of 0 on a number line.

-2 is read "negative two."

A $+$ sign or no sign tells us that the number lies to the right of 0 on a number line. For example, 3 and $+3$ both mean positive three.

PRACTICE 8

Use an integer to express the number in the following. The elevation of New Orleans, Louisiana, is an average of 8 feet below sea level. (*Source: The World Almanac*)

Example 8 Use an integer to express the number in the following. "The lowest temperature ever recorded at South Pole Station, Antarctica, occurred during the month of June. The record-low temperature was 117 degrees below zero." (*Source:* The National Oceanic and Atmospheric Administration)

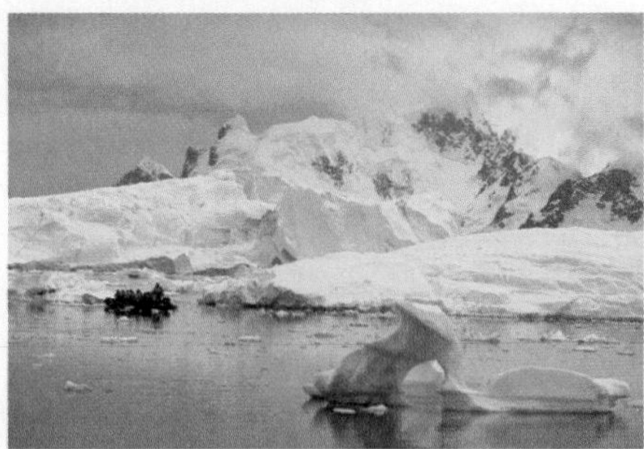

Solution: The integer -117 represents 117 degrees below zero.

Work Practice 8

Answer

8. -8

A problem with integers in real-life settings arises when quantities are smaller than some integer but greater than the next smallest integer. On a number line, these quantities may be visualized by points between integers. Some of these quantities between integers can be represented as a quotient of integers. For example,

The point on the number line halfway between 0 and 1 can be represented by $\frac{1}{2}$, a quotient of integers.

The point on the number line halfway between 0 and -1 can be represented by $-\frac{1}{2}$. Other quotients of integers and their graphs are shown below.

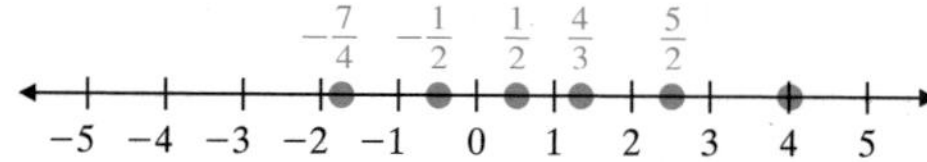

These numbers, each of which can be represented as a quotient of integers, are examples of **rational numbers.** It's not possible to list the set of rational numbers using the notation that we have been using. For this reason, we will use a different notation.

Rational Numbers

$$\left\{\frac{a}{b}\middle|\, a \text{ and } b \text{ are integers and } b \neq 0\right\}$$

We read this set as "the set of numbers $\frac{a}{b}$ such that a and b are integers and ***b* is not equal to 0.**"

Helpful Hint

We commonly refer to rational numbers as fractions.

Notice that every integer is also a rational number since each integer can be written as a quotient of integers. For example, the integer 5 is also a rational number since $5 = \frac{5}{1}$. For the rational number $\frac{5}{1}$, recall that the top number, 5, is called the numerator and the bottom number, 1, is called the denominator.

Let's practice **graphing** numbers on a number line.

Example 9 Graph the numbers on a number line.

$$-\frac{4}{3},\ \frac{1}{4},\ \frac{3}{2},\ -2\frac{1}{8},\ 3.5$$

Solution: To help graph the improper fractions in the list, we first write them as mixed numbers.

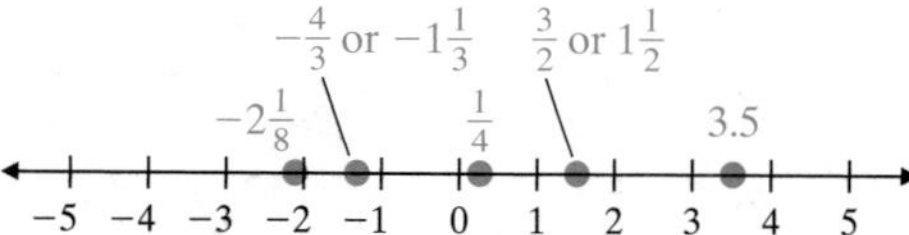

Work Practice 9

Every rational number has a point on the number line that corresponds to it. But not every point on the number line corresponds to a rational number. Those points that do not correspond to rational numbers correspond instead to **irrational numbers.**

PRACTICE 9

Graph the numbers on the number line.

$$-2\frac{1}{2},\ -\frac{2}{3},\ \frac{1}{5},\ \frac{5}{4},\ 2.25$$

−5 −4 −3 −2 −1 0 1 2 3 4 5

Answer

9. 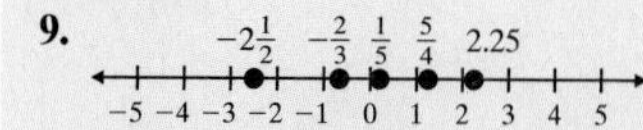

Irrational Numbers

{Nonrational numbers that correspond to points on a number line}

An irrational number that you have probably seen is π. Also, $\sqrt{2}$, the length of the diagonal of the square shown below, is an irrational number.

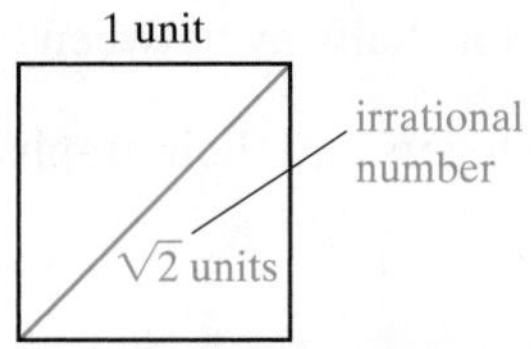

Both rational and irrational numbers can be written as decimal numbers. The decimal equivalent of a rational number will either terminate or repeat in a pattern. For example, upon dividing we find that

$\frac{3}{4} = 0.75$ (Decimal number terminates or ends.)

$\frac{2}{3} = 0.66666\ldots$ (Decimal number repeats in a pattern.)

The decimal representation of an irrational number will neither terminate nor repeat.

The set of numbers, each of which corresponds to a point on a number line, is called the set of **real numbers.** One and only one point on a number line corresponds to each real number.

Real Numbers

{All numbers that correspond to points on a number line}

Several different sets of numbers have been discussed in this section. The following diagram shows the relationships among these sets of real numbers. Notice that, together, the rational numbers and the irrational numbers make up the real numbers.

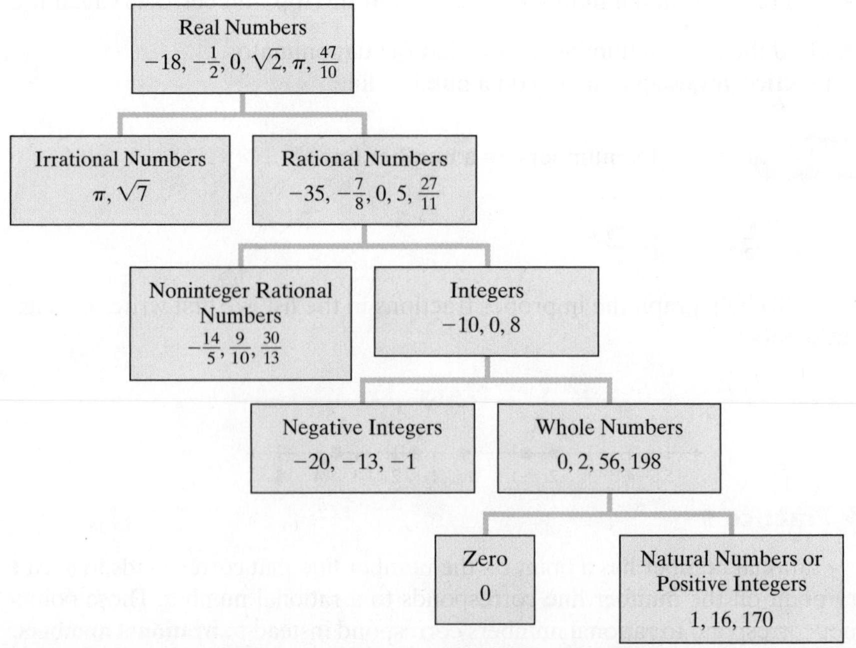

Now that other sets of numbers have been reviewed, let's continue our practice of comparing numbers.

Example 10 Insert $<$, $>$, or $=$ between the pairs of numbers to form true statements.

a. $-5 \quad -6$ **b.** $3.195 \quad 3.2$ **c.** $\frac{1}{4} \quad \frac{1}{3}$

Solution:

a. $-5 > -6$ since -5 lies to the right of -6 on a number line.

b. By comparing digits in the same place values, we find that $3.195 < 3.2$, since $0.1 < 0.2$.

c. By dividing, we find that $\frac{1}{4} = 0.25$ and $\frac{1}{3} = 0.33\ldots$. Since $0.25 < 0.33\ldots$, $\frac{1}{4} < \frac{1}{3}$.

Work Practice 10

PRACTICE 10

Insert $<$, $>$, or $=$ between the pairs of numbers to form true statements.

a. $-11 \quad -9$

b. $4.511 \quad 4.151$

c. $\frac{7}{8} \quad \frac{2}{3}$

Example 11 Given the set $\{-2, 0, \frac{1}{4}, 112, -3, 11, \sqrt{2}\}$, list the numbers in this set that belong to the set of:

a. Natural numbers **b.** Whole numbers **c.** Integers
d. Rational numbers **e.** Irrational numbers **f.** Real numbers

Solution:

a. The natural numbers are 11 and 112.

b. The whole numbers are 0, 11, and 112.

c. The integers are $-3, -2, 0, 11$, and 112.

d. Recall that integers are rational numbers also. The rational numbers are $-3, -2, 0, \frac{1}{4}, 11$, and 112.

e. The only irrational number is $\sqrt{2}$.

f. All numbers in the given set are real numbers.

Work Practice 11

PRACTICE 11

Given the set $\{-100, -\frac{2}{5}, 0, \pi, 6, 913\}$, list the numbers in this set that belong to the set of:

a. Natural numbers

b. Whole numbers

c. Integers

d. Rational numbers

e. Irrational numbers

f. Real numbers

Objective D Finding the Absolute Value of a Number

The number line not only gives us a picture of the real numbers, it also helps us visualize the distance between numbers. The distance between a real number a and 0 is given a special name called the **absolute value** of a. "The absolute value of a" is written in symbols as $|a|$.

Absolute Value

The **absolute value** of a real number a, denoted by $|a|$, is the distance between a and 0 on a number line.

Helpful Hint Since $|a|$ is a distance, $|a|$ is always either positive or 0. It is never negative. That is, **for any real number** a, $|a| \geq 0$.

For example, $|3| = 3$ and $|-3| = 3$ since both 3 and -3 are a distance of 3 units from 0 on the number line.

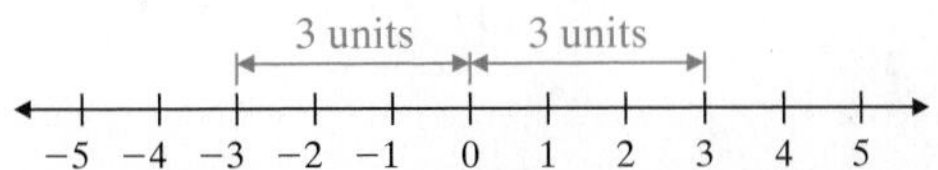

Answers

10. a. $<$ **b.** $>$ **c.** $>$

11. a. 6, 913 **b.** 0, 6, 913

c. $-100, 0, 6, 913$

d. $-100, -\frac{2}{5}, 0, 6, 913$ **e.** π

f. all numbers in the given set

PRACTICE 12

Find the absolute value of each number.

a. $|7|$ **b.** $|-8|$ **c.** $\left|\frac{2}{3}\right|$

d. $|0|$ **e.** $|-3.06|$

Example 12 Find the absolute value of each number.

a. $|4|$ **b.** $|-5|$ **c.** $|0|$

d. $\left|-\frac{2}{9}\right|$ **e.** $|4.93|$

Solution:

a. $|4| = 4$ since 4 is 4 units from 0 on the number line.

b. $|-5| = 5$ since -5 is 5 units from 0 on the number line.

c. $|0| = 0$ since 0 is 0 units from 0 on the number line.

d. $\left|-\frac{2}{9}\right| = \frac{2}{9}$

e. $|4.93| = 4.93$

Work Practice 12

PRACTICE 13

Insert <, >, or = in the appropriate space to make each statement true.

a. $|-4|$ 4

b. -3 $|0|$

c. $|-2.7|$ $|-2|$

d. $|-6|$ $|-16|$

e. $|10|$ $\left|-10\frac{1}{3}\right|$

Example 13 Insert <, >, or = in the appropriate space to make each statement true.

a. $|0|$ 2 **b.** $|-5|$ 5 **c.** $|-3|$ $|-2|$

d. $|-9|$ $|-9.7|$ **e.** $\left|-7\frac{1}{6}\right|$ $|7|$

Solution:

a. $|0| < 2$ since $|0| = 0$ and $0 < 2$.

b. $|-5| = 5$.

c. $|-3| > |-2|$ since $3 > 2$.

d. $|-9| < |-9.7|$ since $9 < 9.7$.

e. $\left|-7\frac{1}{6}\right| > |7|$ since $7\frac{1}{6} > 7$.

Work Practice 13

Answers

12. a. 7 **b.** 8 **c.** $\frac{2}{3}$ **d.** 0 **e.** 3.06

13. a. = **b.** < **c.** > **d.** < **e.** <

Vocabulary and Readiness Check

Use the choices below to fill in each blank. Not all choices will be used.

real	natural	absolute value	$\frac{1}{2}$	$\frac{1}{4}$	$\|a\|$	whole
rational	inequality	integers	0	1	$\|-1\|$	

1. The ____________ numbers are $\{0, 1, 2, 3, 4, \ldots\}$.
2. The ____________ numbers are $\{1, 2, 3, 4, 5, \ldots\}$.
3. The symbols $\neq, \leq$, and $>$ are called ____________ symbols.
4. The ____________ are $\{\ldots, -3, -2, -1, 0, 1, 2, 3, \ldots\}$.
5. The ____________ numbers are {all numbers that correspond to points on a number line}.
6. The ____________ numbers are $\left\{\frac{a}{b} \middle| a \text{ and } b \text{ are integers}, b \neq 0\right\}$.
7. The integer ____________ is neither positive nor negative.
8. The point on the number line halfway between 0 and $\frac{1}{2}$ can be represented by ____________.
9. The distance between a real number a and 0 is called the ____________ of a.
10. The absolute value of a is written in symbols as ____________.

8.1 Exercise Set

FOR EXTRA HELP   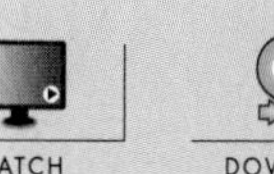  

Objectives A C Mixed Practice *Insert $<$, $>$, or $=$ in the space between the paired numbers to make each statement true. See Examples 1 through 6 and 10.*

1. 4 10

2. 8 5

3. 7 3

4. 9 15

5. 6.26 6.26

6. 1.13 1.13

7. 0 7

8. 20 0

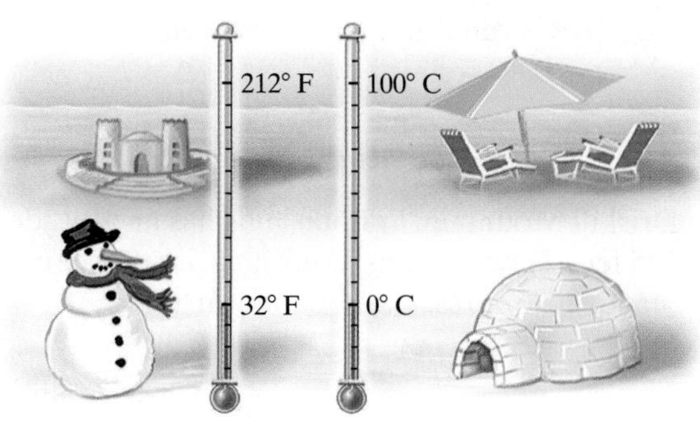

9. The freezing point of water is 32° Fahrenheit. The boiling point of water is 212° Fahrenheit. Write an inequality statement using $<$ or $>$ comparing the numbers 32 and 212.

10. The freezing point of water is 0° Celsius. The boiling point of water is 100° Celsius. Write an inequality statement using $<$ or $>$ comparing the numbers 0 and 100.

△ **11.** An angle measuring 30° and an angle measuring 45° are shown. Write an inequality statement using ≤ or ≥ comparing the numbers 30 and 45.

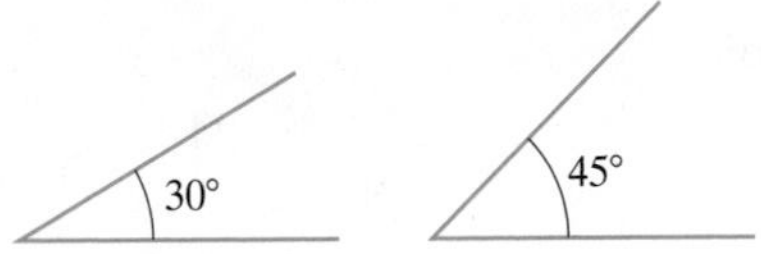

△ **12.** The sum of the measures of the angles of a parallelogram is 360°. The sum of the measures of the angles of a triangle is 180°. Write an inequality statement using ≤ or ≥ comparing the numbers 360 and 180.

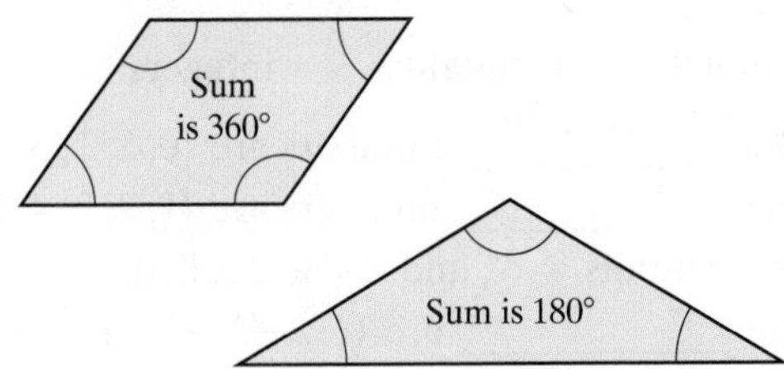

Determine whether each statement is true or false. See Examples 1 through 6 and 10.

13. $11 \leq 11$

14. $8 \geq 9$

15. $-11 > -10$

16. $-16 > -17$

17. $5.092 < 5.902$

18. $1.02 > 1.021$

19. $\frac{9}{10} \leq \frac{8}{9}$

20. $\frac{4}{5} \leq \frac{9}{11}$

Rewrite each inequality so that the inequality symbol points in the opposite direction and the resulting statement has the same meaning as the given one. See Examples 1 through 6 and 10.

21. $25 \geq 20$

22. $-13 \leq 13$

23. $0 < 6$

24. $5 > 3$

25. $-10 > -12$

26. $-4 < -2$

Objectives **B** **C** **Mixed Practice–Translating** *Write each sentence as a mathematical statement. See Examples 7 and 10.*

27. Seven is less than eleven.

28. Twenty is greater than two.

29. Five is greater than or equal to four.

30. Negative ten is less than or equal to thirty-seven.

31. Fifteen is not equal to negative two.

32. Negative seven is not equal to seven.

Use integers to represent the values in each statement. See Example 8.

33. The highest elevation in California is Mt. Whitney, with an altitude of 14,494 feet. The lowest elevation in California is Death Valley, with an altitude of 282 feet below sea level. (*Source:* U.S. Geological Survey)

34. Driskill Mountain, in Louisiana, has an altitude of 535 feet. New Orleans, Louisiana, lies 8 feet below sea level. (*Source:* U.S. Geological Survey)

35. The number of graduate students at the University of Texas at Austin is 28,000 fewer than the number of undergraduate students. (*Source:* University of Texas at Austin)

36. The number of students admitted to the class of 2011 at UCLA is 38,792 fewer students than the number that had applied. (*Source:* UCLA)

37. Gretchen Bertani deposited $475 in her savings account. She later withdrew $195.

38. David Lopez was deep-sea diving. During his dive, he ascended 17 feet and later descended 15 feet.

Graph each set of numbers on the number line. See Example 9.

39. $-4, 0, 2, -2$

40. $-3, 0, 1, -5$

41. $-2, 4, \frac{1}{3}, -\frac{1}{4}$

42. $-5, 3, -\frac{1}{3}, \frac{7}{8}$

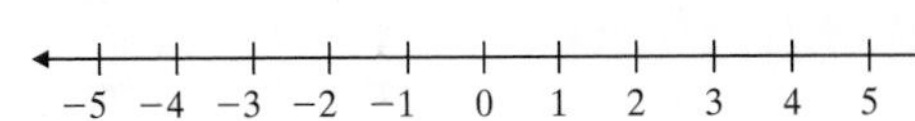

43. $-4.5, \frac{7}{4}, 3.25, -\frac{3}{2}$

44. $4.5, -\frac{9}{4}, 1.75, -\frac{7}{2}$

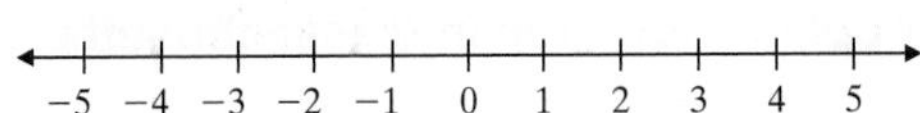

Tell which set or sets each number belongs to: natural numbers, whole numbers, integers, rational numbers, irrational numbers, or real numbers. See Example 11.

45. 0

46. $\frac{1}{4}$

47. -7

48. $-\frac{1}{7}$

49. 265

50. 7941

51. $\frac{2}{3}$

52. $\sqrt{3}$

Determine whether each statement is true or false.

53. Every rational number is also an integer.

54. Every natural number is positive.

55. 0 is a real number.

56. $\frac{1}{2}$ is an integer.

57. Every negative number is also a rational number.

58. Every rational number is also a real number.

59. Every real number is also a rational number.

60. Every whole number is an integer.

Objective **D** *Find each absolute value. See Example 12.*

61. $|8.9|$

62. $|11.2|$

63. $|-20|$

64. $|-17|$

65. $\left|\frac{9}{2}\right|$

66. $\left|\frac{10}{7}\right|$

67. $\left|-\frac{12}{13}\right|$

68. $\left|-\frac{1}{15}\right|$

Insert <, >, or = in the appropriate space to make each statement true. See Examples 12 and 13.

69. $|-5| \quad -4$

70. $|-12| \quad |0|$

71. $\left|-\frac{5}{8}\right| \quad \left|\frac{5}{8}\right|$

72. $\left|\frac{2}{5}\right| \quad \left|-\frac{2}{5}\right|$

73. $|-2| \quad |-2.7|$

74. $|-5.01| \quad |-5|$

75. $|0| \quad |-8|$

76. $|-12| \quad \frac{-24}{2}$

Concept Extensions

The graph below is called a bar graph. This graph shows apple production in Massachusetts from 2003 through 2009. Each bar represents a different year, and the height of each bar represents the apple production for that year in thousands of bushels. (The federal standard for bushel is 48 lb, although 42 lb is also commonly used.)

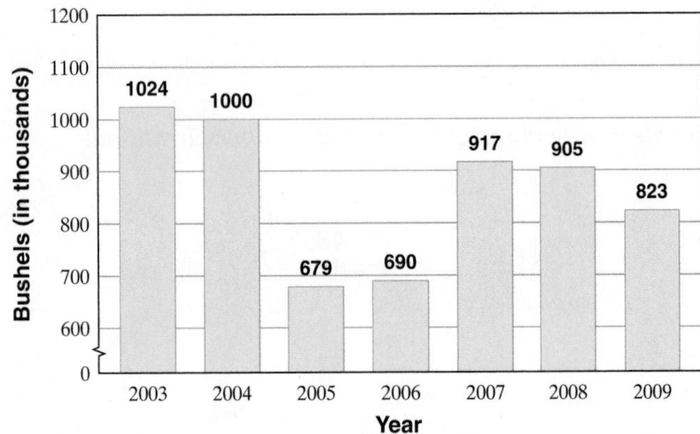

(*Note:* The ⚡ symbol means that some numbers are missing. Along the vertical data line, notice the numbers between 0 and 600 are missing or not shown.) (*Source:* New England Agriculture Statistical Service and Agricultural Statistics Board.)

77. Write an inequality comparing the apple production in 2008 with the apple production in 2009.

78. Write an inequality comparing the apple production in 2006 with the apple production in 2007.

79. Determine the change in apple production between 2003 and 2004.

80. According to the bar graph, which year shown produced the largest crop?

The bar graph shows cranberry production from the top five cranberry-producing states. (Source: National Agricultural Statistics Service)

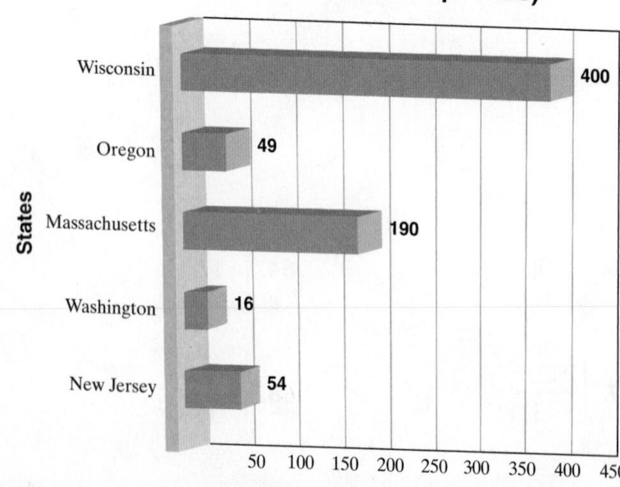

Source: National Agricultural Statistics Service

81. Write an inequality comparing the 2009 cranberry production in Oregon with the 2009 cranberry production in Washington.

82. Write an inequality comparing the 2009 cranberry production in Massachusetts with the 2009 cranberry production in Wisconsin.

83. Determine the difference between the 2009 cranberry production in Washington and the 2009 cranberry production in New Jersey.

84. According to the bar graph, which two states had almost equal 2009 cranberry crops?

The apparent magnitude of a star is the measure of its brightness as seen by someone on Earth. The smaller the apparent magnitude, the brighter the star. Below, the apparent magnitudes of some stars are listed. Use this table to answer Exercises 85 through 90.

Star	Apparent Magnitude	Star	Apparent Magnitude
Arcturus	−0.04	Spica	0.98
Sirius	−1.46	Rigel	0.12
Vega	0.03	Regulus	1.35
Antares	0.96	Canopus	−0.72
Sun	−26.7	Hadar	0.61

(*Source: Norton's 2000.0: Star Atlas and Reference Handbook,* 18th ed., Longman Group, UK, 1989)

85. The apparent magnitude of the sun is −26.7. The apparent magnitude of the star Arcturus is −0.04. Write an inequality statement comparing the numbers −0.04 and −26.7.

86. The apparent magnitude of Antares is 0.96. The apparent magnitude of Spica is 0.98. Write an inequality statement comparing the numbers 0.96 and 0.98.

87. Which is brighter, the sun or Arcturus?

88. Which is dimmer, Antares or Spica?

89. Which star listed is the brightest?

90. Which star listed is the dimmest?

91. In your own words, explain how to find the absolute value of a number.

92. Give an example of a real-life situation that can be described with integers but not with whole numbers.

Objectives

A **Define and Use Exponents and the Order of Operations.**

B **Evaluate Algebraic Expressions, Given Replacement Values for Variables.**

C **Determine Whether a Number Is a Solution of a Given Equation.**

D **Translate Phrases into Expressions and Sentences into Equations.**

8.2 EXPONENTS, ORDER OF OPERATIONS, AND VARIABLE EXPRESSIONS

Objective A Exponents and the Order of Operations

Frequently in algebra, products occur that contain repeated multiplication of the same factor. For example, the volume of a cube whose sides each measure 2 centimeters is $(2 \cdot 2 \cdot 2)$ cubic centimeters. We may use **exponential notation** to write such products in a more compact form. For example,

$2 \cdot 2 \cdot 2$ may be written as 2^3.

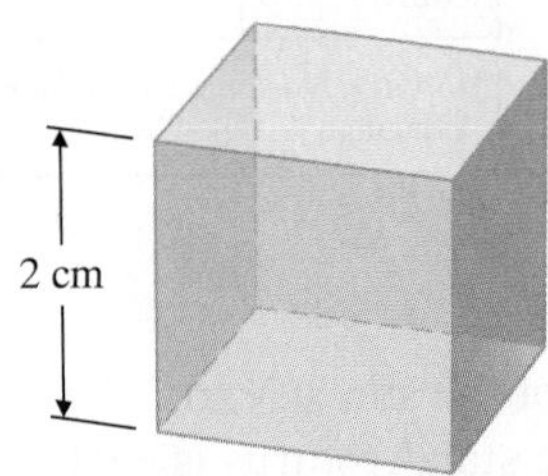

Volume is $(2 \cdot 2 \cdot 2)$ cubic centimeters.

The 2 in 2^3 is called the **base;** it is the repeated factor. The 3 in 2^3 is called the **exponent** and is the number of times the base is used as a factor. The expression 2^3 is called an **exponential expression.**

exponent

$2^3 = 2 \cdot 2 \cdot 2 = 8$

base — 2 is a factor 3 times.

PRACTICE 1

Evaluate each expression.

a. 4^2
b. 2^2
c. 3^4
d. 9^1
e. $\left(\frac{2}{5}\right)^3$
f. $(0.8)^2$

Helpful Hint

$2^3 \neq 2 \cdot 3$ since 2^3 indicates **repeated multiplication of the same factor.**

$2^3 = 2 \cdot 2 \cdot 2 = 8,$

whereas $2 \cdot 3 = 6$

Example 1 Evaluate (find the value of) each expression.

a. 3^2 [read as "3 squared" or as "3 to the second power"]
b. 5^3 [read as "5 cubed" or as "5 to the third power"]
c. 2^4 [read as "2 to the fourth power"]
d. 7^1
e. $\left(\frac{3}{7}\right)^2$
f. $(0.6)^2$

Solution:

a. $3^2 = 3 \cdot 3 = 9$
b. $5^3 = 5 \cdot 5 \cdot 5 = 125$
c. $2^4 = 2 \cdot 2 \cdot 2 \cdot 2 = 16$
d. $7^1 = 7$
e. $\left(\frac{3}{7}\right)^2 = \left(\frac{3}{7}\right)\left(\frac{3}{7}\right) = \frac{3 \cdot 3}{7 \cdot 7} = \frac{9}{49}$
f. $(0.6)^2 = (0.6)(0.6) = 0.36$

Work Practice 1

Answers

1. a. 16 **b.** 4 **c.** 81 **d.** 9 **e.** $\frac{8}{125}$ **f.** 0.64

Using symbols for mathematical operations is a great convenience. The more operation symbols presented in an expression, the more careful we must be when performing the indicated operation. For example, in the expression $2 + 3 \cdot 7$, do we add first or multiply first? To eliminate confusion, **grouping symbols** are used. Examples of grouping symbols are parentheses ( ), brackets [ ], braces { }, absolute value bars | |, and the fraction bar. If we wish $2 + 3 \cdot 7$ to be simplified by adding first, we enclose $2 + 3$ in parentheses.

$$(2 + 3) \cdot 7 = 5 \cdot 7 = 35$$

If we wish to multiply first, $3 \cdot 7$ may be enclosed in parentheses.

$$2 + (3 \cdot 7) = 2 + 21 = 23$$

To eliminate confusion when no grouping symbols are present, we use the following agreed-upon order of operations.

Order of Operations

1. Perform all operations within grouping symbols first, starting with the innermost set.
2. Evaluate exponential expressions.
3. Multiply or divide in order from left to right.
4. Add or subtract in order from left to right.

Using this order of operations, we now simplify $2 + 3 \cdot 7$. There are no grouping symbols and no exponents, so we multiply and then add.

$2 + 3 \cdot 7 = 2 + 21$ Multiply.
$= 23$ Add.

Examples Simplify each expression.

2. $6 \div 3 + 5^2 = 6 \div 3 + 25$ Evaluate 5^2
$= 2 + 25$ Divide.
$= 27$ Add.

3. $20 \div 5 \cdot 4 = 4 \cdot 4$
$= 16$

Helpful Hint Remember to multiply or divide in order from left to right.

4. $\frac{3}{2} \cdot \frac{1}{2} - \frac{1}{2} = \frac{3}{4} - \frac{1}{2}$ Multiply.
$= \frac{3}{4} - \frac{2}{4}$ The least common denominator is 4.
$= \frac{1}{4}$ Subtract.

5. $1 + 2[5(2 \cdot 3 + 1) - 10] = 1 + 2[5(7) - 10]$ Simplify the expression in the innermost set of parentheses. $2 \cdot 3 + 1 = 6 + 1 = 7$.
$= 1 + 2[35 - 10]$ Multiply 5 and 7.
$= 1 + 2[25]$ Subtract inside the brackets.
$= 1 + 50$ Multiply 2 and 25.
$= 51$ Add.

Work Practice 2–5

In the next example, the fraction bar serves as a grouping symbol and separates the numerator and denominator. Simplify each separately.

PRACTICE 2–5

Simplify each expression.

2. $3 \cdot 2 + 4^2$
3. $28 \div 7 \cdot 2$
4. $\frac{9}{5} \cdot \frac{1}{3} - \frac{1}{3}$
5. $5 + 3[2(3 \cdot 4 + 1) - 20]$

Answers
2. 22 **3.** 8 **4.** $\frac{4}{15}$ **5.** 23

PRACTICE 6

Simplify: $\dfrac{1 + |7 - 4| + 3^2}{8 - 5}$

Example 6 Simplify: $\dfrac{3 + |4 - 3| + 2^2}{6 - 3}$

Solution:

$$\frac{3 + |4 - 3| + 2^2}{6 - 3} = \frac{3 + |1| + 2^2}{6 - 3}$$ Simplify the expression inside the absolute value bars.

$$= \frac{3 + 1 + 2^2}{3}$$ Find the absolute value and simplify the denominator.

$$= \frac{3 + 1 + 4}{3}$$ Evaluate the exponential expression.

$$= \frac{8}{3}$$ Simplify the numerator.

Work Practice 6

Helpful Hint

Be careful when evaluating an exponential expression.

$3 \cdot 4^2 = 3 \cdot 16 = 48$ — ↑ Base is 4.

$(3 \cdot 4)^2 = (12)^2 = 144$ — ↑ Base is $3 \cdot 4$.

Objective B Evaluating Algebraic Expressions

Recall that letters used to represent quantities are called **variables.** An **algebraic expression** is a collection of numbers, variables, operation symbols, and grouping symbols. For example,

$$2x, \quad -3, \quad 2x - 10, \quad 5(p^2 + 1), \quad xy, \quad \text{and} \quad \frac{3y^2 - 6y + 1}{5}$$

are algebraic expressions.

Expressions	Meaning
$2x$	$2 \cdot x$
$5(p^2 + 1)$	$5 \cdot (p^2 + 1)$
$3y^2$	$3 \cdot y^2$
xy	$x \cdot y$

If we give a specific value to a variable, we can **evaluate an algebraic expression.** To evaluate an algebraic expression means to find its numerical value once we know the values of the variables.

Algebraic expressions are often used in problem solving. For example, the expression

$$16t^2$$

gives the distance in feet (neglecting air resistance) that an object will fall in t seconds.

Answer

6. $\dfrac{13}{3}$

Example 7 Evaluate each expression when $x = 3$ and $y = 2$.

a. $5x^2$ **b.** $2x - y$ **c.** $\frac{3x}{2y}$ **d.** $\frac{x}{y} + \frac{y}{2}$ **e.** $x^2 - y^2$

Solution:

a. Replace x with 3. Then simplify.

$5x^2 = 5 \cdot (3)^2 = 5 \cdot 9 = 45$

b. Replace x with 3 and y with 2. Then simplify.

$2x - y = 2(3) - 2$ Let $x = 3$ and $y = 2$.
$= 6 - 2$ Multiply.
$= 4$ Subtract.

c. Replace x with 3 and y with 2. Then simplify.

$\frac{3x}{2y} = \frac{3 \cdot 3}{2 \cdot 2} = \frac{9}{4}$ Let $x = 3$ and $y = 2$.

d. Replace x with 3 and y with 2. Then simplify.

$\frac{x}{y} + \frac{y}{2} = \frac{3}{2} + \frac{2}{2} = \frac{5}{2}$

e. Replace x with 3 and y with 2. Then simplify.

$x^2 - y^2 = 3^2 - 2^2 = 9 - 4 = 5$

Work Practice 7

PRACTICE 7

Evaluate each expression when $x = 1$ and $y = 4$.

a. $3y^2$

b. $2y - x$

c. $\frac{11x}{3y}$

d. $\frac{x}{y} + \frac{6}{y}$

e. $y^2 - x^2$

Objective C Solutions of Equations

Many times a problem-solving situation is modeled by an equation. An **equation** is a mathematical statement that two expressions have equal value. The equal symbol "=" is used to equate the two expressions. For example,

$3 + 2 = 5$, $7x = 35$, $\frac{2(x - 1)}{3} = 0$, and $I = PRT$ are all equations.

Helpful Hint

An equation contains the equal symbol "=". An algebraic expression does not.

✓Concept Check Which of the following are equations? Which are expressions?

a. $5x = 8$ **b.** $5x - 8$ **c.** $12y + 3x$ **d.** $12y = 3x$

When an equation contains a variable, deciding which value(s) of the variable make the equation a true statement is called **solving** the equation for the variable. A **solution** of an equation is a value for the variable that makes the equation a true statement. For example, 3 is a solution of the equation $x + 4 = 7$, because if x is replaced with 3 the statement is true.

$x + 4 = 7$
↓
$3 + 4 \stackrel{?}{=} 7$ Replace x with 3.
$7 = 7$

Similarly, 1 is not a solution of the equation $x + 4 = 7$, because $1 + 4 = 7$ is **not** a true statement.

Answers

7. a. 48 **b.** 7 **c.** $\frac{11}{12}$ **d.** $\frac{7}{4}$ **e.** 15

✓ Concept Check Answer

equations: **a, d**; expressions: **b, c**

PRACTICE 8

Decide whether 3 is a solution of $5x - 10 = x + 2$.

Example 8 Decide whether 2 is a solution of $3x + 10 = 8x$.

Solution: Replace x with 2 and see if a true statement results.

$3x + 10 = 8x$ Original equation

$3(2) + 10 \stackrel{?}{=} 8(2)$ Replace x with 2.

$6 + 10 \stackrel{?}{=} 16$ Simplify each side.

$16 = 16$ True

Since we arrived at a true statement after replacing x with 2 and simplifying both sides of the equation, 2 is a solution of the equation.

Work Practice 8

Objective D Translating Words to Symbols

Now that we know how to represent an unknown number by a variable, let's practice translating phrases into algebraic expressions (no "=" symbol) and sentences into equations (with "=" symbol). Oftentimes solving problems involves the ability to translate word phrases and sentences into symbols. Below is a list of key words and phrases to help us translate.

Helpful Hint

Order matters when subtracting and also dividing, so be especially careful with these translations.

Addition (+)	Subtraction (−)	Multiplication (·)	Division (÷)	Equality (=)
Sum	Difference of	Product	Quotient	Equals
Plus	Minus	Times	Divide	Gives
Added to	Subtracted from	Multiply	Into	Is/was/should be
More than	Less than	Twice	Ratio	Yields
Increased by	Decreased by	Of	Divided by	Amounts to
Total	Less			Represents
				Is the same as

PRACTICE 9

Write an algebraic expression that represents each phrase. Let the variable x represent the unknown number.

a. The product of 5 and a number

b. A number added to 7

c. A number divided by 11.2

d. A number subtracted from 8

e. Twice a number, plus 1

Example 9 Write an algebraic expression that represents each phrase. Let the variable x represent the unknown number.

a. The sum of a number and 3

b. The product of 3 and a number

c. The quotient of 7.3 and a number

d. 10 decreased by a number

e. 5 times a number, increased by 7

Solution:

a. $x + 3$ since "sum" means to add

b. $3 \cdot x$ and $3x$ are both ways to denote the product of 3 and x

c. $7.3 \div x$ or $\frac{7.3}{x}$

d. $10 - x$ because "decreased by" means to subtract

e. $\underbrace{5x}_{\text{5 times a number}} + 7$

Work Practice 9

Answers

8. It is a solution.

9. a. $5 \cdot x$ or $5x$. **b.** $7 + x$ **c.** $x \div 11.2$ or $\frac{x}{11.2}$ **d.** $8 - x$ **e.** $2x + 1$

Helpful Hint

Make sure you understand the difference when translating phrases containing "decreased by," "subtracted from," and "less than."

Phrase	Translation	
A number decreased by 10	$x - 10$	Notice the order.
A number subtracted from 10	$10 - x$	
10 less than a number	$x - 10$	
A number less 10	$x - 10$	

Now let's practice translating sentences into equations.

Example 10 Write each sentence as an equation. Let x represent the unknown number.

a. The quotient of 15 and a number is 4.
b. Three subtracted from 12 is a number.
c. 17 added to four times a number is 21.

Solution:

a. In words: the quotient of 15 and a number | is | 4

↓ ↓ ↓

Translate: $\frac{15}{x} = 4$

b. In words: three subtracted **from** 12 | is | a number

↓ ↓ ↓

Translate: $12 - 3 = x$

Care must be taken when the operation is subtraction. The expression $3 - 12$ would be incorrect. Notice that $3 - 12 \neq 12 - 3$.

c. In words: 17 | added to | four times a number | is | 21

↓ ↓ ↓ ↓

Translate: $17 + 4x = 21$

Work Practice 10

PRACTICE 10

Write each sentence as an equation. Let x represent the unknown number.

a. The ratio of a number and 6 is 24.

b. The difference of 10 and a number is 18.

c. One less than twice a number is 99.

Answers

10. a. $\frac{x}{6} = 24$, **b.** $10 - x = 18$, **c.** $2x - 1 = 99$

Calculator Explorations

Exponents

To evaluate exponential expressions on a calculator, find the key marked [y^x] or [∧]. To evaluate, for example, 6^5, press the following keys: [6] [y^x] [5] [=] or [6] [∧] [5] [=].

↕ or

[ENTER]

The display should read [7776]

Order of Operations

Some calculators follow the order of operations, and others do not. To see whether or not your calculator has the order of operations built in, use your calculator to find $2 + 3 \cdot 4$. To do this, press the following sequence of keys:

[2] [+] [3] [×] [4] [=]

↕ or

[ENTER]

The correct answer is 14 because the order of operations is to multiply before we add. If the calculator displays [14], then it has the order of operations built in.

Even if the order of operations is built in, parentheses must sometimes be inserted. For example, to simplify $\frac{5}{12 - 7}$, press the keys

[5] [÷] [(] [1] [2] [−] [7] [)] [=].

↕ or

[ENTER]

The display should read [1].

Use a calculator to evaluate each expression.

1. 5^3
2. 7^4
3. 9^5
4. 8^6
5. $2(20 - 5)$
6. $3(14 - 7) + 21$
7. $24(862 - 455) + 89$
8. $99 + (401 + 962)$
9. $\frac{4623 + 129}{36 - 34}$
10. $\frac{956 - 452}{89 - 86}$

Vocabulary and Readiness Check

Use the choices below to fill in each blank. Some choices may be used more than once.

addition	multiplication	exponent	expression	solution	evaluating the expression
subtraction	division	base	equation	variable(s)	

1. In 2^5, the 2 is called the ____________ and the 5 is called the ____________.
2. True or false: 2^5 means 2.5. ____________.
3. To simplify $8 + 2 \cdot 6$, which operation should be performed first? ____________
4. To simplify $(8 + 2) \cdot 6$, which operation should be performed first? ____________
5. To simplify $9(3 - 2) \div 3 + 6$, which operation should be performed first? ____________
6. To simplify $8 \div 2 \cdot 6$, which operation should be performed first? ____________
7. A combination of operations on letters (variables) and numbers is a(n) ____________.
8. A letter that represents a number is a(n) ____________.
9. $3x - 2y$ is called a(n) ____________ and the letters x and y are ____________.
10. Replacing a variable in an expression by a number and then finding the value of the expression is called ____________.
11. A statement of the form "expression = expression" is called a(n) ____________.
12. A value for the variable that makes the equation a true statement is called a(n) ____________.

8.2 Exercise Set

Objective **A** *Evaluate. See Example 1.*

1. 3^5 **2.** 5^4 **3.** 3^3 **4.** 4^4 **5.** 1^5 **6.** 1^8

7. 5^1 **8.** 8^1 **9.** 7^2 **10.** 9^2 **11.** $\left(\frac{2}{3}\right)^4$ **12.** $\left(\frac{6}{11}\right)^2$

13. $\left(\frac{1}{5}\right)^3$ **14.** $\left(\frac{1}{2}\right)^5$ **15.** $(1.2)^2$ **16.** $(1.5)^2$ **17.** $(0.7)^3$ **18.** $(0.4)^3$

△ **19.** The area of a square whose sides each measure 5 meters is $(5 \cdot 5)$ square meters. Write this area using exponential notation.

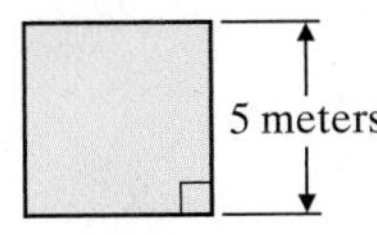

△ **20.** The area of a circle whose radius is 9 meters is $(9 \cdot 9 \cdot \pi)$ square meters. Write this area using exponential notation.

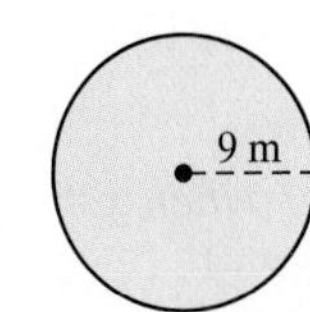

Simplify each expression. See Examples 2 through 6.

21. $5 + 6 \cdot 2$

22. $8 + 5 \cdot 3$

23. $4 \cdot 8 - 6 \cdot 2$

24. $12 \cdot 5 - 3 \cdot 6$

25. $18 \div 3 \cdot 2$

26. $48 \div 6 \cdot 2$

27. $2 + (5 - 2) + 4^2$

28. $6 - 2 \cdot 2 + 2^5$

29. $5 \cdot 3^2$

30. $2 \cdot 5^2$

31. $\frac{1}{4} \cdot \frac{2}{3} - \frac{1}{6}$

32. $\frac{3}{4} \cdot \frac{1}{2} + \frac{2}{3}$

33. $\frac{6 - 4}{9 - 2}$

34. $\frac{8 - 5}{24 - 20}$

35. $2[5 + 2(8 - 3)]$

36. $3[4 + 3(6 - 4)]$

37. $\frac{19 - 3 \cdot 5}{6 - 4}$

38. $\frac{14 - 2 \cdot 3}{12 - 8}$

39. $\frac{|6 - 2| + 3}{8 + 2 \cdot 5}$

40. $\frac{15 - |3 - 1|}{12 - 3 \cdot 2}$

41. $\frac{3 + 3(5 + 3)}{3^2 + 1}$

42. $\frac{3 + 6(8 - 5)}{4^2 + 2}$

43. $\frac{6 + |8 - 2| + 3^2}{18 - 3}$

44. $\frac{16 + |13 - 5| + 4^2}{17 - 5}$

45. $2 + 3[10(4 \cdot 5 - 16) - 30]$

46. $3 + 4[8(5 \cdot 5 - 20) - 41]$

47. $\left(\frac{2}{3}\right)^3 + \frac{1}{9} + \frac{1}{3} \cdot \frac{4}{3}$

48. $\left(\frac{3}{8}\right)^2 + \frac{1}{4} + \frac{1}{8} \cdot \frac{3}{2}$

Objective **B** *Evaluate each expression when $x = 1$, $y = 3$, and $z = 5$. See Example 7.*

49. $3y$

50. $4x$

51. $\frac{z}{5x}$

52. $\frac{y}{2z}$

53. $3x - 2$

54. $6y - 8$

55. $|2x + 3y|$

56. $|5z - 2y|$

57. $xy + z$

58. $yz - x$

59. $5y^2$

60. $2z^2$

Evaluate each expression when $x = 12$, $y = 8$, and $z = 4$. See Example 7.

61. $\frac{x}{z} + 3y$

62. $\frac{y}{z} + 8x$

63. $x^2 - 3y + x$

64. $y^2 - 3x + y$

65. $\frac{x^2 + z}{y^2 + 2z}$

66. $\frac{y^2 + x}{x^2 + 3y}$

Objective C *Decide whether the given number is a solution of the given equation. See Example 8.*

67. $3x - 6 = 9; 5$

68. $2x + 7 = 3x; 6$

69. $2x + 6 = 5x - 1; 0$

70. $4x + 2 = x + 8; 2$

71. $2x - 5 = 5; 8$

72. $3x - 10 = 8; 6$

73. $x + 6 = x + 6; 2$

74. $x + 6 = x + 6; 10$

75. $x = 5x + 15; 0$

76. $4 = 1 - x; 1$

77. $\frac{1}{3}x = 9; 27$

78. $\frac{2}{7}x = \frac{3}{14}; 6$

Objective D *Write each phrase as an algebraic expression. Let x represent the unknown number. See Example 9.*

79. Fifteen more than a number

80. A number increased by 9

81. Five subtracted from a number

82. Five decreased by a number

83. The ratio of a number and 4

84. The quotient of a number and 9

85. Three times a number, increased by 22

86. Twice a number, decreased by 72

Write each sentence as an equation or inequality. Use x to represent any unknown number. See Example 10.

87. One increased by two equals the quotient of nine and three.

88. Four subtracted from eight is equal to two squared.

89. Three is not equal to four divided by two.

90. The difference of sixteen and four is greater than ten.

91. The sum of 5 and a number is 20.

92. Seven subtracted from a number is 0.

93. The product of 7.6 and a number is 17.

94. 9.1 times a number equals 4

95. Thirteen minus three times a number is 13.

96. Eight added to twice a number is 42.

Concept Extensions

97. Are parentheses necessary in the expression $2 + (3 \cdot 5)$? Explain your answer.

98. Are parentheses necessary in the expression $(2 + 3) \cdot 5$? Explain your answer.

For Exercises 99 and 100, match each expression in the first column with its value in the second column.

99. a. $(6 + 2) \cdot (5 + 3)$ 19
b. $(6 + 2) \cdot 5 + 3$ 22
c. $6 + 2 \cdot 5 + 3$ 64
d. $6 + 2 \cdot (5 + 3)$ 43

100. a. $(1 + 4) \cdot 6 - 3$ 15
b. $1 + 4 \cdot (6 - 3)$ 13
c. $1 + 4 \cdot 6 - 3$ 27
d. $(1 + 4) \cdot (6 - 3)$ 22

△ *Recall that perimeter measures the distance around a plane figure and area measures the amount of surface of a plane figure. The expression $2l + 2w$ gives the perimeter of the rectangle below (measured in units), and the expression lw gives its area (measured in square units). Complete the chart below for the given lengths and widths. Be sure to include units.*

	Length: l	Width: w	Perimeter of Rectangle: $2l + 2w$	Area of Rectangle: lw
101.	4 in.	3 in.		
102.	6 in.	1 in.		
103.	5.3 in.	1.7 in.		
104.	4.6 in.	2.4 in.		

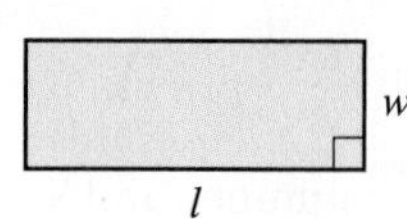

105. Study the perimeters and areas found in the chart to the left. Do you notice any trends?

106. In your own words, explain the difference between an expression and an equation.

107. Insert one set of parentheses so that the following expression simplifies to 32.

$20 - 4 \cdot 4 \div 2$

108. Insert parentheses so that the following expression simplifies to 28.

$2 \cdot 5 + 3^2$

Determine whether each is an expression or an equation. See the Concept Check in this section.

109. a. $5x + 6$
b. $2a = 7$
c. $3a + 2 = 9$
d. $4x + 3y - 8z$
e. $5^2 - 2(6 - 2)$

110. a. $3x^2 - 26$
b. $3x^2 - 26 = 1$
c. $2x - 5 = 7x - 5$
d. $9y + x - 8$
e. $3^2 - 4(5 - 3)$

△ **111.** Why is 4^3 usually read as "four cubed"? (*Hint:* What is the volume of the **cube** below?)

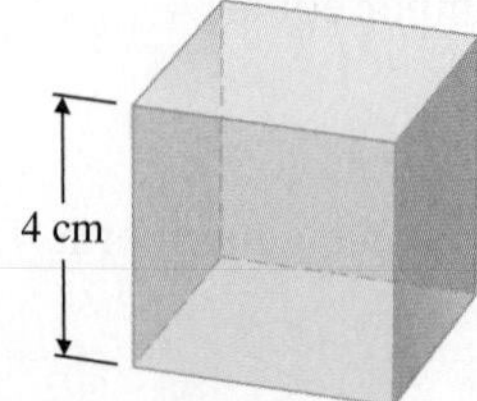

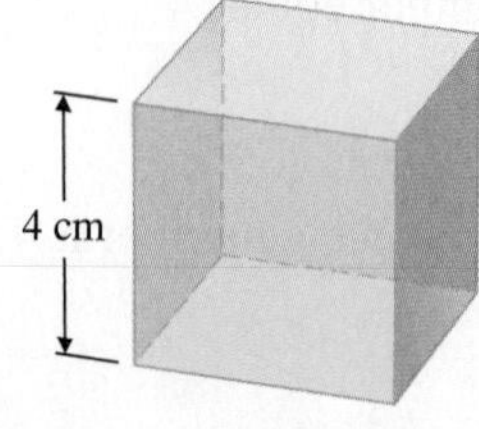

△ **112.** Why is 8^2 usually read as "eight squared"? (*Hint:* What is the area of the **square** below?)

8 inches

113. Write any expression, using 3 or more numbers, that simplifies to −11.

114. Write any expression, using 4 or more numbers, that simplifies to 7.

8.3 ADDING REAL NUMBERS

Objectives

A Add Real Numbers.

B Find the Opposite of a Number.

C Evaluate Algebraic Expressions Using Real Numbers.

D Solve Applications That Involve Addition of Real Numbers.

Real numbers can be added, subtracted, multiplied, divided, and raised to powers, just as whole numbers can.

Objective A Adding Real Numbers

Adding real numbers can be visualized by using a number line. A positive number can be represented on the number line by an arrow of appropriate length pointing to the right, and a negative number by an arrow of appropriate length pointing to the left.

Both arrows represent 2 or +2.

They both point to the right, and they are both 2 units long.

Both arrows represent −3.

They both point to the left, and they are both 3 units long.

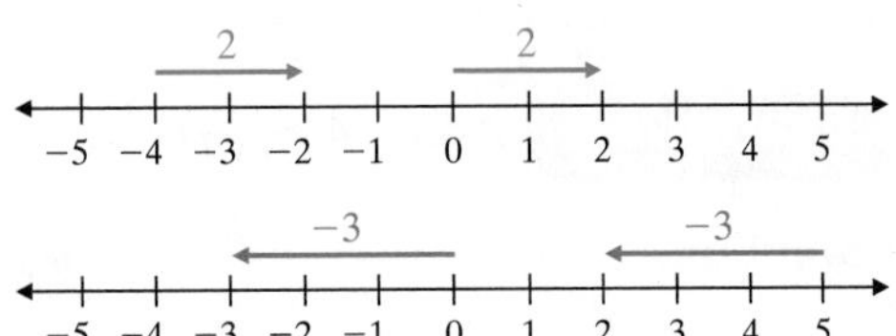

To add signed numbers such as $5 + (-2)$ on a number line, we start at 0 on the number line and draw an arrow representing 5. From the tip of this arrow, we draw another arrow representing −2. The tip of the second arrow ends at their sum, 3.

$$5 + (-2) = 3$$

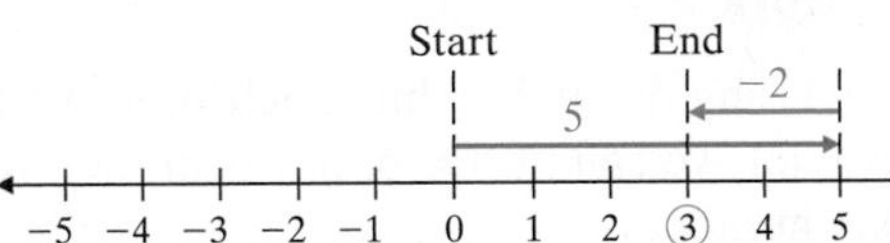

To add $-1 + (-4)$ on the number line, we start at 0 and draw an arrow representing −1. From the tip of this arrow, we draw another arrow representing −4. The tip of the second arrow ends at their sum, −5.

$$-1 + (-4) = -5$$

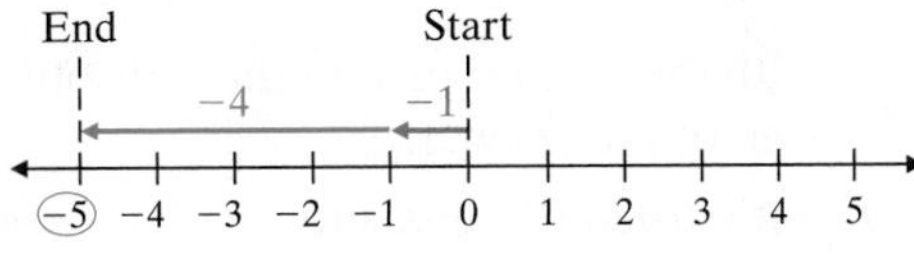

Example 1 Add: $-1 + (-2)$

Solution:

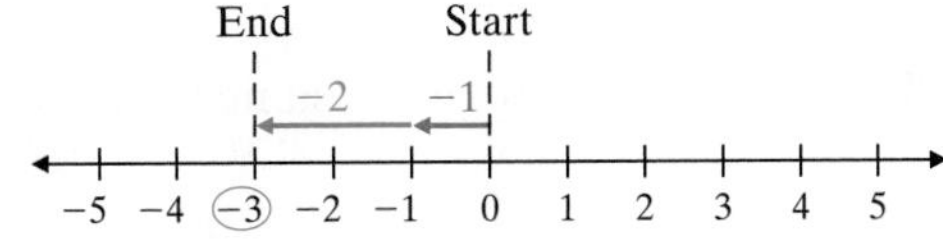

$$-1 + (-2) = -3$$

Work Practice 1

PRACTICE 1

Add using a number line:
$-2 + (-4)$

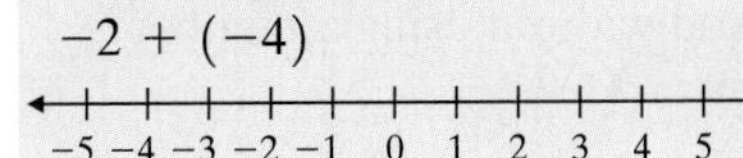

Thinking of integers as money earned or lost might help make addition more meaningful. Earnings can be thought of as positive numbers. If \$1 is earned and later another \$3 is earned, the total amount earned is \$4. In other words, $1 + 3 = 4$.

On the other hand, losses can be thought of as negative numbers. If \$1 is lost and later another \$3 is lost, a total of \$4 is lost. In other words, $(-1) + (-3) = -4$.

In Example 1, we added numbers with the same sign. Adding numbers whose signs are not the same can be pictured on a number line also.

Answer
1. −6

PRACTICE 2

Add using a number line:
$-5 + 8$

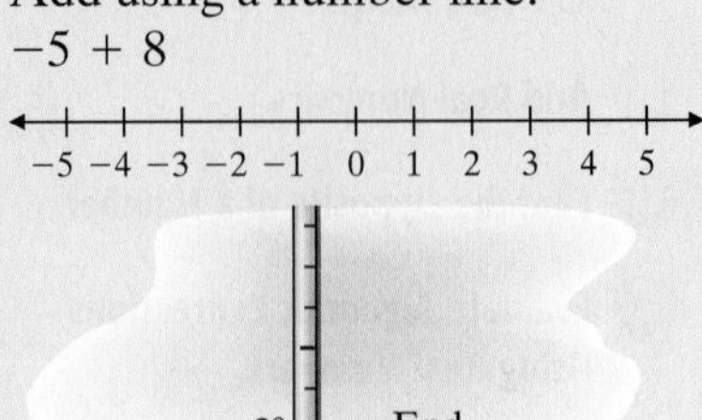

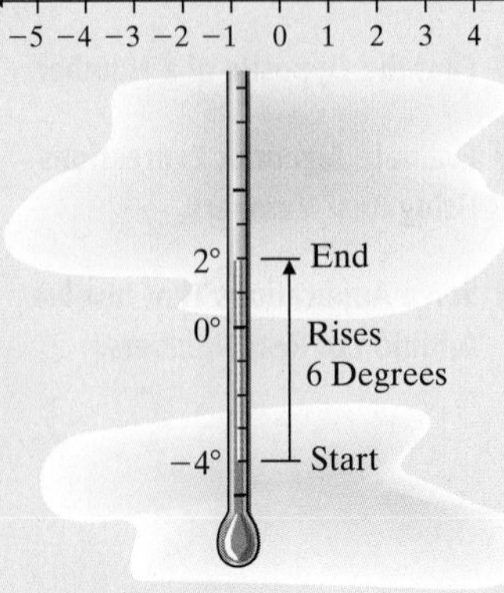

Example 2 Add: $-4 + 6$

Solution:

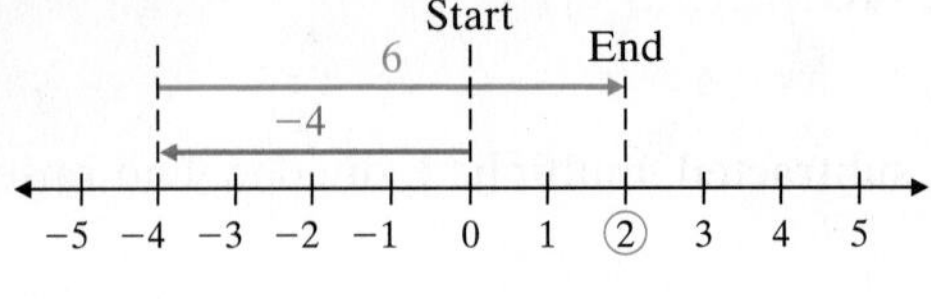

$-4 + 6 = 2$

Work Practice 2

Let's use temperature as an example. If the thermometer registers 4 degrees below 0 degrees and then rises 6 degrees, the new temperature is 2 degrees above 0 degrees. Thus, it is reasonable that $-4 + 6 = 2$. (See the diagram in the margin.)

PRACTICE 3

Add using a number line:
$5 + (-4)$

−5 −4 −3 −2 −1 0 1 2 3 4 5

Example 3 Add: $4 + (-6)$

Solution:

$4 + (-6) = -2$

Start
End
−6
4
−5 −4 −3 −2 −1 0 1 2 3 4 5

Work Practice 3

Using a number line each time we add two numbers can be time consuming. Instead, we can notice patterns in the previous examples and write rules for adding real numbers.

Adding Real Numbers

To add two real numbers

1. with the *same sign,* add their absolute values. Use their common sign as the sign of the answer.
2. with *different signs,* subtract their absolute values. Give the answer the same sign as the number with the larger absolute value.

PRACTICE 4

Add without using a number line: $(-8) + (-5)$

Example 4 Add without using a number line: $(-7) + (-6)$

Solution: Here, we are adding two numbers with the same sign.

$(-7) + (-6) = -13$

↑ same sign
↖ sum of absolute values ($|-7| = 7, |-6| = 6, 7 + 6 = 13$)

Work Practice 4

PRACTICE 5

Add without using a number line: $(-14) + 6$

Example 5 Add without using a number line: $(-10) + 4$

Solution: Here, we are adding two numbers with different signs.

$(-10) + 4 = -6$

↑ sign of number with larger absolute value, -10
↖ difference of absolute values ($|-10| = 10, |4| = 4, 10 - 4 = 6$)

Work Practice 5

Answers
2. 3 **3.** 1 **4.** −13 **5.** −8

Examples Add without using a number line.

6. $(-8) + (-11) = -19$
7. $(-2) + 10 = 8$
8. $0.2 + (-0.5) = -0.3$
9. $-\frac{7}{10} + \left(-\frac{1}{10}\right) = -\frac{8}{10} = -\frac{\overset{1}{\cancel{2}} \cdot 4}{\underset{1}{\cancel{2}} \cdot 5} = -\frac{4}{5}$
10. $11.4 + (-4.7) = 6.7$
11. $-\frac{3}{8} + \frac{2}{5} = -\frac{15}{40} + \frac{16}{40} = \frac{1}{40}$

Work Practice 6–11

PRACTICE 6–11

Add without using a number line.

6. $(-17) + (-10)$
7. $(-4) + 12$
8. $1.5 + (-3.2)$
9. $-\frac{5}{12} + \left(-\frac{1}{12}\right)$
10. $12.1 + (-3.6)$
11. $-\frac{4}{5} + \frac{2}{3}$

In Example 12a, we add three numbers. Remember that by the associative and commutative properties for addition, we may add numbers in any order that we wish. For Example 12a, let's add the numbers from left to right.

Example 12 Find each sum.

a. $3 + (-7) + (-8)$
b. $[7 + (-10)] + [-2 + (-4)]$

Solution:

a. Perform the additions from left to right.

$3 + (-7) + (-8) = -4 + (-8)$ Adding numbers with different signs
$= -12$ Adding numbers with like signs

b. Simplify inside the brackets first.

$[7 + (-10)] + [-2 + (-4)] = [-3] + [-6]$
$= -9$ Add.

Work Practice 12

PRACTICE 12

Find each sum.

a. $16 + (-9) + (-9)$
b. $[3 + (-13)] + [-4 + (-7)]$

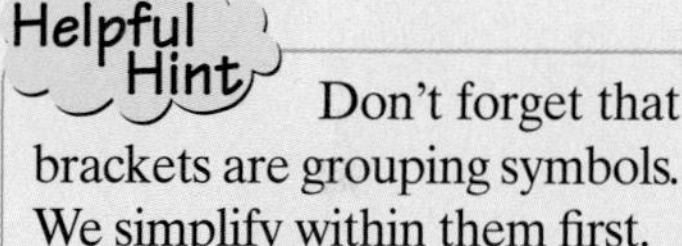

Don't forget that brackets are grouping symbols. We simplify within them first.

Objective B Finding Opposites

To help us subtract real numbers in the next section, we first review what we mean by opposites. The graphs of 4 and −4 are shown on the number line below.

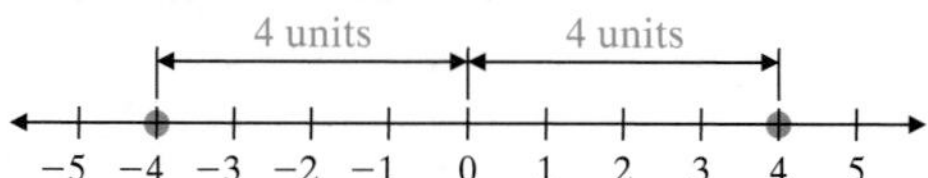

Notice that the graphs of 4 and −4 lie on opposite sides of 0, and each is 4 units away from 0. Such numbers are known as **opposites** or **additive inverses** of each other.

Opposite or Additive Inverse

Two numbers that are the same distance from 0 but lie on opposite sides of 0 are called **opposites** or **additive inverses** of each other.

Answers
6. −27 7. 8 8. −1.7 9. $-\frac{1}{2}$ 10. 8.5 11. $-\frac{2}{15}$ 12. a. −2 b. −21

PRACTICE 13–16

Find the opposite of each number.

13. -35 **14.** 12

15. $-\frac{3}{11}$ **16.** 1.9

Examples Find the opposite of each number.

13. 10 The opposite of 10 is -10.

14. -3 The opposite of -3 is 3.

15. $\frac{1}{2}$ The opposite of $\frac{1}{2}$ is $-\frac{1}{2}$.

16. -4.5 The opposite of -4.5 is 4.5.

Work Practice 13–16

We use the symbol "−" to represent the phrase "the opposite of" or "the additive inverse of." In general, if a is a number, we write the opposite or additive inverse of a as $-a$. We know that the opposite of -3 is 3. Notice that this translates as

the opposite of	−3	is	3
↓	↓	↓	↓
$-$	(-3)	$=$	**3**

This is true in general.

If a is a number, then $-(-a) = a$.

PRACTICE 17

Simplify each expression.

a. $-(-22)$

b. $-\left(-\frac{2}{7}\right)$

c. $-(-x)$

d. $-|-14|$

e. $-|2.3|$

Example 17 Simplify each expression.

a. $-(-10)$ **b.** $-\left(-\frac{1}{2}\right)$ **c.** $-(-2x)$

d. $-|-6|$ **e.** $-|4.1|$

Solution:

a. $-(-10) = 10$

b. $-\left(-\frac{1}{2}\right) = \frac{1}{2}$

c. $-(-2x) = 2x$

d. $-|-6| = -6$ Since $|-6| = 6$.

e. $-|4.1| = -4.1$ Since $|4.1| = 4.1$

Work Practice 17

Let's discover another characteristic about opposites. Notice that the sum of a number and its opposite is always 0.

$10 + (-10) = 0$ (opposites) $-3 + 3 = 0$ (opposites)

$\frac{1}{2} + \left(-\frac{1}{2}\right) = 0$ (opposites)

In general, we can write the following:

The sum of a number a and its opposite $-a$ is 0.

$a + (-a) = 0$ Also, $-a + a = 0$.

Notice that this means that the opposite of 0 is then 0 since $0 + 0 = 0$.

Answers

13. 35 **14.** −12 **15.** $\frac{3}{11}$ **16.** −1.9

17. a. 22 **b.** $\frac{2}{7}$ **c.** x **d.** −14 **e.** −2.3

Examples Add.

18. $-56 + 56 = 0$

19. $17 + (-17) = 0$

Work Practice 18–19

PRACTICE 18–19

Add.

18. $30 + (-30)$

19. $-81 + 81$

✓**Concept Check** What is wrong with the following calculation?

$5 + (-22) = 17$

Objective C Evaluating Algebraic Expressions

We can continue our work with algebraic expressions by evaluating expressions given real-number replacement values.

Example 20 Evaluate $2x + y$ for $x = 3$ and $y = -5$.

Solution: Replace x with 3 and y with -5 in $2x + y$.

$$\begin{aligned} 2x + y &= 2 \cdot 3 + (-5) \\ &= 6 + (-5) \\ &= 1 \end{aligned}$$

Work Practice 20

PRACTICE 20

Evaluate $x + 3y$ for $x = -6$ and $y = 2$.

Example 21 Evaluate $x + y$ for $x = -2$ and $y = -10$.

Solution: $x + y = (-2) + (-10)$ Replace x with -2 and y with -10.

$= -12$

Work Practice 21

PRACTICE 21

Evaluate $x + y$ for $x = -13$ and $y = -9$.

Objective D Solving Applications That Involve Addition

Positive and negative numbers are used in everyday life. Stock market returns show gains and losses as positive and negative numbers. Temperatures in cold climates often dip into the negative range, commonly referred to as "below zero" temperatures. Bank statements report deposits and withdrawals as positive and negative numbers.

Example 22 Calculating Temperature

In Philadelphia, Pennsylvania, the record extreme high temperature is 104°F. Decrease this temperature by 111 degrees, and the result is the record extreme low temperature. Find this temperature. (*Source:* National Climatic Data Center)

Solution:

In words:	extreme low temperature	=	extreme high temperature	+	decrease of 111°
	↓		↓		↓
Translate:	extreme low temperature	=	104	+	(−111)
		= −7			

The record extreme low temperature in Philadelphia, Pennsylvania, is −7°F.

Work Practice 22

PRACTICE 22

If the temperature was −7° Fahrenheit at 6 a.m., and it rose 4 degrees by 7 a.m. and then rose another 7 degrees in the hour from 7 a.m. to 8 a.m., what was the temperature at 8 a.m.?

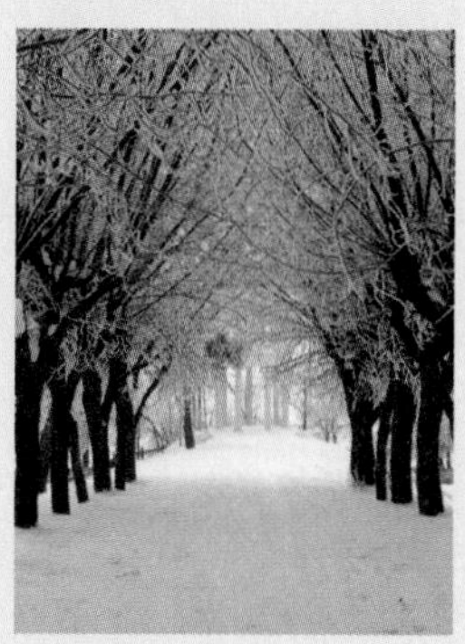

Answers

18. 0 **19.** 0 **20.** 0 **21.** −22 **22.** 4°F

✓ **Concept Check Answer**

$5 + (-22) = -17$

Vocabulary and Readiness Check

Use the choices below to fill in each blank. Not all choices will be used.

$-a$ $\quad a \quad$ 0 $\quad$ commutative $\quad$ associative

1. If n is a number, then $-n + n =$ ___________.
2. Since $x + n = n + x$, we say that addition is ___________.
3. If a is a number, then $-(-a) =$ ___________.
4. Since $n + (x + a) = (n + x) + a$, we say that addition is ___________.

8.3 Exercise Set

FOR EXTRA HELP

PRACTICE

WATCH

DOWNLOAD

READ

REVIEW

Objectives **A B Mixed Practice** *Add. See Examples 1 through 12, 18 and 19.*

1. $6 + (-3)$ **2.** $9 + (-12)$ **3.** $-6 + (-8)$ **4.** $-6 + (-14)$

5. $8 + (-7)$ **6.** $16 + (-4)$ **7.** $-14 + 2$ **8.** $-10 + 5$

9. $-2 + (-3)$ **10.** $-7 + (-4)$ **11.** $-9 + (-3)$ **12.** $-11 + (-5)$

13. $-7 + 3$ **14.** $-5 + 9$ **15.** $10 + (-3)$ **16.** $8 + (-6)$

17. $5 + (-7)$ **18.** $3 + (-6)$ **19.** $-16 + 16$ **20.** $23 + (-23)$

21. $27 + (-46)$ **22.** $53 + (-37)$ **23.** $-18 + 49$ **24.** $-26 + 14$

25. $-33 + (-14)$ **26.** $-18 + (-26)$ **27.** $6.3 + (-8.4)$ **28.** $9.2 + (-11.4)$

29. $117 + (-79)$ **30.** $144 + (-88)$ **31.** $-9.6 + (-3.5)$ **32.** $-6.7 + (-7.6)$

33. $-\frac{3}{8} + \frac{5}{8}$ **34.** $-\frac{5}{12} + \frac{7}{12}$ **35.** $-\frac{7}{16} + \frac{1}{4}$ **36.** $-\frac{5}{9} + \frac{1}{3}$

37. $-\frac{7}{10} + \left(-\frac{3}{5}\right)$ **38.** $-\frac{5}{6} + \left(-\frac{2}{3}\right)$ **39.** $|-8| + (-16)$ **40.** $|-6| + (-61)$

41. $-15 + 9 + (-2)$ **42.** $-9 + 15 + (-5)$ **43.** $-21 + (-16) + (-22)$ **44.** $-18 + (-6) + (-40)$

45. $-23 + 16 + (-2)$ **46.** $-14 + (-3) + 11$ **47.** $|5 + (-10)|$ **48.** $|7 + (-17)|$

49. $6 + (-4) + 9$ **50.** $8 + (-2) + 7$ **51.** $[-17 + (-4)] + [-12 + 15]$

52. $[-2 + (-7)] + [-11 + 22]$ **53.** $|9 + (-12)| + |-16|$ **54.** $|43 + (-73)| + |-20|$

55. $-13 + [5 + (-3) + 4]$

56. $-30 + [1 + (-6) + 8]$

57. Find the sum of -38 and 12.

58. Find the sum of -44 and 16.

Objective B *Find each additive inverse or opposite. See Examples 13 through 17.*

59. 6

60. 4

61. -2

62. -8

63. 0

64. $-\frac{1}{4}$

65. $|-6|$

66. $|-11|$

Simplify each of the following. See Example 17.

67. $-|-2|$

68. $-|-5|$

69. $-(-7)$

70. $-(-14)$

71. $-(-7.9)$

72. $-(-8.4)$

73. $-(-5z)$

74. $-(-7m)$

75. $\left|-\frac{2}{3}\right|$

76. $-\left|-\frac{2}{3}\right|$

Objective C *Evaluate $x + y$ for the given replacement values. See Examples 20 and 21.*

77. $x = -20$ and $y = -50$

78. $x = -1$ and $y = -29$

Evaluate $3x + y$ for the given replacement values. See Examples 20 and 21.

79. $x = 2$ and $y = -3$

80. $x = 7$ and $y = -11$

Objective D **Translating** *Translate each phrase; then simplify. See Example 22.*

81. Find the sum of -6 and 25.

82. Find the sum of -30 and 15.

83. Find the sum of -31, -9, and 30.

84. Find the sum of -49, -2, and 40.

Solve. See Example 22.

85. Suppose a deep-sea diver dives from the surface to 215 feet below the surface. He then dives down 16 more feet. Use positive and negative numbers to represent this situation. Then find the diver's present depth.

86. Suppose a diver dives from the surface to 248 meters below the surface and then swims up 8 meters, down 16 meters, down another 28 meters, and then up 32 meters. Use positive and negative numbers to represent this situation. Then find the diver's depth after these movements.

87. The lowest temperature ever recorded in Massachusetts was -35°F. The highest recorded temperature in Massachusetts was 142° higher than the record low temperature. Find Massachusetts' highest recorded temperature. (*Source:* National Climatic Data Center)

88. On January 2, 1943, the temperature was $-4°$ at 7:30 a.m. in Spearfish, South Dakota. Incredibly, it got 49° warmer in the next 2 minutes. To what temperature did it rise by 7:32?

89. The lowest elevation on Earth is −411 meters (that is, 411 meters below sea level) at the Dead Sea. If you are standing 316 meters above the Dead Sea, what is your elevation? (*Source:* National Geographic Society)

90. The lowest elevation in Australia is −52 feet at Lake Eyre. If you are standing at a point 439 feet above Lake Eyre, what is your elevation? (*Source:* National Geographic Society)

91. During the PGA 2008 Wyndham Championship tournament, the winner, Carl Pettersson, had scores of −6, −9, −4, and −2. What was his total score for the tournament? (*Source:* Professional Golfer's Association)

92. Catriona Matthew won the HSBC LPGA Brasil Cup 2009 Tournament with the following hole scores for round 1: −2, +2, −2, −2, −2. What was her final score for round 1? (*Source:* LPGA of America)

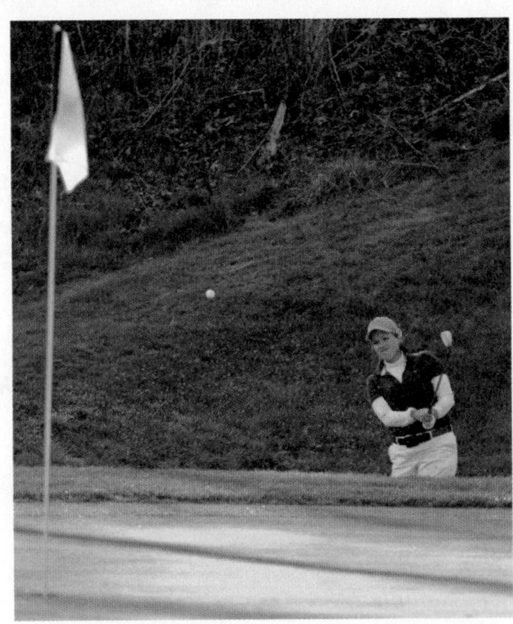

93. A negative net income results when a company spends more money than it brings in. Johnson Outdoors Inc. had the following quarterly net incomes during its 2009 fiscal year. (*Source:* Yahoo Finance)

Quarter of Fiscal 2009	Net Income (in millions)
First	2.5
Second	9
Third	−14.2
Fourth	−4.2

What was the total net income for fiscal year 2009?

94. LeapFrog Enterprises Inc. had the following quarterly net incomes during its 2009 fiscal year. (*Source:* Yahoo Finance)

Quarter of Fiscal 2009	Net Income (in millions)
First	−27.1
Second	−12.2
Third	7.2
Fourth	29.4

What was the total net income for fiscal year 2009?

Concept Extensions

The following bar graph shows each month's average daily low temperature in degrees Fahrenheit for Barrow, Alaska. Use this graph to answer Exercises 95 through 100.

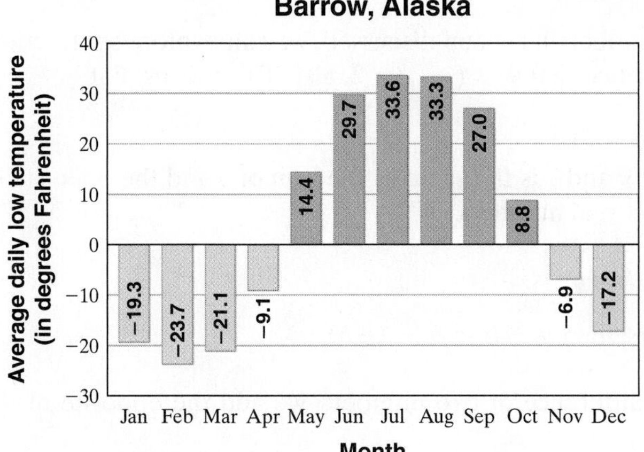

Source: National Climatic Data Center

95. For what month is the graphed temperature the highest?

96. For what month is the graphed temperature the lowest?

97. For what month is the graphed temperature positive *and* closest to 0°?

98. For what month is the graphed temperature negative *and* closest to 0°?

99. Find the average of the temperatures shown for the months of April, May, and October. (To find the average of three temperatures, find their sum and divide by 3.)

100. Find the average of the temperatures shown for the months of January, September, and October. (To find the average of three temperatures, find their sum and divide by 3.)

101. Name 2 numbers whose sum is −17.

102. Name 2 numbers whose sum is −30.

Each calculation below is incorrect. Find the error and correct it. See the Concept Check in this section.

103. $7 + (-10) \stackrel{?}{=} 17$

104. $-4 + 14 \stackrel{?}{=} -18$

105. $-10 + (-12) \stackrel{?}{=} -120$

106. $-15 + (-17) \stackrel{?}{=} 32$

For Exercises 107 through 110, determine whether each statement is true or false.

107. The sum of two negative numbers is always a negative number.

108. The sum of two positive numbers is always a positive number.

109. The sum of a positive number and a negative number is always a negative number.

110. The sum of zero and a negative number is always a negative number.

111. In your own words, explain how to add two negative numbers.

112. In your own words, explain how to add a positive number and a negative number.

Objectives

A Subtract Real Numbers.

B Evaluate Algebraic Expressions Using Real Numbers.

C Determine Whether a Number Is a Solution of a Given Equation.

D Solve Applications That Involve Subtraction of Real Numbers.

E Find Complementary and Supplementary Angles.

8.4 SUBTRACTING REAL NUMBERS

Objective A Subtracting Real Numbers

Now that addition of real numbers has been discussed, we can explore subtraction. We know that $9 - 7 = 2$. Notice that $9 + (-7) = 2$, also. This means that

$$9 - 7 = 9 + (-7)$$

Notice that the *difference* of 9 and 7 is the same as the *sum* of 9 and the opposite of 7. This is how we can subtract real numbers.

Subtracting Real Numbers

If a and b are real numbers, then $a - b = a + (-b)$.

In other words, to find the difference of two numbers, we add the opposite of the number being subtracted.

PRACTICE 1

Subtract.

a. $-20 - 6$
b. $3 - (-5)$
c. $7 - 17$
d. $-4 - (-9)$

Example 1 Subtract.

a. $-13 - 4$ **b.** $5 - (-6)$ **c.** $3 - 6$ **d.** $-1 - (-7)$

Solution:

a. $-13 - 4 = -13 + (-4)$ (add; opposite) Add −13 to the opposite of 4, which is −4.
$= -17$

b. $5 - (-6) = 5 + (6)$ (add; opposite) Add 5 to the opposite of −6, which is 6.
$= 11$

c. $3 - 6 = 3 + (-6)$ Add 3 to the opposite of 6, which is −6.
$= -3$

d. $-1 - (-7) = -1 + (7) = 6$

Work Practice 1

Helpful Hint

Study the patterns indicated.

No change — Change to addition. — Change to opposite.

$$5 - 11 = 5 + (-11) = -6$$
$$-3 - 4 = -3 + (-4) = -7$$
$$7 - (-1) = 7 + (1) = 8$$

PRACTICE 2–4

Subtract.

2. $9.6 - (-5.7)$

3. $-\frac{4}{9} - \frac{2}{9}$

4. $-\frac{1}{4} - \left(\frac{2}{5}\right)$

Examples Subtract.

2. $5.3 - (-4.6) = 5.3 + (4.6) = 9.9$

3. $-\frac{3}{10} - \frac{5}{10} = -\frac{3}{10} + \left(-\frac{5}{10}\right) = -\frac{8}{10} = -\frac{4}{5}$

4. $-\frac{2}{3} - \left(-\frac{4}{5}\right) = -\frac{2}{3} + \left(\frac{4}{5}\right) = -\frac{10}{15} + \frac{12}{15} = \frac{2}{15}$

Work Practice 2–4

Answers

1. a. −26 **b.** 8 **c.** −10 **d.** 5
2. 15.3 **3.** $-\frac{2}{3}$ **4.** $\frac{3}{20}$

Example 5 Write each phrase as an expression and simplify.

a. Subtract 8 from −4. **b.** Decrease 10 by −20.

Solution: Be careful when interpreting these. The order of numbers in subtraction is important.

a. 8 is to be subtracted **from** −4.

$-4 - 8 = -4 + (-8) = -12$

b. To decrease 10 by −20, we find 10 **minus** −20.

$10 - (-20) = 10 + 20 = 30$

Work Practice 5

PRACTICE 5

Write each phrase as an expression and simplify.

a. Subtract 7 from −11.

b. Decrease 35 by −25.

If an expression contains additions and subtractions, just write the subtractions as equivalent additions. Then simplify from left to right.

Example 6 Simplify each expression.

a. $-14 - 8 + 10 - (-6)$ **b.** $1.6 - (-10.3) + (-5.6)$

Solution:

a. $-14 - 8 + 10 - (-6) = -14 + (-8) + 10 + 6 = -6$

b. $1.6 - (-10.3) + (-5.6) = 1.6 + 10.3 + (-5.6) = 6.3$

Work Practice 6

PRACTICE 6

Simplify each expression.

a. $-20 - 5 + 12 - (-3)$

b. $5.2 - (-4.4) + (-8.8)$

When an expression contains parentheses and brackets, remember the order of operations. Start with the innermost set of parentheses or brackets and work your way outward.

Example 7 Simplify each expression.

a. $-3 + [(-2 - 5) - 2]$ **b.** $2^3 - 10 + [-6 - (-5)]$

Solution:

a. Start with the innermost set of parentheses. Rewrite $-2 - 5$ as an addition.

$-3 + [(-2 - 5) - 2] = -3 + [(-2 + (-5)) - 2]$

$= -3 + [(-7) - 2]$ Add: $-2 + (-5)$.

$= -3 + [-7 + (-2)]$ Write $-7 - 2$ as an addition.

$= -3 + [-9]$ Add.

$= -12$ Add.

b. Start simplifying the expression inside the brackets by writing $-6 - (-5)$ as an addition.

$2^3 - 10 + [-6 - (-5)] = 2^3 - 10 + [-6 + 5]$

$= 2^3 - 10 + [-1]$ Add.

$= 8 - 10 + (-1)$ Evaluate 2^3.

$= 8 + (-10) + (-1)$ Write $8 - 10$ as an addition.

$= -2 + (-1)$ Add.

$= -3$ Add.

Work Practice 7

PRACTICE 7

Simplify each expression.

a. $-9 + [(-4 - 1) - 10]$

b. $5^2 - 20 + [-11 - (-3)]$

Answers

5. a. −18 **b.** 60 **6. a.** −10 **b.** 0.8 **7. a.** −24 **b.** −3

Objective B Evaluating Algebraic Expressions

It is important to be able to evaluate expressions for given replacement values. This helps, for example, when checking solutions of equations.

PRACTICE 8

Find the value of each expression when $x = 1$ and $y = -4$.

a. $\dfrac{x - y}{14 + x}$

b. $x^2 - y$

Example 8 Find the value of each expression when $x = 2$ and $y = -5$.

a. $\dfrac{x - y}{12 + x}$ **b.** $x^2 - y$

Solution:

a. Replace x with 2 and y with -5. Be sure to put parentheses around -5 to separate signs. Then simplify the resulting expression.

$$\frac{x - y}{12 + x} = \frac{2 - (-5)}{12 + 2} = \frac{2 + 5}{14} = \frac{7}{14} = \frac{1}{2}$$

b. Replace x with 2 and y with -5 and simplify.

$$x^2 - y = 2^2 - (-5) = 4 - (-5) = 4 + 5 = 9$$

Work Practice 8

Helpful Hint

For additional help when replacing variables with replacement values, first place parentheses about any variables.

For Example 8b above, we have

$$x^2 - y = \underbrace{(x)^2 - (y)}_{\text{Place parentheses about variables}} = \underbrace{(2)^2 - (-5)}_{\text{Replace variables with values}} = 4 - (-5) = 4 + 5 = 9$$

Objective C Solutions of Equations

Recall from Section 8.2 that a solution of an equation is a value for the variable that makes the equation true.

PRACTICE 9

Determine whether -2 is a solution of $-1 + x = 1$.

Example 9 Determine whether -4 is a solution of $x - 5 = -9$.

Solution: Replace x with -4 and see if a true statement results.

$$\begin{aligned} x - 5 &= -9 && \text{Original equation} \\ -4 - 5 &\stackrel{?}{=} -9 && \text{Replace } x \text{ with } -4. \\ -4 + (-5) &\stackrel{?}{=} -9 \\ -9 &= -9 && \text{True} \end{aligned}$$

Thus -4 is a solution of $x - 5 = -9$.

Work Practice 9

Objective D Solving Applications That Involve Subtraction

Another use of real numbers is in recording altitudes above and below sea level, as shown in the next example.

Answers

8. a. $\frac{1}{3}$ **b.** 5 **9.** -2 is not a solution.

Example 10 Finding a Change in Elevation

The highest point in the United States is the top of Mount McKinley, at a height of 20,320 feet above sea level. The lowest point is Death Valley, California, which is 282 feet below sea level. How much higher is Mount McKinley than Death Valley? (*Source:* U.S. Geological Survey)

Solution: To find "how much higher," we subtract. Don't forget that since Death Valley is 282 feet *below* sea level, we represent its height by −282. Draw a diagram to help visualize the problem.

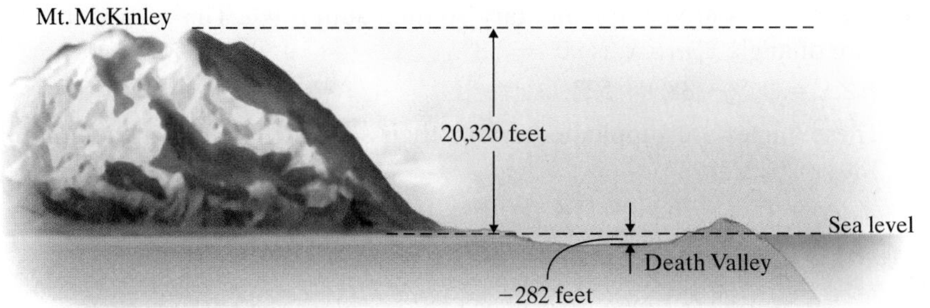

In words:	how much higher is Mt. McKinley	=	height of Mt. McKinley	minus	height of Death Valley
	↓	↓	↓	↓	↓
Translate:	how much higher is Mt. McKinley	=	20,320	−	(−282)

$= 20{,}320 + 282$

$= 20{,}602$

Thus, Mount McKinley is 20,602 feet higher than Death Valley.

Work Practice 10

PRACTICE 10

The highest point in Asia is the top of Mount Everest, at a height of 29,028 feet above sea level. The lowest point is the Dead Sea, which is 1312 feet below sea level. How much higher is Mount Everest than the Dead Sea? (*Source:* National Geographic Society)

Objective E Finding Complementary and Supplementary Angles

A knowledge of geometric concepts is needed by many professionals, such as doctors, carpenters, electronic technicians, gardeners, machinists, and pilots, just to name a few. With this in mind, we review the geometric concepts of **complementary** and **supplementary angles.**

Complementary and Supplementary Angles

Two angles are **complementary** if the sum of their measures is 90°.

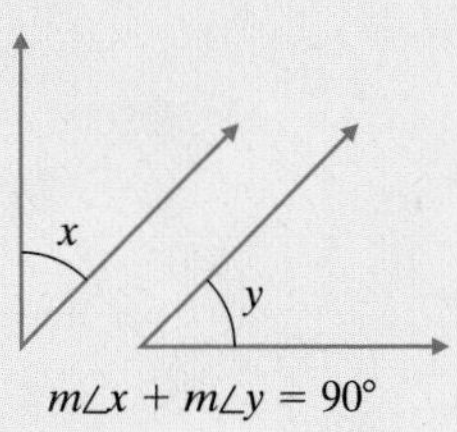

$m\angle x + m\angle y = 90°$

Two angles are **supplementary** if the sum of their measures is 180°.

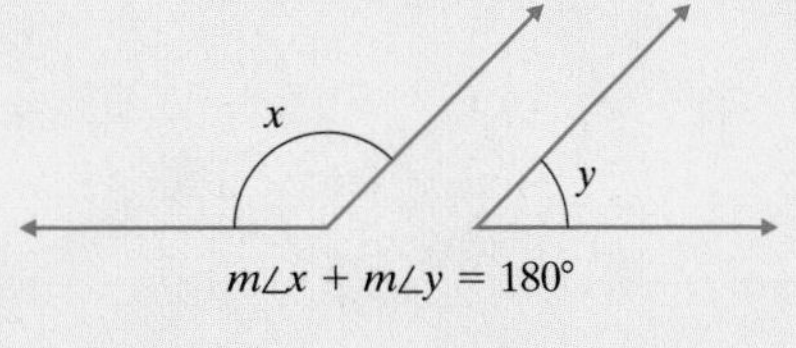

$m\angle x + m\angle y = 180°$

Answer

10. 30,340 ft

PRACTICE 11

Find the measure of each unknown complementary or supplementary angle.

a.

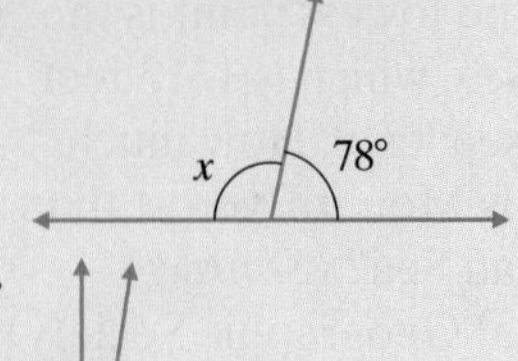

b.

Example 11 Find the measure of each unknown complementary or supplementary angle.

a.

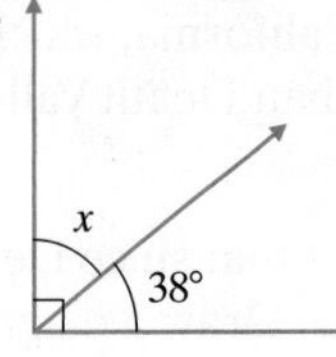

b.

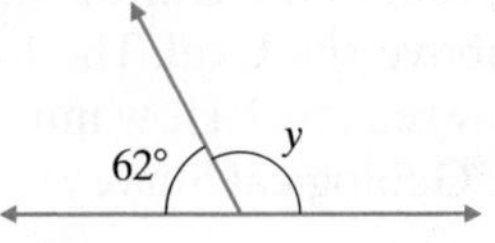

Solution:

a. These angles are complementary, so their sum is 90°. This means that the measure of angle x, $m\angle x$, is $90° - 38°$.

$m\angle x = 90° - 38° = 52°$

b. These angles are supplementary, so their sum is 180°. This means that $m\angle y$ is $180° - 62°$.

$m\angle y = 180° - 62° = 118°$

Work Practice 11

Answers

11. a. 102° **b.** 9°

Vocabulary and Readiness Check

Multiple choice: Select the correct lettered response following each exercise.

1. It is true that $a - b =$ __________.

a. $b - a$ **b.** $a + (-b)$ **c.** $a + b$

2. The opposite of n is __________.

a. $-n$ **b.** $-(-n)$ **c.** n

3. To evaluate $x - y$ for $x = -10$ and $y = -14$, we replace x with -10 and y with -14 and evaluate __________.

a. $10 - 14$ **b.** $-10 - 14$ **c.** $-14 - 10$ **d.** $-10 - (-14)$

4. The expression $-5 - 10$ equals __________.

a. $5 - 10$ **b.** $5 + 10$ **c.** $-5 + (-10)$ **d.** $10 - 5$

8.4 Exercise Set

FOR EXTRA HELP

PRACTICE

WATCH

DOWNLOAD

READ

REVIEW

Objective A *Subtract. See Examples 1 through 4.*

1. $-6 - 4$ **2.** $-12 - 8$ **3.** $4 - 9$ **4.** $8 - 11$ **5.** $16 - (-3)$

6. $12 - (-5)$ **7.** $7 - (-4)$ **8.** $3 - (-6)$ **9.** $-26 - (-18)$ **10.** $-60 - (-48)$

11. $-6 - 5$ **12.** $-8 - 4$ **13.** $16 - (-21)$ **14.** $15 - (-33)$ **15.** $-6 - (-11)$

16. $-4 - (-16)$ **17.** $-44 - 27$ **18.** $-36 - 51$ **19.** $-21 - (-21)$ **20.** $-17 - (-17)$

21. $-\frac{3}{11} - \left(-\frac{5}{11}\right)$ **22.** $-\frac{4}{7} - \left(-\frac{1}{7}\right)$ **23.** $9.7 - 16.1$ **24.** $8.3 - 11.2$ **25.** $-2.6 - (-6.7)$

26. $-6.1 - (-5.3)$ **27.** $\frac{1}{2} - \frac{2}{3}$ **28.** $\frac{3}{4} - \frac{7}{8}$ **29.** $-\frac{1}{6} - \frac{3}{4}$ **30.** $-\frac{1}{10} - \frac{7}{8}$

31. $8.3 - (-0.62)$ **32.** $4.3 - (-0.87)$ **33.** $0 - 8.92$ **34.** $0 - (-4.21)$

Translating *Translate each phrase to an expression and simplify. See Example 5.*

35. Subtract -5 from 8.

36. Subtract -2 from 3.

37. Find the difference between -6 and -1.

38. Find the difference between -17 and -1.

39. Subtract 8 from 7.

40. Subtract 9 from -4.

41. Decrease -8 by 15.

42. Decrease 11 by -14.

Mixed Practice (*Sections 8.2, 8.3, 8.4*) *Simplify each expression. (Remember the order of operations.) See Examples 6 and 7.*

43. $-10 - (-8) + (-4) - 20$

44. $-16 - (-3) + (-11) - 14$

45. $5 - 9 + (-4) - 8 - 8$

46. $7 - 12 + (-5) - 2 + (-2)$

47. $-6 - (2 - 11)$

48. $-9 - (3 - 8)$

49. $3^3 - 8 \cdot 9$

50. $2^3 - 6 \cdot 3$

51. $2 - 3(8 - 6)$

52. $4 - 6(7 - 3)$

53. $(3 - 6) + 4^2$

54. $(2 - 3) + 5^2$

55. $-2 + [(8 - 11) - (-2 - 9)]$

56. $-5 + [(4 - 15) - (-6) - 8]$

57. $|-3| + 2^2 + [-4 - (-6)]$

58. $|-2| + 6^2 + (-3 - 8)$

Objective **B** *Evaluate each expression when $x = -5$, $y = 4$, and $t = 10$. See Example 8.*

59. $x - y$

60. $y - x$

61. $\dfrac{9 - x}{y + 6}$

62. $\dfrac{15 - x}{y + 2}$

63. $|x| + 2t - 8y$

64. $|y| + 3x - 2t$

65. $y^2 - x$

66. $t^2 - x$

67. $\dfrac{|x - (-10)|}{2t}$

68. $\dfrac{|5y - x|}{6t}$

Objective **C** *Decide whether the given number is a solution of the given equation. See Example 9.*

69. $x - 9 = 5$; -4

70. $x - 10 = -7$; 3

71. $-x + 6 = -x - 1$; -2

72. $-x - 6 = -x - 1$; -10

73. $-x - 13 = -15$; 2

74. $4 = 1 - x$; 5

Objectives **D E Mixed Practice** *Solve. See Examples 10 and 11.*

75. The coldest temperature ever recorded on Earth was −129°F in Antarctica. The warmest temperature ever recorded was 136°F in the Sahara Desert. How many degrees warmer is 136°F than −129°F? (*Source: Questions Kids Ask,* Grolier Limited, 1991, and *The World Almanac*)

76. The coldest temperature ever recorded in the United States was −80°F in Alaska. The warmest temperature ever recorded was 134°F in California. How many degrees warmer is 134°F than −80°F? (*Source: The World Almanac,* 2005)

77. Mauna Kea in Hawaii has an elevation of 13,796 feet above sea level. The Mid-America Trench in the Pacific Ocean has an elevation of 21,857 feet below sea level. Find the difference in elevation between those two points. (*Source:* National Geographic Society and Defense Mapping Agency)

78. A woman received a statement of her charge account at Old Navy. She spent \$93 on purchases last month. She returned an \$18 top because she didn't like the color. She also returned a \$26 nightshirt because it was damaged. What does she actually owe on her account?

79. Find x if the angles below are complementary angles.

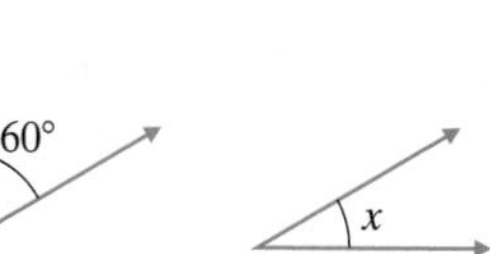

80. Find y if the angles below are supplementary angles.

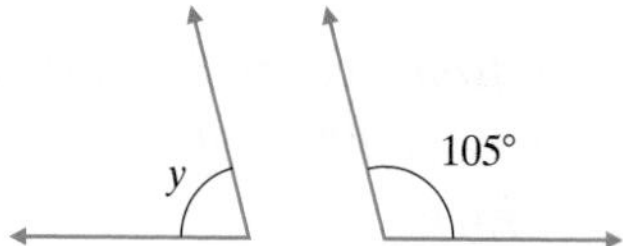

81. A commercial jetliner hits an air pocket and drops 250 feet. After climbing 120 feet, it drops another 178 feet. What is its overall vertical change?

82. In some card games, it is possible to have a negative score. Lavonne Schultz currently has a score of 15 points. She then loses 24 points. What is her new score?

83. The highest point in Africa is Mt. Kilimanjaro, Tanzania, at an elevation of 19,340 feet. The lowest point is Lake Assal, Djibouti, at 512 feet below sea level. How much higher is Mt. Kilimanjaro than Lake Assal? (*Source:* National Geographic Society)

84. The airport in Bishop, California, is at an elevation of 4101 feet above sea level. The nearby Furnace Creek Airport in Death Valley, California, is at an elevation of 226 feet below sea level. How much higher in elevation is the Bishop Airport than the Furnace Creek Airport? (*Source:* National Climatic Data Center)

Find each unknown complementary or supplementary angle.

85.

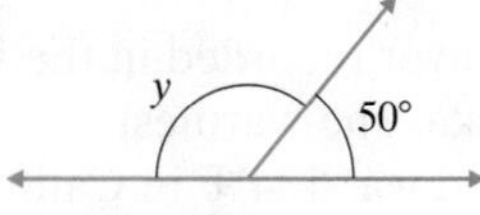

86.

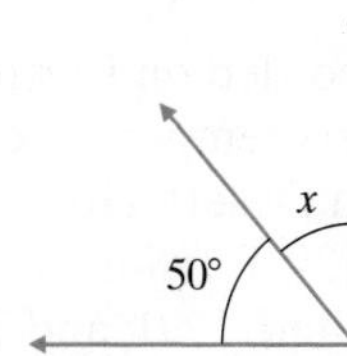

Mixed Practice–Translating (*Sections 8.3, 8.4*) *Translate each phrase to an algebraic expression. Use "x" to represent "a number."*

87. The sum of −5 and a number.

88. The difference of −3 and a number.

89. Subtract a number from −20.

90. Add a number and −36.

Concept Extensions

Recall the bar graph from Section 8.3. It shows each month's average daily low temperature in degrees Fahrenheit for Barrow, Alaska. Use this graph to answer Exercises 91 through 94.

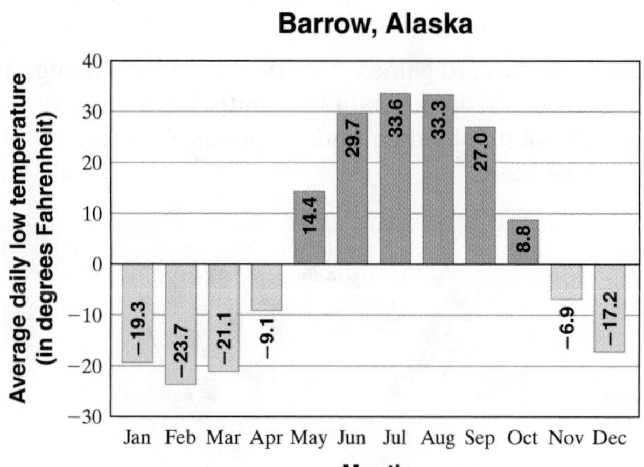

Source: National Climatic Data Center

91. Record the monthly increases and decreases in the low temperature from the previous month.

Month	Monthly Increase or Decrease (from the previous month)
February	
March	
April	
May	
June	

92. Record the monthly increases and decreases in the low temperature from the previous month.

Month	Monthly Increase or Decrease (from the previous month)
July	
August	
September	
October	
November	
December	

93. Which month had the greatest increase in temperature?

94. Which month had the greatest decrease in temperature?

95. Find two numbers whose difference is −5.

96. Find two numbers whose difference is −9.

*Each calculation below is **incorrect.** Find the error and correct it.*

97. $9 - (-7) \stackrel{?}{=} 2$

98. $-4 - 8 \stackrel{?}{=} 4$

99. $10 - 30 \stackrel{?}{=} 20$

100. $-3 - (-10) \stackrel{?}{=} -13$

If p is a positive number and n is a negative number, determine whether each statement is true or false. Explain your answer.

101. $p - n$ is always a positive number.

102. $n - p$ is always a negative number.

103. $|n| - |p|$ is always a positive number.

104. $|n - p|$ is always a positive number.

Without calculating, determine whether each answer is positive or negative. Then use a calculator to find the exact difference.

105. 56,875 − 87,262

106. 4.362 − 7.0086

Answers

1. ______
2. ______
3. ______
4. ______
5. ______
6. ______
7. ______
8. ______
9. ______
10. ______
11. ______
12. ______
13. ______
14. ______
15. ______
16. ______
17. ______
18. ______
19. ______
20. ______
21. ______
22. ______
23. ______
24. ______

Integrated Review Sections 8.1–8.4

Operations on Real Numbers

Answer the following with positive, negative, or 0.

1. The opposite of a positive number is a ________ number.

2. The sum of two negative numbers is a ________ number.

3. The absolute value of a negative number is a ________ number.

4. The absolute value of zero is ________.

5. The sum of two positive numbers is a ________ number.

6. The sum of a number and its opposite is ________.

7. The absolute value of a positive number is a ________ number.

8. The opposite of a negative number is a ________ number.

Fill in the chart:

	Number	Opposite	Absolute Value
9.	$\frac{1}{7}$		
10.	$-\frac{12}{5}$		
11.		-3	
12.		$\frac{9}{11}$	

Perform each indicated operation and simplify. For Exercises 39 and 40, perform the operations within the parentheses first.

13. $-19 + (-23)$ **14.** $7 - (-3)$ **15.** $-15 + 17$ **16.** $-8 - 10$

17. $18 + (-25)$ **18.** $-2 + (-37)$ **19.** $-14 - (-12)$ **20.** $5 - 14$

21. $4.5 - 7.9$ **22.** $-8.6 - 1.2$ **23.** $-\frac{3}{4} - \frac{1}{7}$ **24.** $\frac{2}{3} - \frac{7}{8}$

25. $-9 - (-7) + 4 - 6$

26. $11 - 20 + (-3) - 12$

27. $24 - 6(14 - 11)$

28. $30 - 5(10 - 8)$

29. $(7 - 17) + 4^2$

30. $9^2 + (10 - 30)$

31. $|-9| + 3^2 + (-4 - 20)$

32. $|-4 - 5| + 5^2 + (-50)$

33. $-7 + [(1 - 2) + (-2 - 9)]$

34. $-6 + [(-3 + 7) + (4 - 15)]$

35. Subtract 5 from 1.

36. Subtract -2 from -3.

37. Subtract $-\frac{2}{5}$ from $\frac{1}{4}$.

38. Subtract $\frac{1}{10}$ from $-\frac{5}{8}$.

39. $2(19 - 17)^3 - 3(-7 + 9)^2$

40. $3(10 - 9)^2 + 6(20 - 19)^3$

Evaluate each expression when $x = -2$, $y = -1$, and $z = 9$.

41. $x - y$

42. $x + y$

43. $y + z$

44. $z - y$

45. $\frac{|5z - x|}{y - x}$

46. $\frac{|-x - y + z|}{2z}$

25. ______
26. ______
27. ______
28. ______
29. ______
30. ______
31. ______
32. ______
33. ______
34. ______
35. ______
36. ______
37. ______
38. ______
39. ______
40. ______
41. ______
42. ______
43. ______
44. ______
45. ______
46. ______

8.5 MULTIPLYING AND DIVIDING REAL NUMBERS

Objectives

A Multiply Real Numbers.

B Find the Reciprocal of a Real Number.

C Divide Real Numbers.

D Evaluate Expressions Using Real Numbers.

E Determine Whether a Number is a Solution of a Given Equation.

F Solve Applications That Involve Multiplication or Division of Real Numbers

Objective A Multiplying Real Numbers

Multiplication of real numbers is similar to multiplication of whole numbers. We just need to determine when the answer is positive, when it is negative, and when it is zero. To discover sign patterns for multiplication, recall that multiplication is repeated addition. For example, 3(2) means that 2 is added to itself three times, or

$$3(2) = 2 + 2 + 2 = 6$$

Also,

$$3(-2) = (-2) + (-2) + (-2) = -6$$

Since $3(-2) = -6$, this suggests that the product of a positive number and a negative number is a negative number.

What about the product of two negative numbers? To find out, consider the following pattern.

$-3 \cdot 2 = -6$ Factor decreases by 1 each time.

$-3 \cdot 1 = -3$ Product increases by 3 each time.

$-3 \cdot 0 = 0$

$-3 \cdot -1 = 3$

$-3 \cdot -2 = 6$

This suggests that the product of two negative numbers is a positive number. Our results are given below.

Multiplying Real Numbers

1. The product of two numbers with the *same* sign is a positive number.
2. The product of two numbers with *different* signs is a negative number.

Examples Multiply.

1. $-7(6) = -42$ Different signs, so the product is negative.
2. $2(-10) = -20$
3. $-2(-14) = 28$ Same sign, so the product is positive.
4. $-\frac{2}{3} \cdot \frac{4}{7} = -\frac{2 \cdot 4}{3 \cdot 7} = -\frac{8}{21}$
5. $5(-1.7) = -8.5$
6. $-18(-3) = 54$

Work Practice 1–6

PRACTICE 1–6

Multiply.

1. $-8(3)$ **2.** $5(-30)$

3. $-4(-12)$ **4.** $-\frac{5}{6} \cdot \frac{1}{4}$

5. $6(-2.3)$ **6.** $-15(-2)$

Answers

1. -24 **2.** -150 **3.** 48 **4.** $-\frac{5}{24}$ **5.** -13.8 **6.** 30

We already know that the product of 0 and any whole number is 0. This is true of all real numbers.

Products Involving Zero

If b is a real number, then $b \cdot 0 = 0$. Also $0 \cdot b = 0$.

Example 7 Multiply.

a. $7(0)(-6)$ **b.** $(-2)(-3)(-4)$ **c.** $(-1)(-5)(-9)(-2)$

Solution:

a. By the order of operations, we multiply from left to right. Notice that because one of the factors is 0, the product is 0.

$$7(0)(-6) = 0(-6) = 0$$

b. Multiply two factors at a time, from left to right.

$$(-2)(-3)(-4) = (6)(-4) \quad \text{Multiply } (-2)(-3).$$
$$= -24$$

c. Multiply from left to right.

$$(-1)(-5)(-9)(-2) = (5)(-9)(-2) \quad \text{Multiply } (-1)(-5).$$
$$= -45(-2) \quad \text{Multiply } 5(-9).$$
$$= 90$$

Work Practice 7

PRACTICE 7

Multiply.

a. $5(0)(-3)$

b. $(-1)(-6)(-7)$

c. $(-2)(4)(-8)(-1)$

✓**Concept Check** What is the sign of the product of five negative numbers? Explain.

Helpful Hint

Have you noticed a pattern when multiplying signed numbers?

If we let $(-)$ represent a negative number and $(+)$ represent a positive number, then

$$(-)(-) = (+)$$
$$(-)(-)(-) = (-)$$
$$(-)(-)(-)(-) = (+)$$
$$(-)(-)(-)(-)(-) = (-)$$

The product of an even number of negative numbers is a positive result.

The product of an odd number of negative numbers is a negative result.

Now that we know how to multiply positive and negative numbers, let's see how we find the values of $(-5)^2$ and -5^2, for example. Although these two expressions look similar, the difference between the two is the parentheses. In $(-5)^2$, the parentheses tell us that the base, or repeated factor, is -5. In -5^2, only 5 is the base. Thus,

$$(-5)^2 = (-5)(-5) = 25 \quad \text{The base is } -5.$$
$$-5^2 = -(5 \cdot 5) = -25 \quad \text{The base is } 5.$$

Example 8 Evaluate.

a. $(-2)^3$ **b.** -2^3 **c.** $(-3)^2$ **d.** -3^2 **e.** $\left(-\frac{2}{3}\right)^2$

Solution:

a. $(-2)^3 = (-2)(-2)(-2) = -8$ The base is -2.

b. $-2^3 = -(2 \cdot 2 \cdot 2) = -8$ The base is 2.

c. $(-3)^2 = (-3)(-3) = 9$ The base is -3.

d. $-3^2 = -(3 \cdot 3) = -9$ The base is 3.

e. $\left(-\frac{2}{3}\right)^2 = \left(-\frac{2}{3}\right)\left(-\frac{2}{3}\right) = \frac{4}{9}$ The base is $-\frac{2}{3}$.

Work Practice 8

PRACTICE 8

Evaluate.

a. $(-2)^4$ **b.** -2^4

c. $(-1)^5$ **d.** -1^5

e. $\left(-\frac{7}{9}\right)^2$

Answers

7. a. 0 **b.** -42 **c.** -64

8. a. 16 **b.** -16 **c.** -1 **d.** -1 **e.** $\frac{49}{81}$

✓ **Concept Check Answer**

negative

Helpful Hint

Be careful when identifying the base of an exponential expression.

$(-3)^2$	-3^2
Base is -3	Base is 3
$(-3)^2 = (-3)(-3) = 9$	$-3^2 = -(3 \cdot 3) = -9$

Objective B Finding Reciprocals

Addition and subtraction are related. Every difference of two numbers $a - b$ can be written as the sum $a + (-b)$. Multiplication and division are related also. For example, the quotient $6 \div 3$ can be written as the product $6 \cdot \frac{1}{3}$. Recall that the pair of numbers 3 and $\frac{1}{3}$ has a special relationship. Their product is 1 and they are called **reciprocals** or **multiplicative inverses** of each other.

Reciprocal or Multiplicative Inverse

Two numbers whose product is 1 are called **reciprocals** or **multiplicative inverses** of each other.

PRACTICE 9

Find the reciprocal of each number.

a. 13 **b.** $\frac{7}{15}$

c. -5 **d.** $-\frac{8}{11}$

e. 7.9

Example 9 Find the reciprocal of each number.

a. 22 Reciprocal is $\frac{1}{22}$ since $22 \cdot \frac{1}{22} = 1$.

b. $\frac{3}{16}$ Reciprocal is $\frac{16}{3}$ since $\frac{3}{16} \cdot \frac{16}{3} = 1$.

c. -10 Reciprocal is $-\frac{1}{10}$ since $-10 \cdot -\frac{1}{10} = 1$.

d. $-\frac{9}{13}$ Reciprocal is $-\frac{13}{9}$ since $-\frac{9}{13} \cdot -\frac{13}{9} = 1$.

e. 1.7 Reciprocal is $\frac{1}{1.7}$ since $1.7 \cdot \frac{1}{1.7} = 1$.

Work Practice 9

Helpful Hint

The fraction $\frac{1}{1.7}$ is not simplified since the denominator is a decimal number. For the purpose of finding a reciprocal, we will leave the fraction as is.

Does the number 0 have a reciprocal? If it does, it is a number n such that $0 \cdot n = 1$. Notice that this can never be true since $0 \cdot n = 0$. This means that 0 has no reciprocal.

Quotients Involving Zero

The number 0 does not have a reciprocal.

Answers

9. a. $\frac{1}{13}$ **b.** $\frac{15}{7}$ **c.** $-\frac{1}{5}$ **d.** $-\frac{11}{8}$ **e.** $\frac{1}{7.9}$

Objective C Dividing Real Numbers

We may now write a quotient as an equivalent product.

Quotient of Two Real Numbers

If a and b are real numbers and b is not 0, then

$$a \div b = \frac{a}{b} = a \cdot \frac{1}{b}$$

In other words, the quotient of two real numbers is the product of the first number and the multiplicative inverse or reciprocal of the second number.

Example 10 Use the definition of the quotient of two numbers to find each quotient. $\left(a \div b = a \cdot \frac{1}{b}\right)$

a. $-18 \div 3$ **b.** $\frac{-14}{-2}$ **c.** $\frac{20}{-4}$

Solution:

a. $-18 \div 3 = -18 \cdot \frac{1}{3} = -6$

b. $\frac{-14}{-2} = -14 \cdot -\frac{1}{2} = 7$

c. $\frac{20}{-4} = 20 \cdot -\frac{1}{4} = -5$

Work Practice 10

PRACTICE 10

Use the definition of the quotient of two numbers to find each quotient.

a. $-12 \div 4$ **b.** $\frac{-20}{-10}$

c. $\frac{36}{-4}$

Since the quotient $a \div b$ can be written as the product $a \cdot \frac{1}{b}$, it follows that sign patterns for dividing two real numbers are the same as sign patterns for multiplying two real numbers.

Dividing Real Numbers

1. The quotient of two numbers with the *same* sign is a positive number.
2. The quotient of two numbers with *different* signs is a negative number.

Example 11 Divide.

a. $\frac{-30}{-10} = 3$ Same sign, so the quotient is positive.

b. $\frac{-100}{5} = -20$

c. $\frac{20}{-2} = -10$ Different signs, so the quotient is negative.

d. $\frac{42}{-0.6} = -70$ $0.6\overline{)42.0}$ = 70.

Work Practice 11

PRACTICE 11

Divide.

a. $\frac{-25}{5}$ **b.** $\frac{-48}{-6}$

c. $\frac{50}{-2}$ **d.** $\frac{-72}{0.2}$

✓Concept Check What is wrong with the following calculation?

$\frac{-36}{-9} = -4$ (crossed out)

Answers

10. a. −3 **b.** 2 **c.** −9

11. a. −5 **b.** 8 **c.** −25 **d.** −360

✓ Concept Check Answer

$\frac{-36}{-9} = 4$

In the examples on the previous page, we divided mentally or by long division. When we divide by a fraction, it is usually easier to multiply by its reciprocal.

PRACTICE 12–13

Divide.

12. $-\frac{5}{9} \div \frac{2}{3}$ **13.** $-\frac{2}{7} \div \left(-\frac{1}{5}\right)$

Examples Divide.

12. $\frac{2}{3} \div \left(-\frac{5}{4}\right) = \frac{2}{3} \cdot \left(-\frac{4}{5}\right) = -\frac{8}{15}$

13. $-\frac{1}{6} \div \left(-\frac{2}{3}\right) = -\frac{1}{6} \cdot \left(-\frac{3}{2}\right) = \frac{3}{12} = \frac{\overset{1}{\cancel{3}}}{\underset{1}{\cancel{3}} \cdot 4} = \frac{1}{4}$

Work Practice 12–13

Our definition of the quotient of two real numbers does not allow for division by 0 because 0 does not have a reciprocal. How then do we interpret $\frac{3}{0}$? We say that an expression such as this one is **undefined.** Can we divide 0 by a number other than 0? Yes; for example,

$$\frac{0}{3} = 0 \cdot \frac{1}{3} = 0$$

Division Involving Zero

If a is a nonzero number, then $\frac{0}{a} = 0$ and $\frac{a}{0}$ is undefined.

PRACTICE 14

Divide if possible.

a. $\frac{-7}{0}$ **b.** $\frac{0}{-2}$

Example 14 Divide, if possible.

a. $\frac{1}{0}$ is undefined. **b.** $\frac{0}{-3} = 0$

Work Practice 14

Notice that $\frac{12}{-2} = -6$, $-\frac{12}{2} = -6$, and $\frac{-12}{2} = -6$. This means that

$$\frac{12}{-2} = -\frac{12}{2} = \frac{-12}{2}$$

In other words, a single negative sign in a fraction can be written in the denominator, in the numerator, or in front of the fraction without changing the value of the fraction.

If a and b are real numbers, and $b \neq 0$, then $\frac{a}{-b} = \frac{-a}{b} = -\frac{a}{b}$.

Objective D Evaluating Expressions

Examples combining basic arithmetic operations along with the principles of the order of operations help us to review these concepts of multiplying and dividing real numbers.

Answers

12. $-\frac{5}{6}$ **13.** $\frac{10}{7}$

14. a. undefined **b.** 0

Example 15 Use order of operations to evaluate each expression.

a. $\frac{0(-8)}{2}$ b. $-4(-11) - 5(-2)$

c. $(-2)^2 + 3[(-3 - 2) - |4 - 6|]$ d. $\frac{(-12)(-3) + 4}{-7 - (-2)}$

e. $\frac{2(-3)^2 - 20}{|-5| + 4}$

Solution:

a. $\frac{0(-8)}{2} = \frac{0}{2} = 0$

b. $(-4)(-11) - 5(-2) = 44 - (-10)$ Find the products.
$= 44 + 10$ Add 44 to the opposite of −10.
$= 54$ Add.

c. $(-2)^2 + 3[(-3 - 2) - |4 - 6|] = (-2)^2 + 3[(-5) - |-2|]$ Simplify within innermost sets of grouping symbols.
$= (-2)^2 + 3[-5 - 2]$ Write $|-2|$ as 2.
$= (-2)^2 + 3(-7)$ Combine.
$= 4 + (-21)$ Evaluate $(-2)^2$ and multiply $3(-7)$.
$= -17$ Add.

For parts d and e, first simplify the numerator and denominator separately; then divide.

d. $\frac{(-12)(-3) + 4}{-7 - (-2)} = \frac{36 + 4}{-7 + 2}$
$= \frac{40}{-5}$
$= -8$ Divide.

e. $\frac{2(-3)^2 - 20}{|-5| + 4} = \frac{2 \cdot 9 - 20}{5 + 4} = \frac{18 - 20}{9} = \frac{-2}{9} = -\frac{2}{9}$

Work Practice 15

PRACTICE 15

Use order of operations to evaluate each expression.

a. $\frac{0(-5)}{3}$

b. $-3(-9) - 4(-4)$

c. $(-3)^2 + 2[(5 - 15) - |-4 - 1|]$

d. $\frac{-7(-4) + 2}{-10 - (-5)}$

e. $\frac{5(-2)^3 + 52}{-4 + 1}$

Using what we have learned about multiplying and dividing real numbers, we continue to practice evaluating algebraic expressions.

Example 16 Evaluate each expression when $x = -2$ and $y = -4$.

a. $\frac{3x}{2y}$ b. $x^3 - y^2$ c. $\frac{x - y}{-x}$

Solution: Replace x with −2 and y with −4 and simplify.

a. $\frac{3x}{2y} = \frac{3(-2)}{2(-4)} = \frac{-6}{-8} = \frac{6}{8} = \frac{\cancel{2}^{1} \cdot 3}{\cancel{2}_{1} \cdot 4} = \frac{3}{4}$

Continued on next page

PRACTICE 16

Evaluate each expression when $x = -1$ and $y = -5$.

a. $\frac{3y}{45x}$

b. $x^2 - y^3$

c. $\frac{x + y}{3x}$

Answers

15. a. 0 **b.** 43 **c.** −21 **d.** −6 **e.** −4 **16. a.** $\frac{1}{3}$ **b.** 126 **c.** 2

b. $x^3 - y^2 = (-2)^3 - (-4)^2$ Substitute the given values for the variables.

$= -8 - (16)$ Evaluate $(-2)^3$ and $(-4)^2$.

$= -8 + (-16)$ Write as a sum.

$= -24$ Add.

c. $\frac{x - y}{-x} = \frac{-2 - (-4)}{-(-2)} = \frac{-2 + 4}{2} = \frac{2}{2} = 1$

Work Practice 16

Helpful Hint

Remember: For additional help when replacing variables with replacement values, first place parentheses about any variables.

Evaluate $3x - y^2$ when $x = 5$ and $y = -4$.

$3x - y^2 = 3(x) - (y)^2$ Place parentheses about variables only.

$= 3(5) - (-4)^2$ Replace variables with values.

$= 15 - 16$ Simplify.

$= -1$

Objective E Solutions of Equations

We use our skills in multiplying and dividing real numbers to check possible solutions of an equation.

PRACTICE 17

Determine whether −8 is a solution of $\frac{x}{4} - 3 = x + 3$.

Example 17 Determine whether −10 is a solution of $\frac{-20}{x} + 15 = 2x$.

Solution: $\frac{-20}{x} + 15 = 2x$ Original equation

$\frac{-20}{-10} + 15 \stackrel{?}{=} 2(-10)$ Replace x with −10.

$2 + 15 \stackrel{?}{=} -20$ Divide and multiply.

$17 = -20$ False

Since we have a false statement, −10 is *not* a solution of the equation.

Work Practice 17

Objective F Solving Applications That Involve Multiplying or Dividing Numbers

Many real-life problems involve multiplication and division of numbers.

Answer

17. −8 is a solution

Example 18 Calculating a Total Golf Score

A professional golfer finished seven strokes under par (-7) for each of three days of a tournament. What was her total score for the tournament?

Solution:

Although the key word is "total," since this is repeated addition of the same number, we multiply.

In words:	golfer's total score	=	number of days	·	score each day
	↓	↓	↓	↓	↓
Translate:	golfer's total	=	3	·	(−7)
		= −21			

Thus, the golfer's total score was −21, or 21 strokes under par.

Work Practice 18

PRACTICE 18

A card player had a score of −13 for each of four games. Find the total score.

Answer

18. −52

Calculator Explorations

Entering Negative Numbers on a Scientific Calculator

To enter a negative number on a scientific calculator, find a key marked [+/−]. (On some calculators, this key is marked [CHS] for "change sign.") To enter −8, for example, press the keys [8] [+/−]. The display will read [−8].

Entering Negative Numbers on a Graphing Calculator

To enter a negative number on a graphing calculator, find a key marked [(−)]. Do not confuse this key with the key [−], which is used for subtraction. To enter −8, for example, press the keys [(−)] [8]. The display will read [−8].

Operations with Real Numbers

To evaluate $-2(7 - 9) - 20$ on a calculator, press the keys

[2] [+/−] [×] [(] [7] [−] [9] [)] [−] [2] [0] [=], or [(−)] [2] [(] [7] [−] [9] [)] [−] [2] [0] [ENTER].

The display will read [−16] or [−2(7 − 9) − 20 −16]

Use a calculator to simplify each expression.

1. $-38(26 - 27)$
2. $-59(-8) + 1726$
3. $134 + 25(68 - 91)$
4. $45(32) - 8(218)$
5. $\dfrac{-50(294)}{175 - 205}$
6. $\dfrac{-444 - 444.8}{-181 - (-181)}$
7. $9^5 - 4550$
8. $5^8 - 6259$
9. $(-125)^2$ (Be careful.)
10. -125^2 (Be careful.)

Vocabulary and Readiness Check

Use the choices below to fill in each blank. Each choice may be used more than once.

negative   0

positive   undefined

1. The product of a negative number and a positive number is a(n) _________ number.
2. The product of two negative numbers is a(n) _________ number.
3. The quotient of two negative numbers is a(n) _________ number.
4. The quotient of a negative number and a positive number is a(n) _________ number.
5. The product of a negative number and zero is _________.
6. The reciprocal of a negative number is a _________ number.
7. The quotient of 0 and a negative number is _________.
8. The quotient of a negative number and 0 is _________.

8.5 Exercise Set

FOR EXTRA HELP

MyMathLab

Objective A *Multiply. See Examples 1 through 7.*

1. $-6(4)$ **2.** $-8(5)$ **3.** $2(-1)$ **4.** $7(-4)$

5. $-5(-10)$ **6.** $-6(-11)$ **7.** $-3 \cdot 15$ **8.** $-2 \cdot 37$

9. $-\frac{1}{2}\left(-\frac{3}{5}\right)$ **10.** $-\frac{1}{8}\left(-\frac{1}{3}\right)$ **11.** $5(-1.4)$ **12.** $6(-2.5)$

13. $(-1)(-3)(-5)$ **14.** $(-2)(-3)(-4)$ **15.** $(2)(-1)(-3)(0)$ **16.** $(3)(-5)(-2)(0)$

Evaluate. See Example 8.

17. $(-4)^2$ **18.** $(-3)^3$ **19.** -4^2 **20.** -6^2

21. $\left(-\frac{3}{4}\right)^2$ **22.** $\left(-\frac{2}{7}\right)^2$ **23.** -0.7^2 **24.** -0.8^2

Objective B *Find each reciprocal. See Example 9.*

25. $\frac{2}{3}$ **26.** $\frac{1}{7}$ **27.** -14 **28.** -8

29. $-\frac{3}{11}$ **30.** $-\frac{6}{13}$ **31.** 0.2 **32.** 1.5

Objective C *Divide. See Examples 10 through 14.*

33. $\frac{18}{-2}$ **34.** $\frac{36}{-9}$ **35.** $-48 \div 12$ **36.** $-60 \div 5$

37. $\frac{0}{-4}$ **38.** $\frac{0}{-9}$ **39.** $\frac{5}{0}$ **40.** $\frac{8}{0}$

41. $\frac{6}{7} \div \left(-\frac{1}{3}\right)$ **42.** $\frac{4}{5} \div \left(-\frac{1}{2}\right)$ **43.** $-3.2 \div -0.02$ **44.** $-4.9 \div -0.07$

Objectives A C Mixed Practice *Perform the indicated operation. See Examples 1–14.*

45. $(-8)(-8)$ **46.** $(-7)(-7)$ **47.** $\frac{2}{3}\left(-\frac{4}{9}\right)$ **48.** $\frac{2}{7}\left(-\frac{2}{11}\right)$ **49.** $\frac{-12}{-4}$

50. $\frac{-45}{-9}$ **51.** $\frac{30}{-2}$ **52.** $\frac{14}{-2}$ **53.** $(-5)^3$ **54.** $(-2)^5$

55. $(-0.2)^3$ **56.** $(-0.3)^3$ **57.** $-\frac{3}{4}\left(-\frac{8}{9}\right)$ **58.** $-\frac{5}{6}\left(-\frac{3}{10}\right)$ **59.** $-\frac{5}{9} \div \left(-\frac{3}{4}\right)$

60. $-\frac{1}{10} \div \left(-\frac{8}{11}\right)$ **61.** $-2.1(-0.4)$ **62.** $-1.3(-0.6)$ **63.** $\frac{-48}{1.2}$ **64.** $\frac{-86}{2.5}$

65. $(-3)^4$ **66.** -3^4 **67.** -1^7 **68.** $(-1)^7$

69. Multiply -11 by 11.

70. Multiply -12 by 12.

71. Find the quotient of $-\frac{4}{9}$ and $\frac{4}{9}$.

72. Find the quotient of $-\frac{5}{12}$ and $\frac{5}{12}$.

Mixed Practice (Sections 8.3, 8.4, 8.5) *Perform the indicated operation.*

73. $-9 - 10$ **74.** $-8 - 11$ **75.** $-9(-10)$ **76.** $-8(-11)$

77. $7(-12)$ **78.** $6(-15)$ **79.** $7 + (-12)$ **80.** $6 + (-15)$

Objective D *Evaluate each expression. See Example 15.*

81. $\dfrac{-9(-3)}{-6}$

82. $\dfrac{-6(-3)}{-4}$

83. $-3(2 - 8)$

84. $-4(3 - 9)$

85. $-7(-2) - 3(-1)$

86. $-8(-3) - 4(-1)$

87. $2^2 - 3[(2 - 8) - (-6 - 8)]$

88. $3^2 - 2[(3 - 5) - (2 - 9)]$

89. $\dfrac{-6^2 + 4}{-2}$

90. $\dfrac{3^2 + 4}{5}$

91. $\dfrac{-3 - 5^2}{2(-7)}$

92. $\dfrac{-2 - 4^2}{3(-6)}$

93. $\dfrac{22 + (3)(-2)^2}{-5 - 2}$

94. $\dfrac{-20 + (-4)^2(3)}{1 - 5}$

95. $\dfrac{(-4)^2 - 16}{4 - 12}$

96. $\dfrac{(-2)^2 - 4}{4 - 9}$

97. $\dfrac{6 - 2(-3)}{4 - 3(-2)}$

98. $\dfrac{8 - 3(-2)}{2 - 5(-4)}$

99. $\dfrac{|5 - 9| + |10 - 15|}{|2(-3)|}$

100. $\dfrac{|-3 + 6| + |-2 + 7|}{|-2 \cdot 2|}$

101. $\dfrac{-7(-1) + (-3)4}{(-2)(5) + (-6)(-8)}$

102. $\dfrac{8(-7) + (-2)(-6)}{(-9)(3) + (-10)(-11)}$

Evaluate each expression when $x = -5$ and $y = -3$. See Example 16.

103. $\dfrac{2x - 5}{y - 2}$

104. $\dfrac{2y - 12}{x - 4}$

105. $\dfrac{6 - y}{x - 4}$

106. $\dfrac{10 - y}{x - 8}$

107. $\dfrac{4 - 2x}{y + 3}$

108. $\dfrac{2y + 3}{-5 - x}$

109. $\dfrac{x^2 + y}{3y}$

110. $\dfrac{y^2 - x}{2x}$

Objective E *Decide whether the given number is a solution of the given equation. See Example 17.*

111. $-3x - 5 = -20$; 5

112. $17 - 4x = x + 27$; -2

113. $\dfrac{x}{5} + 2 = -1$; 15

114. $\dfrac{x}{6} - 3 = 5$; 48

115. $\dfrac{x - 3}{7} = -2$; -11

116. $\dfrac{x + 4}{5} = -6$; -30

Objective F **Translating** *Translate each phrase to an expression. Use x to represent "a number." See Example 18.*

117. The product of −71 and a number

118. The quotient of −8 and a number

119. Subtract a number from −16.

120. The sum of a number and −12

121. −29 increased by a number

122. The difference of a number and −10

123. Divide a number by −33.

124. Multiply a number by −17.

Solve. See Example 18.

125. A football team lost four yards on each of three consecutive plays. Represent the total loss as a product of signed numbers and find the total loss.

126. Joe Norstrom lost $400 on each of seven consecutive days in the stock market. Represent his total loss as a product of signed numbers and find his total loss.

127. A deep-sea diver must move up or down in the water in short steps in order to keep from getting a physical condition called the "bends." Suppose a diver moves down from the surface in five steps of 20 feet each. Represent his total movement as a product of signed numbers and find the product.

128. A weather forecaster predicts that the temperature will drop five degrees each hour for the next six hours. Represent this drop as a product of signed numbers and find the total drop in temperature.

Concept Extensions

State whether each statement is true or false.

129. The product of three negative integers is negative.

130. The product of three positive integers is positive.

131. The product of four negative integers is negative.

132. The product of four positive integers is positive.

Study the bar graph below showing the average surface temperatures of planets. Use Exercises 133 and 134 to complete the planet temperatures on the graph. (Pluto is now classified as a dwarf planet.)

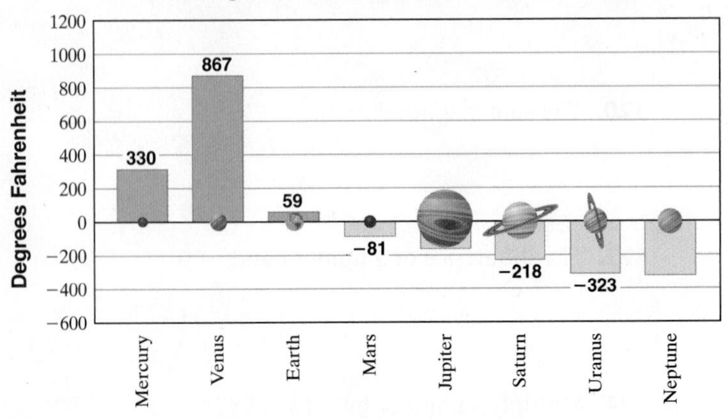

*(For some planets, the temperature given is the temperature where the atmosphere pressure equals 1 Earth atmosphere; Source: *The World Almanac*)

133. The surface temperature of Jupiter is twice the temperature of Mars. Find this temperature.

134. The surface temperature of Neptune is equal to the temperature of Mercury divided by -1. Find this temperature.

135. Explain why the product of an even number of negative numbers is a positive number.

136. If a and b are any real numbers, is the statement $a \cdot b = b \cdot a$ always true? Why or why not?

137. Find two real numbers that are their own reciprocal. Explain why there are only two.

138. Explain why 0 has no reciprocal.

Mixed Practice (1.4, 1.5, 1.6) *Write each as an algebraic expression. Then simplify the expression.*

139. 7 subtracted from the quotient of 0 and 5

140. Twice the sum of -3 and -4

141. -1 added to the product of -8 and -5

142. The difference of -9 and the product of -4 and -6

8.6 PROPERTIES OF REAL NUMBERS

Objectives

A Use the Commutative and Associative Properties.

B Use the Distributive Property.

C Use the Identity and Inverse Properties.

Objective A Using the Commutative and Associative Properties

In this section we review properties of real numbers with which we are already familiar. Throughout this section, the variables *a*, *b*, and *c* represent real numbers.

We know that order does not matter when adding numbers. For example, we know that $7 + 5$ is the same as $5 + 7$. This property is given a special name—the **commutative property of addition.** We also know that order does not matter when multiplying numbers. For example, we know that $-5(6) = 6(-5)$. This property means that multiplication is commutative also and is called the **commutative property of multiplication.**

Commutative Properties

Addition: $a + b = b + a$

Multiplication: $a \cdot b = b \cdot a$

These properties state that the *order* in which any two real numbers are added or multiplied does not change their sum or product. For example, if we let $a = 3$ and $b = 5$, then the commutative properties guarantee that

$3 + 5 = 5 + 3$ and $3 \cdot 5 = 5 \cdot 3$

Helpful Hint

Is subtraction also commutative? Try an example. Is $3 - 2 = 2 - 3$? **No!** The left side of this statement equals 1; the right side equals -1. There is no commutative property of subtraction. Similarly, there is no commutative property of division. For example, $10 \div 2$ does not equal $2 \div 10$.

Example 1 Use a commutative property to complete each statement.

a. $x + 5 =$ _____ **b.** $3 \cdot x =$ _____

Solution:

a. $x + 5 = 5 + x$ By the commutative property of addition

b. $3 \cdot x = x \cdot 3$ By the commutative property of multiplication

Work Practice 1

PRACTICE 1

Use a commutative property to complete each statement.

a. $7 \cdot y =$ _____

b. $4 + x =$ _____

✓**Concept Check** Which of the following pairs of actions are commutative?

a. "raking the leaves" and "bagging the leaves"

b. "putting on your left glove" and "putting on your right glove"

c. "putting on your coat" and "putting on your shirt"

d. "reading a novel" and "reading a newspaper"

Answers

1. a. $y \cdot 7$ **b.** $x + 4$

✓ **Concept Check Answer**

b, d

Let's now discuss grouping numbers. When we add three numbers, the way in which they are grouped or associated does not change their sum. For example, we know that $2 + (3 + 4) = 2 + 7 = 9$. This result is the same if we group the numbers differently. In other words, $(2 + 3) + 4 = 5 + 4 = 9$, also. Thus, $2 + (3 + 4) = (2 + 3) + 4$. This property is called the **associative property of addition.**

In the same way, changing the grouping of numbers when multiplying does not change their product. For example, $2 \cdot (3 \cdot 4) = (2 \cdot 3) \cdot 4$ (check it). This is the **associative property of multiplication.**

Associative Properties

Addition: $(a + b) + c = a + (b + c)$

Multiplication: $(a \cdot b) \cdot c = a \cdot (b \cdot c)$

These properties state that the way in which three numbers are *grouped* does not change their sum or their product.

PRACTICE 2

Use an associative property to complete each statement.

a. $5 \cdot (-3 \cdot 6) =$ _____
b. $(-2 + 7) + 3 =$ _____
c. $(q + r) + 17 =$ _____
d. $(ab) \cdot 21 =$ _____

Example 2 Use an associative property to complete each statement.

a. $5 + (4 + 6) =$ _____ **b.** $(-1 \cdot 2) \cdot 5 =$ _____
c. $(m + n) + 9 =$ _____ **d.** $(xy) \cdot 12 =$ _____

Solution:

a. $5 + (4 + 6) = (5 + 4) + 6$ By the associative property of addition
b. $(-1 \cdot 2) \cdot 5 = -1 \cdot (2 \cdot 5)$ By the associative property of multiplication
c. $(m + n) + 9 = m + (n + 9)$ By the associative property of addition
d. $(xy) \cdot 12 = x \cdot (y \cdot 12)$ Recall that xy means $x \cdot y$.

Work Practice 2

Helpful Hint

Remember the difference between the commutative properties and the associative properties. The commutative properties have to do with the *order* of numbers and the associative properties have to do with the *grouping* of numbers.

PRACTICE 3–4

Determine whether each statement is true by an associative property or a commutative property.

3. $5 \cdot (4 \cdot 7) = 5 \cdot (7 \cdot 4)$
4. $-2 + (4 + 9) = (-2 + 4) + 9$

Examples Determine whether each statement is true by an associative property or a commutative property.

3. $(7 + 10) + 4 = (10 + 7) + 4$ Since the order of two numbers was changed and their grouping was not, this is true by the commutative property of addition.

4. $2 \cdot (3 \cdot 1) = (2 \cdot 3) \cdot 1$ Since the grouping of the numbers was changed and their order was not, this is true by the associative property of multiplication.

Work Practice 3–4

Let's now illustrate how these properties can help us simplify expressions.

Answers

2. a. $(5 \cdot -3) \cdot 6$ **b.** $-2 + (7 + 3)$ **c.** $q + (r + 17)$ **d.** $a \cdot (b \cdot 21)$
3. commutative **4.** associative

Examples Simplify each expression.

5. $10 + (x + 12) = 10 + (12 + x)$ By the commutative property of addition
$= (10 + 12) + x$ By the associative property of addition
$= 22 + x$ Add.

6. $-3(7x) = (-3 \cdot 7)x$ By the associative property of multiplication
$= -21x$ Multiply.

Work Practice 5–6

PRACTICE 5–6

Simplify each expression.

5. $(-3 + x) + 17$

6. $4(5x)$

Objective B Using the Distributive Property

The **distributive property of multiplication over addition** is used repeatedly throughout algebra. It is useful because it allows us to write a product as a sum or a sum as a product.

We know that $7(2 + 4) = 7(6) = 42$. Compare that with

$$7(2) + 7(4) = 14 + 28 = 42$$

Since both original expressions equal 42, they must equal each other, or

$$7(2 + 4) = 7(2) + 7(4)$$

This is an example of the distributive property. The product on the left side of the equal sign is equal to the sum on the right side. We can think of the 7 as being distributed to each number inside the parentheses.

Distributive Property of Multiplication Over Addition

$$a(b + c) = ab + ac$$

Since multiplication is commutative, this property can also be written as

$$(b + c)a = ba + ca$$

The distributive property can also be extended to more than two numbers inside the parentheses. For example,

$$3(x + y + z) = 3(x) + 3(y) + 3(z)$$
$$= 3x + 3y + 3z$$

Since we define subtraction in terms of addition, the distributive property is also true for subtraction. For example,

$$2(x - y) = 2(x) - 2(y)$$
$$= 2x - 2y$$

Examples Use the distributive property to write each expression without parentheses. Then simplify the result.

7. $2(x + y) = 2(x) + 2(y)$
$= 2x + 2y$

8. $-5(-3 + 2z) = -5(-3) + (-5)(2z)$
$= 15 - 10z$

9. $5(x + 3y - z) = 5(x) + 5(3y) - 5(z)$
$= 5x + 15y - 5z$

Continued on next page

PRACTICE 7–12

Use the distributive property to write each expression without parentheses. Then simplify the result.

7. $5(x + y)$

8. $-3(2 + 7x)$

9. $4(x + 6y - 2z)$

10. $-1(3 - a)$

11. $-(8 + a - b)$

12. $\frac{1}{2}(2x + 4) + 9$

Answers

5. $14 + x$ **6.** $20x$ **7.** $5x + 5y$
8. $-6 - 21x$ **9.** $4x + 24y - 8z$
10. $-3 + a$ **11.** $-8 - a + b$
12. $x + 11$

10. $-1(2 - y) = (-1)(2) - (-1)(y)$
$= -2 + y$

11. $-(3 + x - w) = -1(3 + x - w)$
$= (-1)(3) + (-1)(x) - (-1)(w)$
$= -3 - x + w$

Helpful Hint
Notice in Example 11 that $-(3 + x - w)$ can be rewritten as $-1(3 + x - w)$.

12. $\frac{1}{2}(6x + 14) + 10 = \frac{1}{2}(6x) + \frac{1}{2}(14) + 10$ Apply the distributive property.
$= 3x + 7 + 10$ Multiply.
$= 3x + 17$ Add.

Work Practice 7–12

The distributive property can also be used to write a sum as a product.

PRACTICE 13–14

Use the distributive property to write each sum as a product.

13. $9 \cdot 3 + 9 \cdot y$

14. $4x + 4y$

Examples Use the distributive property to write each sum as a product.

13. $8 \cdot 2 + 8 \cdot x = 8(2 + x)$

14. $7s + 7t = 7(s + t)$

Work Practice 13–14

Objective C Using the Identity and Inverse Properties

Next, we look at the **identity properties.**

The number 0 is called the identity for addition because when 0 is added to any real number, the result is the same real number. In other words, the *identity* of the real number is not changed.

The number 1 is called the identity for multiplication because when a real number is multiplied by 1, the result is the same real number. In other words, the *identity* of the real number is not changed.

Identities for Addition and Multiplication

0 is the identity element for addition.

$a + 0 = a$ and $0 + a = a$

1 is the identity element for multiplication.

$a \cdot 1 = a$ and $1 \cdot a = a$

Notice that 0 is the *only* number that can be added to any real number with the result that the sum is the same real number. Also, 1 is the *only* number that can be multiplied by any real number with the result that the product is the same real number.

Additive inverses or **opposites** were introduced in Section 8.3. Two numbers are called additive inverses or opposites if their sum is 0. The additive inverse or opposite of 6 is -6 because $6 + (-6) = 0$. The additive inverse or opposite of -5 is 5 because $-5 + 5 = 0$.

Reciprocals or **multiplicative inverses** were introduced in Section 8.5. Two nonzero numbers are called reciprocals or multiplicative inverses if their product is 1. The reciprocal or multiplicative inverse of $\frac{2}{3}$ is $\frac{3}{2}$ because $\frac{2}{3} \cdot \frac{3}{2} = 1$. Likewise, the reciprocal of -5 is $-\frac{1}{5}$ because $-5\left(-\frac{1}{5}\right) = 1$.

Answers
13. $9(3 + y)$ **14.** $4(x + y)$

Additive or Multiplicative Inverses

The numbers a and $-a$ are additive inverses or opposites of each other because their sum is 0; that is,

$$a + (-a) = 0$$

The numbers b and $\frac{1}{b}$ (for $b \neq 0$) are reciprocals or multiplicative inverses of each other because their product is 1; that is,

$$b \cdot \frac{1}{b} = 1$$

✔**Concept Check** Which of the following is

a. the opposite of $-\frac{3}{10}$, and

b. the reciprocal of $-\frac{3}{10}$?

$1, -\frac{10}{3}, \frac{3}{10}, 0, \frac{10}{3}, -\frac{3}{10}$

Examples Name the property illustrated by each true statement.

15. $3(x + y) = 3 \cdot x + 3 \cdot y$	Distributive property
16. $(x + 7) + 9 = x + (7 + 9)$	Associative property of addition (grouping changed)
17. $(b + 0) + 3 = b + 3$	Identity element for addition
18. $2 \cdot (z \cdot 5) = 2 \cdot (5 \cdot z)$	Commutative property of multiplication (order changed)
19. $-2 \cdot \left(-\frac{1}{2}\right) = 1$	Multiplicative inverse property
20. $-2 + 2 = 0$	Additive inverse property
21. $-6 \cdot (y \cdot 2) = (-6 \cdot 2) \cdot y$	Commutative and associative properties of multiplication (order and grouping changed)

Work Practice 15–21

PRACTICE 15–21

Name the property illustrated by each true statement.

15. $7(a + b) = 7 \cdot a + 7 \cdot b$

16. $12 + y = y + 12$

17. $-4 \cdot (6 \cdot x) = (-4 \cdot 6) \cdot x$

18. $6 + (z + 2) = 6 + (2 + z)$

19. $3\left(\frac{1}{3}\right) = 1$

20. $(x + 0) + 23 = x + 23$

21. $(7 \cdot y) \cdot 10 = y \cdot (7 \cdot 10)$

Answers

15. distributive property
16. commutative property of addition
17. associative property of multiplication
18. commutative property of addition
19. multiplicative inverse property
20. identity element for addition
21. commutative and associative properties of multiplication

✔ **Concept Check Answers**

a. $\frac{3}{10}$ **b.** $-\frac{10}{3}$

Vocabulary and Readiness Check

Use the choices below to fill in each blank.

distributive property	associative property of multiplication	commutative property of addition
opposites or additive inverses	associative property of addition	
reciprocals or multiplicative inverses	commutative property of multiplication	

1. $x + 5 = 5 + x$ is a true statement by the ______.

2. $x \cdot 5 = 5 \cdot x$ is a true statement by the ______.

3. $3(y + 6) = 3 \cdot y + 3 \cdot 6$ is true by the ______.

4. $2 \cdot (x \cdot y) = (2 \cdot x) \cdot y$ is a true statement by the ______.

5. $x + (7 + y) = (x + 7) + y$ is a true statement by the ______.

6. The numbers $-\frac{2}{3}$ and $-\frac{3}{2}$ are called ______.

7. The numbers $-\frac{2}{3}$ and $\frac{2}{3}$ are called ______.

8.6 Exercise Set

FOR EXTRA HELP

Objective A *Use a commutative property to complete each statement. See Examples 1 and 3.*

1. $x + 16 =$ ____ **2.** $8 + y =$ ____ **3.** $-4 \cdot y =$ ____ **4.** $-2 \cdot x =$ ____

5. $xy =$ __ **6.** $ab =$ __ **7.** $2x + 13 =$ ____ **8.** $19 + 3y =$ ____

Use an associative property to complete each statement. See Examples 2 and 4.

9. $(xy) \cdot z =$ ____ **10.** $3 \cdot (x \cdot y) =$ ____ **11.** $2 + (a + b) =$ ____

12. $(y + 4) + z =$ ____ **13.** $4 \cdot (ab) =$ ____ **14.** $(-3y) \cdot z =$ ____

15. $(a + b) + c =$ ____ **16.** $6 + (r + s) =$ ____

Use the commutative and associative properties to simplify each expression. See Examples 5 and 6.

17. $8 + (9 + b)$ **18.** $(r + 3) + 11$ **19.** $4(6y)$ **20.** $2(42x)$ **21.** $\frac{1}{5}(5y)$

22. $\frac{1}{8}(8z)$ **23.** $(13 + a) + 13$ **24.** $7 + (x + 4)$ **25.** $-9(8x)$ **26.** $-3(12y)$

27. $\frac{3}{4}\left(\frac{4}{3}s\right)$ **28.** $\frac{2}{7}\left(\frac{7}{2}r\right)$ **29.** $-\frac{1}{2}(5x)$ **30.** $-\frac{1}{3}(7x)$

Objective B *Use the distributive property to write each expression without parentheses. Then simplify the result, if possible. See Examples 7 through 12.*

31. $4(x + y)$

32. $7(a + b)$

33. $9(x - 6)$

34. $11(y - 4)$

35. $2(3x + 5)$

36. $5(7 + 8y)$

37. $7(4x - 3)$

38. $3(8x - 1)$

39. $3(6 + x)$

40. $2(x + 5)$

41. $-2(y - z)$

42. $-3(z - y)$

43. $-\frac{1}{3}(3y + 5)$

44. $-\frac{1}{2}(2r + 11)$

45. $5(x + 4m + 2)$

46. $8(3y + z - 6)$

47. $-4(1 - 2m + n) + 4$

48. $-4(4 + 2p + 5) + 16$

49. $-(5x + 2)$

50. $-(9r + 5)$

51. $-(r - 3 - 7p)$

52. $-(q - 2 + 6r)$

53. $\frac{1}{2}(6x + 7) + \frac{1}{2}$

54. $\frac{1}{4}(4x - 2) - \frac{7}{2}$

55. $-\frac{1}{3}(3x - 9y)$

56. $-\frac{1}{5}(10a - 25b)$

57. $3(2r + 5) - 7$

58. $10(4s + 6) - 40$

59. $-9(4x + 8) + 2$

60. $-11(5x + 3) + 10$

61. $-0.4(4x + 5) - 0.5$

62. $-0.6(2x + 1) - 0.1$

Use the distributive property to write each sum as a product. See Examples 13 and 14.

63. $4 \cdot 1 + 4 \cdot y$

64. $14 \cdot z + 14 \cdot 5$

65. $11x + 11y$

66. $9a + 9b$

67. $(-1) \cdot 5 + (-1) \cdot x$

68. $(-3)a + (-3)y$

69. $30a + 30b$

70. $25x + 25y$

Objectives A C **Mixed Practice** *Name the property illustrated by each true statement. See Examples 15 through 21.*

71. $3 \cdot 5 = 5 \cdot 3$

72. $4(3 + 8) = 4 \cdot 3 + 4 \cdot 8$

73. $2 + (x + 5) = (2 + x) + 5$

74. $9 \cdot (x \cdot 7) = (9 \cdot x) \cdot 7$

75. $(x + 9) + 3 = (9 + x) + 3$

76. $1 \cdot 9 = 9$

77. $(4 \cdot y) \cdot 9 = 4 \cdot (y \cdot 9)$

78. $-4 \cdot (8 \cdot 3) = (8 \cdot 3) \cdot (-4)$

79. $0 + 6 = 6$

80. $(a + 9) + 6 = a + (9 + 6)$

81. $-4(y + 7) = -4 \cdot y + (-4) \cdot 7$

82. $(11 + r) + 8 = (r + 11) + 8$

83. $6 \cdot \frac{1}{6} = 1$

84. $r + 0 = r$

85. $-6 \cdot 1 = -6$

86. $-\frac{3}{4}\left(-\frac{4}{3}\right) = 1$

Concept Extensions

Fill in the table with the opposite (additive inverse), the reciprocal (multiplicative inverse), or the expression. Assume that the value of each expression is not 0.

	87.	**88.**	**89.**	**90.**	**91.**	**92.**
Expression	8	$-\frac{2}{3}$	x	$4y$		
Opposite						$7x$
Reciprocal					$\frac{1}{2x}$	

Decide whether each statement is true or false. See the second Concept Check in this section.

93. The opposite of $-\frac{a}{2}$ is $-\frac{2}{a}$.

94. The reciprocal of $-\frac{a}{2}$ is $\frac{a}{2}$.

Determine which pairs of actions are commutative. See the first Concept Check in this section.

95. "taking a test" and "studying for the test"

96. "putting on your shoes" and "putting on your socks"

97. "putting on your left shoe" and "putting on your right shoe"

98. "reading the sports section" and "reading the comics section"

99. "mowing the lawn" and "trimming the hedges"

100. "baking a cake" and "eating the cake"

101. "feeding the dog" and "feeding the cat"

102. "dialing a number" and "turning on the cell phone"

Name the property illustrated by each step.

103. **a.** $\triangle + (\square + \bigcirc) = (\square + \bigcirc) + \triangle$

b. $= (\bigcirc + \square) + \triangle$

c. $= \bigcirc + (\square + \triangle)$

104. **a.** $(x + y) + z = x + (y + z)$

b. $= (y + z) + x$

c. $= (z + y) + x$

105. Explain why 0 is called the identity element for addition.

106. Explain why 1 is called the identity element for multiplication.

107. Write an example that shows that division is not commutative.

108. Write an example that shows that subtraction is not commutative.

Objectives

A Identify Terms, Like Terms, and Unlike Terms.

B Combine Like Terms.

C Simplify Expressions Containing Parentheses.

D Write Word Phrases as Algebraic Expressions.

8.7 SIMPLIFYING EXPRESSIONS

As we explore in this section, we will see that an expression such as $3x + 2x$ is not written as simply as possible. This is because—even without replacing x by a value—we can perform the indicated addition.

Objective A Identifying Terms, Like Terms, and Unlike Terms

Before we practice simplifying expressions, we must learn some new language. A **term** is a number or the product of a number and variables raised to powers.

Terms

$-y, \quad 2x^3, \quad -5, \quad 3xz^2, \quad \frac{2}{y}, \quad 0.8z$

The **numerical coefficient** of a term is the numerical factor. The numerical coefficient of $3x$ is 3. Recall that $3x$ means $3 \cdot x$.

Term	Numerical Coefficient
$3x$	3
$\frac{y^3}{5}$	$\frac{1}{5}$ since $\frac{y^3}{5}$ means $\frac{1}{5} \cdot y^3$
$-0.7ab^3c^5$	-0.7
z	1
$-y$	-1
-5	-5

Helpful Hint

The term z means $1z$ and thus has a numerical coefficient of 1.
The term $-y$ means $-1y$ and thus has a numerical coefficient of -1.

PRACTICE 1

Identify the numerical coefficient of each term.

a. $-4x$ **b.** $15y^3$ **c.** x

d. $-y$ **e.** $\frac{z}{4}$

Example 1 Identify the numerical coefficient of each term.

a. $-3y$ **b.** $22z^4$ **c.** y **d.** $-x$ **e.** $\frac{x}{7}$

Solution:

a. The numerical coefficient of $-3y$ is -3.

b. The numerical coefficient of $22z^4$ is 22.

c. The numerical coefficient of y is 1, since y is $1y$.

d. The numerical coefficient of $-x$ is -1, since $-x$ is $-1x$.

e. The numerical coefficient of $\frac{x}{7}$ is $\frac{1}{7}$, since $\frac{x}{7}$ is $\frac{1}{7} \cdot x$.

Work Practice 1

Answers

1. a. -4 **b.** 15 **c.** 1 **d.** -1 **e.** $\frac{1}{4}$

Terms with the same variables raised to exactly the same powers are called **like terms.** Terms that aren't like terms are called **unlike terms.**

Like Terms	Unlike Terms	Reason Why
$3x, 2x$	$5x, 5x^2$	Why? Same variable x, but different powers of x and x^2
$-6x^2y, 2x^2y, 4x^2y$	$7y, 3z, 8x^2$	Why? Different variables
$2ab^2c^3, ac^3b^2$	$6abc^3, 6ab^2$	Why? Different variables and different powers

Helpful Hint

In like terms, each variable and its exponent must match exactly, but these factors don't need to be in the same order.

$2x^2y$ and $3yx^2$ are like terms.

Example 2 Determine whether the terms are like or unlike.

a. $2x, 3x^2$ **b.** $4x^2y, x^2y, -2x^2y$ **c.** $-2yz, -3zy$
d. $-x^4, x^4$ **e.** $-8a^5, 8a^5$

Solution:

a. Unlike terms, since the exponents on x are not the same.
b. Like terms, since each variable and its exponent match.
c. Like terms, since $zy = yz$ by the commutative property.
d. Like terms. The variable and its exponent match.
e. Like terms. The variable and its exponent match.

Work Practice 2

PRACTICE 2

Determine whether the terms are like or unlike.

a. $7x^2, -6x^3$
b. $3x^2y^2, -x^2y^2, 4x^2y^2$
c. $-5ab, 3ba$
d. $2x^3, 4y^3$
e. $-7m^4, 7m^4$

Objective B Combining Like Terms

An algebraic expression containing the sum or difference of like terms can be simplified by applying the distributive property. For example, by the distributive property, we rewrite the sum of the like terms $6x + 2x$ as

$$6x + 2x = (6 + 2)x = 8x$$

Also,

$$-y^2 + 5y^2 = (-1 + 5)y^2 = 4y^2$$

Simplifying the sum or difference of like terms is called **combining like terms.**

Example 3 Simplify each expression by combining like terms.

a. $7x - 3x$ **b.** $10y^2 + y^2$
c. $8x^2 + 2x - 3x$ **d.** $9n^2 - 5n^2 + n^2$

Solution:

a. $7x - 3x = (7 - 3)x = 4x$
b. $10y^2 + y^2 = (10 + 1)y^2 = 11y^2$
c. $8x^2 + 2x - 3x = 8x^2 + (2 - 3)x = 8x^2 - 1x$ or $8x^2 - x$
d. $9n^2 - 5n^2 + n^2 = (9 - 5 + 1)n^2 = 5n^2$

Work Practice 3

PRACTICE 3

Simplify each expression by combining like terms.

a. $9y - 4y$
b. $11x^2 + x^2$
c. $5y - 3x + 4x$
d. $14m^2 - m^2 + 3m^2$

Answers

2. a. unlike **b.** like **c.** like **d.** unlike **e.** like **3. a.** $5y$ **b.** $12x^2$ **c.** $5y + x$ **d.** $16m^2$

The preceding examples suggest the following.

Combining Like Terms

To **combine like terms**, combine the numerical coefficients and multiply the result by the common variable factors.

PRACTICE 4–7

Simplify each expression by combining like terms.

4. $7y + 2y + 6 + 10$
5. $-2x + 4 + x - 11$
6. $3z - 3z^2$
7. $8.9y + 4.2y - 3$

Examples Simplify each expression by combining like terms.

4. $2x + 3x + 5 + 2 = (2 + 3)x + (5 + 2)$
   $= 5x + 7$
5. $-5a - 3 + a + 2 = -5a + 1a + (-3 + 2)$
   $= (-5 + 1)a + (-3 + 2)$
   $= -4a - 1$
6. $4y - 3y^2$
   These two terms cannot be combined because they are unlike terms.
7. $2.3x + 5x - 6 = (2.3 + 5)x - 6$
   $= 7.3x - 6$

Work Practice 4–7

Objective C Simplifying Expressions Containing Parentheses

In simplifying expressions we make frequent use of the distributive property to remove parentheses.

It may be helpful to study the examples below.

$+(3a + 2) = +1(3a + 2) = +1(3a) + (+1)(2) = 3a + 2$ (+ means +1)

$-(3a + 2) = -1(3a + 2) = -1(3a) + (-1)(2) = -3a - 2$ (− means −1)

PRACTICE 8–10

Find each product by using the distributive property to remove parentheses.

8. $3(11y + 6)$
9. $-4(x + 0.2y - 3)$
10. $-(3x + 2y + z - 1)$

Examples Find each product by using the distributive property to remove parentheses.

8. $5(3x + 2) = 5(3x) + 5(2)$ Apply the distributive property.
   $= 15x + 10$ Multiply.
9. $-2(y + 0.3z - 1) = -2(y) + (-2)(0.3z) - (-2)(1)$ Apply the distributive property.
   $= -2y - 0.6z + 2$ Multiply.
10. $-(9x + y - 2z + 6) = -1(9x + y - 2z + 6)$ Distribute −1 over each term.
    $= -1(9x) + (-1)(y) - (-1)(2z) + (-1)(6)$
    $= -9x - y + 2z - 6$

Work Practice 8–10

Answers

4. $9y + 16$ 5. $-x - 7$
6. $3z - 3z^2$ 7. $13.1y - 3$
8. $33y + 18$ 9. $-4x - 0.8y + 12$
10. $-3x - 2y - z + 1$

Helpful Hint

If a "−" sign precedes parentheses, the sign of each term inside the parentheses is changed when the distributive property is applied to remove the parentheses.

Examples:

$$-(2x + 1) = -2x - 1$$
$$-(x - 2y) = -x + 2y$$
$$-(-5x + y - z) = 5x - y + z$$
$$-(-3x - 4y - 1) = 3x + 4y + 1$$

When simplifying an expression containing parentheses, we often use the distributive property first to remove parentheses and then again to combine any like terms.

Examples Simplify each expression.

11. $3(2x - 5) + 1 = 6x - 15 + 1$ Apply the distributive property.
$= 6x - 14$ Combine like terms.

12. $8 - (7x + 2) + 3x = 8 - 7x - 2 + 3x$ Apply the distributive property.
$= -7x + 3x + 8 - 2$
$= -4x + 6$ Combine like terms.

13. $-2(4x + 7) - (3x - 1) = -8x - 14 - 3x + 1$ Apply the distributive property.
$= -11x - 13$ Combine like terms.

14. $9 + 3(4x - 10) = 9 + 12x - 30$ Apply the distributive property.
$= -21 + 12x$ Combine like terms.
or $12x - 21$

Work Practice 11–14

PRACTICE 11–14

Simplify each expression.

11. $4(4x - 6) + 20$
12. $5 - (3x + 9) + 6x$
13. $-3(7x + 1) - (4x - 2)$
14. $8 + 11(2y - 9)$

Helpful Hint Don't forget to use the distributive property and multiply before adding or subtracting like terms.

Example 15 Subtract $4x - 2$ from $2x - 3$.

Solution: We first note that "subtract $4x - 2$ **from** $2x - 3$" translates to $(2x - 3) - (4x - 2)$. Notice that parentheses were placed around each given expression. This is to ensure that the entire expression after the subtraction sign is subtracted. Next, we simplify the algebraic expression.

$(2x - 3) - (4x - 2) = 2x - 3 - 4x + 2$ Apply the distributive property.
$= -2x - 1$ Combine like terms.

Work Practice 15

PRACTICE 15

Subtract $9x - 10$ from $4x - 3$.

Objective D Writing Algebraic Expressions

To prepare for problem solving, we next practice writing word phrases as algebraic expressions.

Answers

11. $16x - 4$ **12.** $3x - 4$
13. $-25x - 1$ **14.** $-91 + 22y$
15. $-5x + 7$

PRACTICE 16–19

Write each phrase as an algebraic expression and simplify if possible. Let x represent the unknown number.

16. Three times a number, subtracted from 10

17. The sum of a number and 2, divided by 5

18. Three times a number, added to the sum of a number and 6

19. Seven times the difference of a number and 4.

Examples Write each phrase as an algebraic expression and simplify if possible. Let x represent the unknown number.

16. Twice a number, plus 6

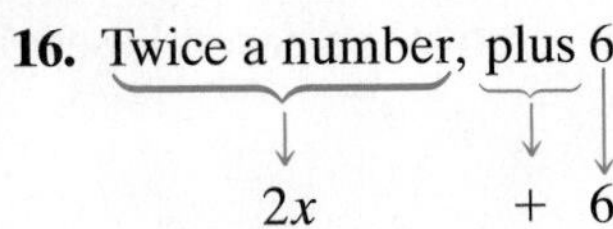

$2x \quad + \quad 6$

This expression cannot be simplified.

17. The difference of a number and 4, divided by 7

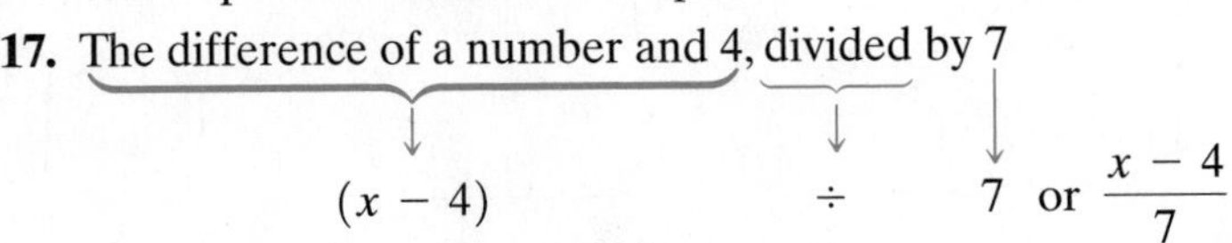

$(x - 4) \quad \div \quad 7$ or $\frac{x - 4}{7}$

This expression cannot be simplified.

18. Five plus the sum of a number and 1

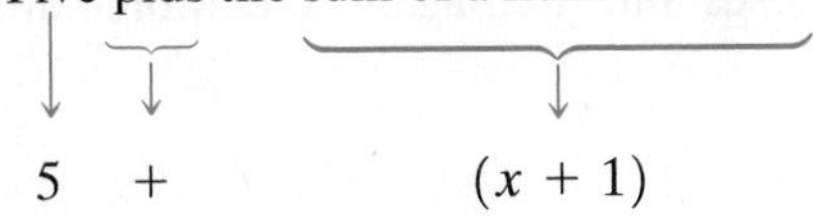

$5 \quad + \quad (x + 1)$

We can simplify this expression.

$$5 + (x + 1) = 5 + x + 1$$
$$= 6 + x$$

19. Four times the sum of a number and 3

$4 \quad \cdot \quad (x + 3)$

Use the distributive property to simplify the expression.

$$4 \cdot (x + 3) = 4(x + 3)$$
$$= 4 \cdot x + 4 \cdot 3$$
$$= 4x + 12$$

Work Practice 16–19

Answers

16. $10 - 3x$ **17.** $(x + 2) \div 5$ or $\frac{x + 2}{5}$

18. $4x + 6$ **19.** $7x - 28$

Vocabulary and Readiness Check

Use the choices below to fill in each blank. Some choices may be used more than once.

numerical coefficient	expression	unlike	distributive
combine like terms	like	term	

1. $14y^2 + 2x - 23$ is called a(n) ________________ while $14y^2$, $2x$, and -23 are each called a(n) ________________.
2. To multiply $3(-7x + 1)$, we use the ________________ property.
3. To simplify an expression like $y + 7y$, we ________________.
4. The term z has an understood ________________ of 1.
5. The terms $-x$ and $5x$ are ________________ terms and the terms $5x$ and $5y$ are ________________ terms.
6. For the term $-3x^2y$, -3 is called the ________________.

Objective A *Identify the numerical coefficient of each term. See Example 1.*

7. $-7y$ 8. $3x$ 9. x 10. $-y$ 11. $17x^2y$ 12. $1.2xyz$

Indicate whether the terms in each list are like or unlike. See Example 2.

13. $5y, -y$ 14. $-2x^2y, 6xy$ 15. $2z, 3z^2$

16. $ab^2, -7ab^2$ 17. $8wz, \frac{1}{7}zw$ 18. $7.4p^3q^2, 6.2p^3q^2r$

8.7 Exercise Set

FOR EXTRA HELP

PRACTICE

WATCH

DOWNLOAD

READ

REVIEW

Objective B *Simplify each expression by combining any like terms. See Examples 3 through 7.*

1. $7y + 8y$ 2. $3x + 2x$ 3. $8w - w + 6w$

4. $c - 7c + 2c$ 5. $3b - 5 - 10b - 4$ 6. $6g + 5 - 3g - 7$

7. $m - 4m + 2m - 6$ 8. $a + 3a - 2 - 7a$ 9. $5g - 3 - 5 - 5g$

10. $8p + 4 - 8p - 15$ 11. $6.2x - 4 + x - 1.2$ 12. $7.9y - 0.7 - y + 0.2$

13. $2k - k - 6$ 14. $7c - 8 - c$ 15. $-9x + 4x + 18 - 10x$

16. $5y - 14 + 7y - 20y$ 17. $6x - 5x + x - 3 + 2x$ 18. $8h + 13h - 6 + 7h - h$

19. $7x^2 + 8x^2 - 10x^2$

20. $8x^3 + x^3 - 11x^3$

21. $3.4m - 4 - 3.4m - 7$

22. $2.8w - 0.9 - 0.5 - 2.8w$

23. $6x + 0.5 - 4.3x - 0.4x + 3$

24. $0.4y - 6.7 + y - 0.3 - 2.6y$

Objective C *Simplify each expression. Use the distributive property to remove any parentheses. See Examples 8 through 10.*

25. $5(y + 4)$

26. $7(r + 3)$

27. $-2(x + 2)$

28. $-4(y + 6)$

29. $-5(2x - 3y + 6)$

30. $-2(4x - 3z - 1)$

31. $-(3x - 2y + 1)$

32. $-(y + 5z - 7)$

Objectives B C **Mixed Practice** *Remove parentheses and simplify each expression. See Examples 8 through 14.*

33. $7(d - 3) + 10$

34. $9(z + 7) - 15$

35. $-4(3y - 4) + 12y$

36. $-3(2x + 5) - 6x$

37. $3(2x - 5) - 5(x - 4)$

38. $2(6x - 1) - (x - 7)$

39. $-2(3x - 4) + 7x - 6$

40. $8y - 2 - 3(y + 4)$

41. $5k - (3k - 10)$

42. $-11c - (4 - 2c)$

43. $(3x + 4) - (6x - 1)$

44. $(8 - 5y) - (4 + 3y)$

45. $5(x + 2) - (3x - 4)$

46. $4(2x - 3) - (x + 1)$

47. $\frac{1}{3}(7y - 1) + \frac{1}{6}(4y + 7)$

48. $\frac{1}{5}(9y + 2) + \frac{1}{10}(2y - 1)$

49. $2 + 4(6x - 6)$

50. $8 + 4(3x - 4)$

51. $0.5(m + 2) + 0.4m$

52. $0.2(k + 8) - 0.1k$

53. $10 - 3(2x + 3y)$

54. $14 - 11(5m + 3n)$

55. $6(3x - 6) - 2(x + 1) - 17x$

56. $7(2x + 5) - 4(x + 2) - 20x$

57. $\frac{1}{2}(12x - 4) - (x + 5)$

58. $\frac{1}{3}(9x - 6) - (x - 2)$

Perform each indicated operation. Don't forget to simplify if possible. See Example 15.

59. Add $6x + 7$ to $4x - 10$.

60. Add $3y - 5$ to $y + 16$.

61. Subtract $7x + 1$ from $3x - 8$.

62. Subtract $4x - 7$ from $12 + x$.

63. Subtract $5m - 6$ from $m - 9$.

64. Subtract $m - 3$ from $2m - 6$.

Objective **D** *Write each phrase as an algebraic expression and simplify if possible. Let x represent the unknown number. See Examples 16 through 19.*

65. Twice a number, decreased by four

66. The difference of a number and two, divided by five

67. Three-fourths of a number, increased by twelve

68. Eight more than triple a number

69. The sum of 5 times a number and −2, added to 7 times the number

70. The sum of 3 times a number and 10, **subtracted from** 9 times the number

71. Eight times the sum of a number and six

72. Six times the difference of a number and five

73. Double a number minus the sum of the number and ten

74. Half a number minus the product of the number and eight

Concept Extensions

Given the following information, determine whether each scale is balanced or not.

1 cone balances 1 cube

1 cylinder balances 2 cubes

75.

76.

77.

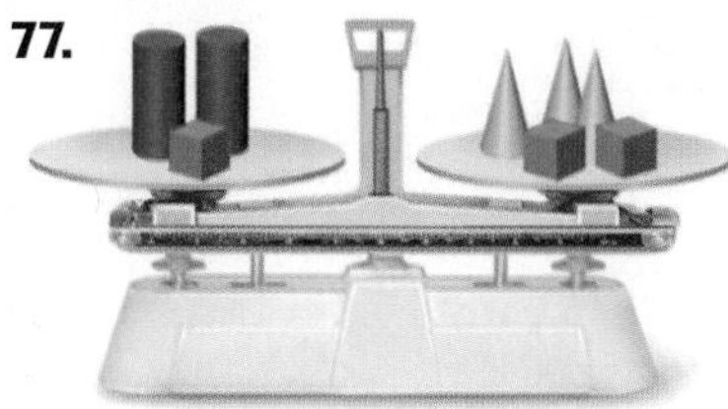

78.

Write each algebraic expression described.

79. Write an expression with 4 terms that simplifies to $3x - 4$.

80. Write an expression of the form _____(_____+_____) whose product is $6x + 24$.

△ **81.** Recall that the perimeter of a figure is the total distance around the figure. Given the following rectangle, express the perimeter as an algebraic expression containing the variable x.

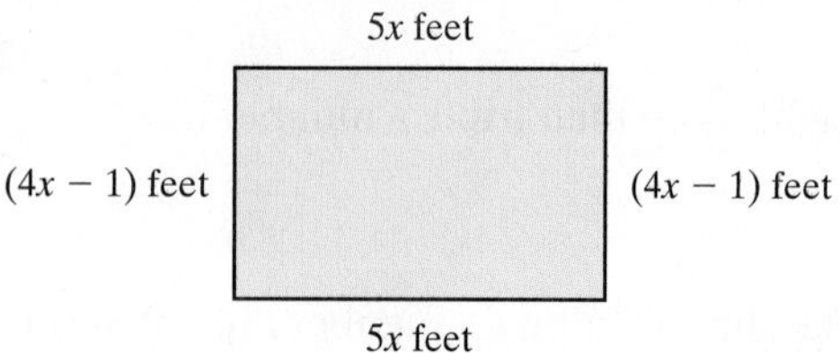

△ **82.** Recall that the perimeter of a figure is the total distance around the figure. Given the following triangle, express its perimeter as an algebraic expression containing the variable x.

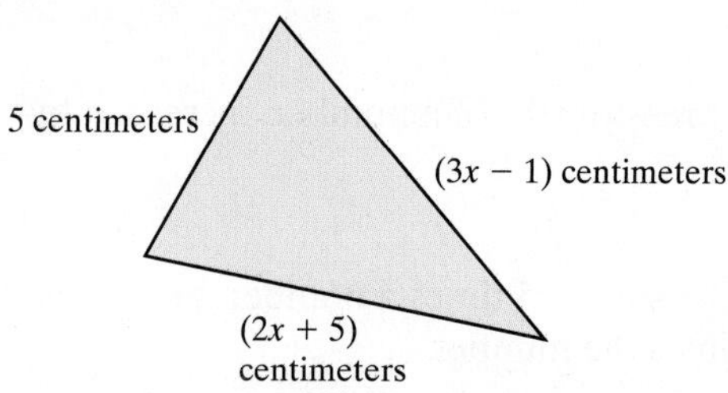

△ **83.** To convert from feet to inches, we multiply by 12. For example, the number of inches in 2 feet is $12 \cdot 2$ inches. If one board has a length of $(x + 2)$ *feet* and a second board has a length of $(3x - 1)$ *inches*, express their total length in inches as an algebraic expression.

84. The value of 7 nickels is $5 \cdot 7$ cents. Likewise, the value of x nickels is $5x$ cents. If the money box in a drink machine contains x *nickels*, $3x$ *dimes*, and $(30x - 1)$ *quarters*, express their total value in cents as an algebraic expression.

85. In your own words, explain how to combine like terms.

86. Do like terms always contain the same numerical coefficients? Explain your answer.

Chapter 8 Group Activity

Magic Squares

Sections 8.2, 8.3, 8.4

A magic square is a set of numbers arranged in a square table so that the sum of the numbers in each column, row, and diagonal is the same. For instance, in the magic square below, the sum of each column, row, and diagonal is 15. Notice that no number is used more than once in the magic square.

2	9	4
7	5	3
6	1	8

The properties of magic squares have been known for a very long time and once were thought to be good luck charms. The ancient Egyptians and Greeks understood their patterns. A magic square even made it into a famous work of art. The engraving titled *Melencolia I,* created by German artist Albrecht Dürer in 1514, features the following four-by-four magic square on the building behind the central figure.

16	3	2	13
5	10	11	8
9	6	7	12
4	15	14	1

Group Exercises

1. Verify that what is shown in the Dürer engraving is, in fact, a magic square. What is the common sum of the columns, rows, and diagonals?

2. Negative numbers can also be used in magic squares. Complete the following magic square:

		−2
	−1	
0		−4

3. Use the numbers $-12, -9, -6, -3, 0, 3, 6, 9,$ and 12 to form a magic square.

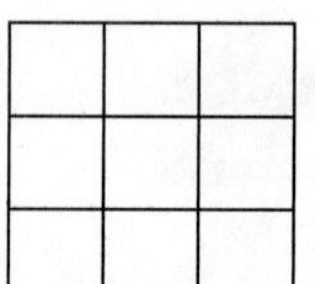

Chapter 8 Vocabulary Check

Fill in each blank with one of the words or phrases listed below.

inequality symbols	exponent	term	numerical coefficient
grouping symbols	solution	like terms	unlike terms
equation	absolute value	numerator	denominator
opposites	base	reciprocals	variable

1. The symbols $\neq$, $<$, and $>$ are called ______________.
2. A mathematical statement that two expressions are equal is called a(n) ______________.
3. The ______________ of a number is the distance between that number and 0 on a number line.
4. A symbol used to represent a number is called a(n) ______________.
5. Two numbers that are the same distance from 0 but lie on opposite sides of 0 are called ______________.
6. The number in a fraction above the fraction bar is called the ______________.
7. A(n) ______________ of an equation is a value for the variable that makes the equation a true statement.
8. Two numbers whose product is 1 are called ______________.
9. In 2^3, the 2 is called the ______________ and the 3 is called the ______________.
10. The ______________ of a term is its numerical factor.
11. The number in a fraction below the fraction bar is called the ______________.
12. Parentheses and brackets are examples of ______________.
13. A(n) ______________ is a number or the product of a number and variables raised to powers.
14. Terms with the same variables raised to the same powers are called ______________.
15. If terms are not like terms, then they are ______________.

Helpful Hint Are you preparing for your test? Don't forget to take the Chapter 8 Test on page 588. Then check your answers at the back of the text and use the Chapter Test Prep Videos to see the fully worked-out solutions to any of the exercises you want to review.

8 Chapter Highlights

Definitions and Concepts	Examples
Section 8.1 Symbols and Sets of Numbers	
A **set** is a collection of objects, called **elements,** enclosed in braces.	$\{a, c, e\}$
Natural numbers: $\{1, 2, 3, 4, \ldots\}$ **Whole numbers:** $\{0, 1, 2, 3, 4, \ldots\}$ **Integers:** $\{\ldots, -3, -2, -1, 0, 1, 2, 3, \ldots\}$	Given the set $\left\{-3.4, \sqrt{3}, 0, \frac{2}{3}, 5, -4\right\}$ list the numbers that belong to the set of Natural numbers: 5 Whole numbers: 0, 5 Integers: $-4, 0, 5$
Rational numbers: { real numbers that can be expressed as a quotient of integers }	Rational numbers: $-3.4, 0, \frac{2}{3}, 5, -4$
Irrational numbers: { real numbers that cannot be expressed as a quotient of integers } A line used to picture numbers is called a **number line.**	Irrational numbers: $\sqrt{3}$ 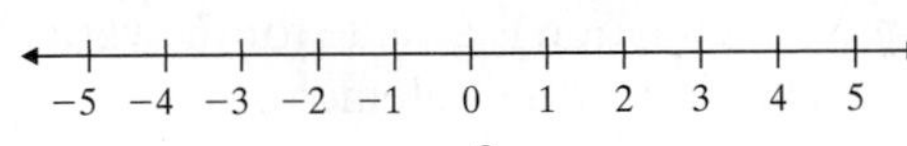
Real numbers: { all numbers that correspond to points on the number line }	Real numbers: $-3.4, \sqrt{3}, 0, \frac{2}{3}, 5, -4$

(*continued*)

Definitions and Concepts	Examples
Section 8.1 Symbols and Sets of Numbers (*continued*)	
The **absolute value** of a real number a denoted by $\lvert a \rvert$ is the distance between a and 0 on a number line.	$\lvert 5 \rvert = 5 \quad \lvert 0 \rvert = 0 \quad \lvert -2 \rvert = 2$
SYMBOLS: $=$ is equal to $\neq$ is not equal to $>$ is greater than $<$ is less than $\leq$ is less than or equal to $\geq$ is greater than or equal to	$-7 = -7$ $3 \neq -3$ $4 > 1$ $1 < 4$ $6 \leq 6$ $18 \geq -\frac{1}{3}$
ORDER PROPERTY FOR REAL NUMBERS For any two real numbers a and b, a is less than b if a is to the left of b on the number line.	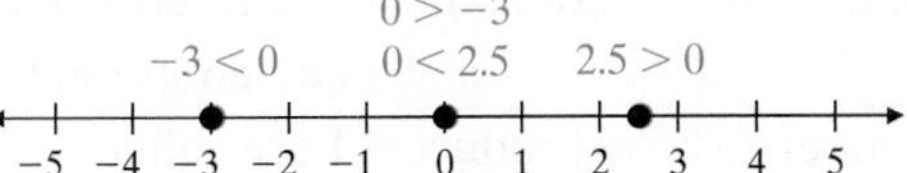
Section 8.2 Exponents, Order of Operations, and Variable Expressions	
The expression a^n is an **exponential expression.** The number a is called the **base;** it is the repeated factor. The number n is called the **exponent;** it is the number of times that the base is a factor.	$4^3 = 4 \cdot 4 \cdot 4 = 64$ $7^2 = 7 \cdot 7 = 49$
ORDER OF OPERATIONS **1.** Perform all operations within grouping symbols first, starting with the innermost set. **2.** Evaluate exponential expressions. **3.** Multiply or divide in order from left to right. **4.** Add or subtract in order from left to right.	$\frac{8^2 + 5(7-3)}{3 \cdot 7} = \frac{8^2 + 5(4)}{21}$ $= \frac{64 + 5(4)}{21}$ $= \frac{64 + 20}{21}$ $= \frac{84}{21}$ $= 4$
A symbol used to represent a number is called a **variable.**	Examples of variables are q, x, z
An **algebraic expression** is a collection of numbers, variables, operation symbols, and grouping symbols.	Examples of algebraic expressions are $5x, \quad 2(y-6), \quad \frac{q^2 - 3q + 1}{6}$
To **evaluate an algebraic expression** containing a variable, substitute a given number for the variable and simplify.	Evaluate $x^2 - y^2$ when $x = 5$ and $y = 3$. $x^2 - y^2 = (5)^2 - 3^2$ $= 25 - 9$ $= 16$
A mathematical statement that two expressions are equal is called an **equation.**	Equations: $3x - 9 = 20$ $A = \pi r^2$
A **solution** of an equation is a value for the variable that makes the equation a true statement.	Determine whether 4 is a solution of $5x + 7 = 27$. $5x + 7 = 27$ $5(4) + 7 \stackrel{?}{=} 27$ $20 + 7 \stackrel{?}{=} 27$ $27 = 27$ True 4 is a solution.

Definitions and Concepts	Examples
Section 8.3 Adding Real Numbers	
To Add Two Numbers with the Same Sign **1.** Add their absolute values. **2.** Use their common sign as the sign of the sum.	Add. $10 + 7 = 17$ $-3 + (-8) = -11$
To Add Two Numbers with Different Signs **1.** Subtract their absolute values. **2.** Use the sign of the number whose absolute value is larger as the sign of the sum.	$-25 + 5 = -20$ $14 + (-9) = 5$
Two numbers that are the same distance from 0 but lie on opposite sides of 0 are called **opposites** or **additive inverses.** The opposite of a number a is denoted by $-a$.	The opposite of -7 is 7. The opposite of 123 is -123.
Section 8.4 Subtracting Real Numbers	
To subtract two numbers a and b, add the first number a to the opposite of the second number, b. $a - b = a + (-b)$	Subtract. $3 - (-44) = 3 + 44 = 47$ $-5 - 22 = -5 + (-22) = -27$ $-30 - (-30) = -30 + 30 = 0$
Section 8.5 Multiplying and Dividing Real Numbers	
Multiplying Real Numbers The product of two numbers with the same sign is a positive number. The product of two numbers with different signs is a negative number.	Multiply. $7 \cdot 8 = 56$ $-7 \cdot (-8) = 56$ $-2 \cdot 4 = -8$ $2 \cdot (-4) = -8$
Products Involving Zero The product of 0 and any number is 0. $b \cdot 0 = 0$ and $0 \cdot b = 0$	$-4 \cdot 0 = 0$ $0 \cdot \left(-\frac{3}{4}\right) = 0$
Quotient of Two Real Numbers $\frac{a}{b} = a \cdot \frac{1}{b}$	Divide. $\frac{42}{2} = 42 \cdot \frac{1}{2} = 21$
Dividing Real Numbers The quotient of two numbers with the same sign is a positive number. The quotient of two numbers with different signs is a negative number.	$\frac{90}{10} = 9$ $\frac{-90}{-10} = 9$ $\frac{42}{-6} = -7$ $\frac{-42}{6} = -7$
Quotients Involving Zero Let a be a nonzero number. $\frac{0}{a} = 0$ and $\frac{a}{0}$ is undefined.	$\frac{0}{18} = 0$ $\frac{0}{-47} = 0$ $\frac{-85}{0}$ is undefined.

Definitions and Concepts	Examples
Section 8.6 Properties of Real Numbers	
COMMUTATIVE PROPERTIES	
Addition: $a + b = b + a$	$3 + (-7) = -7 + 3$
Multiplication: $a \cdot b = b \cdot a$	$-8 \cdot 5 = 5 \cdot (-8)$
ASSOCIATIVE PROPERTIES	
Addition: $(a + b) + c = a + (b + c)$	$(5 + 10) + 20 = 5 + (10 + 20)$
Multiplication: $(a \cdot b) \cdot c = a \cdot (b \cdot c)$	$(-3 \cdot 2) \cdot 11 = -3 \cdot (2 \cdot 11)$
Two numbers whose product is 1 are called **multiplicative inverses** or **reciprocals.** The reciprocal of a nonzero number a is $\frac{1}{a}$ because $a \cdot \frac{1}{a} = 1$.	The reciprocal of 3 is $\frac{1}{3}$. The reciprocal of $-\frac{2}{5}$ is $-\frac{5}{2}$.
DISTRIBUTIVE PROPERTY	
$a(b + c) = a \cdot b + a \cdot c$	$5(6 + 10) = 5 \cdot 6 + 5 \cdot 10$ $-2(3 + x) = -2 \cdot 3 + (-2)(x)$
IDENTITIES	
$a + 0 = a \quad 0 + a = a$ $a \cdot 1 = a \quad 1 \cdot a = a$	$5 + 0 = 5 \quad 0 + (-2) = -2$ $-14 \cdot 1 = -14 \quad 1 \cdot 27 = 27$
INVERSES	
Additive or opposite: $a + (-a) = 0$	$7 + (-7) = 0$
Multiplicative or reciprocal: $b \cdot \frac{1}{b} = 1, \quad b \neq 0$	$3 \cdot \frac{1}{3} = 1$
Section 8.7 Simplifying Expressions	
The **numerical coefficient** of a **term** is its numerical factor.	**Term** / **Numerical Coefficient** $-7y$ / -7 x / 1 $\frac{1}{5}a^2b$ / $\frac{1}{5}$
Terms with the same variables raised to exactly the same powers are **like terms.**	**Like Terms** / **Unlike Terms** $12x, -x$ / $3y, 3y^2$ $-2xy, 5yx$ / $7a^2b, -2ab^2$
To combine like terms, add the numerical coefficients and multiply the result by the common variable factor.	$9y + 3y = 12y$ $-4z^2 + 5z^2 - 6z^2 = -5z^2$
To remove parentheses, apply the distributive property.	$-4(x + 7) + 10(3x - 1)$ $= -4x - 28 + 30x - 10$ $= 26x - 38$

Chapter 8 Review

(8.1) *Insert <, >, or = in the appropriate space to make each statement true.*

1. 8 　 10

2. 7 　 2

3. −4 　 −5

4. $\frac{12}{2}$ 　 −8

5. $|-7|$ 　 $|-8|$

6. $|-9|$ 　 −9

7. $-|-1|$ 　 −1

8. $|-14|$ 　 $-(-14)$

9. 1.2 　 1.02

10. $-\frac{3}{2}$ 　 $-\frac{3}{4}$

Translate each statement into symbols.

11. Four is greater than or equal to negative three.

12. Six is not equal to five.

13. 0.03 is less than 0.3.

14. New York City has 155 museums and 400 art galleries. Write an inequality comparing the numbers 155 and 400. (*Source:* Absolute Trivia.com)

Given the sets of numbers below, list the numbers in each set that also belong to the set of:

a. Natural numbers
b. Whole numbers
c. Integers
d. Rational numbers
e. Irrational numbers
f. Real numbers

15. $\left\{-6, 0, 1, 1\frac{1}{2}, 3, \pi, 9.62\right\}$

16. $\left\{-3, -1.6, 2, 5, \frac{11}{2}, 15.1, \sqrt{5}, 2\pi\right\}$

The following chart shows the gains and losses in dollars of Density Oil and Gas stock for a particular week. Use this chart to answer Exercises 17 and 18.

Day	Gain or Loss (in dollars)
Monday	+1
Tuesday	−2
Wednesday	+5
Thursday	+1
Friday	−4

17. Which day showed the greatest loss?

18. Which day showed the greatest gain?

(8.2) *Choose the correct answer for each statement.*

19. The expression $6 \cdot 3^2 + 2 \cdot 8$ simplifies to
a. −52 **b.** 448 **c.** 70 **d.** 64

20. The expression $68 - 5 \cdot 2^3$ simplifies to
a. −232 **b.** 28 **c.** 38 **d.** 504

Simplify each expression.

21. $3(1 + 2 \cdot 5) + 4$

22. $8 + 3(2 \cdot 6 - 1)$

23. $\dfrac{4 + |6 - 2| + 8^2}{4 + 6 \cdot 4}$

24. $5[3(2 + 5) - 5]$

Translate each word statement to symbols.

25. The difference of twenty and twelve is equal to the product of two and four.

26. The quotient of nine and two is greater than negative five.

Evaluate each expression when $x = 6$, $y = 2$, and $z = 8$.

27. $2x + 3y$

28. $x(y + 2z)$

29. $\dfrac{x}{y} + \dfrac{z}{2y}$

30. $x^2 - 3y^2$

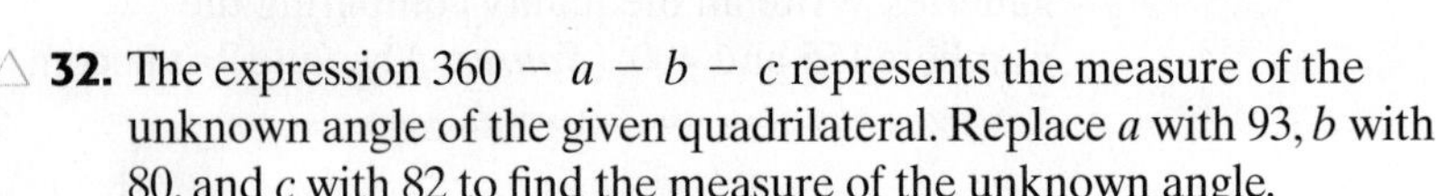

△ **31.** The expression $180 - a - b$ represents the measure of the unknown angle of the given triangle. Replace a with 37 and b with 80 to find the measure of the unknown angle.

△ **32.** The expression $360 - a - b - c$ represents the measure of the unknown angle of the given quadrilateral. Replace a with 93, b with 80, and c with 82 to find the measure of the unknown angle.

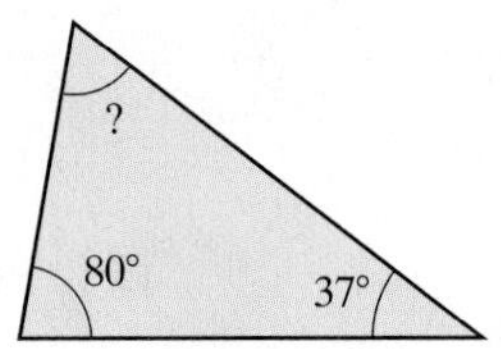

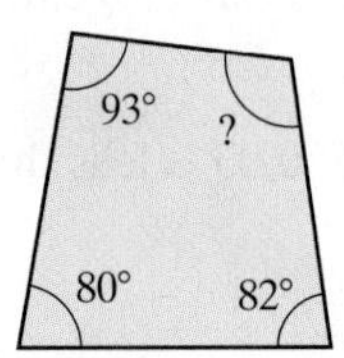

Decide whether the given number is a solution to the given equation.

33. $7x - 3 = 18$; 3

34. $3x^2 + 4 = x - 1$; 1

(8.3) *Find the additive inverse or opposite of each number.*

35. -9

36. $\dfrac{2}{3}$

37. $|-2|$

38. $-|-7|$

Add.

39. $-15 + 4$

40. $-6 + (-11)$

41. $\dfrac{1}{16} + \left(-\dfrac{1}{4}\right)$

42. $-8 + |-3|$

43. $-4.6 + (-9.3)$

44. $-2.8 + 6.7$

(8.4) *Perform each indicated operation.*

45. $6 - 20$

46. $-3.1 - 8.4$

47. $-6 - (-11)$

48. $4 - 15$

49. $-21 - 16 + 3(8 - 2)$

50. $\dfrac{11 - (-9) + 6(8 - 2)}{2 + 3 \cdot 4}$

Evaluate each expression for $x = 3$, $y = -6$, and $z = -9$. Then choose the correct evaluation.

51. $2x^2 - y + z$

a. 15 **b.** 3 **c.** 27 **d.** -3

52. $\dfrac{|y - 4x|}{2x}$

a. 3 **b.** 1 **c.** -1 **d.** -3

53. At the beginning of the week the price of Density Oil and Gas stock from Exercises 17 and 18 is \$50 per share. Find the price of a share of stock at the end of the week.

54. Find the price of a share of stock by the end of the day on Wednesday.

Find each multiplicative inverse or reciprocal.

55. -6

56. $\dfrac{3}{5}$

(8.5) *Simplify each expression.*

57. $6(-8)$

58. $(-2)(-14)$

59. $\dfrac{-18}{-6}$

60. $\dfrac{42}{-3}$

61. $-3(-6)(-2)$

62. $(-4)(-3)(0)(-6)$

63. $\dfrac{4(-3) + (-8)}{2 + (-2)}$

64. $\dfrac{3(-2)^2 - 5}{-14}$

(8.6) *Name the property illustrated in each equation.*

65. $-6 + 5 = 5 + (-6)$

66. $6 \cdot 1 = 6$

67. $3(8 - 5) = 3 \cdot 8 - 3 \cdot 5$

68. $4 + (-4) = 0$

69. $2 + (3 + 9) = (2 + 3) + 9$

70. $2 \cdot 8 = 8 \cdot 2$

71. $6(8 + 5) = 6 \cdot 8 + 6 \cdot 5$

72. $(3 \cdot 8) \cdot 4 = 3 \cdot (8 \cdot 4)$

73. $4 \cdot \frac{1}{4} = 1$

74. $8 + 0 = 8$

75. $4(8 + 3) = 4(3 + 8)$

76. $5(2 + 1) = 5 \cdot 2 + 5 \cdot 1$

(8.7 *Simplify each expression.*

77. $5x - x + 2x$

78. $0.2z - 4.6z - 7.4z$

79. $\frac{1}{2}x + 3 + \frac{7}{2}x - 5$

80. $\frac{4}{5}y + 1 + \frac{6}{5}y + 2$

81. $2(n - 4) + n - 10$

82. $3(w + 2) - (12 - w)$

83. Subtract $7x - 2$ from $x + 5$.

84. Subtract $1.4y - 3$ from $y - 0.7$.

Write each phrase as an algebraic expression. Simplify if possible.

85. Three times a number decreased by 7

86. Twice the sum of a number and 2.8, added to 3 times the number

Mixed Review

Insert $<$, $>$, or $=$ in the space between each pair of numbers.

87. $-|-11| \quad |11.4|$

88. $-1\frac{1}{2} \quad -2\frac{1}{2}$

Perform the indicated operations.

89. $-7.2 + (-8.1)$

90. $14 - 20$

91. $4(-20)$

92. $\frac{-20}{4}$

93. $-\frac{4}{5}\left(\frac{5}{16}\right)$

94. $-0.5(-0.3)$

95. $8 \div 2 \cdot 4$

96. $(-2)^4$

97. $\dfrac{-3 - 2(-9)}{-15 - 3(-4)}$

98. $5 + 2[(7 - 5)^2 + (1 - 3)]$

99. $-\dfrac{5}{8} \div \dfrac{3}{4}$

100. $\dfrac{-15 + (-4)^2 + |-9|}{10 - 2 \cdot 5}$

Remove parentheses and simplify each expression.

101. $7(3x - 3) - 5(x + 4)$

102. $8 + 2(9x - 10)$

Chapter 8 Test

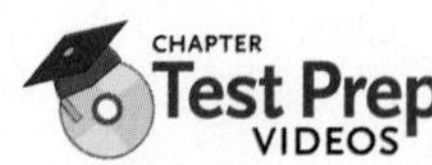

Step-by-step test solutions are found on the Chapter Test Prep Videos available via the Interactive DVD Lecture Series, in MyMathLab or on YouTube (search "MartinGayIntroAlg" and click on "Channels").

Answers

1. ______
2. ______
3. ______
4. ______
5. ______
6. ______
7. ______
8. ______
9. ______
10. ______
11. ______
12. ______
13. ______
14. ______
15. ______
16. ______
17. ______
18. ______
19. ______
20. ______
21. ______

Translate each statement into symbols.

1. The absolute value of negative seven is greater than five.

2. The sum of nine and five is greater than or equal to four.

Simplify each expression.

3. $-13 + 8$

4. $-13 - (-2)$

5. $6 \cdot 3 - 8 \cdot 4$

6. $13(-3)$

7. $(-6)(-2)$

8. $\dfrac{|-16|}{-8}$

9. $\dfrac{-8}{0}$

10. $\dfrac{|-6| + 2}{5 - 6}$

11. $\dfrac{1}{2} - \dfrac{5}{6}$

12. $-1\dfrac{1}{8} + 5\dfrac{3}{4}$

13. $-\dfrac{3}{5} + \dfrac{15}{8}$

14. $3(-4)^2 - 80$

15. $6[5 + 2(3 - 8) - 3]$

16. $\dfrac{-12 + 3 \cdot 8}{4}$

17. $\dfrac{(-2)(0)(-3)}{-6}$

Insert $<$, $>$, or $=$ in the appropriate space to make each statement true.

18. $-3 \quad\quad -7$

19. $4 \quad\quad -8$

20. $|-3| \quad\quad 2$

21. $|-2| \quad\quad -1 - (-3)$

22. Given $\left\{-5, -1, \frac{1}{4}, 0, 1, 7, 11.6, \sqrt{7}, 3\pi\right\}$, list the numbers in this set that also belong to the set of:

a. Natural numbers
b. Whole numbers
c. Integers
d. Rational numbers
e. Irrational numbers
f. Real numbers

Evaluate each expression when $x = 6$, $y = -2$, and $z = -3$.

23. $x^2 + y^2$

24. $x + yz$

25. $2 + 3x - y$

26. $\frac{y + z - 1}{x}$

Identify the property illustrated by each expression.

27. $8 + (9 + 3) = (8 + 9) + 3$

28. $6 \cdot 8 = 8 \cdot 6$

29. $-6(2 + 4) = -6 \cdot 2 + (-6) \cdot 4$

30. $\frac{1}{6}(6) = 1$

31. Find the opposite of -9.

32. Find the reciprocal of $-\frac{1}{3}$.

The New Orleans Saints were 22 yards from the goal when the series of gains and losses shown in the chart occurred. Use this chart to answer Exercises 33 and 34.

	Gains and Losses (in yards)
First down	5
Second down	−10
Third down	−2
Fourth down	29

33. During which down did the greatest loss of yardage occur?

34. Was a touchdown scored?

35. The temperature at the Winter Olympics was a frigid 14° below zero in the morning, but by noon it had risen 31°. What was the temperature at noon?

36. A stockbroker decided to sell 280 shares of stock, which decreased in value by \$1.50 per share yesterday. How much money did she lose?

Simplify each expression.

37. $2y - 6 - y - 4$

38. $2.7x + 6.1 + 3.2x - 4.9$

39. $4(x - 2) - 3(2x - 6)$

40. $-5(y + 1) + 2(3 - 5y)$

22. a. ______
b. ______
c. ______
d. ______
e. ______
f. ______
23. ______
24. ______
25. ______
26. ______
27. ______
28. ______
29. ______
30. ______
31. ______
32. ______
33. ______
34. ______
35. ______
36. ______
37. ______
38. ______
39. ______
40. ______

9

Equations, Inequalities, and Problem Solving

Sections

Check Your Progress

In this chapter, we solve equations and inequalities. Once we know how to solve equations and inequalities, we may solve word problems. Of course, problem solving is an integral topic in algebra and its discussion is continued throughout this text.

A glacier is formed when snow accumulates over time, turns to ice, and begins to flow outwards and downwards under the pressure of its own weight and gravity. Presently 10% of land area is covered with glaciers and about 75% of the fresh water in the world is stored in glacial fields. Glaciers are excellent indicators of past and present climate change. The GLIMS project (Global Land Ice Measurements from Space) is currently creating a glacier database on measurements of the world's estimated 160,000 glaciers. In Section 9.5, Example 1 and Exercise 86 we will examine the distance a glacier covers and the speed at which it travels.

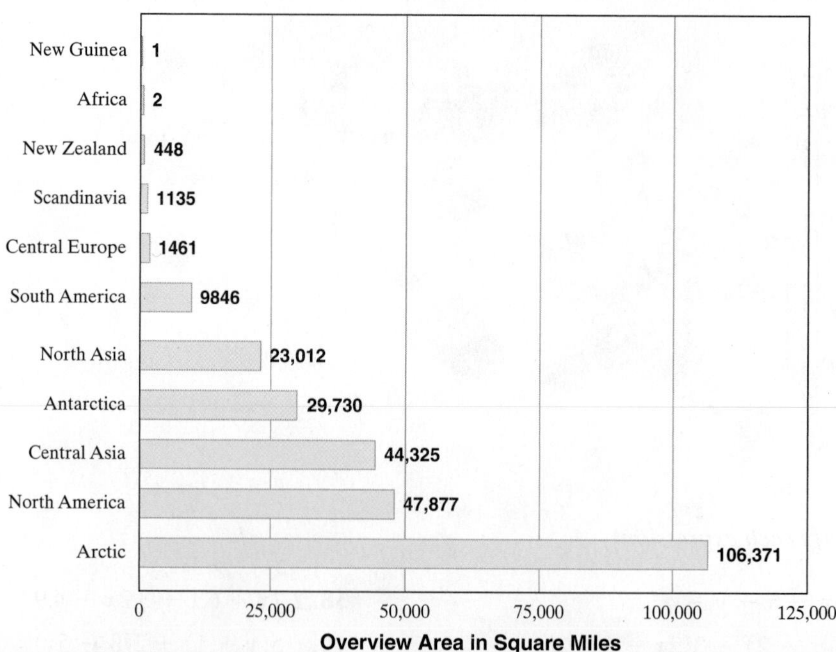

9.1 THE ADDITION PROPERTY OF EQUALITY

Let's recall from Section 1.3 the difference between an equation and an expression. A combination of operations on variables and numbers is an expression, and an equation is of the form "expression = expression."

Equations	Expressions
$3x - 1 = -17$	$3x - 1$
area = length · width	$5(20 - 3) + 10$
$8 + 16 = 16 + 8$	y^3
$-9a + 11b = 14b + 3$	$-x^2 + y - 2$

Now, let's concentrate on equations.

Objective A Using the Addition Property

A value of the variable that makes an equation a true statement is called a solution or root of the equation. The process of finding the solution of an equation is called **solving** the equation for the variable. In this section, we concentrate on solving *linear equations* in one variable.

Linear Equation in One Variable

A **linear equation in one variable** can be written in the form

$$Ax + B = C$$

where A, B, and C are real numbers and $A \neq 0$.

Evaluating each side of a linear equation for a given value of the variable, as we did in Section 1.3, can tell us whether that value is a solution. But we can't rely on this as our method of solving it—with what value would we start?

Instead, to solve a linear equation in x, we write a series of simpler equations, all *equivalent* to the original equation, so that the final equation has the form

$x =$ number or number $= x$

Equivalent equations are equations that have the same solution. This means that the "number" above is the solution to the original equation.

The first property of equality that helps us write simpler equivalent equations is the **addition property of equality.**

Addition Property of Equality

Let a, b, and c represent numbers. Then

$a = b$	Also, $a = b$
and $a + c = b + c$	and $a - c = b - c$
are equivalent equations.	are equivalent equations.

In other words, **the same number may be added to or subtracted from both sides** of an equation without changing the solution of the equation. (We may subtract the same number from both sides since subtraction is defined in terms of addition.)

Let's visualize how we use the addition property of equality to solve an equation. Picture the equation $x - 2 = 1$ as a balanced scale. The left side of the equation has the same value (weight) as the right side.

Objectives

A Use the Addition Property of Equality to Solve Linear Equations.

B Simplify an Equation and Then Use the Addition Property of Equality.

C Write Word Phrases as Algebraic Expressions.

Helpful Hint

Simply stated, an equation contains "=" while an expression does not. Also, we *simplify* expressions and *solve* equations.

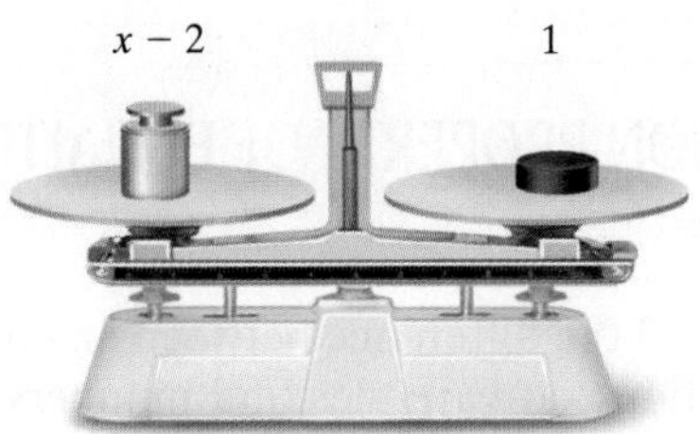

If the same weight is added to each side of a scale, the scale remains balanced. Likewise, if the same number is added to each side of an equation, the left side continues to have the same value as the right side.

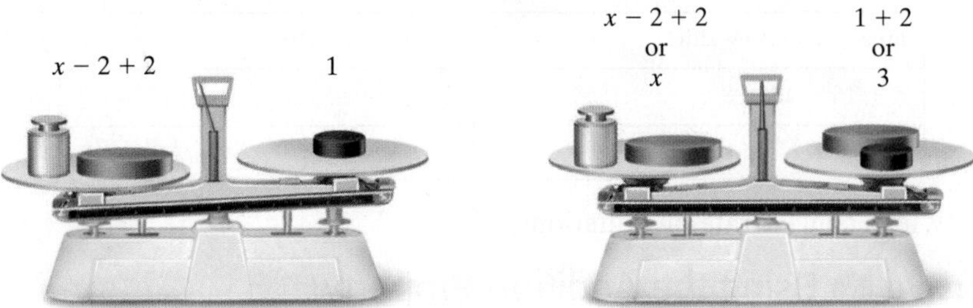

We use the addition property of equality to write equivalent equations until the variable is alone (by itself on one side of the equation) and the equation looks like "x = number" or "number = x."

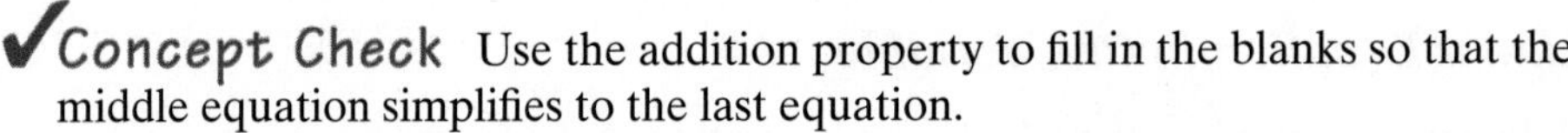

✓Concept Check Use the addition property to fill in the blanks so that the middle equation simplifies to the last equation.

$$x - 5 = 3$$
$$x - 5 + \_\_ = 3 + \_\_$$
$$x = 8$$

PRACTICE 1

Solve: $x - 5 = 8$ for x.

Example 1 Solve $x - 7 = 10$ for x.

Solution: To solve for x, we first get x alone on one side of the equation. To do this, we add 7 to both sides of the equation.

$$x - 7 = 10$$
$$x - 7 + 7 = 10 + 7 \quad \text{Add 7 to both sides.}$$
$$x = 17 \quad \text{Simplify.}$$

The solution of the equation $x = 17$ is obviously 17.
Since we are writing equivalent equations, the solution of the equation $x - 7 = 10$ is also 17.

Check: To check, replace x with 17 in the original equation.

$$x - 7 = 10 \quad \text{Original equation.}$$
$$17 - 7 \stackrel{?}{=} 10 \quad \text{Replace } x \text{ with 17.}$$
$$10 = 10 \quad \text{True}$$

Since the statement is true, 17 is the solution.

Work Practice 1

PRACTICE 2

Solve: $y + 1.7 = 0.3$

Example 2 Solve: $y + 0.6 = -1.0$

Solution: To solve for y (get y alone on one side of the equation), we subtract 0.6 from both sides of the equation.

Answers

1. $x = 13$ **2.** $y = -1.4$

✓ Concept Check Answer

5

$$y + 0.6 = -1.0$$
$$y + 0.6 - 0.6 = -1.0 - 0.6 \quad \text{Subtract 0.6 from both sides.}$$
$$y = -1.6 \quad \text{Combine like terms.}$$

Check:
$$y + 0.6 = -1.0 \quad \text{Original equation.}$$
$$-1.6 + 0.6 \stackrel{?}{=} -1.0 \quad \text{Replace } y \text{ with } -1.6.$$
$$-1.0 = -1.0 \quad \text{True}$$

The solution is -1.6.

Work Practice 2

Example 3 Solve: $\frac{1}{2} = x - \frac{3}{4}$

Solution: To get x alone, we add $\frac{3}{4}$ to both sides.

$$\frac{1}{2} = x - \frac{3}{4}$$
$$\frac{1}{2} + \frac{3}{4} = x - \frac{3}{4} + \frac{3}{4} \quad \text{Add } \frac{3}{4} \text{ to both sides.}$$
$$\frac{1}{2} \cdot \frac{2}{2} + \frac{3}{4} = x \quad \text{The LCD is 4.}$$
$$\frac{2}{4} + \frac{3}{4} = x \quad \text{Add the fractions.}$$
$$\frac{5}{4} = x$$

Check:
$$\frac{1}{2} = x - \frac{3}{4} \quad \text{Original equation.}$$
$$\frac{1}{2} \stackrel{?}{=} \frac{5}{4} - \frac{3}{4} \quad \text{Replace } x \text{ with } \frac{5}{4}.$$
$$\frac{1}{2} \stackrel{?}{=} \frac{2}{4} \quad \text{Subtract.}$$
$$\frac{1}{2} = \frac{1}{2} \quad \text{True}$$

The solution is $\frac{5}{4}$.

Work Practice 3

PRACTICE 3

Solve: $\frac{7}{8} = y - \frac{1}{3}$

Helpful Hint We may solve an equation so that the variable is alone on *either* side of the equation. For example, $\frac{5}{4} = x$ is equivalent to $x = \frac{5}{4}$.

Example 4 Solve: $5t - 5 = 6t$

Solution: To solve for t, we first want all terms containing t on one side of the equation and numbers on the other side. Notice that if we subtract $5t$ from both sides of the equation, then variable terms will be on one side of the equation and the number -5 will be alone on the other side.

$$5t - 5 = 6t$$
$$5t - 5 - 5t = 6t - 5t \quad \text{Subtract } 5t \text{ from both sides.}$$
$$-5 = t \quad \text{Combine like terms.}$$

Check:
$$5t - 5 = 6t \quad \text{Original equation.}$$
$$5(-5) - 5 \stackrel{?}{=} 6(-5) \quad \text{Replace } t \text{ with } -5.$$
$$-25 - 5 \stackrel{?}{=} -30$$
$$-30 = -30 \quad \text{True}$$

The solution is -5.

Work Practice 4

PRACTICE 4

Solve: $3x + 10 = 4x$

Helpful Hint For Example 4, why not subtract $6t$ from both sides? The addition property allows us to do this, and we would have $-t - 5 = 0$. We are just no closer to our goal of having variable terms on one side of the equation and numbers on the other.

Answers

3. $y = \frac{29}{24}$ **4.** $x = 10$

Objective B Simplifying Equations

Many times, it is best to simplify one or both sides of an equation before applying the addition property of equality.

PRACTICE 5

Solve:

$10w + 3 - 4w + 4 = -2w + 3 + 7w$

Example 5 Solve: $2x + 3x - 5 + 7 = 10x + 3 - 6x - 4$

Solution: First we simplify both sides of the equation.

$$2x + 3x - 5 + 7 = 10x + 3 - 6x - 4$$

$$5x + 2 = 4x - 1 \quad \text{Combine like terms on each side of the equation.}$$

Next, we want all terms with a variable on one side of the equation and all numbers on the other side.

$$5x + 2 - 4x = 4x - 1 - 4x \quad \text{Subtract } 4x \text{ from both sides.}$$

$$x + 2 = -1 \quad \text{Combine like terms.}$$

$$x + 2 - 2 = -1 - 2 \quad \text{Subtract 2 from both sides to get } x \text{ alone.}$$

$$x = -3 \quad \text{Combine like terms.}$$

Check:

$$2x + 3x - 5 + 7 = 10x + 3 - 6x - 4 \quad \text{Original equation.}$$

$$2(-3) + 3(-3) - 5 + 7 \stackrel{?}{=} 10(-3) + 3 - 6(-3) - 4 \quad \text{Replace } x \text{ with } -3.$$

$$-6 - 9 - 5 + 7 \stackrel{?}{=} -30 + 3 + 18 - 4 \quad \text{Multiply.}$$

$$-13 = -13 \quad \text{True}$$

The solution is -3.

Work Practice 5

If an equation contains parentheses, we use the distributive property to remove them, as before. Then we combine any like terms.

PRACTICE 6

Solve:

$3(2w - 5) - (5w + 1) = -3$

Example 6 Solve: $6(2a - 1) - (11a + 6) = 7$

Solution:

$$6(2a - 1) - 1(11a + 6) = 7$$

$$6(2a) + 6(-1) - 1(11a) - 1(6) = 7 \quad \text{Apply the distributive property.}$$

$$12a - 6 - 11a - 6 = 7 \quad \text{Multiply.}$$

$$a - 12 = 7 \quad \text{Combine like terms.}$$

$$a - 12 + 12 = 7 + 12 \quad \text{Add 12 to both sides.}$$

$$a = 19 \quad \text{Simplify.}$$

Check: Check by replacing a with 19 in the original equation.

Work Practice 6

PRACTICE 7

Solve: $12 - y = 9$

Example 7 Solve: $3 - x = 7$

Solution: First we subtract 3 from both sides.

$$3 - x = 7$$

$$3 - x - 3 = 7 - 3 \quad \text{Subtract 3 from both sides.}$$

$$-x = 4 \quad \text{Simplify.}$$

We have not yet solved for x since x is not alone. However, this equation does say that the opposite of x is 4. If the opposite of x is 4, then x is the opposite of 4, or $x = -4$.

If $\quad -x = 4,$

then $\quad x = -4.$

Answers

5. $w = -4$ **6.** $w = 13$ **7.** $y = 3$

Check: $3 - x = 7$ Original equation.

$3 - (-4) \stackrel{?}{=} 7$ Replace x with -4.

$3 + 4 \stackrel{?}{=} 7$ Add.

$7 = 7$ True

The solution is -4.

Work Practice 7

Objective C Writing Algebraic Expressions

In this section, we continue to practice writing algebraic expressions.

Example 8

a. The sum of two numbers is 8. If one number is 3, find the other number.

b. The sum of two numbers is 8. If one number is x, write an expression representing the other number.

Solution:

a. If the sum of two numbers is 8 and one number is 3, we find the other number by subtracting 3 from 8. The other number is $8 - 3$, or 5.

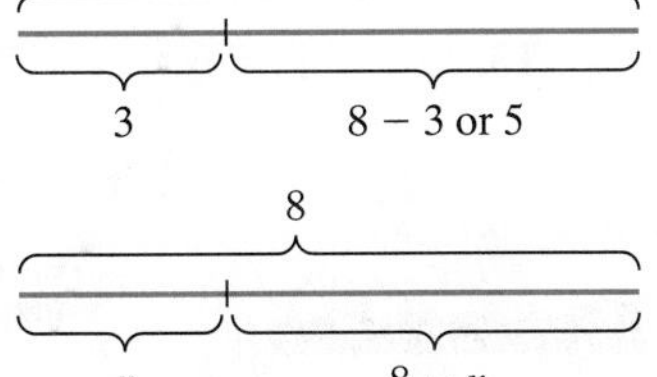

b. If the sum of two numbers is 8 and one number is x, we find the other number by subtracting x from 8. The other number is represented by $8 - x$.

8

x $8 - x$

Work Practice 8

PRACTICE 8

a. The sum of two numbers is 11. If one number is 4, find the other number.

b. The sum of two numbers is 11. If one number is x, write an expression representing the other number.

c. The sum of two numbers is 56. If one number is a, write an expression representing the other number.

Example 9 The Verrazano-Narrows Bridge in New York City is the longest suspension bridge in North America. The Golden Gate Bridge in San Francisco is 60 feet shorter than the Verrazano-Narrows Bridge. If the length of the Verrazano-Narrows Bridge is m feet, express the length of the Golden Gate Bridge as an algebraic expression in m. (*Source:* Survey of State Highway Engineers)

Solution: Since the Golden Gate Bridge is 60 feet shorter than the Verrazano-Narrows Bridge, we have that its length is

In words:	Length of Verrazano-Narrows Bridge	minus	60
Translate:	m	$-$	60

The Golden Gate Bridge is $(m - 60)$ feet long.

Work Practice 9

PRACTICE 9

In a recent House of Representatives race in California, Mike Thompson received 100,445 more votes than Zane Starkewolf. If Zane received n votes, how many did Mike receive? (*Source:* Voter News Service)

Answers

8. a. $11 - 4$ or 7 **b.** $11 - x$ **c.** $56 - a$ **9.** $(n + 100{,}445)$ votes

Vocabulary and Readiness Check

Use the choices below to fill in each blank. Some choices may be used more than once or not at all.

equation	multiplication	addition
expression	solution	equivalent

1. A combination of operations on variables and numbers is called a(n) ____________.
2. A statement of the form "expression = expression" is called a(n) ____________.
3. A(n) ____________ contains an equal sign (=).
4. A(n) ____________ does not contain an equal sign (=).
5. A(n) ____________ may be simplified and evaluated while a(n) ____________ may be solved.
6. A(n) ____________ of an equation is a number that when substituted for a variable makes the equation a true statement.
7. ____________ equations have the same solution.
8. By the ____________ property of equality, the same number may be added to or subtracted from both sides of an equation without changing the solution of the equation.

Solve each equation mentally. See Examples 1 and 2.

9. $x + 4 = 6$ **10.** $x + 7 = 17$ **11.** $n + 18 = 30$

12. $z + 22 = 40$ **13.** $b - 11 = 6$ **14.** $d - 16 = 5$

9.1 Exercise Set

FOR EXTRA HELP

Objective A *Solve each equation. Check each solution. See Examples 1 through 4.*

1. $x + 7 = 10$ **2.** $x + 14 = 25$ **3.** $x - 2 = -4$ **4.** $y - 9 = 1$

5. $-11 = 3 + x$ **6.** $-8 = 8 + z$ **7.** $r - 8.6 = -8.1$ **8.** $t - 9.2 = -6.8$

9. $x - \frac{2}{5} = -\frac{3}{20}$ **10.** $y - \frac{4}{7} = -\frac{3}{14}$ **11.** $\frac{1}{3} + f = \frac{3}{4}$ **12.** $c + \frac{1}{6} = \frac{3}{8}$

Objective B *Solve each equation. Don't forget to first simplify each side of the equation, if possible. Check each solution. See Examples 5 through 7.*

13. $7x + 2x = 8x - 3$ **14.** $3n + 2n = 7 + 4n$ **15.** $\frac{5}{6}x + \frac{1}{6}x = -9$

16. $\frac{13}{11}y - \frac{2}{11}y = -3$ **17.** $2y + 10 = 5y - 4y$ **18.** $4x - 4 = 10x - 7x$

19. $-5(n - 2) = 8 - 4n$ **20.** $-4(z - 3) = 2 - 3z$ **21.** $\frac{3}{7}x + 2 = -\frac{4}{7}x - 5$

22. $\frac{1}{5}x - 1 = -\frac{4}{5}x - 13$ **23.** $5x - 6 = 6x - 5$ **24.** $2x + 7 = x - 10$

25. $8y + 2 - 6y = 3 + y - 10$ **26.** $4p - 11 - p = 2 + 2p - 20$ **27.** $-3(x - 4) = -4x$

28. $-2(x - 1) = -3x$ **29.** $\frac{3}{8}x - \frac{1}{6} = -\frac{5}{8}x - \frac{2}{3}$ **30.** $\frac{2}{5}x - \frac{1}{12} = -\frac{3}{5}x - \frac{3}{4}$

31. $2(x - 4) = x + 3$ **32.** $3(y + 7) = 2y - 5$

33. $3(n - 5) - (6 - 2n) = 4n$

34. $5(3 + z) - (8z + 9) = -4z$

35. $-2(x + 6) + 3(2x - 5) = 3(x - 4) + 10$

36. $-5(x + 1) + 4(2x - 3) = 2(x + 2) - 8$

Objectives **A** **B** **Mixed Practice** *Solve. See Examples 1 through 7.*

37. $13x - 3 = 14x$

38. $18x - 9 = 19x$

39. $5b - 0.7 = 6b$

40. $9x + 5.5 = 10x$

41. $3x - 6 = 2x + 5$

42. $7y + 2 = 6y + 2$

43. $13x - 9 + 2x - 5 = 12x - 1 + 2x$

44. $15x + 20 - 10x - 9 = 25x + 8 - 21x - 7$

45. $7(6 + w) = 6(2 + w)$

46. $6(5 + c) = 5(c - 4)$

47. $n + 4 = 3.6$

48. $m + 2 = 7.1$

49. $10 - (2x - 4) = 7 - 3x$

50. $15 - (6 - 7k) = 2 + 6k$

51. $\frac{1}{3} = x + \frac{2}{3}$

52. $\frac{1}{11} = y + \frac{10}{11}$

53. $-6.5 - 4x - 1.6 - 3x = -6x + 9.8$

54. $-1.4 - 7x - 3.6 - 2x = -8x + 4.4$

Objective **C** *Write each algebraic expression described. See Examples 8 and 9.*

55. A 10-foot board is cut into two pieces. If one piece is x feet long, express the other length in terms of x.

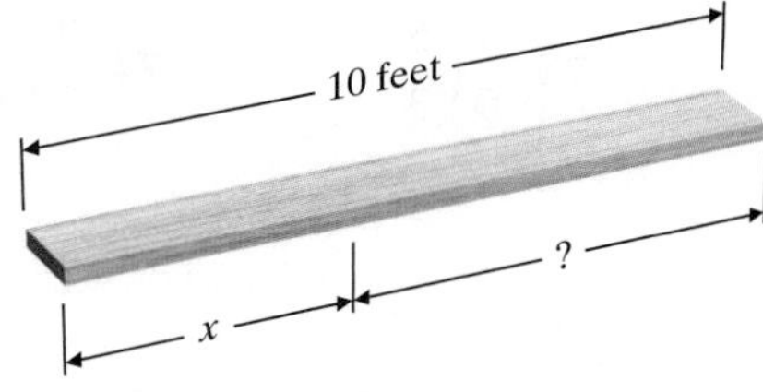

56. A 5-foot piece of string is cut into two pieces. If one piece is x feet long, express the other length in terms of x.

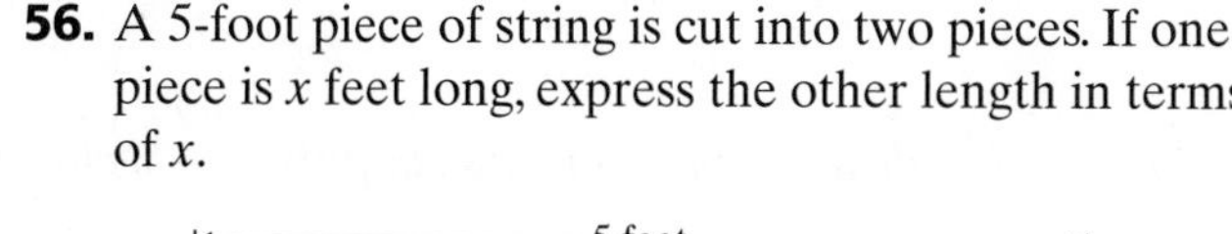

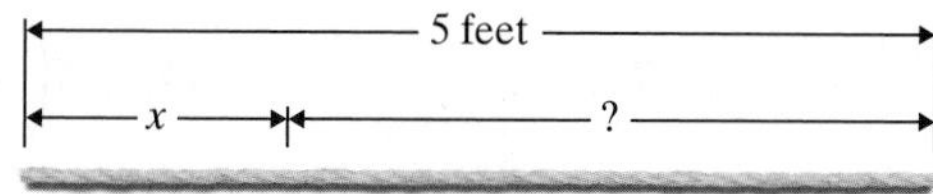

△ **57.** Recall that two angles are *supplementary* if their sum is 180°. If one angle measures $x°$, express the measure of its supplement in terms of x.

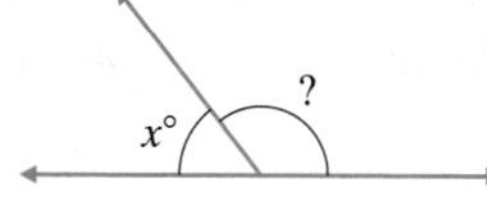

△ **58.** Recall that two angles are *complementary* if their sum is 90°. If one angle measures $x°$, express the measure of its complement in terms of x.

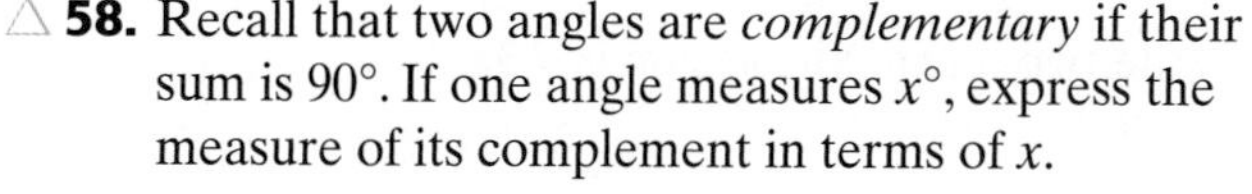

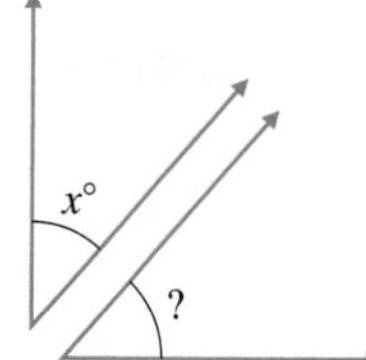

59. In 2009, the number of graduate students at the University of Texas at Austin was approximately 28,000 fewer than the number of undergraduate students. If the number of undergraduate students was n, how many graduate students attend UT Austin? (*Source:* University of Texas at Austin)

60. The longest interstate highway in the U.S. is I-90, which connects Seattle, Washington, and Boston, Massachusetts. The second longest interstate highway, I-80 (connecting San Francisco, California, and Teaneck, New Jersey), is 178.5 miles shorter than I-90. If the length of I-80 is m miles, express the length of I-90 as an algebraic expression in m. (*Source:* U.S. Department of Transportation—Federal Highway Administration)

61. The area of the Sahara Desert in Africa is 7 times the area of the Gobi Desert in Asia. If the area of the Gobi Desert is x square miles, express the area of the Sahara Desert as an algebraic expression in x.

62. The largest meteorite in the world is the Hoba West located in Namibia. Its weight is 3 times the weight of the Armanty meteorite located in Outer Mongolia. If the weight of the Armanty meteorite is y kilograms, express the weight of the Hoba West meteorite as an algebraic expression in y.

Review

Find each multiplicative inverse or reciprocal. See Section 1.7.

63. $\frac{5}{8}$ **64.** $\frac{7}{6}$ **65.** 2 **66.** 5 **67.** $-\frac{1}{9}$ **68.** $-\frac{3}{5}$

Perform each indicated operation and simplify. See Sections 1.6 and 1.8.

69. $\frac{3x}{3}$ **70.** $\frac{-2y}{-2}$ **71.** $-5\left(-\frac{1}{5}y\right)$ **72.** $7\left(\frac{1}{7}r\right)$ **73.** $\frac{3}{5}\left(\frac{5}{3}x\right)$ **74.** $\frac{9}{2}\left(\frac{2}{9}x\right)$

Concept Extensions

75. Write two terms whose sum is $-3x$.

76. Write four terms whose sum is $2y - 6$.

Use the addition property to fill in the blank so that the middle equation simplifies to the last equation. See the Concept Check in this section.

77.
$$x - 4 = -9$$
$$x - 4 + (\quad) = -9 + (\quad)$$
$$x = -5$$

78.
$$a + 9 = 15$$
$$a + 9 + (\quad) = 15 + (\quad)$$
$$a = 6$$

Fill in the blanks with numbers of your choice so that each equation has the given solution. Note: Each blank will be replaced with a different number.

79. ____ + x = ____; Solution: -3

80. x − ____ = ____; Solution: -10

Solve.

△ **81.** The sum of the angles of a triangle is 180°. If one angle of a triangle measures $x°$ and a second angle measures $(2x + 7)°$, express the measure of the third angle in terms of x. Simplify the expression.

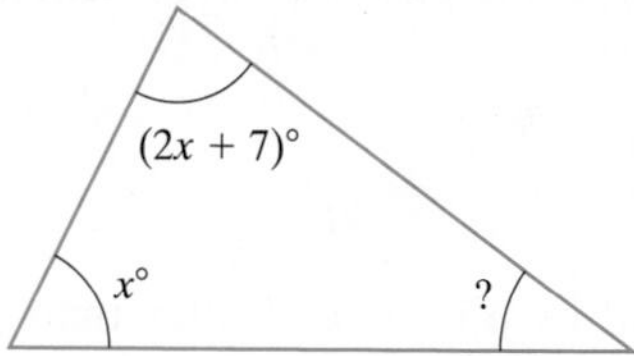

△ **82.** A quadrilateral is a four-sided figure (like the one shown in the figure) whose angle sum is 360°. If one angle measures $x°$, a second angle measures $3x°$, and a third angle measures $5x°$, express the measure of the fourth angle in terms of x. Simplify the expression.

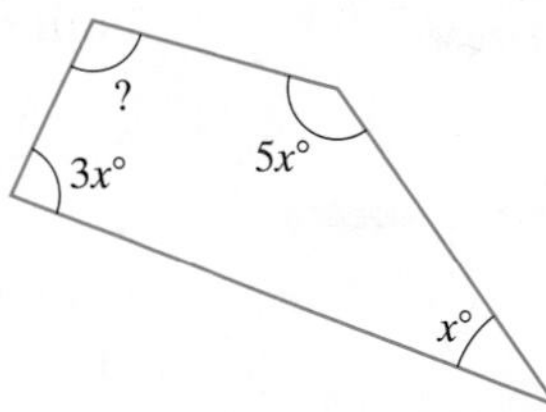

83. In your own words, explain what is meant by the solution of an equation.

84. In your own words, explain how to check a solution of an equation.

Use a calculator to determine the solution of each equation.

85. $36.766 + x = -108.712$

86. $-85.325 = x - 97.985$

Objectives

A **Use the Multiplication Property of Equality to Solve Linear Equations.**

B **Use Both the Addition and Multiplication Properties of Equality to Solve Linear Equations.**

C **Write Word Phrases as Algebraic Expressions.**

9.2 THE MULTIPLICATION PROPERTY OF EQUALITY

Objective A Using the Multiplication Property

As useful as the addition property of equality is, it cannot help us solve every type of linear equation in one variable. For example, adding or subtracting a value on both sides of the equation does not help solve

$$\frac{5}{2}x = 15$$

because the variable x is being multiplied by a number (other than 1). Instead, we apply another important property of equality, the **multiplication property of equality.**

Multiplication Property of Equality

Let a, b, and c represent numbers and let $c \neq 0$. Then

$a = b$	Also, $a = b$
and $a \cdot c = b \cdot c$	and $\frac{a}{c} = \frac{b}{c}$
are equivalent equations.	are equivalent equations.

In other words, **both sides** of an equation **may be multiplied or divided by the same nonzero number** without changing the solution of the equation. (We may divide both sides by the same nonzero number since division is defined in terms of multiplication.)

Picturing again our balanced scale, if we multiply or divide the weight on each side by the same nonzero number, the scale (or equation) remains balanced.

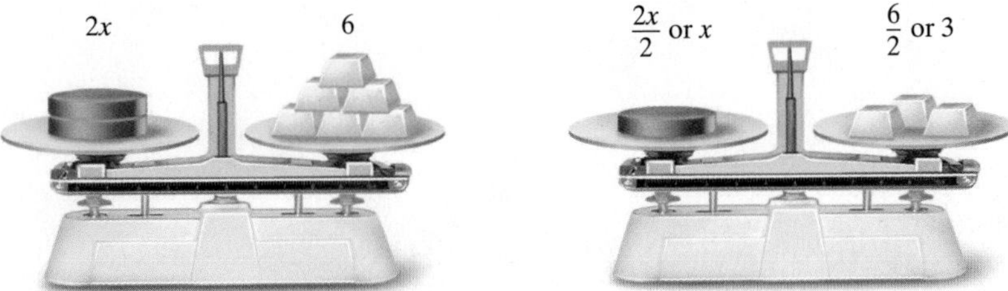

PRACTICE 1

Solve: $\frac{3}{7}x = 9$

Example 1 Solve: $\frac{5}{2}x = 15$

Solution: To get x alone, we multiply both sides of the equation by the reciprocal (or multiplicative inverse) of $\frac{5}{2}$, which is $\frac{2}{5}$.

$$\frac{5}{2}x = 15$$

$$\frac{2}{5} \cdot \left(\frac{5}{2}x\right) = \frac{2}{5} \cdot 15 \quad \text{Multiply both sides by } \frac{2}{5}.$$

$$\left(\frac{2}{5} \cdot \frac{5}{2}\right)x = \frac{2}{5} \cdot 15 \quad \text{Apply the associative property.}$$

$$1x = 6 \quad \text{Simplify.}$$

or

$$x = 6$$

Answer

1. $x = 21$

Check: Replace x with 6 in the original equation.

$$\frac{5}{2}x = 15 \quad \text{Original equation.}$$

$$\frac{5}{2}(6) \stackrel{?}{=} 15 \quad \text{Replace } x \text{ with 6.}$$

$$15 = 15 \quad \text{True}$$

The solution is 6.

Work Practice 1

In the equation $\frac{5}{2}x = 15$, $\frac{5}{2}$ is the coefficient of x. When the coefficient of x is a *fraction,* we will get x alone by multiplying by the reciprocal. When the coefficient of x is an integer or a decimal, it is usually more convenient to divide both sides by the coefficient. (Dividing by a number is, of course, the same as multiplying by the reciprocal of the number.)

Example 2 Solve: $5x = 30$

Solution: To get x alone, we divide both sides of the equation by 5, the coefficient of x.

$$5x = 30$$

$$\frac{5x}{5} = \frac{30}{5} \quad \text{Divide both sides by 5.}$$

$$1 \cdot x = 6 \quad \text{Simplify.}$$

$$x = 6$$

Check: $5x = 30$ Original equation.

$$5 \cdot 6 \stackrel{?}{=} 30 \quad \text{Replace } x \text{ with 6.}$$

$$30 = 30 \quad \text{True}$$

The solution is 6.

Work Practice 2

PRACTICE 2

Solve: $7x = 42$

Example 3 Solve: $-3x = 33$

Solution: Recall that $-3x$ means $-3 \cdot x$. To get x alone, we divide both sides by the coefficient of x, that is, -3.

$$-3x = 33$$

$$\frac{-3x}{-3} = \frac{33}{-3} \quad \text{Divide both sides by } -3.$$

$$1x = -11 \quad \text{Simplify.}$$

$$x = -11$$

Check: $-3x = 33$ Original equation.

$$-3(-11) \stackrel{?}{=} 33 \quad \text{Replace } x \text{ with } -11.$$

$$33 = 33 \quad \text{True}$$

The solution is -11.

Work Practice 3

PRACTICE 3

Solve: $-4x = 52$

Answers

2. $x = 6$ **3.** $x = -13$

PRACTICE 4

Solve: $\frac{y}{5} = 13$

Example 4 Solve: $\frac{y}{7} = 20$

Solution: Recall that $\frac{y}{7} = \frac{1}{7}y$. To get y alone, we multiply both sides of the equation by 7, the reciprocal of $\frac{1}{7}$.

$$\frac{y}{7} = 20$$

$$\frac{1}{7}y = 20$$

$$7 \cdot \frac{1}{7}y = 7 \cdot 20 \quad \text{Multiply both sides by 7.}$$

$$1y = 140 \quad \text{Simplify.}$$

$$y = 140$$

Check: $\frac{y}{7} = 20$ Original equation.

$$\frac{140}{7} \stackrel{?}{=} 20 \quad \text{Replace } y \text{ with 140.}$$

$$20 = 20 \quad \text{True}$$

The solution is 140.

Work Practice 4

PRACTICE 5

Solve: $2.6x = 13.52$

Example 5 Solve: $3.1x = 4.96$

Solution: $3.1x = 4.96$

$$\frac{3.1x}{3.1} = \frac{4.96}{3.1} \quad \text{Divide both sides by 3.1.}$$

$$1x = 1.6 \quad \text{Simplify.}$$

$$x = 1.6$$

Check: Check by replacing x with 1.6 in the original equation. The solution is 1.6.

Work Practice 5

PRACTICE 6

Solve: $-\frac{5}{6}y = -\frac{3}{5}$

Example 6 Solve: $-\frac{2}{3}x = -\frac{5}{2}$

Solution: To get x alone, we multiply both sides of the equation by $-\frac{3}{2}$, the reciprocal of the coefficient of x.

$$-\frac{2}{3}x = -\frac{5}{2}$$

$$-\frac{3}{2} \cdot -\frac{2}{3}x = -\frac{3}{2} \cdot -\frac{5}{2} \quad \text{Multiply both sides by } -\frac{3}{2}\text{, the reciprocal of } -\frac{2}{3}.$$

$$x = \frac{15}{4} \quad \text{Simplify.}$$

Check: Check by replacing x with $\frac{15}{4}$ in the original equation. The solution is $\frac{15}{4}$.

Work Practice 6

Answers

4. $y = 65$ **5.** $x = 5.2$ **6.** $y = \frac{18}{25}$

Objective B Using Both the Addition and Multiplication Properties

We are now ready to combine the skills learned in the last section with the skills learned in this section to solve equations by applying more than one property.

Example 7 Solve: $-z - 4 = 6$

Solution: First, let's get $-z$, the term containing the variable, alone. To do so, we add 4 to both sides of the equation.

$$-z - 4 + 4 = 6 + 4 \quad \text{Add 4 to both sides.}$$
$$-z = 10 \quad \text{Simplify.}$$

Next, recall that $-z$ means $-1 \cdot z$. Thus to get z alone, we either multiply or divide both sides of the equation by -1. In this example, we divide.

$$-z = 10$$
$$\frac{-z}{-1} = \frac{10}{-1} \quad \text{Divide both sides by the coefficient } -1.$$
$$1z = -10 \quad \text{Simplify.}$$
$$z = -10$$

Check:
$$-z - 4 = 6 \quad \text{Original equation.}$$
$$-(-10) - 4 \stackrel{?}{=} 6 \quad \text{Replace } z \text{ with } -10.$$
$$10 - 4 \stackrel{?}{=} 6$$
$$6 = 6 \quad \text{True}$$

The solution is -10.

Work Practice 7

PRACTICE 7

Solve: $-x + 7 = -12$

Don't forget to first simplify one or both sides of an equation, if possible.

Example 8 Solve: $a + a - 10 + 7 = -13$

Solution: First, we simplify the left side of the equation by combining like terms.

$$a + a - 10 + 7 = -13$$
$$2a - 3 = -13 \quad \text{Combine like terms.}$$
$$2a - 3 + 3 = -13 + 3 \quad \text{Add 3 to both sides.}$$
$$2a = -10 \quad \text{Simplify.}$$
$$\frac{2a}{2} = \frac{-10}{2} \quad \text{Divide both sides by 2.}$$
$$a = -5 \quad \text{Simplify.}$$

Check: To check, replace a with -5 in the original equation. The solution is -5.

Work Practice 8

PRACTICE 8

Solve:
$-7x + 2x + 3 - 20 = -2$

Example 9 Solve: $7x - 3 = 5x + 9$

Solution: To get x alone, let's first use the addition property to get variable terms on one side of the equation and numbers on the other side. One way to get variable terms on one side is to subtract $5x$ from both sides.

$$7x - 3 = 5x + 9$$
$$7x - 3 - 5x = 5x + 9 - 5x \quad \text{Subtract } 5x \text{ from both sides.}$$
$$2x - 3 = 9 \quad \text{Simplify.}$$

Continued on next page

PRACTICE 9

Solve: $10x - 4 = 7x + 14$

Answers
7. $x = 19$ **8.** $x = -3$ **9.** $x = 6$

Now, to get numbers on the other side, let's add 3 to both sides.

$$2x - 3 + 3 = 9 + 3 \quad \text{Add 3 to both sides.}$$
$$2x = 12 \quad \text{Simplify.}$$

Use the multiplication property to get x alone.

$$\frac{2x}{2} = \frac{12}{2} \quad \text{Divide both sides by 2.}$$
$$x = 6 \quad \text{Simplify.}$$

Check: To check, replace x with 6 in the original equation to see that a true statement results. The solution is 6.

Work Practice 9

If an equation has parentheses, don't forget to use the distributive property to remove them. Then combine any like terms.

PRACTICE 10

Solve: $4(3x - 2) = -1 + 4$

Example 10 Solve: $5(2x + 3) = -1 + 7$

Solution:

$$5(2x + 3) = -1 + 7$$
$$5(2x) + 5(3) = -1 + 7 \quad \text{Apply the distributive property.}$$
$$10x + 15 = 6 \quad \text{Multiply and write } -1 + 7 \text{ as 6.}$$
$$10x + 15 - 15 = 6 - 15 \quad \text{Subtract 15 from both sides.}$$
$$10x = -9 \quad \text{Simplify.}$$
$$\frac{10x}{10} = -\frac{9}{10} \quad \text{Divide both sides by 10.}$$
$$x = -\frac{9}{10} \quad \text{Simplify.}$$

Check: To check, replace x with $-\frac{9}{10}$ in the original equation to see that a true statement results. The solution is $-\frac{9}{10}$.

Work Practice 10

PRACTICE 11

a. If x is the first of two consecutive integers, express the sum of the two integers in terms of x. Simplify if possible.

b. If x is the first of two consecutive odd integers (see next page), express the sum of the two integers in terms of x. Simplify if possible.

Answers

10. $x = \frac{11}{12}$ **11. a.** $2x + 1$ **b.** $2x + 2$

Objective C Writing Algebraic Expressions

We continue to sharpen our problem-solving skills by writing algebraic expressions.

Example 11 Writing an Expression for Consecutive Integers

If x is the first of three consecutive integers, express the sum of the three integers in terms of x. Simplify if possible.

Solution: An example of three consecutive integers is 7, 8, and 9.

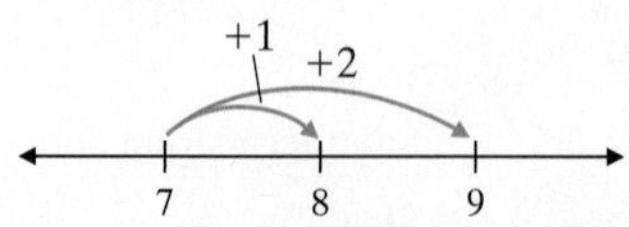

The second consecutive integer is always 1 more than the first, and the third consecutive integer is 2 more than the first. If x is the first of three consecutive integers, the three consecutive integers are x, $x + 1$, and $x + 2$.

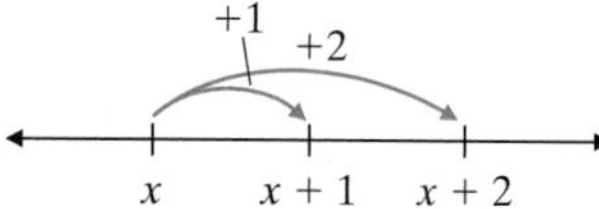

Their sum is shown below.

In words:	first integer	+	second integer	+	third integer
Translate:	x	+	$(x + 1)$	+	$(x + 2)$

This simplifies to $3x + 3$.

Work Practice 11

Study these examples of consecutive even and consecutive odd integers.

Consecutive even integers:

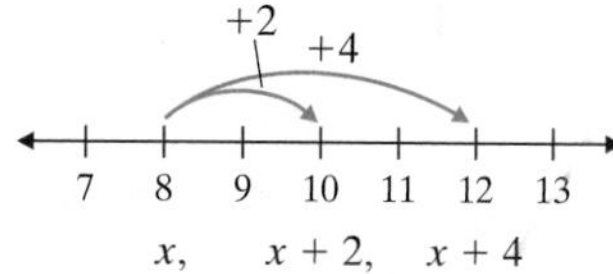

Consecutive odd integers:

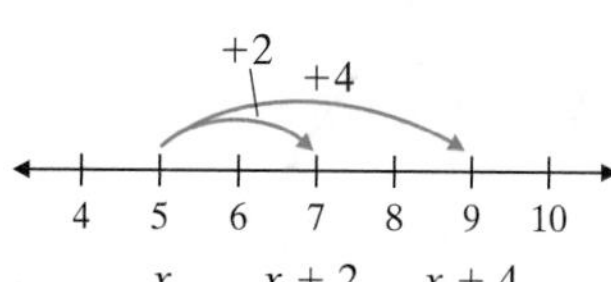

Helpful Hint

If x is an odd integer, then $x + 2$ is the next odd integer. This 2 simply means that odd integers are always 2 units from each other.

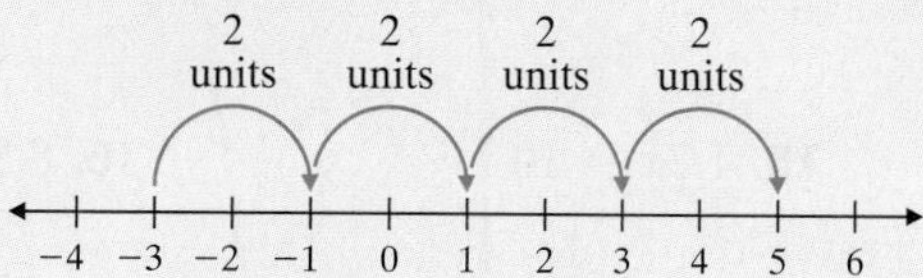

Vocabulary and Readiness Check

Use the choices below to fill in each blank. Some choices may be used more than once. Many of these exercises contain an important review of Section 9.1 also.

equation	multiplication	addition
expression	solution	equivalent

1. By the ___________ property of equality, both sides of an equation may be multiplied or divided by the same nonzero number without changing the solution of the equation.

2. By the ___________ property of equality, the same number may be added to or subtracted from both sides of an equation without changing the solution of the equation.

3. A(n) ___________ may be solved while a(n) ___________ may be simplified and evaluated.

4. A(n) ___________ contains an equal sign (=) while a(n) ___________ does not.

5. ___________ equations have the same solution.

6. A(n) ___________ of an equation is a number that when substituted for a variable makes the equation a true statement.

Solve each equation mentally. See Examples 2 and 3.

7. $3a = 27$ **8.** $9c = 54$ **9.** $5b = 10$ **10.** $7t = 14$ **11.** $6x = -30$ **12.** $8r = -64$

9.2 Exercise Set

FOR EXTRA HELP

PRACTICE WATCH DOWNLOAD READ REVIEW

Objective A *Solve each equation. Check each solution. See Examples 1 through 6.*

1. $-5x = -20$ **2.** $-7x = -49$ **3.** $3x = 0$ **4.** $2x = 0$

5. $-x = -12$ **6.** $-y = 8$ **7.** $\frac{2}{3}x = -8$ **8.** $\frac{3}{4}n = -15$

9. $\frac{1}{6}d = \frac{1}{2}$ **10.** $\frac{1}{8}v = \frac{1}{4}$ **11.** $\frac{a}{2} = 1$ **12.** $\frac{d}{15} = 2$

13. $\frac{k}{-7} = 0$ **14.** $\frac{f}{-5} = 0$ **15.** $1.7x = 10.71$ **16.** $8.5y = 19.55$

Objective B *Solve each equation. Check each solution. See Examples 7 and 8.*

17. $2x - 4 = 16$ **18.** $3x - 1 = 26$ **19.** $-x + 2 = 22$ **20.** $-x + 4 = -24$

21. $6a + 3 = 3$ **22.** $8t + 5 = 5$ **23.** $\frac{x}{3} - 2 = -5$ **24.** $\frac{b}{4} - 1 = -7$

25. $6z - 8 - z + 3 = 0$ **26.** $4a + 1 + a - 11 = 0$ **27.** $1 = 0.4x - 0.6x - 5$ **28.** $19 = 0.4x - 0.9x - 6$

29. $\frac{2}{3}y - 11 = -9$ **30.** $\frac{3}{5}x - 14 = -8$ **31.** $\frac{3}{4}t - \frac{1}{2} = \frac{1}{3}$ **32.** $\frac{2}{7}z - \frac{1}{5} = \frac{1}{2}$

Solve each equation. See Examples 9 and 10.

33. $8x + 20 = 6x + 18$

34. $11x + 13 = 9x + 9$

35. $3(2x + 5) = -18 + 9$

36. $2(4x + 1) = -12 + 6$

37. $2x - 5 = 20x + 4$

38. $6x - 4 = -2x - 10$

39. $2 + 14 = -4(3x - 4)$

40. $8 + 4 = -6(5x - 2)$

41. $-6y - 3 = -5y - 7$

42. $-17z - 4 = -16z - 20$

43. $\frac{1}{2}(2x - 1) = -\frac{1}{7} - \frac{3}{7}$

44. $\frac{1}{3}(3x - 1) = -\frac{1}{10} - \frac{2}{10}$

45. $-10z - 0.5 = -20z + 1.6$

46. $-14y - 1.8 = -24y + 3.9$

47. $-4x + 20 = 4x - 20$

48. $-3x + 15 = 3x - 15$

Objectives **A** **B** **Mixed Practice** *See Examples 1 through 10.*

49. $42 = 7x$

50. $81 = 3x$

51. $4.4 = -0.8x$

52. $6.3 = -0.6x$

53. $6x + 10 = -20$

54. $10y + 15 = -5$

55. $5 - 0.3k = 5$

56. $2 - 0.4p = 2$

57. $13x - 5 = 11x - 11$

58. $20x - 20 = 16x - 40$

59. $9(3x + 1) = 4x - 5x$

60. $7(2x + 1) = 18x - 19x$

61. $-\frac{3}{7}p = -2$

62. $-\frac{4}{5}r = -5$

63. $-\frac{4}{3}x = 12$

64. $-\frac{10}{3}x = 30$

65. $-2x - \frac{1}{2} = \frac{7}{2}$

66. $-3n - \frac{1}{3} = \frac{8}{3}$

67. $10 = 2x - 1$

68. $12 = 3j - 4$

69. $10 - 3x - 6 - 9x = 7$

70. $12x + 30 + 8x - 6 = 10$

71. $z - 5z = 7z - 9 - z$

72. $t - 6t = -13 + t - 3t$

73. $-x - \frac{4}{5} = x + \frac{1}{2} + \frac{2}{5}$

74. $x + \frac{3}{7} = -x + \frac{1}{3} + \frac{4}{7}$

75. $-15 + 37 = -2(x + 5)$

76. $-19 + 74 = -5(x + 3)$

Objective C *Write each algebraic expression described. Simplify if possible. See Example 11.*

77. If x represents the first of two consecutive odd integers, express the sum of the two integers in terms of x.

78. If x is the first of three consecutive even integers, write their sum as an algebraic expression in x.

79. If x is the first of four consecutive integers, express the sum of the first integer and the third integer as an algebraic expression containing the variable x.

80. If x is the first of two consecutive integers, express the sum of 20 and the second consecutive integer as an algebraic expression containing the variable x.

81. Classrooms on one side of the science building are all numbered with consecutive even integers. If the first room on this side of the building is numbered x, write an expression in x for the sum of five classroom numbers in a row. Then simplify this expression.

82. Two sides of a quadrilateral have the same length, x, while the other two sides have the same length, both being the next consecutive odd integer. Write the sum of these lengths. Then simplify this expression.

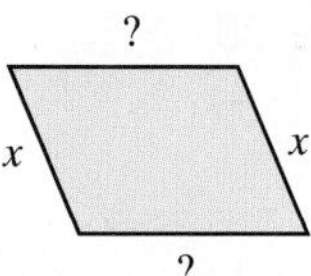

Review

Simplify each expression. See Section 1.8.

83. $5x + 2(x - 6)$

84. $-7y + 2y - 3(y + 1)$

85. $6(2z + 4) + 20$

86. $-(3a - 3) + 2a - 6$

87. $-(x - 1) + x$

88. $8(z - 6) + 7z - 1$

Concept Extensions

Fill in the blank with a number of your choice so that each equation has the given solution.

89. $6x =$ ______; solution: -8

90. ______ $x = 10$; solution: $\frac{1}{2}$

91. The equation $3x + 6 = 2x + 10 + x - 4$ is true for all real numbers. Substitute a few real numbers for x to see that this is so and then try solving the equation. Describe what happens.

92. The equation $6x + 2 - 2x = 4x + 1$ has no solution. Try solving this equation for x and describe what happens.

93. From the results of Exercises 91 and 92, when do you think an equation has all real numbers as its solutions?

94. From the results of Exercises 91 and 92, when do you think an equation has no solution?

Solve.

95. $0.07x - 5.06 = -4.92$

96. $0.06y + 2.63 = 2.5562$

9.3 FURTHER SOLVING LINEAR EQUATIONS

Objectives

A Apply the General Strategy for Solving a Linear Equation.

B Solve Equations Containing Fractions or Decimals.

C Recognize Identities and Equations with No Solution.

Objective A Solving Linear Equations

Let's begin by restating the formal definition of a linear equation in one variable.

A **linear equation in one variable** can be written in the form

$Ax + B = C$

where A, B, and C are real numbers and $A \neq 0$.

We now combine our knowledge from the previous sections into a general strategy for solving linear equations.

To Solve Linear Equations in One Variable

Step 1: If an equation contains fractions, multiply both sides by the LCD to clear the equation of fractions.

Step 2: Use the distributive property to remove parentheses if they are present.

Step 3: Simplify each side of the equation by combining like terms.

Step 4: Get all variable terms on one side and all numbers on the other side by using the addition property of equality.

Step 5: Get the variable alone by using the multiplication property of equality.

Step 6: Check the solution by substituting it into the original equation.

We will use these steps as we solve the equations in Examples 1–5.

Example 1 Solve: $4(2x - 3) + 7 = 3x + 5$

Solution: There are no fractions, so we begin with Step 2.

$4(2x - 3) + 7 = 3x + 5$

Step 2: $8x - 12 + 7 = 3x + 5$ Use the distributive property.

Step 3: $8x - 5 = 3x + 5$ Combine like terms.

Step 4: Get all variable terms on one side of the equation and all numbers on the other side. One way to do this is by subtracting $3x$ from both sides and then adding 5 to both sides.

$8x - 5 - 3x = 3x + 5 - 3x$ Subtract $3x$ from both sides.

$5x - 5 = 5$ Simplify.

$5x - 5 + 5 = 5 + 5$ Add 5 to both sides.

$5x = 10$ Simplify.

Step 5: Use the multiplication property of equality to get x alone.

$\frac{5x}{5} = \frac{10}{5}$ Divide both sides by 5.

$x = 2$ Simplify.

Step 6: Check.

$4(2x - 3) + 7 = 3x + 5$ Original equation

$4[2(2) - 3] + 7 \stackrel{?}{=} 3(2) + 5$ Replace x with 2.

$4(4 - 3) + 7 \stackrel{?}{=} 6 + 5$

$4(1) + 7 \stackrel{?}{=} 11$

$4 + 7 \stackrel{?}{=} 11$

$11 = 11$ True

The solution is 2.

Work Practice 1

PRACTICE 1

Solve:
$5(3x - 1) + 2 = 12x + 6$

Answer
1. $x = 3$

PRACTICE 2

Solve: $9(5 - x) = -3x$

Helpful Hint When checking solutions, use the original equation.

Example 2 Solve: $8(2 - t) = -5t$

Solution: First, we apply the distributive property.

$$8(2 - t) = -5t$$

Step 2: $16 - 8t = -5t$ Use the distributive property.

Step 4: $16 - 8t + 8t = -5t + 8t$ Add $8t$ to both sides.

$16 = 3t$ Combine like terms.

Step 5: $\frac{16}{3} = \frac{3t}{3}$ Divide both sides by 3.

$\frac{16}{3} = t$ Simplify.

Step 6: Check.

$8(2 - t) = -5t$ Original equation

$8\left(2 - \frac{16}{3}\right) \stackrel{?}{=} -5\left(\frac{16}{3}\right)$ Replace t with $\frac{16}{3}$.

$8\left(\frac{6}{3} - \frac{16}{3}\right) \stackrel{?}{=} -\frac{80}{3}$ The LCD is 3.

$8\left(-\frac{10}{3}\right) \stackrel{?}{=} -\frac{80}{3}$ Subtract fractions.

$-\frac{80}{3} = -\frac{80}{3}$ True

The solution is $\frac{16}{3}$.

Work Practice 2

Objective B Solving Equations Containing Fractions or Decimals

If an equation contains fractions, we can clear the equation of fractions by multiplying both sides by the LCD of all denominators. By doing this, we avoid working with time-consuming fractions.

PRACTICE 3

Solve: $\frac{5}{2}x - 1 = \frac{3}{2}x - 4$

Example 3 Solve: $\frac{x}{2} - 1 = \frac{2}{3}x - 3$

Solution: We begin by clearing fractions. To do this, we multiply both sides of the equation by the LCD, which is 6.

$$\frac{x}{2} - 1 = \frac{2}{3}x - 3$$

Step 1: $6\left(\frac{x}{2} - 1\right) = 6\left(\frac{2}{3}x - 3\right)$ Multiply both sides by the LCD, 6.

Step 2: $6\left(\frac{x}{2}\right) - 6(1) = 6\left(\frac{2}{3}x\right) - 6(3)$ Use the distributive property.

$3x - 6 = 4x - 18$ Simplify.

Helpful Hint Don't forget to multiply *each* term by the LCD.

There are no longer grouping symbols and no like terms on either side of the equation, so we continue with Step 4.

Answers

2. $x = \frac{15}{2}$ **3.** $x = -3$

$$3x - 6 = 4x - 18$$

Step 4: $3x - 6 - 3x = 4x - 18 - 3x$ Subtract $3x$ from both sides.
$-6 = x - 18$ Simplify.
$-6 + 18 = x - 18 + 18$ Add 18 to both sides.
$12 = x$ Simplify.

Step 5: The variable is now alone, so there is no need to apply the multiplication property of equality.

Step 6: Check.

$\frac{x}{2} - 1 = \frac{2}{3}x - 3$ Original equation

$\frac{12}{2} - 1 \stackrel{?}{=} \frac{2}{3} \cdot 12 - 3$ Replace x with 12.

$6 - 1 \stackrel{?}{=} 8 - 3$ Simplify.

$5 = 5$ True

The solution is 12.

Work Practice 3

Example 4 Solve: $\frac{2(a + 3)}{3} = 6a + 2$

Solution: We clear the equation of fractions first.

$$\frac{2(a + 3)}{3} = 6a + 2$$

Step 1: $3 \cdot \frac{2(a + 3)}{3} = 3(6a + 2)$ Clear the fraction by multiplying both sides by the LCD, 3.

$2(a + 3) = 3(6a + 2)$ Simplify.

Step 2: Next, we use the distributive property to remove parentheses.

$2a + 6 = 18a + 6$ Use the distributive property.

Step 4: $2a + 6 - 18a = 18a + 6 - 18a$ Subtract $18a$ from both sides.
$-16a + 6 = 6$ Simplify.
$-16a + 6 - 6 = 6 - 6$ Subtract 6 from both sides.
$-16a = 0$

Step 5: $\frac{-16a}{-16} = \frac{0}{-16}$ Divide both sides by -16.
$a = 0$ Simplify.

Step 6: To check, replace a with 0 in the original equation. The solution is 0.

Work Practice 4

PRACTICE 4

Solve: $\frac{3(x - 2)}{5} = 3x + 6$

Helpful Hint

Remember: When solving an equation, it makes no difference on which side of the equation variable terms lie. Just make sure that constant terms lie on the other side.

When solving a problem about money, you may need to solve an equation containing decimals. If you choose, you may multiply to clear the equation of decimals.

Answer

4. $x = -3$

PRACTICE 5

Solve:
$0.06x - 0.10(x - 2) = -0.16$

Helpful Hint If you have trouble with this step, try removing parentheses first.

$0.25x + 0.10(x - 3) = 1.1$

$0.25x + 0.10x - 0.3 = 1.1$

$0.25x + 0.10x - 0.30 = 1.10$

$25x + 10x - 30 = 110$

Then continue.

Example 5 Solve: $0.25x + 0.10(x - 3) = 1.1$

Solution: First we clear this equation of decimals by multiplying both sides of the equation by 100. Recall that multiplying a decimal number by 100 has the effect of moving the decimal point 2 places to the right.

$$0.25x + 0.10(x - 3) = 1.1$$

Step 1: $0.25x + 0.10(x - 3) = 1.10$ Multiply both sides by 100

$$25x + 10(x - 3) = 110$$

Step 2: $25x + 10x - 30 = 110$ Apply the distributive property.

Step 3: $35x - 30 = 110$ Combine like terms.

Step 4: $35x - 30 + 30 = 110 + 30$ Add 30 to both sides.

$35x = 140$ Combine like terms.

Step 5: $\frac{35x}{35} = \frac{140}{35}$ Divide both sides by 35.

$$x = 4$$

Step 6: To check, replace x with 4 in the original equation. The solution is 4.

Work Practice 5

Objective C Recognizing Identities and Equations with No Solution

So far, each equation that we have solved has had a single solution. However, not every equation in one variable has a single solution. Some equations have no solution, while others have an infinite number of solutions. For example,

$$x + 5 = x + 7$$

has **no solution** since no matter which real number we replace x with, the equation is false.

real number + 5 = same real number + 7 FALSE

On the other hand,

$$x + 6 = x + 6$$

has infinitely many solutions since x can be replaced by any real number and the equation will always be true.

real number + 6 = same real number + 6 TRUE

The equation $x + 6 = x + 6$ is called an **identity.** The next two examples illustrate special equations like these.

PRACTICE 6

Solve:
$5(2 - x) + 8x = 3(x - 6)$

Example 6 Solve: $-2(x - 5) + 10 = -3(x + 2) + x$

Solution:

$-2(x - 5) + 10 = -3(x + 2) + x$

$-2x + 10 + 10 = -3x - 6 + x$ Apply the distributive property on both sides.

$-2x + 20 = -2x - 6$ Combine like terms.

$-2x + 20 + 2x = -2x - 6 + 2x$ Add $2x$ to both sides.

$20 = -6$ Combine like terms.

The final equation contains no variable terms, and the result is the false statement $20 = -6$. This means that there is no value for x that makes $20 = -6$ a true equation. Thus, we conclude that there is **no solution** to this equation.

Work Practice 6

Answers
5. $x = 9$ 6. no solution

Example 7 Solve: $3(x - 4) = 3x - 12$

Solution:
$$3(x - 4) = 3x - 12$$
$$3x - 12 = 3x - 12 \quad \text{Apply the distributive property.}$$

The left side of the equation is now identical to the right side. Every real number may be substituted for x and a true statement will result. We arrive at the same conclusion if we continue.

$$3x - 12 = 3x - 12$$
$$3x - 12 - 3x = 3x - 12 - 3x \quad \text{Subtract } 3x \text{ from both sides.}$$
$$-12 = -12 \quad \text{Combine like terms.}$$

Again, the final equation contains no variables, but this time the result is the true statement $-12 = -12$. This means that one side of the equation is identical to the other side. Thus, $3(x - 4) = 3x - 12$ is an **identity** and **every real number** is a solution.

Work Practice 7

PRACTICE 7

Solve:
$-6(2x + 1) - 14$
$= -10(x + 2) - 2x$

Answer

7. Every real number is a solution.

✓Concept Check Suppose you have simplified several equations and obtained the following results. What can you conclude about the solutions to the original equation?

a. $7 = 7$ **b.** $x = 0$ **c.** $7 = -4$

✓ Concept Check Answer

a. Every real number is a solution.
b. The solution is 0.
c. There is no solution.

Calculator Explorations Checking Equations

We can use a calculator to check possible solutions of equations. To do this, replace the variable by the possible solution and evaluate each side of the equation separately.

Equation: $3x - 4 = 2(x + 6)$ Solution: $x = 16$

$$3x - 4 = 2(x + 6)$$
$$3(16) - 4 \stackrel{?}{=} 2(16 + 6)$$

Now evaluate each side with your calculator.

Evaluate left side: [3] [×] [16] [−] [4] [=] or [ENTER]

Display: [44]

Evaluate right side: [2] [(] [16] [+] [6] [)] [=] or [ENTER]

Display: [44]

Since the left side equals the right side, the equation checks.

Use a calculator to check the possible solutions to each equation.

1. $2x = 48 + 6x;\quad x = -12$
2. $-3x - 7 = 3x - 1;\quad x = -1$
3. $5x - 2.6 = 2(x + 0.8);\quad x = 4.4$
4. $-1.6x - 3.9 = -6.9x - 25.6;\quad x = 5$
5. $\dfrac{564x}{4} = 200x - 11(649);\quad x = 121$
6. $20(x - 39) = 5x - 432;\quad x = 23.2$

Vocabulary and Readiness Check

Throughout algebra, it is important to be able to identify equations and expressions.

Remember,

- an equation contains an equal sign and
- an expression does not.

Among other things,

- we solve equations and
- we simplify or perform operations on expressions.

Identify each as an equation or an expression.

1. $x = -7$ ________ **2.** $x - 7$ ________ **3.** $4y - 6 + 9y + 1$ ________

4. $4y - 6 = 9y + 1$ ________ **5.** $\frac{1}{x} - \frac{x-1}{8}$ ________ **6.** $\frac{1}{x} - \frac{x-1}{8} = 6$ ________

7. $0.1x + 9 = 0.2x$ ________ **8.** $0.1x^2 + 9y - 0.2x^2$ ________

9.3 Exercise Set

FOR EXTRA HELP

Powered by CourseCompass and MathXL

MyMathLab

PRACTICE

WATCH

DOWNLOAD

READ

REVIEW

Objective **A** *Solve each equation. See Examples 1 and 2.*

1. $-4y + 10 = -2(3y + 1)$

2. $-3x + 1 = -2(4x + 2)$

3. $15x - 8 = 10 + 9x$

4. $15x - 5 = 7 + 12x$

5. $-2(3x - 4) = 2x$

6. $-(5x - 10) = 5x$

7. $5(2x - 1) - 2(3x) = 1$

8. $3(2 - 5x) + 4(6x) = 12$

9. $-6(x - 3) - 26 = -8$

10. $-4(n - 4) - 23 = -7$

11. $8 - 2(a + 1) = 9 + a$

12. $5 - 6(2 + b) = b - 14$

13. $4x + 3 = -3 + 2x + 14$

14. $6y - 8 = -6 + 3y + 13$

15. $-2y - 10 = 5y + 18$

16. $-7n + 5 = 8n - 10$

Objective **B** *Solve each equation. See Examples 3 through 5.*

17. $\frac{2}{3}x + \frac{4}{3} = -\frac{2}{3}$

18. $\frac{4}{5}x - \frac{8}{5} = -\frac{16}{5}$

19. $\frac{3}{4}x - \frac{1}{2} = 1$

20. $\frac{2}{9}x - \frac{1}{3} = 1$

21. $0.50x + 0.15(70) = 35.5$

22. $0.40x + 0.06(30) = 9.8$

23. $\frac{2(x + 1)}{4} = 3x - 2$

24. $\frac{3(y + 3)}{5} = 2y + 6$

25. $x + \frac{7}{6} = 2x - \frac{7}{6}$

26. $\frac{5}{2}x - 1 = x + \frac{1}{4}$

27. $0.12(y - 6) + 0.06y = 0.08y - 0.7$

28. $0.60(z - 300) + 0.05z = 0.70z - 205$

Objective **C** *Solve each equation. See Examples 6 and 7.*

29. $4(3x + 2) = 12x + 8$

30. $14x + 7 = 7(2x + 1)$

31. $\frac{x}{4} + 1 = \frac{x}{4}$

32. $\frac{x}{3} - 2 = \frac{x}{3}$

33. $3x - 7 = 3(x + 1)$

34. $2(x - 5) = 2x + 10$

35. $-2(6x - 5) + 4 = -12x + 14$

36. $-5(4y - 3) + 2 = -20y + 17$

Objectives **A** **B** **C** **Mixed Practice** *Solve. See Examples 1 through 7.*

37. $\frac{6(3 - z)}{5} = -z$

38. $\frac{4(5 - w)}{3} = -w$

39. $-3(2t - 5) + 2t = 5t - 4$

40. $-(4a - 7) - 5a = 10 + a$

41. $5y + 2(y - 6) = 4(y + 1) - 2$

42. $9x + 3(x - 4) = 10(x - 5) + 7$

43. $\frac{3(x - 5)}{2} = \frac{2(x + 5)}{3}$

44. $\frac{5(x - 1)}{4} = \frac{3(x + 1)}{2}$

45. $0.7x - 2.3 = 0.5$

46. $0.9x - 4.1 = 0.4$

47. $5x - 5 = 2(x + 1) + 3x - 7$

48. $3(2x - 1) + 5 = 6x + 2$

49. $4(2n + 1) = 3(6n + 3) + 1$

50. $4(4y + 2) = 2(1 + 6y) + 8$

51. $x + \frac{5}{4} = \frac{3}{4}x$

52. $\frac{7}{8}x + \frac{1}{4} = \frac{3}{4}x$

53. $\frac{x}{2} - 1 = \frac{x}{5} + 2$

54. $\frac{x}{5} - 7 = \frac{x}{3} - 5$

55. $2(x + 3) - 5 = 5x - 3(1 + x)$

56. $4(2 + x) + 1 = 7x - 3(x - 2)$

57. $0.06 - 0.01(x + 1) = -0.02(2 - x)$

58. $-0.01(5x + 4) = 0.04 - 0.01(x + 4)$

59. $\frac{9}{2} + \frac{5}{2}y = 2y - 4$

60. $3 - \frac{1}{2}x = 5x - 8$

61. $\frac{3}{4}x - 1 + \frac{1}{2}x = \frac{5}{12}x + \frac{1}{6}$

62. $\frac{5}{9}x + 2 - \frac{1}{6}x = \frac{11}{18}x + \frac{1}{3}$

63. $3x + \frac{5}{16} = \frac{3}{4} - \frac{1}{8}x - \frac{1}{2}$

64. $2x - \frac{1}{10} = \frac{2}{5} - \frac{1}{4}x - \frac{17}{20}$

Review

Translating *Write each algebraic expression described. See Section 1.8. Recall that the perimeter of a figure is the total distance around the figure.*

△ 65. A plot of land is in the shape of a triangle. If one side is x meters, a second side is $(2x - 3)$ meters, and a third side is $(3x - 5)$ meters, express the perimeter of the lot as a simplified expression in x.

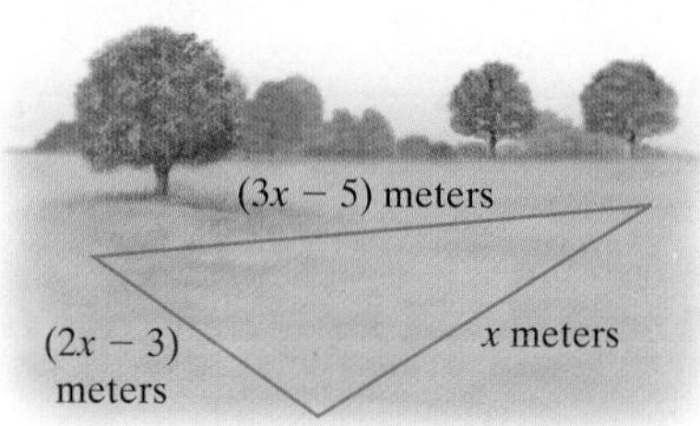

66. A portion of a board has length x feet. The other part has length $(7x - 9)$ feet. Express the total length of the board as a simplified expression in x.

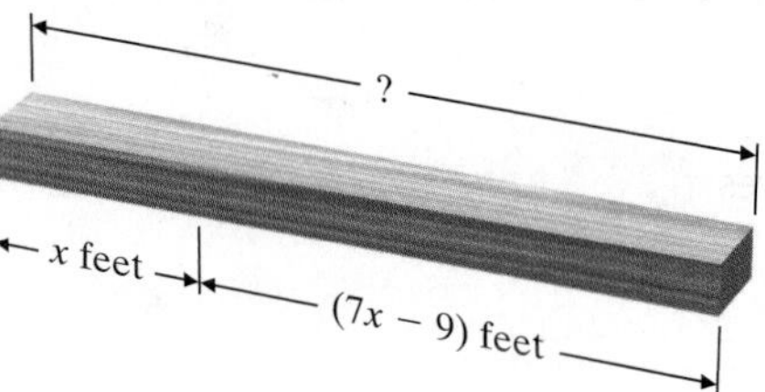

Translating *Write each phrase as an algebraic expression. Use x for the unknown number. See Section 1.8.*

67. A number subtracted from -8

68. Three times a number

69. The sum of -3 and twice a number

70. The difference of 8 and twice a number

71. The product of 9 and the sum of a number and 20

72. The quotient of -12 and the difference of a number and 3

Concept Extensions

See the Concept Check in this section.

73. **a.** Solve: $x + 3 = x + 3$

b. If you simplify an equation (such as the one in part a) and get a true statement such as $3 = 3$ or $0 = 0$, what can you conclude about the solution(s) of the original equation?

c. On your own, construct an equation for which every real number is a solution.

74. **a.** Solve: $x + 3 = x + 5$

b. If you simplify an equation (such as the one in part a) and get a false statement such as $3 = 5$ or $10 = 17$, what can you conclude about the solution(s) of the original equation?

c. On your own, construct an equation that has no solution.

Match each equation in the first column with its solution in the second column. Items in the second column may be used more than once.

75. $5x + 1 = 5x + 1$

76. $3x + 1 = 3x + 2$

77. $2x - 6x - 10 = -4x + 3 - 10$

78. $x - 11x - 3 = -10x - 1 - 2$

79. $9x - 20 = 8x - 20$

80. $-x + 15 = x + 15$

a. all real numbers

b. no solution

c. 0

81. Explain the difference between simplifying an expression and solving an equation.

82. On your own, write an expression and then an equation. Label each.

For Exercises 83 and 84, ***a.*** *Write an equation for perimeter. (Recall that the perimeter of a geometric figure is the sum of the lengths of its sides.)* ***b.*** *Solve the equation in part (a).* ***c.*** *Find the length of each side.*

83. The perimeter of the following pentagon (five-sided figure) is 28 centimeters.

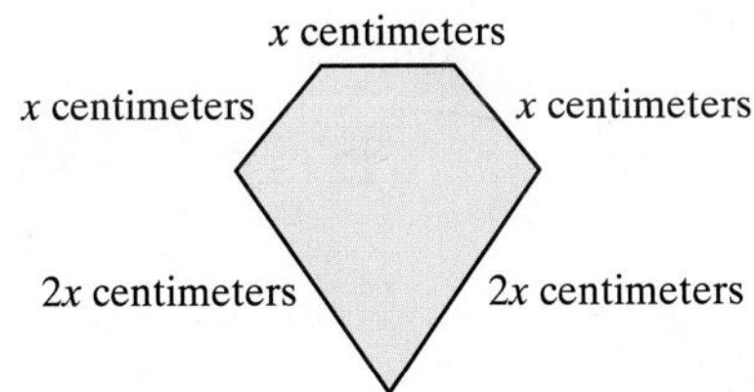

84. The perimeter of the following triangle is 35 meters.

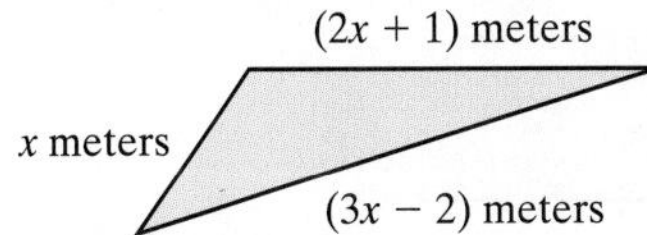

Fill in the blanks with numbers of your choice so that each equation has the given solution. Note: Each blank will be replaced by a different number.

85. $x +$ ____ $= 2x -$ ____; solution: 9

86. $-5x -$ ____ $=$ ____; solution: 2

Solve.

87. $1000(7x - 10) = 50(412 + 100x)$

88. $1000(x + 40) = 100(16 + 7x)$

89. $0.035x + 5.112 = 0.010x + 5.107$

90. $0.127x - 2.685 = 0.027x - 2.38$

Answers

1. ____
2. ____
3. ____
4. ____
5. ____
6. ____
7. ____
8. ____
9. ____
10. ____
11. ____
12. ____
13. ____
14. ____
15. ____
16. ____
17. ____
18. ____
19. ____
20. ____
21. ____
22. ____

Integrated Review Sections 9.1–9.3

Solving Linear Equations

Solve. Feel free to use the steps given in Section 9.3.

1. $x - 10 = -4$

2. $y + 14 = -3$

3. $9y = 108$

4. $-3x = 78$

5. $-6x + 7 = 25$

6. $5y - 42 = -47$

7. $\frac{2}{3}x = 9$

8. $\frac{4}{5}z = 10$

9. $\frac{r}{-4} = -2$

10. $\frac{y}{-8} = 8$

11. $6 - 2x + 8 = 10$

12. $-5 - 6y + 6 = 19$

13. $2x - 7 = 6x - 27$

14. $3 + 8y = 3y - 2$

15. $9(3x - 1) = -4 + 49$

16. $12(2x + 1) = -6 + 66$

17. $-3a + 6 + 5a = 7a - 8a$

18. $4b - 8 - b = 10b - 3b$

19. $-\frac{2}{3}x = \frac{5}{9}$

20. $-\frac{3}{8}y = -\frac{1}{16}$

21. $10 = -6n + 16$

22. $-5 = -2m + 7$

23. $3(5c - 1) - 2 = 13c + 3$

24. $4(3t + 4) - 20 = 3 + 5t$

25. $\frac{2(z + 3)}{3} = 5 - z$

26. $\frac{3(w + 2)}{4} = 2w + 3$

27. $-2(2x - 5) = -3x + 7 - x + 3$

28. $-4(5x - 2) = -12x + 4 - 8x + 4$

29. $0.02(6t - 3) = 0.04(t - 2) + 0.02$

30. $0.03(m + 7) = 0.02(5 - m) + 0.03$

31. $-3y = \frac{4(y - 1)}{5}$

32. $-4x = \frac{5(1 - x)}{6}$

33. $\frac{5}{3}x - \frac{7}{3} = x$

34. $\frac{7}{5}n + \frac{3}{5} = -n$

35. $\frac{1}{10}(3x - 7) = \frac{3}{10}x + 5$

36. $\frac{1}{7}(2x - 5) = \frac{2}{7}x + 1$

37. $5 + 2(3x - 6) = -4(6x - 7)$

38. $3 + 5(2x - 4) = -7(5x + 2)$

23. ______

24. ______

25. ______

26. ______

27. ______

28. ______

29. ______

30. ______

31. ______

32. ______

33. ______

34. ______

35. ______

36. ______

37. ______

38. ______

Objectives

A **Solve Problems Involving Direct Translations.**

B **Solve Problems Involving Relationships Among Unknown Quantities.**

C **Solve Problems Involving Consecutive Integers.**

9.4 AN INTRODUCTION TO PROBLEM SOLVING

First, let's review a list of key words and phrases from Section 1.3 to help us translate.

Helpful Hint

Order matters when subtracting and also dividing, so be especially careful with these translations.

Addition (+)	**Subtraction (−)**	**Multiplication (·)**	**Division (÷)**	**Equality (=)**
Sum	Difference of	Product	Quotient	Equals
Plus	Minus	Times	Divide	Gives
Added to	Subtracted from	Multiply	Into	Is/was/should be
More than	Less than	Twice	Ratio	Yields
Increased by	Decreased by	Of	Divided by	Amounts to
Total	Less			Represents
				Is the same as

We are now ready to put all our translating skills to practical use. To begin, we present a general strategy for problem solving.

General Strategy for Problem Solving

1. UNDERSTAND the problem. During this step, become comfortable with the problem. Some ways of doing this are:

   Read and reread the problem.

   Choose a variable to represent the unknown.

   Construct a drawing.

   Propose a solution and check. Pay careful attention to how you check your proposed solution. This will help when writing an equation to model the problem.
2. TRANSLATE the problem into an equation.
3. SOLVE the equation.
4. INTERPRET the results: *Check* the proposed solution in the stated problem and *state* your conclusion.

Objective A Solving Direct Translation Problems

Much of problem solving involves a direct translation from a sentence to an equation.

PRACTICE 1

Three times a number, minus 6, is the same as two times the number, plus 3. Find the number.

Example 1 Finding an Unknown Number

Twice a number, added to seven, is the same as three subtracted from the number. Find the number.

Solution: Translate the sentence into an equation and solve.

In words:	twice a number	added to	seven	is the same as	three subtracted from the number
	↓	↓	↓	↓	↓
Translate:	$2x$	$+$	7	$=$	$x - 3$

Answer

1. The number is 9.

To solve, begin by subtracting x from both sides to isolate the variable term.

$$2x + 7 = x - 3$$
$$2x + 7 - x = x - 3 - x \quad \text{Subtract } x \text{ from both sides.}$$
$$x + 7 = -3 \quad \text{Combine like terms.}$$
$$x + 7 - 7 = -3 - 7 \quad \text{Subtract 7 from both sides.}$$
$$x = -10 \quad \text{Combine like terms.}$$

Check the solution in the problem as it was originally stated. To do so, replace "number" in the sentence with -10. Twice "-10" added to 7 is the same as 3 subtracted from "-10."

$$2(-10) + 7 = -10 - 3$$
$$-13 = -13$$

The unknown number is -10.

Work Practice 1

Helpful Hint

When checking solutions, go back to the original stated problem rather than to your equation in case errors have been made in translating to an equation.

Example 2 Finding an Unknown Number

Twice the sum of a number and 4 is the same as four times the number decreased by 12. Find the number.

Solution:

1. UNDERSTAND. Read and reread the problem. If we let $x =$ the unknown number, then
"the sum of a number and 4" translates to "$x + 4$" and
"four times the number" translates to "$4x$"
2. TRANSLATE.

twice	sum of a number and 4	is the same as	four times the number	decreased by	12
↓	↓	↓	↓	↓	↓
2	$(x + 4)$	=	$4x$	−	12

3. SOLVE

$$2(x + 4) = 4x - 12$$
$$2x + 8 = 4x - 12 \quad \text{Apply the distributive property.}$$
$$2x + 8 - 4x = 4x - 12 - 4x \quad \text{Subtract } 4x \text{ from both sides.}$$
$$-2x + 8 = -12$$
$$-2x + 8 - 8 = -12 - 8 \quad \text{Subtract 8 from both sides.}$$
$$-2x = -20$$
$$\frac{-2x}{-2} = \frac{-20}{-2} \quad \text{Divide both sides by } -2.$$
$$x = 10$$

4. INTERPRET.

Check: Check this solution in the problem as it was originally stated. To do so, replace "number" with 10. Twice the sum of "10" and 4 is 28, which is the same as 4 times "10" decreased by 12.

State: The number is 10.

Work Practice 2

PRACTICE 2

Three times the difference of a number and 5 is the same as twice the number decreased by 3. Find the number.

Answer

2. The number is 12.

Objective B Solving Problems Involving Relationships Among Unknown Quantities

PRACTICE 3

An 18-foot wire is to be cut so that the length of the longer piece is 5 times the length of the shorter piece. Find the length of each piece.

Example 3 Finding the Length of a Board

A 10-foot board is to be cut into two pieces so that the length of the longer piece is 4 times the length of the shorter. Find the length of each piece.

Solution:

1. UNDERSTAND the problem. To do so, read and reread the problem. You may also want to propose a solution. For example, if 3 feet represents the length of the shorter piece, then $4(3) = 12$ feet is the length of the longer piece, since it is 4 times the length of the shorter piece. This guess gives a total board length of 3 feet + 12 feet = 15 feet, which is too long. However, the purpose of proposing a solution is not to guess correctly, but to help better understand the problem and how to model it.

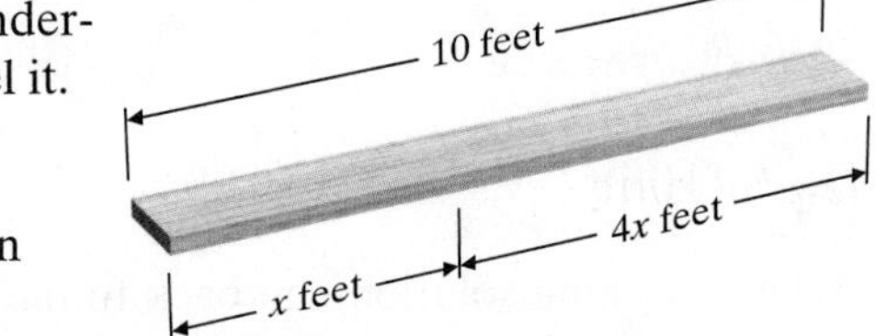

In general, if we let

$x =$ length of shorter piece, then
$4x =$ length of longer piece

2. TRANSLATE the problem. First, we write the equation in words.

length of shorter piece	added to	length of longer piece	equals	total length of board
↓	↓	↓	↓	↓
x	$+$	$4x$	$=$	10

3. SOLVE.

$$x + 4x = 10$$
$$5x = 10 \quad \text{Combine like terms.}$$
$$\frac{5x}{5} = \frac{10}{5} \quad \text{Divide both sides by 5.}$$
$$x = 2$$

4. INTERPRET.

Check: Check the solution in the stated problem. If the length of the shorter piece of board is 2 feet, the length of the longer piece is $4 \cdot (2 \text{ feet}) = 8$ feet and the sum of the lengths of the two pieces is 2 feet + 8 feet = 10 feet.

State: The shorter piece of board is 2 feet and the longer piece of board is 8 feet.

Work Practice 3

Helpful Hint

Make sure that units are included in your answer, if appropriate.

PRACTICE 4

Through the year 2010, the state of California will have 21 more electoral votes for president than the state of Texas. If the total electoral votes for these two states is 89, find the number of electoral votes for each state.

Example 4 Finding the Number of Republican and Democratic Senators

The 111th Congress, which began at noon on January 3, 2009, had a total of 434 Democrats and Republicans. There were 78 more Democratic representatives than Republican. Find the number of representatives from each party. (*Source: New York Times*)

Answers

3. shorter piece: 3 feet; longer piece: 15 feet
4. Texas: 34 electoral votes; California: 55 electoral votes

Solution:

1. UNDERSTAND the problem. Read and reread the problem. Let's suppose that there are 200 Republican representatives. Since there are 78 more Democrats than Republicans, there must be $200 + 78 = 278$ Democrats. The total number of Republicans and Democrats is then $200 + 278 = 478$. This is incorrect since the total should be 434, but we now have a better understanding of the problem.

In general, if we let

$$x = \text{number of Republicans, then}$$
$$x + 78 = \text{number of Democrats}$$

2. TRANSLATE the problem. First, we write the equation in words.

number of Republicans	added to	number of Democrats	equals	434
↓	↓	↓	↓	↓
x	$+$	$(x + 78)$	$=$	434

3. SOLVE.

$$x + (x + 78) = 434$$
$$2x + 78 = 434 \quad \text{Combine like terms.}$$
$$2x + 78 - 78 = 434 - 78 \quad \text{Subtract 78 from both sides.}$$
$$2x = 356$$
$$\frac{2x}{2} = \frac{356}{2} \quad \text{Divide both sides by 2.}$$
$$x = 178$$

4. INTERPRET.

Check: If there were 178 Republican representatives, then there were $178 + 78 = 256$ Democratic representatives. The total number of representatives is then $178 + 256 = 434$. The results check.

State: There were 178 Republican and 256 Democratic representatives at the beginning of the 111th Congress.

Work Practice 4

Example 5 Calculating Hours on the Job

A computer science major at a local university has a part-time job working on computers for his clients. He charges \$20 to come to your home or office and then \$25 per hour. During one month he visited 10 homes or offices and his total income was \$575. How many hours did he spend working on computers?

Solution:

1. UNDERSTAND. Read and reread the problem. Let's propose that the student spent 20 hours working on computers. Pay careful attention as to how his income is calculated. For 20 hours and 10 visits, his income is $20(\$25) + 10(\$20) = \$700$, which is more than \$575. We now have a better understanding of the problem and know that the time working on computers is less than 20 hours.

Let's let

$$x = \text{hours working on computers. Then}$$
$$25x = \text{amount of money made while working on computers}$$

Continued on next page

PRACTICE 5

A car rental agency charges \$28 a day and \$0.15 a mile. If you rent a car for a day and your bill (before taxes) is \$52, how many miles did you drive?

Answer

5. 160 miles

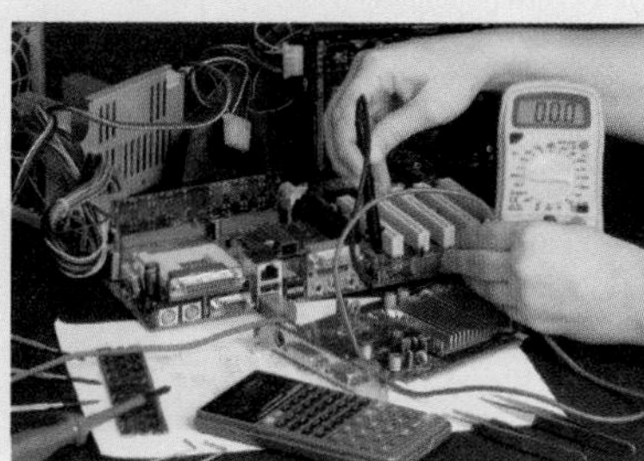

2. TRANSLATE.

money made while working on computers	plus	money made for visits	is equal to	575
↓	↓	↓	↓	↓
$25x$	$+$	$10(20)$	$=$	575

3. SOLVE.

$$25x + 200 = 575$$

$$25x + 200 - 200 = 575 - 200 \quad \text{Subtract 200 from both sides.}$$

$$25x = 375 \quad \text{Simplify.}$$

$$\frac{25x}{25} = \frac{375}{25} \quad \text{Divide both sides by 25.}$$

$$x = 15 \quad \text{Simplify.}$$

4. INTERPRET.

Check: If the student works 15 hours and makes 10 visits, his income is 15(\$25) + 10(\$20) = \$575.

State: The student spent 15 hours working on computers.

Work Practice 5

PRACTICE 6

The measure of the second angle of a triangle is twice the measure of the smallest angle. The measure of the third angle of the triangle is three times the measure of the smallest angle. Find the measures of the angles.

Example 6 Finding Angle Measures

If the two walls of the Vietnam Veterans Memorial in Washington, D.C., were connected, an isosceles triangle would be formed. The measure of the third angle is 97.5° more than the measure of either of the two equal angles. Find the measure of the third angle. (*Source:* National Park Service)

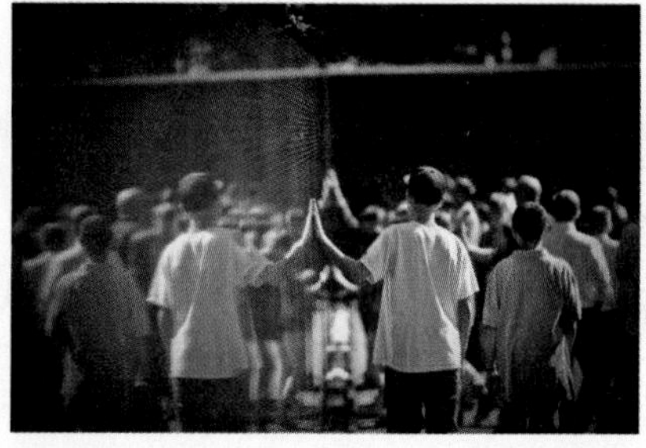

Solution:

1. UNDERSTAND. Read and reread the problem. We then draw a diagram (recall that an isosceles triangle has two angles with the same measure) and let

$$x = \text{degree measure of one angle}$$

$$x = \text{degree measure of the second equal angle}$$

$$x + 97.5 = \text{degree measure of the third angle}$$

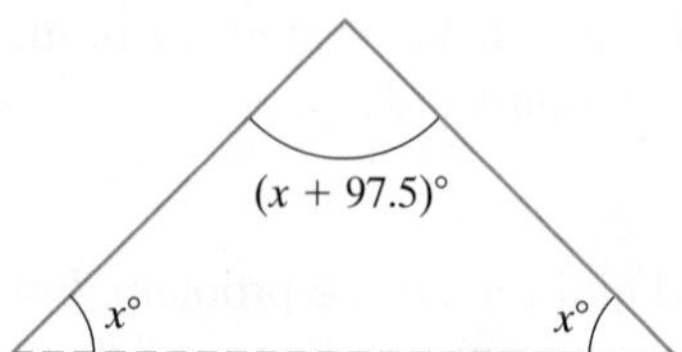

Answer

6. smallest: 30°; second: 60°; third: 90°

2. TRANSLATE. Recall that the sum of the measures of the angles of a triangle equals 180.

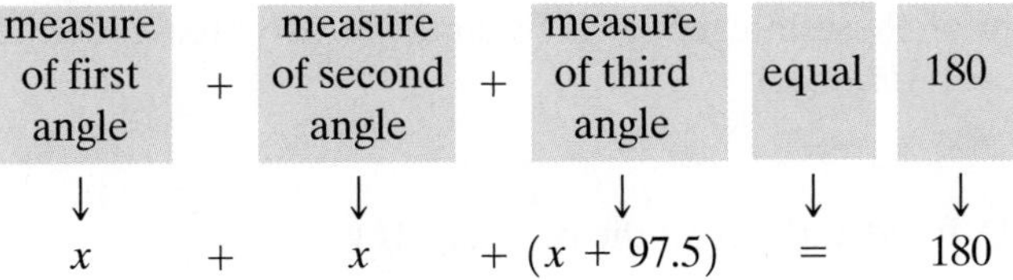

measure of first angle
+
measure of second angle
+
measure of third angle
equal
180

$$x \quad + \quad x \quad + (x + 97.5) \quad = \quad 180$$

3. SOLVE.

$$x + x + (x + 97.5) = 180$$
$$3x + 97.5 = 180 \quad \text{Combine like terms.}$$
$$3x + 97.5 - 97.5 = 180 - 97.5 \quad \text{Subtract 97.5 from both sides.}$$
$$3x = 82.5$$
$$\frac{3x}{3} = \frac{82.5}{3} \quad \text{Divide both sides by 3.}$$
$$x = 27.5$$

4. INTERPRET.

Check: If $x = 27.5$, then the measure of the third angle is $x + 97.5 = 125$. The sum of the angles is then $27.5 + 27.5 + 125 = 180$, the correct sum.

State: The third angle measures 125°.*

Work Practice 6

Objective C Solving Consecutive Integer Problems

The next example has to do with consecutive integers. Recall what we have learned thus far about these integers.

	Example	General Representation
Consecutive Integers	11, 12, 13 (+1, +1)	Let x be an integer. $x,\ x + 1,\ x + 2$ (+1, +1)
Consecutive Even Integers	38, 40, 42 (+2, +2)	Let x be an even integer. $x,\ x + 2,\ x + 4$ (+2, +2)
Consecutive Odd Integers	57, 59, 61 (+2, +2)	Let x be an odd integer. $x,\ x + 2,\ x + 4$ (+2, +2)

The next example has to do with consecutive integers.

*The two walls actually meet at an angle of 125 degrees 12 minutes. The measurement of 97.5° given in the problem is an approximation.

PRACTICE 7

The sum of three consecutive even integers is 144. Find the integers.

Helpful Hint Remember, the 2 here means that odd integers are 2 units apart, for example, the odd integers 13 and $13 + 2 = 15$.

Example 7 Some states have a single area code for the entire state. Two such states have area codes that are consecutive odd integers. If the sum of these integers is 1208, find the two area codes. (*Source: World Almanac*)

Solution:

1. UNDERSTAND. Read and reread the problem. If we let

$$x = \text{the first odd integer, then}$$
$$x + 2 = \text{the next odd integer}$$

2. TRANSLATE.

first odd integer	added to	next odd integer	is	1208
↓	↓	↓		
x	$+$	$(x + 2)$	$=$	1208

3. SOLVE.

$$x + x + 2 = 1208$$
$$2x + 2 = 1208$$
$$2x + 2 - 2 = 1208 - 2$$
$$2x = 1206$$
$$\frac{2x}{2} = \frac{1206}{2}$$
$$x = 603$$

4. INTERPRET.

Check: If $x = 603$, then the next odd integer $x + 2 = 603 + 2 = 605$. Notice their sum, $603 + 605 = 1208$, as needed.

State: The area codes are 603 and 605.

Note: New Hampshire's area code is 603 and South Dakota's area code is 605.

Work Practice 7

Answer

7. 46, 48, 50

Vocabulary and Readiness Check

Fill in the table.

1.	A number: x →	Double the number: →	Double the number, decreased by 31:
2.	A number: x →	Three times the number: →	Three times the number, increased by 17:
3.	A number: x →	The sum of the number and 5: →	Twice the sum of the number and 5:
4.	A number: x →	The difference of the number and 11: →	Seven times the difference of the number and 11:
5.	A number: y →	The difference of 20 and the number: →	The difference of 20 and the number, divided by 3:
6.	A number: y →	The sum of -10 and the number: →	The sum of -10 and the number, divided by 9:

9.4 Exercise Set

Objective A *Solve. For Exercises 1 through 4, write each of the following as equations. Then solve. See Examples 1 and 2.*

1. The sum of twice a number and 7 is equal to the sum of the number and 6. Find the number.

2. The difference of three times a number and 1 is the same as twice the number. Find the number.

3. Three times a number, minus 6, is equal to two times the number, plus 8. Find the number.

4. The sum of 4 times a number and -2 is equal to the sum of 5 times the number and -2. Find the number.

5. Twice the difference of a number and 8 is equal to three times the sum of the number and 3. Find the number.

6. Five times the sum of a number and -1 is the same as 6 times the number. Find the number.

7. The product of twice a number and three is the same as the difference of five times the number and $\frac{3}{4}$. Find the number.

8. If the difference of a number and four is doubled, the result is $\frac{1}{4}$ less than the number. Find the number.

Objective **B** *Solve. For Exercises 9 and 10, the solutions have been started for you. See Examples 3 and 4.*

9. A 25-inch piece of steel is cut into three pieces so that the second piece is twice as long as the first piece, and the third piece is one inch more than five times the length of the first piece. Find the lengths of the pieces.

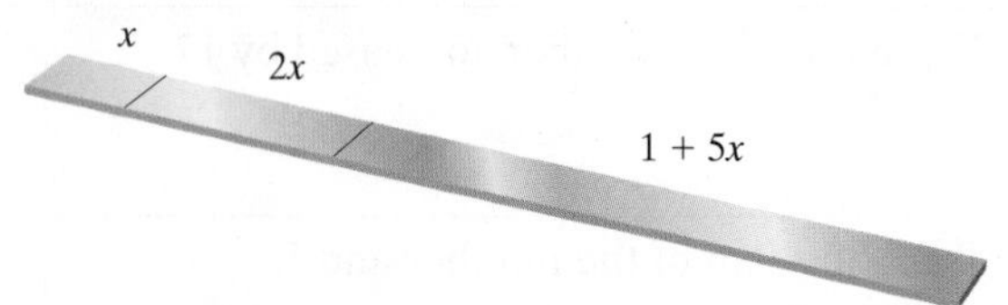

Start the solution:

1. UNDERSTAND the problem. Reread it as many times as needed.

2. TRANSLATE into an equation. (Fill in the blanks below.)

total length of steel	equals	length of first piece	plus	length of second piece	plus	length of third piece
↓	↓	↓	↓	↓	↓	↓
25	=	___	+	___	+	___

Finish with:

3. SOLVE and **4.** INTERPRET

10. A 46-foot piece of rope is cut into three pieces so that the second piece is three times as long as the first piece, and the third piece is two feet more than seven times the length of the first piece. Find the lengths of the pieces.

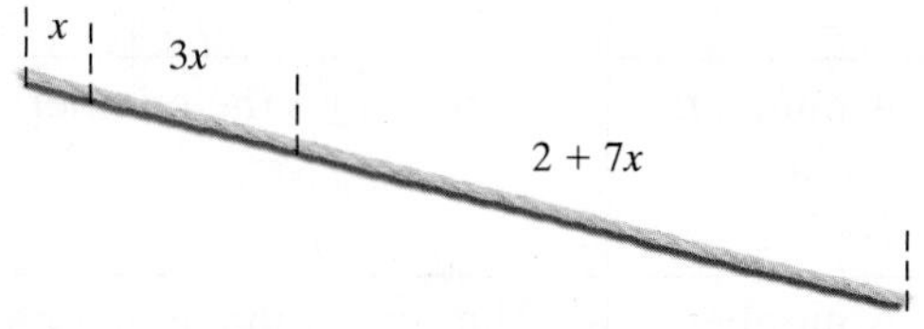

Start the solution:

1. UNDERSTAND the problem. Reread it as many times as needed.

2. TRANSLATE into an equation. (Fill in the blanks below.)

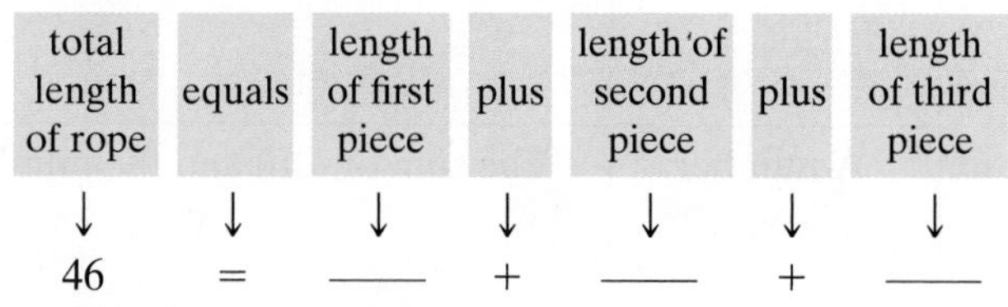

total length of rope	equals	length of first piece	plus	length of second piece	plus	length of third piece
↓	↓	↓	↓	↓	↓	↓
46	=	___	+	___	+	___

Finish with:

3. SOLVE and **4.** INTERPRET

11. A 40-inch board is to be cut into three pieces so that the second piece is twice as long as the first piece and the third piece is 5 times as long as the first piece. If x represents the length of the first piece, find the lengths of all three pieces.

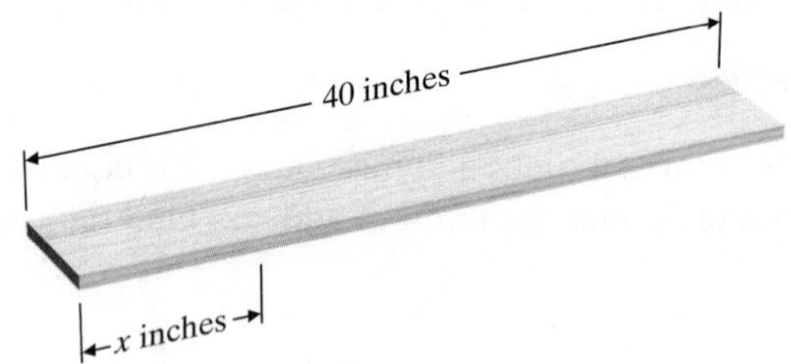

12. A 21-foot beam is to be divided so that the longer piece is 1 foot more than 3 times the length of the shorter piece. If x represents the length of the shorter piece, find the lengths of both pieces.

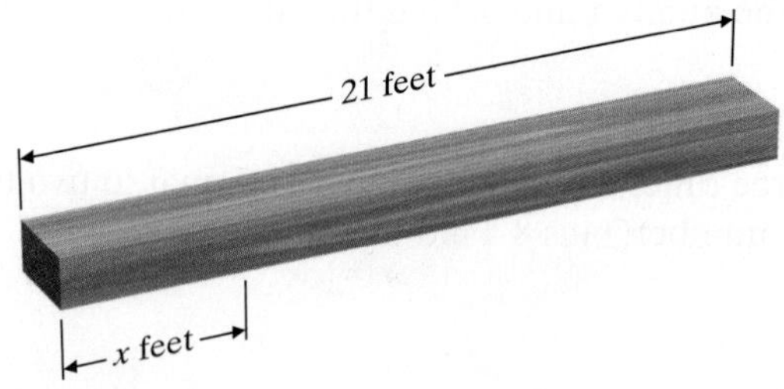

13. In 2008, New Mexico produced 15 million pounds more pecans than Texas. Together, the two states produced 75 million pounds of pecans. Find the amount of pecans grown in New Mexico and Texas in 2008. (*Source:* National Agriculture Statistics Service)

14. In the 2008 Summer Olympics, the U.S. team won 13 more gold medals than the Russian team. If the total number of gold medals won by both teams was 59, find the number of gold medals won by each team. (*Source:* Beijing 2008 Olympic Games)

Solve. See Example 5.

15. A car rental agency advertised renting a Buick Century for \$24.95 per day and \$0.29 per mile. If you rent this car for 2 days, how many whole miles can you drive on a \$100 budget?

16. A plumber gave an estimate for the renovation of a kitchen. Her hourly pay is \$27 per hour and the plumbing parts will cost \$80. If her total estimate is \$404, how many hours does she expect this job to take?

17. In one U.S. city, the taxi cost is \$3 plus \$0.80 per mile. If you are traveling from the airport, there is an additional charge of \$4.50 for tolls. How far can you travel from the airport by taxi for \$27.50?

18. A professional carpet cleaning service charges \$30 plus \$25.50 per hour to come to your home. If your total bill from this company is \$119.25 before taxes, for how many hours were you charged?

Solve. See Example 6.

△ **19.** The flag of Equatorial Guinea contains an isosceles triangle. (Recall that an isosceles triangle contains two angles with the same measure.) If the measure of the third angle of the triangle is 30° more than twice the measure of either of the other two angles, find the measure of each angle of the triangle. (*Hint:* Recall that the sum of the measures of the angles of a triangle is 180°.)

△ **20.** The flag of Brazil contains a parallelogram. One angle of the parallelogram is 15° less than twice the measure of the angle next to it. Find the measure of each angle of the parallelogram. (*Hint:* Recall that opposite angles of a parallelogram have the same measure and that the sum of the measures of the angles is 360°.)

21. The sum of the measures of the angles of a parallelogram is 360°. In the parallelogram below, angles A and D have the same measure as well as angles C and B. If the measure of angle C is twice the measure of angle A, find the measure of each angle.

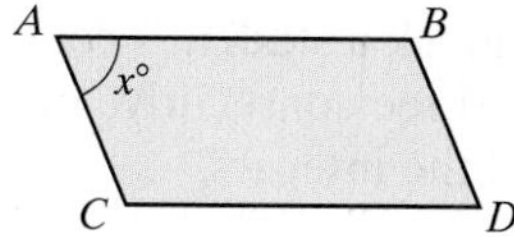

22. Recall that the sum of the measures of the angles of a triangle is 180°. In the triangle below, angle C has the same measure as angle B, and angle A measures 42° less than angle B. Find the measure of each angle.

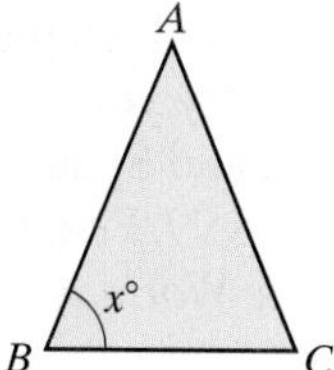

Objective **C** *Solve. See Example 7. Fill in the table. Most of the first row has been completed for you.*

	First Integer →	Next Integers →			Indicated Sum
23. Three consecutive integers:	Integer: x	$x + 1$	$x + 2$		Sum of the three consecutive integers, simplified:
24. Three consecutive integers:	Integer: x				Sum of the second and third consecutive integers, simplified:
25. Three consecutive even integers:	Even integer: x				Sum of the first and third even consecutive integers, simplified:
26. Three consecutive odd integers:	Odd integer: x				Sum of the three consecutive odd integers, simplified:
27. Four consecutive integers:	Integer: x				Sum of the four consecutive integers, simplified:
28. Four consecutive integers:	Integer: x				Sum of the first and fourth consecutive integers, simplified:
29. Three consecutive odd integers:	Odd integer: x				Sum of the second and third consecutive odd integers, simplified:
30. Three consecutive even integers:	Even integer: x				Sum of the three consecutive even integers, simplified:

Solve. See Example 7

31. The left and right page numbers of an open book are two consecutive integers whose sum is 469. Find these page numbers.

32. The room numbers of two adjacent classrooms are two consecutive even numbers. If their sum is 654, find the classroom numbers.

33. To make an international telephone call, you need the code for the country you are calling. The codes for Belgium, France, and Spain are three consecutive integers whose sum is 99. Find the code for each country. (*Source: The World Almanac and Book of Facts*)

34. The code to unlock a student's combination lock happens to be three consecutive odd integers whose sum is 51. Find the integers.

Objectives **A** **B** **C** **Mixed Practice** *Solve. See Examples 1 through 7.*

35. A 17-foot piece of string is cut into two pieces so that the longer piece is 2 feet longer than twice the length of the shorter piece. Find the lengths of both pieces.

36. A 25-foot wire is to be cut so that the longer piece is one foot longer than 5 times the length of the shorter piece. Find the length of each piece.

37. Currently, the two fastest trains are the Japanese Maglev and the French TGV. The sum of their fastest speeds is 718.2 miles per hour. If the speed of the Maglev is 3.8 mph faster than the speed of the TGV, find the speeds of each.

38. The Pentagon is the world's largest office building in terms of floor space. It has three times the amount of floor space as the Empire State Building. If the total floor space for these two buildings is approximately 8700 thousand square feet, find the floor space of each building.

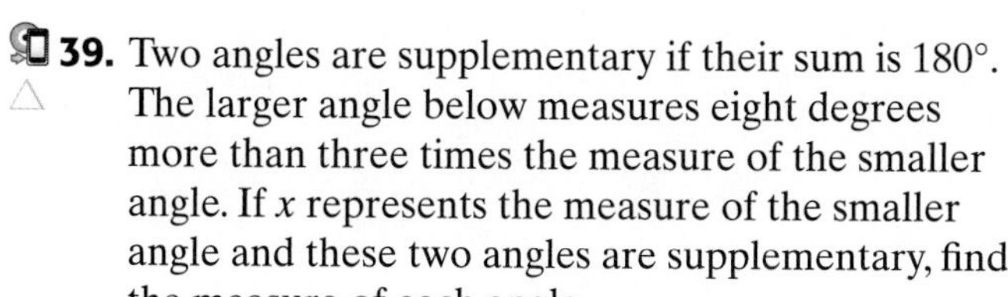

39. Two angles are supplementary if their sum is 180°. The larger angle below measures eight degrees more than three times the measure of the smaller angle. If x represents the measure of the smaller angle and these two angles are supplementary, find the measure of each angle.

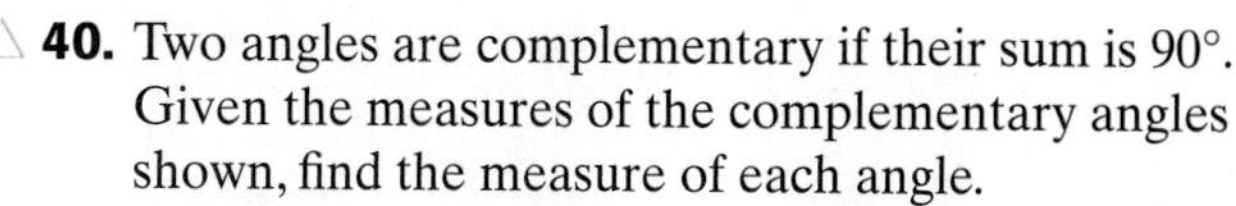

40. Two angles are complementary if their sum is 90°. Given the measures of the complementary angles shown, find the measure of each angle.

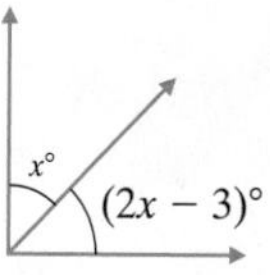

41. The measures of the angles of a triangle are 3 consecutive even integers. Find the measure of each angle.

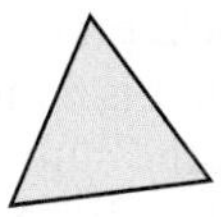

42. A quadrilateral is a polygon with 4 sides. The sum of the measures of the 4 angles in a quadrilateral is 360°. If the measures of the angles of a quadrilateral are consecutive odd integers, find the measures.

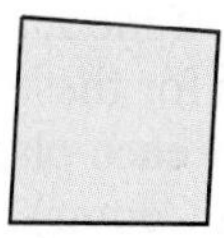

43. The sum of $\frac{1}{5}$ and twice a number is equal to $\frac{4}{5}$ subtracted from three times the number. Find the number.

44. The sum of $\frac{2}{3}$ and four times a number is equal to $\frac{5}{6}$ subtracted from five times the number. Find the number.

45. Hertz Car Rental charges a daily rate of $39 plus $0.20 per mile for a certain car. Suppose that you rent that car for a day and your bill (before taxes) is $95. How many miles did you drive?

46. A woman's $15,000 estate is to be divided so that her husband receives twice as much as her son. Find the amount of money that her husband receives and the amount of money that her son receives.

47. During the 2009 Rose Bowl, University of Southern California beat Pennsylvania State University by 14 points. If their combined scores totaled 62, find the individual team scores.

48. After a recent election, there were 8 more Democratic governors than Republican governors in the United States. How many Democrats and how many Republicans held governors' offices after this election? (*Source:* National Governors Association)

49. The number of counties in California and the number of counties in Montana are consecutive even integers whose sum is 114. If California has more counties than Montana, how many counties does each state have? (*Source: The World Almanac and Book of Facts*)

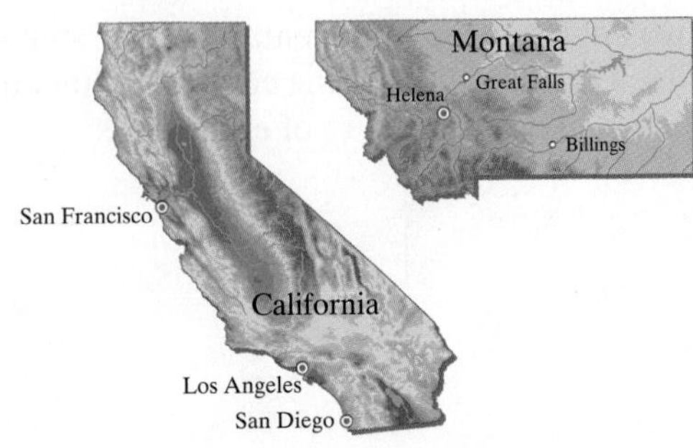

50. A student is building a bookcase with stepped shelves for her dorm room. She buys a 48-inch board and wants to cut the board into three pieces with lengths equal to three consecutive even integers. Find the three board lengths.

51. Over the past few years the satellite Voyager II has passed by the planets Saturn, Uranus, and Neptune, continually updating information about these planets, including the number of moons for each. Uranus is now believed to have 13 more moons than Neptune. Also, Saturn is now believed to have 2 more than twice the number of moons of Neptune. If the total number of moons for these planets is 47, find the number of moons for each planet. (*Source:* National Space Science Data Center)

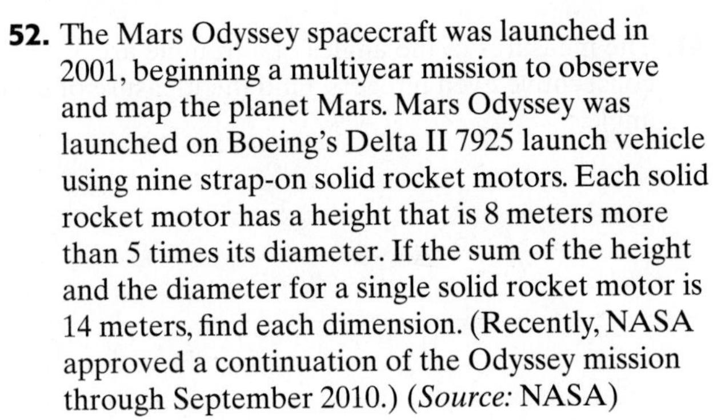

52. The Mars Odyssey spacecraft was launched in 2001, beginning a multiyear mission to observe and map the planet Mars. Mars Odyssey was launched on Boeing's Delta II 7925 launch vehicle using nine strap-on solid rocket motors. Each solid rocket motor has a height that is 8 meters more than 5 times its diameter. If the sum of the height and the diameter for a single solid rocket motor is 14 meters, find each dimension. (Recently, NASA approved a continuation of the Odyssey mission through September 2010.) (*Source:* NASA)

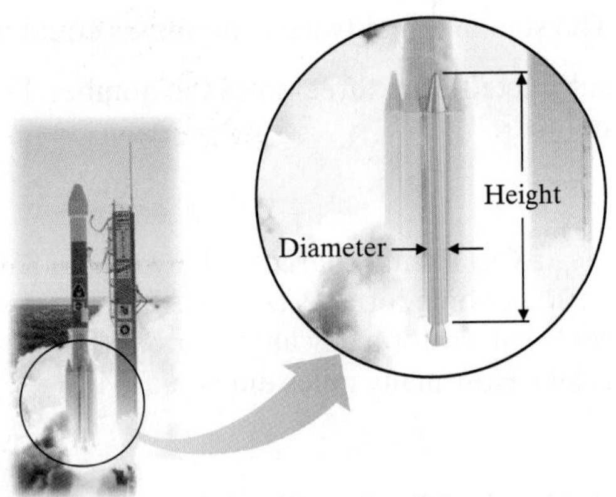

53. If the sum of a number and five is tripled, the result is one less than twice the number. Find the number.

54. Twice the sum of a number and six equals three times the sum of the number and four. Find the number.

55. The area of the Sahara Desert is 7 times the area of the Gobi Desert. If the sum of their areas is 4,000,000 square miles, find the area of each desert.

56. The largest meteorite in the world is the Hoba West, located in Namibia. Its weight is 3 times the weight of the Armanty meteorite, located in Outer Mongolia. If the sum of their weights is 88 tons, find the weight of each.

57. In the 2008 Summer Olympics, Korea won more gold medals than Germany, which won more gold medals than Australia. If the numbers of gold medals won by these three countries are three consecutive integers whose sum is 21, find the number of gold medals won by each. (*Source:* Beijing 2008 Olympics)

58. To make an international telephone call, you need the code for the country you are calling. The codes for Mali Republic, Côte d'Ivoire, and Niger are three consecutive odd integers whose sum is 675. Find the code for each country.

59. In a runoff election in Georgia for a seat in the U.S. Senate, incumbent Senator Saxby Chambliss received 315,217 more votes than challenger Jim Martin. If the total number of votes cast was 2,126,491, find the number of votes for each candidate. (*Source: New York Times*)

60. In Season 7 of *American Idol*, David Cook received 11.7 million more votes than runner-up David Archuleta. If 97.5 million votes were cast in the season finale, find the number of votes for each contestant. (*Source: Los Angeles Times*)

61. A geodesic dome, based on the design by Buckminster Fuller, is composed of two different types of triangular panels. One of these is an isosceles triangle. In one geodesic dome, the measure of the third angle is 76.5° more than the measure of either of the two equal angles. Find the measure of the three angles. (*Source:* Buckminster Fuller Institute)

62. The measures of the angles of a particular triangle are such that the second and third angles are each four times the measure of the smallest angle. Find the measures of the angles of this triangle.

The graph below shows the best-selling albums of all time. Use this graph for Exercises 63 through 66.

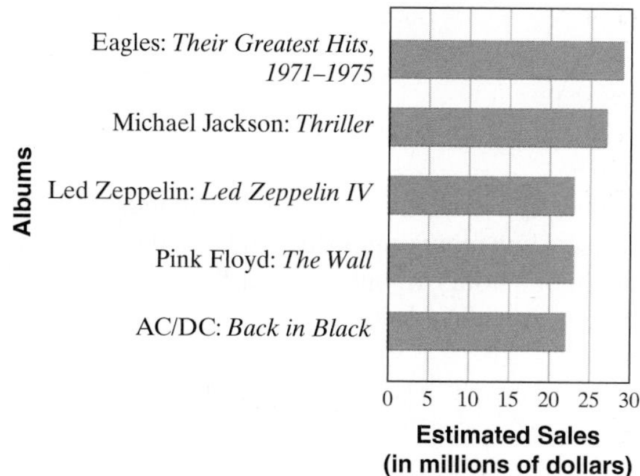

Source: Recording Industry Association of America

63. Which album is the best-selling album of all time?

64. Which albums had total sales between $20 million and $25 million?

65. *Thriller* and *The Wall* had sales worth a total of $50 million. *Thriller* brought in $4 million more than *The Wall*. Find the amount of sales that each album brought in.

66. Eagles: *Their Greatest Hits, 1971–1975*, and AC/DC: *Back in Black* had sales worth $51 million. Eagles: *Their Greatest Hits, 1971–1975*, sold $7 million more than AC/DC: *Back in Black*. Find the amount of sales for each album.

Compare the lengths of the bars in the graph with your results for the exercises below. Are your answers reasonable?

67. Exercise 65

68. Exercise 66

Review

Evaluate each expression for the given values. See Section 1.8.

69. $2W + 2L$; $W = 7$ and $L = 10$

70. $\frac{1}{2}Bh$; $B = 14$ and $h = 22$

71. πr^2; $r = 15$

72. $r \cdot t$; $r = 15$ and $t = 2$

Concept Extensions

△ **73.** A golden rectangle is a rectangle whose length is approximately 1.6 times its width. The early Greeks thought that a rectangle with these dimensions was the most pleasing to the eye and examples of the golden rectangle are found in many early works of art. For example, the Parthenon in Athens contains many examples of golden rectangles.

Mike Hallahan would like to plant a rectangular garden in the shape of a golden rectangle. If he has 78 feet of fencing available, find the dimensions of the garden.

△ **74.** Dr. Dorothy Smith gave the students in her geometry class at the University of New Orleans the following question. Is it possible to construct a triangle such that the second angle of the triangle has a measure that is twice the measure of the first angle and the measure of the third angle is 5 times the measure of the first? If so, find the measure of each angle. (*Hint:* Recall that the sum of the measures of the angles of a triangle is 180°.)

75. Only male crickets chirp. They chirp at different rates depending on their species and the temperature of their environment. Suppose a certain species is currently chirping at a rate of 90 chirps per minute. At this rate, how many chirps occur in one hour? In one 24-hour day? In one year?

76. The human eye blinks once every 5 seconds on average. How many times does the average eye blink in one hour? In one 16-hour day while awake? In one year while awake?

77. In your own words, explain why a solution of a word problem should be checked using the original wording of the problem and not the equation written from the wording.

78. Give an example of how you recently solved a problem using mathematics.

Recall from Exercise 73 that a golden rectangle is a rectangle whose length is approximately 1.6 times its width.

△ **79.** It is thought that for about 75% of adults, a rectangle in the shape of the golden rectangle is the most pleasing to the eye. Draw three rectangles, one in the shape of the golden rectangle, and poll your class. Do the results agree with the percentage given above?

△ **80.** Examples of golden rectangles can be found today in architecture and manufacturing packaging. Find an example of a golden rectangle in your home. A few suggestions: the front face of a book, the floor of a room, the front of a box of food.

For Exercises 81 and 82, measure the dimensions of each rectangle and decide which one best approximates the shape of a golden rectangle.

△ **81.**

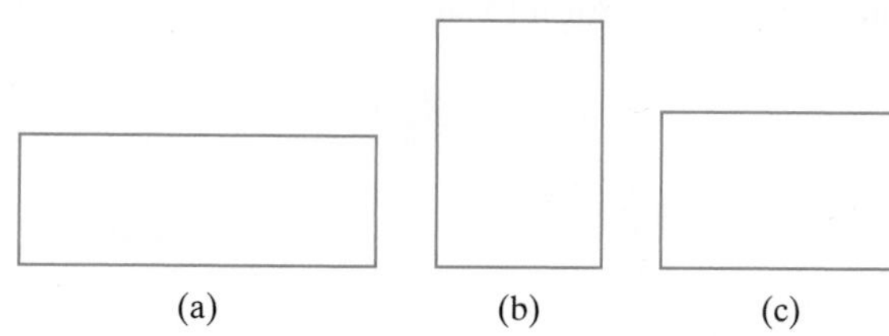

△ **82.**

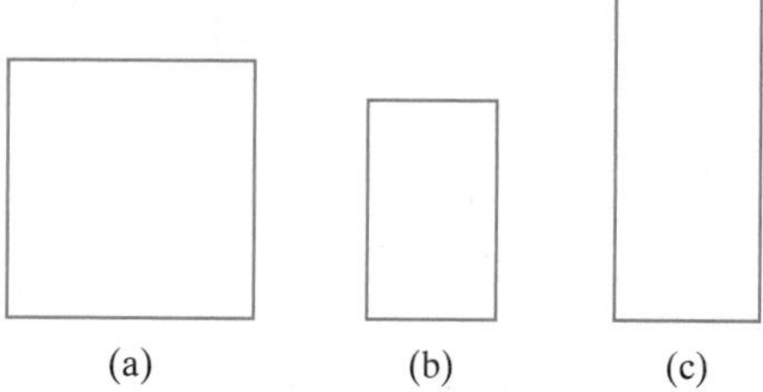

Objectives

A Use Formulas to Solve Problems.

B Solve a Formula or Equation for One of Its Variables.

9.5 FORMULAS AND PROBLEM SOLVING

Objective A Using Formulas to Solve Problems

A **formula** describes a known relationship among quantities. Many formulas are given as equations. For example, the formula

$$d = r \cdot t$$

stands for the relationship

$$\text{distance} = \text{rate} \cdot \text{time}$$

Let's look at one way that we can use this formula.

If we know we traveled a distance of 100 miles at a rate of 40 miles per hour, we can replace the variables d and r in the formula $d = rt$ and find our travel time, t.

$d = rt$ Formula

$100 = 40t$ Replace d with 100 and r with 40.

To solve for t, we divide both sides of the equation by 40.

$\frac{100}{40} = \frac{40t}{40}$ Divide both sides by 40.

$\frac{5}{2} = t$ Simplify.

The travel times was $\frac{5}{2}$ hours, or $2\frac{1}{2}$ hours, or 2.5 hours.

In this section, we solve problems that can be modeled by known formulas. We use the same problem-solving strategy that was introduced in the previous section.

PRACTICE 1

A family is planning their vacation to visit relatives. They will drive from Cincinnati, Ohio, to Rapid City, South Dakota, a distance of 1180 miles. They plan to average a rate of 50 miles per hour. How much time will they spend driving?

Example 1 Finding Time Given Rate and Distance

A glacier is a giant mass of rocks and ice that flows downhill like a river. Portage Glacier in Alaska is about 6 miles, or 31,680 *feet,* long and moves 400 *feet* per year. Icebergs are created when the front end of the glacier flows into Portage Lake. How long does it take for ice at the head (beginning) of the glacier to reach the lake?

Solution:

1. UNDERSTAND. Read and reread the problem. The appropriate formula needed to solve this problem is the distance formula, $d = rt$. To become familiar with this formula, let's find the distance that ice traveling at a rate of 400 feet per year travels in 100 years. To do so, we let time t be 100 years and rate r be the given 400 feet per year, and substitute these values into the formula $d = rt$. We then have that distance $d = 400(100) = 40{,}000$ feet. Since we are interested in finding how long it takes ice to travel 31,680 feet, we now know that it is less than 100 years.

Answer

1. 23.6 hours

Since we are using the formula $d = rt$, we let

t = the time in years for ice to reach the lake

r = rate or speed of ice

d = distance from beginning of glacier to lake

2. TRANSLATE. To translate to an equation, we use the formula $d = rt$ and let distance $d = 31{,}680$ feet and rate $r = 400$ feet per year.

$$d = r \cdot t$$

$$31{,}680 = 400 \cdot t \quad \text{Let } d = 31{,}680 \text{ and } r = 400.$$

3. SOLVE. Solve the equation for t. To solve for t, we divide both sides by 400.

$$\frac{31{,}680}{400} = \frac{400 \cdot t}{400} \quad \text{Divide both sides by 400.}$$

$$79.2 = t \quad \text{Simplify.}$$

4. INTERPRET.

Check: To check, substitute 79.2 for t and 400 for r in the distance formula and check to see that the distance is 31,680 feet.

State: It takes 79.2 years for the ice at the head of Portage Glacier to reach the lake.

Helpful Hint Don't forget to include units, if appropriate.

Work Practice 1

Example 2 Calculating the Length of a Garden

Charles Pecot can afford enough fencing to enclose a rectangular garden with a perimeter of 140 feet. If the width of his garden is to be 30 feet, find the length.

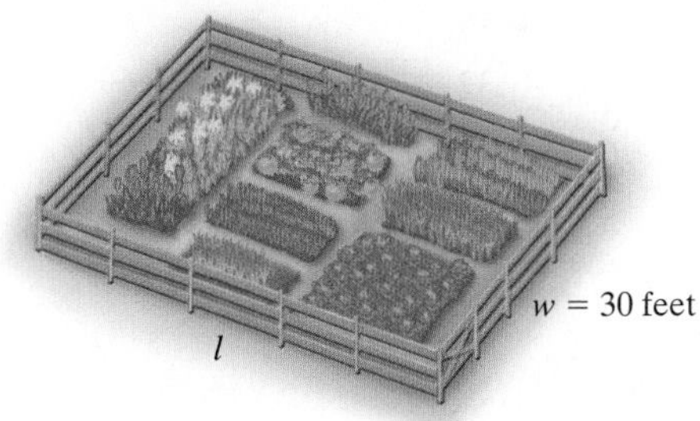

Solution:

1. UNDERSTAND. Read and reread the problem. The formula needed to solve this problem is the formula for the perimeter of a rectangle, $P = 2l + 2w$. Before continuing, let's become familar with this formula.

l = the length of the rectangular garden

w = the width of the rectangular garden

P = perimeter of the garden

2. TRANSLATE. To translate to an equation, we use the formula $P = 2l + 2w$ and let perimeter $P = 140$ feet and width $w = 30$ feet.

$$P = 2l + 2w \quad \text{Let } P = 140 \text{ and } w = 30.$$

$$140 = 2l + 2(30)$$

Continued on next page

PRACTICE 2

A wood deck is being built behind a house. The width of the deck must be 18 feet because of the shape of the house. If there is 450 square feet of decking material, find the length of the deck.

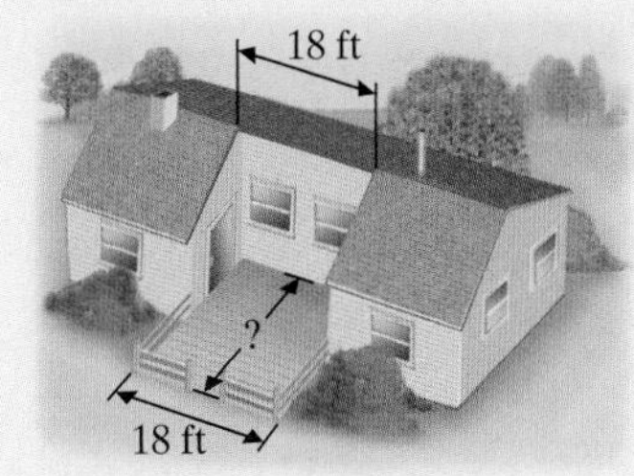

Answer

2. 25 feet

3. SOLVE.

$$140 = 2l + 2(30)$$

$$140 = 2l + 60 \quad \text{Multiply 2(30).}$$

$$140 - 60 = 2l + 60 - 60 \quad \text{Subtract 60 from both sides.}$$

$$80 = 2l \quad \text{Combine like terms.}$$

$$40 = l \quad \text{Divide both sides by 2.}$$

4. INTERPRET.

Check: Substitute 40 for l and 30 for w in the perimeter formula and check to see that the perimeter is 140 feet.

State: The length of the rectangular garden is 40 feet.

Work Practice 2

PRACTICE 3

Convert the temperature 5°C to Fahrenheit.

Example 3 Finding an Equivalent Temperature

The average maximum temperature for January in Algiers, Algeria, is 59° Fahrenheit. Find the equivalent temperature in degrees Celsius.

Solution:

1. UNDERSTAND. Read and reread the problem. A formula that can be used to solve this problem is the formula for converting degrees Celsius to degrees Fahrenheit, $F = \frac{9}{5}C + 32$. Before continuing, become familiar with this formula. Using this formula, we let

C = temperature in degrees Celsius, and
F = temperature in degrees Fahrenheit.

2. TRANSLATE. To translate to an equation, we use the formula $F = \frac{9}{5}C + 32$ and let degrees Fahrenheit $F = 59$.

Formula: $F = \frac{9}{5}C + 32$

Substitute: $59 = \frac{9}{5}C + 32$ Let $F = 59$.

3. SOLVE.

$$59 = \frac{9}{5}C + 32$$

$$59 - 32 = \frac{9}{5}C + 32 - 32 \quad \text{Subtract 32 from both sides.}$$

$$27 = \frac{9}{5}C \quad \text{Combine like terms.}$$

$$\frac{5}{9}\cdot 27 = \frac{5}{9}\cdot\frac{9}{5}C \quad \text{Multiply both sides by } \frac{5}{9}.$$

$$15 = C \quad \text{Simplify.}$$

4. INTERPRET.

Check: To check, replace C with 15 and F with 59 in the formula and see that a true statement results.

State: Thus, 59° Fahrenheit is equivalent to 15° Celsius.

Work Practice 3

Answer

3. 41°F

In the next example, we again use the formula for perimeter of a rectangle as in Example 2. In Example 2, we knew the width of the rectangle. In this example, both the length and width are unknown.

Example 4 Finding Road Sign Dimensions

The length of a rectangular road sign is 2 feet less than three times its width. Find the dimensions if the perimeter is 28 feet.

Solution:

1. UNDERSTAND. Read and reread the problem. Recall that the formula for the perimeter of a rectangle is $P = 2l + 2w$. Draw a rectangle and guess the solution. If the width of the rectangular sign is 5 feet, its length is 2 feet less than 3 times the width, or 3(5 feet) − 2 feet = 13 feet. The perimeter P of the rectangle is then 2(13 feet) + 2(5 feet) = 36 feet, too much. We now know that the width is less than 5 feet.

   Proposed rectangle:

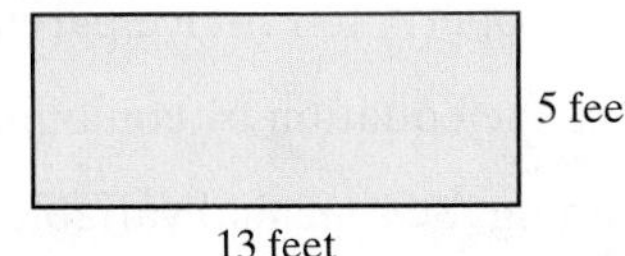

   Let

   w = the width of the rectangular sign; then
   $3w - 2$ = the length of the sign.

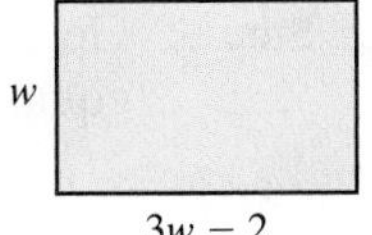

   Draw a rectangle and label it with the assigned variables.

2. TRANSLATE.

   Formula: $P = 2l + 2w$

   Substitute: $28 = 2(3w - 2) + 2w$

3. SOLVE.

$$28 = 2(3w - 2) + 2w$$
$$28 = 6w - 4 + 2w \quad \text{Apply the distributive property.}$$
$$28 = 8w - 4$$
$$28 + 4 = 8w - 4 + 4 \quad \text{Add 4 to both sides.}$$
$$32 = 8w$$
$$\frac{32}{8} = \frac{8w}{8} \quad \text{Divide both sides by 8.}$$
$$4 = w$$

4. INTERPRET.

Check: If the width of the sign is 4 feet, the length of the sign is 3(4 feet) − 2 feet = 10 feet. This gives the rectangular sign a perimeter of P = 2(4 feet) + 2(10 feet) = 28 feet, the correct perimeter.

State: The width of the sign is 4 feet and the length of the sign is 10 feet.

Work Practice 4

PRACTICE 4

The length of a rectangle is one meter more than 4 times its width. Find the dimensions if the perimeter is 52 meters.

Answer

4. length: 21 m; width: 5 m

Objective B Solving a Formula for a Variable

We say that the formula

$$d = rt$$

is solved for d because d is alone on one side of the equation and the other side contains no d's. Suppose that we have a large number of problems to solve where we are given distance d and rate r and asked to find time t. In this case, it may be easier to first solve the formula $d = rt$ for t. To solve for t, we divide both sides of the equation by r.

$$d = rt$$

$$\frac{d}{r} = \frac{rt}{r} \quad \text{Divide both sides by } r.$$

$$\frac{d}{r} = t \quad \text{Simplify.}$$

To solve a formula or an equation for a specified variable, we use the same steps as for solving a linear equation except that we treat the specified variable as the only variable in the equation. These steps are listed next.

Solving Equations for a Specified Variable

Step 1: Multiply on both sides to clear the equation of fractions if they appear.

Step 2: Use the distributive property to remove parentheses if they appear.

Step 3: Simplify each side of the equation by combining like terms.

Step 4: Get all terms containing the specified variable on one side and all other terms on the other side by using the addition property of equality.

Step 5: Get the specified variable alone by using the multiplication property of equality.

PRACTICE 5

Solve $C = 2\pi r$ for r. (This formula is used to find the circumference, C, of a circle given its radius, r.)

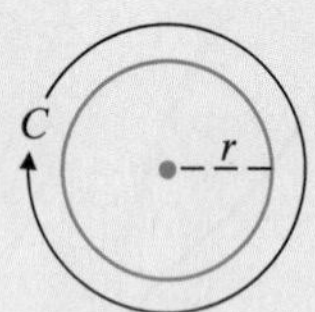

Example 5 Solve $V = lwh$ for l.

Solution: This formula is used to find the volume of a box. To solve for l, we divide both sides by wh.

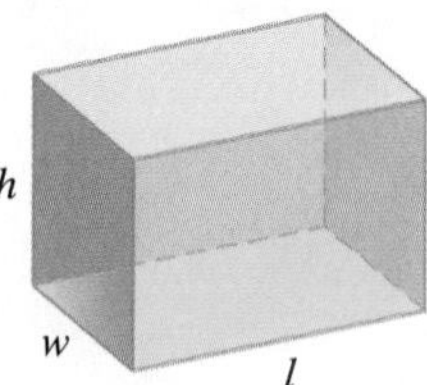

$$V = lwh$$

$$\frac{V}{wh} = \frac{lwh}{wh} \quad \text{Divide both sides by } wh.$$

$$\frac{V}{wh} = l \quad \text{Simplify.}$$

Since we have l alone on one side of the equation, we have solved for l in terms of V, w, and h. Remember that it does not matter on which side of the equation we get the variable alone.

Work Practice 5

Answer

5. $r = \frac{C}{2\pi}$

Example 6 Solve $y = mx + b$ for x.

Solution: First we get mx alone by subtracting b from both sides.

$$y = mx + b$$
$$y - b = mx + b - b \quad \text{Subtract } b \text{ from both sides.}$$
$$y - b = mx \quad \text{Combine like terms.}$$

Next we solve for x by dividing both sides by m.

$$\frac{y-b}{m} = \frac{mx}{m}$$
$$\frac{y-b}{m} = x \quad \text{Simplify.}$$

Work Practice 6

PRACTICE 6

Solve $P = 2l + 2w$ for l.

✓Concept Check Solve:

a. ● = ■ − ■ for ■

b. ● = ■ · ▲ − ■ for ■

Example 7 Solve $P = 2l + 2w$ for w.

Solution: This formula relates the perimeter of a rectangle to its length and width. Find the term containing the variable w. To get this term, $2w$, alone, subtract $2l$ from both sides.

$$P = 2l + 2w$$
$$P - 2l = 2l + 2w - 2l \quad \text{Subtract } 2l \text{ from both sides.}$$
$$P - 2l = 2w \quad \text{Combine like terms.}$$
$$\frac{P-2l}{2} = \frac{2w}{2} \quad \text{Divide both sides by 2.}$$
$$\frac{P-2l}{2} = w \quad \text{Simplify.}$$

Work Practice 7

PRACTICE 7

Solve $P = 2a + b - c$ for a.

Helpful Hint

The 2s may *not* be divided out here. Although 2 is a factor of the denominator, 2 is *not* a factor of the numerator since it is not a factor of both terms in the numerator.

The next example has an equation containing a fraction. We will first clear the equation of fractions and then solve for the specified variable.

Example 8 Solve $F = \frac{9}{5}C + 32$ for C.

Solution:

$$F = \frac{9}{5}C + 32$$
$$5(F) = 5\left(\frac{9}{5}C + 32\right) \quad \text{Clear the fraction by multiplying both sides by the LCD.}$$
$$5F = 9C + 160 \quad \text{Distribute the 5.}$$
$$5F - 160 = 9C + 160 - 160 \quad \text{To get the term containing the variable } C \text{ alone, subtract 160 from both sides.}$$
$$5F - 160 = 9C \quad \text{Combine like terms.}$$
$$\frac{5F-160}{9} = \frac{9C}{9} \quad \text{Divide both sides by 9.}$$
$$\frac{5F-160}{9} = C \quad \text{Simplify.}$$

Work Practice 8

PRACTICE 8

Solve $A = \frac{a+b}{2}$ for b.

Answers

6. $l = \frac{P-2w}{2}$ 7. $a = \frac{P-b+c}{2}$
8. $b = 2A - a$

✓ Concept Check Answer

a. ● + ■ b. $\frac{● + ■}{▲}$

9.5 Exercise Set

FOR EXTRA HELP

PRACTICE

WATCH

DOWNLOAD

READ

REVIEW

Objective A *Substitute the given values into each given formula and solve for the unknown variable. See Examples 1 through 4.*

△ **1.** $A = bh$; $A = 45, b = 15$ (Area of a parallelogram)

2. $d = rt$; $d = 195, t = 3$ (Distance formula)

△ **3.** $S = 4lw + 2wh$; $S = 102, l = 7, w = 3$ (Surface area of a special rectangular box)

△ **4.** $V = lwh$; $l = 14, w = 8, h = 3$ (Volume of a rectangular box)

△ **5.** $A = \frac{1}{2}h(B + b)$; $A = 180, B = 11, b = 7$ (Area of a trapezoid)

△ **6.** $A = \frac{1}{2}h(B + b)$; $A = 60, B = 7, b = 3$ (Area of a trapezoid)

△ **7.** $P = a + b + c$; $P = 30, a = 8, b = 10$ (Perimeter of a triangle)

△ **8.** $V = \frac{1}{3}Ah$; $V = 45, h = 5$ (Volume of a pyramid)

△ **9.** $C = 2\pi r$; $C = 15.7$ (Circumference of a circle) (Use the approximation 3.14 for π.)

△ **10.** $A = \pi r^2$; $r = 4$ (Area of a circle) (Use the approximation 3.14 for π.)

Objective B *Solve each formula for the specified variable. See Examples 5 through 8.*

11. $f = 5gh$ for h

△ **12.** $x = 4\pi y$ for y

△ **13.** $V = lwh$ for w

14. $T = mnr$ for n

15. $3x + y = 7$ for y

16. $-x + y = 13$ for y

17. $A = P + PRT$ for R

18. $A = P + PRT$ for T

△ **19.** $V = \frac{1}{3}Ah$ for A

20. $D = \frac{1}{4}fk$ for k

△ **21.** $P = a + b + c$ for a

22. $PR = x + y + z + w$ for z

△ **23.** $S = 2\pi rh + 2\pi r^2$ for h

△ **24.** $S = 4lw + 2wh$ for h

Objective A *Solve. For Exercises 25 and 26, the solutions have been started for you. See Examples 1 through 4.*

△ **25.** The iconic NASDAQ sign in New York's Times Square has a width of 84 feet and an area of 10,080 square feet. Find the height (or length) of the sign. (*Source:* livedesignonline.com)

Start the solution:

1. UNDERSTAND the problem. Reread it as many times as needed.

2. TRANSLATE into an equation. (Fill in the blanks below.)

Area	=	length	times	width
↓	↓	↓	↓	↓
____	=	x	·	____

Finish with:

3. SOLVE and **4.** INTERPRET

△ **26.** The world's largest sign for Coca-Cola is located in Arica, Chile. The rectangular sign has a length of 400 feet and an area of 52,400 square feet. Find the width of the sign. (*Source:* Fabulous Facts about Coca-Cola, Atlanta, GA)

Start the solution:

1. UNDERSTAND the problem. Reread it as many times as needed.

2. TRANSLATE into an equation. (Fill in the blanks below.)

Area	=	length	times	width
↓	↓	↓	↓	↓
____	=	____	·	x

Finish with:

3. SOLVE and **4.** INTERPRET

△ **27.** A frame shop charges according to both the amount of framing needed to surround the picture and the amount of glass needed to cover the picture.

a. Find the area and perimeter of the picture below.

b. Identify whether the frame has to do with perimeter or area and the same with the glass.

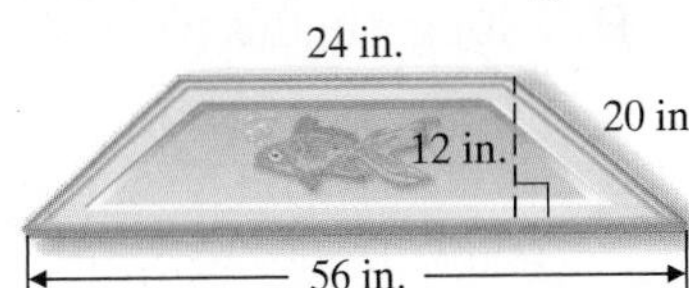

△ **28.** A decorator is painting and placing a border completely around the parallelogram-shaped wall.

a. Find the area and perimeter of the wall below. ($A = bh$)

b. Identify whether the border has to do with perimeter or area and the same with paint.

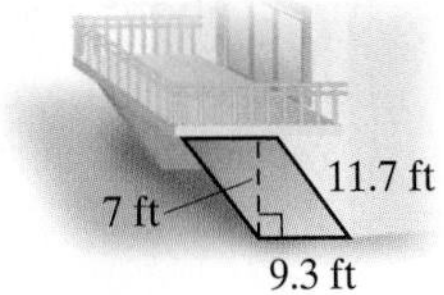

△ **29.** For the purpose of purchasing new baseboard and carpet,

a. Find the area and perimeter of the room below (neglecting doors).

b. Identify whether baseboard has to do with area or perimeter and the same with carpet.

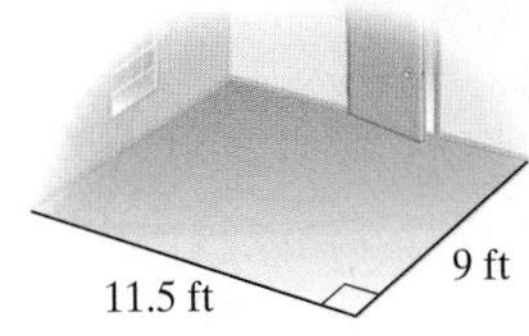

△ **30.** For the purpose of purchasing lumber for a new fence and seed to plant grass,

a. Find the area and perimeter of the yard below.

b. Identify whether a fence has to do with area or perimeter and the same with grass seed.

$\left(A = \frac{1}{2}bh\right)$

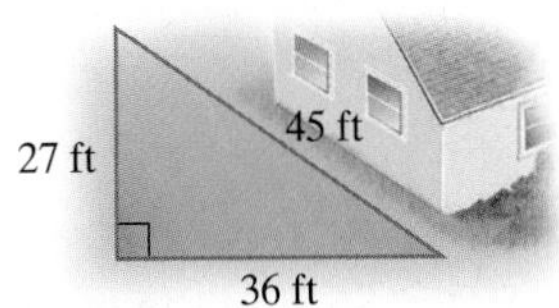

31. Convert Nome, Alaska's 14°F high temperature to Celsius.

32. Convert Paris, France's low temperature of −5°C to Fahrenheit.

33. The X-30 is a "space plane" that skims the edge of space at 4000 miles per hour. Neglecting altitude, if the circumference of Earth is approximately 25,000 miles, how long will it take for the X-30 to travel around Earth?

34. In the United States, a notable hang glider flight was a 303-mile, $8\frac{1}{2}$-hour flight from New Mexico to Kansas. What was the average rate during this flight?

35. An architect designs a rectangular flower garden such that the width is exactly two-thirds of the length. If 260 feet of antique picket fencing are to be used to enclose the garden, find the dimensions of the garden.

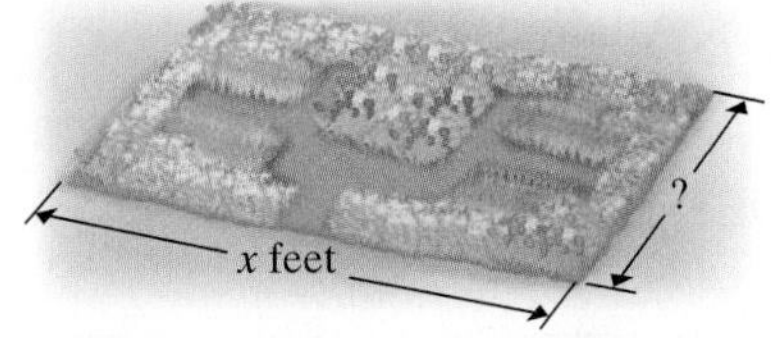

36. If the length of a rectangular parking lot is 10 meters less than twice its width, and the perimeter is 400 meters, find the length of the parking lot.

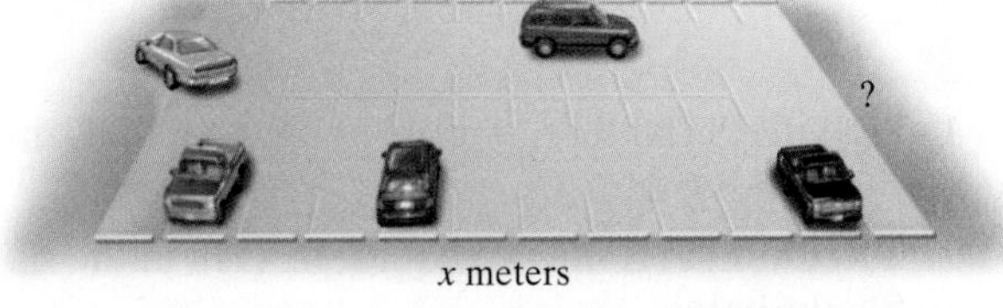

37. A flower bed is in the shape of a triangle with one side twice the length of the shortest side, and the third side is 30 feet more than the length of the shortest side. Find the dimensions if the perimeter is 102 feet.

38. The perimeter of a yield sign in the shape of an isosceles triangle is 22 feet. If the shortest side is 2 feet less than the other two sides, find the length of the shortest side. (*Hint:* An isosceles triangle has two sides the same length.)

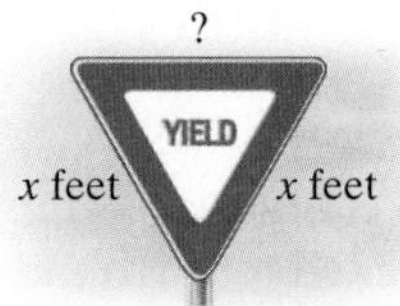

39. The Cat is a high-speed catamaran auto ferry that operates between Bar Harbor, Maine, and Yarmouth, Nova Scotia. The Cat can make the trip in about $2\frac{1}{2}$ hours at a speed of 55 mph. About how far apart are Bar Harbor and Yarmouth? (*Source:* Bay Ferries)

40. A family is planning their vacation to Disney World. They will drive from a small town outside New Orleans, Louisiana, to Orlando, Florida, a distance of 700 miles. They plan to average a rate of 55 mph. How long will this trip take?

Dolbear's Law states the relationship between the rate at which Snowy Tree Crickets chirp and the air temperature of their environment. The formula is

$$T = 50 + \frac{N - 40}{4}, \text{ where } \begin{array}{l} T = \text{temperature in degrees Fahrenheit and} \\ N = \text{number of chirps per minute} \end{array}$$

41. If $N = 86$, find the temperature in degrees Fahrenheit, T.

42. If $N = 94$, find the temperature in degrees Fahrenheit, T.

43. If $T = 55°\text{F}$, find the number of chirps per minute.

44. If $T = 65°\text{F}$, find the number of chirps per minute.

Use the results of Exercises 41–44 to complete each sentence with "increases" or "decreases."

45. As the number of cricket chirps per minute increases, the air temperature of their environment ____________.

46. As the air temperature of their environment decreases, the number of cricket chirps per minute ____________.

Solve. See Examples 1 through 4.

△ **47.** Piranha fish require 1.5 cubic feet of water per fish to maintain a healthy environment. Find the maximum number of piranhas you could put in a tank measuring 8 feet by 3 feet by 6 feet.

△ **48.** Find the maximum number of goldfish you can put in a cylindrical tank whose diameter is 8 meters and whose height is 3 meters, if each goldfish needs 2 cubic meters of water. ($V = \pi r^2 h$)

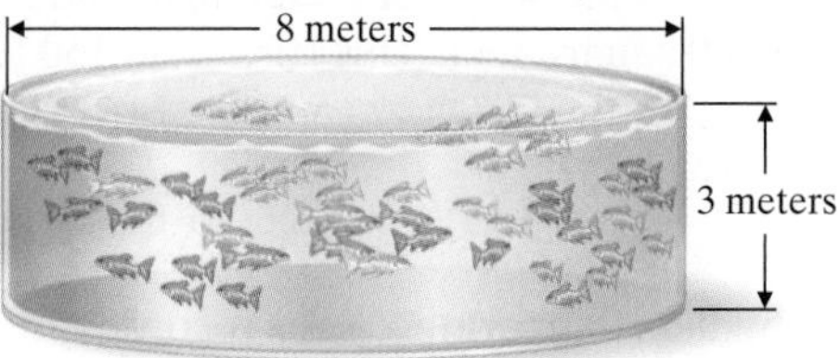

△ **49.** A lawn is in the shape of a trapezoid with a height of 60 feet and bases of 70 feet and 130 feet. How many bags of fertilizer must be purchased to cover the lawn if each bag covers 4000 square feet? $\left(A = \frac{1}{2}h(B + b)\right)$

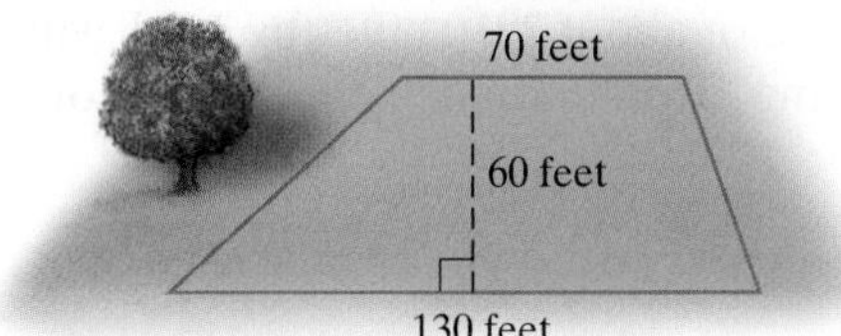

△ **50.** If the area of a right-triangularly shaped sail is 20 square feet and its base is 5 feet, find the height of the sail. $\left(A = \frac{1}{2}bh\right)$

△ **51.** Maria's Pizza sells one 16-inch cheese pizza or two 10-inch cheese pizzas for \$9.99. Determine which size gives more pizza. ($A = \pi r^2$)

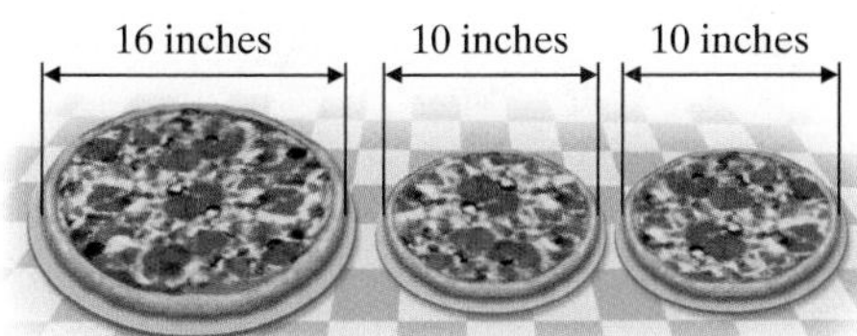

△ **52.** Find how much rope is needed to wrap around Earth at the equator, if the radius of Earth is 4000 miles. (*Hint:* Use 3.14 for π and the formula for circumference.)

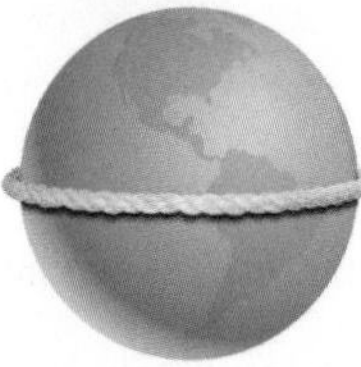

53. A Japanese "bullet" train set a new world record for train speed at 552 kilometers per hour during a manned test run on the Yamanashi Maglev Test Line in April 1999. The Yamanashi Maglev Test Line is 42.8 kilometers long. How many *minutes* would a test run on the Yamanashi Line last at this record-setting speed? Round to the nearest hundredth of a minute. (*Source:* Japan Railways Central Co.)

54. In 1983, the Hawaiian volcano Kilauea began erupting in a series of episodes still occurring at the time of this writing. At times, the lava flows advanced at speeds of up to 0.5 kilometer per hour. In 1983 and 1984 lava flows destroyed 16 homes in the Royal Gardens subdivision, about 6 km away from the eruption site. Roughly how long did it take the lava to reach Royal Gardens? (*Source:* U.S. Geological Survey Hawaiian Volcano Observatory)

△ **55.** The perimeter of an equilateral triangle is 7 inches more than the perimeter of a square, and the side of the triangle is 5 inches longer than the side of the square. Find the side of the triangle. (*Hint:* An equilateral triangle has three sides the same length.)

△ **56.** A square animal pen and a pen shaped like an equilateral triangle have equal perimeters. Find the length of the sides of each pen if the sides of the triangular pen are fifteen less than twice a side of the square pen. (*Hint:* An equilateral triangle has three sides the same length.)

57. Find how long it takes Tran Nguyen to drive 135 miles on I-10 if he merges onto I-10 at 10 a.m. and drives nonstop with his cruise control set on 60 mph.

58. Beaumont, Texas, is about 150 miles from Toledo Bend. If Leo Miller leaves Beaumont at 4 a.m. and averages 45 mph, when should he arrive at Toledo Bend?

△ **59.** The longest runway at Los Angeles International Airport has the shape of a rectangle and an area of 1,813,500 square feet. This runway is 150 feet wide. How long is the runway? (*Source:* Los Angeles World Airports)

60. The return stroke of a bolt of lightning can travel at a speed of 87,000 miles per second (almost half the speed of light). At this speed, how many times can an object travel around the world in one second? (See Exercise 52.) Round to the nearest tenth. (*Source: The Handy Science Answer Book*)

61. The highest temperature ever recorded in Europe was 122°F in Seville, Spain, in August of 1881. Convert this record high temperature to Celsius. (*Source:* National Climatic Data Center)

62. The lowest temperature ever recorded in Oceania was −10°C at the Haleakala Summit in Maui, Hawaii, in January 1961. Convert this record low temperature to Fahrenheit. (*Source:* National Climatic Data Center)

△ **63.** The CART FedEx Championship Series is an open-wheeled race car competition based in the United States. A CART car has a maximum length of 199 inches, a maximum width of 78.5 inches, and a maximum height of 33 inches. When the CART series travels to another country for a grand prix, teams must ship their cars. Find the volume of the smallest shipping crate needed to ship a CART car of maximum dimensions. (*Source:* Championship Auto Racing Teams, Inc.)

CART Racing Car

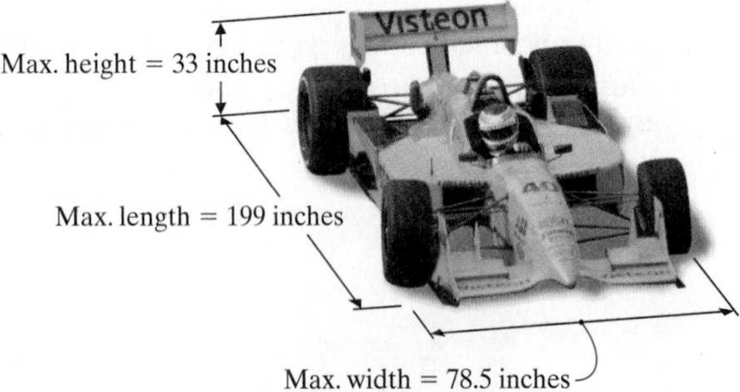

64. On a road course, a CART car's speed can average up to around 105 mph. Based on this speed, how long would it take a CART driver to travel from Los Angeles to New York City, a distance of about 2810 miles by road, without stopping? Round to the nearest tenth of an hour.

△ **65.** The Hoberman Sphere is a toy ball that expands and contracts. When it is completely closed, it has a diameter of 9.5 inches. Find the volume of the Hoberman Sphere when it is completely closed. Use 3.14 for π. Round to the nearest whole cubic inch. (*Hint:* volume of a sphere $= \frac{4}{3}\pi r^3$. *Source:* Hoberman Designs, Inc.)

△ **66.** When the Hoberman Sphere (see Exercise 65) is completely expanded, its diameter is 30 inches. Find the volume of the Hoberman Sphere when it is completely expanded. Use 3.14 for π. (*Source:* Hoberman Designs, Inc.)

67. The average temperature on the planet Mercury is 167°C. Convert this temperature to degrees Fahrenheit. Round to the nearest degree. (*Source:* National Space Science Data Center)

68. The average temperature on the planet Jupiter is −227°F. Convert this temperature to degrees Celsius. Round to the nearest degree. (*Source:* National Space Science Data Center)

Review

Write each percent as a decimal.

69. 32% **70.** 8% **71.** 200% **72.** 0.5%

Write each decimal as a percent.

73. 0.17 **74.** 0.03 **75.** 7.2 **76.** 5

Concept Extensions

Solve.

77. $N = R + \frac{V}{G}$ for V (Urban forestry: tree plantings per year)

78. $B = \frac{F}{P - V}$ for V (Business: break-even point)

79. The formula $V = lwh$ is used to find the volume of a box. If the length of a box is doubled, the width is doubled, and the height is doubled, how does this affect the volume? Explain your answer.

80. The formula $A = bh$ is used to find the area of a parallelogram. If the base of a parallelogram is doubled and its height is doubled, how does this affect the area? Explain your answer.

81. Use the Dolbear's Law formula for Exercises 41–46 and calculate when the number of cricket chirps per minute is the same as the temperature in degrees Fahrenheit. (*Hint:* Replace T with N and solve for N or replace N with T and solve for T.)

82. Find the temperature at which the Celsius measurement and the Fahrenheit measurement are the same number.

Solve. See the Concept Check in this section.

83. ▲ − ● · ▮ = ◻ for ●

84. ⬟ · ■ + ▲ = ● for ■

85. Flying fish do not *actually* fly, but glide. They have been known to travel a distance of 1300 feet at a rate of 20 miles per hour. How many seconds would it take to travel this distance? (*Hint:* First convert miles per hour to feet per second. Recall that 1 mile = 5280 feet.) Round to the nearest tenth of a second.

86. A glacier is a giant mass of rocks and ice that flows downhill like a river. Exit Glacier, near Seward, Alaska, moves at a rate of 20 inches a day. Find the distance in feet the glacier moves in a year. (Assume 365 days a year.) Round to two decimal places.

Substitute the given values into each given formula and solve for the unknown variable. If necessary, round to one decimal place.

87. $I = PRT$; $I = 1{,}056{,}000$, $R = 0.055$, $T = 6$ (Simple interest formula)

88. $I = PRT$; $I = 3750$, $P = 25{,}000$, $R = 0.05$ (Simple interest formula)

89. $V = \frac{4}{3}\pi r^3$; $r = 3$ (Volume of a sphere) (Use a calculator approximation for π.)

90. $V = \frac{1}{3}\pi r^2 h$; $V = 565.2$, $r = 6$ (Volume of a cone) (Use a calculator approximation for π.)

Objectives

A Solve Percent Equations.

B Solve Discount and Mark-Up Problems.

C Solve Percent Increase and Percent Decrease Problems.

D Solve Mixture Problems.

9.6 PERCENT AND MIXTURE PROBLEM SOLVING

This section is devoted to solving problems in the categories listed. The same problem-solving steps used in previous sections are also followed in this section. They are listed below for review.

General Strategy for Problem Solving

1. UNDERSTAND the problem. During this step, become comfortable with the problem. Some ways of doing this are as follows:

   Read and reread the problem.

   Choose a variable to represent the unknown.

   Construct a drawing, whenever possible.

   Propose a solution and check. Pay careful attention to how you check your proposed solution. This will help writing an equation to model the problem.
2. TRANSLATE the problem into an equation.
3. SOLVE the equation.
4. INTERPRET the results: *Check* the proposed solution in the stated problem and *state* your conclusion.

Objective A Solving Percent Equations

Many of today's statistics are given in terms of percent: a basketball player's free throw percent, current interest rates, stock market trends, and nutrition labeling, just to name a few. In this section, we first explore percent, percent equations, and applications involving percents.

PRACTICE 1

The number 22 is what percent of 40?

Example 1 The number 63 is what percent of 72?

Solution:

1. UNDERSTAND. Read and reread the problem. Next, let's suppose that the percent is 80%. To check, we find 80% of 72.

   $80\% \text{ of } 72 = 0.80(72) = 57.6$

   This is close, but not 63. At this point, though, we have a better understanding of the problem; we know the correct answer is close to and greater than 80%, and we know how to check our proposed solution later.

   Let $x =$ the unknown percent.

2. TRANSLATE. Recall that "is" means "equals" and "of" signifies multiplying. Let's translate the sentence directly.

the number 63	is	what percent	of	72
↓	↓	↓	↓	↓
63	=	x	·	72

3. SOLVE.

$$63 = 72x$$

$$0.875 = x \quad \text{Divide both sides by 72.}$$

$$87.5\% = x \quad \text{Write as a percent.}$$

Answer

1. 55%

4. INTERPRET.

Check: Verify that 87.5% of 72 is 63.

State: The number 63 is 87.5% of 72.

Work Practice 1

Example 2 The number 120 is 15% of what number?

Solution:

1. UNDERSTAND. Read and reread the problem.

Let $x =$ the unknown number.

2. TRANSLATE.

the number 120	is	15%	of	what number
↓	↓	↓	↓	↓
120	=	15%	·	x

3. SOLVE.

$120 = 0.15x$ Write 15% as 0.15.

$800 = x$ Divide both sides by 0.15.

4. INTERPRET.

Check: Check the proposed solution by finding 15% of 800 and verifying that the result is 120.

State: Thus, 120 is 15% of 800.

Work Practice 2

PRACTICE 2

The number 150 is 40% of what number?

Example 3 The circle graph below shows the purpose of trips made by American travelers. Use this graph to answer the questions below.

Purpose of Trip

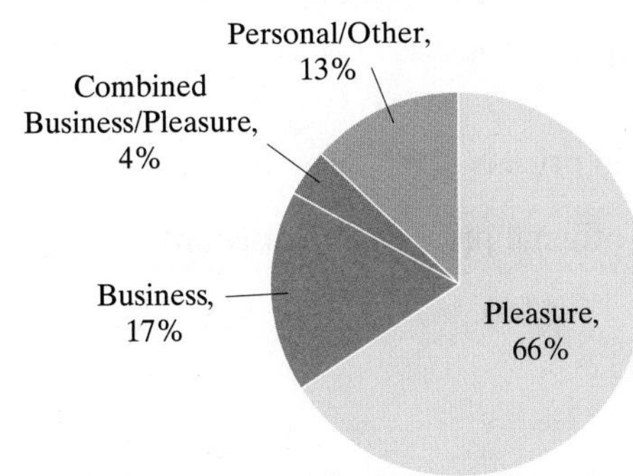

Source: Travel Industry Association of America

a. What percent of trips made by American travelers are solely for the purpose of business?

b. What percent of trips made by American travelers are for the purpose of business or combined business/pleasure?

c. On an airplane flight of 253 Americans, how many of these people might we expect to be traveling solely for business?

Solution:

a. From the circle graph, we see that 17% of trips made by American travelers are solely for the purpose of business.

Continued on next page

PRACTICE 3

Use the circle graph to answer each question.

a. What percent of trips made by American travelers are solely for pleasure?

b. What percent of trips made by American travelers are for the purpose of pleasure or combined business/pleasure?

c. On an airplane flight of 250 Americans, how many of these people might we expect to be traveling solely for pleasure?

Answers

2. 375 **3. a.** 66% **b.** 70% **c.** 165 people

b. From the circle graph, we know that 17% of trips are solely for business and 4% of trips are for combined business/pleasure. The sum 17% + 4% or 21% of trips made by American travelers are for the purpose of business or combined business/pleasure.

c. Since 17% of trips made by American travelers are for business, we find 17% of 253. Remember that "of" translates to "multiplication."

$$17\% \text{ of } 253 = 0.17(253) \quad \text{Replace "of" with the operation of multiplication.}$$
$$= 43.01$$

We might then expect that about 43 American travelers on the flight are traveling solely for business.

Work Practice 3

Objective B Solving Discount and Mark-Up Problems

The next example has to do with discounting the price of a cell phone.

PRACTICE 4

A surfboard, originally purchased for $400, was sold on eBay at a discount of 40% of the original price. What is the discount and the new price?

Example 4 Cell Phones Unlimited recently reduced the price of a $140 phone by 20%. What is the discount and the new price?

Solution:

1. UNDERSTAND. Read and reread the problem. Make sure you understand the meaning of the word "discount." Discount is the amount of money by which an item has been decreased. To find the discount, we simply find 20% of $140. In other words, we have the formulas,

discount = percent · original price   Then

new price = original price − discount

2, 3. TRANSLATE and SOLVE.

discount	=	percent	·	original price
	=	20%	·	$140
	=	0.20	·	$140
	= $28			

Thus, the discount in price is $28.

new price	=	original price	−	discount
	=	$140	−	$28
	= $112			

3. INTERPRET.

Check: Check your calculations in the formulas, and also see if our results are reasonable. They are.

State: The discount in price is $28 and the new price is $112.

Work Practice 4

A concept similar to discount is mark-up. What is the difference between the two? A discount is subtracted from the original price while a mark-up is added to the original price. For mark-ups,

mark-up = percent · original price

new price = original price + mark-up

Mark-up exercises can be found in Exercise Set 2.6.

Answer

4. discount: $160; new price: $240

Objective C Solving Percent Increase and Percent Decrease Problems

Percent increase or percent decrease is a common way to describe how some measurement has increased or decreased. For example, crime increased by 8%, teachers received a 5.5% increase in salary, or a company decreased its employees by 10%. The next example is a review of percent increase.

Example 5 Calculating the Percent Increase of Attending College

The tuition and fees cost of attending a public college rose from \$2928 in 2003 to \$5246 in 2009. Find the percent increase. (*Source*: The College Board) *Note*: These costs are an average of two-year and four-year colleges.

Solution:

1. UNDERSTAND. Read and reread the problem. Notice that the new tuition, \$5246, is almost double the old tuition of \$2928. Because of that, we know that the percent increase is close to 100%. To see this, let's guess that the percent increase is 100%. To check, we find 100% of \$2928 to find the *increase* in cost. Then we add this increase to \$2928 to find the *new cost*. In other words, 100%(\$2928) = 1.00(\$2928) = \$2928, the *increase* in cost. The *new cost* would be old cost + increase = \$2928 + \$2928 = \$5856, close to the actual new cost of \$5246. We now know that the increase is close to, but less than 100% and we know how to check our proposed solution.

Let $x =$ the percent increase.

2. TRANSLATE. First, find the **increase,** and then the **percent increase.** The increase in cost is found by:

In words:	increase	=	new cost	−	old cost	or
Translate:	increase	=	\$5246	−	\$2928	
		=	\$2318			

Next, find the percent increase. The percent increase or percent decrease is always a percent of the original number or, in this case, the old cost.

In words:	increase	is	what percent	of	old cost
Translate:	\$2318	=	x	·	\$2928

3. SOLVE.

$2318 = 2928x$

$0.792 \approx x$ Divide both sides by 2928 and round to 3 decimal places.

$79.2\% \approx x$ Write as a percent.

4. INTERPRET.

Check: Check the proposed solution

State: The percent increase in cost is approximately 79.2%.

Work Practice 5

PRACTICE 5

If a number increases from 120 to 200, find the percent increase. Round to the nearest tenth of a percent.

Percent decrease is found using a similar method. First find the decrease, then determine what percent of the original or first amount is that decrease.

Read the next example carefully. For Example 5, we were asked to find percent increase. In Example 6, we are given the percent increase and asked to find the number before the increase.

Answer

5. 66.7%

PRACTICE 6

Find the original price of a suit if the sale price is \$46 after a 20% discount.

Example 6 The fastest-growing sector of digital theater screens is 3D. Find the number of digital 3D screens in the United States and Canada last year if after a 134% increase, the number this year is 3548. Round to the nearest whole. (*Source:* MPAA)

Solution:

1. UNDERSTAND. Read and reread the problem. Let's guess a solution and see how we would check our guess. If the number of digital 3D screens last year was 1000, we would see if 1000 plus the increase is 3548; that is,

$$1000 + 134\%(1000) = 1000 + 1.34(1000) = 1000 + 1340 = 2340$$

Since 2340 is too small, we know that our guess of 1000 is too small. We also have a better understanding of the problem. Let

x = number of digital 3D screens last year

2. TRANSLATE. To translate to an equation, we remember that

In words:	number of digital 3D screens last year	plus	increase	equals	number of digital 3D screens this year
Translate:	x	$+$	$1.34x$	$=$	3548

3. SOLVE.

$$2.34x = 3548$$
$$x = \frac{3548}{2.34}$$
$$x \approx 1516$$

4. INTERPRET.

Check: Recall that x represents the number of digital 3D screens last year. If this number is approximately 1516, let's see if 1516 plus the increase is close to 3548. (We use the word "close" since 1516 is rounded.)

$$1516 + 134\%(1516) = 1516 + 1.34(1516) = 1516 + 2031.44 = 3547.44$$

which is close to 3548.

State: There were approximately 1516 digital 3D screens last year.

Work Practice 6

Objective D Solving Mixture Problems

Mixture problems involve two or more different quantities being combined to form a new mixture. These applications range from Dow Chemical's need to form a chemical mixture of a required strength to Planter's Peanut Company's need to find the correct mixture of peanuts and cashews, given taste and price constraints.

PRACTICE 7

How much 20% dye solution and 50% dye solution should be mixed to obtain 6 liters of a 40% solution?

Example 7 Calculating Percent for a Lab Experiment

A chemist working on his doctoral degree at Massachusetts Institute of Technology needs 12 liters of a 50% acid solution for a lab experiment. The stockroom has only 40% and 70% solutions. How much of each solution should be mixed together to form 12 liters of a 50% solution?

Solution:

1. UNDERSTAND. First, read and reread the problem a few times. Next, guess a solution. Suppose that we need 7 liters of the 40% solution. Then we need $12 - 7 = 5$ liters of the 70% solution. To see if this is indeed the solution, find

Answers

6. \$57.50 **7.** 2 liters of the 20% solution; 4 liters of the 50% solution

the amount of pure acid in 7 liters of the 40% solution, in 5 liters of the 70% solution, and in 12 liters of a 50% solution, the required amount and strength.

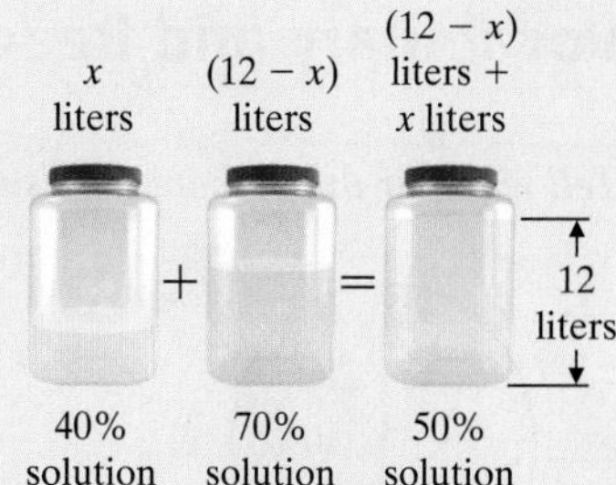

number of liters	×	acid strength	=	amount of pure acid
7 liters	×	40%	=	7(0.40) or 2.8 liters
5 liters	×	70%	=	5(0.70) or 3.5 liters
12 liters	×	50%	=	12(0.50) or 6 liters

Since 2.8 liters + 3.5 liters = 6.3 liters and not 6, our guess is incorrect, but we have gained some valuable insight into how to model and check this problem.

Let

x = number of liters of 40% solution; then

$12 - x$ = number of liters of 70% solution.

2. TRANSLATE. To help us translate to an equation, the following table summarizes the information given. Recall that the amount of acid in each solution is found by multiplying the acid strength of each solution by the number of liters.

	No. of Liters	·	Acid Strength	=	Amount of Acid
40% Solution	x		40%		$0.40x$
70% Solution	$12 - x$		70%		$0.70(12 - x)$
50% Solution Needed	12		50%		0.50(12)

The amount of acid in the final solution is the sum of the amounts of acid in the two beginning solutions.

In words:	acid in 40% solution	+	acid in 70% solution	=	acid in 50% mixture
Translate:	$0.40x$	+	$0.70(12 - x)$	=	$0.50(12)$

3. SOLVE.

$$0.40x + 0.70(12 - x) = 0.50(12)$$

$$0.4x + 8.4 - 0.7x = 6 \quad \text{Apply the distributive property.}$$

$$-0.3x + 8.4 = 6 \quad \text{Combine like terms.}$$

$$-0.3x = -2.4 \quad \text{Subtract 8.4 from both sides.}$$

$$x = 8 \quad \text{Divide both sides by } -0.3.$$

4. INTERPRET.

Check: To check, recall how we checked our guess.

State: If 8 liters of the 40% solution are mixed with 12 − 8 or 4 liters of the 70% solution, the result is 12 liters of a 50% solution.

Work Practice 7

Vocabulary and Readiness Check

Tell whether the percent labels in the circle graphs are correct.

1.

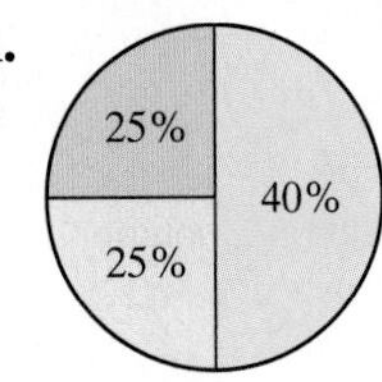

2.

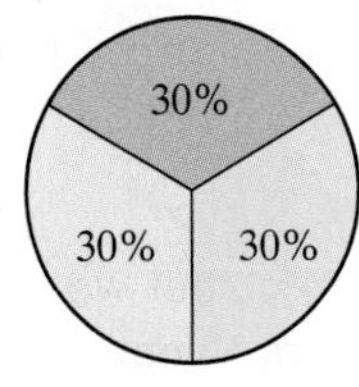

3.

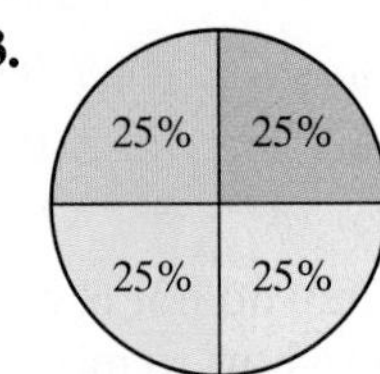

4.

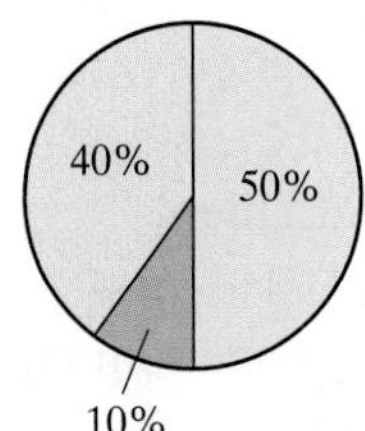

9.6 Exercise Set

FOR EXTRA HELP

MyMathLab

PRACTICE

WATCH

DOWNLOAD

READ

REVIEW

Objective A *Find each number described. For Exercises 1 and 2, the solutions have been started for you. See Examples 1 and 2.*

1. What number is 16% of 70?

Start the solution:

1. UNDERSTAND the problem. Reread it as many times as needed.

2. TRANSLATE into an equation. (Fill in the blanks below.)

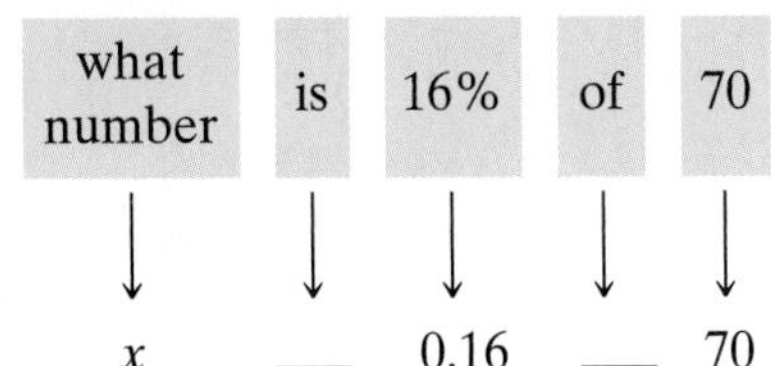

Finish with:

3. SOLVE and **4.** INTERPRET

2. What number is 88% of 1000?

Start the solution:

1. UNDERSTAND the problem. Reread it as many times as needed.

2. TRANSLATE into an equation. (Fill in the blanks below.)

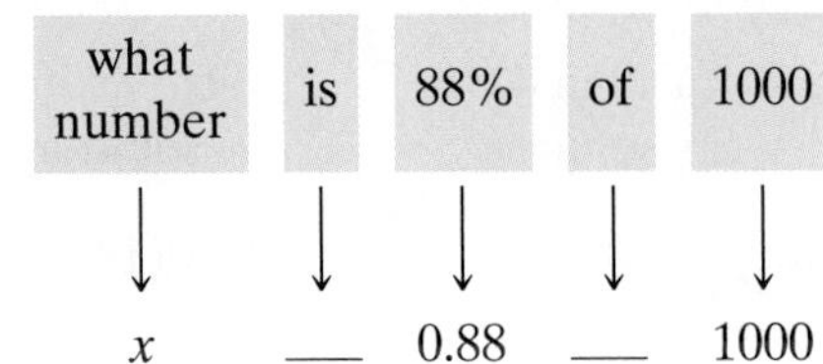

Finish with:

3. SOLVE and **4.** INTERPRET

3. The number 28.6 is what percent of 52?

4. The number 87.2 is what percent of 436?

5. The number 45 is 25% of what number?

6. The number 126 is 35% of what number?

The circle graph below shows the number of minutes that adults spend on their home phone each day. Use this graph for Exercises 7 through 10. See Example 3.

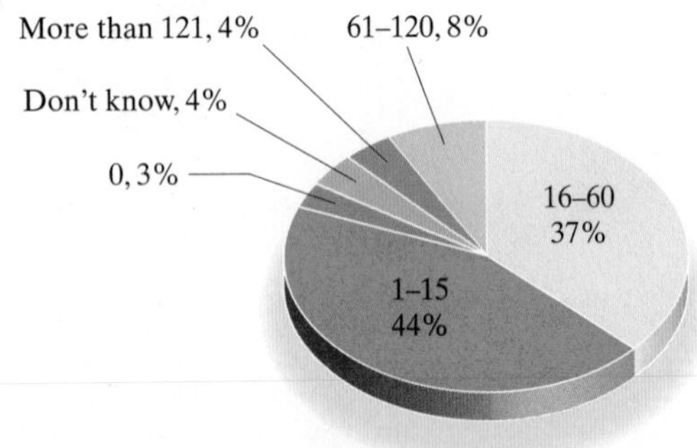

Source: Bruskin/Goldring Research for Sony Electronics

7. What percent of adults spend more than 121 minutes on the phone each day?

8. What percent of adults spend no time on the phone each day?

9. Florence is a town in Alabama whose adult population is approximately 27,000. How many of these adults might you expect to talk 16–60 minutes on the phone each day?

10. Columbus is a town in Indiana whose adult population is approximately 29,250. How many of these adults might you expect to talk 61–120 minutes on the phone each day?

Objective **B** *Solve. If needed, round answers to the nearest cent. See Example 4.*

11. A used automobile dealership recently reduced the price of a used sports car by 8%. If the price of the car before discount was $18,500, find the discount and the new price.

12. A music store is advertising a 25%-off sale on all new releases. Find the discount and the sale price of a newly released CD that regularly sells for $12.50.

13. A birthday celebration meal is $40.50 including tax. Find the total cost if a 15% tip is added to the cost.

14. A retirement dinner for two is $65.40 including tax. Find the total cost if a 20% tip is added to the cost.

Objective **C** *Solve. See Example 5.*

15. The number of fraud complaints for Internet auction sites decreased from 148,600 in 2005 to 73,900 in 2007. Find the percent decrease. Round to the nearest whole percent. (*Source:* FBI)

16. The number of text messages rose from 996 million in June to 1100 million in December. Find the percent increase. Round to the nearest whole percent.

17. By decreasing each dimension by 1 unit, the area of a rectangle decreased from 40 square feet (on the left) to 28 square feet (on the right). Find the percent decrease in area.

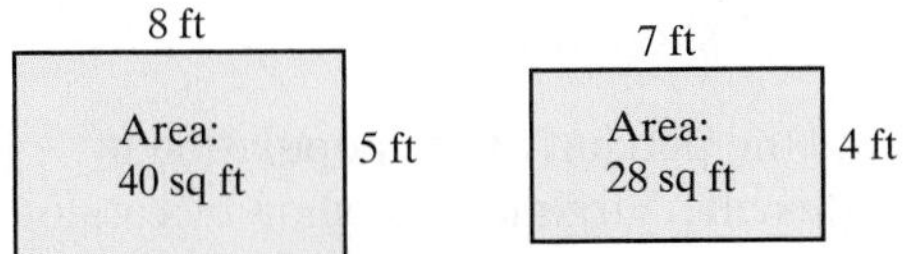

18. By decreasing the length of the side by one unit, the area of a square decreased from 100 square meters to 81 square meters. Find the percent decrease in area.

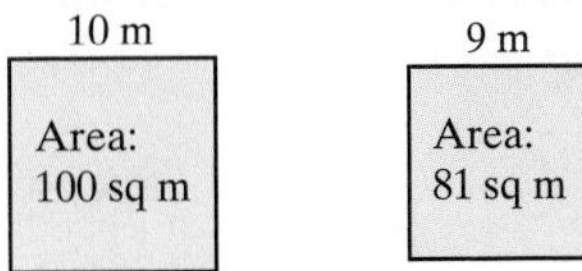

Solve. See Example 6.

19. Find the original price of a pair of shoes if the sale price is $78 after a 25% discount.

20. Find the original price of a popular pair of shoes if the increased price is $80 after a 25% increase.

21. Find last year's salary if after a 4% pay raise, this year's salary is $44,200.

22. Find last year's salary if after a 3% pay raise, this year's salary is $55,620.

Objective **D** *Solve. For each exercise, a table is given for you to complete and use to write an equation that models the situation. See Example 7.*

23. How much pure acid should be mixed with 2 gallons of a 40% acid solution in order to get a 70% acid solution?

	Number of Gallons ·	Acid Strength =	Amount of Acid
Pure Acid		100%	
40% Acid Solution			
70% Acid Solution Needed			

24. How many cubic centimeters (cc) of a 25% antibiotic solution should be added to 10 cubic centimeters of a 60% antibiotic solution in order to get a 30% antibiotic solution?

	Number of Cubic cm ·	Antibiotic Strength =	Amount of Antibiotic
25% Antibiotic Solution			
60% Antibiotic Solution			
30% Antibiotic Solution Needed			

25. Community Coffee Company wants a new flavor of Cajun coffee. How many pounds of coffee worth \$7 a pound should be added to 14 pounds of coffee worth \$4 a pound to get a mixture worth \$5 a pound?

	Number of Pounds ·	Cost per Pound =	Value
\$7 per lb Coffee			
\$4 per lb Coffee			
\$5 per lb Coffee Wanted			

26. Planter's Peanut Company wants to mix 20 pounds of peanuts worth \$3 a pound with cashews worth \$5 a pound in order to make an experimental mix worth \$3.50 a pound. How many pounds of cashews should be added to the peanuts?

	Number of Pounds ·	Cost per Pound =	Value
\$3 per lb Peanuts			
\$5 per lb Cashews			
\$3.50 per lb Mixture Wanted			

Objectives A B C **Mixed Practice** *Solve. If needed, round money amounts to two decimal places and all other amounts to one decimal place. See Examples 1 through 6.*

27. Find 23% of 20.

28. Find 140% of 86.

29. The number 40 is 80% of what number?

30. The number 56.25 is 45% of what number?

31. The number 144 is what percent of 480?

32. The number 42 is what percent of 35?

The graph shows the communities in the United States that have the highest percentages of citizens that shop by catalog. Use the graph to answer Exercises 33 through 36.

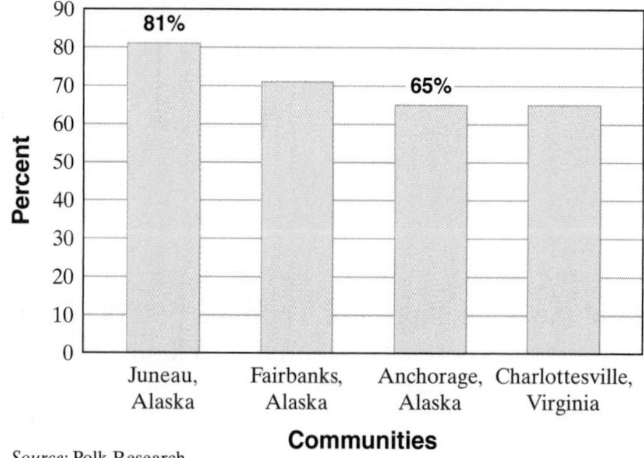

33. Estimate the percent of the population in Fairbanks, Alaska, who shop by catalog.

34. Estimate the percent of the population in Charlottesville, Virginia, who shop by catalog.

35. According to CNN, in 2008, Anchorage had a population of 278,700. How many catalog shoppers might we predict lived in Anchorage? Round to the nearest whole number.

36. According to CNN, in 2008, Juneau had a population of 30,700. How many catalog shoppers might we predict lived in Juneau? Round to the nearest whole number.

For Exercises 37 and 38, fill in the percent column in each table. Each table contains a worked-out example.

37.

Top Cranberry-Producing States in 2008 (in millions of pounds)

	Millions of Pounds	Percent of Total (rounded to nearest percent)
Wisconsin	385	
Oregon	50	
Massachusetts	190	
Washington	15	
New Jersey	49	Example: $\frac{49}{689} \approx 7\%$
Total	689	

Source: National Agricultural Statistics Service

38.

The Gap, Inc. Brands North American Stores in 2008

Store Brand/Location	Number of Stores	Percent of Total (rounded to nearest percent)
The Gap U.S.	1136	
The Gap Canada	91	
Banana Republic U.S.	540	Example: $\frac{540}{2876} \approx 19\%$
Banana Republic Canada	33	
Old Navy–U.S.	1012	
Old Navy–Canada	64	
Total	2876	

39. Iceberg lettuce is grown and shipped to stores for about 40 cents a head, and consumers purchase it for about 70 cents a head. Find the percent increase.

40. The lettuce consumption per capita in 1990 was 31.5 pounds, and in 2007 the consumption dropped to 29.5 pounds. Find the percent decrease.

41. A student at the University of New Orleans makes money by buying and selling used cars. Charles bought a used car and later sold it for a 20% profit. If he sold it for $4680, how much did Charles pay for the car?

42. The number of registered vehicles on the road in the United States is constantly increasing. In 2007, there were approximately 246 million registered vehicles. This represents a 3% increase over 2002. How many registered vehicles were there in the United States in 2002? Round to the nearest million. (*Source:* Federal Highway Administration)

43. By doubling each dimension, the area of a parallelogram increased from 36 square centimeters to 144 square centimeters. Find the percent increase in area.

44. By doubling each dimension, the area of a triangle increased from 6 square miles to 24 square miles. Find the percent increase in area.

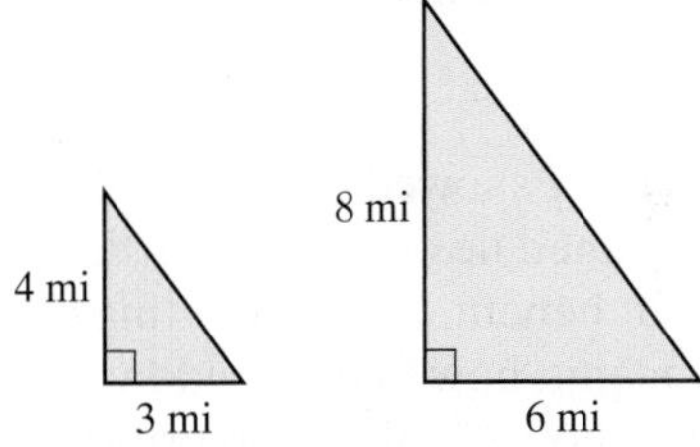

45. A gasoline station recently increased the price of one grade of gasoline by 5%. If this gasoline originally cost $2.20 per gallon, find the mark-up and the new price.

46. The price of a biology book recently increased by 10%. If this book originally cost $89.90, find the mark-up and the new price.

47. How much of an alloy that is 20% copper should be mixed with 200 ounces of an alloy that is 50% copper in order to get an alloy that is 30% copper?

48. How much water should be added to 30 gallons of a solution that is 70% antifreeze in order to get a mixture that is 60% antifreeze?

49. During the 1982–1983 term, the Supreme Court made 151 decisions while during the 2007–2008 term, they only made 72. Find the percent decrease in number of decisions. Round to the nearest tenth of a percent.

50. The number of farms in the United States is decreasing. In 1940, there were approximately 6.3 million farms, while in 2007 there were only 2.1 million farms. Find the percent decrease in the number of farms. Round to the nearest tenth of a percent.

51. A company recently downsized its number of employees by 35%. If there are still 78 employees, how many employees were there prior to the layoffs?

52. The average number of children born to each U.S. woman has decreased by 44% since 1920. If this average is now 1.9, find the average in 1920. Round to the nearest tenth.

53. Nordstrom advertised a 25%-off sale. If a London Fog coat originally sold for $256, find the decrease in price and the sale price.

54. A gasoline station decreased the price of a $0.95 cola by 15%. Find the decrease in price and the new price.

55. Scoville units are used to measure the hotness of a pepper. Measuring 577 thousand Scoville units, the "Red Savina" habañero pepper was known as the hottest chili pepper. That has recently changed with the discovery of Naga Jolokia pepper from India. It measures 48% hotter than the habañero. Find the measure of the Naga Jolokia pepper. Round to the nearest thousand units.

56. As of this writing, the women's record for throwing a disc (like a heavy Frisbee) was set by Valarie Jenkins of the United States in 2008. Her throw was 148.00 meters. The men's world record was set by Christian Sandstrom of Sweden in 2002. His throw was 68.9% farther than Valarie's. Find the distance of his throw. Round to the nearest meter. (*Source:* World Flying Disc Federation)

57. A recent survey showed that 42% of recent college graduates named flexible hours as their most desired employment benefit. In a graduating class of 860 college students, how many would you expect to rank flexible hours as their top priority in job benefits? (Round to the nearest whole.) (*Source:* JobTrak.com)

58. A recent survey showed that 64% of U.S. colleges have Internet access in their classrooms. There are approximately 9800 post-secondary institutions in the United States. How many of these would you expect to have Internet access in their classrooms? (*Source:* Market Data Retrieval, National Center for Education Statistics)

59. A new self-tanning lotion for everyday use is to be sold. First, an experimental lotion mixture is made by mixing 800 ounces of everyday moisturizing lotion worth $0.30 an ounce with self-tanning lotion worth $3 per ounce. If the experimental lotion is to cost $1.20 per ounce, how many ounces of the self-tanning lotion should be in the mixture?

60. The owner of a local chocolate shop wants to develop a new trail mix. How many pounds of chocolate-covered peanuts worth $5 a pound should be mixed with 10 pounds of granola bites worth $2 a pound to get a mixture worth $3 per pound?

Review

Place <, >, or = in the appropriate space to make each a true statement. See Sections 8.1, 8.2, and 8.3.

61. $-5 \quad -7$

62. $\frac{12}{3} \quad 2^2$

63. $|-5| \quad -(-5)$

64. $-3^3 \quad (-3)^3$

65. $(-3)^2 \quad -3^2$

66. $|-2| \quad -|-2|$

Concept Extensions

67. Is it possible to mix a 10% acid solution and a 40% acid solution to obtain a 60% acid solution? Why or why not?

68. Must the percents in a circle graph have a sum of 100%? Why or why not?

Standardized nutrition labels like the one below have been displayed on food items since 1994. The percent column on the right shows the percent of daily values (based on a 2000-calorie diet) shown at the bottom of the label. For example, a serving of this food contains 4 grams of total fat, where the recommended daily fat based on a 2000-calorie diet is less than 65 grams of fat. This means that $\frac{4}{65}$ *or approximately 6% (as shown) of your daily recommended fat is taken in by eating a serving of this food. Use this nutrition label to answer Exercises 69 through 71.*

Nutrition Facts

Serving Size	**18 Crackers (31g)**
Servings Per Container	**About 9**
Amount Per Serving	
Calories 130	Calories from Fat 35
	% Daily Value*
Total Fat 4g	**6%**
Saturated Fat 0.5g	**3%**
Polyunsaturated Fat 0g	
Monounsaturated Fat 1.5g	
Cholesterol 0mg	**0%**
Sodium 230mg	x
Total Carbohydrate 23g	y
Dietary Fiber 2g	**8%**
Sugars 3g	
Protein 2g	
Vitamin A 0% •	Vitamin C 0%
Calcium 2% •	Iron 6%

* Percent Daily Values are based on a 2,000 calorie diet. Your daily values may be higher or lower depending on your calorie needs.

	Calories	2,000	2,500
Total Fat	Less than	65g	80g
Sat. Fat	Less than	20g	25g
Cholesterol	Less than	300mg	300mg
Sodium	Less than	2400mg	2400mg
Total Carbohydrate		300g	375g
Dietary Fiber		25g	30g

69. Based on a 2000-calorie diet, what percent of daily value of sodium is contained in a serving of this food? In other words, find x in the label. (Round to the nearest tenth of a percent.)

70. Based on a 2000-calorie diet, what percent of daily value of total carbohydrate is contained in a serving of this food? In other words, find y in the label. (Round to the nearest tenth of a percent.)

71. Notice on the nutrition label that one serving of this food contains 130 calories and 35 of these calories are from fat. Find the percent of calories from fat. (Round to the nearest tenth of a percent.) It is recommended that no more than 30% of calorie intake come from fat. Does this food satisfy this recommendation?

Use the nutrition label below to answer Exercises 72 through 74.

NUTRITIONAL INFORMATION PER SERVING

Serving Size: 9.8 oz.		**Servings Per Container: 1**	
Calories	280	Polyunsaturated Fat	1g
Protein	12g	Saturated Fat	3g
Carbohydrate	45g	Cholesterol	20mg
Fat	6g	Sodium	520mg
Percent of Calories from Fat	?	Potassium	220mg

72. If fat contains approximately 9 calories per gram, find the percent of calories from fat in one serving of this food. (Round to the nearest tenth of a percent.)

73. If protein contains approximately 4 calories per gram, find the percent of calories from protein from one serving of this food. (Round to the nearest tenth of a percent.)

74. Find a food that contains more than 30% of its calories per serving from fat. Analyze the nutrition label and verify that the percents shown are correct.

Objectives

A **Graph Inequalities on a Number Line.**

B **Use the Addition Property of Inequality to Solve Inequalities.**

C **Use the Multiplication Property of Inequality to Solve Inequalities.**

D **Use Both Properties to Solve Inequalities.**

E **Solve Problems Modeled by Inequalities.**

9.7 LINEAR INEQUALITIES AND PROBLEM SOLVING

In Chapter 8, we reviewed these inequality symbols and their meanings:

$<$ means "is less than" $\quad\quad$ $\le$ means "is less than or equal to"
$>$ means "is greater than" $\quad\quad$ $\ge$ means "is greater than or equal to"

An **inequality** is a statement that contains one of the symbols above.

Equations	Inequalities
$x = 3$	$x \le 3$
$5n - 6 = 14$	$5n - 6 > 14$
$12 = 7 - 3y$	$12 \le 7 - 3y$
$\frac{x}{4} - 6 = 1$	$\frac{x}{4} - 6 > 1$

Objective A Graphing Inequalities on a Number Line

Recall that the single solution to the equation $x = 3$ is 3. The solutions of the inequality $x \le 3$ include 3 and *all real numbers less than 3* (for example, -10, $\frac{1}{2}$, 2, and 2.9). Because we can't list all numbers less than 3, we show instead a picture of the solutions by graphing them on a number line.

To graph the solutions of $x \le 3$, we shade the numbers to the left of 3 since they are less than 3. Then we place a closed circle on the point representing 3. The closed circle indicates that 3 *is* a solution: 3 *is* less than or equal to 3.

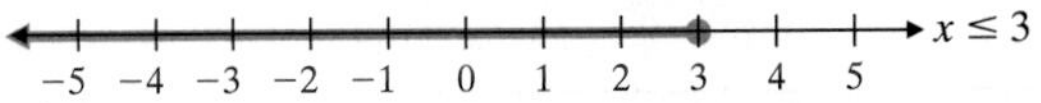

To graph the solutions of $x < 3$, we shade the numbers to the left of 3. Then we place an open circle on the point representing 3. The open circle indicates that 3 *is not* a solution: 3 *is not* less than 3.

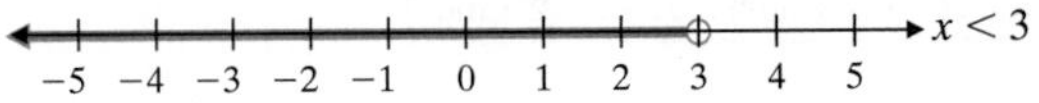

Example 1 Graph: $x \ge -1$

Solution: To graph the solutions of $x \ge -1$, we place a closed circle at -1 since the inequality symbol is $\ge$ and -1 is greater than or equal to -1. Then we shade to the right of -1.

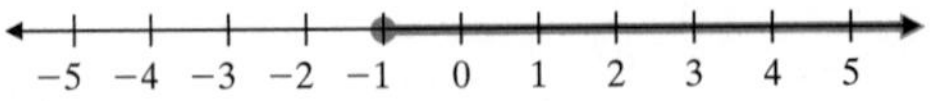

Work Practice 1

Example 2 Graph: $-1 > x$

Solution: Recall from Section 8.1 that $-1 > x$ means the same as $x < -1$. The graph of the solutions of $x < -1$ is shown below.

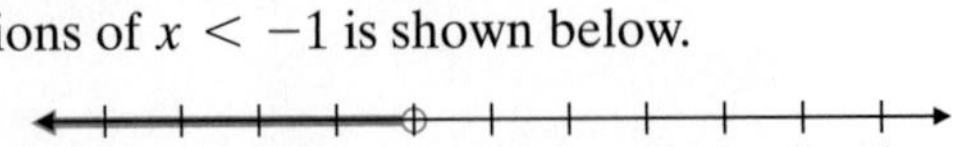

Work Practice 2

PRACTICE 1

Graph: $x \ge -2$

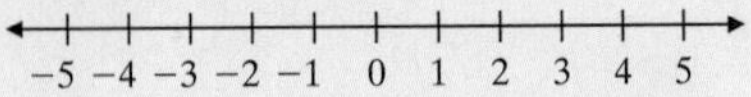

PRACTICE 2

Graph: $5 > x$

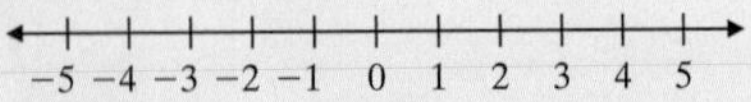

Answers

1. 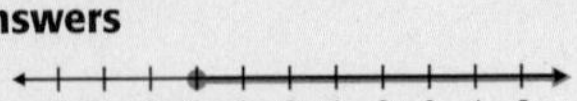

2. 

Example 3 Graph: $-4 < x \le 2$

Solution: We read $-4 < x \le 2$ as "-4 is less than x and x is less than or equal to 2," or as "x is greater than -4 and x is less than or equal to 2." To graph the solutions of this inequality, we place an open circle at -4 (-4 is not part of the graph), a closed circle at 2 (2 is part of the graph), and we shade all numbers between -4 and 2. Why? All numbers between -4 and 2 are greater than -4 *and* also less than 2.

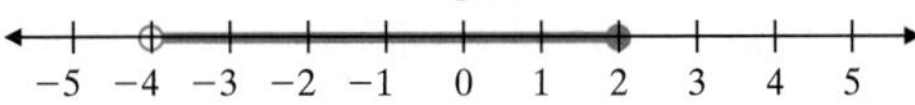

Work Practice 3

PRACTICE 3

Graph: $-3 \le x < 1$

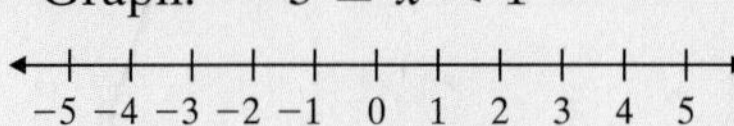

Objective B Using the Addition Property

When solutions of a linear inequality are not immediately obvious, they are found through a process similar to the one used to solve a linear equation. Our goal is to get the variable alone on one side of the inequality. We use properties of inequality similar to properties of equality.

Addition Property of Inequality

If a, b, and c are real numbers, then

$a < b$ and $a + c < b + c$

are equivalent inequalities.

This property also holds true for subtracting values, since subtraction is defined in terms of addition. In other words, adding or subtracting the same quantity from both sides of an inequality does not change the solutions of the inequality.

Example 4 Solve $x + 4 \le -6$. Graph the solutions.

Solution: To solve for x, subtract 4 from both sides of the inequality.

$x + 4 \le -6$ Original inequality

$x + 4 - 4 \le -6 - 4$ Subtract 4 from both sides.

$x \le -10$ Simplify.

The graph of the solutions is shown below.

−14 −13 −12 −11 −10 −9 −8 −7 −6 −5 −4

Work Practice 4

PRACTICE 4

Solve $x - 6 \ge -11$. Graph the solutions.

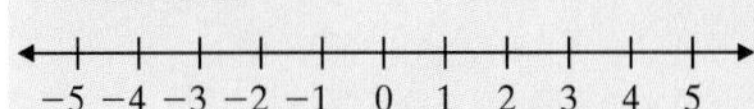

Helpful Hint

Notice that any number less than or equal to -10 is a solution to $x \le -10$. For example, solutions include

-10, -200, $-11\frac{1}{2}$, $-\sqrt{130}$, and -50.3

Objective C Using the Multiplication Property

An important difference between solving linear equations and solving linear inequalities is shown when we multiply or divide both sides of an inequality by a nonzero real number. For example, start with the true statement $6 < 8$ and multiply both sides by 2. As we see below, the resulting inequality is also true.

$6 < 8$ True

$2(6) < 2(8)$ Multiply both sides by 2.

$12 < 16$ True

Answers

3. −5 −4 −3 −2 −1 0 1 2 3 4 5

4. $x \ge -5$

But if we start with the same true statement $6 < 8$ and multiply both sides by -2, the resulting inequality is not a true statement.

$6 < 8$ True
$-2(6) < -2(8)$ Multiply both sides by -2.
$-12 < -16$ False

Notice, however, that if we reverse the direction of the inequality symbol, the resulting inequality is true.

$-12 < -16$ False
$-12 > -16$ True

This demonstrates the multiplication property of inequality.

Multiplication Property of Inequality

1. If a, b, and c are real numbers, and c is **positive**, then

$$a < b \quad \text{and} \quad ac < bc$$

are equivalent inequalities.

2. If a, b, and c are real numbers, and c is **negative**, then

$$a < b \quad \text{and} \quad ac > bc$$

are equivalent inequalities.

Because division is defined in terms of multiplication, this property also holds true when dividing both sides of an inequality by a nonzero number: If we multiply or divide both sides of an inequality by a negative number, **the direction of the inequality sign must be reversed for the inequalities to remain equivalent.**

✓**Concept Check** Fill in the box with <, >, ≤, or ≥.

a. Since $-8 < -4$, then $3(-8) \square 3(-4)$.

b. Since $5 \geq -2$, then $\frac{5}{-7} \square \frac{-2}{-7}$.

c. If $a < b$, then $2a \square 2b$.

d. If $a \geq b$, then $\frac{a}{-3} \square \frac{b}{-3}$.

PRACTICE 5

Solve $-3x \leq 12$. Graph the solutions.

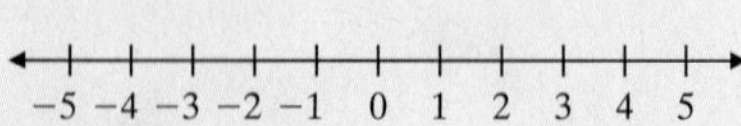

Example 5 Solve $-2x \leq -4$. Graph the solutions.

Solution: Remember to reverse the direction of the inequality symbol when dividing by a negative number.

$-2x \leq -4$

$\frac{-2x}{-2} \geq \frac{-4}{-2}$ Divide both sides by -2 and reverse the inequality sign.

$x \geq 2$ Simplify.

The graph of the solutions is shown.

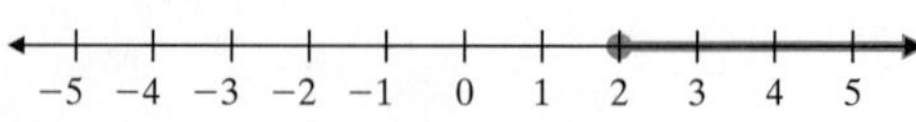

Work Practice 5

Answer

5. $x \geq -4$

✓ **Concept Check Answer**

a. < b. ≤ c. < d. ≤

Example 6 Solve $2x < -4$. Graph the solutions.

Solution: $2x < -4$

$\frac{2x}{2} < \frac{-4}{2}$ Divide both sides by 2. Do not reverse the inequality sign.

$x < -2$ Simplify.

The graph of the solutions is shown.

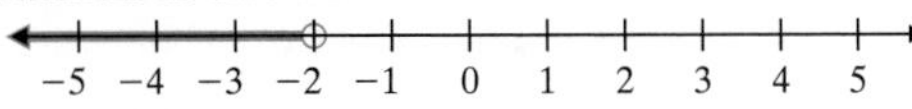

Work Practice 6

PRACTICE 6

Solve $5x > -20$. Graph the solutions.

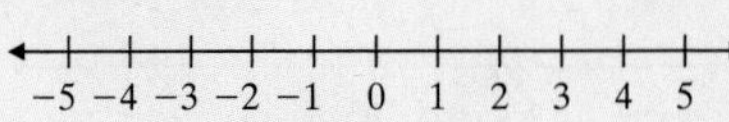

Since we cannot list all solutions to an inequality such as $x < -2$, we will use the set notation $\{x \mid x < -2\}$. Recall from Section 8.1 that this is read "the set of all x such that x is less than -2." We will use this notation when solving inequalities.

Objective D Using Both Properties of Inequality

The following steps may be helpful when solving inequalities in one variable. Notice that these steps are similar to the ones given in Section 9.3 for solving equations.

To Solve Linear Inequalities in One Variable

Step 1: If an inequality contains fractions, multiply both sides by the LCD to clear the inequality of fractions.

Step 2: Use the distributive property to remove parentheses if they appear.

Step 3: Simplify each side of the inequality by combining like terms.

Step 4: Get all variable terms on one side and all numbers on the other side by using the addition property of inequality.

Step 5: Get the variable alone by using the multiplication property of inequality.

Helpful Hint

Don't forget that if both sides of an inequality are multiplied or divided by a negative number, the direction of the inequality sign must be reversed.

Example 7 Solve $-4x + 7 \geq -9$. Graph the solution set.

Solution: $-4x + 7 \geq -9$

$-4x + 7 - 7 \geq -9 - 7$ Subtract 7 from both sides.

$-4x \geq -16$ Simplify.

$\frac{-4x}{-4} \leq \frac{-16}{-4}$ Divide both sides by -4 and reverse the direction of the inequality sign.

$x \leq 4$ Simplify.

The graph of the solution set $\{x \mid x \leq 4\}$ is shown.

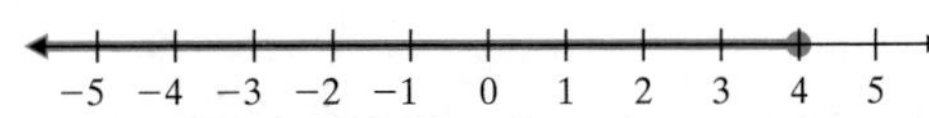

Work Practice 7

PRACTICE 7

Solve $-3x + 11 \leq -13$. Graph the solution set.

Answers

6. $x > -4$

7. $\{x \mid x \geq 8\}$

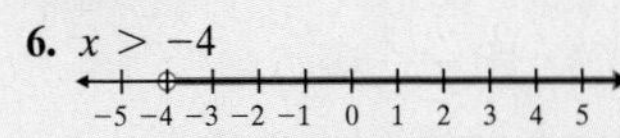

PRACTICE 8

Solve $2x - 3 > 4(x - 1)$. Graph the solution set.

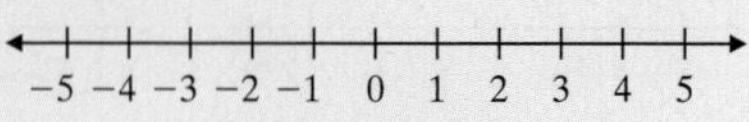

Example 8 Solve $-5x + 7 < 2(x - 3)$. Graph the solution set.

Solution: $-5x + 7 < 2(x - 3)$

$-5x + 7 < 2x - 6$ Apply the distributive property.

$-5x + 7 - 2x < 2x - 6 - 2x$ Subtract $2x$ from both sides.

$-7x + 7 < -6$ Combine like terms.

$-7x + 7 - 7 < -6 - 7$ Subtract 7 from both sides.

$-7x < -13$ Combine like terms.

$\frac{-7x}{-7} > \frac{-13}{-7}$ Divide both sides by -7 and reverse the direction of the inequality sign.

$x > \frac{13}{7}$ Simplify.

The graph of the solution set $\left\{x \mid x > \frac{13}{7}\right\}$ is shown.

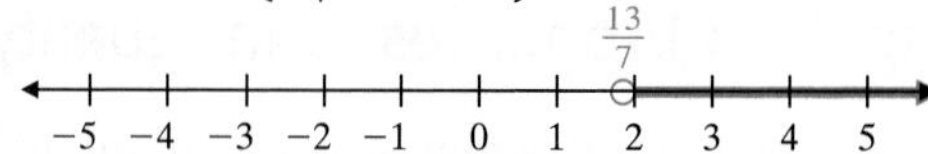

Work Practice 8

PRACTICE 9

Solve:

$3(x + 5) - 1 \geq 5(x - 1) + 7$

Example 9 Solve: $2(x - 3) - 5 \leq 3(x + 2) - 18$

Solution: $2(x - 3) - 5 \leq 3(x + 2) - 18$

$2x - 6 - 5 \leq 3x + 6 - 18$ Apply the distributive property.

$2x - 11 \leq 3x - 12$ Combine like terms.

$-x - 11 \leq -12$ Subtract $3x$ from both sides.

$-x \leq -1$ Add 11 to both sides.

$\frac{-x}{-1} \geq \frac{-1}{-1}$ Divide both sides by -1 and reverse the direction of the inequality sign.

$x \geq 1$ Simplify.

The solution set is $\{x \mid x \geq 1\}$.

Work Practice 9

Objective E Solving Problems Modeled by Inequalities

Problems containing words such as "at least," "at most," "between," "no more than," and "no less than" usually indicate that an inequality should be solved instead of an equation. In solving applications involving linear inequalities, we use the same procedure we used to solve applications involving linear equations.

Some Inequality Translations

≥	≤	<	>
at least	at most	is less than	is greater than
no less than	no more than		

PRACTICE 10

Twice a number, subtracted from 35, is greater than 15. Find all numbers that make this true.

Example 10 12 subtracted from 3 times a number is less than 21. Find all numbers that make this statement true.

Solution:

1. UNDERSTAND. Read and reread the problem. This is a direct translation problem, and let's let

$x =$ the unknown number

Answers

8. $\left\{x \mid x < \frac{1}{2}\right\}$

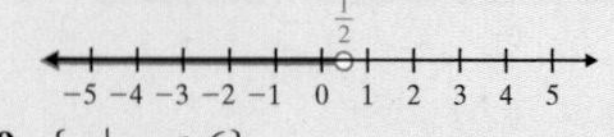

9. $\{x \mid x \leq 6\}$
10. all numbers less than 10

2. TRANSLATE.

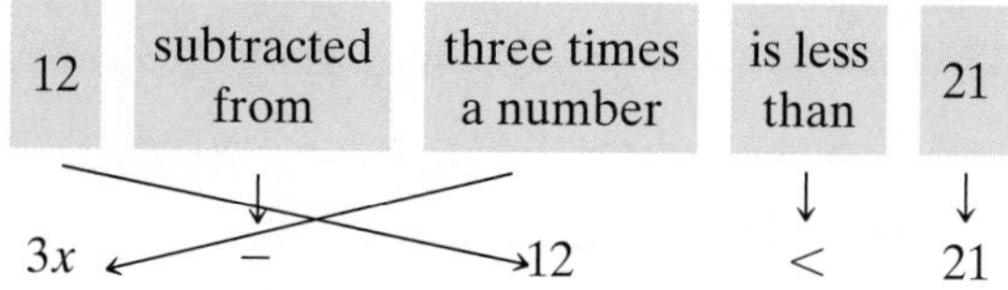
12
subtracted from
three times a number
is less than
21
3x
−
12
<
21

3. SOLVE. $3x - 12 < 21$

$3x < 33$ Add 12 to both sides.

$\frac{3x}{3} < \frac{33}{3}$ Divide both sides by 3 and do not reverse the direction of the inequality sign.

$x < 11$ Simplify.

4. INTERPRET.

Check: Check the translation; then let's choose a number less than 11 to see if it checks. For example, let's check 10. 12 subtracted from 3 times 10 is 12 subtracted from 30, or 18. Since 18 is less than 21, the number 10 checks.

State: All numbers less than 11 make the original statement true.

Work Practice 10

Example 11 Budgeting for a Wedding

Marie Chase and Jonathan Edwards are having their wedding reception at the Gallery reception hall. They may spend at most $1000 for the reception. If the reception hall charges a $100 cleanup fee plus $14 per person, find the greatest number of people that they can invite and still stay within their budget.

Solution:

1. UNDERSTAND. Read and reread the problem. Suppose that 50 people attend the reception. The cost is then $\$100 + \$14(50) = \$100 + \$700 = \$800$.

Let $x =$ the number of people who attend the reception.

2. TRANSLATE.

cleanup fee	+	cost per person	times	number of people	must be less than or equal to	$1000
↓		↓	↓	↓	↓	↓
100	+	14	·	x	≤	1000

3. SOLVE.

$100 + 14x \leq 1000$

$14x \leq 900$ Subtract 100 from both sides.

$x \leq 64\frac{2}{7}$ Divide both sides by 14.

4. INTERPRET.

Check: Since x represents the number of people, we round down to the nearest whole, or 64. Notice that if 64 people attend, the cost is $\$100 + \$14(64) = \$996$. If 65 people attend, the cost is $\$100 + \$14(65) = \$1010$, which is more than the given $1000.

State: Marie Chase and Jonathan Edwards can invite at most 64 people to the reception.

Work Practice 11

PRACTICE 11

Alex earns $600 per month plus 4% of all his sales. Find the minimum sales that will allow Alex to earn at least $3000 per month.

Answer

11. $60,000

Vocabulary and Readiness Check

Identify each as an equation, expression, or inequality.

1. $6x - 7(x + 9)$ __________

2. $6x = 7(x + 9)$ __________

3. $6x < 7(x + 9)$ __________

4. $5y - 2 \geq -38$ __________

5. $\frac{9}{7} = \frac{x + 2}{14}$ __________

6. $\frac{9}{7} - \frac{x + 2}{14}$ __________

Decide which number listed is not a solution to each given inequality.

7. $x \geq -3$; $-3, 0, -5, \pi$ __________

8. $x < 6$; $-6, |-6|, 0, -3.2$ __________

9. $x < 4.01$; $4, -4.01, 4.1, -4.1$ __________

10. $x \geq -3$; $-4, -3, -2, -(-2)$ __________

9.7 Exercise Set

FOR EXTRA HELP

MyMathLab

PRACTICE

WATCH

DOWNLOAD

READ

REVIEW

Objective **A** *Graph each inequality on the number line. See Examples 1 and 2.*

1. $x \leq -1$

−5 −4 −3 −2 −1 0 1 2 3 4 5

2. $y < 0$

−5 −4 −3 −2 −1 0 1 2 3 4 5

3. $x > \frac{1}{2}$

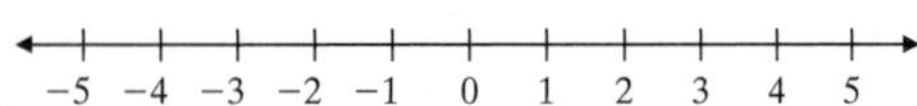

4. $z \geq -\frac{2}{3}$

−5 −4 −3 −2 −1 0 1 2 3 4 5

5. $y < 4$

−5 −4 −3 −2 −1 0 1 2 3 4 5

6. $x > 3$

−5 −4 −3 −2 −1 0 1 2 3 4 5

7. $-2 \leq m$

−5 −4 −3 −2 −1 0 1 2 3 4 5

8. $-5 \geq x$

−5 −4 −3 −2 −1 0 1 2 3 4 5

Graph each inequality on the number line. See Example 3.

9. $-1 < x < 3$

−5 −4 −3 −2 −1 0 1 2 3 4 5

10. $-2 \leq x \leq 3$

−5 −4 −3 −2 −1 0 1 2 3 4 5

11. $0 \leq y < 2$

−5 −4 −3 −2 −1 0 1 2 3 4 5

12. $-4 < x \leq 0$

−5 −4 −3 −2 −1 0 1 2 3 4 5

Objective **B** *Solve each inequality. Graph the solution set. Write each answer using solution set notation. See Example 4.*

13. $x - 2 \geq -7$

−5 −4 −3 −2 −1 0 1 2 3 4 5

14. $x + 4 \leq 1$

−5 −4 −3 −2 −1 0 1 2 3 4 5

15. $-9 + y < 0$

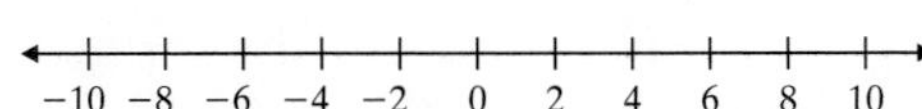

16. $-3 + m > 5$

−10 −8 −6 −4 −2 0 2 4 6 8 10

17. $3x - 5 > 2x - 8$

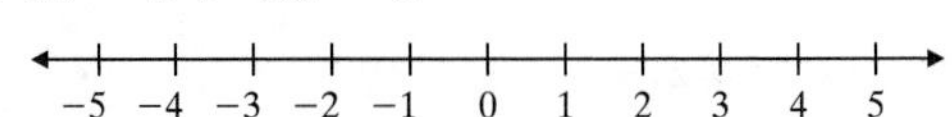

18. $3 - 7x \geq 10 - 8x$

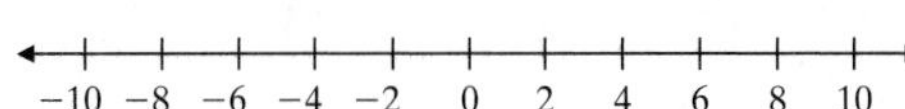

19. $4x - 1 \leq 5x - 2x$

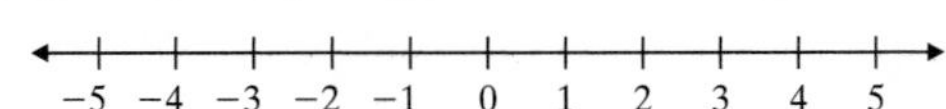

20. $7x + 3 < 9x - 3x$

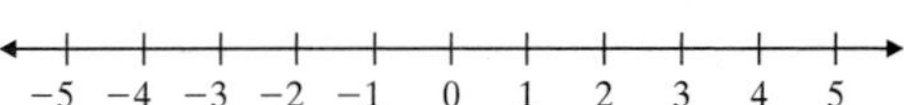

Objective **C** *Solve each inequality. Graph the solution set. See Examples 5 and 6.*

21. $2x < -6$

−5 −4 −3 −2 −1 0 1 2 3 4 5

22. $3x > -9$

−5 −4 −3 −2 −1 0 1 2 3 4 5

23. $-8x \leq 16$

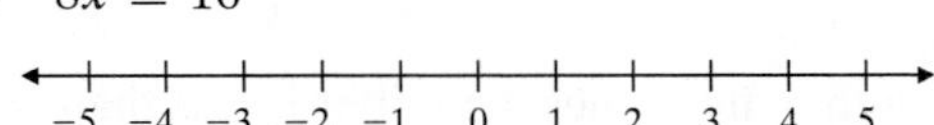

24. $-5x < 20$

−5 −4 −3 −2 −1 0 1 2 3 4 5

25. $-x > 0$

−5 −4 −3 −2 −1 0 1 2 3 4 5

26. $-y \geq 0$

−5 −4 −3 −2 −1 0 1 2 3 4 5

27. $\frac{3}{4}y \geq -2$

−5 −4 −3 −2 −1 0 1 2 3 4 5

28. $\frac{5}{6}x \leq -8$

−10 −8 −6 −4 −2 0 2 4 6 8 10

29. $-0.6y < -1.8$

−5 −4 −3 −2 −1 0 1 2 3 4 5

30. $-0.3x > -2.4$

−10 −8 −6 −4 −2 0 2 4 6 8 10

Objectives **B C D Mixed Practice** *Solve each inequality. Write each answer using solution set notation. See Examples 4 through 9.*

31. $-8 < x + 7$

32. $-11 > x + 4$

33. $7(x + 1) - 6x \geq -4$

34. $10(x + 2) - 9x \leq -1$

35. $4x > 1$

36. $6x < 5$

37. $-\frac{2}{3}y \leq 8$

38. $-\frac{3}{4}y \geq 9$

39. $4(2z + 1) < 4$

40. $6(2 - z) \geq 12$

41. $3x - 7 < 6x + 2$

42. $2x - 1 \geq 4x - 5$

43. $5x - 7x \leq x + 2$

44. $4 - x < 8x + 2x$

45. $-6x + 2 \geq 2(5 - x)$

46. $-7x + 4 > 3(4 - x)$

47. $3(x - 5) < 2(2x - 1)$

48. $5(x - 2) \leq 3(2x - 1)$

49. $4(3x - 1) \leq 5(2x - 4)$

50. $3(5x - 4) \leq 4(3x - 2)$

51. $3(x + 2) - 6 > -2(x - 3) + 14$

52. $7(x - 2) + x \leq -4(5 - x) - 12$

53. $-5(1 - x) + x \leq -(6 - 2x) + 6$

54. $-2(x - 4) - 3x < -(4x + 1) + 2x$

55. $\frac{1}{4}(x + 4) < \frac{1}{5}(2x + 3)$

56. $\frac{1}{2}(x - 5) < \frac{1}{3}(2x - 1)$

57. $-5x + 4 \leq -4(x - 1)$

58. $-6x + 2 < -3(x + 4)$

Objective **E** *Solve the following. For Exercises 61 and 62, the solutions have been started for you. See Examples 10 and 11.*

59. Six more than twice a number is greater than negative fourteen. Find all numbers that make this statement true.

60. One more than five times a number is less than or equal to ten. Find all such numbers.

△ **61.** The perimeter of a rectangle is to be no greater than 100 centimeters and the width must be 15 centimeters. Find the maximum length of the rectangle.

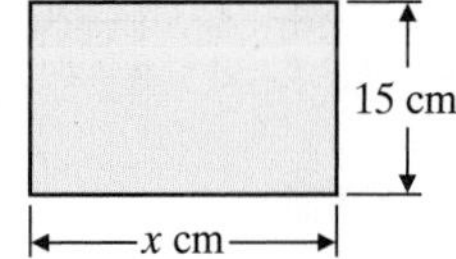

△ **62.** One side of a triangle is three times as long as another side, and the third side is 12 inches long. If the perimeter can be no longer than 32 inches, find the maximum lengths of the other two sides.

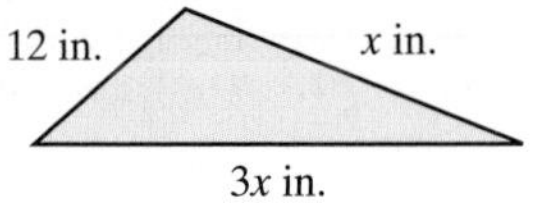

Start the solution:

1. UNDERSTAND the problem. Reread it as many times as needed.

2. TRANSLATE into an equation. (Fill in the blanks below.)

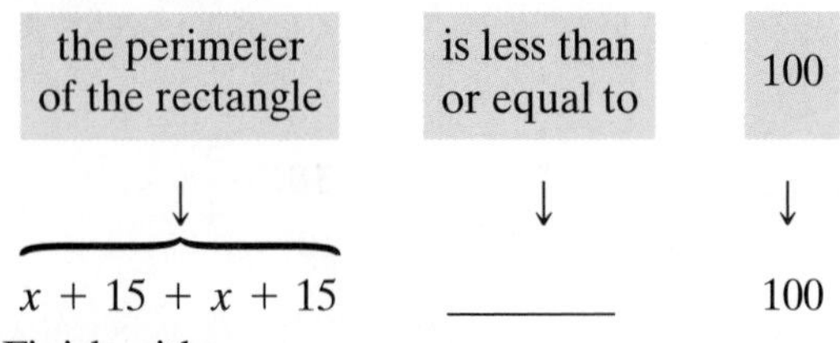

Finish with:

3. SOLVE and **4.** INTERPRET

Start the solution:

1. UNDERSTAND the problem. Reread it as many times as needed.

2. TRANSLATE into an equation. (Fill in the blanks below.)

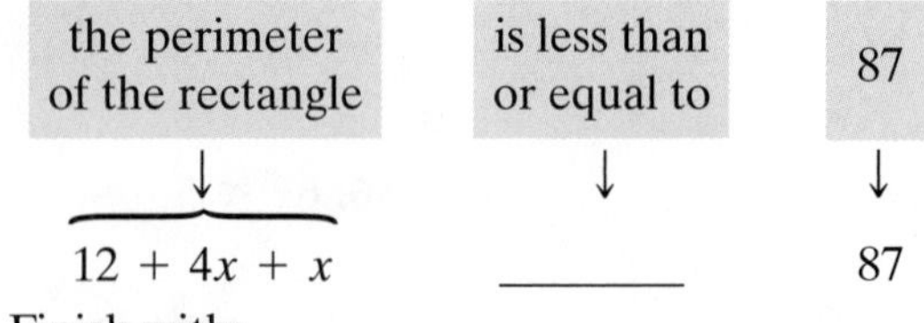

Finish with:

3. SOLVE and **4.** INTERPRET

63. Ben Holladay bowled 146 and 201 in his first two games. What must he bowl in his third game to have an average of at least 180? (*Hint:* The average of a list of numbers is their sum divided by the number of numbers in the list.)

64. On an NBA team the two forwards measure 6′8″ and 6′6″ tall and the two guards measure 6′0″ and 5′9″ tall. How tall should the center be if they wish to have a starting team average height of at least 6′5″?

65. Dennis and Nancy Wood are celebrating their 30th wedding anniversary by having a reception at Tiffany Oaks reception hall. They have budgeted $3000 for their reception. If the reception hall charges a $50.00 cleanup fee plus $34 per person, find the greatest number of people that they may invite and still stay within their budget.

66. A surprise retirement party is being planned for Pratap Puri. A total of $860 has been collected for the event, which is to be held at a local reception hall. This reception hall charges a cleanup fee of $40 and $15 per person for drinks and light snacks. Find the greatest number of people that may be invited and still stay within the $860 budget.

67. A 150-pound person uses 5.8 calories per minute when walking at a speed of 4 mph. How long must a person walk at this speed to use at least 200 calories? Round up to the nearest minute. (*Source:* Home & Garden Bulletin No. 72)

68. A 170-pound person uses 5.3 calories per minute when bicycling at a speed of 5.5 mph. How long must a person ride a bike at this speed in order to use at least 200 calories? Round up to the nearest minute. (*Source:* Same as Exercise 67)

Review

Evaluate each expression. See Section 8.2.

69. 3^4 **70.** 4^3 **71.** 1^8 **72.** 0^7 **73.** $\left(\frac{7}{8}\right)^2$ **74.** $\left(\frac{2}{3}\right)^3$

The graph shows the number of U.S. Starbucks locations from 2002 to 2008. The height of the graph for each year shown corresponds to the number of Starbucks locations in the United States. Use this graph to answer Exercises 75 through 80. (We study graphs such as this further in Section 6.1.)

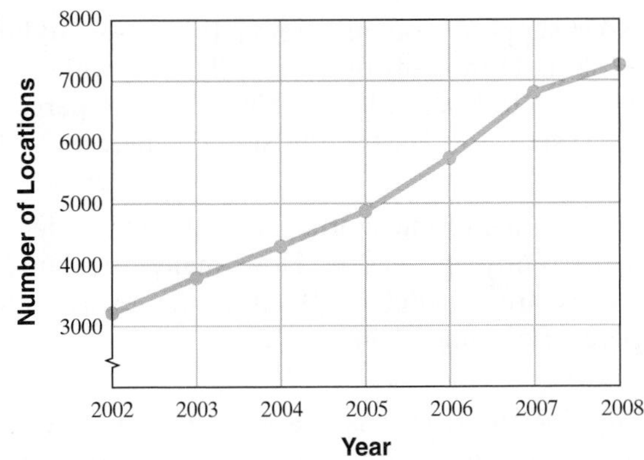

75. How many Starbucks locations were there in 2002?

76. How many Starbucks locations were there in 2007?

77. Between which two years did the greatest increase in the number of Starbucks locations occur?

78. In what year were there approximately 4900 Starbucks locations?

79. During which year did the number of Starbucks locations rise above 5000?

80. During which year did the number of Starbucks locations rise above 6000?

Concept Extensions

Fill in the box with $<, >, \leq,$ or $\geq$. See the Concept Check in this section.

81. Since $3 < 5$, then $3(-4) \square 5(-4)$.

82. If $m \leq n$, then $2m \square 2n$.

83. If $m \leq n$, then $-2m \square -2n$.

84. If $-x < y$, then $x \square -y$.

85. When solving an inequality, when must you reverse the direction of the inequality symbol?

86. If both sides of the inequality $-3x < -30$ are divided by 3, do you reverse the direction of the inequality symbol? Why or why not?

Solve.

87. Eric Daly has scores of 75, 83, and 85 on his history tests. Use an inequality to find the scores he can make on his final exam to receive a B in the class. The final exam counts as **two** tests, and a B is received if the final course average is greater than or equal to 80.

88. Maria Lipco has scores of 85, 95, and 92 on her algebra tests. Use an inequality to find the scores she can make on her final exam to receive an A in the course. The final exam counts as **three** tests, and an A is received if the final course average is greater than or equal to 90. Round to one decimal place.

Chapter 9 Group Activity

Investigating Averages

Sections 9.1–9.6

Materials:

- small rubber ball or crumpled paper ball
- bucket or waste can

This activity may be completed by working in groups or individually.

1. Try shooting the ball into the bucket or waste can 5 times. Record your results below.

Shots Made **Shots Missed**

2. Find your shooting percent for the 5 shots (that is, the percent of the shots you actually made out of the number you tried).

3. Suppose you are going to try an additional 5 shots. How many of the next 5 shots will you have to make to have a 50% shooting percent for all 10 shots? An 80% shooting percent?

4. Did you solve an equation in Question 3? If so, explain what you did. If not, explain how you could use an equation to find the answers.

5. Now suppose you are going to try an additional 22 shots. How many of the next 22 shots will you have to make to have at least a 50% shooting percent for all 27 shots? At least a 70% shooting percent?

6. Choose one of the sports played at your college that is currently in season. How many regular-season games are scheduled? What is the team's current percent of games won?

7. Suppose the team has a goal of finishing the season with a winning percent better than 110% of their current wins. At least how many of the remaining games must they win to achieve their goal?

Chapter 9 Vocabulary Check

Fill in each blank with one of the words or phrases listed below.

no solution	all real numbers	linear equation in one variable
equivalent equations	formula	reversed
linear inequality in one variable	the same	

1. A(n) ____________________ can be written in the form $ax + b = c$.
2. Equations that have the same solution are called ____________________.
3. An equation that describes a known relationship among quantities is called a(n) ____________________.
4. A(n) ____________________ can be written in the form $ax + b < c$, (or $>$, $\leq$, $\geq$).
5. The solution(s) to the equation $x + 5 = x + 5$ is/are ____________________.
6. The solution(s) to the equation $x + 5 = x + 4$ is/are ____________________.
7. If both sides of an inequality are multiplied or divided by the same positive number, the direction of the inequality symbol is ____________________.
8. If both sides of an inequality are multiplied by the same negative number, the direction of the inequality symbol is ____________________.

Helpful Hint Are you preparing for your test? Don't forget to take the Chapter 9 Test on page 579. Then check your answers at the back of the text and use the Chapter Test Prep Videos to see the fully worked-out solutions to any of the exercises you want to review.

9 Chapter Highlights

Definitions and Concepts	**Examples**
Section 9.1 The Addition Property of Equality	
A **linear equation in one variable** can be written in the form $Ax + B = C$ where A, B, and C are real numbers and $A \neq 0$.	$-3x + 7 = 2$ $3(x - 1) = -8(x + 5) + 4$
Equivalent equations are equations that have the same solution.	$x - 7 = 10$ and $x = 17$ are equivalent equations.
Addition Property of Equality Adding the same number to or subtracting the same number from both sides of an equation does not change its solution.	$y + 9 = 3$ $y + 9 - 9 = 3 - 9$ $y = -6$
Section 9.2 The Multiplication Property of Equality	
Multiplication Property of Equality Multiplying both sides or dividing both sides of an equation by the same nonzero number does not change its solution.	$\frac{2}{3}a = 18$ $\frac{3}{2}\left(\frac{2}{3}a\right) = \frac{3}{2}(18)$ $a = 27$

Definitions and Concepts	Examples
Section 9.3 Further Solving Linear Equations	
To Solve Linear Equations	*Solve:* $\frac{5(-2x+9)}{6} + 3 = \frac{1}{2}$
1. Clear the equation of fractions.	**1.** $6 \cdot \frac{5(-2x+9)}{6} + 6 \cdot 3 = 6 \cdot \frac{1}{2}$
2. Remove any grouping symbols such as parentheses.	**2.** $5(-2x+9) + 18 = 3$ Apply the distributive property. $-10x + 45 + 18 = 3$
3. Simplify each side by combining like terms.	**3.** $-10x + 63 = 3$ Combine like terms.
4. Get all variable terms on one side and all numbers on the other side by using the addition property of equality.	**4.** $-10x + 63 - 63 = 3 - 63$ Subtract 63. $-10x = -60$
5. Get the variable alone by using the multiplication property of equality.	**5.** $\frac{-10x}{-10} = \frac{-60}{-10}$ Divide by -10. $x = 6$
6. Check the solution by substituting it into the original equation.	
Section 9.4 An Introduction to Problem Solving	
Problem-Solving Steps	The height of the Hudson volcano in Chile is twice the height of the Kiska volcano in the Aleutian Islands. If the sum of their heights is 12,870 feet, find the height of each.
1. UNDERSTAND the problem.	**1.** Read and reread the problem. Guess a solution and check your guess. Let x be the height of the Kiska volcano. Then $2x$ is the height of the Hudson volcano. 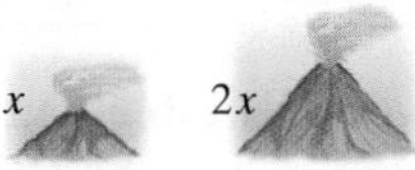
2. TRANSLATE the problem.	**2.** height of Kiska ↓ x · added to ↓ $+$ · height of Hudson ↓ $2x$ · is ↓ $=$ · 12,870 ↓ 12,870
3. SOLVE the equation.	**3.** $x + 2x = 12{,}870$ $3x = 12{,}870$ $x = 4290$
4. INTERPRET the results.	**4.** *Check:* If x is 4290, then $2x$ is 2(4290) or 8580. Their sum is 4290 + 8580 or 12,870, the required amount. *State:* The Kiska volcano is 4290 feet tall, and the Hudson volcano is 8580 feet tall.

Definitions and Concepts	Examples
Section 9.5 Formulas and Problem Solving	
An equation that describes a known relationship among quantities is called a **formula.**	$A = lw$ (area of a rectangle) $I = PRT$ (simple interest)
To solve a formula for a specified variable, use the same steps as for solving a linear equation. Treat the specified variable as the only variable of the equation.	*Solve:* $P = 2l + 2w$ for l. $P = 2l + 2w$ $P - 2w = 2l + 2w - 2w$ Subtract $2w$. $P - 2w = 2l$ $\frac{P - 2w}{2} = \frac{2l}{2}$ Divide by 2. $\frac{P - 2w}{2} = l$
Section 9.6 Percent and Mixture Problem Solving	
Use the same problem-solving steps to solve a problem containing percents.	32% of what number is 36.8?
1. UNDERSTAND.	**1.** Read and reread. Propose a solution and check. Let $x =$ the unknown number.
2. TRANSLATE.	**2.** 32% of what number is 36.8 ↓ ↓ ↓ ↓ ↓ $32\% \cdot x = 36.8$
3. SOLVE.	**3.** *Solve:* $32\% \cdot x = 36.8$ $0.32x = 36.8$ $\frac{0.32x}{0.32} = \frac{36.8}{0.32}$ Divide by 0.32. $x = 115$ Simplify.
4. INTERPRET.	**4.** *Check, then state:* 32% of 115 is 36.8.
	How many liters of a 20% acid solution must be mixed with a 50% acid solution in order to obtain 12 liters of a 30% solution?
1. UNDERSTAND.	**1.** Read and reread. Guess a solution and check. Let $x =$ number of liters of 20% solution. Then $12 - x =$ number of liters of 50% solution.
2. TRANSLATE.	**2.** (see table below)

	No. of Liters	· Acid Strength	= Amount of Acid
20% Solution	x	20%	$0.20x$
50% Solution	$12 - x$	50%	$0.50(12 - x)$
30% Solution Needed	12	30%	$0.30(12)$

In words: acid in 20% solution + acid in 50% solution = acid in 30% solution

Translate: $0.20x + 0.50(12 - x) = 0.30(12)$

(continued)

Definitions and Concepts	Examples
Section 9.6 Percent and Mixture Problem Solving (*continued*)	
3. SOLVE.	**3.** *Solve:* $0.20x + 0.50(12 - x) = 0.30(12)$ $0.20x + 6 - 0.50x = 3.6$ Apply the distributive property. $-0.30x + 6 = 3.6$ Combine like terms. $-0.30x = -2.4$ Subtract 6. $x = 8$ Divide by -0.30.
4. INTERPRET.	**4.** *Check, then state:* If 8 liters of a 20% acid solution are mixed with $12 - 8$ or 4 liters of a 50% acid solution, the result is 12 liters of a 30% solution.
Section 9.7 Linear Inequalities and Problem Solving	
Properties of inequalities are similar to properties of equations. However, if you multiply or divide both sides of an inequality by the same *negative* number, you must reverse the direction of the inequality symbol.	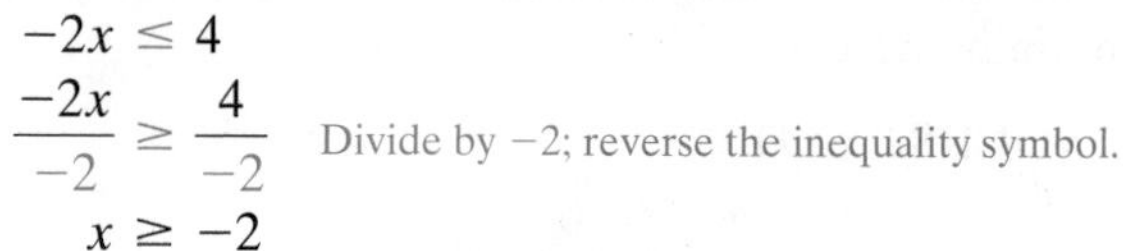 $-2x \le 4$ $\frac{-2x}{-2} \ge \frac{4}{-2}$ Divide by -2; reverse the inequality symbol. $x \ge -2$ 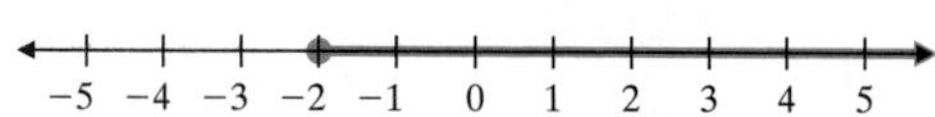
To Solve Linear Inequalities **1.** Clear the inequality of fractions. **2.** Remove grouping symbols. **3.** Simplify each side by combining like terms. **4.** Write all variable terms on one side and all numbers on the other side using the addition property of inequality. **5.** Get the variable alone by using the multiplication property of inequality.	*Solve:* $3(x + 2) \le -2 + 8$ **1.** $3(x + 2) \le -2 + 8$ No fractions to clear. **2.** $3x + 6 \le -2 + 8$ Apply the distributive property. **3.** $3x + 6 \le 6$ Combine like terms. **4.** $3x + 6 - 6 \le 6 - 6$ Subtract 6. $3x \le 0$ **5.** $\frac{3x}{3} \le \frac{0}{3}$ Divide by 3. $x \le 0$ The solution set is $\{x \mid x \le 0\}$. 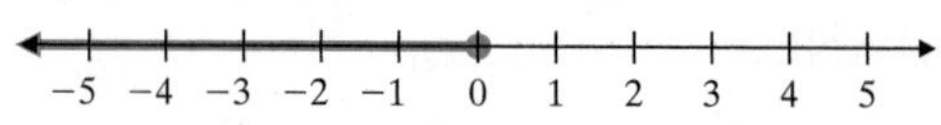

Chapter 9 Review

(9.1) *Solve each equation.*

1. $8x + 4 = 9x$

2. $5y - 3 = 6y$

3. $\frac{2}{7}x + \frac{5}{7}x = 6$

4. $3x - 5 = 4x + 1$

5. $2x - 6 = x - 6$

6. $4(x + 3) = 3(1 + x)$

7. $6(3 + n) = 5(n - 1)$

8. $5(2 + x) - 3(3x + 2) = -5(x - 6) + 2$

Choose the correct algebraic expression.

9. The sum of two numbers is 10. If one number is x, express the other number in terms of x.

a. $x - 10$
b. $10 - x$
c. $10 + x$
d. $10x$

10. Mandy is 5 inches taller than Melissa. If x inches represents the height of Mandy, express Melissa's height in terms of x.

a. $x - 5$
b. $5 - x$
c. $5 + x$
d. $5x$

△ **11.** If one angle measures $x°$, express the measure of its complement in terms of x.

a. $(180 - x)°$
b. $(90 - x)°$
c. $(x - 180)°$
d. $(x - 90)°$

△ **12.** If one angle measures $(x + 5)°$, express the measure of its supplement in terms of x.

a. $(185 + x)°$
b. $(95 + x)°$
c. $(175 - x)°$
d. $(x - 170)°$

(x + 5)°
?

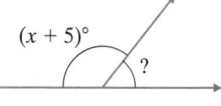

(9.2) *Solve each equation.*

13. $\frac{3}{4}x = -9$

14. $\frac{x}{6} = \frac{2}{3}$

15. $-5x = 0$

16. $-y = 7$

17. $0.2x = 0.15$

18. $\frac{-x}{3} = 1$

19. $-3x + 1 = 19$

20. $5x + 25 = 20$

21. $7(x - 1) + 9 = 5x$

22. $7x - 6 = 5x - 3$

23. $-5x + \frac{3}{7} = \frac{10}{7}$

24. $5x + x = 9 + 4x - 1 + 6$

25. Write the sum of three consecutive integers as an expression in x. Let x be the first integer.

26. Write the sum of the first and fourth of four consecutive even integers. Let x be the first even integer.

(9.3) *Solve each equation.*

27. $\frac{5}{3}x + 4 = \frac{2}{3}x$

28. $\frac{7}{8}x + 1 = \frac{5}{8}x$

29. $-(5x + 1) = -7x + 3$

30. $-4(2x + 1) = -5x + 5$

31. $-6(2x - 5) = -3(9 + 4x)$

32. $3(8y - 1) = 6(5 + 4y)$

33. $\frac{3(2 - z)}{5} = z$

34. $\frac{4(n + 2)}{5} = -n$

35. $0.5(2n - 3) - 0.1 = 0.4(6 + 2n)$

36. $-9 - 5a = 3(6a - 1)$

37. $\frac{5(c + 1)}{6} = 2c - 3$

38. $\frac{2(8 - a)}{3} = 4 - 4a$

39. $200(70x - 3560) = -179(150x - 19{,}300)$

40. $1.72y - 0.04y = 0.42$

(9.4) *Solve each of the following.*

41. The height of the Washington Monument is 50.5 inches more than 10 times the length of a side of its square base. If the sum of these two dimensions is 7327 inches, find the height of the Washington Monument. (*Source:* National Park Service)

42. A 12-foot board is to be divided into two pieces so that one piece is twice as long as the other. If x represents the length of the shorter piece, find the length of each piece.

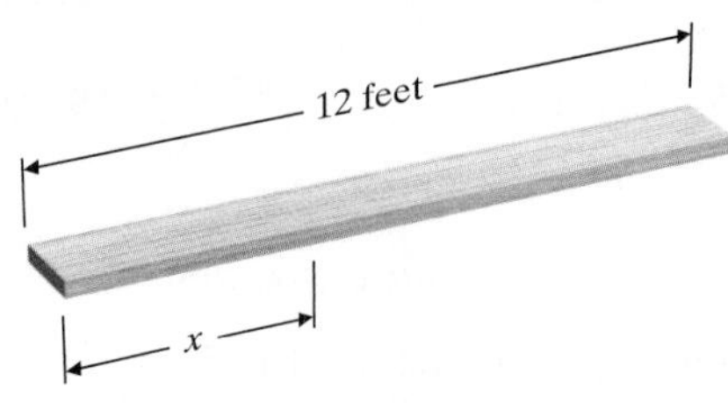

43. The Harvard University library system and the Cornell University library system consist of a total of 119 different library sites. The number of Harvard libraries is two more than twice the number of Cornell libraries. How many libraries does each university support? (*Source*: Harvard University, Cornell University)

44. Find three consecutive integers whose sum is -114.

45. The quotient of a number and 3 is the same as the difference of the number and two. Find the number.

46. Double the sum of a number and 6 is the opposite of the number. Find the number.

(9.5) *Substitute the given values into the given formulas and solve for the unknown variable.*

47. $P = 2l + 2w$; $P = 46, l = 14$

48. $V = lwh$; $V = 192, l = 8, w = 6$

Solve each equation for the indicated variable or constant.

49. $y = mx + b$ for m

50. $r = vst - 5$ for s

51. $2y - 5x = 7$ for x

52. $3x - 6y = -2$ for y

△ **53.** $C = \pi D$ for π

△ **54.** $C = 2\pi r$ for π

△ **55.** A swimming pool holds 900 cubic meters of water. If its length is 20 meters and its height is 3 meters, find its width.

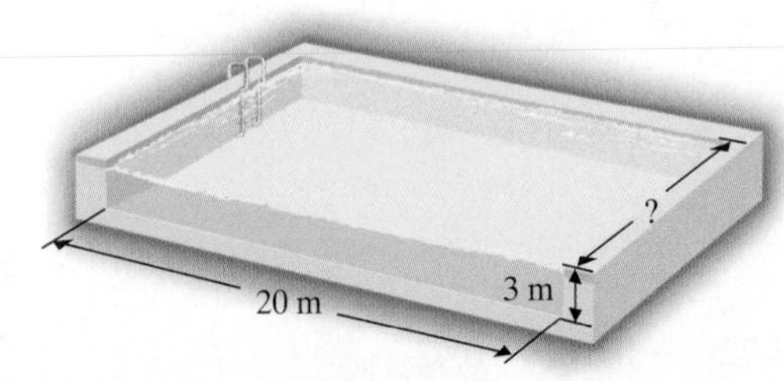

56. The perimeter of a rectangular billboard is 60 feet and the billboard has a length 6 feet longer than its width. Find the dimensions of the billboard.

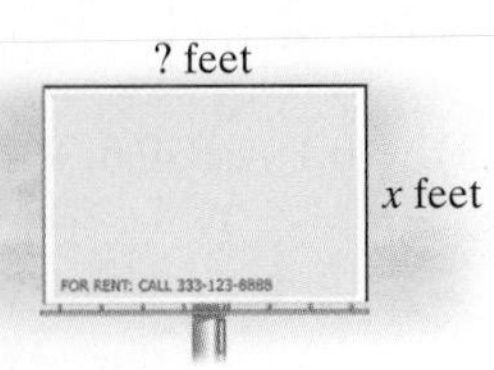

57. A charity 10K race is given annually to benefit a local hospice organization. How long will it take to run/walk a 10K race (10 kilometers or 10,000 meters) if your average pace is 125 **meters** per minute? Give your time in hours and minutes.

58. On April 28, 2001, the highest temperature recorded in the United States was 104°F, which occurred in Death Valley, California. Convert this temperature to degrees Celsius. (*Source:* National Weather Service)

(9.6) *Find each of the following.*

59. The number 9 is what percent of 45?

60. The number 59.5 is what percent of 85?

61. The number 137.5 is 125% of what number?

62. The number 768 is 60% of what number?

63. The price of a small diamond ring was recently increased by 11%. If the ring originally cost \$1900, find the mark-up and the new price of the ring.

64. A recent survey found that 66.9% of Americans use the Internet. If a city has a population of 76,000 how many people in that city would you expect to use the Internet? (*Source:* UCLA Center for Communication Policy)

65. Thirty gallons of a 20% acid solution are needed for an experiment. Only 40% and 10% acid solutions are available. How much of each should be mixed to form the needed solution?

66. The ACT Assessment is a college entrance exam taken by about 60% of college-bound students. The national average was 20.7 in 1993 and rose to 21.1 in 2008. Find the percent increase. (Round to the nearest tenth of a percent.)

The graph below shows the percent(s) of cell phone users who have engaged in various behaviors while driving and talking on their cell phones. Use this graph to answer Exercises 67 through 70.

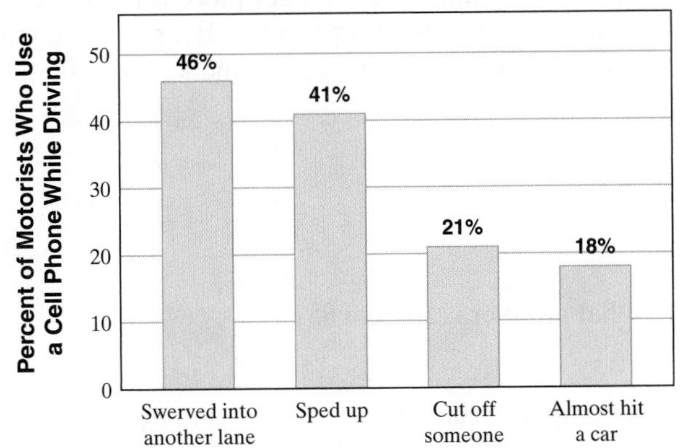

Source: Progressive Insurance

67. What percent of motorists who use a cell phone while driving have almost hit another car?

68. What is the most common effect of cell phone use on driving?

69. If a cell phone service has an estimated 4600 customers who use their cell phones while driving, how many of these customers would you expect to have cut someone off while driving and talking on their cell phones?

70. Do the percents in the graph to the left have a sum of 100%? Why or why not?

(9.7) *Graph on a number line.*

71. $x \leq -2$

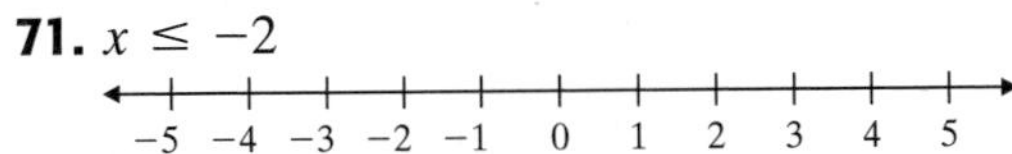

72. $0 < x \leq 5$

−5 −4 −3 −2 −1 0 1 2 3 4 5

Solve each inequality.

73. $x - 5 \leq -4$

74. $x + 7 > 2$

75. $-2x \geq -20$

76. $-3x > 12$

77. $5x - 7 > 8x + 5$

78. $x + 4 \geq 6x - 16$

79. $\frac{2}{3}y > 6$

80. $-0.5y \leq 7.5$

81. $-2(x - 5) > 2(3x - 2)$

82. $4(2x - 5) \leq 5x - 1$

83. Carol Abolafia earns \$175 per week plus a 5% commission on all her sales. Find the minimum amount of sales she must make to ensure that she earns at least \$300 per week.

84. Joseph Barrow shot rounds of 76, 82, and 79 golfing. What must he shoot on his next round so that his average will be below 80?

Mixed Review

Solve each equation.

85. $6x + 2x - 1 = 5x + 11$

86. $2(3y - 4) = 6 + 7y$

87. $4(3 - a) - (6a + 9) = -12a$

88. $\frac{x}{3} - 2 = 5$

89. $2(y + 5) = 2y + 10$

90. $7x - 3x + 2 = 2(2x - 1)$

Solve.

91. The sum of six and twice a number is equal to seven less than the number. Find the number.

92. A 23-inch piece of string is to be cut into two pieces so that the length of the longer piece is three more than four times the shorter piece. If x represents the length of the shorter piece, find the lengths of both pieces.

Solve for the specified variable.

93. $V = \frac{1}{3}Ah$ for h

94. What number is 26% of 85?

95. The number 72 is 45% of what number?

96. A company recently increased its number of employees from 235 to 282. Find the percent increase.

Solve each inequality. Graph the solution set.

97. $4x - 7 > 3x + 2$

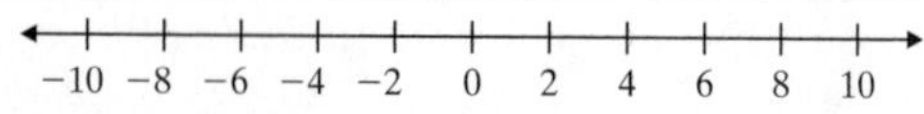

98. $-5x < 20$

−5 −4 −3 −2 −1 0 1 2 3 4 5

99. $-3(1 + 2x) + x \geq -(3 - x)$

−5 −4 −3 −2 −1 0 1 2 3 4 5

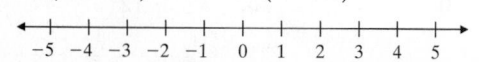

Chapter 9 Test

Step-by-step test solutions are found on the Chapter Test Prep Videos available via the Interactive DVD Lecture Series, in MyMathLab or on YouTube (search "MartinGayIntroAlg" and click on "Channels").

Solve each equation.

1. $-\frac{4}{5}x = 4$

2. $4(n - 5) = -(4 - 2n)$

3. $5y - 7 + y = -(y + 3y)$

4. $4z + 1 - z = 1 + z$

5. $\frac{2(x + 6)}{3} = x - 5$

6. $\frac{4(y - 1)}{5} = 2y + 3$

7. $\frac{1}{2} - x + \frac{3}{2} = x - 4$

8. $\frac{1}{3}(y + 3) = 4y$

9. $-0.3(x - 4) + x = 0.5(3 - x)$

10. $-4(a + 1) - 3a = -7(2a - 3)$

11. $-2(x - 3) = x + 5 - 3x$

Solve each application.

12. A number increased by two-thirds of the number is 35. Find the number.

△ 13. A gallon of water seal covers 200 square feet. How many gallons are needed to paint two coats of water seal on a deck that measures 20 feet by 35 feet?

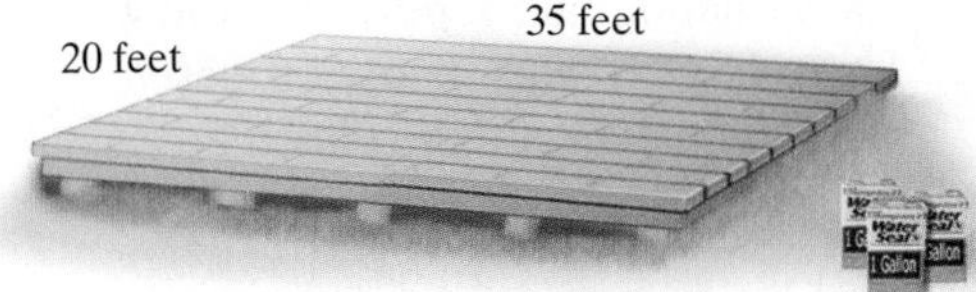

14. Find the value of x if $y = -14$, $m = -2$, and $b = -2$ in the formula $y = mx + b$.

Solve each equation for the indicated variable.

15. $V = \pi r^2 h$ for h

16. $3x - 4y = 10$ for y

Answers

1. ____

2. ____

3. ____

4. ____

5. ____

6. ____

7. ____

8. ____

9. ____

10. ____

11. ____

12. ____

13. ____

14. ____

15. ____

16. ____

17. ______

Solve each inequality. Graph the solution set.

17. $3x - 5 \geq 7x + 3$

−5 −4 −3 −2 −1 0 1 2 3 4 5

18. $x + 6 > 4x - 6$

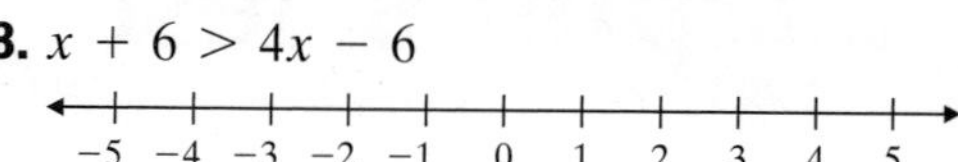

18. ______

Solve each inequality.

19. $-0.3x \geq 2.4$

20. $-5(x - 1) + 6 \leq -3(x + 4) + 1$

19. ______

21. $\dfrac{2(5x + 1)}{3} > 2$

The following graph shows the breakdown of tornadoes occurring in the United States by strength. The corresponding Fujita Tornado Scale categories are shown in parentheses. Use this graph to answer Exercise 22.

20. ______

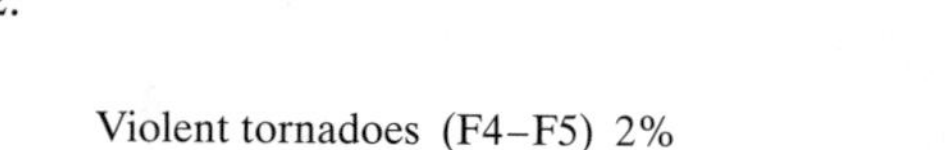

21. ______

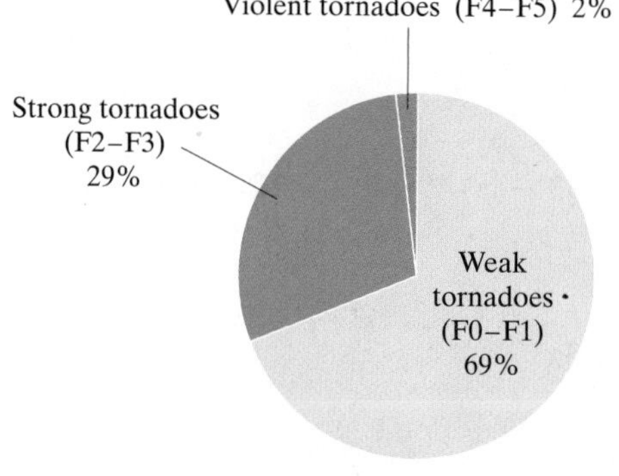

Source: National Climatic Data Center

22. ______

22. According to the National Climatic Data Center, in an average year, about 800 tornadoes are reported in the United States. How many of these would you expect to be classified as "weak" tornadoes?

23. The number 72 is what percent of 180?

23. ______

24. Some states have a single area code for the entire state. Two such states have area codes where one is double the other. If the sum of these integers is 1203, find the two area codes.

25. New York State has more public libraries than any other state. It has 696 more public libraries than Georgia does. If the total number of public libraries for these states is 812, find the number of public libraries in New York and the number in Georgia. (*Source: The World Almanac and Book of Facts*)

24. ______

25. ______

Cumulative Review Chapters 8–9

Determine whether each statement is true or false.

1. $8 \geq 8$

2. $-4 < -6$

3. $8 \leq 8$

4. $3 > -3$

5. $23 \leq 0$

6. $-8 \geq -8$

7. $0 \leq 23$

8. $-8 \leq -8$

9. Insert $<$, $>$, or $=$ in the appropriate space to make each statement true.

a. $|0| \quad 2$

b. $|-5| \quad 5$

c. $|-3| \quad |-2|$

d. $|-9| \quad |-9.7|$

e. $\left|-7\frac{1}{6}\right| \quad |7|$

10. Find the absolute value of each number.

a. $|5|$

b. $|-8|$

c. $\left|-\frac{2}{3}\right|$

Simplify.

11. $\dfrac{3 + |4 - 3| + 2^2}{6 - 3}$

12. $1 + 2(9 - 7)^3 + 4^2$

Add without using number lines.

13. $(-8) + (-11)$

14. $-2 + (-8)$

15. $(-2) + 10$

16. $-10 + 20$

17. $0.2 + (-0.5)$

18. $1.2 + (-1.2)$

Answers

1. ______
2. ______
3. ______
4. ______
5. ______
6. ______
7. ______
8. ______
9. a. ______
   b. ______
   c. ______
   d. ______
   e. ______
10. a. ______
    b. ______
    c. ______
11. ______
12. ______
13. ______
14. ______
15. ______
16. ______
17. ______
18. ______

19. a. ______
b. ______
20. a. ______
b. ______
c. ______
d. ______
21. a. ______
b. ______
c. ______
22. a. ______
b. ______
c. ______
23. a. ______
b. ______
c. ______
24. a. ______
b. ______
25. ______
26. ______
27. ______
28. ______
29. a. ______
b. ______
c. ______
d. ______
e. ______

19. Simplify each expression.

a. $-3 + [(-2 - 5) - 2]$

b. $2^3 - 10 + [-6 - (-5)]$

20. Simplify each expression.

a. $-(-5)$

b. $-\left(-\frac{2}{3}\right)$

c. $-(-a)$

d. $-|-3|$

21. Multiply.

a. $7(0)(-6)$

b. $(-2)(-3)(-4)$

c. $(-1)(-5)(-9)(-2)$

22. Subtract.

a. $-2.7 - 8.4$

b. $-\frac{4}{5} - \left(-\frac{3}{5}\right)$

c. $\frac{1}{4} - \left(-\frac{1}{2}\right)$

23. Use the definition of the quotient of two numbers to find each quotient.

a. $-18 \div 3$

b. $\frac{-14}{-2}$

c. $\frac{20}{-4}$

24. Find each product.

a. $(4.5)(-0.08)$

b. $-\frac{3}{4} \cdot -\frac{8}{17}$

Use the distributive property to write each expression without parentheses. Then simplify the result.

25. $-5(-3 + 2z)$

26. $2(x^2 - 3x + 4)$

27. $\frac{1}{2}(6x + 14) + 10$

28. $-(x + 4) + 3(x + 4)$

29. Determine whether the terms are like or unlike.

a. $2x, 3x^2$

b. $4x^2y, x^2y, -2x^2y$

c. $-2yz, -3zy$

d. $-x^4, x^4$

e. $-8a^5, 8a^5$

30. Find each quotient.

a. $\frac{-32}{8}$ **b.** $\frac{-108}{-12}$

c. $-\frac{5}{7} \div \left(-\frac{9}{2}\right)$

31. Subtract $4x - 2$ from $2x - 3$.

32. Subtract $10x + 3$ from $-5x + 1$.

33. Solve: $x - 7 = 10$

Solve.

34. $\frac{5}{6} + x = \frac{2}{3}$

35. $-z - 4 = 6$

36. $-3x + 1 - (-4x - 6) = 10$

37. $\frac{2(a + 3)}{3} = 6a + 2$

38. $\frac{x}{4} = 18$

39. The 111th Congress, which began at noon on January 3, 2009, had a total of 434 Democrats and Republicans. There were 78 more Democratic representatives than Republican. Find the number of representatives from each party. (*Source: New York Times*)

40. $6x + 5 = 4(x + 4) - 1$

41. A glacier is a giant mass of rocks and ice that flows downhill like a river. Portage Glacier in Alaska is about 6 miles, or 31,680 feet, long and moves 400 feet per year. Icebergs are created when the front end of the glacier flows into Portage Lake. How long does it take for ice at the head (beginning) of the glacier to reach the lake?

42. A number increased by 4 is the same as 3 times the number decreased by 8. Find the number.

43. The number 63 is what percent of 72?

44. Solve: $C = 2\pi r$ for r.

45. Solve: $5(2x + 3) = -1 + 7$

46. Solve: $x - 3 > 2$

47. Graph $-1 > x$.

−5 −4 −3 −2 −1 0 1 2 3 4 5

48. Solve: $3x - 4 \leq 2x - 14$

49. Solve: $2(x - 3) - 5 \leq 3(x + 2) - 18$

50. Solve: $-3x \geq 9$

30. a. ______

b. ______

c. ______

31. ______

32. ______

33. ______

34. ______

35. ______

36. ______

37. ______

38. ______

39. ______

40. ______

41. ______

42. ______

43. ______

44. ______

45. ______

46. ______

47. ______

48. ______

49. ______

50. ______

10 Exponents and Polynomials

Sections

Recall from Chapter 8 that an exponent is a shorthand notation for repeated factors. This chapter explores additional concepts about exponents and exponential expressions. An especially useful type of exponential expression is a polynomial. Polynomials model many real-world phenomena. Our goal in this chapter is to become proficient with operations on polynomials.

According to a recent survey, the average American adult owns 2.4 cell phones, and over 56% of those surveyed still have their old cell phones. In fact, it is estimated that 130 million cell phones will be retired this year. With new cell phone models having new features and increased technologies, this number of retired cell phones will probably only increase. The good news is that the number of cell phones being recycled is increasing. Below is a graph showing the growth of cell phones recycled by the largest recycler. (*Source:* Recycling for Charities) In Exercises 25 and 26 of Section 10.3, you will explore some information about the growth of wireless technology.

Cell Phones Recycled by Largest Recycler

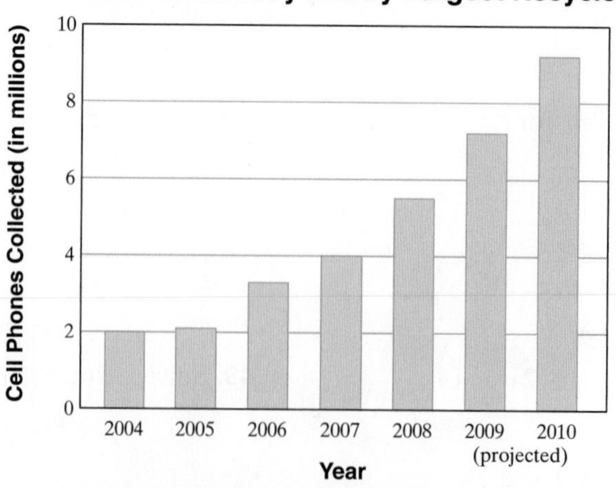

Source: ReCellular.com (independent projections)

10.1 EXPONENTS

Objectives

A Evaluate Exponential Expressions.

B Use the Product Rule for Exponents.

C Use the Power Rule for Exponents.

D Use the Power Rules for Products and Quotients.

E Use the Quotient Rule for Exponents, and Define a Number Raised to the 0 Power.

F Decide Which Rule(s) to Use to Simplify an Expression.

Objective A Evaluating Exponential Expressions

In this section, we continue our work with integer exponents. Recall from Section 8.2 that repeated multiplication of the same factor can be written using exponents. For example,

$$2 \cdot 2 \cdot 2 \cdot 2 \cdot 2 = 2^5$$

The exponent 5 tells us how many times 2 is a factor. The expression 2^5 is called an **exponential expression.** It is also called the fifth **power** of 2, or we can say that 2 is **raised** to the fifth power.

$$5^6 = \underbrace{5 \cdot 5 \cdot 5 \cdot 5 \cdot 5 \cdot 5}_{\text{6 factors; each factor is 5}} \quad \text{and} \quad (-3)^4 = \underbrace{(-3) \cdot (-3) \cdot (-3) \cdot (-3)}_{\text{4 factors; each factor is } -3}$$

The base of an exponential expression is the repeated factor. The exponent is the number of times that the base is used as a factor.

$$a^n = \underbrace{a \cdot a \cdot a \cdots a}_{n \text{ factors; each factor is } a}$$

(n: exponent or power; a: base)

Examples Evaluate each expression.

1. $2^3 = 2 \cdot 2 \cdot 2 = 8$
2. $3^1 = 3$. To raise 3 to the first power means to use 3 as a factor only once. When no exponent is shown, the exponent is assumed to be 1.
3. $(-4)^2 = (-4)(-4) = 16$
4. $-4^2 = -(4 \cdot 4) = -16$
5. $\left(\frac{1}{2}\right)^4 = \frac{1}{2} \cdot \frac{1}{2} \cdot \frac{1}{2} \cdot \frac{1}{2} = \frac{1}{16}$
6. $4 \cdot 3^2 = 4 \cdot 9 = 36$

Work Practice 1–6

PRACTICE 1–6

Evaluate each expression.

1. 3^4
2. 7^1
3. $(-2)^3$
4. -2^3
5. $\left(\frac{2}{3}\right)^2$
6. $5 \cdot 6^2$

Notice how similar -4^2 is to $(-4)^2$ in the examples above. The difference between the two is the parentheses. In $(-4)^2$, the parentheses tell us that the base, or the repeated factor, is -4. In -4^2, only 4 is the base.

Helpful Hint

Be careful when identifying the base of an exponential expression. Pay close attention to the use of parentheses.

$(-3)^2$	-3^2	$2 \cdot 3^2$
The base is -3.	The base is 3.	The base is 3.
$(-3)^2 = (-3)(-3) = 9$	$-3^2 = -(3 \cdot 3) = -9$	$2 \cdot 3^2 = 2 \cdot 3 \cdot 3 = 18$

An exponent has the same meaning whether the base is a number or a variable. If x is a real number and n is a positive integer, then x^n is the product of n factors, each of which is x.

$$x^n = \underbrace{x \cdot x \cdot x \cdot x \cdot x \cdots x}_{n \text{ factors; each factor is } x}$$

Answers

1. 81 2. 7 3. −8 4. −8 5. $\frac{4}{9}$ 6. 180

PRACTICE 7

Evaluate each expression for the given value of x.

a. $3x^2$ when x is 4

b. $\frac{x^4}{-8}$ when x is -2

Example 7 Evaluate each expression for the given value of x.

a. $2x^3$ when x is 5 **b.** $\frac{9}{x^2}$ when x is -3

Solution:

a. When x is 5, $2x^3 = 2 \cdot 5^3$

$$= 2 \cdot (5 \cdot 5 \cdot 5)$$
$$= 2 \cdot 125$$
$$= 250$$

b. When x is -3, $\frac{9}{x^2} = \frac{9}{(-3)^2}$

$$= \frac{9}{(-3)(-3)}$$
$$= \frac{9}{9} = 1$$

Work Practice 7

Objective B Using the Product Rule

Exponential expressions can be multiplied, divided, added, subtracted, and themselves raised to powers. Let's see if we can discover a shortcut method for multiplying exponential expressions with the same base. By our definition of an exponent,

$$5^4 \cdot 5^3 = \underbrace{(5 \cdot 5 \cdot 5 \cdot 5)}_{\text{4 factors of 5}} \cdot \underbrace{(5 \cdot 5 \cdot 5)}_{\text{3 factors of 5}}$$
$$= \underbrace{5 \cdot 5 \cdot 5 \cdot 5 \cdot 5 \cdot 5 \cdot 5}_{\text{7 factors of 5}}$$
$$= 5^7$$

Also,

$$x^2 \cdot x^3 = \underbrace{(x \cdot x)}_{\text{2 factors of } x} \cdot \underbrace{(x \cdot x \cdot x)}_{\text{3 factors of } x}$$
$$= x \cdot x \cdot x \cdot x \cdot x$$
$$= x^5$$

In both cases, notice that the result is exactly the same if the exponents are added.

$$5^4 \cdot 5^3 = 5^{4+3} = 5^7 \quad \text{and} \quad x^2 \cdot x^3 = x^{2+3} = x^5$$

This suggests the following rule.

Product Rule for Exponents

If m and n are positive integers and a is a real number, then

$$a^m \cdot a^n = a^{m+n}$$ ← Add exponents. (Keep common base.)

For example,

$$3^5 \cdot 3^7 = 3^{5+7} = 3^{12}$$ ← Add exponents. (Keep common base.)

Answers

7. a. 48 **b.** -2

Helpful Hint

Don't forget that

$3^5 \cdot 3^7 \neq 9^{12}$ ← Add exponents.
↑ Common base *not* kept.

$3^5 \cdot 3^7 = \underbrace{3 \cdot 3 \cdot 3 \cdot 3 \cdot 3}_{\text{5 factors of 3}} \cdot \underbrace{3 \cdot 3 \cdot 3 \cdot 3 \cdot 3 \cdot 3 \cdot 3}_{\text{7 factors of 3}}$

$= 3^{12}$ 12 factors of 3, *not* 9

In other words, to multiply two exponential expressions with the **same base,** we keep the base and add the exponents. We call this **simplifying** the exponential expression.

Examples Use the product rule to simplify each expression.

8. $4^2 \cdot 4^5 = 4^{2+5} = 4^7$ ← Add exponents.
↑ Keep common base.

9. $x^2 \cdot x^5 = x^{2+5} = x^7$

10. $y^3 \cdot y = y^3 \cdot y^1$
$= y^{3+1}$
$= y^4$

Helpful Hint Don't forget that if no exponent is written, it is assumed to be 1.

11. $y^3 \cdot y^2 \cdot y^7 = y^{3+2+7} = y^{12}$

12. $(-5)^7 \cdot (-5)^8 = (-5)^{7+8} = (-5)^{15}$

Work Practice 8–12

PRACTICE 8–12

Use the product rule to simplify each expression.

8. $7^3 \cdot 7^2$ **9.** $x^4 \cdot x^9$
10. $r^5 \cdot r$ **11.** $s^6 \cdot s^2 \cdot s^3$
12. $(-3)^9 \cdot (-3)$

✓**Concept Check** Where possible, use the product rule to simplify the expression.

a. $z^2 \cdot z^{14}$ **b.** $x^2 \cdot z^{14}$ **c.** $9^8 \cdot 9^3$ **d.** $9^8 \cdot 2^7$

Example 13 Use the product rule to simplify $(2x^2)(-3x^5)$.

Solution: Recall that $2x^2$ means $2 \cdot x^2$ and $-3x^5$ means $-3 \cdot x^5$.

$(2x^2)(-3x^5) = (2 \cdot x^2) \cdot (-3 \cdot x^5)$

$= (2 \cdot -3) \cdot (x^2 \cdot x^5)$ Group factors with common bases (using commutative and associative properties).

$= -6x^7$ Simplify.

Work Practice 13

PRACTICE 13

Use the product rule to simplify $(6x^3)(-2x^9)$.

Examples Simplify.

14. $(x^2y)(x^3y^2) = (x^2 \cdot x^3) \cdot (y^1 \cdot y^2)$ Group like bases and write y as y^1.
$= x^5 \cdot y^3$ or x^5y^3 Multiply.

15. $(-a^7b^4)(3ab^9) = (-1 \cdot 3) \cdot (a^7 \cdot a^1) \cdot (b^4 \cdot b^9)$
$= -3a^8b^{13}$

Work Practice 14–15

PRACTICE 14–15

Simplify.

14. $(m^5n^{10})(mn^8)$
15. $(-x^9y)(4x^2y^{11})$

Answers

8. 7^5 **9.** x^{13} **10.** r^6 **11.** s^{11}
12. $(-3)^{10}$ **13.** $-12x^{12}$
14. m^6n^{18} **15.** $-4x^{11}y^{12}$

✓ **Concept Check Answers**

a. z^{16} **b.** cannot be simplified
c. 9^{11} **d.** cannot be simplified

Helpful Hint

These examples will remind you of the difference between adding and multiplying terms.

Addition

$5x^3 + 3x^3 = (5 + 3)x^3 = 8x^3$ By the distributive property

$7x + 4x^2 = 7x + 4x^2$ Cannot be combined

Multiplication

$(5x^3)(3x^3) = 5 \cdot 3 \cdot x^3 \cdot x^3 = 15x^{3+3} = 15x^6$ By the product rule

$(7x)(4x^2) = 7 \cdot 4 \cdot x \cdot x^2 = 28x^{1+2} = 28x^3$ By the product rule

Objective C Using the Power Rule

Exponential expressions can themselves be raised to powers. Let's try to discover a rule that simplifies an expression like $(x^2)^3$. By the definition of a^n,

$(x^2)^3 = (x^2)(x^2)(x^2)$ $(x^2)^3$ means 3 factors of (x^2).

which can be simplified by the product rule for exponents.

$$(x^2)^3 = (x^2)(x^2)(x^2) = x^{2+2+2} = x^6$$

Notice that the result is exactly the same if we multiply the exponents.

$$(x^2)^3 = x^{2\cdot 3} = x^6$$

The following rule states this result.

Power Rule for Exponents

If m and n are positive integers and a is a real number, then

$(a^m)^n = a^{mn}$ ← Multiply exponents. ← Keep the base.

For example,

$(7^2)^5 = 7^{2\cdot 5} = 7^{10}$ ← Multiply exponents. ← Keep the base.

$[(-5)^3]^7 = (-5)^{3\cdot 7} = (-5)^{21}$ ← Multiply exponents. ← Keep the base.

In other words, to raise an exponential expression to a power, we keep the base and multiply the exponents.

PRACTICE 16–17

Use the power rule to simplify each expression.

16. $(9^4)^{10}$ **17.** $(z^6)^3$

Examples Use the power rule to simplify each expression.

16. $(5^3)^6 = 5^{3\cdot 6} = 5^{18}$

17. $(y^8)^2 = y^{8\cdot 2} = y^{16}$

Work Practice 16–17

Helpful Hint

Take a moment to make sure that you understand when to apply the product rule and when to apply the power rule.

Product Rule → Add Exponents	Power Rule → Multiply Exponents
$x^5 \cdot x^7 = x^{5+7} = x^{12}$	$(x^5)^7 = x^{5\cdot 7} = x^{35}$
$y^6 \cdot y^2 = y^{6+2} = y^8$	$(y^6)^2 = y^{6\cdot 2} = y^{12}$

Answers

16. 9^{40} **17.** z^{18}

Objective D Using the Power Rules for Products and Quotients

When the base of an exponential expression is a product, the definition of a^n still applies. For example, simplify $(xy)^3$ as follows.

$$(xy)^3 = (xy)(xy)(xy) \quad (xy)^3 \text{ means 3 factors of } (xy).$$
$$= x \cdot x \cdot x \cdot y \cdot y \cdot y \quad \text{Group factors with common bases.}$$
$$= x^3y^3 \quad \text{Simplify.}$$

Notice that to simplify the expression $(xy)^3$, we raise each factor within the parentheses to a power of 3.

$$(xy)^3 = x^3y^3$$

In general, we have the following rule.

Power of a Product Rule

If n is a positive integer and a and b are real numbers, then

$$(ab)^n = a^nb^n$$

For example,

$$(3x)^5 = 3^5x^5$$

In other words, to raise a product to a power, we raise each factor to the power.

Examples Simplify each expression.

18. $(st)^4 = s^4 \cdot t^4 = s^4t^4$ Use the power of a product rule.

19. $(2a)^3 = 2^3 \cdot a^3 = 8a^3$ Use the power of a product rule.

20. $(-5x^2y^3z)^2 = (-5)^2 \cdot (x^2)^2 \cdot (y^3)^2 \cdot (z^1)^2$ Use the power of a product rule.
$= 25x^4y^6z^2$

21. $(-xy^3)^5 = (-1xy^3)^5 = (-1)^5 \cdot x^5 \cdot (y^3)^5$ Use the power of a product rule.
$= -1x^5y^{15}$ or $-x^5y^{15}$

Work Practice 18–21

PRACTICE 18–21

Simplify each expression.

18. $(xy)^7$ **19.** $(3y)^4$

20. $(-2p^4q^2r)^3$ **21.** $(-a^4b)^7$

Let's see what happens when we raise a quotient to a power. For example, we simplify $\left(\frac{x}{y}\right)^3$ as follows.

$$\left(\frac{x}{y}\right)^3 = \left(\frac{x}{y}\right)\left(\frac{x}{y}\right)\left(\frac{x}{y}\right) \quad \left(\frac{x}{y}\right)^3 \text{ means 3 factors of } \left(\frac{x}{y}\right).$$
$$= \frac{x \cdot x \cdot x}{y \cdot y \cdot y} \quad \text{Multiply fractions.}$$
$$= \frac{x^3}{y^3} \quad \text{Simplify.}$$

Notice that to simplify the expression $\left(\frac{x}{y}\right)^3$, we raise both the numerator and the denominator to a power of 3.

$$\left(\frac{x}{y}\right)^3 = \frac{x^3}{y^3}$$

In general, we have the following rule.

Answers

18. x^7y^7 **19.** $81y^4$ **20.** $-8p^{12}q^6r^3$
21. $-a^{28}b^7$

Power of a Quotient Rule

If n is a positive integer and a and c are real numbers, then

$$\left(\frac{a}{c}\right)^n = \frac{a^n}{c^n}, \quad c \neq 0$$

For example,

$$\left(\frac{y}{7}\right)^3 = \frac{y^3}{7^3}$$

In other words, to raise a quotient to a power, we raise both the numerator and the denominator to the power.

PRACTICE 22–23

Simplify each expression.

22. $\left(\frac{r}{s}\right)^6$ **23.** $\left(\frac{5x^6}{9y^3}\right)^2$

Examples Simplify each expression.

22. $\left(\frac{m}{n}\right)^7 = \frac{m^7}{n^7}, \quad n \neq 0$ Use the power of a quotient rule.

23. $\left(\frac{2x^4}{3y^5}\right)^4 = \frac{2^4 \cdot (x^4)^4}{3^4 \cdot (y^5)^4}$ Use the power of a quotient rule and the power of a product rule.

$= \frac{16x^{16}}{81y^{20}}, \quad y \neq 0$ Use the power rule for exponents.

Work Practice 22–23

Objective E Using the Quotient Rule and Defining the Zero Exponent

Another pattern for simplifying exponential expressions involves quotients.

$$\begin{aligned}\frac{x^5}{x^3} &= \frac{x \cdot x \cdot x \cdot x \cdot x}{x \cdot x \cdot x} \\ &= \frac{x \cdot x \cdot x \cdot x \cdot x}{x \cdot x \cdot x} \\ &= 1 \cdot 1 \cdot 1 \cdot x \cdot x \\ &= x \cdot x \\ &= x^2\end{aligned}$$

Notice that the result is exactly the same if we subtract exponents of the common bases.

$$\frac{x^5}{x^3} = x^{5-3} = x^2$$

The following rule states this result in a general way.

Quotient Rule for Exponents

If m and n are positive integers and a is a real number, then

$$\frac{a^m}{a^n} = a^{m-n}, \quad a \neq 0$$

For example,

$$\frac{x^6}{x^2} = x^{6-2} = x^4, \quad x \neq 0$$

Answers

22. $\frac{r^6}{s^6}, \quad s \neq 0$ **23.** $\frac{25x^{12}}{81y^6}, \quad y \neq 0$

In other words, to divide one exponential expression by another with a common base, we keep the base and subtract the exponents.

Examples Simplify each quotient.

24. $\frac{x^5}{x^2} = x^{5-2} = x^3$ Use the quotient rule.

25. $\frac{4^7}{4^3} = 4^{7-3} = 4^4 = 256$ Use the quotient rule.

26. $\frac{(-3)^5}{(-3)^2} = (-3)^3 = -27$ Use the quotient rule.

27. $\frac{2x^5y^2}{xy} = 2 \cdot \frac{x^5}{x^1} \cdot \frac{y^2}{y^1}$

$= 2 \cdot (x^{5-1}) \cdot (y^{2-1})$ Use the quotient rule.

$= 2x^4y^1$ or $2x^4y$

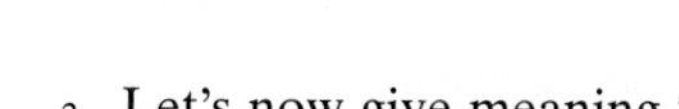

Work Practice 24–27

PRACTICE 24–27

Simplify each quotient.

24. $\frac{y^7}{y^3}$ **25.** $\frac{5^9}{5^6}$

26. $\frac{(-2)^{14}}{(-2)^{10}}$ **27.** $\frac{7a^4b^{11}}{ab}$

Let's now give meaning to an expression such as x^0. To do so, we will simplify $\frac{x^3}{x^3}$ in two ways and compare the results.

$\frac{x^3}{x^3} = x^{3-3} = x^0$ Apply the quotient rule.

$\frac{x^3}{x^3} = \frac{x \cdot x \cdot x}{x \cdot x \cdot x} = 1$ Divide the numerator and denominator by all common factors.

Since $\frac{x^3}{x^3} = x^0$ and $\frac{x^3}{x^3} = 1$, we define that $x^0 = 1$ as long as x is not 0.

Zero Exponent

$a^0 = 1$, as long as a is not 0.

For example, $5^0 = 1$.

In other words, a base raised to the 0 power is 1, as long as the base is not 0.

Examples Simplify each expression.

28. $3^0 = 1$

29. $(5x^3y^2)^0 = 1$

30. $(-4)^0 = 1$

31. $-4^0 = -1 \cdot 4^0 = -1 \cdot 1 = -1$

32. $5x^0 = 5 \cdot x^0 = 5 \cdot 1 = 5$

Work Practice 28–32

PRACTICE 28–32

Simplify each expression.

28. 8^0 **29.** $(2r^2s)^0$

30. $(-7)^0$ **31.** -7^0

32. $7y^0$

Answers

24. y^4 **25.** 125 **26.** 16 **27.** $7a^3b^{10}$ **28.** 1 **29.** 1 **30.** 1 **31.** -1 **32.** 7

✓**Concept Check** Suppose you are simplifying each expression. Tell whether you would *add* the exponents, *subtract* the exponents, *multiply* the exponents, *divide* the exponents, or *none of these.*

a. $(x^{63})^{21}$ **b.** $\dfrac{y^{15}}{y^3}$ **c.** $z^{16} + z^8$ **d.** $w^{45} \cdot w^9$

Objective F Deciding Which Rule to Use

Let's practice deciding which rule to use to simplify an expression. We will continue this discussion with more examples in the next section.

PRACTICE 33

Simplify each expression.

a. $\dfrac{x^7}{x^4}$ **b.** $(3y^4)^4$ **c.** $\left(\dfrac{x}{4}\right)^3$

Example 33 Simplify each expression.

a. $x^7 \cdot x^4$ **b.** $\left(\dfrac{t}{2}\right)^4$ **c.** $(9y^5)^2$

Solution:

a. Here, we have a product, so we use the product rule to simplify.

$x^7 \cdot x^4 = x^{7+4} = x^{11}$

b. This is a quotient raised to a power, so we use the power of a quotient rule.

$\left(\dfrac{t}{2}\right)^4 = \dfrac{t^4}{2^4} = \dfrac{t^4}{16}$

c. This is a product raised to a power, so we use the power of a product rule.

$(9y^5)^2 = 9^2(y^5)^2 = 81y^{10}$

Work Practice 33

PRACTICE 34

Simplify each expression.

a. $2^3 - 2^0$ **b.** $(y^0)^7 + (5^0)^3$

c. $\left(\dfrac{7x^9}{14y^6}\right)^2$ **d.** $\dfrac{(3a^2b^5)^3}{-27a^6b^4}$

Example 34 Simplify each expression.

a. $4^2 - 4^0$ **b.** $(x^0)^3 + (2^0)^5$ **c.** $\left(\dfrac{3y^7}{6x^5}\right)^2$ **d.** $\dfrac{(2a^3b^4)^3}{-8a^9b^2}$

Solution:

a. $4^2 - 4^0 = 16 - 1 = 15$ Remember that $4^0 = 1$.

b. $(x^0)^3 + (2^0)^5 = 1^3 + 1^5 = 1 + 1 = 2$

c. $\left(\dfrac{3y^7}{6x^5}\right)^2 = \dfrac{3^2(y^7)^2}{6^2(x^5)^2} = \dfrac{9 \cdot y^{14}}{36 \cdot x^{10}} = \dfrac{y^{14}}{4x^{10}}$

d. $\dfrac{(2a^3b^4)^3}{-8a^9b^2} = \dfrac{2^3(a^3)^3(b^4)^3}{-8a^9b^2} = \dfrac{8a^9b^{12}}{-8a^9b^2} = -1 \cdot (a^{9-9}) \cdot (b^{12-2})$

$= -1 \cdot a^0 \cdot b^{10} = -1 \cdot 1 \cdot b^{10} = -b^{10}$

Work Practice 34

Answers

33. a. x^3 **b.** $81y^{16}$ **c.** $\dfrac{x^3}{64}$

34. a. 7 **b.** 2 **c.** $\dfrac{x^{18}}{4y^{12}}$ **d.** $-b^{11}$

✓ **Concept Check Answers**

a. multiply **b.** subtract **c.** none of these **d.** add

Vocabulary and Readiness Check

Use the choices below to fill in each blank. Some choices may be used more than once.

0	base	add
1	exponent	multiply

1. Repeated multiplication of the same factor can be written using a(n) __________.
2. In 5^2, the 2 is called the __________ and the 5 is called the __________.
3. To simplify $x^2 \cdot x^7$, keep the base and __________ the exponents.
4. To simplify $(x^3)^6$, keep the base and __________ the exponents.
5. The understood exponent on the term y is __________.
6. If $x^{\square} = 1$, the exponent is __________.

For each of the following expressions, state the exponent shown and its corresponding base.

7. 3^2

8. $(-3)^6$

9. -4^2

10. $5 \cdot 3^4$

11. $5x^2$

12. $(5x)^2$

10.1 Exercise Set

FOR EXTRA HELP

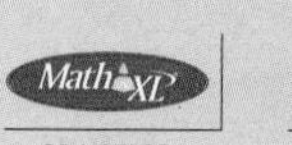

PRACTICE

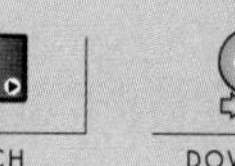

WATCH

DOWNLOAD

READ

REVIEW

Objective A *Evaluate each expression. See Examples 1 through 6.*

1. 7^2

2. -3^2

3. $(-5)^1$

4. $(-3)^2$

5. -2^4

6. -4^3

7. $(-2)^4$

8. $(-4)^3$

9. $\left(\frac{1}{3}\right)^3$

10. $\left(-\frac{1}{9}\right)^2$

11. $7 \cdot 2^4$

12. $9 \cdot 2^2$

Evaluate each expression with the given replacement values. See Example 7.

13. x^2 when $x = -2$

14. x^3 when $x = -2$

15. $5x^3$ when $x = 3$

16. $4x^2$ when $x = 5$

17. $2xy^2$ when $x = 3$ and $y = -5$

18. $-4x^2y^3$ when $x = 2$ and $y = -1$

19. $\frac{2z^4}{5}$ when $z = -2$

20. $\frac{10}{3y^3}$ when $y = -3$

Objective B *Use the product rule to simplify each expression. See Examples 8 through 15.*

21. $x^2 \cdot x^5$

22. $y^2 \cdot y$

23. $(-3)^3 \cdot (-3)^9$

24. $(-5)^7 \cdot (-5)^6$

25. $(5y^4)(3y)$

26. $(-2z^3)(-2z^2)$

27. $(x^9y)(x^{10}y^5)$

28. $(a^2b)(a^{13}b^{17})$

29. $(-8mn^6)(9m^2n^2)$

30. $(-7a^3b^3)(7a^{19}b)$

31. $(4z^{10})(-6z^7)(z^3)$

32. $(12x^5)(-x^6)(x^4)$

△ **33.** The rectangle below has width $4x^2$ feet and length $5x^3$ feet. Find its area as an expression in x.

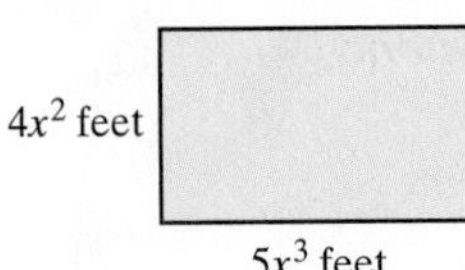

△ **34.** The parallelogram below has base length $9y^7$ meters and height $2y^{10}$ meters. Find its area as an expression in y.

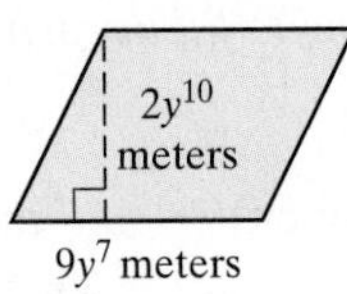

Objectives C D Mixed Practice *Use the power rule and the power of a product or quotient rule to simplify each expression. See Examples 16 through 23.*

35. $(x^9)^4$

36. $(y^7)^5$

37. $(pq)^8$

38. $(ab)^6$

39. $(2a^5)^3$

40. $(4x^6)^2$

41. $(x^2y^3)^5$

42. $(a^4b)^7$

43. $(-7a^2b^5c)^2$

44. $(-3x^7yz^2)^3$

45. $\left(\frac{r}{s}\right)^9$

46. $\left(\frac{q}{t}\right)^{11}$

47. $\left(\frac{mp}{n}\right)^9$

48. $\left(\frac{xy}{7}\right)^2$

49. $\left(\frac{-2xz}{y^5}\right)^2$

50. $\left(\frac{xy^4}{-3z^3}\right)^3$

△ **51.** The square shown has sides of length $8z^5$ decimeters. Find its area.

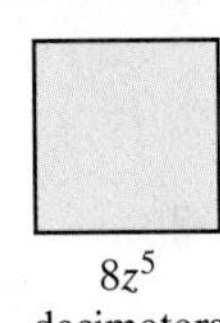

△ **52.** Given the circle below with radius $5y$ centimeters, find its area. Do not approximate π.

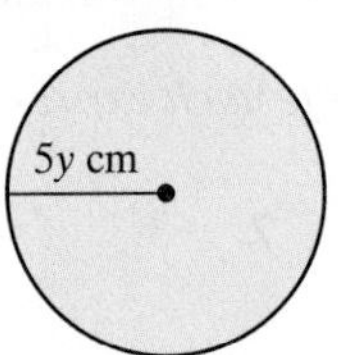

△ **53.** The vault below is in the shape of a cube. If each side is $3y^4$ feet, find its volume.

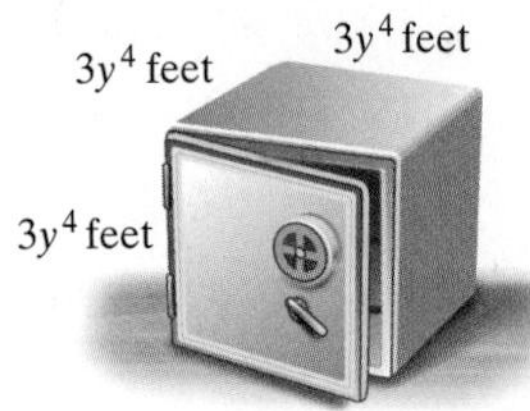

△ **54.** The silo shown is in the shape of a cylinder. If its radius is $4x$ meters and its height is $5x^3$ meters, find its volume. Do not approximate π.

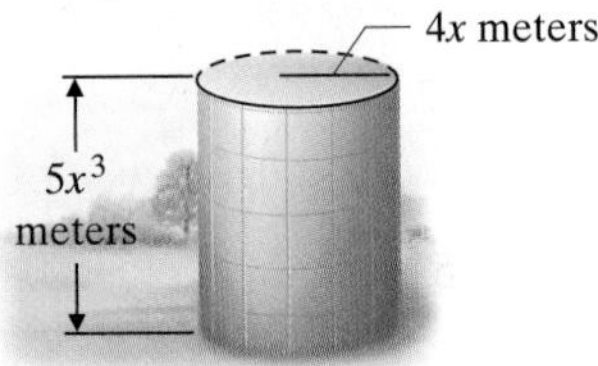

Objective E *Use the quotient rule and simplify each expression. See Examples 24 through 27.*

55. $\frac{x^3}{x}$

56. $\frac{y^{10}}{y^9}$

57. $\frac{(-4)^6}{(-4)^3}$

58. $\frac{(-6)^{13}}{(-6)^{11}}$

59. $\frac{p^7q^{20}}{pq^{15}}$

60. $\frac{x^8y^6}{xy^5}$

61. $\frac{7x^2y^6}{14x^2y^3}$

62. $\frac{9a^4b^7}{27ab^2}$

Simplify each expression. See Examples 28 through 32.

63. 7^0

64. 23^0

65. $(2x)^0$

66. $(4y)^0$

67. $-7x^0$

68. $-2x^0$

69. $5^0 + y^0$

70. $-3^0 + 4^0$

Objectives **A B C D E F Mixed Practice** *Simplify each expression. See Examples 1 through 6, and 8 through 34.*

71. -9^2

72. $(-9)^2$

73. $\left(\frac{1}{4}\right)^3$

74. $\left(\frac{2}{3}\right)^3$

75. b^4b^2

76. y^4y

77. $a^2a^3a^4$

78. $x^2x^{15}x^9$

79. $(2x^3)(-8x^4)$

80. $(3y^4)(-5y)$

81. $(a^7b^{12})(a^4b^8)$

82. $(y^2z^2)(y^{15}z^{13})$

83. $(-2mn^6)(-13m^8n)$

84. $(-3s^5t)(-7st^{10})$

85. $(z^4)^{10}$

86. $(t^5)^{11}$

87. $(4ab)^3$

88. $(2ab)^4$

89. $(-6xyz^3)^2$

90. $(-3xy^2a^3)^3$

91. $\frac{3x^5}{x^4}$

92. $\frac{5x^9}{x^3}$

93. $(9xy)^2$

94. $(2ab)^5$

95. $2^3 + 2^0$

96. $7^2 - 7^0$

97. $\left(\frac{3y^5}{6x^4}\right)^3$

98. $\left(\frac{2ab}{6yz}\right)^4$

99. $\frac{2x^3y^2z}{xyz}$

100. $\frac{x^{12}y^{13}}{x^5y^7}$

101. $(5^0)^3 + (y^0)^7$

102. $(9^0)^4 + (z^0)^5$

103. $\left(\frac{5x^9}{10y^{11}}\right)^2$

104. $\left(\frac{3a^4}{9b^5}\right)^2$

105. $\frac{(2a^5b^3)^4}{-16a^{20}b^7}$

106. $\frac{(2x^6y^2)^5}{-32x^{20}y^{10}}$

Review

Subtract. See Section 8.4.

107. $5 - 7$

108. $9 - 12$

109. $3 - (-2)$

110. $5 - (-10)$

111. $-11 - (-4)$

112. $-15 - (-21)$

Concept Extensions

Solve. See the Concept Checks in this section. For Exercises 113 through 116, match the expression with the operation needed to simplify each. A letter may be used more than once and a letter may not be used at all.

113. $(x^{14})^{23}$

114. $x^{14} \cdot x^{23}$

115. $x^{14} + x^{23}$

116. $\frac{x^{35}}{x^{17}}$

a. Add the exponents.
b. Subtract the exponents.
c. Multiply the exponents.
d. Divide the exponents.
e. None of these

Fill in the boxes so that each statement is true. (More than one answer is possible for each exercise.)

117. $x^{\square} \cdot x^{\square} = x^{12}$

118. 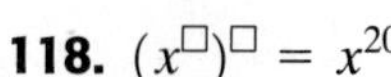 $(x^{\square})^{\square} = x^{20}$

119. $\dfrac{y^{\square}}{y^{\square}} = y^7$

120. $(y^{\square})^{\square} \cdot (y^{\square})^{\square} = y^{30}$

△ **121.** The formula $V = x^3$ can be used to find the volume V of a cube with side length x. Find the volume of a cube with side length 7 meters. (Volume is measured in cubic units.)

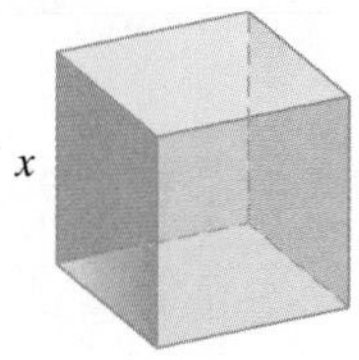

△ **122.** The formula $S = 6x^2$ can be used to find the surface area S of a cube with side length x. Find the surface area of a cube with side length 5 meters. (Surface area is measured in square units.)

△ **123.** To find the amount of water that a swimming pool in the shape of a cube can hold, do we use the formula for volume of the cube or surface area of the cube? (See Exercises 121 and 122.)

△ **124.** To find the amount of material needed to cover an ottoman in the shape of a cube, do we use the formula for volume of the cube or surface area of the cube? (See Exercises 121 and 122.)

125. Explain why $(-5)^4 = 625$, while $-5^4 = -625$.

126. Explain why $5 \cdot 4^2 = 80$, while $(5 \cdot 4)^2 = 400$.

127. In your own words, explain why $5^0 = 1$.

128. In your own words, explain when $(-3)^n$ is positive and when it is negative.

Simplify each expression. Assume that variables represent positive integers.

129. $x^{5a}x^{4a}$

130. $b^{9a}b^{4a}$

131. $(a^b)^5$

132. $(2a^{4b})^4$

133. $\dfrac{x^{9a}}{x^{4a}}$

134. $\dfrac{y^{15b}}{y^{6b}}$

10.2 NEGATIVE EXPONENTS AND SCIENTIFIC NOTATION

Objectives

A Simplify Expressions Containing Negative Exponents.

B Use the Rules and Definitions for Exponents to Simplify Exponential Expressions.

C Write Numbers in Scientific Notation.

D Convert Numbers in Scientific Notation to Standard Form.

Objective A Simplifying Expressions Containing Negative Exponents

Our work with exponential expressions so far has been limited to exponents that are positive integers or 0. Here we will also give meaning to an expression like x^{-3}.

Suppose that we wish to simplify the expression $\frac{x^2}{x^5}$. If we use the quotient rule for exponents, we subtract exponents:

$$\frac{x^2}{x^5} = x^{2-5} = x^{-3}, \quad x \neq 0$$

But what does x^{-3} mean? Let's simplify $\frac{x^2}{x^5}$ using the definition of a^n.

$$\frac{x^2}{x^5} = \frac{x \cdot x}{x \cdot x \cdot x \cdot x \cdot x}$$

$$= \frac{x \cdot x}{x \cdot x \cdot x \cdot x \cdot x} \quad \text{Divide numerator and denominator by common factors.}$$

$$= \frac{1}{x^3}$$

If the quotient rule is to hold true for negative exponents, then x^{-3} must equal $\frac{1}{x^3}$.

From this example, we state the definition for negative exponents.

Negative Exponents

If a is a real number other than 0 and n is an integer, then

$$a^{-n} = \frac{1}{a^n}$$

For example,

$$x^{-3} = \frac{1}{x^3}$$

In other words, another way to write a^{-n} is to take its reciprocal and change the sign of its exponent.

Examples Simplify by writing each expression with positive exponents only.

1. $3^{-2} = \frac{1}{3^2} = \frac{1}{9}$ — Use the definition of negative exponents.
2. $2x^{-3} = 2^1 \cdot \frac{1}{x^3} = \frac{2^1}{x^3}$ or $\frac{2}{x^3}$ — Use the definition of negative exponents.
3. $2^{-1} + 4^{-1} = \frac{1}{2} + \frac{1}{4} = \frac{2}{4} + \frac{1}{4} = \frac{3}{4}$
4. $(-2)^{-4} = \frac{1}{(-2)^4} = \frac{1}{(-2)(-2)(-2)(-2)} = \frac{1}{16}$

Helpful Hint Don't forget that since there are no parentheses, only x is the base for the exponent -3.

Work Practice 1–4

PRACTICE 1–4

Simplify by writing each expression with positive exponents only.

1. 5^{-3}
2. $7x^{-4}$
3. $5^{-1} + 3^{-1}$
4. $(-3)^{-4}$

Answers

1. $\frac{1}{125}$ 2. $\frac{7}{x^4}$ 3. $\frac{8}{15}$ 4. $\frac{1}{81}$

Helpful Hint

A negative exponent *does not affect* the sign of its base.

Remember: Another way to write a^{-n} is to take its reciprocal and change the sign of its exponent: $a^{-n} = \frac{1}{a^n}$. For example,

$$x^{-2} = \frac{1}{x^2}, \qquad 2^{-3} = \frac{1}{2^3} \text{ or } \frac{1}{8}$$

$$\frac{1}{y^{-4}} = \frac{1}{\frac{1}{y^4}} = y^4, \qquad \frac{1}{5^{-2}} = 5^2 \text{ or } 25$$

From the preceding Helpful Hint, we know that $x^{-2} = \frac{1}{x^2}$ and $\frac{1}{y^{-4}} = y^4$. We can use this to include another statement in our definition of negative exponents.

Negative Exponents

If a is a real number other than 0 and n is an integer, then

$$a^{-n} = \frac{1}{a^n} \quad \text{and} \quad \frac{1}{a^{-n}} = a^n$$

PRACTICE 5–8

Simplify each expression. Write each result using positive exponents only.

5. $\left(\frac{6}{7}\right)^{-2}$ 6. $\frac{x}{x^{-4}}$

7. $\frac{y^{-9}}{z^{-5}}$ 8. $\frac{y^{-4}}{y^6}$

Examples Simplify each expression. Write each result using positive exponents only.

5. $\left(\frac{2}{x}\right)^{-3} = \frac{2^{-3}}{x^{-3}} = \frac{2^{-3}}{1} \cdot \frac{1}{x^{-3}} = \frac{1}{2^3} \cdot \frac{x^3}{1} = \frac{x^3}{2^3} = \frac{x^3}{8}$ Use the negative exponents rule.

6. $\frac{y}{y^{-2}} = \frac{y^1}{y^{-2}} = y^{1-(-2)} = y^3$ Use the quotient rule.

7. $\frac{p^{-4}}{q^{-9}} = p^{-4} \cdot \frac{1}{q^{-9}} = \frac{1}{p^4} \cdot q^9 = \frac{q^9}{p^4}$ Use the negative exponents rule.

8. $\frac{x^{-5}}{x^7} = x^{-5-7} = x^{-12} = \frac{1}{x^{12}}$

Work Practice 5–8

Objective B Simplifying Exponential Expressions

All the previously stated rules for exponents apply for negative exponents also. Here is a summary of the rules and definitions for exponents.

Summary of Exponent Rules

If m and n are integers and a, b, and c are real numbers, then

Product rule for exponents: $a^m \cdot a^n = a^{m+n}$

Power rule for exponents: $(a^m)^n = a^{m \cdot n}$

Power of a product: $(ab)^n = a^n b^n$

Power of a quotient: $\left(\frac{a}{c}\right)^n = \frac{a^n}{c^n}, \quad c \neq 0$

Quotient rule for exponents: $\frac{a^m}{a^n} = a^{m-n}, \quad a \neq 0$

Zero exponent: $a^0 = 1, \quad a \neq 0$

Negative exponent: $a^{-n} = \frac{1}{a^n}, \quad a \neq 0$

Answers

5. $\frac{49}{36}$ 6. x^5 7. $\frac{z^5}{y^9}$ 8. $\frac{1}{y^{10}}$

Examples Simplify each expression. Write each result using positive exponents only.

9. $\dfrac{(2x^3)^4x}{x^7} = \dfrac{2^4 \cdot x^{12} \cdot x}{x^7} = \dfrac{16 \cdot x^{12+1}}{x^7}$ Use the power rule.

$= \dfrac{16 \cdot x^{13}}{x^7} = 16 \cdot x^{13-7} = 16x^6$

10. $\left(\dfrac{3a^2}{b}\right)^{-3} = \dfrac{3^{-3}(a^2)^{-3}}{b^{-3}}$ Raise each factor in the numerator and the denominator to the -3 power.

$= \dfrac{3^{-3}a^{-6}}{b^{-3}}$ Use the power rule.

$= \dfrac{b^3}{3^3a^6}$ Use the negative exponent rule.

$= \dfrac{b^3}{27a^6}$ Write 3^3 as 27.

11. $(y^{-3}z^6)^{-6} = (y^{-3})^{-6}(z^6)^{-6}$ Raise each factor to the -6 power.

$= y^{18}z^{-36} = \dfrac{y^{18}}{z^{36}}$

12. $\dfrac{x^{-7}}{(x^4)^3} = \dfrac{x^{-7}}{x^{12}} = x^{-7-12} = x^{-19} = \dfrac{1}{x^{19}}$

13. $(5y^3)^{-2} = 5^{-2}(y^3)^{-2} = 5^{-2}y^{-6} = \dfrac{1}{5^2y^6} = \dfrac{1}{25y^6}$

14. $\dfrac{3a^4b^0c^6}{6ab^2c^8} = \dfrac{3}{6} \cdot a^{4-1} \cdot b^{0-2} \cdot c^{6-8} = \dfrac{1}{2} \cdot a^3b^{-2}c^{-2} = \dfrac{a^3}{2b^2c^2}$

Note: Since $b^0 = 1$, another way to proceed above is to first replace b^0 with 1, then continue.

15. $-\dfrac{22a^7b^{-5}}{11a^{-2}b^3} = -\dfrac{22}{11} \cdot a^{7-(-2)}b^{-5-3} = -2a^9b^{-8} = -\dfrac{2a^9}{b^8}$

16. $\dfrac{(2xy)^{-3}}{(x^2y^3)^2} = \dfrac{2^{-3}x^{-3}y^{-3}}{(x^2)^2(y^3)^2} = \dfrac{2^{-3}x^{-3}y^{-3}}{x^4y^6} = 2^{-3}x^{-3-4}y^{-3-6}$

$= 2^{-3}x^{-7}y^{-9} = \dfrac{1}{2^3x^7y^9}$ or $\dfrac{1}{8x^7y^9}$

Work Practice 9–16

PRACTICE 9–16

Simplify each expression. Write each result using positive exponents only.

9. $\dfrac{(3x^5)^3x}{x^4}$

10. $\left(\dfrac{9x^3}{y}\right)^{-2}$

11. $(a^{-4}b^7)^{-5}$

12. $\dfrac{y^{-10}}{(y^5)^4}$

13. $(4a^2)^{-3}$

14. $\dfrac{5x^7y^3z^0}{15xy^8z^3}$

15. $-\dfrac{32x^{-3}y^{-6}}{8x^{-5}y^{-2}}$

16. $\dfrac{(3x^{-2}y)^{-2}}{(2x^7y)^3}$

Objective C Writing Numbers in Scientific Notation

Both very large and very small numbers frequently occur in many fields of science. For example, the distance between the sun and the dwarf planet Pluto is approximately 5,906,000,000 kilometers, and the mass of a proton is approximately 0.00000000000000000000000165 gram. It can be tedious to write these numbers in this standard decimal notation, so **scientific notation** is used as a convenient shorthand for expressing very large and very small numbers.

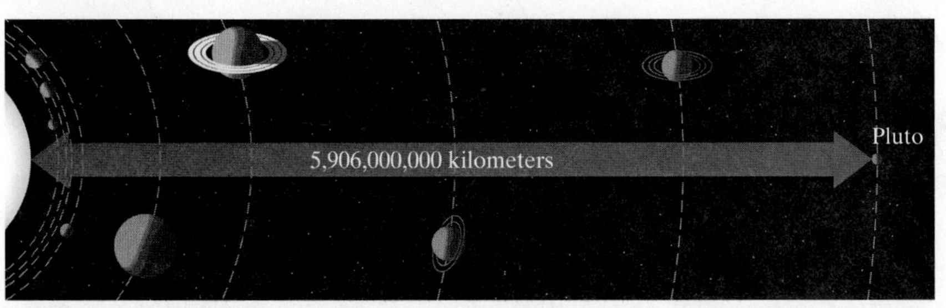

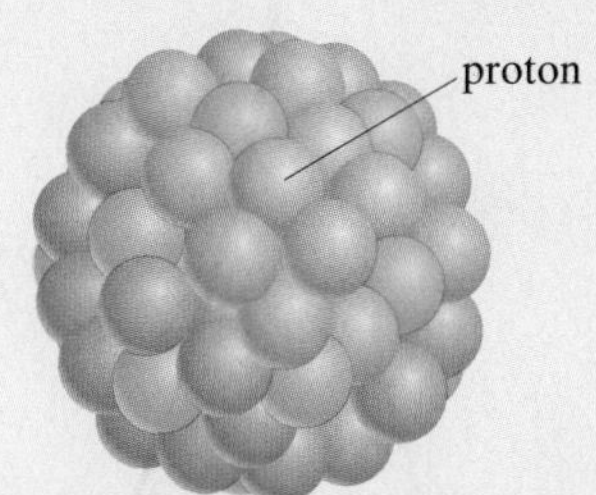

Mass of proton is approximately 0.00000000000000000000000165 gram

Answers

9. $27x^{12}$ 10. $\dfrac{y^2}{81x^6}$ 11. $\dfrac{a^{20}}{b^{35}}$ 12. $\dfrac{1}{y^{30}}$ 13. $\dfrac{1}{64a^6}$ 14. $\dfrac{x^6}{3y^5z^3}$ 15. $-\dfrac{4x^2}{y^4}$ 16. $\dfrac{1}{72x^{17}y^5}$

Scientific Notation

A positive number is written in scientific notation if it is written as the product of a number a, where $1 \leq a < 10$, and an integer power r of 10: $a \times 10^r$.

The following numbers are written in scientific notation. The $\times$ sign for multiplication is used as part of the notation.

2.03×10^2 $\quad 7.362 \times 10^7$ $\quad 5.906 \times 10^9$ (Distance between the sun and Pluto)

1×10^{-3} $\quad 8.1 \times 10^{-5}$ $\quad 1.65 \times 10^{-24}$ (Mass of a proton)

The following steps are useful when writing numbers in scientific notation.

To Write a Number in Scientific Notation

Step 1: Move the decimal point in the original number so that the new number has a value between 1 and 10.

Step 2: Count the number of decimal places the decimal point is moved in Step 1. If the original number is 10 or greater, the count is positive. If the original number is less than 1, the count is negative.

Step 3: Multiply the new number in Step 1 by 10 raised to an exponent equal to the count found in Step 2.

PRACTICE 17

Write each number in scientific notation.

a. 420,000 **b.** 0.00017
c. 9,060,000,000 **d.** 0.000007

Example 17 Write each number in scientific notation.

a. 367,000,000 **b.** 0.000003
c. 20,520,000,000 **d.** 0.00085

Solution:

a. Step 1: Move the decimal point until the number is between 1 and 10.

367,000,000.
8 places

Step 2: The decimal point is moved 8 places and the original number is 10 or greater, so the count is positive 8.

Step 3: $367{,}000{,}000 = 3.67 \times 10^8$

b. Step 1: Move the decimal point until the number is between 1 and 10.

0.000003
6 places

Step 2: The decimal point is moved 6 places and the original number is less than 1, so the count is -6.

Step 3: $0.000003 = 3.0 \times 10^{-6}$

c. $20{,}520{,}000{,}000 = 2.052 \times 10^{10}$

d. $0.00085 = 8.5 \times 10^{-4}$

Work Practice 17

Objective D Converting Numbers to Standard Form

A number written in scientific notation can be rewritten in standard form. For example, to write 8.63×10^3 in standard form, recall that $10^3 = 1000$.

$$8.63 \times 10^3 = 8.63(1000) = 8630$$

Notice that the exponent on the 10 is positive 3, and we moved the decimal point 3 places to the right.

Answers

17. a. 4.2×10^5 **b.** 1.7×10^{-4} **c.** 9.06×10^9 **d.** 7×10^{-6}

To write 7.29×10^{-3} in standard form, recall that $10^{-3} = \frac{1}{10^3} = \frac{1}{1000}$.

$$7.29 \times 10^{-3} = 7.29\left(\frac{1}{1000}\right) = \frac{7.29}{1000} = 0.00729$$

The exponent on the 10 is negative 3, and we moved the decimal to the left 3 places.

In general, **to write a scientific notation number in standard form,** move the decimal point the same number of places as the exponent on 10. If the exponent is positive, move the decimal point to the right; if the exponent is negative, move the decimal point to the left.

✓Concept Check Which number in each pair is larger?

a. 7.8×10^3 or 2.1×10^5
b. 9.2×10^{-2} or 2.7×10^4
c. 5.6×10^{-4} or 6.3×10^{-5}

Example 18 Write each number in standard form, without exponents.

a. 1.02×10^5 **b.** 7.358×10^{-3}
c. 8.4×10^7 **d.** 3.007×10^{-5}

Solution:

a. Move the decimal point 5 places to the right.

$1.02 \times 10^5 = 102{,}000.$

b. Move the decimal point 3 places to the left.

$7.358 \times 10^{-3} = 0.007358$

c. $8.4 \times 10^7 = 84{,}000{,}000.$ 7 places to the right

d. $3.007 \times 10^{-5} = 0.00003007$ 5 places to the left

Work Practice 18

PRACTICE 18

Write the numbers in standard form, without exponents.

a. 3.062×10^{-4}
b. 5.21×10^4
c. 9.6×10^{-5}
d. 6.002×10^6

Performing operations on numbers written in scientific notation makes use of the rules and definitions for exponents.

Example 19 Perform each indicated operation. Write each result in standard decimal notation.

a. $(8 \times 10^{-6})(7 \times 10^3)$

b. $\frac{12 \times 10^2}{6 \times 10^{-3}}$

Solution:

a.
$$\begin{aligned}(8 \times 10^{-6})(7 \times 10^3) &= 8 \cdot 7 \cdot 10^{-6} \cdot 10^3\\ &= 56 \times 10^{-3}\\ &= 0.056\end{aligned}$$

b. $\frac{12 \times 10^2}{6 \times 10^{-3}} = \frac{12}{6} \times 10^{2-(-3)} = 2 \times 10^5 = 200{,}000$

Work Practice 19

PRACTICE 19

Perform each indicated operation. Write each result in standard decimal notation.

a. $(9 \times 10^7)(4 \times 10^{-9})$

b. $\frac{8 \times 10^4}{2 \times 10^{-3}}$

Answers

18. a. 0.0003062 **b.** 52,100 **c.** 0.000096 **d.** 6,002,000
19. a. 0.36 **b.** 40,000,000

✓ Concept Check Answers

a. 2.1×10^5 **b.** 2.7×10^4 **c.** 5.6×10^{-4}

Calculator Explorations Scientific Notation

To enter a number written in scientific notation on a scientific calculator, locate the scientific notation key, which may be marked EE or EXP. To enter 3.1×10^7, press 3.1 EE 7. The display should read 3.1 07.

Enter each number written in scientific notation on your calculator.

1. 5.31×10^3
2. -4.8×10^{14}
3. 6.6×10^{-9}
4. -9.9811×10^{-2}

Multiply each of the following on your calculator. Notice the form of the result.

5. $3{,}000{,}000 \times 5{,}000{,}000$
6. $230{,}000 \times 1000$

Multiply each of the following on your calculator. Write the product in scientific notation.

7. $(3.26 \times 10^6)(2.5 \times 10^{13})$
8. $(8.76 \times 10^{-4})(1.237 \times 10^9)$

Vocabulary and Readiness Check

Fill in each blank with the correct choice.

1. The expression x^{-3} equals ______________.

a. $-x^3$ **b.** $\frac{1}{x^3}$ **c.** $\frac{-1}{x^3}$ **d.** $\frac{1}{x^{-3}}$

2. The expression 5^{-4} equals ______________.

a. -20 **b.** -625 **c.** $\frac{1}{20}$ **d.** $\frac{1}{625}$

3. The number 3.021×10^{-3} is written in ______________.

a. standard form **b.** expanded form
c. scientific notation

4. The number 0.0261 is written in ______________.

a. standard form **b.** expanded form
c. scientific notation

Write each expression using positive exponents only.

5. $5x^{-2}$ **6.** $3x^{-3}$ **7.** $\frac{1}{y^{-6}}$ **8.** $\frac{1}{x^{-3}}$ **9.** $\frac{4}{y^{-3}}$ **10.** $\frac{16}{y^{-7}}$

10.2 Exercise Set

FOR EXTRA HELP

Objective A *Simplify each expression. Write each result using positive exponents only. See Examples 1 through 8.*

1. 4^{-3} **2.** 6^{-2} **3.** $7x^{-3}$ **4.** $(7x)^{-3}$ **5.** $\left(-\frac{1}{4}\right)^{-3}$ **6.** $\left(-\frac{1}{8}\right)^{-2}$

7. $3^{-1} + 2^{-1}$ **8.** $4^{-1} + 4^{-2}$ **9.** $\frac{1}{p^{-3}}$ **10.** $\frac{1}{q^{-5}}$ **11.** $\frac{p^{-5}}{q^{-4}}$ **12.** $\frac{r^{-5}}{s^{-2}}$

13. $\frac{x^{-2}}{x}$ **14.** $\frac{y}{y^{-3}}$ **15.** $\frac{z^{-4}}{z^{-7}}$ **16.** $\frac{x^{-4}}{x^{-1}}$ **17.** $3^{-2} + 3^{-1}$ **18.** $4^{-2} - 4^{-3}$

19. $(-3)^{-2}$ **20.** $(-2)^{-6}$ **21.** $\frac{-1}{p^{-4}}$ **22.** $\frac{-1}{y^{-6}}$ **23.** $-2^0 - 3^0$ **24.** $5^0 + (-5)^0$

Objective B *Simplify each expression. Write each result using positive exponents only. See Examples 9 through 16.*

25. $\frac{x^2x^5}{x^3}$ **26.** $\frac{y^4y^5}{y^6}$ **27.** $\frac{p^2p}{p^{-1}}$ **28.** $\frac{y^3y}{y^{-2}}$ **29.** $\frac{(m^5)^4m}{m^{10}}$ **30.** $\frac{(x^2)^8x}{x^9}$

31. $\frac{r}{r^{-3}r^{-2}}$ **32.** $\frac{p}{p^{-3}p^{-5}}$ **33.** $(x^5y^3)^{-3}$ **34.** $(z^5x^5)^{-3}$ **35.** $\frac{(x^2)^3}{x^{10}}$ **36.** $\frac{(y^4)^2}{y^{12}}$

37. $\frac{(a^5)^2}{(a^3)^4}$ **38.** $\frac{(x^2)^5}{(x^4)^3}$ **39.** $\frac{8k^4}{2k}$ **40.** $\frac{27r^6}{3r^4}$ **41.** $\frac{-6m^4}{-2m^3}$ **42.** $\frac{15a^4}{-15a^5}$

43. $\frac{-24a^6b}{6ab^2}$ **44.** $\frac{-5x^4y^5}{15x^4y^2}$ **45.** $\frac{6x^2y^3z^0}{-7x^2y^5z^5}$ **46.** $\frac{-8xa^2b^0}{-5xa^5b}$ **47.** $(3a^2b^{-4})^3$ **48.** $(5x^3y^{-2})^2$

49. $(a^{-5}b^2)^{-6}$ **50.** $(4^{-1}x^5)^{-2}$ **51.** $\left(\frac{x^{-2}y^4z^0}{x^3y^7}\right)^2$ **52.** $\left(\frac{a^5bc^0}{a^7b^{-2}}\right)^{-3}$ **53.** $\frac{4^2z^{-3}}{4^3z^{-5}}$ **54.** $\frac{5^{-1}z^7}{5^{-2}z^9}$

55. $\frac{3^{-1}x^4}{3^3x^{-7}}$ **56.** $\frac{2^{-3}x^{-4}}{2^2x}$ **57.** $\frac{7ab^{-4}}{7^{-1}a^{-3}b^2}$ **58.** $\frac{6^{-5}x^{-1}y^2}{6^{-2}x^{-4}y^4}$ **59.** $\frac{-12m^5n^{-7}}{4m^{-2}n^{-3}}$ **60.** $\frac{-15r^{-6}s}{5r^{-4}s^{-3}}$

61. $\left(\frac{a^{-5}b}{ab^3}\right)^{-4}$ **62.** $\left(\frac{r^{-2}s^{-3}}{r^{-4}s^{-3}}\right)^{-3}$ **63.** $(5^2)(8)(2^0)$ **64.** $(3^4)(7^0)(2)$ **65.** $\frac{(xy^3)^5}{(xy)^{-4}}$ **66.** $\frac{(rs)^{-3}}{(r^2s^3)^2}$

67. $\frac{(-2xy^{-3})^{-3}}{(xy^{-1})^{-1}}$ **68.** $\frac{(-3x^2y^2)^{-2}}{(xyz)^{-2}}$ **69.** $\frac{(a^4b^{-7})^{-5}}{(5a^2b^{-1})^{-2}}$ **70.** $\frac{(a^6b^{-2})^4}{(4a^{-3}b^{-3})^3}$

△ **71.** Find the volume of the cube.

$\frac{3x^{-2}}{z}$ inches

△ **72.** Find the area of the triangle.

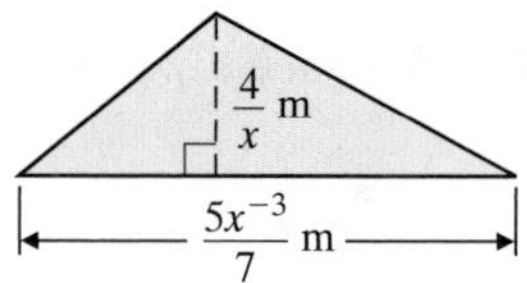

Objective **C** *Write each number in scientific notation. See Example 17.*

73. 78,000 **74.** 9,300,000,000 **75.** 0.00000167 **76.** 0.00000017

77. 0.00635 **78.** 0.00194 **79.** 1,160,000 **80.** 700,000

81. As of this writing, the world's largest optical telescope is the Gran Telescopio Canaris, located in La Palma, Canary Islands, Spain. The elevation of this telescope is 2400 meters above sea level. Write 2400 in scientific notation.

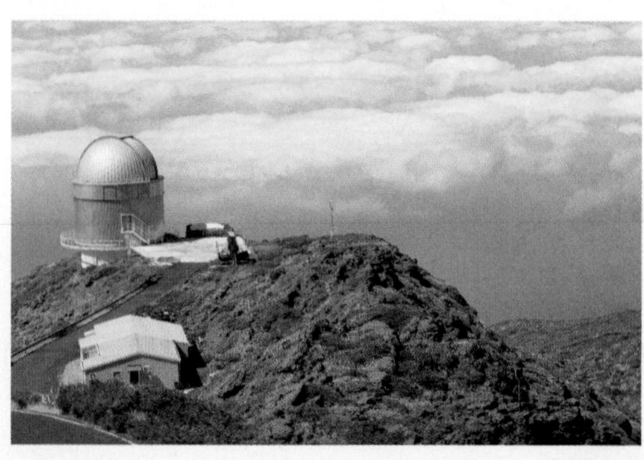

82. In January 2009, the twin Mars rovers, Spirit and Opportunity, celebrated their fifth anniversary of landing on Mars. These rovers, which were expected to last about 90 days, have defied all expectations, and have been transmitting signals back to Earth from as far away as 250,000,000 miles. Write 250,000,000 in scientific notation. (*Source:* NASA)

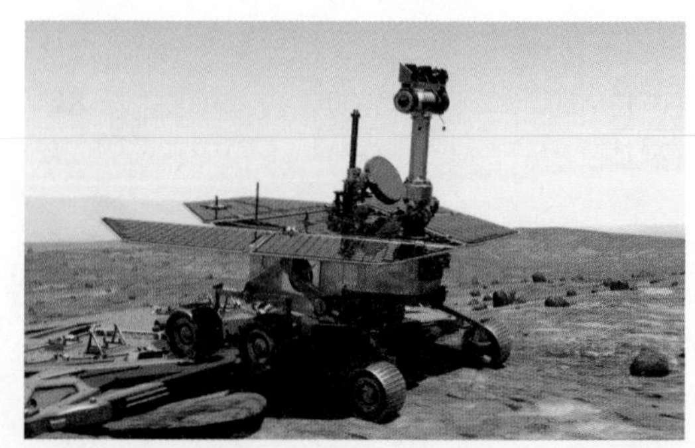

Objective D *Write each number in standard form. See Example 18.*

83. 8.673×10^{-10}

84. 9.056×10^{-4}

85. 3.3×10^{-2}

86. 4.8×10^{-6}

87. 2.032×10^{4}

88. 9.07×10^{10}

89. Each second, the sun converts 7.0×10^{8} tons of hydrogen into helium and energy in the form of gamma rays. Write this number in standard form. (*Source:* Students for the Exploration and Development of Space)

90. In chemistry, Avogadro's number is the number of atoms in one mole of an element. Avogadro's number is $6.02214199 \times 10^{23}$. Write this number in standard form. (*Source:* National Institute of Standards and Technology)

Objectives C D **Mixed Practice** *See Examples 17 and 18. Below are some interesting facts about selected countries' national debts during a certain time period. If a number is written in standard form, write it in scientific notation. If a number is written in scientific notation, write it in standard form. (Source:* CIA World Factbook*)*

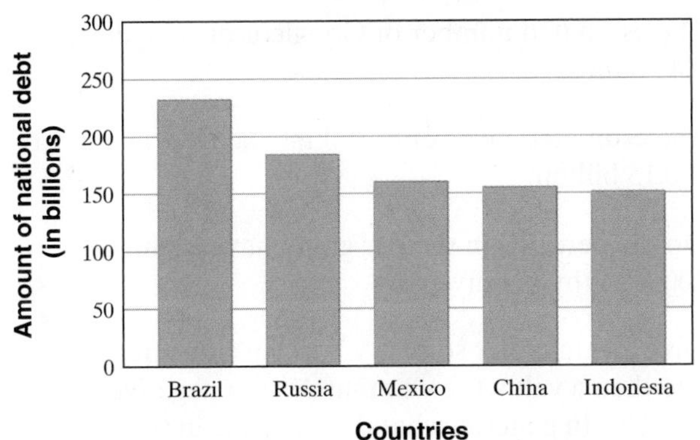

91. The national debt of Russia during a certain time period was \$184,000,000,000.

92. The amount by which Russia's debt is greater than Mexico's debt is \$24,000,000,000.

93. At a certain time period, China's national debt was $\$1.55 \times 10^{11}$.

94. At a certain time period, the national debt of the United States was $\$1.1 \times 10^{13}$.

95. At a certain time period, the estimated per person share of the United States' national debt was $\$3.5 \times 10^{4}$.

96. The bar graph shows the national debt of five different countries. Estimate the height of the tallest bar and the shortest bar in standard notation. Then write each number in scientific notation.

Objective D *Evaluate each expression using exponential rules. Write each result in standard form. See Example 19.*

97. $(1.2 \times 10^{-3})(3 \times 10^{-2})$

98. $(2.5 \times 10^{6})(2 \times 10^{-6})$

99. $(4 \times 10^{-10})(7 \times 10^{-9})$

100. $(5 \times 10^{6})(4 \times 10^{-8})$

101. $\dfrac{8 \times 10^{-1}}{16 \times 10^{5}}$

102. $\dfrac{25 \times 10^{-4}}{5 \times 10^{-9}}$

103. $\dfrac{1.4 \times 10^{-2}}{7 \times 10^{-8}}$

104. $\dfrac{0.4 \times 10^{5}}{0.2 \times 10^{11}}$

105. Although the actual amount varies by season and time of day, the average volume of water that flows over Niagara Falls (the American and Canadian falls combined) each second is 7.5×10^{5} gallons. How much water flows over Niagara Falls in an hour? Write the result in scientific notation. (*Hint:* 1 hour equals 3600 seconds.) (*Source:* niagarafallslive.com)

106. A beam of light travels 9.460×10^{12} kilometers per year. How far does light travel in 10,000 years? Write the result in scientific notation.

Review

Simplify each expression by combining any like terms. See Section 8.7.

107. $3x - 5x + 7$

108. $7w + w - 2w$

109. $y - 10 + y$

110. $-6z + 20 - 3z$

111. $7x + 2 - 8x - 6$

112. $10y - 14 - y - 14$

Concept Extensions

For Exercises 113–118, write each number in standard form. Then write the number in scientific notation.

113. The Facebook Web site has more than 90 million active users.

114. Facebook has more than 24 million photos uploaded daily.

115. There are over 1 billion Internet users worldwide.

116. The English version of Wikipedia has more than 2.3 million articles.

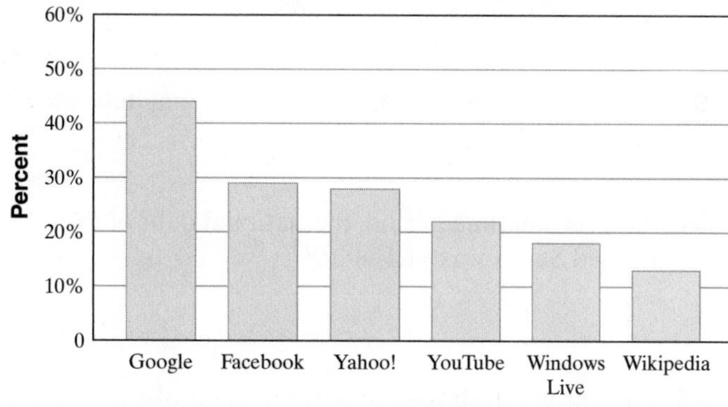

117. The estimated number of Google users in a day is 0.44 billion.

118. The estimated number of Wikipedia users in a day is 0.13 billion.

119. Do the percents in the bar graph have a sum of 100%? Why or why not?

120. Give a value for x so that x^{-1} is a positive number, and then a value for x so that x^{-1} is a negative number. In general, what does this mean?

Simplify.

121. $(2a^3)^3a^4 + a^5a^8$

122. $(2a^3)^3a^{-3} + a^{11}a^{-5}$

Fill in the boxes so that each statement is true. (More than one answer may be possible for these exercises.)

123. $x^{\square} = \frac{1}{x^5}$

124. $7^{\square} = \frac{1}{49}$

125. $z^{\square} \cdot z^{\square} = z^{-10}$

126. $(x^{\square})^{\square} = x^{-15}$

127. Which is larger? See the Concept Check in this section.

a. 9.7×10^{-2} or 1.3×10^1

b. 8.6×10^5 or 4.4×10^7

c. 6.1×10^{-2} or 5.6×10^{-4}

128. Determine whether each statement is true or false.

a. $5^{-1} < 5^{-2}$

b. $\left(\frac{1}{5}\right)^{-1} < \left(\frac{1}{5}\right)^{-2}$

c. $a^{-1} < a^{-2}$ for all nonzero numbers.

129. It was stated earlier that for an integer n,

$$x^{-n} = \frac{1}{x^n}, \quad x \neq 0$$

Explain why x may not equal 0.

130. The quotient rule states that

$$\frac{a^m}{a^n} = a^{m-n}, a \neq 0.$$

Explain why a may not equal 0.

Simplify each expression. Assume that variables represent positive integers.

131. $(x^{-3s})^3$

132. $a^{-4m} \cdot a^{5m}$

133. $a^{4m+1} \cdot a^4$

134. $(3y^{2z})^3$

10.3 INTRODUCTION TO POLYNOMIALS

Objective A Defining Term and Coefficient

In this section, we introduce a special algebraic expression called a polynomial. Let's first review some definitions presented in Section 8.7.

Recall that a term is a number or the product of a number and variables raised to powers. The terms of an expression are separated by plus signs. The terms of the expression $4x^2 + 3x$ are $4x^2$ and $3x$. The terms of the expression $9x^4 - 7x - 1$, or $9x^4 + (-7x) + (-1)$, are $9x^4$, $-7x$, and -1.

Expression	Terms
$4x^2 + 3x$	$4x^2, 3x$
$9x^4 - 7x - 1$	$9x^4, -7x, -1$
$7y^3$	$7y^3$

The **numerical coefficient** of a term, or simply the **coefficient,** is the numerical factor of each term. If no numerical factor appears in the term, then the coefficient is understood to be 1. If the term is a number only, it is called a **constant term** or simply a **constant.**

Term	Coefficient
x^5	1
$3x^2$	3
$-4x$	-4
$-x^2y$	-1
3 (constant)	3

Example 1 Complete the table for the expression $7x^5 - 8x^4 + x^2 - 3x + 5$.

Term	Coefficient
x^2	
	-8
$-3x$	
	7
5	

Solution: The completed table is shown below.

Term	Coefficient
x^2	1
$-8x^4$	-8
$-3x$	-3
$7x^5$	7
5	5

Work Practice 1

Objectives

A Define Term and Coefficient of a Term.

B Define Polynomial, Monomial, Binomial, Trinomial, and Degree.

C Evaluate Polynomials for Given Replacement Values.

D Simplify a Polynomial by Combining Like Terms.

E Simplify a Polynomial in Several Variables.

F Write a Polynomial in Descending Powers of the Variable and with No Missing Powers of the Variable.

PRACTICE 1

Complete the table for the expression $-6x^6 + 4x^5 + 7x^3 - 9x^2 - 1$.

Term	Coefficient
$7x^3$	
	-9
$-6x^6$	
	4
-1	

Answer

1. term: $-9x^2, 4x^5$; coefficient: $7, -6, -1$

Objective B Defining Polynomial, Monomial, Binomial, Trinomial, and Degree

Now we are ready to define what we mean by a polynomial.

Polynomial

A **polynomial in x** is a finite sum of terms of the form ax^n, where a is a real number and n is a whole number.

For example,

$$x^5 - 3x^3 + 2x^2 - 5x + 1$$

is a polynomial in x. Notice that this polynomial is written in **descending powers** of x, because the powers of x decrease from left to right. (Recall that the term 1 can be thought of as $1x^0$.)

On the other hand,

$$x^{-5} + 2x - 3$$

is **not** a polynomial because one of its terms contains a variable with an exponent, -5, that is not a whole number.

Types of Polynomials

A **monomial** is a polynomial with exactly one term.
A **binomial** is a polynomial with exactly two terms.
A **trinomial** is a polynomial with exactly three terms.

The following are examples of monomials, binomials, and trinomials. Each of these examples is also a polynomial.

Polynomials			
Monomials	**Binomials**	**Trinomials**	**More than Three Terms**
ax^2	$x + y$	$x^2 + 4xy + y^2$	$5x^3 - 6x^2 + 3x - 6$
$-3z$	$3p + 2$	$x^5 + 7x^2 - x$	$-y^5 + y^4 - 3y^3 - y^2 + y$
4	$4x^2 - 7$	$-q^4 + q^3 - 2q$	$x^6 + x^4 - x^3 + 1$

Each term of a polynomial has a degree. The **degree of a term in one variable** is the exponent on the variable.

PRACTICE 2

Identify the degree of each term of the trinomial $-15x^3 + 2x^2 - 5$.

Example 2 Identify the degree of each term of the trinomial $12x^4 - 7x + 3$.

Solution: The term $12x^4$ has degree 4.
The term $-7x$ has degree 1 since $-7x$ is $-7x^1$.
The term 3 has degree 0 since 3 is $3x^0$.

Work Practice 2

Each polynomial also has a degree.

Degree of a Polynomial

The **degree of a polynomial** is the greatest degree of any term of the polynomial.

Answer
2. 3; 2; 0

Example 3 Find the degree of each polynomial and tell whether the polynomial is a monomial, binomial, trinomial, or none of these.

a. $-2t^2 + 3t + 6$ **b.** $15x - 10$ **c.** $7x + 3x^3 + 2x^2 - 1$

Solution:

a. The degree of the trinomial $-2t^2 + 3t + 6$ is 2, the greatest degree of any of its terms.

b. The degree of the binomial $15x - 10$ or $15x^1 - 10$ is 1.

c. The degree of the polynomial $7x + 3x^3 + 2x^2 - 1$ is 3. The polynomial is neither a monomial, binomial, nor trinomial.

Work Practice 3

PRACTICE 3

Find the degree of each polynomial and tell whether the polynomial is a monomial, binomial, trinomial, or none of these.

a. $-6x + 14$

b. $9x - 3x^6 + 5x^4 + 2$

c. $10x^2 - 6x - 6$

Objective C Evaluating Polynomials

Polynomials have different values depending on the replacement values for the variables. When we find the value of a polynomial for a given replacement value, we are evaluating the polynomial for that value.

Example 4 Evaluate each polynomial when $x = -2$.

a. $-5x + 6$ **b.** $3x^2 - 2x + 1$

Solution:

a. $-5x + 6 = -5(-2) + 6$ Replace x with -2.
$= 10 + 6$
$= 16$

b. $3x^2 - 2x + 1 = 3(-2)^2 - 2(-2) + 1$ Replace x with -2.
$= 3(4) + 4 + 1$
$= 12 + 4 + 1$
$= 17$

Work Practice 4

PRACTICE 4

Evaluate each polynomial when $x = -1$.

a. $-2x + 10$

b. $6x^2 + 11x - 20$

Many physical phenomena can be modeled by polynomials.

Example 5 Finding Free-Fall Time

The Swiss Re Building, completed in London in 2003, is a unique building. Londoners often refer to it as the "pickle building." The building is 592.1 feet tall. An object is dropped from the highest point of this building. Neglecting air resistance, the height in feet of the object above ground at time t seconds is given by the polynomial $-16t^2 + 592.1$. Find the height of the object when $t = 1$ second and when $t = 6$ seconds.

Solution: To find each height, we evaluate the polynomial when $t = 1$ and when $t = 6$.

$-16t^2 + 592.1 = -16(1)^2 + 592.1$ Replace t with 1.
$= -16(1) + 592.1$
$= -16 + 592.1$
$= 576.1$

Continued on next page

PRACTICE 5

Find the height of the object in Example 5 when $t = 2$ seconds and $t = 4$ seconds.

Answers

3. a. binomial, 1 **b.** none of these, 6 **c.** trinomial, 2 **4. a.** 12 **b.** −25 **5.** 528.1 feet, 336.1 feet

The height of the object at 1 second is 576.1 feet.

$$-16t^2 + 592.1 = -16(6)^2 + 592.1 \quad \text{Replace } t \text{ with 6.}$$
$$= -16(36) + 592.1$$
$$= -576 + 592.1 = 16.1$$

The height of the object at 6 seconds is 16.1 feet.

Work Practice 5

Objective D Simplifying Polynomials by Combining Like Terms

We can simplify polynomials with like terms by combining the like terms. Recall from Section 8.7 that like terms are terms that contain exactly the same variables raised to exactly the same powers.

Like Terms	Unlike Terms
$5x^2, -7x^2$	$3x, 3y$
$y, 2y$	$-2x^2, -5x$
$\frac{1}{2}a^2b, -a^2b$	$6st^2, 4s^2t$

Only like terms can be combined. We combine like terms by applying the distributive property.

PRACTICE 6–10

Simplify each polynomial by combining any like terms.

6. $-6y + 8y$
7. $14y^2 + 3 - 10y^2 - 9$
8. $7x^3 + x^3$
9. $23x^2 - 6x - x - 15$
10. $\frac{2}{7}x^3 - \frac{1}{4}x + 2 - \frac{1}{2}x^3 + \frac{3}{8}x$

Answers

6. $2y$ 7. $4y^2 - 6$ 8. $8x^3$
9. $23x^2 - 7x - 15$
10. $-\frac{3}{14}x^3 + \frac{1}{8}x + 2$

Examples Simplify each polynomial by combining any like terms.

6. $-3x + 7x = (-3 + 7)x = 4x$

7. $11x^2 + 5 + 2x^2 - 7 = 11x^2 + 2x^2 + 5 - 7$
$= 13x^2 - 2$

8. $9x^3 + x^3 = 9x^3 + 1x^3$ Write x^3 as $1x^3$.
$= 10x^3$

9. $5x^2 + 6x - 9x - 3 = 5x^2 - 3x - 3$ Combine like terms $6x$ and $-9x$.

10. $\frac{2}{5}x^4 + \frac{2}{3}x^3 - x^2 + \frac{1}{10}x^4 - \frac{1}{6}x^3$

$$= \left(\frac{2}{5} + \frac{1}{10}\right)x^4 + \left(\frac{2}{3} - \frac{1}{6}\right)x^3 - x^2$$
$$= \left(\frac{4}{10} + \frac{1}{10}\right)x^4 + \left(\frac{4}{6} - \frac{1}{6}\right)x^3 - x^2$$

$$= \frac{5}{10}x^4 + \frac{3}{6}x^3 - x^2$$

$$= \frac{1}{2}x^4 + \frac{1}{2}x^3 - x^2$$

Work Practice 6–10

Example 11 Write a polynomial that describes the total area of the squares and rectangles shown below. Then simplify the polynomial.

Solution: Recall that the area of a rectangle is length times width.

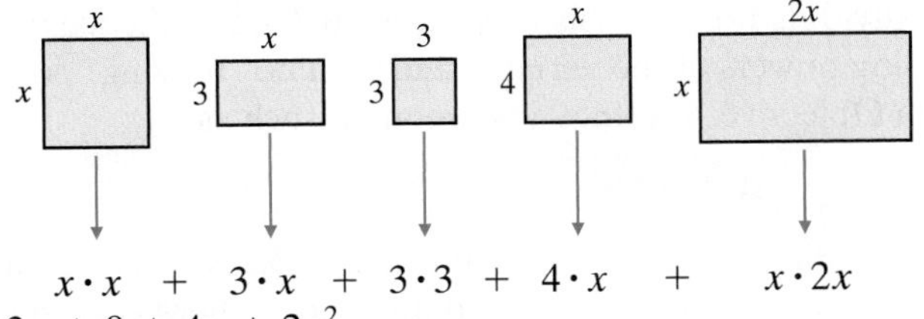

Area: $x \cdot x + 3 \cdot x + 3 \cdot 3 + 4 \cdot x + x \cdot 2x$

$= x^2 + 3x + 9 + 4x + 2x^2$

$= 3x^2 + 7x + 9$ Combine like terms.

Work Practice 11

PRACTICE 11

Write a polynomial that describes the total area of the squares and rectangles shown below. Then simplify the polynomial.

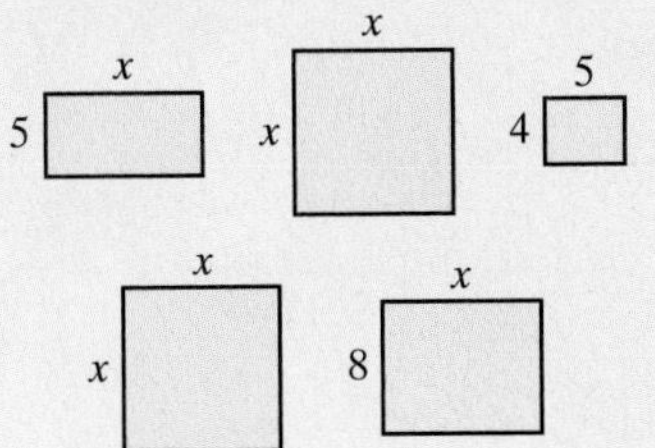

Objective E Simplifying Polynomials Containing Several Variables

A polynomial may contain more than one variable. One example is

$$5x + 3xy^2 - 6x^2y^2 + x^2y - 2y + 1$$

We call this expression a polynomial in several variables.

The **degree of a term** with more than one variable is the sum of the exponents on the variables. The **degree of a polynomial** in several variables is still the greatest degree of the terms of the polynomial.

Example 12 Identify the degrees of the terms and the degree of the polynomial $5x + 3xy^2 - 6x^2y^2 + x^2y - 2y + 1$.

Solution: To organize our work, we use a table.

Terms of Polynomial	Degree of Term	Degree of Polynomial
$5x$	1	
$3xy^2$	1 + 2, or 3	
$-6x^2y^2$	2 + 2, or 4	4 (greatest degree)
x^2y	2 + 1, or 3	
$-2y$	1	
1	0	

Work Practice 12

PRACTICE 12

Identify the degrees of the terms and the degree of the polynomial $-2x^3y^2 + 4 - 8xy + 3x^3y + 5xy^2$.

To simplify a polynomial containing several variables, we combine any like terms.

Answers

11. $5x + x^2 + 20 + x^2 + 8x$; $2x^2 + 13x + 20$

12. 5, 0, 2, 4, 3; 5

PRACTICE 13–14

Simplify each polynomial by combining any like terms.

13. $11ab - 6a^2 - ba + 8b^2$

14. $7x^2y^2 + 2y^2 - 4y^2x^2 + x^2 - y^2 + 5x^2$

Helpful Hint This term can be written as $7yx$ or $7xy$.

Examples Simplify each polynomial by combining any like terms.

13. $3xy - 5y^2 + 7yx - 9x^2 = (3 + 7)xy - 5y^2 - 9x^2$
$= 10xy - 5y^2 - 9x^2$

14. $9a^2b - 6a^2 + 5b^2 + a^2b - 11a^2 + 2b^2$
$= 10a^2b - 17a^2 + 7b^2$

Work Practice 13–14

Objective F Inserting "Missing" Terms

To prepare for dividing polynomials in Section 10.7, let's practice writing a polynomial in descending powers of the variable and with no "missing" powers.

Recall from Objective B that a polynomial such as

$$x^5 - 3x^3 + 2x^2 - 5x + 1$$

is written in descending powers of x because the powers of x decrease from left to right. Study the decreasing powers of x and notice that there is a "missing" power of x. This missing power is x^4. Writing a polynomial in decreasing powers of the variable helps you immediately determine important features of the polynomial, such as its degree. It is also sometimes helpful to write a polynomial so that there are no "missing" powers of x. For our polynomial above, if we simply insert a term of $0x^4$, which equals 0, we have an equivalent polynomial with no missing powers of x.

$$x^5 - 3x^3 + 2x^2 - 5x + 1 = x^5 + 0x^4 - 3x^3 + 2x^2 - 5x + 1$$

PRACTICE 15

Write each polynomial in descending powers of the variable with no missing powers.

a. $x^2 + 9$

b. $9m^3 + m^2 - 5$

c. $-3a^3 + a^4$

Example 15 Write each polynomial in descending powers of the variable with no missing powers.

a. $x^2 - 4$

b. $3m^3 - m + 1$

c. $2x + x^4$

Solution:

a. $x^2 - 4 = x^2 + 0x^1 - 4$ or $x^2 + 0x - 4$ — Insert a missing term of $0x^1$ or $0x$.

b. $3m^3 - m + 1 = 3m^3 + 0m^2 - m + 1$ — Insert a missing term of $0m^2$.

c. $2x + x^4 = x^4 + 2x$ — Write in descending powers of variable.
$= x^4 + 0x^3 + 0x^2 + 2x + 0x^0$ — Insert missing terms of $0x^3$, $0x^2$, and $0x^0$ (or 0).

Work Practice 15

Helpful Hint

Since there is no constant as a last term, we insert a $0x^0$. This $0x^0$ (or 0) is the final power of x in our polynomial.

Answers

13. $10ab - 6a^2 + 8b^2$
14. $3x^2y^2 + y^2 + 6x^2$
15. a. $x^2 + 0x + 9$
b. $9m^3 + m^2 + 0m - 5$
c. $a^4 - 3a^3 + 0a^2 + 0a + 0a^0$

Vocabulary and Readiness Check

Use the choices below to fill in each blank. Not all choices will be used.

least	monomial	trinomial	coefficient
greatest	binomial	constant	

1. A __________ is a polynomial with exactly two terms.
2. A __________ is a polynomial with exactly one term.
3. A __________ is a polynomial with exactly three terms.
4. The numerical factor of a term is called the __________.
5. A number term is also called a __________.
6. The degree of a polynomial is the __________ degree of any term of the polynomial.

10.3 Exercise Set

FOR EXTRA HELP MyMathLab

PRACTICE WATCH DOWNLOAD READ REVIEW

Objective A *Complete each table for each polynomial. See Example 1.*

1. $x^2 - 3x + 5$

Term	Coefficient
x^2	
	-3
5	

2. $2x^3 - x + 4$

Term	Coefficient
	2
$-x$	
4	

3. $-5x^4 + 3.2x^2 + x - 5$

Term	Coefficient
$-5x^4$	
$3.2x^2$	
x	
-5	

4. $9.7x^7 - 3x^5 + x^3 - \frac{1}{4}x^2$

Term	Coefficient
$9.7x^7$	
$-3x^5$	
x^3	
$-\frac{1}{4}x^2$	

Objective B *Find the degree of each polynomial and determine whether it is a monomial, binomial, trinomial, or none of these. See Examples 2 and 3.*

5. $x + 2$

6. $-6y + 4$

7. $9m^3 - 5m^2 + 4m - 8$

8. $a + 5a^2 + 3a^3 - 4a^4$

9. $12x^4 - x^6 - 12x^2$

10. $7r^2 + 2r - 3r^5$

11. $3z - 5z^4$

12. $5y^6 + 2$

Objective C *Evaluate each polynomial when* **(a)** $x = 0$ *and* **(b)** $x = -1$. *See Examples 4 and 5.*

13. $5x - 6$

14. $2x - 10$

15. $x^2 - 5x - 2$

16. $x^2 + 3x - 4$

17. $-x^3 + 4x^2 - 15$

18. $-2x^3 + 3x^2 - 6$

A rocket is fired upward from the ground with an initial velocity of 200 feet per second. Neglecting air resistance, the height of the rocket at any time t can be described in feet by the polynomial $-16t^2 + 200t$. *Find the height of the rocket at the time given in Exercises 19 through 22. See Example 5.*

	Time, t (in seconds)	Height $-16t^2 + 200t$
19.	1	
20.	5	
21.	7.6	
22.	10.3	

23. The polynomial $-7.5x^2 + 93x - 100$ models the yearly number of visitors (in thousands) x years after 2000 at Apostle Islands National Park. Use this polynomial to estimate the number of visitors to the park in 2008 ($x = 8$).

24. The polynomial $8x^2 - 90.6x + 752$ models the yearly number of visitors (in thousands) x years after 2000 at Cedar Breaks National Park. Use this polynomial to estimate the number of visitors to the park in 2007 ($x = 7$).

25. The number of wireless telephone subscribers (in millions) x years after 1995 is given by the polynomial $0.52x^2 + 11.4x + 27.87$ for 1995 through 2008. Use this model to predict the number of wireless telephone subscribers in 2012 ($x = 17$). (*Source:* Based on data from Cellular Telecommunications & Internet Association)

26. The penetration rate of American wireless telephone subscribers—that is, the percent of the population who have cell phones—x years after 1995 is given by $0.1x^2 + 4.4x + 10.7$ for 1995 through 2008. Assuming the same rate of growth, use this model to predict the penetration rate of wireless subscribers in the United States in 2010 ($x = 15$). (*Source:* Based on data from Cellular Telecommunications & Internet Association)

Objective **D** *Simplify each expression by combining like terms. See Examples 6 through 10.*

27. $9x - 20x$

28. $14y - 30y$

29. $14x^3 + 9x^3$

30. $18x^3 + 4x^3$

31. $7x^2 + 3 + 9x^2 - 10$

32. $8x^2 + 4 + 11x^2 - 20$

33. $15x^2 - 3x^2 - 13$

34. $12k^3 - 9k^3 + 11$

35. $8s - 5s + 4s$

36. $5y + 7y - 6y$

37. $0.1y^2 - 1.2y^2 + 6.7 - 1.9$

38. $7.6y + 3.2y^2 - 8y - 2.5y^2$

39. $\frac{2}{3}x^4 + 12x^3 + \frac{1}{6}x^4 - 19x^3 - 19$

40. $\frac{2}{5}x^4 - 23x^2 + \frac{1}{15}x^4 + 5x^2 - 5$

41. $\frac{3}{20}x^3 + \frac{1}{10} - \frac{3}{10}x - \frac{1}{5} - \frac{7}{20}x + 6x^2$

42. $\frac{5}{16}x^3 - \frac{1}{8} + \frac{3}{8}x + \frac{1}{4} - \frac{9}{16}x - 14x^2$

Write a polynomial that describes the total area of each set of rectangles and squares shown in Exercises 43 and 44. Then simplify the polynomial. See Example 11.

△ **43.** 2x, 2x; 7, x; x, x; 5, x

△ **44.** 7, x; 2x, 2x; 2x, 2x; 6, 3; 4, 4

Recall that the perimeter of a figure such as the ones shown in Exercises 45 and 46 is the sum of the lengths of its sides. Write each perimeter as a polynomial. Then simplify the polynomial.

△ **45.**

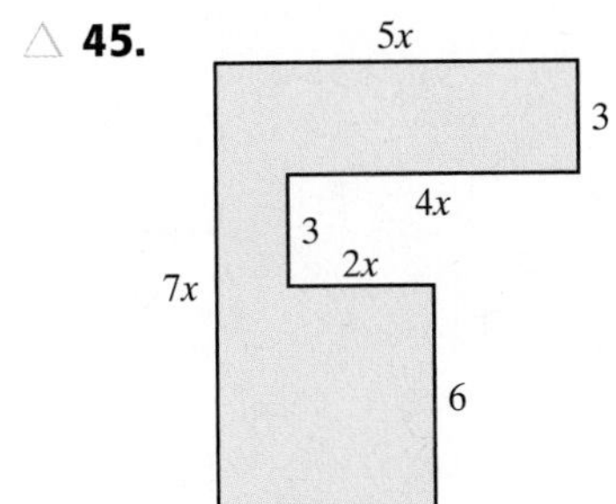

△ **46.**

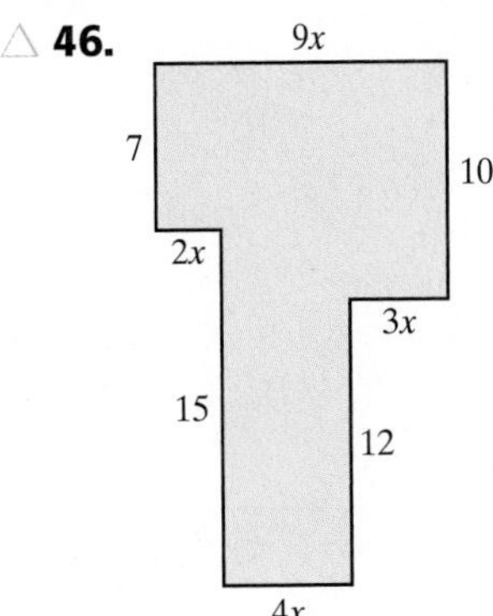

Objective E *Identify the degrees of the terms and the degree of the polynomial. See Example 12.*

47. $9ab - 6a + 5b - 3$

48. $y^4 - 6y^3x + 2x^2y^2 - 5y^2 + 3$

49. $x^3y - 6 + 2x^2y^2 + 5y^3$

50. $2a^2b + 10a^4b - 9ab + 6$

Simplify each polynomial by combining any like terms. See Examples 13 and 14.

51. $3ab - 4a + 6ab - 7a$

52. $-9xy + 7y - xy - 6y$

53. $4x^2 - 6xy + 3y^2 - xy$

54. $3a^2 - 9ab + 4b^2 - 7ab$

55. $5x^2y + 6xy^2 - 5yx^2 + 4 - 9y^2x$

56. $17a^2b - 16ab^2 + 3a^3 + 4ba^3 - b^2a$

57. $14y^3 - 9 + 3a^2b^2 - 10 - 19b^2a^2$

58. $18x^4 + 2x^3y^3 - 1 - 2y^3x^3 - 17x^4$

Objective **F** *Write each polynomial in descending powers of the variable and with no missing powers. See Example 15.*

59. $7x^2 + 3$

60. $5x^2 - 2$

61. $x^3 - 64$

62. $x^3 - 8$

63. $5y^3 + 2y - 10$

64. $6m^3 - 3m + 4$

65. $8y + 2y^4$

66. $11z + 4z^4$

67. $6x^5 + x^3 - 3x + 15$

68. $9y^5 - y^2 + 2y - 11$

Review

Simplify each expression. See Section 8.7.

69. $4 + 5(2x + 3)$

70. $9 - 6(5x + 1)$

71. $2(x - 5) + 3(5 - x)$

72. $-3(w + 7) + 5(w + 1)$

Concept Extensions

73. Describe how to find the degree of a term.

74. Describe how to find the degree of a polynomial.

75. Explain why xyz is a monomial while $x + y + z$ is a trinomial.

76. Explain why the degree of the term $5y^3$ is 3 and the degree of the polynomial $2y + y + 2y$ is 1.

Simplify, if possible.

77. $x^4 \cdot x^9$

78. $x^4 + x^9$

79. $a \cdot b^3 \cdot a^2 \cdot b^7$

80. $a + b^3 + a^2 + b^7$

81. $(y^5)^4 + (y^2)^{10}$

82. $x^5y^2 + y^2x^5$

Fill in the boxes so that the terms in each expression can be combined. Then simplify. Each exercise has more than one solution.

83. $7x^{\square} + 2x^{\square}$

84. $(3y^2)^{\square} + (4y^3)^{\square}$

85. Explain why the height of the rocket in Exercises 19 through 22 increases and then decreases as time passes.

86. Approximate (to the nearest tenth of a second) how long before the rocket in Exercises 19 through 22 hits the ground.

Simplify each polynomial by combining like terms.

87. $1.85x^2 - 3.76x + 9.25x^2 + 10.76 - 4.21x$

88. $7.75x + 9.16x^2 - 1.27 - 14.58x^2 - 18.34$

10.4 ADDING AND SUBTRACTING POLYNOMIALS

Objectives

A **Add Polynomials.**

B **Subtract Polynomials.**

C **Add or Subtract Polynomials in One Variable.**

D **Add or Subtract Polynomials in Several Variables.**

Objective A Adding Polynomials

To add polynomials, we use commutative and associative properties and then combine like terms. To see if you are ready to add polynomials, try the Concept Check.

✓**Concept Check** When combining like terms in the expression $5x - 8x^2 - 8x$, which of the following is the proper result?

a. $-11x^2$ **b.** $-3x - 8x^2$ **c.** $-11x$ **d.** $-11x^4$

To Add Polynomials

To add polynomials, combine all like terms.

PRACTICE 1–2

Add.

1. $(3x^5 - 7x^3 + 2x - 1) + (3x^3 - 2x)$

2. $(5x^2 - 2x + 1) + (-6x^2 + x - 1)$

Examples Add.

1. $(4x^3 - 6x^2 + 2x + 7) + (5x^2 - 2x)$

$= 4x^3 - 6x^2 + 2x + 7 + 5x^2 - 2x$ Remove parentheses.

$= 4x^3 + (-6x^2 + 5x^2) + (2x - 2x) + 7$ Combine like terms.

$= 4x^3 - x^2 + 7$ Simplify.

2. $(-2x^2 + 5x - 1) + (-2x^2 + x + 3)$

$= -2x^2 + 5x - 1 - 2x^2 + x + 3$ Remove parentheses.

$= (-2x^2 - 2x^2) + (5x + 1x) + (-1 + 3)$ Combine like terms.

$= -4x^2 + 6x + 2$ Simplify.

Work Practice 1–2

Just as we can add numbers vertically, polynomials can be added vertically if we line up like terms underneath one another.

PRACTICE 3

Add $(9y^2 - 6y + 5)$ and $(4y + 3)$ using a vertical format.

Example 3 Add $(7y^3 - 2y^2 + 7)$ and $(6y^2 + 1)$ using a vertical format.

Solution: Vertically line up like terms and add.

$$\begin{array}{r} 7y^3 - 2y^2 + 7 \\ 6y^2 + 1 \\ \hline 7y^3 + 4y^2 + 8 \end{array}$$

Work Practice 3

Objective B Subtracting Polynomials

To subtract one polynomial from another, recall the definition of subtraction. To subtract a number, we add its opposite: $a - b = a + (-b)$. To subtract a polynomial, we also add its opposite. Just as $-b$ is the opposite of b, $-(x^2 + 5)$ is the opposite of $(x^2 + 5)$.

To Subtract Polynomials

To subtract two polynomials, change the signs of the terms of the polynomial being subtracted and then add.

Answers

1. $3x^5 - 4x^3 - 1$ **2.** $-x^2 - x$

3. $9y^2 - 2y + 8$

✓ **Concept Check Answer**

b

Example 4 Subtract: $(5x - 3) - (2x - 11)$

Solution: From the definition of subtraction, we have

$$\begin{aligned}(5x - 3) - (2x - 11) &= (5x - 3) + [-(2x - 11)] && \text{Add the opposite.}\\ &= (5x - 3) + (-2x + 11) && \text{Apply the distributive property.}\\ &= 5x - 3 - 2x + 11 && \text{Remove parentheses.}\\ &= 3x + 8 && \text{Combine like terms.}\end{aligned}$$

Work Practice 4

PRACTICE 4

Subtract:
$(9x + 5) - (4x - 3)$

Example 5 Subtract: $(2x^3 + 8x^2 - 6x) - (2x^3 - x^2 + 1)$

Solution: First, we change the sign of each term of the second polynomial; then we add.

$$\begin{aligned}&(2x^3 + 8x^2 - 6x) - (2x^3 - x^2 + 1)\\ &= (2x^3 + 8x^2 - 6x) + (-2x^3 + x^2 - 1)\\ &= 2x^3 + 8x^2 - 6x - 2x^3 + x^2 - 1\\ &= 2x^3 - 2x^3 + 8x^2 + x^2 - 6x - 1\\ &= 9x^2 - 6x - 1 && \text{Combine like terms.}\end{aligned}$$

Work Practice 5

PRACTICE 5

Subtract:
$(4x^3 - 10x^2 + 1)$
$-(-4x^3 + x^2 - 11)$

Just as polynomials can be added vertically, so can they be subtracted vertically.

Example 6 Subtract $(5y^2 + 2y - 6)$ from $(-3y^2 - 2y + 11)$ using a vertical format.

Solution: Arrange the polynomials in a vertical format, lining up like terms.

$$\begin{array}{r} -3y^2 - 2y + 11 \\ \underline{-(5y^2 + 2y - 6)} \end{array} \qquad \begin{array}{r} -3y^2 - 2y + 11 \\ \underline{-5y^2 - 2y + 6} \\ -8y^2 - 4y + 17 \end{array}$$

Work Practice 6

PRACTICE 6

Subtract $(6y^2 - 3y + 2)$ from $(2y^2 - 2y + 7)$ using a vertical format.

Helpful Hint

Don't forget to change the sign of each term in the polynomial being subtracted.

Objective C Adding and Subtracting Polynomials in One Variable

Let's practice adding and subtracting polynomials in one variable.

Example 7 Subtract $(5z - 7)$ from the sum of $(8z + 11)$ and $(9z - 2)$.

Solution: Notice that $(5z - 7)$ is to be subtracted **from** a sum. The translation is

$$\begin{aligned}&[(8z + 11) + (9z - 2)] - (5z - 7)\\ &= 8z + 11 + 9z - 2 - 5z + 7 && \text{Remove grouping symbols.}\\ &= 8z + 9z - 5z + 11 - 2 + 7 && \text{Group like terms.}\\ &= 12z + 16 && \text{Combine like terms.}\end{aligned}$$

Work Practice 7

PRACTICE 7

Subtract $(3x + 1)$ from the sum of $(4x - 3)$ and $(12x - 5)$.

Answers

4. $5x + 8$ **5.** $8x^3 - 11x^2 + 12$
6. $-4y^2 + y + 5$ **7.** $13x - 9$

Objective D Adding and Subtracting Polynomials in Several Variables

Now that we know how to add or subtract polynomials in one variable, we can also add and subtract polynomials in several variables.

PRACTICE 8–9

Add or subtract as indicated.

8. $(2a^2 - ab + 6b^2) + (-3a^2 + ab - 7b^2)$

9. $(5x^2y^2 + 3 - 9x^2y + y^2) - (-x^2y^2 + 7 - 8xy^2 + 2y^2)$

Examples Add or subtract as indicated.

8. $(3x^2 - 6xy + 5y^2) + (-2x^2 + 8xy - y^2)$
$= 3x^2 - 6xy + 5y^2 - 2x^2 + 8xy - y^2$
$= x^2 + 2xy + 4y^2$ Combine like terms.

9. $(9a^2b^2 + 6ab - 3ab^2) - (5b^2a + 2ab - 3 - 9b^2)$
$= 9a^2b^2 + 6ab - 3ab^2 - 5b^2a - 2ab + 3 + 9b^2$
$= 9a^2b^2 + 4ab - 8ab^2 + 9b^2 + 3$ Combine like terms.

Work Practice 8–9

✓**Concept Check** If possible, simplify each expression by performing the indicated operation.

a. $2y + y$
b. $2y \cdot y$
c. $-2y - y$
d. $(-2y)(-y)$
e. $2x + y$

Answers

8. $-a^2 - b^2$
9. $6x^2y^2 - 4 - 9x^2y + 8xy^2 - y^2$

✓ **Concept Check Answers**

a. $3y$ **b.** $2y^2$ **c.** $-3y$ **d.** $2y^2$
e. cannot be simplified

Vocabulary and Readiness Check

Simplify by combining like terms if possible.

1. $-9y - 5y$ **2.** $6m^5 + 7m^5$ **3.** $x + 6x$

4. $7z - z$ **5.** $5m^2 + 2m$ **6.** $8p^3 + 3p^2$

10.4 Exercise Set

FOR EXTRA HELP

MyMathLab

PRACTICE

WATCH

DOWNLOAD

READ

REVIEW

Objective A *Add. See Examples 1 and 2.*

1. $(3x + 7) + (9x + 5)$

2. $(-y - 2) + (3y + 5)$

3. $(-7x + 5) + (-3x^2 + 7x + 5)$

4. $(3x - 8) + (4x^2 - 3x + 3)$

5. $(-5x^2 + 3) + (2x^2 + 1)$

6. $(3x^2 + 7) + (3x^2 + 9)$

7. $(-3y^2 - 4y) + (2y^2 + y - 1)$

8. $(7x^2 + 2x - 9) + (-3x^2 + 5)$

9. $(1.2x^3 - 3.4x + 7.9) + (6.7x^3 + 4.4x^2 - 10.9)$

10. $(9.6y^3 + 2.7y^2 - 8.6) + (1.1y^3 - 8.8y + 11.6)$

11. $\left(\frac{3}{4}m^2 - \frac{2}{5}m + \frac{1}{8}\right) + \left(-\frac{1}{4}m^2 - \frac{3}{10}m + \frac{11}{16}\right)$

12. $\left(-\frac{4}{7}n^2 + \frac{5}{6}m - \frac{1}{20}\right) + \left(\frac{3}{7}n^2 - \frac{5}{12}m - \frac{3}{10}\right)$

Add using a vertical format. See Example 3.

13. $\begin{array}{r} 3t^2 + 4 \\ \underline{5t^2 - 8} \end{array}$

14. $\begin{array}{r} 7x^3 + 3 \\ \underline{2x^3 - 7} \end{array}$

15. $\begin{array}{r} 10a^3 - 8a^2 + 4a + 9 \\ \underline{5a^3 + 9a^2 - 7a + 7} \end{array}$

16. $\begin{array}{r} 2x^3 - 3x^2 + x - 4 \\ \underline{5x^3 + 2x^2 - 3x + 2} \end{array}$

Objective B *Subtract. See Examples 4 and 5.*

17. $(2x + 5) - (3x - 9)$

18. $(4 + 5a) - (-a - 5)$

19. $(5x^2 + 4) - (-2y^2 + 4)$

20. $(-7y^2 + 5) - (-8y^2 + 12)$

21. $3x - (5x - 9)$

22. $4 - (-y - 4)$

23. $(2x^2 + 3x - 9) - (-4x + 7)$

24. $(-7x^2 + 4x + 7) - (-8x + 2)$

25. $(5x + 8) - (-2x^2 - 6x + 8)$

26. $(-6y^2 + 3y - 4) - (9y^2 - 3y)$

27. $(0.7x^2 + 0.2x - 0.8) - (0.9x^2 + 1.4)$

28. $(-0.3y^2 + 0.6y - 0.3) - (0.5y^2 + 0.3)$

29. $\left(\frac{1}{4}z^2 - \frac{1}{5}z\right) - \left(-\frac{3}{20}z^2 + \frac{1}{10}z - \frac{7}{20}\right)$

30. $\left(\frac{1}{3}x^2 - \frac{2}{7}x\right) - \left(\frac{4}{21}x^2 + \frac{1}{21}x - \frac{2}{3}\right)$

Subtract using a vertical format. See Example 6.

31. $\begin{array}{r} 4z^2 - 8z + 3 \\ -(6z^2 + 8z - 3) \\ \hline \end{array}$

32. $\begin{array}{r} 7a^2 - 9a + 6 \\ -(11a^2 - 4a + 2) \\ \hline \end{array}$

33. $\begin{array}{r} 5u^5 - 4u^2 + 3u - 7 \\ -(3u^5 + 6u^2 - 8u + 2) \\ \hline \end{array}$

34. $\begin{array}{r} 5x^3 - 4x^2 + 6x - 2 \\ -(3x^3 - 2x^2 - x - 4) \\ \hline \end{array}$

Objectives **A B C Mixed Practice** *Add or subtract as indicated. See Examples 1 through 7.*

35. $(3x + 5) + (2x - 14)$

36. $(2y + 20) + (5y - 30)$

37. $(9x - 1) - (5x + 2)$

38. $(7y + 7) - (y - 6)$

39. $(14y + 12) + (-3y - 5)$

40. $(26y + 17) + (-20y - 10)$

41. $(x^2 + 2x + 1) - (3x^2 - 6x + 2)$

42. $(5y^2 - 3y - 1) - (2y^2 + y + 1)$

43. $(3x^2 + 5x - 8) + (5x^2 + 9x + 12) - (8x^2 - 14)$

44. $(2x^2 + 7x - 9) + (x^2 - x + 10) - (3x^2 - 30)$

45. $(-a^2 + 1) - (a^2 - 3) + (5a^2 - 6a + 7)$

46. $(-m^2 + 3) - (m^2 - 13) + (6m^2 - m + 1)$

Translating *Perform each indicated operation. See Examples 3, 6, and 7.*

47. Subtract $4x$ from $(7x - 3)$.

48. Subtract y from $(y^2 - 4y + 1)$.

49. Add $(4x^2 - 6x + 1)$ and $(3x^2 + 2x + 1)$.

50. Add $(-3x^2 - 5x + 2)$ and $(x^2 - 6x + 9)$.

51. Subtract $(5x + 7)$ from $(7x^2 + 3x + 9)$.

52. Subtract $(5y^2 + 8y + 2)$ from $(7y^2 + 9y - 8)$.

53. Subtract $(4y^2 - 6y - 3)$ from the sum of $(8y^2 + 7)$ and $(6y + 9)$.

54. Subtract $(4x^2 - 2x + 2)$ from the sum of $(x^2 + 7x + 1)$ and $(7x + 5)$.

55. Subtract $(3x^2 - 4)$ from the sum of $(x^2 - 9x + 2)$ and $(2x^2 - 6x + 1)$.

56. Subtract $(y^2 - 9)$ from the sum of $(3y^2 + y + 4)$ and $(2y^2 - 6y - 10)$.

Objective D *Add or subtract as indicated. See Examples 8 and 9.*

57. $(9a + 6b - 5) + (-11a - 7b + 6)$

58. $(3x - 2 + 6y) + (7x - 2 - y)$

59. $(4x^2 + y^2 + 3) - (x^2 + y^2 - 2)$

60. $(7a^2 - 3b^2 + 10) - (-2a^2 + b^2 - 12)$

61. $(x^2 + 2xy - y^2) + (5x^2 - 4xy + 20y^2)$

62. $(a^2 - ab + 4b^2) + (6a^2 + 8ab - b^2)$

63. $(11r^2s + 16rs - 3 - 2r^2s^2) - (3sr^2 + 5 - 9r^2s^2)$

64. $(3x^2y - 6xy + x^2y^2 - 5) - (11x^2y^2 - 1 + 5yx^2)$

For Exercises 65 through 68, find the perimeter of each figure.

65.

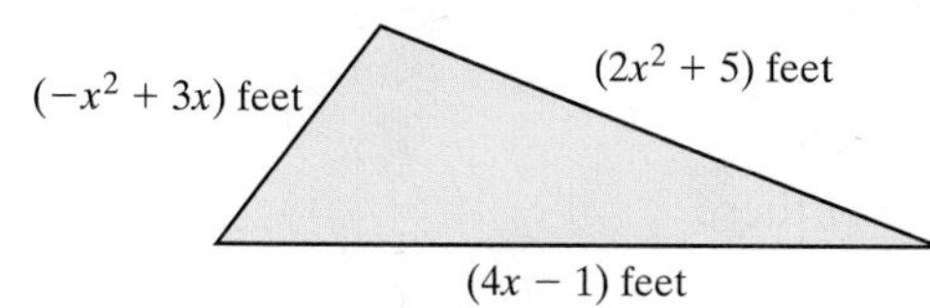

66.

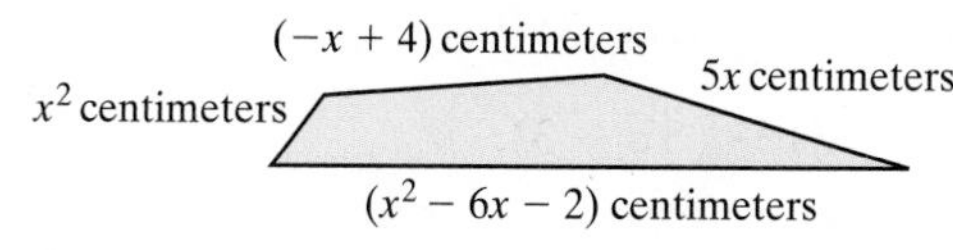

67.

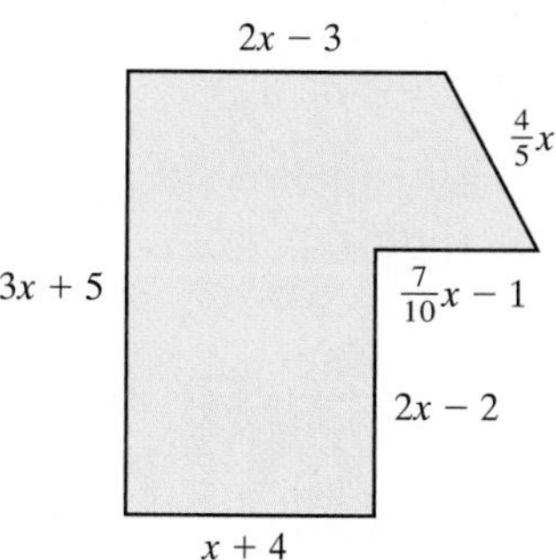

68.

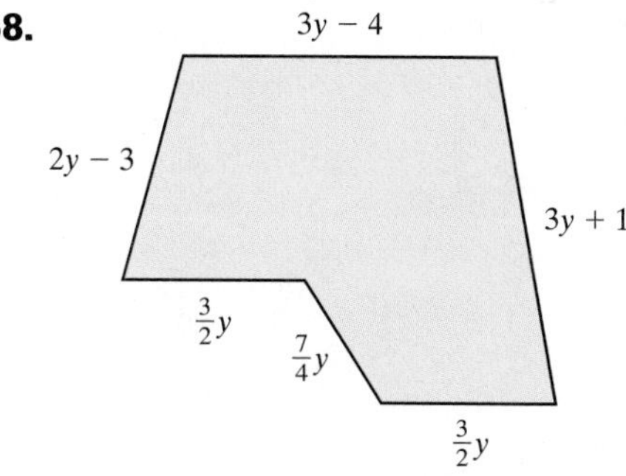

69. A wooden beam is $(4y^2 + 4y + 1)$ meters long. If a piece $(y^2 - 10)$ meters is cut off, express the length of the remaining piece of beam as a polynomial in y.

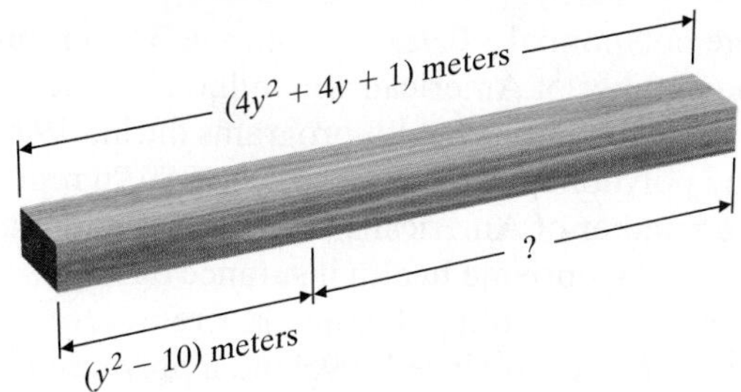

70. A piece of quarter-round molding is $(13x - 7)$ inches long. If a piece $(2x + 2)$ inches long is removed, express the length of the remaining piece of molding as a polynomial in x.

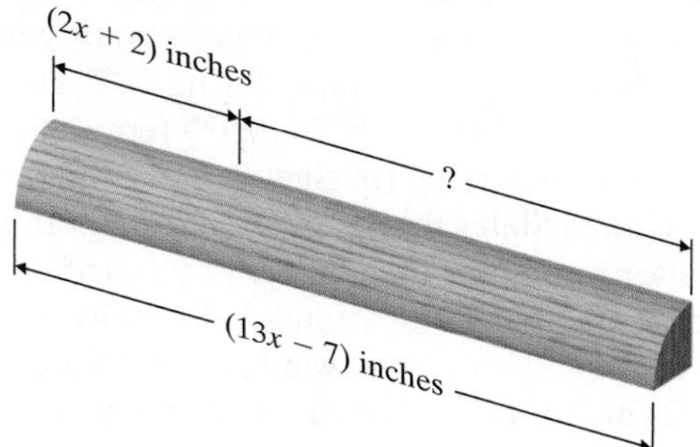

Perform each indicated operation.

71. $[(1.2x^2 - 3x + 9.1) - (7.8x^2 - 3.1 + 8)] + (1.2x - 6)$

72. $[(7.9y^4 - 6.8y^3 + 3.3y) + (6.1y^3 - 5)] - (4.2y^4 + 1.1y - 1)$

Review

Multiply. See Section 10.1.

73. $3x(2x)$

74. $-7x(x)$

75. $(12x^3)(-x^5)$

76. $6r^3(7r^{10})$

77. $10x^2(20xy^2)$

78. $-z^2y(11zy)$

Concept Extensions

Fill in the squares so that each is a true statement.

79. $3x^{\square} + 4x^2 = 7x^{\square}$

80. $9y^7 + 3y^{\square} = 12y^7$

81. $2x^{\square} + 3x^{\square} - 5x^{\square} + 4x^{\square} = 6x^4 - 2x^3$

82. $3y^{\square} + 7y^{\square} - 2y^{\square} - y^{\square} = 10y^5 - 3y^2$

Match each expression on the left with its simplification on the right. Not all letters on the right must be used and a letter may be used more than once.

83. $10y - 6y^2 - y$

84. $5x + 5x$

85. $(5x - 3) + (5x - 3)$

86. $(15x - 3) - (5x - 3)$

a. $3y$
b. $9y - 6y^2$
c. $10x$
d. $25x^2$
e. $10x - 6$
f. none of these

Simplify each expression by performing the indicated operation. Explain how you arrived at each answer. See the last Concept Check in this section.

87. a. $z + 3z$
b. $z \cdot 3z$
c. $-z - 3z$
d. $(-z)(-3z)$

88. a. $2y + y$
b. $2y \cdot y$
c. $-2y - y$
d. $(-2y)(-y)$

89. a. $m \cdot m \cdot m$
b. $m + m + m$
c. $(-m)(-m)(-m)$
d. $-m - m - m$

90. a. $x + x$
b. $x \cdot x$
c. $-x - x$
d. $(-x)(-x)$

91. The polynomial $-20x^2 + 156x + 14{,}437$ represents the electricity generated (in gigawatts) by geothermal sources in the United States during 2002–2007. The polynomial $894x^2 - 90x + 10{,}939$ represents the electricity generated (in gigawatts) by wind power in the United States during 2002–2007. In both polynomials, x represents the number of years after 2002. Find a polynomial for the total electricity generated by both geothermal and wind power during 2002–2007. (*Source:* Based on information from the Energy Information Administration)

92. The polynomial $-0.92x^2 + 2.43x + 34.85$ represents the number of Americans (in millions) under age 65 covered by public health programs during 1999–2007. The polynomial $0.07x^2 - 0.64x + 180.96$ represents the number of Americans (in millions) under age 65 covered by private health insurance during 1999–2007. In both polynomials, x represents the number of years since 1999. Find a polynomial for the total number of Americans (in millions) under age 65 with some form of health coverage during this period. (*Source:* Based on data from U.S. Census Bureau)

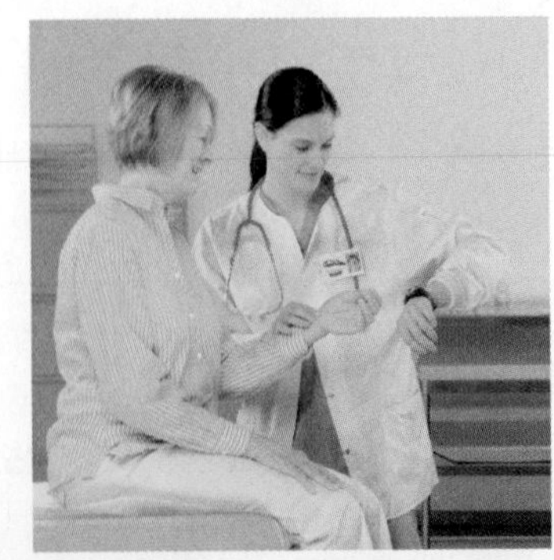

10.5 MULTIPLYING POLYNOMIALS

Objectives

A Multiply Monomials.

B Multiply a Monomial by a Polynomial.

C Multiply Two Polynomials.

D Multiply Polynomials Vertically.

Objective A Multiplying Monomials

Recall from Section 10.1 that to multiply two monomials such as $(-5x^3)$ and $(-2x^4)$, we use the associative and commutative properties and regroup. Remember also that to multiply exponential expressions with a common base, we use the product rule for exponents and add exponents.

$(-5x^3)(-2x^4) = (-5)(-2)(x^3 \cdot x^4)$ Use the commutative and associative properties.

$= 10x^7$ Multiply.

Examples Multiply.

1. $6x \cdot 4x = (6 \cdot 4)(x \cdot x)$ Use the commutative and associative properties.

$= 24x^2$ Multiply.

2. $-7x^2 \cdot 2x^5 = (-7 \cdot 2)(x^2 \cdot x^5)$

$= -14x^7$

3. $(-12x^5)(-x) = (-12x^5)(-1x)$

$= (-12)(-1)(x^5 \cdot x)$

$= 12x^6$

Work Practice 1–3

PRACTICE 1–3

Multiply.

1. $10x \cdot 9x$

2. $8x^3(-11x^7)$

3. $(-5x^4)(-x)$

✓Concept Check Simplify.

a. $3x \cdot 2x$ **b.** $3x + 2x$

Objective B Multiplying Monomials by Polynomials

To multiply a monomial such as $7x$ by a trinomial such as $x^2 + 2x + 5$, we use the distributive property.

Examples Multiply.

4. $7x(x^2 + 2x + 5) = 7x(x^2) + 7x(2x) + 7x(5)$ Apply the distributive property.

$= 7x^3 + 14x^2 + 35x$ Multiply.

5. $5x(2x^3 + 6) = 5x(2x^3) + 5x(6)$ Apply the distributive property.

$= 10x^4 + 30x$ Multiply.

6. $-3x^2(5x^2 + 6x - 1)$

$= (-3x^2)(5x^2) + (-3x^2)(6x) + (-3x^2)(-1)$ Apply the distributive property.

$= -15x^4 - 18x^3 + 3x^2$ Multiply.

Work Practice 4–6

PRACTICE 4–6

Multiply.

4. $4x(x^2 + 4x + 3)$

5. $8x(7x^4 + 1)$

6. $-2x^3(3x^2 - x + 2)$

Answers

1. $90x^2$ **2.** $-88x^{10}$ **3.** $5x^5$

4. $4x^3 + 16x^2 + 12x$ **5.** $56x^5 + 8x$

6. $-6x^5 + 2x^4 - 4x^3$

✓ **Concept Check Answers**

a. $6x^2$ **b.** $5x$

Objective C Multiplying Two Polynomials

We also use the distributive property to multiply two binomials.

PRACTICE 7

Multiply:

a. $(x + 5)(x + 10)$

b. $(4x + 5)(3x - 4)$

Example 7 Multiply.

a. $(m + 4)(m + 6)$ **b.** $(3x + 2)(2x - 5)$

Solution:

a. $(m + 4)(m + 6) = m(m + 6) + 4(m + 6)$ Use the distributive property.

$= m \cdot m + m \cdot 6 + 4 \cdot m + 4 \cdot 6$ Use the distributive property.

$= m^2 + 6m + 4m + 24$ Multiply.

$= m^2 + 10m + 24$ Combine like terms.

b. $(3x + 2)(2x - 5) = 3x(2x - 5) + 2(2x - 5)$ Use the distributive property.

$= 3x(2x) + 3x(-5) + 2(2x) + 2(-5)$

$= 6x^2 - 15x + 4x - 10$ Multiply.

$= 6x^2 - 11x - 10$ Combine like terms.

Work Practice 7

This idea can be expanded so that we can multiply any two polynomials.

To Multiply Two Polynomials

Multiply each term of the first polynomial by each term of the second polynomial, and then combine like terms.

PRACTICE 8–9

Multiply.

8. $(3x - 2y)^2$

9. $(x + 3)(2x^2 - 5x + 4)$

Examples Multiply.

8. $(2x - y)^2$

$= (2x - y)(2x - y)$ Using the meaning of an exponent, we have 2 factors of $(2x - y)$.

$= 2x(2x) + 2x(-y) + (-y)(2x) + (-y)(-y)$

$= 4x^2 - 2xy - 2xy + y^2$ Multiply.

$= 4x^2 - 4xy + y^2$ Combine like terms.

9. $(t + 2)(3t^2 - 4t + 2)$

$= t(3t^2) + t(-4t) + t(2) + 2(3t^2) + 2(-4t) + 2(2)$

$= 3t^3 - 4t^2 + 2t + 6t^2 - 8t + 4$

$= 3t^3 + 2t^2 - 6t + 4$ Combine like terms.

Work Practice 8–9

✓**Concept Check** Square where indicated. Simplify if possible.

a. $(4a)^2 + (3b)^2$ **b.** $(4a + 3b)^2$

Objective D Multiplying Polynomials Vertically

Another convenient method for multiplying polynomials is to multiply vertically, similar to the way we multiply real numbers. This method is shown in the next examples.

Answers

7. a. $x^2 + 15x + 50$

b. $12x^2 - x - 20$

8. $9x^2 - 12xy + 4y^2$

9. $2x^3 + x^2 - 11x + 12$

✓ **Concept Check Answers**

a. $16a^2 + 9b^2$ **b.** $16a^2 + 24ab + 9b^2$

Example 10 Multiply vertically: $(2y^2 + 5)(y^2 - 3y + 4)$

Solution:

$$\begin{array}{rrrrrl} & & y^2 & - 3y & + 4 & \\ & & 2y^2 & & + 5 & \\ \hline & & 5y^2 & - 15y & + 20 & \text{Multiply } y^2 - 3y + 4 \text{ by } 5. \\ 2y^4 & - 6y^3 & + 8y^2 & & & \text{Multiply } y^2 - 3y + 4 \text{ by } 2y^2. \\ \hline 2y^4 & - 6y^3 & + 13y^2 & - 15y & + 20 & \text{Combine like terms.} \end{array}$$

Work Practice 10

PRACTICE 10

Multiply vertically: $(3y^2 + 1)(y^2 - 4y + 5)$

Example 11 Find the product of $(2x^2 - 3x + 4)$ and $(x^2 + 5x - 2)$ using a vertical format.

Solution: First, we arrange the polynomials in a vertical format. Then we multiply each term of the second polynomial by each term of the first polynomial.

$$\begin{array}{rrrrrl} & & 2x^2 & - 3x & + 4 & \\ & & x^2 & + 5x & - 2 & \\ \hline & & -4x^2 & + 6x & - 8 & \text{Multiply } 2x^2 - 3x + 4 \text{ by } -2. \\ & 10x^3 & - 15x^2 & + 20x & & \text{Multiply } 2x^2 - 3x + 4 \text{ by } 5x. \\ 2x^4 & - 3x^3 & + 4x^2 & & & \text{Multiply } 2x^2 - 3x + 4 \text{ by } x^2. \\ \hline 2x^4 & + 7x^3 & - 15x^2 & + 26x & - 8 & \text{Combine like terms.} \end{array}$$

Work Practice 11

PRACTICE 11

Find the product of $(4x^2 - x - 1)$ and $(3x^2 + 6x - 2)$ using a vertical format.

Answers

10. $3y^4 - 12y^3 + 16y^2 - 4y + 5$

11. $12x^4 + 21x^3 - 17x^2 - 4x + 2$

Vocabulary and Readiness Check

Fill in each blank with the correct choice.

1. The expression $5x(3x + 2)$ equals $5x \cdot 3x + 5x \cdot 2$ by the ______________ property.
   a. commutative **b.** associative **c.** distributive
2. The expression $(x + 4)(7x - 1)$ equals $x(7x - 1) + 4(7x - 1)$ by the ______________ property.
   a. commutative **b.** associative **c.** distributive
3. The expression $(5y - 1)^2$ equals ______________.
   a. $2(5y - 1)$ **b.** $(5y - 1)(5y + 1)$ **c.** $(5y - 1)(5y - 1)$
4. The expression $9x \cdot 3x$ equals ______________.
   a. $27x$ **b.** $27x^2$ **c.** $12x$ **d.** $12x^2$

Perform the indicated operation, if possible.

5. $x^3 \cdot x^5$ **6.** $x^2 \cdot x^6$ **7.** $x^3 + x^5$ **8.** $x^2 + x^6$

9. $x^7 \cdot x^7$ **10.** $x^{11} \cdot x^{11}$ **11.** $x^7 + x^7$ **12.** $x^{11} + x^{11}$

13. $9y^2 \cdot 11y^2$ **14.** $6z^3 \cdot 7z^3$ **15.** $9y^2 + 11y^2$ **16.** $6z^3 + 7z^3$

10.5 Exercise Set

FOR EXTRA HELP

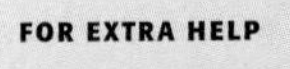

Objective **A** *Multiply. See Examples 1 through 3.*

1. $8x^2 \cdot 3x$ **2.** $6x \cdot 3x^2$ **3.** $(-x^3)(-x)$ **4.** $(-x^6)(-x)$

5. $-4n^3 \cdot 7n^7$ **6.** $9t^6(-3t^5)$ **7.** $(-3.1x^3)(4x^9)$ **8.** $(-5.2x^4)(3x^4)$

9. $\left(-\frac{1}{3}y^2\right)\left(\frac{2}{5}y\right)$ **10.** $\left(-\frac{3}{4}y^7\right)\left(\frac{1}{7}y^4\right)$ **11.** $(2x)(-3x^2)(4x^5)$ **12.** $(x)(5x^4)(-6x^7)$

Objective **B** *Multiply. See Examples 4 through 6.*

13. $3x(2x + 5)$ **14.** $2x(6x + 3)$ **15.** $7x(x^2 + 2x - 1)$ **16.** $5y(y^2 + y - 10)$

17. $-2a(a + 4)$ **18.** $-3a(2a + 7)$ **19.** $3x(2x^2 - 3x + 4)$ **20.** $4x(5x^2 - 6x - 10)$

21. $3a^2(4a^3 + 15)$ **22.** $9x^3(5x^2 + 12)$ **23.** $-2a^2(3a^2 - 2a + 3)$ **24.** $-4b^2(3b^3 - 12b^2 - 6)$

25. $3x^2y(2x^3 - x^2y^2 + 8y^3)$

26. $4xy^2(7x^3 + 3x^2y^2 - 9y^3)$

27. $-y(4x^3 - 7x^2y + xy^2 + 3y^3)$

28. $-x(6y^3 - 5xy^2 + x^2y - 5x^3)$

29. $\frac{1}{2}x^2(8x^2 - 6x + 1)$

30. $\frac{1}{3}y^2(9y^2 - 6y + 1)$

Objective **C** *Multiply. See Examples 7 through 9.*

31. $(x + 4)(x + 3)$

32. $(x + 2)(x + 9)$

33. $(a + 7)(a - 2)$

34. $(y - 10)(y + 11)$

35. $\left(x + \frac{2}{3}\right)\left(x - \frac{1}{3}\right)$

36. $\left(x + \frac{3}{5}\right)\left(x - \frac{2}{5}\right)$

37. $(3x^2 + 1)(4x^2 + 7)$

38. $(5x^2 + 2)(6x^2 + 2)$

39. $(4x - 3)(3x - 5)$

40. $(8x - 3)(2x - 4)$

41. $(1 - 3a)(1 - 4a)$

42. $(3 - 2a)(2 - a)$

43. $(2y - 4)^2$

44. $(6x - 7)^2$

45. $(x - 2)(x^2 - 3x + 7)$

46. $(x + 3)(x^2 + 5x - 8)$

47. $(x + 5)(x^3 - 3x + 4)$

48. $(a + 2)(a^3 - 3a^2 + 7)$

49. $(2a - 3)(5a^2 - 6a + 4)$

50. $(3 + b)(2 - 5b - 3b^2)$

51. $(7xy - y)^2$

52. $(x^2 - 4)^2$

Objective **D** *Multiply vertically. See Examples 10 and 11.*

53. $(2x - 11)(6x + 1)$

54. $(4x - 7)(5x + 1)$

55. $(x + 3)(2x^2 + 4x - 1)$

56. $(4x - 5)(8x^2 + 2x - 4)$

57. $(x^2 + 5x - 7)(2x^2 - 7x - 9)$

58. $(3x^2 - x + 2)(x^2 + 2x + 1)$

Objectives **A B C D** **Mixed Practice** *Multiply. See Examples 1 through 11.*

59. $-1.2y(-7y^6)$

60. $-4.2x(-2x^5)$

61. $-3x(x^2 + 2x - 8)$

62. $-5x(x^2 - 3x + 10)$

63. $(x + 19)(2x + 1)$

64. $(3y + 4)(y + 11)$

65. $\left(x + \frac{1}{7}\right)\left(x - \frac{3}{7}\right)$

66. $\left(m + \frac{2}{9}\right)\left(m - \frac{1}{9}\right)$

67. $(3y + 5)^2$

68. $(7y + 2)^2$

69. $(a + 4)(a^2 - 6a + 6)$

70. $(t + 3)(t^2 - 5t + 5)$

Express as the product of polynomials. Then multiply.

△ **71.** Find the area of the rectangle.

$(2x + 5)$ yards

$(2x - 5)$ yards

△ **72.** Find the area of the square field.

△ **73.** Find the area of the triangle.

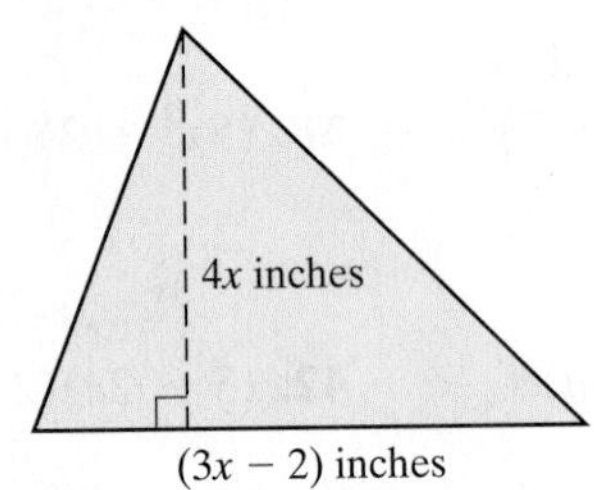

△ **74.** Find the volume of the cube-shaped glass block.

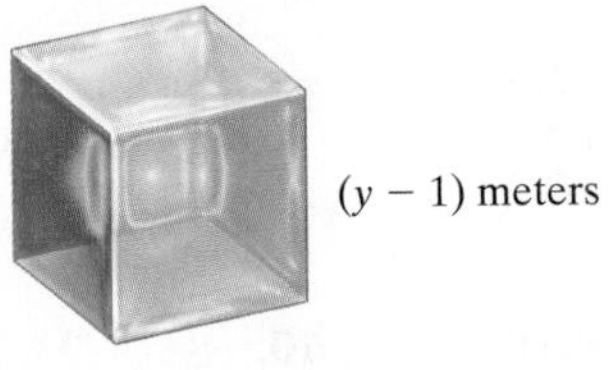

Review

In this section, we review operations on monomials. Study the box below, then proceed. See Sections 8.7, 10.1, and 10.2.

Operations on Monomials	
Multiply	Review the product rule for exponents.
Divide	Review the quotient rule for exponents.
Add or Subtract	Remember, we may only combine like terms.

Perform the operations on the monomials, if possible. The first two rows have been completed for you.

	Monomials	Add	Subtract	Multiply	Divide
	$6x, 3x$	$6x + 3x = 9x$	$6x - 3x = 3x$	$6x \cdot 3x = 18x^2$	$\frac{6x}{3x} = 2$
	$-12x^2, 2x$	$-12x^2 + 2x$; can't be simplified	$-12x^2 - 2x$; can't be simplified	$-12x^2 \cdot 2x = -24x^3$	$\frac{-12x^2}{2x} = -6x$
75.	$5a, 15a$				
76.	$4y^3, 4y^7$				
77.	$-3y^5, 9y^4$				
78.	$-14x^2, 2x^2$				

Concept Extensions

79. Perform each indicated operation. Explain the difference between the two expressions.

a. $(3x + 5) + (3x + 7)$
b. $(3x + 5)(3x + 7)$

80. Perform each indicated operation. Explain the difference between the two expressions.

a. $(8x - 3) - (5x - 2)$
b. $(8x - 3)(5x - 2)$

Mixed Practice *Perform the indicated operations. See Sections 10.4 and 10.5.*

81. $(3x - 1) + (10x - 6)$

82. $(2x - 1) + (10x - 7)$

83. $(3x - 1)(10x - 6)$

84. $(2x - 1)(10x - 7)$

85. $(3x - 1) - (10x - 6)$

86. $(2x - 1) - (10x - 7)$

87. The area of the largest rectangle below is $x(x + 3)$. Find another expression for this area by finding the sum of the areas of the smaller rectangles.

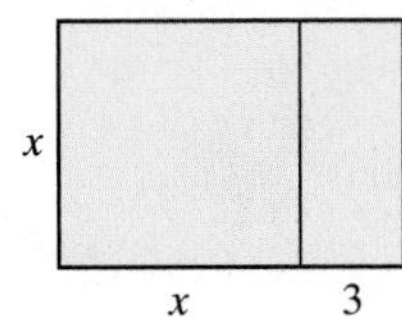

88. The area of the figure below is $(x + 2)(x + 3)$. Find another expression for this area by finding the sum of the areas of the smaller rectangles.

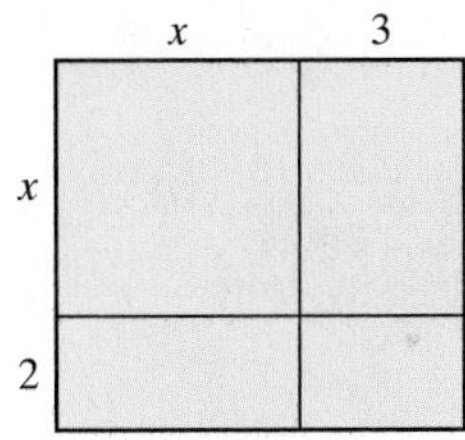

89. Write an expression for the area of the largest rectangle below in two different ways.

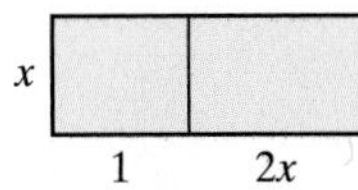

90. Write an expression for the area of the figure below in two different ways.

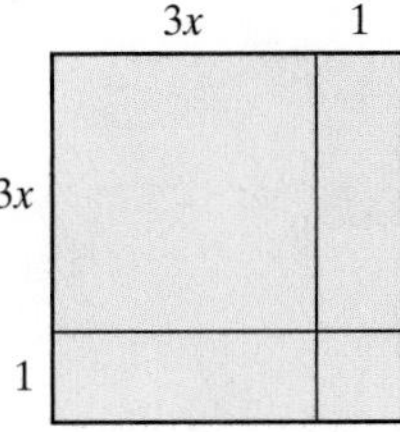

Simplify. See the Concept Checks in this section.

91. $5a + 6a$

92. $5a \cdot 6a$

Square where indicated. Simplify if possible.

93. $(5x)^2 + (2y)^2$

94. $(5x + 2y)^2$

95. Multiply each of the following polynomials.

a. $(a + b)(a - b)$
b. $(2x + 3y)(2x - 3y)$
c. $(4x + 7)(4x - 7)$
d. Can you make a general statement about all products of the form $(x + y)(x - y)$?

96. Evaluate each of the following.

a. $(2 + 3)^2$; $2^2 + 3^2$
b. $(8 + 10)^2$; $8^2 + 10^2$
c. Does $(a + b)^2 = a^2 + b^2$ no matter what the values of a and b are? Why or why not?

10.6 SPECIAL PRODUCTS

Objective A Using the FOIL Method

In this section, we multiply binomials using special products. First, we introduce a special order for multiplying binomials called the FOIL order or method. This order, or pattern, is a result of the distributive property. We demonstrate by multiplying $(3x + 1)$ by $(2x + 5)$.

The FOIL Method

F stands for the product of the **First** terms. $(3x + 1)(2x + 5)$ $(3x)(2x) = 6x^2$ F

O stands for the product of the **Outer** terms. $(3x + 1)(2x + 5)$ $(3x)(5) = 15x$ O

I stands for the product of the **Inner** terms. $(3x + 1)(2x + 5)$ $(1)(2x) = 2x$ I

L stands for the product of the **Last** terms. $(3x + 1)(2x + 5)$ $(1)(5) = 5$ L

$$\begin{aligned}(3x + 1)(2x + 5) &= \overset{F}{6x^2} + \overset{O}{15x} + \overset{I}{2x} + \overset{L}{5} \\ &= 6x^2 + 17x + 5 \quad \text{Combine like terms.}\end{aligned}$$

Let's practice multiplying binomials using the FOIL method.

Example 1 Multiply: $(x - 3)(x + 4)$

Solution:

$$\begin{aligned}(x - 3)(x + 4) &= \overset{F}{(x)(x)} + \overset{O}{(x)(4)} + \overset{I}{(-3)(x)} + \overset{L}{(-3)(4)} \\ &= x^2 + 4x - 3x - 12 \\ &= x^2 + x - 12 \quad \text{Combine like terms.}\end{aligned}$$

Work Practice 1

Example 2 Multiply: $(5x - 7)(x - 2)$

Solution:

$$\begin{aligned}(5x - 7)(x - 2) &= \overset{F}{5x(x)} + \overset{O}{5x(-2)} + \overset{I}{(-7)(x)} + \overset{L}{(-7)(-2)} \\ &= 5x^2 - 10x - 7x + 14 \\ &= 5x^2 - 17x + 14 \quad \text{Combine like terms.}\end{aligned}$$

Work Practice 2

Objectives

A Multiply Two Binomials Using the FOIL Method.

B Square a Binomial.

C Multiply the Sum and Difference of Two Terms.

D Use Special Products to Multiply Binomials.

PRACTICE 1

Multiply: $(x + 7)(x - 5)$

Helpful Hint Remember that the FOIL order for multiplying can be used only for the product of 2 binomials.

PRACTICE 2

Multiply: $(6x - 1)(x - 4)$

Answers

1. $x^2 + 2x - 35$ 2. $6x^2 - 25x + 4$

PRACTICE 3

Multiply: $(2y^2 + 3)(y - 4)$

Example 3 Multiply: $(y^2 + 6)(2y - 1)$

Solution: F O I L

$(y^2 + 6)(2y - 1) = 2y^3 - 1y^2 + 12y - 6$

Notice in this example that there are no like terms that can be combined, so the product is $2y^3 - y^2 + 12y - 6$.

Work Practice 3

Objective B Squaring Binomials

An expression such as $(3y + 1)^2$ is called the square of a binomial. Since $(3y + 1)^2 = (3y + 1)(3y + 1)$, we can use the FOIL method to find this product.

PRACTICE 4

Multiply: $(2x + 9)^2$

Example 4 Multiply: $(3y + 1)^2$

Solution:
$$(3y + 1)^2 = (3y + 1)(3y + 1)$$
F O I L
$$= (3y)(3y) + (3y)(1) + 1(3y) + 1(1)$$
$$= 9y^2 + 3y + 3y + 1$$
$$= 9y^2 + 6y + 1$$

Work Practice 4

Notice the pattern that appears in Example 4.

$(3y + 1)^2 = 9y^2 + 6y + 1$

- $9y^2$ is the first term of the binomial squared: $(3y)^2 = 9y^2$.
- $6y$ is 2 times the product of both terms of the binomial: $(2)(3y)(1) = 6y$.
- 1 is the second term of the binomial squared: $(1)^2 = 1$.

This pattern leads to the formulas below, which can be used when squaring a binomial. We call these **special products.**

Squaring a Binomial

A binomial squared is equal to the square of the first term plus or minus twice the product of both terms plus the square of the second term.

$$(a + b)^2 = a^2 + 2ab + b^2$$
$$(a - b)^2 = a^2 - 2ab + b^2$$

This product can be visualized geometrically.

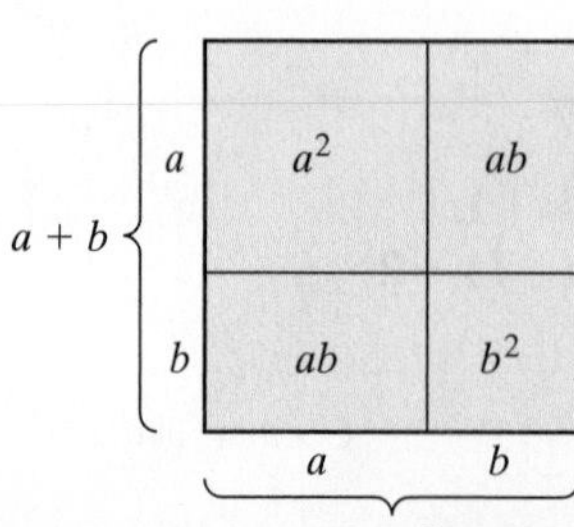

The area of the large square is side · side.

Area $= (a + b)(a + b) = (a + b)^2$

The area of the large square is also the sum of the areas of the smaller rectangles.

Area $= a^2 + ab + ab + b^2 = a^2 + 2ab + b^2$

Thus, $(a + b)^2 = a^2 + 2ab + b^2$.

Answers

3. $2y^3 - 8y^2 + 3y - 12$

4. $4x^2 + 36x + 81$

Examples Use a special product to square each binomial.

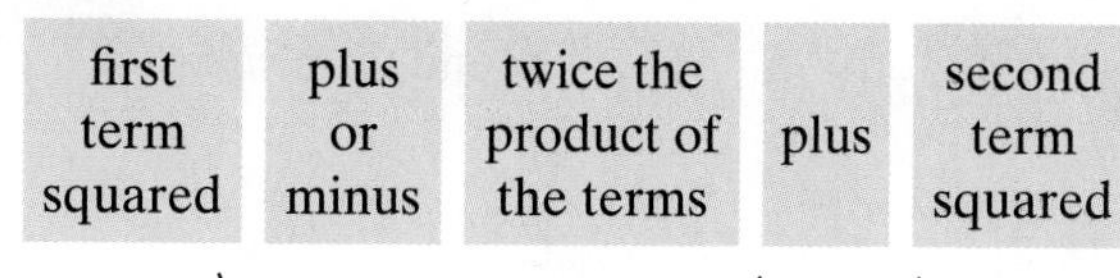

5. $(t + 2)^2 = t^2 + 2(t)(2) + 2^2 = t^2 + 4t + 4$

6. $(p - q)^2 = p^2 - 2(p)(q) + q^2 = p^2 - 2pq + q^2$

7. $(2x + 5)^2 = (2x)^2 + 2(2x)(5) + 5^2 = 4x^2 + 20x + 25$

8. $(x^2 - 7y)^2 = (x^2)^2 - 2(x^2)(7y) + (7y)^2 = x^4 - 14x^2y + 49y^2$

Work Practice 5–8

PRACTICE 5–8

Use a special product to square each binomial.

5. $(y + 3)^2$

6. $(r - s)^2$

7. $(6x + 5)^2$

8. $(x^2 - 3y)^2$

Helpful Hint

Notice that

$(a + b)^2 \neq a^2 + b^2$ The middle term, $2ab$, is missing.

$(a + b)^2 = (a + b)(a + b) = a^2 + 2ab + b^2$

Likewise,

$(a - b)^2 \neq a^2 - b^2$

$(a - b)^2 = (a - b)(a - b) = a^2 - 2ab + b^2$

Objective C Multiplying the Sum and Difference of Two Terms

Another special product is the product of the sum and difference of the same two terms, such as $(x + y)(x - y)$. Finding this product by the FOIL method, we see a pattern emerge.

$$(x + y)(x - y) = \overset{F}{x^2} - \overset{O}{xy} + \overset{I}{xy} - \overset{L}{y^2}$$
$$= x^2 - y^2$$

Notice that the two middle terms subtract out. This is because the **O**uter product is the opposite of the **I**nner product. Only the **difference of squares** remains.

Multiplying the Sum and Difference of Two Terms

The product of the sum and difference of two terms is the square of the first term minus the square of the second term.

$(a + b)(a - b) = a^2 - b^2$

Answers

5. $y^2 + 6y + 9$ **6.** $r^2 - 2rs + s^2$
7. $36x^2 + 60x + 25$
8. $x^4 - 6x^2y + 9y^2$

PRACTICE 9–13

Use a special product to multiply.

9. $(x + 9)(x - 9)$
10. $(5 + 4y)(5 - 4y)$
11. $\left(x - \frac{1}{3}\right)\left(x + \frac{1}{3}\right)$
12. $(3a - b)(3a + b)$
13. $(2x^2 - 6y)(2x^2 + 6y)$

Examples Use a special product to multiply.

first term squared — minus — second term squared

9. $(x + 4)(x - 4) = x^2 - 4^2 = x^2 - 16$

10. $(6t + 7)(6t - 7) = (6t)^2 - 7^2 = 36t^2 - 49$

11. $\left(x - \frac{1}{4}\right)\left(x + \frac{1}{4}\right) = x^2 - \left(\frac{1}{4}\right)^2 = x^2 - \frac{1}{16}$

12. $(2p - q)(2p + q) = (2p)^2 - q^2 = 4p^2 - q^2$

13. $(3x^2 - 5y)(3x^2 + 5y) = (3x^2)^2 - (5y)^2 = 9x^4 - 25y^2$

Work Practice 9–13

✓**Concept Check** Match each expression on the left to the equivalent expression or expressions in the list on the right.

$(a + b)^2$
$(a + b)(a - b)$

a. $(a + b)(a + b)$
b. $a^2 - b^2$
c. $a^2 + b^2$
d. $a^2 - 2ab + b^2$
e. $a^2 + 2ab + b^2$

Objective D Using Special Products

Let's now practice using our special products on a variety of multiplication problems. This practice will help us recognize when to apply what special product formula.

PRACTICE 14–17

Use a special product to multiply, if possible.

14. $(7x - 1)^2$
15. $(5y + 3)(2y - 5)$
16. $(2a - 1)(2a + 1)$
17. $\left(5y - \frac{1}{9}\right)^2$

Examples Use a special product to multiply, if possible.

14. $(4x - 9)(4x + 9)$
$= (4x)^2 - 9^2 = 16x^2 - 81$

This is the sum and difference of the same two terms.

15. $(3y + 2)^2$
$= (3y)^2 + 2(3y)(2) + 2^2$
$= 9y^2 + 12y + 4$

This is a binomial squared.

16. $(6a + 1)(a - 7)$

No special product applies.

F O I L — Use the FOIL method.

$= 6a \cdot a + 6a(-7) + 1 \cdot a + 1(-7)$
$= 6a^2 - 42a + a - 7$
$= 6a^2 - 41a - 7$

17. $\left(4x - \frac{1}{11}\right)^2$

This is a binomial squared.

$= (4x)^2 - 2(4x)\left(\frac{1}{11}\right) + \left(\frac{1}{11}\right)^2$

$= 16x^2 - \frac{8}{11}x + \frac{1}{121}$

Work Practice 14–17

Helpful Hint

- When multiplying two binomials, you may always use the FOIL order or method.
- When multiplying any two polynomials, you may always use the distributive property to find the product.

Answers

9. $x^2 - 81$ **10.** $25 - 16y^2$ **11.** $x^2 - \frac{1}{9}$ **12.** $9a^2 - b^2$ **13.** $4x^4 - 36y^2$ **14.** $49x^2 - 14x + 1$ **15.** $10y^2 - 19y - 15$ **16.** $4a^2 - 1$ **17.** $25y^2 - \frac{10}{9}y + \frac{1}{81}$

✓ **Concept Check Answer**

a and e, b

Vocabulary and Readiness Check

Answer each exercise true or false.

1. $(x + 4)^2 = x^2 + 16$
2. For $(x + 6)(2x - 1)$, the product of the first terms is $2x^2$.
3. $(x + 4)(x - 4) = x^2 + 16$
4. The product $(x - 1)(x^3 + 3x - 1)$ is a polynomial of degree 5.

10.6 Exercise Set

FOR EXTRA HELP

PRACTICE

WATCH

DOWNLOAD

READ

REVIEW

Objective A *Multiply using the FOIL method. See Examples 1 through 3.*

1. $(x + 3)(x + 4)$
2. $(x + 5)(x + 1)$
3. $(x - 5)(x + 10)$
4. $(y - 12)(y + 4)$
5. $(5x - 6)(x + 2)$
6. $(3y - 5)(2y + 7)$
7. $(y - 6)(4y - 1)$
8. $(2x - 9)(x - 11)$
9. $(2x + 5)(3x - 1)$
10. $(6x + 2)(x - 2)$
11. $(y^2 + 7)(6y + 4)$
12. $(y^2 + 3)(5y + 6)$
13. $\left(x - \frac{1}{3}\right)\left(x + \frac{2}{3}\right)$
14. $\left(x - \frac{2}{5}\right)\left(x + \frac{1}{5}\right)$
15. $(0.4 - 3a)(0.2 - 5a)$
16. $(0.3 - 2a)(0.6 - 5a)$
17. $(x + 5y)(2x - y)$
18. $(x + 4y)(3x - y)$

Objective B *Multiply. See Examples 4 through 8.*

19. $(x + 2)^2$
20. $(x + 7)^2$
21. $(2a - 3)^2$
22. $(7x - 3)^2$
23. $(3a - 5)^2$
24. $(5a - 2)^2$
25. $(x^2 + 0.5)^2$
26. $(x^2 + 0.3)^2$
27. $\left(y - \frac{2}{7}\right)^2$
28. $\left(y - \frac{3}{4}\right)^2$
29. $(2x - 1)^2$
30. $(5b - 4)^2$
31. $(5x + 9)^2$
32. $(6s + 2)^2$
33. $(3x - 7y)^2$
34. $(4s - 2y)^2$
35. $(4m + 5n)^2$
36. $(3n + 5m)^2$
37. $(5x^4 - 3)^2$
38. $(7x^3 - 6)^2$

Objective C *Multiply. See Examples 9 through 13.*

39. $(a - 7)(a + 7)$ **40.** $(b + 3)(b - 3)$ **41.** $(x + 6)(x - 6)$ **42.** $(x - 8)(x + 8)$

43. $(3x - 1)(3x + 1)$ **44.** $(7x - 5)(7x + 5)$ **45.** $(x^2 + 5)(x^2 - 5)$ **46.** $(a^2 + 6)(a^2 - 6)$

47. $(2y^2 - 1)(2y^2 + 1)$ **48.** $(3x^2 + 1)(3x^2 - 1)$ **49.** $(4 - 7x)(4 + 7x)$ **50.** $(8 - 7x)(8 + 7x)$

51. $\left(3x - \frac{1}{2}\right)\left(3x + \frac{1}{2}\right)$ **52.** $\left(10x + \frac{2}{7}\right)\left(10x - \frac{2}{7}\right)$ **53.** $(9x + y)(9x - y)$ **54.** $(2x - y)(2x + y)$

55. $(2m + 5n)(2m - 5n)$ **56.** $(5m + 4n)(5m - 4n)$

Objectives D **Mixed Practice** *Multiply. See Examples 14 through 17.*

57. $(a + 5)(a + 4)$ **58.** $(a + 5)(a + 7)$ **59.** $(a - 7)^2$ **60.** $(b - 2)^2$

61. $(4a + 1)(3a - 1)$ **62.** $(6a + 7)(6a + 5)$ **63.** $(x + 2)(x - 2)$ **64.** $(x - 10)(x + 10)$

65. $(3a + 1)^2$ **66.** $(4a + 2)^2$ **67.** $(x + y)(4x - y)$ **68.** $(3x + 2)(4x - 2)$

69. $\left(\frac{1}{3}a^2 - 7\right)\left(\frac{1}{3}a^2 + 7\right)$ **70.** $\left(\frac{a}{2} + 4y\right)\left(\frac{a}{2} - 4y\right)$ **71.** $(3b + 7)(2b - 5)$ **72.** $(3y - 13)(y - 3)$

73. $(x^2 + 10)(x^2 - 10)$ **74.** $(x^2 + 8)(x^2 - 8)$ **75.** $(4x + 5)(4x - 5)$ **76.** $(3x + 5)(3x - 5)$

77. $(5x - 6y)^2$ **78.** $(4x - 9y)^2$ **79.** $(2r - 3s)(2r + 3s)$ **80.** $(6r - 2x)(6r + 2x)$

Express each as a product of polynomials in x. Then multiply and simplify.

81. Find the area of the square rug if its side is $(2x + 1)$ feet.

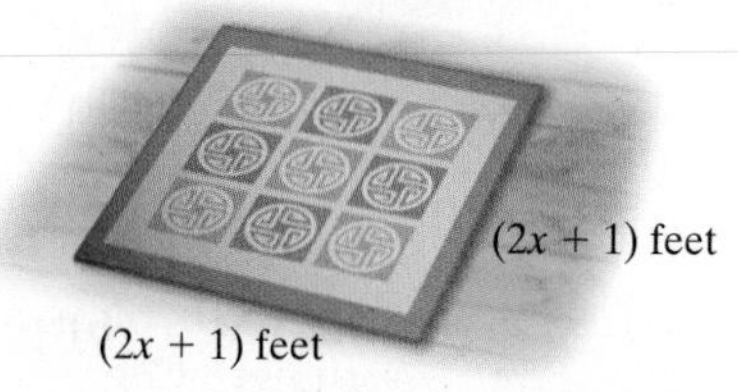

82. Find the area of the rectangular canvas if its length is $(3x - 2)$ inches and its width is $(x - 4)$ inches.

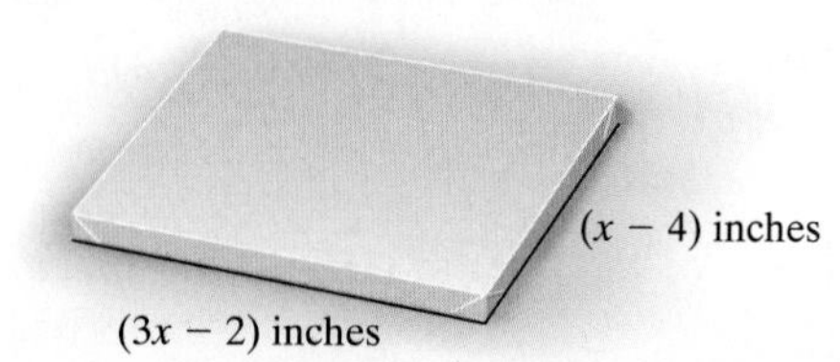

Review

Simplify each expression. See Sections 10.1 and 10.2.

83. $\frac{50b^{10}}{70b^5}$ **84.** $\frac{60y^6}{80y^2}$ **85.** $\frac{8a^{17}b^5}{-4a^7b^{10}}$ **86.** $\frac{-6a^8y}{3a^4y}$ **87.** $\frac{2x^4y^{12}}{3x^4y^4}$ **88.** $\frac{-48ab^6}{32ab^3}$

Concept Extensions

Match each expression on the left to the equivalent expression on the right. See the Concept Check in this section. (Not all choices will be used.)

89. $(a - b)^2$

90. $(a - b)(a + b)$

91. $(a + b)^2$

92. $(a + b)^2(a - b)^2$

a. $a^2 - b^2$
b. $a^2 + b^2$
c. $a^2 - 2ab + b^2$
d. $a^2 + 2ab + b^2$
e. none of these

Fill in the squares so that a true statement forms.

93. $(x^{\square} + 7)(x^{\square} + 3) = x^4 + 10x^2 + 21$

94. $(5x^{\square} - 2)^2 = 25x^6 - 20x^3 + 4$

Find the area of the shaded figure. To do so, subtract the area of the smaller square(s) from the area of the larger geometric figure.

△ **95.**

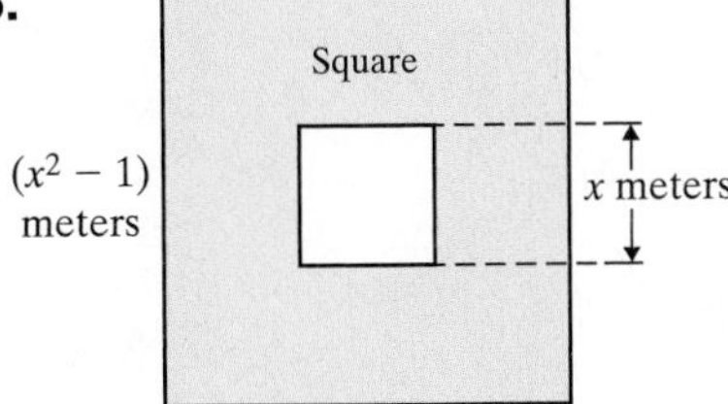

△ **96.**

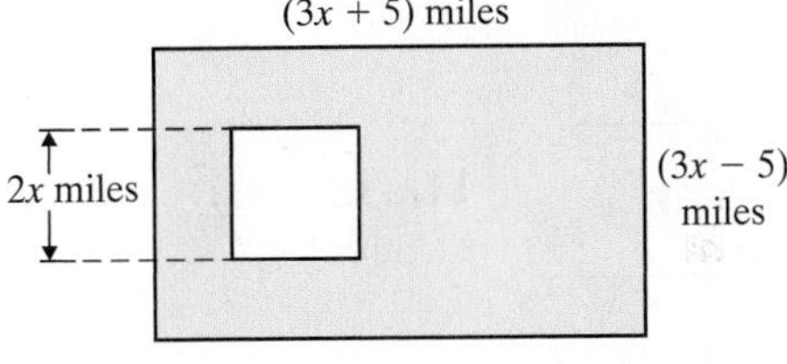

△ **97.**

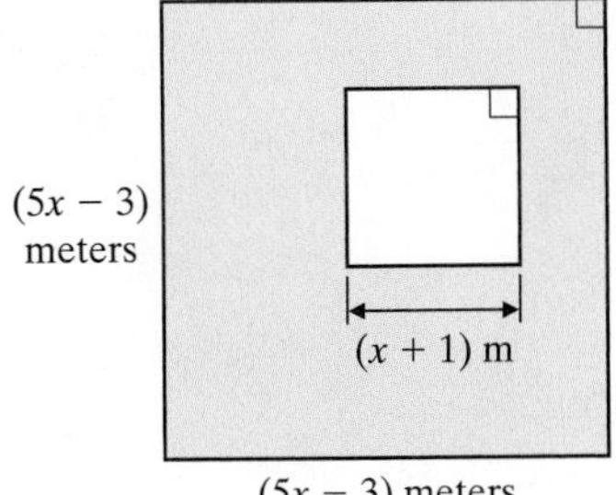

△ **98.**

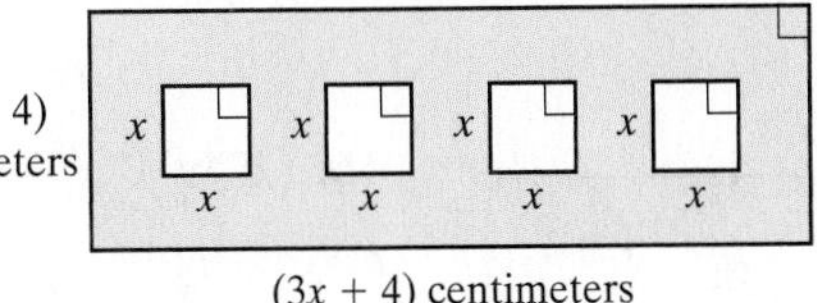

99. In your own words, describe the different methods that can be used to find the product: $(2x - 5)(3x + 1)$.

100. In your own words, describe the different methods that can be used to find the product: $(5x + 1)^2$.

101. Suppose that a classmate asked you why $(2x + 1)^2$ is **not** $(4x^2 + 1)$. Write down your response to this classmate.

102. Suppose that a classmate asked you why $(2x + 1)^2$ is $(4x^2 + 4x + 1)$. Write down your response to this classmate.

Answers

1. ____
2. ____
3. ____
4. ____
5. ____
6. ____
7. ____
8. ____
9. ____
10. ____
11. ____
12. ____
13. ____
14. ____
15. ____
16. ____
17. ____
18. ____
19. ____
20. ____

Integrated Review Sections 10.1–10.6

Exponents and Operations on Polynomials

Perform operations and simplify.

1. $(5x^2)(7x^3)$

2. $(4y^2)(-8y^7)$

3. -4^2

4. $(-4)^2$

5. $(x - 5)(2x + 1)$

6. $(3x - 2)(x + 5)$

7. $(x - 5) + (2x + 1)$

8. $(3x - 2) + (x + 5)$

9. $\dfrac{7x^9y^{12}}{x^3y^{10}}$

10. $\dfrac{20a^2b^8}{14a^2b^2}$

11. $(12m^7n^6)^2$

12. $(4y^9z^{10})^3$

13. $(4y - 3)(4y + 3)$

14. $(7x - 1)(7x + 1)$

15. $(x^{-7}y^5)^9$

16. 8^{-2}

17. $(3^{-1}x^9)^3$

18. $\dfrac{(r^7s^{-5})^6}{(2r^{-4}s^{-4})^4}$

19. $(7x^2 - 2x + 3) - (5x^2 + 9)$

20. $(10x^2 + 7x - 9) - (4x^2 - 6x + 2)$

21. $0.7y^2 - 1.2 + 1.8y^2 - 6y + 1$

22. $7.8x^2 - 6.8x - 3.3 + 0.6x^2 - 0.9$

23. Subtract $y^2 + 2$ from $3y^2 - 6y + 1$.

24. $(z^2 + 5) - (3z^2 - 1) + \left(8z^2 + 2z - \frac{1}{2}\right)$

25. $(x + 4)^2$

26. $(y - 9)^2$

27. $(x + 4) + (x + 4)$

28. $(y - 9) + (y - 9)$

29. $7x^2 - 6xy + 4(y^2 - xy)$

30. $5a^2 - 3ab + 6(b^2 - a^2)$

31. $(x - 3)(x^2 + 5x - 1)$

32. $(x + 1)(x^2 - 3x - 2)$

33. $(2x - 7)(3x + 10)$

34. $(5x - 1)(4x + 5)$

35. $(2x - 7)(x^2 - 6x + 1)$

36. $(5x - 1)(x^2 + 2x - 3)$

37. $\left(2x + \frac{5}{9}\right)\left(2x - \frac{5}{9}\right)$

38. $\left(12y + \frac{3}{7}\right)\left(12y - \frac{3}{7}\right)$

21. ______

22. ______

23. ______

24. ______

25. ______

26. ______

27. ______

28. ______

29. ______

30. ______

31. ______

32. ______

33. ______

34. ______

35. ______

36. ______

37. ______

38. ______

Objectives

A **Divide a Polynomial by a Monomial.**

B **Use Long Division to Divide a Polynomial by a Polynomial Other than a Monomial.**

10.7 DIVIDING POLYNOMIALS

Objective A Dividing by a Monomial

To divide a polynomial by a monomial, recall addition of fractions. Fractions that have a common denominator are added by adding the numerators:

$$\frac{a}{c} + \frac{b}{c} = \frac{a + b}{c}$$

If we read this equation from right to left and let a, b, and c be monomials, $c \neq 0$, we have the following.

To Divide a Polynomial by a Monomial

Divide each term of the polynomial by the monomial.

$$\frac{a + b}{c} = \frac{a}{c} + \frac{b}{c}, \quad c \neq 0$$

Throughout this section, we assume that denominators are not 0.

PRACTICE 1

Divide: $(25x^3 + 5x^2) \div 5x^2$

Example 1 Divide: $(6m^2 + 2m) \div 2m$

Solution: We begin by writing the quotient in fraction form. Then we divide each term of the polynomial $6m^2 + 2m$ by the monomial $2m$ and use the quotient rule for exponents to simplify.

$$\frac{6m^2 + 2m}{2m} = \frac{6m^2}{2m} + \frac{2m}{2m}$$

$$= 3m + 1 \quad \text{Simplify.}$$

Check: To check, we multiply.

$$2m(3m + 1) = 2m(3m) + 2m(1) = 6m^2 + 2m$$

The quotient $3m + 1$ checks.

Work Practice 1

✓Concept Check In which of the following is $\frac{x + 5}{5}$ simplified correctly?

a. $\frac{x}{5} + 1$ **b.** x **c.** $x + 1$

PRACTICE 2

Divide: $\frac{24x^7 + 12x^2 - 4x}{4x^2}$

Example 2 Divide: $\frac{9x^5 - 12x^2 + 3x}{3x^2}$

Solution: $\frac{9x^5 - 12x^2 + 3x}{3x^2} = \frac{9x^5}{3x^2} - \frac{12x^2}{3x^2} + \frac{3x}{3x^2}$ Divide each term by $3x^2$.

$$= 3x^3 - 4 + \frac{1}{x} \quad \text{Simplify.}$$

Notice that the quotient is not a polynomial because of the term $\frac{1}{x}$. This expression is called a rational expression—we will study rational expressions in Chapter 12. Although the quotient of two polynomials is not always a polynomial, we may still check by multiplying.

Answers

1. $5x + 1$ **2.** $6x^5 + 3 - \frac{1}{x}$

✓ Concept Check Answer

a

Check: $3x^2\left(3x^3 - 4 + \frac{1}{x}\right) = 3x^2(3x^3) - 3x^2(4) + 3x^2\left(\frac{1}{x}\right)$

$= 9x^5 - 12x^2 + 3x$

Work Practice 2

Example 3 Divide: $\frac{8x^2y^2 - 16xy + 2x}{4xy}$

Solution: $\frac{8x^2y^2 - 16xy + 2x}{4xy} = \frac{8x^2y^2}{4xy} - \frac{16xy}{4xy} + \frac{2x}{4xy}$ Divide each term by $4xy$.

$= 2xy - 4 + \frac{1}{2y}$ Simplify.

Check: $4xy\left(2xy - 4 + \frac{1}{2y}\right) = 4xy(2xy) - 4xy(4) + 4xy\left(\frac{1}{2y}\right)$

$= 8x^2y^2 - 16xy + 2x$

Work Practice 3

PRACTICE 3

Divide: $\frac{12x^3y^3 - 18xy + 6y}{3xy}$

Objective B Dividing by a Polynomial Other than a Monomial

To divide a polynomial by a polynomial other than a monomial, we use a process known as long division. Polynomial long division is similar to number long division, so we review long division by dividing 13 into 3660.

$$\begin{array}{r} 281 \\ 13\overline{)3660} \\ \underline{26\downarrow} \\ 106 \\ \underline{104\downarrow} \\ 20 \\ \underline{13} \\ 7 \end{array}$$

$2 \cdot 13 = 26$

Subtract and bring down the next digit in the dividend.

$8 \cdot 13 = 104$

Subtract and bring down the next digit in the dividend.

$1 \cdot 13 = 13$

Subtract. There are no more digits to bring down, so the remainder is 7.

Helpful Hint Recall that 3660 is called the dividend.

The quotient is 281 R 7, which can be written as $281\frac{7}{13}$. (7 ← remainder, 13 ← divisor)

Recall that division can be checked by multiplication. To check this division problem, we see that

$13 \cdot 281 + 7 = 3660$, the dividend.

Now we demonstrate long division of polynomials.

Example 4 Divide $x^2 + 7x + 12$ by $x + 3$ using long division.

Solution:

To subtract, change the signs of these terms and add.

$$\begin{array}{r} x \\ x + 3\overline{)x^2 + 7x + 12} \\ \underline{-x^2 - 3x \downarrow} \\ 4x + 12 \end{array}$$

How many times does x divide x^2? $\frac{x^2}{x} = x$.

Multiply: $x(x + 3)$

Subtract and bring down the next term.

Continued on next page

PRACTICE 4

Divide $x^2 + 12x + 35$ by $x + 5$ using long division.

Answers

3. $4x^2y^2 - 6 + \frac{2}{x}$ **4.** $x + 7$

Now we repeat this process.

$$\begin{array}{r} x + 4 \\ x + 3\overline{)x^2 + 7x + 12} \\ \underline{x^2 + 3x} \\ 4x + 12 \\ \underline{\overset{-}{4x} \overset{-}{+} 12} \\ 0 \end{array}$$

How many times does x divide $4x$? $\frac{4x}{x} = 4$.

To subtract, change the signs of these terms and add. → Multiply: $4(x + 3)$

Subtract. The remainder is 0.

The quotient is $x + 4$.

Check: We check by multiplying.

divisor	·	quotient	+	remainder	=	dividend
or ↓		↓		↓		↓
$(x + 3)$	·	$(x + 4)$	+	0		$= x^2 + 7x + 12$

The quotient checks.

Work Practice 4

PRACTICE 5

Divide: $8x^2 + 2x - 7$ by $2x - 1$

Example 5 Divide $6x^2 + 10x - 5$ by $3x - 1$ using long division.

Solution:

$$\begin{array}{r} 2x + 4 \\ 3x - 1\overline{)6x^2 + 10x - 5} \\ \underline{\overset{-}{6x^2} \overset{+}{-} 2x} \\ 12x - 5 \\ \underline{\overset{-}{12x} \overset{+}{-} 4} \\ -1 \end{array}$$

$\frac{6x^2}{3x} = 2x$, so $2x$ is a term of the quotient.

Multiply: $2x(3x - 1)$

Subtract and bring down the next term.

$\frac{12x}{3x} = 4$. Multiply: $4(3x - 1)$

Subtract. The remainder is -1.

Thus $(6x^2 + 10x - 5)$ divided by $(3x - 1)$ is $(2x + 4)$ with a remainder of -1. This can be written as follows.

$$\frac{6x^2 + 10x - 5}{3x - 1} = 2x + 4 + \frac{-1}{3x - 1} \quad \begin{array}{l} \leftarrow \text{remainder} \\ \leftarrow \text{divisor} \end{array}$$

$$\text{or } 2x + 4 - \frac{1}{3x - 1}$$

Check: To check, we multiply $(3x - 1)(2x + 4)$. Then we add the remainder, -1, to this product.

$$(3x - 1)(2x + 4) + (-1) = (6x^2 + 12x - 2x - 4) - 1$$
$$= 6x^2 + 10x - 5$$

The quotient checks.

Work Practice 5

Notice that the division process is continued until the degree of the remainder polynomial is less than the degree of the divisor polynomial.

Recall that in Section 10.3 we practiced writing polynomials in descending order of powers and with no missing terms. For example, $2 - 4x^2$ written in this form is $-4x^2 + 0x + 2$. Writing the dividend and divisor in this form is helpful when dividing polynomials.

Answer

5. $4x + 3 + \frac{-4}{2x - 1}$ or $4x + 3 - \frac{4}{2x - 1}$

Example 6 Divide: $(2 - 4x^2) \div (x + 1)$

Solution: We use the rewritten form of $2 - 4x^2$ from the previous page.

$$\begin{array}{r l}
-4x + 4 & \\
x + 1\overline{)-4x^2 + 0x + 2} & \frac{-4x^2}{x} = -4x, \text{ so } -4x \text{ is a term of the quotient.} \\
\underline{-4x^2 - 4x} & \text{Multiply: } -4x(x+1) \\
4x + 2 & \text{Subtract and bring down the next term.} \\
\underline{4x + 4} & \frac{4x}{x} = 4. \text{ Multiply: } 4(x+1) \\
-2 & \text{Remainder}
\end{array}$$

Thus, $\frac{-4x^2 + 0x + 2}{x + 1}$ or $\frac{2 - 4x^2}{x + 1} = -4x + 4 + \frac{-2}{x + 1}$ or $-4x + 4 - \frac{2}{x + 1}$.

Check: To check, see that $(x + 1)(-4x + 4) + (-2) = 2 - 4x^2$.

Work Practice 6

PRACTICE 6

Divide: $(15 - 2x^2) \div (x - 3)$

Example 7 Divide: $\frac{4x^2 + 7 + 8x^3}{2x + 3}$

Solution: Before we begin the division process, we rewrite $4x^2 + 7 + 8x^3$ as $8x^3 + 4x^2 + 0x + 7$. Notice that we have written the polynomial in descending order and have represented the missing x-term by $0x$.

$$\begin{array}{r l}
4x^2 - 4x + 6 & \\
2x + 3\overline{)8x^3 + 4x^2 + 0x + 7} & \\
\underline{8x^3 + 12x^2} & \\
-8x^2 + 0x & \\
\underline{-8x^2 - 12x} & \\
12x + 7 & \\
\underline{12x + 18} & \\
-11 & \text{Remainder}
\end{array}$$

Thus, $\frac{4x^2 + 7 + 8x^3}{2x + 3} = 4x^2 - 4x + 6 + \frac{-11}{2x + 3}$ or $4x^2 - 4x + 6 - \frac{11}{2x + 3}$.

Work Practice 7

PRACTICE 7

Divide: $\frac{5 - x + 9x^3}{3x + 2}$

Example 8 Divide $x^3 - 8$ by $x - 2$.

Solution: Notice that the polynomial $x^3 - 8$ is missing an x^2-term and an x-term. We'll represent these terms by inserting $0x^2$ and $0x$.

$$\begin{array}{r}
x^2 + 2x + 4 \\
x - 2\overline{)x^3 + 0x^2 + 0x - 8} \\
\underline{x^3 - 2x^2} \\
2x^2 + 0x \\
\underline{2x^2 - 4x} \\
4x - 8 \\
\underline{4x - 8} \\
0
\end{array}$$

Thus, $\frac{x^3 - 8}{x - 2} = x^2 + 2x + 4$.

Check: To check, see that $(x^2 + 2x + 4)(x - 2) = x^3 - 8$.

Work Practice 8

PRACTICE 8

Divide: $x^3 - 1$ by $x - 1$

Answers

6. $-2x - 6 + \frac{-3}{x - 3}$ or $-2x - 6 - \frac{3}{x - 3}$

7. $3x^2 - 2x + 1 + \frac{3}{3x + 2}$

8. $x^2 + x + 1$

Vocabulary and Readiness Check

Use the choices below to fill in each blank. Choices may be used more than once

dividend   divisor   quotient

1. In $6\overline{)18}$ with quotient 3, the 18 is the ________, the 3 is the ________ and the 6 is the ________.

2. In $x + 1\overline{)x^2 + 3x + 2}$ with quotient $x + 2$, the $x + 1$ is the ________, the $x^2 + 3x + 2$ is the ________, and the $x + 2$ is the ________.

Simplify each expression mentally.

3. $\dfrac{a^6}{a^4}$ **4.** $\dfrac{p^8}{p^3}$ **5.** $\dfrac{y^2}{y}$ **6.** $\dfrac{a^3}{a}$

10.7 Exercise Set

FOR EXTRA HELP

MyMathLab

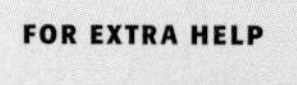

Objective A *Perform each division. See Examples 1 through 3.*

1. $\dfrac{12x^4 + 3x^2}{x}$ **2.** $\dfrac{15x^2 - 9x^5}{x}$ **3.** $\dfrac{20x^3 - 30x^2 + 5x + 5}{5}$ **4.** $\dfrac{8x^3 - 4x^2 + 6x + 2}{2}$

5. $\dfrac{15p^3 + 18p^2}{3p}$ **6.** $\dfrac{6x^5 + 3x^4}{3x^4}$ **7.** $\dfrac{-9x^4 + 18x^5}{6x^5}$ **8.** $\dfrac{14m^2 - 27m^3}{7m}$

9. $\dfrac{-9x^5 + 3x^4 - 12}{3x^3}$ **10.** $\dfrac{6a^2 - 4a + 12}{-2a^2}$ **11.** $\dfrac{4x^4 - 6x^3 + 7}{-4x^4}$ **12.** $\dfrac{-12a^3 + 36a - 15}{3a}$

Objective B *Find each quotient using long division. See Examples 4 and 5.*

13. $\dfrac{x^2 + 4x + 3}{x + 3}$ **14.** $\dfrac{x^2 + 7x + 10}{x + 5}$ **15.** $\dfrac{2x^2 + 13x + 15}{x + 5}$ **16.** $\dfrac{3x^2 + 8x + 4}{x + 2}$

17. $\dfrac{2x^2 - 7x + 3}{x - 4}$ **18.** $\dfrac{3x^2 - x - 4}{x - 1}$ **19.** $\dfrac{9a^3 - 3a^2 - 3a + 4}{3a + 2}$ **20.** $\dfrac{4x^3 + 12x^2 + x - 14}{2x + 3}$

21. $\dfrac{8x^2 + 10x + 1}{2x + 1}$ **22.** $\dfrac{3x^2 + 17x + 7}{3x + 2}$ **23.** $\dfrac{2x^3 + 2x^2 - 17x + 8}{x - 2}$ **24.** $\dfrac{4x^3 + 11x^2 - 8x - 10}{x + 3}$

Find each quotient using long division. Don't forget to write the polynomials in descending order and fill in any missing terms. See Examples 6 through 8.

25. $\dfrac{x^2 - 36}{x - 6}$

26. $\dfrac{a^2 - 49}{a - 7}$

27. $\dfrac{x^3 - 27}{x - 3}$

28. $\dfrac{x^3 + 64}{x + 4}$

29. $\dfrac{1 - 3x^2}{x + 2}$

30. $\dfrac{7 - 5x^2}{x + 3}$

31. $\dfrac{-4b + 4b^2 - 5}{2b - 1}$

32. $\dfrac{-3y + 2y^2 - 15}{2y + 5}$

Objectives **A B Mixed Practice** *Divide. If the divisor contains 2 or more terms, use long division. See Examples 1 through 8.*

33. $\dfrac{a^2b^2 - ab^3}{ab}$

34. $\dfrac{m^3n^2 - mn^4}{mn}$

35. $\dfrac{8x^2 + 6x - 27}{2x - 3}$

36. $\dfrac{18w^2 + 18w - 8}{3w + 4}$

37. $\dfrac{2x^2y + 8x^2y^2 - xy^2}{2xy}$

38. $\dfrac{11x^3y^3 - 33xy + x^2y^2}{11xy}$

39. $\dfrac{2b^3 + 9b^2 + 6b - 4}{b + 4}$

40. $\dfrac{2x^3 + 3x^2 - 3x + 4}{x + 2}$

41. $\dfrac{y^3 + 3y^2 + 4}{y - 2}$

42. $\dfrac{3x^3 + 11x + 12}{x + 4}$

43. $\dfrac{5 - 6x^2}{x - 2}$

44. $\dfrac{3 - 7x^2}{x - 3}$

45. $\dfrac{x^5 + x^2}{x^2 + x}$

46. $\dfrac{x^6 - x^3}{x^3 - x^2}$

Review

Fill in each blank. See Section 10.1

47. $12 = 4 \cdot$ ____

48. $12 = 2 \cdot$ ____

49. $20 = -5 \cdot$ ____

50. $20 = -4 \cdot$ ____

51. $9x^2 = 3x \cdot$ ____

52. $9x^2 = 9x \cdot$ ____

53. $36x^2 = 4x \cdot$ ____

54. $36x^2 = 2x \cdot$ ____

Concept Extensions

Solve.

△ **55.** The perimeter of a square is $(12x^3 + 4x - 16)$ feet. Find the length of its side.

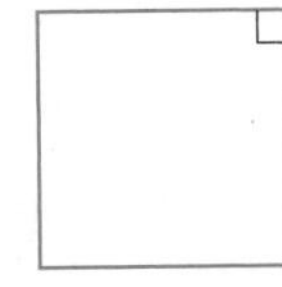

Perimeter is $(12x^3 + 4x - 16)$ feet

△ **56.** The volume of the swimming pool shown is $(36x^5 - 12x^3 + 6x^2)$ cubic feet. If its height is $2x$ feet and its width is $3x$ feet, find its length.

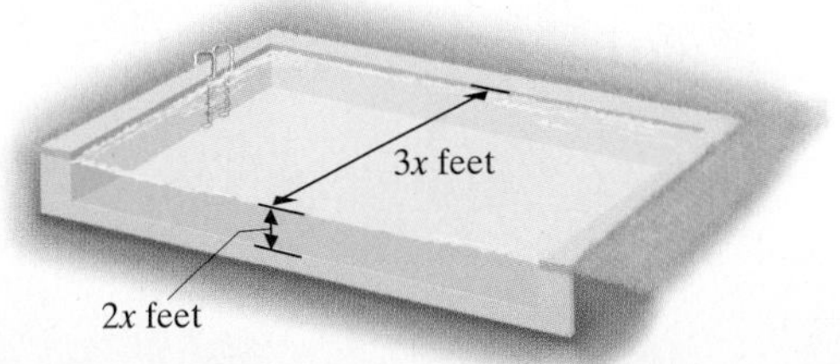

△ **57.** The area of the parallelogram shown is $(10x^2 + 31x + 15)$ square meters. If its base is $(5x + 3)$ meters, find its height.

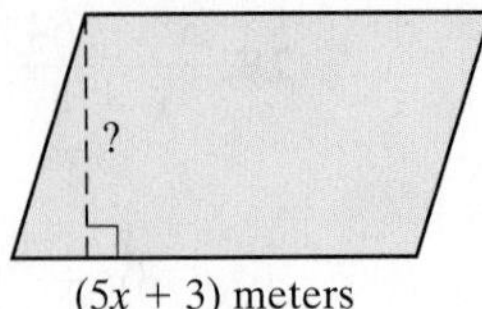

△ **58.** The area of the top of the Ping-Pong table shown is $(49x^2 + 70x - 200)$ square inches. If its length is $(7x + 20)$ inches, find its width.

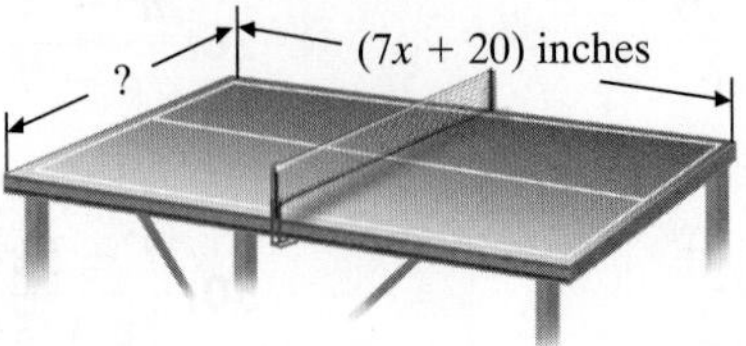

59. Explain how to check a polynomial long division result when the remainder is 0.

60. Explain how to check a polynomial long division result when the remainder is not 0.

61. In which of the following is $\frac{a+7}{7}$ simplified correctly? See the Concept Check in this section.

a. $a + 1$
b. a
c. $\frac{a}{7} + 1$

62. In which of the following is $\frac{5x+15}{5}$ simplified correctly? See the Concept Check in this section.

a. $x + 15$
b. $x + 3$
c. $x + 1$

Chapter 10 Group Activity

Modeling with Polynomials

Materials

Calculator

This activity may be completed by working in groups or individually.

The polynomial model $-16x^2 + 150x + 8945$ gives the average daily total supply of motor gasoline (in thousand barrels per day) in the United States for the period 2003–2007. The polynomial model $8x^2 + 80x + 8443$ gives the average daily supply of domestically produced motor gasoline (in thousand barrels per day) in the United States for the same period. In both models, x is the number of years after 2003. The other source of motor gasoline in the United States, contributing to the total supply, is imported motor gasoline. (*Source:* Based on data from the Energy Information Administration)

1. Use the given polynomials to complete the following table showing the average daily supply (both total and domestic) over the period 2003–2007 by evaluating each polynomial at the given values of x. Then subtract each value in the fourth column from the corresponding value in the third column. Record the result in the last column, labeled "Difference." What do you think these values represent?

Year	x	Average Daily Total Supply (thousand barrels per day)	Average Daily Domestic Supply (thousand barrels per day)	Difference
2003	0			
2004	1			
2005	2			
2006	3			
2007	4			

2. Use the polynomial models to find a new polynomial model representing the average daily supply of imported motor gasoline. Then evaluate your new polynomial model to complete the accompanying table.

Year	x	Average Daily Imported Supply (thousand barrels per day)
2003	0	
2004	1	
2005	2	
2006	3	
2007	4	

3. Compare the values in the last column of the table in Question 1 to the values in the last column of the table in Question 2. What do you notice? What can you conclude?

4. Make a bar graph of the data in the table in Question 2. Describe what you see.

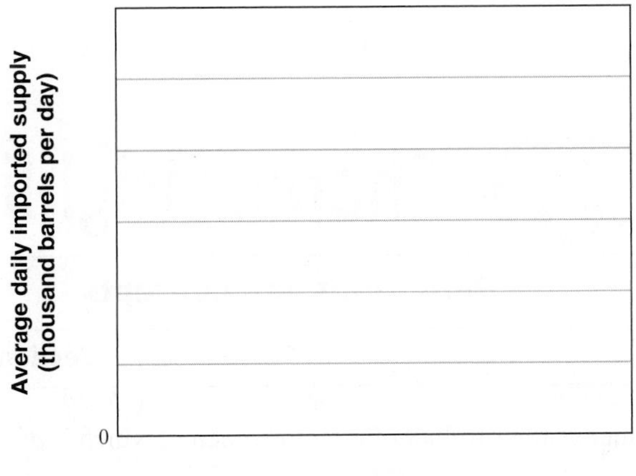

Chapter 10 Vocabulary Check

Fill in each blank with one of the words or phrases listed below.

term	coefficient	monomial	binomial	trinomial
polynomials	degree of a term	degree of a polynomial	distributive	FOIL

1. A ____________________ is a number or the product of a number and variables raised to powers.
2. The ____________________ method may be used when multiplying two binomials.
3. A polynomial with exactly 3 terms is called a ____________________.
4. The ____________________ is the greatest degree of any term of the polynomial.
5. A polynomial with exactly 2 terms is called a ____________________.
6. The ____________________ of a term is its numerical factor.
7. The ____________________ is the sum of the exponents on the variables in the term.
8. A polynomial with exactly 1 term is called a ____________________.
9. Monomials, binomials, and trinomials are all examples of ____________________.
10. The ____________________ property is used to multiply $2x(x - 4)$.

Helpful Hint Are you preparing for your test? Don't forget to take the Chapter 10 Test on page 758. Then check your answers at the back of the text and use the Chapter Test Prep Videos to see the fully worked-out solutions to any of the exercises you want to review.

10 Chapter Highlights

Definitions and Concepts	Examples
Section 10.1 Exponents	
a^n means the product of n factors, each of which is a.	$3^2 = 3 \cdot 3 = 9$ $(-5)^3 = (-5)(-5)(-5) = -125$ $\left(\frac{1}{2}\right)^4 = \frac{1}{2}\cdot\frac{1}{2}\cdot\frac{1}{2}\cdot\frac{1}{2} = \frac{1}{16}$
Let m and n be integers and no denominators be 0.	
Product Rule: $a^m \cdot a^n = a^{m+n}$	$x^2 \cdot x^7 = x^{2+7} = x^9$
Power Rule: $(a^m)^n = a^{mn}$	$(5^3)^8 = 5^{3\cdot 8} = 5^{24}$
Power of a Product Rule: $(ab)^n = a^n b^n$	$(7y)^4 = 7^4 y^4$
Power of a Quotient Rule: $\left(\frac{a}{b}\right)^n = \frac{a^n}{b^n}$	$\left(\frac{x}{8}\right)^3 = \frac{x^3}{8^3}$
Quotient Rule: $\frac{a^m}{a^n} = a^{m-n}$	$\frac{x^9}{x^4} = x^{9-4} = x^5$
Zero Exponent: $a^0 = 1, a \neq 0$	$5^0 = 1; x^0 = 1, x \neq 0$

Definitions and Concepts	Examples
Section 10.2 Negative Exponents and Scientific Notation	
If $a \neq 0$ and n is an integer, $a^{-n} = \frac{1}{a^n}$	$3^{-2} = \frac{1}{3^2} = \frac{1}{9}$; $5x^{-2} = \frac{5}{x^2}$ Simplify: $\left(\frac{x^{-2}y}{x^5}\right)^{-2} = \frac{x^4y^{-2}}{x^{-10}} = x^{4-(-10)}y^{-2} = \frac{x^{14}}{y^2}$
A positive number is written in scientific notation if it is written as the product of a number a, where $1 \leq a < 10$, and an integer power r of 10. $a \times 10^r$	$1200 = 1.2 \times 10^3$ $0.000000568 = 5.68 \times 10^{-7}$
Section 10.3 Introduction to Polynomials	
A **term** is a number or the product of a number and variables raised to powers.	$-5x, 7a^2b, \frac{1}{4}y^4, 0.2$
The **numerical coefficient,** or **coefficient,** of a term is its numerical factor.	**Term** / **Coefficient** $7x^2$ — 7 y — 1 $-a^2b$ — -1
A **polynomial** is a finite sum of terms of the form ax^n where a is a real number and n is a whole number.	$5x^3 - 6x^2 + 3x - 6$ (Polynomial)
A **monomial** is a polynomial with exactly 1 term.	$\frac{5}{6}y^3$ (Monomial)
A **binomial** is a polynomial with exactly 2 terms.	$-0.2a^2b - 5b^2$ (Binomial)
A **trinomial** is a polynomial with exactly 3 terms.	$3x^2 - 2x + 1$ (Trinomial)
The **degree of a polynomial** is the greatest degree of any term of the polynomial.	**Polynomial** / **Degree** $5x^2 - 3x + 2$ — 2 $7y + 8y^2z^3 - 12$ — $2 + 3 = 5$
Section 10.4 Adding and Subtracting Polynomials	
To add polynomials, combine like terms.	Add. $(7x^2 - 3x + 2) + (-5x - 6)$ $= 7x^2 - 3x + 2 - 5x - 6$ $= 7x^2 - 8x - 4$
To subtract two polynomials, change the signs of the terms of the second polynomial, and then add.	Subtract. $(17y^2 - 2y + 1) - (-3y^3 + 5y - 6)$ $= (17y^2 - 2y + 1) + (3y^3 - 5y + 6)$ $= 17y^2 - 2y + 1 + 3y^3 - 5y + 6$ $= 3y^3 + 17y^2 - 7y + 7$

Definitions and Concepts	Examples
Section 10.5 Multiplying Polynomials	
To multiply two polynomials, multiply each term of one polynomial by each term of the other polynomial, and then combine like terms.	Multiply. $(2x + 1)(5x^2 - 6x + 2)$ $= 2x(5x^2 - 6x + 2) + 1(5x^2 - 6x + 2)$ $= 10x^3 - 12x^2 + 4x + 5x^2 - 6x + 2$ $= 10x^3 - 7x^2 - 2x + 2$
Section 10.6 Special Products	
The **FOIL method** may be used when multiplying two binomials.	Multiply: $(5x - 3)(2x + 3)$ First, Last, Inner, Outer: $(5x - 3)(2x + 3)$ F O I L $= (5x)(2x) + (5x)(3) + (-3)(2x) + (-3)(3)$ $= 10x^2 + 15x - 6x - 9$ $= 10x^2 + 9x - 9$
Squaring a Binomial $(a + b)^2 = a^2 + 2ab + b^2$ $(a - b)^2 = a^2 - 2ab + b^2$	Square each binomial. $(x + 5)^2 = x^2 + 2(x)(5) + 5^2 = x^2 + 10x + 25$ $(3x - 2y)^2 = (3x)^2 - 2(3x)(2y) + (2y)^2 = 9x^2 - 12xy + 4y^2$
Multiplying the Sum and Difference of Two Terms $(a + b)(a - b) = a^2 - b^2$	Multiply. $(6y + 5)(6y - 5) = (6y)^2 - 5^2 = 36y^2 - 25$
Section 10.7 Dividing Polynomials	
To divide a polynomial by a monomial, $\frac{a + b}{c} = \frac{a}{c} + \frac{b}{c}, c \neq 0$	Divide. $\frac{15x^5 - 10x^3 + 5x^2 - 2x}{5x^2}$ $= \frac{15x^5}{5x^2} - \frac{10x^3}{5x^2} + \frac{5x^2}{5x^2} - \frac{2x}{5x^2}$ $= 3x^3 - 2x + 1 - \frac{2}{5x}$
To divide a polynomial by a polynomial other than a monomial, use long division.	$2x + 3\overline{)10x^2 + 13x - 7}$ with quotient $5x - 1 + \frac{-4}{2x + 3}$; $\underline{10x^2 \not+ 15x}$; $-2x - 7$; $\underline{\not-2x \not- 3}$; -4 or $5x - 1 - \frac{4}{2x + 3}$

Chapter 10 Review

(10.1) *State the base and the exponent for each expression.*

1. 3^2 **2.** $(-5)^4$ **3.** -5^4 **4.** x^6

Evaluate each expression.

5. 8^3 **6.** $(-6)^2$ **7.** -6^2 **8.** $-4^3 - 4^0$ **9.** $(3b)^0$ **10.** $\frac{8b}{8b}$

Simplify each expression.

11. $y^2 \cdot y^7$ **12.** $x^9 \cdot x^5$ **13.** $(2x^5)(-3x^6)$ **14.** $(-5y^3)(4y^4)$ **15.** $(x^4)^2$

16. $(y^3)^5$ **17.** $(3y^6)^4$ **18.** $(2x^3)^3$ **19.** $\frac{x^9}{x^4}$ **20.** $\frac{z^{12}}{z^5}$

21. $\frac{3x^4y^{10}}{12xy^6}$ **22.** $\frac{2x^7y^8}{8xy^2}$ **23.** $5a^7(2a^4)^3$ **24.** $(2x)^2(9x)$ **25.** $\frac{(4a^5b)^2}{-16ab^2}$

26. $\frac{(2x^3y)^4}{-16x^5y^4}$ **27.** $(-5a)^0 + 7^0 + 8^0$ **28.** $8x^0 + 9^0$

Simplify the given expression and choose the correct result.

29. $\left(\frac{3x^4}{4y}\right)^3$

a. $\frac{27x^{64}}{64y^3}$ **b.** $\frac{27x^{12}}{64y^3}$

c. $\frac{9x^{12}}{12y^3}$ **d.** $\frac{3x^{12}}{4y^3}$

30. $\left(\frac{5a^6}{b^3}\right)^2$

a. $\frac{10a^{12}}{b^6}$ **b.** $\frac{25a^{36}}{b^9}$

c. $\frac{25a^{12}}{b^6}$ **d.** $25a^{12}b^6$

(10.2) *Simplify each expression.*

31. 7^{-2} **32.** -7^{-2} **33.** $2x^{-4}$ **34.** $(2x)^{-4}$

35. $\left(\frac{1}{5}\right)^{-3}$ **36.** $\left(\frac{-2}{3}\right)^{-2}$ **37.** $2^0 + 2^{-4}$ **38.** $6^{-1} - 7^{-1}$

Simplify each expression. Write each answer using positive exponents only.

39. $\dfrac{r^{-3}}{r^{-4}}$

40. $\dfrac{y^{-2}}{y^{-5}}$

41. $\left(\dfrac{bc^{-2}}{bc^{-3}}\right)^4$

42. $\left(\dfrac{x^{-3}y^{-4}}{x^{-2}y^{-5}}\right)^{-3}$

43. $\dfrac{10a^3b^4c^0}{50ab^{11}c^3}$

44. $\dfrac{8a^0b^4c^5}{40a^6bc^{12}}$

45. $\dfrac{9x^{-4}y^{-6}}{x^2y^7}$

46. $\dfrac{3a^5b^{-5}}{a^{-5}b^5}$

Write each number in scientific notation.

47. 0.00027

48. 0.8868

49. 80,800,000

50. 868,000

51. In November 2008, approximately 127,000,000 Americans voted in the U.S. presidential election. Write this number in scientific notation. (*Source:* CNN)

52. The approximate diameter of the Milky Way galaxy is 150,000 light years. Write this number in scientific notation. (*Source:* NASA IMAGE/POETRY Education and Public Outreach Program)

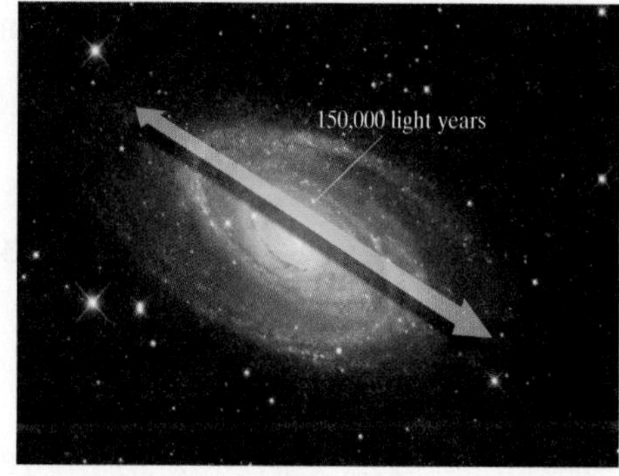

Write each number in standard form.

53. 8.67×10^5

54. 3.86×10^{-3}

55. 8.6×10^{-4}

56. 8.936×10^5

57. The volume of the planet Jupiter is 1.43128×10^{15} cubic kilometers. Write this number in standard form. (*Source:* National Space Science Data Center)

58. An angstrom is a unit of measure, equal to 1×10^{-10} meter, used for measuring wavelengths or the diameters of atoms. Write this number in standard form. (*Source:* National Institute of Standards and Technology)

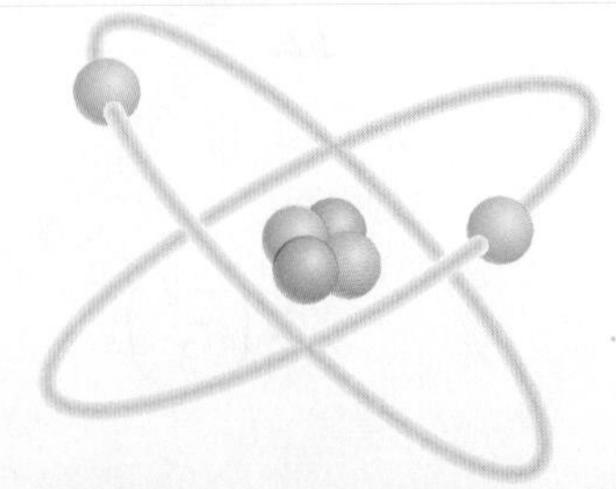

Simplify. Express each result in standard form.

59. $(8 \times 10^4)(2 \times 10^{-7})$

60. $\dfrac{8 \times 10^4}{2 \times 10^{-7}}$

(10.3) *Find the degree of each polynomial.*

61. $y^5 + 7x - 8x^4$

62. $9y^2 + 30y + 25$

63. $-14x^2y - 28x^2y^3 - 42x^2y^2$

64. $6x^2y^2z^2 + 5x^2y^3 - 12xyz$

65. The Glass Bridge Skywalk is suspended 4000 feet over the Colorado River at the very edge of the Grand Canyon. Neglecting air resistance, the height of an object dropped from the Skywalk at time t seconds is given by the polynomial $-16t^2 + 4000$. Find the height of the object at the given times below.

t	0 seconds	1 second	3 seconds	5 seconds
$-16t^2 + 4000$				

△ **66.** The surface area of a box with a square base and a height of 5 units is given by the polynomial $2x^2 + 20x$. Fill in the table below by evaluating $2x^2 + 20x$ for the given values of x.

x	1	3	5.1	10
$2x^2 + 20x$				

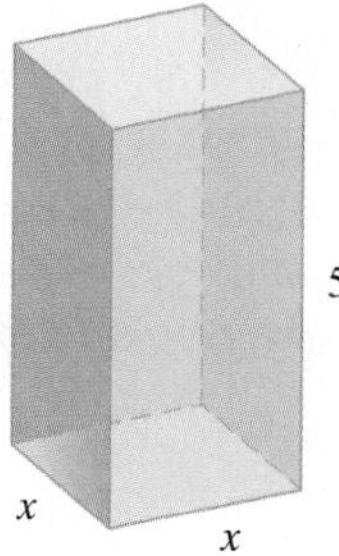

Combine like terms in each expression.

67. $7a^2 - 4a^2 - a^2$

68. $9y + y - 14y$

69. $6a^2 + 4a + 9a^2$

70. $21x^2 + 3x + x^2 + 6$

71. $4a^2b - 3b^2 - 8q^2 - 10a^2b + 7q^2$

72. $2s^{14} + 3s^{13} + 12s^{12} - s^{10}$

(10.4) *Add or subtract as indicated.*

73. $(3x^2 + 2x + 6) + (5x^2 + x)$

74. $(2x^5 + 3x^4 + 4x^3 + 5x^2) + (4x^2 + 7x + 6)$

75. $(-5y^2 + 3) - (2y^2 + 4)$

76. $(2m^7 + 3x^4 + 7m^6) - (8m^7 + 4m^2 + 6x^4)$

77. $(3x^2 - 7xy + 7y^2) - (4x^2 - xy + 9y^2)$

78. $(8x^6 - 5xy - 10y^2) - (7x^6 - 9xy - 12y^2)$

Translating *Perform the indicated operations.*

79. Add $(-9x^2 + 6x + 2)$ and $(4x^2 - x - 1)$.

80. Subtract $(4x^2 + 8x - 7)$ from the sum of $(x^2 + 7x + 9)$ and $(x^2 + 4)$.

(10.5) *Multiply each expression.*

81. $6(x + 5)$

82. $9(x - 7)$

83. $4(2a + 7)$

84. $9(6a - 3)$

85. $-7x(x^2 + 5)$

86. $-8y(4y^2 - 6)$

87. $-2(x^3 - 9x^2 + x)$

88. $-3a(a^2b + ab + b^2)$

89. $(-2a)(3a^3 - 4a + 1)$

90. $(7b)(6b^3 - 4b + 2)$

91. $(2x + 2)(x - 7)$

92. $(2x - 5)(3x + 2)$

93. $(4a - 1)(a + 7)$

94. $(6a - 1)(7a + 3)$

95. $(x + 7)(x^3 + 4x - 5)$

96. $(x + 2)(x^5 + x + 1)$

97. $(x^2 + 2x + 4)(x^2 + 2x - 4)$

98. $(x^3 + 4x + 4)(x^3 + 4x - 4)$

99. $(x + 7)^3$

100. $(2x - 5)^3$

(10.6) *Use special products to multiply each of the following.*

101. $(x + 7)^2$

102. $(x - 5)^2$

103. $(3x - 7)^2$

104. $(4x + 2)^2$

105. $(5x - 9)^2$

106. $(5x + 1)(5x - 1)$

107. $(7x + 4)(7x - 4)$

108. $(a + 2b)(a - 2b)$

109. $(2x - 6)(2x + 6)$

110. $(4a^2 - 2b)(4a^2 + 2b)$

Express each as a product of polynomials in x. Then multiply and simplify.

111. Find the area of the square if its side is $(3x - 1)$ meters.

112. Find the area of the rectangle.

(10.7) *Divide.*

113. $\dfrac{x^2 + 21x + 49}{7x^2}$

114. $\dfrac{5a^3b - 15ab^2 + 20ab}{-5ab}$

115. $(a^2 - a + 4) \div (a - 2)$

116. $(4x^2 + 20x + 7) \div (x + 5)$

117. $\dfrac{a^3 + a^2 + 2a + 6}{a - 2}$

118. $\dfrac{9b^3 - 18b^2 + 8b - 1}{3b - 2}$

119. $\dfrac{4x^4 - 4x^3 + x^2 + 4x - 3}{2x - 1}$

120. $\dfrac{-10x^2 - x^3 - 21x + 18}{x - 6}$

△ **121.** The area of the rectangle below is $(15x^3 - 3x^2 + 60)$ square feet. If its length is $3x^2$ feet, find its width.

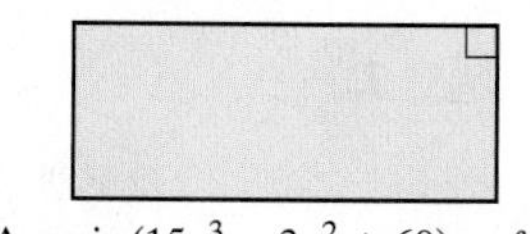

Area is $(15x^3 - 3x^2 + 60)$ sq feet

122. The perimeter of the equilateral triangle below is $(21a^3b^6 + 3a - 3)$ units. Find the length of a side.

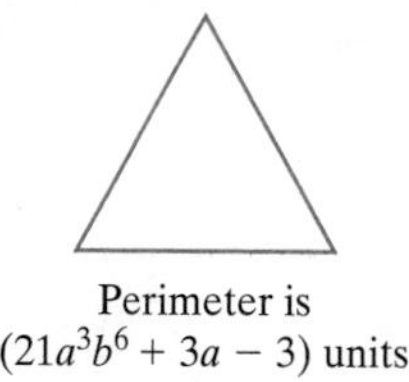

Perimeter is $(21a^3b^6 + 3a - 3)$ units

Mixed Review

Evaluate.

123. 3^3

124. $\left(-\dfrac{1}{2}\right)^3$

Simplify each expression. Write each answer using positive exponents only.

125. $(4xy^2)(x^3y^5)$

126. $\dfrac{18x^9}{27x^3}$

127. $\left(\dfrac{3a^4}{b^2}\right)^3$

128. $(2x^{-4}y^3)^{-4}$

129. $\dfrac{a^{-3}b^6}{9^{-1}a^{-5}b^{-2}}$

Perform the indicated operations and simplify.

130. $(-y^2 - 4) + (3y^2 - 6)$

131. $(6x + 2) + (5x - 7)$

132. $(5x^2 + 2x - 6) - (-x - 4)$

133. $(8y^2 - 3y + 1) - (3y^2 + 2)$

134. $(2x + 5)(3x - 2)$

135. $4x(7x^2 + 3)$

136. $(7x - 2)(4x - 9)$

137. $(x - 3)(x^2 + 4x - 6)$

Use special products to multiply.

138. $(5x + 4)^2$

139. $(6x + 3)(6x - 3)$

Divide.

140. $\dfrac{8a^4 - 2a^3 + 4a - 5}{2a^3}$

141. $\dfrac{x^2 + 2x + 10}{x + 5}$

142. $\dfrac{4x^3 + 8x^2 - 11x + 4}{2x - 3}$

Chapter 10 Test

Answers

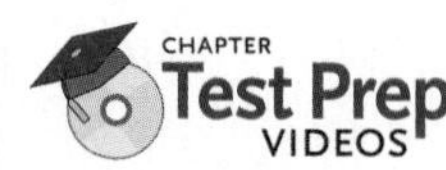

Step-by-step test solutions are found on the Chapter Test Prep Videos available via the Interactive DVD Lecture Series, in MyMathLab or on YouTube (search "MartinGayIntroAlg" and click on "Channels").

1. ______
2. ______
3. ______
4. ______
5. ______
6. ______
7. ______
8. ______
9. ______
10. ______
11. ______
12. ______
13. ______
14. ______
15. a. ______
 b. ______
16. ______
17. ______
18. ______
19. ______

Evaluate each expression.

1. 2^5

2. $(-3)^4$

3. -3^4

4. 4^{-3}

Simplify each expression. Write the result using only positive exponents.

5. $(3x^2)(-5x^9)$

6. $\dfrac{y^7}{y^2}$

7. $\dfrac{r^{-8}}{r^{-3}}$

8. $\left(\dfrac{4x^2y^3}{x^3y^{-4}}\right)^2$

9. $\dfrac{6^2x^{-4}y^{-1}}{6^3x^{-3}y^7}$

Express each number in scientific notation.

10. 563,000

11. 0.0000863

Write each number in standard form.

12. 1.5×10^{-3}

13. 6.23×10^4

14. Simplify. Write the answer in standard form.
$(1.2 \times 10^5)(3 \times 10^{-7})$

15. a. Complete the table for the polynomial $4xy^2 + 7xyz + x^3y - 2$.

Term	Numerical Coefficient	Degree of Term
$4xy^2$		
$7xyz$		
x^3y		
-2		

b. What is the degree of the polynomial?

16. Simplify by combining like terms.
$5x^2 + 4x - 7x^2 + 11 + 8x$

Perform each indicated operation.

17. $(8x^3 + 7x^2 + 4x - 7) + (8x^3 - 7x - 6)$

18.
$$\begin{array}{r} 5x^3 + x^2 + 5x - 2 \\ -(8x^3 - 4x^2 + x - 7) \\ \hline \end{array}$$

19. Subtract $(4x + 2)$ from the sum of $(8x^2 + 7x + 5)$ and $(x^3 - 8)$.

Multiply in Exercises 20 through 26.

20. $(3x + 7)(x^2 + 5x + 2)$

21. $3x^2(2x^2 - 3x + 7)$

22. $(x + 7)(3x - 5)$

23. $\left(3x - \frac{1}{5}\right)\left(3x + \frac{1}{5}\right)$

24. $(4x - 2)^2$

25. $(8x + 3)^2$

26. $(x^2 - 9b)(x^2 + 9b)$

27. The height of the Bank of China in Hong Kong is 1001 feet. Neglecting air resistance, the height of an object dropped from this building at time t seconds is given by the polynomial $-16t^2 + 1001$. Find the height of the object at the given times below.

t	0 seconds	1 second	3 seconds	5 seconds
$-16t^2 + 1001$				

△ **28.** Find the area of the top of the table. Express the area as a product, then multiply and simplify.

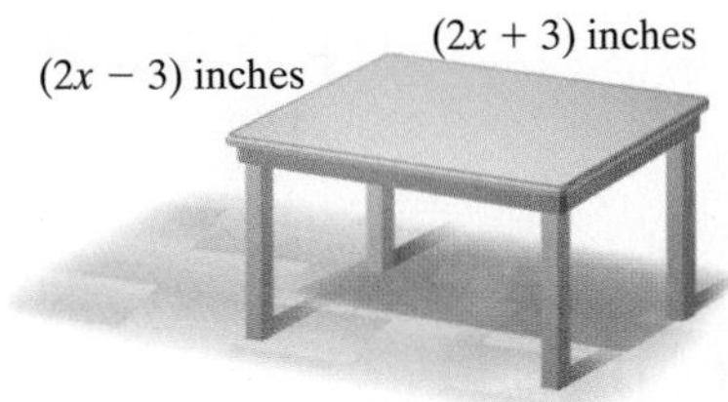

Divide.

29. $\dfrac{4x^2 + 2xy - 7x}{8xy}$

30. $(x^2 + 7x + 10) \div (x + 5)$

31. $\dfrac{27x^3 - 8}{3x + 2}$

20. ______

21. ______

22. ______

23. ______

24. ______

25. ______

26. ______

27. ______

28. ______

29. ______

30. ______

31. ______

Answers

1. a. ____
b. ____
c. ____
d. ____
e. ____
f. ____
2. a. ____
b. ____
c. ____
3. a. ____
b. ____
c. ____
d. ____
e. ____
f. ____
4. a. ____
b. ____
5. ____
6. ____
7. a. ____
b. ____
c. ____
d. ____
e. ____

Cumulative Review Chapters 8–10

1. Given the set $\left\{-2, 0, \frac{1}{4}, 112, -3, 11, \sqrt{2}\right\}$, list the numbers in this set that belong to the set of:

a. Natural numbers
b. Whole numbers
c. Integers
d. Rational numbers
e. Irrational numbers
f. Real numbers

2. Find the absolute value of each number.

a. $|-7.2|$
b. $|0|$
c. $\left|-\frac{1}{2}\right|$

3. Evaluate (find the value of) the following:

a. 3^2
b. 5^3
c. 2^4
d. 7^1
e. $\left(\frac{3}{7}\right)^2$
f. $(0.6)^2$

4. Multiply. Write products in lowest terms.

a. $\frac{3}{4} \cdot \frac{7}{21}$
b. $\frac{1}{2} \cdot 4\frac{5}{6}$

5. Simplify: $\frac{3}{2} \cdot \frac{1}{2} - \frac{1}{2}$

6. Evaluate $\frac{2x - 7y}{x^2}$ for $x = 5$ and $y = 1$.

7. Write an algebraic expression that represents each phrase. Let the variable x represent the unknown number.

a. The sum of a number and 3
b. The product of 3 and a number
c. The quotient of 7.3 and a number
d. 10 decreased by a number
e. 5 times a number, increased by 7

8. Simplify: $8 + 3(2 \cdot 6 - 1)$

9. Add: $11.4 + (-4.7)$

10. Is $x = 1$ a solution of $5x^2 + 2 = x - 8$?

11. Find the value of each expression when $x = 2$ and $y = -5$.

a. $\frac{x - y}{12 + x}$ **b.** $x^2 - y$

12. Subtract:

a. $7 - 40$

b. $-5 - (-10)$

Divide.

13. $\frac{-30}{-10}$ **14.** $\frac{-48}{6}$ **15.** $\frac{42}{-0.6}$ **16.** $\frac{-30}{-0.2}$

Find each product by using the distributive property to remove parentheses.

17. $5(3x + 2)$ **18.** $-3(2x - 3)$ **19.** $-2(y + 0.3z - 1)$

20. $4x(-x^2 + 6x - 1)$ **21.** $-(9x + y - 2z + 6)$ **22.** $-(-4xy + 6y - 2)$

23. Solve: $6(2a - 1) - (11a + 6) = 7$

24. Solve: $2x + \frac{1}{8} = x - \frac{3}{8}$

25. Solve: $\frac{y}{7} = 20$

26. Solve: $10 = 5j - 2$

27. Solve: $0.25x + 0.10(x - 3) = 1.1$

28. Solve: $\frac{7x + 5}{3} = x + 3$

29. Twice the sum of a number and 4 is the same as four times the number decreased by 12. Find the number.

30. Write the phrase as an algebraic expression and simplify if possible. Double a number, subtracted from the sum of a number and seven.

8. ______
9. ______
10. ______
11. a. ______
b. ______
12. a. ______
b. ______
13. ______
14. ______
15. ______
16. ______
17. ______
18. ______
19. ______
20. ______
21. ______
22. ______
23. ______
24. ______
25. ______
26. ______
27. ______
28. ______
29. ______
30. ______

31. ____
32. ____
33. ____
34. ____
35. ____
36. a. ____
b. ____
c. ____
37. a. ____
b. ____
c. ____
38. ____
39. ____
40. ____
41. ____
42. ____
43. ____
44. ____
45. ____
46. ____
47. ____
48. ____
49. ____

△ **31.** Charles Pecot can afford enough fencing to enclose a rectangular garden with a perimeter of 140 feet. If the width of his garden is to be 30 feet, find the length.

32. Simplify: $\dfrac{4(-3) + (-8)}{5 + (-5)}$

33. The number 120 is 15% of what number?

34. Graph $x < 5$.

−5 −4 −3 −2 −1 0 1 2 3 4 5

35. Solve: $-4x + 7 \geq -9$. Graph the solution set.

−5 −4 −3 −2 −1 0 1 2 3 4 5

36. Evaluate.

a. $(-5)^2$ **b.** -5^2 **c.** $2 \cdot 5^2$

37. Simplify each expression.

a. $x^7 \cdot x^4$

b. $\left(\dfrac{t}{2}\right)^4$

c. $(9y^5)^2$

38. Simplify: $\dfrac{(z^2)^3 \cdot z^7}{z^9}$

Simplify the following expressions. Write each result using positive exponents only.

39. $\left(\dfrac{3a^2}{b}\right)^{-3}$

40. $(5x^7)(-3x^9)$

41. $(5y^3)^{-2}$

42. $(-3)^{-2}$

Simplify each polynomial by combining any like terms.

43. $9x^3 + x^3$

44. $(5y^2 - 6) - (y^2 + 2)$

45. $5x^2 + 6x - 9x - 3$

46. Multiply: $(10x^2 - 3)(10x^2 + 3)$.

47. Multiply: $7x(x^2 + 2x + 5)$

48. Multiply: $(10x^2 + 3)^2$.

49. Divide: $\dfrac{9x^5 - 12x^2 + 3x}{3x^2}$

Factoring Polynomials

11

Sections

Check Your Progress

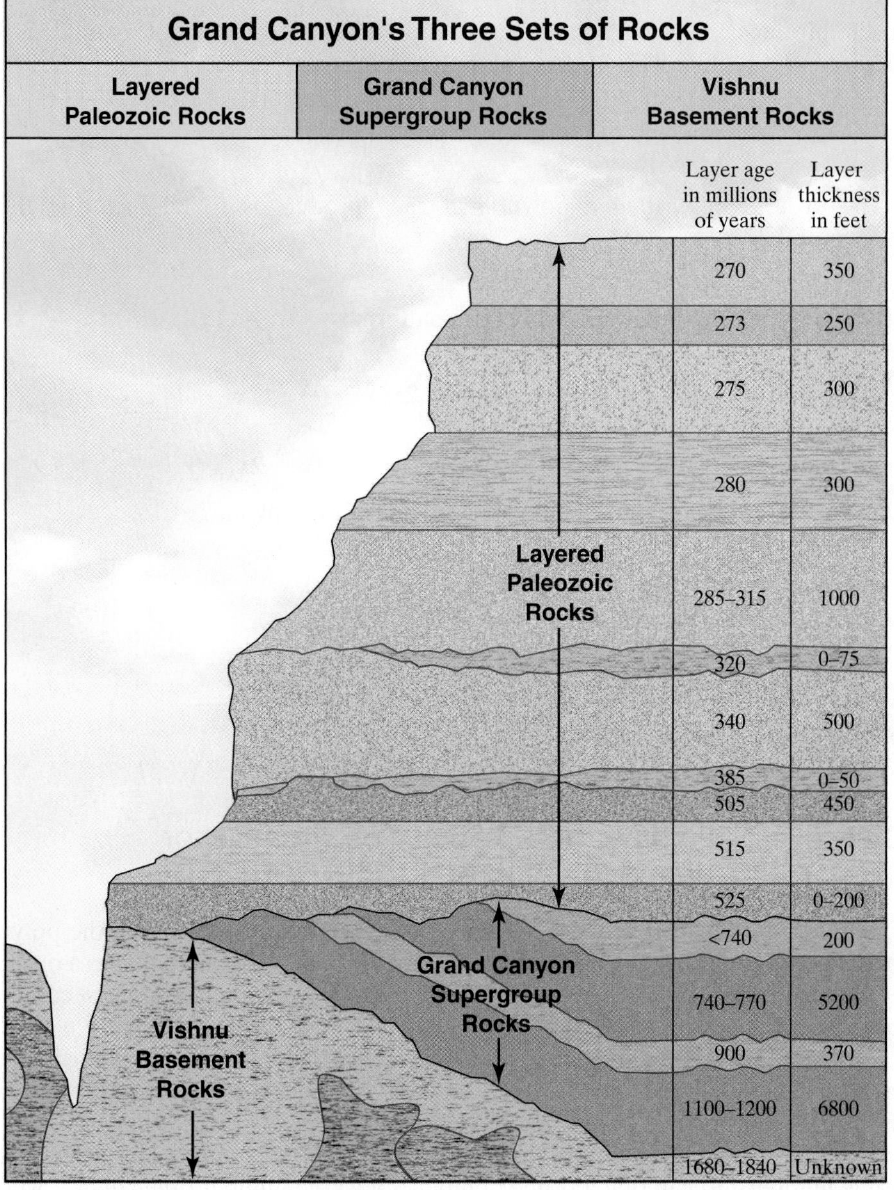

Grand Canyon's Three Sets of Rocks
Layered Paleozoic Rocks
Grand Canyon Supergroup Rocks
Vishnu Basement Rocks
Layer age in millions of years
Layer thickness in feet
270 350
273 250
275 300
280 300
285–315 1000
320 0–75
340 500
385 0–50
505 450
515 350
525 0–200
<740 200
740–770 5200
900 370
1100–1200 6800
1680–1840 Unknown
Layered Paleozoic Rocks
Grand Canyon Supergroup Rocks
Vishnu Basement Rocks

In Chapter 10, we learned how to multiply polynomials. Now we will deal with an operation that is the reverse process of multiplying–factoring. Factoring is an important algebraic skill because it allows us to write a sum as a product. As we will see in Sections 11.6 and 11.7, factoring can be used to solve equations other than linear equations. In Chapter 12, we will also use factoring to simplify and perform arithmetic operations on rational expressions.

The Grand Canyon is a part of the Colorado River basin. It is truly one of this nation's most stirring natural wonders. Grand Canyon National Park comprises more than a million acres of land, has 277 miles of rivers, and is up to 18 miles wide and a mile deep. Recent studies (somewhat controversial) have increased the estimation of the origin of the canyon from 5 to 6 million years ago to somewhere around 17 million years ago.

The diagram above depicts the Grand Canyon's layers of rock along with—most interestingly—each layer's age and thickness.

In Exercise 105, Section 11.5, you will explore information about the height of the Toroweap Overlook, on the North Rim of the canyon.

Objectives

A **Find the Greatest Common Factor of a List of Numbers.**

B **Find the Greatest Common Factor of a List of Terms.**

C **Factor Out the Greatest Common Factor from the Terms of a Polynomial.**

D **Factor by Grouping.**

11.1 THE GREATEST COMMON FACTOR

In the product $2 \cdot 3 = 6$, the numbers 2 and 3 are called **factors** of 6 and $2 \cdot 3$ is a **factored form** of 6. This is true of polynomials also. Since $(x + 2)(x + 3) = x^2 + 5x + 6$, then $(x + 2)$ and $(x + 3)$ are factors of $x^2 + 5x + 6$, and $(x + 2)(x + 3)$ is a factored form of the polynomial.

The process of writing a polynomial as a product is called **factoring** the polynomial.

Study the examples below and look for a pattern.

Multiplying: $5(x^2 + 3) = 5x^2 + 15$ $\quad 2x(x - 7) = 2x^2 - 14x$

Factoring: $5x^2 + 15 = 5(x^2 + 3)$ $\quad 2x^2 - 14x = 2x(x - 7)$

Do you see that factoring is the reverse process of multiplying?

factoring

$$x^2 + 5x + 6 = (x + 2)(x + 3)$$

multiplying

✓Concept Check Multiply: $2(x - 4)$
What do you think the result of factoring $2x - 8$ would be? Why?

Objective A Finding the Greatest Common Factor of a List of Numbers

The first step in factoring a polynomial is to see whether the terms of the polynomial have a common factor. If there is one, we can write the polynomial as a product by **factoring out** the common factor. We will usually factor out the *greatest* common factor (GCF).

The GCF of a list of integers is the largest integer that is a factor of all the integers in the list. For example, the GCF of 12 and 20 is 4 because 4 is the largest integer that is a factor of both 12 and 20. With large integers, the GCF may not be easily found by inspection. When this happens, we will write each integer as a product of prime numbers. Recall that a prime number is a whole number other than 1, whose only factors are 1 and itself.

PRACTICE 1

Find the GCF of each list of numbers.

a. 45 and 75 **b.** 32 and 33
c. 14, 24, and 60

Example 1 Find the GCF of each list of numbers.

a. 28 and 40 **b.** 55 and 21 **c.** 15, 18, and 66

Solution:

a. Write each number as a product of primes.

$28 = 2 \cdot 2 \cdot 7 = 2^2 \cdot 7$

$40 = 2 \cdot 2 \cdot 2 \cdot 5 = 2^3 \cdot 5$

There are two common factors, each of which is 2, so the GCF is

$\text{GCF} = 2 \cdot 2 = 4$

Answers

1. a. 15 **b.** 1 **c.** 2

✓ Concept Check Answer

$2x - 8$; the result would be $2(x - 4)$ because factoring is the reverse process of multiplying.

b. $55 = 5 \cdot 11$

$21 = 3 \cdot 7$

There are no common prime factors; thus, the GCF is 1.

c. $15 = 3 \cdot 5$

$18 = 2 \cdot 3 \cdot 3 = 2 \cdot 3^2$

$66 = 2 \cdot 3 \cdot 11$

The only prime factor common to all three numbers is 3, so the GCF is

$\text{GCF} = 3$

Work Practice 1

Objective B Finding the Greatest Common Factor of a List of Terms

The greatest common factor of a list of variables raised to powers is found in a similar way. For example, the GCF of x^2, x^3, and x^5 is x^2 because each term contains a factor of x^2 and no higher power of x is a factor of each term.

$x^2 = x \cdot x$

$x^3 = x \cdot x \cdot x$

$x^5 = x \cdot x \cdot x \cdot x \cdot x$

There are two common factors, each of which is x, so the GCF $= x \cdot x$ or x^2. From this example, we see that **the GCF of a list of common variables raised to powers is the variable raised to the smallest exponent in the list.**

Example 2 Find the GCF of each list of terms.

a. x^3, x^7, and x^5

b. y, y^4, and y^7

Solution:

a. The GCF is x^3, since 3 is the smallest exponent to which x is raised.

b. The GCF is y^1 or y, since 1 is the smallest exponent on y.

Work Practice 2

PRACTICE 2

Find the GCF of each list of terms.

a. y^4, y^5, and y^8

b. x and x^{10}

The **greatest common factor (GCF) of a list of terms** is the product of the GCF of the numerical coefficients and the GCF of the variable factors.

$20x^2y^2 = 2 \cdot 2 \cdot 5 \cdot x \cdot x \cdot y \cdot y$

$6xy^3 = 2 \cdot 3 \cdot x \cdot y \cdot y \cdot y$

$\text{GCF} = 2 \cdot x \cdot y \cdot y = 2xy^2$

Helpful Hint

Remember that the GCF of a list of terms contains the smallest exponent on each common variable.

The GCF of x^5y^6, x^2y^7, and x^3y^4 is x^2y^4. (Smallest exponent on x; Smallest exponent on y)

Answers

2. a. y^4 **b.** x

PRACTICE 3

Find the greatest common factor of each list of terms.

a. $6x^2$, $9x^4$, and $-12x^5$

b. $-16y$, $-20y^6$, and $40y^4$

c. a^5b^4, ab^3, and a^3b^2

Example 3 Find the greatest common factor of each list of terms.

a. $6x^2$, $10x^3$, and $-8x$

b. $-18y^2$, $-63y^3$, and $27y^4$

c. a^3b^2, a^5b, and a^6b^2

Solution:

a.
$$\left.\begin{aligned} 6x^2 &= 2\cdot 3\cdot x^2 \\ 10x^3 &= 2\cdot 5\cdot x^3 \\ -8x &= -1\cdot 2\cdot 2\cdot 2\cdot x^1 \end{aligned}\right\} \rightarrow \text{The GCF of } x^2, x^3, \text{ and } x^1 \text{ is } x^1 \text{ or } x.$$
$$\text{GCF} = 2\cdot x^1 \quad \text{or} \quad 2x$$

b.
$$\left.\begin{aligned} -18y^2 &= -1\cdot 2\cdot 3\cdot 3\cdot y^2 \\ -63y^3 &= -1\cdot 3\cdot 3\cdot 7\cdot y^3 \\ 27y^4 &= 3\cdot 3\cdot 3\cdot y^4 \end{aligned}\right\} \rightarrow \text{The GCF of } y^2, y^3, \text{ and } y^4 \text{ is } y^2.$$
$$\text{GCF} = 3\cdot 3\cdot y^2 \quad \text{or} \quad 9y^2$$

c. The GCF of a^3, a^5, and a^6 is a^3.
The GCF of b^2, b, and b^2 is b.
Thus, the GCF of a^3b^2, a^5b, and a^6b^2 is a^3b.

Work Practice 3

Objective C Factoring Out the Greatest Common Factor

To factor a polynomial such as $8x + 14$, we first see whether the terms have a greatest common factor other than 1. In this case, they do: The GCF of $8x$ and 14 is 2.

We factor out 2 from each term by writing each term as the product of 2 and the term's remaining factors.

$$8x + 14 = 2\cdot 4x + 2\cdot 7$$

Using the distributive property, we can write

$$\begin{aligned} 8x + 14 &= 2\cdot 4x + 2\cdot 7 \\ &= 2(4x + 7) \end{aligned}$$

Thus, a factored form of $8x + 14$ is $2(4x + 7)$. We can check by multiplying:

$$2(4x + 7) = 2\cdot 4x + 2\cdot 7 = 8x + 14.$$

Helpful Hint

A factored form of $8x + 14$ is *not*

$$2\cdot 4x + 2\cdot 7$$

Although the *terms* have been factored (written as products), the *polynomial* $8x + 14$ has not been factored. A factored form of $8x + 14$ is the *product* $2(4x + 7)$.

✓Concept Check Which of the following is/are factored form(s) of $6t + 18$?

a. 6

b. $6\cdot t + 6\cdot 3$

c. $6(t + 3)$

d. $3(t + 6)$

Answers

3. a. $3x^2$ **b.** $4y$ **c.** ab^2

✓ Concept Check Answer

c

Example 4 Factor each polynomial by factoring out the greatest common factor (GCF).

a. $5ab + 10a$ **b.** $y^5 - y^{12}$

Solution:

a. The GCF of terms $5ab$ and $10a$ is $5a$. Thus,

$$5ab + 10a = 5a \cdot b + 5a \cdot 2$$
$$= 5a(b + 2) \quad \text{Apply the distributive property.}$$

We can check our work by multiplying $5a$ and $(b + 2)$.
$5a(b + 2) = 5a \cdot b + 5a \cdot 2 = 5ab + 10a$, the original polynomial.

b. The GCF of y^5 and y^{12} is y^5. Thus,

$$y^5 - y^{12} = y^5(1) - y^5(y^7)$$
$$= y^5(1 - y^7)$$

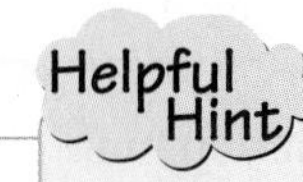

Don't forget the 1.

Work Practice 4

PRACTICE 4

Factor each polynomial by factoring out the greatest common factor (GCF).

a. $10y + 25$

b. $x^4 - x^9$

Example 5 Factor: $-9a^5 + 18a^2 - 3a$

Solution:

$$-9a^5 + 18a^2 - 3a = 3a(-3a^4) + 3a(6a) + 3a(-1)$$
$$= 3a(-3a^4 + 6a - 1)$$

Don't forget the -1.

Work Practice 5

PRACTICE 5

Factor: $-10x^3 + 8x^2 - 2x$

In Example 5, we could have chosen to factor out $-3a$ instead of $3a$. If we factor out $-3a$, we have

$$-9a^5 + 18a^2 - 3a = (-3a)(3a^4) + (-3a)(-6a) + (-3a)(1)$$
$$= -3a(3a^4 - 6a + 1)$$

Helpful Hint

Notice the changes in signs when factoring out $-3a$.

Examples Factor.

6. $6a^4 - 12a = 6a(a^3 - 2)$

7. $\frac{3}{7}x^4 + \frac{1}{7}x^3 - \frac{5}{7}x^2 = \frac{1}{7}x^2(3x^2 + x - 5)$

8. $15p^2q^4 + 20p^3q^5 + 5p^3q^3 = 5p^2q^3(3q + 4pq^2 + p)$

Work Practice 6–8

PRACTICE 6–8

Factor.

6. $4x^3 + 12x$

7. $\frac{2}{5}a^5 - \frac{4}{5}a^3 + \frac{1}{5}a^2$

8. $6a^3b + 3a^3b^2 + 9a^2b^4$

Example 9 Factor: $5(x + 3) + y(x + 3)$

Solution: The binomial $(x + 3)$ is present in both terms and is the greatest common factor. We use the distributive property to factor out $(x + 3)$.

$$5(x + 3) + y(x + 3) = (x + 3)(5 + y)$$

Work Practice 9

PRACTICE 9

Factor: $7(p + 2) + q(p + 2)$

Answers

4. a. $5(2y + 5)$ **b.** $x^4(1 - x^5)$
5. $2x(-5x^2 + 4x - 1)$
6. $4x(x^2 + 3)$ **7.** $\frac{1}{5}a^2(2a^3 - 4a + 1)$
8. $3a^2b(2a + ab + 3b^3)$
9. $(p + 2)(7 + q)$

Objective D Factoring by Grouping

Once the GCF is factored out, we can often continue to factor the polynomial, using a variety of techniques. We discuss here a technique called **factoring by grouping.** This technique can be used to factor some polynomials with four terms.

PRACTICE 10

Factor $ab + 7a + 2b + 14$ by grouping.

Example 10 Factor $xy + 2x + 3y + 6$ by grouping.

Solution: Notice that the first two terms of this polynomial have a common factor of x and the second two terms have a common factor of 3. Because of this, group the first two terms, then the last two terms, and then factor out these common factors.

$$xy + 2x + 3y + 6 = (xy + 2x) + (3y + 6) \quad \text{Group terms.}$$
$$= x(y + 2) + 3(y + 2) \quad \text{Factor out GCF from each grouping.}$$

Helpful Hint Notice that this form, $x(y + 2) + 3(y + 2)$, is *not* a factored form of the original polynomial. It is a sum, not a product.

Next we factor out the common binomial factor, $(y + 2)$.

$$x(y + 2) + 3(y + 2) = (y + 2)(x + 3)$$

Now the result is a factored form because it is a product. We were able to write the polynomial as a product because of the common binomial factor, $(y + 2)$, that appeared. If this does not happen, try rearranging the terms of the original polynomial.

Check: Multiply $(y + 2)$ by $(x + 3)$.

$$(y + 2)(x + 3) = xy + 2x + 3y + 6,$$

the original polynomial.
Thus, the factored form of $xy + 2x + 3y + 6$ is the product $(y + 2)(x + 3)$.

Work Practice 10

You may want to try these steps when factoring by grouping.

To Factor by Grouping

Step 1: Group the terms in two groups so that each group has a common factor.

Step 2: Factor out the GCF from each group.

Step 3: If there is a common binomial factor, factor it out.

Step 4: If not, rearrange the terms and try these steps again.

PRACTICE 11–13

Factor by grouping.

11. $28x^3 - 7x^2 + 12x - 3$

12. $2xy + 5y^2 - 4x - 10y$

13. $3x^2 + 4xy + 3x + 4y$

Examples Factor by grouping.

11. $15x^3 - 10x^2 + 6x - 4$

$$= (15x^3 - 10x^2) + (6x - 4) \quad \text{Group the terms.}$$
$$= 5x^2(3x - 2) + 2(3x - 2) \quad \text{Factor each group.}$$
$$= (3x - 2)(5x^2 + 2) \quad \text{Factor out the common factor, } (3x - 2).$$

12. $3x^2 + 4xy - 3x - 4y$

$$= (3x^2 + 4xy) + (-3x - 4y)$$
$$= x(3x + 4y) - 1(3x + 4y) \quad \text{Factor each group. A } -1 \text{ is factored from the second pair of terms so that there is a common factor, } (3x + 4y).$$
$$= (3x + 4y)(x - 1) \quad \text{Factor out the common factor, } (3x + 4y).$$

Answers

10. $(b + 7)(a + 2)$
11. $(4x - 1)(7x^2 + 3)$
12. $(2x + 5y)(y - 2)$
13. $(3x + 4y)(x + 1)$

13. $2a^2 + 5ab + 2a + 5b$

$= (2a^2 + 5ab) + (2a + 5b)$ Factor each group.

$= a(2a + 5b) + 1(2a + 5b)$ An understood 1 is written before $(2a + 5b)$ to help remember that $(2a + 5b)$ is $1(2a + 5b)$.

$= (2a + 5b)(a + 1)$ Factor out the common factor, $(2a + 5b)$.

Work Practice 11–13

Helpful Hint Notice that the factor of 1 is written when $(2a + 5b)$ is factored out.

Examples Factor by grouping.

14. $3x^3 - 2x - 9x^2 + 6$

$= x(3x^2 - 2) - 3(3x^2 - 2)$ Factor each group. A -3 is factored from the second pair of terms so that there is a common factor, $(3x^2 - 2)$.

$= (3x^2 - 2)(x - 3)$ Factor out the common factor, $(3x^2 - 2)$.

15. $3xy + 2 - 3x - 2y$

Notice that the first two terms have no common factor other than 1. However, if we rearrange these terms, a grouping emerges that does lead to a common factor.

$3xy + 2 - 3x - 2y$

$= (3xy - 3x) + (-2y + 2)$

$= 3x(y - 1) - 2(y - 1)$ Factor -2 from the second group.

$= (y - 1)(3x - 2)$ Factor out the common factor, $(y - 1)$.

16. $5x - 10 + x^3 - x^2 = 5(x - 2) + x^2(x - 1)$

There is no common binomial factor that can now be factored out. No matter how we rearrange the terms, no grouping will lead to a common factor. Thus, this polynomial is not factorable by grouping.

Work Practice 14–16

Helpful Hint

Throughout this chapter, we will be factoring polynomials. Even when the instructions do not so state, it is always a good idea to check your answers by multiplying.

PRACTICE 14–16

Factor by grouping.

14. $4x^3 + x - 20x^2 - 5$

15. $3xy - 4 + x - 12y$

16. $2x - 2 + x^3 - 3x^2$

Answers

14. $(4x^2 + 1)(x - 5)$

15. $(3y + 1)(x - 4)$

16. cannot be factored by grouping

Vocabulary and Readiness Check

Use the choices below to fill in each blank. Some choices may be used more than once and some may not be used at all.

greatest common factor   factors   factoring   true   false   least   greatest

1. Since $5 \cdot 4 = 20$, the numbers 5 and 4 are called ________________ of 20.

2. The ________________ of a list of integers is the largest integer that is a factor of all the integers in the list.

3. The greatest common factor of a list of common variables raised to powers is the variable raised to the ________________ exponent in the list.

4. The process of writing a polynomial as a product is called ________________.

5. True or false: A factored form of $7x + 21 + xy + 3y$ is $7(x + 3) + y(x + 3)$. ________________

6. True or false: A factored form of $3x^3 + 6x + x^2 + 2$ is $3x(x^2 + 2)$. ________________

Write the prime factorization of the following integers.

7. 14   **8.** 15

Write the GCF of the following pairs of integers.

9. 18, 3   **10.** 7, 35   **11.** 20, 15   **12.** 6, 15

11.1 Exercise Set

FOR EXTRA HELP

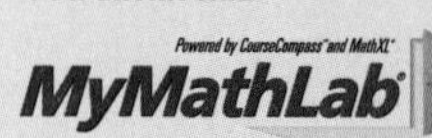

PRACTICE

WATCH

DOWNLOAD

READ

REVIEW

Objectives A B Mixed Practice *Find the GCF for each list. See Examples 1 through 3.*

1. 32, 36   **2.** 36, 90   **3.** 18, 42, 84   **4.** 30, 75, 135

5. 24, 14, 21   **6.** 15, 25, 27   **7.** y^2, y^4, y^7 **8.** x^3, x^2, x^5

9. z^7, z^9, z^{11} **10.** y^8, y^{10}, y^{12} **11.** $x^{10}y^2, xy^2, x^3y^3$ **12.** p^7q, p^8q^2, p^9q^3

13. $14x, 21$ **14.** $20y, 15$ **15.** $12y^4, 20y^3$ **16.** $32x^5, 18x^2$

17. $-10x^2, 15x^3$ **18.** $-21x^3, 14x$ **19.** $12x^3, -6x^4, 3x^5$ **20.** $15y^2, 5y^7, -20y^3$

21. $-18x^2y, 9x^3y^3, 36x^3y$ **22.** $7x^3y^3, -21x^2y^2, 14xy^4$ **23.** $20a^6b^2c^8, 50a^7b$ **24.** $40x^7y^2z, 64x^9y$

Objective C *Factor out the GCF from each polynomial. See Examples 4 through 9.*

25. $3a + 6$ **26.** $18a + 12$ **27.** $30x - 15$ **28.** $42x - 7$ **29.** $x^3 + 5x^2$

30. $y^5 + 6y^4$

31. $6y^4 + 2y^3$

32. $5x^2 + 10x^6$

33. $32xy - 18x^2$

34. $10xy - 15x^2$

35. $4x - 8y + 4$

36. $7x + 21y - 7$

37. $6x^3 - 9x^2 + 12x$

38. $12x^3 + 16x^2 - 8x$

39. $a^7b^6 - a^3b^2 + a^2b^5 - a^2b^2$

40. $x^9y^6 + x^3y^5 - x^4y^3 + x^3y^3$

41. $5x^3y - 15x^2y + 10xy$

42. $14x^3y + 7x^2y - 7xy$

43. $8x^5 + 16x^4 - 20x^3 + 12$

44. $9y^6 - 27y^4 + 18y^2 + 6$

45. $\frac{1}{3}x^4 + \frac{2}{3}x^3 - \frac{4}{3}x^5 + \frac{1}{3}x$

46. $\frac{2}{5}y^7 - \frac{4}{5}y^5 + \frac{3}{5}y^2 - \frac{2}{5}y$

47. $y(x^2 + 2) + 3(x^2 + 2)$

48. $x(y^2 + 1) - 3(y^2 + 1)$

49. $z(y + 4) + 3(y + 4)$

50. $8(x + 2) - y(x + 2)$

51. $r(z^2 - 6) + (z^2 - 6)$

52. $q(b^3 - 5) + (b^3 - 5)$

Factor a "−1" from each polynomial. See Example 5.

53. $-x - 7$

54. $-y - 3$

55. $-2 + z$

56. $-5 + y$

57. $3a - b + 2$

58. $2y - z - 11$

Objective **D** *Factor each four-term polynomial by grouping. If this is not possible, write "not factorable by grouping." See Examples 10 through 16.*

59. $x^3 + 2x^2 + 5x + 10$

60. $x^3 + 4x^2 + 3x + 12$

61. $5x + 15 + xy + 3y$

62. $xy + y + 2x + 2$

63. $6x^3 - 4x^2 + 15x - 10$

64. $16x^3 - 28x^2 + 12x - 21$

65. $5m^3 + 6mn + 5m^2 + 6n$

66. $8w^2 + 7wv + 8w + 7v$

67. $2y - 8 + xy - 4x$

68. $6x - 42 + xy - 7y$

69. $2x^3 + x^2 + 8x + 4$

70. $2x^3 - x^2 - 10x + 5$

71. $3x - 3 + x^3 - 4x^2$

72. $7x - 21 + x^3 - 2x^2$

73. $4x^2 - 8xy - 3x + 6y$

74. $5xy - 15x - 6y + 18$

75. $5q^2 - 4pq - 5q + 4p$

76. $6m^2 - 5mn - 6m + 5n$

Objectives C D Mixed Practice *Factor out the GCF from each polynomial. Then factor by grouping.*

77. $12x^2y - 42x^2 - 4y + 14$

78. $90 + 15y^2 - 18x - 3xy^2$

79. $6a^2 + 9ab^2 + 6ab + 9b^3$

80. $16x^2 + 4xy^2 + 8xy + 2y^3$

Review

Multiply. See section 10.5.

81. $(x + 2)(x + 5)$

82. $(y + 3)(y + 6)$

83. $(b + 1)(b - 4)$

84. $(x - 5)(x + 10)$

Fill in the chart by finding two numbers that have the given product and sum. The first column is filled in for you.

		85.	86.	87.	88.	89.	90.	91.	92.
Two Numbers	4, 7								
Their Product	28	12	20	8	16	−10	−9	−24	−36
Their Sum	11	8	9	−9	−10	3	0	−5	−5

Concept Extensions

See the Concept Checks in this section.

93. Which of the following is/are factored form(s) of $-2x + 14$?

a. $-2(x + 7)$ **b.** $-2 \cdot x + 14$
c. $-2(x - 14)$ **d.** $-2(x - 7)$

94. Which of the following is/are factored form(s) of $8a - 24$?

a. $8 \cdot a - 24$ **b.** $8(a - 3)$
c. $4(2a - 12)$ **d.** $8 \cdot a - 2 \cdot 12$

Which of the following expressions are factored?

95. $(a + 6)(a + 2)$

96. $(x + 5)(x + y)$

97. $5(2y + z) - b(2y + z)$

98. $3x(a + 2b) + 2(a + 2b)$

99. The annual cotton crop yield (in 1000 bales) in the United States for the period 2003–2007 can be approximated by the polynomial $-1264x^2 + 5056x + 18{,}960$, where x is the number of years after 2003. (*Source:* Based on data from the National Agricultural Statistics Service)

a. Find the approximate amount of the cotton harvest in 2004. To do so, let $x = 1$ and evaluate $-1264x^2 + 5056x + 18{,}960$.

b. Find the approximate amount of cotton harvested in 2007.

c. Factor the polynomial $-1264x^2 + 5056x + 18{,}960$.

100. The polynomial $-30x^2 + 180x + 210$ represents the approximate number of visitors (in thousands) per year to the White House during 2003–2007. In this polynomial, x represents the years since 2003. (*Source:* Based on data from the National Park Service)

a. Find the approximate number of visitors to the White House in 2005. To do so, let $x = 2$ and evaluate $-30x^2 + 180x + 210$.

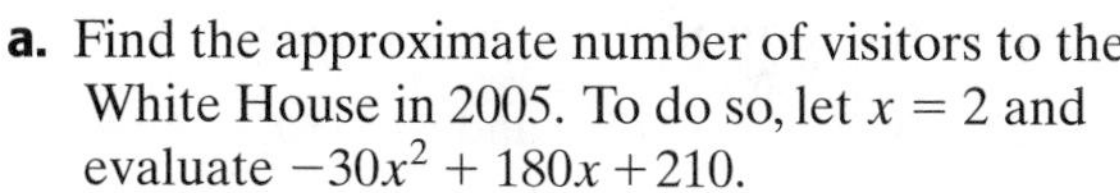

b. Find the approximate number of visitors to the White House in 2006.

c. Factor out the GCF from the polynomial $-30x^2 + 180x + 210$.

Write an expression for the area of each shaded region. Then write the expression as a factored polynomial.

△ **101.**

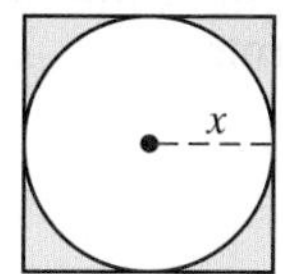

△ **102.**

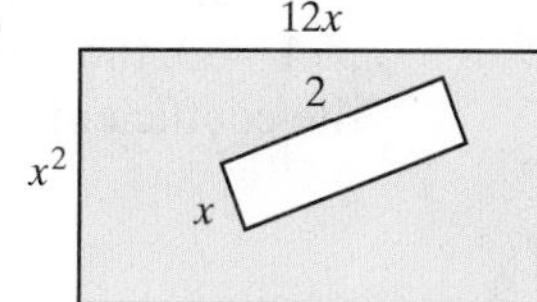

Write an expression for the length of each rectangle. (Hint: Factor the area binomial and recall that Area = width · length.)

△ **103.**

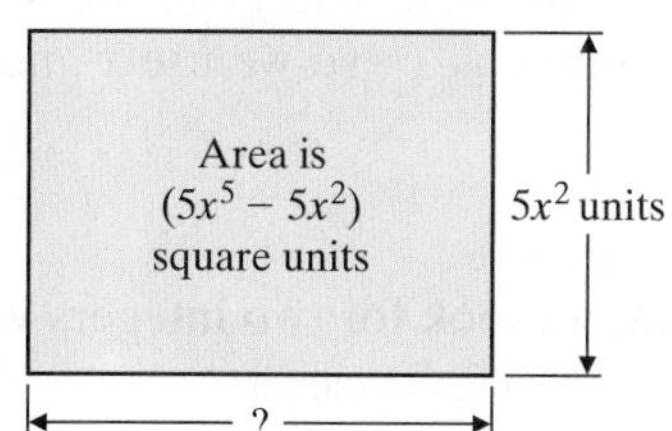

△ **104.**

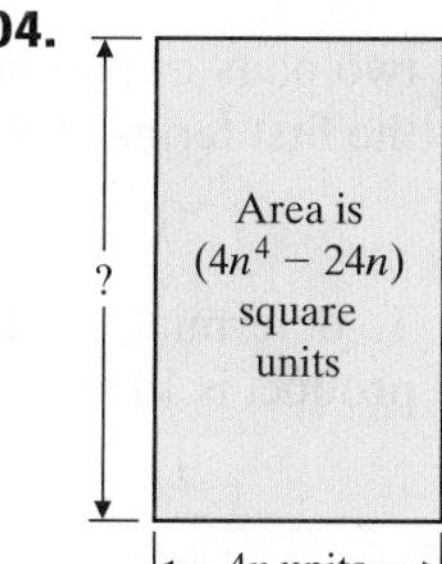

105. Construct a binomial whose greatest common factor is $5a^3$. (*Hint:* Multiply $5a^3$ by a binomial whose terms contain no common factor other than 1: $5a^3(\square + \square)$.)

106. Construct a trinomial whose greatest common factor is $2x^2$. See the hint for Exercise 105.

107. Explain how you can tell whether a polynomial is written in factored form.

108. Construct a four-term polynomial that can be factored by grouping. Explain how you constructed the polynomial.

Objectives

A **Factor Trinomials of the Form $x^2 + bx + c$.**

B **Factor Out the Greatest Common Factor and Then Factor a Trinomial of the Form $x^2 + bx + c$.**

11.2 FACTORING TRINOMIALS OF THE FORM $x^2 + bx + c$

Objective A Factoring Trinomials of the Form $x^2 + bx + c$

In this section, we factor trinomials of the form $x^2 + bx + c$, such as

$$x^2 + 7x + 12, \quad x^2 - 12x + 35, \quad x^2 + 4x - 12, \quad \text{and} \quad r^2 - r - 42$$

Notice that for these trinomials, the coefficient of the squared variable is 1.

Recall that factoring means to write as a product and that factoring and multiplying are reverse processes. Using the FOIL method of multiplying binomials, we have the following.

$$\begin{aligned} & \quad\ \ \text{F} \quad \text{O} \quad \text{I} \quad \text{L} \\ (x + 3)(x + 1) &= x^2 + 1x + 3x + 3 \\ &= x^2 + 4x + 3 \end{aligned}$$

Thus, a factored form of $x^2 + 4x + 3$ is $(x + 3)(x + 1)$.

Notice that the product of the first terms of the binomials is $x \cdot x = x^2$, the first term of the trinomial. Also, the product of the last two terms of the binomials is $3 \cdot 1 = 3$, the third term of the trinomial. The sum of these same terms is $3 + 1 = 4$, the coefficient of the middle, x, term of the trinomial.

The product of these numbers is 3.

$$x^2 + 4x + 3 = (x + 3)(x + 1)$$

The sum of these numbers is 4.

Many trinomials, such as the one above, factor into two binomials. To factor $x^2 + 7x + 10$, let's assume that it factors into two binomials and begin by writing two pairs of parentheses. The first term of the trinomial is x^2, so we use x and x as the first terms of the binomial factors.

$$x^2 + 7x + 10 = (x + \square)(x + \square)$$

To determine the last term of each binomial factor, we look for two integers whose product is 10 and whose sum is 7. The integers are 2 and 5. Thus,

$$x^2 + 7x + 10 = (x + 2)(x + 5)$$

Check: To see if we have factored correctly, we multiply.

$$\begin{aligned} (x + 2)(x + 5) &= x^2 + 5x + 2x + 10 \\ &= x^2 + 7x + 10 \qquad \text{Combine like terms.} \end{aligned}$$

Helpful Hint

Since multiplication is commutative, the factored form of $x^2 + 7x + 10$ can be written as either $(x + 2)(x + 5)$ or $(x + 5)(x + 2)$.

To Factor a Trinomial of the Form $x^2 + bx + c$

The product of these numbers is c.

$$x^2 + bx + c = (x + \square)(x + \square)$$

The sum of these numbers is b.

Example 1 Factor: $x^2 + 7x + 12$

Solution: We begin by writing the first terms of the binomial factors.

$$(x + \square)(x + \square)$$

Next we look for two numbers whose product is 12 and whose sum is 7. Since our numbers must have a positive product and a positive sum, we look at pairs of positive factors of 12 only.

Factors of 12	Sum of Factors
1, 12	13
2, 6	8
3, 4	7

Correct sum, so the numbers are 3 and 4.

Thus, $x^2 + 7x + 12 = (x + 3)(x + 4)$

Check: $(x + 3)(x + 4) = x^2 + 4x + 3x + 12 = x^2 + 7x + 12$

Work Practice 1

Example 2 Factor: $x^2 - 12x + 35$

Solution: Again, we begin by writing the first terms of the binomials.

$$(x + \square)(x + \square)$$

Now we look for two numbers whose product is 35 and whose sum is -12. Since our numbers must have a positive product and a negative sum, we look at pairs of negative factors of 35 only.

Factors of 35	Sum of Factors
−1, −35	−36
−5, −7	−12

Correct sum, so the numbers are −5 and −7.

$$x^2 - 12x + 35 = (x - 5)(x - 7)$$

Check: To check, multiply $(x - 5)(x - 7)$.

Work Practice 2

Example 3 Factor: $x^2 + 4x - 12$

Solution: $x^2 + 4x - 12 = (x + \square)(x + \square)$

We look for two numbers whose product is -12 and whose sum is 4. Since our numbers must have a negative product, we look at pairs of factors with opposite signs.

Factors of −12	Sum of Factors
−1, 12	11
1, −12	−11
−2, 6	4
2, −6	−4
−3, 4	1
3, −4	−1

Correct sum, so the numbers are −2 and 6.

$$x^2 + 4x - 12 = (x - 2)(x + 6)$$

Work Practice 3

PRACTICE 1

Factor: $x^2 + 12x + 20$

PRACTICE 2

Factor each trinomial.

a. $x^2 - 23x + 22$
b. $x^2 - 27x + 50$

PRACTICE 3

Factor: $x^2 + 5x - 36$

Answers

1. $(x + 10)(x + 2)$
2. **a.** $(x - 1)(x - 22)$ **b.** $(x - 2)(x - 25)$
3. $(x + 9)(x - 4)$

PRACTICE 4

Factor each trinomial.

a. $q^2 - 3q - 40$

b. $y^2 + 2y - 48$

Example 4 Factor: $r^2 - r - 42$

Solution: Because the variable in this trinomial is r, the first term of each binomial factor is r.

$$r^2 - r - 42 = (r + \square)(r + \square)$$

Now we look for two numbers whose product is -42 and whose sum is -1, the numerical coefficient of r. The numbers are 6 and -7. Therefore,

$$r^2 - r - 42 = (r + 6)(r - 7)$$

Work Practice 4

PRACTICE 5

Factor: $x^2 + 6x + 15$

Example 5 Factor: $a^2 + 2a + 10$

Solution: Look for two numbers whose product is 10 and whose sum is 2. Neither 1 and 10 nor 2 and 5 give the required sum, 2. We conclude that $a^2 + 2a + 10$ is not factorable with integers. A polynomial such as $a^2 + 2a + 10$ is called a **prime polynomial.**

Work Practice 5

PRACTICE 6

Factor each trinomial.

a. $x^2 + 9xy + 14y^2$

b. $a^2 - 13ab + 30b^2$

Example 6 Factor: $x^2 + 5xy + 6y^2$

Solution: $x^2 + 5xy + 6y^2 = (x + \square)(x + \square)$

Recall that the middle term, $5xy$, is the same as $5yx$. Thus, we can see that $5y$ is the "coefficient" of x. We then look for two terms whose product is $6y^2$ and whose sum is $5y$. The terms are $2y$ and $3y$ because $2y \cdot 3y = 6y^2$ and $2y + 3y = 5y$. Therefore,

$$x^2 + 5xy + 6y^2 = (x + 2y)(x + 3y)$$

Work Practice 6

PRACTICE 7

Factor: $x^4 + 8x^2 + 12$

Example 7 Factor: $x^4 + 5x^2 + 6$

Solution: As usual, we begin by writing the first terms of the binomials. Since the greatest power of x in this polynomial is x^4, we write

$$(x^2 + \square)(x^2 + \square) \quad \text{Since } x^2 \cdot x^2 = x^4$$

Now we look for two factors of 6 whose sum is 5. The numbers are 2 and 3. Thus,

$$x^4 + 5x^2 + 6 = (x^2 + 2)(x^2 + 3)$$

Work Practice 7

If the terms of a polynomial are not written in descending powers of the variable, you may want to rearrange the terms before factoring.

PRACTICE 8

Factor: $48 - 14x + x^2$

Example 8 Factor: $40 - 13t + t^2$

Solution: First, we rearrange terms so that the trinomial is written in descending powers of t.

$$40 - 13t + t^2 = t^2 - 13t + 40$$

Next, try to factor.

$$t^2 - 13t + 40 = (t + \square)(t + \square)$$

Now we look for two factors of 40 whose sum is -13. The numbers are -8 and -5. Thus,

$$t^2 - 13t + 40 = (t - 8)(t - 5)$$

Work Practice 8

Answers

4. a. $(q - 8)(q + 5)$ **b.** $(y + 8)(y - 6)$

5. prime polynomial

6. a. $(x + 2y)(x + 7y)$ **b.** $(a - 3b)(a - 10b)$

7. $(x^2 + 6)(x^2 + 2)$

8. $(x - 6)(x - 8)$

The following sign patterns may be useful when factoring trinomials.

Helpful Hint

A positive constant in a trinomial tells us to look for two numbers with the same sign. The sign of the coefficient of the middle term tells us whether the signs are both positive or both negative.

both positive — same sign

$x^2 + 10x + 16 = (x + 2)(x + 8)$

both negative — same sign

$x^2 - 10x + 16 = (x - 2)(x - 8)$

A negative constant in a trinomial tells us to look for two numbers with opposite signs.

opposite signs

$x^2 + 6x - 16 = (x + 8)(x - 2)$

opposite signs

$x^2 - 6x - 16 = (x - 8)(x + 2)$

Objective B Factoring Out the Greatest Common Factor

Remember that the first step in factoring any polynomial is to factor out the greatest common factor (if there is one other than 1 or −1).

Example 9 Factor: $3m^2 - 24m - 60$

Solution: First we factor out the greatest common factor, 3, from each term.

$$3m^2 - 24m - 60 = 3(m^2 - 8m - 20)$$

Now we factor $m^2 - 8m - 20$ by looking for two factors of −20 whose sum is −8. The factors are −10 and 2. Therefore, the complete factored form is

$$3m^2 - 24m - 60 = 3(m + 2)(m - 10)$$

Work Practice 9

PRACTICE 9

Factor each trinomial.

a. $4x^2 - 24x + 36$

b. $x^3 + 3x^2 - 4x$

Helpful Hint

Remember to write the common factor, 3, as part of the factored form.

Example 10 Factor: $2x^4 - 26x^3 + 84x^2$

Solution:

$$2x^4 - 26x^3 + 84x^2 = 2x^2(x^2 - 13x + 42) \quad \text{Factor out common factor, } 2x^2.$$

$$= 2x^2(x - 6)(x - 7) \quad \text{Factor } x^2 - 13x + 42.$$

Work Practice 10

PRACTICE 10

Factor: $5x^5 - 25x^4 - 30x^3$

Answers

9. a. $4(x - 3)(x - 3)$ **b.** $x(x + 4)(x - 1)$

10. $5x^3(x + 1)(x - 6)$

Vocabulary and Readiness Check

Fill in each blank with "true" or "false."

1. To factor $x^2 + 7x + 6$, we look for two numbers whose product is 6 and whose sum is 7. ______
2. We can write the factorization $(y + 2)(y + 4)$ also as $(y + 4)(y + 2)$. ______
3. The factorization $(4x - 12)(x - 5)$ is completely factored. ______
4. The factorization $(x + 2y)(x + y)$ may also be written as $(x + 2y)^2$. ______

Complete each factored form.

5. $x^2 + 9x + 20 = (x + 4)(x \quad)$
6. $x^2 + 12x + 35 = (x + 5)(x \quad)$
7. $x^2 - 7x + 12 = (x - 4)(x \quad)$
8. $x^2 - 13x + 22 = (x - 2)(x \quad)$
9. $x^2 + 4x + 4 = (x + 2)(x \quad)$
10. $x^2 + 10x + 24 = (x + 6)(x \quad)$

11.2 Exercise Set

FOR EXTRA HELP

MyMathLab

PRACTICE

WATCH

DOWNLOAD

READ

REVIEW

Objective A *Factor each trinomial completely. If a polynomial can't be factored, write "prime." See Examples 1 through 8.*

1. $x^2 + 7x + 6$
2. $x^2 + 6x + 8$
3. $y^2 - 10y + 9$
4. $y^2 - 12y + 11$
5. $x^2 - 6x + 9$
6. $x^2 - 10x + 25$
7. $x^2 - 3x - 18$
8. $x^2 - x - 30$
9. $x^2 + 3x - 70$
10. $x^2 + 4x - 32$
11. $x^2 + 5x + 2$
12. $x^2 - 7x + 5$
13. $x^2 + 8xy + 15y^2$
14. $x^2 + 6xy + 8y^2$
15. $a^4 - 2a^2 - 15$
16. $y^4 - 3y^2 - 70$
17. $13 + 14m + m^2$
18. $17 + 18n + n^2$
19. $10t - 24 + t^2$
20. $6q - 27 + q^2$
21. $a^2 - 10ab + 16b^2$
22. $a^2 - 9ab + 18b^2$

Objectives A B Mixed Practice *Factor each trinomial completely. Some of these trinomials contain a greatest common factor (other than 1). Don't forget to factor out the GCF first. See Examples 1 through 10.*

23. $2z^2 + 20z + 32$
24. $3x^2 + 30x + 63$
25. $2x^3 - 18x^2 + 40x$
26. $3x^3 - 12x^2 - 36x$
27. $x^2 - 3xy - 4y^2$
28. $x^2 - 4xy - 77y^2$
29. $x^2 + 15x + 36$
30. $x^2 + 19x + 60$
31. $x^2 - x - 2$
32. $x^2 - 5x - 14$
33. $r^2 - 16r + 48$
34. $r^2 - 10r + 21$
35. $x^2 + xy - 2y^2$
36. $x^2 - xy - 6y^2$
37. $3x^2 + 9x - 30$
38. $4x^2 - 4x - 48$

39. $3x^2 - 60x + 108$

40. $2x^2 - 24x + 70$

41. $x^2 - 18x - 144$

42. $x^2 + x - 42$

43. $r^2 - 3r + 6$

44. $x^2 + 4x - 10$

45. $x^2 - 8x + 15$

46. $x^2 - 9x + 14$

47. $6x^3 + 54x^2 + 120x$

48. $3x^3 + 3x^2 - 126x$

49. $4x^2y + 4xy - 12y$

50. $3x^2y - 9xy + 45y$

51. $x^2 - 4x - 21$

52. $x^2 - 4x - 32$

53. $x^2 + 7xy + 10y^2$

54. $x^2 - 3xy - 4y^2$

55. $64 + 24t + 2t^2$

56. $50 + 20t + 2t^2$

57. $x^3 - 2x^2 - 24x$

58. $x^3 - 3x^2 - 28x$

59. $2t^5 - 14t^4 + 24t^3$

60. $3x^6 + 30x^5 + 72x^4$

61. $5x^3y - 25x^2y^2 - 120xy^3$

62. $7a^3b - 35a^2b^2 + 42ab^3$

63. $162 - 45m + 3m^2$

64. $48 - 20n + 2n^2$

65. $-x^2 + 12x - 11$ (Factor out -1 first.)

66. $-x^2 + 8x - 7$ (Factor out -1 first.)

67. $\frac{1}{2}y^2 - \frac{9}{2}y - 11$ (Factor out $\frac{1}{2}$ first.)

68. $\frac{1}{3}y^2 - \frac{5}{3}y - 8$ (Factor out $\frac{1}{3}$ first.)

69. $x^3y^2 + x^2y - 20x$

70. $a^2b^3 + ab^2 - 30b$

Review

Multiply. See Section 10.5.

71. $(2x + 1)(x + 5)$

72. $(3x + 2)(x + 4)$

73. $(5y - 4)(3y - 1)$

74. $(4z - 7)(7z - 1)$

75. $(a + 3b)(9a - 4b)$

76. $(y - 5x)(6y + 5x)$

Concept Extensions

77. Write a polynomial that factors as $(x - 3)(x + 8)$.

78. To factor $x^2 + 13x + 42$, think of two numbers whose ______ is 42 and whose ______ is 13.

Complete each sentence in your own words.

79. If $x^2 + bx + c$ is factorable and c is negative, then the signs of the last-term factors of the binomials are opposite because...

80. If $x^2 + bx + c$ is factorable and c is positive, then the signs of the last-term factors of the binomials are the same because . . .

Remember that perimeter means distance around. Write the perimeter of each rectangle as a simplified polynomial. Then factor the polynomial completely.

△ **81.** Rectangle with sides $4x + 33$ and $x^2 + 10x$

△ **82.** Rectangle with sides $12x^2$ and $2x^3 + 16x$

83. An object is thrown upward from the top of an 80-foot building with an initial velocity of 64 feet per second. Neglecting air resistance, the height of the object after t seconds is given by $-16t^2 + 64t + 80$. Factor this polynomial.

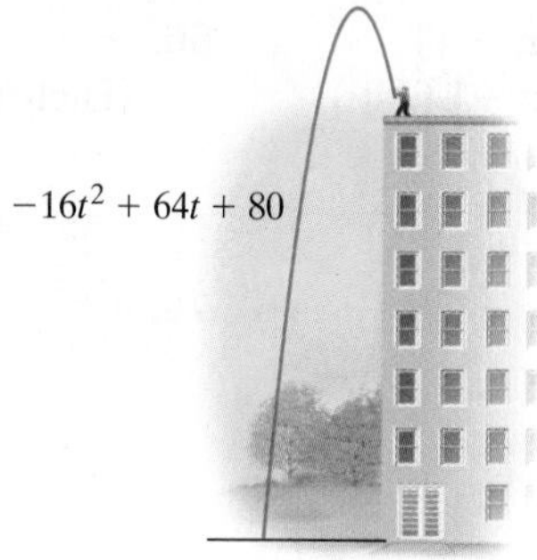

84. An object is thrown upward from the top of a 112-foot building with an initial velocity of 96 feet per second. Neglecting air resistance, the height of the object after t seconds is given by $-16t^2 + 96t + 112$. Factor this polynomial.

Factor each trinomial completely.

85. $x^2 + \frac{1}{2}x + \frac{1}{16}$

86. $x^2 + x + \frac{1}{4}$

87. $z^2(x + 1) - 3z(x + 1) - 70(x + 1)$

88. $y^2(x + 1) - 2y(x + 1) - 15(x + 1)$

Find all positive values of c so that each trinomial is factorable.

89. $n^2 - 16n + c$

90. $y^2 - 4y + c$

Find all positive values of b so that each trinomial is factorable.

91. $y^2 + by + 20$

92. $x^2 + bx + 15$

Factor each trinomial. (Hint: *Notice that* $x^{2n} + 4x^n + 3$ *factors as* $(x^n + 1)(x^n + 3)$. Remember: $x^n \cdot x^n = x^{n+n}$ *or* x^{2n}.)

93. $x^{2n} + 8x^n - 20$

94. $x^{2n} + 5x^n + 6$

11.3 FACTORING TRINOMIALS OF THE FORM $ax^2 + bx + c$

Objectives

A **Factor Trinomials of the Form $ax^2 + bx + c$, where $a \neq 1$.**

B **Factor Out the GCF Before Factoring a Trinomial of the Form $ax^2 + bx + c$.**

Objective A Factoring Trinomials of the Form $ax^2 + bx + c$

In this section, we factor trinomials of the form $ax^2 + bx + c$, such as

$$3x^2 + 11x + 6, \quad 8x^2 - 22x + 5, \quad \text{and} \quad 2x^2 + 13x - 7$$

Notice that the coefficient of the squared variable in these trinomials is a number other than 1. We will factor these trinomials using a trial-and-check method based on our work in the last section.

To begin, let's review the relationship between the numerical coefficients of the trinomial and the numerical coefficients of its factored form. For example, since

$$(2x + 1)(x + 6) = 2x^2 + 13x + 6,$$

a factored form of $2x^2 + 13x + 6$ is $(2x + 1)(x + 6)$.

Notice that $2x$ and x are factors of $2x^2$, the first term of the trinomial. Also, 6 and 1 are factors of 6, the last term of the trinomial, as shown:

$$2x^2 + 13x + 6 = (2x + 1)(x + 6)$$

$2x \cdot x$

$1 \cdot 6$

Also notice that $13x$, the middle term, is the sum of the following products:

$$2x^2 + 13x + 6 = (2x + 1)(x + 6)$$

$1x$
$+12x$
$13x$ Middle term

Let's use this pattern to factor $5x^2 + 7x + 2$. First, we find factors of $5x^2$. Since all numerical coefficients in this trinomial are positive, we will use factors with positive numerical coefficients only. Thus, the factors of $5x^2$ are $5x$ and x. Let's try these factors as first terms of the binomials. Thus far, we have

$$5x^2 + 7x + 2 = (5x + \square)(x + \square)$$

Next, we need to find positive factors of 2. Positive factors of 2 are 1 and 2. Now we try possible combinations of these factors as second terms of the binomials until we obtain a middle term of $7x$.

$$(5x + 1)(x + 2) = 5x^2 + 11x + 2$$

$1x$
$+10x$
$11x$ ⟶ **Incorrect** middle term

Let's try switching factors 2 and 1.

$$(5x + 2)(x + 1) = 5x^2 + 7x + 2$$

$2x$
$+5x$
$7x$ ⟶ **Correct** middle term

Thus a factored form of $5x^2 + 7x + 2$ is $(5x + 2)(x + 1)$. To check, we multiply $(5x + 2)$ and $(x + 1)$. The product is $5x^2 + 7x + 2$.

PRACTICE 1

Factor each trinomial.

a. $5x^2 + 27x + 10$

b. $4x^2 + 12x + 5$

Example 1 Factor: $3x^2 + 11x + 6$

Solution: Since all numerical coefficients are positive, we use factors with positive numerical coefficients. We first find factors of $3x^2$.

Factors of $3x^2$: $3x^2 = 3x \cdot x$

If factorable, the trinomial will be of the form

$$3x^2 + 11x + 6 = (3x + \square)(x + \square)$$

Next we factor 6.

Factors of 6: $6 = 1 \cdot 6, \quad 6 = 2 \cdot 3$

Now we try combinations of factors of 6 until a middle term of $11x$ is obtained. Let's try 1 and 6 first.

$$(3x + 1)(x + 6) = 3x^2 + 19x + 6$$

$1x$
$+18x$
$19x$ → **Incorrect** middle term

Now let's next try 6 and 1.

$$(3x + 6)(x + 1)$$

Before multiplying, notice that the terms of the factor $3x + 6$ have a common factor of 3. The terms of the original trinomial $3x^2 + 11x + 6$ have no common factor other than 1, so the terms of its factors will also contain no common factor other than 1. This means that $(3x + 6)(x + 1)$ is not a factored form.

Next let's try 2 and 3 as last terms.

$$(3x + 2)(x + 3) = 3x^2 + 11x + 6$$

$2x$
$+9x$
$11x$ → **Correct** middle term

Thus a factored form of $3x^2 + 11x + 6$ is $(3x + 2)(x + 3)$.

Work Practice 1

Helpful Hint This is true in general: If the terms of a trinomial have no common factor (other than 1), then the terms of each of its binomial factors will contain no common factor (other than 1).

✓Concept Check Do the terms of $3x^2 + 29x + 18$ have a common factor? Without multiplying, decide which of the following factored forms could not be a factored form of $3x^2 + 29x + 18$.

a. $(3x + 18)(x + 1)$ **b.** $(3x + 2)(x + 9)$

c. $(3x + 6)(x + 3)$ **d.** $(3x + 9)(x + 2)$

PRACTICE 2

Factor each trinomial.

a. $2x^2 - 11x + 12$

b. $6x^2 - 5x + 1$

Example 2 Factor: $8x^2 - 22x + 5$

Solution: Factors of $8x^2$: $8x^2 = 8x \cdot x, \quad 8x^2 = 4x \cdot 2x$

We'll try $8x$ and x.

$$8x^2 - 22x + 5 = (8x + \square)(x + \square)$$

Since the middle term, $-22x$, has a negative numerical coefficient, we factor 5 into negative factors.

Factors of 5: $5 = -1 \cdot -5$

Answers

1. a. $(5x + 2)(x + 5)$
   b. $(2x + 5)(2x + 1)$
2. a. $(2x - 3)(x - 4)$
   b. $(3x - 1)(2x - 1)$

✓ Concept Check Answer

no; a, c, d

Let's try -1 and -5.

$$(8x - 1)(x - 5) = 8x^2 - 41x + 5$$

$-1x$
$+(-40x)$
$-41x$ ⟶ **Incorrect** middle term

Now let's try -5 and -1.

$$(8x - 5)(x - 1) = 8x^2 - 13x + 5$$

$-5x$
$+(-8x)$
$-13x$ ⟶ **Incorrect** middle term

Don't give up yet! We can still try other factors of $8x^2$. Let's try $4x$ and $2x$ with -1 and -5.

$$(4x - 1)(2x - 5) = 8x^2 - 22x + 5$$

$-2x$
$+(-20x)$
$-22x$ ⟶ **Correct** middle term

A factored form of $8x^2 - 22x + 5$ is $(4x - 1)(2x - 5)$.

Work Practice 2

Example 3 Factor: $2x^2 + 13x - 7$

Solution: Factors of $2x^2$: $2x^2 = 2x \cdot x$

Factors of -7: $-7 = -1 \cdot 7$, $\quad -7 = 1 \cdot -7$

We try possible combinations of these factors:

$(2x + 1)(x - 7) = 2x^2 - 13x - 7$ **Incorrect** middle term
$(2x - 1)(x + 7) = 2x^2 + 13x - 7$ **Correct** middle term

A factored form of $2x^2 + 13x - 7$ is $(2x - 1)(x + 7)$.

Work Practice 3

Example 4 Factor: $10x^2 - 13xy - 3y^2$

Solution: Factors of $10x^2$: $10x^2 = 10x \cdot x$, $\quad 10x^2 = 2x \cdot 5x$

Factors of $-3y^2$: $-3y^2 = -3y \cdot y$, $\quad -3y^2 = 3y \cdot -y$

We try some combinations of these factors:

Correct ↓ Correct ↓

$(10x - 3y)(x + y) = 10x^2 + 7xy - 3y^2$
$(x + 3y)(10x - y) = 10x^2 + 29xy - 3y^2$
$(5x + 3y)(2x - y) = 10x^2 + xy - 3y^2$
$(2x - 3y)(5x + y) = 10x^2 - 13xy - 3y^2$ **Correct** middle term

A factored form of $10x^2 - 13xy - 3y^2$ is $(2x - 3y)(5x + y)$.

Work Practice 4

Example 5 Factor: $3x^4 - 5x^2 - 8$

Solution: Factors of $3x^4$: $3x^4 = 3x^2 \cdot x^2$

Factors of -8: $-8 = -2 \cdot 4, 2 \cdot -4, -1 \cdot 8, 1 \cdot -8$

Continued on next page

PRACTICE 3

Factor each trinomial.

a. $3x^2 + 14x - 5$
b. $35x^2 + 4x - 4$

PRACTICE 4

Factor each trinomial.

a. $14x^2 - 3xy - 2y^2$
b. $12a^2 - 16ab - 3b^2$

PRACTICE 5

Factor: $2x^4 - 5x^2 - 7$

Answers

3. a. $(3x - 1)(x + 5)$ **b.** $(5x + 2)(7x - 2)$
4. a. $(7x + 2y)(2x - y)$ **b.** $(6a + b)(2a - 3b)$
5. $(2x^2 - 7)(x^2 + 1)$

Try combinations of these factors:

Correct ↓ (first term) Correct ↓ (last term)

$(3x^2 - 2)(x^2 + 4) = 3x^4 + 10x^2 - 8$ **Incorrect** middle term

$(3x^2 + 4)(x^2 - 2) = 3x^4 - 2x^2 - 8$ **Incorrect** middle term

$(3x^2 + 8)(x^2 - 1) = 3x^4 + 5x^2 - 8$ **Incorrect sign** on middle term, so switch signs in binomial factors.

$(3x^2 - 8)(x^2 + 1) = 3x^4 - 5x^2 - 8$ **Correct** middle term

Work Practice 5

Helpful Hint

Study the last two lines of Example 5. If a factoring attempt gives you a middle term whose numerical coefficient is the opposite of the desired numerical coefficient, try switching the signs of the last terms in the binomials.

Switched signs

$(3x^2 + 8)(x^2 - 1) = 3x^4 + 5x^4 - 8$ Middle term: $+5x$

$(3x^2 - 8)(x^2 + 1) = 3x^4 - 5x^2 - 8$ Middle term: $-5x$

Objective B Factoring Out the Greatest Common Factor

Don't forget that the first step in factoring any polynomial is to look for a common factor to factor out.

PRACTICE 6

Factor each trinomial.

a. $3x^3 + 17x^2 + 10x$

b. $6xy^2 + 33xy - 18x$

Example 6 Factor: $24x^4 + 40x^3 + 6x^2$

Solution: Notice that all three terms have a common factor of $2x^2$. Thus we factor out $2x^2$ first.

$$24x^4 + 40x^3 + 6x^2 = 2x^2(12x^2 + 20x + 3)$$

Next we factor $12x^2 + 20x + 3$.

Factors of $12x^2$: $12x^2 = 4x \cdot 3x$, $12x^2 = 12x \cdot x$, $12x^2 = 6x \cdot 2x$

Since all terms in the trinomial have positive numerical coefficients, we factor 3 using positive factors only.

Factors of 3: $3 = 1 \cdot 3$

We try some combinations of the factors.

$2x^2(4x + 3)(3x + 1) = 2x^2(12x^2 + 13x + 3)$

$2x^2(12x + 1)(x + 3) = 2x^2(12x^2 + 37x + 3)$

$2x^2(2x + 3)(6x + 1) = 2x^2(12x^2 + 20x + 3)$ **Correct** middle term

A factored form of $24x^4 + 40x^3 + 6x^2$ is $2x^2(2x + 3)(6x + 1)$.

Helpful Hint Don't forget to include the common factor in the factored form.

Work Practice 6

When the term containing the squared variable has a negative coefficient, you may want to first factor out a common factor of -1.

PRACTICE 7

Factor: $-5x^2 - 19x + 4$

Example 7 Factor: $-6x^2 - 13x + 5$

Solution: We begin by factoring out a common factor of -1.

$-6x^2 - 13x + 5 = -1(6x^2 + 13x - 5)$ Factor out -1.

$= -1(3x - 1)(2x + 5)$ Factor $6x^2 + 13x - 5$.

Work Practice 7

Answers

6. a. $x(3x + 2)(x + 5)$ b. $3x(2y - 1)(y + 6)$
7. $-1(x + 4)(5x - 1)$

Vocabulary and Readiness Check

Complete each factorization.

1. $2x^2 + 5x + 3$ factors as $(2x + 3)(\ ?\ )$.
   a. $(x + 3)$ **b.** $(2x + 1)$ **c.** $(3x + 4)$ **d.** $(x + 1)$
2. $7x^2 + 9x + 2$ factors as $(7x + 2)(\ ?\ )$.
   a. $(3x + 1)$ **b.** $(x + 1)$ **c.** $(x + 2)$ **d.** $(7x + 1)$
3. $3x^2 + 31x + 10$ factors as __________.
   a. $(3x + 2)(x + 5)$ **b.** $(3x + 5)(x + 2)$ **c.** $(3x + 1)(x + 10)$
4. $5x^2 + 61x + 12$ factors as __________.
   a. $(5x + 1)(x + 12)$ **b.** $(5x + 3)(x + 4)$ **c.** $(5x + 2)(x + 6)$

11.3 Exercise Set

FOR EXTRA HELP

PRACTICE

WATCH

DOWNLOAD

READ

REVIEW

Objective A *Complete each factored form. See Examples 1 through 5.*

1. $5x^2 + 22x + 8 = (5x + 2)(\qquad)$

2. $2y^2 + 15y + 25 = (2y + 5)(\qquad)$

3. $50x^2 + 15x - 2 = (5x + 2)(\qquad)$

4. $6y^2 + 11y - 10 = (2y + 5)(\qquad)$

5. $20x^2 - 7x - 6 = (5x + 2)(\qquad)$

6. $8y^2 - 2y - 55 = (2y + 5)(\qquad)$

Factor each trinomial completely. See Examples 1 through 5.

7. $2x^2 + 13x + 15$

8. $3x^2 + 8x + 4$

9. $8y^2 - 17y + 9$

10. $21x^2 - 41x + 10$

11. $2x^2 - 9x - 5$

12. $36r^2 - 5r - 24$

13. $20r^2 + 27r - 8$

14. $3x^2 + 20x - 63$

15. $10x^2 + 31x + 3$

16. $12x^2 + 17x + 5$

17. $x + 3x^2 - 2$

18. $y + 8y^2 - 9$

19. $6x^2 - 13xy + 5y^2$

20. $8x^2 - 14xy + 3y^2$

21. $15m^2 - 16m - 15$

22. $25n^2 - 5n - 6$

23. $-9x + 20 + x^2$

24. $-7x + 12 + x^2$

25. $2x^2 - 7x - 99$

26. $2x^2 + 7x - 72$

27. $-27t + 7t^2 - 4$

28. $-3t + 4t^2 - 7$

29. $3a^2 + 10ab + 3b^2$

30. $2a^2 + 11ab + 5b^2$

31. $49p^2 - 7p - 2$

32. $3r^2 + 10r - 8$

33. $18x^2 - 9x - 14$

34. $42a^2 - 43a + 6$

35. $2m^2 + 17m + 10$

36. $3n^2 + 20n + 5$

37. $24x^2 + 41x + 12$

38. $24x^2 - 49x + 15$

Objectives A B **Mixed Practice** *Factor each trinomial completely. See Examples 1 through 7.*

39. $12x^3 + 11x^2 + 2x$

40. $8a^3 + 14a^2 + 3a$

41. $21b^2 - 48b - 45$

42. $12x^2 - 14x - 10$

43. $7z + 12z^2 - 12$

44. $16t + 15t^2 - 15$

45. $6x^2y^2 - 2xy^2 - 60y^2$

46. $8x^2y + 34xy - 84y$

47. $4x^2 - 8x - 21$

48. $6x^2 - 11x - 10$

49. $3x^2 - 42x + 63$

50. $5x^2 - 75x + 60$

51. $8x^2 + 6xy - 27y^2$

52. $54a^2 + 39ab - 8b^2$

53. $-x^2 + 2x + 24$

54. $-x^2 + 4x + 21$

55. $4x^3 - 9x^2 - 9x$

56. $6x^3 - 31x^2 + 5x$

57. $24x^2 - 58x + 9$

58. $36x^2 + 55x - 14$

59. $40a^2b + 9ab - 9b$

60. $24y^2x + 7yx - 5x$

61. $30x^3 + 38x^2 + 12x$

62. $6x^3 - 28x^2 + 16x$

63. $6y^3 - 8y^2 - 30y$

64. $12x^3 - 34x^2 + 24x$

65. $10x^4 + 25x^3y - 15x^2y^2$

66. $42x^4 - 99x^3y - 15x^2y^2$

67. $-14x^2 + 39x - 10$

68. $-15x^2 + 26x - 8$

69. $16p^4 - 40p^3 + 25p^2$

70. $9q^4 - 42q^3 + 49q^2$

71. $-2x^2 + 9x + 5$

72. $-3x^2 + 8x + 16$

73. $-4 + 52x - 48x^2$

74. $-5 + 55x - 50x^2$

75. $2t^4 + 3t^2 - 27$

76. $4r^4 - 17r^2 - 15$

77. $5x^2y^2 + 20xy + 1$

78. $3a^2b^2 + 12ab + 1$

79. $6a^5 + 37a^3b^2 + 6ab^4$

80. $5m^5 + 26m^3h^2 + 5mh^4$

Review

Multiply. See Section 10.6.

81. $(x - 4)(x + 4)$

82. $(2x - 9)(2x + 9)$

83. $(x + 2)^2$

84. $(x + 3)^2$

85. $(2x - 1)^2$

86. $(3x - 5)^2$

Concept Extensions

See the Concept Check in this section.

87. Do the terms of $4x^2 + 19x + 12$ have a common factor (other than 1)?

88. Without multiplying, decide which of the following factored forms is not a factored form of $4x^2 + 19x + 12$.

a. $(2x + 4)(2x + 3)$ **b.** $(4x + 4)(x + 3)$
c. $(4x + 3)(x + 4)$ **d.** $(2x + 2)(2x + 6)$

Write the perimeter of each figure as a simplified polynomial. Then factor the polynomial completely.

89.

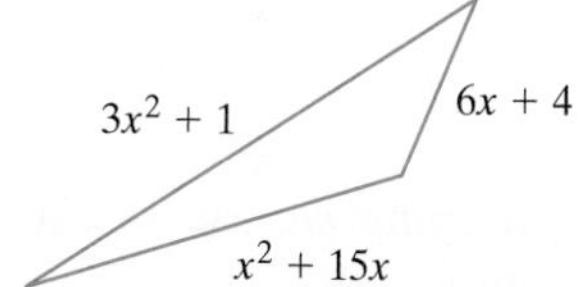

90.

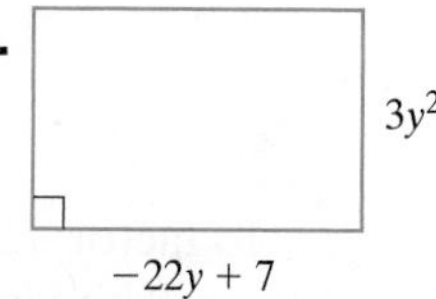

Factor each trinomial completely.

91. $4x^2 + 2x + \frac{1}{4}$

92. $27x^2 + 2x - \frac{1}{9}$

93. $4x^2(y - 1)^2 + 25x(y - 1)^2 + 25(y - 1)^2$

94. $3x^2(a + 3)^3 - 28x(a + 3)^3 + 25(a + 3)^3$

Find all positive values of b so that each trinomial is factorable.

95. $3x^2 + bx - 5$

96. $2z^2 + bz - 7$

Find all positive values of c so that each trinomial is factorable.

97. $5x^2 + 7x + c$

98. $3x^2 - 8x + c$

99. In your own words, describe the steps you use to factor a trinomial.

100. A student in your class factored $6x^2 + 7x + 1$ as $(3x + 1)(2x + 1)$. Write down how you would explain the student's error.

Objective

A **Use the Grouping Method to Factor Trinomials of the Form $ax^2 + bx + c$.**

11.4 FACTORING TRINOMIALS OF THE FORM $ax^2 + bx + c$ BY GROUPING

Objective A Using the Grouping Method

There is an alternative method that can be used to factor trinomials of the form $ax^2 + bx + c, a \neq 1$. This method is called the **grouping method** because it uses factoring by grouping as we learned in Section 11.1.

To see how this method works, recall from Section 11.2 that to factor a trinomial such as $x^2 + 11x + 30$, we find two numbers such that

Product is 30.

$$x^2 + 11x + 30$$

Sum is 11.

To factor a trinomial such as $2x^2 + 11x + 12$ by grouping, we use an extension of the method in Section 11.1. Here we look for two numbers such that

Product is $2 \cdot 12 = 24$.

$$2x^2 + 11x + 12$$

Sum is 11.

This time, we use the two numbers to write

$$2x^2 + 11x + 12 \text{ as}$$
$$= 2x^2 + \square x + \square x + 12$$

Then we factor by grouping. Since we want a positive product, 24, and a positive sum, 11, we consider pairs of positive factors of 24 only.

Factors of 24	Sum of Factors	
1, 24	25	
2, 12	14	
3, 8	11	Correct sum

The factors are 3 and 8. Now we use these factors to write the middle term, $11x$, as $3x + 8x$ (or $8x + 3x$). We replace $11x$ with $3x + 8x$ in the original trinomial and then we can factor by grouping.

$$\begin{aligned} 2x^2 + 11x + 12 &= 2x^2 + 3x + 8x + 12 \\ &= (2x^2 + 3x) + (8x + 12) && \text{Group the terms.} \\ &= x(2x + 3) + 4(2x + 3) && \text{Factor each group.} \\ &= (2x + 3)(x + 4) && \text{Factor out } (2x + 3). \end{aligned}$$

In general, we have the following procedure.

To Factor Trinomials by Grouping

Step 1: Factor out a greatest common factor, if there is one other than 1.

Step 2: For the resulting trinomial $ax^2 + bx + c$, find two numbers whose product is $a \cdot c$ and whose sum is b.

Step 3: Write the middle term, bx, using the factors found in Step 2.

Step 4: Factor by grouping.

Example 1 Factor $8x^2 - 14x + 5$ by grouping.

Solution:

Step 1: The terms of this trinomial contain no greatest common factor other than 1.

Step 2: This trinomial is of the form $ax^2 + bx + c$, with $a = 8$, $b = -14$, and $c = 5$. Find two numbers whose product is $a \cdot c$ or $8 \cdot 5 = 40$, and whose sum is b or -14.

The numbers are -4 and -10.

Factors of 40	Sum of Factors
$-40, -1$	-41
$-20, -2$	-22
$-10, -4$	-14

Correct sum

Step 3: Write $-14x$ as $-4x - 10x$ so that

$$8x^2 - 14x + 5 = 8x^2 - 4x - 10x + 5$$

Step 4: Factor by grouping.

$$8x^2 - 4x - 10x + 5 = 4x(2x - 1) - 5(2x - 1)$$
$$= (2x - 1)(4x - 5)$$

Work Practice 1

Example 2 Factor $6x^2 - 2x - 20$ by grouping.

Solution:

Step 1: First factor out the greatest common factor, 2.

$$6x^2 - 2x - 20 = 2(3x^2 - x - 10)$$

Step 2: Next notice that $a = 3$, $b = -1$, and $c = -10$ in the resulting trinomial. Find two numbers whose product is $a \cdot c$ or $3(-10) = -30$ and whose sum is b, -1. The numbers are -6 and 5.

Step 3: $3x^2 - x - 10 = 3x^2 - 6x + 5x - 10$

Step 4: $3x^2 - 6x + 5x - 10 = 3x(x - 2) + 5(x - 2)$
$= (x - 2)(3x + 5)$

The factored form of $6x^2 - 2x - 20 = 2(x - 2)(3x + 5)$.

Don't forget to include the common factor of 2.

Work Practice 2

Example 3 Factor $18y^4 + 21y^3 - 60y^2$ by grouping.

Solution:

Step 1: First factor out the greatest common factor, $3y^2$.

$$18y^4 + 21y^3 - 60y^2 = 3y^2(6y^2 + 7y - 20)$$

Step 2: Notice that $a = 6$, $b = 7$, and $c = -20$ in the resulting trinomial. Find two numbers whose product is $a \cdot c$ or $6(-20) = -120$ and whose sum is 7. It may help to factor -120 as a product of primes and -1.

$$-120 = 2 \cdot 2 \cdot 2 \cdot 3 \cdot 5 \cdot (-1)$$

Then choose pairings of factors until you have two pairings whose sum is 7.

$$2 \cdot 2 \cdot 2 \cdot 3 \cdot 5 \cdot (-1)$$

($2 \cdot 2 \cdot 2 \cdot (-1) = -8$; $3 \cdot 5 = 15$) The numbers are -8 and 15.

Step 3: $6y^2 + 7y - 20 = 6y^2 - 8y + 15y - 20$

Step 4: $6y^2 - 8y + 15y - 20 = 2y(3y - 4) + 5(3y - 4)$
$= (3y - 4)(2y + 5)$

The factored form of $18y^4 + 21y^3 - 60y^2$ is $3y^2(3y - 4)(2y + 5)$.

Don't forget to include the common factor of $3y^2$.

Work Practice 3

PRACTICE 1

Factor each trinomial by grouping.

a. $3x^2 + 14x + 8$
b. $12x^2 + 19x + 5$

PRACTICE 2

Factor each trinomial by grouping.

a. $30x^2 - 26x + 4$
b. $6x^2y - 7xy - 5y$

PRACTICE 3

Factor $12y^5 + 10y^4 - 42y^3$ by grouping.

Answers

1. a. $(x + 4)(3x + 2)$ **b.** $(4x + 5)(3x + 1)$
2. a. $2(5x - 1)(3x - 2)$ **b.** $y(2x + 1)(3x - 5)$
3. $2y^3(3y + 7)(2y - 3)$

Vocabulary and Readiness Check

For each trinomial ax^2+bx+c, choose two numbers whose product is $a \cdot c$ and whose sum is b.

1. $x^2 + 6x + 8$

a. 4, 2 **b.** 7, 1 **c.** 6, 2 **d.** 6, 8

2. $x^2 + 11x + 24$

a. 6, 4 **b.** 24, 1 **c.** 8, 3 **d.** 2, 12

3. $2x^2 + 13x + 6$

a. 2, 6 **b.** 12, 1 **c.** 13, 1 **d.** 3, 4

4. $4x^2 + 8x + 3$

a. 4, 3 **b.** 4, 4 **c.** 12, 1 **d.** 2, 6

11.4 Exercise Set

FOR EXTRA HELP MyMathLab

PRACTICE

WATCH

DOWNLOAD

READ

REVIEW

Objective A *Factor each polynomial by grouping. Notice that Step 3 has already been done in these exercises. See Examples 1 through 3.*

1. $x^2 + 3x + 2x + 6$ **2.** $x^2 + 5x + 3x + 15$ **3.** $y^2 + 8y - 2y - 16$ **4.** $z^2 + 10z - 7z - 70$

5. $8x^2 - 5x - 24x + 15$ **6.** $4x^2 - 9x - 32x + 72$ **7.** $5x^4 - 3x^2 + 25x^2 - 15$ **8.** $2y^4 - 10y^2 + 7y^2 - 35$

Factor each trinomial by grouping. Exercises 9 through 12 are broken into parts to help you get started. See Examples 1 through 3.

9. $6x^2 + 11x + 3$

a. Find two numbers whose product is $6 \cdot 3 = 18$ and whose sum is 11.
b. Write $11x$ using the factors from part (a).
c. Factor by grouping.

10. $8x^2 + 14x + 3$

a. Find two numbers whose product is $8 \cdot 3 = 24$ and whose sum is 14.
b. Write $14x$ using the factors from part (a).
c. Factor by grouping.

11. $15x^2 - 23x + 4$

a. Find two numbers whose product is $15 \cdot 4 = 60$ and whose sum is -23.
b. Write $-23x$ using the factors from part (a).
c. Factor by grouping.

12. $6x^2 - 13x + 5$

a. Find two numbers whose product is $6 \cdot 5 = 30$ and whose sum is -13.
b. Write $-13x$ using the factors from part (a).
c. Factor by grouping.

13. $21y^2 + 17y + 2$ **14.** $15x^2 + 11x + 2$ **15.** $7x^2 - 4x - 11$ **16.** $8x^2 - x - 9$

17. $10x^2 - 9x + 2$ **18.** $30x^2 - 23x + 3$ **19.** $2x^2 - 7x + 5$ **20.** $2x^2 - 7x + 3$

21. $12x + 4x^2 + 9$ **22.** $20x + 25x^2 + 4$ **23.** $4x^2 - 8x - 21$ **24.** $6x^2 - 11x - 10$

25. $10x^2 - 23x + 12$ **26.** $21x^2 - 13x + 2$ **27.** $2x^3 + 13x^2 + 15x$ **28.** $3x^3 + 8x^2 + 4x$

29. $16y^2 - 34y + 18$

30. $4y^2 - 2y - 12$

31. $-13x + 6 + 6x^2$

32. $-25x + 12 + 12x^2$

33. $54a^2 - 9a - 30$

34. $30a^2 + 38a - 20$

35. $20a^3 + 37a^2 + 8a$

36. $10a^3 + 17a^2 + 3a$

37. $12x^3 - 27x^2 - 27x$

38. $30x^3 - 155x^2 + 25x$

39. $3x^2y + 4xy^2 + y^3$

40. $6r^2t + 7rt^2 + t^3$

41. $20z^2 + 7z + 1$

42. $36z^2 + 6z + 1$

43. $24a^2 - 6ab - 30b^2$

44. $30a^2 + 5ab - 25b^2$

45. $15p^4 + 31p^3q + 2p^2q^2$

46. $20s^4 + 61s^3t + 3s^2t^2$

47. $35 + 12x + x^2$

48. $33 + 14x + x^2$

49. $6 - 11x + 5x^2$

50. $5 - 12x + 7x^2$

Review

Multiply. See Section 10.6.

51. $(x - 2)(x + 2)$

52. $(y - 5)(y + 5)$

53. $(y + 4)(y + 4)$

54. $(x + 7)(x + 7)$

55. $(9z + 5)(9z - 5)$

56. $(8y + 9)(8y - 9)$

57. $(4x - 3)^2$

58. $(2z - 1)^2$

Concept Extensions

Write the perimeter of each figure as a simplified polynomial. Then factor the polynomial.

59.

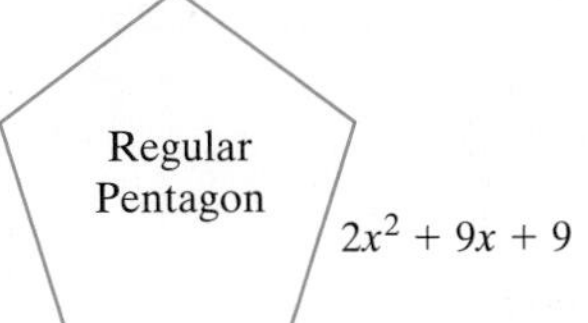

60.

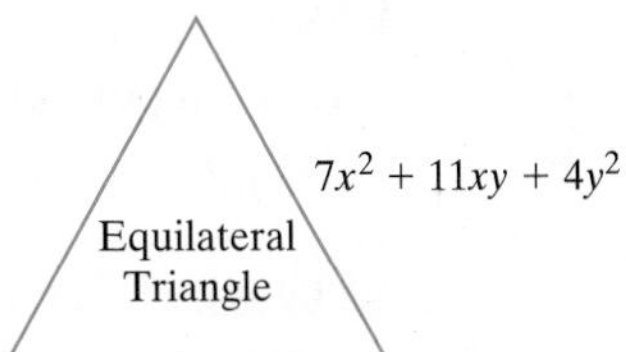

Factor each polynomial by grouping.

61. $x^{2n} + 2x^n + 3x^n + 6$
(*Hint:* Don't forget that $x^{2n} = x^n \cdot x^n$.)

62. $x^{2n} + 6x^n + 10x^n + 60$

63. $3x^{2n} + 16x^n - 35$

64. $12x^{2n} - 40x^n + 25$

65. In your own words, explain how to factor a trinomial by grouping.

Objectives

A **Factor Perfect Square Trinomials.**

B **Factor the Difference of Two Squares.**

C **Factor the Sum or Difference of Two Cubes.**

11.5 FACTORING BY SPECIAL PRODUCTS

Objective A Factoring Perfect Square Trinomials

A trinomial that is the square of a binomial is called a **perfect square trinomial.** For example,

$$(x + 3)^2 = (x + 3)(x + 3)$$
$$= x^2 + 6x + 9$$

Thus $x^2 + 6x + 9$ is a perfect square trinomial.

In Chapter 12, we discovered special product formulas for squaring binomials.

$$(a + b)^2 = a^2 + 2ab + b^2 \quad \text{and} \quad (a - b)^2 = a^2 - 2ab + b^2$$

Because multiplication and factoring are reverse processes, we can now use these special products to help us factor perfect square trinomials. If we reverse these equations, we have the following.

Factoring Perfect Square Trinomials

$$a^2 + 2ab + b^2 = (a + b)^2$$
$$a^2 - 2ab + b^2 = (a - b)^2$$

To use these equations to help us factor, we must first be able to recognize a perfect square trinomial. A trinomial is a perfect square trinomial if it can be written so that its first term is the square of some quantity a, its last term is the square of some quantity b, and its middle term is twice the product of the quantities a and b.

PRACTICE 1

Factor: $x^2 + 8x + 16$

Example 1 Factor: $m^2 + 10m + 25$

Solution: Notice that the first term is a square: $m^2 = (m)^2$, the last term is a square: $25 = 5^2$, and the middle term $10m = 2 \cdot 5 \cdot m$.
This is a perfect square trinomial. Thus,

$$m^2 + 10m + 25 = m^2 + 2(m)(5) + 5^2 = (m + 5)^2$$

Work Practice 1

PRACTICE 2–3

Factor.

2. $9x^2 + 6x + 1$

3. $25x^2 - 20x + 4$

Examples Factor each trinomial.

2. $4x^2 + 4x + 1 = (2x)^2 + 2 \cdot 2x \cdot 1 + 1^2$ See whether it is a perfect square trinomial.
$= (2x + 1)^2$ Factor.

3. $9x^2 - 12x + 4 = (3x)^2 - 2(3x)(2) + 2^2$ See whether it is a perfect square trinomial.
$= (3x - 2)^2$ Factor.

Work Practice 2–3

Answers

1. $(x + 4)^2$ **2.** $(3x + 1)^2$
3. $(5x - 2)^2$

Example 4 Factor: $3a^2x - 12abx + 12b^2x$

Solution: The terms of this trinomial have a greatest common factor of $3x$, which we factor out first.

$$3a^2x - 12abx + 12b^2x = 3x(a^2 - 4ab + 4b^2)$$

The polynomial $a^2 - 4ab + 4b^2$ is a perfect square trinomial. Notice that the first term is a square: $a^2 = (a)^2$, the last term is a square: $4b^2 = (2b)^2$, and $4ab = 2(a)(2b)$. The factoring can now be completed as

$$3x(a^2 - 4ab + 4b^2) = 3x(a - 2b)^2$$

Work Practice 4

PRACTICE 4

Factor: $4x^3 - 32x^2y + 64xy^2$

Helpful Hint

If you recognize a trinomial as a perfect square trinomial, use the special formulas to factor. However, general methods for factoring trinomials from Sections 13.3 and 13.4 will also result in the correct factored form.

Objective B Factoring the Difference of Two Squares

We now factor special types of binomials, beginning with the **difference of two squares.** The special product pattern presented in Section 12.6 for the product of a sum and a difference of two terms is used again here. However, the emphasis is now on factoring rather than on multiplying.

Difference of Two Squares

$$a^2 - b^2 = (a + b)(a - b)$$

Notice that a binomial is a difference of two squares when it is the difference of the square of some quantity a and the square of some quantity b.

Examples Factor.

5. $x^2 - 9 = x^2 - 3^2$
$= (x + 3)(x - 3)$

6. $16y^2 - 9 = (4y)^2 - 3^2$
$= (4y + 3)(4y - 3)$

7. $50 - 8y^2 = 2(25 - 4y^2)$ Factor out the common factor of 2.
$= 2[5^2 - (2y)^2]$
$= 2(5 + 2y)(5 - 2y)$

8. $x^2 - \frac{1}{4} = x^2 - \left(\frac{1}{2}\right)^2$
$= \left(x + \frac{1}{2}\right)\left(x - \frac{1}{2}\right)$

Work Practice 5–8

PRACTICE 5–8

Factor:

5. $x^2 - 49$
6. $4y^2 - 81$
7. $12 - 3a^2$
8. $y^2 - \frac{1}{25}$

The binomial $x^2 + 9$ is a **sum of two squares** and cannot be factored by using real numbers. *In general, except for factoring out a greatest common factor, the sum of two squares usually cannot be factored by using real numbers.*

Answers

4. $4x(x - 4y)^2$ **5.** $(x + 7)(x - 7)$
6. $(2y + 9)(2y - 9)$
7. $3(2 + a)(2 - a)$
8. $\left(y + \frac{1}{5}\right)\left(y - \frac{1}{5}\right)$

Helpful Hint

The sum of two squares whose greatest common factor is 1 usually cannot be factored by using real numbers.

PRACTICE 9

Factor: $a^4 - 81$

Example 9 Factor: $p^4 - 16$

Solution:

$$p^4 - 16 = (p^2)^2 - 4^2$$
$$= (p^2 + 4)(p^2 - 4)$$

The binomial factor $p^2 + 4$ cannot be factored by using real numbers, but the binomial factor $p^2 - 4$ is a difference of squares.

$$(p^2 + 4)(p^2 - 4) = (p^2 + 4)(p + 2)(p - 2)$$

Work Practice 9

Helpful Hint

1. Don't forget to first see whether there's a greatest common factor (other than 1) that can be factored out.
2. Factor completely. In other words, check to see whether any factors can be factored further (as in Example 9).

PRACTICE 10–12

Factor each binomial.

10. $9x^3 - 25x$
11. $48x^4 - 3$
12. $-9x^2 + 100$

Examples Factor each binomial.

10. $4x^3 - 49x = x(4x^2 - 49)$ — Factor out the common factor, x.
$= x[(2x)^2 - 7^2]$
$= x(2x + 7)(2x - 7)$ — Factor the difference of two squares.

11. $162x^4 - 2 = 2(81x^4 - 1)$ — Factor out the common factor, 2.
$= 2(9x^2 + 1)(9x^2 - 1)$ — Factor the difference of two squares.
$= 2(9x^2 + 1)(3x + 1)(3x - 1)$ — Factor the difference of two squares.

12. $-49x^2 + 16 = -1(49x^2 - 16)$ — Factor out -1.
$= -1(7x + 4)(7x - 4)$ — Factor the difference of two squares.

Work Practice 10–12

✓**Concept Check** Is $(x - 4)(y^2 - 9)$ completely factored? Why or why not?

PRACTICE 13

Factor: $(x + 1)^2 - 9$

Example 13 Factor: $(x + 3)^2 - 36$

Solution:

$(x + 3)^2 - 36 = (x + 3)^2 - 6^2$
$= [(x + 3) + 6][(x + 3) - 6]$ — Factor as the difference of two squares.
$= [x + 3 + 6][x + 3 - 6]$ — Remove parentheses.
$= (x + 9)(x - 3)$ — Simplify.

Work Practice 13

Answers

9. $(a^2 + 9)(a + 3)(a - 3)$
10. $x(3x - 5)(3x + 5)$
11. $3(4x^2 + 1)(2x + 1)(2x - 1)$
12. $-1(3x - 10)(3x + 10)$
13. $(x - 2)(x + 4)$

✓ **Concept Check Answer**

no; $(y^2 - 9)$ can be factored

Example 14 Factor: $x^2 + 4x + 4 - y^2$

Solution: Factoring by grouping comes to mind since the sum of the first three terms of this polynomial is a perfect square trinomial.

$$x^2 + 4x + 4 - y^2 = (x^2 + 4x + 4) - y^2 \quad \text{Group the first three terms.}$$
$$= (x + 2)^2 - y^2 \quad \text{Factor the perfect square trinomial.}$$

This is not completely factored yet since we have a *difference*, not a *product*. Since $(x + 2)^2 - y^2$ is a difference of squares, we have

$$(x + 2)^2 - y^2 = [(x + 2) + y][(x + 2) - y]$$
$$= (x + 2 + y)(x + 2 - y)$$

Work Practice 14

PRACTICE 14

Factor: $a^2 + 2a + 1 - b^2$

Objective C Factoring the Sum or Difference of Two Cubes

Although the sum of two squares usually cannot be factored, the sum of two cubes, as well as the difference of two cubes, can be factored as follows.

Sum and Difference of Two Cubes

$$a^3 + b^3 = (a + b)(a^2 - ab + b^2)$$
$$a^3 - b^3 = (a - b)(a^2 + ab + b^2)$$

To check the first pattern, let's find the product of $(a + b)$ and $(a^2 - ab + b^2)$.

$$(a + b)(a^2 - ab + b^2) = a(a^2 - ab + b^2) + b(a^2 - ab + b^2)$$
$$= a^3 - a^2b + ab^2 + a^2b - ab^2 + b^3$$
$$= a^3 + b^3$$

Example 15 Factor: $x^3 + 8$

Solution: First we write the binomial in the form $a^3 + b^3$. Then we use the formula

$$a^3 + b^3 = (a + b)(a^2 - a \cdot b + b^2), \quad \text{where } a \text{ is } x \text{ and } b \text{ is 2.}$$
$$\downarrow \quad \downarrow \qquad \downarrow \quad \downarrow \downarrow \qquad \downarrow \downarrow \quad \downarrow$$
$$x^3 + 8 = x^3 + 2^3 = (x + 2)(x^2 - x \cdot 2 + 2^2)$$

Thus, $x^3 + 8 = (x + 2)(x^2 - 2x + 4)$

Work Practice 15

PRACTICE 15

Factor: $x^3 + 27$

Example 16 Factor: $p^3 + 27q^3$

Solution:
$$p^3 + 27q^3 = p^3 + (3q)^3$$
$$= (p + 3q)[p^2 - (p)(3q) + (3q)^2]$$
$$= (p + 3q)(p^2 - 3pq + 9q^2)$$

Work Practice 16

PRACTICE 16

Factor: $x^3 + 64y^3$

Example 17 Factor: $y^3 - 64$

Solution: This is a difference of cubes since $y^3 - 64 = y^3 - 4^3$.

From $a^3 - b^3 = (a - b)(a^2 + a \cdot b + b^2)$ we have that

$$\downarrow \quad \downarrow \qquad \downarrow \quad \downarrow \downarrow \qquad \downarrow \downarrow \quad \downarrow$$
$$y^3 - 4^3 = (y - 4)(y^2 + y \cdot 4 + 4^2)$$
$$= (y - 4)(y^2 + 4y + 16)$$

Work Practice 17

PRACTICE 17

Factor: $y^3 - 8$

Answers

14. $(a + 1 + b)(a + 1 - b)$
15. $(x + 3)(x^2 - 3x + 9)$
16. $(x + 4y)(x^2 - 4xy + 16y^2)$
17. $(y - 2)(y^2 + 2y + 4)$

Helpful Hint

When factoring sums or differences of cubes, be sure to notice the sign patterns.

same sign

$$x^3 + y^3 = (x + y)(x^2 - xy + y^2)$$

opposite signs — always positive

same sign

$$x^3 - y^3 = (x - y)(x^2 + xy + y^2)$$

opposite signs — always positive

PRACTICE 18

Factor: $27a^2 - b^3a^2$

Example 18 Factor: $125q^2 - n^3q^2$

Solution: First we factor out a common factor of q^2.

$$\begin{aligned} 125q^2 - n^3q^2 &= q^2(125 - n^3) \\ &= q^2(5^3 - n^3) \end{aligned}$$

Opposite sign — Positive

$$\begin{aligned} &= q^2(5 - n)[5^2 + (5)(n) + (n^2)] \\ &= q^2(5 - n)(25 + 5n + n^2) \end{aligned}$$

Thus, $125q^2 - n^3q^2 = q^2(5 - n)(25 + 5n + n^2)$. The trinomial $25 + 5n + n^2$ cannot be factored further.

Work Practice 18

Answer

18. $a^2(3 - b)(9 + 3b + b^2)$

Calculator Explorations Graphing

A graphing calculator is a convenient tool for evaluating an expression at a given replacement value. For example, let's evaluate $x^2 - 6x$ when $x = 2$. To do so, store the value 2 in the variable x and then enter and evaluate the algebraic expression.

```
2→X
                2
X²-6X
               -8
```

The value of $x^2 - 6x$ when $x = 2$ is -8. You may want to use this method for evaluating expressions as you explore the following.

We can use a graphing calculator to explore factoring patterns numerically. Use your calculator to evaluate $x^2 - 2x + 1$, $x^2 - 2x - 1$, and $(x - 1)^2$ for each value of x given in the table. What do you observe?

	$x^2 - 2x + 1$	$x^2 - 2x - 1$	$(x - 1)^2$
$x = 5$			
$x = -3$			
$x = 2.7$			
$x = -12.1$			
$x = 0$			

Notice in each case that $x^2 - 2x - 1 \neq (x - 1)^2$. Because for each x in the table the value of $x^2 - 2x + 1$ and the value of $(x - 1)^2$ are the same, we might guess that $x^2 - 2x + 1 = (x - 1)^2$. We can verify our guess algebraically with multiplication:

$$(x - 1)(x - 1) = x^2 - x - x + 1 = x^2 - 2x + 1$$

Vocabulary and Readiness Check

Write each number as a square.

1. 1 **2.** 25 **3.** 81 **4.** 64 **5.** 9 **6.** 100

Write each term as a square.

7. $9x^2$ **8.** $16y^2$ **9.** $25a^2$ **10.** $81b^2$ **11.** $36p^4$ **12.** $4q^4$

11.5 Exercise set

FOR EXTRA HELP

Objective **A** *Determine whether each trinomial is a perfect square trinomial. See Examples 1 through 4.*

1. $x^2 + 16x + 64$ **2.** $x^2 + 22x + 121$ **3.** $y^2 + 5y + 25$ **4.** $y^2 + 4y + 16$

5. $4x^2 + 12xy + 8y^2$ **6.** $25x^2 + 20xy + 2y^2$ **7.** $25a^2 - 40ab + 16b^2$

8. $36a^2 - 12ab + b^2$ **9.** $m^2 - 2m + 1$ **10.** $p^2 - 4p + 4$

Factor each trinomial completely. See Examples 1 through 4.

11. $x^2 + 22x + 121$ **12.** $x^2 + 18x + 81$ **13.** $x^2 - 16x + 64$ **14.** $x^2 - 12x + 36$ **15.** $16a^2 - 24a + 9$

16. $25x^2 + 20x + 4$ **17.** $3x^2 - 24x + 48$ **18.** $2n^2 - 28n + 98$ **19.** $x^2y^2 - 10xy + 25$ **20.** $4x^2y^2 - 28xy + 49$

21. $m^3 + 18m^2 + 81m$ **22.** $y^3 + 12y^2 + 36y$ **23.** $1 + 6x^2 + x^4$ **24.** $1 + 16x^2 + x^4$

25. $9x^2 - 24xy + 16y^2$ **26.** $25x^2 - 60xy + 36y^2$ **27.** $x^4 + 4x^2 + 4$ **28.** $m^4 + 10m^2 + 25$

Objective **B** *Factor each completely. See Examples 5 through 14.*

29. $x^2 - 25$ **30.** $y^2 - 100$ **31.** $9 - 4z^2$ **32.** $16x^2 - y^2$

33. $16r^2 + 1$ **34.** $49y^2 + 9$ **35.** $x^3y - 121xy^3$ **36.** $25xy^2 - 4x$

37. $(y + 2)^2 - 49$ **38.** $(x - 1)^2 - z^2$ **39.** $64x^2 - 100$ **40.** $4x^2 - 36$

41. $18x^2y - 2y$ **42.** $12xy^2 - 108x$ **43.** $9x^2 - 49$ **44.** $25x^2 - 4$

45. $x^4 - 81$ **46.** $x^4 - 256$ **47.** $(x + 2y)^2 - 9$

48. $(3x + y)^2 - 25$ **49.** $x^2 + 16x + 64 - x^4$ **50.** $x^2 + 20x + 100 - x^4$

51. $x^2 - 10x + 25 - y^2$ **52.** $x^2 - 18x + 81 - y^2$ **53.** $4x^2 + 4x + 1 - z^2$

54. $9y^2 + 12y + 4 - x^2$

55. $m^4 - 1$

56. $n^4 - 16$

Objective C *Factor. See Examples 15 through 18.*

57. $x^3 + 27$

58. $y^3 + 1$

59. $z^3 - 1$

60. $8 - z^3$

61. $m^3 + n^3$

62. $r^3 + 125$

63. $x^3y^2 - 27y^2$

64. $64 - p^3$

65. $a^3b + 8b^4$

66. $8ab^3 + 27a^4$

67. $125y^3 - 8x^3$

68. $54y^3 - 128$

69. $x^6 - y^3$

70. $x^3 - y^6$

71. $8x^3 + 27y^3$

72. $125x^3 + 8y^3$

73. $x^3 - 1$

74. $x^3 - 8$

75. $x^3 + 125$

76. $x^3 + 216$

77. $3x^6y^2 + 81y^2$

78. $x^2y^9 + x^2y^3$

Review

Solve each equation. See Section 9.3.

79. $x - 5 = 0$

80. $x + 7 = 0$

81. $3x + 1 = 0$

82. $5x - 15 = 0$

83. $-2x = 0$

84. $3x = 0$

85. $-5x + 25 = 0$

86. $-4x - 16 = 0$

Concept Extensions

Factor each expression completely.

87. $x^2 - \frac{2}{3}x + \frac{1}{9}$

88. $x^2 - \frac{1}{25}$

89. $(x + 2)^2 - y^2$

90. $(y - 6)^2 - z^2$

91. $a^2(b - 4) - 16(b - 4)$

92. $m^2(n + 8) - 9(n + 8)$

93. $(x^2 + 6x + 9) - 4y^2$ (*Hint:* Factor the trinomial in parentheses first.)

94. $(x^2 + 2x + 1) - 36y^2$ (*Hint:* Factor the trinomial in parentheses first.)

95. $x^{2n} - 100$

96. $x^{2n} - 81$

97. Fill in the blank so that $x^2 +$ ______ $x + 16$ is a perfect square trinomial.

98. Fill in the blank so that $9x^2 +$ ______ $x + 25$ is a perfect square trinomial.

99. Describe a perfect square trinomial.

100. Write a perfect square trinomial that factors as $(x + 3y)^2$.

101. What binomial multiplied by $(x - 6)$ gives the difference of two squares?

102. What binomial multiplied by $(5 + y)$ gives the difference of two squares?

The area of the largest square in the figure is $(a + b)^2$. Use this figure to answer Exercises 103 and 104.

103. Write the area of the largest square as the sum of the areas of the smaller squares and rectangles.

104. What factoring formula from this section is visually represented by this square?

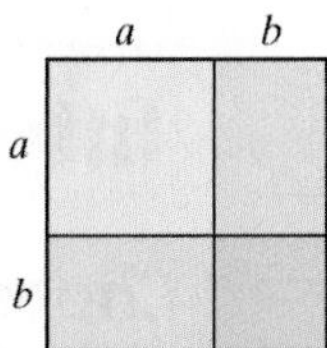

105. The Toroweap Overlook, on the North Rim of the Grand Canyon, lies 3000 vertical feet above the Colorado River. The view is spectacular, and the sheer drop is dramatic. A film crew creating a documentary about the Grand Canyon has suspended a camera platform 296 feet below the Overlook. A camera filter comes loose and falls to the river below. The height of the filter above the river after t seconds is given by the expression $2704 - 16t^2$.

a. Find the height of the filter above the river after 3 seconds.

b. Find the height of the filter above the river after 7 seconds.

c. To the nearest whole second, estimate when the filter lands in the river.

d. Factor $2704 - 16t^2$.

106. An object is dropped from the top of Pittsburgh's USX Towers, which is 841 feet tall. (*Source: World Almanac* research) The height of the object after t seconds is given by the expression $841 - 16t^2$.

a. Find the height of the object after 2 seconds.

b. Find the height of the object after 5 seconds.

c. To the nearest whole second, estimate when the object hits the ground.

d. Factor $841 - 16t^2$.

107. At this writing, the world's tallest building is the Taipei 101 in Taipei, Taiwan, at a height of 1671 feet. (*Source:* Council on Tall Buildings and Urban Habitat) Suppose a worker is suspended 71 feet below the top of the pinnacle atop the building, at a height of 1600 feet above the ground. If the worker accidentally drops a bolt, the height of the bolt after t seconds is given by the expression $1600 - 16t^2$.

a. Find the height of the bolt after 3 seconds.

b. Find the height of the bolt after 7 seconds.

c. To the nearest whole second, estimate when the bolt hits the ground.

d. Factor $1600 - 16t^2$.

108. A performer with the Moscow Circus is planning a stunt involving a free fall from the top of the Moscow State University building, which is 784 feet tall. (*Source:* Council on Tall Buildings and Urban Habitat) Neglecting air resistance, the performer's height above gigantic cushions positioned at ground level after t seconds is given by the expression $784 - 16t^2$.

a. Find the performer's height after 2 seconds.

b. Find the performer's height after 5 seconds.

c. To the nearest whole second, estimate when the performer reaches the cushions positioned at ground level.

d. Factor $784 - 16t^2$.

Answers

1.
2.
3.
4.
5.
6.
7.
8.
9.
10.
11.
12.
13.
14.
15.
16.
17.
18.
19.
20.
21.
22.
23.
24.
25.
26.
27.
28.
29.
30.
31.
32.
33.
34.
35.
36.
37.
38.
39.
40.
41.
42.

Integrated Review Sections 11.1–11.5

Choosing a Factoring Strategy

The key to proficiency in factoring polynomials is to practice until you are comfortable with each technique. A strategy for factoring polynomials completely is given next.

Factoring a Polynomial

Step 1: Are there any common factors? If so, factor out the greatest common factor.

Step 2: How many terms are in the polynomial?

a. If there are *two* terms, decide if one of the following formulas may be applied:

i. Difference of two squares: $a^2 - b^2 = (a + b)(a - b)$

ii. Difference of two cubes: $a^3 - b^3 = (a - b)(a^2 + ab + b^2)$

iii. Sum of two cubes: $a^3 + b^3 = (a + b)(a^2 - ab + b^2)$

b. If there are *three* terms, try one of the following:

i. Perfect square trinomial: $a^2 + 2ab + b^2 = (a + b)^2$

$a^2 - 2ab + b^2 = (a - b)^2$

ii. If not a perfect square trinomial, factor by using the methods presented in Sections 13.2 through 13.4.

c. If there are *four* or more terms, try factoring by grouping.

Step 3: See whether any factors in the factored polynomial can be factored further.

Factor each polynomial completely.

1. $x^2 + x - 12$

2. $x^2 - 10x + 16$

3. $x^2 - x - 6$

4. $x^2 + 2x + 1$

5. $x^2 - 6x + 9$

6. $x^2 + x - 2$

7. $x^2 + x - 6$

8. $x^2 + 7x + 12$

9. $x^2 - 7x + 10$

10. $x^2 - x - 30$

11. $2x^2 - 98$

12. $3x^2 - 75$

13. $x^2 + 3x + 5x + 15$

14. $3y - 21 + xy - 7x$

15. $x^2 + 6x - 16$

16. $x^2 - 3x - 28$

17. $4x^3 + 20x^2 - 56x$

18. $6x^3 - 6x^2 - 120x$

19. $12x^2 + 34x + 24$

20. $8a^2 + 6ab - 5b^2$

21. $4a^2 - b^2$

22. $x^2 - 25y^2$

23. $28 - 13x - 6x^2$

24. $20 - 3x - 2x^2$

25. $x^2 - 2x + 4$

26. $a^2 + a - 3$

27. $6y^2 + y - 15$

28. $4x^2 - x - 5$

29. $18x^3 - 63x^2 + 9x$

30. $12a^3 - 24a^2 + 4a$

31. $16a^2 - 56a + 49$

32. $25p^2 - 70p + 49$

33. $14 + 5x - x^2$

34. $3 - 2x - x^2$

35. $3x^4y + 6x^3y - 72x^2y$

36. $2x^3y + 8x^2y^2 - 10xy^3$

37. $12x^3y + 243xy$

38. $6x^3y^2 + 8xy^2$

39. $2xy - 72x^3y$

40. $2x^3 - 18x$

41. $x^3 + 6x^2 - 4x - 24$

42. $x^3 - 2x^2 - 36x + 72$

43. $6a^3 + 10a^2$

44. $4n^2 - 6n$

45. $3x^3 - x^2 + 12x - 4$

46. $x^3 - 2x^2 + 3x - 6$

47. $6x^2 + 18xy + 12y^2$

48. $12x^2 + 46xy - 8y^2$

49. $5(x + y) + x(x + y)$

50. $7(x - y) + y(x - y)$

51. $14t^2 - 9t + 1$

52. $3t^2 - 5t + 1$

53. $3x^2 + 2x - 5$

54. $7x^2 + 19x - 6$

55. $1 - 8a - 20a^2$

56. $1 - 7a - 60a^2$

57. $x^4 - 10x^2 + 9$

58. $x^4 - 13x^2 + 36$

59. $x^2 - 23x + 120$

60. $y^2 + 22y + 96$

61. $x^2 - 14x - 48$

62. $16a^2 - 56ab + 49b^2$

63. $25p^2 - 70pq + 49q^2$

64. $7x^2 + 24xy + 9y^2$

65. $-x^2 - x + 30$

66. $-x^2 + 6x - 8$

67. $3rs - s + 12r - 4$

68. $x^3 - 2x^2 + x - 2$

69. $4x^2 - 8xy - 3x + 6y$

70. $4x^2 - 2xy - 7yz + 14xz$

71. $x^2 + 9xy - 36y^2$

72. $3x^2 + 10xy - 8y^2$

73. $x^4 - 14x^2 - 32$

74. $x^4 - 22x^2 - 75$

75. $x^4 - x$

76. $x^6 + x^3$

77. $8x^3 + 125y^3$

78. $27x^3 - 64y^3$

79. Explain why it makes good sense to factor out the GCF first, before using other methods of factoring.

80. The sum of two squares usually does not factor. Is the sum of two squares $9x^2 + 81y^2$ factorable?

43. ______
44. ______
45. ______
46. ______
47. ______
48. ______
49. ______
50. ______
51. ______
52. ______
53. ______
54. ______
55. ______
56. ______
57. ______
58. ______
59. ______
60. ______
61. ______
62. ______
63. ______
64. ______
65. ______
66. ______
67. ______
68. ______
69. ______
70. ______
71. ______
72. ______
73. ______
74. ______
75. ______
76. ______
77. ______
78. ______
79. ______
80.

Objectives

A Solve Quadratic Equations by Factoring.

B Solve Equations with Degree Greater than Two by Factoring.

11.6 SOLVING QUADRATIC EQUATIONS BY FACTORING

In this section, we introduce a new type of equation—the **quadratic equation.**

Quadratic Equation

A quadratic equation is one that can be written in the form

$$ax^2 + bx + c = 0$$

where a, b, and c are real numbers and $a \neq 0$.

Some examples of quadratic equations are shown below.

$$x^2 - 9x - 22 = 0 \qquad 4x^2 - 28 = -49 \qquad x(2x - 7) = 4$$

The form $ax^2 + bx + c = 0$ is called the **standard form** of a quadratic equation. The quadratic equation $x^2 - 9x - 22 = 0$ is the only equation above that is in standard form.

Quadratic equations model many real-life situations. For example, let's suppose we want to know how long before a person diving from a 144-foot cliff reaches the ocean. The answer to this question is found by solving the quadratic equation $-16t^2 + 144 = 0$. (See Example 1 in Section 11.7.)

Objective A Solving Quadratic Equations by Factoring

Some quadratic equations can be solved by making use of factoring and the **zero-factor property.**

Zero-Factor Property

If a and b are real numbers and if $ab = 0$, then $a = 0$ or $b = 0$.

In other words, if the product of two numbers is 0, then at least one of the numbers must be 0.

PRACTICE 1

Solve: $(x - 7)(x + 2) = 0$

Example 1 Solve: $(x - 3)(x + 1) = 0$

Solution: If this equation is to be a true statement, then either the factor $x - 3$ must be 0 or the factor $x + 1$ must be 0. In other words, either

$$x - 3 = 0 \quad \text{or} \quad x + 1 = 0$$

If we solve these two linear equations, we have

$$x = 3 \quad \text{or} \quad x = -1$$

Continued on next page

Answer

1. 7 and −2

Thus, 3 and −1 are both solutions of the equation $(x - 3)(x + 1) = 0$. To check, we replace x with 3 in the original equation. Then we replace x with −1 in the original equation.

Check:

$(x - 3)(x + 1) = 0$ | $(x - 3)(x + 1) = 0$

$(3 - 3)(3 + 1) \stackrel{?}{=} 0$ Replace x with 3. | $(-1 - 3)(-1 + 1) \stackrel{?}{=} 0$ Replace x with −1.

$0(4) = 0$ True | $(-4)(0) = 0$ True

The solutions are 3 and −1.

Work Practice 1

Helpful Hint

The zero-factor property says that *if a product is 0, then a factor is 0.*

If $a \cdot b = 0$, then $a = 0$ or $b = 0$.

If $x(x + 5) = 0$, then $x = 0$ or $x + 5 = 0$.

If $(x + 7)(2x - 3) = 0$, then $x + 7 = 0$ or $2x - 3 = 0$.

Use this property only when the product is 0. For example, if $a \cdot b = 8$, we do not know the value of a or b. The values may be $a = 2, b = 4$ or $a = 8, b = 1$, or any other two numbers whose product is 8.

Example 2 Solve: $(x - 5)(2x + 7) = 0$

Solution: The product is 0. By the zero-factor property, this is true only when a factor is 0. To solve, we set each factor equal to 0 and solve the resulting linear equations.

$$(x - 5)(2x + 7) = 0$$

$$x - 5 = 0 \quad \text{or} \quad 2x + 7 = 0$$

$$x = 5 \qquad 2x = -7$$

$$x = -\frac{7}{2}$$

Check: Let $x = 5$.

$$(x - 5)(2x + 7) = 0$$

$$(5 - 5)(2 \cdot 5 + 7) \stackrel{?}{=} 0 \quad \text{Replace } x \text{ with 5.}$$

$$0 \cdot 17 \stackrel{?}{=} 0$$

$$0 = 0 \quad \text{True}$$

Let $x = -\frac{7}{2}$.

$$(x - 5)(2x + 7) = 0$$

$$\left(-\frac{7}{2} - 5\right)\left(2\left(-\frac{7}{2}\right) + 7\right) \stackrel{?}{=} 0 \quad \text{Replace } x \text{ with } -\frac{7}{2}.$$

$$\left(-\frac{17}{2}\right)(-7 + 7) \stackrel{?}{=} 0$$

$$\left(-\frac{17}{2}\right) \cdot 0 \stackrel{?}{=} 0$$

$$0 = 0 \quad \text{True}$$

The solutions are 5 and $-\frac{7}{2}$.

Work Practice 2

PRACTICE 2

Solve: $(x - 10)(3x + 1) = 0$

Answer

2. 10 and $-\frac{1}{3}$

PRACTICE 3

Solve each equation.

a. $y(y + 3) = 0$

b. $x(4x - 3) = 0$

Example 3 Solve: $x(5x - 2) = 0$

Solution: $x(5x - 2) = 0$

$x = 0$ or $5x - 2 = 0$ Use the zero-factor property.

$5x = 2$

$x = \frac{2}{5}$

Check these solutions in the original equation. The solutions are 0 and $\frac{2}{5}$.

Work Practice 3

PRACTICE 4

Solve: $x^2 - 3x - 18 = 0$

Example 4 Solve: $x^2 - 9x - 22 = 0$

Solution: One side of the equation is 0. However, to use the zero-factor property, one side of the equation must be 0 *and* the other side must be written as a product (must be factored). Thus, we must first factor this polynomial.

$x^2 - 9x - 22 = 0$

$(x - 11)(x + 2) = 0$ Factor.

Now we can apply the zero-factor property.

$x - 11 = 0$ or $x + 2 = 0$

$x = 11$ $\quad x = -2$

Check: Let $x = 11$.

$x^2 - 9x - 22 = 0$

$11^2 - 9 \cdot 11 - 22 \stackrel{?}{=} 0$

$121 - 99 - 22 \stackrel{?}{=} 0$

$22 - 22 \stackrel{?}{=} 0$

$0 = 0$ True

Let $x = -2$.

$x^2 - 9x - 22 = 0$

$(-2)^2 - 9(-2) - 22 \stackrel{?}{=} 0$

$4 + 18 - 22 \stackrel{?}{=} 0$

$22 - 22 \stackrel{?}{=} 0$

$0 = 0$ True

The solutions are 11 and -2.

Work Practice 4

PRACTICE 5

Solve: $9x^2 - 24x = -16$

Example 5 Solve: $4x^2 - 28x = -49$

Solution: First we rewrite the equation in standard form so that one side is 0. Then we factor the polynomial.

$4x^2 - 28x = -49$

$4x^2 - 28x + 49 = 0$ Write in standard form by adding 49 to both sides.

$(2x - 7)(2x - 7) = 0$ Factor.

Next we use the zero-factor property and set each factor equal to 0. Since the factors are the same, the related equations will give the same solution.

$2x - 7 = 0$ or $2x - 7 = 0$ Set each factor equal to 0.

$2x = 7$ $\quad 2x = 7$ Solve.

$x = \frac{7}{2}$ $\quad x = \frac{7}{2}$

Check this solution in the original equation. The solution is $\frac{7}{2}$.

Work Practice 5

Answers

3. a. 0 and -3 **b.** 0 and $\frac{3}{4}$

4. 6 and -3 **5.** $\frac{4}{3}$

The following steps may be used to solve a quadratic equation by factoring.

To Solve Quadratic Equations by Factoring

Step 1: Write the equation in standard form so that one side of the equation is 0.

Step 2: Factor the quadratic equation completely.

Step 3: Set each factor containing a variable equal to 0.

Step 4: Solve the resulting equations.

Step 5: Check each solution in the original equation.

Since it is not always possible to factor a quadratic polynomial, not all quadratic equations can be solved by factoring. Other methods of solving quadratic equations are presented in Chapter 9.

Example 6 Solve: $x(2x - 7) = 4$

Solution: First we write the equation in standard form; then we factor.

$$x(2x - 7) = 4$$

$$2x^2 - 7x = 4 \quad \text{Multiply.}$$

$$2x^2 - 7x - 4 = 0 \quad \text{Write in standard form.}$$

$$(2x + 1)(x - 4) = 0 \quad \text{Factor.}$$

$$2x + 1 = 0 \quad \text{or} \quad x - 4 = 0 \quad \text{Set each factor equal to zero.}$$

$$2x = -1 \qquad x = 4 \quad \text{Solve.}$$

$$x = -\frac{1}{2}$$

Check the solutions in the original equation. The solutions are $-\frac{1}{2}$ and 4.

Work Practice 6

PRACTICE 6

Solve each equation.

a. $x(x - 4) = 5$

b. $x(3x + 7) = 6$

Helpful Hint

To solve the equation $x(2x - 7) = 4$, do **not** set each factor equal to 4. Remember that to apply the zero-factor property, one side of the equation must be 0 and the other side of the equation must be in factored form.

✓Concept Check Explain the error and solve the equation correctly.

$$(x - 3)(x + 1) = 5$$

$$x - 3 = 0 \quad \text{or} \quad x + 1 = 0$$

$$x = 3 \quad \text{or} \quad x = -1$$

Objective B Solving Equations with Degree Greater than Two by Factoring

Some equations with degree greater than 2 can be solved by factoring and then using the zero-factor property.

Answers

6. a. 5 and −1 **b.** $\frac{2}{3}$ and −3

✓ Concept Check Answer

To use the zero-factor property, one side of the equation must be 0, not 5. Correctly, $(x - 3)(x + 1) = 5$, $x^2 - 2x - 3 = 5$, $x^2 - 2x - 8 = 0$, $(x - 4)(x + 2) = 0$, $x - 4 = 0$ or $x + 2 = 0$, $x = 4$ or $x = -2$.

PRACTICE 7

Solve: $2x^3 - 18x = 0$

Example 7 Solve: $3x^3 - 12x = 0$

Solution: To factor the left side of the equation, we begin by factoring out the greatest common factor, $3x$.

$$3x^3 - 12x = 0$$

$$3x(x^2 - 4) = 0 \quad \text{Factor out the GCF, } 3x.$$

$$3x(x + 2)(x - 2) = 0 \quad \text{Factor } x^2 - 4 \text{, a difference of two squares.}$$

$$3x = 0 \quad \text{or} \quad x + 2 = 0 \quad \text{or} \quad x - 2 = 0 \quad \text{Set each factor equal to 0.}$$

$$x = 0 \qquad x = -2 \qquad x = 2 \quad \text{Solve.}$$

Thus, the equation $3x^3 - 12x = 0$ has three solutions: 0, −2, and 2.

Check: Replace x with each solution in the original equation.

Let $x = 0$.

$$3(0)^3 - 12(0) \stackrel{?}{=} 0$$

$$0 = 0 \quad \text{True}$$

Let $x = -2$.

$$3(-2)^3 - 12(-2) \stackrel{?}{=} 0$$

$$3(-8) + 24 \stackrel{?}{=} 0$$

$$0 = 0 \quad \text{True}$$

Let $x = 2$.

$$3(2)^3 - 12(2) \stackrel{?}{=} 0$$

$$3(8) - 24 \stackrel{?}{=} 0$$

$$0 = 0 \quad \text{True}$$

The solutions are 0, −2, and 2.

Work Practice 7

PRACTICE 8

Solve:
$(x + 3)(3x^2 - 20x - 7) = 0$

Example 8 Solve: $(5x - 1)(2x^2 + 15x + 18) = 0$

Solution:

$$(5x - 1)(2x^2 + 15x + 18) = 0$$

$$(5x - 1)(2x + 3)(x + 6) = 0 \quad \text{Factor the trinomial.}$$

$$5x - 1 = 0 \quad \text{or} \quad 2x + 3 = 0 \quad \text{or} \quad x + 6 = 0 \quad \text{Set each factor equal to 0.}$$

$$5x = 1 \qquad 2x = -3 \qquad x = -6 \quad \text{Solve.}$$

$$x = \frac{1}{5} \qquad x = -\frac{3}{2}$$

Check each solution in the original equation. The solutions are $\frac{1}{5}$, $-\frac{3}{2}$, and −6.

Work Practice 8

Answers

7. 0, 3, and −3 **8.** −3, $-\frac{1}{3}$, and 7

Vocabulary and Readiness Check

Use the choices below to fill in each blank. Not all choices will be used.

$-3, 5$	$a = 0$ or $b = 0$	0	linear
$3, -5$	quadratic	1	

1. An equation that can be written in the form $ax^2 + bx + c = 0$ (with $a \neq 0$) is called a ______________ equation.

2. If the product of two numbers is 0, then at least one of the numbers must be ______________.

3. The solutions to $(x - 3)(x + 5) = 0$ are ______________.

4. If $a \cdot b = 0$, then ______________.

11.6 Exercise Set

FOR EXTRA HELP

PRACTICE

WATCH

DOWNLOAD

READ

REVIEW

Objective A *Solve each equation. See Examples 1 through 3.*

1. $(x - 2)(x + 1) = 0$

2. $(x + 3)(x + 2) = 0$

3. $(x - 6)(x - 7) = 0$

4. $(x + 4)(x - 10) = 0$

5. $(x + 9)(x + 17) = 0$

6. $(x - 11)(x - 1) = 0$

7. $x(x + 6) = 0$

8. $x(x - 7) = 0$

9. $3x(x - 8) = 0$

10. $2x(x + 12) = 0$

11. $(2x + 3)(4x - 5) = 0$

12. $(3x - 2)(5x + 1) = 0$

13. $(2x - 7)(7x + 2) = 0$

14. $(9x + 1)(4x - 3) = 0$

15. $\left(x - \frac{1}{2}\right)\left(x + \frac{1}{3}\right) = 0$

16. $\left(x + \frac{2}{9}\right)\left(x - \frac{1}{4}\right) = 0$

17. $(x + 0.2)(x + 1.5) = 0$

18. $(x + 1.7)(x + 2.3) = 0$

Solve. See Examples 4 through 6.

19. $x^2 - 13x + 36 = 0$

20. $x^2 + 2x - 63 = 0$

21. $x^2 + 2x - 8 = 0$

22. $x^2 - 5x + 6 = 0$

23. $x^2 - 7x = 0$

24. $x^2 - 3x = 0$

25. $x^2 + 20x = 0$

26. $x^2 + 15x = 0$

27. $x^2 = 16$

28. $x^2 = 9$

29. $x^2 - 4x = 32$

30. $x^2 - 5x = 24$

31. $(x + 4)(x - 9) = 4x$

32. $(x + 3)(x + 8) = x$

33. $x(3x - 1) = 14$

34. $x(4x - 11) = 3$

35. $3x^2 + 19x - 72 = 0$

36. $36x^2 + x - 21 = 0$

Objectives **A** **B** and Section 8.3 **Mixed Practice** *Solve each equation. See Examples 1 through 8. (A few exercises are linear equations.)*

37. $4x^3 - x = 0$

38. $4y^3 - 36y = 0$

39. $4(x - 7) = 6$

40. $5(3 - 4x) = 9$

41. $(4x - 3)(16x^2 - 24x + 9) = 0$

42. $(2x + 5)(4x^2 + 20x + 25) = 0$

43. $4y^2 - 1 = 0$

44. $4y^2 - 81 = 0$

45. $(2x + 3)(2x^2 - 5x - 3) = 0$

46. $(2x - 9)(x^2 + 5x - 36) = 0$

47. $x^2 - 15 = -2x$

48. $x^2 - 26 = -11x$

49. $30x^2 - 11x = 30$

50. $9x^2 + 7x = 2$

51. $5x^2 - 6x - 8 = 0$

52. $12x^2 + 7x - 12 = 0$

53. $6y^2 - 22y - 40 = 0$

54. $3x^2 - 6x - 9 = 0$

55. $(y - 2)(y + 3) = 6$

56. $(y - 5)(y - 2) = 28$

57. $x^3 - 12x^2 + 32x = 0$

58. $x^3 - 14x^2 + 49x = 0$

59. $x^2 + 14x + 49 = 0$

60. $x^2 + 22x + 121 = 0$

61. $12y = 8y^2$

62. $9y = 6y^2$

63. $7x^3 - 7x = 0$

64. $3x^3 - 27x = 0$

65. $3x^2 + 8x - 11 = 13 - 6x$

66. $2x^2 + 12x - 1 = 4 + 3x$

67. $3x^2 - 20x = -4x^2 - 7x - 6$

68. $4x^2 - 20x = -5x^2 - 6x - 5$

Review

Perform each indicated operation. Write all results in lowest terms.

69. $\frac{3}{5} + \frac{4}{9}$

70. $\frac{2}{3} + \frac{3}{7}$

71. $\frac{7}{10} - \frac{5}{12}$

72. $\frac{5}{9} - \frac{5}{12}$

73. $\frac{4}{5} \cdot \frac{7}{8}$

74. $\frac{3}{7} \cdot \frac{12}{17}$

Concept Extensions

For Exercises 75 and 76, see the Concept Check in this section.

75. Explain the error and solve correctly:

$x(x - 2) = 8$

$x = 8$ or $x - 2 = 8$

$x = 10$

76. Explain the error and solve correctly:

$(x - 4)(x + 2) = 0$

$x = -4$ or $x = 2$

77. Write a quadratic equation that has two solutions, 6 and -1. Leave the polynomial in the equation in factored form.

78. Write a quadratic equation that has two solutions, 0 and -2. Leave the polynomial in the equation in factored form.

79. Write a quadratic equation in standard form that has two solutions, 5 and 7.

80. Write an equation that has three solutions, 0, 1, and 2.

81. A compass is accidentally thrown upward and out of an air balloon at a height of 300 feet. The height, y, of the compass at time x is given by the equation $y = -16x^2 + 20x + 300$.

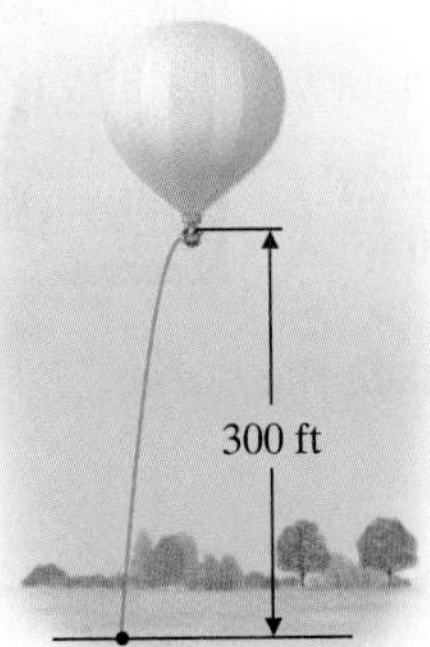

a. Find the height of the compass at the given times by filling in the table below.

Time, x (in seconds)	0	1	2	3	4	5	6
Height, y (in feet)							

b. Use the table to determine when the compass strikes the ground.

c. Use the table to approximate the maximum height of the compass.

82. A rocket is fired upward from the ground with an initial velocity of 100 feet per second. The height, y, of the rocket at any time x is given by the equation $y = -16x^2 + 100x$.

a. Find the height of the rocket at the given times by filling in the table below.

Time, x (in seconds)	0	1	2	3	4	5	6	7
Height, y (in feet)								

b. Use the table to determine between what two whole-numbered seconds the rocket strikes the ground.

c. Use the table to approximate the maximum height of the rocket.

Solve each equation.

83. $(x - 3)(3x + 4) = (x + 2)(x - 6)$

84. $(2x - 3)(x + 6) = (x - 9)(x + 2)$

85. $(2x - 3)(x + 8) = (x - 6)(x + 4)$

86. $(x + 6)(x - 6) = (2x - 9)(x + 4)$

Objective

A Solve Problems That Can Be Modeled by Quadratic Equations.

11.7 QUADRATIC EQUATIONS AND PROBLEM SOLVING

Objective A Solving Problems Modeled by Quadratic Equations

Some problems may be modeled by quadratic equations. To solve these problems, we use the same problem-solving steps that were introduced in Section 9.4. When solving these problems, keep in mind that a solution of an equation that models a problem may not be a solution to the problem. For example, a person's age or the length of a rectangle is always a positive number. Thus we discard solutions that do not make sense as solutions of the problem.

PRACTICE 1

Cliff divers also frequent the falls at Waimea Falls Park in Oahu, Hawaii. Here, a diver can jump from a ledge 64 feet up the waterfall into a rocky pool below. Neglecting air resistance, the height of a diver above the pool after t seconds is $h = -16t^2 + 64$. Find how long it takes the diver to reach the pool.

Example 1 Finding Free-Fall Time

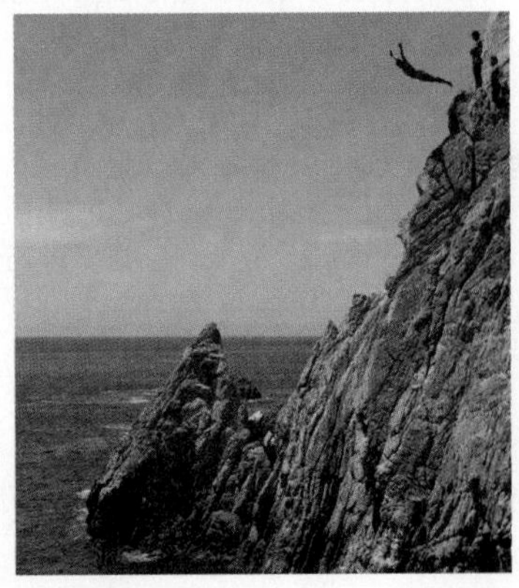

Since the 1940s, one of the top tourist attractions in Acapulco, Mexico, is watching the cliff divers off La Quebrada. The divers' platform is about 144 feet above the sea. These divers must time their descent just right, since they land in the crashing Pacific, in an inlet that is at most $9\frac{1}{2}$ feet deep. Neglecting air resistance, the height h in feet of a cliff diver above the ocean after t seconds is given by the quadratic equation $h = -16t^2 + 144$.

Find out how long it takes the diver to reach the ocean.

Solution:

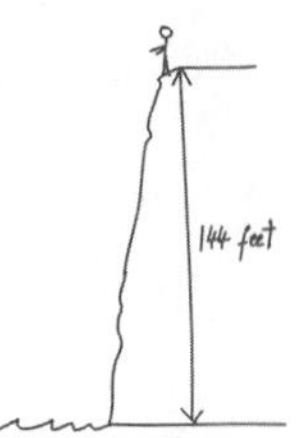

1. UNDERSTAND. Read and reread the problem. Then draw a picture of the problem.

   The equation $h = -16t^2 + 144$ models the height of the falling diver at time t. Familiarize yourself with this equation by finding the height of the diver at time $t = 1$ second and $t = 2$ seconds.

   When $t = 1$ second, the height of the diver is $h = -16(1)^2 + 144 = 128$ feet.

   When $t = 2$ seconds, the height of the diver is $h = -16(2)^2 + 144 = 80$ feet.

2. TRANSLATE. To find out how long it takes the diver to reach the ocean, we want to know the value of t for which $h = 0$.

3. SOLVE. Solve the equation.

$$0 = -16t^2 + 144$$

$$0 = -16(t^2 - 9) \quad \text{Factor out } -16.$$

$$0 = -16(t - 3)(t + 3) \quad \text{Factor completely.}$$

$$t - 3 = 0 \quad \text{or} \quad t + 3 = 0 \quad \text{Set each factor containing a variable equal to 0.}$$

$$t = 3 \quad \text{or} \quad t = -3 \quad \text{Solve.}$$

4. INTERPRET. Since the time t cannot be negative, the proposed solution is 3 seconds.

Check: Verify that the height of the diver when t is 3 seconds is 0.

When $t = 3$ seconds, $h = -16(3)^2 + 144 = -144 + 144 = 0$.

Work Practice 1

Answer

1. 2 sec

Example 2 Finding a Number

The square of a number plus three times the number is 70. Find the number.

Solution:

1. UNDERSTAND. Read and reread the problem. Suppose that the number is 5. The square of 5 is 5^2 or 25. Three times 5 is 15. Then $25 + 15 = 40$, not 70, so the number must be greater than 5. Remember, the purpose of proposing a number, such as 5, is to better understand the problem. Now that we do, we will let $x =$ the number.
2. TRANSLATE.

the square of a number	plus	three times the number	is	70
↓	↓	↓	↓	↓
x^2	$+$	$3x$	$=$	70

3. SOLVE.

$$x^2 + 3x = 70$$

$$x^2 + 3x - 70 = 0 \quad \text{Subtract 70 from both sides.}$$

$$(x + 10)(x - 7) = 0 \quad \text{Factor.}$$

$$x + 10 = 0 \quad \text{or} \quad x - 7 = 0 \quad \text{Set each factor equal to 0.}$$

$$x = -10 \qquad x = 7 \quad \text{Solve.}$$

4. INTERPRET.

Check: The square of -10 is $(-10)^2$, or 100. Three times -10 is $3(-10)$ or -30. Then $100 + (-30) = 70$, the correct sum, so -10 checks.

The square of 7 is 7^2 or 49. Three times 7 is 3(7), or 21. Then $49 + 21 = 70$, the correct sum, so 7 checks.

State: There are two numbers. They are -10 and 7.

Work Practice 2

PRACTICE 2

The square of a number minus twice the number is 63. Find the number.

Example 3 Finding the Dimensions of a Sail

The height of a triangular sail is 2 meters less than twice the length of the base. If the sail has an area of 30 square meters, find the length of its base and the height.

Solution:

1. UNDERSTAND. Read and reread the problem. Since we are finding the length of the base and the height, we let

   $x =$ the length of the base

   Since the height is 2 meters less than twice the length of the base,

   $2x - 2 =$ the height

   An illustration is shown in the margin.
2. TRANSLATE. We are given that the area of the triangle is 30 square meters, so we use the formula for area of a triangle.

area of triangle	$=$	$\frac{1}{2}$	$\cdot$	base	$\cdot$	height
↓		↓		↓		↓
30	$=$	$\frac{1}{2}$	$\cdot$	x	$\cdot$	$(2x - 2)$

PRACTICE 3

The length of a rectangular garden is 5 feet more than its width. The area of the garden is 176 square feet. Find the length and the width of the garden.

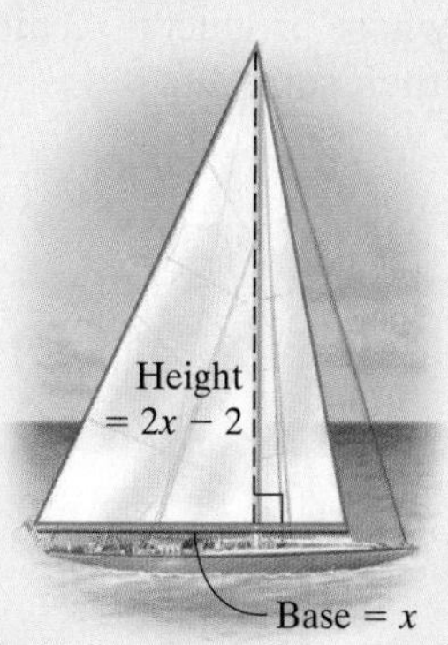

Answers

2. 9 and −7
3. length: 16 ft; width: 11 ft

3. SOLVE. Now we solve the quadratic equation.

$$30 = \frac{1}{2}x(2x - 2)$$
$$30 = x^2 - x \qquad \text{Multiply.}$$
$$0 = x^2 - x - 30 \qquad \text{Write in standard form.}$$
$$0 = (x - 6)(x + 5) \qquad \text{Factor.}$$
$$x - 6 = 0 \quad \text{or} \quad x + 5 = 0 \qquad \text{Set each factor equal to 0.}$$
$$x = 6 \qquad\qquad x = -5$$

4. INTERPRET. Since x represents the length of the base, we discard the solution -5. The base of a triangle cannot be negative. The base is then 6 meters and the height is $2(6) - 2 = 10$ meters.

Check: To check this problem, we recall that

$$\text{area} = \frac{1}{2} \cdot \text{base} \cdot \text{height or}$$
$$30 \stackrel{?}{=} \frac{1}{2}(6)(10)$$
$$30 = 30 \qquad \text{True}$$

State: The base of the triangular sail is 6 meters and the height is 10 meters.

Work Practice 3

The next example has to do with consecutive integers. Study the following diagrams for a review of consecutive integers.

Examples

If x is the first integer, then consecutive integers are $x, x + 1, x + 2, \ldots$

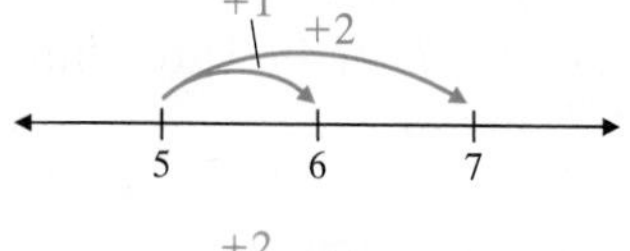

If x is the first even integer, then consecutive even integers are $x, x + 2, x + 4, \ldots$

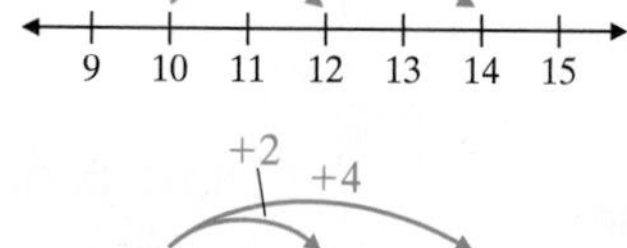

If x is the first odd integer, then consecutive odd integers are $x, x + 2, x + 4, \ldots$

+2 +4

8 9 10 11 12 13 14

PRACTICE 4

Find two consecutive odd integers whose product is 23 more than their sum.

Example 4 Finding Consecutive Even Integers

Find two consecutive even integers whose product is 34 more than their sum.

Solution:

1. UNDERSTAND. Read and reread the problem. Let's just choose two consecutive even integers to help us better understand the problem. Let's choose 10 and 12. Their product is $10(12) = 120$ and their sum is $10 + 12 = 22$. The product is $120 - 22$, or 98 greater than the sum. Thus our guess is incorrect, but we have a better understanding of this example.

   Let's let x and $x + 2$ be the consecutive even integers.

2. TRANSLATE.

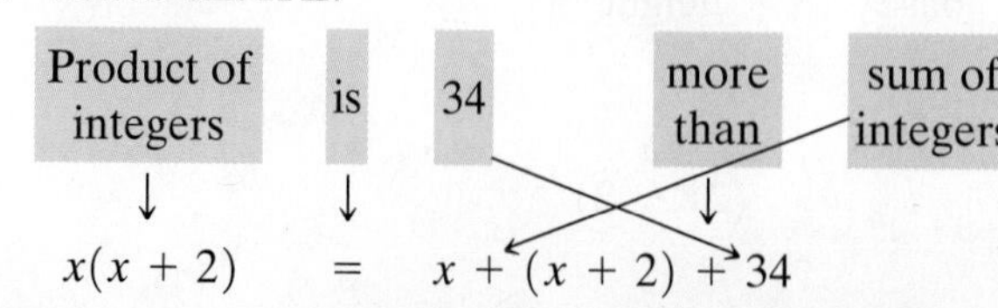

Continued on next page

Answer

4. 5 and 7 or -5 and -3

3. SOLVE. Now we solve the equation.

$$x(x + 2) = x + (x + 2) + 34 \quad \text{Multiply.}$$
$$x^2 + 2x = x + x + 2 + 34 \quad \text{Combine like terms.}$$
$$x^2 + 2x = 2x + 36 \quad \text{Write in standard form.}$$
$$x^2 - 36 = 0 \quad \text{Factor.}$$
$$(x + 6)(x - 6) = 0 \quad \text{Set each factor equal to 0.}$$
$$x + 6 = 0 \quad \text{or} \quad x - 6 = 0 \quad \text{Solve.}$$
$$x = -6 \qquad x = 6$$

4. INTERPRET. If $x = -6$, then $x + 2 = -6 + 2$, or -4.
If $x = 6$, then $x + 2 = 6 + 2$, or 8.

Check: $-6, -4$ | $6, 8$

$-6(-4) \stackrel{?}{=} -6 + (-4) + 34$ | $6(8) \stackrel{?}{=} 6 + 8 + 34$

$24 \stackrel{?}{=} -10 + 34$ | $48 \stackrel{?}{=} 14 + 34$

$24 = 24$ True | $48 = 48$ True

State: The two consecutive even integers are -6 and -4 or 6 and 8.

Work Practice 4

The next example makes use of the **Pythagorean theorem.** Before we review this theorem, recall that a **right triangle** is a triangle that contains a 90° or right angle. The **hypotenuse** of a right triangle is the side opposite the right angle and is the longest side of the triangle. The **legs** of a right triangle are the other sides of the triangle.

Pythagorean Theorem

In a right triangle, the sum of the squares of the lengths of the two legs is equal to the square of the length of the hypotenuse.

$$(\text{leg})^2 + (\text{leg})^2 = (\text{hypotenuse})^2 \quad \text{or} \quad a^2 + b^2 = c^2$$

Hypotenuse c
Leg b
Leg a

Helpful Hint If you use this formula, don't forget that c represents the length of the hypotenuse.

Example 5 Finding the Dimensions of a Triangle

Find the lengths of the sides of a right triangle if the lengths can be expressed as three consecutive even integers.

Solution:

1. UNDERSTAND. Read and reread the problem. Let's suppose that the length of one leg of the right triangle is 4 units. Then the other leg is the next even integer, or 6 units, and the hypotenuse of the triangle is the next even integer, or 8 units. Remember that the hypotenuse is the longest side. Let's see if a triangle with sides of these lengths forms a right triangle. To do this, we check to see whether the Pythagorean theorem holds true.

$$4^2 + 6^2 \stackrel{?}{=} 8^2$$
$$16 + 36 \stackrel{?}{=} 64$$
$$52 = 64 \quad \text{False}$$

4 units
8 units
6 units

PRACTICE 5

The length of one leg of a right triangle is 7 meters less than the length of the other leg. The length of the hypotenuse is 13 meters. Find the lengths of the legs.

Answer

5. 5 meters, 12 meters

Our proposed numbers do not check, but we now have a better understanding of the problem.

We let x, $x + 2$, and $x + 4$ be three consecutive even integers. Since these integers represent lengths of the sides of a right triangle, we have the following.

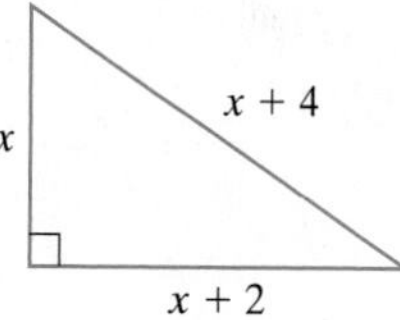

x = one leg
$x + 2$ = other leg
$x + 4$ = hypotenuse (longest side)

2. TRANSLATE. By the Pythagorean theorem, we have that

$$(\text{leg})^2 + (\text{leg})^2 = (\text{hypotenuse})^2$$
$$(x)^2 + (x + 2)^2 = (x + 4)^2$$

3. SOLVE. Now we solve the equation.

$$x^2 + (x + 2)^2 = (x + 4)^2$$
$$x^2 + x^2 + 4x + 4 = x^2 + 8x + 16 \quad \text{Multiply.}$$
$$2x^2 + 4x + 4 = x^2 + 8x + 16 \quad \text{Combine like terms.}$$
$$x^2 - 4x - 12 = 0 \quad \text{Write in standard form.}$$
$$(x - 6)(x + 2) = 0 \quad \text{Factor.}$$
$$x - 6 = 0 \quad \text{or} \quad x + 2 = 0 \quad \text{Set each factor equal to 0.}$$
$$x = 6 \qquad x = -2$$

4. INTERPRET. We discard $x = -2$ since length cannot be negative. If $x = 6$, then $x + 2 = 8$ and $x + 4 = 10$.

Check: Verify that

$$(\text{leg})^2 + (\text{leg})^2 = (\text{hypotenuse})^2$$
$$6^2 + 8^2 \stackrel{?}{=} 10^2$$
$$36 + 64 \stackrel{?}{=} 100$$
$$100 = 100 \quad \text{True}$$

State: The sides of the right triangle have lengths 6 units, 8 units, and 10 units.

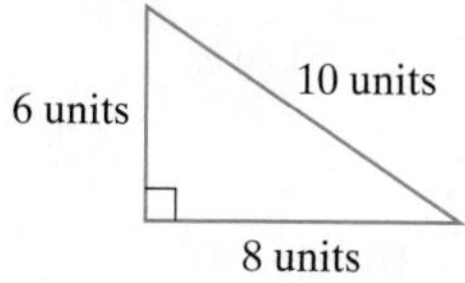

Work Practice 5

11.7 Exercise Set

FOR EXTRA HELP

MyMathLab

Objective A *See Examples 1 through 5 for all exercises.*

Translating *For Exercises 1 through 6, represent each given condition using a single variable, x.*

△ **1.** The length and width of a rectangle whose length is 4 centimeters more than its width

△ **2.** The length and width of a rectangle whose length is twice its width

3. Two consecutive odd integers

4. Two consecutive even integers

△ **5.** The base and height of a triangle whose height is one more than four times its base

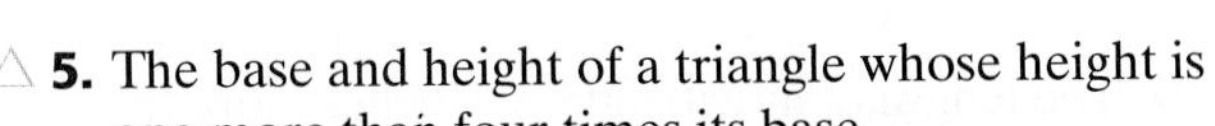

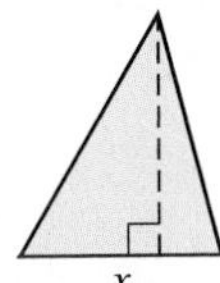

△ **6.** The base and height of a trapezoid whose base is three less than five times its height

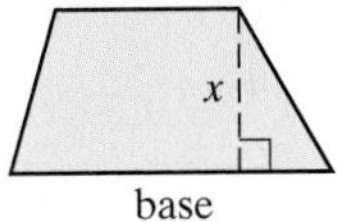

Use the information given to find the dimensions of each figure.

△ **7.**

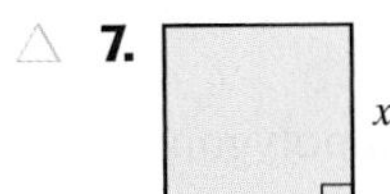

The *area* of the square is 121 square units. Find the length of its sides.

△ **8.**

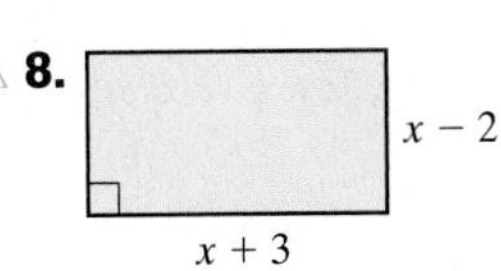

The *area* of the rectangle is 84 square inches. Find its length and width.

△ **9.**

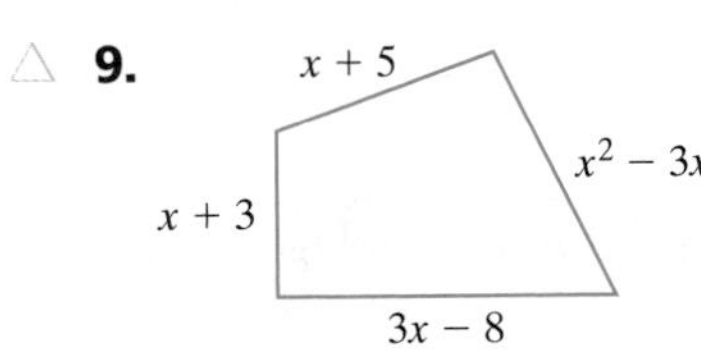

The *perimeter* of the quadrilateral is 120 centimeters. Find the lengths of its sides.

10.

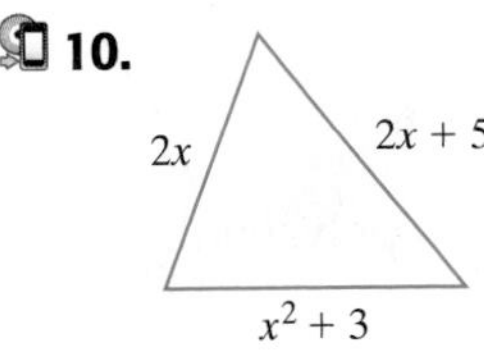

The *perimeter* of the triangle is 85 feet. Find the lengths of its sides.

△ **11.**

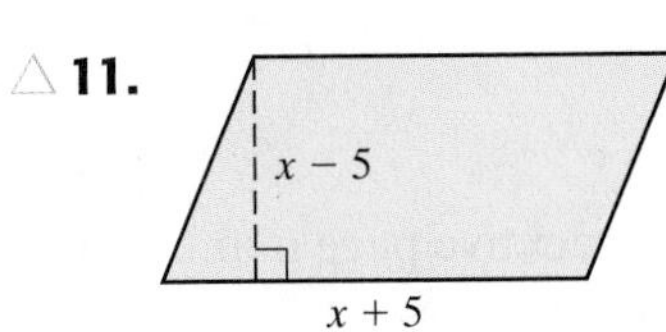

The *area* of the parallelogram is 96 square miles. Find its base and height.

△ **12.**

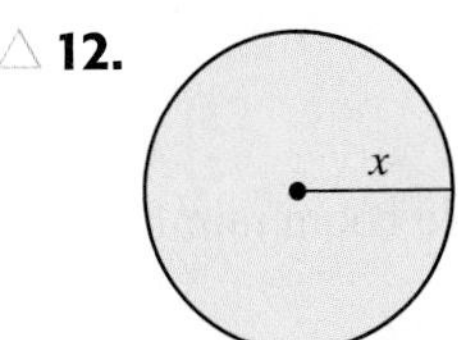

The *area* of the circle is 25π square kilometers. Find its radius.

Solve.

13. An object is thrown upward from the top of an 80-foot building with an initial velocity of 64 feet per second. The height h of the object after t seconds is given by the quadratic equation $h = -16t^2 + 64t + 80$. When will the object hit the ground?

14. A hang glider accidentally drops her compass from the top of a 400-foot cliff. The height h of the compass after t seconds is given by the quadratic equation $h = -16t^2 + 400$. When will the compass hit the ground?

15. The width of a rectangle is 7 centimeters less than twice its length. Its area is 30 square centimeters. Find the dimensions of the rectangle.

16. The length of a rectangle is 9 inches more than its width. Its area is 112 square inches. Find the dimensions of the rectangle.

△ *The equation* $D = \frac{1}{2}n(n - 3)$ *gives the number of diagonals D for a polygon with n sides. For example, a polygon with 6 sides has* $D = \frac{1}{2} \cdot 6(6 - 3)$ *or* $D = 9$ *diagonals. (See if you can count all 9 diagonals. Some are shown in the figure.) Use this equation,* $D = \frac{1}{2}n(n - 3)$, *for Exercises 17 through 20.*

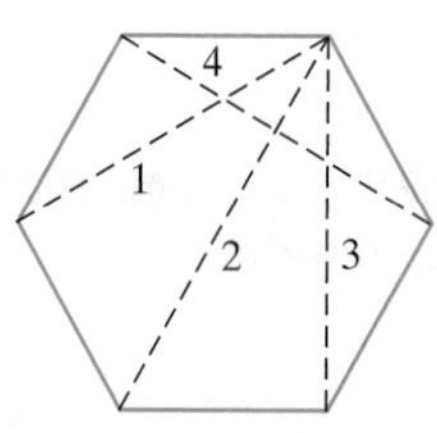

17. Find the number of diagonals for a polygon that has 12 sides.

18. Find the number of diagonals for a polygon that has 15 sides.

19. Find the number of sides n for a polygon that has 35 diagonals.

20. Find the number of sides n for a polygon that has 14 diagonals.

21. The sum of a number and its square is 132. Find the number.

22. The sum of a number and its square is 182. Find the number.

23. The product of two consecutive room numbers is 210. Find the room numbers.

24. The product of two consecutive page numbers is 420. Find the page numbers.

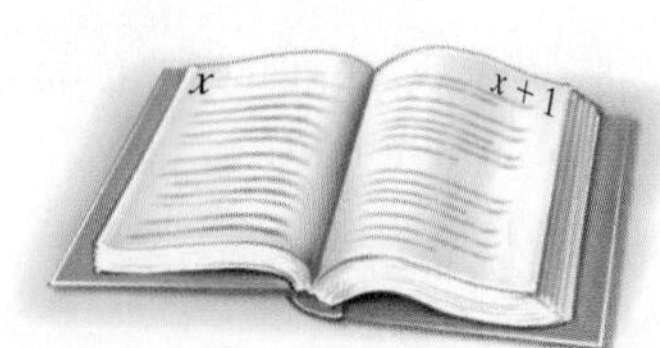

△ **25.** A ladder is leaning against a building so that the distance from the ground to the top of the ladder is one foot less than the length of the ladder. Find the length of the ladder if the distance from the bottom of the ladder to the building is 5 feet.

△ **26.** Use the given figure to find the length of the guy wire.

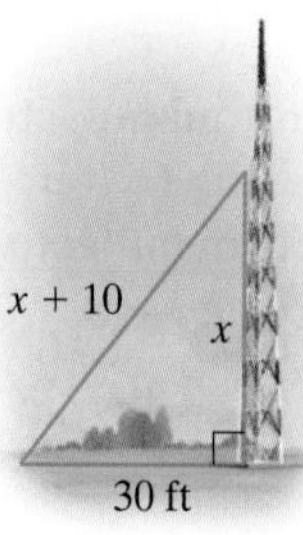

△ **27.** If the sides of a square are increased by 3 inches, the area becomes 64 square inches. Find the length of the sides of the original square.

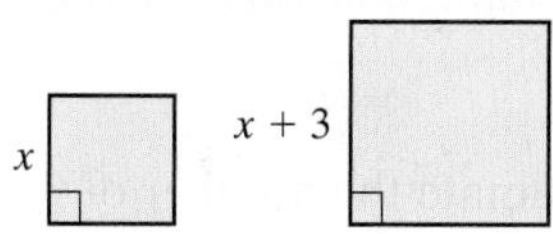

△ **28.** If the sides of a square are increased by 5 meters, the area becomes 100 square meters. Find the length of the sides of the original square.

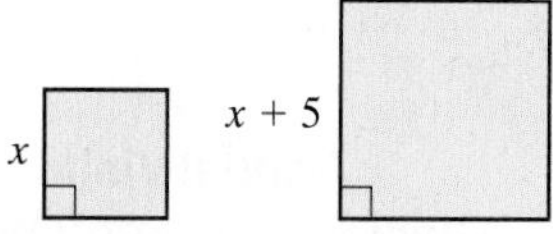

△ **29.** One leg of a right triangle is 4 millimeters longer than the smaller leg and the hypotenuse is 8 millimeters longer than the smaller leg. Find the lengths of the sides of the triangle.

△ **30.** One leg of a right triangle is 9 centimeters longer than the other leg and the hypotenuse is 45 centimeters. Find the lengths of the legs of the triangle.

△ **31.** The length of the base of a triangle is twice its height. If the area of the triangle is 100 square kilometers, find the height.

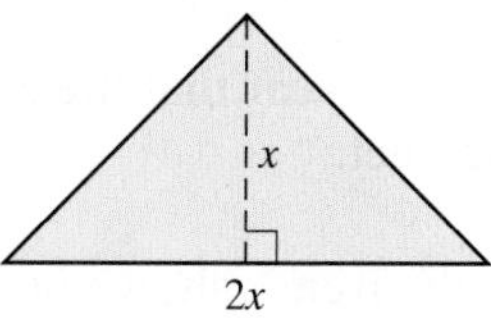

△ **32.** The height of a triangle is 2 millimeters less than the base. If the area is 60 square millimeters, find the base.

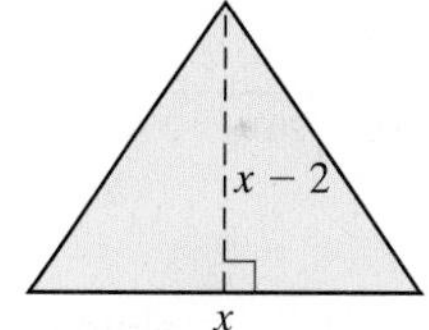

△ **33.** Find the length of the shorter leg of a right triangle if the longer leg is 12 feet more than the shorter leg and the hypotenuse is 12 feet less than twice the shorter leg.

△ **34.** Find the length of the shorter leg of a right triangle if the longer leg is 10 miles more than the shorter leg and the hypotenuse is 10 miles less than twice the shorter leg.

35. An object is dropped from 39 feet below the tip of the pinnacle atop one of the 1483-foot-tall Petronas Twin Towers in Kuala Lumpur, Malaysia. (*Source:* Council on Tall Buildings and Urban Habitat) The height h of the object after t seconds is given by the equation $h = -16t^2 + 1444$. Find how many seconds pass before the object reaches the ground.

36. An object is dropped from the top of 311 South Wacker Drive, a 961-foot-tall office building in Chicago. (*Source:* Council on Tall Buildings and Urban Habitat) The height h of the object after t seconds is given by the equation $h = -16t^2 + 961$. Find how many seconds pass before the object reaches the ground.

37. At the end of 2 years, P dollars invested at an interest rate r compounded annually increases to an amount, A dollars, given by

$$A = P(1 + r)^2$$

Find the interest rate if \$100 increased to \$144 in 2 years. Write your answer as a percent.

38. At the end of 2 years, P dollars invested at an interest rate r compounded annually increases to an amount, A dollars, given by

$$A = P(1 + r)^2$$

Find the interest rate if \$2000 increased to \$2420 in 2 years. Write your answer as a percent.

△ **39.** Find the dimensions of a rectangle whose width is 7 miles less than its length and whose area is 120 square miles.

△ **40.** Find the dimensions of a rectangle whose width is 2 inches less than half its length and whose area is 160 square inches.

41. If the cost, C, for manufacturing x units of a certain product is given by $C = x^2 - 15x + 50$, find the number of units manufactured at a cost of \$9500.

42. If a switchboard handles n telephones, the number C of telephone connections it can make simultaneously is given by the equation $C = \frac{n(n-1)}{2}$. Find how many telephones are handled by a switchboard making 120 telephone connections simultaneously.

Review

The following double line graph shows a comparison of the number of annual visitors (in millions) to Glacier National Park and Gettysburg National Military Park for the years shown. Use this graph to answer Exercises 43 through 49. See Section 9.4.

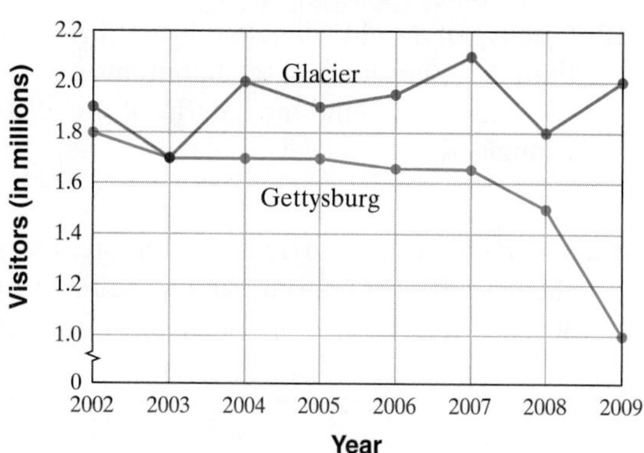

43. Approximate the number of visitors to Glacier National Park in 2002.

44. Approximate the number of visitors to Gettysburg National Military Park in 2009.

45. Approximate the number of visitors to Glacier National Park in 2005.

46. Approximate the number of visitors to Gettysburg National Military Park in 2005.

47. Determine the year that the colored lines in this graph intersect.

48. In your own words, explain the meaning of the point of intersection in the graph.

49. Describe the trends shown in this graph and speculate as to why these trends have occurred.

Concept Extensions

△ **50.** Two boats travel at right angles to each other after leaving the same dock at the same time. One hour later the boats are 17 miles apart. If one boat travels 7 miles per hour faster than the other boat, find the rate of each boat.

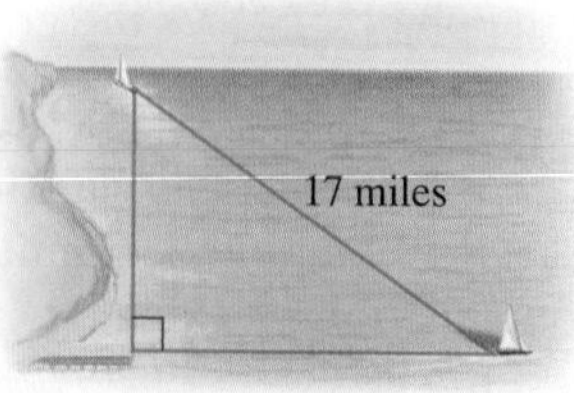

△ **51.** The side of a square equals the width of a rectangle. The length of the rectangle is 6 meters longer than its width. The sum of the areas of the square and the rectangle is 176 square meters. Find the side of the square.

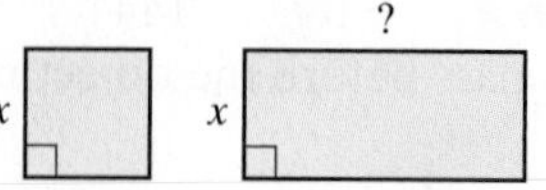

52. The sum of two numbers is 20, and the sum of their squares is 218. Find the numbers.

53. The sum of two numbers is 25, and the sum of their squares is 325. Find the numbers.

△ **54.** A rectangular garden is surrounded by a walk of uniform width. The area of the garden is 180 square yards. If the dimensions of the garden plus the walk are 16 yards by 24 yards, find the width of the walk.

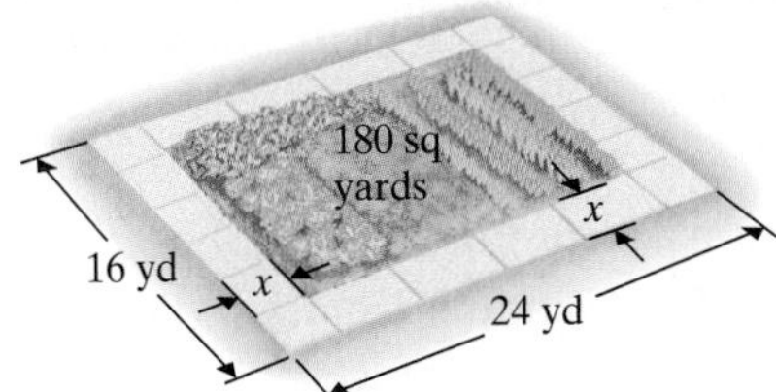

△ **55.** A rectangular pool is surrounded by a walk 4 meters wide. The pool is 6 meters longer than its width. If the total area of the pool and walk is 576 square meters more than the area of the pool, find the dimensions of the pool.

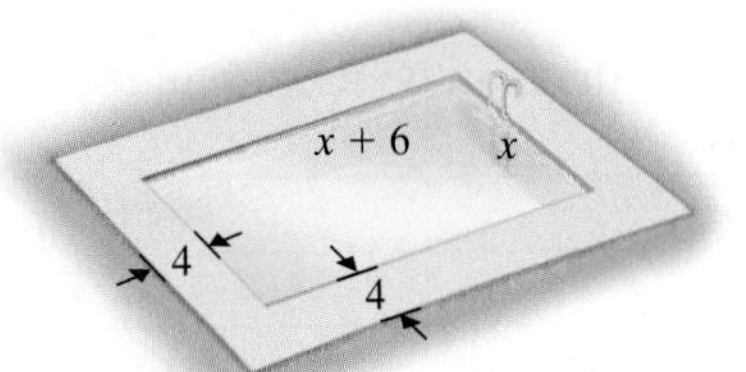

△ **56.** According to the International America's Cup Class (IACC) rule, a sailboat competing in the America's Cup match must have a 110-foot-tall mast and a combined mainsail and jib sail area of 3000 square feet. (*Source:* America's Cup Organizing Committee) A design for an IACC-class sailboat calls for the mainsail to be 60% of the combined sail area. If the height of the triangular mainsail is 28 feet more than twice the length of the boom, find the length of the boom and the height of the mainsail.

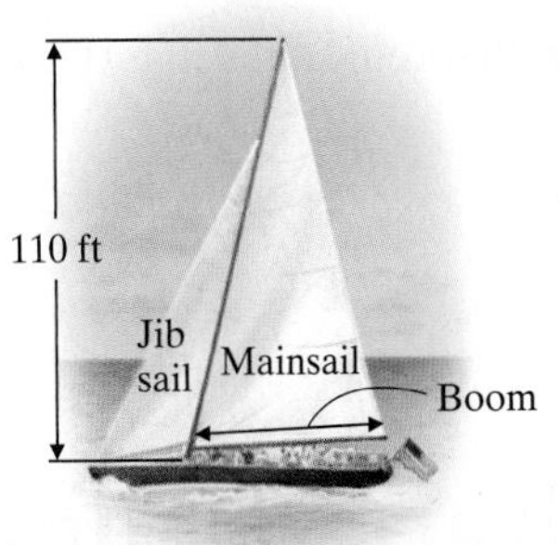

Answers

Chapter 11 Group Activity

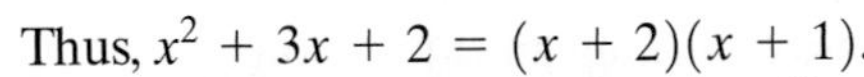

Factoring polynomials can be visualized using areas of rectangles. To see this, let's first find the areas of the following squares and rectangles. (Recall that Area = Length · Width.)

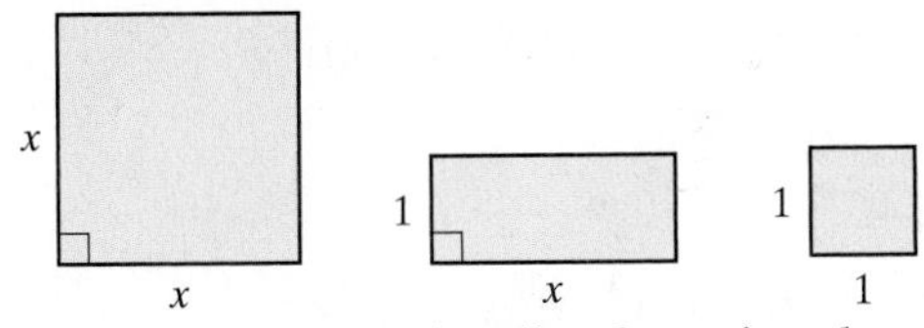

To use these areas to visualize factoring the polynomial $x^2 + 3x + 2$, for example, use the shapes below to form a rectangle. The factored form is found by reading the length and the width of the rectangle as shown below.

Thus, $x^2 + 3x + 2 = (x + 2)(x + 1)$.

Try using this method to visualize the factored form of each polynomial below.

Work in a group and use tiles to find the factored form of the polynomials below. (Tiles can be handmade from index cards.)

1. $x^2 + 6x + 5$

2. $x^2 + 5x + 6$

3. $x^2 + 5x + 4$

4. $x^2 + 4x + 3$

5. $x^2 + 6x + 9$

6. $x^2 + 4x + 4$

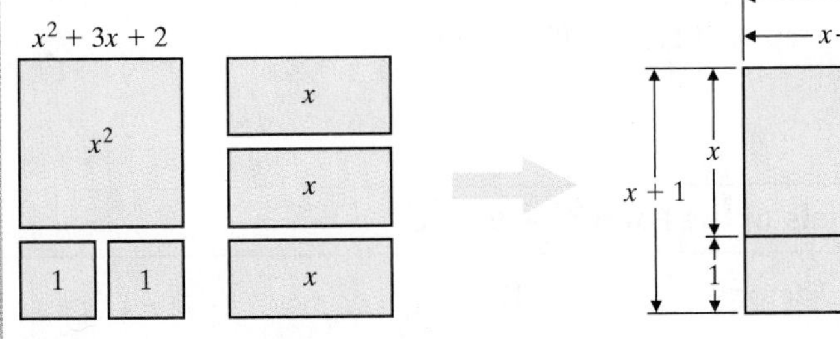

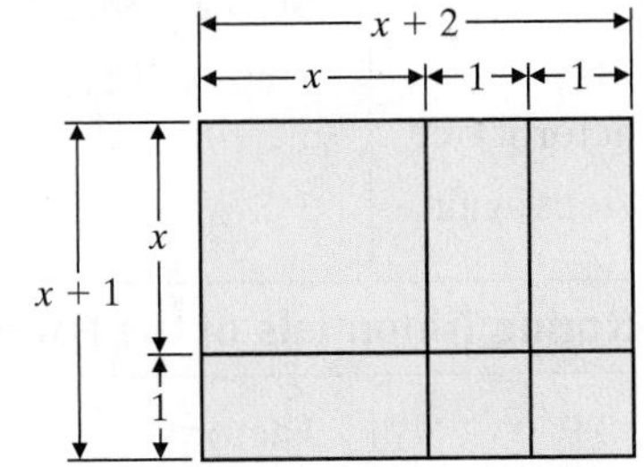

Chapter 11 Vocabulary Check

Fill in each blank with one of the words or phrases listed below. Some words or phrases may be used more than once.

factoring	leg	hypotenuse
greatest common factor	perfect square trinomial	quadratic equation

1. An equation that can be written in the form $ax^2 + bx + c = 0$ (with a not 0) is called a ______________.
2. ______________ is the process of writing an expression as a product.
3. The ______________ of a list of terms is the product of all common factors.
4. A trinomial that is the square of some binomial is called a ______________.
5. In a right triangle, the side opposite the right angle is called the ______________.
6. In a right triangle, each side adjacent to the right angle is called a ______________.
7. The Pythagorean theorem states that $(\text{leg})^2 + (\text{leg})^2 = (\_\_\_\_\_\_)^2$.

Helpful Hint Are you preparing for your test? Don't forget to take the Chapter 11 Test on page 827. Then check your answers at the back of the text and use the Chapter Test Prep Videos to see the fully worked-out solutions to any of the exercises you want to review.

11 Chapter Highlights

Definitions and Concepts	Examples
Section 11.1 The Greatest Common Factor	
Factoring is the process of writing an expression as a product.	Factor: $6 = 2 \cdot 3$ Factor: $x^2 + 5x + 6 = (x + 2)(x + 3)$
The GCF of a list of variable terms contains the smallest exponent on each common variable.	The GCF of z^5, z^3, and z^{10} is z^3.
The GCF of a list of terms is the product of all common factors.	Find the GCF of $8x^2y$, $10x^3y^2$, and $50x^2y^3$. $8x^2y = 2 \cdot 2 \cdot 2 \cdot x^2 \cdot y$ $10x^3y^2 = 2 \cdot 5 \cdot x^3 \cdot y^2$ $50x^2y^3 = 2 \cdot 5 \cdot 5 \cdot x^2 \cdot y^3$ $\text{GCF} = 2 \cdot x^2 \cdot y$ or $2x^2y$
To Factor by Grouping **Step 1.** Group the terms in two groups so that each group has a common factor. **Step 2.** Factor out the GCF from each group. **Step 3.** If there is a common binomial factor, factor it out. **Step 4.** If not, rearrange the terms and try these steps again.	Factor: $10ax + 15a - 6xy - 9y$ **Step 1.** $(10ax + 15a) + (-6xy - 9y)$ **Step 2.** $5a(2x + 3) - 3y(2x + 3)$ **Step 3.** $(2x + 3)(5a - 3y)$
Section 11.2 Factoring Trinomials of the Form $x^2 + bx + c$	
The product of these numbers is c. $x^2 + bx + c = (x + \square)(x + \square)$ The sum of these numbers is b.	Factor: $x^2 + 7x + 12$ $3 + 4 = 7$ $\quad 3 \cdot 4 = 12$ $x^2 + 7x + 12 = (x + 3)(x + 4)$

Definitions and Concepts	Examples
Section 11.3 Factoring Trinomials of the Form $ax^2 + bx + c$	
To factor $ax^2 + bx + c$, try various combinations of factors of ax^2 and c until a middle term of bx is obtained when checking.	Factor: $3x^2 + 14x - 5$ Factors of $3x^2$: $3x, x$ Factors of -5: $-1, 5$ and $1, -5$ $(3x - 1)(x + 5)$ $-1x$ $+15x$ Correct middle term $14x$
Section 11.4 Factoring Trinomials of the Form $ax^2 + bx + c$ by Grouping	
To Factor $ax^2 + bx + c$ by Grouping **Step 1.** Find two numbers whose product is $a \cdot c$ and whose sum is b. **Step 2.** Rewrite bx, using the factors found in Step 1. **Step 3.** Factor by grouping.	Factor: $3x^2 + 14x - 5$ **Step 1.** Find two numbers whose product is $3 \cdot (-5)$ or -15 and whose sum is 14. They are 15 and -1. **Step 2.** $3x^2 + 14x - 5$ $= 3x^2 + 15x - 1x - 5$ **Step 3.** $= 3x(x + 5) - 1(x + 5)$ $= (x + 5)(3x - 1)$
Section 11.5 Factoring by Special Products	
A **perfect square trinomial** is a trinomial that is the square of some binomial.	**Perfect Square Trinomial = Square of Binomial** $x^2 + 4x + 4 = (x + 2)^2$ $25x^2 - 10x + 1 = (5x - 1)^2$
Factoring Perfect Square Trinomials $a^2 + 2ab + b^2 = (a + b)^2$ $a^2 - 2ab + b^2 = (a - b)^2$	Factor. $x^2 + 6x + 9 = x^2 + 2 \cdot x \cdot 3 + 3^2 = (x + 3)^2$ $4x^2 - 12x + 9 = (2x)^2 - 2 \cdot 2x \cdot 3 + 3^2$ $= (2x - 3)^2$
Difference of Two Squares $a^2 - b^2 = (a + b)(a - b)$	Factor. $x^2 - 9 = x^2 - 3^2 = (x + 3)(x - 3)$
Sum and Difference of Two Cubes $a^3 + b^3 = (a + b)(a^2 - ab + b^2)$ $a^3 - b^3 = (a - b)(a^2 + ab + b^2)$	Factor. $8y^3 + 1 = (2y + 1)(4y^2 - 2y + 1)$ $27p^3 - 64q^3 = (3p - 4q)(9p^2 + 12pq + 16q^2)$
Section 11.6 Solving Quadratic Equations by Factoring	
A **quadratic equation** is an equation that can be written in the form $ax^2 + bx + c = 0$ with a not 0. The form $ax^2 + bx + c = 0$ is called the **standard form** of a quadratic equation. **Zero-Factor Property** If a and b are real numbers and if $ab = 0$, then $a = 0$ or $b = 0$.	**Quadratic Equation** — **Standard Form** $x^2 = 16$ — $x^2 - 16 = 0$ $y = -2y^2 + 5$ — $2y^2 + y - 5 = 0$ If $(x + 3)(x - 1) = 0$, then $x + 3 = 0$ or $x - 1 = 0$. *(continued)*

Definitions and Concepts	Examples
Section 11.6 Solving Quadratic Equations by Factoring *(continued)*	
TO SOLVE QUADRATIC EQUATIONS BY FACTORING	Solve: $3x^2 = 13x - 4$
Step 1. Write the equation in standard form so that one side of the equation is 0.	**Step 1.** $3x^2 - 13x + 4 = 0$
Step 2. Factor completely.	**Step 2.** $(3x - 1)(x - 4) = 0$
Step 3. Set each factor containing a variable equal to 0.	**Step 3.** $3x - 1 = 0$ or $x - 4 = 0$
Step 4. Solve the resulting equations.	**Step 4.** $3x = 1$ $\quad x = 4$ $x = \frac{1}{3}$
Step 5. Check solutions in the original equation.	**Step 5.** Check both $\frac{1}{3}$ and 4 in the original equation.
Section 11.7 Quadratic Equations and Problem Solving	
PROBLEM-SOLVING STEPS	A garden is in the shape of a rectangle whose length is two feet more than its width. If the area of the garden is 35 square feet, find its dimensions.
1. UNDERSTAND the problem.	1. Read and reread the problem. Guess a solution and check your guess. Draw a diagram. Let x be the width of the rectangular garden. Then $x + 2$ is the length. 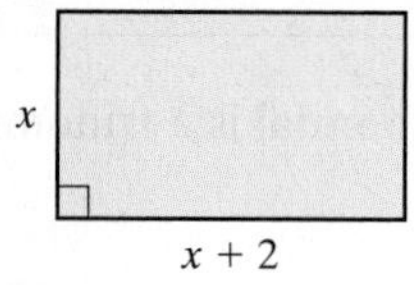
2. TRANSLATE.	2. length · width = area $\downarrow \quad \downarrow \quad \downarrow$ $(x + 2) \cdot x = 35$
3. SOLVE.	3. $(x + 2)x = 35$ $x^2 + 2x - 35 = 0$ $(x - 5)(x + 7) = 0$ $x - 5 = 0$ or $x + 7 = 0$ $x = 5$ $\quad x = -7$
4. INTERPRET.	4. Discard the solution $x = -7$ since x represents width. *Check:* If x is 5 feet, then $x + 2 = 5 + 2 = 7$ feet. The area of a rectangle whose width is 5 feet and whose length is 7 feet is (5 feet)(7 feet) or 35 square feet. *State:* The garden is 5 feet by 7 feet.

Chapter 11 Review

(11.1) *Complete each factoring.*

1. $6x^2 - 15x = 3x(\qquad)$

2. $4x^5 + 2x - 10x^4 = 2x(\qquad\qquad)$

Factor out the GCF from each polynomial.

3. $5m + 30$

4. $20x^3 + 12x^2 + 24x$

5. $3x(2x + 3) - 5(2x + 3)$

6. $5x(x + 1) - (x + 1)$

Factor each polynomial by grouping.

7. $3x^2 - 3x + 2x - 2$

8. $3a^2 + 9ab + 3b^2 + ab$

9. $10a^2 + 5ab + 7b^2 + 14ab$

10. $6x^2 + 10x - 3x - 5$

(11.2) *Factor each trinomial.*

11. $x^2 + 6x + 8$

12. $x^2 - 11x + 24$

13. $x^2 + x + 2$

14. $x^2 - 5x - 6$

15. $x^2 + 2x - 8$

16. $x^2 + 4xy - 12y^2$

17. $x^2 + 8xy + 15y^2$

18. $72 - 18x - 2x^2$

19. $32 + 12x - 4x^2$

20. $5y^3 - 50y^2 + 120y$

21. To factor $x^2 + 2x - 48$, think of two numbers whose product is ______ and whose sum is ______.

22. What is the first step in factoring $3x^2 + 15x + 30$?

(11.3) or (11.4) *Factor each trinomial.*

23. $2x^2 + 13x + 6$

24. $4x^2 + 4x - 3$

25. $6x^2 + 5xy - 4y^2$

26. $x^2 - x + 2$

27. $2x^2 - 23x - 39$

28. $18x^2 - 9xy - 20y^2$

29. $10y^3 + 25y^2 - 60y$

30. $60y^3 - 39y^2 + 6y$

Write the perimeter of each figure as a simplified polynomial. Then factor each polynomial completely.

△ **31.**

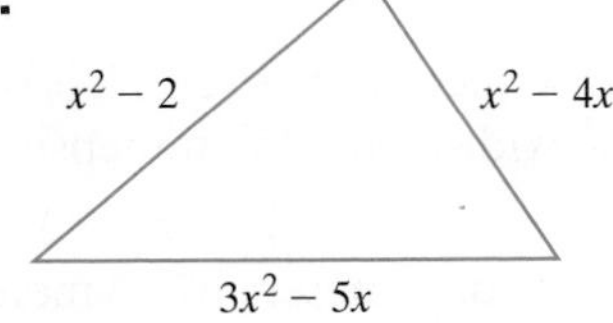

△ **32.**

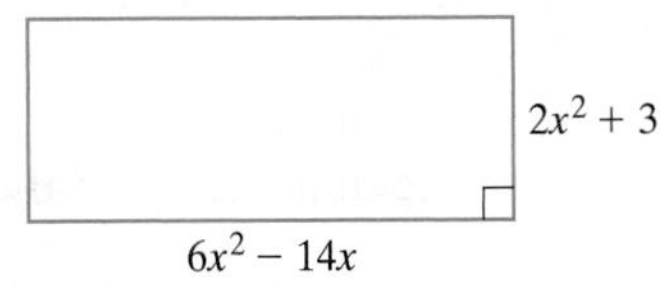

(11.5) *Factor each polynomial completely.*

33. $x^2 - 81$

34. $x^2 + 12x + 36$

35. $4x^2 - 9$

36. $9t^2 - 25s^2$

37. $16x^2 + y^2$

38. $n^2 - 18n + 81$

39. $3r^2 + 36r + 108$

40. $9y^2 - 42y + 49$

41. $5m^8 - 5m^6$

42. $4x^2 - 28xy + 49y^2$

43. $3x^2y + 6xy^2 + 3y^3$

44. $16x^4 - 1$

45. $(y + 2)^2 - 25$

46. $(x - 3)^2 - 16$

47. $8 - 27y^3$

48. $1 - 64y^3$

49. $6x^4y + 48xy$

50. $2x^5 + 16x^2y^3$

51. $x^2 - 2x + 1 - y^2$

△ **52.** The volume of the cylindrical shell is $\pi R^2h - \pi r^2h$ cubic units. Write this volume as a factored expression.

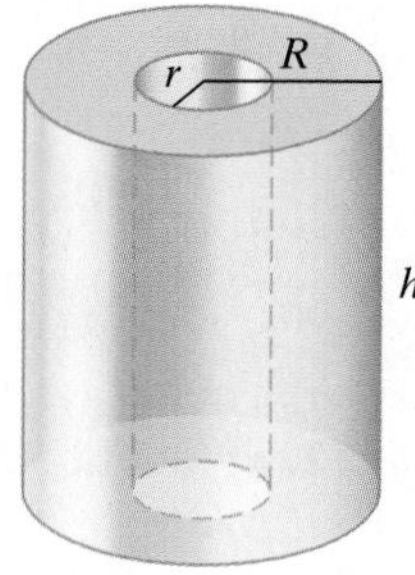

(11.6) *Solve each equation.*

53. $(x + 6)(x - 2) = 0$

54. $(x - 7)(x + 11) = 0$

55. $3x(x + 1)(7x - 2) = 0$

56. $4(5x + 1)(x + 3) = 0$

57. $x^2 + 8x + 7 = 0$

58. $x^2 - 2x - 24 = 0$

59. $x^2 + 10x = -25$

60. $x(x - 10) = -16$

61. $(3x - 1)(9x^2 + 3x + 1) = 0$

62. $56x^2 - 5x - 6 = 0$

63. $m^2 = 6m$

64. $r^2 = 25$

65. Write a quadratic equation that has the two solutions 4 and 5.

66. Write a quadratic equation that has two solutions, both -1.

(11.7) *Use the given information to choose the correct dimensions.*

△ **67.** The perimeter of a rectangle is 24 inches. The length is twice the width. Find the dimensions of the rectangle.

a. 5 inches by 7 inches
b. 5 inches by 10 inches
c. 4 inches by 8 inches
d. 2 inches by 10 inches

△ **68.** The area of a rectangle is 80 meters. The length is one more than three times the width. Find the dimensions of the rectangle.

a. 8 meters by 10 meters
b. 4 meters by 13 meters
c. 4 meters by 20 meters
d. 5 meters by 16 meters

Use the given information to find the dimensions of each figure.

△ **69.** The *area* of the square is 81 square units. Find the length of a side.

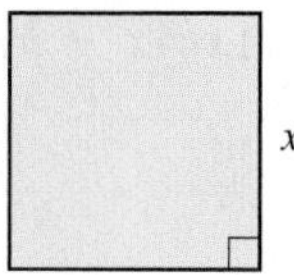

△ **70.** The *perimeter* of the quadrilateral is 47 units. Find the lengths of the sides.

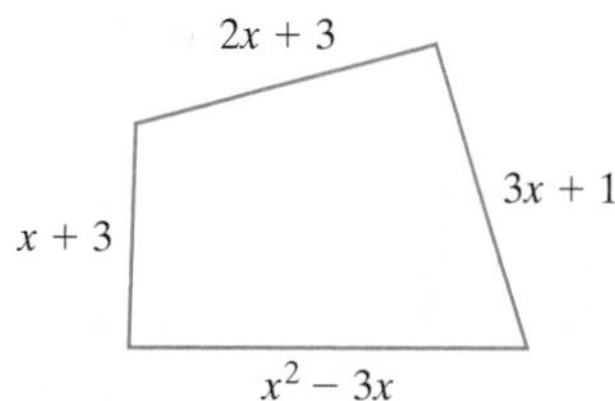

Solve.

△ **71.** A flag for a local organization is in the shape of a rectangle whose length is 15 inches less than twice its width. If the area of the flag is 500 square inches, find its dimensions.

△ **72.** The base of a triangular sail is four times its height. If the area of the triangle is 162 square yards, find the base.

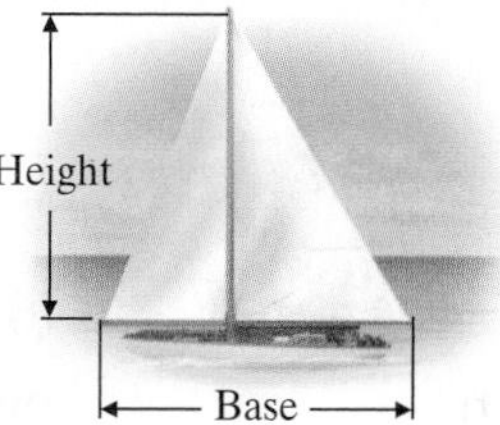

73. Find two consecutive positive integers whose product is 380.

74. Find two consecutive positive even integers whose product is 440.

75. A rocket is fired from the ground with an initial velocity of 440 feet per second. Its height h after t seconds is given by the equation $h = -16t^2 + 440t$.

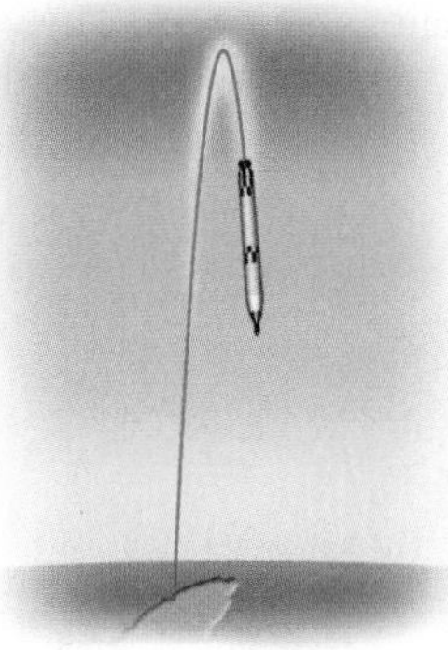

a. Find how many seconds pass before the rocket reaches a height of 2800 feet. Explain why two answers are obtained.

b. Find how many seconds pass before the rocket reaches the ground again.

△ **76.** An architect's squaring instrument is in the shape of a right triangle. Find the length of the longer leg of the right triangle if the hypotenuse is 8 centimeters longer than the longer leg and the shorter leg is 8 centimeters shorter than the longer leg.

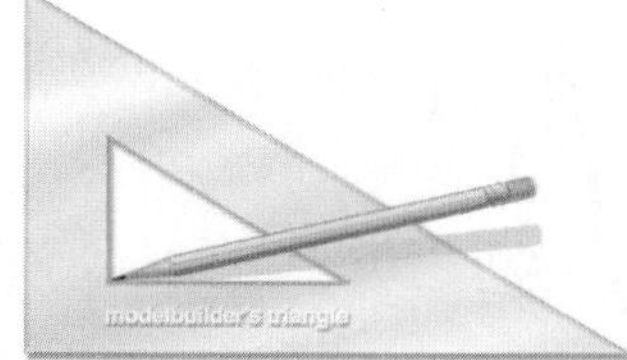

Mixed Review

Factor completely.

77. $6x + 24$

78. $7x - 63$

79. $11x(4x - 3) - 6(4x - 3)$

80. $2x(x - 5) - (x - 5)$

81. $3x^3 - 4x^2 + 6x - 8$

82. $xy + 2x - y - 2$

83. $2x^2 + 2x - 24$

84. $3x^3 - 30x^2 + 27x$

85. $4x^2 - 81$

86. $2x^2 - 18$

87. $16x^2 - 24x + 9$

88. $5x^2 + 20x + 20$

Solve.

89. $2x^2 - x - 28 = 0$

90. $x^2 - 2x = 15$

91. $2x(x + 7)(x + 4) = 0$

92. $x(x - 5) = -6$

93. $x^2 = 16x$

94. The perimeter of the following triangle is 48 inches. Find the lengths of its sides.

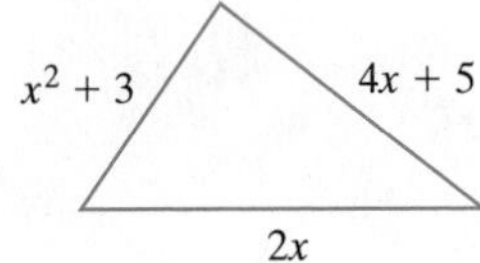

95. The width of a rectangle is 4 inches less than its length. Its area is 12 square inches. Find the dimensions of the rectangle.

Chapter 11 Test

Step-by-step test solutions are found on the Chapter Test Prep Videos available via the Interactive DVD Lecture Series, in MyMathLab or on YouTube (search "MartinGayAlgebra" and click on "Channels").

Factor each polynomial completely. If a polynomial cannot be factored, write "prime."

1. $9x^2 - 3x$

2. $x^2 + 11x + 28$

3. $49 - m^2$

4. $y^2 + 22y + 121$

5. $x^4 - 16$

6. $4(a + 3) - y(a + 3)$

7. $x^2 + 4$

8. $y^2 - 8y - 48$

9. $3a^2 + 3ab - 7a - 7b$

10. $3x^2 - 5x + 2$

11. $180 - 5x^2$

12. $9x^3 + 39x^2 + 12x$

13. $6t^2 - t - 5$

14. $xy^2 - 7y^2 - 4x + 28$

15. $x - x^5$

16. $x^2 + 14xy + 24y^2$

17. $x^3 + 64$

18. $81xy^3 - 3xz^3$

Solve each equation.

19. $(x - 3)(x + 9) = 0$

20. $x^2 + 5x = 14$

Answers

1. ________
2. ________
3. ________
4. ________
5. ________
6. ________
7. ________
8. ________
9. ________
10. ________
11. ________
12. ________
13. ________
14. ________
15. ________
16. ________
17. ________
18. ________
19. ________
20. ________

21. $x(x + 6) = 7$

22. $3x(2x - 3)(3x + 4) = 0$

23. $t^2 - 2t - 15 = 0$

24. $3x^2 = -12x$

25. $5t^3 - 45t = 0$

26. $(x - 1)(3x^2 - x - 2) = 0$

Solve.

27. A deck for a home is in the shape of a triangle. The length of the base of the triangle is 9 feet longer than its height. If the area of the triangle is 68 square feet, find the length of the base.

28. An object is dropped from the top of the Woolworth Building on Broadway in New York City. The height h of the object after t seconds is given by the equation

$$h = -16t^2 + 784$$

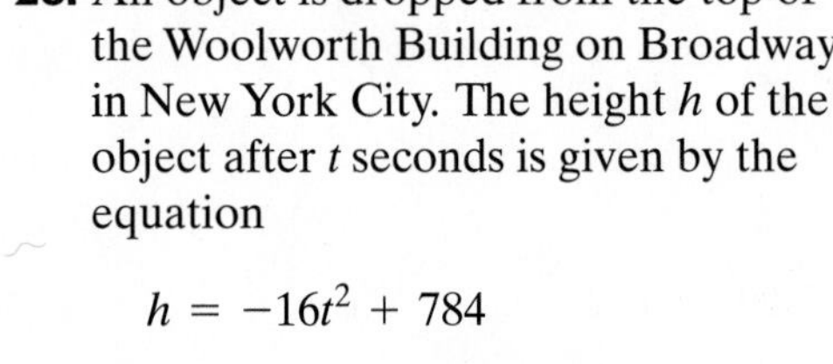

Find how many seconds pass before the object reaches the ground.

△ **29.** The *area* of the rectangle is 54 square units. Find the dimensions of the rectangle.

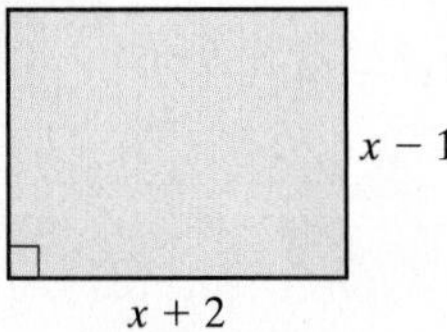

△ **30.** Find the lengths of the sides of a right triangle if the hypotenuse is 10 centimeters longer than the shorter leg and 5 centimeters longer than the longer leg.

31. A window washer is suspended 38 feet below the roof of the 1127-foot-tall John Hancock Center in Chicago. (*Source:* Council on Tall Buildings and Urban Habitat) If the window washer drops an object from this height, the object's height h after t seconds is given by the equation $h = -16t^2 + 1089$. Find how many seconds pass before the object reaches the ground.

21. ______
22. ______
23. ______
24. ______
25. ______
26. ______
27. ______
28. ______
29. ______
30. ______
31. ______

Cumulative Review Chapters 8–11

1. Translate each sentence into a mathematical statement.
   a. Nine is less than or equal to eleven.
   b. Eight is greater than one.
   c. Three is not equal to four.

2. Insert $<$ or $>$ in the space to make each statement true.
   a. $|-5| \quad |-3|$
   b. $|0| \quad |-2|$

3. Decide whether 2 is a solution of $3x + 10 = 8x$.

4. Evaluate $\frac{x}{y} + 5x$ if $x = 20$ and $y = 10$.

5. Subtract 8 from -4.

6. Evaluate $\frac{x}{y} + 5x$ if $x = -20$ and $y = 10$.

7. Evaluate each expression when $x = -2$ and $y = -4$.
   a. $\frac{3x}{2y}$
   b. $x^3 - y^2$
   c. $\frac{x - y}{-x}$

8. Evaluate $\frac{x}{y} + 5x$ if $x = -20$ and $y = -10$.

Simplify each expression by combining like terms.

9. $2x + 3x + 5 + 2$

10. $5 - 2(3x - 7)$

11. $-5a - 3 + a + 2$

12. $5(x - 6) + 9(-2x + 1)$

13. $2.3x + 5x - 6$

Solve each equation.

14. $0.8y + 0.2(y - 1) = 1.8$

15. $-3x = 33$

16. $\frac{x}{-7} = -4$

17. $3(x - 4) = 3x - 12$

18. $-\frac{2}{3}x = -22$

19. Solve $V = lwh$ for l.

20. Solve $3x + 2y = -7$ for y.

Simplify each expression.

21. $(5^3)^6$

22. $5^2 + 5^1$

23. $(y^8)^2$

24. $y^8 \cdot y^2$

Simplify the following expressions. Write each result using positive exponents only.

25. $\frac{(2x^3)^4 x}{x^7}$

26. 3^{-2}

27. $(y^{-3}z^6)^{-6}$

Answers

1. a. ______
   b. ______
   c. ______
2. a. ______
   b. ______
3. ______
4. ______
5. ______
6. ______
7. a. ______
   b. ______
   c. ______
8. ______
9. ______
10. ______
11. ______
12. ______
13. ______
14. ______
15. ______
16. ______
17. ______
18. ______
19. ______
20. ______
21. ______
22. ______
23. ______
24. ______
25. ______
26. ______
27. ______

28. ______
29. ______
30. ______
31. ______
32. ______
33. ______
34. ______
35. ______
36. ______
37. ______
38. ______
39. ______
40. ______
41. ______
42. ______
43. ______
44. ______
45. ______
46. ______
47. ______
48. ______
49. ______
50. ______
51. ______
52. ______
53. ______

28. $\dfrac{x^{-3}}{x^{-7}}$ **29.** $\dfrac{x^{-7}}{(x^4)^3}$ **30.** $\dfrac{(5a^7)^2}{a^5}$

Simplify each polynomial by combining any like terms.

31. $-3x + 7x$

32. $\dfrac{2}{3}x + 23 + \dfrac{1}{6}x - 100$

33. $11x^2 + 5 + 2x^2 - 7$

34. $0.2x - 1.1 + 2.3 - 0.7x$

35. Multiply: $(2x - y)^2$

36. Multiply: $(3x - 7y)^2$

Use a special product to square each binomial.

37. $(t + 2)^2$ **38.** $(x - 13)^2$ **39.** $(x^2 - 7y)^2$

40. $(7x + y)^2$

41. Divide: $\dfrac{8x^2y^2 - 16xy + 2x}{4xy}$

Factor each polynomial.

42. $z^3 + 7z + z^2 + 7$

43. $5(x + 3) + y(x + 3)$

44. $2x^3 + 2x^2 - 84x$

45. $x^4 + 5x^2 + 6$

46. $-4x^2 - 23x + 6$

47. $6x^2 - 2x - 20$

48. $9xy^2 - 16x$

49. $-a^3 - 8$

50. $x^3 - 216y^3$

51. $8x^3 + 27$

52. The platform for the cliff divers in Acapulco, Mexico, is about 144 feet above the sea. Neglecting air resistance, the height h in feet of a cliff diver above the ocean after t seconds is given by the quadratic equation $h = -16t^2 + 144$. Find how long it takes the diver to reach the ocean.

53. Solve $x^2 - 13x = -36$.

Rational Expressions

12

Sections

Check Your Progress

In this chapter, we expand our knowledge of algebraic expressions to include algebraic fractions, called *rational expressions*. We explore the operations of addition, subtraction, multiplication, and division using principles similar to the principles for numerical fractions.

Many sport statistics are calculated using formulas containing rational expressions. Below are a few examples:

Sport	Formula	Explanation
Baseball	$S = \dfrac{h + d + 2t + 3r}{b}$	A baseball player's slugging percentage S, where h = number of hits, d = number of doubles, t = number of triples, r = number of home runs, and b = number of at bats
NCAA Football	$R_{\text{NCAA}} = \dfrac{100C + 330T - 200I + 8.4Y}{A}$	A quarterback's rating in NCAA football R, where C = the number of completed passes, A = the number of attempted passes, T = the number of touchdown passes, Y = the number of yards in the completed passes, and I = the number of interceptions
NFL Football	$R_{\text{NFL}} = \dfrac{a + b + c + d}{6} \times 100$	A quarterback's rating in NFL football R, where a, b, c, and d are each formulas containing rational expressions.
(*Source:* Wikipedia.org.)		

In Section 12.1, Exercises 87 and 88, you will have the opportunity to calculate some sport statistics.

Objectives

A Find the Value of a Rational Expression Given a Replacement Number.

B Identify Values for Which a Rational Expression Is Undefined.

C Simplify, or Write Rational Expressions in Lowest Terms.

D Write Equivalent Forms of Rational Expressions.

12.1 SIMPLIFYING RATIONAL EXPRESSIONS

Objective A Evaluating Rational Expressions

A rational number is a number that can be written as a quotient of integers. A *rational expression* is also a quotient; it is a quotient of polynomials. Examples are

$$\frac{2}{3}, \quad \frac{3y^3}{8}, \quad \frac{-4p}{p^3 + 2p + 1}, \quad \text{and} \quad \frac{5x^2 - 3x + 2}{3x + 7}$$

Rational Expression

A **rational expression** is an expression that can be written in the form

$$\frac{P}{Q}$$

where P and Q are polynomials and $Q \neq 0$.

Rational expressions have different numerical values depending on what values replace the variables.

Example 1 Find the numerical value of $\frac{x + 4}{2x - 3}$ for each replacement value.

a. $x = 5$ **b.** $x = -2$

Solution:

a. We replace each x in the expression with 5 and then simplify.

$$\frac{x + 4}{2x - 3} = \frac{5 + 4}{2(5) - 3} = \frac{9}{10 - 3} = \frac{9}{7}$$

b. We replace each x in the expression with -2 and then simplify.

$$\frac{x + 4}{2x - 3} = \frac{-2 + 4}{2(-2) - 3} = \frac{2}{-7} \quad \text{or} \quad -\frac{2}{7}$$

Work Practice 1

PRACTICE 1

Find the value of $\frac{x - 3}{5x + 1}$ for each replacement value.

a. $x = 4$

b. $x = -3$

In the example above, we wrote $\frac{2}{-7}$ as $-\frac{2}{7}$. For a negative fraction such as $\frac{2}{-7}$, recall from Section 8.6 that

$$\frac{2}{-7} = \frac{-2}{7} = -\frac{2}{7}$$

In general, for any fraction,

$$\frac{-a}{b} = \frac{a}{-b} = -\frac{a}{b}, \quad b \neq 0$$

This is also true for rational expressions. For example,

$$\underbrace{\frac{-(x + 2)}{x}}_{\uparrow} = \frac{x + 2}{-x} = -\frac{x + 2}{x}$$

Notice the parentheses.

Answers

1. a. $\frac{1}{21}$ **b.** $\frac{3}{7}$

Objective B Identifying When a Rational Expression Is Undefined

In the definition of rational expression (first "box" in this section), notice that we wrote $Q \neq 0$ for the denominator Q. The denominator of a rational expression must not equal 0 since division by 0 is not defined. (See the Helpful Hint to the right.) This means we must be careful when replacing the variable in a rational expression by a number. For example, suppose we replace x with 5 in the rational expression $\frac{3+x}{x-5}$. The expression becomes

$$\frac{3+x}{x-5} = \frac{3+5}{5-5} = \frac{8}{0}$$

But division by 0 is undefined. Therefore, in this expression we can allow x to be any real number *except* 5. **A rational expression is undefined for values that make the denominator 0.** Thus,

> To find values for which a rational expression is undefined, find values for which the denominator is 0.

Helpful Hint **Do you recall why division by 0 is not defined?** Remember, for example, that

$\frac{8}{4} = 2$ because $2 \cdot 4 = 8$.

Thus, if $\frac{8}{0} =$ *a number*,

then *the number* $\cdot\, 0 = 8$.

There is no number that when multiplied by 0 equals 8; thus $\frac{8}{0}$ is undefined. This is true in general for fractions and rational expressions.

Example 2 Are there any values for x for which each expression is undefined?

a. $\frac{x}{x-3}$ **b.** $\frac{x^2+2}{x^2-3x+2}$ **c.** $\frac{x^3-6x^2-10x}{3}$

Solution: To find values for which a rational expression is undefined, we find values that make the denominator 0.

a. The denominator of $\frac{x}{x-3}$ is 0 when $x - 3 = 0$ or when $x = 3$. Thus, when $x = 3$, the expression $\frac{x}{x-3}$ is undefined.

b. We set the denominator equal to 0.

$$x^2 - 3x + 2 = 0$$
$$(x-2)(x-1) = 0 \quad \text{Factor.}$$
$$x - 2 = 0 \quad \text{or} \quad x - 1 = 0 \quad \text{Set each factor equal to 0.}$$
$$x = 2 \qquad\qquad x = 1 \quad \text{Solve.}$$

Thus, when $x = 2$ or $x = 1$, the denominator $x^2 - 3x + 2$ is 0. So the rational expression $\frac{x^2+2}{x^2-3x+2}$ is undefined when $x = 2$ or when $x = 1$.

c. The denominator of $\frac{x^3-6x^2-10x}{3}$ is never 0, so there are no values of x for which this expression is undefined.

Work Practice 2

PRACTICE 2

Are there any values for x for which each rational expression is undefined?

a. $\frac{x}{x+8}$

b. $\frac{x-3}{x^2+5x+4}$

c. $\frac{x^2-3x+2}{5}$

Note: Unless otherwise stated, we will now assume that variables in rational expressions are replaced only by values for which the expressions are defined.

Objective C Simplifying Rational Expressions

A fraction is said to be written in lowest terms or simplest form when the numerator and denominator have no common factors other than 1 (or -1). For example, the fraction $\frac{7}{10}$ is written in lowest terms since the numerator and denominator have no common factors other than 1 (or -1).

The process of writing a rational expression in lowest terms or simplest form is called **simplifying** a rational expression.

Answers

2. a. $x = -8$ **b.** $x = -4, x = -1$ **c.** no

Simplifying a rational expression is similar to simplifying a fraction. To simplify a fraction, we essentially "remove factors of 1." Our ability to do this comes from these facts:

- Any nonzero number over itself simplifies to 1 $\left(\frac{5}{5} = 1, \frac{-7.26}{-7.26} = 1, \text{ and } \frac{c}{c} = 1\right.$ as long as c is not $\left.0\right)$, and
- The product of any number and 1 is that number $\left(19 \cdot 1 = 19, -8.9 \cdot 1 = -8.9, \frac{a}{b} \cdot 1 = \frac{a}{b}\right)$.

In other words, we have the following:

$$\frac{a \cdot c}{b \cdot c} = \frac{a}{b} \cdot \frac{c}{c} = \frac{a}{b}$$

Since $\frac{a}{b} \cdot 1 = \frac{a}{b}$

Simplify: $\frac{15}{20}$

$$\frac{15}{20} = \frac{3 \cdot 5}{2 \cdot 2 \cdot 5}$$ Factor the numerator and the denominator.

$$= \frac{3 \cdot 5}{2 \cdot 2 \cdot 5}$$ Look for common factors.

$$= \frac{3}{2 \cdot 2} \cdot \frac{5}{5}$$ Common factors in the numerator and denominator form factors of 1.

$$= \frac{3}{2 \cdot 2} \cdot 1$$ Write $\frac{5}{5}$ as 1.

$$= \frac{3}{2 \cdot 2} = \frac{3}{4}$$ Multiply.

Before we use the same technique to simplify a rational expression, remember that as long as the denominator is not 0, $\frac{a^3b}{a^3b} = 1, \frac{x+3}{x+3} = 1, \text{ and } \frac{7x^2 + 5x - 100}{7x^2 + 5x - 100} = 1.$

Simplify: $\frac{x^2 - 9}{x^2 + x - 6}$

$$\frac{x^2 - 9}{x^2 + x - 6} = \frac{(x-3)(x+3)}{(x-2)(x+3)}$$ Factor the numerator and the denominator.

$$= \frac{(x-3)(x+3)}{(x-2)(x+3)}$$ Look for common factors.

$$= \frac{x-3}{x-2} \cdot \frac{x+3}{x+3}$$

$$= \frac{x-3}{x-2} \cdot 1$$ Write $\frac{x+3}{x+3}$ as 1.

$$= \frac{x-3}{x-2}$$ Multiply.

Just as for numerical fractions, we can use a shortcut notation. Remember that as long as exact factors in both the numerator and denominator are divided out, we are "removing a factor of 1." We will use the following notation to show this:

$$\frac{x^2 - 9}{x^2 + x - 6} = \frac{(x-3)(x+3)}{(x-2)(x+3)}$$ A factor of 1 is identified by the shading.

$$= \frac{x-3}{x-2}$$ Remove a factor of 1.

Thus, the rational expression $\frac{x^2 - 9}{x^2 + x - 6}$ has the same value as the rational expression $\frac{x - 3}{x - 2}$ for all values of x except 2 and -3. (Remember that when x is 2, the denominator of both rational expressions is 0 and when x is -3, the original rational expression has a denominator of 0.)

As we simplify rational expressions, we will assume that the simplified rational expression is equal to the original rational expression for all real numbers except those for which either denominator is 0. The following steps may be used to simplify rational expressions.

To Simplify a Rational Expression

Step 1: Completely factor the numerator and denominator.

Step 2: Divide out factors common to the numerator and denominator. (This is the same as "removing a factor of 1.")

Example 3 Simplify: $\frac{5x - 5}{x^3 - x^2}$

Solution: To begin, we factor the numerator and denominator if possible. Then we look for common factors.

$$\frac{5x - 5}{x^3 - x^2} = \frac{5(x - 1)}{x^2(x - 1)} = \frac{5}{x^2}$$

Work Practice 3

PRACTICE 3

Simplify: $\frac{x^4 + x^3}{5x + 5}$

Example 4 Simplify: $\frac{x^2 + 8x + 7}{x^2 - 4x - 5}$

Solution: We factor the numerator and denominator and then look for common factors.

$$\frac{x^2 + 8x + 7}{x^2 - 4x - 5} = \frac{(x + 7)(x + 1)}{(x - 5)(x + 1)} = \frac{x + 7}{x - 5}$$

Work Practice 4

PRACTICE 4

Simplify: $\frac{x^2 + 11x + 18}{x^2 + x - 2}$

Example 5 Simplify: $\frac{x^2 + 4x + 4}{x^2 + 2x}$

Solution: We factor the numerator and denominator and then look for common factors.

$$\frac{x^2 + 4x + 4}{x^2 + 2x} = \frac{(x + 2)(x + 2)}{x(x + 2)} = \frac{x + 2}{x}$$

Work Practice 5

PRACTICE 5

Simplify: $\frac{x^2 + 10x + 25}{x^2 + 5x}$

Helpful Hint

When simplifying a rational expression, we look for **common *factors,* not common *terms.***

$$\frac{x \cdot (x + 2)}{x \cdot x} = \frac{x + 2}{x}$$

Common factors. These can be divided out.

$$\frac{x + 2}{x}$$

Common terms. There is no factor of 1 that can be generated.

Answers

3. $\frac{x^3}{5}$ 4. $\frac{x + 9}{x - 1}$ 5. $\frac{x + 5}{x}$

✓Concept Check Recall that we can remove only *factors* of 1. Which of the following are *not* true? Explain why.

a. $\frac{3-1}{3+5}$ simplifies to $-\frac{1}{5}$ **b.** $\frac{2x+10}{2}$ simplifies to $x+5$

c. $\frac{37}{72}$ simplifies to $\frac{3}{2}$ **d.** $\frac{2x+3}{2}$ simplifies to $x+3$

PRACTICE 6

Simplify: $\frac{x+5}{x^2-25}$

Example 6 Simplify: $\frac{x+9}{x^2-81}$

Solution: We factor and then divide the numerator and denominator by all common factors.

$$\frac{x+9}{x^2-81} = \frac{x+9}{(x+9)(x-9)} = \frac{1}{x-9}$$

Work Practice 6

PRACTICE 7

Simplify each rational expression.

a. $\frac{x+4}{4+x}$

b. $\frac{x-4}{4-x}$

Example 7 Simplify each rational expression.

a. $\frac{x+y}{y+x}$ **b.** $\frac{x-y}{y-x}$

Solution:

a. The expression $\frac{x+y}{y+x}$ can be simplified by using the commutative property of addition to rewrite the denominator $y+x$ as $x+y$.

$$\frac{x+y}{y+x} = \frac{x+y}{x+y} = 1$$

b. The expression $\frac{x-y}{y-x}$ can be simplified by recognizing that $y-x$ and $x-y$ are opposites. In other words, $y-x=-1(x-y)$. We proceed as follows:

$$\frac{x-y}{y-x} = \frac{1\cdot(x-y)}{(-1)(x-y)} = \frac{1}{-1} = -1$$

Work Practice 7

Objective D Writing Equivalent Forms of Rational Expressions

From Example 7a, we have $y+x=x+y$. $y+x$ and $x+y$ are equivalent.

From Example 7b, we have $y-x=-1(x-y)$. $y-x$ and $x-y$ are opposites.

Thus, $\frac{x+y}{y+x} = \frac{x+y}{x+y} = 1$ and $\frac{x-y}{y-x} = \frac{x-y}{-1(x-y)} = \frac{1}{-1} = -1.$

When performing operations on rational expressions, equivalent forms of answers often result. For this reason, it is very important to be able to recognize equivalent answers.

Answers

6. $\frac{1}{x-5}$ 7. a. 1 b. -1

✓ Concept Check Answer

a, c, d

Example 8 List some equivalent forms of $-\frac{5x - 1}{x + 9}$.

Solution: To do so, recall that $-\frac{a}{b} = \frac{-a}{b} = \frac{a}{-b}$. Thus

$$-\frac{5x - 1}{x + 9} = \frac{-(5x - 1)}{x + 9} = \frac{-5x + 1}{x + 9} \quad \text{or} \quad \frac{1 - 5x}{x + 9}$$

Also,

$$-\frac{5x - 1}{x + 9} = \frac{5x - 1}{-(x + 9)} = \frac{5x - 1}{-x - 9} \quad \text{or} \quad \frac{5x - 1}{-9 - x}$$

Thus $-\frac{5x - 1}{x + 9} = \frac{-(5x - 1)}{x + 9} = \frac{-5x + 1}{x + 9} = \frac{5x - 1}{-(x + 9)} = \frac{5x - 1}{-x - 9}$

Work Practice 8

Keep in mind that many rational expressions may look different but in fact are equivalent.

PRACTICE 8

List 4 equivalent forms of $-\frac{3x + 7}{x - 6}$.

Helpful Hint Remember, a negative sign in front of a fraction or rational expression may be moved to the numerator or the denominator, but *not* both.

Answer

8. $\frac{-(3x + 7)}{x - 6}$; $\frac{-3x - 7}{x - 6}$; $\frac{3x + 7}{-(x - 6)}$; $\frac{3x + 7}{-x + 6}$

Vocabulary and Readiness Check

Use the choices below to fill in each blank. Not all choices will be used.

-1	0	simplifying	$\frac{-a}{-b}$	$\frac{-a}{b}$	$\frac{a}{-b}$
1	2	rational expression			

1. A ______________ is an expression that can be written in the form $\frac{P}{Q}$ where P and Q are polynomials and $Q \neq 0$.

2. The expression $\frac{x+3}{3+x}$ simplifies to ______________.

3. The expression $\frac{x-3}{3-x}$ simplifies to ______________.

4. A rational expression is undefined for values that make the denominator ______________.

5. The expression $\frac{7x}{x-2}$ is undefined for $x =$ ______________.

6. The process of writing a rational expression in lowest terms is called ______________.

7. For a rational expression, $-\frac{a}{b} =$ ______________ $=$ ______________.

Decide which rational expression can be simplified. (Do not actually simplify.)

8. $\frac{x}{x+7}$ **9.** $\frac{3+x}{x+3}$ **10.** $\frac{5-x}{x-5}$ **11.** $\frac{x+2}{x+8}$

12.1 Exercise Set

FOR EXTRA HELP

PRACTICE

WATCH

DOWNLOAD

READ

REVIEW

Objective A *Find the value of the following expressions when $x = 2$, $y = -2$, and $z = -5$. See Example 1.*

1. $\frac{x+5}{x+2}$

2. $\frac{x+8}{x+1}$

3. $\frac{y^3}{y^2-1}$

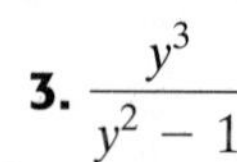

4. $\frac{z}{z^2-5}$

5. $\frac{x^2+8x+2}{x^2-x-6}$

6. $\frac{x+5}{x^2+4x-8}$

7. The average cost per DVD, in dollars, for a company to produce x DVDs on exercising is given by the formula $A = \frac{3x+400}{x}$, where A is the average cost per DVD and x is the number of DVDs produced.

a. Find the cost for producing 1 DVD.

b. Find the average cost for producing 100 DVDs.

c. Does the cost per DVD decrease or increase when more DVDs are produced? Explain your answer.

8. For a certain model of fax machine, the manufacturing cost C per machine is given by the equation

$$C = \frac{250x + 10{,}000}{x}$$

where x is the number of fax machines manufactured and cost C is in dollars per machine.

a. Find the cost per fax machine when manufacturing 100 fax machines.

b. Find the cost per fax machine when manufacturing 1000 fax machines.

c. Does the cost per machine decrease or increase when more machines are manufactured? Explain why this is so.

Objective B *Find any numbers for which each rational expression is undefined. See Example 2.*

9. $\frac{7}{2x}$

10. $\frac{3}{5x}$

11. $\frac{x+3}{x+2}$

12. $\frac{5x+1}{x-9}$

13. $\frac{x-4}{2x-5}$

14. $\frac{x+1}{5x-2}$

15. $\frac{9x^3+4}{15x^2+30x}$

16. $\frac{19x^3+2}{x^2-x}$

17. $\frac{x^2-5x-2}{4}$

18. $\frac{9y^5+y^3}{9}$

19. $\frac{3x^2+9}{x^2-5x-6}$

20. $\frac{11x^2+1}{x^2-5x-14}$

21. $\frac{x}{3x^2+13x+14}$

22. $\frac{x}{2x^2+15x+27}$

Objective C *Simplify each expression. See Examples 3 through 7.*

23. $\frac{x+7}{7+x}$

24. $\frac{y+9}{9+y}$

25. $\frac{x-7}{7-x}$

26. $\frac{y-9}{9-y}$

27. $\frac{2}{8x+16}$

28. $\frac{3}{9x+6}$

29. $\frac{x-2}{x^2-4}$

30. $\frac{x+5}{x^2-25}$

31. $\frac{2x-10}{3x-30}$

32. $\frac{3x-9}{4x-16}$

33. $\frac{-5a-5b}{a+b}$

34. $\frac{-4x-4y}{x+y}$

35. $\frac{7x+35}{x^2+5x}$

36. $\frac{9x+99}{x^2+11x}$

37. $\frac{x+5}{x^2-4x-45}$

38. $\frac{x-3}{x^2-6x+9}$

39. $\frac{5x^2+11x+2}{x+2}$

40. $\frac{12x^2+4x-1}{2x+1}$

41. $\frac{x^3+7x^2}{x^2+5x-14}$

42. $\frac{x^4-10x^3}{x^2-17x+70}$

43. $\frac{14x^2-21x}{2x-3}$

44. $\frac{4x^2+24x}{x+6}$

45. $\frac{x^2+7x+10}{x^2-3x-10}$

46. $\frac{2x^2+7x-4}{x^2+3x-4}$

47. $\frac{3x^2+7x+2}{3x^2+13x+4}$

48. $\frac{4x^2-4x+1}{2x^2+9x-5}$

49. $\frac{2x^2-8}{4x-8}$

50. $\frac{5x^2-500}{35x+350}$

51. $\frac{4-x^2}{x-2}$

52. $\frac{49-y^2}{y-7}$

53. $\frac{x^2-1}{x^2-2x+1}$

54. $\frac{x^2-16}{x^2-8x+16}$

Simplify each expression. Each exercise contains a four-term polynomial that should be factored by grouping. See Examples 3 through 7.

55. $\frac{x^2+xy+2x+2y}{x+2}$

56. $\frac{ab+ac+b^2+bc}{b+c}$

57. $\dfrac{5x + 15 - xy - 3y}{2x + 6}$

58. $\dfrac{xy - 6x + 2y - 12}{y^2 - 6y}$

59. $\dfrac{2xy + 5x - 2y - 5}{3xy + 4x - 3y - 4}$

60. $\dfrac{2xy + 2x - 3y - 3}{2xy + 4x - 3y - 6}$

Objective **D** *Study Example 8. Then list four equivalent forms for each rational expression.*

61. $-\dfrac{x - 10}{x + 8}$

62. $-\dfrac{x + 11}{x - 4}$

63. $-\dfrac{5y - 3}{y - 12}$

64. $-\dfrac{8y - 1}{y - 15}$

Objectives **C** **D** **Mixed Practice** *Simplify each expression. Then determine whether the given answer is correct. See Examples 3 through 8.*

65. $\dfrac{9 - x^2}{x - 3}$; Answer: $-3 - x$

66. $\dfrac{100 - x^2}{x - 10}$; Answer: $-10 - x$

67. $\dfrac{7 - 34x - 5x^2}{25x^2 - 1}$; Answer: $\dfrac{x + 7}{-5x - 1}$

68. $\dfrac{2 - 15x - 8x^2}{64x^2 - 1}$; Answer: $\dfrac{x + 2}{-8x - 1}$

Review

Perform each indicated operation.

69. $\dfrac{1}{3} \cdot \dfrac{9}{11}$

70. $\dfrac{5}{27} \cdot \dfrac{2}{5}$

71. $\dfrac{1}{3} \div \dfrac{1}{4}$

72. $\dfrac{7}{8} \div \dfrac{1}{2}$

73. $\dfrac{13}{20} \div \dfrac{2}{9}$

74. $\dfrac{8}{15} \div \dfrac{5}{8}$

Concept Extensions

Which of the following are incorrect and why? See the Concept Check in this section.

75. $\dfrac{5a - 15}{5}$ simplifies to $a - 3$

76. $\dfrac{7m - 9}{7}$ simplifies to $m - 9$

77. $\dfrac{1 + 2}{1 + 3}$ simplifies to $\dfrac{2}{3}$

78. $\dfrac{46}{54}$ simplifies to $\dfrac{6}{5}$

79. Explain how to write a fraction in lowest terms.

80. Explain how to write a rational expression in lowest terms.

81. Explain why the denominator of a fraction or a rational expression must not equal 0.

82. Does $\dfrac{(x - 3)(x + 3)}{x - 3}$ have the same value as $x + 3$ for all real numbers? Explain why or why not.

83. The dose of medicine prescribed for a child depends on the child's age A in years and the adult dose D for the medication. Young's Rule is a formula used by pediatricians that gives a child's dose C as

$$C = \frac{DA}{A + 12}$$

Suppose that an 8-year-old child needs medication, and the normal adult dose is 1000 mg. What size dose should the child receive?

84. Calculating body-mass index is a way to gauge whether a person should lose weight. Doctors recommend that body-mass index values fall between 19 and 25. The formula for body-mass index B is

$$B = \frac{705w}{h^2}$$

where w is weight in pounds and h is height in inches. Should a 148-pound person who is 5 feet 6 inches tall lose weight?

85. Anthropologists and forensic scientists use a measure called the cephalic index to help classify skulls. The cephalic index of a skull with width W and length L from front to back is given by the formula

$$C = \frac{100W}{L}$$

A long skull has an index value less than 75, a medium skull has an index value between 75 and 85, and a broad skull has an index value over 85. Find the cephalic index of a skull that is 5 inches wide and 6.4 inches long. Classify the skull.

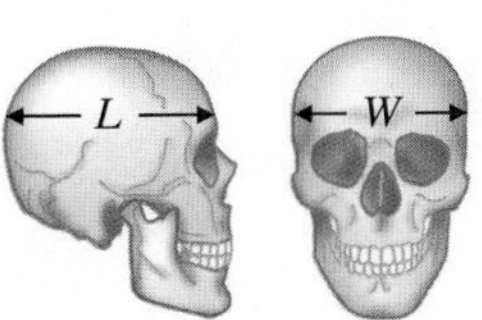

86. A company's gross profit margin P can be computed with the formula $P = \frac{R - C}{R}$, where R = the company's revenue and C = cost of goods sold. For the fiscal year 2008, computer company Apple had revenues of \$32.5 billion and cost of goods sold \$21.3 billion. (*Source:* Apple, Inc.) What was Apple's gross profit margin in 2008? Express the answer as a percent, rounded to the nearest tenth of a percent.

87. A baseball player's slugging percentage S can be calculated with the following formula:

$S = \frac{h + d + 2t + 3r}{b}$, where h = number of hits, d = number of doubles, t = number of triples, r = number of home runs, and b = number of at bats. In 2008, Albert Pujols of the St. Louis Cardinals led Major League Baseball in slugging percentage. During the 2008 season, Pujols had 524 at bats, 187 hits, 44 doubles, no triples, and 37 home runs. (*Source:* Major League Baseball) Calculate Pujols' 2008 slugging percentage. Round to the nearest tenth of a percent.

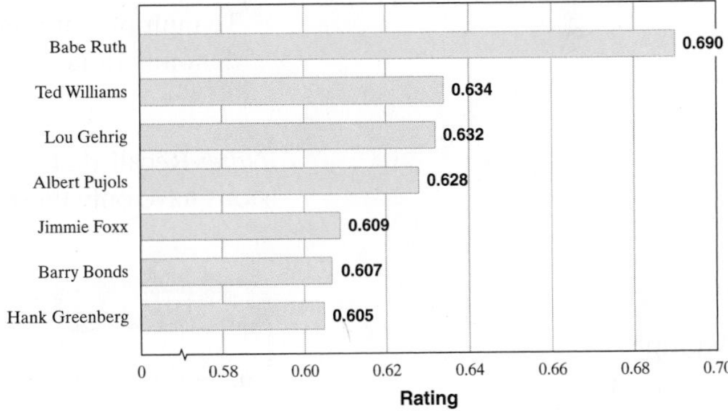

88. To calculate a quarterback's rating in NCAA football, you may use the formula $\frac{100C + 330T - 200I + 8.4Y}{A}$, where C = the number of completed passes, A = the number of attempted passes, T = the number of touchdown passes, Y = the number of yards in the completed passes, and I = the number of interceptions. Sam Bradford of the University of Oklahoma was selected as the 2008 winner of the Heisman Memorial Trophy as the Most Outstanding Football Player. Bradford, a sophomore quarterback with the Sooners, ended the season with 442 attempts, 302 completions, 4464 yards, 53 touchdowns, and only 6 interceptions. Calculate Bradford's quarterback rating for the 2008 season. (*Source:* NCAA) Round the answer to the nearest tenth.

Objectives

A **Multiply Rational Expressions.**

B **Divide Rational Expressions.**

C **Multiply and Divide Rational Expressions.**

D **Convert Between Units of Measure.**

12.2 MULTIPLYING AND DIVIDING RATIONAL EXPRESSIONS

Objective A Multiplying Rational Expressions

Just as simplifying rational expressions is similar to simplifying number fractions, multiplying and dividing rational expressions is similar to multiplying and dividing number fractions.

Fractions	**Rational Expressions**
Multiply: $\frac{3}{5} \cdot \frac{10}{11}$	Multiply: $\frac{x-3}{x+5} \cdot \frac{2x+10}{x^2-9}$

Multiply numerators and then multiply denominators.

$$\frac{3}{5} \cdot \frac{10}{11} = \frac{3 \cdot 10}{5 \cdot 11} \qquad \frac{x-3}{x+5} \cdot \frac{2x+10}{x^2-9} = \frac{(x-3) \cdot (2x+10)}{(x+5) \cdot (x^2-9)}$$

Simplify by factoring numerators and denominators.

$$= \frac{3 \cdot 2 \cdot 5}{5 \cdot 11} \qquad = \frac{(x-3) \cdot 2(x+5)}{(x+5)(x+3)(x-3)}$$

Divide numerators and denominators by all common factors.

$$= \frac{3 \cdot 2}{11} \text{ or } \frac{6}{11} \qquad = \frac{2}{x+3}$$

Multiplying Rational Expressions

If $\frac{P}{Q}$ and $\frac{R}{S}$ are rational expressions, then

$$\frac{P}{Q} \cdot \frac{R}{S} = \frac{PR}{QS}$$

To multiply rational expressions, multiply the numerators and then multiply the denominators.

Note: Recall that, unless otherwise stated, we assume variables in rational expressions have only those replacement values for which the expressions are defined.

PRACTICE 1

Multiply.

a. $\frac{16y}{3} \cdot \frac{1}{x^2}$

b. $\frac{-5a^3}{3b^3} \cdot \frac{2b^2}{15a}$

Example 1 Multiply.

a. $\frac{25x}{2} \cdot \frac{1}{y^3}$ **b.** $\frac{-7x^2}{5y} \cdot \frac{3y^5}{14x^2}$

Solution: To multiply rational expressions, we first multiply the numerators and then multiply the denominators of both expressions. Then we write the product in lowest terms.

a. $\frac{25x}{2} \cdot \frac{1}{y^3} = \frac{25x \cdot 1}{2 \cdot y^3} = \frac{25x}{2y^3}$

The expression $\frac{25x}{2y^3}$ is in lowest terms.

b. $\frac{-7x^2}{5y} \cdot \frac{3y^5}{14x^2} = \frac{-7x^2 \cdot 3y^5}{5y \cdot 14x^2}$ Multiply.

Answers

1. a. $\frac{16y}{3x^2}$ **b.** $-\frac{2a^2}{9b}$

The expression $\frac{-7x^2 \cdot 3y^5}{5y \cdot 14x^2}$ is not in lowest terms, so we factor the numerator and the denominator and "remove factors of 1."

$$= \frac{-1 \cdot 7 \cdot 3 \cdot x^2 \cdot y \cdot y^4}{5 \cdot 2 \cdot 7 \cdot x^2 \cdot y}$$ Common factors in the numerator and denominator form factors of 1.

$$= -\frac{3y^4}{10}$$ Divide out common factors. (This is the same as "removing a factor of 1.")

Work Practice 1

When multiplying rational expressions, it is usually best to factor each numerator and denominator first. This will help us write the product in lowest terms.

Example 2 Multiply: $\frac{x^2 + x}{3x} \cdot \frac{6}{5x + 5}$

Solution:

$$\frac{x^2 + x}{3x} \cdot \frac{6}{5x + 5} = \frac{x(x + 1)}{3x} \cdot \frac{2 \cdot 3}{5(x + 1)}$$ Factor numerators and denominators.

$$= \frac{x(x + 1) \cdot 2 \cdot 3}{3x \cdot 5\,(x + 1)}$$ Multiply.

$$= \frac{2}{5}$$ Divide out common factors.

Work Practice 2

PRACTICE 2

Multiply: $\frac{3x + 6}{14} \cdot \frac{7x^2}{x^3 + 2x^2}$

The following steps may be used to multiply rational expressions.

To Multiply Rational Expressions

Step 1: Completely factor numerators and denominators.

Step 2: Multiply numerators and multiply denominators.

Step 3: Simplify or write the product in lowest terms by dividing out common factors.

✓Concept Check Which of the following is a true statement?

a. $\frac{1}{3} \cdot \frac{1}{2} = \frac{1}{5}$ **b.** $\frac{2}{x} \cdot \frac{5}{x} = \frac{10}{x}$ **c.** $\frac{3}{x} \cdot \frac{1}{2} = \frac{3}{2x}$ **d.** $\frac{x}{7} \cdot \frac{x + 5}{4} = \frac{2x + 5}{28}$

Example 3 Multiply: $\frac{3x + 3}{5x^2 - 5x} \cdot \frac{2x^2 + x - 3}{4x^2 - 9}$

Solution:

$$\frac{3x + 3}{5x^2 - 5x} \cdot \frac{2x^2 + x - 3}{4x^2 - 9} = \frac{3(x + 1)}{5x(x - 1)} \cdot \frac{(2x + 3)(x - 1)}{(2x - 3)(2x + 3)}$$ Factor.

$$= \frac{3(x + 1)(2x + 3)(x - 1)}{5x\,(x - 1)\,(2x - 3)\,(2x + 3)}$$ Multiply.

$$= \frac{3(x + 1)}{5x(2x - 3)}$$ Simplify.

Work Practice 3

PRACTICE 3

Multiply:
$\frac{4x + 8}{7x^2 - 14x} \cdot \frac{3x^2 - 5x - 2}{9x^2 - 1}$

Answers

2. $\frac{3}{2}$ **3.** $\frac{4(x + 2)}{7x(3x - 1)}$

✓Concept Check Answer

c

Objective B Dividing Rational Expressions

We can divide by a rational expression in the same way we divide by a number fraction. Recall that to divide by a fraction, we multiply by its reciprocal.

For example, to divide $\frac{3}{2}$ by $\frac{7}{8}$, we multiply $\frac{3}{2}$ by $\frac{8}{7}$.

$$\frac{3}{2} \div \frac{7}{8} = \frac{3}{2} \cdot \frac{8}{7} = \frac{3 \cdot 4 \cdot 2}{2 \cdot 7} = \frac{12}{7}$$

Helpful Hint

Don't forget how to find reciprocals. The reciprocal of $\frac{a}{b}$ is $\frac{b}{a}$, $a \neq 0$, $b \neq 0$.

Dividing Rational Expressions

If $\frac{P}{Q}$ and $\frac{R}{S}$ are rational expressions and $\frac{R}{S}$ is not 0, then

$$\frac{P}{Q} \div \frac{R}{S} = \frac{P}{Q} \cdot \frac{S}{R} = \frac{PS}{QR}$$

To divide two rational expressions, multiply the first rational expression by the reciprocal of the second rational expression.

PRACTICE 4

Divide: $\frac{7x^2}{6} \div \frac{x}{2y}$

Example 4 Divide: $\frac{3x^3}{40} \div \frac{4x^3}{y^2}$

Solution:

$$\frac{3x^3}{40} \div \frac{4x^3}{y^2} = \frac{3x^3}{40} \cdot \frac{y^2}{4x^3} \quad \text{Multiply by the reciprocal of } \frac{4x^3}{y^2}.$$

$$= \frac{3x^3 \cdot y^2}{160x^3}$$

$$= \frac{3y^2}{160} \quad \text{Simplify.}$$

Work Practice 4

PRACTICE 5

Divide: $\frac{(x-4)^2}{6} \div \frac{3x-12}{2}$

Example 5 Divide: $\frac{(x+2)^2}{10} \div \frac{2x+4}{5}$

Solution:

$$\frac{(x+2)^2}{10} \div \frac{2x+4}{5} = \frac{(x+2)^2}{10} \cdot \frac{5}{2x+4} \quad \text{Multiply by the reciprocal of } \frac{2x+4}{5}.$$

$$= \frac{(x+2)(x+2) \cdot 5}{5 \cdot 2 \cdot 2 \cdot (x+2)} \quad \text{Factor and multiply.}$$

$$= \frac{x+2}{4} \quad \text{Simplify.}$$

Work Practice 5

Remember, **to Divide by a Rational Expression**, multiply by its reciprocal.

Answers

4. $\frac{7xy}{3}$ 5. $\frac{x-4}{9}$

Example 6 Divide: $\frac{6x + 2}{x^2 - 1} \div \frac{3x^2 + x}{x - 1}$

Solution:

$$\frac{6x + 2}{x^2 - 1} \div \frac{3x^2 + x}{x - 1} = \frac{6x + 2}{x^2 - 1} \cdot \frac{x - 1}{3x^2 + x}$$ Multiply by the reciprocal.

$$= \frac{2(3x + 1)(x - 1)}{(x + 1)(x - 1) \cdot x(3x + 1)}$$ Factor and multiply.

$$= \frac{2}{x(x + 1)}$$ Simplify.

Work Practice 6

PRACTICE 6

Divide: $\frac{10x + 4}{x^2 - 4} \div \frac{5x^3 + 2x^2}{x + 2}$

Example 7 Divide: $\frac{2x^2 - 11x + 5}{5x - 25} \div \frac{4x - 2}{10}$

Solution:

$$\frac{2x^2 - 11x + 5}{5x - 25} \div \frac{4x - 2}{10} = \frac{2x^2 - 11x + 5}{5x - 25} \cdot \frac{10}{4x - 2}$$ Multiply by the reciprocal.

$$= \frac{(2x - 1)(x - 5) \cdot 2 \cdot 5}{5(x - 5) \cdot 2(2x - 1)}$$ Factor and multiply.

$$= \frac{1}{1} \text{ or } 1$$ Simplify.

Work Practice 7

PRACTICE 7

Divide:

$\frac{3x^2 - 10x + 8}{7x - 14} \div \frac{9x - 12}{21}$

Objective C Multiplying and Dividing Rational Expressions

Let's make sure that we understand the difference between multiplying and dividing rational expressions.

Rational Expressions	
Multiplication	Multiply the numerators and multiply the denominators.
Division	Multiply by the reciprocal of the divisor.

Example 8 Multiply or divide as indicated.

a. $\frac{x - 4}{5} \cdot \frac{x}{x - 4}$

b. $\frac{x - 4}{5} \div \frac{x}{x - 4}$

c. $\frac{x^2 - 4}{2x + 6} \cdot \frac{x^2 + 4x + 3}{2 - x}$

Solution:

a. $\frac{x - 4}{5} \cdot \frac{x}{x - 4} = \frac{(x - 4) \cdot x}{5 \cdot (x - 4)} = \frac{x}{5}$

b. $\frac{x - 4}{5} \div \frac{x}{x - 4} = \frac{x - 4}{5} \cdot \frac{x - 4}{x} = \frac{(x - 4)^2}{5x}$

c. $\frac{x^2 - 4}{2x + 6} \cdot \frac{x^2 + 4x + 3}{2 - x} = \frac{(x - 2)(x + 2) \cdot (x + 1)(x + 3)}{2(x + 3) \cdot (2 - x)}$ Factor and multiply.

Continued on next page

PRACTICE 8

Multiply or divide as indicated.

a. $\frac{x + 3}{x} \cdot \frac{7}{x + 3}$

b. $\frac{x + 3}{x} \div \frac{7}{x + 3}$

c. $\frac{3 - x}{x^2 + 6x + 5} \cdot \frac{2x + 10}{x^2 - 7x + 12}$

Answers

6. $\frac{2}{x^2(x - 2)}$ 7. 1

8. a. $\frac{7}{x}$ b. $\frac{(x + 3)^2}{7x}$

c. $-\frac{2}{(x + 1)(x - 4)}$

Recall from Section 12.1 that $x - 2$ and $2 - x$ are opposites. This means that $\frac{x-2}{2-x} = -1$. Thus,

$$\frac{(x-2)(x+2)\cdot(x+1)(x+3)}{2(x+3)\cdot(2-x)} = \frac{-1(x+2)(x+1)}{2}$$
$$= -\frac{(x+2)(x+1)}{2}$$

Work Practice 8

Objective D Converting Between Units of Measure

How many square inches are in 1 square foot?

How many cubic feet are in a cubic yard?

If you have trouble answering these questions, this section will be helpful to you.

Now that we know how to multiply fractions and rational expressions, we can use this knowledge to help us convert between units of measure. To do so, we will use **unit fractions.** A unit fraction is a fraction that equals 1. For example, since 12 in. = 1 ft, we have the unit fractions

$$\frac{12 \text{ in.}}{1 \text{ ft}} = 1 \quad \text{and} \quad \frac{1 \text{ ft}}{12 \text{ in.}} = 1$$

PRACTICE 9

288 square inches = ____ square feet

Example 9 18 square feet = ____ square yards

Solution: Let's multiply 18 square feet by a unit fraction that has square feet in the denominator and square yards in the numerator. From the diagram, you can see that

1 square yard = 9 square feet

Thus,

$$18 \text{ sq ft} = \frac{18 \text{ sq ft}}{1} \cdot 1 = \frac{\overset{2}{\cancel{18}} \cancel{\text{sq ft}}}{1} \cdot \frac{1 \text{ sq yd}}{\underset{1}{\cancel{9}} \cancel{\text{sq ft}}}$$
$$= \frac{2 \cdot 1}{1 \cdot 1} \text{sq yd} = 2 \text{ sq yd}$$

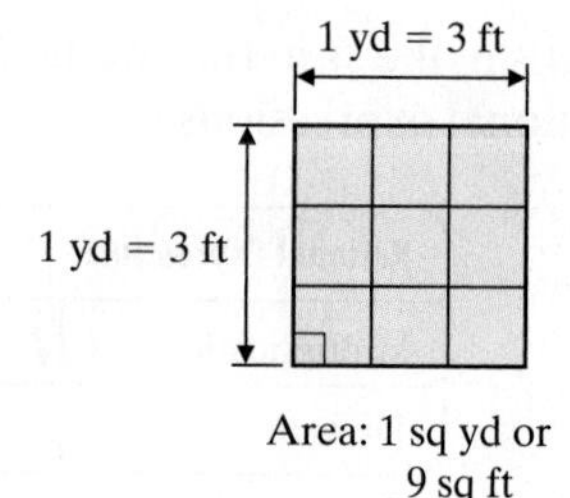

Area: 1 sq yd or 9 sq ft

Thus, 18 sq ft = 2 sq yd.

Draw a diagram of 18 sq ft to help you see that this is reasonable.

Work Practice 9

PRACTICE 10

3.5 square feet = ____ square inches

Example 10 5.2 square yards = ____ square feet

Solution:

$$5.2 \text{ sq yd} = \frac{5.2 \text{ sq yd}}{1} \cdot 1 = \frac{5.2 \cancel{\text{sq yd}}}{1} \cdot \frac{9 \text{ sq ft}}{1 \cancel{\text{sq yd}}} \begin{matrix} \leftarrow \text{Units converting to} \\ \leftarrow \text{Units given} \end{matrix}$$
$$= \frac{5.2 \cdot 9}{1 \cdot 1} \text{sq ft}$$
$$= 46.8 \text{ sq ft}$$

Thus, 5.2 sq yd = 46.8 sq ft.

Draw a diagram to see that this is reasonable.

Work Practice 10

Answers

9. 2 sq ft **10.** 504 sq in.

Example 11 Converting from Cubic Feet to Cubic Yards

The largest building in the world by volume is The Boeing Company's Everett, Washington, factory complex, where Boeing's wide-body jetliners, the 747, 767, and 777, are built. The volume of this factory complex is 472,370,319 cubic feet. Find the volume of this Boeing facility in cubic yards. (*Source:* The Boeing Company)

Solution: There are 27 cubic feet in 1 cubic yard. (See the diagram.)

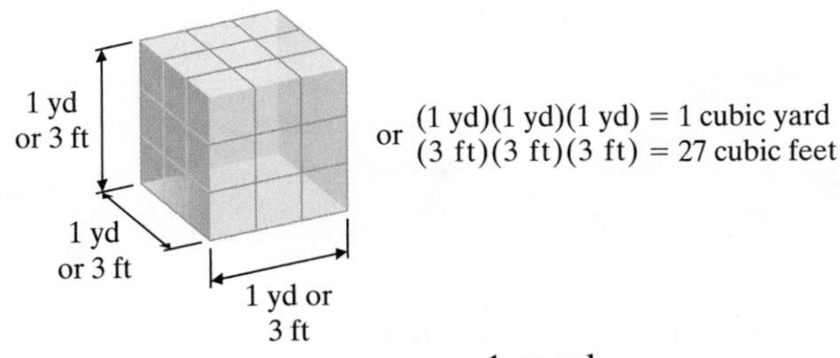

$$472{,}370{,}319 \text{ cu ft} = 472{,}370{,}319 \cancel{\text{cu ft}} \cdot \frac{1 \text{ cu yd}}{27 \cancel{\text{cu ft}}}$$
$$= \frac{472{,}370{,}319}{27} \text{ cu yd}$$
$$= 17{,}495{,}197 \text{ cu yd}$$

Work Practice 11

Helpful Hint

When converting among units of measurement, if possible write the unit fraction so that **the numerator contains the units you are converting to** and **the denominator contains the original units.**

$$48 \text{ in.} = \frac{48 \cancel{\text{in.}}}{1} \cdot \overbrace{\frac{1 \text{ ft}}{12 \cancel{\text{in.}}}}^{\text{Unit fraction}} \begin{matrix} \leftarrow \text{Units converting to} \\ \leftarrow \text{Original units} \end{matrix}$$
$$= \frac{48}{12} \text{ ft} = 4 \text{ ft}$$

Example 12

At the 2008 Summer Olympics, Jamaican athlete Usain Bolt won the gold medal in the men's 100-meter track event. He ran the distance at an average speed of 33.9 feet per second. Convert this speed to miles per hour. (*Source:* Beijing 2008 Olympics Committee)

Solution: Recall that 1 mile = 5280 feet and 1 hour = 3600 seconds $(60 \cdot 60)$.

$$33.9 \text{ feet/second} = \frac{33.9 \text{ feet}}{1 \text{ second}} \cdot \overbrace{\frac{3600 \text{ seconds}}{1 \text{ hour}} \cdot \frac{1 \text{ mile}}{5280 \text{ feet}}}^{\text{Unit fractions}}$$
$$= \frac{33.9 \cdot 3600}{5280} \text{ miles/hour}$$
$$\approx 23.1 \text{ miles/hour (rounded to the nearest tenth)}$$

Work Practice 12

PRACTICE 11

The largest casino in the world is the Venetian, in Macau, on the southern tip of China. The gaming area for this casino is approximately 61,000 *square yards*. Find the size of the gaming area in *square feet*. (*Source: USA Today*)

PRACTICE 12

The cheetah is the fastest land animal, being clocked at about 102.7 feet per second. Convert this to miles per hour. Round to the nearest tenth. (*Source: World Almanac and Book of Facts*)

Answers

11. 549,000 sq ft

12. 70.0 miles per hour

Vocabulary and Readiness Check

Use the choices below to fill in each blank. Not all choices will be used.

opposites $\quad \frac{a \cdot d}{b \cdot c} \quad \frac{a \cdot c}{b \cdot d} \quad \frac{x}{42} \quad \frac{x^2}{42} \quad \frac{2x}{42} \quad \frac{6}{7} \quad \frac{7}{6}$

reciprocals

1. The expressions $\frac{x}{2y}$ and $\frac{2y}{x}$ are called __________.

2. $\frac{a}{b} \cdot \frac{c}{d} =$ __________

3. $\frac{a}{b} \div \frac{c}{d} =$ __________

4. $\frac{x}{7} \cdot \frac{x}{6} =$ __________

5. $\frac{x}{7} \div \frac{x}{6} =$ __________

12.2 Exercise Set

FOR EXTRA HELP

PRACTICE

WATCH

DOWNLOAD

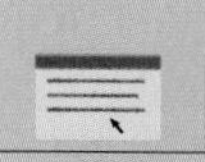
READ

REVIEW

Objective A *Find each product and simplify if possible. See Examples 1 through 3.*

1. $\frac{3x}{y^2} \cdot \frac{7y}{4x}$

2. $\frac{9x^2}{y} \cdot \frac{4y}{3x^3}$

3. $\frac{8x}{2} \cdot \frac{x^5}{4x^2}$

4. $\frac{6x^2}{10x^3} \cdot \frac{5x}{12}$

5. $-\frac{5a^2b}{30a^2b^2} \cdot b^3$

6. $-\frac{9x^3y^2}{18xy^5} \cdot y^3$

7. $\frac{x}{2x - 14} \cdot \frac{x^2 - 7x}{5}$

8. $\frac{4x - 24}{20x} \cdot \frac{5}{x - 6}$

9. $\frac{6x + 6}{5} \cdot \frac{10}{36x + 36}$

10. $\frac{x^2 + x}{8} \cdot \frac{16}{x + 1}$

11. $\frac{(m + n)^2}{m - n} \cdot \frac{m}{m^2 + mn}$

12. $\frac{(m - n)^2}{m + n} \cdot \frac{m}{m^2 - mn}$

13. $\frac{x^2 - 25}{x^2 - 3x - 10} \cdot \frac{x + 2}{x}$

14. $\frac{a^2 - 4a + 4}{a^2 - 4} \cdot \frac{a + 3}{a - 2}$

15. $\frac{x^2 + 6x + 8}{x^2 + x - 20} \cdot \frac{x^2 + 2x - 15}{x^2 + 8x + 16}$

16. $\frac{x^2 + 9x + 20}{x^2 - 15x + 44} \cdot \frac{x^2 - 11x + 28}{x^2 + 12x + 35}$

Objective B *Find each quotient and simplify. See Examples 4 through 7.*

17. $\frac{5x^7}{2x^5} \div \frac{15x}{4x^3}$

18. $\frac{9y^4}{6y} \div \frac{y^2}{3}$

19. $\frac{8x^2}{y^3} \div \frac{4x^2y^3}{6}$

20. $\frac{7a^2b}{3ab^2} \div \frac{21a^2b^2}{14ab}$

21. $\frac{(x - 6)(x + 4)}{4x} \div \frac{2x - 12}{8x^2}$

22. $\frac{(x + 3)^2}{5} \div \frac{5x + 15}{25}$

23. $\frac{3x^2}{x^2 - 1} \div \frac{x^5}{(x + 1)^2}$

24. $\frac{9x^5}{a^2 - b^2} \div \frac{27x^2}{3b - 3a}$

25. $\frac{m^2 - n^2}{m + n} \div \frac{m}{m^2 + nm}$

26. $\frac{(m - n)^2}{m + n} \div \frac{m^2 - mn}{m}$

27. $\dfrac{x+2}{7-x} \div \dfrac{x^2-5x+6}{x^2-9x+14}$

28. $\dfrac{x-3}{2-x} \div \dfrac{x^2+3x-18}{x^2+2x-8}$

29. $\dfrac{x^2+7x+10}{x-1} \div \dfrac{x^2+2x-15}{x-1}$

30. $\dfrac{x+1}{2x^2+5x+3} \div \dfrac{20x+100}{2x+3}$

Objective **C** **Mixed Practice** *Multiply or divide as indicated. See Example 8.*

31. $\dfrac{5x-10}{12} \div \dfrac{4x-8}{8}$

32. $\dfrac{6x+6}{5} \div \dfrac{9x+9}{10}$

33. $\dfrac{x^2+5x}{8} \cdot \dfrac{9}{3x+15}$

34. $\dfrac{3x^2+12x}{6} \cdot \dfrac{9}{2x+8}$

35. $\dfrac{7}{6p^2+q} \div \dfrac{14}{18p^2+3q}$

36. $\dfrac{3x+6}{20} \div \dfrac{4x+8}{8}$

37. $\dfrac{3x+4y}{x^2+4xy+4y^2} \cdot \dfrac{x+2y}{2}$

38. $\dfrac{x^2-y^2}{3x^2+3xy} \cdot \dfrac{3x^2+6x}{3x^2-2xy-y^2}$

39. $\dfrac{(x+2)^2}{x-2} \div \dfrac{x^2-4}{2x-4}$

40. $\dfrac{x+3}{x^2-9} \div \dfrac{5x+15}{(x-3)^2}$

41. $\dfrac{x^2-4}{24x} \div \dfrac{2-x}{6xy}$

42. $\dfrac{3y}{3-x} \div \dfrac{12xy}{x^2-9}$

43. $\dfrac{a^2+7a+12}{a^2+5a+6} \cdot \dfrac{a^2+8a+15}{a^2+5a+4}$

44. $\dfrac{b^2+2b-3}{b^2+b-2} \cdot \dfrac{b^2-4}{b^2+6b+8}$

45. $\dfrac{5x-20}{3x^2+x} \cdot \dfrac{3x^2+13x+4}{x^2-16}$

46. $\dfrac{9x+18}{4x^2-3x} \cdot \dfrac{4x^2-11x+6}{x^2-4}$

47. $\dfrac{8n^2-18}{2n^2-5n+3} \div \dfrac{6n^2+7n-3}{n^2-9n+8}$

48. $\dfrac{36n^2-64}{3n^2-10n+8} \div \dfrac{3n^2-5n-12}{n^2-9n+14}$

Objective **D** *Convert as indicated. See Examples 9 through 12.*

49. 10 square feet = ________ square inches.

50. 1008 square inches = ________ square feet.

51. 45 square feet = ________ square yards.

52. 2 square yards = ________ square inches.

53. 3 cubic yards = ________ cubic feet.

54. 2 cubic yards = ________ cubic inches.

55. 50 miles per hour = ________ feet per second (round to the nearest whole).

56. 10 feet per second = ________ miles per hour (round to the nearest tenth).

57. 6.3 square yards = ________ square feet.

58. 3.6 square yards = ________ square feet.

59. In January 2010, the Burj Khalifa Tower officially became the tallest building in the world. This tower has a curtain wall (the exterior skin of the building) that is approximately 133,500 square yards. Convert this to square feet. (*Source:* Burj Khalifa)

60. The Pentagon, headquarters for the Department of Defense, contains 3,705,793 square feet of office and storage space. Convert this to square yards. Round to the nearest square yard. (*Source:* U.S. Department of Defense)

61. On October 9, 2007, Russ Wicks set a new stock car world speed record of 359.2 feet/second on the Bonneville Salt Flats in Utah. Convert this speed to miles/hour. Round to the nearest tenth. (*Source:* RussWicks.com)

62. On October 4, 2004, the rocket plane *SpaceShipOne* shot to an altitude of more than 100 km for the second time inside a week to claim the $10 million Ansari X-Prize. At one point in its flight, *SpaceShipOne* was traveling past Mach 1, about 930 miles per hour. Find this speed in feet per second. (*Source:* Space.com)

Review

Perform each indicated operation.

63. $\frac{1}{5} + \frac{4}{5}$

64. $\frac{3}{15} + \frac{6}{15}$

65. $\frac{9}{9} - \frac{19}{9}$

66. $\frac{4}{3} - \frac{8}{3}$

67. $\frac{6}{5} + \left(\frac{1}{5} - \frac{8}{5}\right)$

68. $-\frac{3}{2} + \left(\frac{1}{2} - \frac{3}{2}\right)$

Concept Extensions

Identify each statement as true or false. If false, correct the multiplication. See the Concept Check in this section.

69. $\frac{4}{a} \cdot \frac{1}{b} = \frac{4}{ab}$

70. $\frac{2}{3} \cdot \frac{2}{4} = \frac{2}{7}$

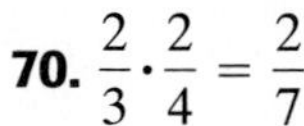

71. $\frac{x}{5} \cdot \frac{x+3}{4} = \frac{2x+3}{20}$

72. $\frac{7}{a} \cdot \frac{3}{a} = \frac{21}{a}$

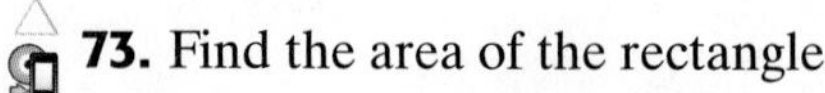

73. Find the area of the rectangle.

$\frac{2x}{x^2 - 25}$ feet

$\frac{x+5}{9x}$ feet

74. Find the area of the square.

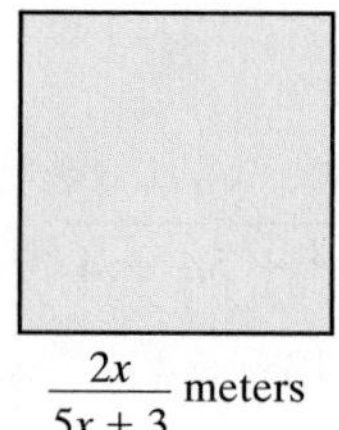

$\frac{2x}{5x+3}$ meters

Multiply or divide as indicated.

75. $\left(\frac{x^2 - y^2}{x^2 + y^2} \div \frac{x^2 - y^2}{3x}\right) \cdot \frac{x^2 + y^2}{6}$

76. $\left(\frac{x^2 - 9}{x^2 - 1} \cdot \frac{x^2 + 2x + 1}{2x^2 + 9x + 9}\right) \div \frac{2x + 3}{1 - x}$

77. $\left(\frac{2a + b}{b^2} \cdot \frac{3a^2 - 2ab}{ab + 2b^2}\right) \div \frac{a^2 - 3ab + 2b^2}{5ab - 10b^2}$

78. $\left(\frac{x^2y^2 - xy}{4x - 4y} \div \frac{3y - 3x}{8x - 8y}\right) \cdot \frac{y - x}{8}$

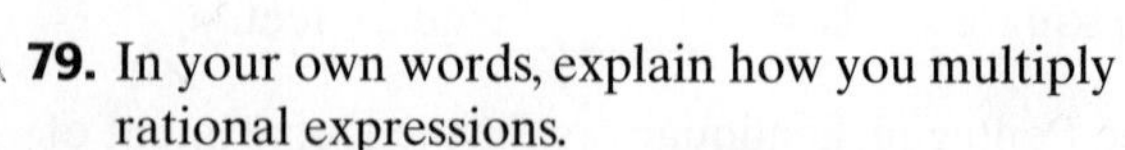

79. In your own words, explain how you multiply rational expressions.

80. Explain how dividing rational expressions is similar to dividing rational numbers.

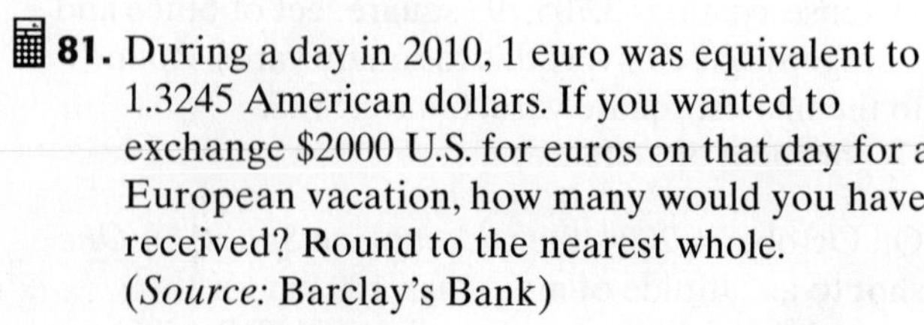

81. During a day in 2010, 1 euro was equivalent to 1.3245 American dollars. If you wanted to exchange \$2000 U.S. for euros on that day for a European vacation, how many would you have received? Round to the nearest whole. (*Source:* Barclay's Bank)

82. An environmental technician finds that warm water from an industrial process is being discharged into a nearby pond at a rate of 30 gallons per minute. Plant regulations state that the flow rate should be no more than 0.1 cubic feet per second. Is the flow rate of 30 gallons per minute in violation of the plant regulations? (*Hint:* 1 cubic foot is equivalent to 7.48 gallons.)

Chapter 12 Vocabulary Check

Fill in each blank with one of the words or phrases listed below. Not all choices will be used.

rational expression	simplifying	unit	reciprocals	
numerator	denominator	$\frac{-a}{b}$	$\frac{-a}{-b}$	$\frac{a}{-b}$

1. A(n) ______________ is an expression that can be written in the form $\frac{P}{Q}$, where P and Q are polynomials and Q is not 0.

2. For a rational expression, $-\frac{a}{b} =$ ______________ $=$ ______________.

3. A rational expression is undefined when the ______________ is 0.

4. The process of writing a rational expression in lowest terms is called ______________.

5. The expressions $\frac{2x}{7}$ and $\frac{7}{2x}$ are called ______________.

6. A(n) ______________ fraction is a fraction that equals 1.

Helpful Hint Are you preparing for your test? Don't forget to take the Chapter 12 Test on page 854. Then check your answers at the back of the text and use the Chapter Test Prep Videos to see the fully worked-out solutions to any of the exercises you want to review.

12 Chapter Highlights

Definitions and Concepts	Examples
Section 12.1 Simplifying Rational Expressions	
A **rational expression** is an expression that can be written in the form $\frac{P}{Q}$, where P and Q are polynomials and Q does not equal 0.	$\frac{7y^3}{4}, \frac{x^2+6x+1}{x-3}, \frac{-5}{s^3+8}$
To find values for which a rational expression is undefined, find values for which the denominator is 0.	Find any values for which the expression $\frac{5y}{y^2-4y+3}$ is undefined. $y^2 - 4y + 3 = 0$ Set the denominator equal to 0. $(y-3)(y-1) = 0$ Factor. $y - 3 = 0$ or $y - 1 = 0$ Set each factor equal to 0. $y = 3$ $\quad y = 1$ Solve. The expression is undefined when y is 3 and when y is 1.

(*continued*)

Definitions and Concepts	Examples
Section 12.1 Simplifying Rational Expressions (*continued*)	
To Simplify a Rational Expression **Step 1.** Factor the numerator and denominator. **Step 2.** Divide out factors common to the numerator and denominator. (This is the same as removing a factor of 1.)	Simplify: $\dfrac{4x+20}{x^2-25}$ $\dfrac{4x+20}{x^2-25} = \dfrac{4(x+5)}{(x+5)(x-5)} = \dfrac{4}{x-5}$
Section 12.2 Multiplying and Dividing Rational Expressions	
To Multiply Rational Expressions **Step 1.** Factor numerators and denominators. **Step 2.** Multiply numerators and multiply denominators. **Step 3.** Write the product in lowest terms. $\dfrac{P}{Q}\cdot\dfrac{R}{S} = \dfrac{PR}{QS}$	Multiply: $\dfrac{4x+4}{2x-3}\cdot\dfrac{2x^2+x-6}{x^2-1}$ $\dfrac{4x+4}{2x-3}\cdot\dfrac{2x^2+x-6}{x^2-1}$ $= \dfrac{4(x+1)}{2x-3}\cdot\dfrac{(2x-3)(x+2)}{(x+1)(x-1)}$ $= \dfrac{4(x+1)(2x-3)(x+2)}{(2x-3)(x+1)(x-1)}$ $= \dfrac{4(x+2)}{x-1}$
To divide by a rational expression, multiply by the reciprocal. $\dfrac{P}{Q} \div \dfrac{R}{S} = \dfrac{P}{Q}\cdot\dfrac{S}{R} = \dfrac{PS}{QR}$	Divide: $\dfrac{15x+5}{3x^2-14x-5} \div \dfrac{15}{3x-12}$ $\dfrac{15x+5}{3x^2-14x-5} \div \dfrac{15}{3x-12}$ $= \dfrac{5(3x+1)}{(3x+1)(x-5)}\cdot\dfrac{3(x-4)}{3\cdot 5}$ $= \dfrac{x-4}{x-5}$

Chapter 12 Review

(12.1) *Find any real number for which each rational expression is undefined.*

1. $\dfrac{x+5}{x^2-4}$

2. $\dfrac{5x+9}{4x^2-4x-15}$

Find the value of each rational expression when $x = 5$, $y = 7$, and $z = -2$.

3. $\dfrac{2-z}{z+5}$

4. $\dfrac{x^2+xy-y^2}{x+y}$

Simplify each rational expression.

5. $\dfrac{2x+6}{x^2+3x}$

6. $\dfrac{3x-12}{x^2-4x}$

7. $\dfrac{x+2}{x^2-3x-10}$

8. $\dfrac{x+4}{x^2+5x+4}$

9. $\dfrac{x^3-4x}{x^2+3x+2}$

10. $\dfrac{5x^2-125}{x^2+2x-15}$

11. $\dfrac{x^2-x-6}{x^2-3x-10}$

12. $\dfrac{x^2-2x}{x^2+2x-8}$

Simplify each expression. First, factor the four-term polynomials by grouping.

13. $\dfrac{x^2+xa+xb+ab}{x^2-xc+bx-bc}$

14. $\dfrac{x^2+5x-2x-10}{x^2-3x-2x+6}$

(12.2) *Perform each indicated operation and simplify.*

15. $\dfrac{15x^3y^2}{z}\cdot\dfrac{z}{5xy^3}$

16. $\dfrac{-y^3}{8}\cdot\dfrac{9x^2}{y^3}$

17. $\dfrac{x^2-9}{x^2-4}\cdot\dfrac{x-2}{x+3}$

18. $\dfrac{2x+5}{x-6}\cdot\dfrac{2x}{-x+6}$

19. $\dfrac{x^2-5x-24}{x^2-x-12}\div\dfrac{x^2-10x+16}{x^2+x-6}$

20. $\dfrac{4x+4y}{xy^2}\div\dfrac{3x+3y}{x^2y}$

21. $\dfrac{x^2+x-42}{x-3}\cdot\dfrac{(x-3)^2}{x+7}$

22. $\dfrac{2a+2b}{3}\cdot\dfrac{a-b}{a^2-b^2}$

23. $\dfrac{2x^2-9x+9}{8x-12}\div\dfrac{x^2-3x}{2x}$

24. $\dfrac{x^2-y^2}{x^2+xy}\div\dfrac{3x^2-2xy-y^2}{3x^2+6x}$

Mixed Review

Simplify each rational expression.

25. $\dfrac{4x+12}{8x^2+24x}$

26. $\dfrac{x^3-6x^2+9x}{x^2+4x-21}$

Perform the indicated operations and simplify.

27. $\dfrac{x^2+9x+20}{x^2-25}\cdot\dfrac{x^2-9x+20}{x^2+8x+16}$

28. $\dfrac{x^2-x-72}{x^2-x-30}\div\dfrac{x^2+6x-27}{x^2-9x+18}$

Chapter 12 Test

Step-by-step test solutions are found on the Chapter Test Prep Videos available via the Interactive DVD Lecture Series, in MyMathLab or on YouTube (search "MartinGayIntroAlg" and click on "Channels").

Answers

1. ______

2. a. ______

b. ______

3. ______

4. ______

5. ______

6. ______

7. ______

8. ______

9. ______

10. ______

11. ______

1. Find any real numbers for which the following expression is undefined.

$$\frac{x+5}{x^2+4x+3}$$

2. For a certain computer desk, the average manufacturing cost C per desk (in dollars) is

$$C = \frac{100x + 3000}{x}$$

where x is the number of desks manufactured.

a. Find the average cost per desk when manufacturing 200 computer desks.

b. Find the average cost per desk when manufacturing 1000 computer desks.

Simplify each rational expression.

3. $\dfrac{3x-6}{5x-10}$

4. $\dfrac{x+6}{x^2+12x+36}$

5. $\dfrac{7-x}{x-7}$

6. $\dfrac{y-x}{x^2-y^2}$

7. $\dfrac{2m^3-2m^2-12m}{m^2-5m+6}$

8. $\dfrac{ay+3a+2y+6}{ay+3a+5y+15}$

Perform each indicated operation and simplify if possible.

9. $\dfrac{x^2-13x+42}{x^2+10x+21} \div \dfrac{x^2-4}{x^2+x-6}$

10. $\dfrac{3}{x-1} \cdot (5x-5)$

11. $\dfrac{y^2-5y+6}{2y+4} \cdot \dfrac{y+2}{2y-6}$

Cumulative Review Chapters 8–12

1. Write each sentence as an equation. Let x represent the unknown number.

a. The quotient of 15 and a number is 4.

b. Three subtracted from 12 is a number.

c. 17 added to four times a number is 21.

2. Write each sentence as an equation. Let x represent the unknown number.

a. The difference of 12 and a number is -45.

b. The product of 12 and a number is -45.

c. A number less 10 is twice the number.

3. Find the sums.

a. $3 + (-7) + (-8)$

b. $[7 + (-10)] + [-2 + (-4)]$

4. Find the differences.

a. $28 - 6 - 30$

b. $7 - 2 - 22$

For Exercises 5 through 8, name the property illustrated by each true statement.

5. $3(x + y) = 3 \cdot x + 3 \cdot y$

6. $3 + y = y + 3$

7. $(x + 7) + 9 = x + (7 + 9)$

8. $(x \cdot 7) \cdot 9 = x \cdot (7 \cdot 9)$

9. Solve: $3 - x = 7$

10. Solve: $7x - 6 = 6x - 6$

11. A 10-foot board is to be cut into two pieces so that the length of the longer piece is 4 times the length of the shorter. Find the length of each piece.

12. Find two consecutive even integers whose sum is 382.

13. Solve: $y = mx + b$ for x.

14. Solve: $3x - 2y = 6$ for x.

15. Solve $x + 4 \le -6$. Graph the solutions.

−10 −8 −6 −4 −2 0 2 4 6 8 10

16. Solve: $-3x + 7 > -x + 9$

Simplify.

17. $\frac{x^5}{x^2}$

18. $\frac{y^{14}}{y^{14}}$

19. $\frac{4^7}{4^3}$

20. $(x^5y^2)^3$

Answers

1. a. ______
b. ______
c. ______
2. a. ______
b. ______
c. ______
3. a. ______
b. ______
4. a. ______
b. ______
5. ______
6. ______
7. ______
8. ______
9. ______
10. ______
11. ______
12. ______
13. ______
14. ______
15. ______
16. ______
17. ______
18. ______
19. ______
20. ______

21. ______
22. ______
23. ______
24. ______
25. ______
26. ______
27. ______
28. ______
29. ______
30. ______
31. ______
32. ______
33. ______
34. ______
35. ______
36. ______
37. ______
38. ______
39. ______
40. ______
41. ______
42. ______
43. ______
44. ______
45. ______
46. ______
47. ______
48. ______

21. $\dfrac{(-3)^5}{(-3)^2}$ **22.** $\dfrac{x^{19}y^5}{xy}$ **23.** $\dfrac{2x^5y^2}{xy}$ **24.** $(-3a^2b)(5a^3b)$

Simplify by writing each expression with positive exponents only.

25. $2x^{-3}$ **26.** 7^{-2} **27.** $(-2)^{-4}$ **28.** $5z^{-7}$

Multiply.

29. $5x(2x^3 + 6)$ **30.** $(x + 9)^2$

31. $-3x^2(5x^2 + 6x - 1)$ **32.** $(2x + 1)(2x - 1)$

Perform the indicated operations.

33. Divide: $\dfrac{4x^2 + 7 + 8x^3}{2x + 3}$ **34.** Divide $(4x^3 - 9x + 2)$ by $(x - 4)$.

35. Factor: $x^2 + 7x + 12$ **36.** Factor: $-2a^2 + 10a + 12$

37. Factor: $25x^2 + 20xy + 4y^2$ **38.** Factor: $x^2 - 4$

39. Solve: $x^2 - 9x - 22 = 0$ **40.** Solve: $3x^2 + 5x = 2$

41. Multiply: $\dfrac{x^2 + x}{3x} \cdot \dfrac{6}{5x + 5}$ **42.** Simplify: $\dfrac{2x^2 - 50}{4x^4 - 20x^3}$

43. $1 - a^3$ **44.** Factor: $7x^6 - 7x^5 + 7x^4$

45. $x^3 - 64$ **46.** Factor: $4x^2 + 12x + 9$

47. $8x^4 - x$ **48.** Multiply: $\dfrac{6x^2 - 18x}{3x^2 - 2x} \cdot \dfrac{15x - 10}{x^2 - 9}$

Graphing Equations and Inequalities

13

Sections

Check Your Progress

In Chapter 9 we learned to solve and graph the solutions of linear equations and inequalities in one variable on number lines. Now we define and present techniques for solving and graphing linear equations and inequalities in two variables on grids. Two-variable equations lead directly to the concept of *function,* perhaps the most important concept in all mathematics. Functions are introduced in Section 13.6.

"Neither snow, nor rain, nor heat, nor gloom of night stays these couriers from the swift completion of their appointed rounds." This familiar quotation, adapted from Herodotus, is inscribed in the New York City post office. By land and sea and air, on horseback, steamboats, and jets, the U.S. mail has been delivered to its destinations for more than 200 years. To this day, the most unusual delivery method is by mule, to the most remote mail location in the country, Supai, Arizona, located deep below the south rim of the Grand Canyon.

The Post Office Department, the predecessor of the U.S. Postal Service, was created by the Second Continental Congress on July 26, 1775. This agency was an arm of the U.S. government until 1982, the last year the Postal Service accepted public subsidy. You will explore the way that some postage is calculated.

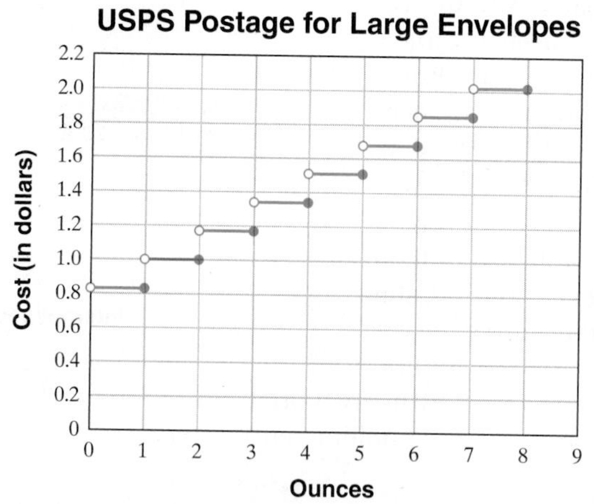

Objectives

A **Read Bar and Line Graphs.**

B **Plot Ordered Pairs of Numbers on the Rectangular Coordinate System.**

C **Graph Paired Data to Create a Scatter Diagram.**

D **Find the Missing Coordinate of an Ordered Pair Solution, Given One Coordinate of the Pair.**

13.1 READING GRAPHS AND THE RECTANGULAR COORDINATE SYSTEM

In today's world, where the exchange of information must be fast and entertaining, graphs are becoming increasingly popular. They provide a quick way of making comparisons, drawing conclusions, and approximating quantities.

Objective A Reading Bar and Line Graphs

A **bar graph** consists of a series of bars arranged vertically or horizontally. The bar graph in Example 1 shows a comparison of worldwide Internet users by region. The names of the regions are listed vertically and a bar is shown for each region. Corresponding to the length of the bar for each region is a number along a horizontal axis. These horizontal numbers are numbers of Internet users in millions.

Example 1

The following bar graph shows the estimated number of Internet users worldwide by region, as of a recent year.

a. Find the region that has the most Internet users and approximate the number of users.

b. How many more users are in the North America region than the Latin America/Caribbean region?

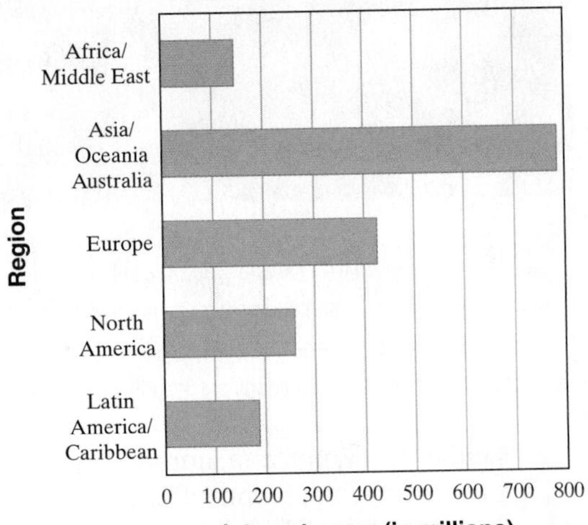

PRACTICE 1

Use the graph from Example 1 to answer the following.

a. Find the region with the fewest Internet users and approximate the number of users.

b. How many more users are in the Asia/Oceania/Australia region than in the Africa/Middle East region?

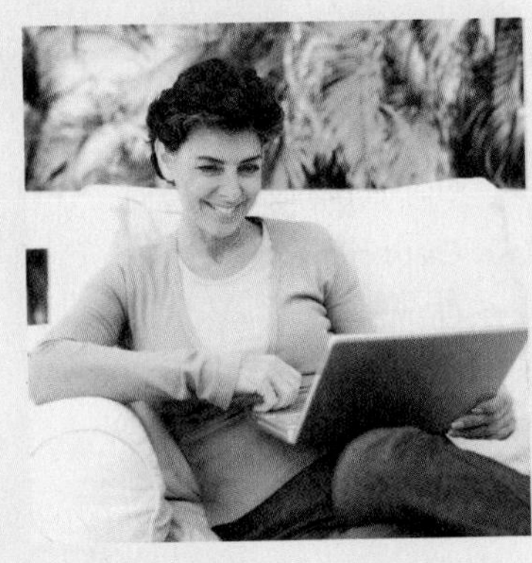

Solution:

a. Since these bars are arranged horizontally, we look for the longest bar, which is the bar representing Asia/Oceania/Australia. To approximate the number associated with this region, we move from the right edge of this bar vertically downward to the Internet user axis. This region has approximately 785 million Internet users.

b. The North America region has approximately 260 million Internet users. The Latin America/Caribbean region has approximately 187 million Internet users. To find how many more users are in the North America region, we subtract $260 - 187 = 73$ million more Internet users.

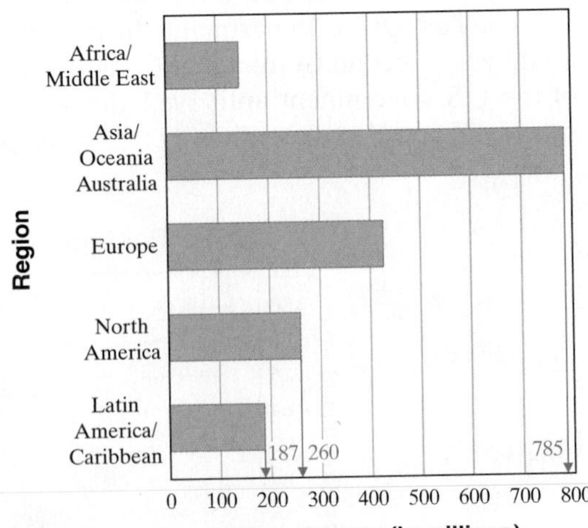

Work Practice 1

Answers

1. a. Africa/Middle East region, 145 million Internet users, **b.** 640 million more Internet users

A **line graph** consists of a series of points connected by a line. The next graph is an example of a line graph. It is also sometimes called a **broken line graph.**

Example 2

The line graph shows the relationship between time since smoking a cigarette and pulse rate. Time is recorded along the horizontal axis in minutes, with 0 minutes being the moment a smoker lights a cigarette. Pulse is recorded along the vertical axis in heartbeats per minute.

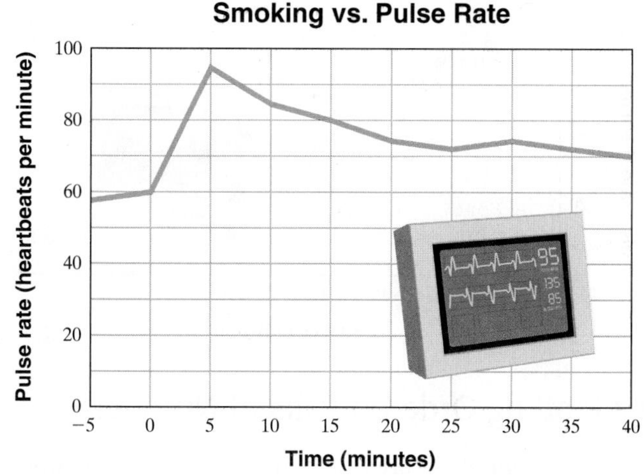

a. What is the pulse rate 15 minutes after a cigarette is lit?

b. When is the pulse rate the lowest?

c. When does the pulse rate show the greatest change?

Solution:

a. We locate the number 15 along the time axis and move vertically upward until the line is reached. From this point on the line, we move horizontally to the left until the pulse rate axis is reached. Reading the number of beats per minute, we find that the pulse rate is 80 beats per minute 15 minutes after a cigarette is lit.

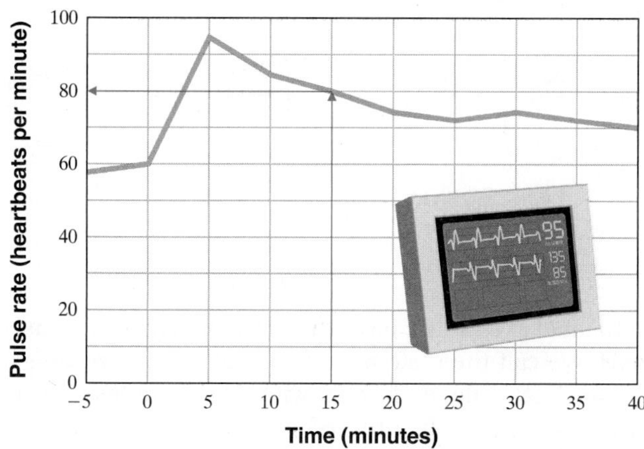

b. We find the lowest point of the line graph, which represents the lowest pulse rate. From this point, we move vertically downward to the time axis. We find that the pulse rate is the lowest at −5 minutes, which means 5 minutes *before* lighting a cigarette.

c. The pulse rate shows the greatest change during the 5 minutes between 0 and 5. Notice that the line graph is *steepest* between 0 and 5 minutes.

Work Practice 2

PRACTICE 2

Use the graph from Example 2 to answer the following.

a. What is the pulse rate 40 minutes after lighting a cigarette?

b. What is the pulse rate when the cigarette is being lit?

c. When is the pulse rate the highest?

Answers

2. a. 70 beats per minute **b.** 60 beats per minute **c.** 5 minutes after lighting

Notice in the graph on the previous page that there are two numbers associated with each point of the graph. For example, we discussed earlier that 15 minutes after "lighting up," the pulse rate is 80 beats per minute. If we agree to write the time first and the pulse rate second, we can say there is a point on the graph corresponding to the **ordered pair** of numbers (15, 80). A few more ordered pairs are shown alongside their corresponding points.

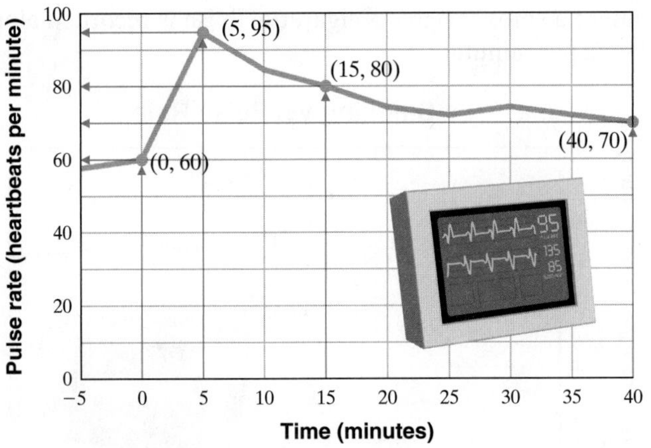

Objective B Plotting Ordered Pairs of Numbers

In general, we use the idea of ordered pairs to describe the location of a point in a plane (such as a piece of paper). We start with a horizontal and a vertical axis. Each axis is a number line, and for the sake of consistency we construct our axes to intersect at the 0 coordinate of both. This point of intersection is called the **origin.** Notice that these two number lines or axes divide the plane into four regions called **quadrants.** The quadrants are usually numbered with Roman numerals as shown. The axes are not considered to be in any quadrant.

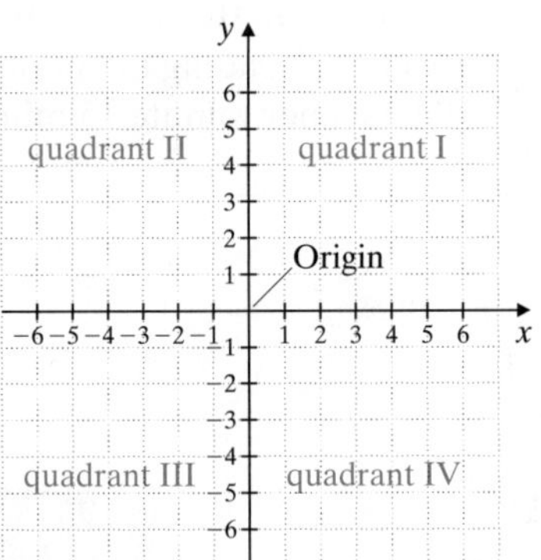

It is helpful to label axes, so we label the horizontal axis the ***x*-axis** and the vertical axis the ***y*-axis.** We call the system described above the **rectangular coordinate system,** or the **coordinate plane.** Just as with other graphs shown, we can then describe the locations of points by ordered pairs of numbers. We list the horizontal ***x*-axis** measurement first and the vertical ***y*-axis** measurement second.

To plot or graph the point corresponding to the ordered pair (a, b) we start at the origin. We then move a units left or right (right if a is positive, left if a is negative). From there, we move b units up or down (up if b is positive, down if b is negative). For example, to plot the point corresponding to the ordered pair (3, 2), we start at the origin, move 3 units right, and from there move 2 units up. (See the figure on the next page.) The x-value, 3, is also called the ***x*-coordinate** and the y-value, 2, is also called the ***y*-coordinate.** From now on, we will call the point with coordinates (3, 2) simply the point (3, 2). The point (−2, 5) is also graphed on the next page.

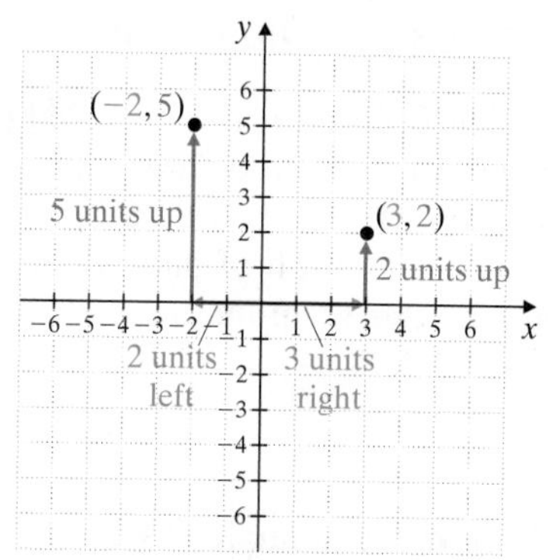

Helpful Hint

Don't forget that **each ordered pair corresponds to exactly one point in the plane and that each point in the plane corresponds to exactly one ordered pair.**

✓**Concept Check** Is the graph of the point $(-5, 1)$ in the same location as the graph of the point $(1, -5)$? Explain.

Example 3 On a single coordinate system, plot each ordered pair. State in which quadrant, or on which axis, each point lies.

a. $(5, 3)$ **b.** $(-2, -4)$ **c.** $(1, -2)$ **d.** $(-5, 3)$ **e.** $(0, 0)$

f. $(0, 2)$ **g.** $(-5, 0)$ **h.** $\left(0, -5\frac{1}{2}\right)$ **i.** $\left(4\frac{2}{3}, -3\right)$

Solution:

a. Point $(5, 3)$ lies in quadrant I.

b. Point $(-2, -4)$ lies in quadrant III.

c. Point $(1, -2)$ lies in quadrant IV.

d. Point $(-5, 3)$ lies in quadrant II.

e.–h. Points $(0, 0)$, $(0, 2)$, and $\left(0, -5\frac{1}{2}\right)$ lie on the y-axis. Points $(0, 0)$ and $(-5, 0)$ lie on the x-axis.

i. Point $\left(4\frac{2}{3}, -3\right)$ lies in quadrant IV.

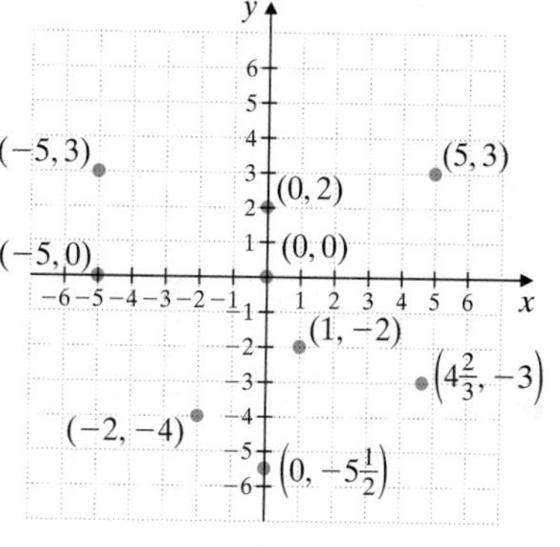

Work Practice 3

Helpful Hint

In Example 3, notice that the point $(0, 0)$ lies on both the x-axis and the y-axis. It is the only point in the entire rectangular coordinate system that has this feature. Why? It is the only point of intersection of the x-axis and the y-axis.

✓**Concept Check** For each description of a point in the rectangular coordinate system, write an ordered pair that represents it.

a. Point A is located three units to the left of the y-axis and five units above the x-axis.

b. Point B is located six units below the origin.

From Example 3, notice that the y-coordinate of any point on the x-axis is 0. For example, the point $(-5, 0)$ lies on the x-axis. Also, the x-coordinate of any point on the y-axis is 0. For example, the point $(0, 2)$ lies on the y-axis.

PRACTICE 3

On a single coordinate system, plot each ordered pair. State in which quadrant, or on which axis, each point lies.

a. $(4, 2)$ **b.** $(-1, -3)$

c. $(2, -2)$ **d.** $(-5, 1)$

e. $(0, 3)$ **f.** $(3, 0)$

g. $(0, -4)$ **h.** $\left(-2\frac{1}{2}, 0\right)$

i. $\left(1, -3\frac{3}{4}\right)$

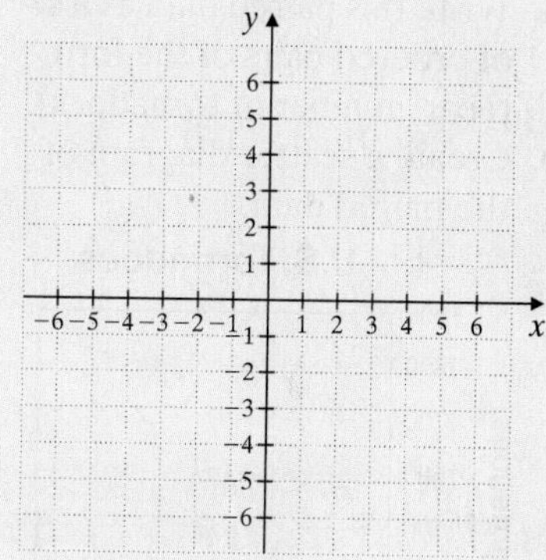

Answers

3.

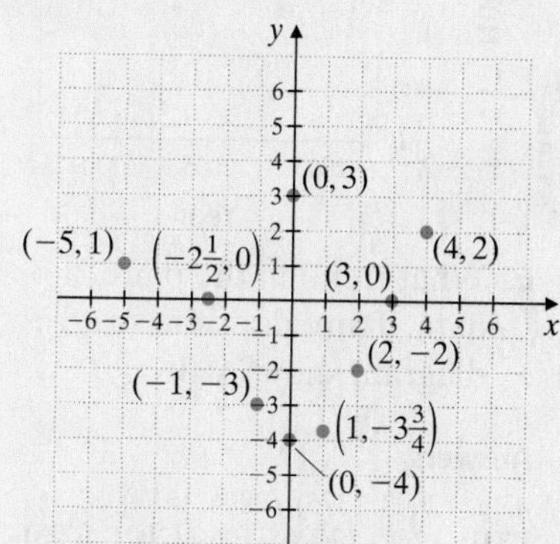

a. Point $(4, 2)$ lies in quadrant I.

b. Point $(-1, -3)$ lies in quadrant III.

c. Point $(2, -2)$ lies in quadrant IV.

d. Point $(-5, 1)$ lies in quadrant II.

e–h. Points $(3, 0)$ and $\left(-2\frac{1}{2}, 0\right)$ lie on the x-axis. Points $(0, 3)$ and $(0, -4)$ lie on the y-axis.

i. Point $\left(1, -3\frac{3}{4}\right)$ lies in quadrant IV.

✓ **Concept Check Answer**

The graph of point $(-5, 1)$ lies in quadrant II and the graph of point $(1, -5)$ lies in quadrant IV. They are *not* in the same location.

✓ **Concept Check Answers**

a. $(-3, 5)$ **b.** $(0, -6)$

Objective C Creating Scatter Diagrams

Data that can be represented as ordered pairs are called **paired data.** Many types of data collected from the real world are paired data. For instance, the annual measurements of a child's height can be written as ordered pairs of the form (year, height in inches) and are paired data. The graph of paired data as points in a rectangular coordinate system is called a **scatter diagram.** Scatter diagrams can be used to look for patterns and trends in paired data.

Example 4 The table gives the annual net sales for PetSmart for the years shown. (*Source:* PetSmart)

Year	PetSmart Net Sales (in billions of dollars)
2003	3.0
2004	3.4
2005	3.8
2006	4.2
2007	4.7
2008	5.1

a. Write this paired data as a set of ordered pairs of the form (year, net sales in billions of dollars).
b. Create a scatter diagram of the paired data.
c. What trend in the paired data does the scatter diagram show?

Solution:

a. The ordered pairs are (2003, 3.0), (2004, 3.4), (2005, 3.8), (2006, 4.2), (2007, 4.7), and (2008, 5.1).

b. We begin by plotting the ordered pairs. Because the x-coordinate in each ordered pair is a year, we label the x-axis "Year" and mark the horizontal axis with the years given. Then we label the y-axis or vertical axis "Net Sales (in billions of dollars)." In this case, it is convenient to mark the vertical axis in multiples of 0.5, starting with 0. In Practice 4, since there are no years when the number of tornadoes is less than 1000, we use the notation ⌇ to skip to 1000, and then proceed by multiples of 100.

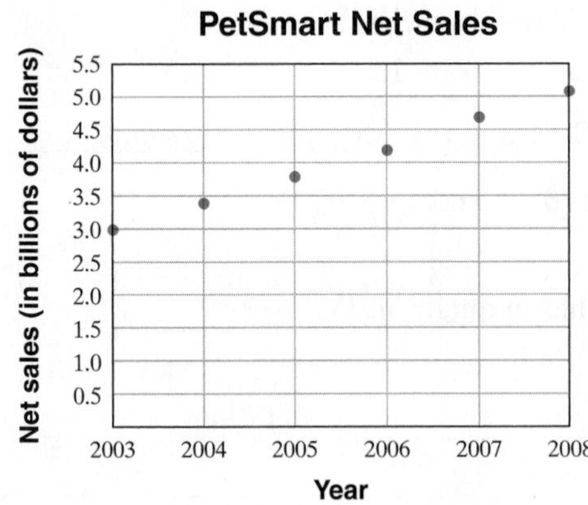

c. The scatter diagram shows that PetSmart net sales steadily increased over the years 2003–2008.

Work Practice 4

Objective D Completing Ordered Pair Solutions

Let's see how we can use ordered pairs to record solutions of equations containing two variables. An equation in one variable such as $x + 1 = 5$ has one solution, 4: the number 4 is the value of the variable x that makes the equation true.

An equation in two variables, such as $2x + y = 8$, has solutions consisting of two values, one for x and one for y. For example, $x = 3$ and $y = 2$ is a

PRACTICE 4

The table gives the number of tornadoes that have occurred in the United States for the years shown. (*Source:* Storm Prediction Center, National Weather Service)

Year	Tornadoes
2003	1376
2004	1817
2005	1264
2006	1106
2007	1093
2008	1621

a. Write this paired data as a set of ordered pairs of the form (year, number of tornadoes).
b. Create a scatter diagram of the paired data.

U.S. Tornadoes

Number of tornadoes: 1900, 1800, 1700, 1600, 1500, 1400, 1300, 1200, 1100, 1000, 0

Year: 2003, 2005, 2007

c. What trend in the paired data, if any, does the scatter diagram show?

Answers

4. a. (2003, 1376), (2004, 1817), (2005, 1264), (2006, 1106), (2007, 1093), (2008, 1621)

b.

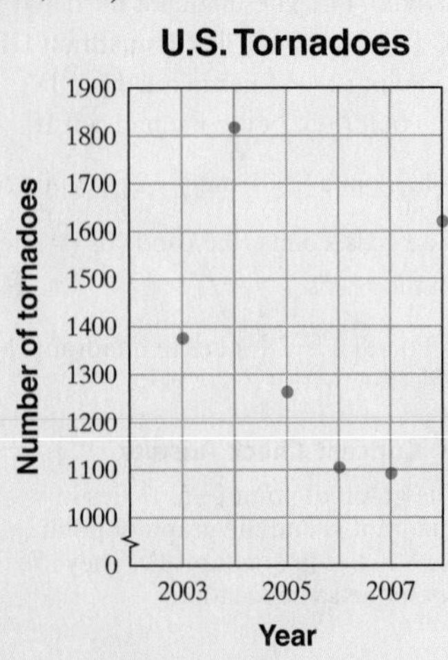

c. The number of tornadoes varies greatly from year to year.

solution of $2x + y = 8$ because, if x is replaced with 3 and y with 2, we get a true statement.

Replace x with 3 and y with 2.

$8 = 8$ True

The solution $x = 3$ and can be written as $(3, 2)$, an ordered pair of numbers.

In general, an ordered pair is a **solution** of an equation in two variables if replacing the variables by the values of the ordered pair results in a *true statement.*

For example, another ordered pair solution of $2x + y = 8$ is $(5, -2)$. Replacing x with 5 and y with -2 results in a true statement.

$$2x + y = 8$$

$$2(5) + (-2) \stackrel{?}{=} 8 \quad \text{Replace } x \text{ with 5 and } y \text{ with } -2.$$

$$10 - 2 \stackrel{?}{=} 8$$

$$8 = 8 \quad \text{True}$$

Example 5 Complete each ordered pair so that it is a solution to the equation $3x + y = 12$.

a. $(0, \ )$ **b.** $(\ , 6)$ **c.** $(-1, \ )$

Solution:

a. In the ordered pair $(0, \ )$, the x-value is 0. We let $x = 0$ in the equation and solve for y.

$$3x + y = 12$$

$$3(0) + y = 12 \quad \text{Replace } x \text{ with 0.}$$

$$0 + y = 12$$

$$y = 12$$

The completed ordered pair is $(0, 12)$.

b. In the ordered pair $(\ , 6)$, the y-value is 6. We let $y = 6$ in the equation and solve for x.

$$3x + y = 12$$

$$3x + 6 = 12 \quad \text{Replace } y \text{ with 6.}$$

$$3x = 6 \quad \text{Subtract 6 from both sides.}$$

$$x = 2 \quad \text{Divide both sides by 3.}$$

The ordered pair is $(2, 6)$.

c. In the ordered pair $(-1, \ )$, the x-value is -1. We let $x = -1$ in the equation and solve for y.

$$3x + y = 12$$

$$3(-1) + y = 12 \quad \text{Replace } x \text{ with } -1.$$

$$-3 + y = 12$$

$$y = 15 \quad \text{Add 3 to both sides.}$$

The ordered pair is $(-1, 15)$.

Work Practice 5

PRACTICE 5

Complete each ordered pair so that it is a solution to the equation $x + 2y = 8$.

a. $(0, \ )$

b. $(\ , 3)$

c. $(-4, \ )$

Solutions of equations in two variables can also be recorded in a **table of paired values,** as shown in the next example.

Answers

5. a. $(0, 4)$ **b.** $(2, 3)$ **c.** $(-4, 6)$

PRACTICE 6

Complete the table for the equation $y = -2x$.

	x	y
a.	-3	
b.		0
c.		10

Example 6 Complete the table for the equation $y = 3x$.

	x	y
a.	-1	
b.		0
c.		-9

Solution:

a. We replace x with -1 in the equation and solve for y.

$y = 3x$

$y = 3(-1)$ Let $x = -1$.

$y = -3$

The ordered pair is $(-1, -3)$.

b. We replace y with 0 in the equation and solve for x.

$y = 3x$

$0 = 3x$ Let $y = 0$.

$0 = x$ Divide both sides by 3.

The ordered pair is $(0, 0)$.

c. We replace y with -9 in the equation and solve for x.

$y = 3x$

$-9 = 3x$ Let $y = -9$.

$-3 = x$ Divide both sides by 3.

The ordered pair is $(-3, -9)$. The completed table is shown to the right.

x	y
-1	-3
0	0
-3	-9

Work Practice 6

PRACTICE 7

Complete the table for the equation $y = \frac{1}{3}x - 1$.

	x	y
a.	-3	
b.	0	
c.		0

Example 7 Complete the table for the equation

$$y = \frac{1}{2}x - 5.$$

	x	y
a.	-2	
b.	0	
c.		0

Solution:

a. Let $x = -2$.

$y = \frac{1}{2}x - 5$

$y = \frac{1}{2}(-2) - 5$

$y = -1 - 5$

$y = -6$

b. Let $x = 0$.

$y = \frac{1}{2}x - 5$

$y = \frac{1}{2}(0) - 5$

$y = 0 - 5$

$y = -5$

c. Let $y = 0$.

$y = \frac{1}{2}x - 5$

$0 = \frac{1}{2}x - 5$ Now, solve for x.

$5 = \frac{1}{2}x$ Add 5.

$10 = x$ Multiply by 2.

Ordered Pairs: $(-2, -6)$ $(0, -5)$ $(10, 0)$

The completed table is

x	y
-2	-6
0	-5
10	0

Work Practice 7

Answers

6.

	x	y
a.	-3	6
b.	0	0
c.	-5	10

7.

	x	y
a.	-3	-2
b.	0	-1
c.	3	0

By now, you have noticed that equations in two variables often have more than one solution. We discuss this more in the next section.

A table showing ordered pair solutions may be written vertically or horizontally, as shown in the next example.

Example 8 A small business purchased a computer for \$2000. The business predicts that the computer will be used for 5 years and the value in dollars y of the computer in x years is $y = -300x + 2000$. Complete the table.

x	0	1	2	3	4	5
y						

Solution:

To find the value of y when x is 0, we replace x with 0 in the equation. We use this same procedure to find y when x is 1 and when x is 2.

When $x = 0$,

$y = -300x + 2000$
$y = -300 \cdot 0 + 2000$
$y = 0 + 2000$
$y = 2000$

When $x = 1$,

$y = -300x + 2000$
$y = -300 \cdot 1 + 2000$
$y = -300 + 2000$
$y = 1700$

When $x = 2$,

$y = -300x + 2000$
$y = -300 \cdot 2 + 2000$
$y = -600 + 2000$
$y = 1400$

We have the ordered pairs (0, 2000), (1, 1700), and (2, 1400). This means that in 0 years the value of the computer is \$2000, in 1 year the value of the computer is \$1700, and in 2 years the value is \$1400. To complete the table of values, we continue the procedure for $x = 3$, $x = 4$, and $x = 5$.

When $x = 3$,

$y = -300x + 2000$
$y = -300 \cdot 3 + 2000$
$y = -900 + 2000$
$y = 1100$

When $x = 4$,

$y = -300x + 2000$
$y = -300 \cdot 4 + 2000$
$y = -1200 + 2000$
$y = 800$

When $x = 5$,

$y = -300x + 2000$
$y = -300 \cdot 5 + 2000$
$y = -1500 + 2000$
$y = 500$

The completed table is shown below.

x	0	1	2	3	4	5
y	2000	1700	1400	1100	800	500

Work Practice 8

PRACTICE 8

A company purchased a fax machine for \$400. The business manager of the company predicts that the fax machine will be used for 7 years and the value in dollars y of the machine in x years is $y = -50x + 400$. Complete the table.

x	1	2	3	4	5	6	7
y							

The ordered pair solutions recorded in the completed table for Example 8 are another set of paired data. They are graphed next. Notice that this scatter diagram gives a visual picture of the decrease in value of the computer.

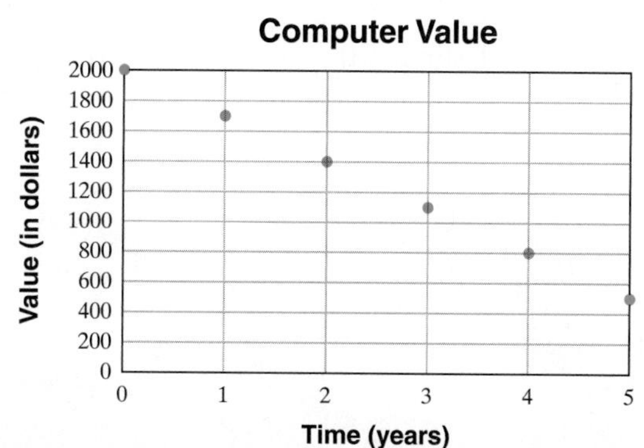

Answer

8.

x	1	2	3	4	5	6	7
y	350	300	250	200	150	100	50

Vocabulary and Readiness Check

Use the choices below to fill in each blank. The exercises below all have to do with the rectangular coordinate system.

origin	x-coordinate	x-axis	scatter diagram	four
quadrants	y-coordinate	y-axis	solution	one

1. The horizontal axis is called the ______________.
2. The vertical axis is called the ______________.
3. The intersection of the horizontal axis and the vertical axis is a point called the ______________.
4. The axes divide the plane into regions, called ______________. There are ______________ of these regions.
5. In the ordered pair of numbers $(-2, 5)$, the number -2 is called the ______________ and the number 5 is called the ______________.
6. Each ordered pair of numbers corresponds to ______________ point in the plane.
7. An ordered pair is a(n) ______________ of an equation in two variables if replacing the variables by the coordinates of the ordered pair results in a true statement.
8. The graph of paired data as points in a rectangular coordinate system is called a(n) ______________.

13.1 Exercise Set

FOR EXTRA HELP

MyMathLab

PRACTICE

WATCH

DOWNLOAD

READ

REVIEW

Objective A *The following bar graph shows the top 10 tourist destinations and the number of tourists that visit each country per year. Use this graph to answer Exercises 1 through 6. See Example 1.*

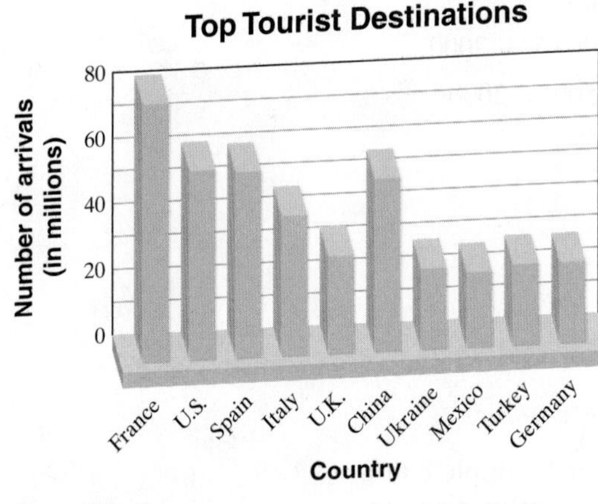

Source: Wikipedia

1. Which country shown is the most popular tourist destination?

2. Which country shown is the least popular tourist destination?

3. Which countries shown have more than 40 million tourists per year?

4. Which countries shown have fewer than 30 million tourists per year?

5. Estimate the number of tourists per year whose destination is Italy.

6. Estimate the number of tourists per year whose destination is the U.K.

The following line graph shows the paid attendance at each Super Bowl game from 2003 through 2009. Use this graph to answer Exercises 7 through 10. See Example 2.

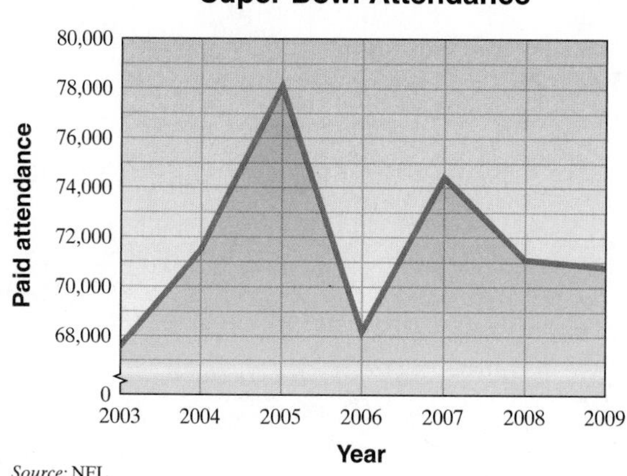

Source: NFL

7. Estimate the Super Bowl attendance in 2009.

8. Estimate the Super Bowl attendance in 2004.

9. Find the year on the graph with the greatest Super Bowl attendance and approximate that attendance.

10. Find the year on the graph with the least Super Bowl attendance and approximate that attendance.

The line graph below shows the number of students per computer in U.S. public schools. Use this graph for Exercises 11 through 16. See Example 2.

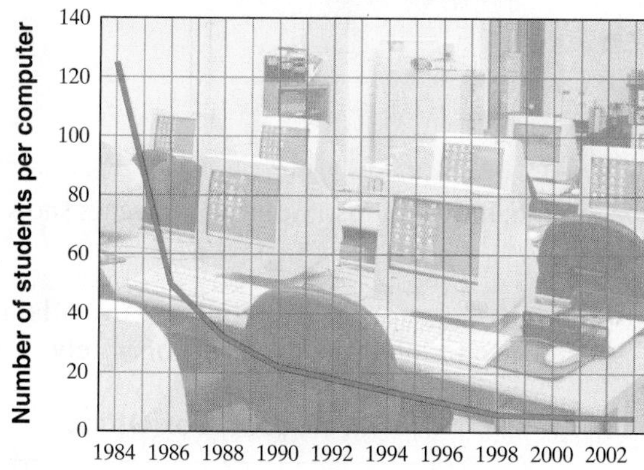

Source: World Almanac, 2005

11. Approximate the number of students per computer in 1986.

12. Approximate the number of students per computer in 2002.

13. Between what years did the greatest decrease in number of students per computer occur?

14. What was the first year that the number of students per computer fell below 20?

15. What was the first year that the number of students per computer fell below 15?

16. Discuss any trends shown by this line graph.

Objective **B** *Plot each ordered pair. State in which quadrant or on which axis each point lies. See Example 3.*

17. **a.** $(1, 5)$ **b.** $(-5, -2)$ **c.** $(-3, 0)$ **d.** $(0, -1)$
e. $(2, -4)$ **f.** $\left(-1, 4\frac{1}{2}\right)$ **g.** $(3.7, 2.2)$ **h.** $\left(\frac{1}{2}, -3\right)$

18. **a.** $(2, 4)$ **b.** $(0, 2)$ **c.** $(-2, 1)$ **d.** $(-3, -3)$
e. $\left(3\frac{3}{4}, 0\right)$ **f.** $(5, -4)$ **g.** $(-3.4, 4.8)$ **h.** $\left(\frac{1}{3}, -5\right)$

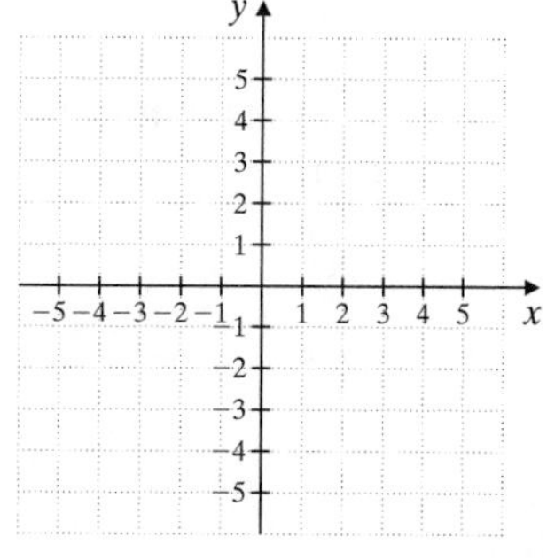

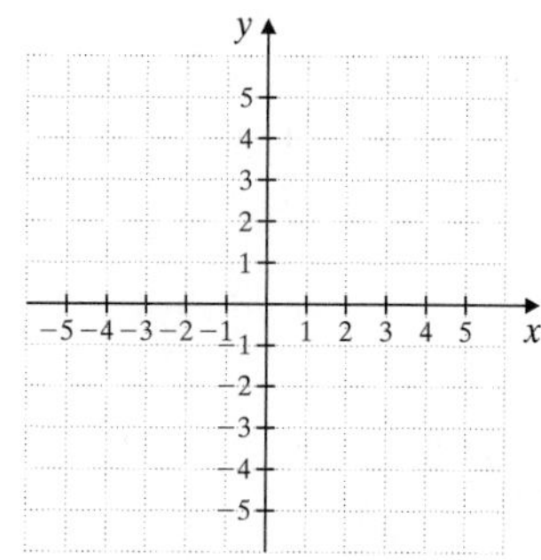

Find the x- and y-coordinates of each labeled point. See Example 3.

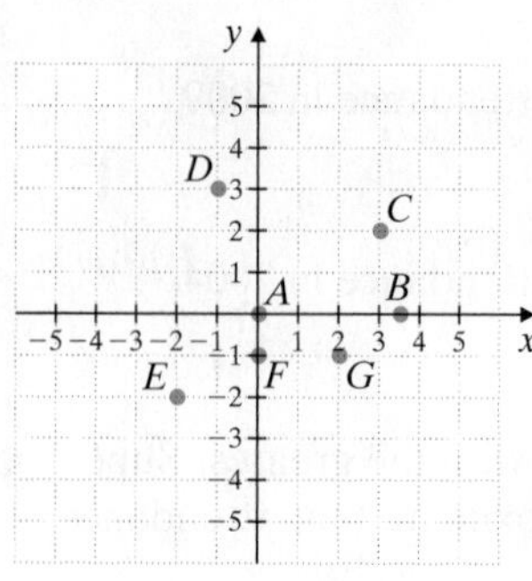

19. A **20.** B **21.** C

22. D **23.** E **24.** F

25. G

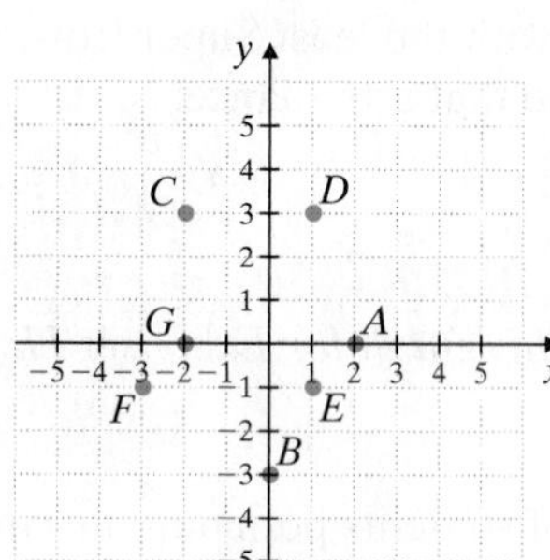

26. A **27.** B **28.** C

29. D **30.** E **31.** F

32. G

Objective C *Solve. See Example 4.*

33. The table shows the domestic box office (in billions of dollars) for the U.S. movie industry during the years shown. (*Source:* Motion Picture Association of America)

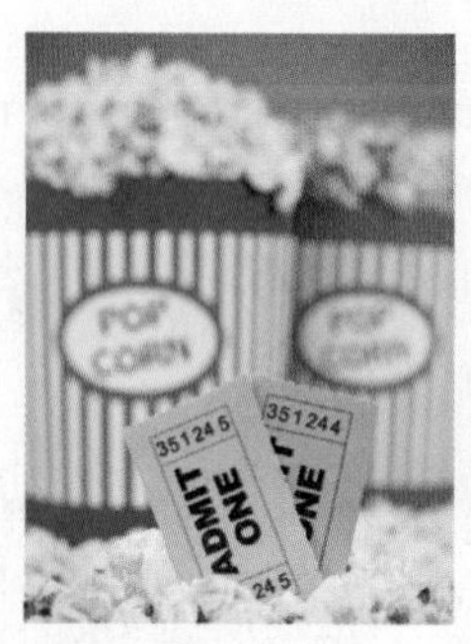

Year	Box Office (in billions of dollars)
2003	9.17
2004	9.22
2005	8.83
2006	9.14
2007	9.63
2008	9.79

a. Write this paired data as a set of ordered pairs of the form (year, box office).

b. In your own words, write the meaning of the ordered pair (2006, 9.14).

c. Create a scatter diagram of the paired data. Be sure to label the axes appropriately.

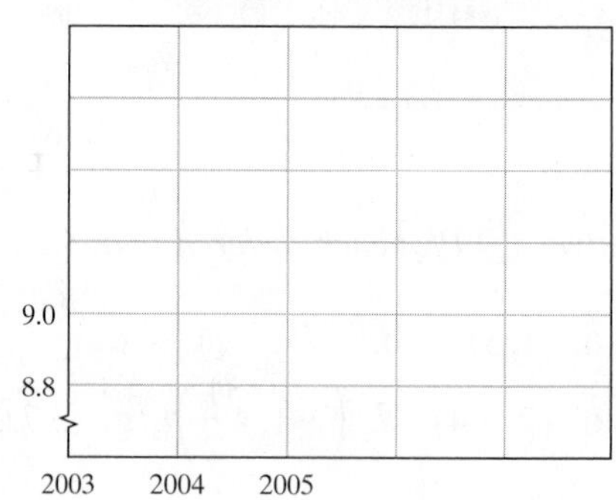

d. What trend in the paired data does the scatter diagram show?

34. The table shows the amount of money (in billions of dollars) that Americans spent on their pets for the years shown. (*Source:* American Pet Products Manufacturers Association)

Year	Pet-Related Expenditures (in billions of dollars)
2005	36.3
2006	38.5
2007	41.2
2008	43.4

a. Write this paired data as a set of ordered pairs of the form (year, pet-related expenditures).

b. In your own words, write the meaning of the ordered pair (2007, 41.2).

c. Create a scatter diagram of the paired data. Be sure to label the axes appropriately.

Pet-Related Expenditures

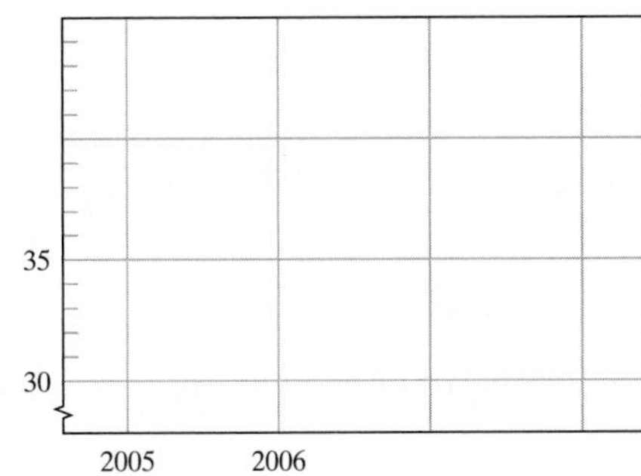

d. What trend in the paired data does the scatter diagram show?

35. Minh, a psychology student, kept a record of how much time she spent studying for each of her 20-point psychology quizzes and her score on each quiz.

Hours Spent Studying	0.50	0.75	1.00	1.25	1.50	1.50	1.75	2.00
Quiz Score	10	12	15	16	18	19	19	20

a. Write the data as ordered pairs of the form (hours spent studying, quiz score).

b. In your own words, write the meaning of the ordered pair (1.25, 16).

c. Create a scatter diagram of the paired data. Be sure to label the axes appropriately.

d. What might Minh conclude from the scatter diagram?

Minh's Chart for Psychology

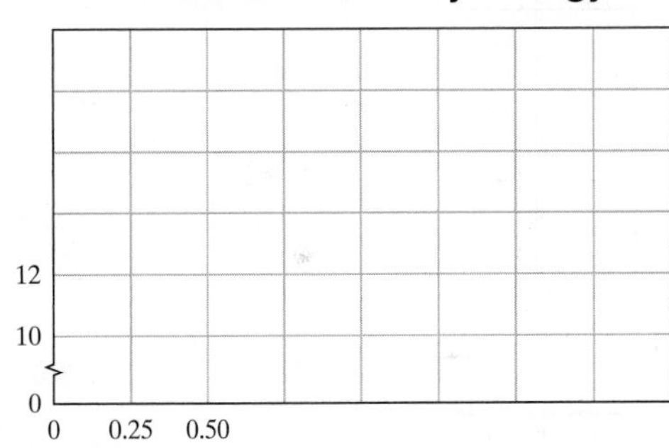

36. A local lumberyard uses quantity pricing. The table shows the price per board for different amounts of lumber purchased.

Price per Board (in dollars)	Number of Boards Purchased
8.00	1
7.50	10
6.50	25
5.00	50
2.00	100

a. Write the data as ordered pairs of the form (price per board, number of boards purchased).

b. In your own words, write the meaning of the ordered pair (2.00, 100).

c. Create a scatter diagram of the paired data. Be sure to label the axes appropriately.

Lumberyard Board Pricing

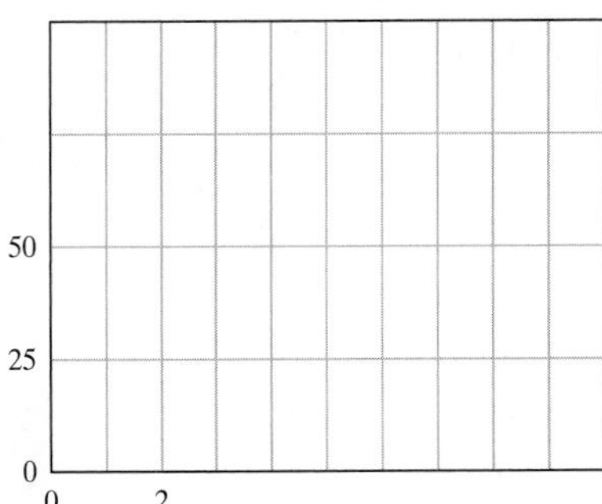

d. What trend in the paired data does the scatter diagram show?

Objective D *Complete each ordered pair so that it is a solution of the given linear equation. See Example 5.*

37. $x - 4y = 4$; (, −2), (4,)

38. $x - 5y = -1$; (, −2), (4,)

39. $y = \frac{1}{4}x - 3$; (−8,), (, 1)

40. $y = \frac{1}{5}x - 2$; (−10,), (, 1)

Complete the table of ordered pairs for each linear equation. See Examples 6 and 7.

41. $y = -7x$

x	y
0	
−1	
	2

42. $y = -9x$

x	y
	0
−3	
	2

43. $x = -y + 2$

x	y
0	
	0
−3	

44. $x = -y + 4$

x	y
	0
0	
	−3

45. $y = \frac{1}{2}x$

x	y
0	
−6	
	1

46. $y = \frac{1}{3}x$

x	y
0	
−6	
	1

47. $x + 3y = 6$

x	y
0	
	0
	1

48. $2x + y = 4$

x	y
0	
	0
	2

49. $y = 2x - 12$

x	y
0	
	−2
3	

50. $y = 5x + 10$

x	y
	0
	5
0	

51. $2x + 7y = 5$

x	y
0	
	0
	1

52. $x - 6y = 3$

x	y
0	
1	
	−1

Objectives B C D Mixed Practice *Complete the table of ordered pairs for each equation. Then plot the ordered pair solutions. See Examples 3 through 7.*

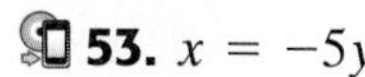

53. $x = -5y$

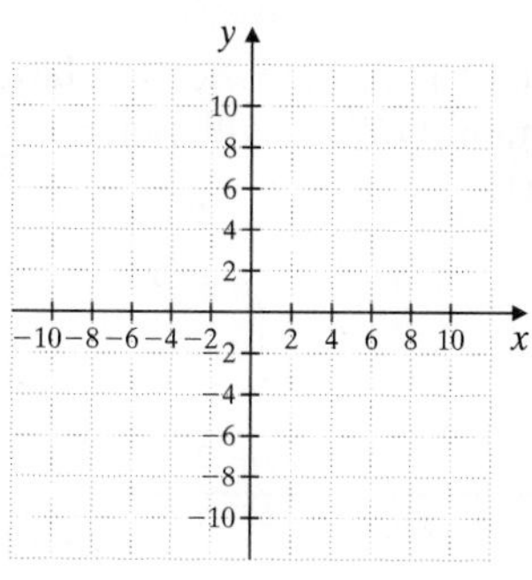

x	y
	0
	1
10	

54. $y = -3x$

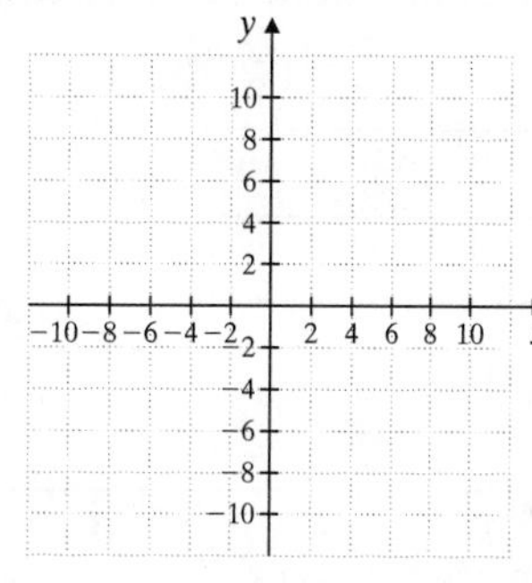

x	y
0	
−2	
	9

55. $y = \frac{1}{3}x + 2$

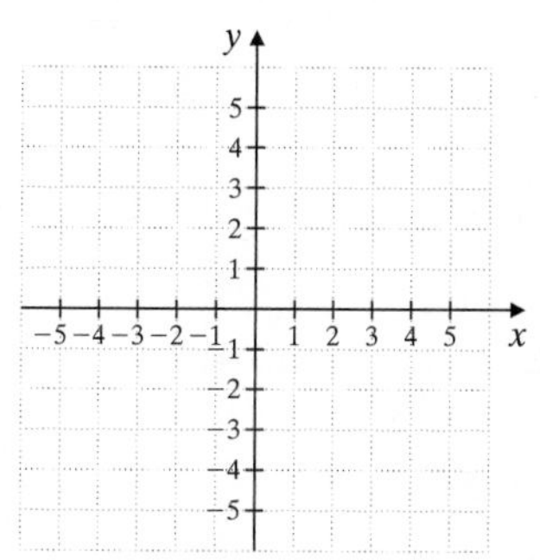

x	y
0	
−3	
	0

56. $y = \frac{1}{2}x + 3$

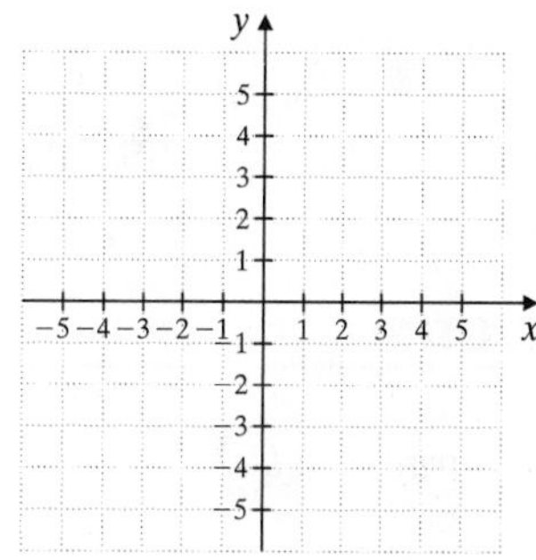

x	y
0	
−4	
	0

Solve. See Example 8.

57. The cost in dollars y of producing x computer desks is given by $y = 80x + 5000$.

a. Complete the table.

x	100	200	300
y			

b. Find the number of computer desks that can be produced for \$8600. (*Hint:* Find x when $y = 8600$.)

58. The hourly wage y of an employee at a certain production company is given by $y = 0.25x + 9$ where x is the number of units produced by the employee in an hour.

a. Complete the table.

x	0	1	5	10
y				

b. Find the number of units that an employee must produce each hour to earn an hourly wage of \$12.25. (*Hint:* Find x when $y = 12.25$.)

59. The average annual cinema admission price y (in dollars) from 2000 through 2008 is given by $y = 0.2x + 5.39$. In this equation, x represents the number of years after 2000. (*Source:* Motion Picture Association of America)

a. Complete the table.

x	1	3	5
y			

b. Find the year in which the average cinema admission price was approximately \$6.40. (*Hint:* Find x when $y = 6.40$ and round to the nearest whole number.)

c. Use the given equation to predict when the cinema admission price might be \$8.00. (Use the hint for part b.)

60. The amount y of land occupied by farms in the United States (in millions of acres) from 1997 through 2007 is given by $y = -4x + 967$. In the equation, x represents the number of years after 1997. (*Source:* National Agricultural Statistics Service)

a. Complete the table.

x	4	7	10
y			

b. Find the year in which there were approximately 930 million acres of land occupied by farms. (*Hint:* Find x when $y = 930$ and round to the nearest whole number.)

c. Use the given equation to predict when the land occupied by farms might be 900 million acres. (Use the hint for part b.)

Review

Solve each equation for y. See Section 9.5.

61. $x + y = 5$

62. $x - y = 3$

63. $2x + 4y = 5$

64. $5x + 2y = 7$

65. $10x = -5y$

66. $4y = -8x$

Concept Extensions

Answer each exercise with true or false.

67. Point $(-1, 5)$ lies in quadrant IV.

68. Point $(3, 0)$ lies on the y-axis.

69. For the point $\left(-\frac{1}{2}, 1.5\right)$, the first value, $-\frac{1}{2}$, is the x-coordinate and the second value, 1.5, is the y-coordinate.

70. The ordered pair $\left(2, \frac{2}{3}\right)$ is a solution of $2x - 3y = 6$.

For Exercises 71 through 75, fill in each blank with "0," "positive," or "negative." For Exercises 76 and 77, fill in each blank with "x" or "y."

	Point	Location
71.	(_______, _______)	quadrant III
72.	(_______, _______)	quadrant I
73.	(_______, _______)	quadrant IV
74.	(_______, _______)	quadrant II
75.	(_______, _______)	origin
76.	(number, 0)	__-axis
77.	(0, number)	__-axis

78. Give an example of an ordered pair whose location is in (or on)

a. quadrant I **b.** quadrant II **c.** quadrant III
d. quadrant IV **e.** x-axis **f.** y-axis

Solve. See the Concept Checks in this section.

79. Is the graph of $(3, 0)$ in the same location as the graph of $(0, 3)$? Explain why or why not.

80. Give the coordinates of a point such that if the coordinates are reversed, the location is the same.

81. In general, what points can have coordinates reversed and still have the same location?

82. In your own words, describe how to plot or graph an ordered pair of numbers.

83. Discuss any similarities in the graphs of the ordered pair solutions for Exercises 53–56.

84. Discuss any differences in the graphs of the ordered pair solution for Exercises 53–56.

Write an ordered pair for each point described.

85. Point C is four units to the right of the y-axis and seven units below the x-axis.

86. Point D is three units to the left of the origin.

△ **87.** Find the perimeter of the rectangle whose vertices are the points with coordinates $(-1, 5)$, $(3, 5)$, $(3, -4)$, and $(-1, -4)$.

△ **88.** Find the area of the rectangle whose vertices are the points with coordinates $(5, 2)$, $(5, -6)$, $(0, -6)$, and $(0, 2)$.

The scatter diagram below shows Target's annual revenues. The horizontal axis represents the number of years after 2003.

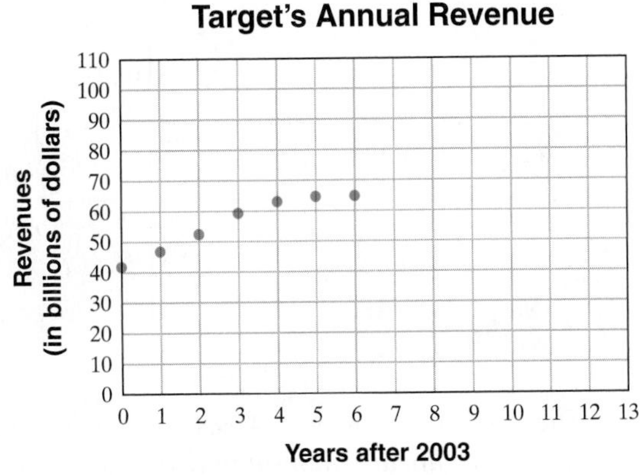

89. Estimate the annual revenues for years 1, 2, 3, and 4.

90. Use a straightedge or ruler and this scatter diagram to predict Target's revenue in the year 2015.

Objective

A **Graph a Linear Equation by Finding and Plotting Ordered Pair Solutions.**

13.2 GRAPHING LINEAR EQUATIONS

In the previous section, we found that equations in two variables may have more than one solution. For example, both (2, 2) and (0, 4) are solutions of the equation $x + y = 4$. In fact, this equation has an infinite number of solutions. Other solutions include $(-2, 6)$, $(4, 0)$, and $(6, -2)$. Notice the pattern that appears in the graph of these solutions.

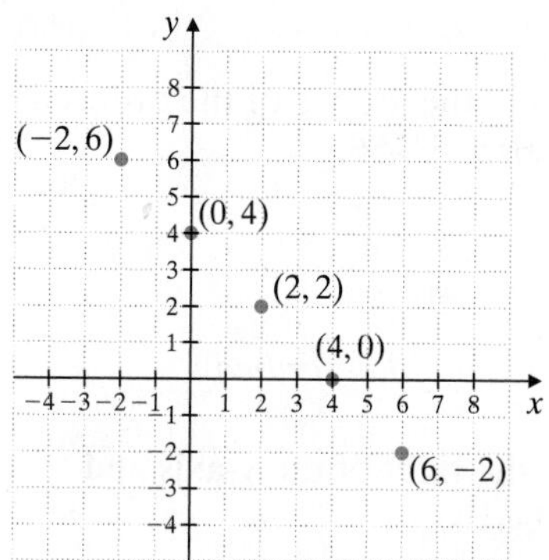

These solutions all appear to lie on the same line, as seen in the second graph. It can be shown that every ordered pair solution of the equation corresponds to a point on this line, and every point on this line corresponds to an ordered pair solution. Thus, we say that this line is the **graph of the equation** $x + y = 4$. Notice that we can show only a part of a line on a graph. The arrowheads on each end of the line below remind us that the line actually extends indefinitely in both directions.

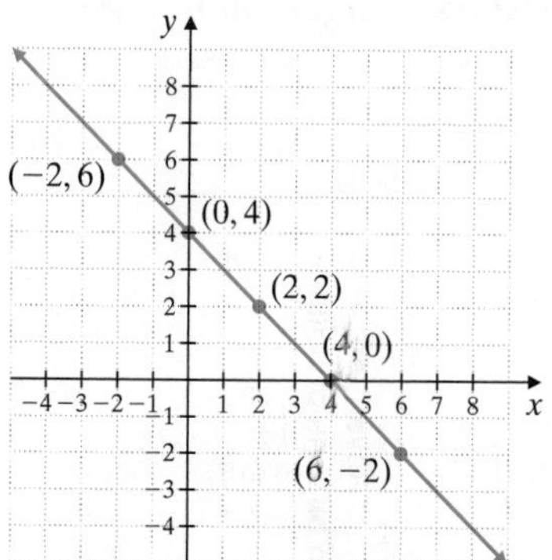

The equation $x + y = 4$ is called a *linear equation in two variables* and *the graph of every linear equation in two variables is a straight line.*

Linear Equation in Two Variables

A **linear equation in two variables** is an equation that can be written in the form

$$Ax + By = C$$

where A, B, and C are real numbers and A and B are not both 0. This form is called **standard form. The graph of a linear equation in two variables is a straight line.**

A linear equation in two variables may be written in many forms. Standard form, $Ax + By = C$, is just one of many of these forms.

Following are examples of linear equations in two variables.

$2x + y = 8 \qquad -2x = 7y \qquad y = \frac{1}{3}x + 2 \qquad y = 7$

(Standard Form)

Objective A Graphing Linear Equations

From geometry, we know that a straight line is determined by just two points. Thus, to graph a linear equation in two variables, we need to find just two of its infinitely many solutions. Once we do so, we plot the solution points and draw the line connecting the points. Usually, we find a third solution as well, as a check.

Example 1 Graph the linear equation $2x + y = 5$.

Solution: To graph this equation, we find three ordered pair solutions of $2x + y = 5$. To do this, we choose a value for one variable, x or y, and solve for the other variable. For example, if we let $x = 1$, then $2x + y = 5$ becomes

$$\begin{aligned} 2x + y &= 5 \\ 2(1) + y &= 5 \quad \text{Replace } x \text{ with 1.} \\ 2 + y &= 5 \quad \text{Multiply.} \\ y &= 3 \quad \text{Subtract 2 from both sides.} \end{aligned}$$

Since $y = 3$ when $x = 1$, the ordered pair $(1, 3)$ is a solution of $2x + y = 5$. Next, we let $x = 0$.

$$\begin{aligned} 2x + y &= 5 \\ 2(0) + y &= 5 \quad \text{Replace } x \text{ with 0.} \\ 0 + y &= 5 \\ y &= 5 \end{aligned}$$

The ordered pair $(0, 5)$ is a second solution.

The two solutions found so far allow us to draw the straight line that is the graph of all solutions of $2x + y = 5$. However, we will find a third ordered pair as a check. Let $y = -1$.

$$\begin{aligned} 2x + y &= 5 \\ 2x + (-1) &= 5 \quad \text{Replace } y \text{ with } -1. \\ 2x - 1 &= 5 \\ 2x &= 6 \quad \text{Add 1 to both sides.} \\ x &= 3 \quad \text{Divide both sides by 2.} \end{aligned}$$

The third solution is $(3, -1)$. These three ordered pair solutions are listed in the table and plotted on the coordinate plane. The graph of $2x + y = 5$ is the line through the three points.

x	y
1	3
0	5
3	−1

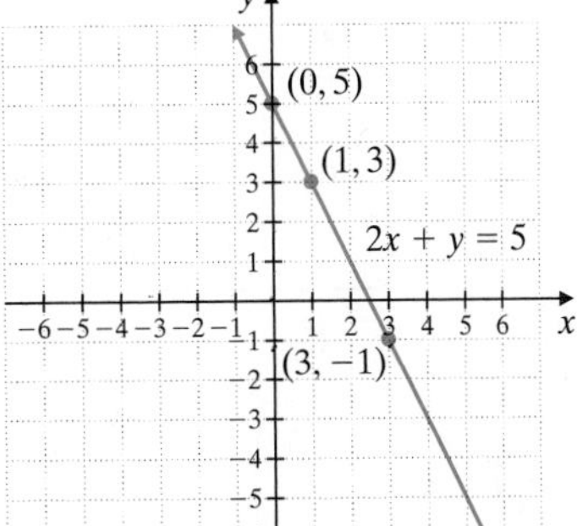

Work Practice 1

PRACTICE 1

Graph the linear equation $x + 3y = 6$.

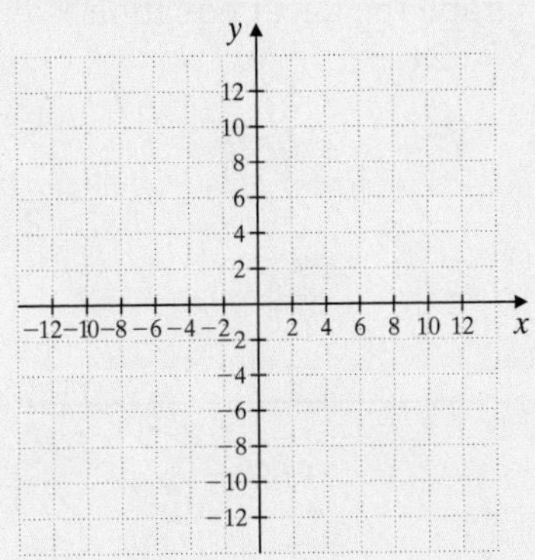

Helpful Hint All three points should fall on the same straight line. If not, check your ordered pair solutions for a mistake.

Answer

1.

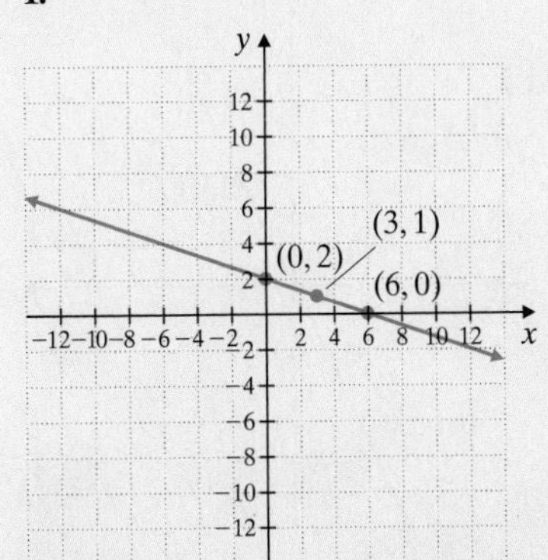

PRACTICE 2

Graph the linear equation $-2x + 4y = 8$.

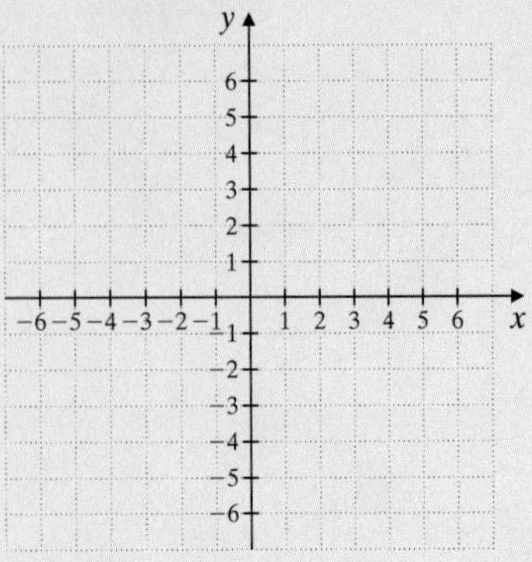

PRACTICE 3

Graph the linear equation $y = 2x$.

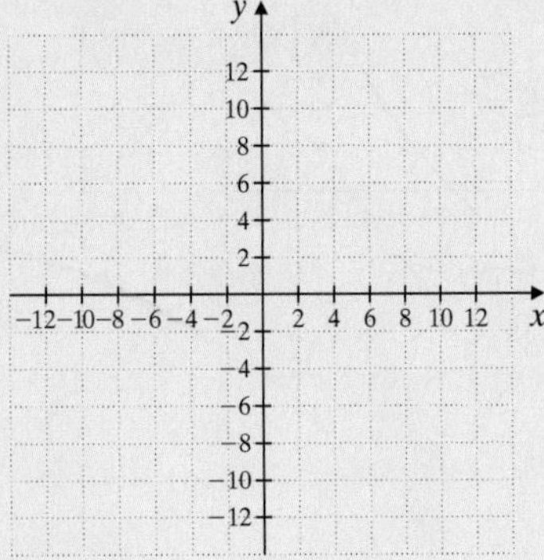

Answers

2.

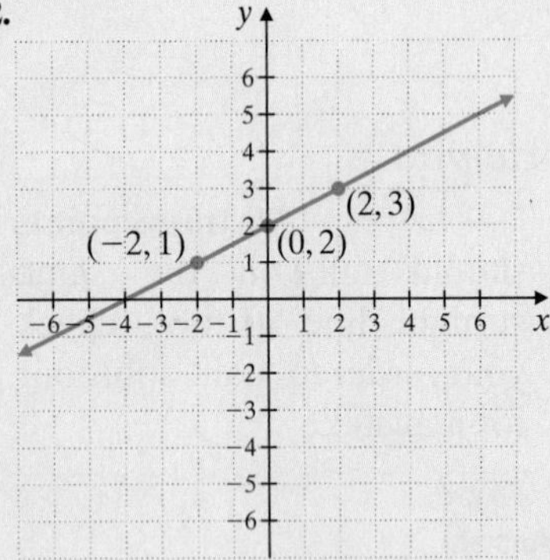

3.

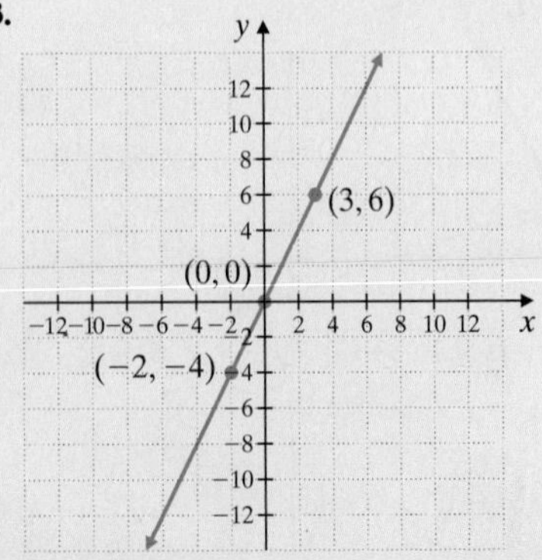

Example 2 Graph the linear equation $-5x + 3y = 15$.

Solution: We find three ordered pair solutions of $-5x + 3y = 15$.

Let $x = 0$.

$$-5x + 3y = 15$$
$$-5 \cdot 0 + 3y = 15$$
$$0 + 3y = 15$$
$$3y = 15$$
$$y = 5$$

Let $y = 0$.

$$-5x + 3y = 15$$
$$-5x + 3 \cdot 0 = 15$$
$$-5x + 0 = 15$$
$$-5x = 15$$
$$x = -3$$

Let $x = -2$.

$$-5x + 3y = 15$$
$$-5 \cdot -2 + 3y = 15$$
$$10 + 3y = 15$$
$$3y = 5$$
$$y = \frac{5}{3} \text{ or } 1\frac{2}{3}$$

The ordered pairs are $(0, 5)$, $(-3, 0)$, and $\left(-2, 1\frac{2}{3}\right)$. The graph of $-5x + 3y = 15$ is the line through the three points.

x	y
0	5
−3	0
−2	$1\frac{2}{3}$

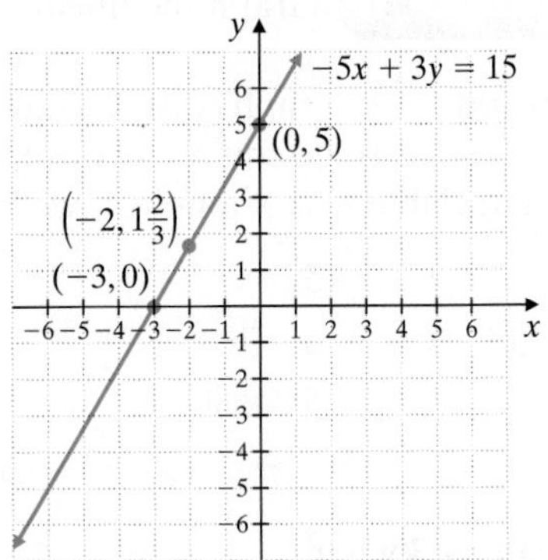

Work Practice 2

Example 3 Graph the linear equation $y = 3x$.

Solution: We find three ordered pair solutions. Since this equation is solved for y, we'll choose three x-values.

If $x = 2$, $y = 3 \cdot 2 = 6$.

If $x = 0$, $y = 3 \cdot 0 = 0$.

If $x = -1$, $y = 3 \cdot -1 = -3$.

Next, we plot the ordered pair solutions and draw a line through the plotted points. The line is the graph of $y = 3x$.

Think about the following for a moment: A line is made up of an infinite number of points. Every point on the line defined by $y = 3x$ represents an ordered pair solution of the equation and every ordered pair solution is a point on this line.

x	y
2	6
0	0
−1	−3

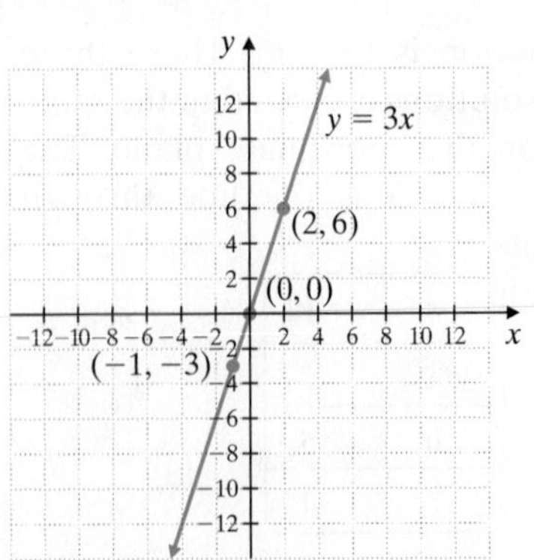

Work Practice 3

Helpful Hint

When graphing a linear equation in two variables, if it is

- solved for y, it may be easier to find ordered pair solutions by choosing x-values. If it is
- solved for x, it may be easier to find ordered pair solutions by choosing y-values.

Example 4 Graph the linear equation $y = -\frac{1}{3}x + 2$.

Solution: We find three ordered pair solutions, plot the solutions, and draw a line through the plotted solutions. To avoid fractions, we'll choose x-values that are multiples of 3 to substitute into the equation.

If $x = 6$, then $y = -\frac{1}{3} \cdot 6 + 2 = -2 + 2 = 0$

If $x = 0$, then $y = -\frac{1}{3} \cdot 0 + 2 = 0 + 2 = 2$

If $x = -3$, then $y = -\frac{1}{3} \cdot -3 + 2 = 1 + 2 = 3$

x	y
6	0
0	2
−3	3

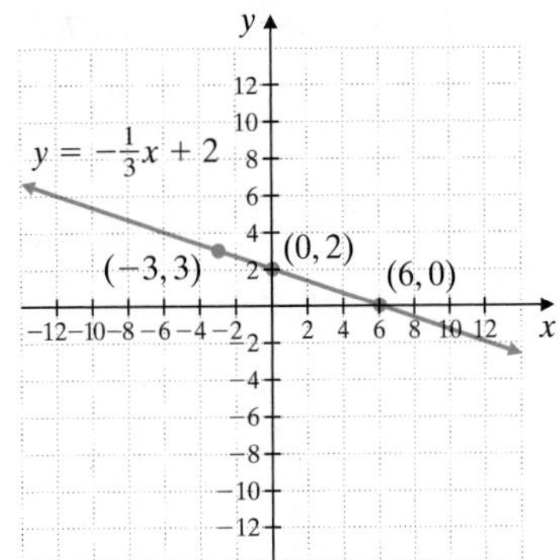

Work Practice 4

Let's take a moment and compare the graphs in Examples 3 and 4. The graph of $y = 3x$ tilts upward (as we follow the line from left to right) and the graph of $y = -\frac{1}{3}x + 2$ tilts downward (as we follow the line from left to right). We will learn more about the tilt, or slope, of a line in Section 6.4.

Example 5 Graph the linear equation $y = -2$.

Solution: The equation $y = -2$ can be written in standard form as $0x + y = -2$. No matter what value we replace x with, y is always -2.

x	y
0	−2
3	−2
−2	−2

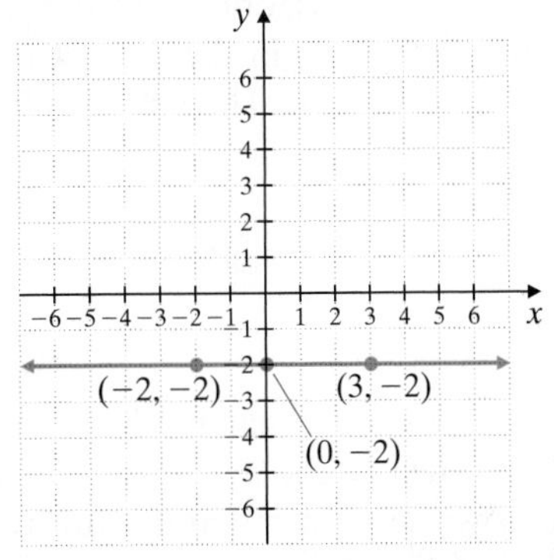

Notice that the graph of $y = -2$ is a horizontal line.

Work Practice 5

Linear equations are often used to model real data, as seen in the next example.

PRACTICE 4

Graph the linear equation $y = -\frac{1}{2}x + 4$.

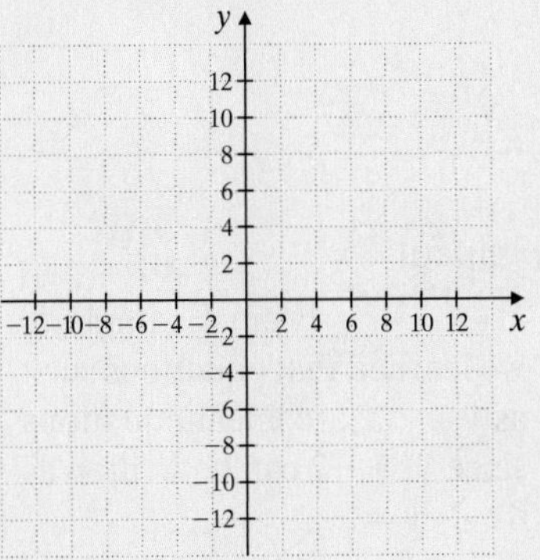

PRACTICE 5

Graph the linear equation $x = 3$.

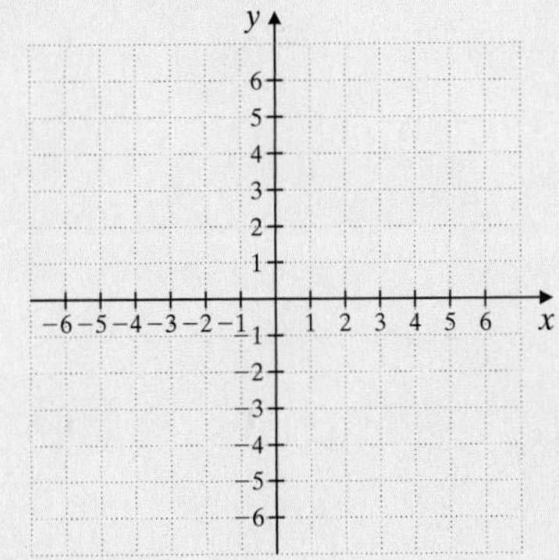

Answers

4.

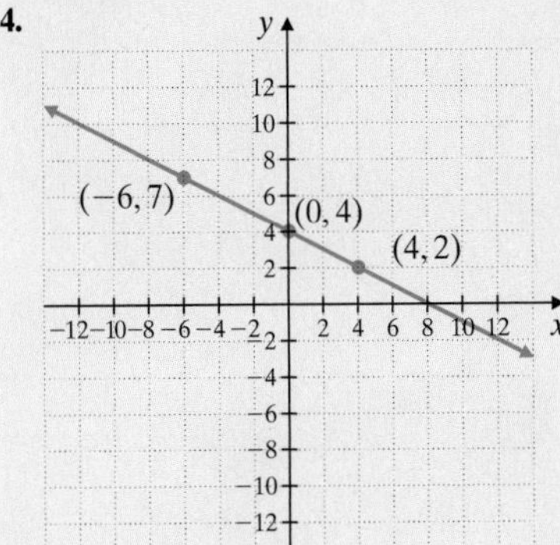

5.

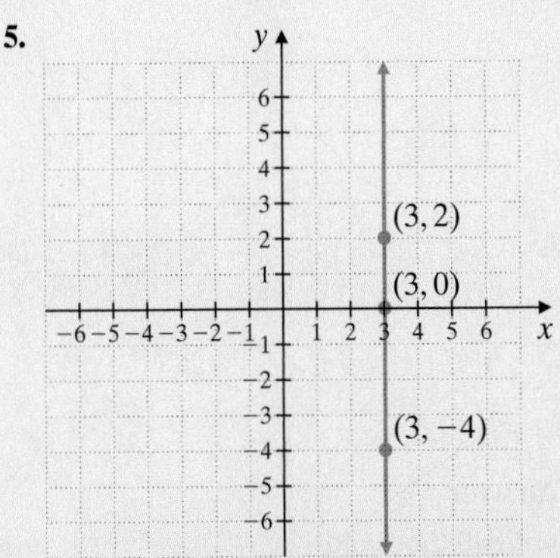

PRACTICE 6

Use the graph in Example 6 to predict the number of registered nurses in 2015.

Helpful Hint From Example 5, we learned that equations such as $y = -2$ are linear equations since $y = -2$ can be written as $0x + y = -2$.

Example 6 Estimating the Number of Registered Nurses

One of the occupations expected to have the most growth in the next few years is registered nurse. The number of people y (in thousands) employed as registered nurses in the United States can be estimated by the linear equation $y = 46.7x + 2279$, where x is the number of years after the year 2003. (*Source:* Based on data from the Bureau of Labor Statistics)

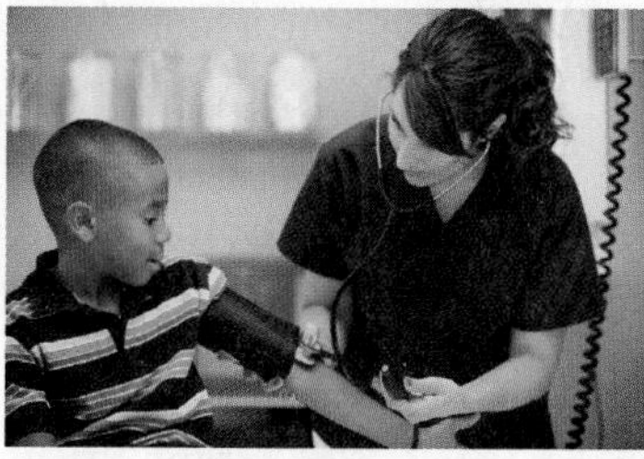

a. Graph the equation.

b. Use the graph to predict the number of registered nurses in the year 2014.

Solution:

a. To graph $y = 46.7x + 2279$, choose x-values and substitute in the equation.

If $x = 0$, then $y = 46.7(0) + 2279 = 2279$.

If $x = 2$, then $y = 46.7(2) + 2279 = 2372.4$.

If $x = 5$, then $y = 46.7(5) + 2279 = 2512.5$.

x	y
0	2279
2	2372.4
5	2512.5

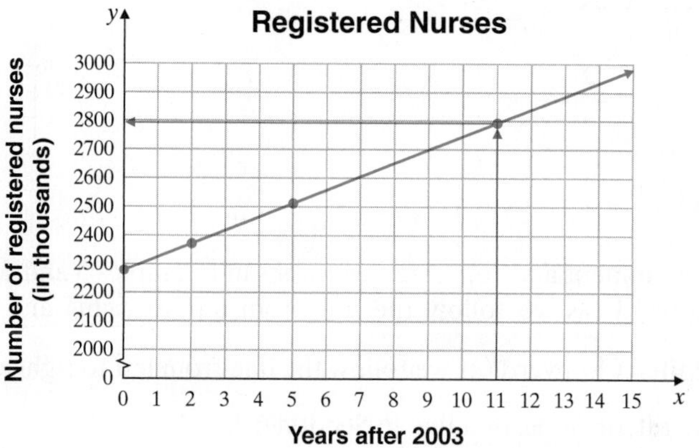

b. To use the graph to *predict* the number of registered nurses in the year 2014, we need to find the y-coordinate that corresponds to $x = 11$. (11 years after 2003 is the year 2014.) To do so, find 11 on the x-axis. Move vertically upward to the graphed line and then horizontally to the left. We approximate the number on the y-axis to be 2800. Thus, in the year 2014, we predict that there will be 2800 thousand registered nurses. (The actual value, using 11 for x, is 2792.7.)

Work Practice 6

Helpful Hint

Make sure you understand that models are mathematical approximations of the data for the known years. (For example, see the model in Example 6.) Any number of unknown factors can affect future years, so be cautious when using models to make predictions.

Answer

6. 2840 thousand

Calculator Explorations Graphing

In this section, we begin an optional study of graphing calculators and graphing software packages for computers. These graphers use the same point plotting technique that was introduced in this section. The advantage of this graphing technology is, of course, that graphing calculators and computers can find and plot ordered pair solutions much faster than we can. Note, however, that the features described in these boxes may not be available on all graphing calculators.

The rectangular screen where a portion of the rectangular coordinate system is displayed is called a **window.** We call it a **standard window** for graphing when both the x- and y-axes show coordinates between -10 and 10. This information is often displayed in the window menu on a graphing calculator as follows.

Xmin = −10
Xmax = 10
Xscl = 1 The scale on the x-axis is one unit per tick mark.
Ymin = −10
Ymax = 10
Yscl = 1 The scale on the y-axis is one unit per tick mark.

To use a graphing calculator to graph the equation $y = 2x + 3$, press the [Y=] key and enter the keystrokes [2] [x] [+] [3]. The top row should now read $Y_1 = 2x + 3$. Next press the [GRAPH] key, and the display should look like this:

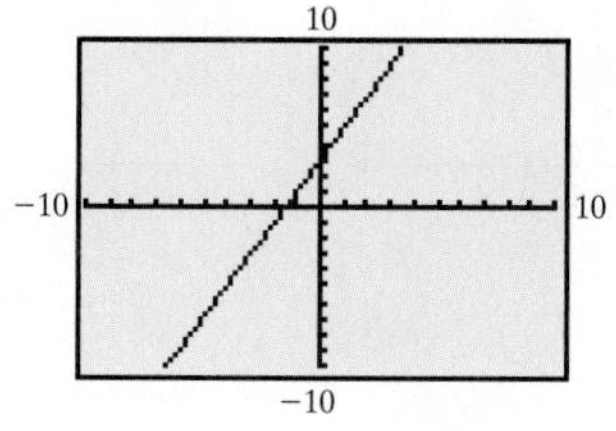

Graph the following linear equations. (Unless otherwise stated, use a standard window when graphing.)

1. $y = -3x + 7$

2. $y = -x + 5$

3. $y = 2.5x - 7.9$

4. $y = -1.3x + 5.2$

5. $y = -\frac{3}{10}x + \frac{32}{5}$

6. $y = \frac{2}{9}x - \frac{22}{3}$

13.2 Exercise Set

FOR EXTRA HELP

MyMathLab

PRACTICE

WATCH

DOWNLOAD

READ

REVIEW

Objective A *For each equation, find three ordered pair solutions by completing the table. Then use the ordered pairs to graph the equation. See Examples 1 through 5.*

1. $x - y = 6$

x	y
	0
4	
	−1

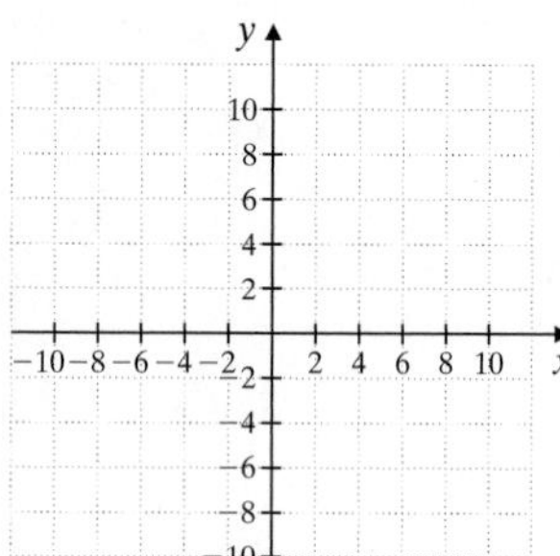

2. $x - y = 4$

x	y
0	
	2
−1	

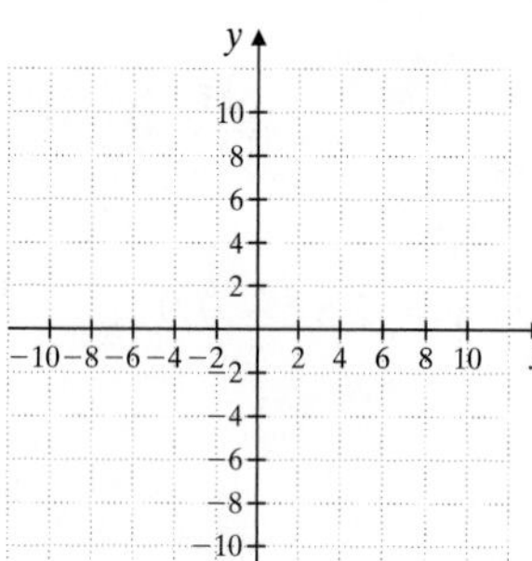

3. $y = -4x$

x	y
1	
0	
−1	

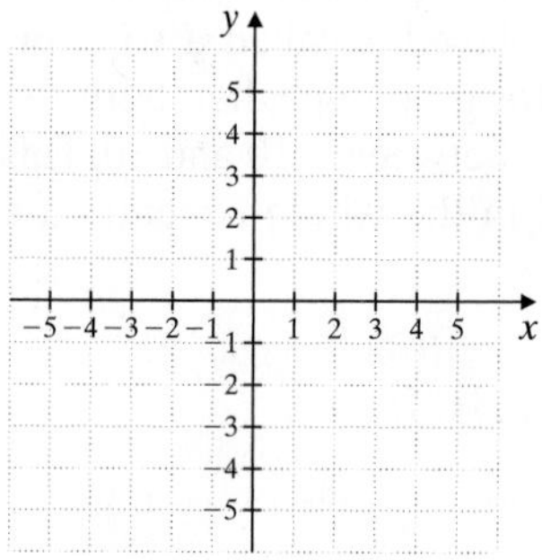

4. $y = -5x$

x	y
1	
0	
−1	

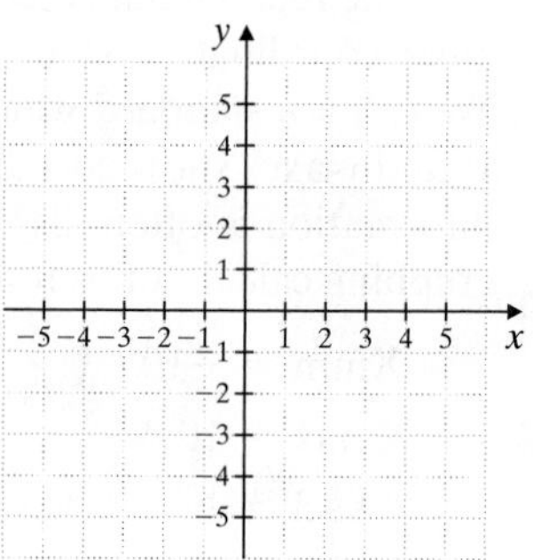

5. $y = \frac{1}{3}x$

x	y
0	
6	
−3	

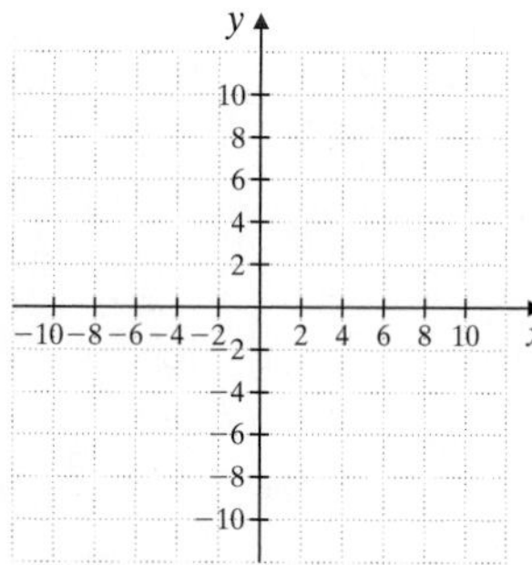

6. $y = \frac{1}{2}x$

x	y
0	
−4	
2	

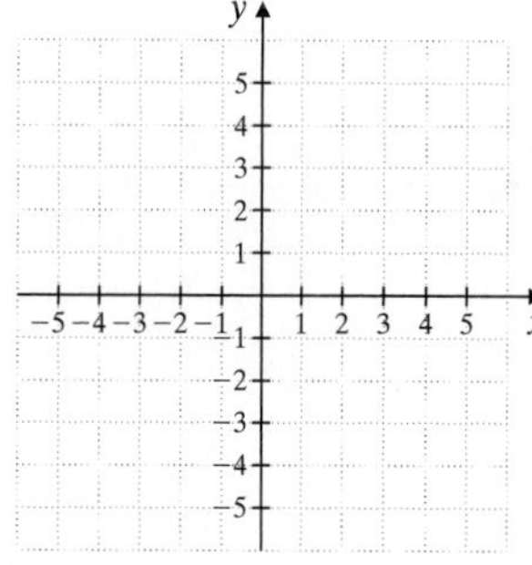

7. $y = -4x + 3$

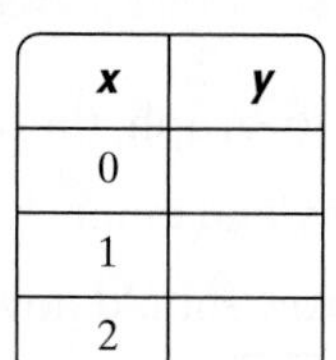

x	y
0	
1	
2	

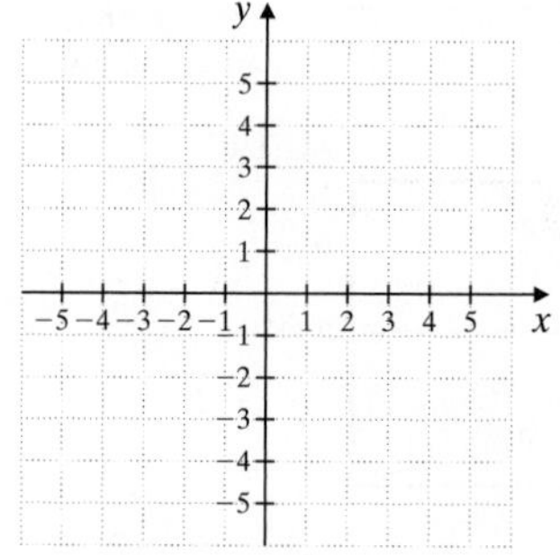

8. $y = -5x + 2$

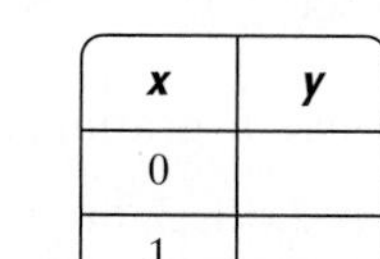

x	y
0	
1	
2	

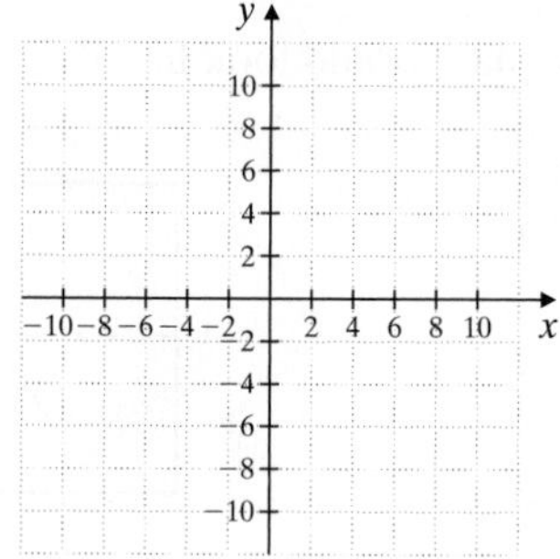

Graph each linear equation. See Examples 1 through 5.

9. $x + y = 1$

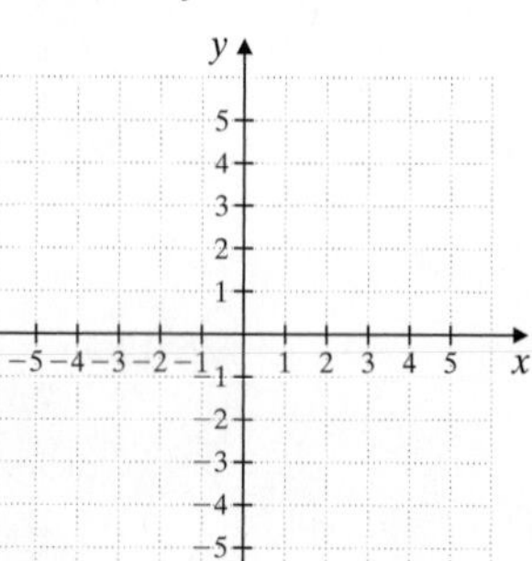

10. $x + y = 7$

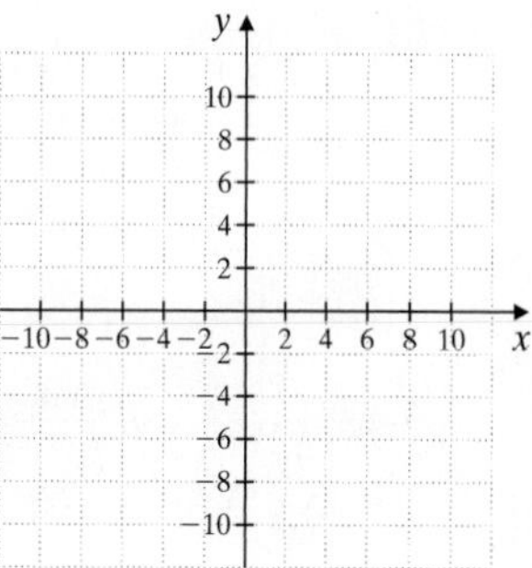

11. $x - y = -2$

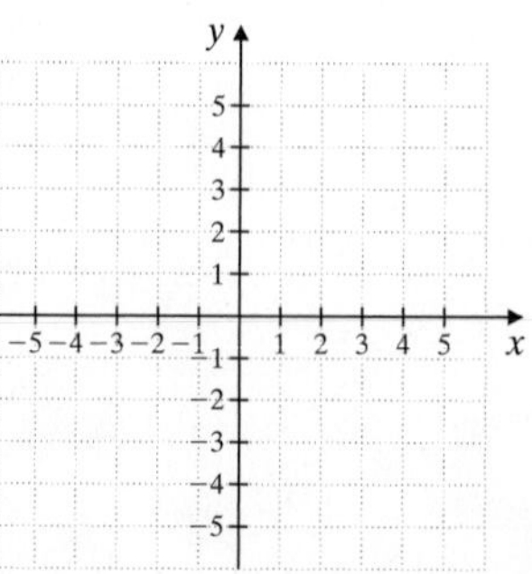

12. $-x + y = 6$

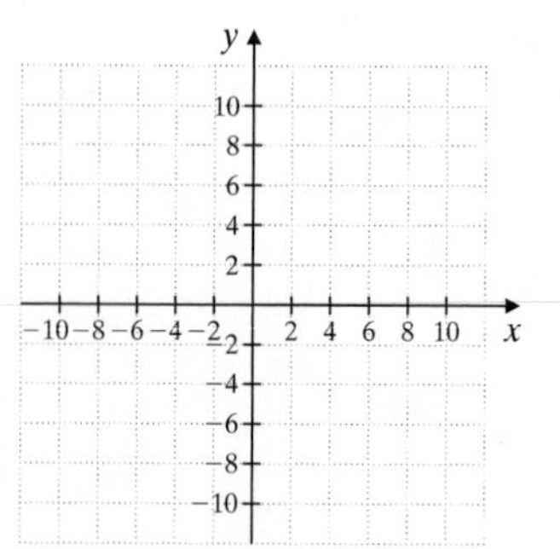

13. $x - 2y = 6$

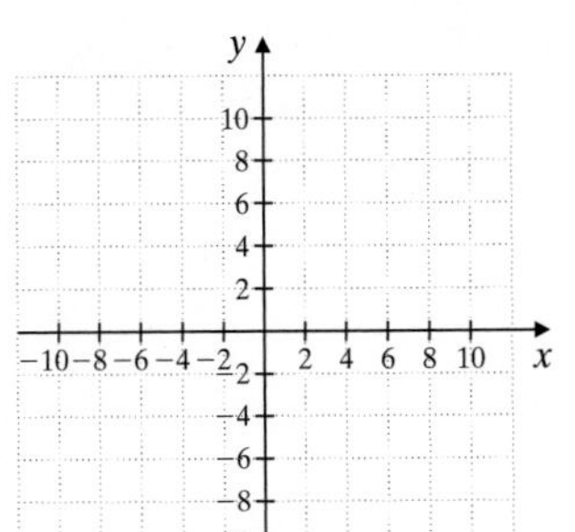

14. $-x + 5y = 5$

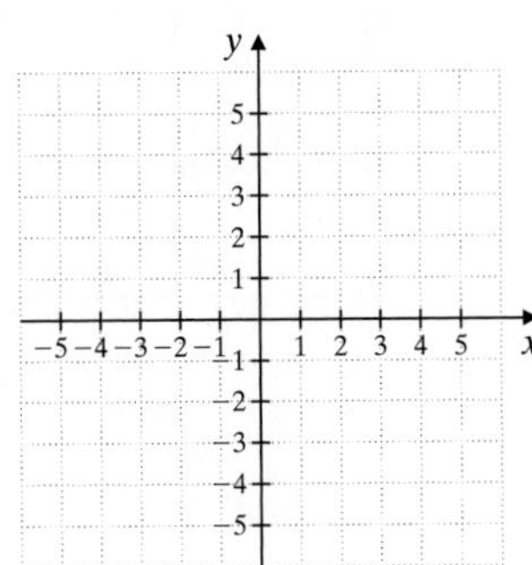

15. $y = 6x + 3$

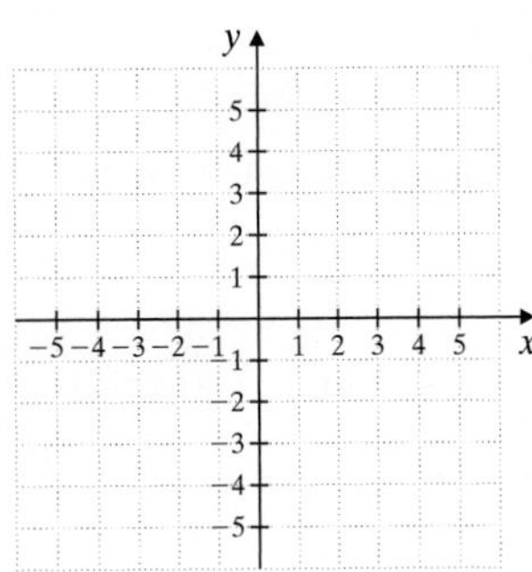

16. $y = -2x + 7$

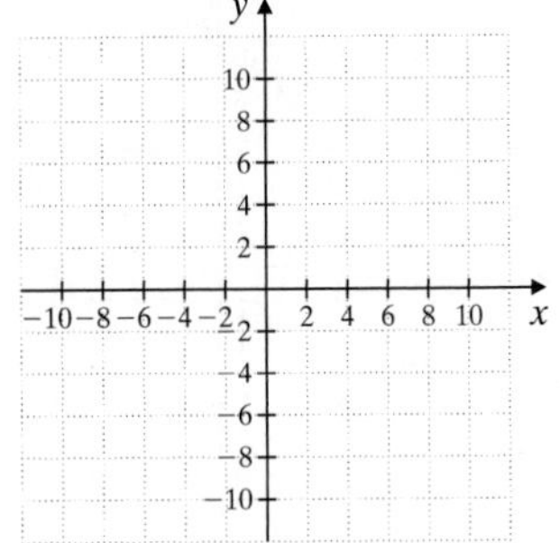

17. $x = -4$

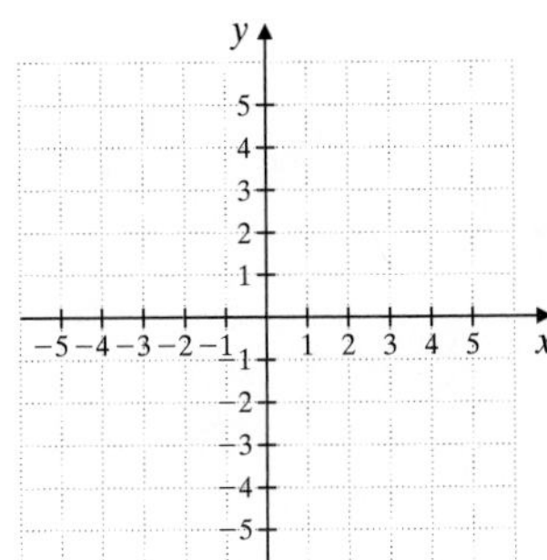

18. $y = 5$

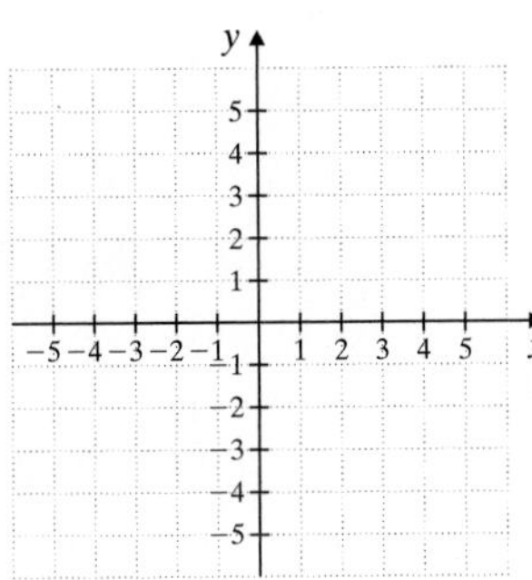

19. $y = 3$

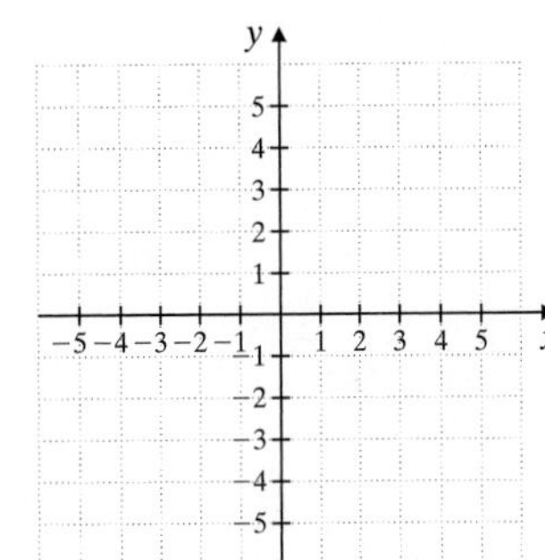

20. $x = -1$

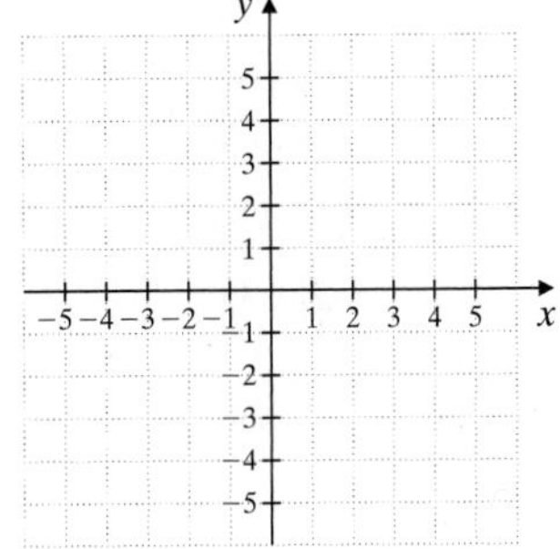

21. $y = x$

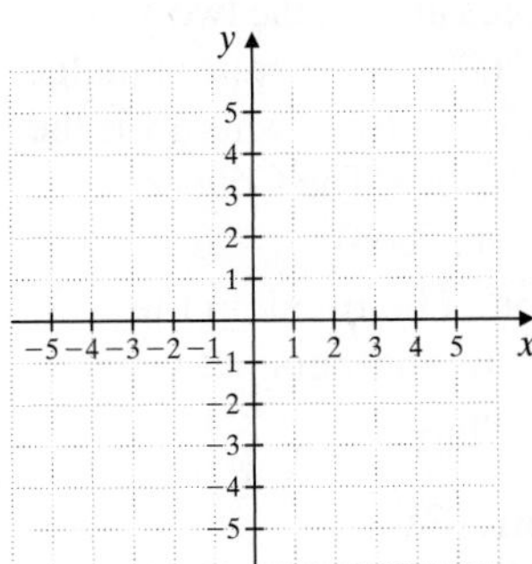

22. $y = -x$

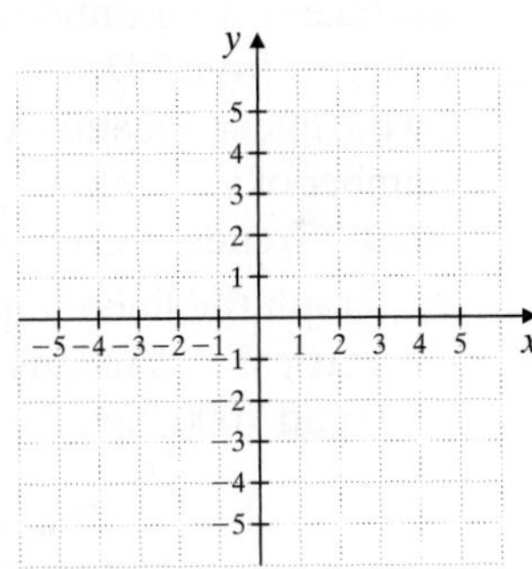

23. $x = -3y$

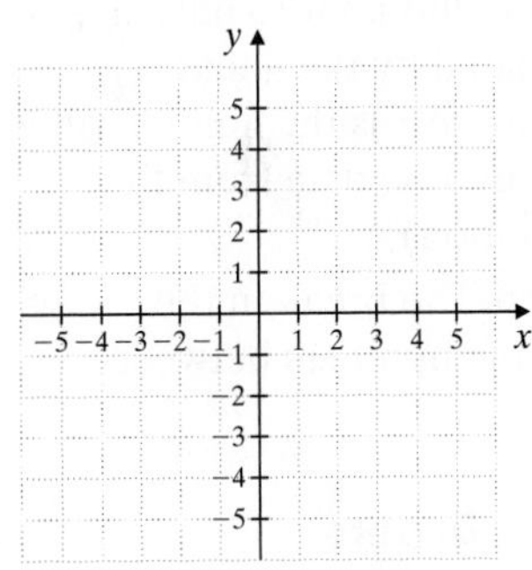

24. $x = 4y$

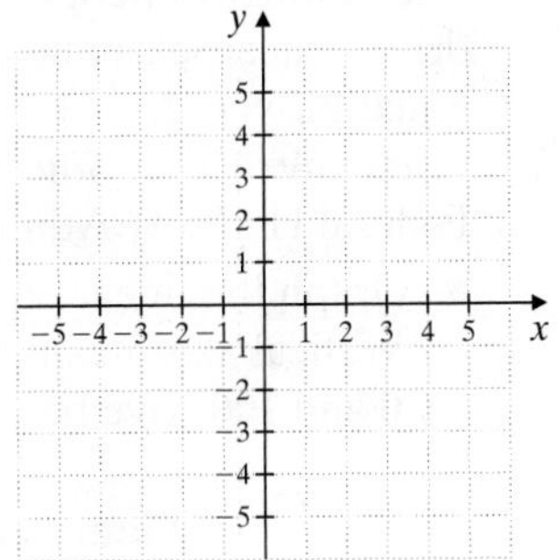

25. $x + 3y = 9$

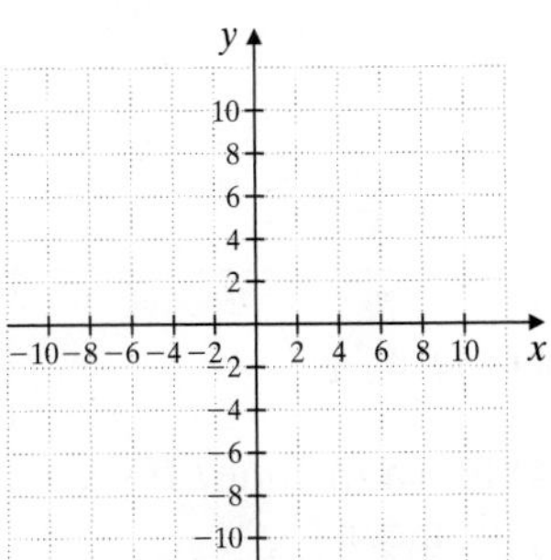

26. $2x + y = 2$

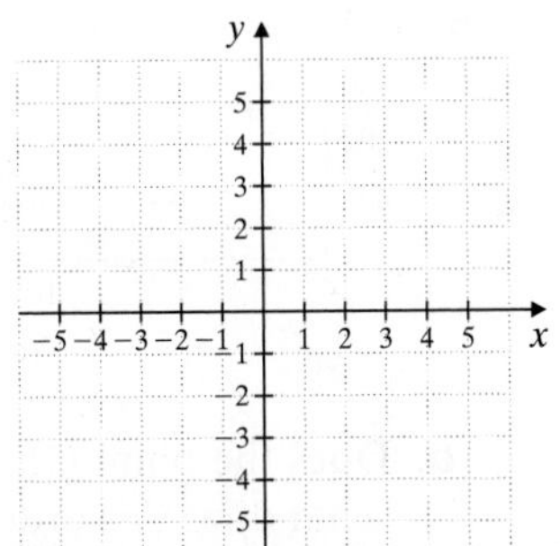

27. $y = \frac{1}{2}x + 2$

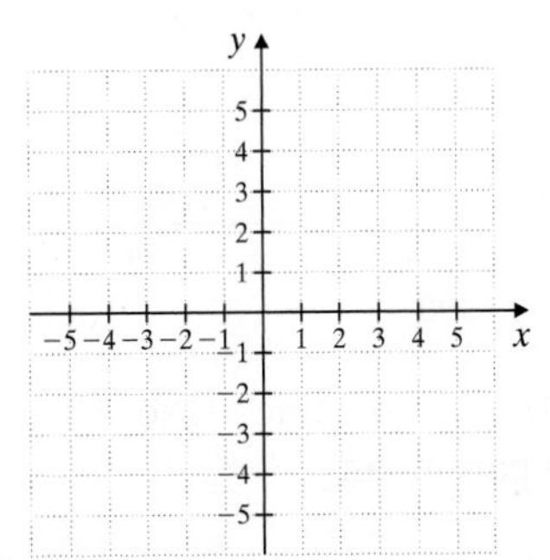

28. $y = \frac{1}{4}x + 3$

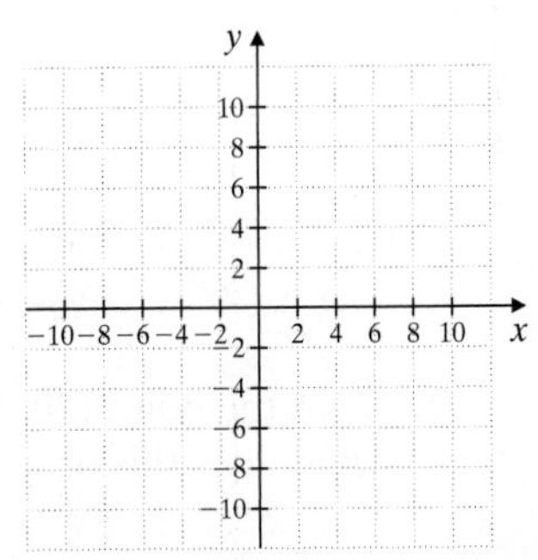

29. $3x - 2y = 12$

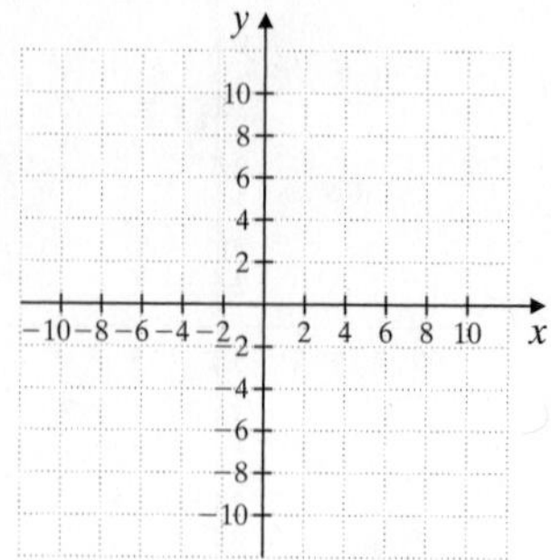

30. $2x - 7y = 14$

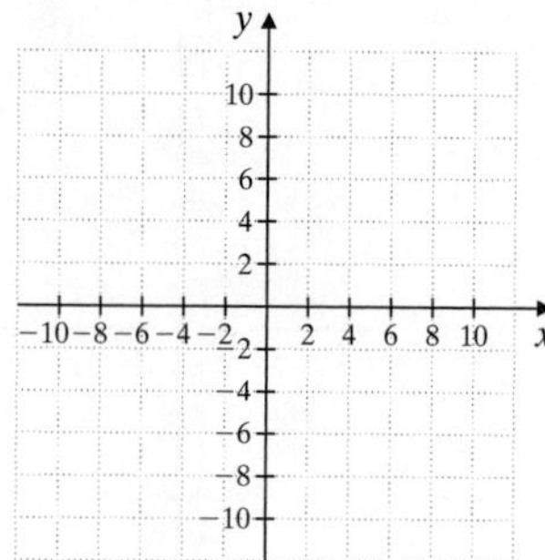

31. $y = -3.5x + 4$

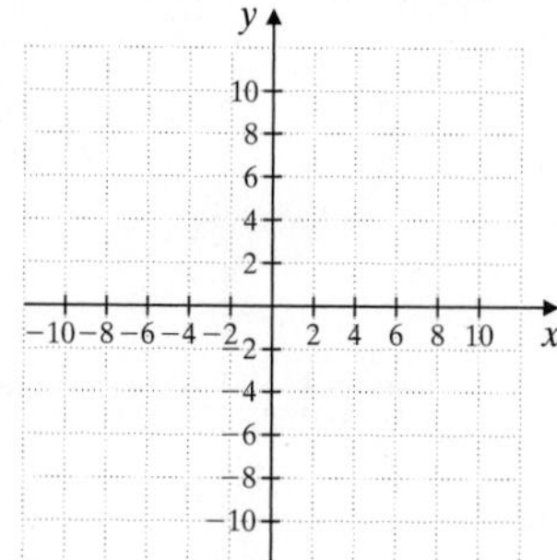

32. $y = -1.5x - 3$

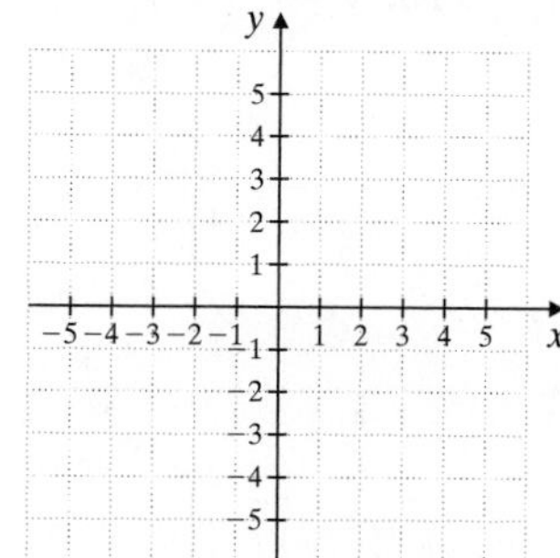

Solve. See Example 6.

33. One American rite of passage is a driver's license. The number of people y (in millions) who have a driver's license can be estimated by the linear equation $y = 2.2x + 145$, where x is the number of years after 1990. (*Source:* Based on data from the Federal Highway Administration)

a. Graph the linear equation. The break in the vertical axis means that the numbers between 0 and 100 have been skipped.

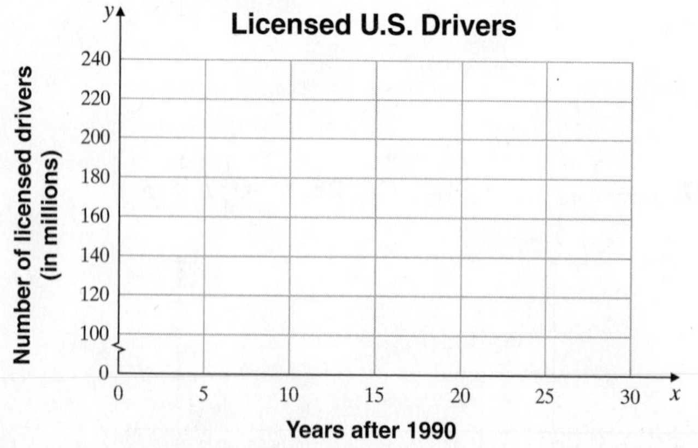

b. Does the point (20, 189) lie on the line? If so, what does this ordered pair mean?

34. College is getting more expensive every year. The average cost for tuition and fees at a public two-year college y from 1978 through 2009 can be approximated by the linear equation $y = 45x + 1089$, where x is the number of years after 1978. (*Source:* The College Board: Trends in College Pricing 2008)

a. Graph the linear equation. The break in the vertical axis means that the numbers between 0 and 1000 have been skipped.

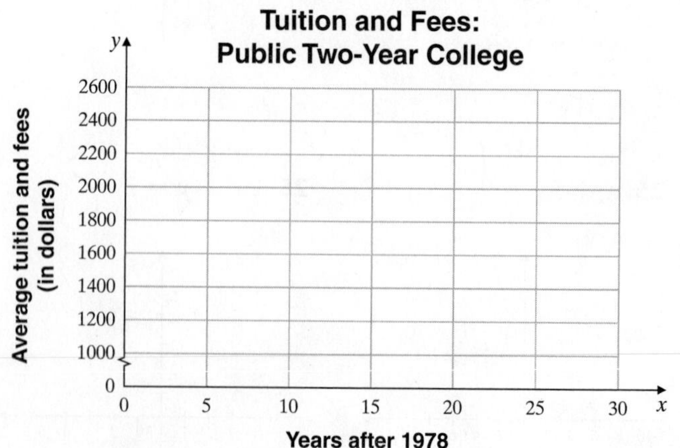

b. Does the point (15, 1764) lie on the line? If so, what does this ordered pair mean?

35. The percent of U.S. households y that have at least one computer can be approximated by the linear equation $y = 5.6x + 38.5$, where x is the number of years since 1998. (*Source: Statistical Abstract of the United States*)

a. Graph the linear equation.

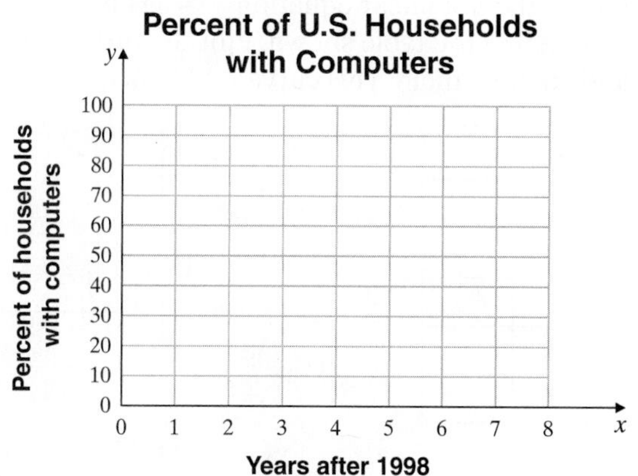

b. Complete the ordered pair (5,).

c. Write a sentence explaining the meaning of the ordered pair found in part b.

36. The restaurant industry is still busier than ever. The yearly revenue for restaurants in the United States can be estimated by $y = 13.4x + 6.2$, where x is the number of years after 1970 and y is the revenue in billions of dollars. (*Source:* National Restaurant Association)

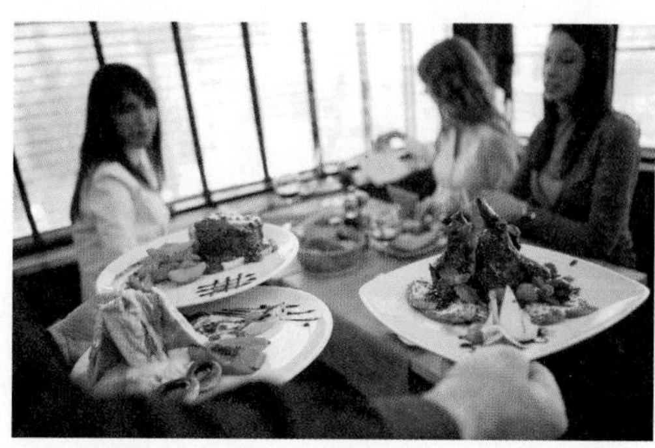

a. Graph the linear equation.

b. Complete the ordered pair (25,).

c. Write a sentence explaining the meaning of the ordered pair found in part b.

Review

△ **37.** The coordinates of three vertices of a rectangle are $(-2, 5)$, $(4, 5)$, and $(-2, -1)$. Find the coordinates of the fourth vertex. See Section 13.1.

△ **38.** The coordinates of two vertices of a square are $(-3, -1)$ and $(2, -1)$. Find the coordinates of two pairs of points possible for the third and fourth vertices. See Section 13.1.

Complete each table. See Section 13.1.

39. $x - y = -3$

x	y
0	
	0

40. $y - x = 5$

x	y
0	
	0

41. $y = 2x$

x	y
0	
	0

42. $x = -3y$

x	y
0	
	0

Concept Extensions

Graph each pair of linear equations on the same set of axes. Discuss how the graphs are similar and how they are different.

43. $y = 5x$
$y = 5x + 4$

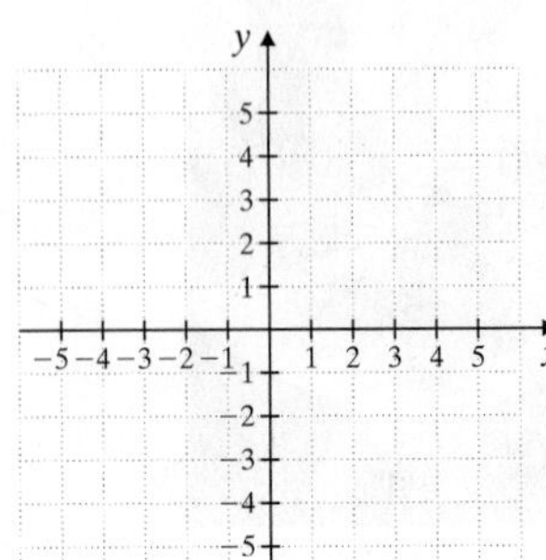

44. $y = 2x$
$y = 2x + 5$

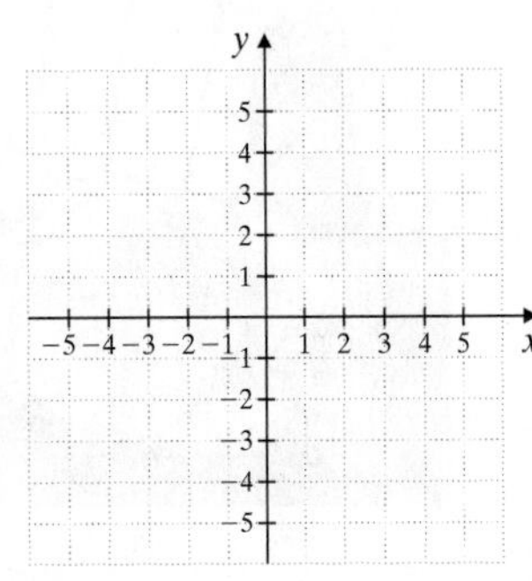

45. $y = -2x$
$y = -2x - 3$

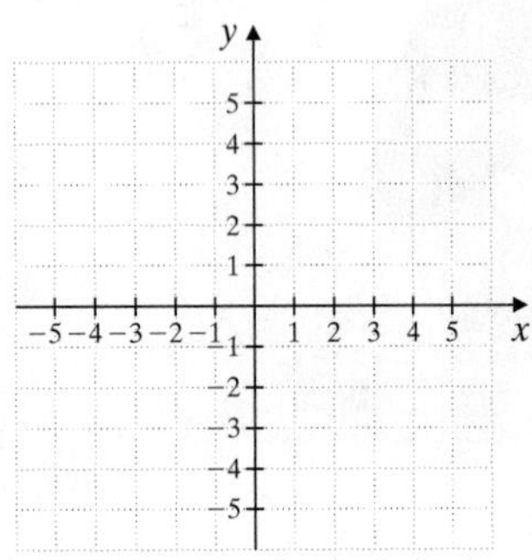

46. $y = x$
$y = x - 7$

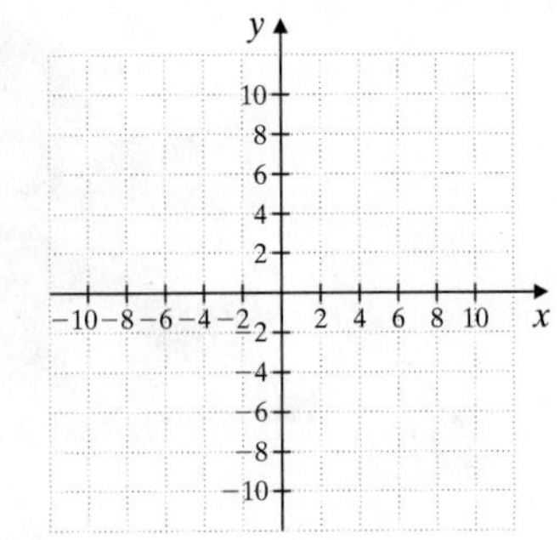

47. Graph the nonlinear equation $y = x^2$ by completing the table shown. Plot the ordered pairs and connect them with a smooth curve.

x	y
0	
1	
−1	
2	
−2	

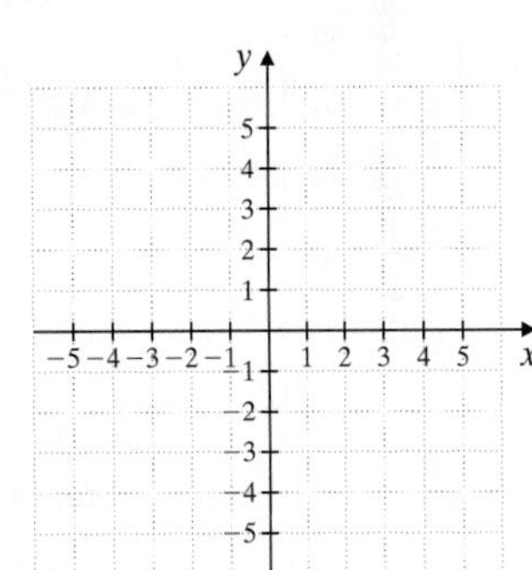

48. Graph the nonlinear equation $y = |x|$ by completing the table shown. Plot the ordered pairs and connect them. This curve is "V" shaped.

x	y
0	
1	
−1	
2	
−2	

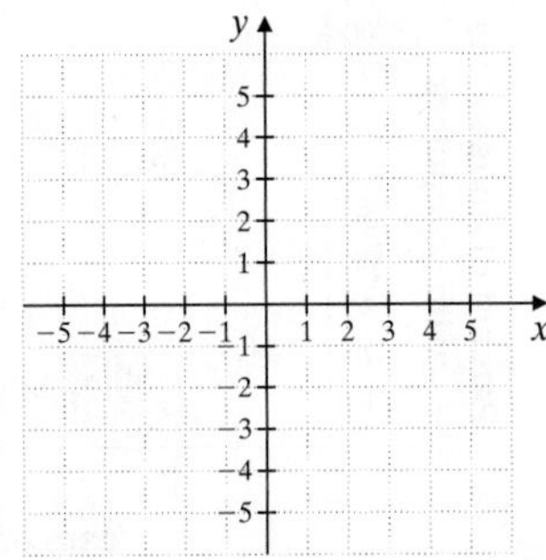

△ **49.** The perimeter of the trapezoid below is 22 centimeters. Write a linear equation in two variables for the perimeter. Find y if x is 3 centimeters.

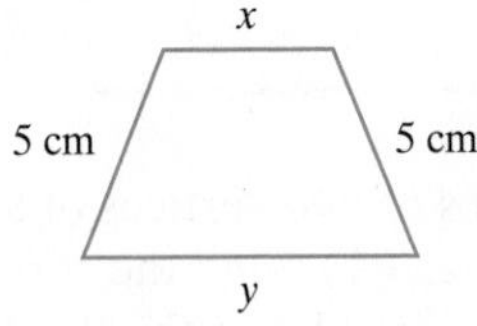

△ **50.** The perimeter of the rectangle below is 50 miles. Write a linear equation in two variables for the perimeter. Use this equation to find x when y is 20 miles.

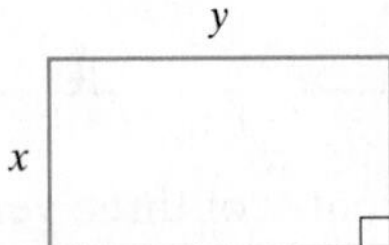

51. If (a, b) is an ordered pair solution of $x + y = 5$, is (b, a) also a solution? Explain why or why not.

52. If (a, b) is an ordered pair solution of $x - y = 5$, is (b, a) also a solution? Explain why or why not.

13.3 INTERCEPTS

Objectives

A Identify Intercepts of a Graph.

B Graph a Linear Equation by Finding and Plotting Intercept Points.

C Identify and Graph Vertical and Horizontal Lines.

Objective A Identifying Intercepts

The graph of $y = 4x - 8$ is shown below. Notice that this graph crosses the y-axis at the point $(0, -8)$. This point is called the ***y*-intercept.** Likewise the graph crosses the x-axis at $(2, 0)$. This point is called the ***x*-intercept.**

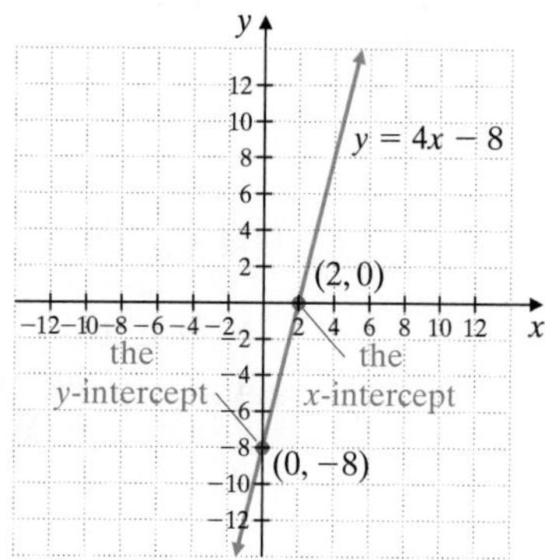

The intercepts are $(2, 0)$ and $(0, -8)$.

Helpful Hint

If a graph crosses the x-axis at $(2, 0)$ and the y-axis at $(0, -8)$, then

$(2, 0)$ ↑ x-intercept $(0, -8)$ ↑ y-intercept

Notice that for the x-intercept, the y-value is 0 and for the y-intercept, the x-value is 0.

Note: Sometimes in mathematics, you may see just the number -8 stated as the y-intercept, and 2 stated as the x-intercept.

Examples Identify the x- and y-intercepts.

1.

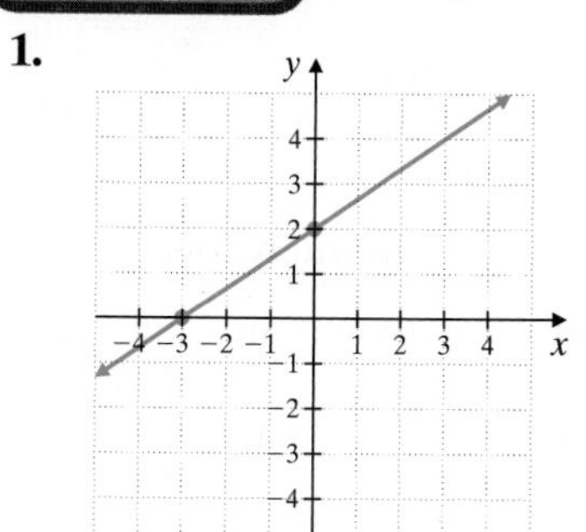

Solution:

x-intercept: $(-3, 0)$

y-intercept: $(0, 2)$

Continued on next page

PRACTICE 1

Identify the x- and y-intercepts.

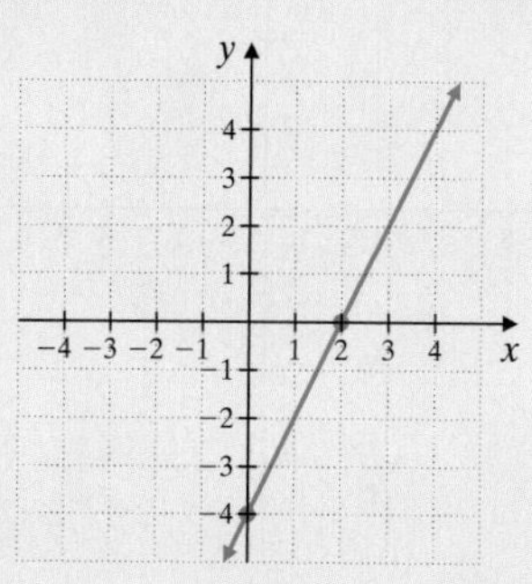

Answer

1. x-intercept: $(2, 0)$; y-intercept: $(0, -4)$

PRACTICE 2–3

Identify the x- and y-intercepts.

2.

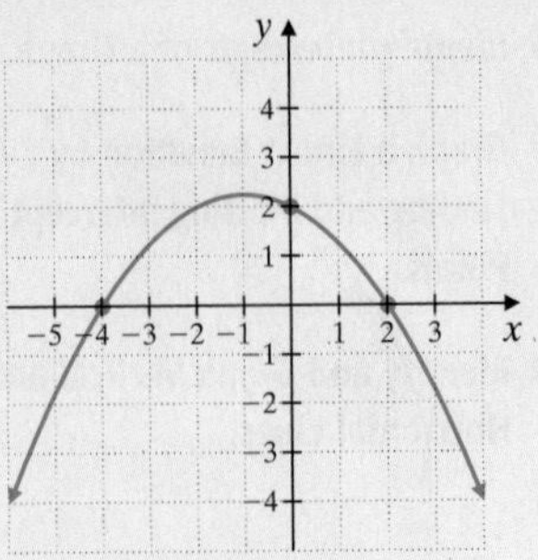

3.

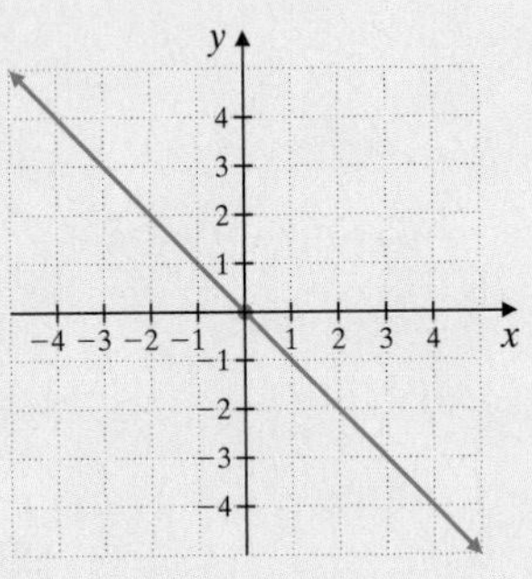

2.

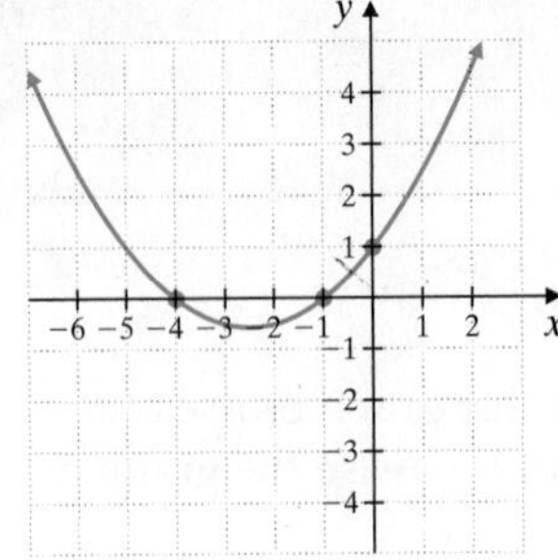

Solution:

x-intercepts: $(-4, 0)$, $(-1, 0)$
y-intercept: $(0, 1)$

3.

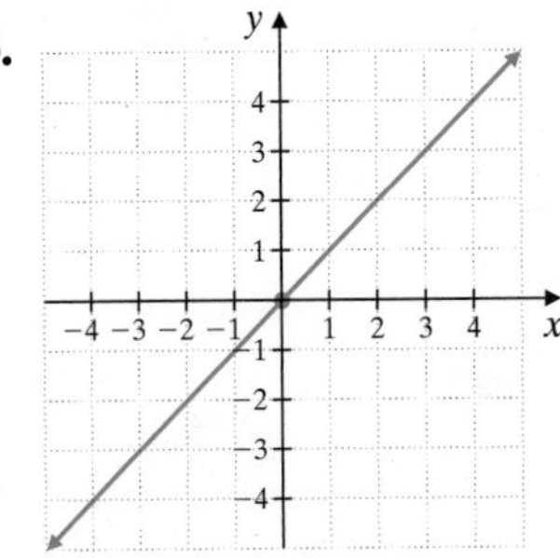

Solution:

x-intercept: $(0, 0)$
y-intercept: $(0, 0)$

Here, the x- and y-intercepts happen to be the same point.

Work Practice 1–3

Helpful Hint

Notice that any time $(0, 0)$ is a point of a graph, then it is an x-intercept and a y-intercept. Why? It is the *only* point that lies on both axes.

Objective B Finding and Plotting Intercepts

Given an equation of a line, we can usually find intercepts easily since one coordinate is 0.

To find the x-intercept of a line from its equation, let $y = 0$, since a point on the x-axis has a y-coordinate of 0. To find the y-intercept of a line from its equation, let $x = 0$, since a point on the y-axis has an x-coordinate of 0.

PRACTICE 4

Graph $2x - y = 4$ by finding and plotting its intercepts.

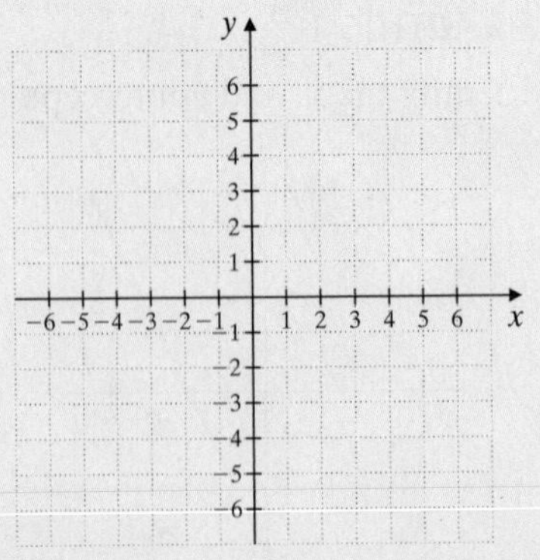

Finding x- and y-Intercepts

To find the x-intercept, let $y = 0$ and solve for x.
To find the y-intercept, let $x = 0$ and solve for y.

Example 4 Graph $x - 3y = 6$ by finding and plotting its intercepts.

Solution: We let $y = 0$ to find the x-intercept and $x = 0$ to find the y-intercept.

Let $y = 0$.	Let $x = 0$.
$x - 3y = 6$	$x - 3y = 6$
$x - 3(0) = 6$	$0 - 3y = 6$
$x - 0 = 6$	$-3y = 6$
$x = 6$	$y = -2$

The x-intercept is $(6, 0)$ and the y-intercept is $(0, -2)$. We find a third ordered pair solution to check our work. If we let $y = -1$, then $x = 3$. We plot the points $(6, 0)$,

Answers

2. x-intercepts: $(-4, 0)(2, 0)$; y-intercept: $(0, 2)$
3. x-intercept and y-intercept: $(0, 0)$
4. See page 901.

(0, −2), and (3, −1). The graph of $x - 3y = 6$ is the line drawn through these points as shown.

x	y
6	0
0	−2
3	−1

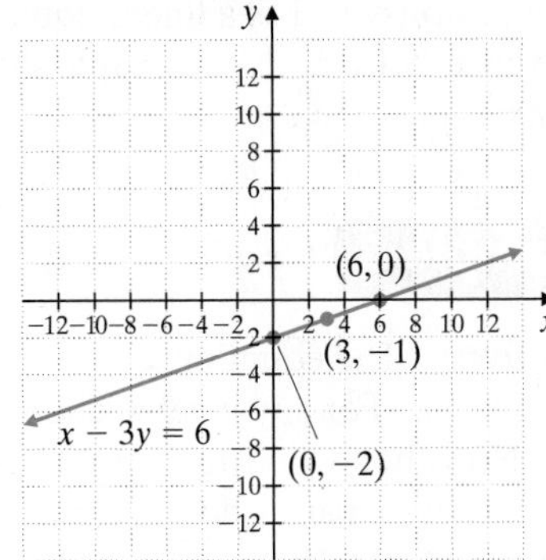

Work Practice 4

Example 5 Graph $x = -2y$ by finding and plotting its intercepts.

Solution: We let $y = 0$ to find the x-intercept and $x = 0$ to find the y-intercept.

Let $y = 0$.
$x = -2y$
$x = -2(0)$
$x = 0$

Let $x = 0$.
$x = -2y$
$0 = -2y$
$0 = y$

Both the x-intercept and y-intercept are (0, 0). In other words, when $x = 0$, then $y = 0$, which gives the ordered pair (0, 0). Also, when $y = 0$, then $x = 0$, which gives the same ordered pair, (0, 0). This happens when the graph passes through the origin. Since two points are needed to determine a line, we must find at least one more ordered pair that satisfies $x = -2y$. Since the equation is solved for x, we choose y-values so that there is no need to solve to find the corresponding x-value. We let $y = -1$ to find a second ordered pair solution and let $y = 1$ as a check point.

Let $y = -1$.
$x = -2(-1)$
$x = 2$ Multiply.

Let $y = 1$.
$x = -2(1)$
$x = -2$ Multiply.

The ordered pairs are (0, 0), (2, −1), and (−2, 1). We plot these points to graph $x = -2y$.

x	y
0	0
2	−1
−2	1

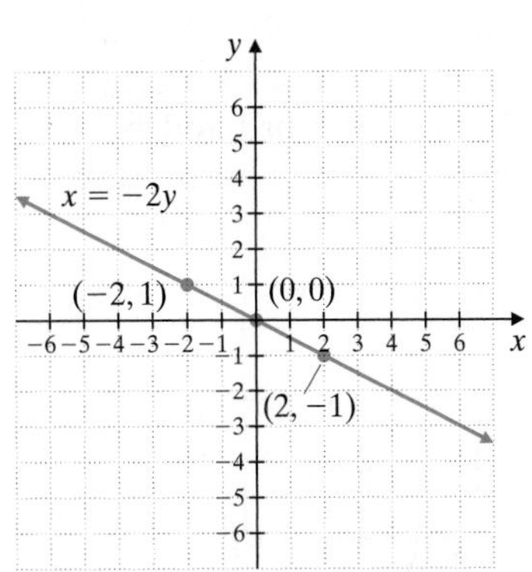

Work Practice 5

PRACTICE 5

Graph $y = 3x$ by finding and plotting its intercepts.

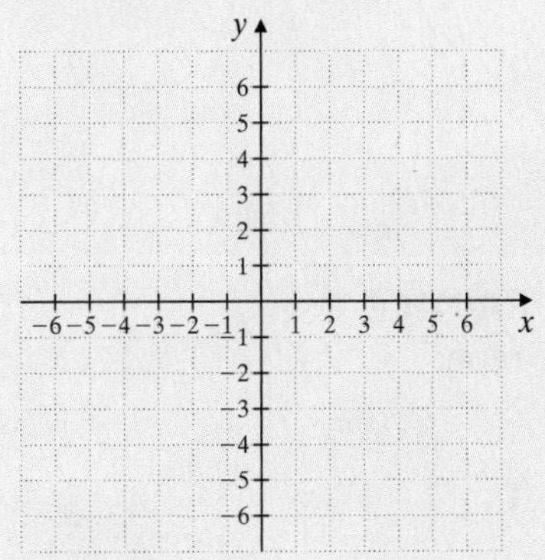

Answers

4.

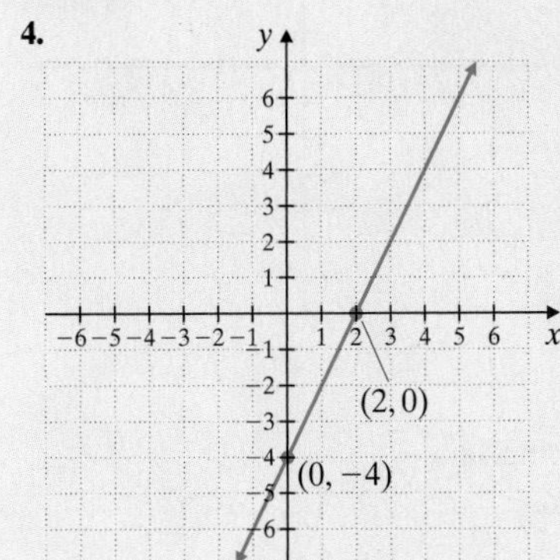

5.

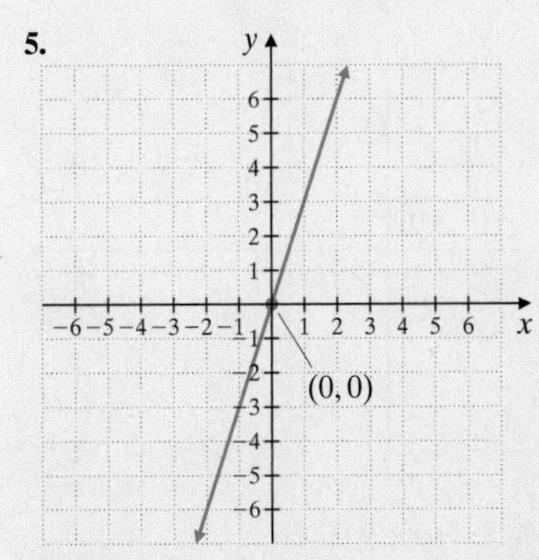

Objective C Graphing Vertical and Horizontal Lines

The equation $x = 2$ is a linear equation in two variables because it can be written in the form $x + 0y = 2$. The graph of this equation is a vertical line, as reviewed in the next example.

PRACTICE 6
Graph: $x = -3$

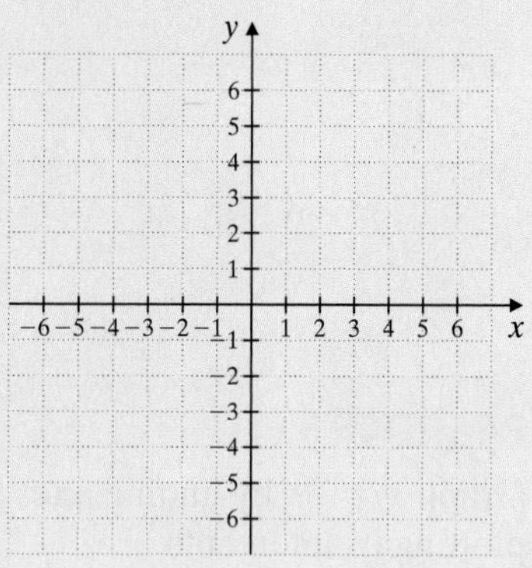

Example 6 Graph: $x = 2$

Solution: The equation $x = 2$ can be written as $x + 0y = 2$. For any y-value chosen, notice that x is 2. No other value for x satisfies $x + 0y = 2$. Any ordered pair whose x-coordinate is 2 is a solution of $x + 0y = 2$. We will use the ordered pair solutions (2, 3), (2, 0), and (2, −3) to graph $x = 2$.

x	y
2	3
2	0
2	−3

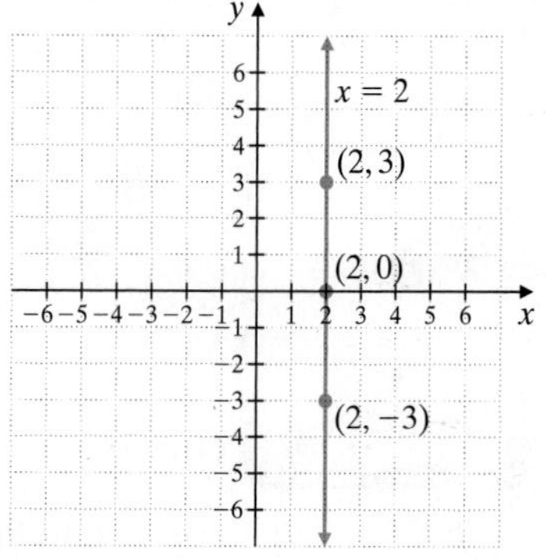

The graph is a vertical line with x-intercept 2. Note that this graph has no y-intercept because x is never 0.

Work Practice 6

PRACTICE 7
Graph: $y = 4$

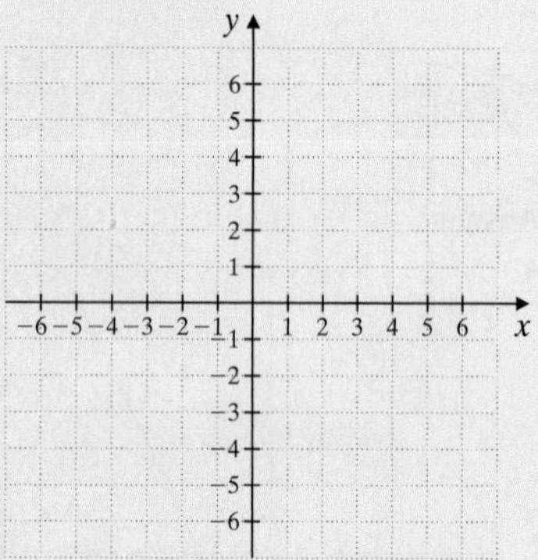

In general, we have the following.

Vertical Lines

The graph of $x = c$, where c is a real number, is a **vertical line** with x-intercept $(c, 0)$.

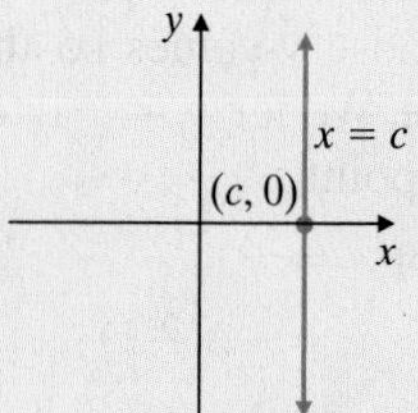

Example 7 Graph: $y = -3$

Solution: The equation $y = -3$ can be written as $0x + y = -3$. For any x-value chosen, y is −3. If we choose 4, 1, and −2 as x-values, the ordered pair solutions are (4, −3), (1, −3), and (−2, −3). We use these ordered pairs to graph $y = -3$. The graph is a horizontal line with y-intercept −3 and no x-intercept.

x	y
4	−3
1	−3
−2	−3

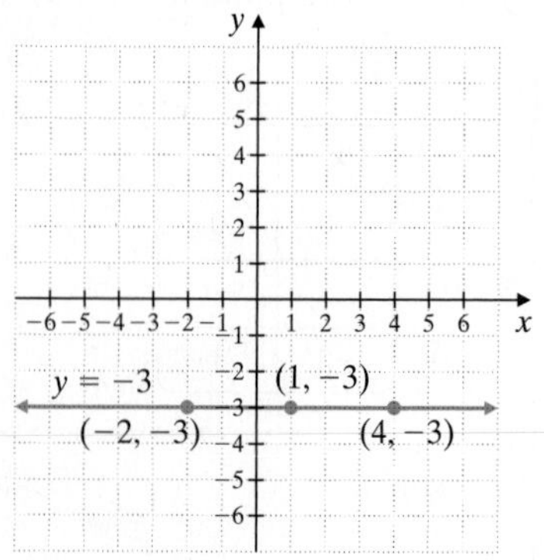

Work Practice 7

Answers

6.

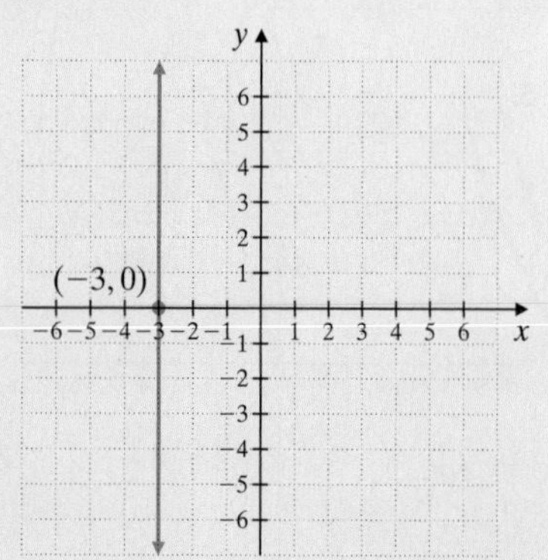

7. See page 903.

In general, we have the following.

Horizontal Lines

The graph of $y = c$, where c is a real number, is a **horizontal line** with y-intercept $(0, c)$.

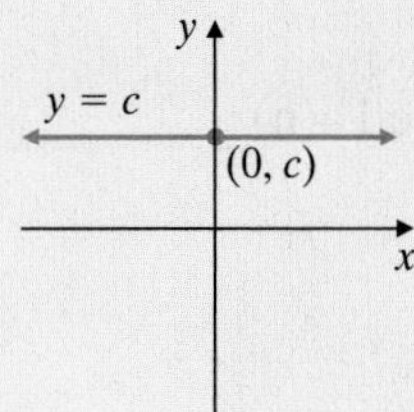

Answer

7.

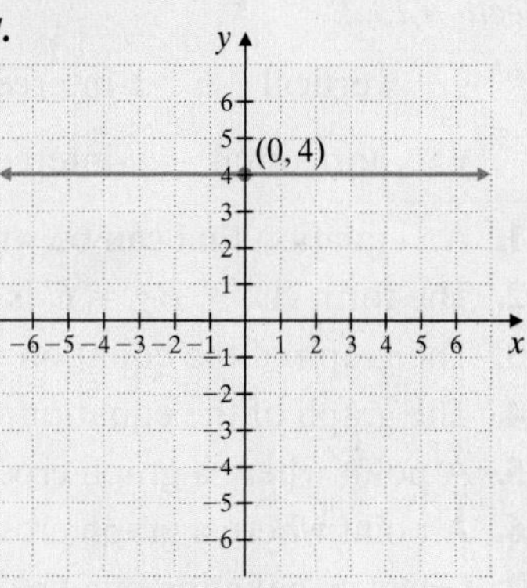

Calculator Explorations Graphing

You may have noticed that to use the Y= key on a graphing calculator to graph an equation, the equation must be solved for y. For example, to graph $2x + 3y = 7$, we solve this equation for y.

$$2x + 3y = 7$$

$$3y = -2x + 7 \quad \text{Subtract } 2x \text{ from both sides.}$$

$$\frac{3y}{3} = -\frac{2x}{3} + \frac{7}{3} \quad \text{Divide both sides by 3.}$$

$$y = -\frac{2}{3}x + \frac{7}{3} \quad \text{Simplify.}$$

To graph $2x + 3y = 7$ or $y = -\frac{2}{3}x + \frac{7}{3}$, press the Y= key and enter

$$Y_1 = -\frac{2}{3}x + \frac{7}{3}$$

$2x + 3y = 7$ or $y = -\frac{2}{3}x + \frac{7}{3}$

10

−10 10

−10

Graph each linear equation.

1. $x = 3.78y$

2. $-2.61y = x$

3. $3x + 7y = 21$

4. $-4x + 6y = 12$

5. $-2.2x + 6.8y = 15.5$

6. $5.9x - 0.8y = -10.4$

Vocabulary and Readiness Check

Use the choices below to fill in each blank. Some choices may be used more than once. Exercises 1 and 2 come from Section 13.2.

x	vertical	x-intercept	linear
y	horizontal	y-intercept	standard

1. An equation that can be written in the form $Ax + By = C$ is called a(n) __________ equation in two variables.
2. The form $Ax + By = C$ is called __________ form.
3. The graph of the equation $y = -1$ is a(n) __________ line.
4. The graph of the equation $x = 5$ is a(n) __________ line.
5. A point where a graph crosses the y-axis is called a(n) __________.
6. A point where a graph crosses the x-axis is called a(n) __________.
7. Given an equation of a line, to find the x-intercept (if there is one), let __________ = 0 and solve for __________.
8. Given an equation of a line, to find the y-intercept (if there is one), let __________ = 0 and solve for __________.

Answer the following true or false.

9. All lines have an x-intercept *and* a y-intercept.
10. The graph of $y = 4x$ contains the point $(0, 0)$.
11. The graph of $x + y = 5$ has an x-intercept of $(5, 0)$ and a y-intercept of $(0, 5)$.
12. The graph of $y = 5x$ contains the point $(5, 1)$.

13.3 Exercise Set

FOR EXTRA HELP

PRACTICE

WATCH

DOWNLOAD

READ

REVIEW

Objective **A** *Identify the intercepts. See Examples 1 through 3.*

1.

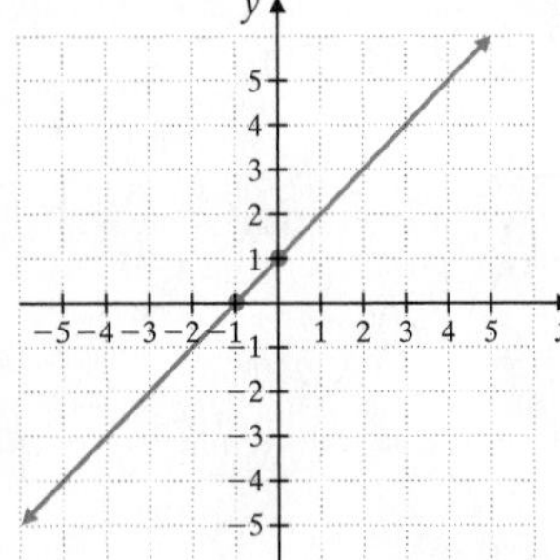

2.

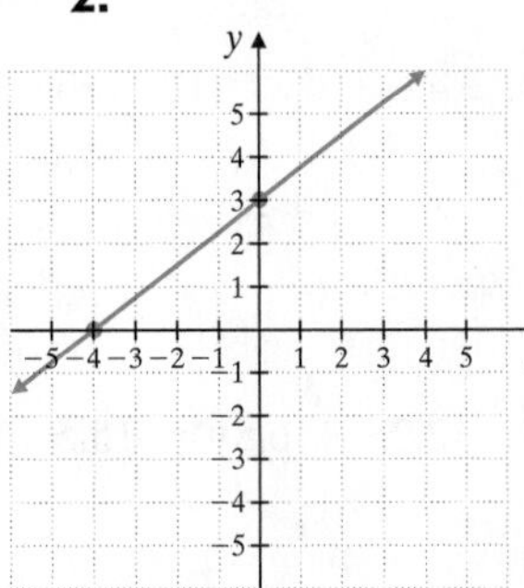

3.

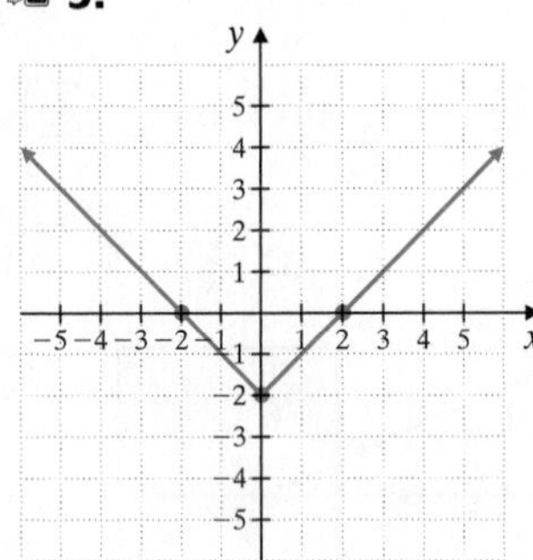

4.

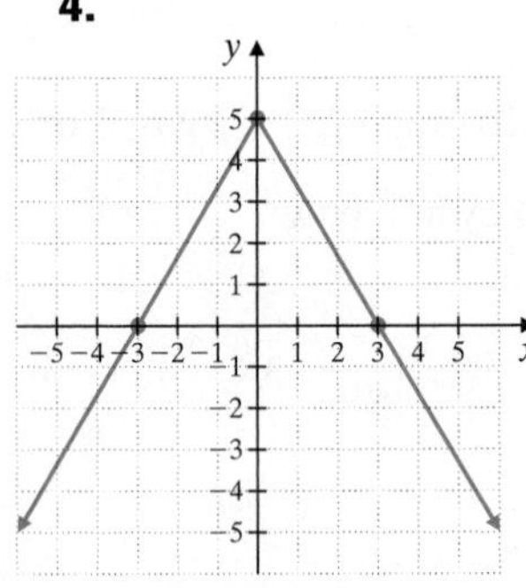

5.

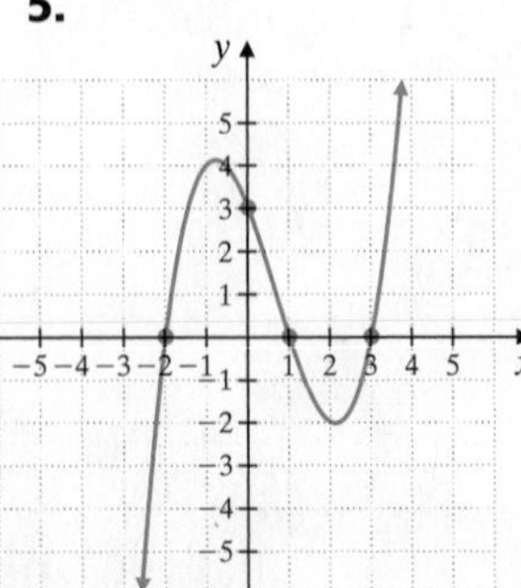

6.

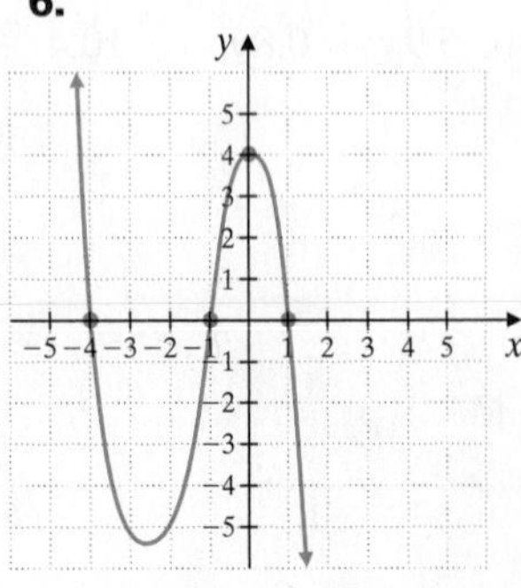

7.

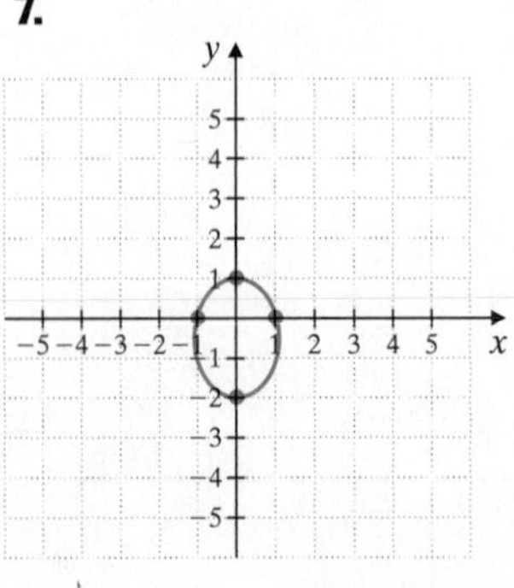

8.

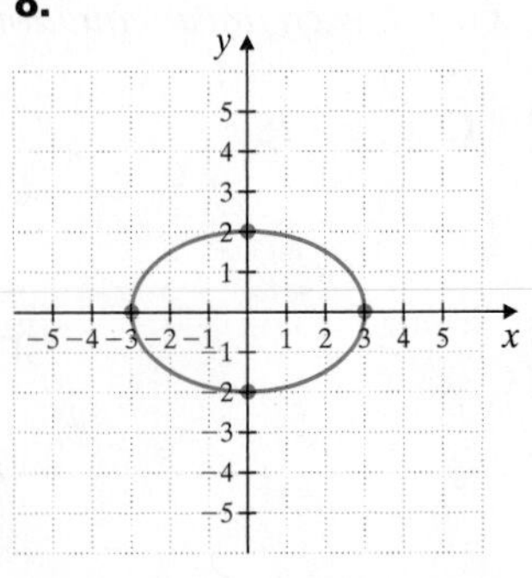

Objective B *Graph each linear equation by finding and plotting its intercepts. See Examples 4 and 5.*

9. $x - y = 3$

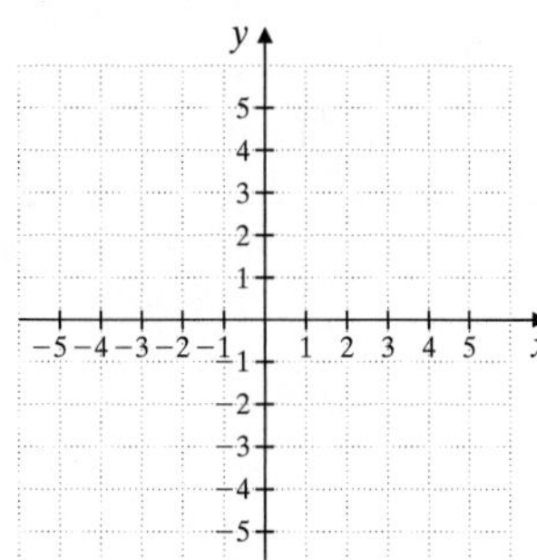

10. $x - y = -4$

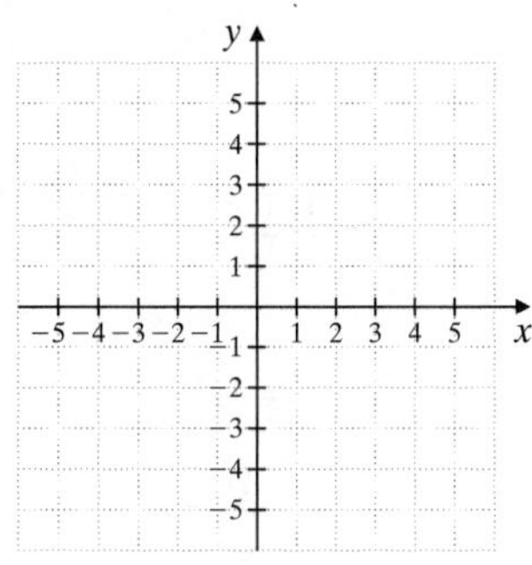

11. $x = 5y$

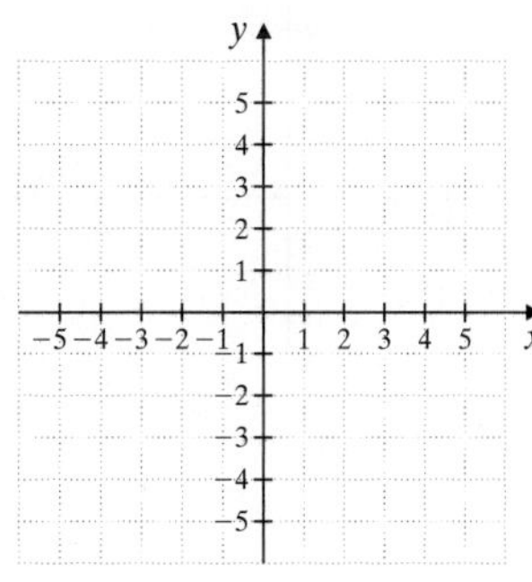

12. $x = 2y$

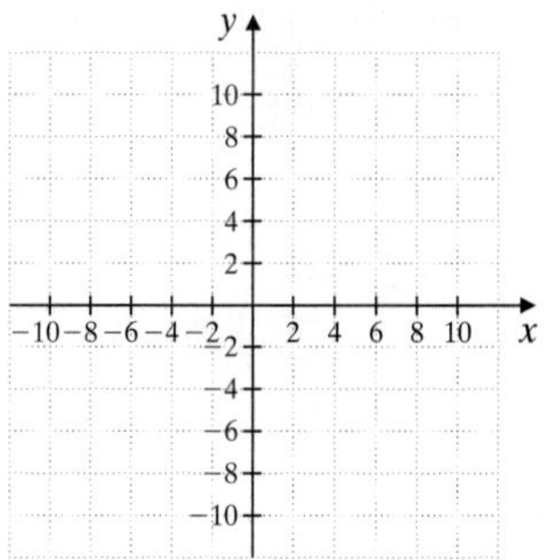

13. $-x + 2y = 6$

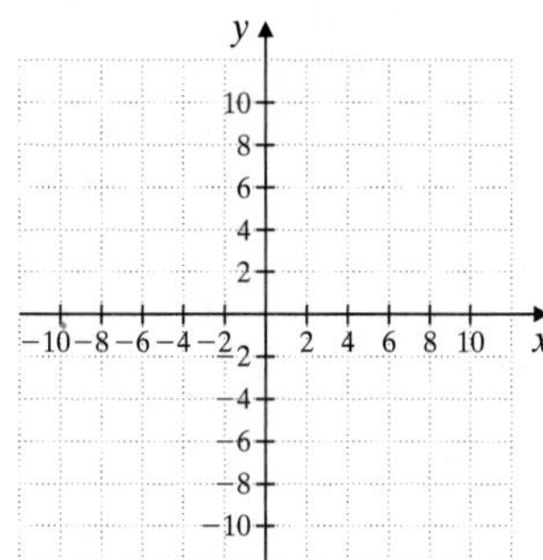

14. $x - 2y = -8$

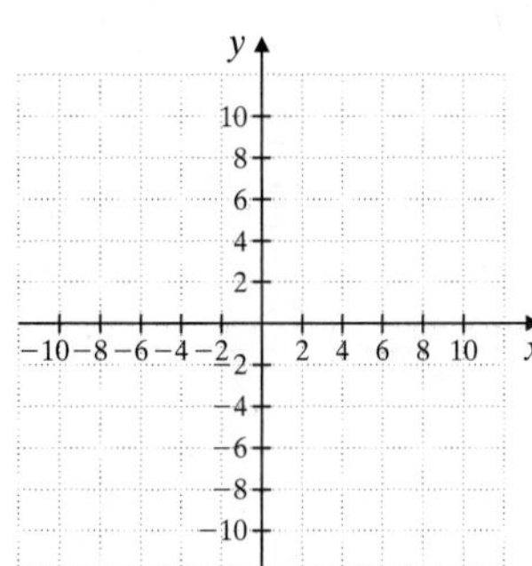

15. $2x - 4y = 8$

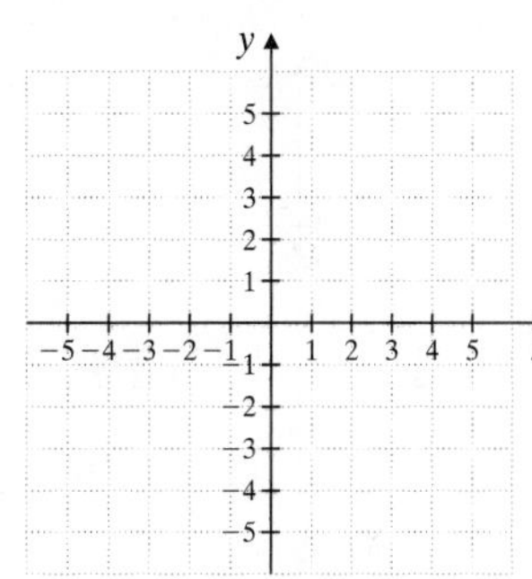

16. $2x + 3y = 6$

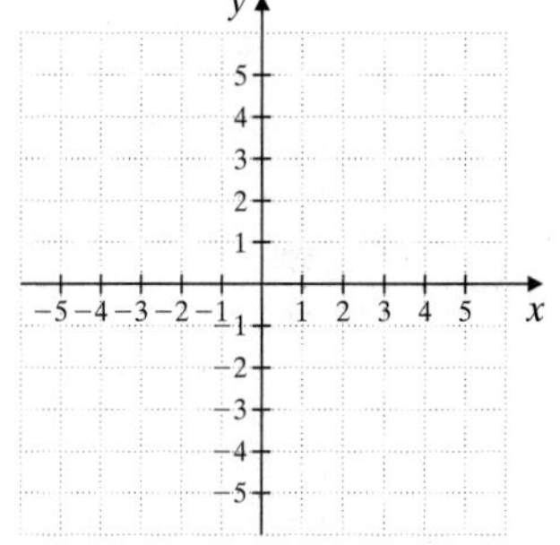

17. $y = 2x$

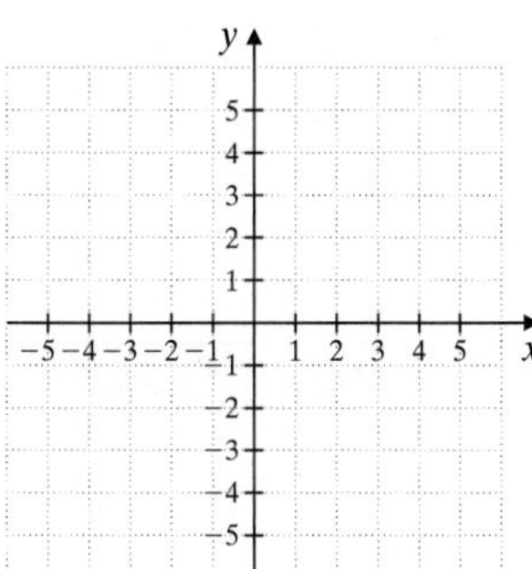

18. $y = -2x$

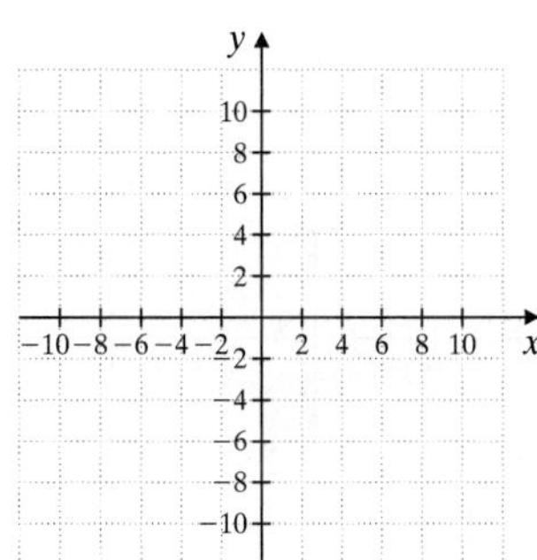

19. $y = 3x + 6$

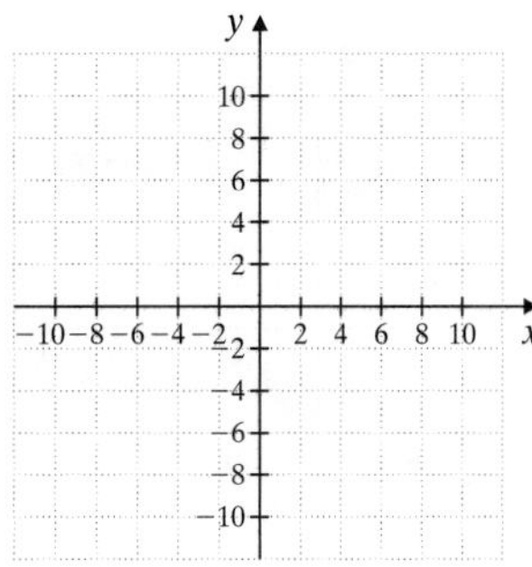

20. $y = 2x + 10$

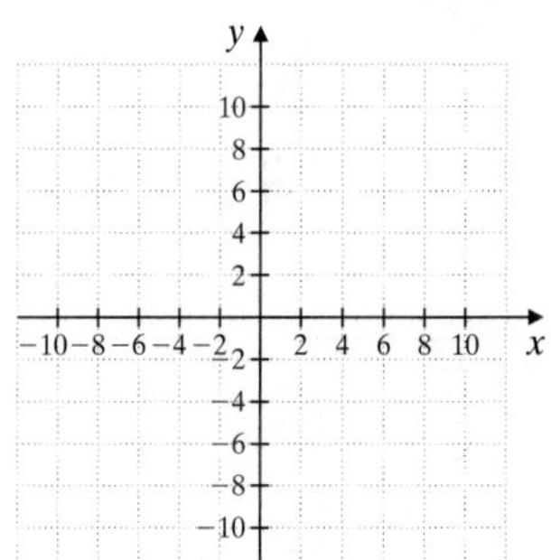

Objective C *Graph each linear equation. See Examples 6 and 7.*

21. $x = -1$

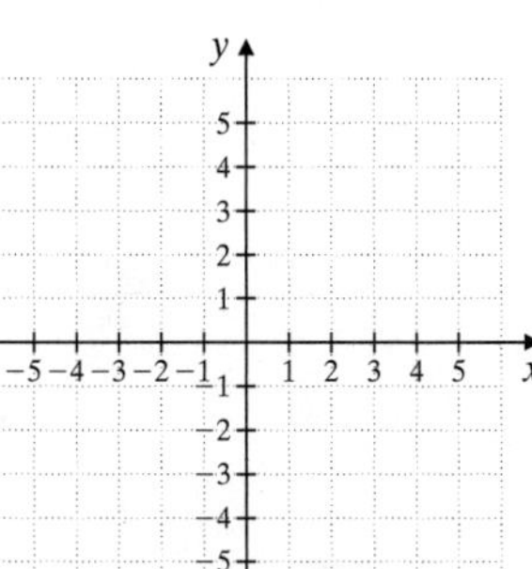

22. $y = 5$

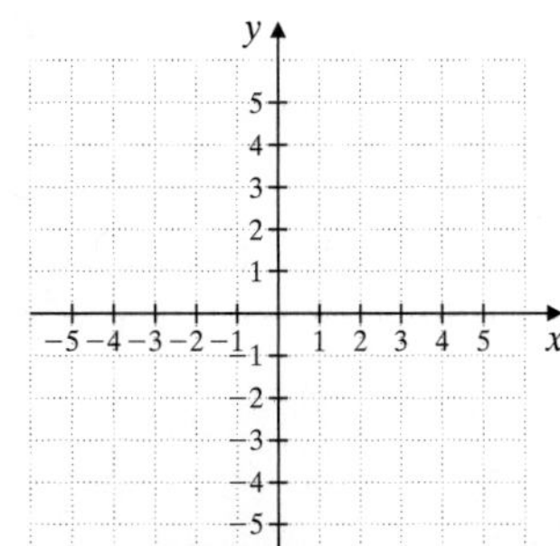

23. $y = 0$

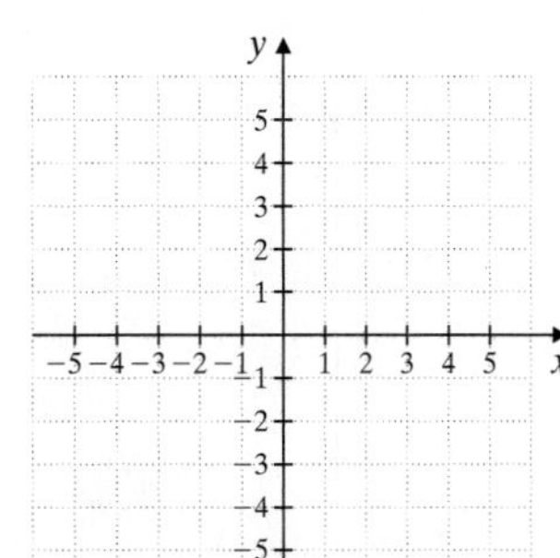

24. $x = 0$

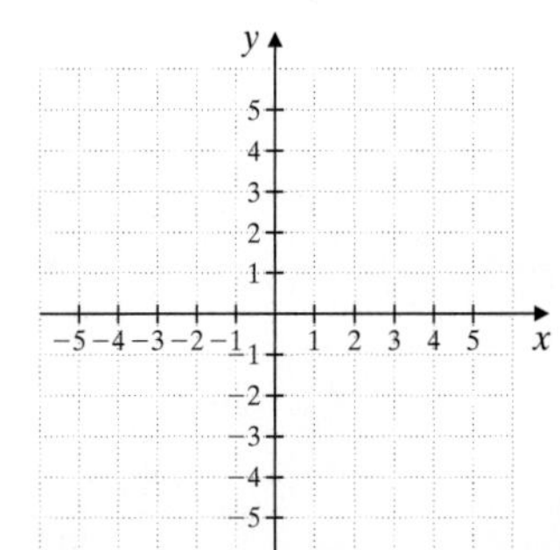

25. $y + 7 = 0$

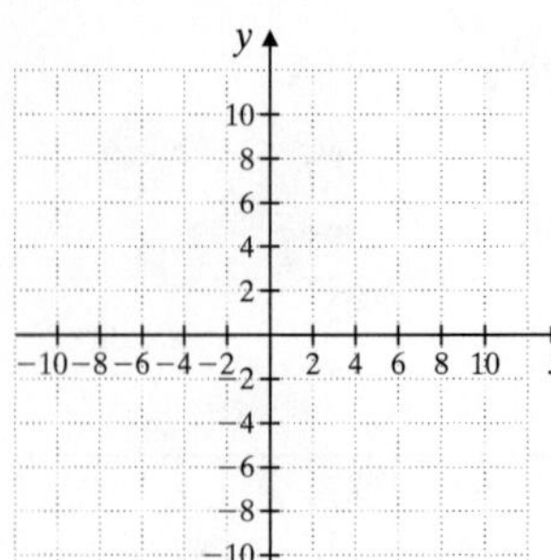

26. $x - 2 = 0$

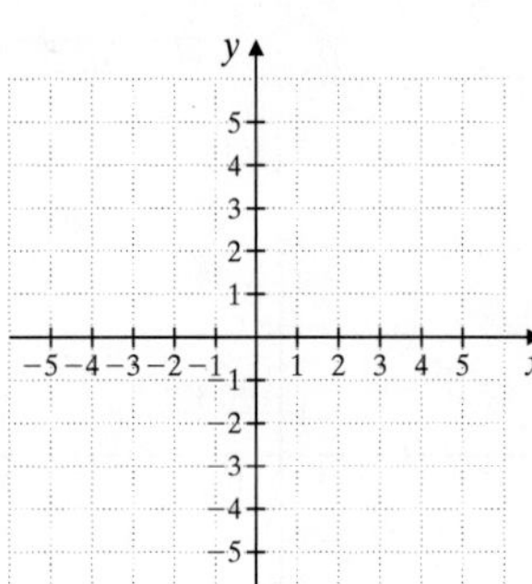

27. $x + 3 = 0$

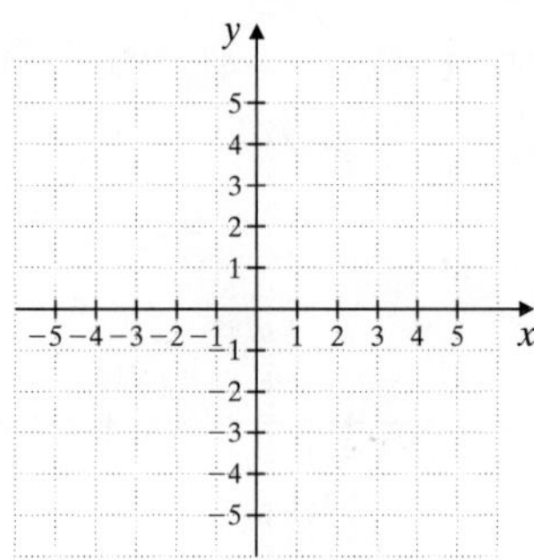

28. $y - 6 = 0$

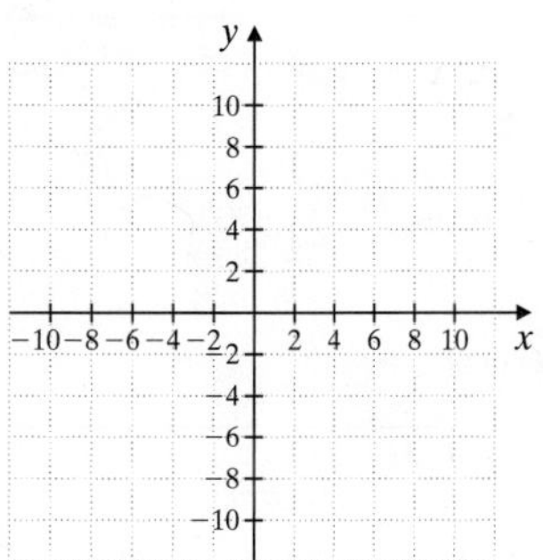

Objectives **B C Mixed Practice** *Graph each linear equation. See Examples 4 through 7.*

29. $x = y$

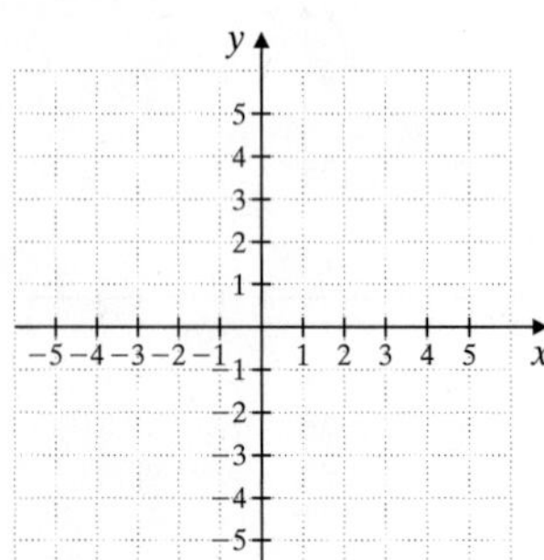

30. $x = -y$

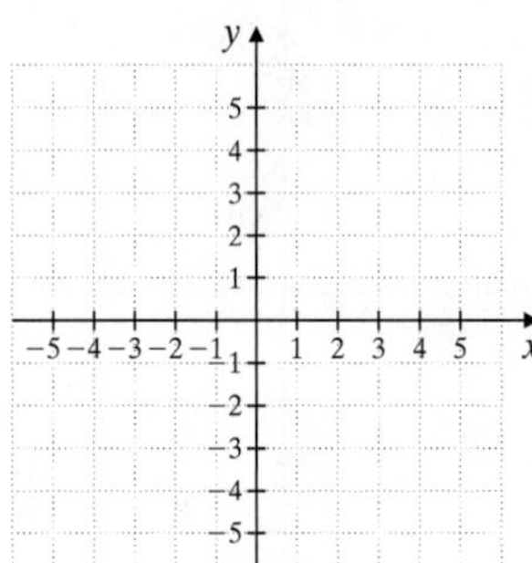

31. $x + 8y = 8$

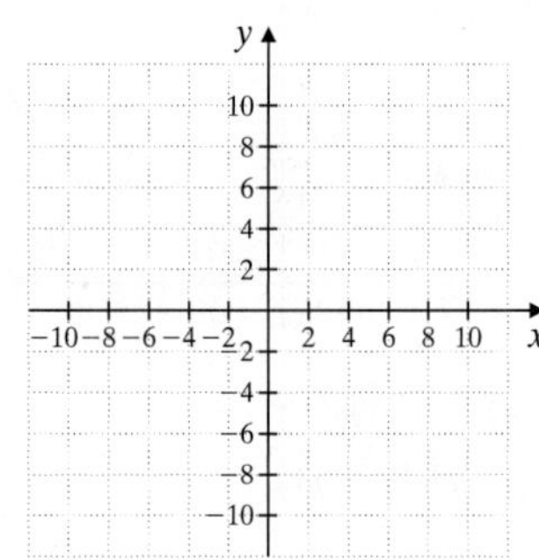

32. $x + 3y = 9$

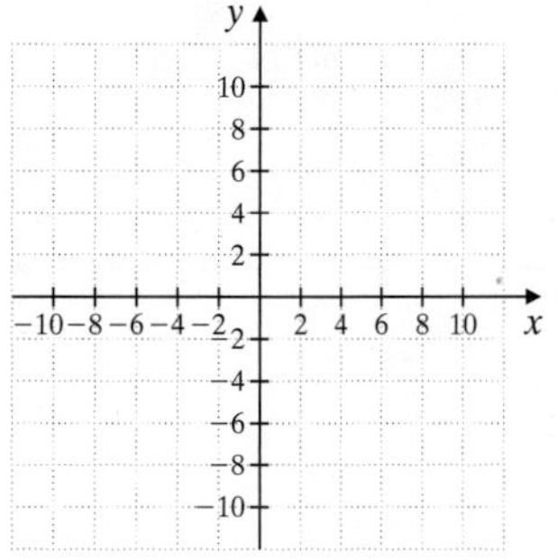

33. $5 = 6x - y$

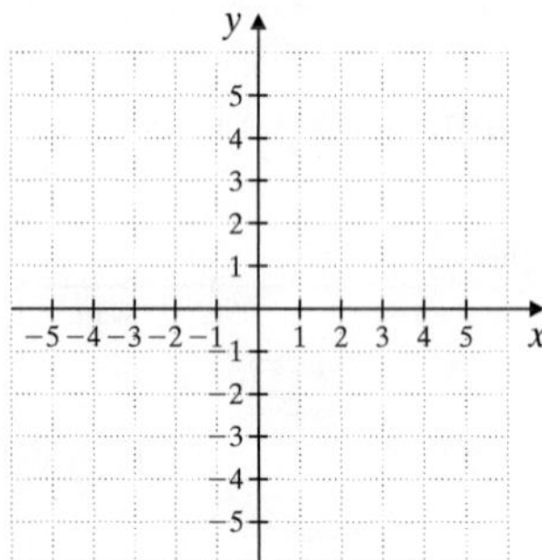

34. $4 = x - 3y$

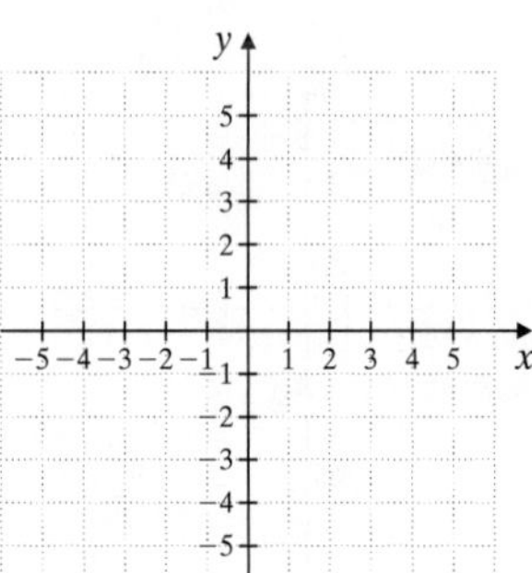

35. $-x + 10y = 11$

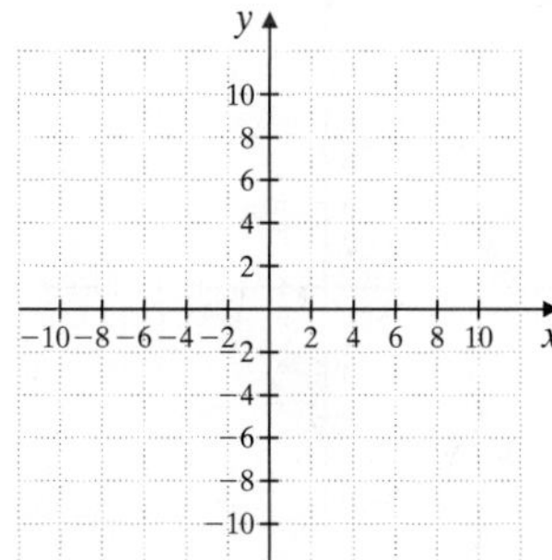

36. $-x + 9y = 10$

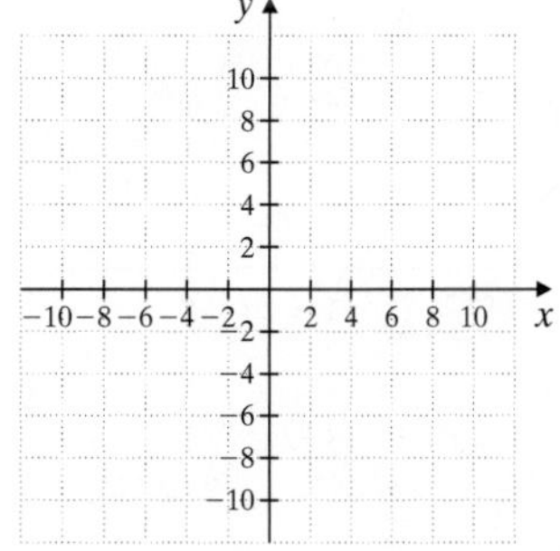

37. $x = -4\frac{1}{2}$

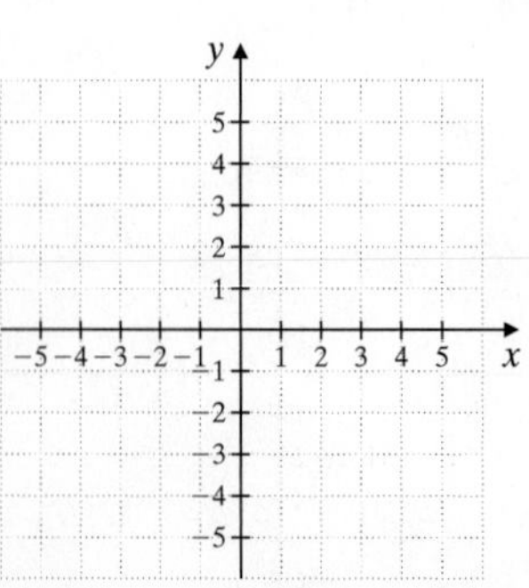

38. $x = -1\frac{3}{4}$

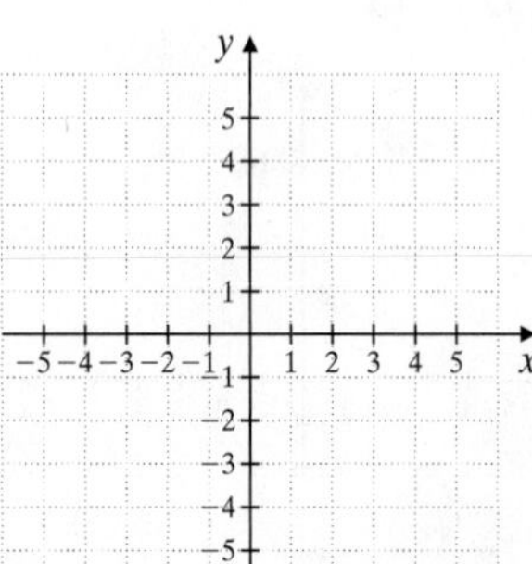

39. $y = 3\frac{1}{4}$

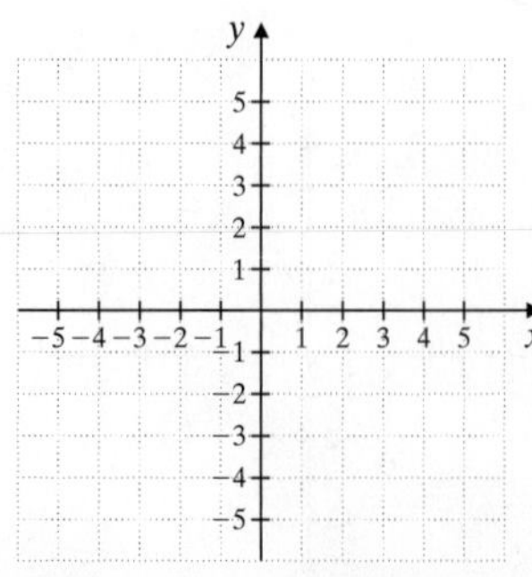

40. $y = 2\frac{1}{2}$

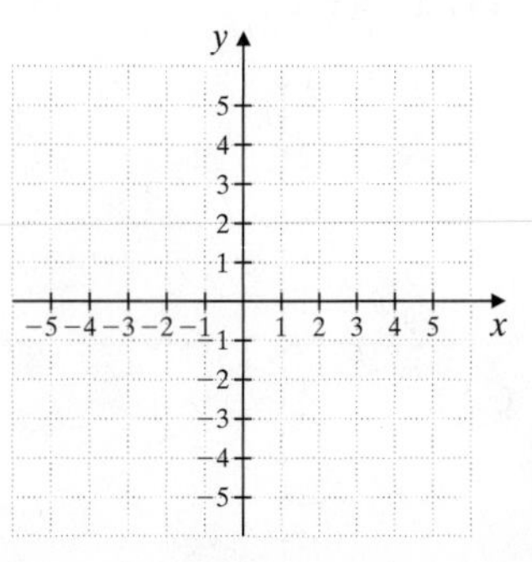

41. $y = -\frac{2}{3}x + 1$

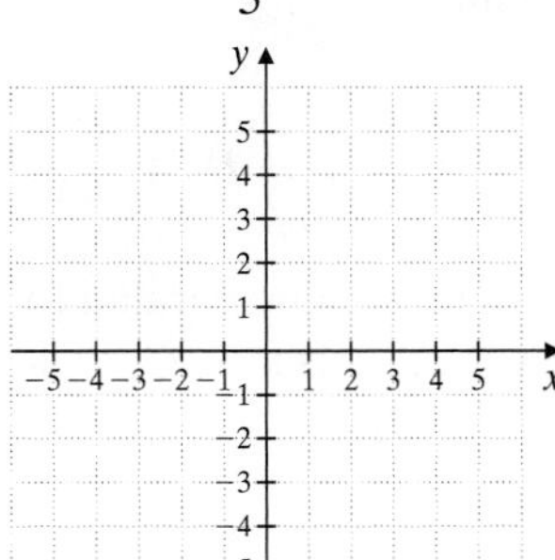

42. $y = -\frac{3}{5}x + 3$

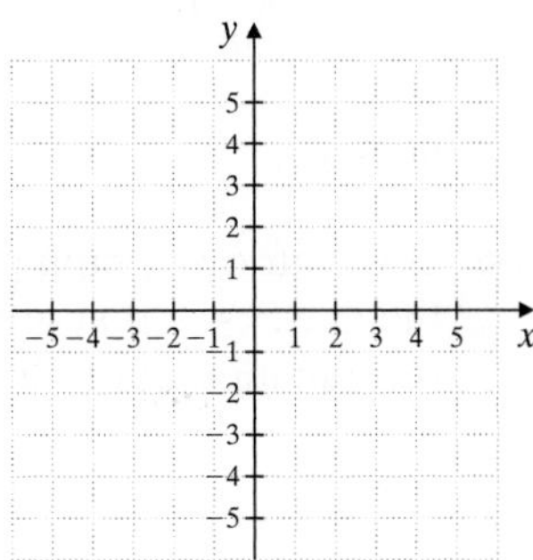

43. $4x - 6y + 2 = 0$

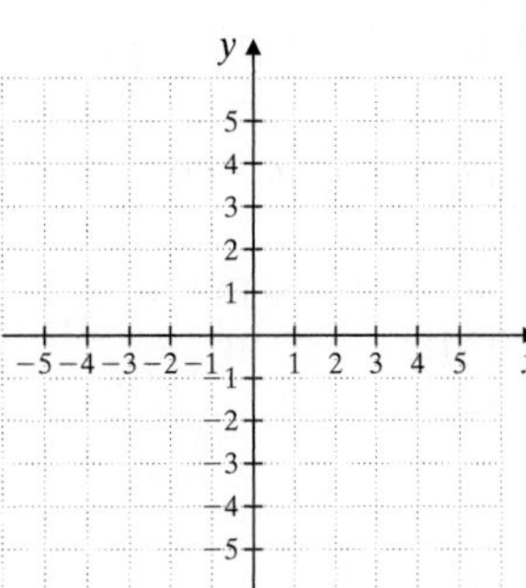

44. $9x - 6y + 3 = 0$

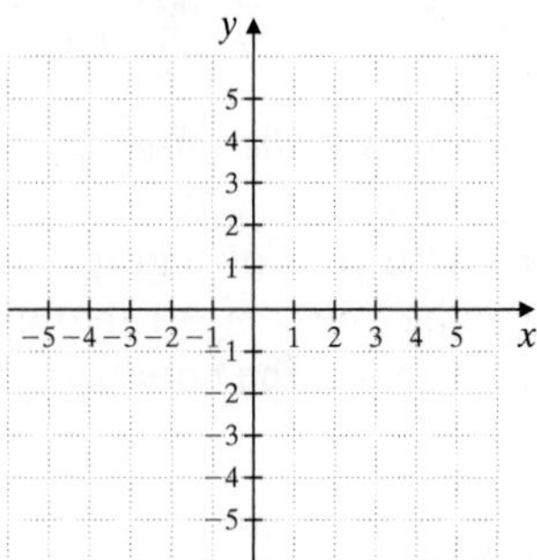

Review

Simplify. See Sections 8.4, and 8.5.

45. $\frac{-6 - 3}{2 - 8}$

46. $\frac{4 - 5}{-1 - 0}$

47. $\frac{-8 - (-2)}{-3 - (-2)}$

48. $\frac{12 - 3}{10 - 9}$

49. $\frac{0 - 6}{5 - 0}$

50. $\frac{2 - 2}{3 - 5}$

Concept Extensions

Match each equation with its graph.

51. $y = 3$

52. $y = 2x + 2$

53. $x = 3$

54. $y = 2x + 3$

a.

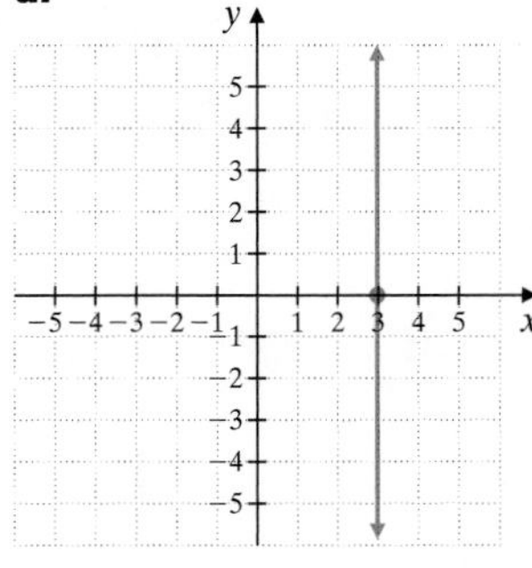

b.

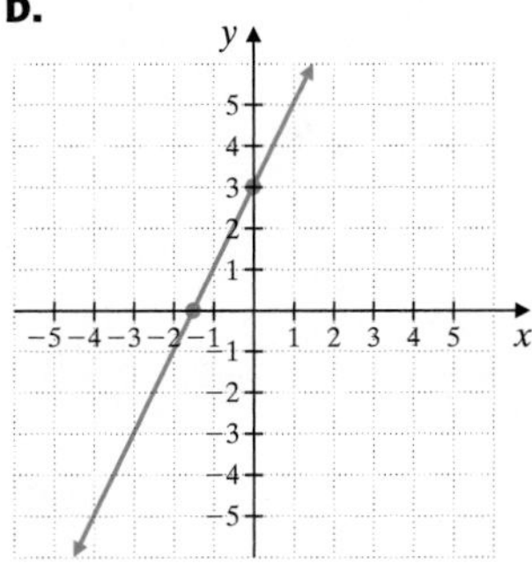

c.

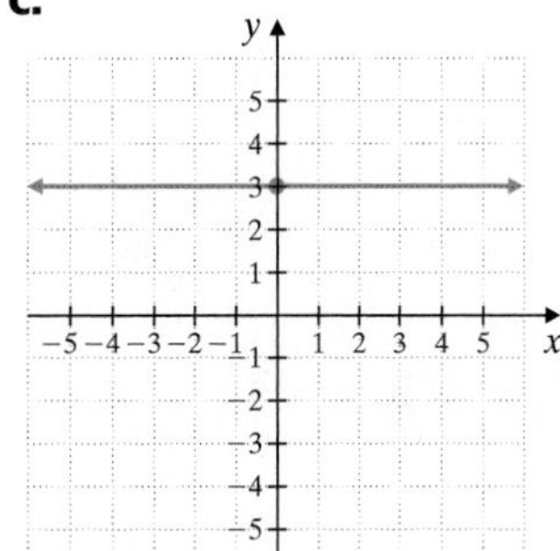

d.

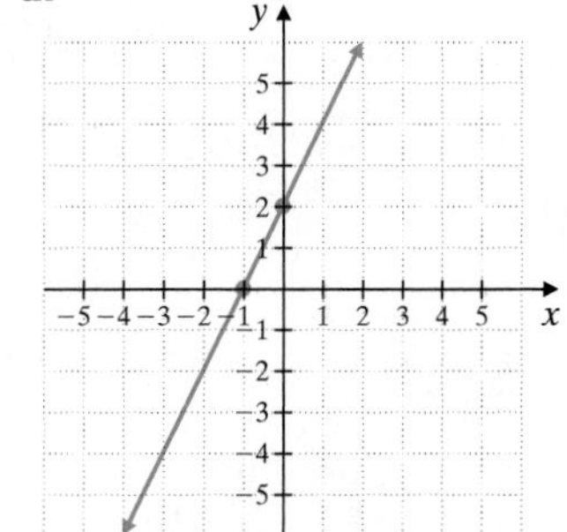

55. What is the greatest number of x- and y-intercepts that a line can have?

56. What is the smallest number of x- and y-intercepts that a line can have?

57. What is the smallest number of x- and y-intercepts that a circle can have?

58. What is the greatest number of x- and y-intercepts that a circle can have?

59. Discuss whether a vertical line ever has a y-intercept.

60. Discuss whether a horizontal line ever has an x-intercept.

The production supervisor at Alexandra's Office Products finds that it takes 3 hours to manufacture a particular office chair and 6 hours to manufacture an office desk. A total of 1200 hours is available to produce office chairs and desks of this style. The linear equation that models this situation is $3x + 6y = 1200$*, where x represents the number of chairs produced and y the number of desks manufactured.*

61. Complete the ordered pair solution (0,   ) of this equation. Describe the manufacturing situation that corresponds to this solution.

62. Complete the ordered pair solution (, 0) of this equation. Describe the manufacturing situation that corresponds to this solution.

63. If 50 desks are manufactured, find the greatest number of chairs that can be made.

64. If 50 chairs are manufactured, find the greatest number of desks that can be made.

Two lines in the same plane that do not intersect are called ***parallel lines.***

65. Use your own graph paper to draw a line parallel to the line $y = -1$ that intersects the y-axis at -4. What is the equation of this line?

66. Use your own graph paper to draw a line parallel to the line $x = 5$ that intersects the x-axis at 1. What is the equation of this line?

Solve.

67. It has been said that newspapers are disappearing, replaced by various electronic media. The average circulation of newspapers in the United States y, in millions, from 2003 to 2007 can be modeled by the equation $y = -1.9x + 59$, where x represents the number of years after 2003. (*Source:* Newspaper Association of America)

a. Find the x-intercept of this equation (round to the nearest tenth).

b. What does this x-intercept mean?

68. The number of a certain chain of stores y for the years 2003–2007 can be modeled by the equation $y = -198x + 3991$, where x represents the number of years after 2003. (*Source:* Limited Brands)

a. Find the y-intercept of this equation.

b. What does this y-intercept mean?

13.4 SLOPE AND RATE OF CHANGE

Objective A Finding the Slope of a Line Given Two Points

Thus far, much of this chapter has been devoted to graphing lines. You have probably noticed by now that a key feature of a line is its slant or steepness. In mathematics, the slant or steepness of a line is formally known as its **slope.** We measure the slope of a line by the ratio of vertical change (rise) to the corresponding horizontal change (run) as we move along the line.

On the line below, for example, suppose that we begin at the point (1, 2) and move to the point (4, 6). The vertical change is the change in y-coordinates: $6 - 2$ or 4 units. The corresponding horizontal change is the change in x-coordinates: $4 - 1 = 3$ units. The ratio of these changes is

$$\text{slope} = \frac{\text{change in } y \text{ (vertical change or rise)}}{\text{change in } x \text{ (horizontal change or run)}} = \frac{4}{3}$$

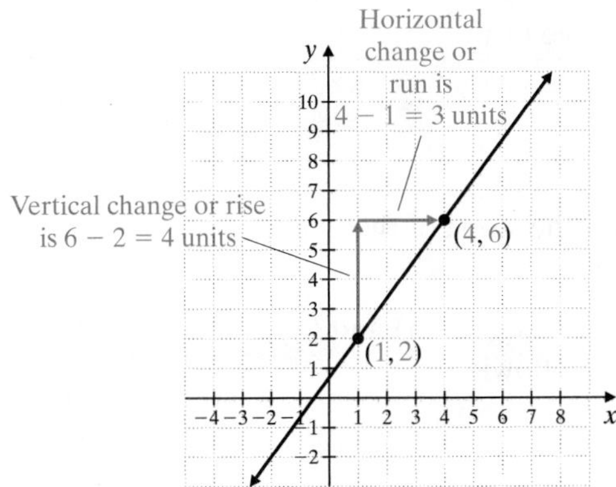

The slope of this line, then, is $\frac{4}{3}$. This means that for every 4 units of change in y-coordinates, there is a corresponding change of 3 units in x-coordinates.

Helpful Hint

It makes no difference what two points of a line are chosen to find its slope. The slope of a line is the same everywhere on the line.

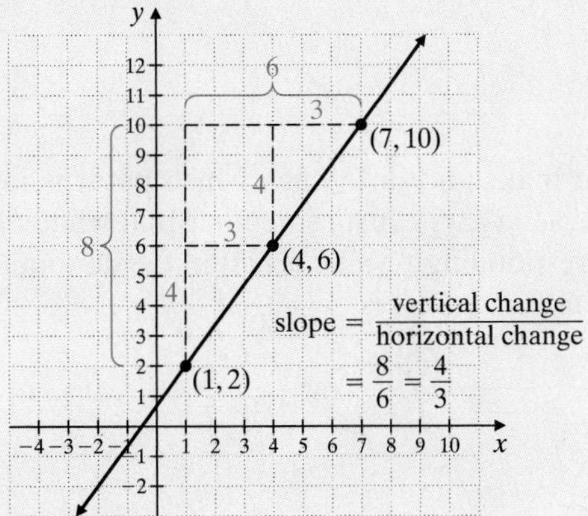

To find the slope of a line, then, choose two points of the line. Label the two x-coordinates of the two points x_1 and x_2 (read "x sub one" and "x sub two"), and label the corresponding y-coordinates y_1 and y_2.

Objectives

A Find the Slope of a Line Given Two Points of the Line.

B Find the Slope of a Line Given Its Equation.

C Find the Slopes of Horizontal and Vertical Lines.

D Compare the Slopes of Parallel and Perpendicular Lines.

E Slope as a Rate of Change.

The vertical change or **rise** between these points is the difference in the y-coordinates: $y_2 - y_1$. The horizontal change or **run** between the points is the difference of the x-coordinates: $x_2 - x_1$. The slope of the line is the ratio of $y_2 - y_1$ to $x_2 - x_1$, and we traditionally use the letter m to denote slope $m = \dfrac{y_2 - y_1}{x_2 - x_1}$.

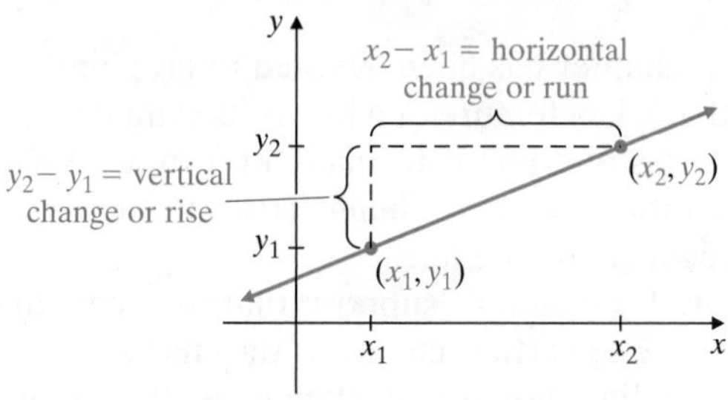

Slope of a Line

The slope m of the line containing the points (x_1, y_1) and (x_2, y_2) is given by

$$m = \frac{\text{rise}}{\text{run}} = \frac{\text{change in } y}{\text{change in } x} = \frac{y_2 - y_1}{x_2 - x_1}, \qquad \text{as long as } x_2 \neq x_1$$

PRACTICE 1

Find the slope of the line through $(-2, 3)$ and $(4, -1)$. Graph the line.

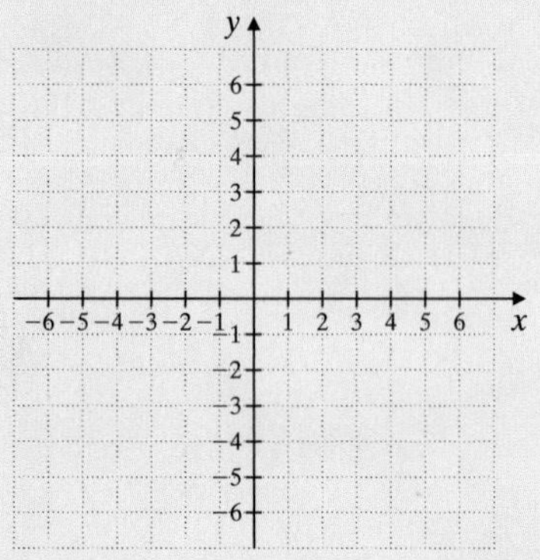

Example 1 Find the slope of the line through $(-1, 5)$ and $(2, -3)$. Graph the line.

Solution: Let (x_1, y_1) be $(-1, 5)$ and (x_2, y_2) be $(2, -3)$. Then, by the definition of slope, we have the following.

$$m = \frac{y_2 - y_1}{x_2 - x_1} = \frac{-3 - 5}{2 - (-1)} = \frac{-8}{3} = -\frac{8}{3}$$

The slope of the line is $-\dfrac{8}{3}$.

Work Practice 1

Answer

1. $-\dfrac{2}{3}$

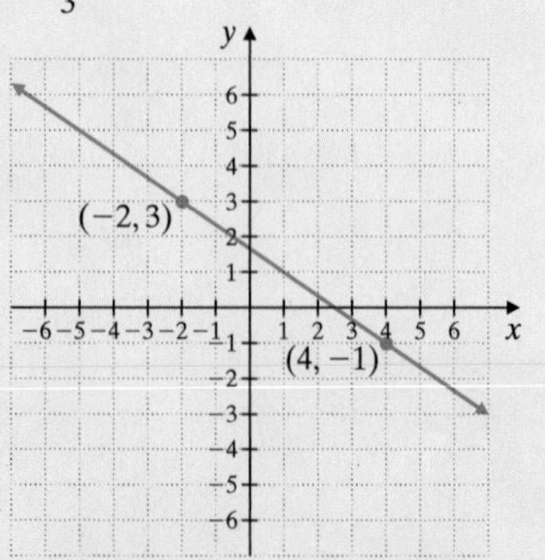

Helpful Hint

When finding slope, it makes no difference which point is identified as (x_1, y_1) and which is identified as (x_2, y_2). Just remember that whatever y-value is first in the numerator, its corresponding x-value is first in the denominator. Another way to calculate the slope in Example 1 is

$$m = \frac{y_2 - y_1}{x_2 - x_1} = \frac{5 - (-3)}{-1 - 2} = \frac{8}{-3} \text{ or } -\frac{8}{3} \quad \leftarrow \text{Same slope as found in Example 1}$$

✓Concept Check The points $(-2, -5)$, $(0, -2)$, $(4, 4)$, and $(10, 13)$ all lie on the same line. Work with a partner and verify that the slope is the same no matter which points are used to find slope.

✓ Concept Check Answer

$m = \dfrac{3}{2}$

Example 2 Find the slope of the line through $(-1, -2)$ and $(2, 4)$. Graph the line.

Solution: Let (x_1, y_1) be $(2, 4)$ and (x_2, y_2) be $(-1, -2)$.

$$m = \frac{y_2 - y_1}{x_2 - x_1}$$

$$= \frac{-2 - 4}{-1 - 2} \quad \begin{array}{l}\text{y-value}\\ \text{corresponding x-value}\end{array}$$

$$= \frac{-6}{-3} = 2$$

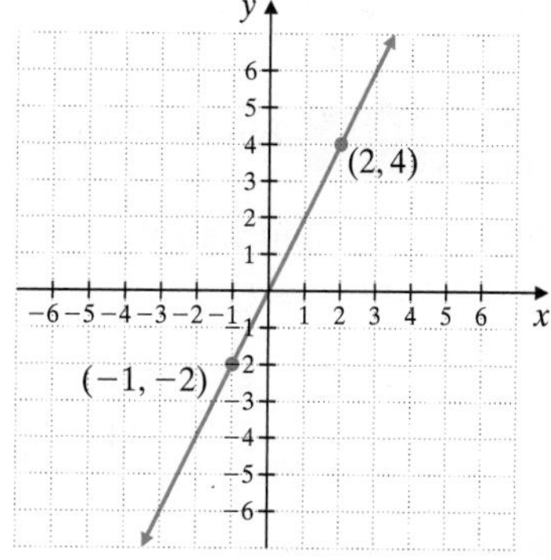

The slope is 2.

Work Practice 2

PRACTICE 2

Find the slope of the line through $(-2, 1)$ and $(3, 5)$. Graph the line.

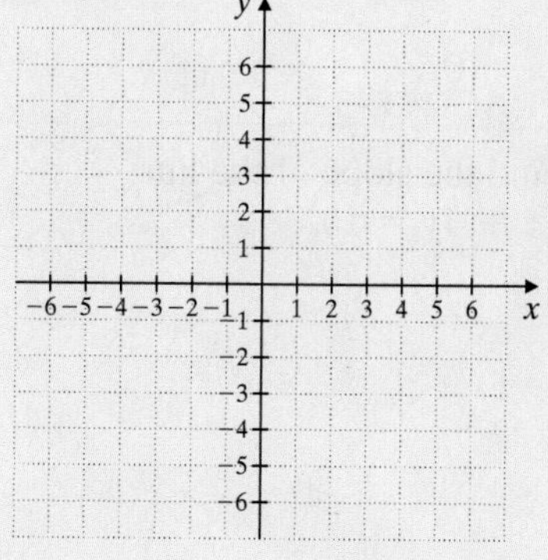

✓Concept Check What is wrong with the following slope calculation for the points $(3, 5)$ and $(-2, 6)$?

$$m = \frac{5 - 6}{-2 - 3} = \frac{-1}{-5} = \frac{1}{5}$$

Notice that the slope of the line in Example 1 is negative and that the slope of the line in Example 2 is positive. Let your eye follow the line with negative slope from left to right and notice that the line "goes down." If you follow the line with positive slope from left to right, you will notice that the line "goes up." This is true in general.

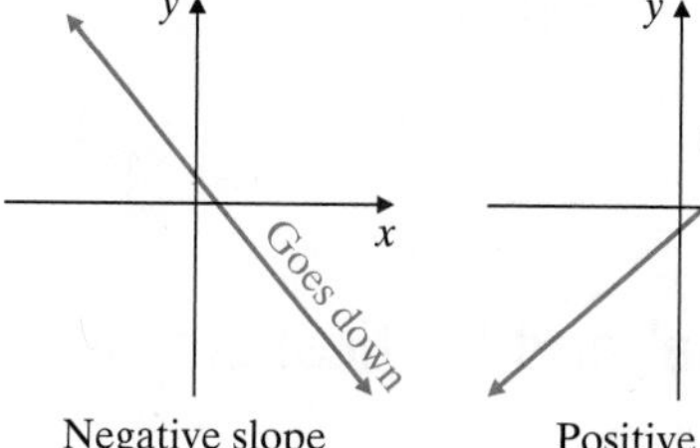

Negative slope

Positive slope

Helpful Hint To decide whether a line "goes up" or "goes down," always follow the line from left to right.

Objective B Finding the Slope of a Line Given Its Equation

As we have seen, the slope of a line is defined by two points on the line. Thus, if we know the equation of a line, we can find its slope by finding two of its points. For example, let's find the slope of the line

$$y = 3x - 2$$

To find two points, we can choose two values for x and substitute to find corresponding y-values. If $x = 0$, for example, $y = 3 \cdot 0 - 2$ or $y = -2$. If $x = 1$, $y = 3 \cdot 1 - 2$ or $y = 1$. This gives the ordered pairs $(0, -2)$ and $(1, 1)$. Using the definition for slope, we have

$$m = \frac{1 - (-2)}{1 - 0} = \frac{3}{1} = 3 \quad \text{The slope is 3.}$$

Notice that the slope, 3, is the same as the coefficient of x in the equation $y = 3x - 2$. This is true in general.

Answer

2. $\frac{4}{5}$

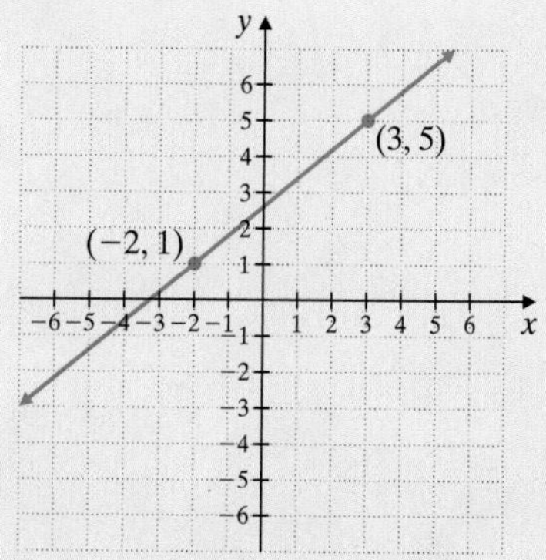

✓ Concept Check Answer

$$m = \frac{5 - 6}{3 - (-2)} = \frac{-1}{5} = -\frac{1}{5}$$

If a linear equation is solved for y, the coefficient of x is the line's slope. In other words, the slope of the line given by $y = mx + b$ is m, the coefficient of x.

$$y = mx + b$$
↑ slope

PRACTICE 3

Find the slope of the line $5x + 4y = 10$.

Example 3 Find the slope of the line $-2x + 3y = 11$.

Solution: When we solve for y, the coefficient of x is the slope.

$$-2x + 3y = 11$$

$$3y = 2x + 11 \quad \text{Add } 2x \text{ to both sides.}$$

$$y = \frac{2}{3}x + \frac{11}{3} \quad \text{Divide both sides by 3.}$$

The slope is $\frac{2}{3}$.

Work Practice 3

PRACTICE 4

Find the slope of the line $-y = -2x + 7$.

Example 4 Find the slope of the line $-y = 5x - 2$.

Solution: Remember, the equation must be solved for y (not $-y$) in order for the coefficient of x to be the slope.

To solve for y, let's divide both sides of the equation by -1.

$$-y = 5x - 2 \quad \text{Divide both sides by } -1.$$

$$\frac{-y}{-1} = \frac{5x}{-1} - \frac{2}{-1} \quad \text{Simplify.}$$

$$y = -5x + 2$$

The slope is -5.

Work Practice 4

Objective C Finding Slopes of Horizontal and Vertical Lines

PRACTICE 5

Find the slope of $y = 3$.

Example 5 Find the slope of the line $y = -1$.

Solution: Recall that $y = -1$ is a horizontal line with y-intercept -1. To find the slope, we find two ordered pair solutions of $y = -1$, knowing that solutions of $y = -1$ must have a y-value of -1. We will use $(2, -1)$ and $(-3, -1)$. We let (x_1, y_1) be $(2, -1)$ and (x_2, y_2) be $(-3, -1)$.

$$m = \frac{y_2 - y_1}{x_2 - x_1} = \frac{-1 - (-1)}{-3 - 2} = \frac{0}{-5} = 0$$

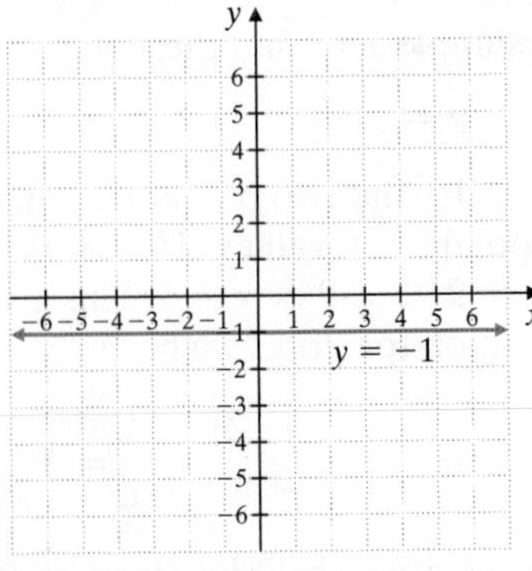

The slope of the line $y = -1$ is 0. Since the y-values will have a difference of 0 for every horizontal line, we can say that all **horizontal lines have a slope of 0.**

Work Practice 5

Answers

3. $-\frac{5}{4}$ 4. 2 5. 0

Example 6 Find the slope of the line $x = 5$.

Solution: Recall that the graph of $x = 5$ is a vertical line with x-intercept 5. To find the slope, we find two ordered pair solutions of $x = 5$. Ordered pair solutions of $x = 5$ must have an x-value of 5. We will use (5, 0) and (5, 4). We let $(x_1, y_1) = (5, 0)$ and $(x_2, y_2) = (5, 4)$.

$$m = \frac{y_2 - y_1}{x_2 - x_1} = \frac{4 - 0}{5 - 5} = \frac{4}{0}$$

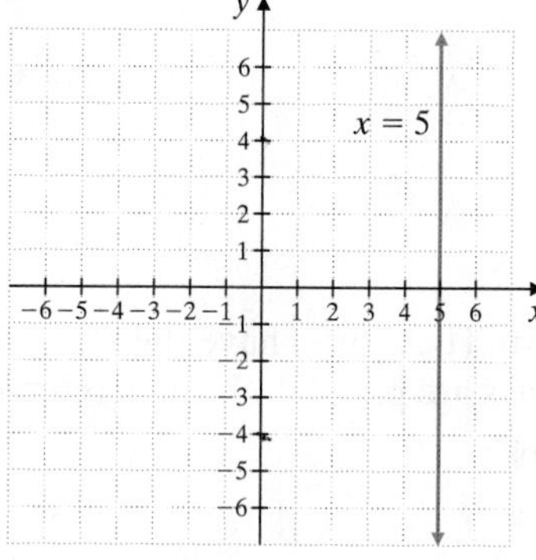

Since $\frac{4}{0}$ is undefined, we say that the slope of the vertical line $x = 5$ is undefined. Since the x-values will have a difference of 0 for every vertical line, we can say that all **vertical lines have undefined slope.**

Work Practice 6

PRACTICE 6

Find the slope of the line $x = -2$.

Helpful Hint

Slope of 0 and undefined slope are not the same. Vertical lines have undefined slope, while horizontal lines have a slope of 0.

Here is a general review of slope.

Summary of Slope

Slope m of the line through (x_1, y_1) and (x_2, y_2) is given by the equation

$$m = \frac{y_2 - y_1}{x_2 - x_1}.$$

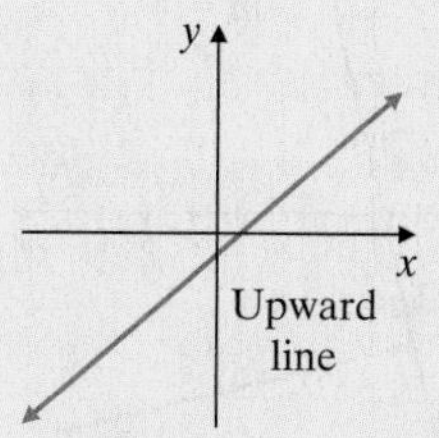

Positive slope: $m > 0$

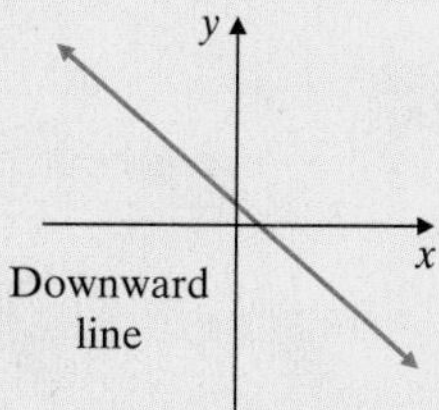

Negative slope: $m < 0$

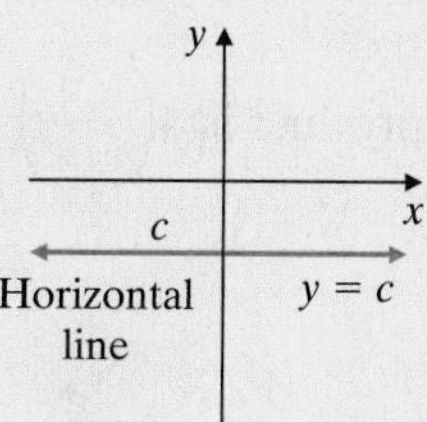

Zero slope: $m = 0$

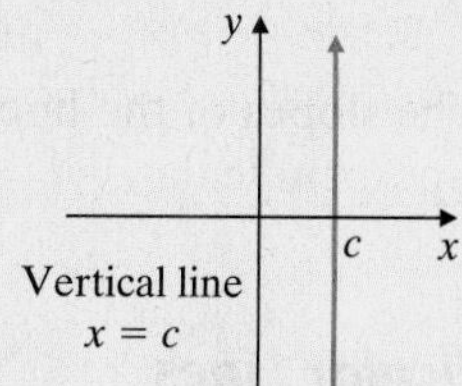

No slope or undefined slope

Objective D Slopes of Parallel and Perpendicular Lines

Two lines in the same plane are **parallel** if they do not intersect. Slopes of lines can help us determine whether lines are parallel. Since parallel lines have the same steepness, it follows that they have the same slope.

Answer

6. undefined slope

For example, the graphs of

$$y = -2x + 4$$

and

$$y = -2x - 3$$

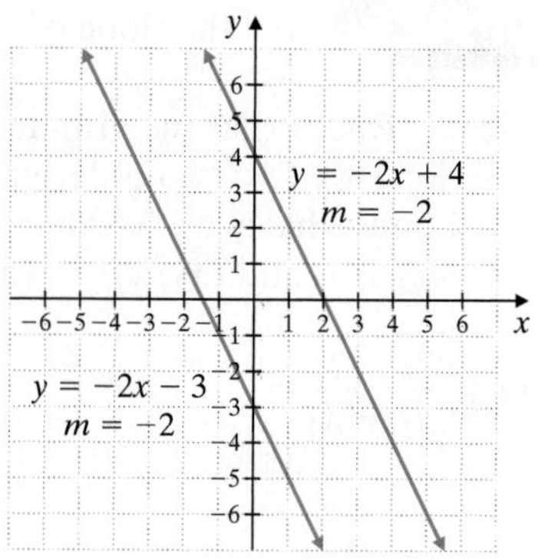

are shown. These lines have the same slope, -2. They also have different y-intercepts, so the lines are parallel. (If the y-intercepts were the same also, the lines would be the same.)

Parallel Lines

Nonvertical parallel lines have the same slope and different y-intercepts.

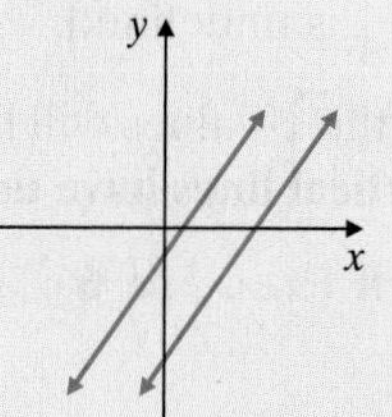

Two lines are **perpendicular** if they lie in the same plane and meet at a 90° (right) angle. How do the slopes of perpendicular lines compare? The product of the slopes of two perpendicular lines is -1.

For example, the graphs of

$$y = 4x + 1$$

and

$$y = -\frac{1}{4}x - 3$$

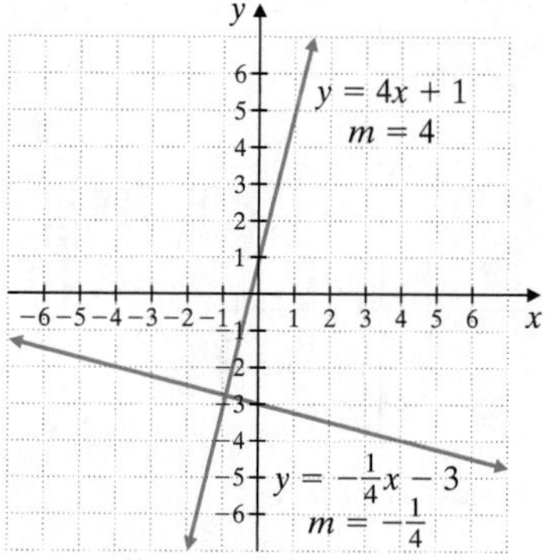

are shown. The slopes of the lines are 4 and $-\frac{1}{4}$. Their product is $4\left(-\frac{1}{4}\right) = -1$, so the lines are perpendicular.

Perpendicular Lines

If the product of the slopes of two lines is -1, then the lines are perpendicular.

(Two nonvertical lines are perpendicular if the slope of one is the negative reciprocal of the slope of the other.)

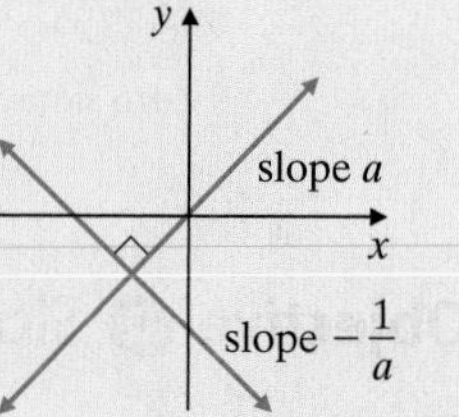

Helpful Hint

Here are examples of numbers that are negative (opposite) reciprocals.

Number	Negative Reciprocal	Their product is −1.
$\frac{2}{3}$	$-\frac{3}{2}$	$\frac{2}{3} \cdot -\frac{3}{2} = -\frac{6}{6} = -1$
-5 or $-\frac{5}{1}$	$\frac{1}{5}$	$-5 \cdot \frac{1}{5} = -\frac{5}{5} = -1$

Here are a few important points about vertical and horizontal lines.

- Two distinct vertical lines are parallel.
- Two distinct horizontal lines are parallel.
- A horizontal line and a vertical line are always perpendicular.

Example 7 Determine whether each pair of lines is parallel, perpendicular, or neither.

a. $y = -\frac{1}{5}x + 1$
$2x + 10y = 3$

b. $x + y = 3$
$-x + y = 4$

c. $3x + y = 5$
$2x + 3y = 6$

Solution:

a. The slope of the line $y = -\frac{1}{5}x + 1$ is $-\frac{1}{5}$. We find the slope of the second line by solving its equation for y.

$2x + 10y = 3$

$10y = -2x + 3$ Subtract $2x$ from both sides.

$y = \frac{-2}{10}x + \frac{3}{10}$ Divide both sides by 10.

$y = -\frac{1}{5}x + \frac{3}{10}$ Simplify.

The slope of this line is $-\frac{1}{5}$ also. Since the lines have the same slope and different y-intercepts, they are parallel, as shown in the figure on the left below.

b. To find each slope, we solve each equation for y.

$x + y = 3$
$y = -x + 3$
The slope is −1.

$-x + y = 4$
$y = x + 4$
The slope is 1.

The slopes are not the same, so the lines are not parallel. Next we check the product of the slopes: $(-1)(1) = -1$. Since the product is −1, the lines are perpendicular, as shown in the figure on the right below.

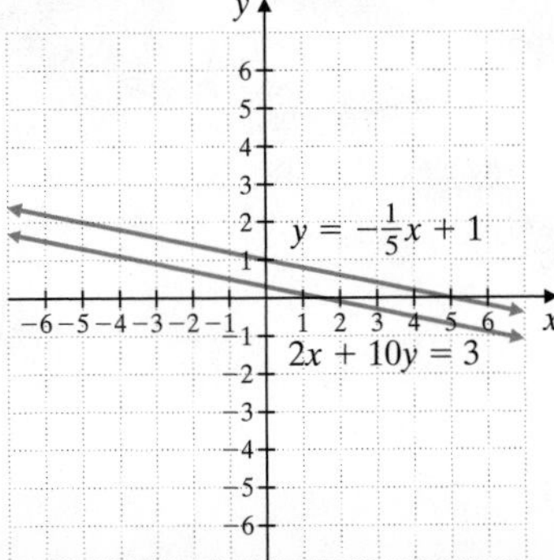

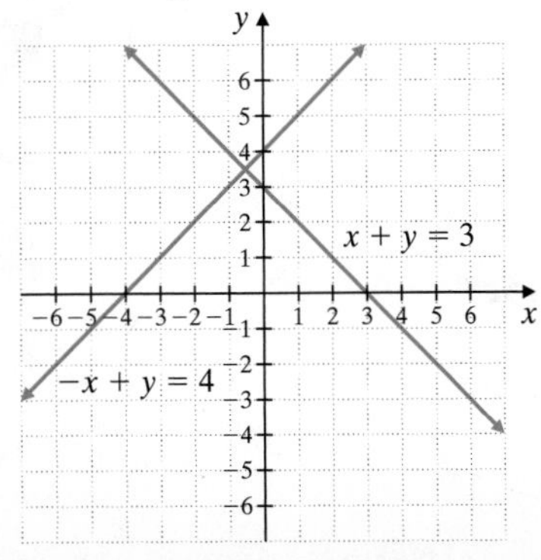

Continued on next page

PRACTICE 7

Determine whether each pair of lines is parallel, perpendicular, or neither.

a. $x + y = 5$
$2x + y = 5$

b. $5y = 2x - 3$
$5x + 2y = 1$

c. $y = 2x + 1$
$4x - 2y = 8$

Answers

7. a. neither **b.** perpendicular **c.** parallel

c. We solve each equation for y to find each slope. The slopes are -3 and $-\frac{2}{3}$. The slopes are not the same and their product is not -1. Thus, the lines are neither parallel nor perpendicular.

Work Practice 7

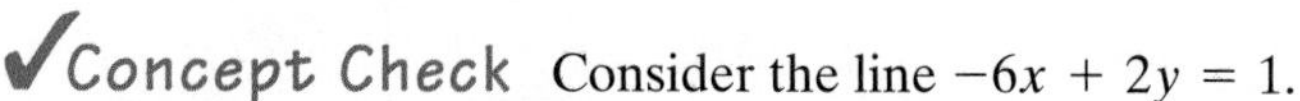

✓Concept Check Consider the line $-6x + 2y = 1$.

a. Write the equations of two lines parallel to this line.

b. Write the equations of two lines perpendicular to this line.

Objective E Slope as a Rate of Change

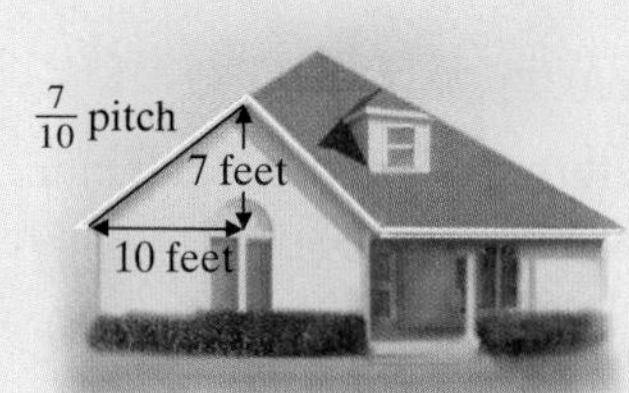

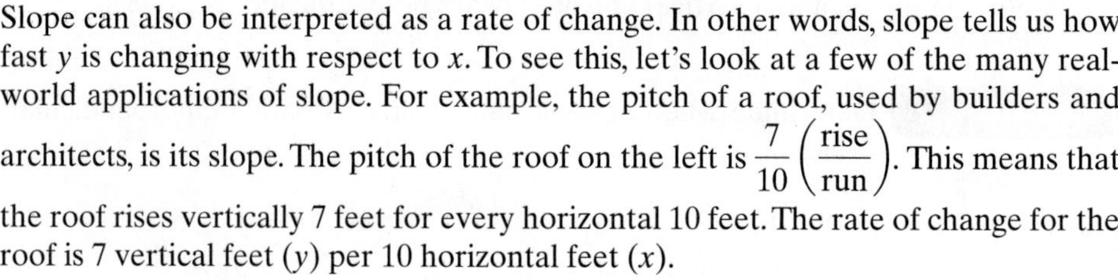

Slope can also be interpreted as a rate of change. In other words, slope tells us how fast y is changing with respect to x. To see this, let's look at a few of the many real-world applications of slope. For example, the pitch of a roof, used by builders and architects, is its slope. The pitch of the roof on the left is $\frac{7}{10}\left(\frac{\text{rise}}{\text{run}}\right)$. This means that the roof rises vertically 7 feet for every horizontal 10 feet. The rate of change for the roof is 7 vertical feet (y) per 10 horizontal feet (x).

The grade of a road is its slope written as a percent. A 7% grade, as shown below, means that the road rises (or falls) 7 feet for every horizontal 100 feet. $\left(\text{Recall that } 7\% = \frac{7}{100}.\right)$ Here, the slope of $\frac{7}{100}$ gives us the rate of change. The road rises (in our diagram) 7 vertical feet (y) for every 100 horizontal feet (x).

PRACTICE 8

Find the grade of the road shown.

Example 8 Finding the Grade of a Road

At one part of the road to the summit of Pike's Peak, the road rises 15 feet for a horizontal distance of 250 feet. Find the grade of the road.

Solution: Recall that the grade of a road is its slope written as a percent.

$$\text{grade} = \frac{\text{rise}}{\text{run}} = \frac{15}{250} = 0.06 = 6\%$$

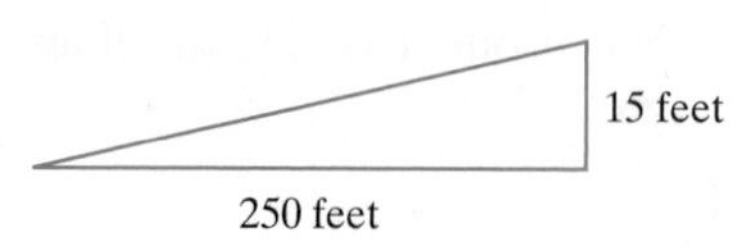

The grade is 6%.

Work Practice 8

Answer

8. 15%

✓ Concept Check Answers

Answers may vary; for example,

a. $y = 3x - 3,\ y = 3x - 1$

b. $y = -\frac{1}{3}x,\ y = -\frac{1}{3}x + 1$

Slope can also be interpreted as a rate of change. In other words, slope tells us how fast y is changing with respect to x.

Example 9 Finding the Slope of a Line

The following graph shows the cost y (in cents) of a nationwide long-distance telephone call from Texas with a certain telephone-calling plan, where x is the length of the call in minutes. Find the slope of the line and attach the proper units for the rate of change. Then write a sentence explaining the meaning of slope in this application.

Solution: Use (2, 34) and (6, 62) to calculate slope.

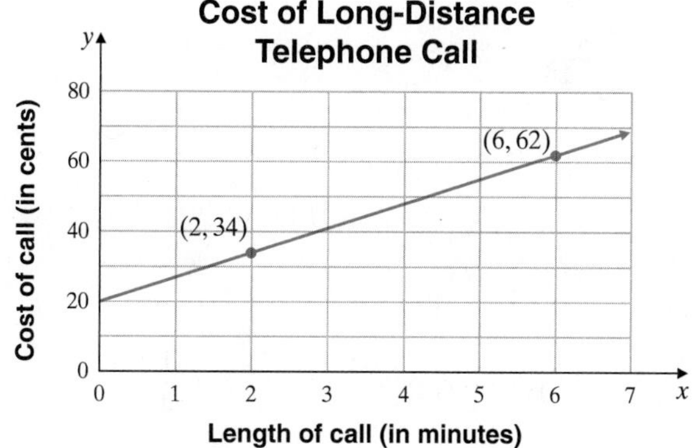

$$m = \frac{62 - 34}{6 - 2} = \frac{28}{4} = \frac{7 \text{ cents}}{1 \text{ minute}}$$

This means that the rate of change of a phone call is 7 cents per 1 minute, or the cost of the phone call is 7 cents per minute.

Work Practice 9

PRACTICE 9

Find the slope of the line and write the slope as a rate of change. This graph represents annual food and drink sales y (in billions of dollars) for year x. Write a sentence explaining the meaning of slope in this application.

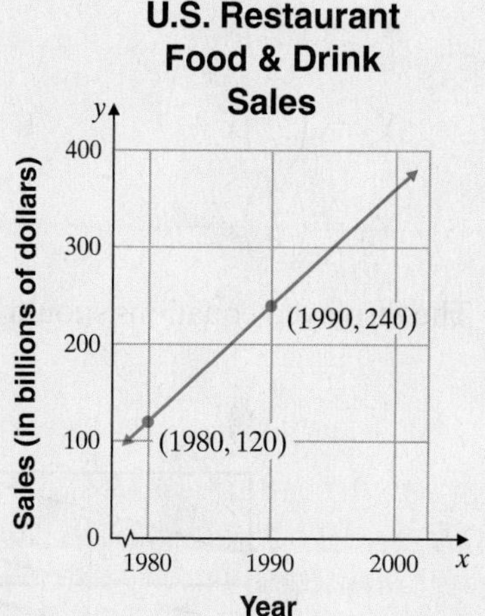

Source: National Restaurant Assn.

Answer

9. $m = 12$; The sales of food and drink from restaurants increases by $12 billion per year.

Calculator Explorations Graphing

It is possible to use a graphing calculator and sketch the graph of more than one equation on the same set of axes. This feature can be used to see that parallel lines have the same slope. For example, graph the equations $y = \frac{2}{5}x$, $y = \frac{2}{5}x + 7$, and $y = \frac{2}{5}x - 4$ on the same set of axes. To do so, press the Y= key and enter the equations on the first three lines.

$$Y_1 = \left(\frac{2}{5}\right)x$$

$$Y_2 = \left(\frac{2}{5}\right)x + 7$$

$$Y_3 = \left(\frac{2}{5}\right)x - 4$$

The displayed equations should look like this:

$y_2 = \frac{2}{5}x + 7$ $y_1 = \frac{2}{5}x$

10

−10 10

−10

$y_3 = \frac{2}{5}x - 4$

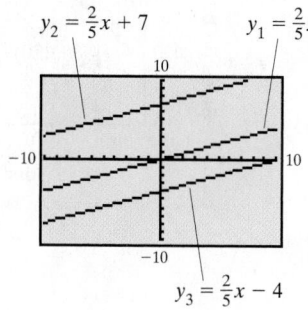

These lines are parallel as expected since they all have a slope of $\frac{2}{5}$. The graph of $y = \frac{2}{5}x + 7$ is the graph of $y = \frac{2}{5}x$ moved 7 units upward with a y-intercept of 7. Also, the graph of $y = \frac{2}{5}x - 4$ is the graph of $y = \frac{2}{5}x$ moved 4 units downward with a y-intercept of −4.

Graph the parallel lines on the same set of axes. Describe the similarities and differences in their graphs.

1. $y = 3.8x$, $y = 3.8x - 3$, $y = 3.8x + 9$

2. $y = -4.9x$, $y = -4.9x + 1$, $y = -4.9x + 8$

3. $y = \frac{1}{4}x$, $y = \frac{1}{4}x + 5$, $y = \frac{1}{4}x - 8$

4. $y = -\frac{3}{4}x$, $y = -\frac{3}{4}x - 5$, $y = -\frac{3}{4}x + 6$

Vocabulary and Readiness Check

Use the choices below to fill in each blank. Not all choices will be used.

m	x	0	positive	undefined
b	y	slope	negative	

1. The measure of the steepness or tilt of a line is called ____________.
2. If an equation is written in the form $y = mx + b$, the value of the letter ____________ is the value of the slope of the graph.
3. The slope of a horizontal line is ____________.
4. The slope of a vertical line is ____________.
5. If the graph of a line moves upward from left to right, the line has ____________ slope.
6. If the graph of a line moves downward from left to right, the line has ____________ slope.
7. Given two points of a line, slope $= \dfrac{\text{change in \_\_\_\_\_\_}}{\text{change in \_\_\_\_\_\_}}$.

State whether the slope of the line is positive, negative, 0, or undefined.

8. 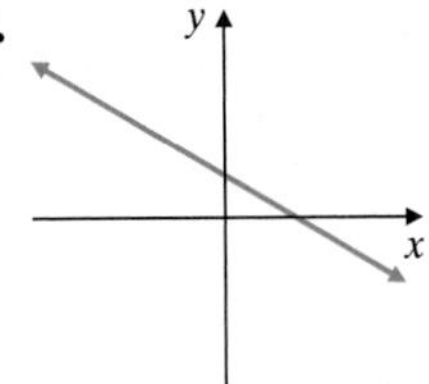

9. 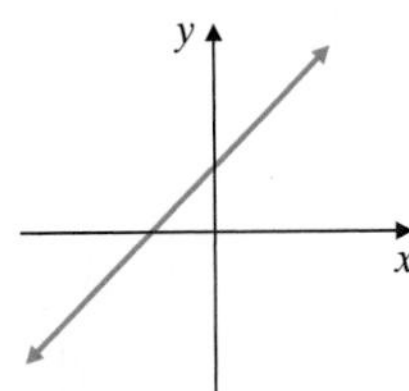

10. 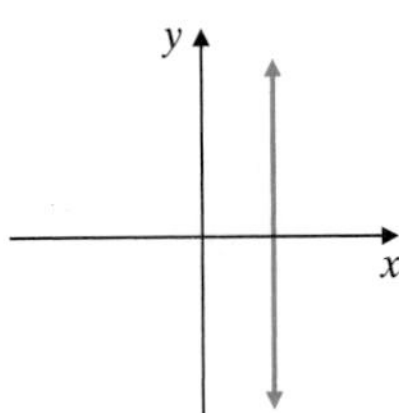

11. 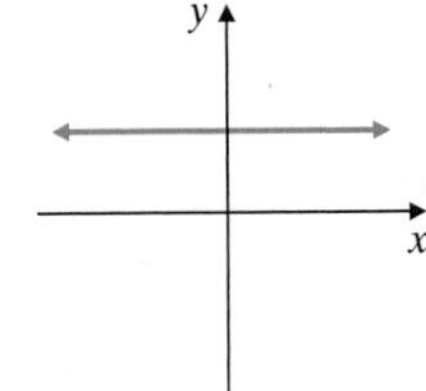

Decide whether a line with the given slope slants upward or downward or is horizontal or vertical.

12. $m = \dfrac{7}{6}$ ____________ **13.** $m = -3$ ____________ **14.** $m = 0$ ____________ **15.** m is undefined. ____________

13.4 Exercise Set

FOR EXTRA HELP MyMathLab

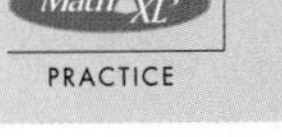
PRACTICE

WATCH

DOWNLOAD

READ

REVIEW

Objective A *Find the slope of the line that passes through the given points. See Examples 1 and 2.*

1. $(-1, 5)$ and $(6, -2)$ **2.** $(-1, 16)$ and $(3, 4)$ **3.** $(1, 4)$ and $(5, 3)$ **4.** $(3, 1)$ and $(2, 6)$

5. $(5, 1)$ and $(-2, 1)$ **6.** $(-8, 3)$ and $(-2, 3)$ **7.** $(-4, 3)$ and $(-4, 5)$ **8.** $(-2, -3)$ and $(-2, 5)$

Use the points shown on each graph to find the slope of each line. See Examples 1 and 2.

9. 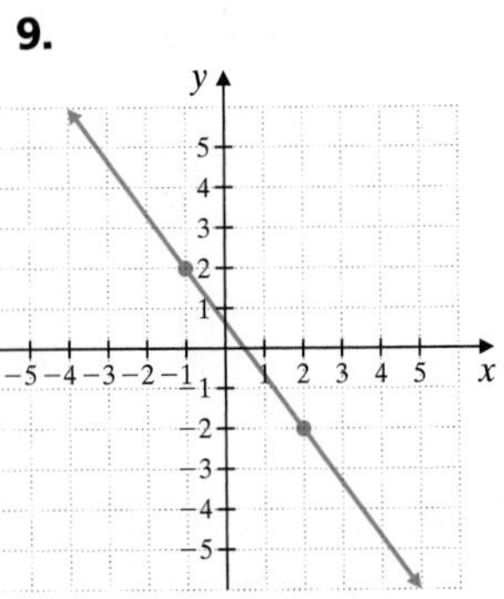

10. 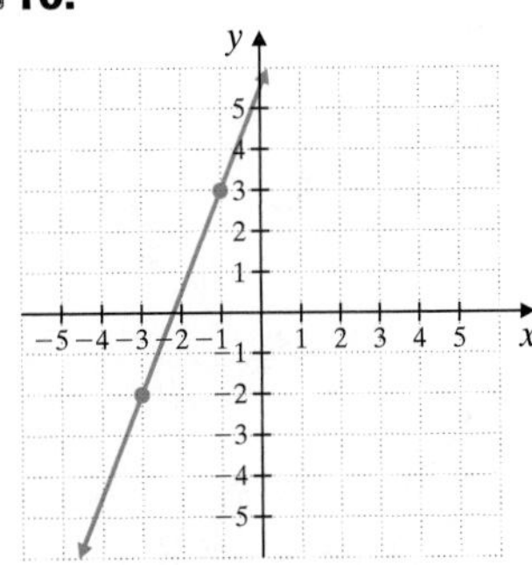

11. 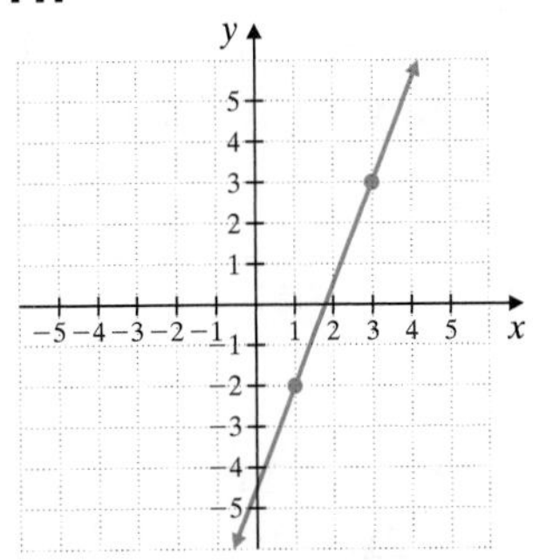

12. 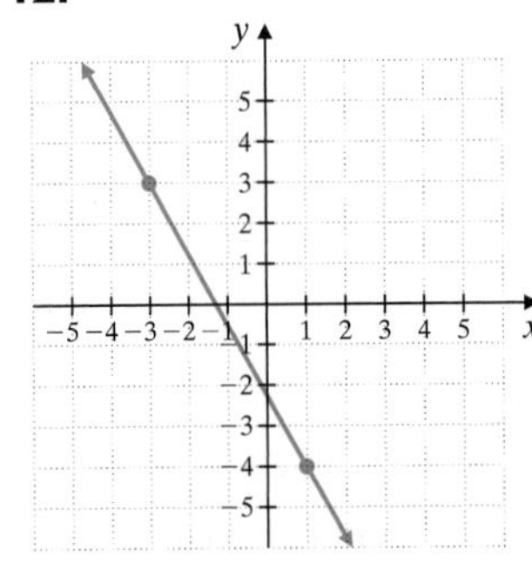

For each graph, determine which line has the greater slope.

13.
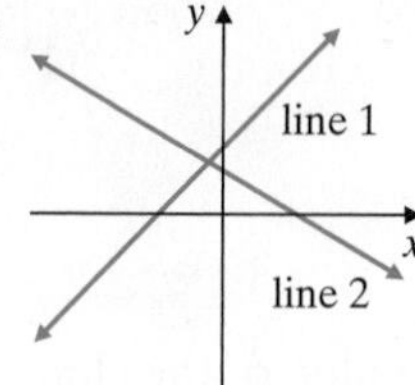

14.
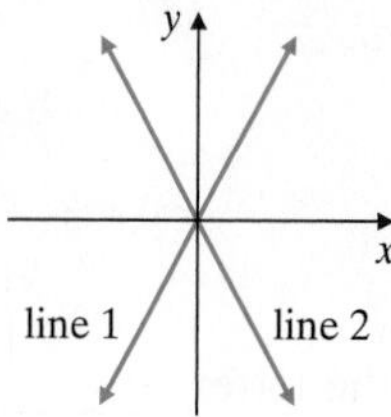

15.
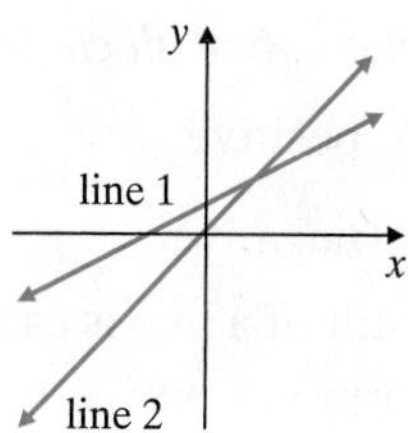

16.
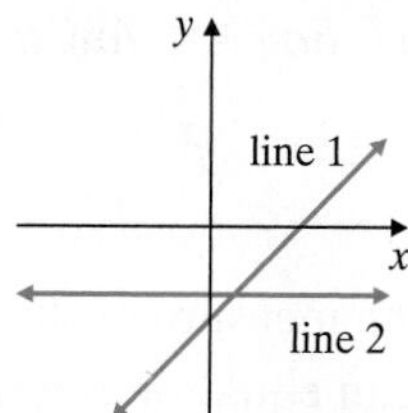

Objectives B C **Mixed Practice** *Find the slope of each line. See Examples 3 through 6.*

17. $y = 5x - 2$

18. $y = -2x + 6$

19. $y = -0.3x + 2.5$

20. $y = -7.6x - 0.1$

21. $2x + y = 7$

22. $-5x + y = 10$

23.
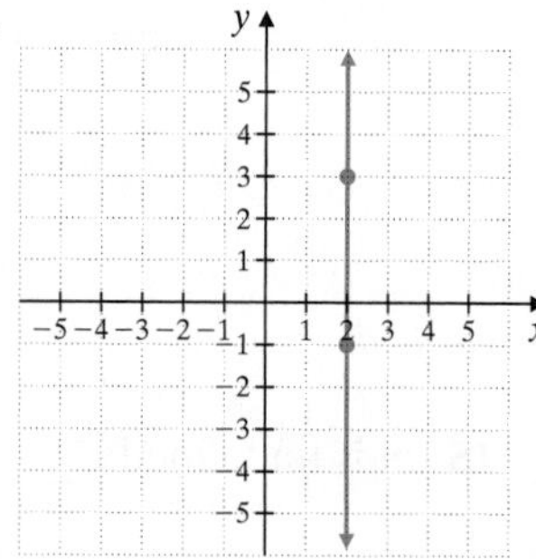

24.
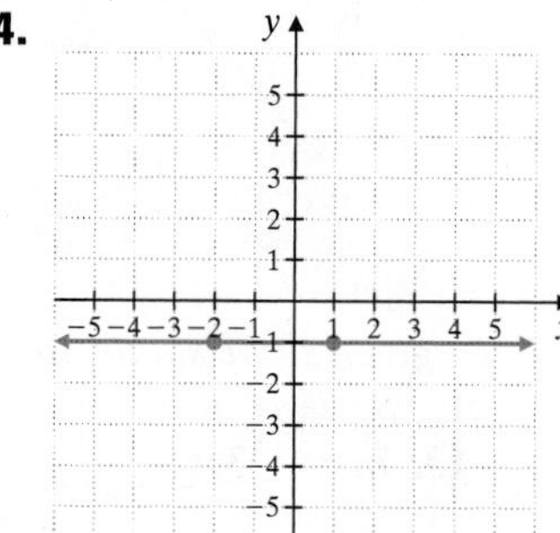

25. $2x - 3y = 10$

26. $3x - 5y = 1$

27. $x = 1$

28. $y = -2$

29. $x = 2y$

30. $x = -4y$

31. $y = -3$

32. $x = 5$

33. $-3x - 4y = 6$

34. $-4x - 7y = 9$

35. $20x - 5y = 1.2$

36. $24x - 3y = 5.7$

△ Objective D *Determine whether each pair of lines is parallel, perpendicular, or neither. See Example 7.*

37. $y = \frac{2}{9}x + 3$
$y = -\frac{2}{9}x$

38. $y = \frac{1}{5}x + 20$
$y = -\frac{1}{5}x$

39. $x - 3y = -6$
$y = 3x - 9$

40. $y = 4x - 2$
$4x + y = 5$

41. $6x = 5y + 1$
$-12x + 10y = 1$

42. $-x + 2y = -2$
$2x = 4y + 3$

43. $6 + 4x = 3y$
$3x + 4y = 8$

44. $10 + 3x = 5y$
$5x + 3y = 1$

△ *Find the slope of the line that is (a) parallel and (b) perpendicular to the line through each pair of points. See Example 7.*

45. $(-3, -3)$ and $(0, 0)$

46. $(6, -2)$ and $(1, 4)$

47. $(-8, -4)$ and $(3, 5)$

48. $(6, -1)$ and $(-4, -10)$

Objective E *The pitch of a roof is its slope. Find the pitch of each roof shown. See Example 8.*

49.

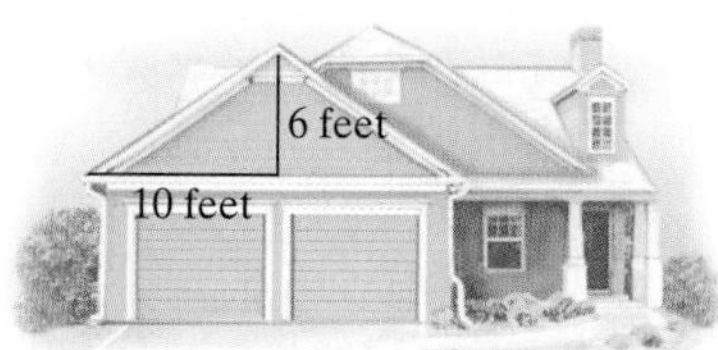

50.

The grade of a road is its slope written as a percent. Find the grade of each road shown. See Example 8.

51.

52.

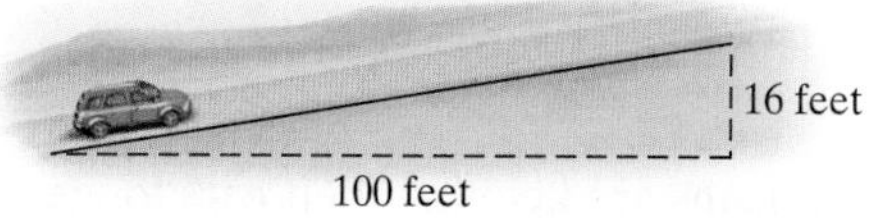

53. One of Japan's superconducting "bullet" trains is researched and tested at the Yamanashi Maglev Test Line near Otsuki City. The steepest section of the track has a rise of 2580 meters for a horizontal distance of 6450 meters. What is the grade (slope written as a percent) of this section of track? (*Source:* Japan Railways Central Co.)

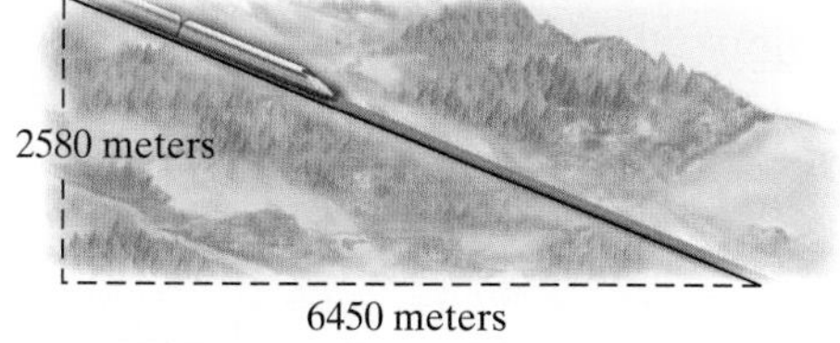

54. Professional plumbers suggest that a sewer pipe should rise 0.25 inch for every horizontal foot. Find the recommended slope for a sewer pipe and write the slope as a grade, or percent. Round to the nearest percent.

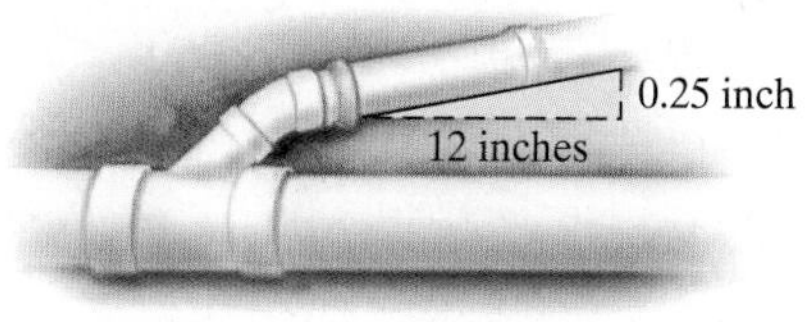

55. There has been controversy over the past few years about the world's steepest street. The *Guinness Book of Records* actually listed Baldwin Street, in Dunedin, New Zealand, as the world's steepest street, but Canton Avenue in the Pittsburgh neighborhood of Beechview may be steeper. Calculate each grade to the nearest percent.

		Grade (%)
Canton Avenue	for every 30 meters of horizontal distance, the vertical change is 11 meters	
Baldwin Street	for every 2.86 meters of horizontal distance, the vertical change is 1 meter	

56. According to federal regulations, a wheelchair ramp should rise no more than 1 foot for a horizontal distance of 12 feet. Write the slope as a grade. Round to the nearest tenth of a percent.

Find the slope of each line and write a sentence using the slope as a rate of change. Don't forget to attach the proper units. See Example 9.

57. This graph approximates the number of U.S. households that have televisions y (in millions) for year x.

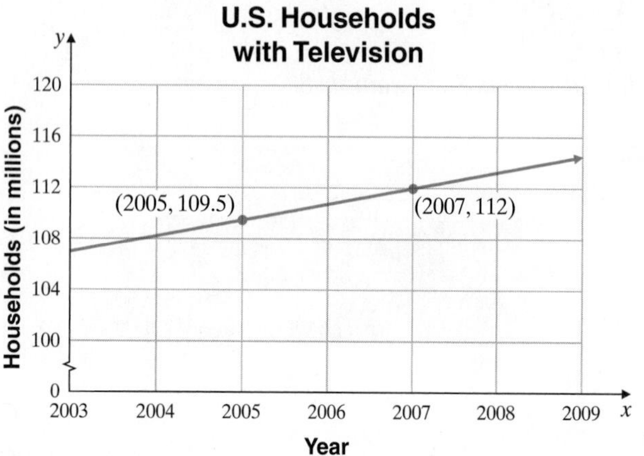

Source: Nielson Media Research

58. The graph approximates the amount of money y (in billions of dollars) spent worldwide on tourism for year x. (*Source:* World Tourism Organization)

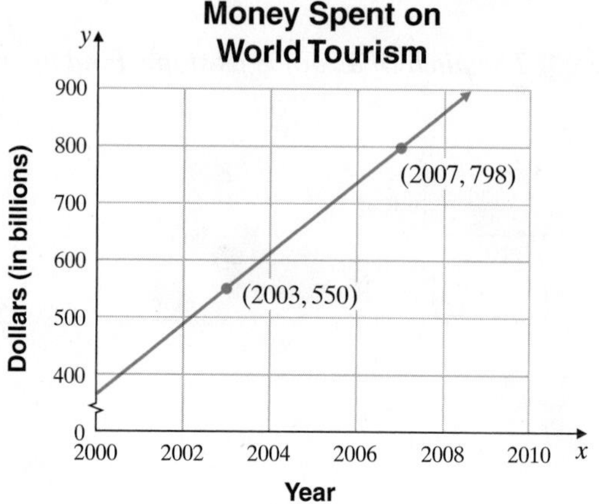

59. Americans are keeping their cars longer. The graph below shows the median age y (in years) of automobiles in the United States for the years shown. (*Source:* Bureau of Transportation Statistics)

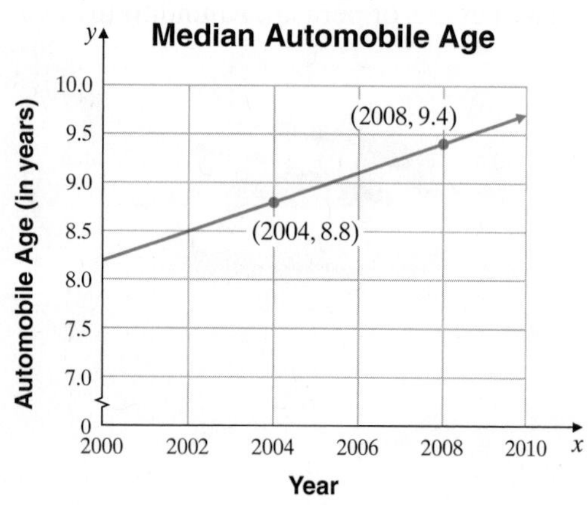

60. The graph below shows the total cost y (in dollars) of owning and operating a compact car (excluding the cost of the car), where x is the number of miles driven.

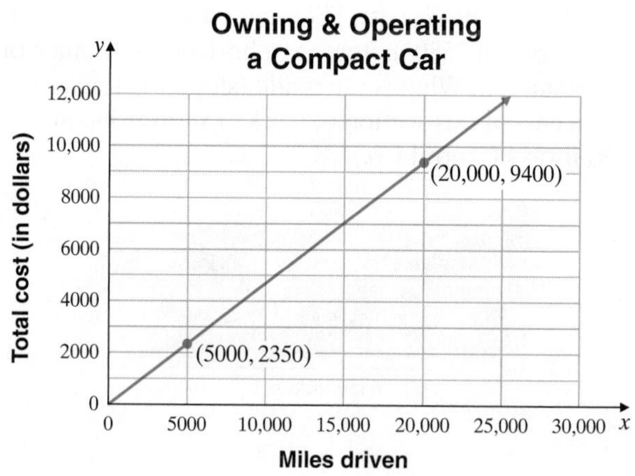

Source: AAA

Review

Solve each equation for y. See Section 9.5.

61. $y - (-6) = 2(x - 4)$

62. $y - 7 = -9(x - 6)$

63. $y - 1 = -6(x - (-2))$

64. $y - (-3) = 4(x - (-5))$

Concept Extensions

Match each line with its slope.

a. $m = 0$ **b.** undefined slope **c.** $m = 3$

d. $m = 1$ **e.** $m = -\frac{1}{2}$ **f.** $m = -\frac{3}{4}$

65.

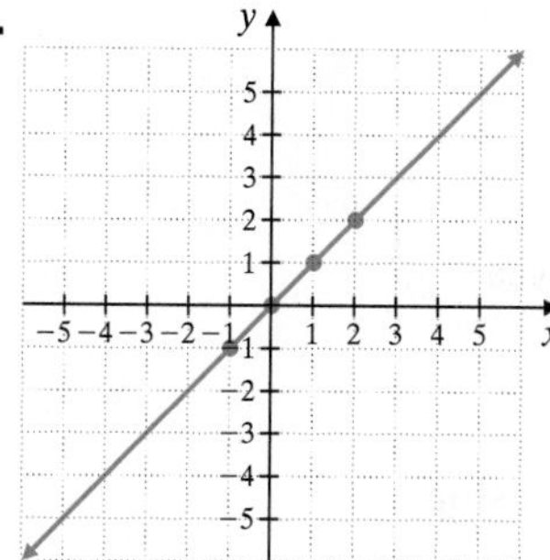

66.

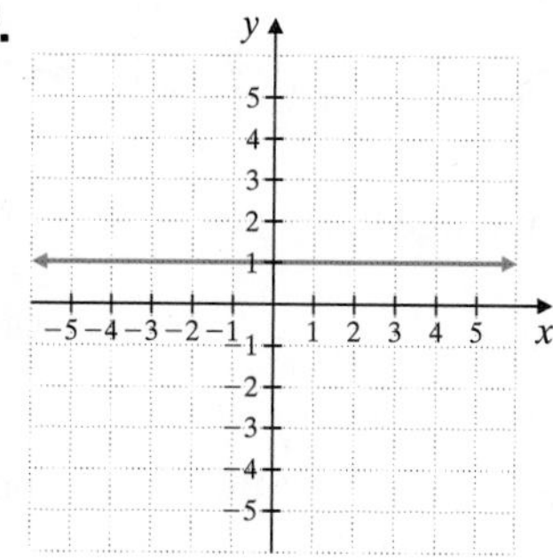

67.

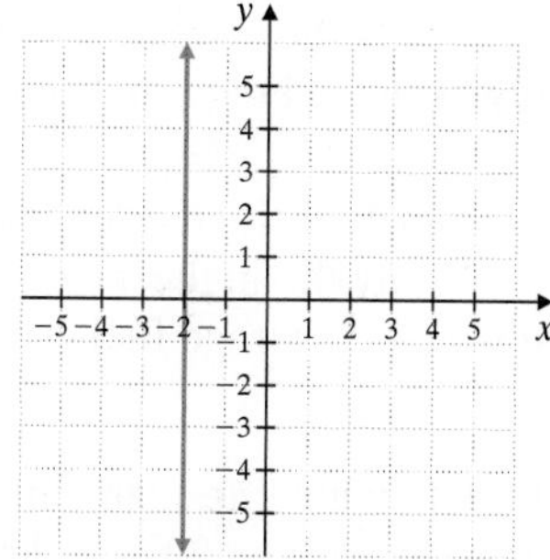

68.

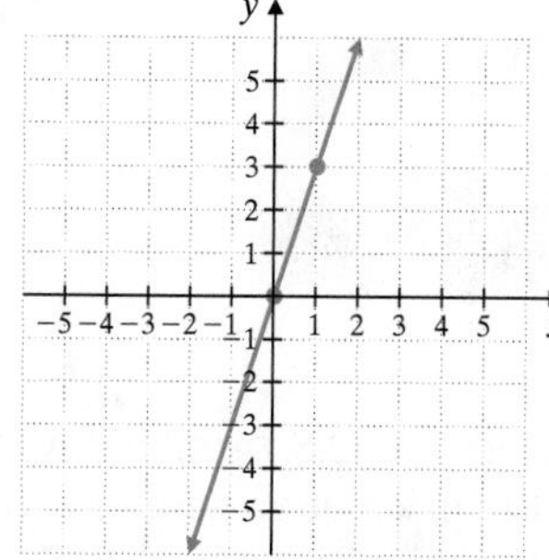

69.

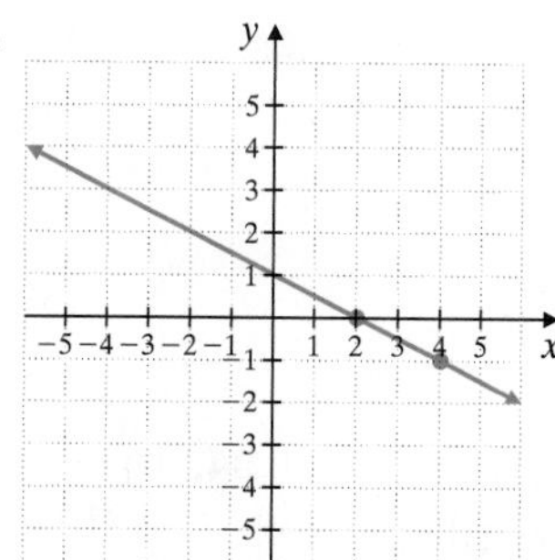

70.

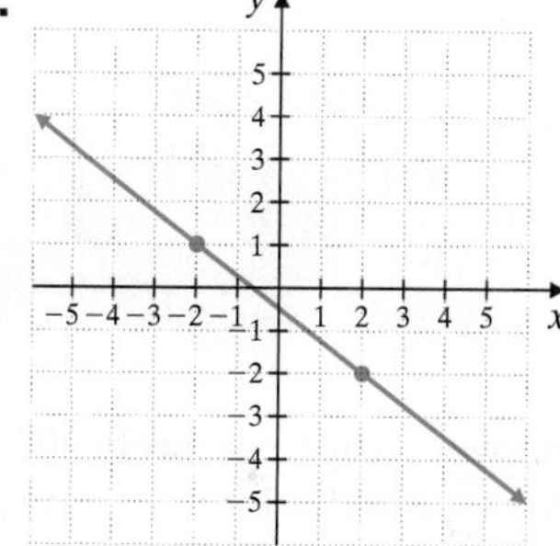

Solve. See a Concept Check in this section.

71. Verify that the points $(2, 1), (0, 0), (-2, -1)$, and $(-4, -2)$ are all on the same line by computing the slope between each pair of points. (See the first Concept Check.)

72. Given the points $(2, 3)$ and $(-5, 1)$, can the slope of the line through these points be calculated by $\frac{1 - 3}{2 - (-5)}$? Why or why not? (See the second Concept Check.)

73. Write the equations of three lines parallel to $10x - 5y = -7$. (See the third Concept Check.)

74. Write the equations of two lines perpendicular to $10x - 5y = -7$. (See the third Concept Check.)

The following line graph shows the average fuel economy (in miles per gallon) of passenger automobiles produced during each of the model years shown. Use this graph to answer Exercises 75 through 80.

75. What was the average fuel economy (in miles per gallon) for automobiles produced during 2004?

76. Find the decrease in average fuel economy for automobiles between the years 1998 and 1999.

77. During which of the model years shown was average fuel economy the lowest?
What was the average fuel economy for that year?

78. During which of the model years shown was average fuel economy the highest?
What was the average fuel economy for that year?

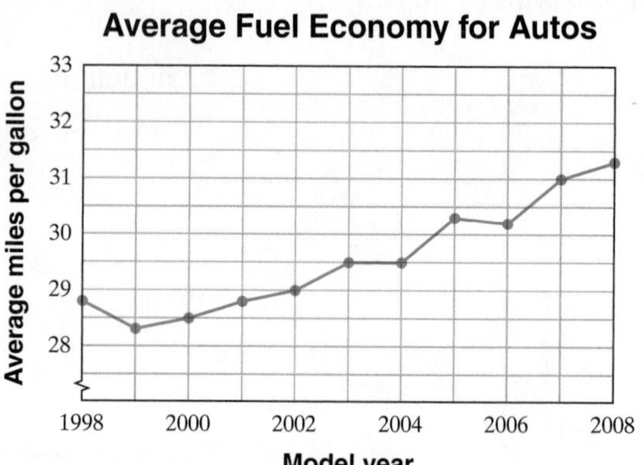

Source: Bureau of Transportation Statistics

79. Of the following line segments, which has the greatest slope: from 2002 to 2003, from 2006 to 2007, or from 2007 to 2008?

80. What line segment has a slope of 0?

81. Find x so that the pitch of the roof is $\frac{2}{5}$.

82. Find x so that the pitch of the roof is $\frac{1}{3}$.

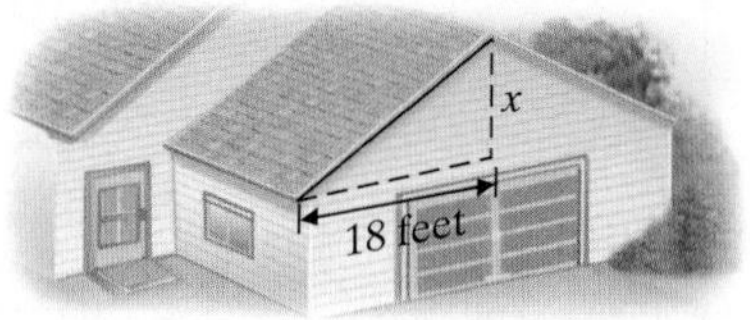

83. There were approximately 2025 heart transplants performed in the United States in 2004. In 2007, the number of heart transplants in the United States rose to 2208. (*Source:* Organ Procurement and Transplantation Network)

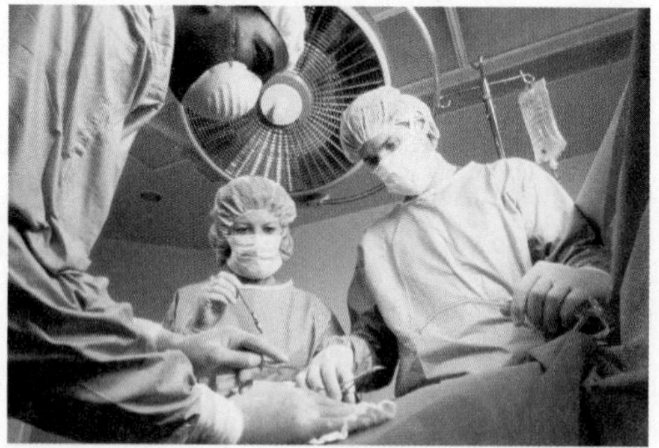

a. Write two ordered pairs of the form (year, number of heart transplants).

b. Find the slope of the line between the two points.

c. Write a sentence explaining the meaning of the slope as a rate of change.

84. The average price of an acre of U.S. farmland was \$1210 in 2002. In 2008, the price of an acre rose to \$2350. (*Source:* National Agricultural Statistics Services)

a. Write two ordered pairs of the form (year, price of an acre).

b. Find the slope of the line through the two points.

c. Write a sentence explaining the meaning of the slope as a rate of change.

85. Show that the quadrilateral with vertices $(1, 3)$, $(2, 1)$, $(-4, 0)$, and $(-3, -2)$ is a parallelogram.

86. Show that a triangle with vertices at the points $(1, 1)$, $(-4, 4)$, and $(-3, 0)$ is a right triangle.

Find the slope of the line through the given points.

87. $(-3.8, 1.2)$ and $(-2.2, 4.5)$

88. $(2.1, 6.7)$ and $(-8.3, 9.3)$

89. $(14.3, -10.1)$ and $(9.8, -2.9)$

90. $(2.3, 0.2)$ and $(7.9, 5.1)$

91. The graph of $y = \frac{1}{2}x$ has a slope of $\frac{1}{2}$. The graph of $y = 3x$ has a slope of 3. The graph of $y = 5x$ has a slope of 5. Graph all three equations on a single coordinate system. As the slope becomes larger, how does the steepness of the line change?

92. The graph of $y = -\frac{1}{3}x + 2$ has a slope of $-\frac{1}{3}$. The graph of $y = -2x + 2$ has a slope of -2. The graph of $y = -4x + 2$ has a slope of -4. Graph all three equations on a single coordinate system. As the absolute value of the slope becomes larger, how does the steepness of the line change?

Objectives

A Use the Slope-Intercept Form to Graph a Linear Equation.

B Use the Slope-Intercept Form to Write an Equation of a Line.

C Use the Point-Slope Form to Find an Equation of a Line Given Its Slope and a Point of the Line.

D Use the Point-Slope Form to Find an Equation of a Line Given Two Points of the Line.

E Use the Point-Slope Form to Solve Problems.

13.5 EQUATIONS OF LINES

We know that when a linear equation is solved for y, the coefficient of x is the slope of the line. For example, the slope of the line whose equation is $y = 3x + 1$ is 3. In this equation, $y = 3x + 1$, what does 1 represent? To find out, let $x = 0$ and watch what happens.

$$y = 3x + 1$$

$$y = 3 \cdot 0 + 1 \quad \text{Let } x = 0.$$

$$y = 1$$

We now have the ordered pair $(0, 1)$, which means that 1 is the y-intercept.

This is true in general. To see this, let $x = 0$ and solve for y in $y = mx + b$.

$$y = m \cdot 0 + b \quad \text{Let } x = 0.$$

$$y = b$$

We obtain the ordered pair $(0, b)$, which means that point is the y-intercept.

The form $y = mx + b$ is appropriately called the *slope-intercept form* of a linear equation. (m: slope; b: y-intercept is $(0, b)$)

Slope-Intercept Form

When a linear equation in two variables is written in **slope-intercept form**,

$$y = mx + b$$

(m: slope; $(0, b)$, y-intercept)

then m is the slope of the line and $(0, b)$ is the y-intercept of the line.

PRACTICE 1

Use the slope-intercept form to graph the equation $y = \frac{2}{3}x - 4$.

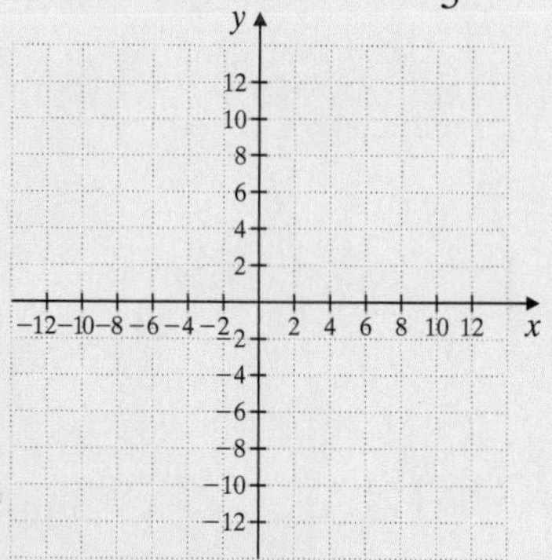

Answer

1.

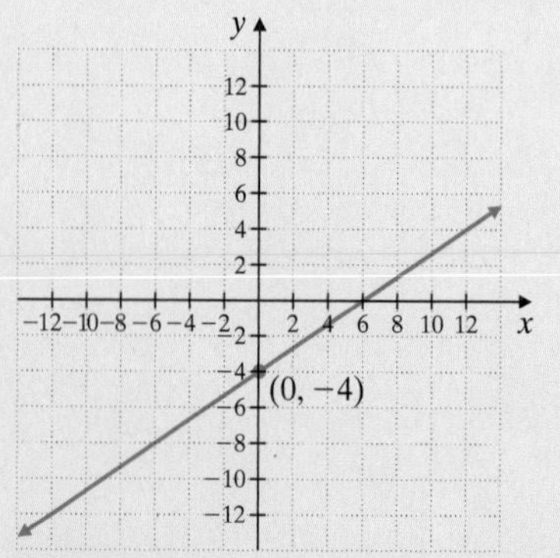

Objective A Using the Slope-Intercept Form to Graph an Equation

We can use the slope-intercept form of the equation of a line to graph a linear equation.

Example 1 Use the slope-intercept form to graph the equation

$$y = \frac{3}{5}x - 2.$$

Solution: Since the equation $y = \frac{3}{5}x - 2$ is written in slope-intercept form $y = mx + b$, the slope of its graph is $\frac{3}{5}$ and the y-intercept is $(0, -2)$. To graph this equation, we begin by plotting the point $(0, -2)$. From this point, we can find another point of the graph by using the slope $\frac{3}{5}$ and recalling that slope is $\frac{\text{rise}}{\text{run}}$. We start at the y-intercept and move 3 units up since the

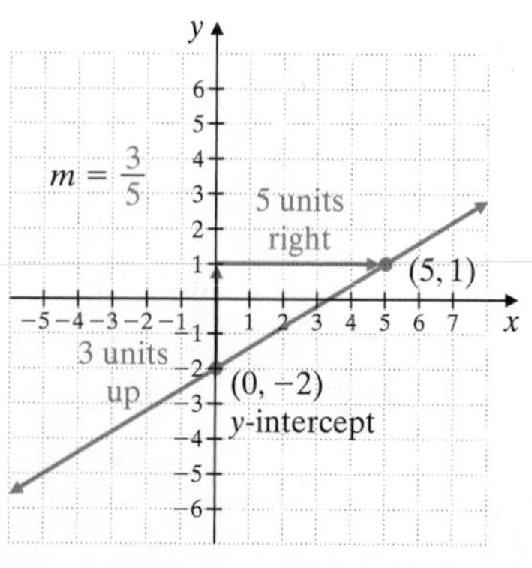

numerator of the slope is 3; then we move 5 units to the right since the denominator of the slope is 5. We stop at the point (5, 1). The line through (0, −2) and (5, 1) is the graph of $y = \frac{3}{5}x - 2$.

Work Practice 1

Example 2 Use the slope-intercept form to graph the equation $4x + y = 1$.

Solution: First we write the given equation in slope-intercept form.

$$4x + y = 1$$
$$y = -4x + 1$$

The graph of this equation will have slope −4 and y-intercept (0, 1). To graph this line, we first plot the point (0, 1). To find another point of the graph, we use the slope −4, which can be written as $\frac{-4}{1}$ $\left(\frac{4}{-1} \text{ could also be used}\right)$. We start at the point (0, 1) and move 4 units down (since the numerator of the slope is −4), and then 1 unit to the right (since the denominator of the slope is 1).

We arrive at the point (1, −3). The line through (0, 1) and (1, −3) is the graph of $4x + y = 1$.

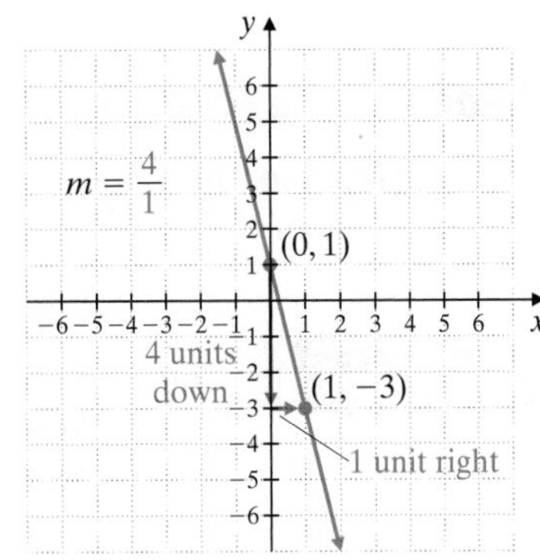

Work Practice 2

PRACTICE 2

Use the slope-intercept form to graph $3x + y = 2$.

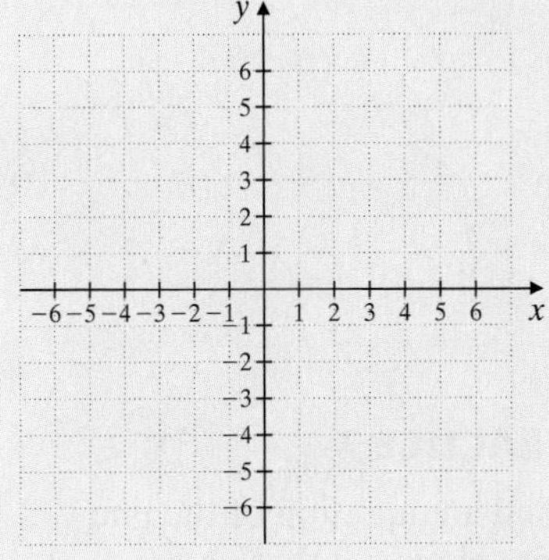

Helpful Hint

In Example 2, if we interpret the slope of −4 as $\frac{4}{-1}$, we arrive at (−1, 5) for a second point. Notice that this point is also on the line.

PRACTICE 3

Find an equation of the line with y-intercept (0, −4) and slope of $\frac{1}{5}$.

Objective B Using the Slope-Intercept Form to Write an Equation

The slope-intercept form can also be used to write the equation of a line when we know its slope and y-intercept.

Example 3 Find an equation of the line with y-intercept (0, −3) and slope of $\frac{1}{4}$.

Solution: We are given the slope and the y-intercept. We let $m = \frac{1}{4}$ and $b = -3$ and write the equation in slope-intercept form, $y = mx + b$.

$y = mx + b$

$y = \frac{1}{4}x + (-3)$ Let $m = \frac{1}{4}$ and $b = -3$.

$y = \frac{1}{4}x - 3$ Simplify.

Work Practice 3

Answers

2.

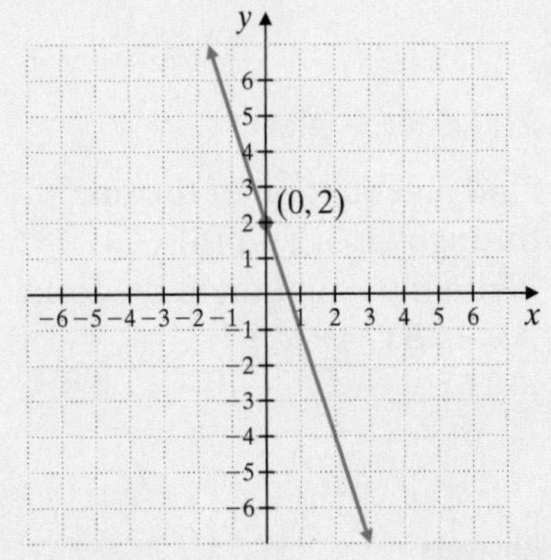

3. $y = \frac{1}{5}x - 4$

Objective C Writing an Equation Given Its Slope and a Point

Thus far, we have written an equation of a line by knowing its slope and y-intercept. We can also write an equation of a line if we know its slope and any point on the line. To see how we do this, let m represent slope and (x_1, y_1) represent the point on the line. Then if (x, y) is any other point of the line, we have that

$$\frac{y - y_1}{x - x_1} = m$$

$$y - y_1 = m(x - x_1) \quad \text{Multiply both sides by } (x - x_1).$$

↑ slope

This is the *point-slope form* of the equation of a line.

Point-Slope Form of the Equation of a Line

The **point-slope form** of the equation of a line is $y - y_1 = m(x - x_1)$, where m is the slope of the line and (x_1, y_1) is a point on the line.

PRACTICE 4

Find an equation of the line with slope -3 that passes through $(2, -4)$. Write the equation in slope-intercept form, $y = mx + b$, and in standard form, $Ax + By = C$.

Example 4 Find an equation of the line with slope -2 that passes through $(-1, 5)$. Write the equation in slope-intercept form, $y = mx + b$, and in standard form, $Ax + By = C$.

Solution: Since the slope and a point on the line are given, we use point-slope form $y - y_1 = m(x - x_1)$ to write the equation. Let $m = -2$ and $(-1, 5) = (x_1, y_1)$.

$$y - y_1 = m(x - x_1)$$

$$y - 5 = -2[x - (-1)] \quad \text{Let } m = -2 \text{ and } (x_1, y_1) = (-1, 5).$$

$$y - 5 = -2(x + 1) \quad \text{Simplify.}$$

$$y - 5 = -2x - 2 \quad \text{Use the distributive property.}$$

To write the equation in slope-intercept form, $y = mx + b$, we simply solve the equation for y. To do this, we add 5 to both sides.

$$y - 5 = -2x - 2$$

$$y = -2x + 3 \quad \text{Slope-intercept form}$$

$$2x + y = 3 \quad \text{Add } 2x \text{ to both sides and we have standard form.}$$

Work Practice 4

Objective D Writing an Equation Given Two Points

We can also find the equation of a line when we are given any two points of the line.

PRACTICE 5

Find an equation of the line through $(1, 3)$ and $(5, -2)$. Write the equation in the form $Ax + By = C$.

Example 5 Find an equation of the line through $(2, 5)$ and $(-3, 4)$. Write the equation in the form $Ax + By = C$.

Solution: First, use the two given points to find the slope of the line.

$$m = \frac{4 - 5}{-3 - 2} = \frac{-1}{-5} = \frac{1}{5}$$

Next we use the slope $\frac{1}{5}$ and either one of the given points to write the equation in point-slope form. We use $(2, 5)$. Let $x_1 = 2$, $y_1 = 5$, and $m = \frac{1}{5}$.

Answers

4. $y = -3x + 2$; $3x + y = 2$
5. $5x + 4y = 17$

$$y - y_1 = m(x - x_1) \quad \text{Use point-slope form.}$$

$$y - 5 = \frac{1}{5}(x - 2) \quad \text{Let } x_1 = 2,\ y_1 = 5, \text{ and } m = \frac{1}{5}.$$

$$5(y - 5) = 5 \cdot \frac{1}{5}(x - 2) \quad \text{Multiply both sides by 5 to clear fractions.}$$

$$5y - 25 = x - 2 \quad \text{Use the distributive property and simplify.}$$

$$-x + 5y - 25 = -2 \quad \text{Subtract } x \text{ from both sides.}$$

$$-x + 5y = 23 \quad \text{Add 25 to both sides.}$$

Work Practice 5

Helpful Hint

When you multiply both sides of the equation from Example 5, $-x + 5y = 23$, by -1, it becomes $x - 5y = -23$.

Both $-x + 5y = 23$ and $x - 5y = -23$ are in the form $Ax + By = C$ and both are equations of the same line.

Objective E Using the Point-Slope Form to Solve Problems

Problems occurring in many fields can be modeled by linear equations in two variables. The next example is from the field of marketing and shows how consumer demand for a product depends on the price of the product.

Example 6 The Whammo Company has learned that by pricing a newly released Frisbee at \$6, sales will reach 2000 Frisbees per day. Raising the price to \$8 will cause the sales to fall to 1500 Frisbees per day.

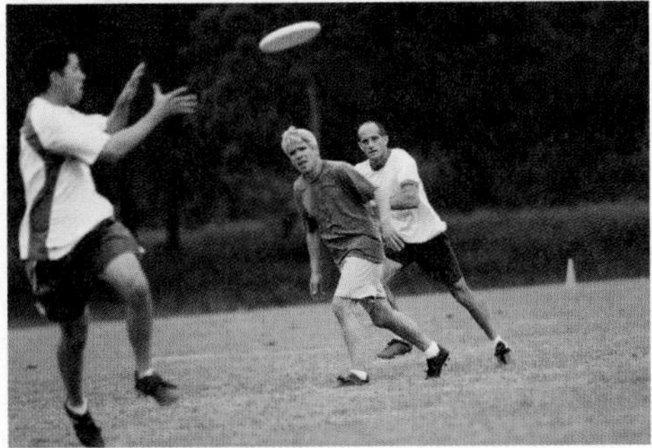

a. Assume that the relationship between sales price and number of Frisbees sold is linear and write an equation describing this relationship. Write the equation in slope-intercept form. Use ordered pairs of the form (sales price, number sold).

b. Predict the daily sales of Frisbees if the sales price is \$7.50.

Solution:

a. We use the given information and write two ordered pairs. Our ordered pairs are (6, 2000) and (8, 1500). To use the point-slope form to write an equation, we find the slope of the line that contains these points.

$$m = \frac{2000 - 1500}{6 - 8} = \frac{500}{-2} = -250$$

Next we use the slope and either one of the points to write the equation in point-slope form. We use (6, 2000).

Continued on next page

PRACTICE 6

The Pool Entertainment Company learned that by pricing a new pool toy at \$10, local sales will reach 200 a week. Lowering the price to \$9 will cause sales to rise to 250 a week.

a. Assume that the relationship between sales price and number of toys sold is linear, and write an equation describing this relationship. Write the equation in slope-intercept form. Use ordered pairs of the form (sales price, number sold).

b. Predict the weekly sales of the toy if the price is \$7.50.

Answers

6. a. $y = -50x + 700$ **b.** 325

$$y - y_1 = m(x - x_1) \quad \text{Use point-slope form.}$$
$$y - 2000 = -250(x - 6) \quad \text{Let } x_1 = 6,\ y_1 = 2000, \text{ and } m = -250.$$
$$y - 2000 = -250x + 1500 \quad \text{Use the distributive property.}$$
$$y = -250x + 3500 \quad \text{Write in slope-intercept form.}$$

b. To predict the sales if the price is \$7.50, we find y when $x = 7.50$.

$$y = -250x + 3500$$
$$y = -250(7.50) + 3500 \quad \text{Let } x = 7.50.$$
$$y = -1875 + 3500$$
$$y = 1625$$

If the sales price is \$7.50, sales will reach 1625 Frisbees per day.

Work Practice 6

We could have solved Example 6 by using ordered pairs of the form (number sold, sales price).

Here is a summary of our discussion on linear equations thus far.

Forms of Linear Equations

$Ax + By = C$	**Standard form** of a linear equation. A and B are not both 0.
$y = mx + b$	**Slope-intercept form** of a linear equation. The slope is m and the y-intercept is $(0, b)$.
$y - y_1 = m(x - x_1)$	**Point-slope form** of a linear equation. The slope is m and (x_1, y_1) is a point on the line.
$y = c$	**Horizontal line** The slope is 0 and the y-intercept is $(0, c)$.
$x = c$	**Vertical line** The slope is undefined and the x-intercept is $(c, 0)$.

Parallel and Perpendicular Lines

Nonvertical parallel lines have the same slope.
The product of the slopes of two nonvertical perpendicular lines is -1.

Calculator Explorations Graphing

A graphing calculator is a very useful tool for discovering patterns. To discover the change in the graph of a linear equation caused by a change in slope, try the following. Use a standard window and graph a linear equation in the form $y = mx + b$. Recall that the graph of such an equation will have slope m and y-intercept $(0, b)$.

First graph $y = x + 3$. To do so, press the Y= key and enter $Y_1 = x + 3$. Notice that this graph has slope 1 and that the y-intercept is 3. Next, on the same set of axes, graph $y = 2x + 3$ and $y = 3x + 3$ by pressing Y= and entering $Y_2 = 2x + 3$ and $Y_3 = 3x + 3$.

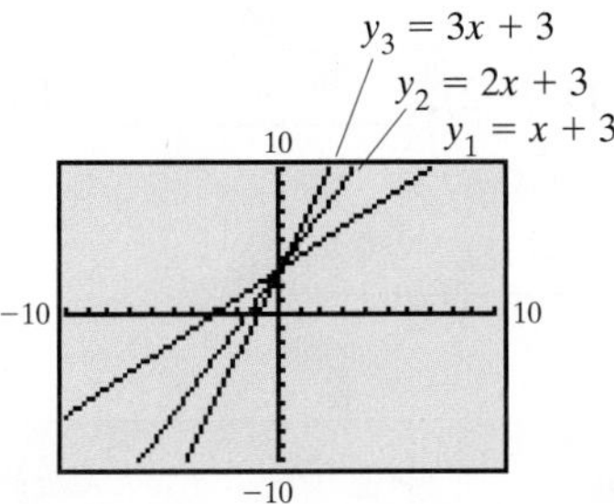

Notice the difference in the graph of each equation as the slope changes from 1 to 2 to 3. How would the graph of $y = 5x + 3$ appear? To see the change in the graph caused by a change in negative slope, try graphing $y = -x + 3$, $y = -2x + 3$, and $y = -3x + 3$ on the same set of axes.

Use a graphing calculator to graph the following equations. For each exercise, graph the first equation and use its graph to predict the appearance of the other equations. Then graph the other equations on the same set of axes and check your prediction.

1. $y = x$; $y = 6x$, $y = -6x$

2. $y = -x$; $y = -5x$, $y = -10x$

3. $y = \frac{1}{2}x + 2$; $y = \frac{3}{4}x + 2$, $y = x + 2$

4. $y = x + 1$; $y = \frac{5}{4}x + 1$, $y = \frac{5}{2}x + 1$

Vocabulary and Readiness Check

Use the choices below to fill in each blank. Some choices may be used more than once and some not at all.

b	(y_1, x_1)	point-slope	vertical	standard
m	(x_1, y_1)	slope-intercept	horizontal	

1. The form $y = mx + b$ is called ______________ form. When a linear equation in two variables is written in this form, ______________ is the slope of its graph and (0, ______________) is its y-intercept.

2. The form $y - y_1 = m(x - x_1)$ is called ______________ form. When a linear equation in two variables is written in this form, ______________ is the slope of its graph and ______________ is a point on the graph.

For Exercises 3 through 6 identify the form that the linear equation in two variables is written in. For Exercises 7 and 8, identify the appearance of the graph of the equation.

3. $y - 7 = 4(x + 3)$; ______________ form

4. $5x - 9y = 11$; ______________ form

5. $y = \frac{3}{4}x - \frac{1}{3}$; ______________ form

6. $y + 2 = \frac{-1}{3}(x - 2)$; ______________ form

7. $y = \frac{1}{2}$; ______________ line

8. $x = -17$; ______________ line

13.5 Exercise Set

FOR EXTRA HELP

MyMathLab

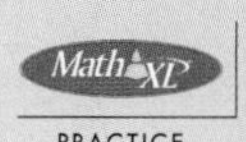
PRACTICE

WATCH

DOWNLOAD

READ

REVIEW

Objective A *Use the slope-intercept form to graph each equation. See Examples 1 and 2.*

1. $y = 2x + 1$

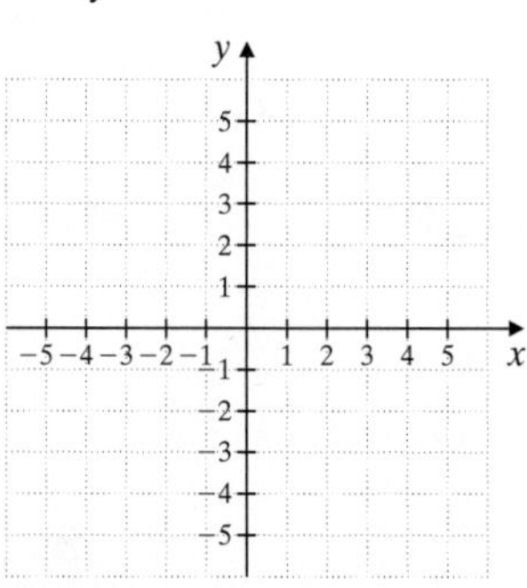

2. $y = -4x - 1$

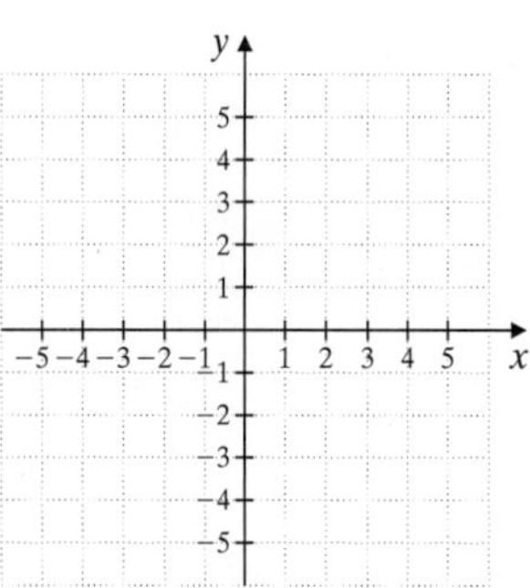

3. $y = \frac{2}{3}x + 5$

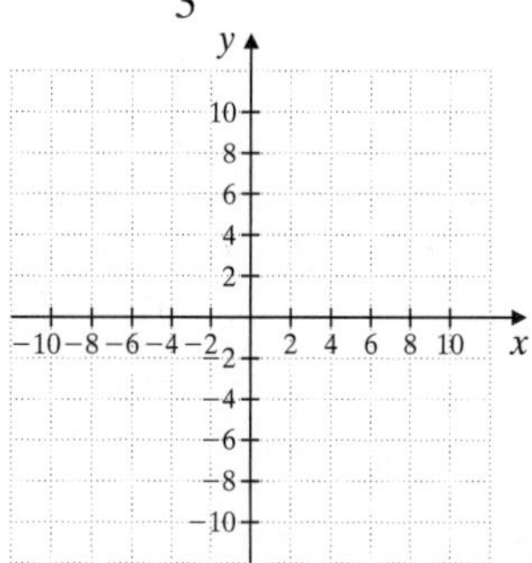

4. $y = \frac{1}{4}x - 3$

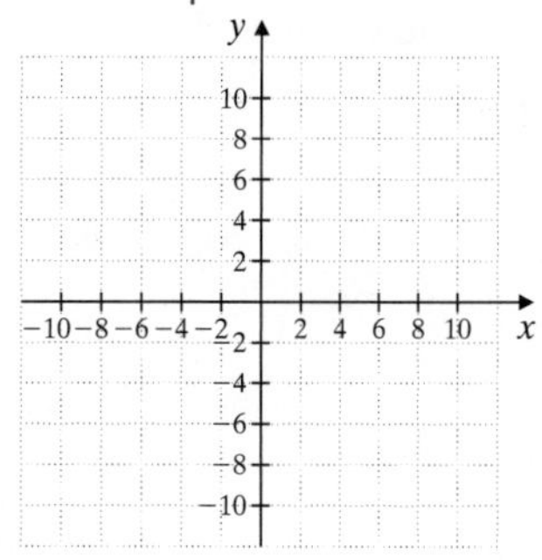

5. $y = -5x$

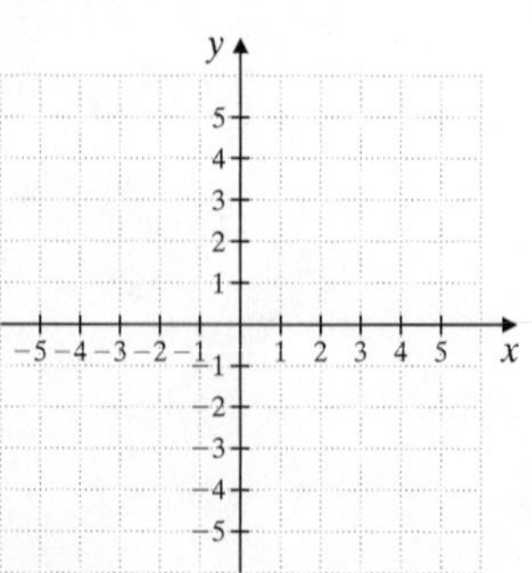

6. $y = -6x$

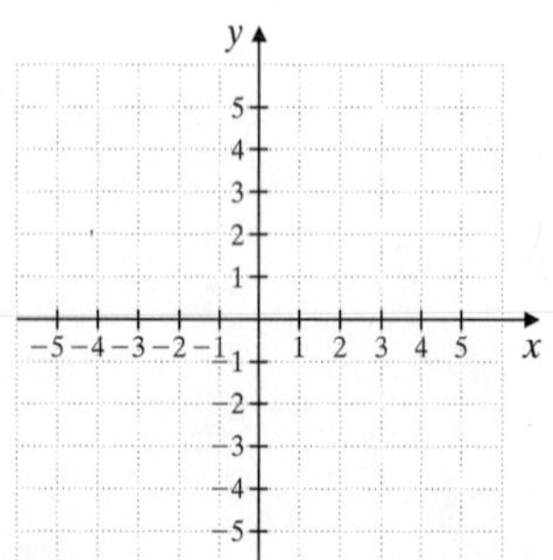

7. $4x + y = 6$

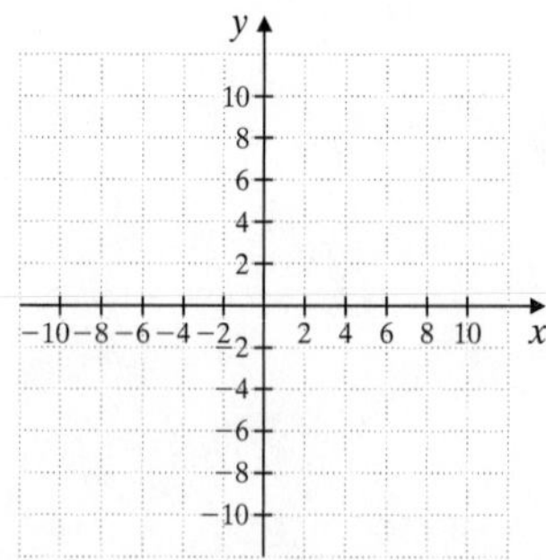

8. $-3x + y = 2$

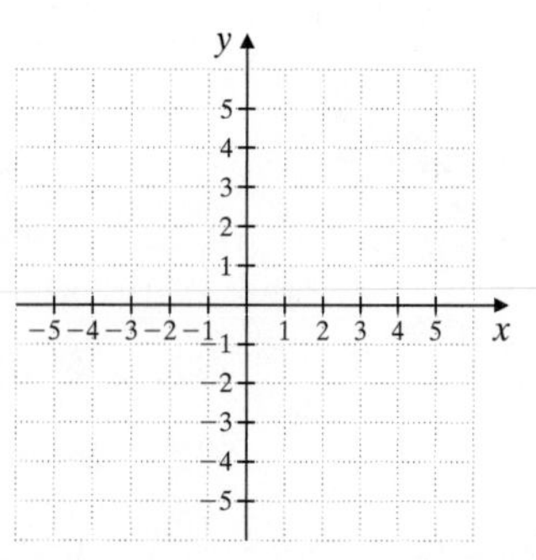

9. $4x - 7y = -14$

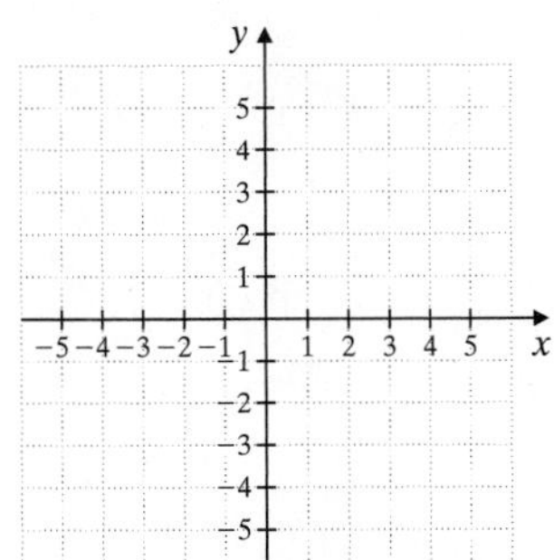

10. $3x - 4y = 4$

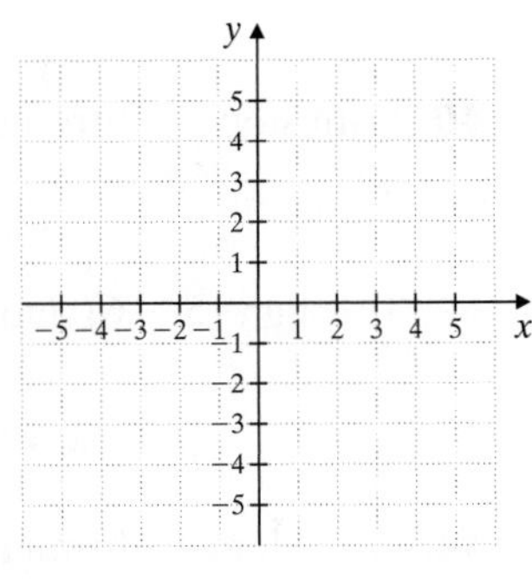

11. $x = \frac{5}{4}y$

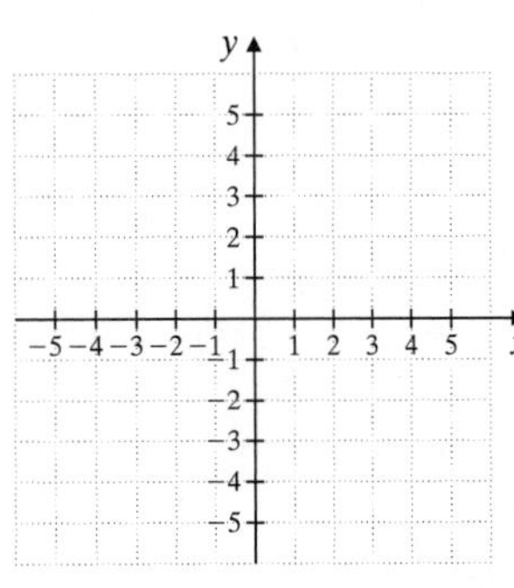

12. $x = \frac{3}{2}y$

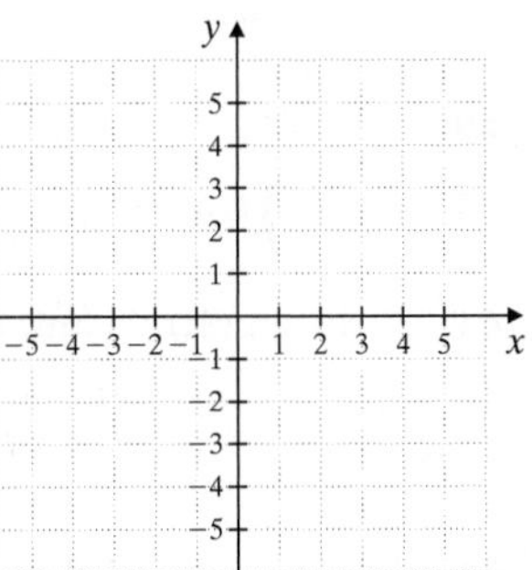

Objective **B** *Write an equation of the line with each given slope, m, and y-intercept, (0, b). See Example 3.*

13. $m = 5, b = 3$

14. $m = -3, b = -3$

15. $m = -4, b = -\frac{1}{6}$

16. $m = 2, b = \frac{3}{4}$

17. $m = \frac{2}{3}, b = 0$

18. $m = -\frac{4}{5}, b = 0$

19. $m = 0, b = -8$

20. $m = 0, b = -2$

21. $m = -\frac{1}{5}, b = \frac{1}{9}$

22. $m = \frac{1}{2}, b = -\frac{1}{3}$

Objective **C** *Find an equation of each line with the given slope that passes through the given point. Write the equation in the form $Ax + By = C$. See Example 4.*

23. $m = 6;\ (2, 2)$

24. $m = 4;\ (1, 3)$

25. $m = -8;\ (-1, -5)$

26. $m = -2;\ (-11, -12)$

27. $m = \frac{3}{2};\ (5, -6)$

28. $m = \frac{2}{3};\ (-8, 9)$

29. $m = -\frac{1}{2};\ (-3, 0)$

30. $m = -\frac{1}{5};\ (4, 0)$

Objective **D** *Find an equation of the line passing through each pair of points. Write the equation in the form $Ax + By = C$. See Example 5.*

31. $(3, 2)$ and $(5, 6)$

32. $(6, 2)$ and $(8, 8)$

33. $(-1, 3)$ and $(-2, -5)$

34. $(-4, 0)$ and $(6, -1)$

35. $(2, 3)$ and $(-1, -1)$

36. $(7, 10)$ and $(-1, -1)$

37. $(0, 0)$ and $\left(-\frac{1}{8}, \frac{1}{13}\right)$

38. $(0, 0)$ and $\left(-\frac{1}{2}, \frac{1}{3}\right)$

Objectives B C D **Mixed Practice** *See Examples 3 through 5. Find an equation of each line described. Write each equation in slope-intercept form when possible.*

39. With slope $-\frac{1}{2}$, through $\left(0, \frac{5}{3}\right)$

40. With slope $\frac{5}{7}$, through $(0, -3)$

41. Through $(10, 7)$ and $(7, 10)$

42. Through $(5, -6)$ and $(-6, 5)$

43. With undefined slope, through $\left(-\frac{3}{4}, 1\right)$

44. With slope 0, through $(6.7, 12.1)$

45. Slope 1, through $(-7, 9)$

46. Slope 5, through $(6, -8)$

47. Slope -5, y-intercept $(0, 7)$

48. Slope -2, y-intercept $(0, -4)$

49. Through $(1, 2)$, parallel to $y = 5$

50. Through $(1, -5)$, parallel to the y-axis

51. Through $(2, 3)$ and $(0, 0)$

52. Through $(4, 7)$ and $(0, 0)$

53. Through $(-2, -3)$, perpendicular to the y-axis

54. Through $(0, 12)$, perpendicular to the x-axis

55. Slope $-\frac{4}{7}$, through $(-1, -2)$

56. Slope $-\frac{3}{5}$, through $(4, 4)$

Objective E *Solve. Assume each exercise describes a linear relationship. Write the equations in slope-intercept form. See Example 6.*

57. In 2003, there were 302 million magazine subscriptions in the United States. By 2007, this number was 322 million. (*Source:* Audit Bureau of Circulation, Magazine Publishers Association)

a. Write two ordered pairs of the form (years after 2003, millions of magazine subscriptions) for this situation.

b. Assume the relationship between years after 2003 and millions of magazine subscriptions is linear over this period. Use the ordered pairs from part (a) to write an equation for the line relating year after 2003 to millions of magazine subscriptions.

c. Use this linear equation in part (b) to estimate the millions of magazine subscriptions in 2005.

58. In 2000, crude oil field production in the United States was 2130 thousand barrels. In 2007, U.S. crude oil field production dropped to 1850 thousand barrels. (*Source:* Energy Information Administration)

a. Write two ordered pairs of the form (years after 2000, crude oil production).

b. Assume the relationship between years after 2000 and crude oil production is linear over this period. Use the ordered pairs from part (a) to write an equation of the line relating years after 2000 to crude oil production.

c. Use the linear equation from part (b) to estimate crude oil production in the United States in 2010, if this trend were to continue.

59. A rock is dropped from the top of a 400-foot cliff. After 1 second, the rock is traveling 32 feet per second. After 3 seconds, the rock is traveling 96 feet per second.

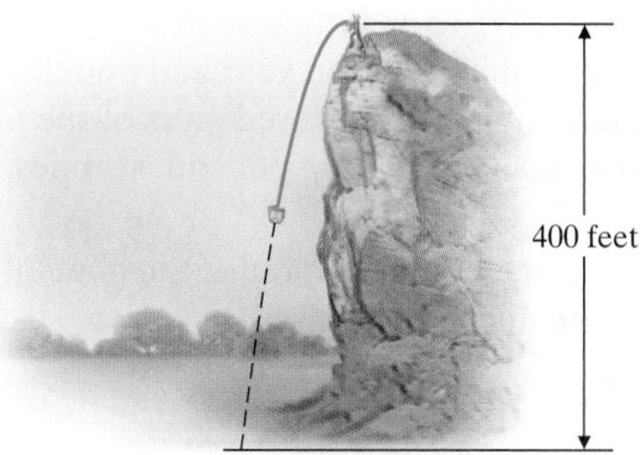

a. Assume that the relationship between time and speed is linear and write an equation describing this relationship. Use ordered pairs of the form (time, speed).

b. Use this equation to determine the speed of the rock 4 seconds after it is dropped.

60. A Hawaiian fruit company is studying the sales of a pineapple sauce to see if this product is to be continued. At the end of its first year, profits on this product amounted to \$30,000. At the end of the fourth year, profits were \$66,000.

a. Assume that the relationship between years on the market and profit is linear and write an equation describing this relationship. Use ordered pairs of the form (years on the market, profit).

b. Use this equation to predict the profit at the end of 7 years.

61. In 2004 there were approximately 83,000 gas-electric hybrid vehicles sold in the United States. In 2007, there were approximately 353,000 such vehicles sold. (*Source:* Energy Information Administration, Department of Energy)

a. Assume the relationship between years past 2004 and the number of vehicles sold is linear over this period. Write an equation describing the relationship between time and the number of gas-electric hybrid vehicles sold. Use ordered pairs of the form (years past 2004, number of vehicles sold).

b. Use this equation to estimate the number of gas-electric hybrid sales in 2009.

62. In 2008, there were approximately 945 thousand restaurants in the United States. In 2004, there were 875 thousand restaurants. (*Source:* National Restaurant Association)

a. Assume the relationship between years past 2004 and the number of restaurants is linear over this period. Write an equation describing the relationship between time and the number of restaurants. Use ordered pairs of the form (years past 2004, numbers of restaurants in thousands).

b. Use this equation to predict the number of eating establishments in 2012.

63. In 2007 there were approximately 5540 cinema sites in the United States. In 2003 there were 5700 cinema sites. (*Source:* National Association of Theater Owners)

a. Assume the relationship between years past 2003 and the number of cinema sites is linear over this period. Write an equation describing this relationship. Use ordered pairs of the form (years past 2003, number of cinema sites).

b. Use this equation to predict the number of cinema sites in 2010.

64. In 2006, the U.S. population per square mile of land area was approximately 83.6. In 2000, the population per square mile was 79.6.

a. Assume the relationship between years past 2000 and population per square mile is linear over this period. Write an equation describing the relationship between year and population per square mile. Use ordered pairs of the form (years past 2000, population per square mile).

b. Use this equation to predict the population per square mile in 2010.

65. The Pool Fun Company has learned that, by pricing a newly released Fun Noodle at \$3, sales will reach 10,000 Fun Noodles per day during the summer. Raising the price to \$5 will cause sales to fall to 8000 Fun Noodles per day.

a. Assume that the relationship between price and number of Fun Noodles sold is linear and write an equation describing this relationship. Use ordered pairs of the form (price, number sold).

b. Predict the daily sales of Fun Noodles if the price is \$3.50.

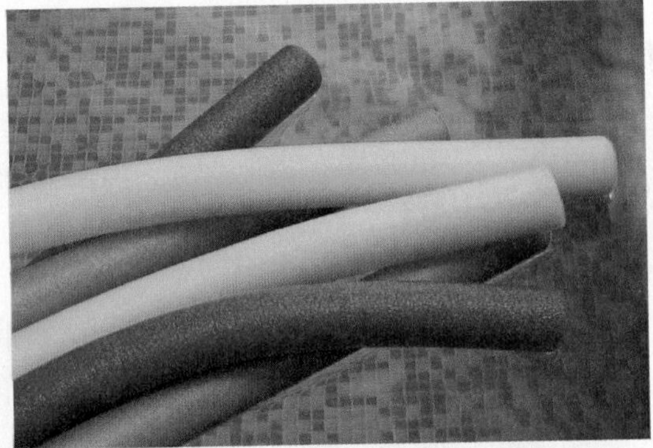

66. The value of a building bought in 1995 may be depreciated (or decreased) as time passes for income tax purposes. Seven years after the building was bought, this value was \$225,000 and 12 years after it was bought, this value was \$195,000.

a. If the relationship between number of years past 1995 and the depreciated value of the building is linear, write an equation describing this relationship. Use ordered pairs of the form (years past 1995, value of building).

b. Use this equation to estimate the depreciated value of the building in 2013.

Review

Find the value of $x^2 - 3x + 1$ for each given value of x. See Section 8.2.

67. 2 **68.** 5 **69.** -1 **70.** -3

Concept Extensions

Match each linear equation with its graph.

71. $y = 2x + 1$

72. $y = -x + 1$

73. $y = -3x - 2$

74. $y = \frac{5}{3}x - 2$

a.

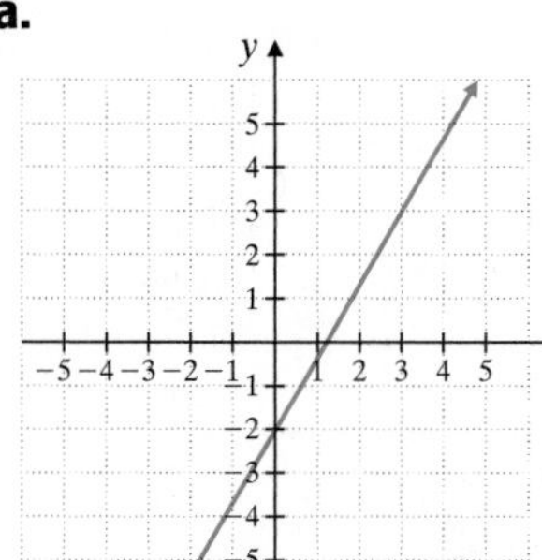

b.

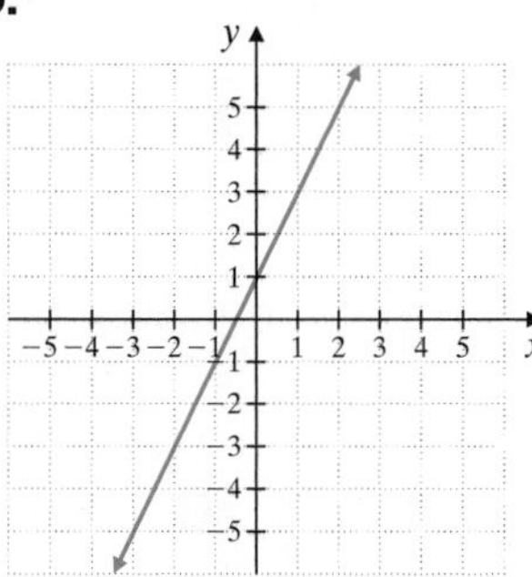

c.

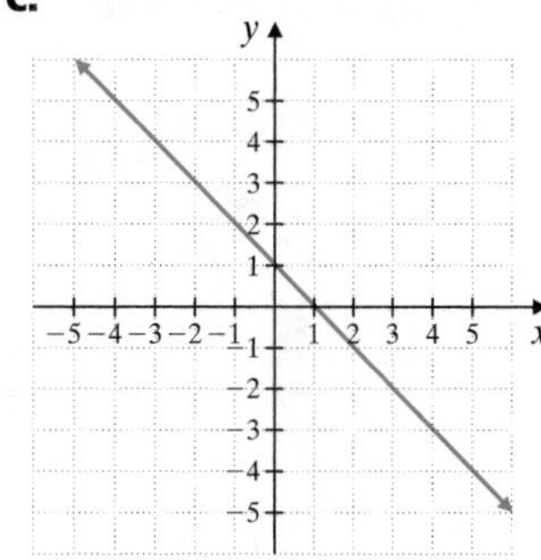

d.

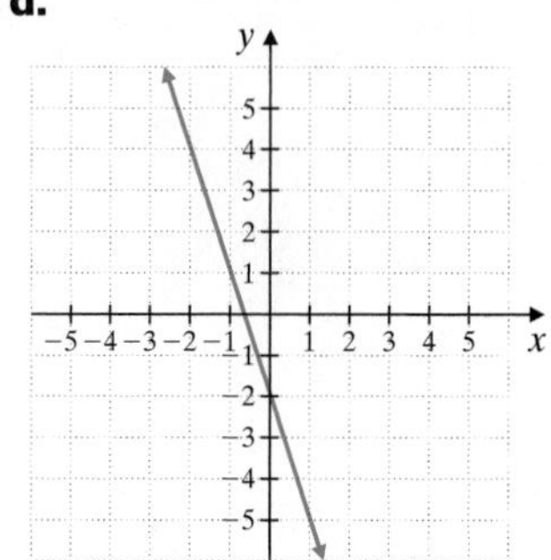

75. Write an equation in standard form of the line that contains the point $(-1, 2)$ and is parallel to (has the same slope as) the line $y = 3x - 1$.

76. Write an equation in standard form of the line that contains the point $(4, 0)$ and is parallel to (has the same slope as) the line $y = -2x + 3$.

△ **77.** Write an equation in standard form of the line that contains the point $(-1, 2)$ and is perpendicular to the line $y = 3x - 1$.

△ **78.** Write an equation in standard form of the line that contains the point $(4, 0)$ and is perpendicular to the line $y = -2x + 3$.

Integrated Review Sections 13.1–13.5

Answers

1. ________

2. ________

3. ________

4. ________

5. ________

6. ________

7. ________

8. ________

Summary on Linear Equations

Find the slope of each line.

1.

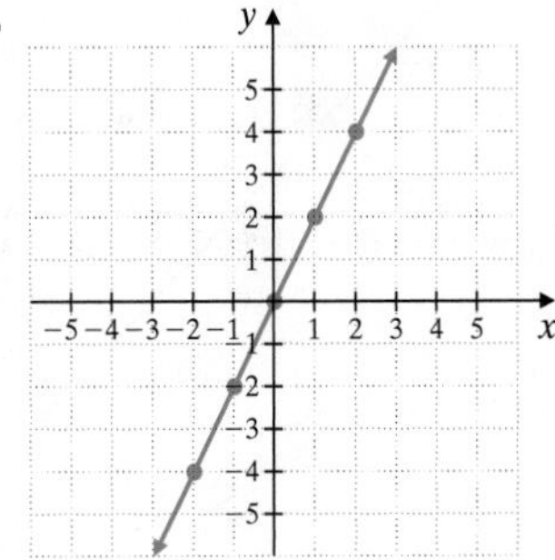

2.

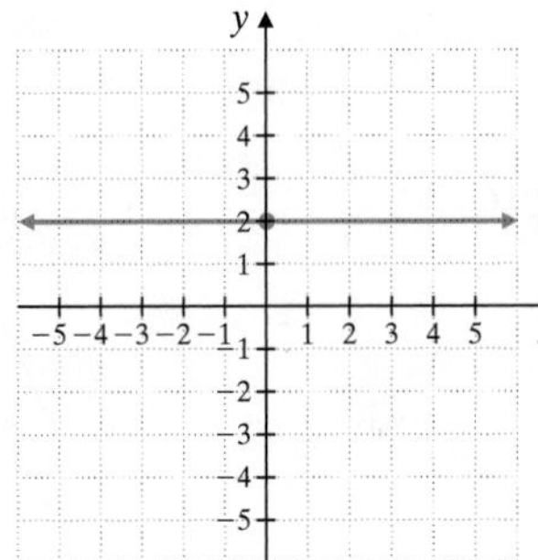

3.

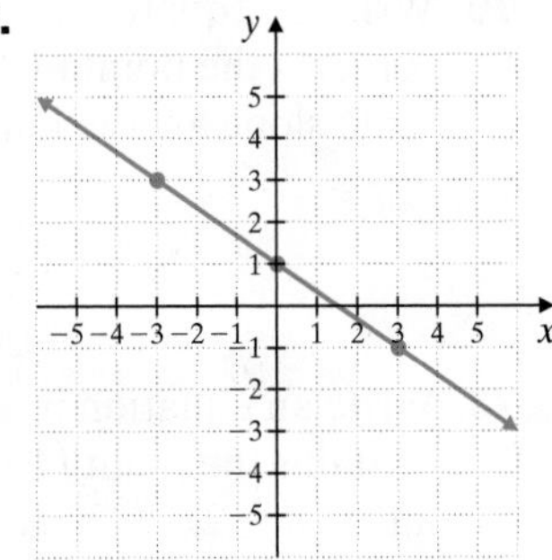

4.

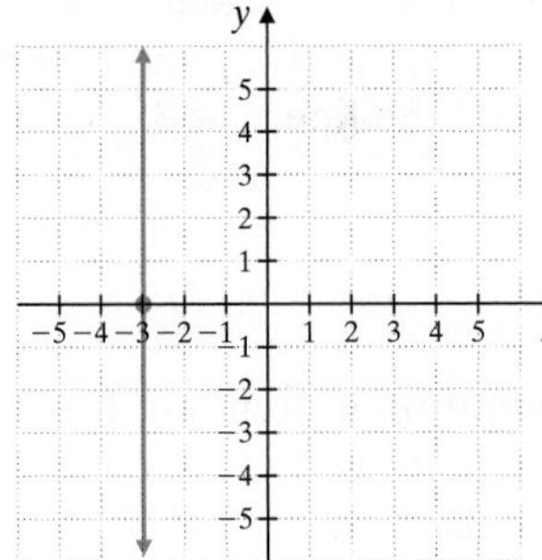

Graph each linear equation. For Exercises 11 and 12, label the intercepts.

5. $y = -2x$

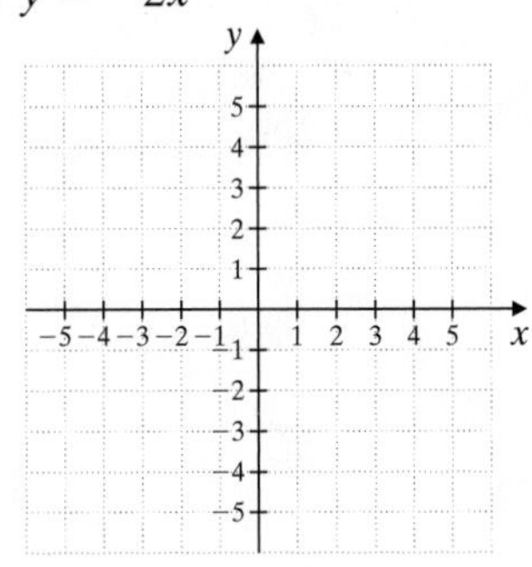

6. $x + y = 3$

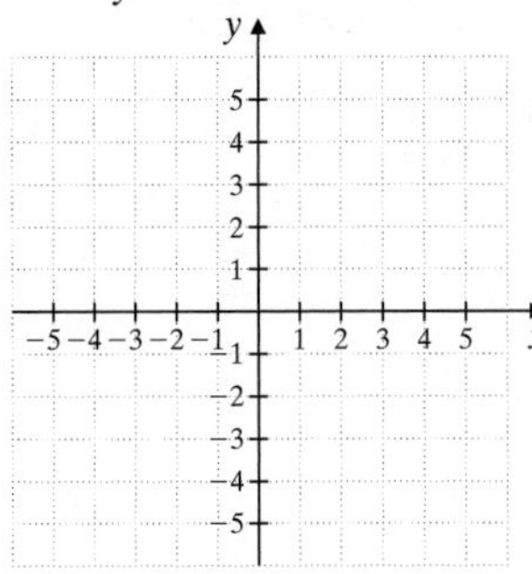

7. $x = -1$

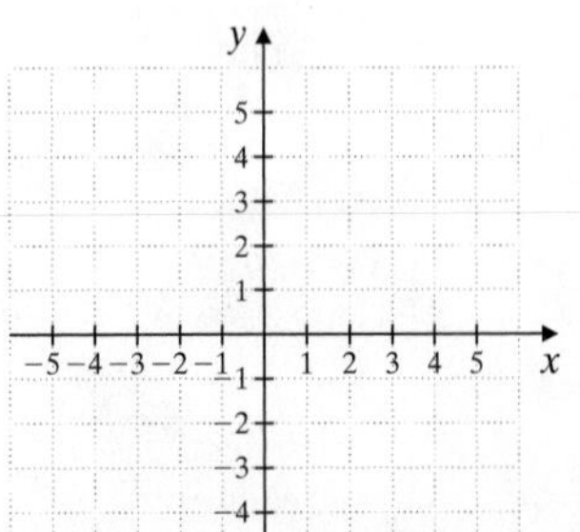

8. $y = 4$

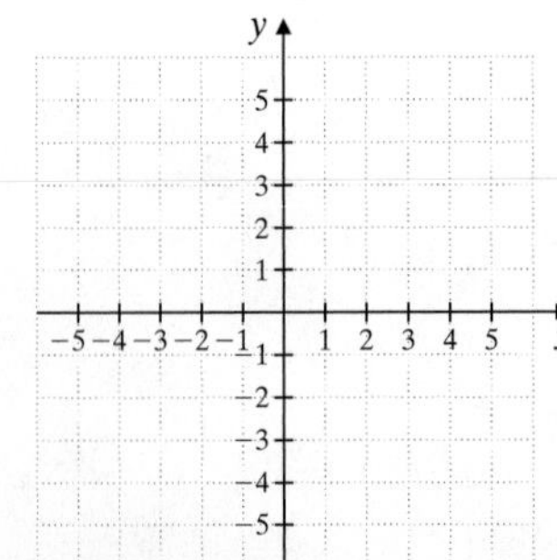

9. $x - 2y = 6$

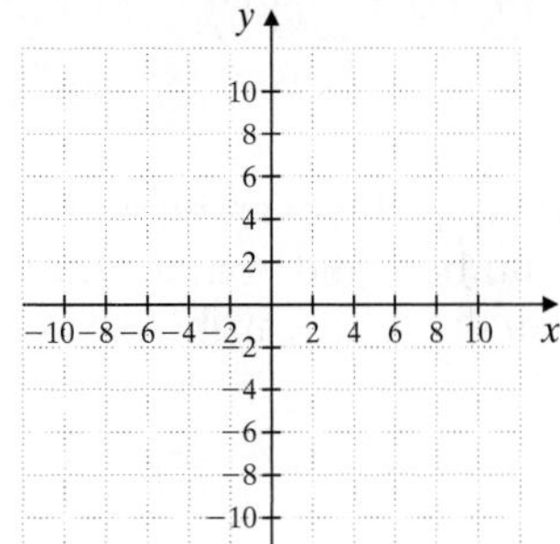

10. $y = 3x + 2$

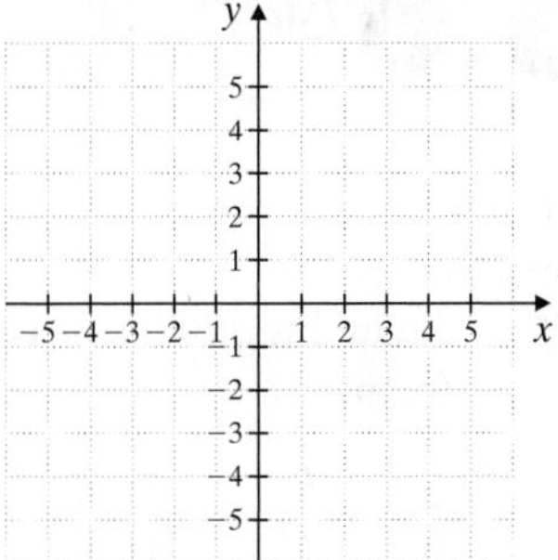

11. $y = -\frac{3}{4}x + 3$

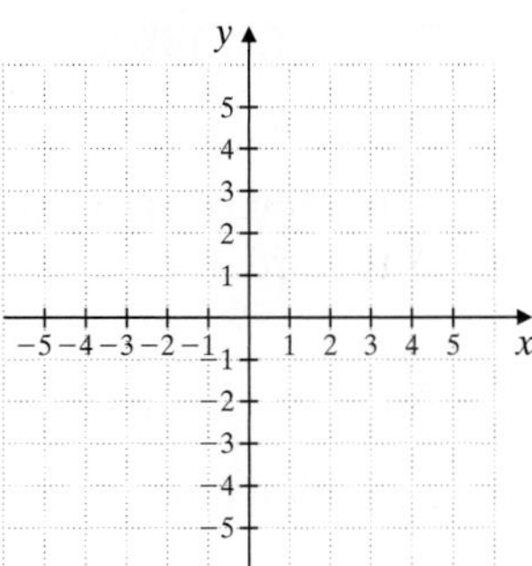

12. $5x - 2y = 8$

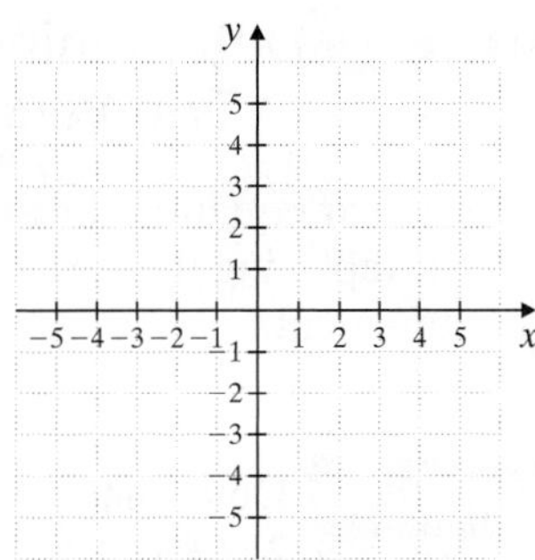

Find the slope of each line by writing the equation in slope-intercept form.

13. $y = 3x - 1$ **14.** $y = -6x + 2$ **15.** $7x + 2y = 11$ **16.** $2x - y = 0$

Find the slope of each line.

17. $x = 2$ **18.** $y = -4$

19. Write an equation of the line with slope $m = 2$ and y-intercept $\left(0, -\frac{1}{3}\right)$. Write the equation in the form $y = mx + b$.

20. Find an equation of the line with slope $m = -4$ that passes through the point $(-1, 3)$. Write the equation in the form $y = mx + b$.

21. Find an equation of the line that passes through the points $(2, 0)$ and $(-1, -3)$. Write the equation in the form $Ax + By = C$.

Determine whether each pair of lines is parallel, perpendicular, or neither.

22. $6x - y = 7$
$2x + 3y = 4$

23. $3x - 6y = 4$
$y = -2x$

24. Yogurt is an ever more popular food item. In 2002, American Dairy affiliates produced 2133 million pounds of yogurt. In 2007, this number rose to 3478 million pounds of yogurt.

a. Write two ordered pairs of the form (year, millions of pounds of yogurt produced).

b. Find the slope of the line between these two points.

c. Write a sentence explaining the meaning of the slope as a rate of change.

9. ______
10. ______
11. ______
12. ______
13. ______
14. ______
15. ______
16. ______
17. ______
18. ______
19. ______
20. ______
21. ______
22. ______
23. ______
24. a. ______
b. ______
c. ______

Objectives

A **Determine Whether an Ordered Pair Is a Solution of a Linear Inequality in Two Variables.**

B **Graph a Linear Inequality in Two Variables.**

13.6 GRAPHING LINEAR INEQUALITIES IN TWO VARIABLES

Recall that a linear equation in two variables is an equation that can be written in the form $Ax + By = C$, where A, B, and C are real numbers and A and B are not both 0. A **linear inequality in two variables** is an inequality that can be written in one of the forms

$$Ax + By < C \qquad Ax + By \le C$$
$$Ax + By > C \qquad Ax + By \ge C$$

where A, B, and C are real numbers and A and B are not both 0.

Objective A Determining Solutions of Linear Inequalities in Two Variables

Just as for linear equations in x and y, an ordered pair is a **solution** of an inequality in x and y if replacing the variables with the coordinates of the ordered pair results in a true statement.

PRACTICE 1

Determine whether each ordered pair is a solution of $x - 4y > 8$.

a. $(-3, 2)$
b. $(9, 0)$

Example 1 Determine whether each ordered pair is a solution of the inequality $2x - y < 6$.

a. $(5, -1)$ **b.** $(2, 7)$

Solution:

a. We replace x with 5 and y with -1 and see if a true statement results.

$$2x - y < 6$$
$$2(5) - (-1) < 6 \quad \text{Replace } x \text{ with 5 and } y \text{ with } -1.$$
$$10 + 1 < 6$$
$$11 < 6 \quad \text{False}$$

The ordered pair $(5, -1)$ is not a solution since $11 < 6$ is a false statement.

b. We replace x with 2 and y with 7 and see if a true statement results.

$$2x - y < 6$$
$$2(2) - (7) < 6 \quad \text{Replace } x \text{ with 2 and } y \text{ with 7.}$$
$$4 - 7 < 6$$
$$-3 < 6 \quad \text{True}$$

The ordered pair $(2, 7)$ is a solution since $-3 < 6$ is a true statement.

Work Practice 1

Objective B Graphing Linear Inequalities in Two Variables

The linear equation $x - y = 1$ is graphed next. Recall that all points on the line correspond to ordered pairs that satisfy the equation $x - y = 1$.

Notice that the line defined by $x - y = 1$ divides the rectangular coordinate system plane into 2 sides. All points on one side of the line satisfy the inequality $x - y < 1$ and all points on the other side satisfy the inequality $x - y > 1$. The graph on the next page shows a few examples of this.

Answers
1. a. no b. yes

$x - y < 1$	
$1 - 3 < 1$	True
$-2 - 1 < 1$	True
$-4 - (-4) < 1$	True

$x - y > 1$	
$4 - 1 > 1$	True
$2 - (-2) > 1$	True
$0 - (-4) > 1$	True

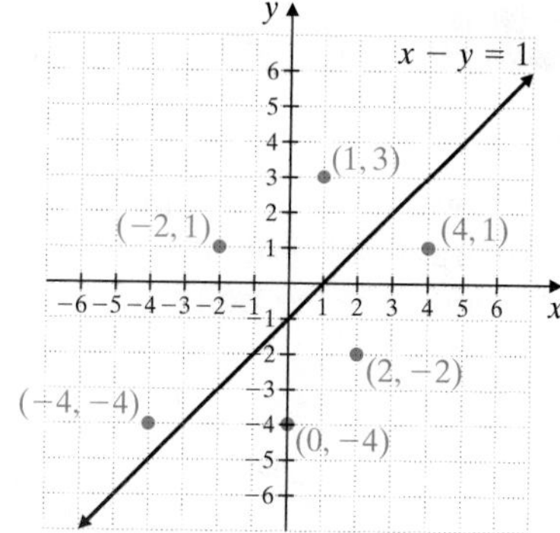

The graph of $x - y < 1$ is the region shaded blue and the graph of $x - y > 1$ is the region shaded red below.

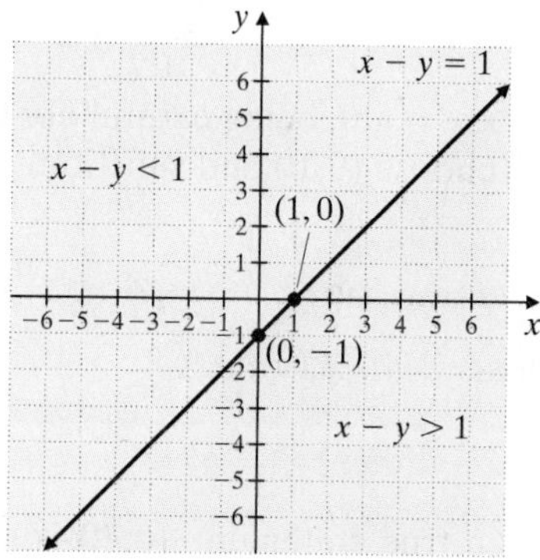

The region to the left of the line and the region to the right of the line are called **half-planes.** Every line divides the plane (similar to a sheet of paper extending indefinitely in all directions) into two half-planes; the line is called the **boundary.**

Recall that the inequality $x - y \le 1$ means

$$x - y = 1 \quad \text{or} \quad x - y < 1$$

Thus, the graph of $x - y \le 1$ is the half-plane $x - y < 1$ along with the boundary line $x - y = 1$.

To Graph a Linear Inequality in Two Variables

Step 1: Graph the boundary line found by replacing the inequality sign with an equal sign. If the inequality sign is $>$ or $<$, graph a dashed boundary line (indicating that the points on the line are not solutions of the inequality). If the inequality sign is $\ge$ or $\le$, graph a solid boundary line (indicating that the points on the line are solutions of the inequality).

Step 2: Choose a point *not* on the boundary line as a test point. Substitute the coordinates of this test point into the *original* inequality.

Step 3: If a true statement is obtained in Step 2, shade the half-plane that contains the test point. If a false statement is obtained, shade the half-plane that does not contain the test point.

PRACTICE 2

Graph: $x - y > 3$

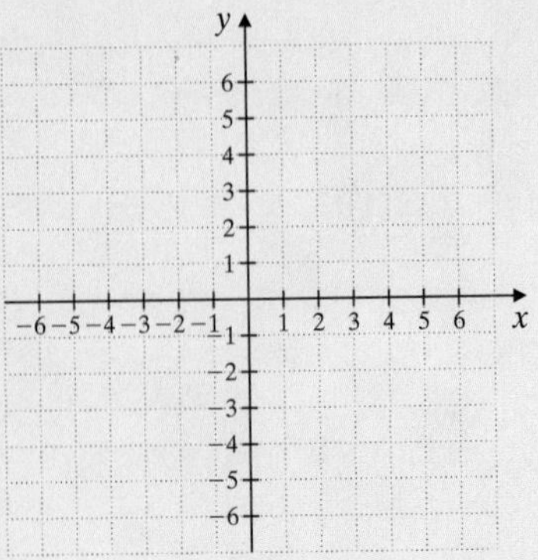

Example 2 Graph: $x + y < 7$

Solution:

Step 1: First we graph the boundary line by graphing the equation $x + y = 7$. We graph this boundary as a *dashed line* because the inequality sign is $<$, and thus the points on the line are not solutions of the inequality $x + y < 7$.

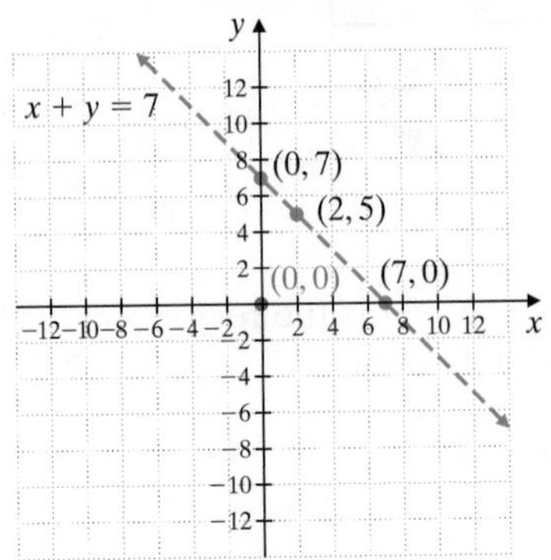

Step 2: Next we choose a test point, being careful *not* to choose a point on the boundary line. We choose (0, 0) and substitute the coordinates of (0, 0) into $x + y < 7$.

$x + y < 7$ Original inequality

$0 + 0 < 7$ Replace x with 0 and y with 0.

$0 < 7$ True

Step 3: Since the result is a true statement, (0, 0) is a solution of $x + y < 7$, and every point in the same half-plane as (0, 0) is also a solution. To indicate this, we shade the entire half-plane containing (0, 0), as shown.

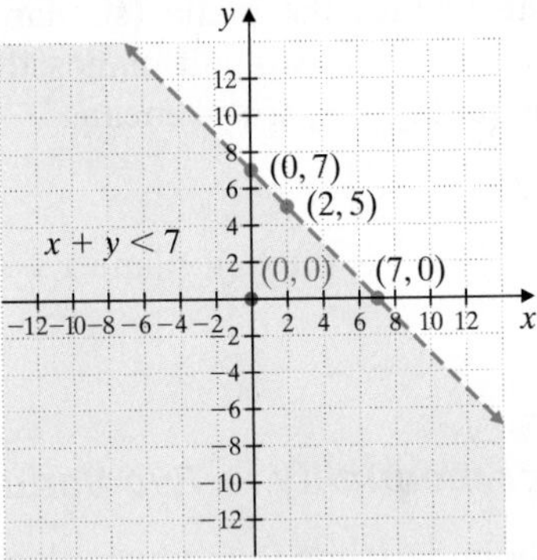

Work Practice 2

✓**Concept Check** Determine whether (0, 0) is included in the graph of

a. $y \geq 2x + 3$

b. $x < 7$

c. $2x - 3y < 6$

Answer

2.

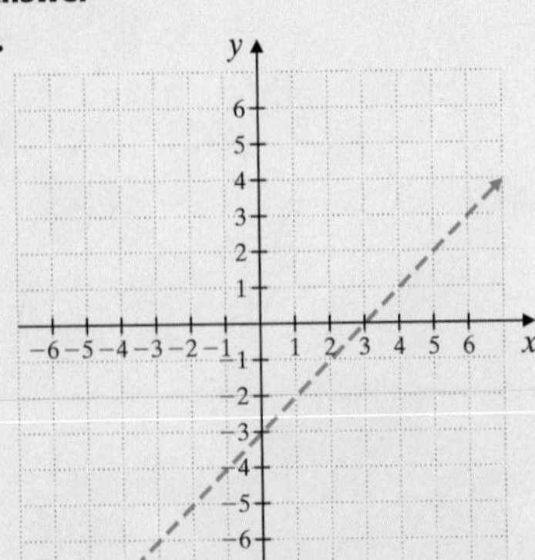

✓ **Concept Check Answers**

a. no **b.** yes **c.** yes

Example 3 Graph: $2x - y \geq 3$

Solution:

Step 1: We graph the boundary line by graphing $2x - y = 3$. We draw this line as a solid line because the inequality sign is $\geq$, and thus the points on the line are solutions of $2x - y \geq 3$.

Step 2: Once again, (0, 0) is a convenient test point since it is not on the boundary line.

We substitute 0 for x and 0 for y into the original inequality.

$2x - y \geq 3$

$2(0) - 0 \geq 3$ Let $x = 0$ and $y = 0$.

$0 \geq 3$ False

Step 3: Since the statement is false, no point in the half-plane containing (0, 0) is a solution. Therefore, we shade the half-plane that does not contain (0, 0). Every point in the shaded half-plane and every point on the boundary line is a solution of $2x - y \geq 3$.

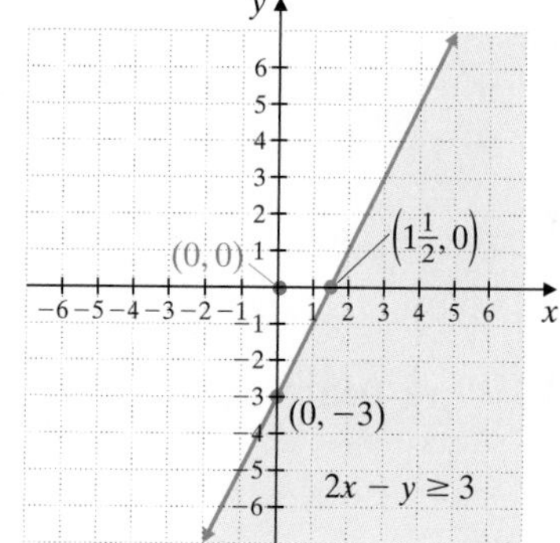

Work Practice 3

Helpful Hint

When graphing an inequality, make sure the test point is substituted into the **original inequality.** For Example 3, we substituted the test point (0, 0) into the **original inequality** $2x - y \geq 3$, *not* $2x - y = 3$.

Example 4 Graph: $x > 2y$

Solution:

Step 1: We find the boundary line by graphing $x = 2y$. The boundary line is a dashed line since the inequality symbol is $>$.

Step 2: We cannot use $(0, 0)$ as a test point because it is a point on the boundary line. We choose instead $(0, 2)$.

$x > 2y$

$0 > 2(2)$ Let $x = 0$ and $y = 2$.

$0 > 4$ False

Step 3: Since the statement is false, we shade the half-plane that does not contain the test point $(0, 2)$, as shown.

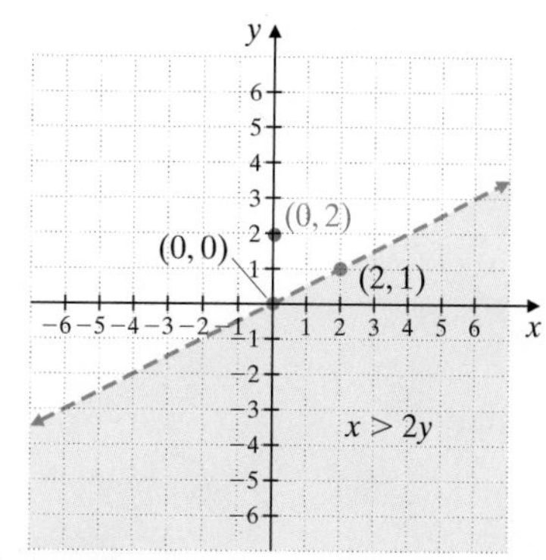

Work Practice 4

PRACTICE 3

Graph: $x - 4y \leq 4$

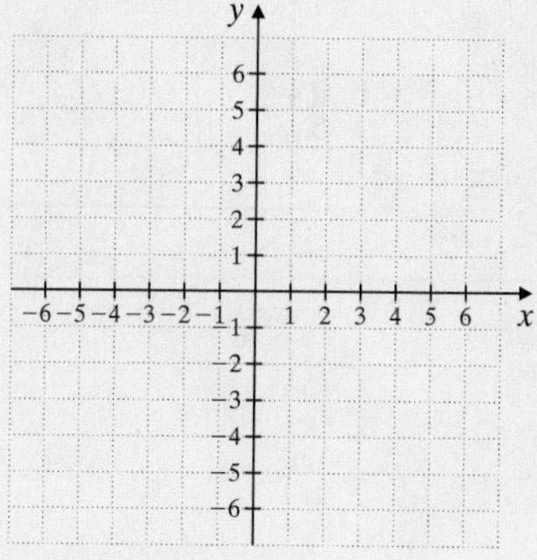

PRACTICE 4

Graph: $y < 3x$

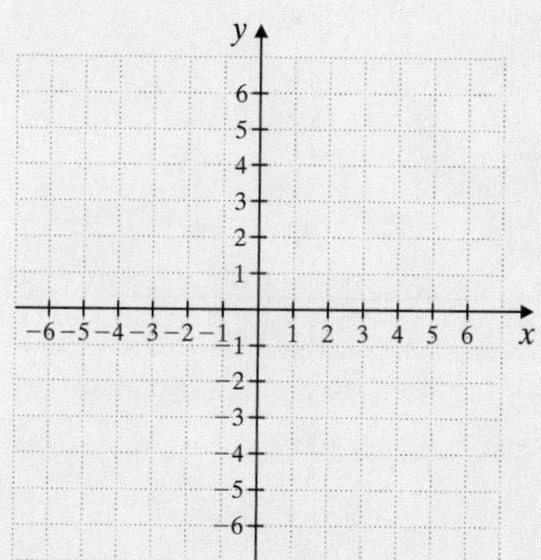

Answers

3.

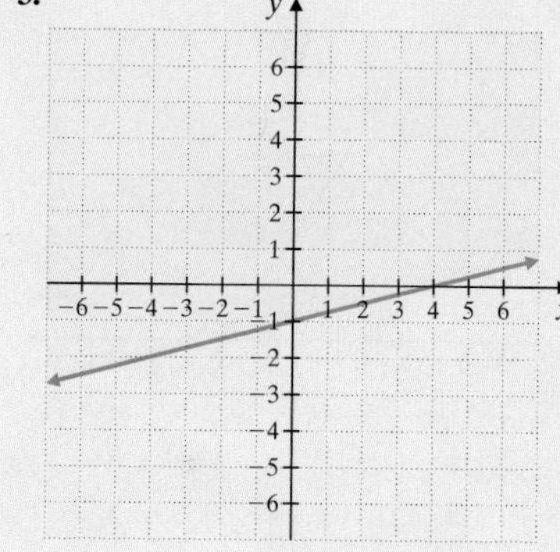

4.

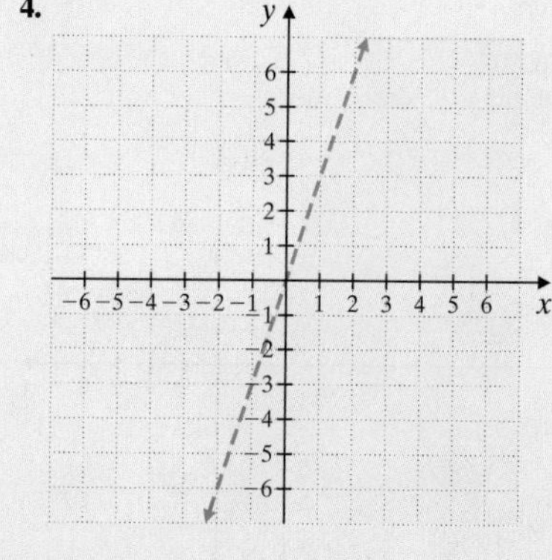

PRACTICE 5

Graph: $3x + 2y \geq 12$

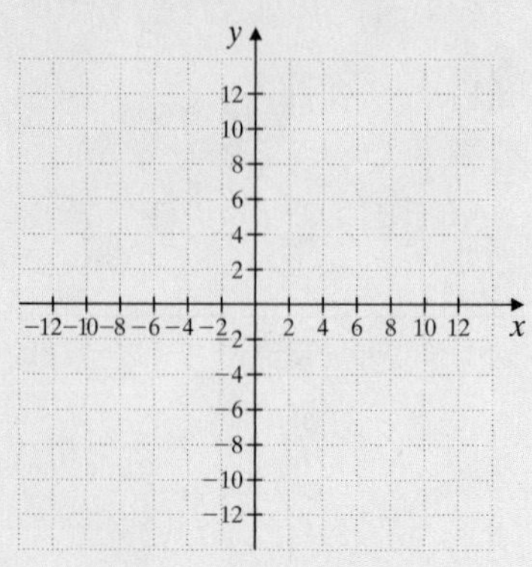

PRACTICE 6

Graph: $x < 2$

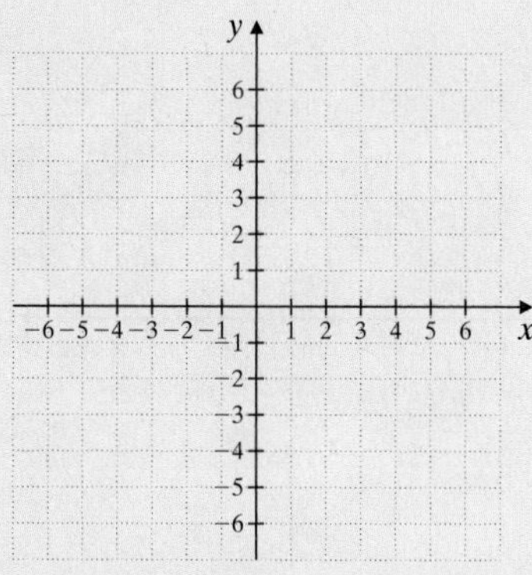

Answers

5.

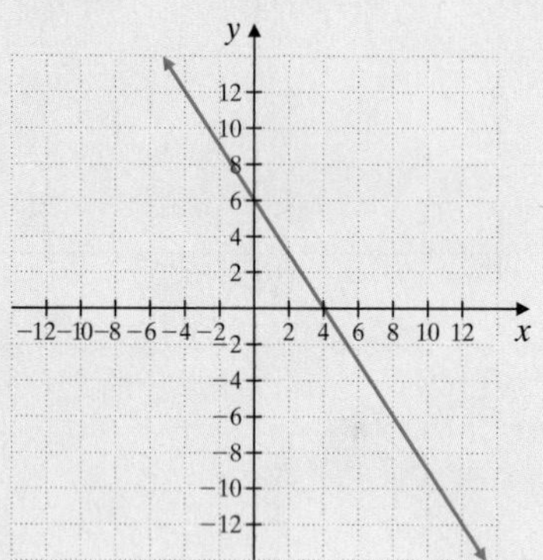

6.

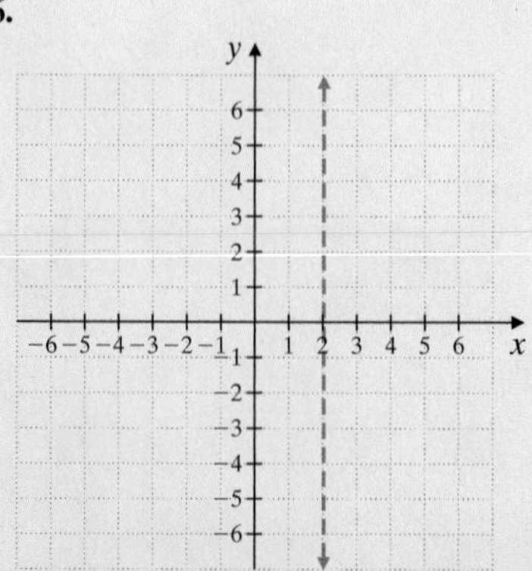

Example 5 Graph: $5x + 4y \leq 20$

Solution: We graph the solid boundary line $5x + 4y = 20$ and choose $(0, 0)$ as the test point.

$$5x + 4y \leq 20$$

$$5(0) + 4(0) \leq 20 \quad \text{Let } x = 0 \text{ and } y = 0.$$

$$0 \leq 20 \quad \text{True}$$

We shade the half-plane that contains $(0, 0)$, as shown.

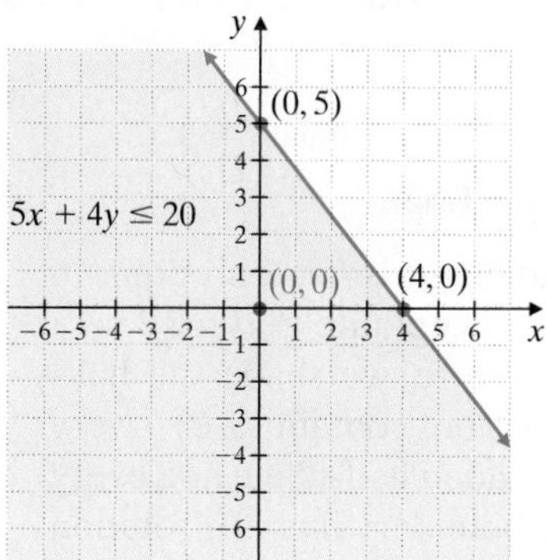

Work Practice 5

Example 6 Graph: $y > 3$

Solution: We graph the dashed boundary line $y = 3$ and choose $(0, 0)$ as the test point. (Recall that the graph of $y = 3$ is a horizontal line with y-intercept 3.)

$$y > 3$$

$$0 > 3 \quad \text{Let } y = 0.$$

$$0 > 3 \quad \text{False}$$

We shade the half-plane that does not contain $(0, 0)$, as shown.

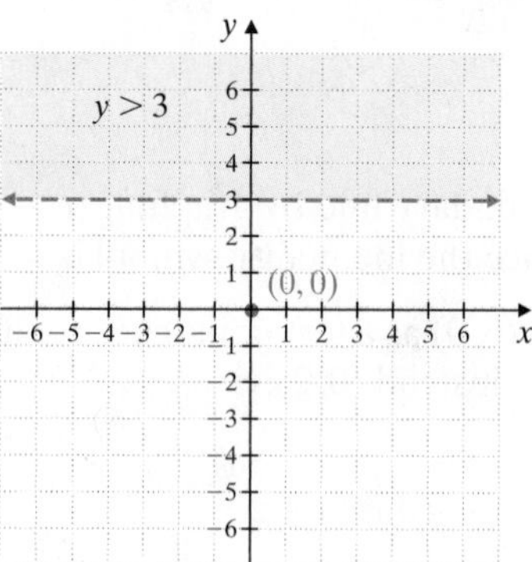

Work Practice 6

Example 7 Graph: $y \le \frac{2}{3}x - 4$

Solution: Graph the solid boundary line $y = \frac{2}{3}x - 4$. This equation is in slope-intercept form with slope $\frac{2}{3}$ and y-intercept -4.

We use this information to graph the line. Then we choose (0, 0) as our test point.

$$y \le \frac{2}{3}x - 4$$
$$0 \le \frac{2}{3} \cdot 0 - 4$$
$$0 \le -4 \quad \text{False}$$

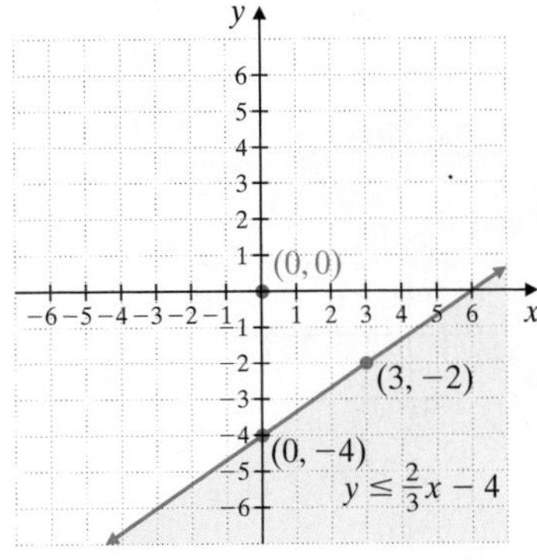

We shade the half-plane that does not contain (0, 0), as shown.

Work Practice 7

PRACTICE 7

Graph: $y \ge \frac{1}{4}x + 3$

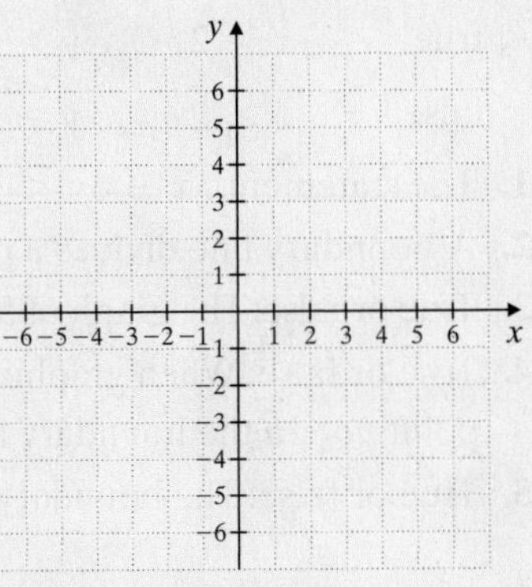

Answer

7.

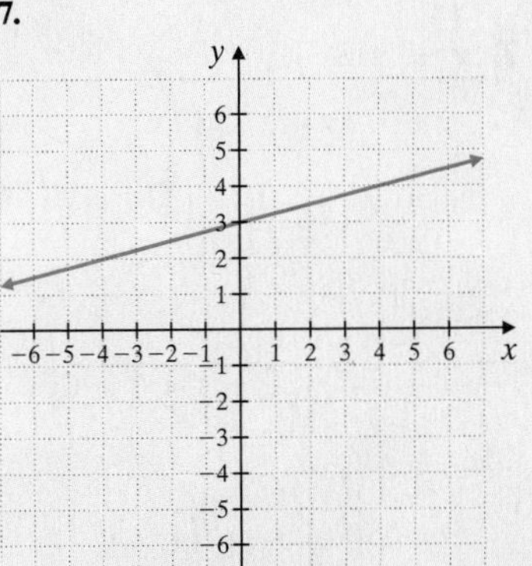

Vocabulary and Readiness Check

Use the choices below to fill in each blank. Some choices may be used more than once, and some not at all.

true	$x > 2$	$y > 2$	half-planes
false	$x \geq 2$	$y \geq 2$	linear inequality in two variables

1. The statement $5x - 6y < 7$ is an example of a ______________.

2. A boundary line divides a plane into two regions called ______________.

3. True or false: The graph of $5x - 6y < 7$ includes its corresponding boundary line. ______________

4. True or false: When graphing a linear inequality, to determine which side of the boundary line to shade, choose a point *not* on the boundary line. ______________

5. True or false: The boundary line for the inequality $5x - 6y < 7$ is the graph of $5x - 6y = 7$.
____

6. The graph of ______________ is

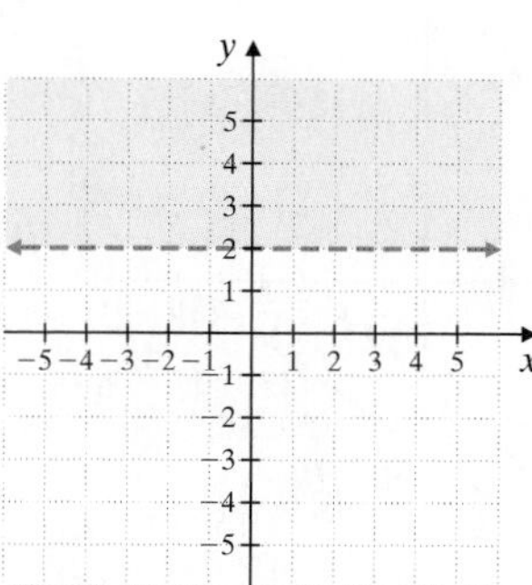

13.6 Exercise Set

Objective A *Determine whether the ordered pairs given are solutions of the linear inequality in two variables. See Example 1.*

1. $x - y > 3$; $(0, 3)$, $(2, -1)$

2. $y - x < -2$; $(2, 1)$, $(5, -1)$

3. $3x - 5y \leq -4$; $(2, 3)$, $(-1, -1)$

4. $2x + y \geq 10$; $(0, 11)$, $(5, 0)$

5. $x < -y$; $(0, 2)$, $(-5, 1)$

6. $y > 3x$; $(0, 0)$, $(1, 4)$

Objective B *Graph each inequality. See Examples 2 through 7.*

7. $x + y \leq 1$

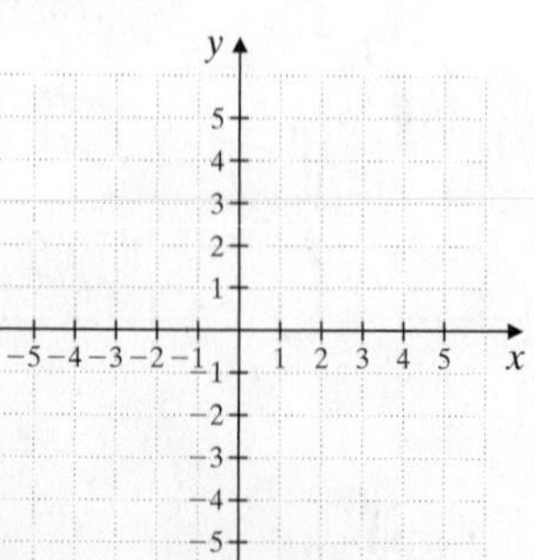

8. $x + y \geq -2$

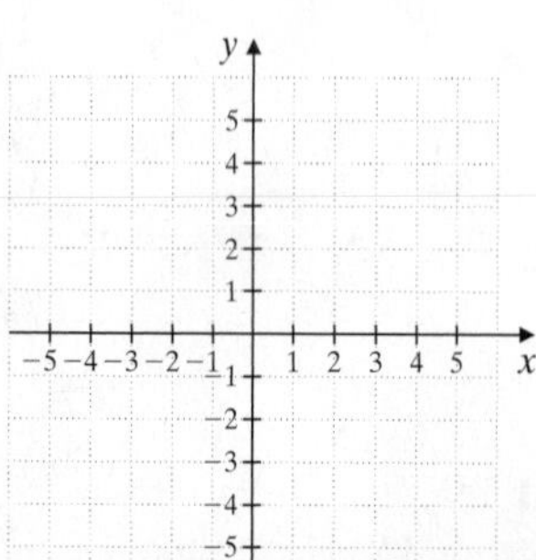

9. $2x - y > -4$

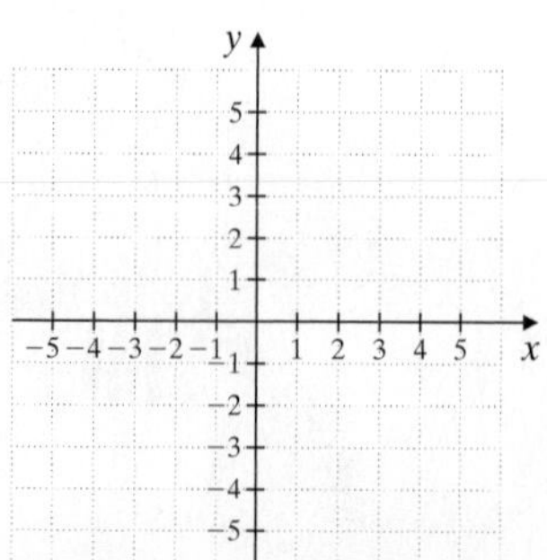

10. $x - 3y < 3$

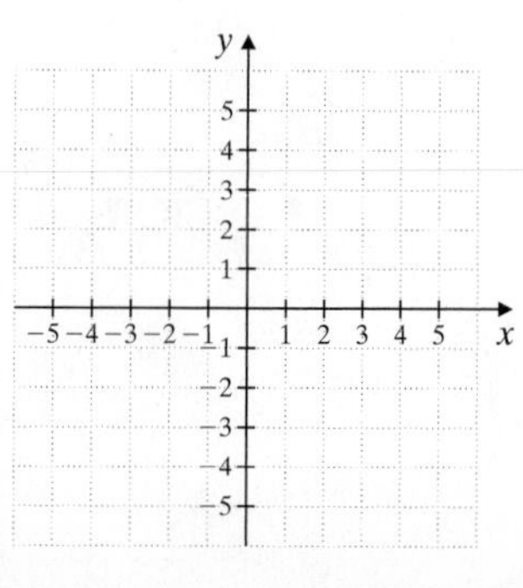

11. $y \geq 2x$

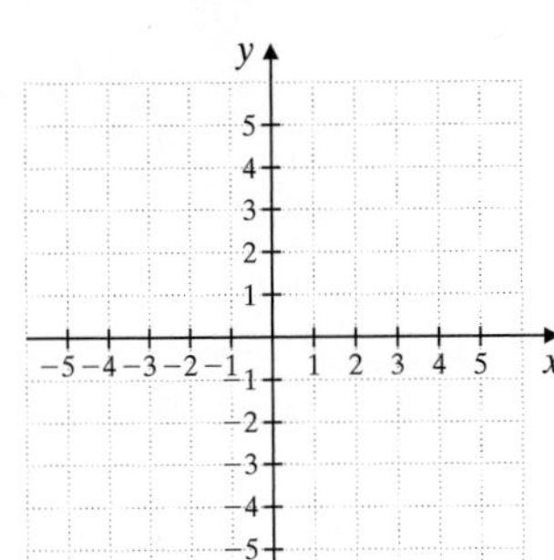

12. $y \leq 3x$

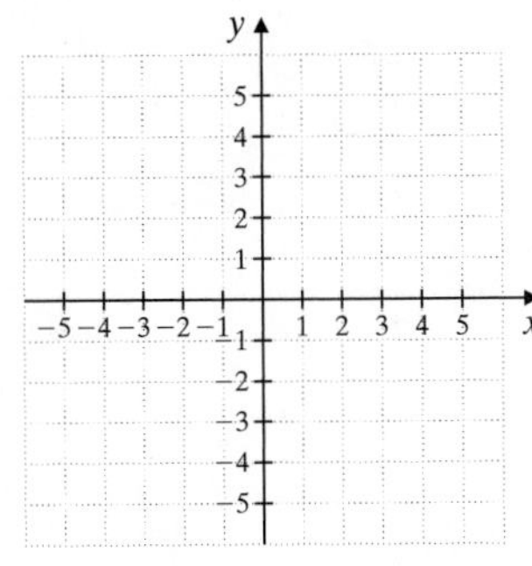

13. $x < -3y$

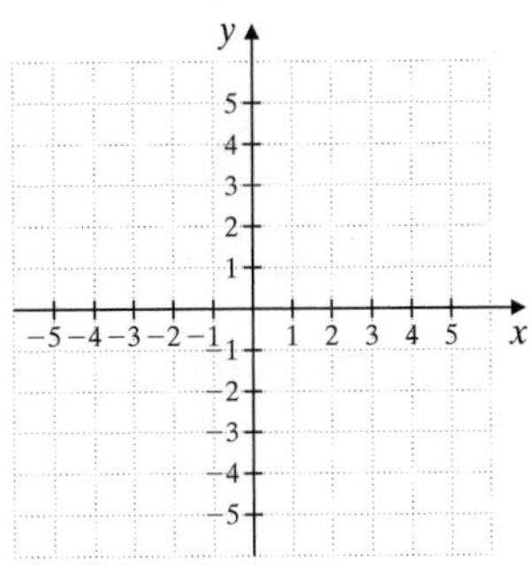

14. $x > -2y$

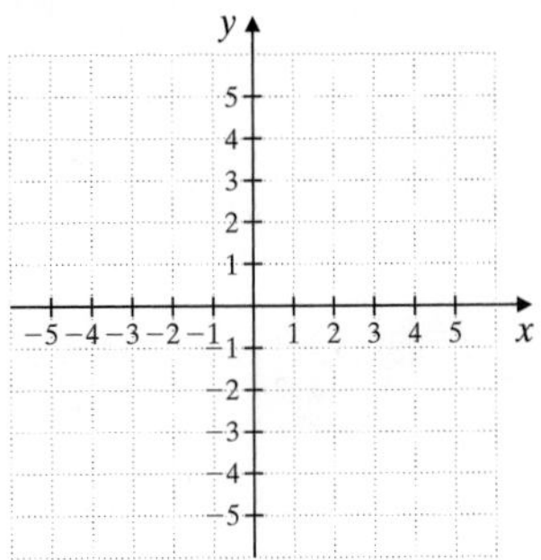

15. $y \geq x + 5$

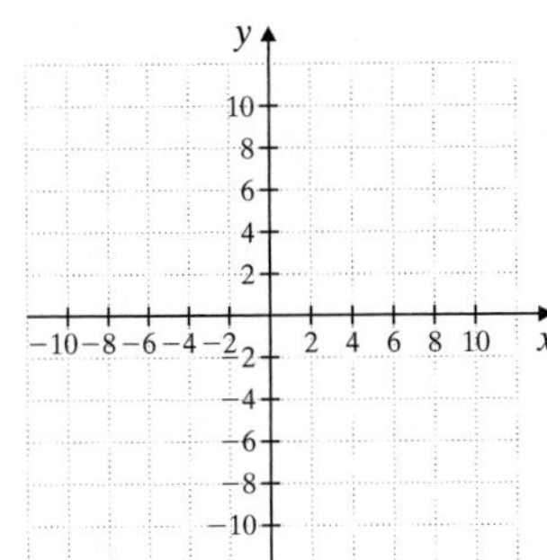

16. $y \leq x + 1$

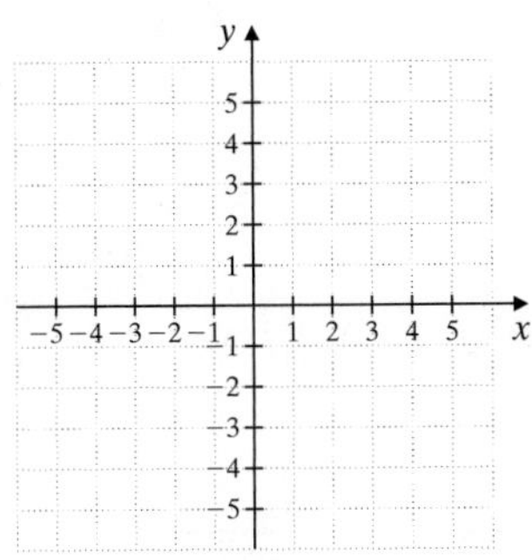

17. $y < 4$

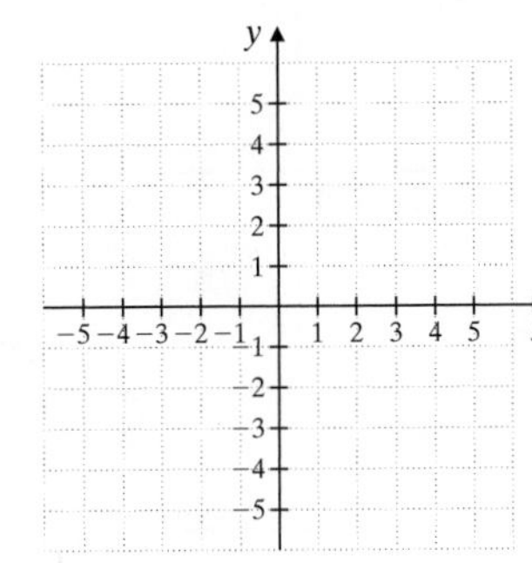

18. $y > 2$

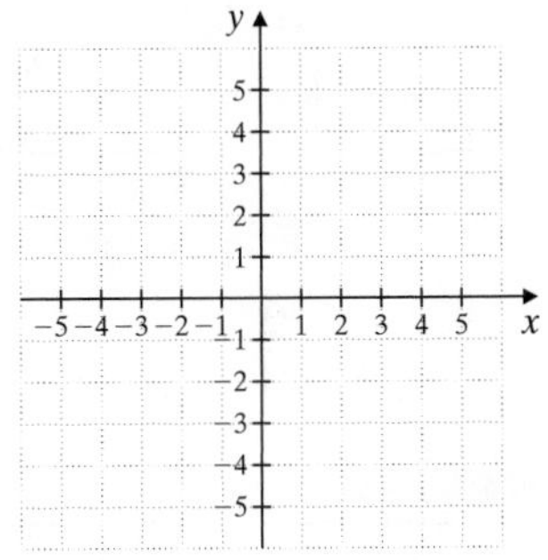

19. $x \geq -3$

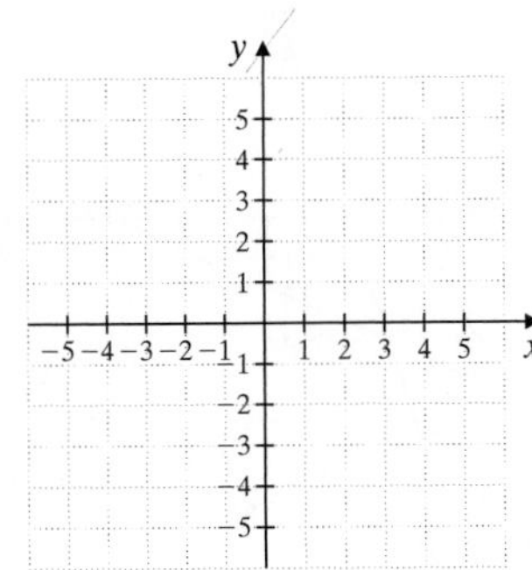

20. $x \leq -1$

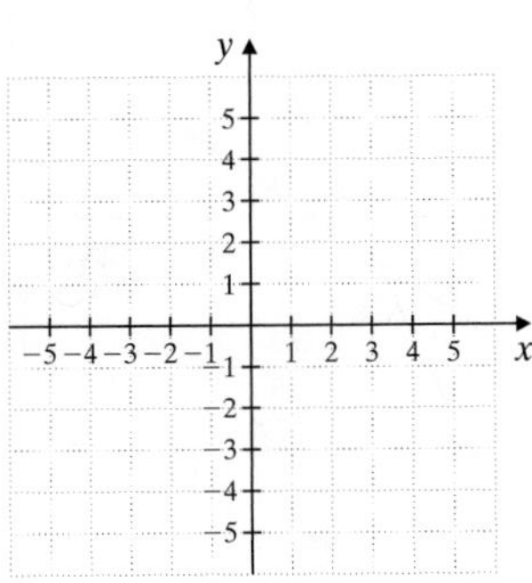

21. $5x + 2y \leq 10$

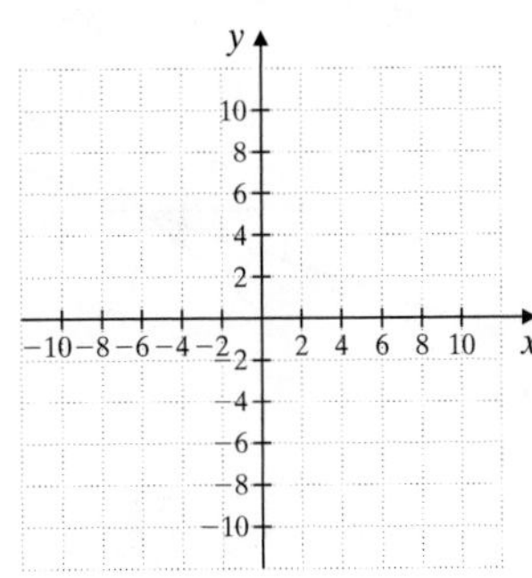

22. $4x + 3y \geq 12$

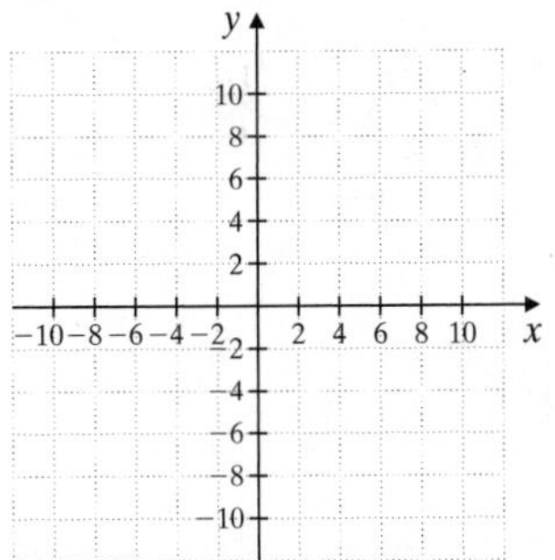

23. $x > y$

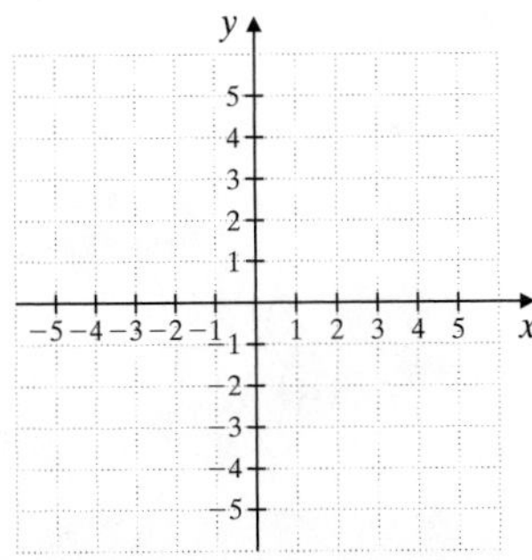

24. $x \leq -y$

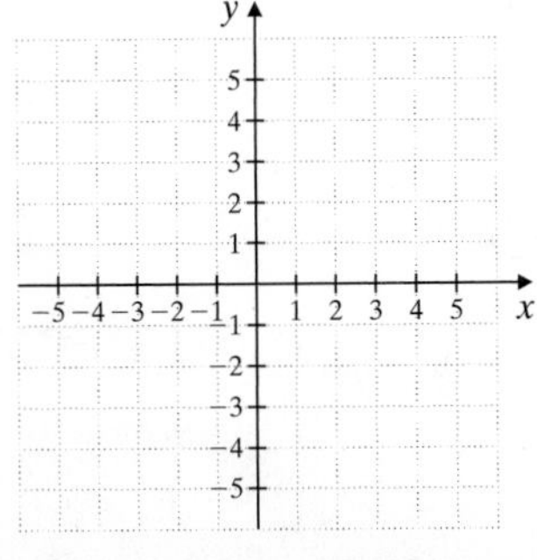

25. $x - y \leq 6$

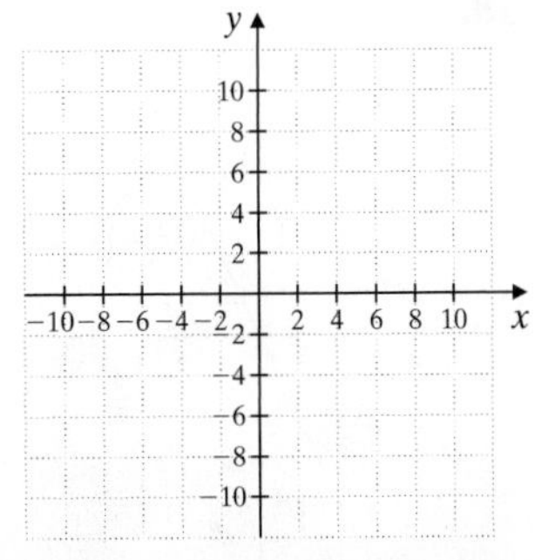

26. $x - y > 10$

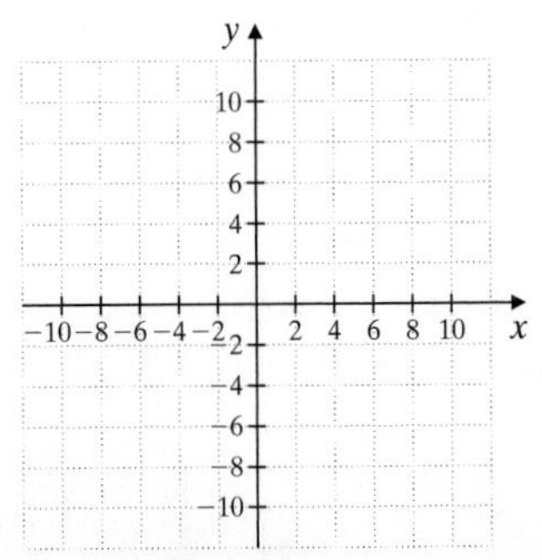

27. $x \geq 0$

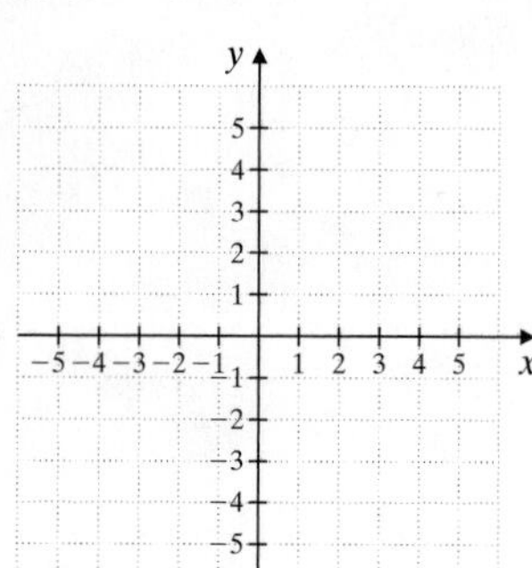

28. $y \leq 0$

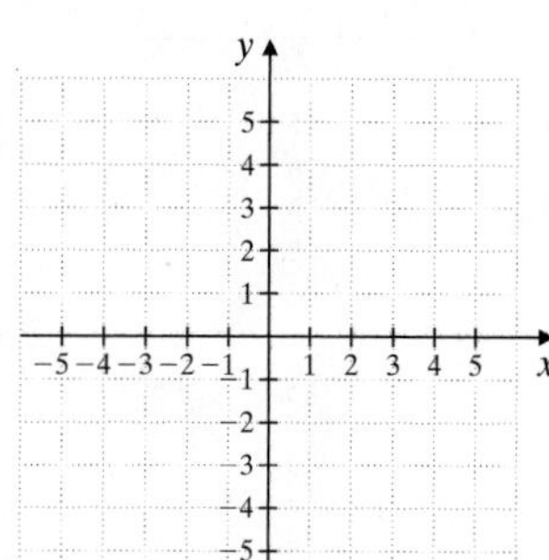

29. $2x + 7y > 5$

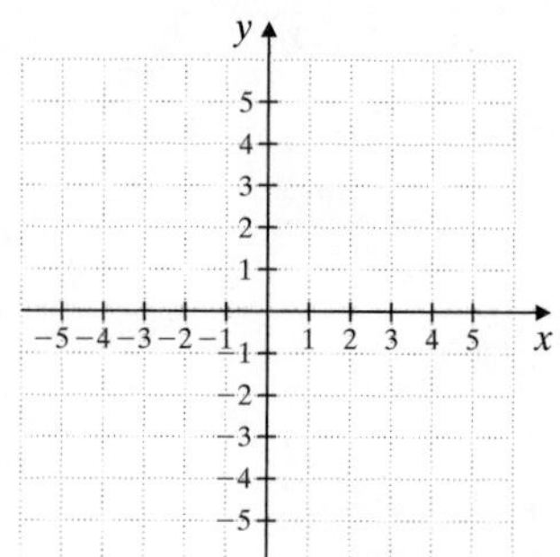

30. $3x + 5y \leq -2$

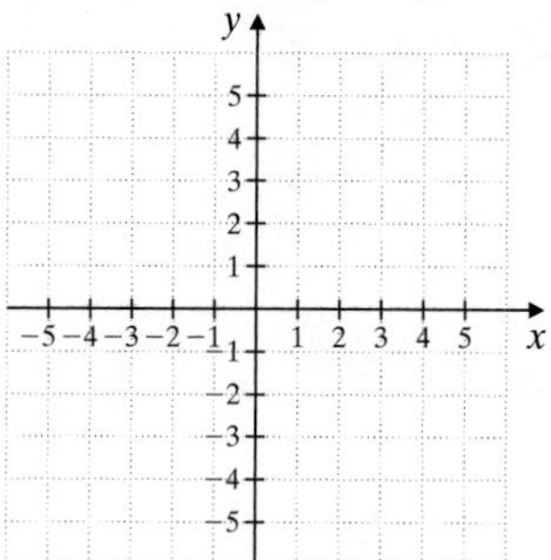

31. $y \geq \frac{1}{2}x - 4$

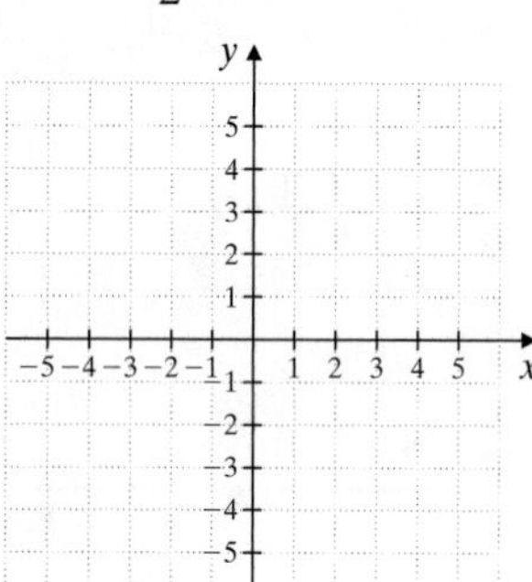

32. $y < \frac{2}{5}x - 3$

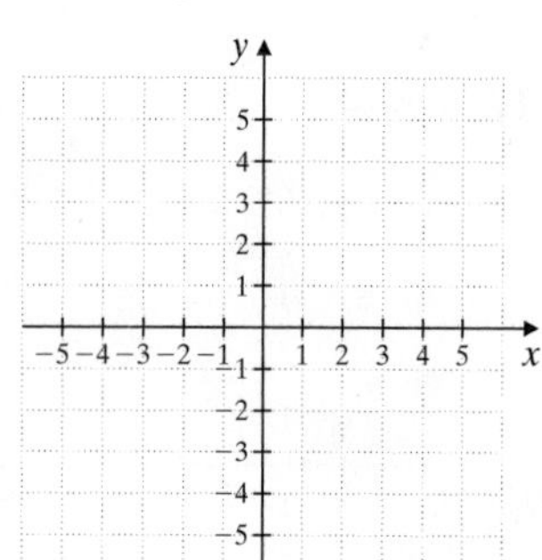

Review

Approximate the coordinates of each point of intersection. See Section 13.1.

33.

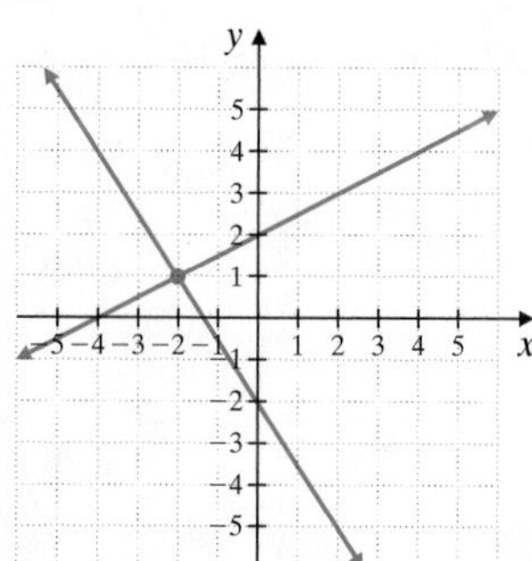

34.

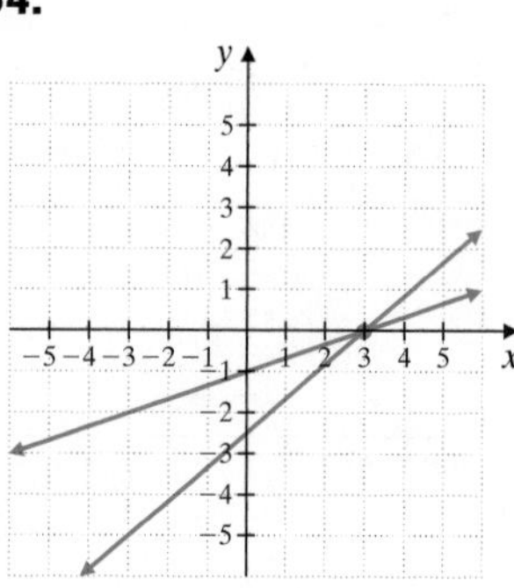

35.

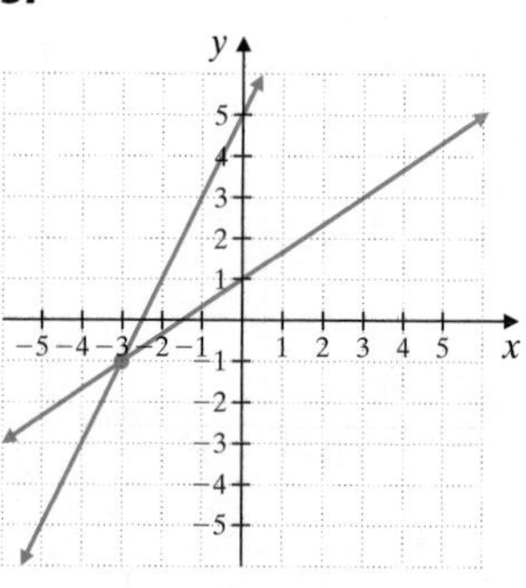

36.

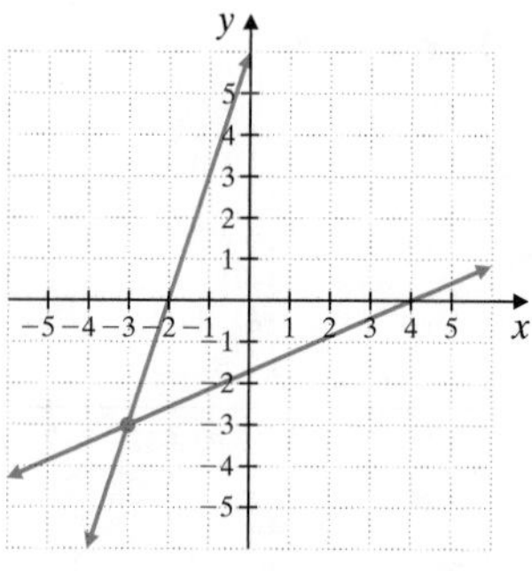

Concept Extensions

Match each inequality with its graph.

a. $x > 2$

b. $y < 2$

c. $y \leq 2x$

d. $y \leq -3x$

37.

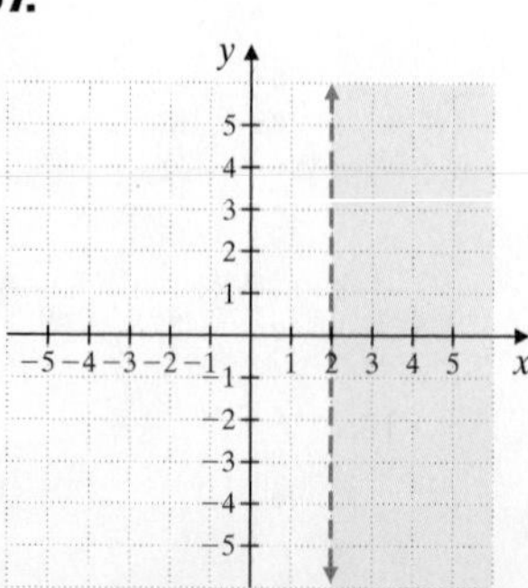

38.

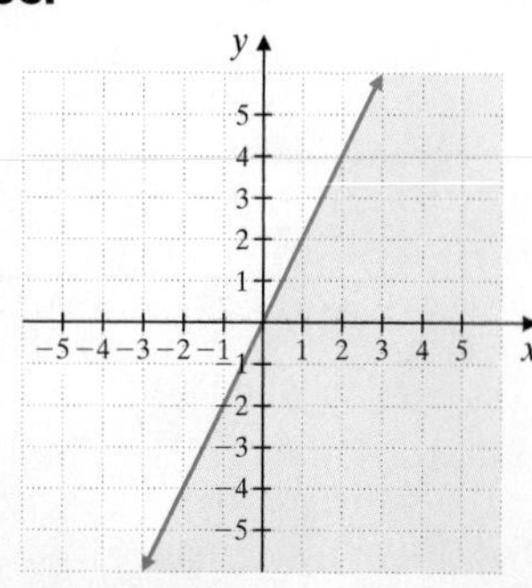

39.

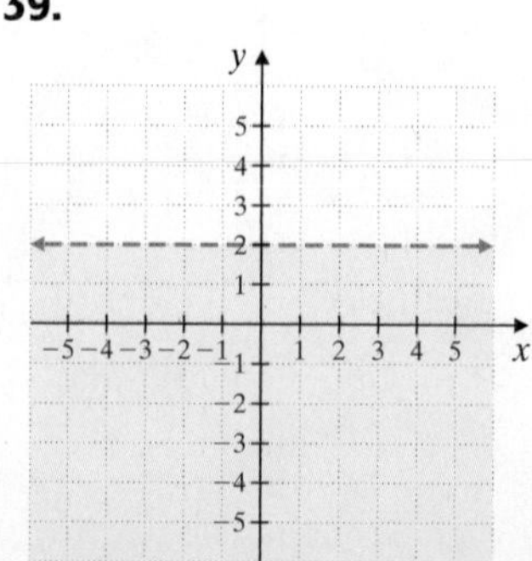

40.

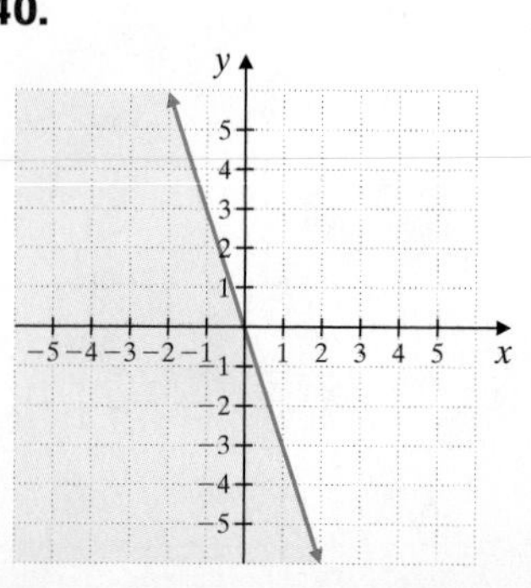

41. Explain why a point on the boundary line should not be chosen as the test point.

42. Write an inequality whose solutions are all points with coordinates whose sum is at least 13.

Determine whether (1, 1) *is included in each graph. See the Concept Check in this section.*

43. $3x + 4y < 8$

44. $y > 5x$

45. $y \geq -\frac{1}{2}x$

46. $x > 3$

47. It's the end of the budgeting period for Dennis Fernandes and he has $500 left in his budget for car rental expenses. He plans to spend this budget on a sales trip throughout southern Texas. He will rent a car that costs $30 per day and $0.15 per mile and he can spend no more than $500.

a. Write an inequality describing this situation. Let x = number of days and let y = number of miles.

b. Graph this inequality below.

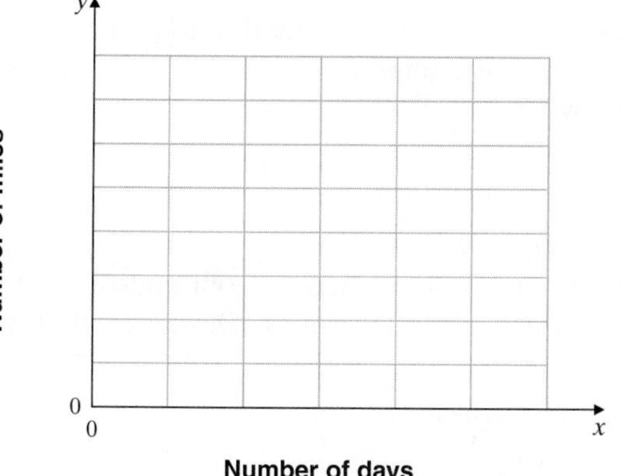

c. Why is the grid showing quadrant I only?

48. Scott Sambracci and Sara Thygeson are planning their wedding. They have calculated that they want the cost of their wedding ceremony x plus the cost of their reception y to be no more than $5000.

a. Write an inequality describing this relationship.

b. Graph this inequality below.

c. Why is the grid showing quadrant I only?

Chapter 13 Group Activity

Finding a Linear Model

This activity may be completed by working in groups or individually.

The following table shows the actual number of foreign visitors (in millions) to the United States for the years 2005 through 2011. (The last two years are predictions.)

Year	Foreign Visitors to the United States (in millions)
2005	48.1
2006	51.0
2007	56.0
2008	61.1
2009	57.4
2010	59.5
2011	61.4

(*Source:* Tourism Industries/International Trade Administration, U.S. Department of Commerce)

1. Make a scatter diagram of the paired data in the table.

2. Use what you have learned in this chapter to write an equation of the line representing the paired data in the table. Explain how you found the equation, and what each variable represents.

3. What is the slope of your line? What does the slope mean in this context?

4. Use your linear equation to predict the number of foreign visitors to the United States in 2014.

5. Compare your linear equation to that found by other students or groups. Is it the same, similar, or different? How?

6. Compare your prediction from question 4 to that of other students or groups. Describe what you find.

7. The number of visitors to the United States for 2012 was estimated to be 65.1 million. If this data point is added to the chart, how does it affect your results?

Chapter 13 Vocabulary Check

Fill in each blank with one of the words listed below.

y-axis	x-axis	solution	linear	standard	slope-intercept
x-intercept	y-intercept	y	x	slope	point-slope

1. An ordered pair is a(n) of an equation in two variables if replacing the variables by the coordinates of the ordered pair results in a true statement.
2. The vertical number line in the rectangular coordinate system is called the ____________.
3. A(n) ____________ equation can be written in the form $Ax + By = C$.
4. A(n) ____________ is a point of the graph where the graph crosses the x-axis.
5. The form $Ax + By = C$ is called ____________ form.
6. A(n) ____________ is a point of the graph where the graph crosses the y-axis.
7. The equation $y = 7x - 5$ is written in ____________ form.
8. The equation $y + 1 = 7(x - 2)$ is written in ____________ form.
9. To find an x-intercept of a graph, let ____________ = 0.
10. The horizontal number line in the rectangular coordinate system is called the ____________.
11. To find a y-intercept of a graph, let ____________ = 0.
12. The ____________ of a line measures the steepness or tilt of the line.

Helpful Hint Are you preparing for your test? Don't forget to take the Chapter 13 Test on page 946. Then check your answers at the back of the text and use the Chapter Test Prep Videos to see the fully worked-out solutions to any of the exercises you want to review.

13 Chapter Highlights

Definitions and Concepts	Examples
Section 13.1 Reading Graphs and the Rectangular Coordinate System	
The **rectangular coordinate system** consists of a plane and a vertical and a horizontal number line intersecting at their 0 coordinates. The vertical number line is called the ***y*-axis** and the horizontal number line is called the ***x*-axis.** The point of intersection of the axes is called the **origin.** To **plot** or **graph** an ordered pair means to find its corresponding point on a rectangular coordinate system. To plot or graph an ordered pair such as $(3, -2)$, start at the origin. Move 3 units to the right and from there, 2 units down. To plot or graph $(-3, 4)$, start at the origin. Move 3 units to the left and from there, 4 units up. An ordered pair is a **solution** of an equation in two variables if replacing the variables with the coordinates of the ordered pair results in a true statement.	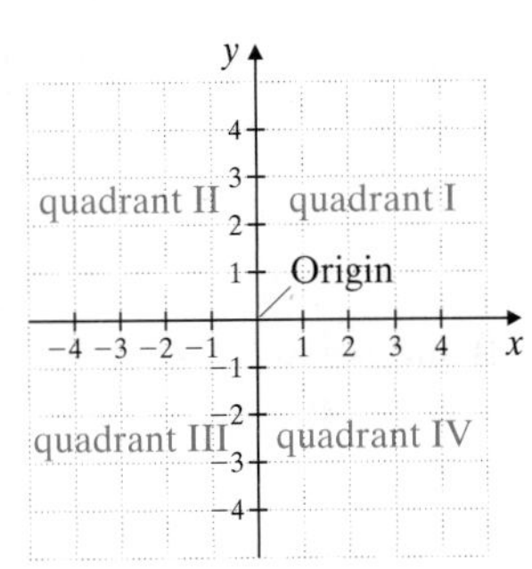 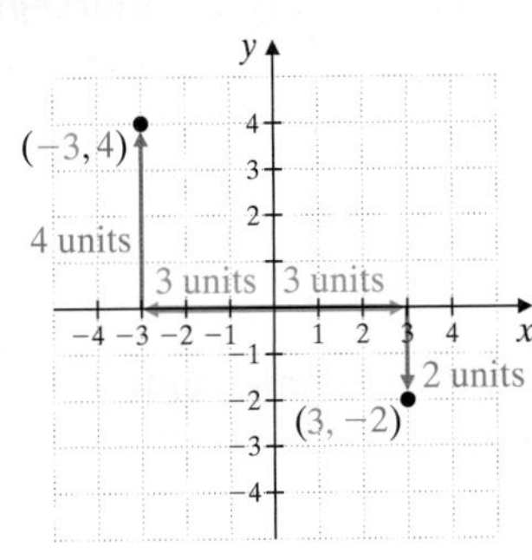

(continued)

Definitions and Concepts	Examples

Section 13.1 Reading Graphs and the Rectangular Coordinate System (*continued*)

If one coordinate of an ordered pair solution of an equation is known, the other value can be determined by substitution.

Complete the ordered pair (0,) for the equation $x - 6y = 12$.

$$x - 6y = 12$$
$$0 - 6y = 12 \quad \text{Let } x = 0.$$
$$\frac{-6y}{-6} = \frac{12}{-6} \quad \text{Divide by } -6.$$
$$y = -2$$

The ordered pair solution is $(0, -2)$.

Section 13.2 Graphing Linear Equations

A **linear equation in two variables** is an equation that can be written in the form $Ax + By = C$, where A and B are not both 0. The form $Ax + By = C$ is called **standard form.**

$3x + 2y = -6 \qquad x = -5$

$y = 3 \qquad y = -x + 10$

$x + y = 10$ is in standard form.

To graph a linear equation in two variables, find three ordered pair solutions. Plot the solution points and draw the line connecting the points.

Graph: $x - 2y = 5$

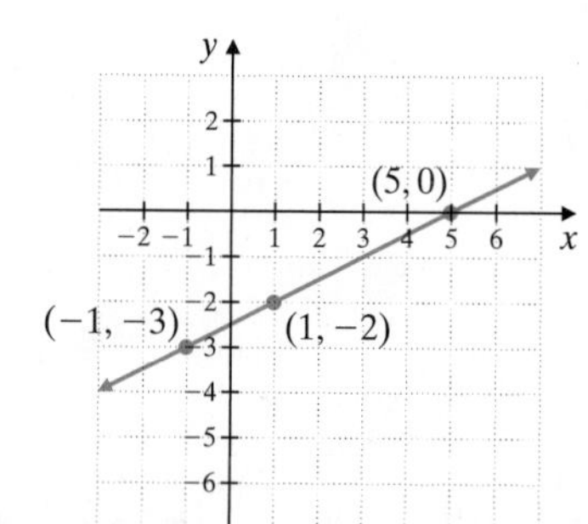

x	y
5	0
1	−2
−1	−3

Section 13.3 Intercepts

An **intercept** of a graph is a point where the graph intersects an axis. If a graph intersects the x-axis at a, then $(a, 0)$ is an ***x*-intercept.** If a graph intersects the y-axis at b, then $(0, b)$ is a ***y*-intercept.**

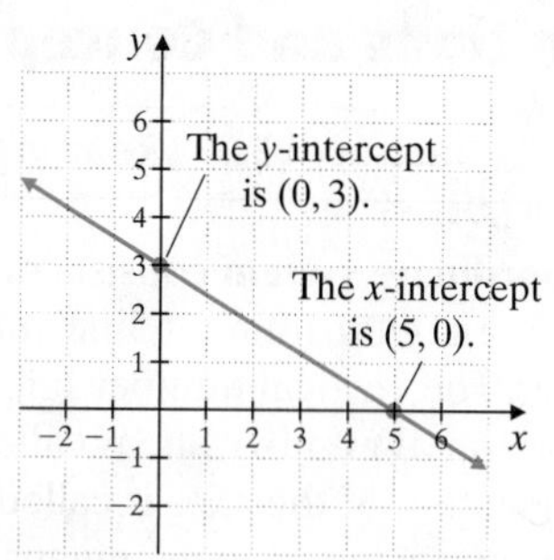

To find the *x*-intercept(s), let $y = 0$ and solve for x.
To find the *y*-intercept(s), let $x = 0$ and solve for y.

Find the intercepts for $2x - 5y = -10$ and graph the line.

If $y = 0$, then

$$2x - 5 \cdot 0 = -10$$
$$2x = -10$$
$$\frac{2x}{2} = \frac{-10}{2}$$
$$x = -5$$

If $x = 0$, then

$$2 \cdot 0 - 5y = -10$$
$$-5y = -10$$
$$\frac{-5y}{-5} = \frac{-10}{-5}$$
$$y = 2$$

Definitions and Concepts	Examples
Section 13.3 Intercepts (*continued*)	
	The x-intercept is $(-5, 0)$. The y-intercept is $(0, 2)$. 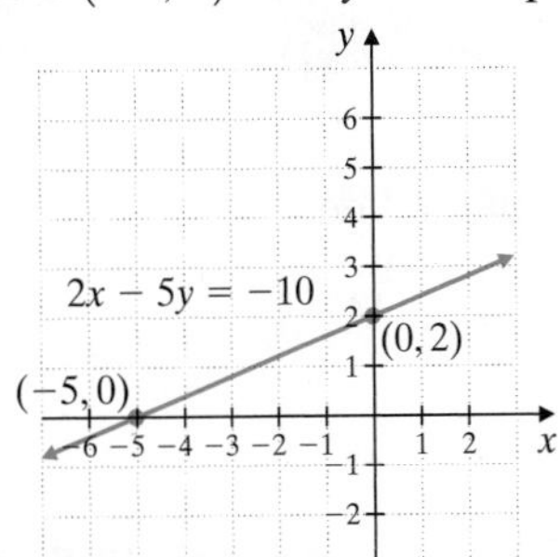
The graph of $x = c$ is a vertical line with x-intercept $(c, 0)$. The graph of $y = c$ is a horizontal line with y-intercept $(0, c)$.	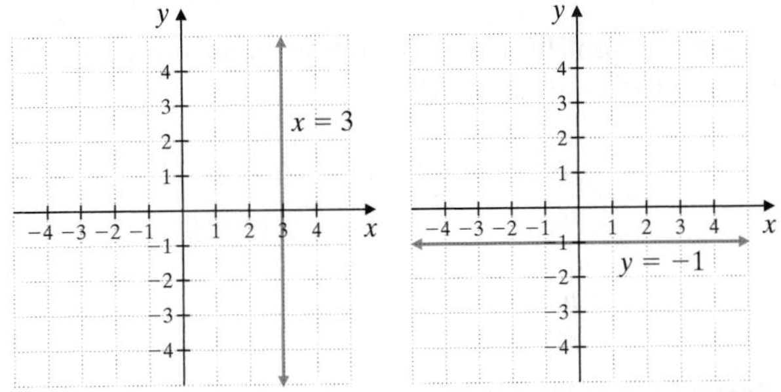
Section 13.4 Slope and Rate of Change	
The **slope m** of the line through points (x_1, y_1) and (x_2, y_2) is given by $$m = \frac{y_2 - y_1}{x_2 - x_1} \quad \text{as long as } x_2 \neq x_1$$ A horizontal line has slope 0. The slope of a vertical line is undefined. Nonvertical parallel lines have the same slope. Two nonvertical lines are perpendicular if the slope of one is the negative reciprocal of the slope of the other.	The slope of the line through points $(-1, 6)$ and $(-5, 8)$ is $$m = \frac{y_2 - y_1}{x_2 - x_1} = \frac{8 - 6}{-5 - (-1)} = \frac{2}{-4} = -\frac{1}{2}$$ The slope of the line $y = -5$ is 0. The line $x = 3$ has undefined slope. 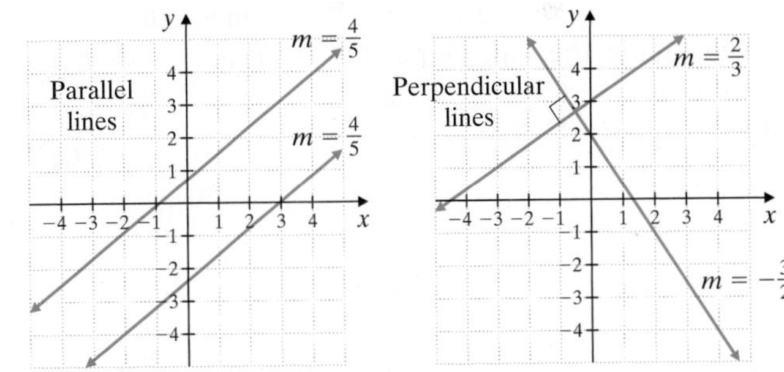
Section 13.5 Equations of Lines	
SLOPE-INTERCEPT FORM $$y = mx + b$$ m is the slope of the line. $(0, b)$ is the y-intercept.	Find the slope and the y-intercept of the line $2x + 3y = 6$. Solve for y: $$2x + 3y = 6$$ $$3y = -2x + 6 \quad \text{Subtract } 2x.$$ $$y = -\frac{2}{3}x + 2 \quad \text{Divide by 3.}$$ The slope of the line is $-\frac{2}{3}$ and the y-intercept is $(0, 2)$.

(*continued*)

Definitions and Concepts	Examples
Section 13.5 Equations of Lines (*continued*)	
POINT-SLOPE FORM $y - y_1 = m(x - x_1)$ m is the slope. (x_1, y_1) is a point of the line.	Find an equation of the line with slope $\frac{3}{4}$ that contains the point $(-1, 5)$. $y - 5 = \frac{3}{4}[x - (-1)]$ $4(y - 5) = 3(x + 1)$ Multiply by 4. $4y - 20 = 3x + 3$ Distribute. $-3x + 4y = 23$ Subtract $3x$ and add 20.
Section 13.6 Graphing Linear Inequalities in Two Variables	
A **linear inequality in two variables** is an inequality that can be written in one of these forms: $Ax + By < C$ $Ax + By \le C$ $Ax + By > C$ $Ax + By \ge C$ where A and B are not both 0.	$2x - 5y < 6$ $x \ge -5$ $y > -8x$ $y \le 2$
TO GRAPH A LINEAR INEQUALITY **1.** Graph the boundary line by graphing the related equation. Draw the line solid if the inequality symbol is $\le$ or $\ge$. Draw the line dashed if the inequality symbol is $<$ or $>$. **2.** Choose a test point not on the line. Substitute its coordinates into the original inequality. **3.** If the resulting inequality is true, shade the half-plane that contains the test point. If the inequality is not true, shade the half-plane that does not contain the test point.	Graph: $2x - y \le 4$ **1.** Graph $2x - y = 4$. Draw a solid line because the inequality symbol is $\le$. **2.** Check the test point $(0, 0)$ in the original inequality, $2x - y \le 4$. $2 \cdot 0 - 0 \le 4$ Let $x = 0$ and $y = 0$. $0 \le 4$ True **3.** The inequality is true, so shade the half-plane containing $(0, 0)$ as shown. 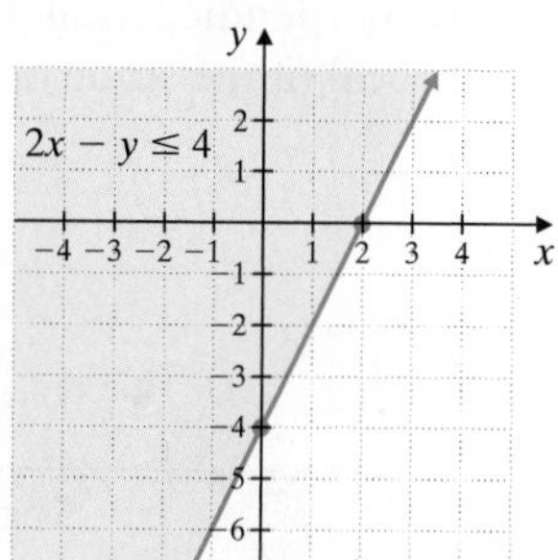

Chapter 13 Review

(13.1) *Plot each ordered pair on the same rectangular coordinate system.*

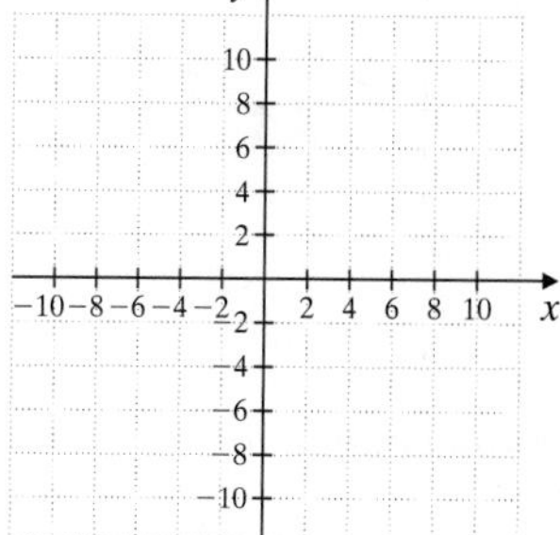

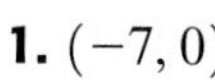

1. $(-7, 0)$

2. $\left(0, 4\frac{4}{5}\right)$

3. $(-2, -5)$

4. $(1, -3)$

5. $(0.7, 0.7)$

6. $(-6, 4)$

Complete each ordered pair so that it is a solution of the given equation.

7. $-2 + y = 6x$; $(7, \quad)$

8. $y = 3x + 5$; $(\quad, -8)$

Complete the table of values for each given equation.

9. $9 = -3x + 4y$

x	y
	0
	3
9	

10. $y = 5$

x	y
7	
−7	
0	

11. $x = 2y$

x	y
	0
	5
	−5

12. The cost in dollars of producing x compact disc holders is given by $y = 5x + 2000$.

a. Complete the table.

x	1	100	1000
y			

b. Find the number of compact disc holders that can be produced for $6430.

(13.2) *Graph each linear equation.*

13. $x - y = 1$

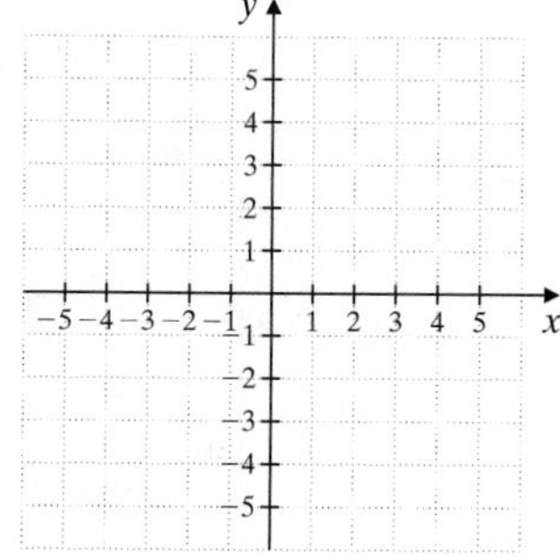

14. $x + y = 6$

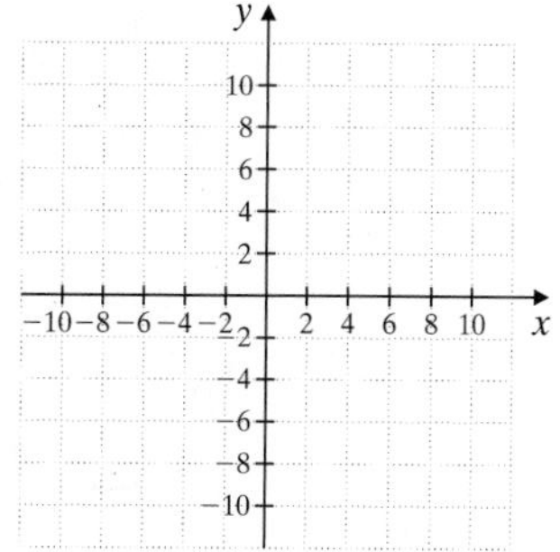

15. $x - 3y = 12$

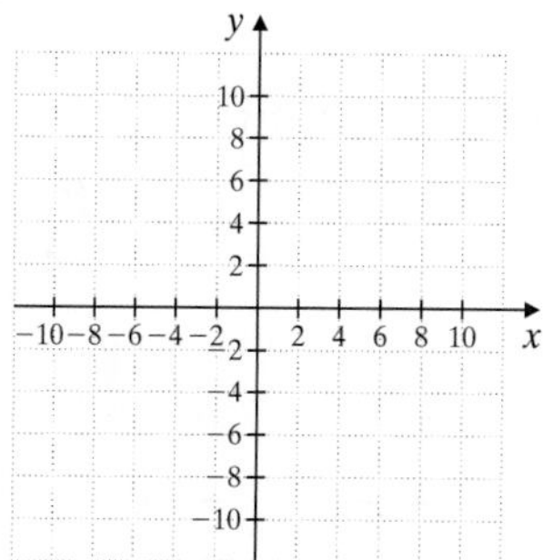

16. $5x - y = -8$

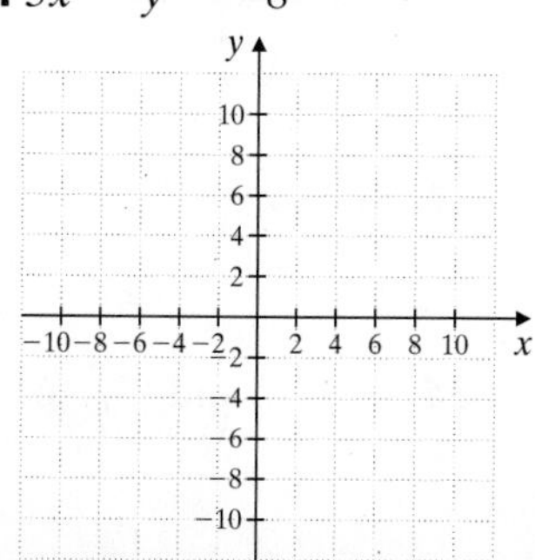

17. $x = 3y$

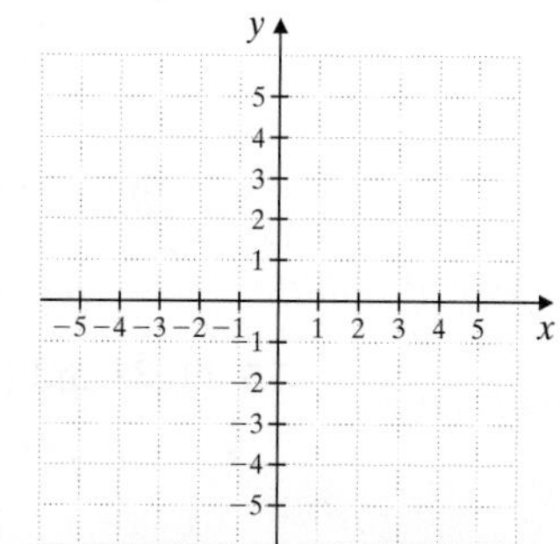

18. $y = -2x$

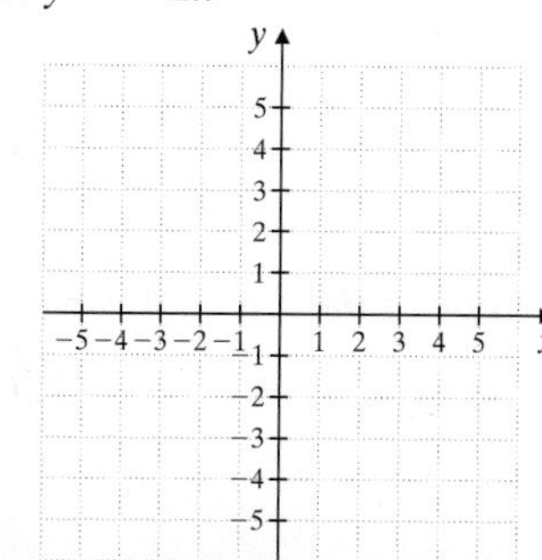

(13.3) *Identify the intercepts in each graph.*

19.

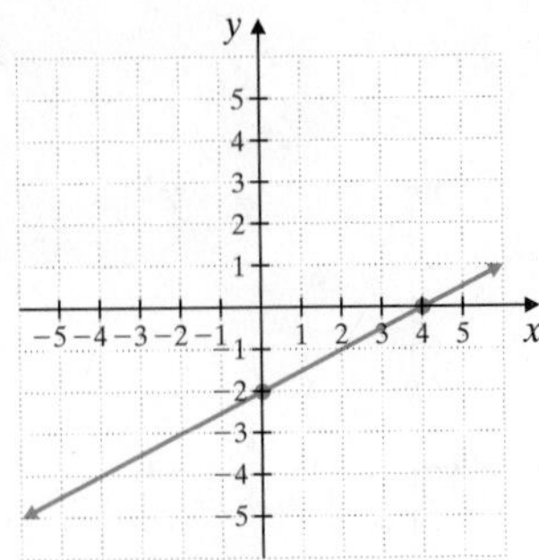

20.

Graph each linear equation.

21. $y = -3$

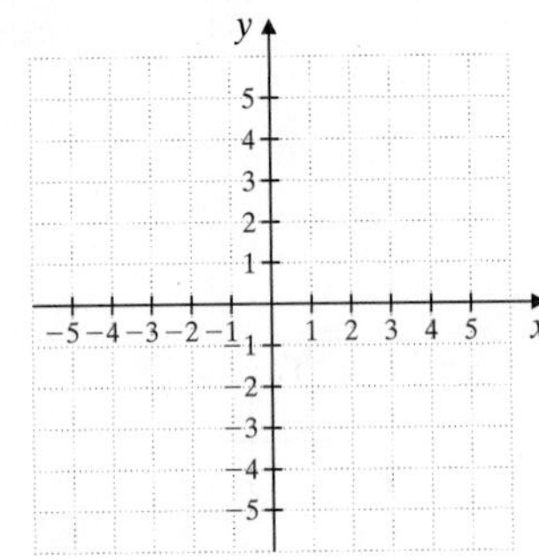

22. $x = 5$

Find the intercepts of each equation.

23. $x - 3y = 12$

24. $-4x + y = 8$

(13.4) *Find the slope of each line.*

25.

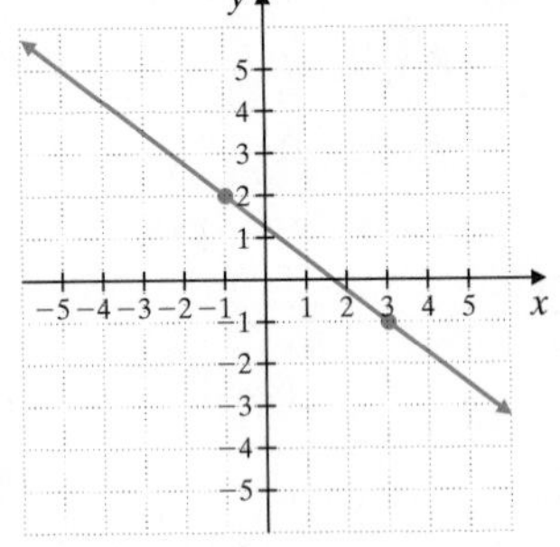

26.

Match each line with its slope.

a.

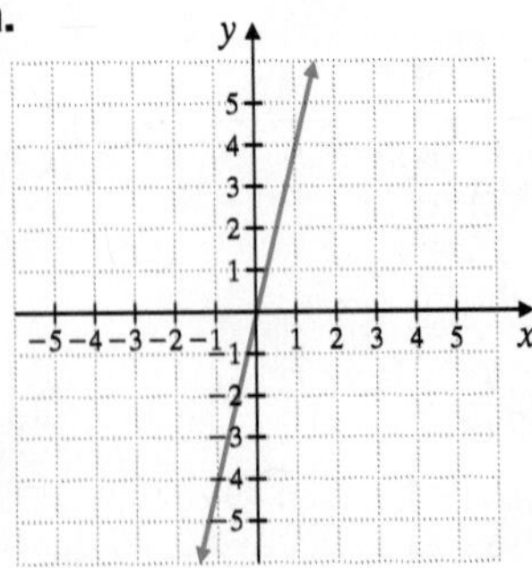

b.

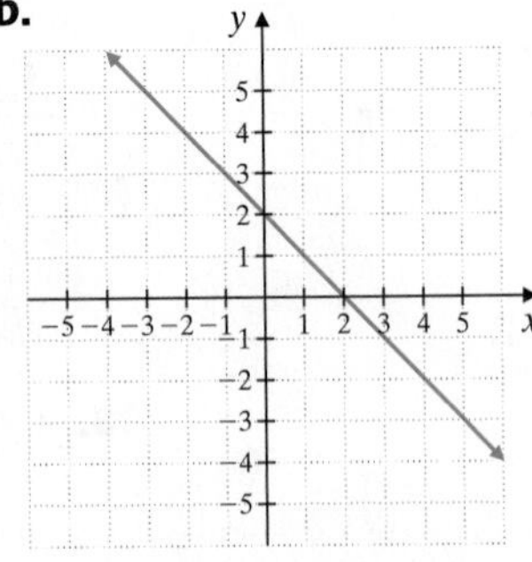

c.

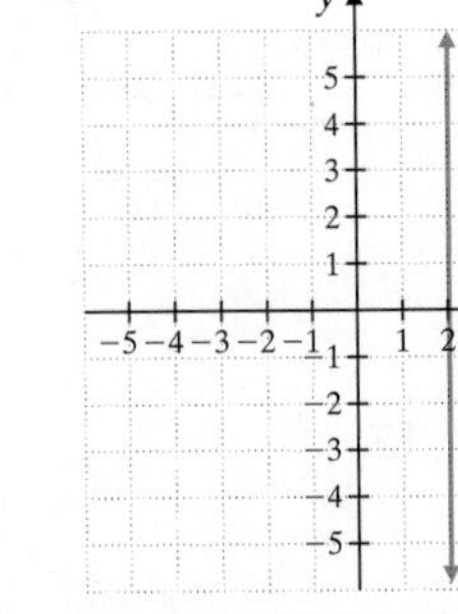

d.

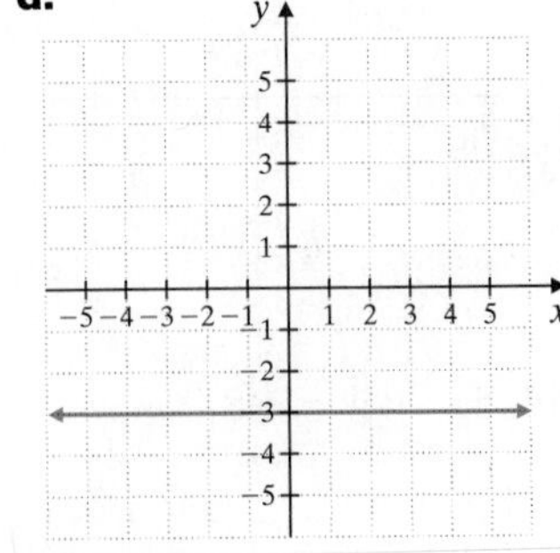

27. $m = 0$

28. $m = -1$

29. undefined slope

30. $m = 4$

Find the slope of the line that passes through each pair of points.

31. $(2, 5)$ and $(6, 8)$

32. $(4, 7)$ and $(1, 2)$

33. $(1, 3)$ and $(-2, -9)$

34. $(-4, 1)$ and $(3, -6)$

Find the slope of each line.

35. $y = 3x + 7$ **36.** $x - 2y = 4$ **37.** $y = -2$ **38.** $x = 0$

△ *Determine whether each pair of lines is parallel, perpendicular, or neither.*

39. $x - y = -6$
$x + y = 3$

40. $3x + y = 7$
$-3x - y = 10$

41. $y = 4x + \frac{1}{2}$
$4x + 2y = 1$

42. $y = 6x - \frac{1}{3}$
$x + 6y = 6$

Find the slope of each line and write the slope as a rate of change. Don't forget to attach the proper units.

43. The graph below approximates the number of U.S. college students (in millions) earning a bachelor's degree for each year x.

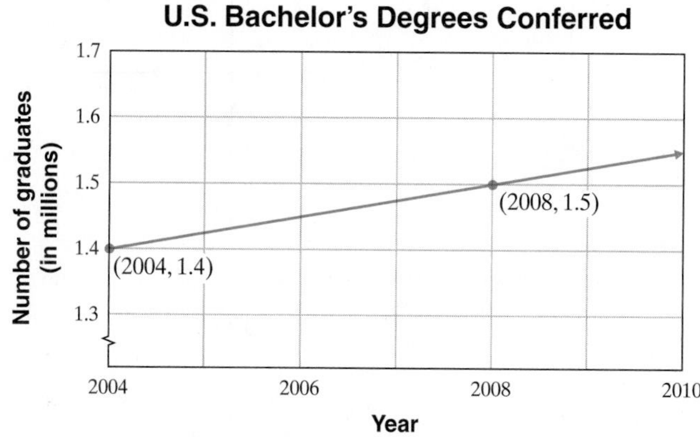

Source: Digest of Education Statistics

44. The graph below approximates the number of kidney transplants y in the United States for year x.

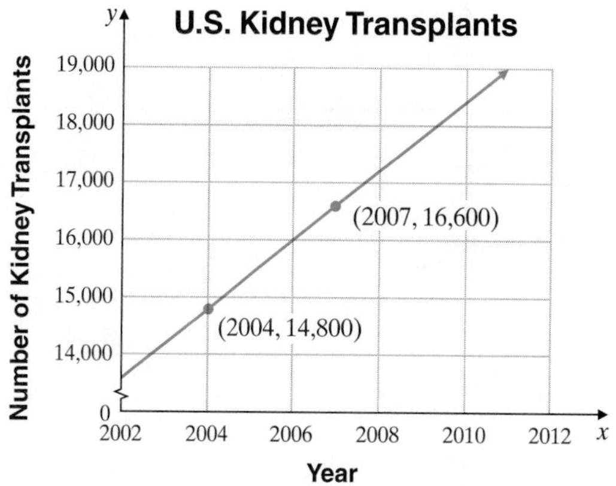

(13.5) *Determine the slope and the y-intercept of the graph of each equation.*

45. $x - 6y = -1$ **46.** $3x + y = 7$

Write an equation of each line.

47. slope -5; y-intercept $\left(0, \frac{1}{2}\right)$ **48.** slope $\frac{2}{3}$; y-intercept $(0, 6)$

Match each equation with its graph.

49. $y = 2x + 1$ **50.** 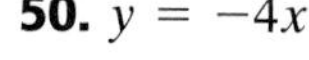 $y = -4x$ **51.** $y = 2x$ **52.** 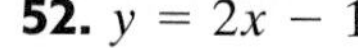 $y = 2x - 1$

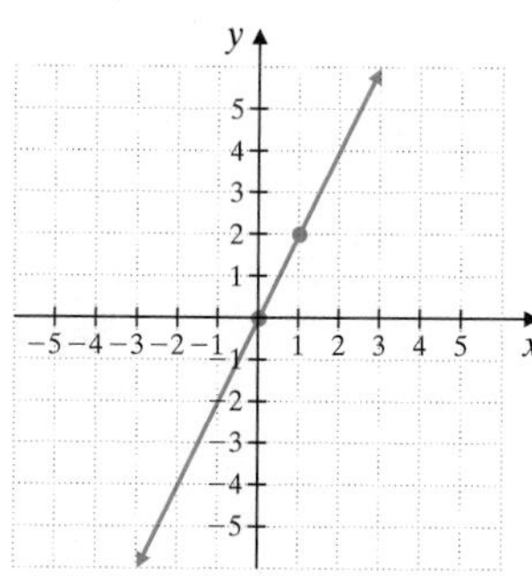

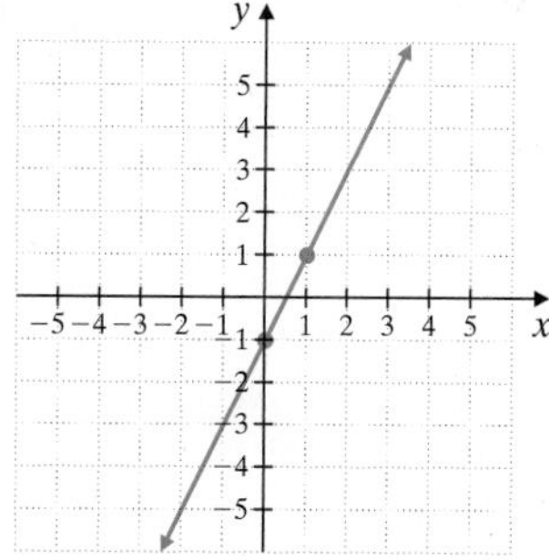

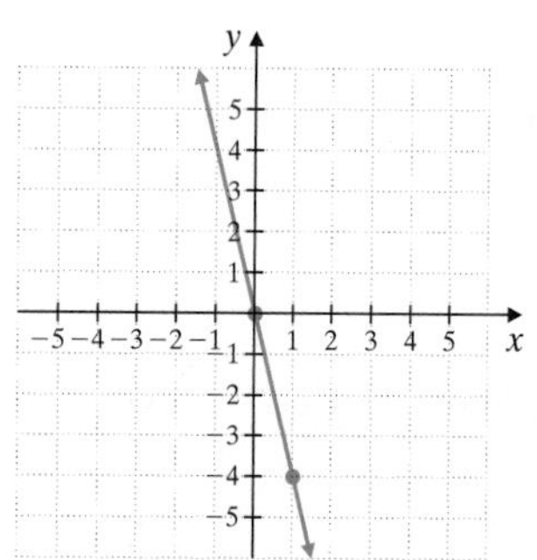

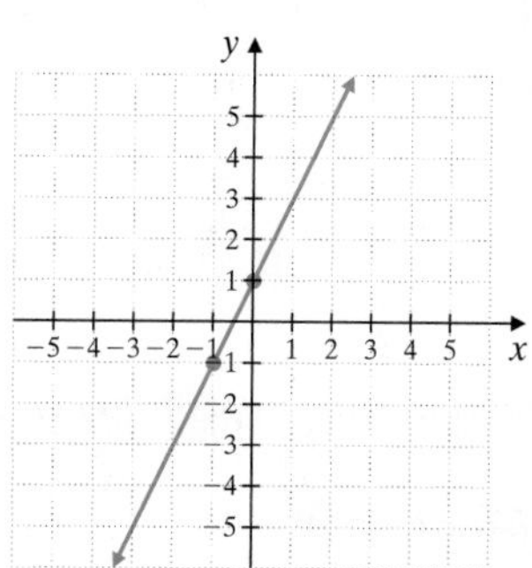

Write an equation of the line with the given slope that passes through the given point. Write the equation in the form $Ax + By = C$.

53. $m = 4; (2, 0)$

54. $m = -3; (0, -5)$

55. $m = \frac{3}{5}; (1, 4)$

56. $m = -\frac{1}{3}; (-3, 3)$

Write an equation of the line passing through each pair of points. Write the equation in the form $y = mx + b$.

57. $(1, 7)$ and $(2, -7)$

58. $(-2, 5)$ and $(-4, 6)$

(13.6) *Graph each inequality.*

59. $x + 6y < 6$

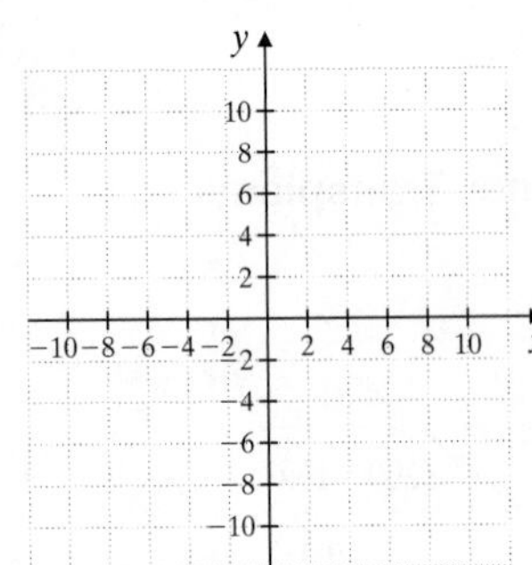

60. $x + y > -2$

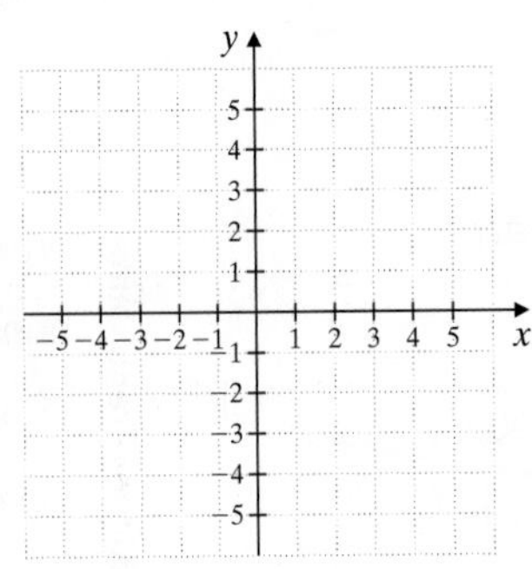

61. $y \geq -7$

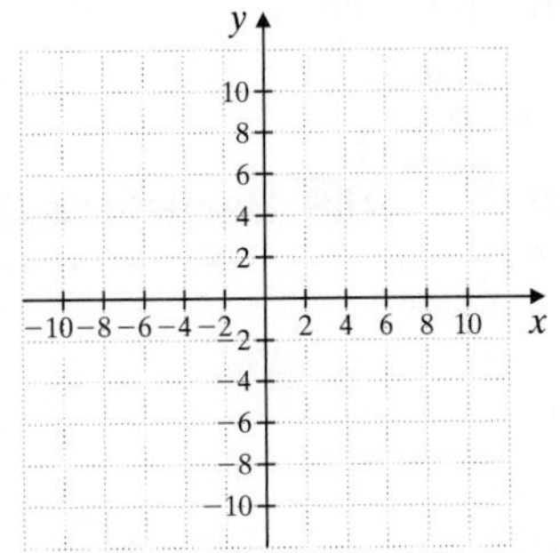

62. $y \leq -4$

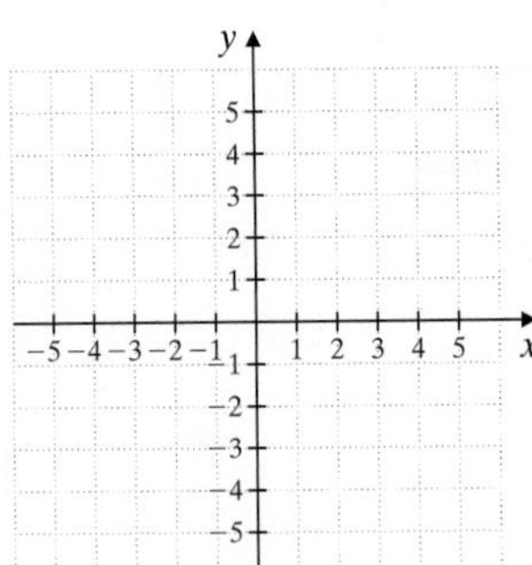

63. $-x \leq y$

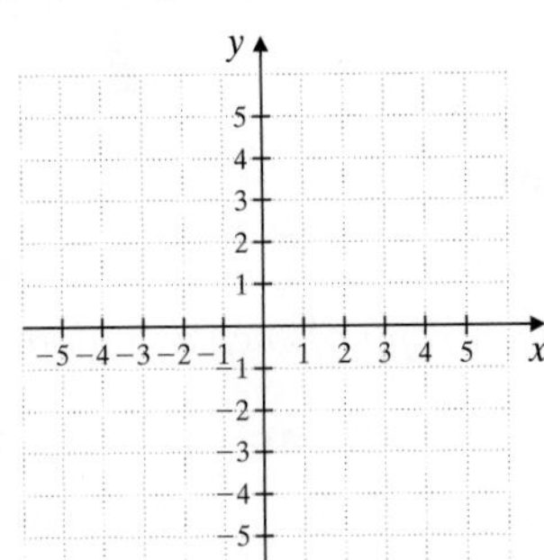

64. $x \geq -y$

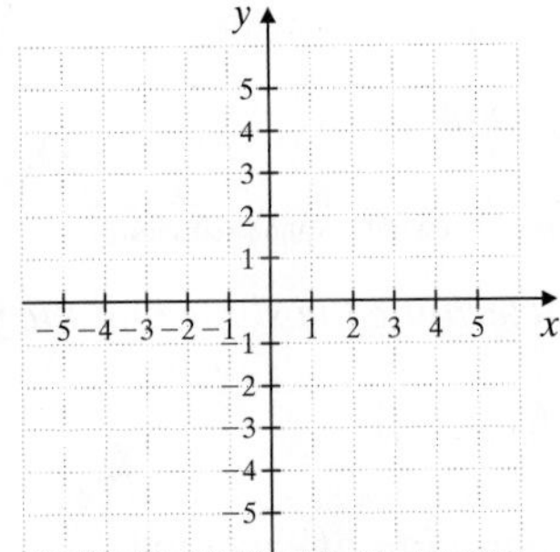

Mixed Review

Complete the table of values for each given equation.

65. $2x - 5y = 9$

x	y
	1
2	
	−3

66. $x = -3y$

x	y
0	
	1
6	

Find the intercepts for each equation.

67. $2x - 3y = 6$

68. $-5x + y = 10$

Graph each linear equation.

69. $x - 5y = 10$

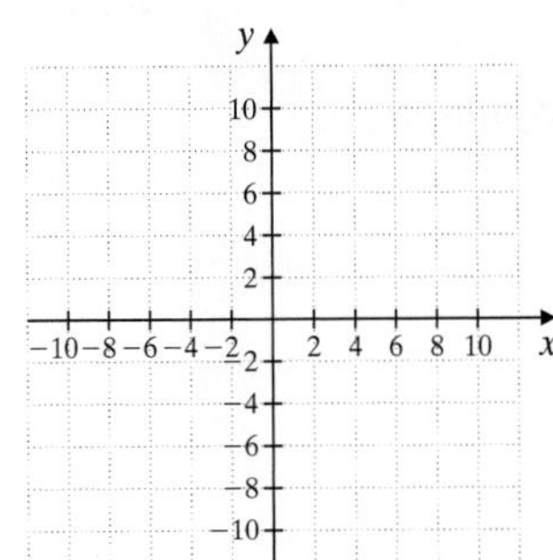

70. $x + y = 4$

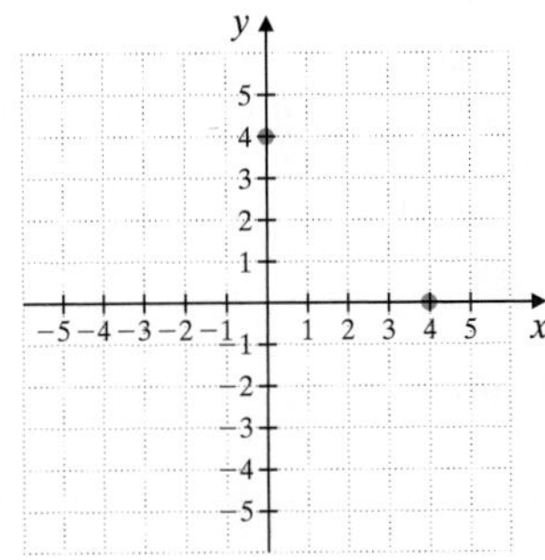

71. $y = -4x$

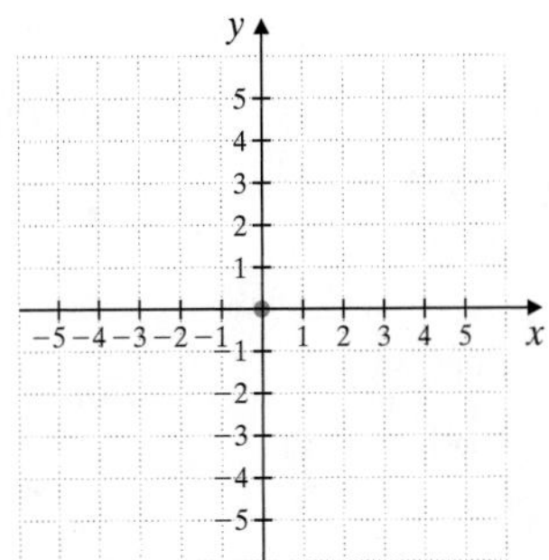

72. $2x + 3y = -6$

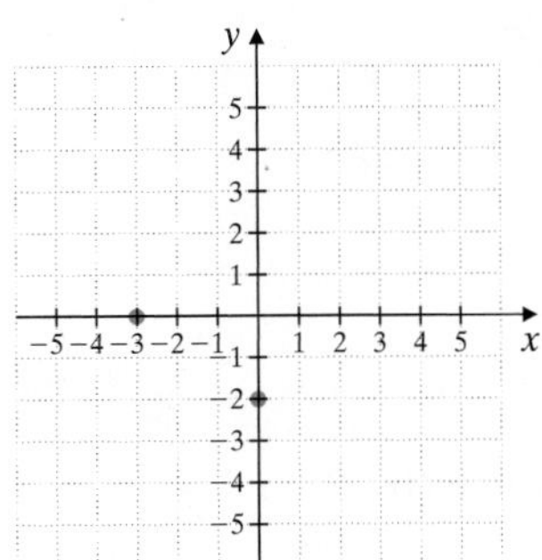

73. $x = 3$

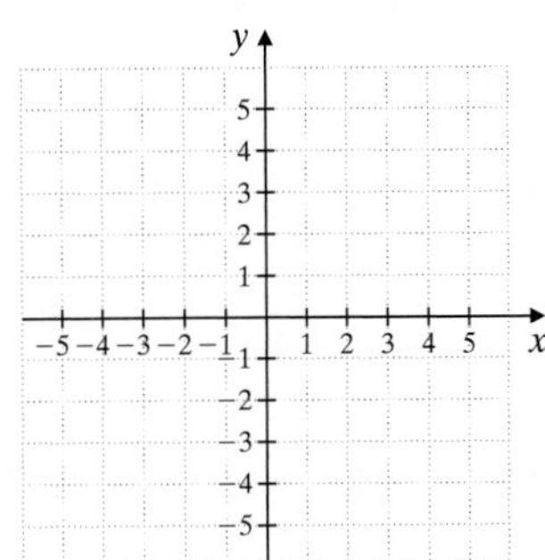

74. $y = -2$

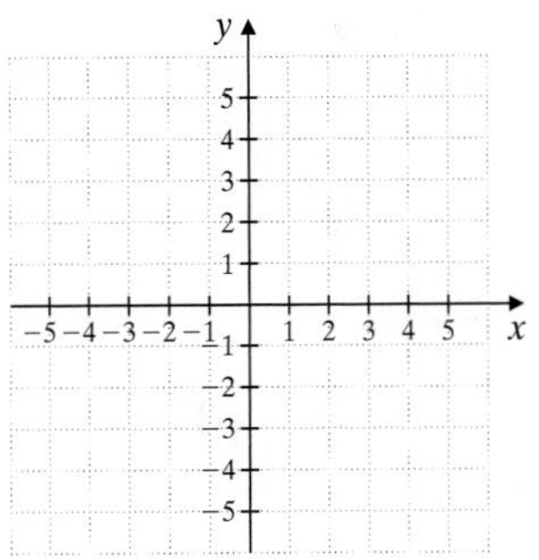

Find the slope of the line that passes through each pair of points.

75. $(3, -5)$ and $(-4, 2)$

76. $(1, 3)$ and $(-6, -8)$

Find the slope of each line.

77.

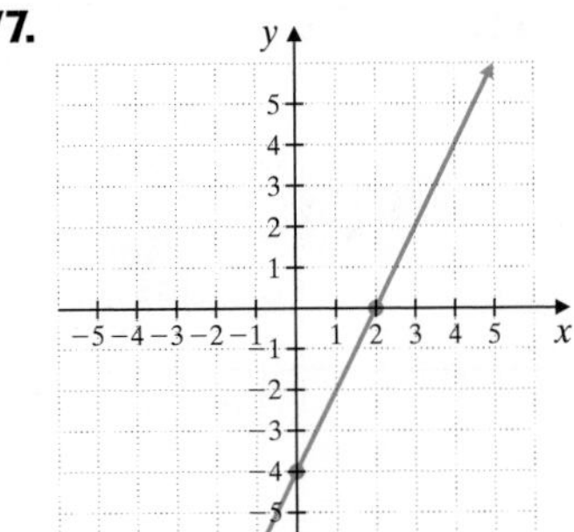

78.

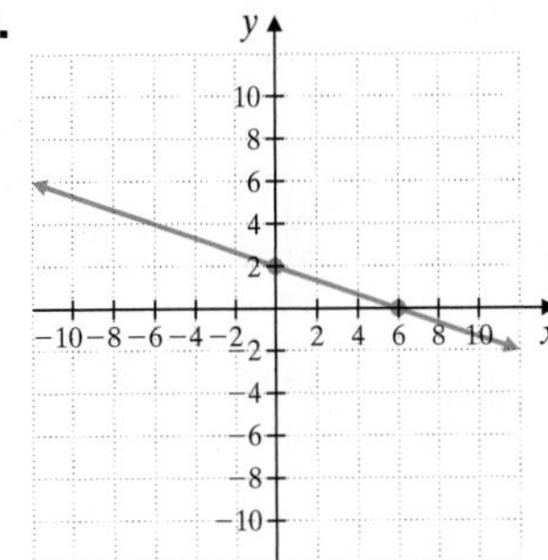

Determine the slope and y-intercept of the graph of each equation.

79. $-2x + 3y = -15$

80. $6x + y - 2 = 0$

Write an equation of the line with the given slope that passes through the given point. Write the equation in the form $Ax + By = C$.

81. $m = -5$; $(3, -7)$

82. $m = 3$; $(0, 6)$

Write an equation of the line passing through each pair of points. Write the equation in the form $Ax + By = C$.

83. $(-3, 9)$ and $(-2, 5)$

84. $(3, 1)$ and $(5, -9)$

Chapter 13 Test

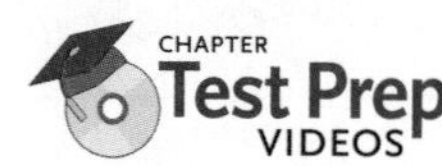

Step-by-step test solutions are found on the Chapter Test Prep Videos available via the Interactive DVD Lecture Series, in MyMathLab or on YouTube (search "MartinGayIntroAlg" and click on "Channels").

Answers

1. ________

2. ________

3. ________

4. ________

5. ________

6. ________

7. ________

8. ________

9. ________

10. ________

11. ________

12. ________

13. ________

14. ________

Complete each ordered pair so that it is a solution of the given equation.

1.

2.

Find the slope of each line.

3.

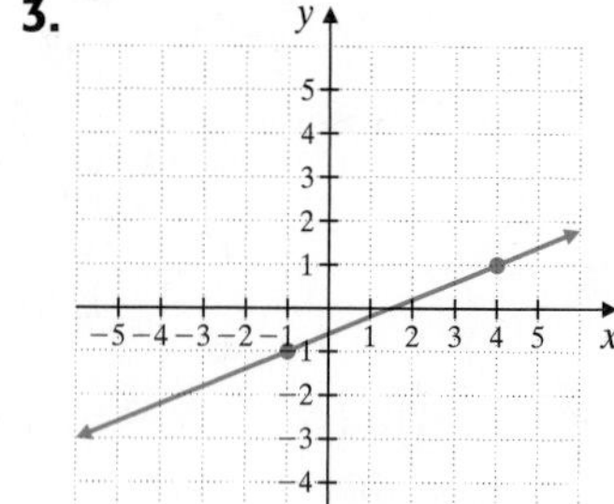

4.

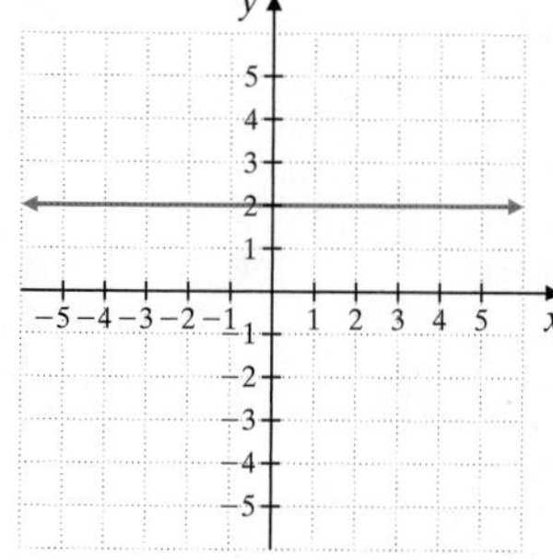

5. Passes through $(6, -5)$ and $(-1, 2)$

6. Passes through $(0, -8)$ and $(-1, -1)$

7. $-3x + y = 5$

8. $x = 6$

Graph.

9. **10.**

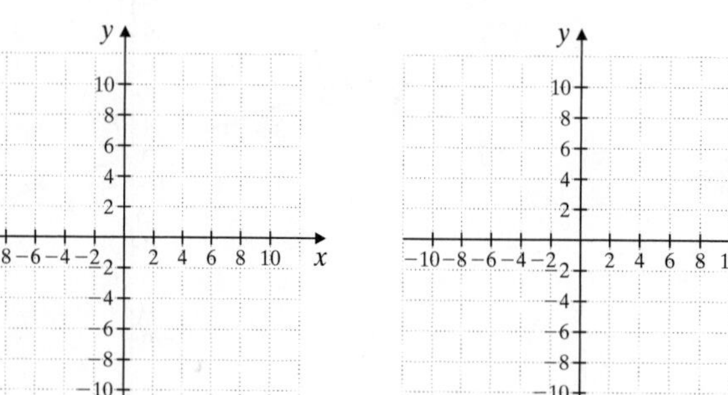

11.

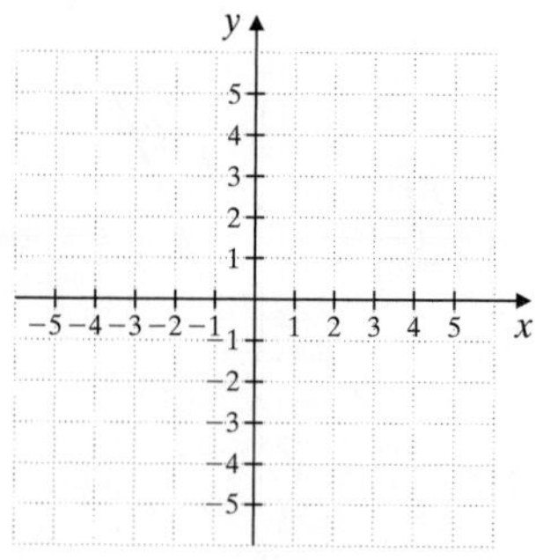

12.

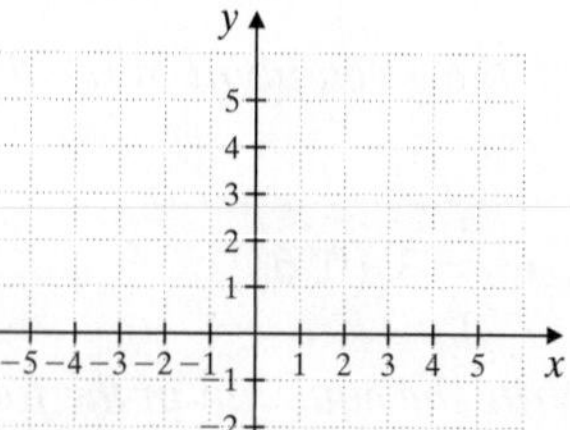

13.

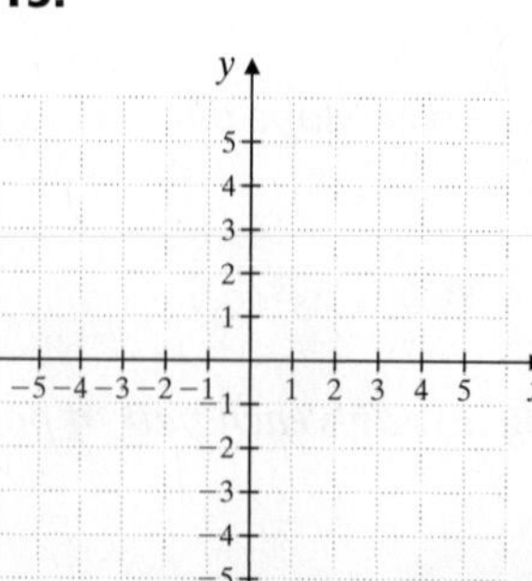

14.

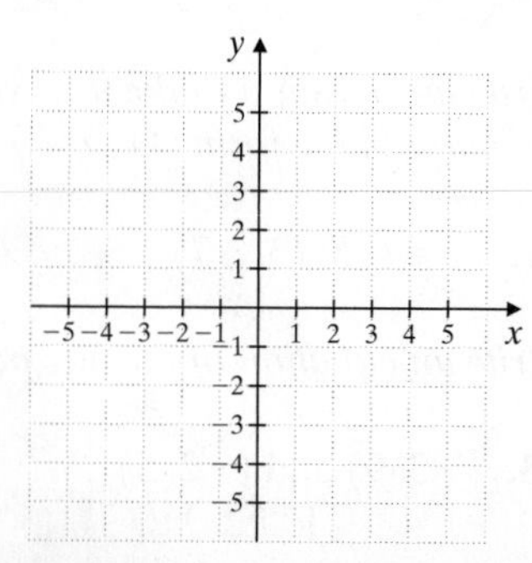

15.

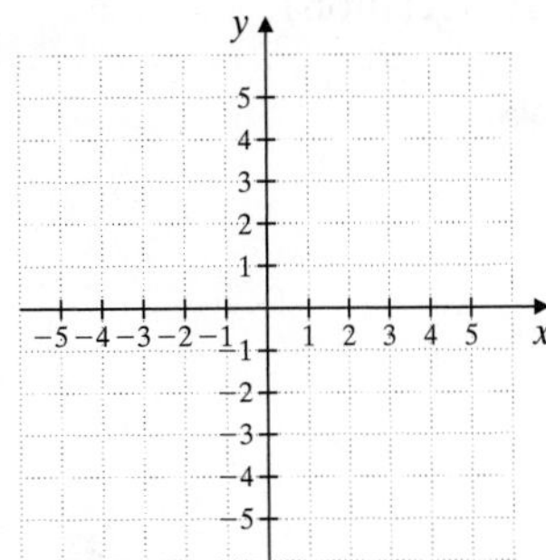

16.

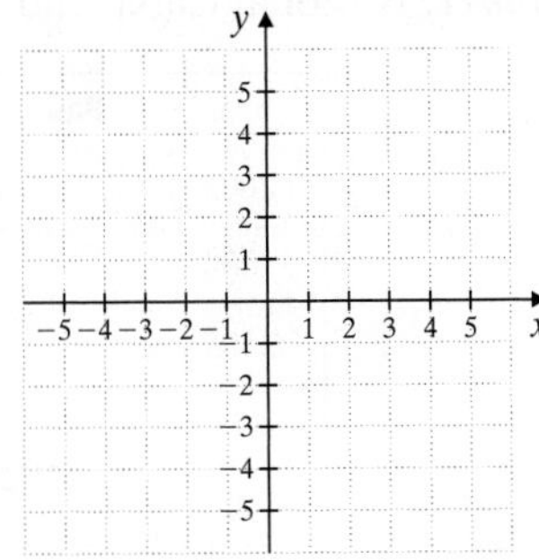

17. Determine whether the graphs of and $-4x = 2y$ are parallel lines, perpendicular lines, or neither.

Find the equation of each line. Write the equation in the form $Ax + By = C$.

18. Slope $-\frac{1}{4}$, passes through $(2, 2)$

19. Passes through the origin and $(6, -7)$

20. Passes through $(2, -5)$ and $(1, 3)$

21. Slope $\frac{1}{8}$; y-intercept $(0, 12)$

△ **22.** The perimeter of the parallelogram below is 42 meters. Write a linear equation in two variables for the perimeter. Use this equation to find x when y is 8 meters.

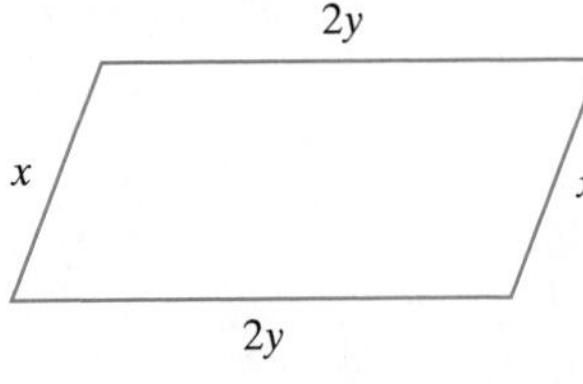

15. ______

16. ______

17. ______

18. ______

19. ______

20. ______

21. ______

22. ______

23. a. ______

b. ______

23. The table gives the number of basic cable TV subscribers (in millions) for the years shown. (*Source:* National Cable and Telecommunications Association)

Year	Basic Cable TV Subscribers (in millions)
2003	66.0
2004	65.4
2005	65.4
2006	65.6
2007	64.9
2008	63.7
2009	62.1

a. Write this data as a set of ordered pairs of the form (year, number of basic cable TV subscribers in millions).

b. Create a scatter diagram of the data. Be sure to label the axes properly.

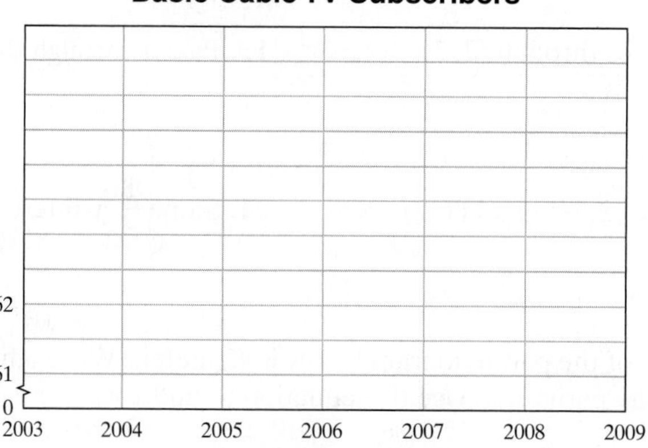

Cumulative Review Chapters 8–13

Simplify each expression.

1. $6 \div 3 + 5^2$

2. $\frac{10}{3} + \frac{5}{21}$

3. $1 + 2[5(2 \cdot 3 + 1) - 10]$

4. $16 - 3 \cdot 3 + 2^4$

5. The highest point in the United States is the top of Mount McKinley, at a height of 20,320 feet above sea level. The lowest point is Death Valley, California, which is 282 feet below sea level. How much higher is Mount McKinley than Death Valley? (*Source:* U.S. Geological Society)

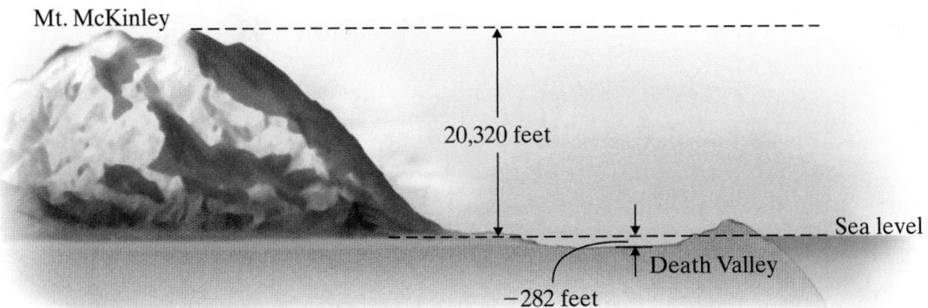

6. Simplify: $1.7x - 11 - 0.9x - 25$

Write each phrase as an algebraic expression and simplify if possible. Let x represent the unknown number.

7. Twice a number, plus 6.

8. The product of -15 and the sum of a number and $\frac{2}{3}$.

9. The difference of a number and 4, divided by 7.

10. The quotient of -9 and twice a number.

11. Five plus the sum of a number and 1.

12. A number subtracted from -86.

13. Solve for x: $\frac{5}{2}x = 15$

14. Solve for x: $\frac{x}{4} - 1 = -7$

15. Solve $2x < -4$. Graph the solutions.

−5 −4 −3 −2 −1 0 1 2 3 4 5

16. Solve: $5(x + 4) \geq 4(2x + 3)$

17. Find the degree of each polynomial and tell whether the polynomial is a monomial, binomial, trinomial, or none of these.

a. $-2t^2 + 3t + 6$

b. $15x - 10$

c. $7x + 3x^3 + 2x^2 - 1$

18. Solve $x + 2y = 6$ for y.

Answers

1. ________
2. ________
3. ________
4. ________
5. ________
6. ________
7. ________
8. ________
9. ________
10. ________
11. ________
12. ________
13. ________
14. ________
15. ________
16. ________
17. a. ________
b. ________
c. ________
18. ________

19. ______

20. ______

21. ______

22. ______

23. ______

24. ______

25. ______

26. ______

27. ______

28. ______

29. ______

30. ______

31. ______

32. ______

33. ______

34. ______

35. ______

19. Add: $(-2x^2 + 5x - 1) + (-2x^2 + x + 3)$

20. Subtract: $(-2x^2 + 5x - 1) - (-2x^2 + x + 3)$

21. Multiply: $(3y + 1)^2$

22. Multiply: $(x - 12)^2$

23. Factor: $-9a^5 + 18a^2 - 3a$

24. Factor: $4x^2 - 36$

25. Factor: $x^2 + 4x - 12$

26. Factor: $3x^2 - 20xy - 7y^2$

27. Factor: $8x^2 - 22x + 5$

28. Factor: $18x^2 + 35x - 2$

29. Solve: $x^2 - 9x - 22 = 0$

30. Solve: $x^2 = x$

31. Divide: $\dfrac{2x^2 - 11x + 5}{5x - 25} \div \dfrac{4x - 2}{10}$

32. Simplify: $\dfrac{2x^2 - 50}{4x^4 - 20x^3}$

Write the rational expression as an equivalent rational expression with the given denominator.

33. $\dfrac{4b}{9a} = \dfrac{\quad}{27a^2b}$

34. $\dfrac{1}{2x} = \dfrac{\quad}{14x^3}$

35. Solve: $3x^2 + 5x = 2$

36. Complete each ordered pair so that it is a solution to the equation $3x + y = 12$.

a. $(0, \quad)$

b. $(\quad, 6)$

c. $(-1, \quad)$

37. Complete the table for $y = -5x$.

x	y
0	
−1	
	10

38. Graph: $2x + y = 5$

39. Find the slope of the line through $(0, 5)$ and $(-5, 4)$.

40. Find the slope of the line $-2x + 3y = 11$.

41. Find the slope of the line $x = -10$.

42. Find an equation of the line with slope -2 that passes through $(-1, 5)$. Write the equation in slope-intercept form, $y = mx + b$, and in standard form, $Ax + By = C$.

43. Find the slope and y-intercept of the line whose equation is $2x - 5y = 10$.

44. Write an equation of the line through $(2, 3)$ and $(0, 0)$. Write the equation in standard form.

36. a. ________

b. ________

c. ________

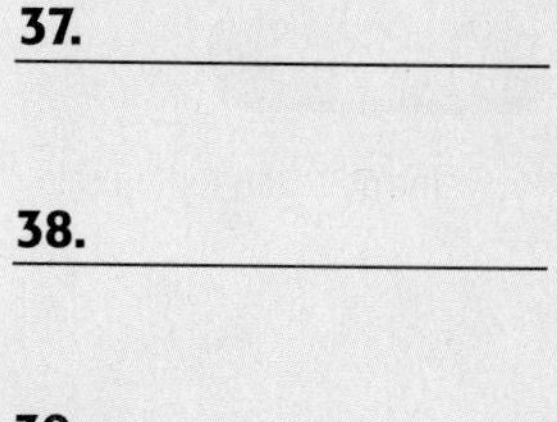

37. ________

38. ________

39. ________

40. ________

41. ________

42. ________

43. ________

44. ________

14 Roots and Radicals

Sections

Having spent the last chapter studying equations, we return now to algebraic expressions. We expand on our skills of operating on expressions–adding, subtracting, multiplying, dividing, and raising to powers–to include finding roots. Just as subtraction is defined by addition and division by multiplication, finding roots is defined by raising to powers. As we master finding roots, we will work with equations that contain roots and solve problems that can be modeled by such equations.

Check Your Progress

One of the structures at the Beijing Olympics that captured everyone's imagination was the swimming and diving competition venue, the National Aquatics Center, better known as the Water Cube. It has a concrete and steel base, but it is the outside membrane of the center that makes it special. The complete structure of the Water Cube is covered with a plastic skin that is meant to simulate the shape of soap bubbles. The bubble covering is not just for looks; rather, the temperature of the building is regulated by controlling the air temperature lodged within the bubbles. Many people believe the Water Cube to be the fastest Olympic pool in the world; and in fact, between this pool and the faster Speedo swimsuit, 25 world records were broken. (*Source:* ARUP East Asia)

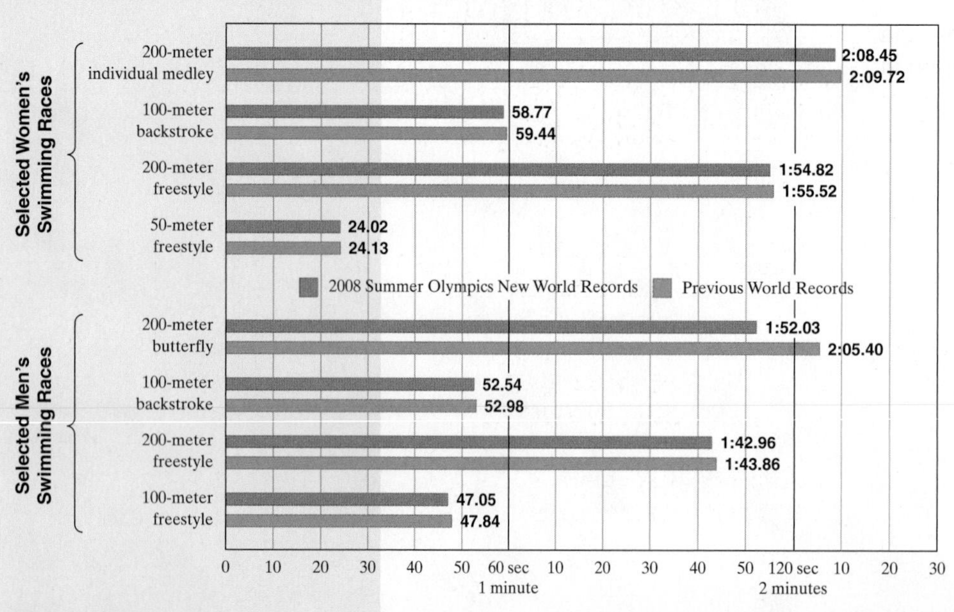

14.1 INTRODUCTION TO RADICALS

Objectives

A Find Square Roots.

B Find Cube Roots.

C Find nth Roots.

D Approximate Square Roots.

E Simplify Radicals Containing Variables.

Objective A Finding Square Roots

In this section, we define finding the **root** of a number by its reverse operation, raising a number to a power. We begin with squares and square roots.

The *square* of 5 is $5^2 = 25$.

The *square* of -5 is $(-5)^2 = 25$.

The *square* of $\frac{1}{2}$ is $\left(\frac{1}{2}\right)^2 = \frac{1}{4}$.

The reverse operation of squaring a number is finding a **square root** of a number. For example,

A *square root* of 25 is 5, because $5^2 = 25$.

A *square root* of 25 is also -5, because $(-5)^2 = 25$.

A *square root* of $\frac{1}{4}$ is $\frac{1}{2}$, because $\left(\frac{1}{2}\right)^2 = \frac{1}{4}$.

In general, the number b is a square root of a number a if $b^2 = a$.

The symbol $\sqrt{}$ is used to denote the **positive** or **principal square root** of a number. For example,

$\sqrt{25} = 5$ only, since $5^2 = 25$ and 5 is positive.

The symbol $-\sqrt{}$ is used to denote the **negative square root.** For example,

$-\sqrt{25} = -5$

The symbol $\sqrt{}$ is called a **radical** or **radical sign.** The expression within or under a radical sign is called the **radicand.** An expression containing a radical is called a **radical expression.**

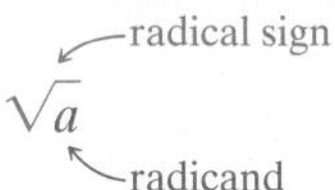

Square Root

If a is a positive number, then

$\sqrt{a}$ is the **positive square root** of a and

$-\sqrt{a}$ is the **negative square root** of a.

Also, $\sqrt{0} = 0$.

Examples Find each square root.

1. $\sqrt{36} = 6$, because $6^2 = 36$ and 6 is positive.
2. $-\sqrt{16} = -4$. The negative sign in front of the radical indicates the negative square root of 16.
3. $\sqrt{\frac{9}{100}} = \frac{3}{10}$ because $\left(\frac{3}{10}\right)^2 = \frac{9}{100}$ and $\frac{3}{10}$ is positive.
4. $\sqrt{0} = 0$ because $0^2 = 0$.
5. $\sqrt{0.64} = 0.8$ because $(0.8)^2 = 0.64$ and 0.8 is positive.

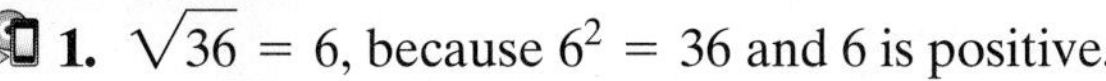
Work Practice 1–5

PRACTICE 1–5

Find each square root.

1. $\sqrt{100}$
2. $-\sqrt{81}$
3. $\sqrt{\frac{25}{81}}$
4. $\sqrt{1}$
5. $\sqrt{0.81}$

Answers

1. 10 **2.** -9 **3.** $\frac{5}{9}$ **4.** 1 **5.** 0.9

Is the square root of a negative number a real number? For example, is $\sqrt{-4}$ a real number? To answer this question, we ask ourselves, is there a real number whose square is -4? Since there is no real number whose square is -4, we say that $\sqrt{-4}$ is not a real number. In general,

A square root of a negative number is not a real number.

Study the following table to make sure you understand the differences discussed earlier.

Number	Square Roots of Number	$\sqrt{\text{number}}$	$-\sqrt{\text{number}}$
25	$-5, 5$	$\sqrt{25} = 5$ only	$-\sqrt{25} = -5$
$\frac{1}{4}$	$-\frac{1}{2}, \frac{1}{2}$	$\sqrt{\frac{1}{4}} = \frac{1}{2}$ only	$-\sqrt{\frac{1}{4}} = -\frac{1}{2}$
-9	No real square roots.	$\sqrt{-9}$ is not a real number.	

Objective B Finding Cube Roots

We can find roots other than square roots. For example, since $2^3 = 8$, we call 2 the **cube root** of 8. In symbols, we write

$\sqrt[3]{8} = 2$ The number 3 is called the **index.**

Also,

$\sqrt[3]{-64} = -4$ Since $(-4)^3 = -64$

Notice that unlike the square root of a negative number, the cube root of a negative number is a real number. This is so because while we cannot find a real number whose *square* is negative, we *can* find a real number whose *cube* is negative. In fact, the cube of a negative number is a negative number. Therefore, the cube root of a negative number is a negative number.

PRACTICE 6–8

Find each cube root.

6. $\sqrt[3]{27}$
7. $\sqrt[3]{-8}$
8. $\sqrt[3]{\frac{1}{64}}$

Examples Find each cube root.

6. $\sqrt[3]{1} = 1$ because $1^3 = 1$.
7. $\sqrt[3]{-27} = -3$ because $(-3)^3 = -27$.
8. $\sqrt[3]{\frac{1}{125}} = \frac{1}{5}$ because $\left(\frac{1}{5}\right)^3 = \frac{1}{125}$.

Work Practice 6–8

Objective C Finding *n*th Roots

Just as we can raise a real number to powers other than 2 or 3, we can find roots other than square roots and cube roots. In fact, we can take the nth root of a number where n is any natural number. An ***n*th root** of a number a is a number whose nth power is a.

In symbols, the nth root of a is written as $\sqrt[n]{a}$. Recall that n is called the **index.** The index 2 is usually omitted for square roots.

Helpful Hint

If the index is even, as it is in $\sqrt{\quad}$, $\sqrt[4]{\quad}$, $\sqrt[6]{\quad}$, and so on, the radicand must be nonnegative for the root to be a real number. For example,

$\sqrt[4]{81} = 3$ but $\sqrt[4]{-81}$ is not a real number.

$\sqrt[6]{64} = 2$ but $\sqrt[6]{-64}$ is not a real number.

Answers

6. 3 7. -2 8. $\frac{1}{4}$

✓**Concept Check** Which of the following is a real number?

a. $\sqrt{-64}$ **b.** $\sqrt[4]{-64}$ **c.** $\sqrt[5]{-64}$ **d.** $\sqrt[6]{-64}$

Examples Find each root.

9. $\sqrt[4]{16} = 2$ because $2^4 = 16$ and 2 is positive.

10. $\sqrt[5]{-32} = -2$ because $(-2)^5 = -32$.

11. $-\sqrt[6]{1} = -1$ because $\sqrt[6]{1} = 1$.

12. $\sqrt[4]{-81}$ is not a real number since the index, 4, is even and the radicand, -81, is negative. In other words, there is no real number that when raised to the 4th power gives -81.

Work Practice 9–12

PRACTICE 9–12

Find each root.

9. $\sqrt[4]{-16}$

10. $\sqrt[5]{-1}$

11. $\sqrt[4]{256}$

12. $\sqrt[6]{-1}$

Objective D Approximating Square Roots

Recall that numbers such as 1, 4, 9, 25, and $\frac{4}{25}$ are called **perfect squares,** since $1^2 = 1, 2^2 = 4, 3^2 = 9, 5^2 = 25$, and $\left(\frac{2}{5}\right)^2 = \frac{4}{25}$. Square roots of perfect square radicands simplify to rational numbers.

What happens when we try to simplify a root such as $\sqrt{3}$? Since 3 is not a perfect square, $\sqrt{3}$ is not a rational number. It cannot be written as a quotient of integers. It is called an **irrational number** and we can find a decimal **approximation** of it. To find decimal approximations, use a calculator. (For calculator help, see the next example or the box at the end of this section.)

Example 13 Use a calculator to approximate $\sqrt{3}$ to three decimal places.

Solution: We may use a calculator to approximate $\sqrt{3}$. To use a calculator, find the square root key $\boxed{\sqrt{\ }}$.

$$\sqrt{3} \approx 1.732050808$$

To three decimal places, $\sqrt{3} \approx 1.732$.

Work Practice 13

PRACTICE 13

Use a calculator to approximate $\sqrt{22}$ to three decimal places.

From Example 13, we found that

$$\sqrt{3} \approx 1.732$$

To see if the approximation is reasonable, notice that since

$1 < 3 < 4$, then

$\sqrt{1} < \sqrt{3} < \sqrt{4}$, or

$1 < \sqrt{3} < 2$.

Since $\sqrt{3}$ is a number between 1 and 2, our result of $\sqrt{3} \approx 1.732$ is reasonable.

Objective E Simplifying Radicals Containing Variables

Radicals can also contain variables. To simplify radicals containing variables, special care must be taken. To see how we simplify $\sqrt{x^2}$, let's look at a few examples in this form.

If $x = 3$, we have $\sqrt{3^2} = \sqrt{9} = 3$, or x.

If x is 5, we have $\sqrt{5^2} = \sqrt{25} = 5$, or x.

From these two examples, you may think that $\sqrt{x^2}$ simplifies to x. Let's now look at an example where x is a negative number. If $x = -3$, we have $\sqrt{(-3)^2} = \sqrt{9} = 3$, not -3, our original x. To make sure that $\sqrt{x^2}$ simplifies to a nonnegative number, we have the following.

Answers

9. not a real number **10.** -1 **11.** 4 **12.** not a real number **13.** 4.690

✓ **Concept Check Answer**

c

For any real number a,

$$\sqrt{a^2} = |a|$$

Thus,

$$\sqrt{x^2} = |x|,$$

$$\sqrt{(-8)^2} = |-8| = 8,$$

$$\sqrt{(7y)^2} = |7y|, \quad \text{and so on.}$$

To avoid this confusion, for the rest of the chapter we assume that **if a variable appears in the radicand of a radical expression, it represents positive numbers only.** Then

$\sqrt{x^2} = |x| = x$ since x is a positive number.

$\sqrt{y^2} = y$ Because $(y)^2 = y^2$

$\sqrt{x^8} = x^4$ Because $(x^4)^2 = x^8$

$\sqrt{9x^2} = 3x$ Because $(3x)^2 = 9x^2$

PRACTICE 14–19

Simplify each expression. Assume that all variables represent positive numbers.

14. $\sqrt{z^8}$ **15.** $\sqrt{x^{20}}$

16. $\sqrt{4x^6}$ **17.** $\sqrt[3]{8y^{12}}$

18. $\sqrt{\dfrac{z^8}{81}}$ **19.** $\sqrt[3]{-64x^9y^{24}}$

Answers

14. z^4 **15.** x^{10} **16.** $2x^3$ **17.** $2y^4$ **18.** $\dfrac{z^4}{9}$ **19.** $-4x^3y^8$

Examples Simplify each expression. Assume that all variables represent positive numbers.

14. $\sqrt{z^2} = z$ because $(z)^2 = z^2$.

15. $\sqrt{x^6} = x^3$ because $(x^3)^2 = x^6$.

16. $\sqrt[3]{27y^6} = 3y^2$ because $(3y^2)^3 = 27y^6$.

17. $\sqrt{16x^{16}} = 4x^8$ because $(4x^8)^2 = 16x^{16}$.

18. $\sqrt{\dfrac{x^4}{25}} = \dfrac{x^2}{5}$ because $\left(\dfrac{x^2}{5}\right)^2 = \dfrac{x^4}{25}$.

19. $\sqrt[3]{-125a^{12}b^{15}} = -5a^4b^5$ because $(-5a^4b^5)^3 = -125a^{12}b^{15}$.

Work Practice 14–19

Calculator Explorations Simplifying Square Roots

To simplify or approximate square roots using a calculator, locate the key marked $\boxed{\sqrt{\ }}$. To simplify $\sqrt{25}$ using a scientific calculator, press $\boxed{25}$ $\boxed{\sqrt{\ }}$. The display should read $\boxed{5}$. To simplify $\sqrt{25}$ using a graphing calculator, press $\boxed{\sqrt{\ }}$ $\boxed{25}$ $\boxed{\text{ENTER}}$.

To approximate $\sqrt{30}$, press $\boxed{30}$ $\boxed{\sqrt{\ }}$ (or $\boxed{\sqrt{\ }}$ $\boxed{30}$). The display should read $\boxed{5.477225575}$. This is an approximation for $\sqrt{30}$. A three-decimal-place approximation is

$$\sqrt{30} \approx 5.477$$

Is this answer reasonable? Since 30 is between perfect squares 25 and 36, $\sqrt{30}$ is between $\sqrt{25} = 5$ and $\sqrt{36} = 6$. The calculator result is then reasonable since 5.477225575 is between 5 and 6.

Use a calculator to approximate each expression to three decimal places. Decide whether each result is reasonable.

1. $\sqrt{6}$ **2.** $\sqrt{14}$

3. $\sqrt{11}$ **4.** $\sqrt{200}$

5. $\sqrt{82}$ **6.** $\sqrt{46}$

Many scientific calculators have a key, such as $\boxed{\sqrt[x]{y}}$, that can be used to approximate roots other than square roots. To approximate these roots using a graphing calculator, look under the $\boxed{\text{MATH}}$ menu or consult your manual. To use a $\boxed{\sqrt[x]{y}}$ key to find $\sqrt[3]{8}$, press $\boxed{3}$ $\boxed{\sqrt[x]{y}}$ $\boxed{8}$ (press $\boxed{\text{ENTER}}$ if needed). The display should read $\boxed{2}$.

Use a calculator to approximate each expression to three decimal places. Decide whether each result is reasonable.

7. $\sqrt[3]{40}$ **8.** $\sqrt[3]{71}$

9. $\sqrt[4]{20}$ **10.** $\sqrt[4]{15}$

11. $\sqrt[5]{18}$ **12.** $\sqrt[6]{2}$

Vocabulary and Readiness Check

Use the choices below to fill in each blank.

positive	index	radical sign	power
negative	principal	square root	radicand

1. The symbol $\sqrt{}$ is used to denote the positive, or __________, square root.
2. In the expression $\sqrt[4]{16}$, the number 4 is called the __________, the number 16 is called the __________, and $\sqrt{}$ is called the __________.
3. The reverse operation of squaring a number is finding a(n) __________ of a number.
4. For a positive number a,

   $-\sqrt{a}$ is the ________ square root of a and

   $\sqrt{a}$ is the ________ square root of a.
5. An nth root of a number a is a number whose nth __________ is a.

Answer each true or false.

6. $\sqrt{4} = -2$ __________
7. $\sqrt{-9} = -3$ __________
8. $\sqrt{1000} = 100$ __________
9. $\sqrt{1} = 1$ and $\sqrt{0} = 0$ __________
10. $\sqrt{64} = 8$ and $\sqrt[3]{64} = 4$ __________

14.1 Exercise Set

FOR EXTRA HELP

MyMathLab

PRACTICE

WATCH

DOWNLOAD

READ

REVIEW

Objective A *Find each square root. See Examples 1 through 5.*

1. $\sqrt{16}$
2. $\sqrt{64}$
3. $\sqrt{\frac{1}{25}}$
4. $\sqrt{\frac{1}{64}}$
5. $-\sqrt{100}$
6. $-\sqrt{36}$
7. $\sqrt{-4}$
8. $\sqrt{-25}$
9. $-\sqrt{121}$
10. $-\sqrt{49}$
11. $\sqrt{\frac{9}{25}}$
12. $\sqrt{\frac{4}{81}}$
13. $\sqrt{900}$
14. $\sqrt{400}$
15. $\sqrt{144}$
16. $\sqrt{169}$
17. $\sqrt{\frac{1}{100}}$
18. $\sqrt{\frac{1}{121}}$
19. $\sqrt{0.25}$
20. $\sqrt{0.49}$

Objective B *Find each cube root. See Examples 6 through 8.*

21. $\sqrt[3]{125}$
22. $\sqrt[3]{64}$
23. $\sqrt[3]{-64}$
24. $\sqrt[3]{-27}$
25. $-\sqrt[3]{8}$
26. $-\sqrt[3]{27}$
27. $\sqrt[3]{\frac{1}{8}}$
28. $\sqrt[3]{\frac{1}{64}}$
29. $\sqrt[3]{-125}$
30. $\sqrt[3]{-1}$

Objectives **A B C Mixed Practice** *Find each root. See Examples 1 through 12.*

31. $\sqrt[5]{32}$ **32.** $\sqrt[4]{81}$ **33.** $\sqrt{81}$ **34.** $\sqrt{49}$

35. $\sqrt[4]{-16}$ **36.** $\sqrt{-9}$ **37.** $\sqrt[3]{-\frac{27}{64}}$ **38.** $\sqrt[3]{-\frac{8}{27}}$

39. $-\sqrt[4]{625}$ **40.** $-\sqrt[5]{32}$ **41.** $\sqrt[6]{1}$ **42.** $\sqrt[5]{1}$

Objective **D** *Approximate each square root to three decimal places. See Example 13.*

43. $\sqrt{7}$ **44.** $\sqrt{10}$ **45.** $\sqrt{37}$ **46.** $\sqrt{27}$ **47.** $\sqrt{136}$ **48.** $\sqrt{8}$

49. A standard baseball diamond is a square with 90-foot sides connecting the bases. The distance from home plate to second base is $90 \cdot \sqrt{2}$ feet. Approximate $\sqrt{2}$ to two decimal places and use your result to approximate the distance $90 \cdot \sqrt{2}$ feet.

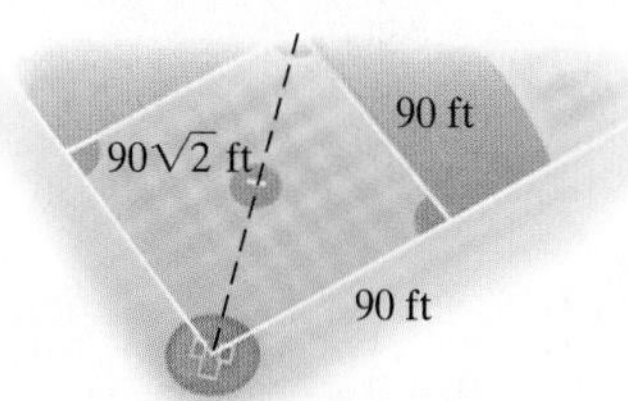

50. The roof of the warehouse shown needs to be shingled. The total area of the roof is exactly $480 \cdot \sqrt{29}$ square feet. Approximate $\sqrt{29}$ to two decimal places and use your result to approximate the area $480 \cdot \sqrt{29}$ square feet. Approximate this area to the nearest whole number.

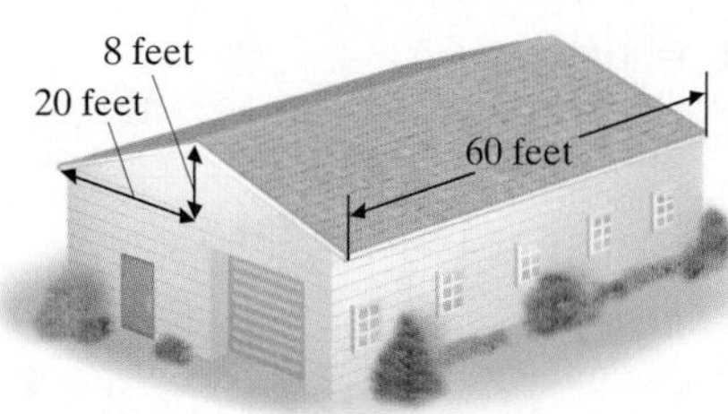

Objective **E** *Find each root. Assume that all variables represent positive numbers. See Examples 14 through 19.*

51. $\sqrt{m^2}$ **52.** $\sqrt{y^{10}}$ **53.** $\sqrt{x^4}$ **54.** $\sqrt{x^6}$

55. $\sqrt{9x^8}$ **56.** $\sqrt{36x^{12}}$ **57.** $\sqrt{81x^2}$ **58.** $\sqrt{100z^4}$

59. $\sqrt{a^2b^4}$ **60.** $\sqrt{x^{12}y^{20}}$ **61.** $\sqrt{16a^6b^4}$ **62.** $\sqrt{4m^{14}n^2}$

63. $\sqrt[3]{a^6b^{18}}$ **64.** $\sqrt[3]{x^{12}y^{18}}$ **65.** $\sqrt[3]{-8x^3y^{27}}$ **66.** $\sqrt[3]{-27a^6b^{30}}$

67. $\sqrt{\frac{x^6}{36}}$ **68.** $\sqrt{\frac{y^8}{49}}$ **69.** $\sqrt{\frac{25y^2}{9}}$ **70.** $\sqrt{\frac{4x^2}{81}}$

Review

Write each integer as a product of two integers such that one of the factors is a perfect square. For example, we can write $18 = 9 \cdot 2$, where 9 is a perfect square.

71. 50 **72.** 8 **73.** 32 **74.** 75

75. 28 **76.** 44 **77.** 27 **78.** 90

Concept Extensions

Solve. See the Concept Check in this section.

79. Which of the following is a real number?
a. $\sqrt[7]{-1}$ **b.** $\sqrt[3]{-125}$
c. $\sqrt[6]{-128}$ **d.** $\sqrt[8]{-1}$

80. Which of the following is a real number?
a. $\sqrt{-1}$ **b.** $\sqrt[3]{-1}$
c. $\sqrt[4]{-1}$ **d.** $\sqrt[5]{-1}$

The length of a side of a square is given by the expression $\sqrt{A}$, where A is the square's area. Use this expression for Exercises 81 through 84. Be sure to attach the appropriate units.

△ **81.** The area of a square is 49 square miles. Find the length of a side of the square.

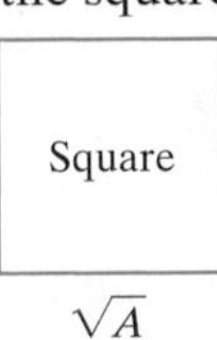

△ **82.** The area of a square is $\frac{1}{81}$ square meters. Find the length of a side of the square.

△ **83.** Sony currently makes the smallest portable mini disc player. It is approximately in the shape of a square with top area of 9.61 square inches. Find the length of a side. (*Source:* SONY)

△ **84.** A parking lot is in the shape of a square with area 2500 square yards. Find the length of a side.

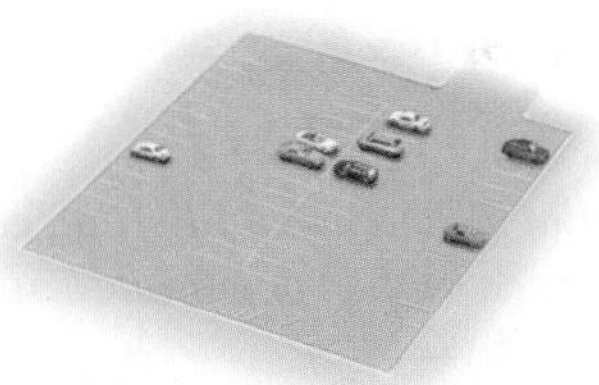

85. Simplify $\sqrt{\sqrt{81}}$.

86. Simplify $\sqrt[3]{\sqrt[3]{1}}$.

87. Simplify $\sqrt{\sqrt{10{,}000}}$.

88. Simplify $\sqrt{\sqrt{1{,}600{,}000{,}000}}$.

For each square root below, give two whole numbers that the square root lies between. For example,

since $\sqrt{11}$ is between $\sqrt{9}$ and $\sqrt{16}$, then

$\sqrt{11}$ is between 3 and 4.

89. $\sqrt{18}$

90. $\sqrt{28}$

91. $\sqrt{80}$

92. $\sqrt{98}$

93. The formula for calculating the period (one back-and-forth swing) of a pendulum is $T = 2\pi\sqrt{\frac{L}{g}}$, where T is time of the period of the swing, L is the length of the pendulum, and g is the acceleration of gravity. At the California Academy of Sciences, one can see a Foucault's pendulum with length = 30 ft and g = 32 ft/sec^2. Using $\pi \approx 3.14$, find the period of this pendulum. (Round to the nearest tenth of a second.)

94. If the amount of gold discovered by humankind could be assembled in one place, it would be a cube with a volume of 195,112 cubic feet. Each side of the cube would be $\sqrt[3]{195{,}112}$ feet long. How long would one side of the cube be? (*Source: Reader's Digest*)

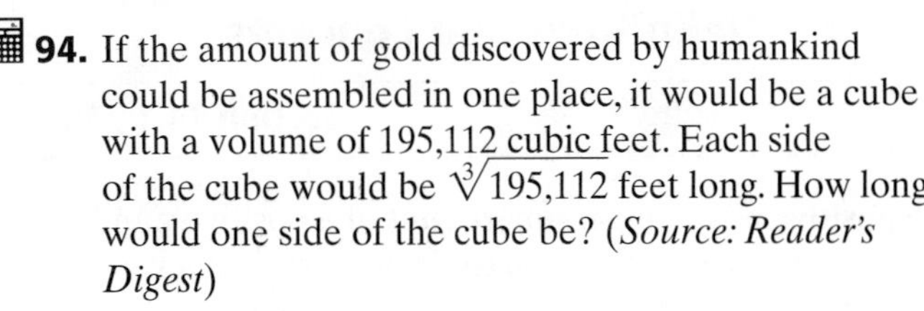

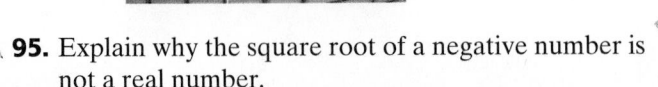

95. Explain why the square root of a negative number is not a real number.

96. Explain why the cube root of a negative number is a real number.

97. Graph $y = \sqrt{x}$. (Complete the table below, plot the ordered pair solutions, and draw a smooth curve through the points. Remember that since the radicand cannot be negative, this particular graph begins at the point with coordinates (0, 0).)

x	y
0	0
1	
3	(approximate)
4	
9	

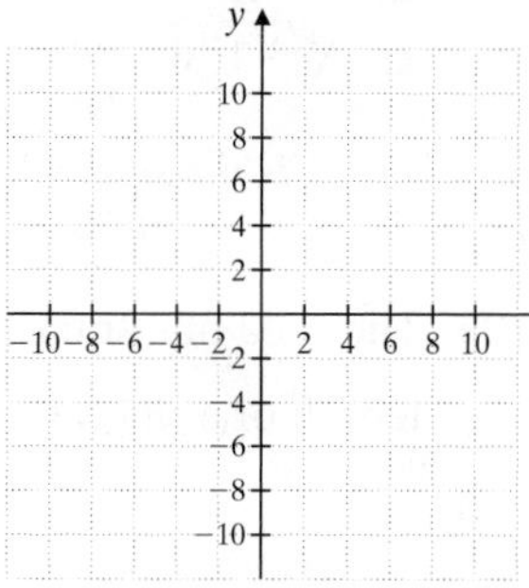

98. Graph $y = \sqrt[3]{x}$. (Complete the table below, plot the ordered pair solutions, and draw a smooth curve through the points.)

x	y
−8	
−2	(approximate)
−1	
0	
1	
2	(approximate)
8	

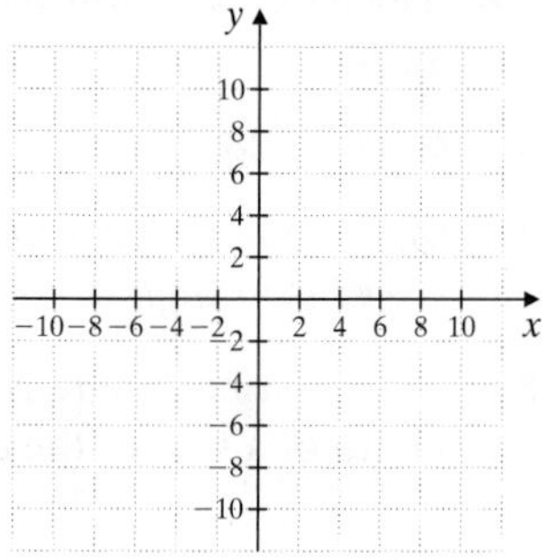

Recall from this section that $\sqrt{a^2} = |a|$ for any real number a. Simplify the following given that x represents any real number.

99. $\sqrt{x^2}$

100. $\sqrt{4x^2}$

101. $\sqrt{(x + 2)^2}$

102. $\sqrt{x^2 + 6x + 9}$
(*Hint:* First factor $x^2 + 6x + 9$.)

Use a graphing calculator and graph each function. Observe the graph from left to right and give the ordered pair that corresponds to the "beginning" of the graph. Then tell why the graph starts at that point.

103. $y = \sqrt{x - 2}$

104. $y = \sqrt{x + 3}$

105. $y = \sqrt{x + 4}$

106. $y = \sqrt{x - 5}$

14 Chapter Highlights

Definitions and Concepts	**Examples**
Section 14.1 Introduction to Radicals	
The **positive or principal square root** of a positive number a is written as $\sqrt{a}$. The **negative square root** of a is written as $-\sqrt{a}$. $\sqrt{a} = b$ only if $b^2 = a$ and $b > 0$.	$\sqrt{25} = 5$ $\quad \sqrt{100} = 10$ $-\sqrt{9} = -3$ $\quad \sqrt{\frac{4}{49}} = \frac{2}{7}$
A square root of a negative number is not a real number.	$\sqrt{-4}$ is not a real number.
The **cube root** of a real number a is written as $\sqrt[3]{a}$ and $\sqrt[3]{a} = b$ only if $b^3 = a$.	$\sqrt[3]{64} = 4$ $\quad \sqrt[3]{-8} = -2$
The ***n*th root** of a number a is written as $\sqrt[n]{a}$ and $\sqrt[n]{a} = b$ only if $b^n = a$.	$\sqrt[4]{81} = 3$
In $\sqrt[n]{a}$, the natural number n is called the **index,** the symbol $\sqrt{\ }$ is called a **radical,** and the expression within the radical is called the **radicand.** (*Note:* If the index is even, the radicand must be nonnegative for the root to be a real number.)	$\sqrt[5]{-32} = -2$ index ↓ $\sqrt[n]{a}$ ↖ radicand

Chapter 14 Review

(14.1) *Find each root.*

1. $\sqrt{81}$

2. $-\sqrt{49}$

3. $\sqrt[3]{27}$

4. $\sqrt[4]{81}$

5. $-\sqrt{\frac{9}{64}}$

6. $\sqrt{\frac{36}{81}}$

7. $\sqrt[4]{16}$

8. $\sqrt[3]{-8}$

9. Which radical(s) is not a real number?
a. $\sqrt{4}$ **b.** $-\sqrt{4}$ **c.** $\sqrt{-4}$ **d.** $\sqrt[3]{-4}$

10. Which radical(s) is not a real number?
a. $\sqrt{-5}$ **b.** $\sqrt[3]{-5}$ **c.** $\sqrt[4]{-5}$ **d.** $\sqrt[5]{-5}$

Find each root. Assume that all variables represent positive numbers.

11. $\sqrt{x^{12}}$

12. $\sqrt{x^8}$

13. $\sqrt{9y^2}$

14. $\sqrt{25x^4}$

Answers

1. ______
2. ______
3. ______
4. ______
5. ______
6. ______
7. a. ______
b. ______
c. ______
8. a. ______
b. ______
9. a. ______
b. ______
c. ______
d. ______
10. a. ______
b. ______
11. ______

Cumulative Review Chapters 8–14

Multiply.

1. $-2(-14)$

2. $9(-5.2)$

3. $-\frac{2}{3} \cdot \frac{4}{7}$

4. $-3\frac{3}{8} \cdot 5\frac{1}{3}$

5. Solve: $4(2x - 3) + 7 = 3x + 5$

6. Solve: $6y - 11 + 4 + 2y = 8 + 15y - 8y$

7. The circle graph below shows the purpose of trips made by American travelers. Use this graph to answer the questions below.

a. What percent of trips made by American travelers is solely for the purpose of business?

b. What percent of trips made by American travelers is for the purpose of business or combined business/pleasure?

c. On an airplane flight of 253 Americans, how many of these people might we expect to be traveling solely for business?

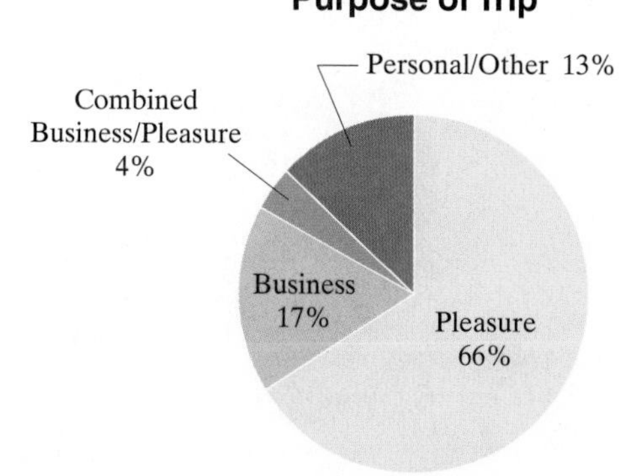

Source: Travel Industry Association of America

8. Simplify each expression.

a. $\frac{4(-3) - (-6)}{-8 + 4}$

b. $\frac{3 + (-3)(-2)^3}{-1 - (-4)}$

9. Write the following numbers in standard form, without exponents.

a. 1.02×10^5

b. 7.358×10^{-3}

c. 8.4×10^7

d. 3.007×10^{-5}

10. Write the following numbers in scientific notation.

a. 7,200,000

b. 0.000308

11. Multiply: $(3x + 2)(2x - 5)$

12. Multiply: $(7x + 1)^2$

13. Factor $xy + 2x + 3y + 6$ by grouping.

14. Factor $xy^2 + 5x - y^2 - 5$ by grouping.

15. Factor: $3x^2 + 11x + 6$

16. Factor: $3x^2 + 15x + 18$

17. Find an equation of the line with y-intercept $(0, 4)$ and slope of -2.

18. Combine like terms to simplify.
$4a^2 + 3a - 2a^2 + 7a - 5$

19. Graph $y = -3$.

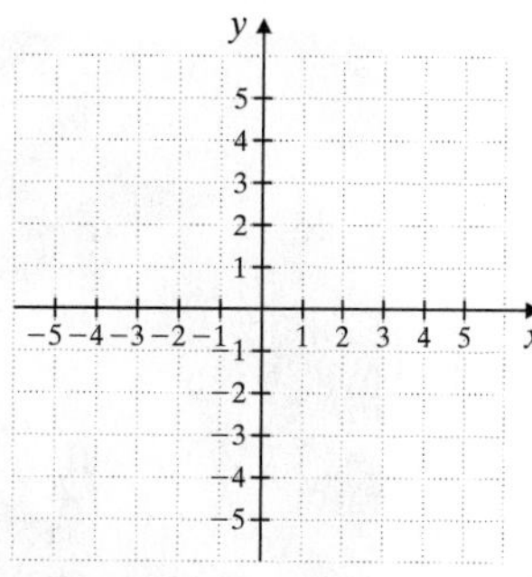

20. Complete the table for the equation $2x + y = 6$.

x	y
0	
	−2
3	

21. Find an equation of the line with y-intercept $(0, -3)$ and slope of $\frac{1}{4}$.

22. Find an equation of the line perpendicular to $y = 2x + 4$ and passing through $(1, 5)$.

Find each root.

23. $\sqrt[3]{1}$

24. $\sqrt{121}$

25. $\sqrt[3]{-27}$

26. $\sqrt{\frac{1}{4}}$

27. $\sqrt[3]{\frac{1}{125}}$

28. $\sqrt{\frac{25}{144}}$

Simplify.

29. $\sqrt{54}$

30. $\sqrt{63}$

31. $\sqrt{200}$

32. $\sqrt{500}$

12. ______
13. ______
14. ______
15. ______
16. ______
17. ______
18. ______
19. ______
20. ______
21. ______
22. ______
23. ______
24. ______
25. ______
26. ______
27. ______
28. ______
29. ______
30. ______
36. ______
32. ______

15 Graphs and Functions

The linear equations we explored in are statements about a single variable. This chapter examines statements about two variables: linear equations in two variables. We focus particularly on graphs of those equations which lead to the notion of relation and to the notion of function, perhaps the single most important and useful concept in all of mathematics.

Over the past few years, diamonds have gained much higher visibility by increased media advertising. Strong consumer demand has caused the industry to increase production and is the basis for the bar graph below. By a method called least squares (Section 15.2), the function $f(x) = 0.42x + 10.5$ approximates the data below where $f(x)$ is world diamond production value (in billions of dollars) and where x is the number of years past 2000. In Section 15.1, Exercises 101 and 102, page 996, we will use this linear equation to predict diamond production.

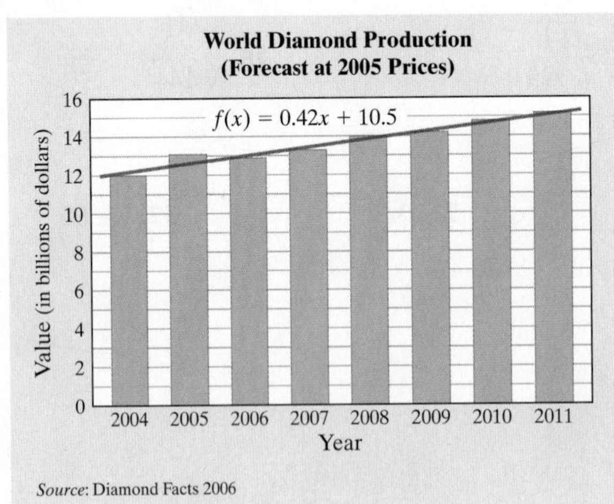

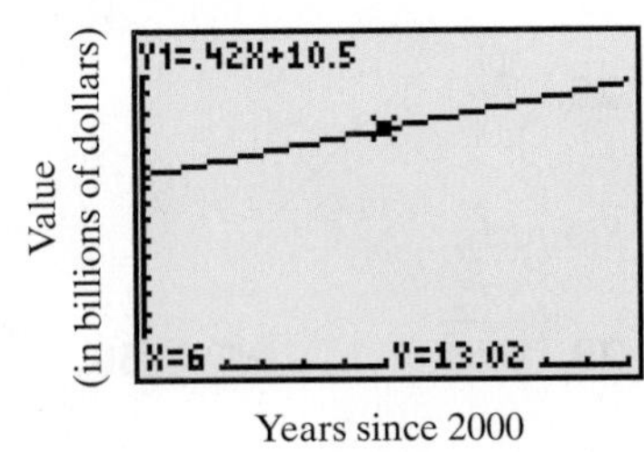

15.1 INTRODUCTION TO FUNCTIONS

OBJECTIVES

1. Define relation, domain, and range.
2. Identify functions.
3. Use the vertical line test for functions.
4. Find the domain and range of a function.
5. Use function notation.

OBJECTIVE 1 ▶ Defining relation, domain, and range. Recall our example from the last section about products sold and monthly salary. We modeled the data given by the equation $y = 3000 + \frac{1}{5}x$. This equation describes a relationship between x-values and y-values. For example, if $x = 1000$, then this equation describes how to find the y-value related to $x = 1000$. In words, the equation $y = 3000 + \frac{1}{5}x$ says that 3000 plus $\frac{1}{5}$ of the x-value gives the corresponding y-value. The x-value of 1000 corresponds to the y-value of $3000 + \frac{1}{5} \cdot 1000 = 3200$ for this equation, and we have the ordered pair $(1000, 3200)$.

There are other ways of describing relations or correspondences between two numbers or, in general, a first set (sometimes called the set of *inputs*) and a second set (sometimes called the set of *outputs*). For example,

First Set: Input	→	*Correspondence*	→	*Second Set: Output*
People in a certain city	→	Each person's age	→	The set of nonnegative integers

A few examples of ordered pairs from this relation might be (Ana, 4); (Bob, 36); (Trey, 21); and so on.

Below are just a few other ways of describing relations between two sets and the ordered pairs that they generate.

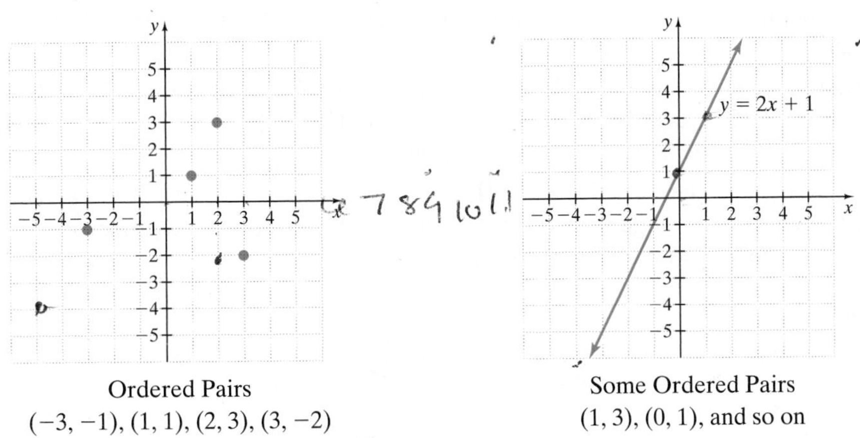

Ordered Pairs
$(-3, -1), (1, 1), (2, 3), (3, -2)$

Some Ordered Pairs
$(1, 3), (0, 1)$, and so on

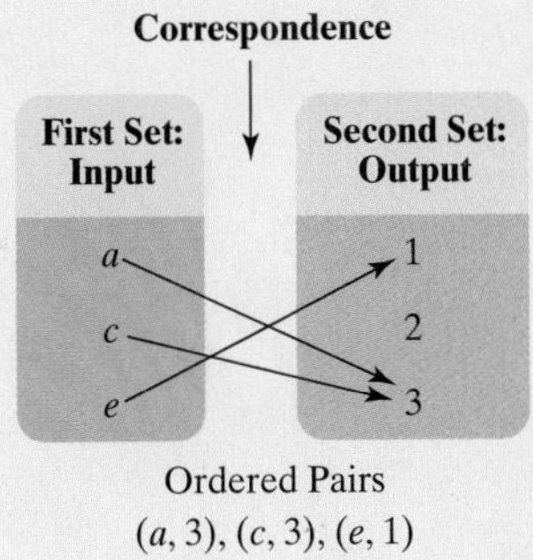

Ordered Pairs
$(a, 3), (c, 3), (e, 1)$

Relation, Domain, and Range

A **relation** is a set of ordered pairs.
The **domain** of the relation is the set of all first components of the ordered pairs.
The **range** of the relation is the set of all second components of the ordered pairs.

For example, the domain for our relation as shown above to the left is $\{a, c, e\}$ and the range is $\{1, 3\}$. Notice that the range does not include the element 2 of the second set. This is because no element of the first set is assigned to this element. If a relation is defined in terms of x- and y-values, we will agree that the domain corresponds to x-values and that the range corresponds to y-values that have x-values assigned to them.

Helpful Hint

Remember that the range only includes elements that are paired with domain values. For the correspondence below, the range is $\{a\}$.

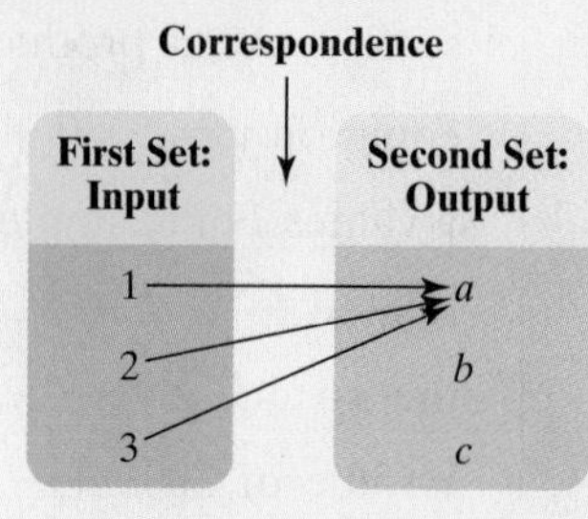

EXAMPLE 1 Determine the domain and range of each relation.

a. $\{(2, 3), (2, 4), (0, -1), (3, -1)\}$

b.

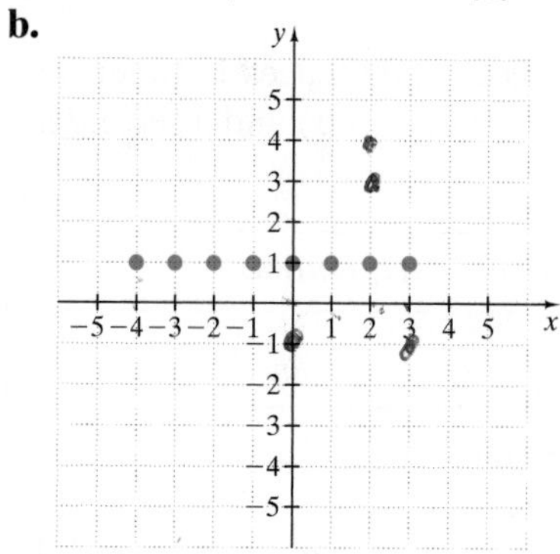

c.

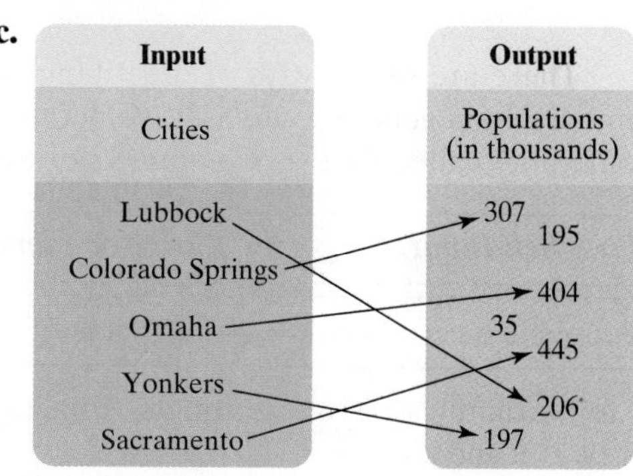

Solution

a. The domain is the set of all first coordinates of the ordered pairs, $\{2, 0, 3\}$. The range is the set of all second coordinates, $\{3, 4, -1\}$.

b. Ordered pairs are not listed here, but are given in graph form. The relation is $\{(-4, 1), (-3, 1), (-2, 1), (-1, 1), (0, 1), (1, 1), (2, 1), (3, 1)\}$. The domain is $\{-4, -3, -2, -1, 0, 1, 2, 3\}$. The range is $\{1\}$.

c. The domain is the set of inputs, {Lubbock, Colorado Springs, Omaha, Yonkers, Sacramento}. The range is the numbers in the set of outputs that correspond to elements in the set of inputs {307, 404, 445, 206, 197}. □

Helpful Hint

Domain or range elements that occur more than once need only to be listed once.

PRACTICE

1 Determine the domain and range of each relation.

a. {(4, 1)(4, −3)(5, −2)(5, 6)}

b.

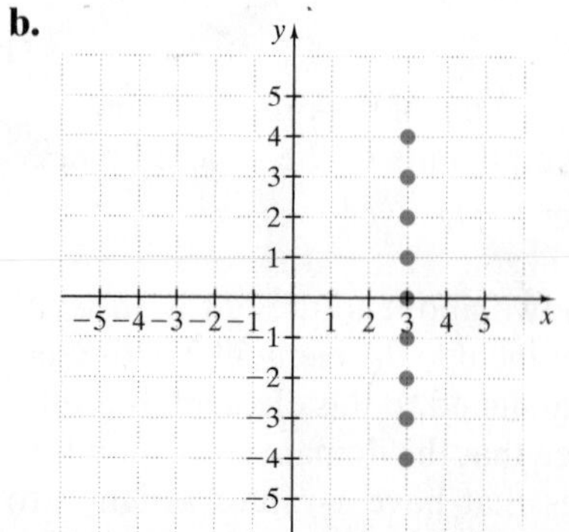

c.

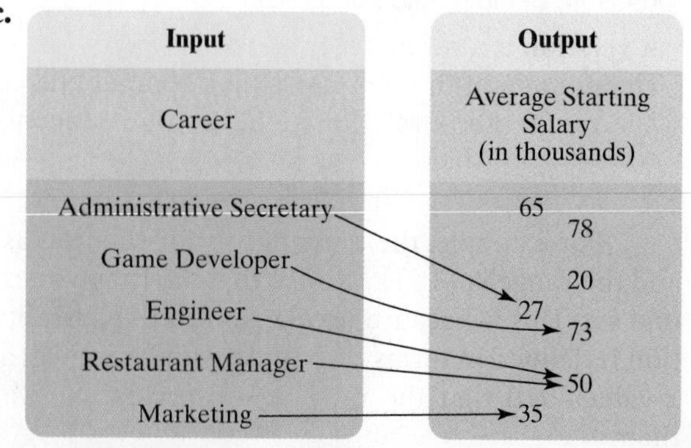

OBJECTIVE 2 ▶ Identifying functions. Now we consider a special kind of relation called a function.

Function

A **function** is a relation in which each first component in the ordered pairs corresponds to *exactly* one second component.

▶ **Helpful Hint**

A function is a special type of relation, so all functions are relations, but not all relations are functions.

EXAMPLE 2 Which of the following relations are also functions?

a. $\{(-2,5), (2,7), (-3,5), (9,9)\}$

b.

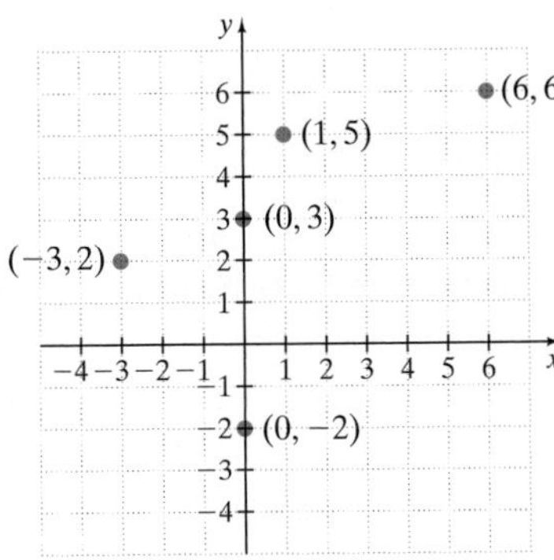

c.

Input	Correspondence	Output
People in a certain city	Each person's age	The set of nonnegative integers

Solution

a. Although the ordered pairs $(-2,5)$ and $(-3,5)$ have the same y-value, each x-value is assigned to only one y-value, so this set of ordered pairs is a function.

b. The x-value 0 is assigned to two y-values, -2 and 3, in this graph so this relation does not define a function.

c. This relation is a function because although two different people may have the same age, each person has only one age. This means that each element in the first set is assigned to only one element in the second set. □

PRACTICE 2 Which of the following relations are also functions?

a. $\{(3, 1), (-3, -4), (8, 5), (9, 1)\}$

b.

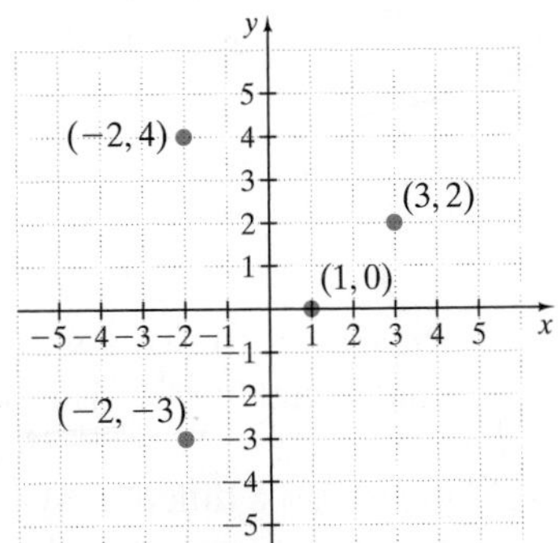

c.

Input	Correspondence	Output
People in a certain city	Birth date (day of month)	Set of positive integers

Answer to Concept Check:
Two different ordered pairs can have the same y-value, but not the same x-value in a function.

Concept Check ✓

Explain why a function can contain both the ordered pairs $(1, 3)$ and $(2, 3)$ but not both $(3, 1)$ and $(3, 2)$.

We will call an equation such as $y = 2x + 1$ a **relation** since this equation defines a set of ordered pair solutions.

EXAMPLE 3 Is the relation $y = 2x + 1$ also a function?*

Solution The relation $y = 2x + 1$ is a function if each x-value corresponds to just one y-value. For each x-value substituted in the equation $y = 2x + 1$, the multiplication and addition performed on each gives a single result, so only one y-value will be associated with each x-value. Thus, $y = 2x + 1$ is a function.

*For further discussion including the graph, see Objective 3. □

PRACTICE 3 Is the relation $y = -3x + 5$ also a function?

EXAMPLE 4 Is the relation $x = y^2$ also a function?*

Solution In $x = y^2$, if $y = 3$, then $x = 9$. Also, if $y = -3$, then $x = 9$. In other words, we have the ordered pairs $(9, 3)$ and $(9, -3)$. Since the x-value 9 corresponds to two y-values, 3 and -3, $x = y^2$ is not a function.

*For further discussion including the graph, see Objective 3. □

PRACTICE 4 Is the relation $y = -x^2$ also a function?

OBJECTIVE 3 ▶ Using the vertical line test. As we have seen so far, not all relations are functions. Consider the graphs of $y = 2x + 1$ and $x = y^2$ shown next. For the graph of $y = 2x + 1$, notice that each x-value corresponds to only one y-value. Recall from Example 3 that $y = 2x + 1$ is a function.

Graph of Example 3:
$y = 2x + 1$

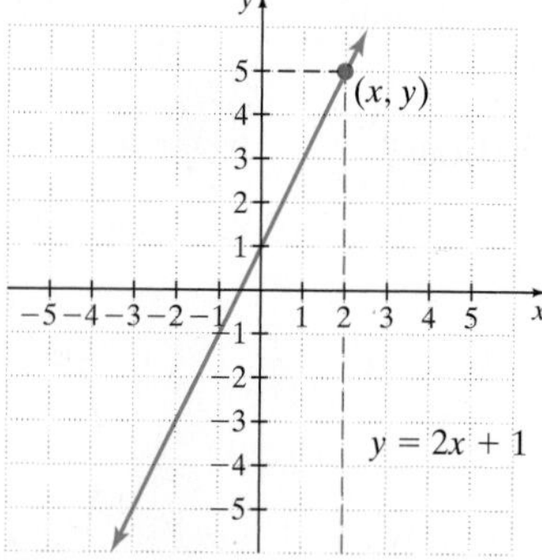

Graph of Example 4:
$x = y^2$

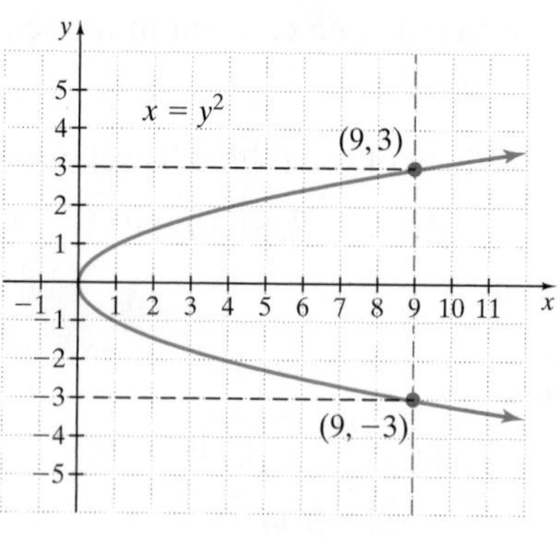

For the graph of $x = y^2$ the x-value 9, for example, corresponds to two y-values, 3 and -3, as shown by the vertical line. Recall from Example 4 that $x = y^2$ is not a function.

Graphs can be used to help determine whether a relation is also a function by the following vertical line test.

Vertical Line Test

If no vertical line can be drawn so that it intersects a graph more than once, the graph is the graph of a function.

EXAMPLE 5 Which of the following graphs are graphs of functions?

a.

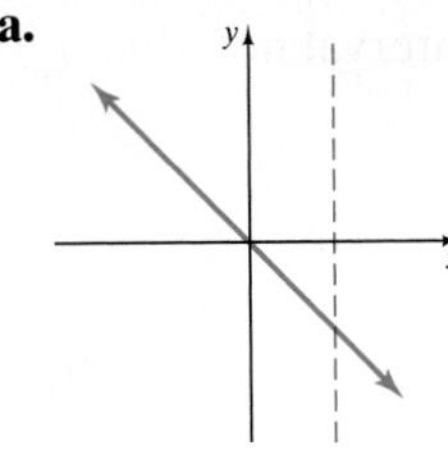

b.

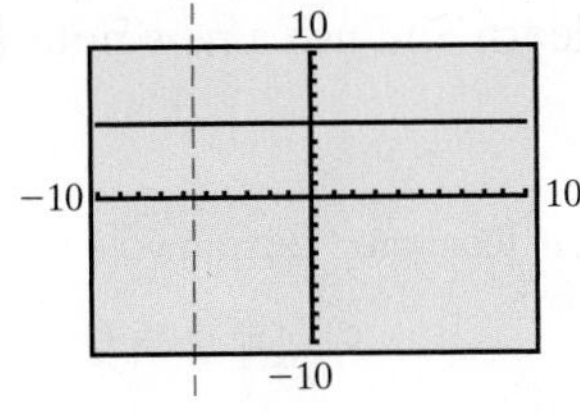

c.

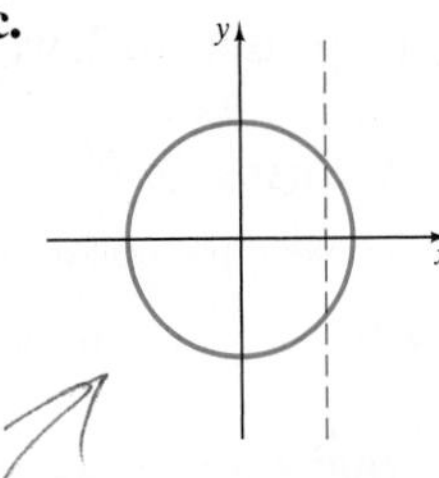

Solution

a. Yes, this is the graph of a function since no vertical line will intersect this graph more than once.

b. Yes, this is the graph of a function.

c. No, this is not the graph of a function. Note that vertical lines can be drawn that intersect the graph in two points.

d.

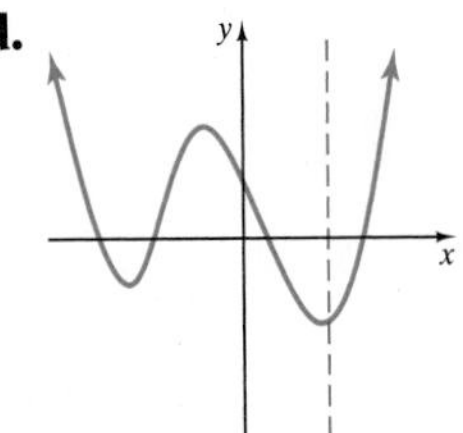

e.

f.

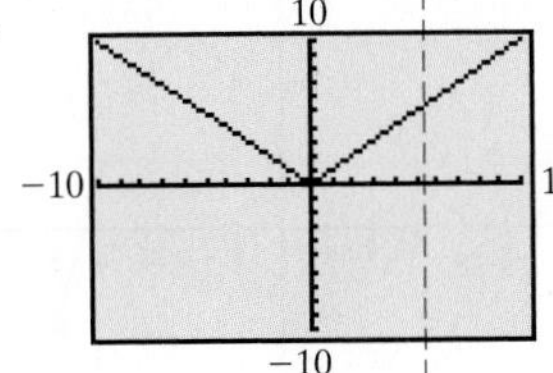

Solution

d. Yes, this is the graph of a function.

e. No, this is not the graph of a function. A vertical line can be drawn that intersects this line at every point.

f. Yes, this is the graph of a function. □

PRACTICE 5 Which of the following graphs are graphs of functions?

a.

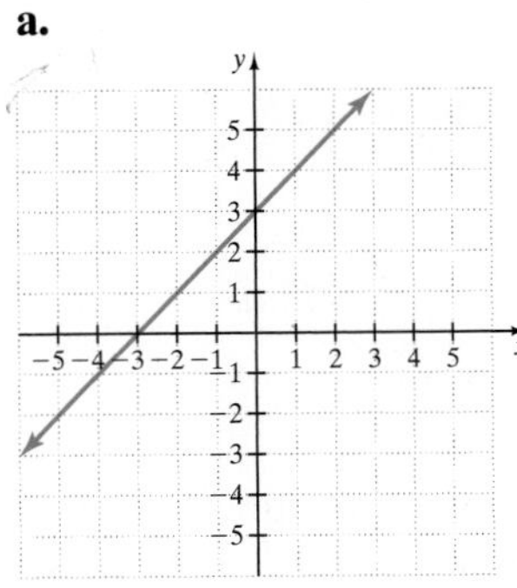

b.

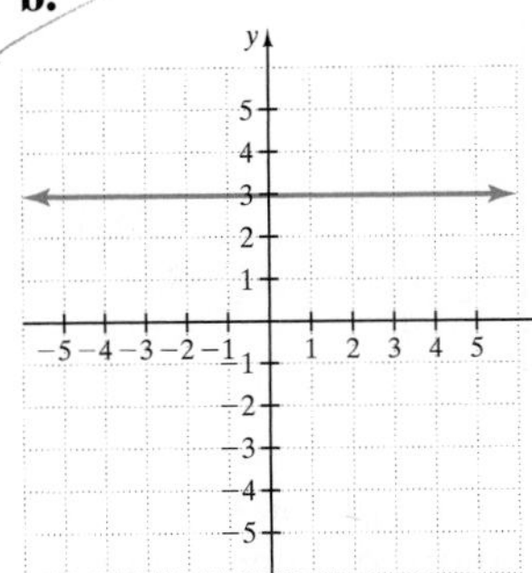

c.

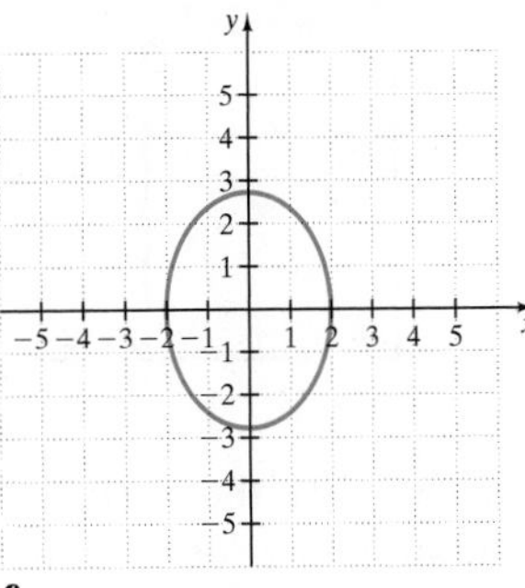

d.

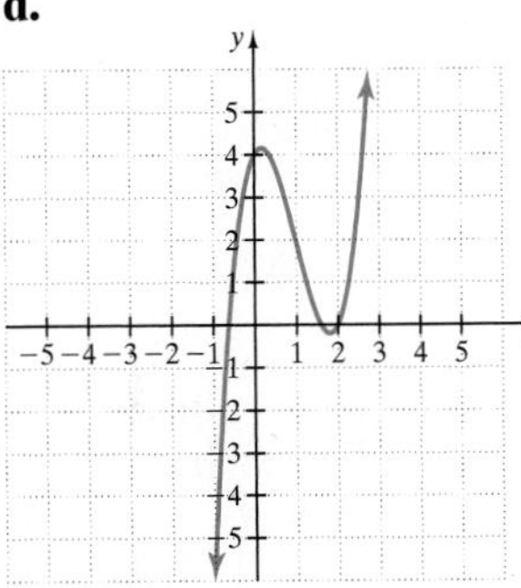

e.

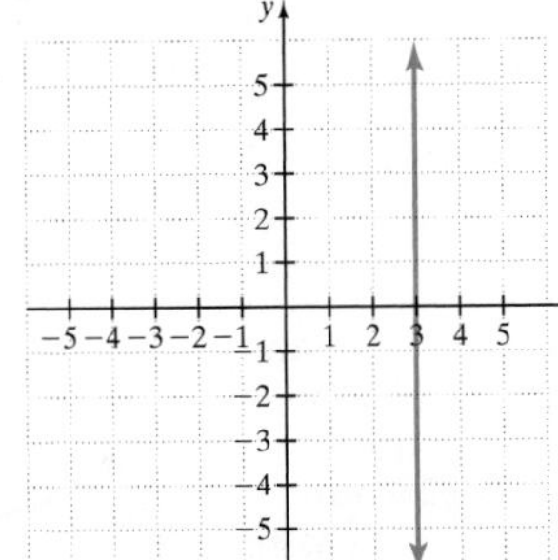

f.

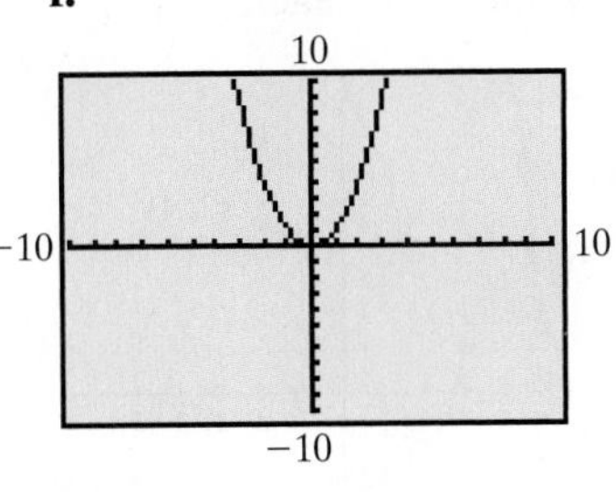

Recall that the graph of a linear equation in two variables is a line, and a line that is not vertical will pass the vertical line test. Thus, **all linear equations are functions except those whose graph is a vertical line.** For now, we will use set builder notation to write domains and ranges.

For ease of writing, if the domain or range is all real numbers, we simply write "all real numbers" instead of $\{x \mid x \text{ is a real number}\}$ or $\{y \mid y \text{ is a real number}\}$.

In Section 16.2, we will learn and use a new notation called interval notation.

Concept Check ☑

Determine which equations represent functions. Explain your answer.

a. $y = |x|$ **b.** $y = x^2$ **c.** $x + y = 6$

OBJECTIVE 4 ▶ Finding the domain and range of a function. Next, we practice finding the domain and range of a relation from its graph.

EXAMPLE 6 Find the domain and range of each relation. Determine whether the relation is also a function.

a. (−3, 1) (2, 4) (5, −2)

b.

c. Y1=X²+3 X=0 Y=3

d.

e. Y1=abs(X+5)−2 X=−5 Y=−2

Solution By the vertical line test, graphs **a**, **c**, **d**, and **e** are graphs of functions. The domain is the set of values of x and the range is the set of values of y. We read these values from each graph.

a. (−3, 1) (2, 4) (5, −2)

Range: The y-values graphed are from −2 to 4, or $\{y \mid -2 \le y \le 4\}$.

Domain: The x-values graphed are from −3 to 5, or $\{x \mid -3 \le x \le 5\}$.

b.

Range: $\{y \mid -2 \le y \le 2\}$

Domain: $\{x \mid -4 \le x \le 4\}$

Answer to Concept Check: a, b, c

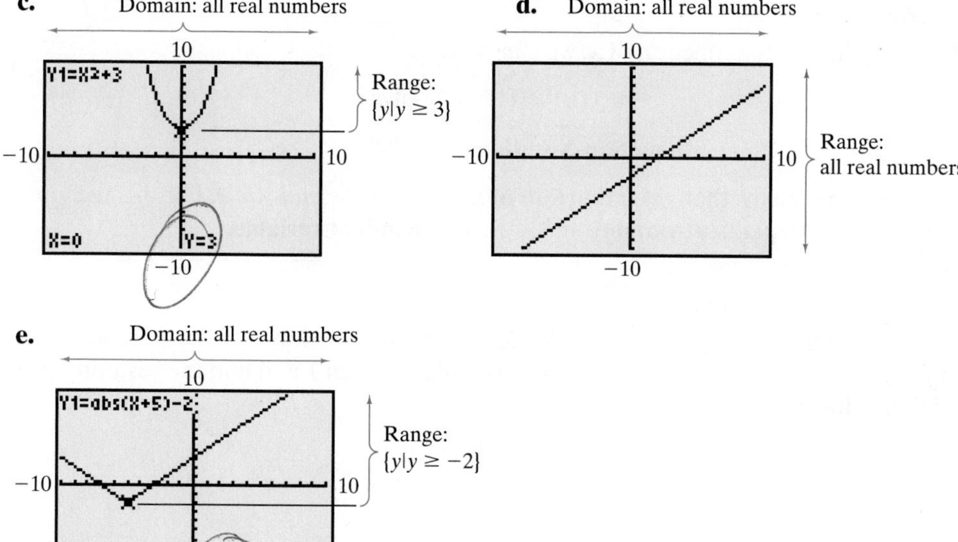

PRACTICE

6 Find the domain and range of each relation. Determine whether each relation is also a function.

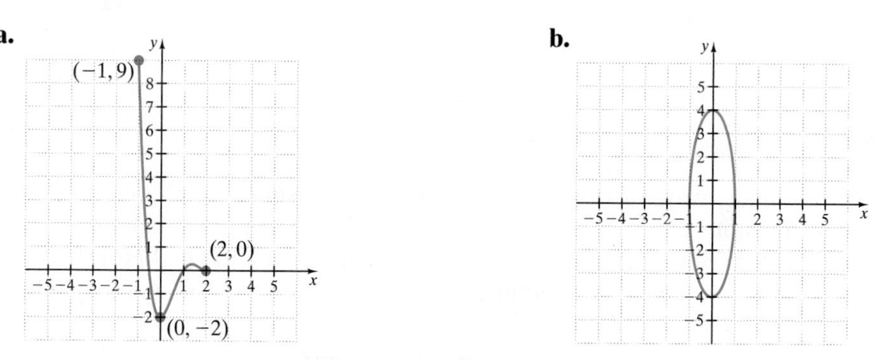

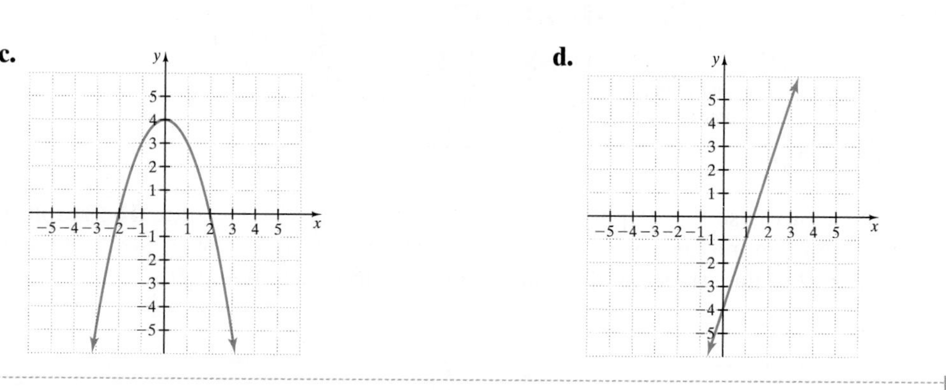

OBJECTIVE 5 ▶ Using function notation. Many times letters such as f, g, and h are used to name functions.

Function Notation

To denote that y is a function of x, we can write

$$y = \underbrace{f(x)}_{\text{Function Notation}} \quad (\text{Read "}f\text{ of }x\text{."})$$

This notation means that **y is a function of x** or that y *depends on* x. For this reason, y is called the **dependent variable** and x the **independent variable.**

For example, to use function notation with the function $y = 4x + 3$, we write $f(x) = 4x + 3$. The notation $f(1)$ means to replace x with 1 and find the resulting y or function value. Since

$$f(x) = 4x + 3$$

then

$$f(1) = 4(1) + 3 = 7$$

This means that when $x = 1$, y or $f(x) = 7$. The corresponding ordered pair is $(1, 7)$. Here, the input is 1 and the output is $f(1)$ or 7. Now let's find $f(2)$, $f(0)$, and $f(-1)$.

$$\begin{aligned} f(x) &= 4x + 3 \\ f(2) &= 4(2) + 3 \\ &= 8 + 3 \\ &= 11 \end{aligned} \qquad \begin{aligned} f(x) &= 4x + 3 \\ f(0) &= 4(0) + 3 \\ &= 0 + 3 \\ &= 3 \end{aligned} \qquad \begin{aligned} f(x) &= 4(x) + 3 \\ f(-1) &= 4(-1) + 3 \\ &= -4 + 3 \\ &= -1 \end{aligned}$$

Ordered Pairs:

$(2, 11)$ $(0, 3)$ $(-1, -1)$

Helpful Hint

Make sure you remember that $f(2) = 11$ corresponds to the ordered pair $(2, 11)$.

There are many ways of evaluating function values using a graphing utility. One way is to use the store feature. For example, to find $f(2)$ when $f(x) = 4x + 3$, store the number 2, enter the expression, and calculate. To find $f(0)$ and $f(-1)$ for the same function and save time, have your graphing utility replay the last entry and then edit it.

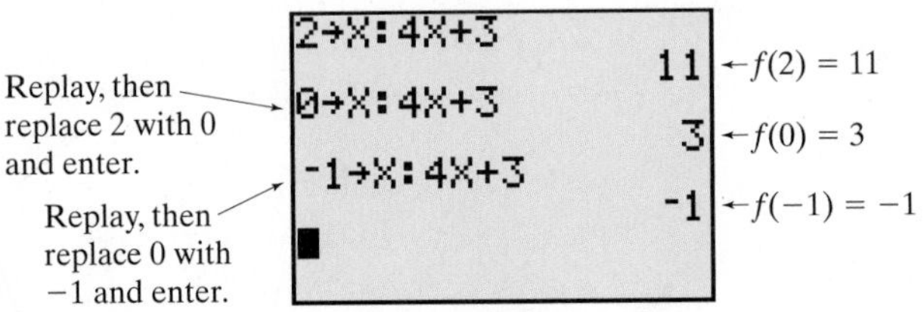

We can also use the graph to evaluate a function at a given value. The graph of $y_1 = 4x + 3$ in an integer window is shown below. Move the cursor to the point with x-coordinate 2 to find $f(2)$. Continue in this manner to find $f(0)$ and $f(-1)$.

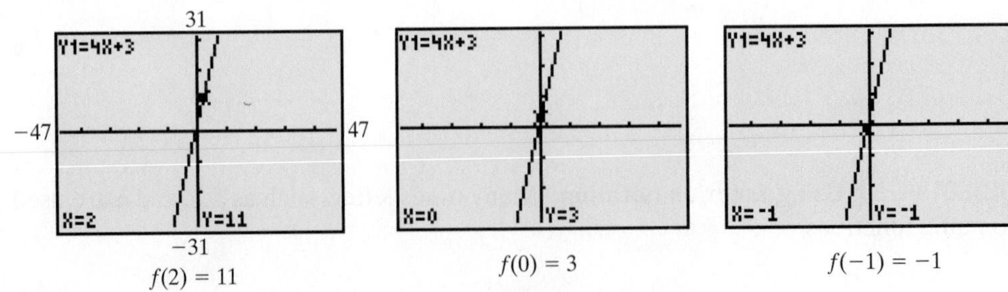

$f(2) = 11$ $f(0) = 3$ $f(-1) = -1$

A third method for finding function values is by using a table.

$f(-1) = -1$ ⟶
$f(0) = 3$ ⟶
$f(2) = 11$ ⟶

X	Y1
-1	-1
0	3
1	7
2	11
3	15
4	19
5	23

Y1=4X+3

The method you use to find function values depends on the particular situation. For instance, in Example 7, we evaluate several different functions for various values of x, so we calculate by hand and use the store feature to check. However, in Example 8 we evaluate the same function, but for different values of x, so we choose to look at the graph of the function. These are just a few methods that can be used to evaluate functions at given values.

Helpful Hint

Note that $f(x)$ is a special symbol in mathematics used to denote a function. The symbol $f(x)$ is read "f of x." It does *not* mean $f \cdot x$ (f times x).

EXAMPLE 7 If $f(x) = 7x^2 - 3x + 1, g(x) = 3x - 2$, and $h(x) = x^2$ find the following.

a. $f(1)$ **b.** $g(3)$ **c.** $h(-2)$

Solution

a. Substitute 1 for x in $f(x) = 7x^2 - 3x + 1$ and simplify.

$f(x) = 7x^2 - 3x + 1$

$f(1) = 7(1)^2 - 3(1) + 1 = 5$

b. $g(x) = 3x - 2$

$g(3) = 3(3) - 2 = 7$

c. $h(x) = x^2$

$h(-2) = (-2)^2 = 4$

A calculator check is in the margin. □

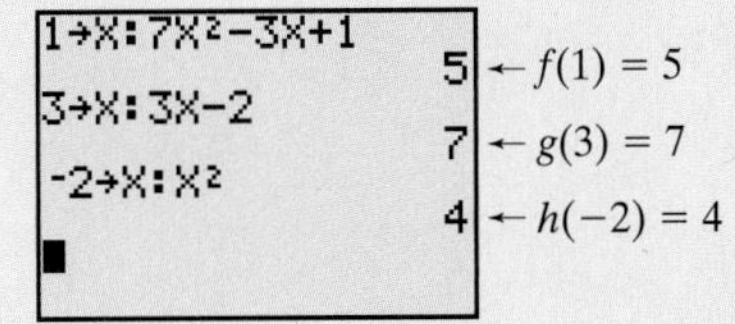

PRACTICE 7 If $f(x) = 3x - 2$ and $g(x) = 5x^2 + 2x - 1$, find the following.

a. $f(1)$ **b.** $g(1)$ **c.** $f(0)$ **d.** $g(-2)$

Concept Check ✓

Suppose $y = f(x)$ and we are told that $f(3) = 9$. Which is not true?

a. When $x = 3, y = 9$.

b. A possible function is $f(x) = x^2$.

c. A point on the graph of the function is $(3, 9)$.

d. A possible function is $f(x) = 2x + 4$.

Answer to Concept Check: d

If it helps, think of a function, f, as a machine that has been programmed with a certain correspondence or rule. An input value (a member of the domain) is then fed into the machine, the machine does the correspondence or rule, and the result is the output (a member of the range).

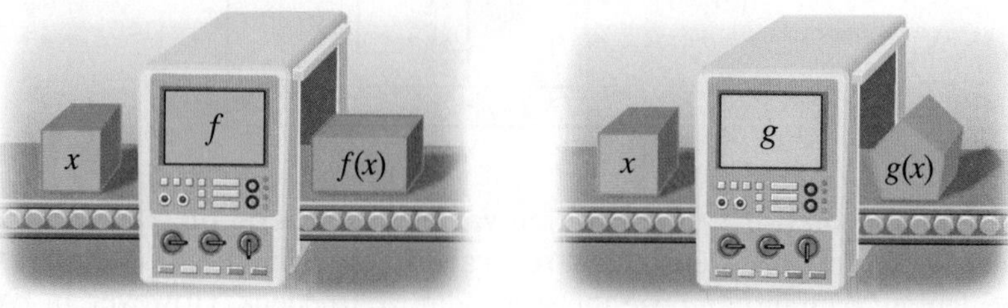

EXAMPLE 8 If $f(x) = 0.5x - 25$, find

a. $f(-10)$ **b.** $f(18)$ **c.** $f(11)$ **d.** $f(0)$

Solution

a. We choose to use a graphical method to evaluate. Define $y_1 = 0.5x - 25$ and graph using an integer window. Move the cursor to find $x = -10$. In the screen shown below, we see that -10 is paired with $y = -30$; therefore $f(-10) = -30$.

b. Move the cursor to $x = 18$ and see that it is paired with -16 and thus $f(18) = -16$.

c. Move the cursor to $x = 11$ and see that $y = -19.5$, so $f(11) = -19.5$.

d. Move the cursor to $x = 0$ and see that $y = -25$, so $f(0) = -25$.

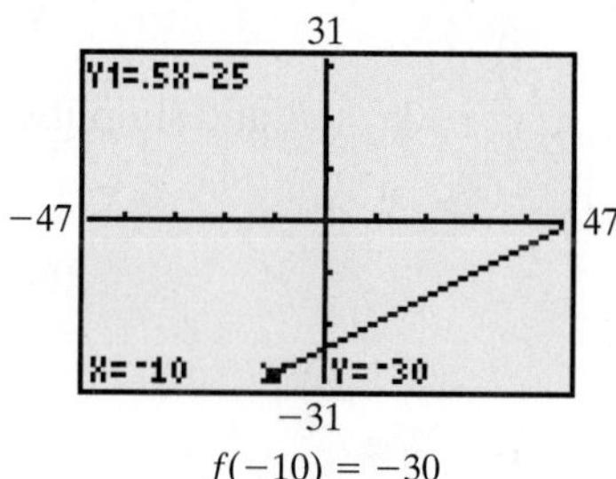

$f(-10) = -30$

□

PRACTICE 8 If $f(x) = 2.6x^2 - 4$, find:

a. $f(2)$ **b.** $f(-4)$ **c.** $f(0)$ **d.** $f(0.7)$

Many formulas that are familiar to you describe functions. For example, we have used the formula for finding the area of a circle, $A = \pi r^2$. The area of the circle is actually a function of the length of the radius. Using this function notation, we write

$$A(r) = \pi r^2$$

$A(r)$ can be read as the area with respect to r. To find the area of the circle whose radius is 3 cm, we write

$$A(r) = \pi r^2$$
$$A(3) = \pi(3)^2 = 9\pi \text{ square centimeters}$$

An approximation to two decimal places is

$$9\pi \text{ sq cm} \approx 28.27 \text{ sq cm}$$

EXAMPLE 9 Given the graphs of the functions f and g, find each function value by inspecting the graphs.

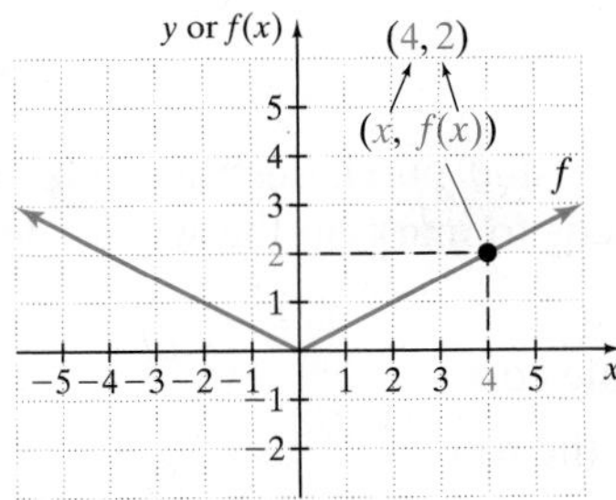

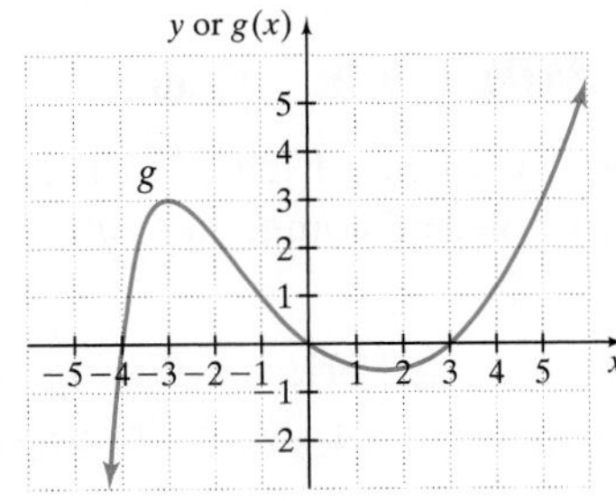

a. $f(4)$ **b.** $f(-2)$ **c.** $g(5)$ **d.** $g(0)$

e. Find all x-values such that $f(x) = 1$.

f. Find all x-values such that $g(x) = 0$.

Solution

a. To find $f(4)$, find the y-value when $x = 4$. We see from the graph that when $x = 4$, y or $f(x) = 2$. Thus, $f(4) = 2$.

b. $f(-2) = 1$ from the ordered pair $(-2, 1)$.

c. $g(5) = 3$ from the ordered pair $(5, 3)$.

d. $g(0) = 0$ from the ordered pair $(0, 0)$.

e. To find x-values such that $f(x) = 1$, we are looking for any ordered pairs on the graph of f whose $f(x)$ or y-value is 1. They are $(2, 1)$ and $(-2, 1)$. Thus $f(2) = 1$ and $f(-2) = 1$. The x-values are 2 and -2.

f. Find ordered pairs on the graph of g whose $g(x)$ or y-value is 0. They are $(3, 0)$ $(0, 0)$, and $(-4, 0)$. Thus $g(3) = 0$, $g(0) = 0$, and $g(-4) = 0$. The x-values are 3, 0, and -4. □

PRACTICE

9 Given the graphs of the functions f and g, find each function value by inspecting the graphs.

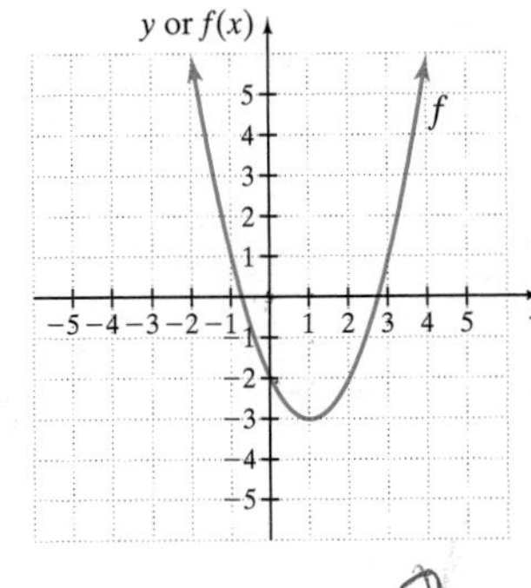

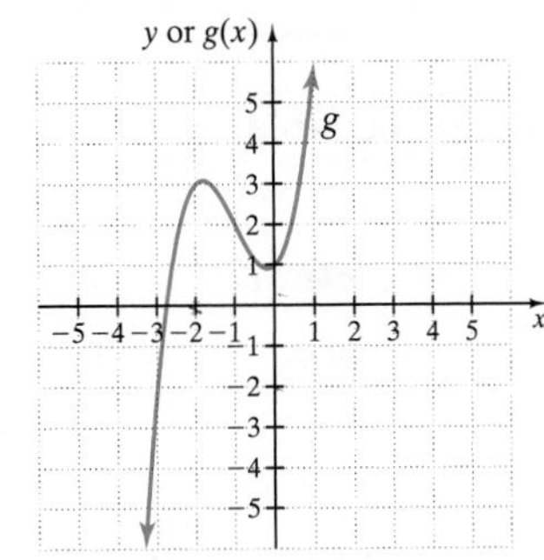

a. $f(1)$ **b.** $f(0)$ **c.** $g(-2)$ **d.** $g(0)$

e. Find all x-values such that $f(x) = 1$.

f. Find all x-values such that $g(x) = -2$.

When a store manager is setting the retail price of an article, the price may be dependent on the wholesale price of the article. When this happens, we say that the retail price is a function of the wholesale price.

EXAMPLE 10 **Finding Retail Prices**

Elizabeth Lockwood manages the college bookstore and purchases the books from several wholesale companies. She finds that she needs to mark up the wholesale cost by 25%.

a. Write the retail price as a function of the wholesale cost.

b. Find the retail price of the following books given the wholesale cost.

Wholesale Cost	\$15.00	\$22.75	\$38.50	\$53.00
Retail Price				

Solution

a. Let w = the wholesale cost of a book. To denote that the retail price is a function of wholesale cost, we define the function $R(w)$.

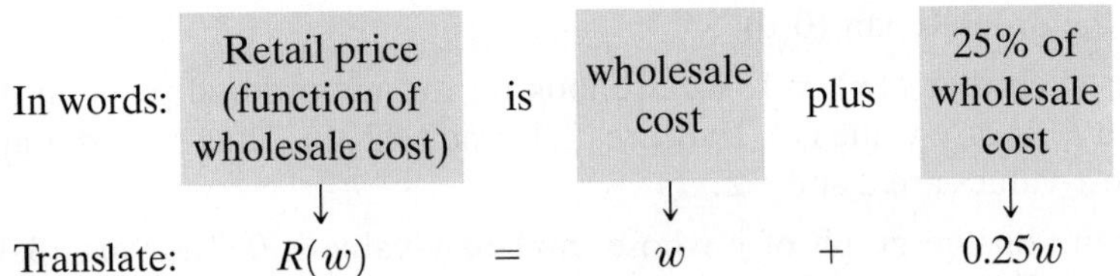

b. Here we evaluate $R(w) = w + 0.25w$ for the given values of w.

Completing the table, we have

Wholesale Cost	w	\$15.00	\$22.75	\$38.50	\$53.00
Retail Price	$R(w)$	\$18.75	\$28.44	\$48.13	\$66.25

□

PRACTICE 10 Find the cost of each book in Example 10 if the mark-up is 15%.

Many types of real-world paired data form functions. The following broken-line graph shows the research and development spending by the Pharmaceutical Manufacturers Association.

EXAMPLE 11 The following graph shows the research and development expenditures by the Pharmaceutical Manufacturers Association as a function of time.

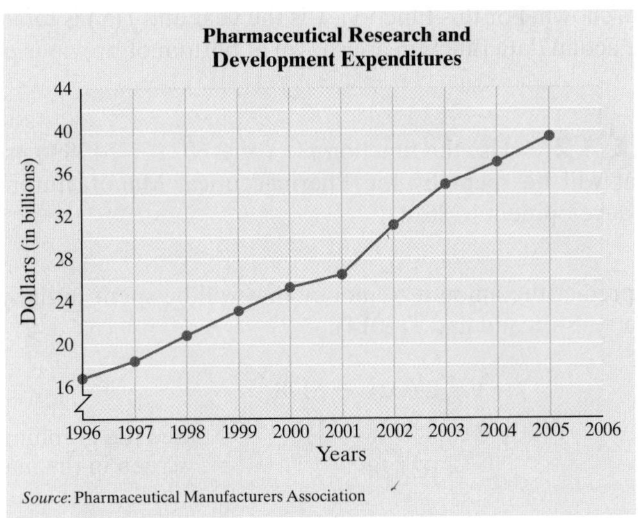

a. Approximate the money spent on research and development in 2002.

b. In 1958, research and development expenditures were \$200 million. Find the increase in expenditures from 1958 to 2004.

Solution

a. Find the year 2002 and move upward until you reach the graph. From the point on the graph move horizontally, to the left, until the other axis is reached. In 2002, approximately \$31 billion was spent.

b. In 2004, approximately \$37 billion, or \$37,000 million was spent. The increase in spending from 1958 to 2004 is \$37,000 − \$200 = \$36,800 million or \$36.8 billion. □

PRACTICE 11 Use the graph in Example 11 and approximate the money spent in 2003.

Notice that the graph in Example 11 is the graph of a function since for each year there is only one total amount of money spent by the Pharmaceutical Manufacturers Association on research and development. Also notice that the graph resembles the

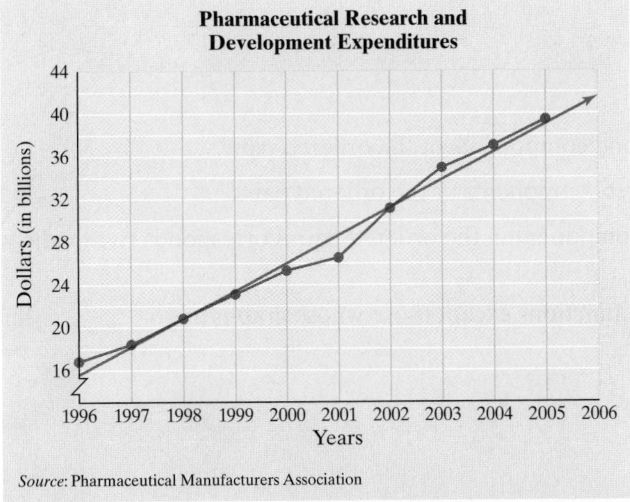

graph of a line. Often, businesses depend on equations that "closely fit" data-defined functions like this one in order to model the data and predict future trends. For example, by a method called **least squares,** the function $f(x) = 2.602x - 5178$ approximates the data shown. For this function, x is the year and $f(x)$ is total money spent. Its graph and the actual data function are shown at bottom of previous page.

EXAMPLE 12 Use the function $f(x) = 2.602x - 5178$ to predict the amount of money that will be spent by the Pharmaceutical Manufacturers Association on research and development in 2014.

Solution To predict the amount of money that will be spent in the year 2014 we use $f(x) = 2.602x - 5178$ and find $f(2014)$.

```
2014→X
                2014
2.602X-5178
              62.428
```

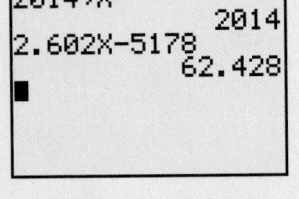

A calculator check for Example 12.

$$f(x) = 2.602x - 5178$$
$$f(2014) = 2.602(2014) - 5178$$ See the graphing calculator screen in the margin.
$$= 62.428$$

We predict that in the year 2014, \$62.428 billion dollars will be spent on research and development by the Pharmaceutical Manufacturers Association. □

PRACTICE
12 Use $f(x) = 2.602x - 5178$ to approximate the money spent in 2012.

VOCABULARY & READINESS CHECK

Use the choices below to fill in each blank. Some choices may not be used. These exercises have to do with functions and the rectangular coordinate system (Sections 15.1 and 15.2).

x	domain	vertical	relation	$(1.7, -2)$	line	parabola
y	range	horizontal	function	$(-2, 1.7)$	origin	V-shaped

1. The intersection of the x-axis and y-axis is a point, called the ________.
2. To find an x-intercept, let _____ = 0 and solve for _____.
3. To find a y-intercept, let _____ = 0 and solve for _____.
4. The graph of $Ax + By = C$, where A and B are not both 0, is a _______.
5. The graph of $y = |x|$ looks _________.
6. The graph of $y = x^2$ is a _________.
7. A ________ is a set of ordered pairs.
8. The ________ of a relation is the set of all second components of the ordered pairs.
9. The _________ of a relation is the set of all first components of the ordered pairs.
10. A _________ is a relation in which each first component in the ordered pairs corresponds to *exactly* one second component.
11. By the vertical line test, all linear equations are functions except those whose graphs are ________ lines.
12. If $f(-2) = 1.7$, the corresponding ordered pair is ________.

15.1 EXERCISE SET

Find the domain and the range of each relation. Also determine whether the relation is a function. See Examples 1 and 2.

1. $\{(-1,7),(0,6),(-2,2),(5,6)\}$

2. $\{(4,9),(-4,9),(2,3),(10,-5)\}$

3. $\{(-2,4),(6,4),(-2,-3),(-7,-8)\}$

4. $\{(6,6),(5,6),(5,-2),(7,6)\}$

5. $\{(1,1),(1,2),(1,3),(1,4)\}$

6. $\{(1,1),(2,1),(3,1),(4,1)\}$

7. $\left\{\left(\frac{3}{2},\frac{1}{2}\right),\left(1\frac{1}{2},-7\right),\left(0,\frac{4}{5}\right)\right\}$

8. $\{(\pi,0),(0,\pi),(-2,4),(4,-2)\}$

9. $\{(-3,-3),(0,0),(3,3)\}$

10. $\left\{\left(\frac{1}{2},\frac{1}{4}\right),\left(0,\frac{7}{8}\right),(0.5,\pi)\right\}$

11.

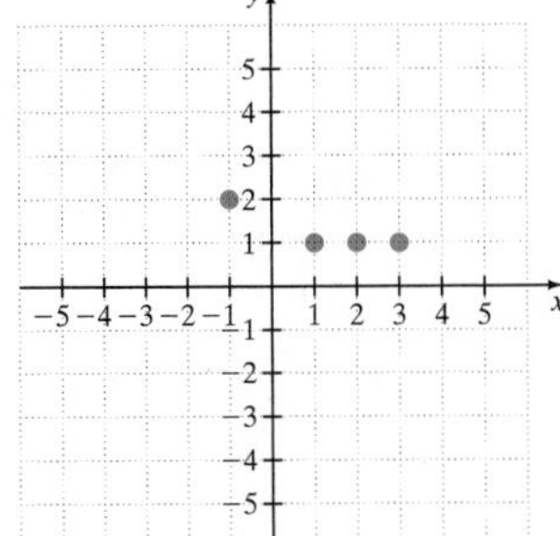

12.

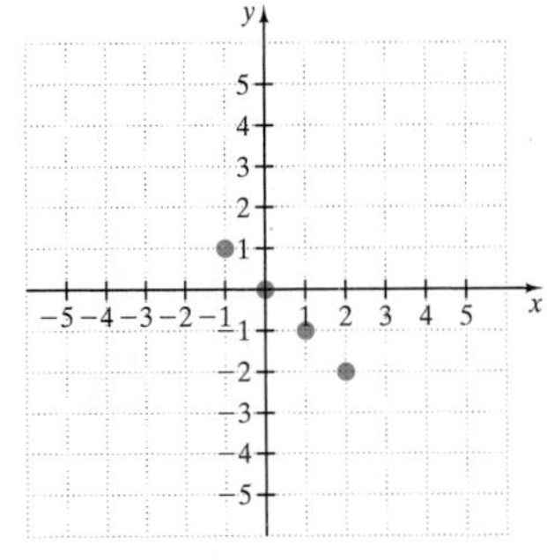

13.

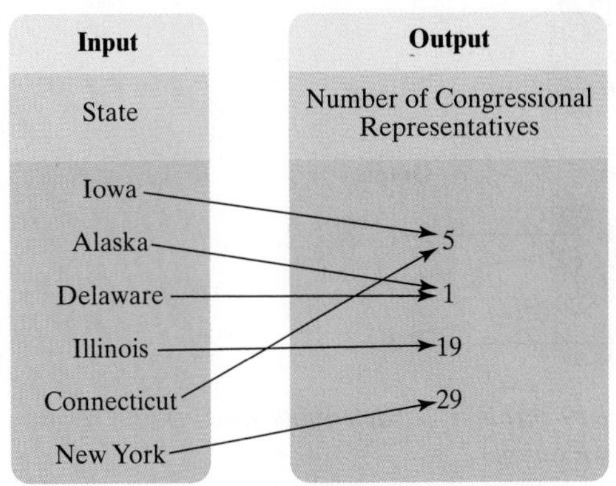

14.

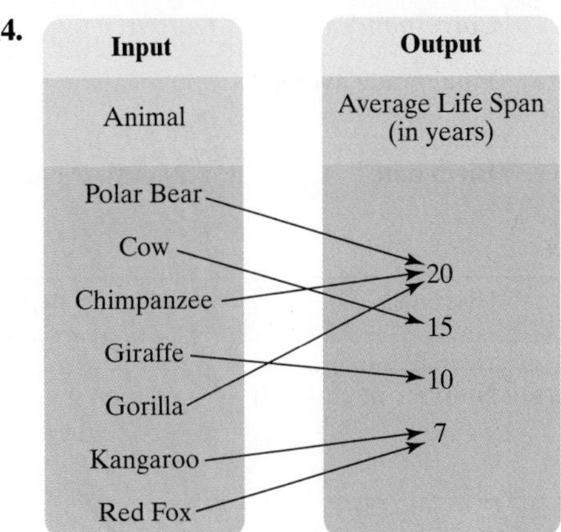

15.

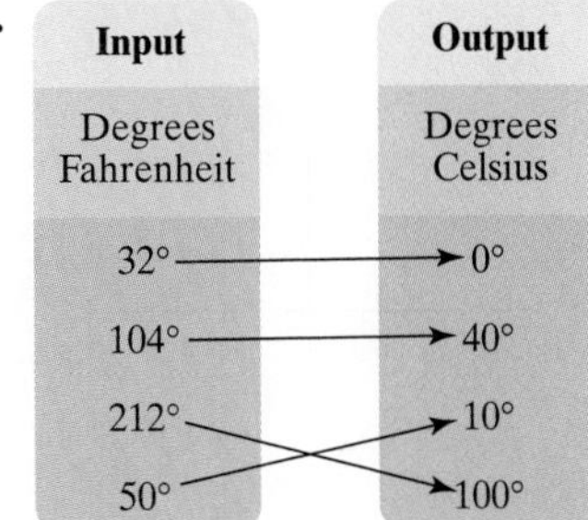

16.

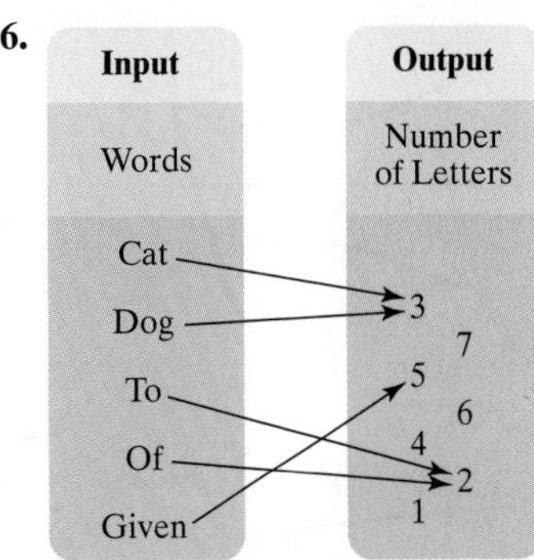

17.

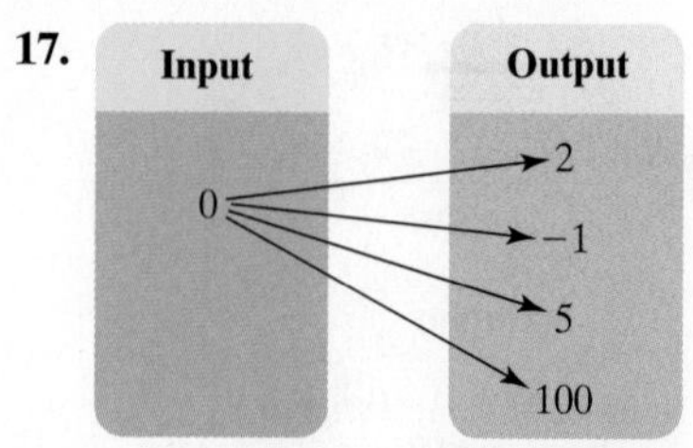

18.

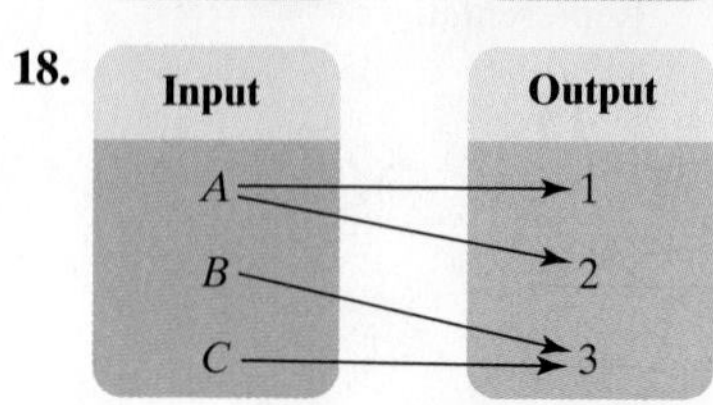

In Exercises 19 through 22, determine whether the relation is a function. See Example 2.

	First Set: Input	***Correspondence***	***Second Set: Output***
19.	Class of algebra students	Final grade average	nonnegative numbers
20.	People who live in Cincinnati, Ohio	Birth date	days of the year
21.	blue, green, brown	Eye color	People who live in Cincinnati, Ohio
22.	Whole numbers from 0 to 4	Number of children	50 Women in a water aerobics class

Use the vertical line test to determine whether each graph is the graph of a function. See Example 5.

23.

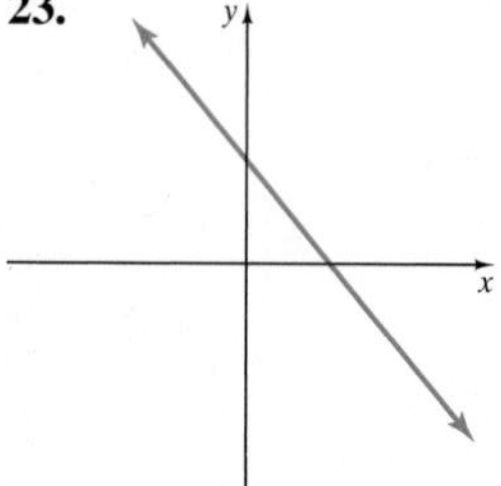

24.

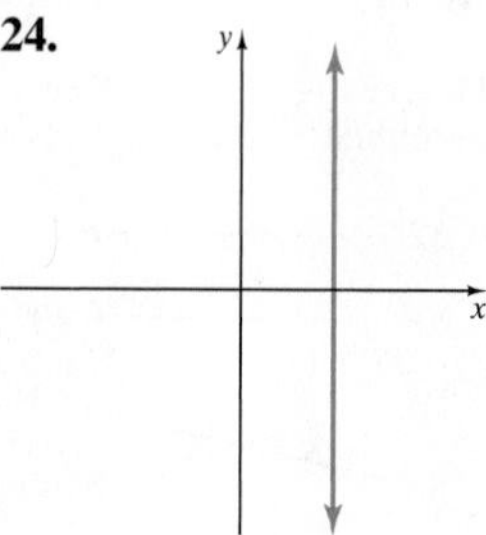

25.

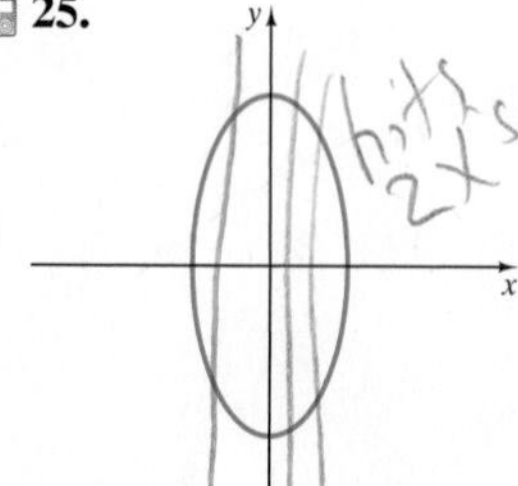

26.

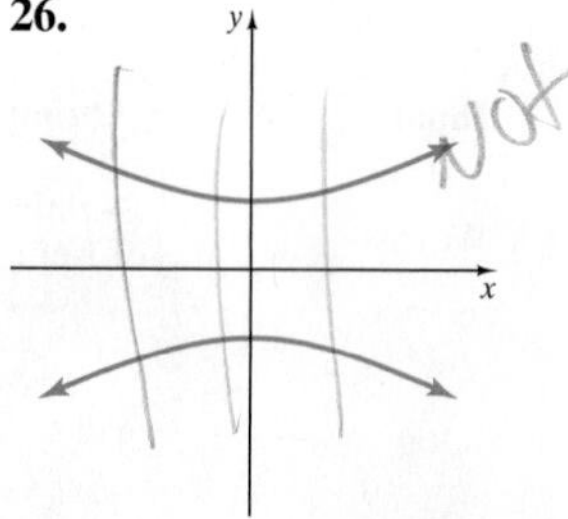

27.

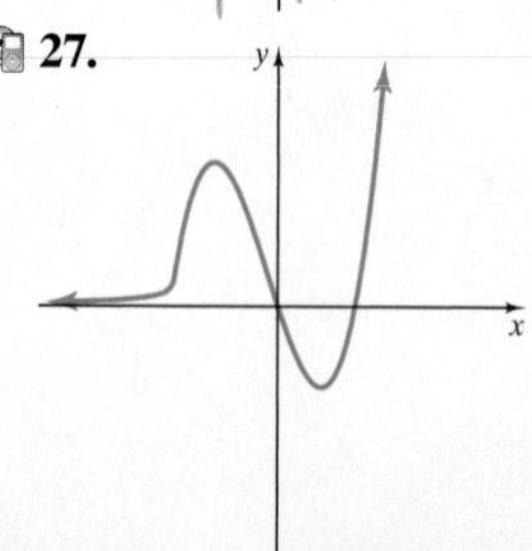

28.

29.

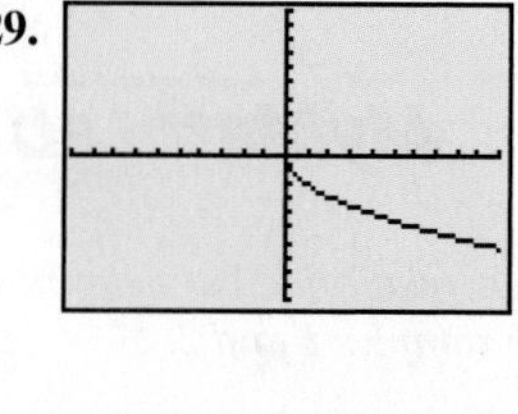

30.

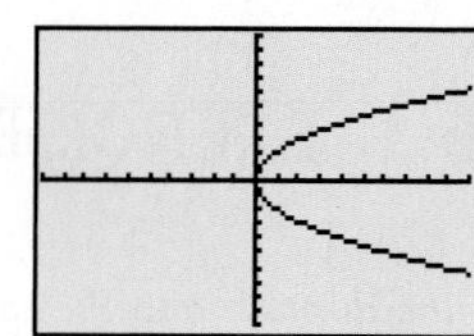

31.

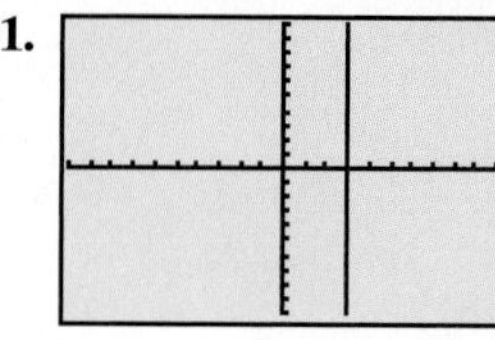

32.

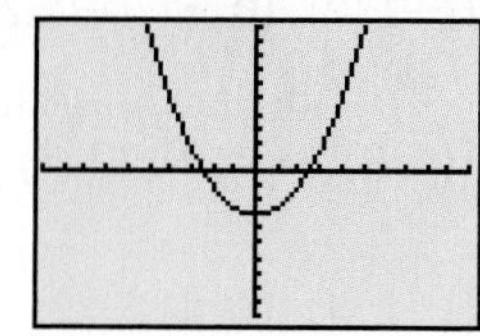

Find the domain and the range of each relation. Use the vertical line test to determine whether each graph is the graph of a function. See Example 6.

33.

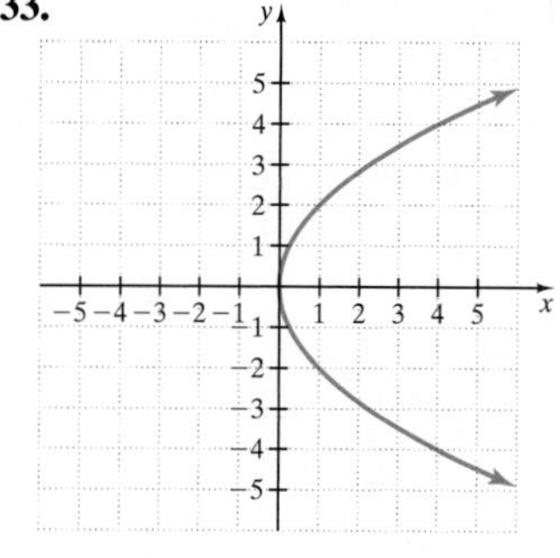

34.

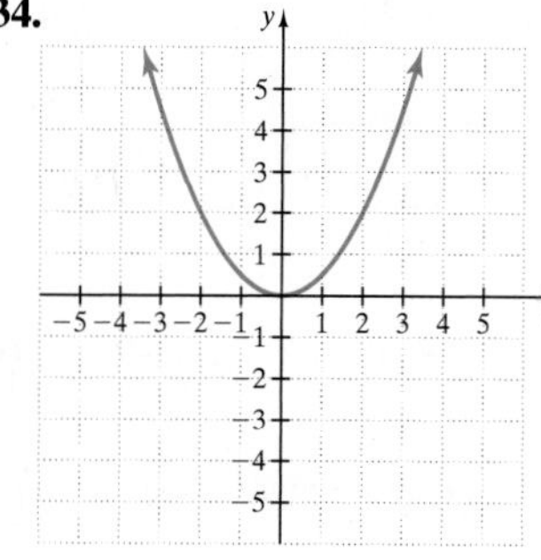

35.

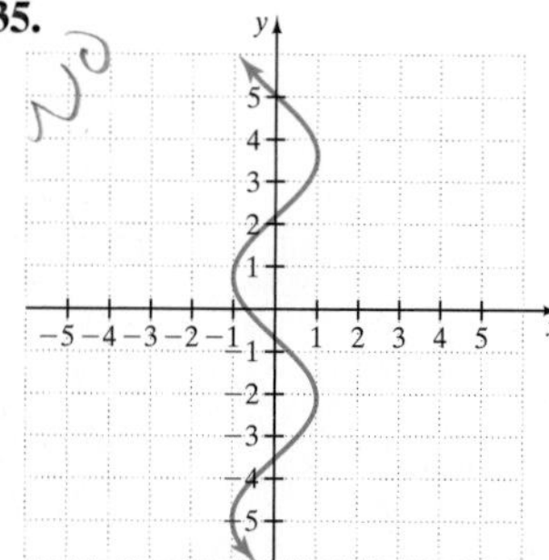

36.

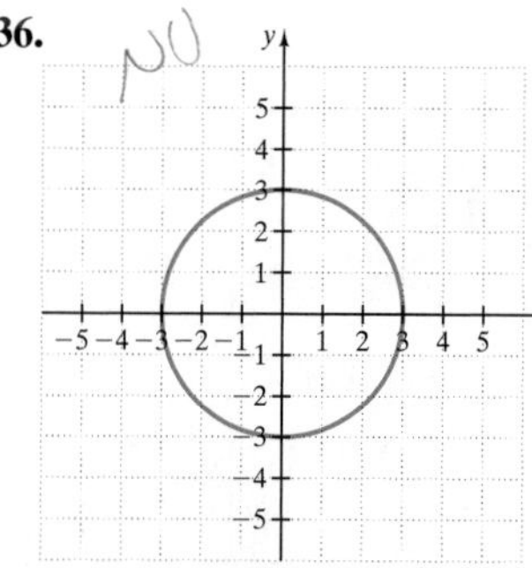

37.

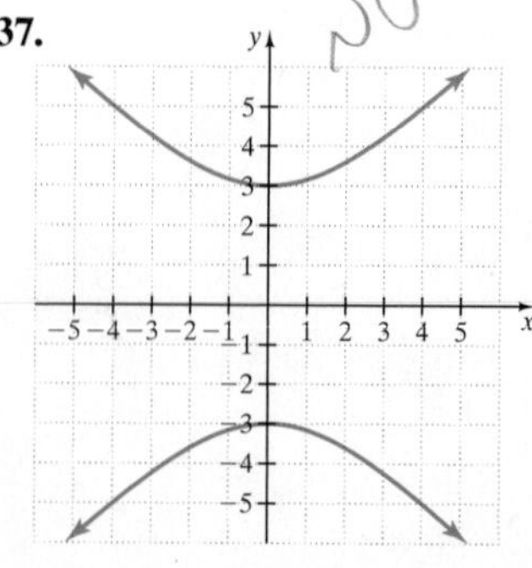

38.

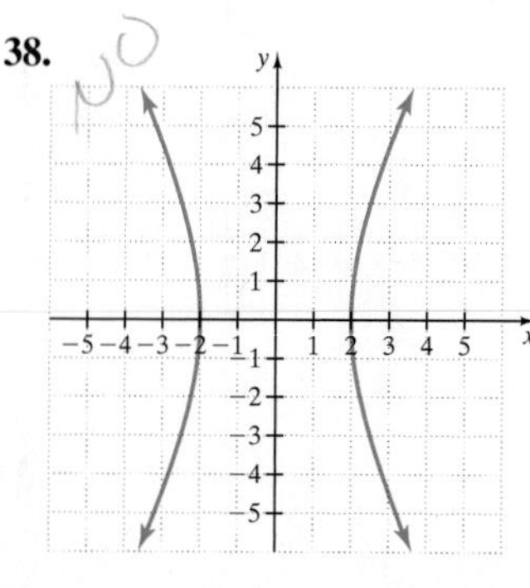

39.
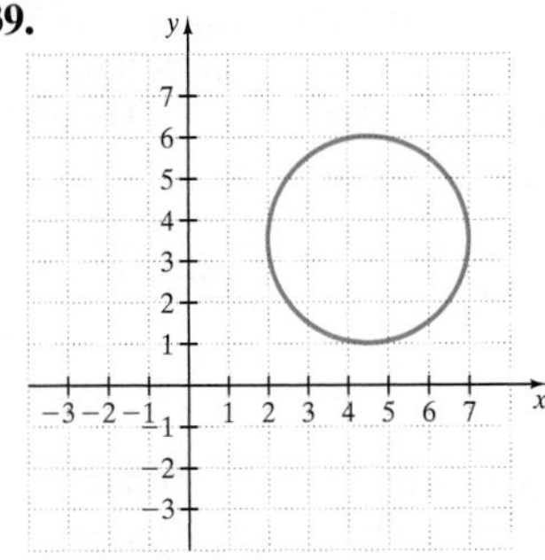

40.
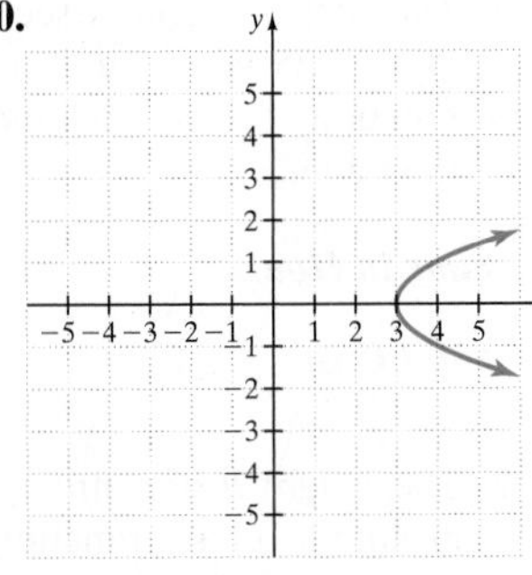

41.
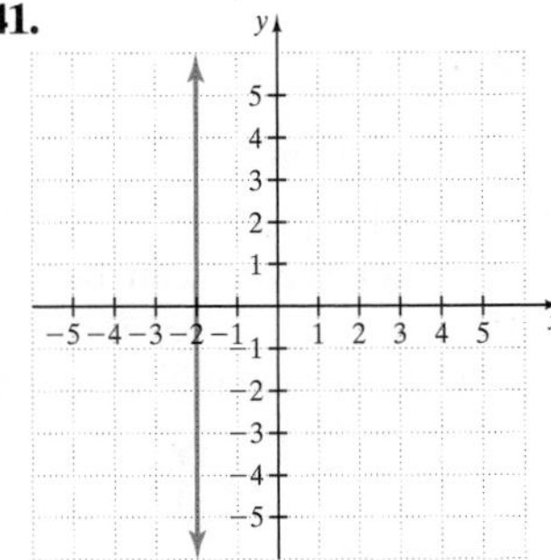

42.
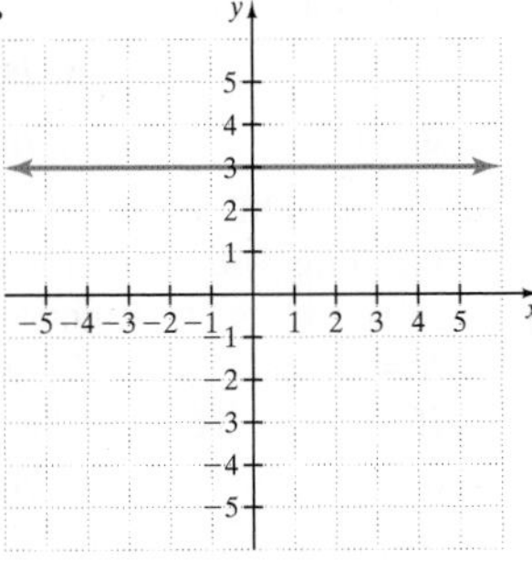

43.
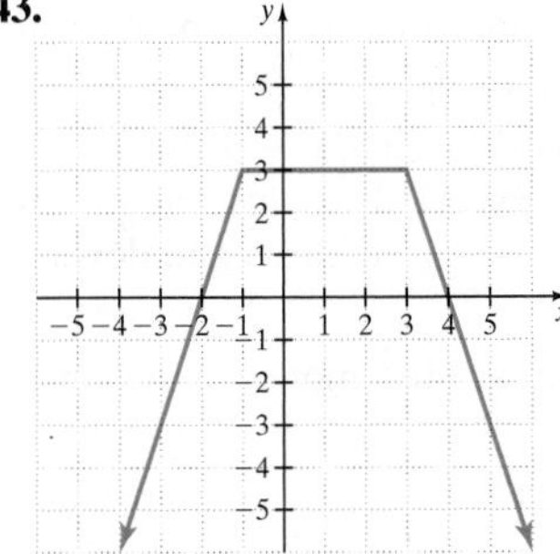

44.
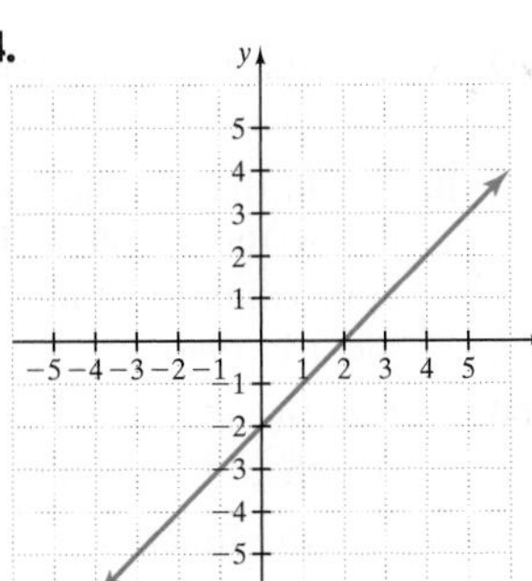

45.
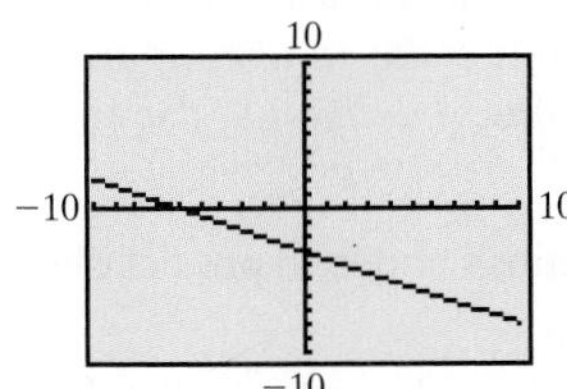

46.
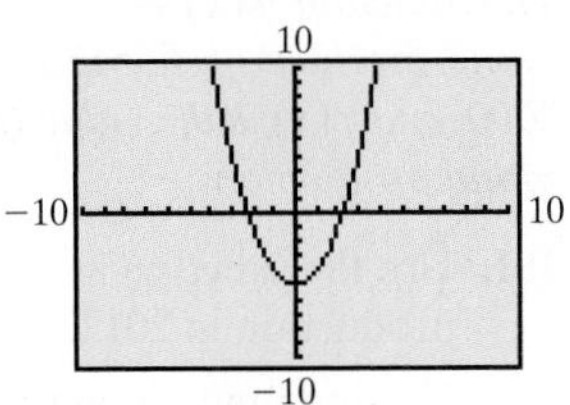

47. In your own words define **(a)** function; **(b)** domain; **(c)** range.

48. Explain the vertical line test and how it is used.

MIXED PRACTICE

Decide whether each is a function. See Examples 3 through 6.

49. $y = x + 1$

50. $y = x - 1$

51. $x = 2y^2$

52. $y = x^2$

53 $y - x = 7$

54. $2x - 3y = 9$

55. $y = \frac{1}{x}$

56. $y = \frac{1}{x - 3}$

57. $y = 5x - 12$

58. $y = \frac{1}{2}x + 4$

59. $x = y^2$

60. $x = |y|$

If $f(x) = 3x + 3$, $g(x) = 4x^2 - 6x + 3$, and $h(x) = 5x^2 - 7$, find the following. See Examples 7 and 8.

61. $f(4)$

62. $f(-1)$

63. $h(-3)$

64. $h(0)$

65. $g(2)$

66. $g(1)$

67. $g(0)$

68. $h(-2)$

Given the following functions, find the indicated values. See Examples 7 and 8.

69. $f(x) = \frac{1}{2}x$;
a. $f(0)$ **b.** $f(2)$ **c.** $f(-2)$

70. $g(x) = -\frac{1}{3}x$;
a. $g(0)$ **b.** $g(-1)$ **c.** $g(3)$

71. $g(x) = 2x^2 + 4$;
a. $g(-11)$ **b.** $g(-1)$ **c.** $g\left(\frac{1}{2}\right)$

72. $h(x) = -x^2$;
a. $h(-5)$ **b.** $h\left(-\frac{1}{3}\right)$ **c.** $h\left(\frac{1}{3}\right)$

73. $f(x) = -5$;
a. $f(2)$ **b.** $f(0)$ **c.** $f(606)$

74. $h(x) = 7$;
a. $h(7)$ **b.** $h(542)$ **c.** $h\left(-\frac{3}{4}\right)$

75. $f(x) = 1.3x^2 - 2.6x + 5.1$
a. $f(2)$ **b.** $f(-2)$ **c.** $f(3.1)$

76. $g(x) = 2.7x^2 + 6.8x - 10.2$
a. $g(1)$ **b.** $g(-5)$ **c.** $g(7.2)$

77. Given the following table of values for $f(x) = |2x - 5| + 8$, find the indicated values.
a. $f(-5)$ **b.** $f(10)$ **c.** $f(15)$

X	Y1
-5	23
0	13
5	13
10	23
15	33
20	43
25	53

Y1=abs(2X-5)+8

78. Given the following table of values for $f(x) = -2x^3 + x$, find the indicated values.
a. $f(-4)$ **b.** $f(2)$ **c.** $f(6)$

X	Y1
-4	124
-2	14
0	0
2	-14
4	-124
6	-426
8	-1016

Y1=-2X³+X

79. Given the graph of the function $f(x) = x^2 + x + 1$, find the value of $f(2)$.

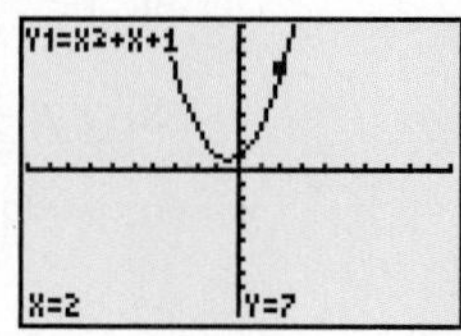

80. Given the graph of the function $f(x) = x^3 + x^2 + 1$, find $f(-2)$.

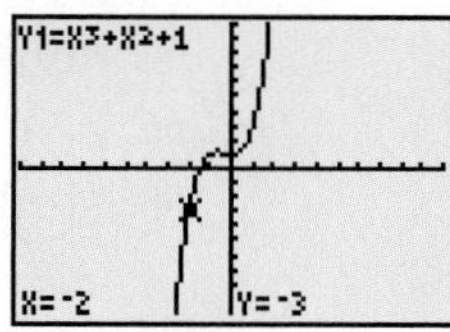

Use the graph of the functions below to answer Exercises 81 through 92. See Example 9.

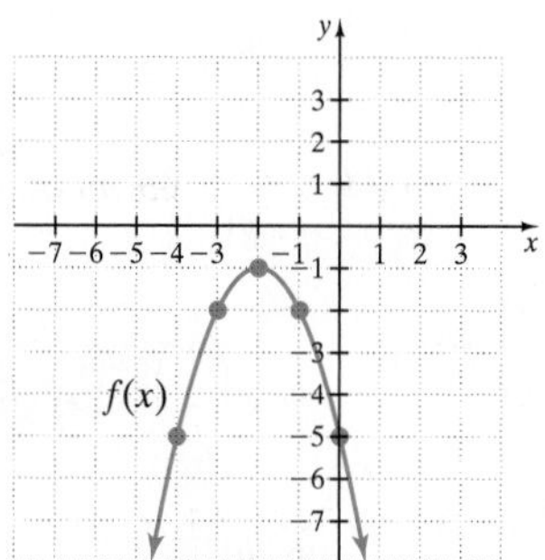

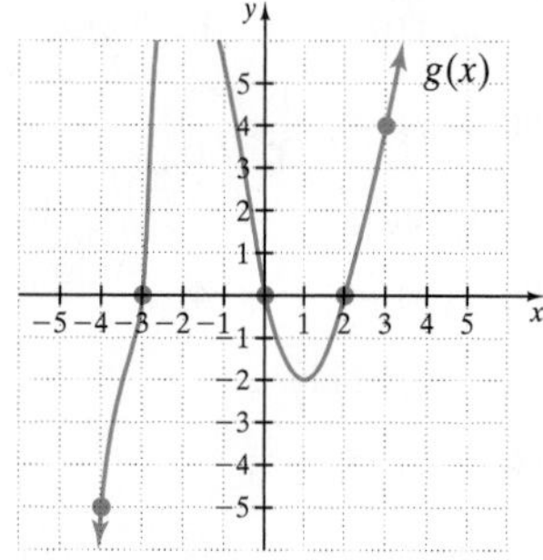

81. If $f(1) = -10$, write the corresponding ordered pair.

82. If $f(-5) = -10$, write the corresponding ordered pair.

83. If $g(4) = 56$, write the corresponding ordered pair.

84. If $g(-2) = 8$, write the corresponding ordered pair.

85. Find $f(-1)$.

86. Find $f(-2)$.

87. Find $g(2)$.

88. Find $g(-4)$.

89. Find all values of x such that $f(x) = -5$.

90. Find all values of x such that $f(x) = -2$.

91. Find all values of x such that $g(x) = -5$

92. Find all values of x such that $g(x) = 0$.

93. What is the greatest number of x-intercepts that a function may have? Explain your answer.

94. What is the greatest number of y-intercepts that a function may have? Explain your answer.

Solve. See Examples 10 and 11.

95. Julie needs to hire a plumber. The cost of hiring a plumber, C, in dollars is a function of the time spent on the job, t, in hours. If the plumber charges a one-time fee of \$20 plus \$35 per hour, we can write this in function notation as $C(t) = 20 + 35t$. Complete the table.

Time in Hours	t	***1***	***2***	***3***	***4***	***5***
Total Cost	$C(t)$					

96. The cost of hiring a secretary to type a term paper is \$10 plus \$5.25 per hour. Therefore, the cost, C, in dollars is a function of time, t, in hours, or $C(t) = 10 + 5.25t$. Complete the table.

Time in Hours	t	***0.5***	***1***	***1.5***	***2.5***	***3***
Total Cost	$C(t)$					

97. The height h of a firecracker being shot into the air from ground level is a function of time t and can be represented using the following formula from physics: $h = -16t^2 + vt$, where v is initial velocity. If the velocity is 80 feet per second, the height in terms of time is $h(t) = -16t^2 + 80t$. Find the following:

a. $h(0.5)$ **b.** $h(1)$ **c.** $h(1.5)$
d. $h(2)$ **e.** $h(2.5)$ **f.** $h(5)$

98. The height h of a rocket launched from a 200-foot-high building with velocity of 120 feet per second can be expressed as a function of time t using the formula $h = -16t^2 + vt + h_0$, where h_0 stands for the initial height. If $h(t) = -16t^2 + 120t + 200$, find the following:

a. $h(0.2)$ **b.** $h(0.6)$ **c.** $h(2.25)$
d. $h(3)$ **e.** $h(4)$

Use the graph in Example 11 to answer the following. Also see Example 12.

99. a. Use the graph to approximate the money spent on research and development in 1996.

b. Recall that the function $f(x) = 2.602x - 5178$ approximates the graph in Example 11. Use this equation to approximate the money spent on research and development in 1996.

100. a. Use the graph to approximate the money spent on research and development in 1999.

b. Use the function $f(x) = 2.602x - 5178$ to approximate the money spent on research and development in 1999.

The function $f(x) = 0.42x + 10.5$, can be used to predict diamond production. For this function, x is the number of years after 2000, and $f(x)$ is the value (in billions of dollars) of the year's diamond production.

101. Use the function in the directions above to predict diamond production in 2012.

102. Use the function in the directions above to predict diamond production in 2015.

103. Since $y = x + 7$ describes a function, rewrite the equation using function notation.

104. In your own words, explain how to find the domain of a function given its graph.

The function $A(r) = \pi r^2$ may be used to find the area of a circle if we are given its radius.

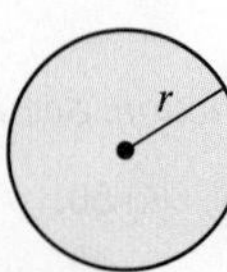

△ **105.** Find the area of a circle whose radius is 5 centimeters. (Do not approximate π.)

△ **106.** Find the area of a circular garden whose radius is 8 feet. (Do not approximate π.)

The function $V(x) = x^3$ may be used to find the volume of a cube if we are given the length x of a side.

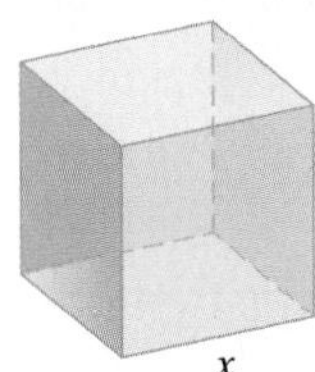

107. Find the volume of a cube whose side is 14 inches.

108. Find the volume of a die whose side is 1.7 centimeters.

Forensic scientists use the following functions to find the height of a woman if they are given the height of her femur bone f or her tibia bone t in centimeters.

$$H(f) = 2.59f + 47.24$$
$$H(t) = 2.72t + 61.28$$

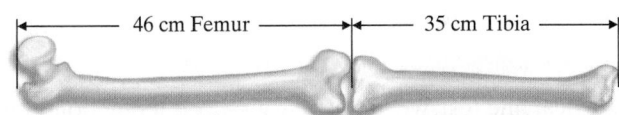

46 cm Femur — 35 cm Tibia

109. Find the height of a woman whose femur measures 46 centimeters.

110. Find the height of a woman whose tibia measures 35 centimeters.

The dosage in milligrams D of Ivermectin, a heartworm preventive, for a dog who weighs x pounds is given by

$$D(x) = \frac{136}{25}x$$

111. Find the proper dosage for a dog that weighs 30 pounds.

112. Find the proper dosage for a dog that weighs 50 pounds.

113. The per capita consumption (in pounds) of all poultry in the United States is approximated by the function $C(x) = 2.28x + 94.86$, where x is the number of years since 2001. (*Source*: Based on actual and estimated data from the Economic Research Service, U.S. Department of Agriculture)

a. Find and interpret $C(5)$.

b. Estimate the per capita consumption of all poultry in the United States in 2007.

114. The average length of U.S. hospital stays has been decreasing, following the equation $y = -0.09x + 8.02$, where x is the number of years since 1970 and y is the length of the average stay in days. (*Source:* National Center for Health Statistics)

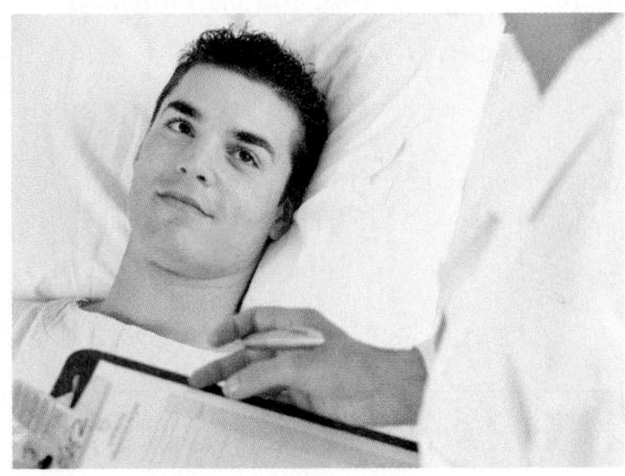

a. What was the length of the average hospital stay in 1995?

b. If this trend continues, what will the average length be in 2011?

REVIEW AND PREVIEW

Complete the given table and use the table to graph the linear equation. See Section 15.1.

115. $x - y = -5$

x	0		1
y		0	

116. $2x + 3y = 10$

x	0		
y		0	2

117. $7x + 4y = 8$

x	0		
y		0	−1

118. $5y - x = -15$

x	0		−2
y		0	

119. $y = 6x$

x	0		−1
y		0	

120. $y = -2x$

x	0		−2
y		0	

△ **121.** Is it possible to find the perimeter of the following geometric figure? If so, find the perimeter.

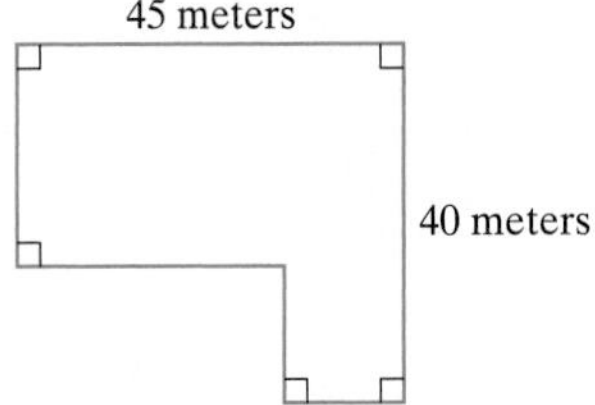

CONCEPT EXTENSIONS

For Exercises 122 through 125, suppose that $y = f(x)$ and it is true that $f(7) = 50$. Determine whether each is true or false. See the second Concept Check in this section.

122. An ordered pair solution of the function is (7, 50).

123. When x is 50, y is 7.

124. A possible function is $f(x) = x^2 + 1$.

125. A possible function is $f(x) = 10x - 20$.

Given the following functions, find the indicated values.

126. $f(x) = 2x + 7;$

a. $f(2)$ **b.** $f(a)$

127. $g(x) = -3x + 12;$

a. $g(s)$ **b.** $g(r)$

128. $h(x) = x^2 + 7;$

a. $h(3)$ **b.** $h(a)$

129. $f(x) = x^2 - 12;$

a. $f(12)$ **b.** $f(a)$

130. Describe a function whose domain is the set of people in your hometown.

131. Describe a function whose domain is the set of people in your algebra class.

15.2 GRAPHING LINEAR FUNCTIONS

OBJECTIVES

1. Graph linear functions.
2. Graph linear functions by finding intercepts.
3. Graph vertical and horizontal lines.
4. Use graphs to solve problems.

OBJECTIVE 1 ▶ Graphing linear functions. In this section, we identify and graph linear functions. By the vertical line test, we know that all linear equations except those whose graphs are vertical lines are functions. For example, we know from Section 15.1 that $y = 2x$ is a linear equation in two variables. Its graph is shown.

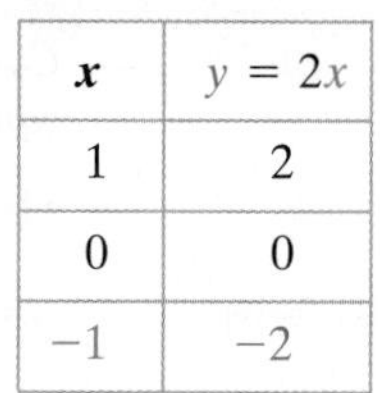

x	$y = 2x$
1	2
0	0
−1	−2

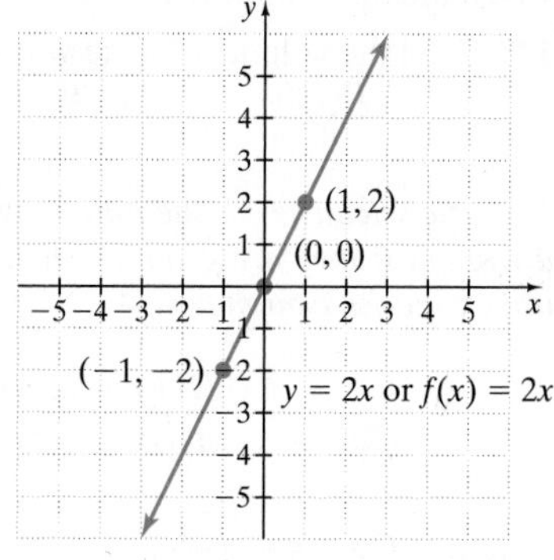

Because this graph passes the vertical line test, we know that $y = 2x$ is a function. If we want to emphasize that this equation describes a function, we may write $y = 2x$ as $f(x) = 2x$.

A graphing utility is a very versatile tool for exploring the graphs of functions.

DISCOVER THE CONCEPT

a. On your graphing utility, graph both $f(x) = 2x$ as $y_1 = 2x$, and $g(x) = 2x + 10$ as $y_2 = 2x + 10$ using an integer window.

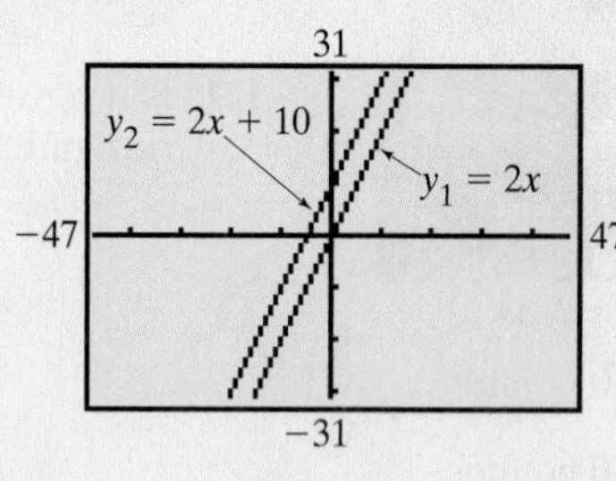

Integer Window

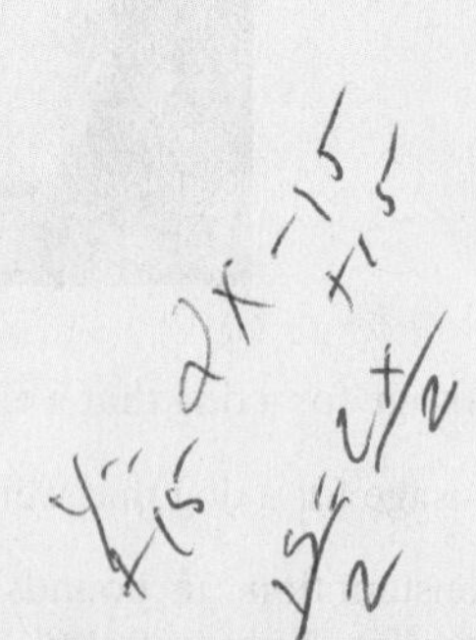

b. Trace on the graph of $y_1 = 2x$ to find the point whose ordered pair has x-coordinate 3 and find the corresponding y-coordinate. Now, press the down arrow key and find the corresponding y-coordinate on the graph of $y_2 = 2x + 10$. Compare the two y-coordinates for the same x-coordinate.

c. Trace to another point on the graph of y_1 and repeat this process. Compare the two lines, and see if you can state how we could sketch the graph of $g(x) = 2x + 10$ from the graph of $f(x) = 2x$.

d. Predict how the graph of $h(x) = 2x - 15$ could be drawn. Graph $y_3 = 2x - 15$ and see if your prediction is correct.

The y-values for the graph of $g(x)$ or $y = 2x + 10$ are obtained by adding 10 to the y-value of each corresponding point of the graph of $f(x)$ or $y = 2x$. The graph of $g(x) = 2x + 10$ is the same as the graph of $f(x) = 2x$ shifted upward 10 units.

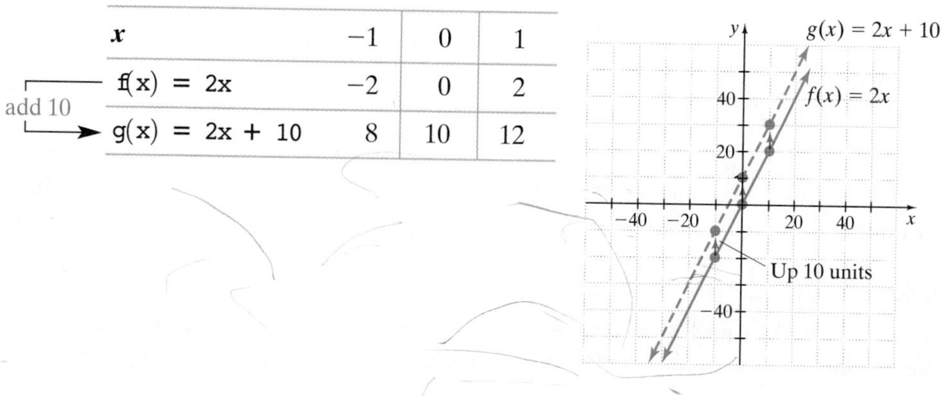

x	−1	0	1
$f(x) = 2x$	−2	0	2
$g(x) = 2x + 10$	8	10	12

Also, the graph of $h(x)$ or $y = 2x - 15$ is obtained by subtracting 15 from the y-value of each corresponding point of the graph of $f(x)$ or $y = 2x$. Thus, the graph of $h(x) = 2x - 15$ is the same as the graph of $f(x) = 2x$ shifted downward 15 units.

The functions $f(x) = 2x$, $g(x) = 2x + 10$, and $h(x) = 2x - 15$ are called linear functions—"linear" because each graph is a line, and "function" because each graph passes the vertical line test.

In general, a **linear function** is a function that can be written in the form $f(x) = mx + b$. For example, $g(x) = 2x + 10$ is in this form, with $m = 2$ and $b = 10$.

Note: Ordered pairs may be listed in a variety of ways, including tables. In Section 15.1, the tables were written vertically. Above, we see a table written horizontally. Throughout this section, you will see ordered-pair tables written vertically and horizontally. Both ways of writing tables are useful and have advantages.

EXAMPLE 1 Graph $g(x) = 2x + 1$. Compare this graph with the graph of $f(x) = 2x$.

Solution To graph $g(x) = 2x + 1$, find three ordered pair solutions.

add 1

x	$f(x) = 2x$	$g(x) = 2x + 1$
0	0	1
−1	−2	−1
1	2	3

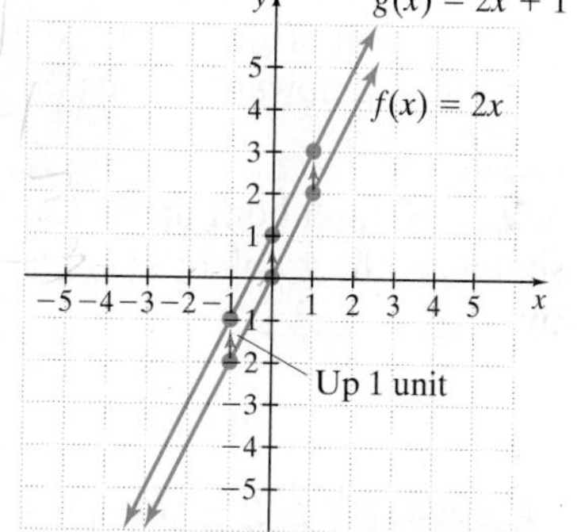

Notice that y-values for the graph of $g(x) = 2x + 1$ are obtained by adding 1 to each y-value of each corresponding point of the graph of $f(x) = 2x$. The graph of $g(x) = 2x + 1$ is the same as the graph of $f(x) = 2x$ shifted upward 1 unit. □

PRACTICE

1 Graph $g(x) = 4x - 3$ and $f(x) = 4x$ on the same axes.

Notice that $g(x) = 2x + 1$ above is a **linear function** in the form $g(x) = mx + b$. For this function, $g(x) = 2x + 1$, $m = 2$ and $b = 1$.

EXAMPLE 2 Graph both linear functions $f(x) = 0.5x$ and $g(x) = 0.5x + 8$ using the same integer window.

a. Use the graphs to complete the following table of solution pairs.

x	−6	0	5	13	18
$f(x) = 0.5x$					
$g(x) = 0.5x + 8$					

b. Complete the following sentence. The graph of $g(x) = 0.5x + 8$ can be obtained from the graph of $f(x) = 0.5x$ by ____________.

Solution

a. Define $y_1 = 0.5x$ and $y_2 = 0.5x + 8$ and graph in the integer window. The screens below show the values of $f(x)$ and $g(x)$ when $x = 4$. In other words, $f(4) = 2$ and $g(4) = 10$.

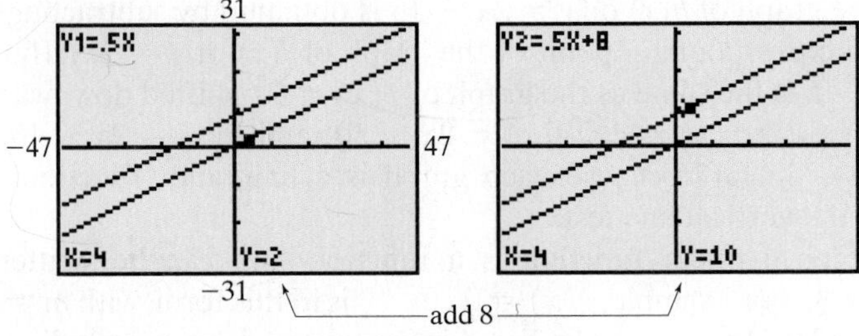

Trace along each graph to complete the table as follows:

x	−6	0	5	13	18
$f(x) = 0.5x$	−3	0	2.5	6.5	9
$g(x) = 0.5x + 8$	5	8	10.5	14.5	17

b. The graph of $g(x) = 0.5x + 8$ can be obtained from the graph of $f(x) = 0.5x$ by shifting it upward 8 units. □

PRACTICE 2 Graph both linear functions $f(x) = -3x$ and $g(x) = -3x + 2$. Complete the sentence. The graph of $g(x) = -3x + 2$ can be obtained from the graph of $f(x) = -3x$ by ____________.

EXAMPLE 3 Graph both linear functions $f(x) = -x$ and $g(x) = -x - 16$ using an integer window. Complete the following statement. The graph of $g(x) = -x - 16$ can be obtained from the graph of $f(x) = -x$ by ____________.

Solution Graph $y_1 = -x$ and $y_2 = -x - 16$ using an integer window as shown on the next page. We can complete the statement as follows. The graph of $g(x) = -x - 16$ can be obtained from the graph of $f(x)$ by shifting it downward 16 units. To further illustrate this fact, see the table on the next page. And compare the y_1 and y_2 values for the same x-value.

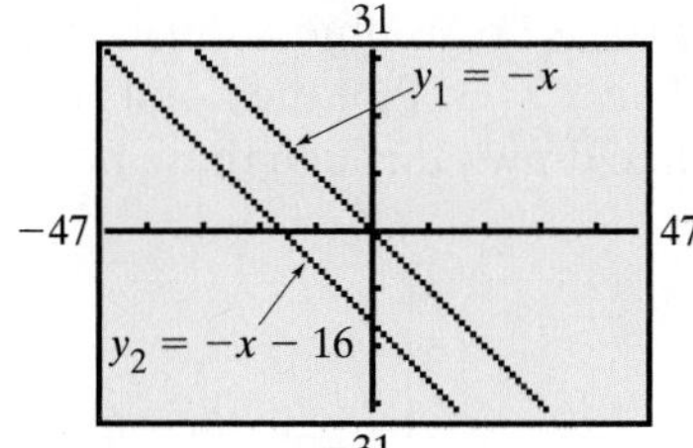

X	Y1	Y2
0	0	-16
1	-1	-17
2	-2	-18
3	-3	-19
4	-4	-20
5	-5	-21
6	-6	-22

Y2=-22

subtract 16

□

PRACTICE

3 Complete the sentence. The graph of $y_2 = -x - 5$ can be obtained from the graph of $y = -x$ by ______________.

In general, for any function $f(x)$, the graph of $y = f(x) + K$ is the same as the graph of $y = f(x)$ shifted $|K|$ units upward if K is positive and downward if K is negative.

OBJECTIVE 2 ▶ Graphing linear functions using intercepts. The graph of $y = 2x + 10$ is shown in both screens below. Notice that this graph crosses both the x-axis and the y-axis. Recall that a point where a graph crosses the x-axis is called the ***x*-intercept,** and a point where a graph crosses the y-axis is called the ***y*-intercept.**

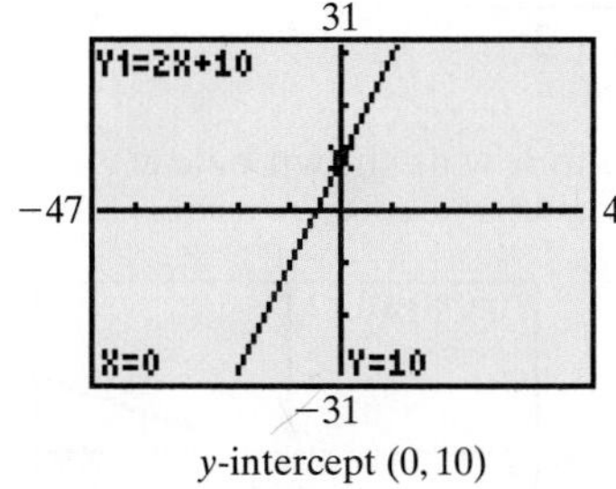

y-intercept (0, 10)

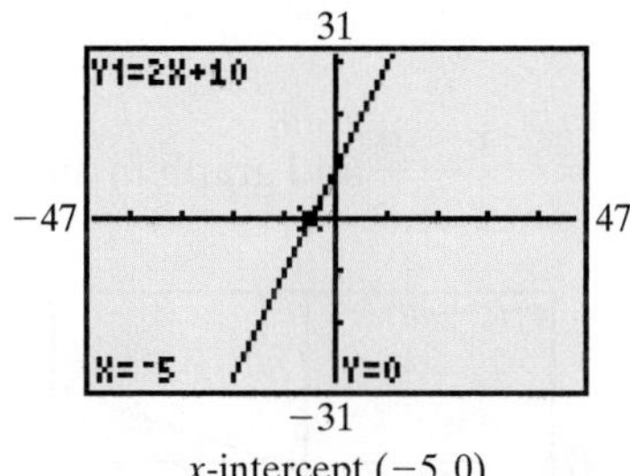

x-intercept (−5, 0)

By tracing along the graph, we can see that the y-intercept of the graph of $y = 2x + 10$ is (0, 10). Also the x-intercept of the graph is (−5, 0).

One way to find the y-intercept of the graph of an equation is to let $x = 0$, since a point on the y-axis has an x-coordinate of 0. To find the x-intercept, let $y = 0$ or $f(x) = 0$, since a point on the x-axis has a y-coordinate of 0.

Finding *x*- and *y*-Intercepts

To find an x-intercept, let $y = 0$ or $f(x) = 0$ and solve for x.
To find a y-intercept, let $x = 0$ and solve for y.

Intercepts are usually easy to find and plot since one coordinate is 0.

In the next example, we sketch a linear function by plotting x- and y-intercepts.

EXAMPLE 4 Graph $x - 3y = 6$ by plotting intercepts. Check using a graphing utility.

Solution Let $y = 0$ to find the x-intercept and $x = 0$ to find the y-intercept.

If $y = 0$ then	If $x = 0$ then
$x - 3(0) = 6$	$0 - 3y = 6$
$x - 0 = 6$	$-3y = 6$
$x = 6$	$y = -2$

The x-intercept is $(6, 0)$ and the y-intercept is $(0, -2)$. We find a third ordered pair solution to check our work. If we let $y = -1$, then $x = 3$. Plot the points $(6, 0)$, $(0, -2)$, and $(3, -1)$. The graph of $x - 3y = 6$ is the line drawn through these points, as shown.

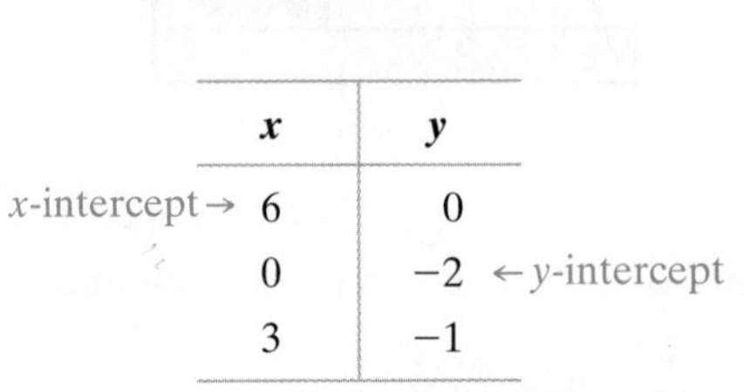

	x	y	
x-intercept →	6	0	
	0	−2	← y-intercept
	3	−1	

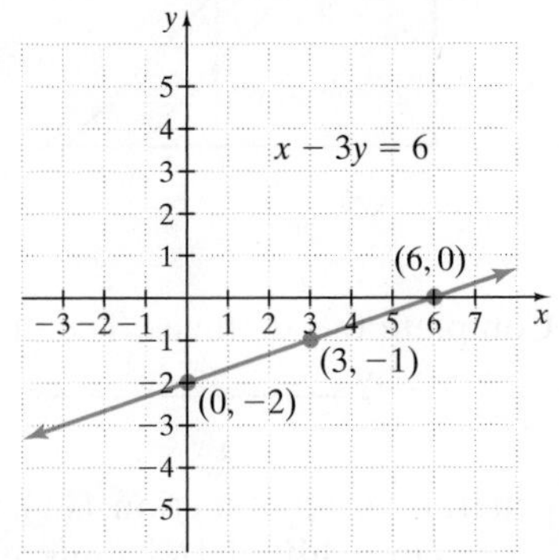

To check using a graphing utility, solve for y to enter the equation in the Y= editor.

$$x - 3y = 6$$
$$-3y = -x + 6$$
$$y = \frac{-x + 6}{-3}$$

Define $y_1 = \dfrac{-x + 6}{-3}$ and graph in an integer window as shown below.

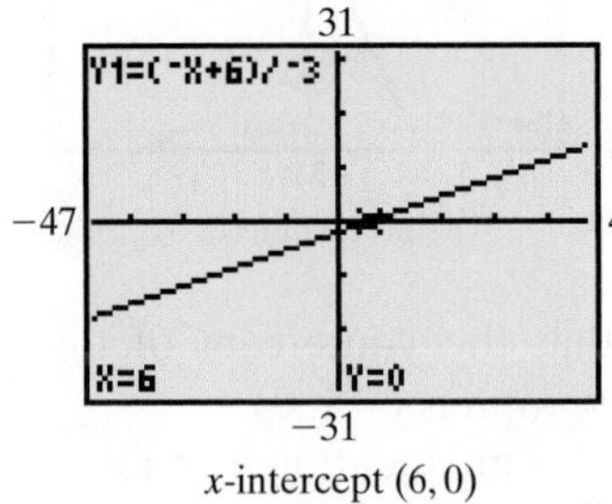

x-intercept $(6, 0)$

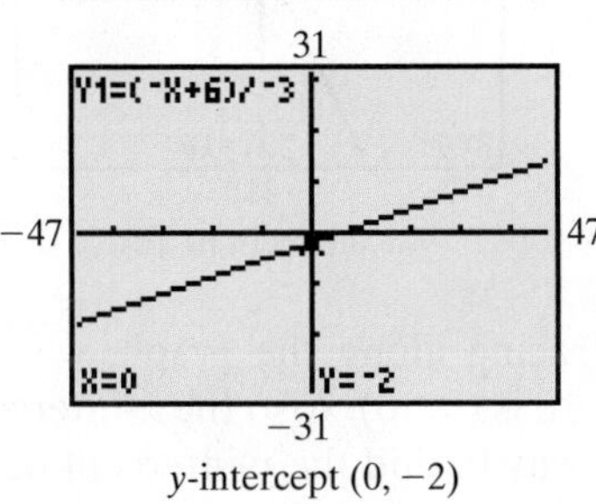

y-intercept $(0, -2)$

□

PRACTICE 4 Graph $4x - 5y = -20$ by plotting intercepts. Check using a graphing utility.

Notice that the equation $x - 3y = 6$ describes a linear function—"linear" because its graph is a line and "function" because the graph passes the vertical line test.

If we want to emphasize that the equation $x - 3y = 6$ from Example 4 describes a function, we first solve the equation for y.

$$x - 3y = 6$$
$$-3y = -x + 6 \quad \text{Subtract } x \text{ from both sides.}$$
$$\frac{-3y}{-3} = \frac{-x}{-3} + \frac{6}{-3} \quad \text{Divide both sides by } -3.$$
$$y = \frac{1}{3}x - 2 \quad \text{Simplify.}$$

Next, let $y = f(x)$.

$$f(x) = \frac{1}{3}x - 2$$

Helpful Hint

Any linear equation that describes a function can be written using function notation. To do so,

1. Solve the equation for y and then
2. Replace y with $f(x)$, as we did above.

Helpful Hint

Recall that when generating a graph using a graphing utility, we first solve for the variable y. When a function is given in the $f(x)$ notation, it is already solved for y and can be entered in the Y= editor directly.

DISCOVER THE CONCEPT

a. Use an integer setting and graph each linear function.

$$y_1 = x + 15 \qquad y_2 = x \qquad y_3 = x - 11$$

b. Decide how the y-intercept of the graph of the equation compares with the equation.

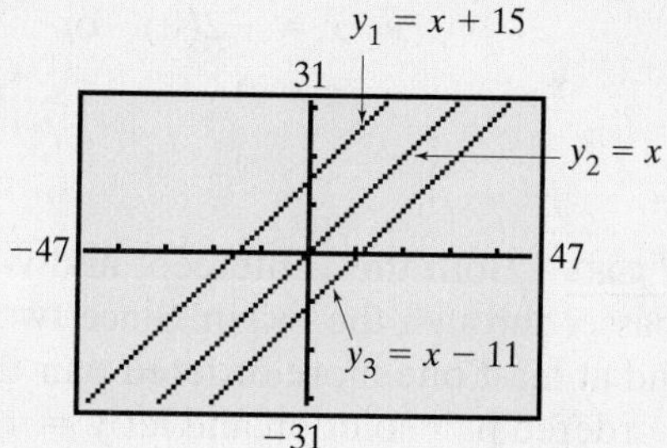

From the discovery above, we found the following:

Equation	***y-intercept***
$y = x + 15$	$(0, 15)$
$y = x$	$(0, 0)$
$y = x - 11$	$(0, -11)$

In general,

$$y = mx + b \qquad (0, b)$$

Notice that the y-intercept of the graph of the equation of the form $y = mx + b$ is $(0, b)$ each time. This is because we find the y-intercept of the graph of an equation by letting $x = 0$. Thus,

$$y = mx + b$$
$$y = m \cdot 0 + b \quad \text{Let } x = 0.$$
$$y = b$$

The intercept is $(0, b)$.

EXAMPLE 5 Find the y-intercept of the graph of each equation.

a. $f(x) = \frac{1}{2}x + \frac{3}{7}$ **b.** $y = -2.5x - 3.2$

Solution

a. The y-intercept of $f(x) = \frac{1}{2}x + \frac{3}{7}$ is $\left(0, \frac{3}{7}\right)$.

b. The y-intercept of $y = -2.5x - 3.2$ is $(0, -3.2)$. □

Y1=-2.5X-3.2
X=0 Y=-3.2
[−10, 10] by [−10, 10]

A calculator check of Example 5b.

PRACTICE 5 Find the y-intercept of the graph of each equation.

a. $f(x) = \frac{3}{4}x - \frac{2}{5}$ **b.** $y = 2.6x + 4.1$

EXAMPLE 6 Graph $x = -2y$ by plotting intercepts.

Solution Let $y = 0$ to find the x-intercept and $x = 0$ to find the y-intercept.

If $y = 0$ then	If $x = 0$ then
$x = -2(0)$ or	$0 = -2y$ or
$x = 0$	$0 = y$
$(0, 0)$	$(0, 0)$

Ordered pairs Both the x-intercept and y-intercept are $(0, 0)$. This happens when the graph passes through the origin. Since two points are needed to determine a line, we must find at least one more ordered pair that satisfies $x = -2y$. Let $y = -1$ to find a second ordered pair solution and let $y = 1$ as a check point.

If $y = -1$ then	If $y = 1$ then
$x = -2(-1)$ or	$x = -2(1)$ or
$x = 2$	$x = -2$

The ordered pairs are $(0, 0)$, $(2, -1)$, and $(-2, 1)$. Plot these points to graph $x = -2y$.

x	y
0	0
2	−1
−2	1

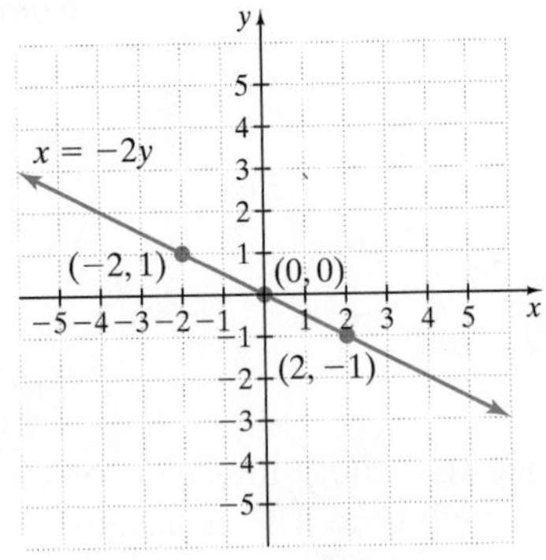

□

PRACTICE 6 Graph $y = -3x$ by plotting intercepts.

OBJECTIVE 3 ▶ Graphing vertical and horizontal lines. The equations $x = c$ and $y = c$, where c is a real number constant, are both linear equations in two variables. Why? Because $x = c$ can be written as $x + 0y = c$ and $y = c$ can be written as $0x + y = c$. We graph these two special linear equations on the next page.

EXAMPLE 7 Graph $x = 2$.

Solution The equation $x = 2$ can be written as $x + 0y = 2$. For any y-value chosen, notice that x is 2. No other value for x satisfies $x + 0y = 2$. Any ordered pair whose x-coordinate is 2 is a solution to $x + 0y = 2$ because 2 added to 0 times any value of y is $2 + 0$, or 2. We will use the ordered pairs $(2, 3)$, $(2, 0)$, and $(2, -3)$ to graph $x = 2$.

	x	y
	2	3
x-intercept :	2	0
	2	−3

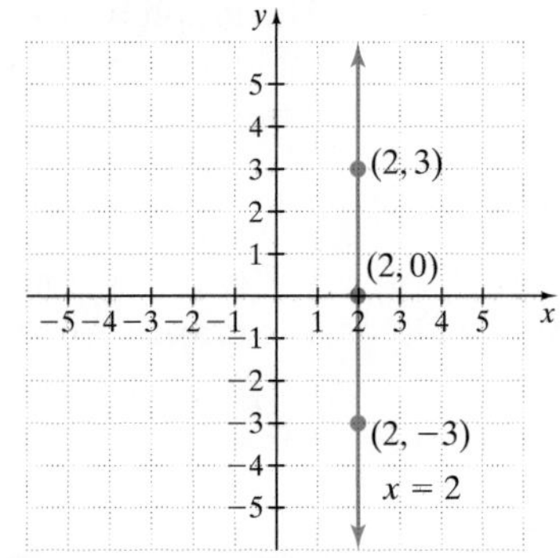

The graph is a vertical line with x-intercept $(2, 0)$. Notice that this graph is not the graph of a function, and it has no y-intercept because x is never 0. □

PRACTICE 7 Graph $x = -4$.

TECHNOLOGY NOTE

Since the graph of $x = c$ is a vertical line and is not a function, we cannot enter this equation in the Y= editor.

However, most graphing utilities have a draw feature that allows you to draw the vertical line, but you cannot use trace on it since it is not a function. See if your graphing utility has this feature.

EXAMPLE 8 Graph $y = -3$.

Solution The equation $y = -3$ can be written as $0x + y = -3$. For any x-value chosen, y is -3. If we choose 4, 0, and -2 as x-values, the ordered pair solutions are $(4, -3)$, $(0, -3)$, and $(-2, -3)$. We will use these ordered pairs to graph $y = -3$.

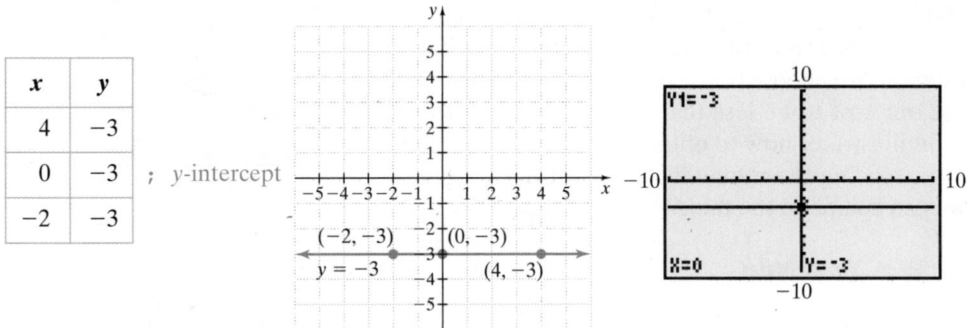

x	y	
4	−3	
0	−3	; y-intercept
−2	−3	

The graph is a horizontal line with y-intercept $(0, -3)$ and no x-intercept. Notice that this graph is the graph of a function. Above to the right is the graph of $y = -3$ using a graphing utility. Trace along the line to see that all ordered pair solutions have a y-coordinate of -3. □

PRACTICE 8 Graph $y = 4$.

From Examples 7 and 8, we have the following generalization.

Graphing Vertical and Horizontal Lines

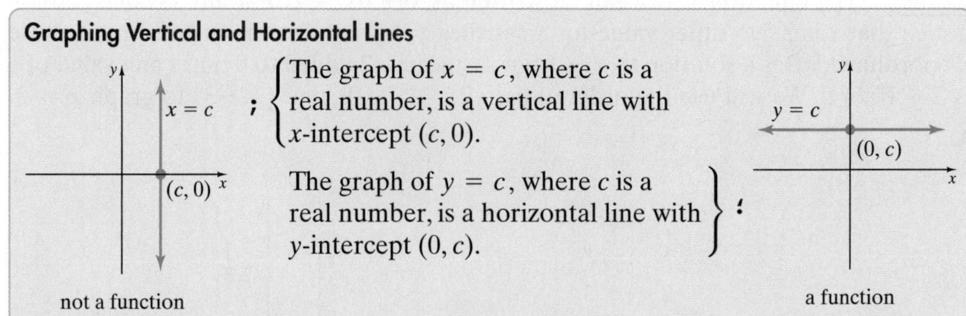

x = c
(c, 0)
not a function
The graph of x = c, where c is a real number, is a vertical line with x-intercept (c, 0).
The graph of y = c, where c is a real number, is a horizontal line with y-intercept (0, c).
y = c
(0, c)
a function

Notice the graph of $x = c$ is not a function, so it cannot be graphed in function mode on the calculator. The graph of $y = c$ is a function, so it can be graphed on the calculator.

OBJECTIVE 4 ▶ Using graphs to solve problems. We can use the graph of a linear equation to solve problems.

EXAMPLE 9 **Cost of Renting a Car**

The cost of renting a car for a day is given by the linear function $C(x) = 35 + 0.15x$, where $C(x)$ represents the cost in dollars and x is the number of miles driven. Use the graph of the function to complete the table below in dollars, and find the cost $C(x)$ for the given number of miles.

No. of Miles	x	150	200	325	500
Cost	$C(x) = 35 + 0.15x$				

Solution Define $y_1 = 35 + 0.15x$ and graph in a [0, 600, 100] by [0, 200, 50] window. We choose $0 \le x \le 600$ since the values in the table are in this interval. We choose $0 \le y \le 200$ as we are estimating our cost to be less than \$200. The graph to the right illustrates how to obtain the cost for 150 miles.

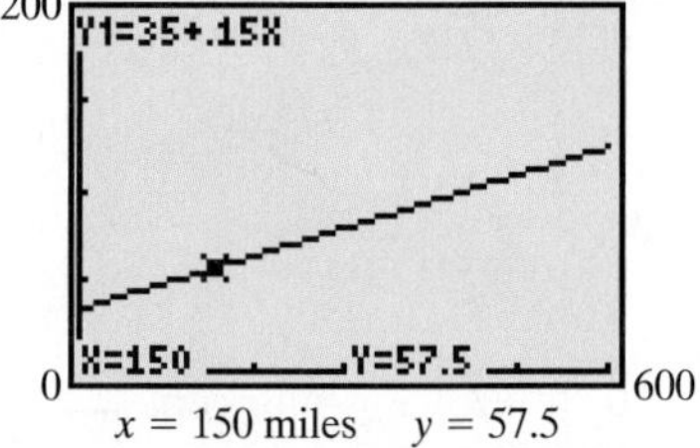

Finding the remaining values from the graph, we can complete the table.

No. of Miles	x	150	200	325	500
Cost	$C(x) = 35 + 0.15x$	57.5	65	83.75	110

Notice from the graph that the cost $C(x)$ increases as the number of miles, x, increases. □

PRACTICE 9 The cost of renting a premium car for a day is given by the linear function $C(x) = 79 + 0.10x$, where x is the number of miles driven. Use this function to complete the table.

No. of Miles	x	50	175	230	450
Cost	$C(x)$				

VOCABULARY & READINESS CHECK

Use the choices below to fill in each blank. Some choices may be used more than once and some not at all.

horizontal	y	$(c, 0)$	$(b, 0)$	$(m, 0)$	linear
vertical	x	$(0, c)$	$(0, b)$	$(0, m)$	$f(x)$

1. A ________ function can be written in the form $f(x) = mx + b$.

2. In the form $f(x) = mx + b$, the y-intercept is ________.

3. The graph of $x = c$ is a ________ line with x-intercept ________.

4. The graph of $y = c$ is a ________ line with y-intercept ________.

5. To find an x-intercept, let ____ = 0 or ______ = 0 and solve for ____.

6. To find a y-intercept, let ____ = 0 and solve for ____.

15.2 EXERCISE SET

Graph each linear function. See Examples 1 and 2.

1. $f(x) = -2x$

2. $f(x) = 2x$

3. $f(x) = -2x + 3$

4. $f(x) = 2x + 6$

5. $f(x) = \frac{1}{2}x$

6. $f(x) = \frac{1}{3}x$

7. $f(x) = \frac{1}{2}x - 4$

8. $f(x) = \frac{1}{3}x - 2$

The graph of $f(x) = 5x$ in a standard window follows. Use this graph to match each linear function with its graph. See Examples 1 and 2.

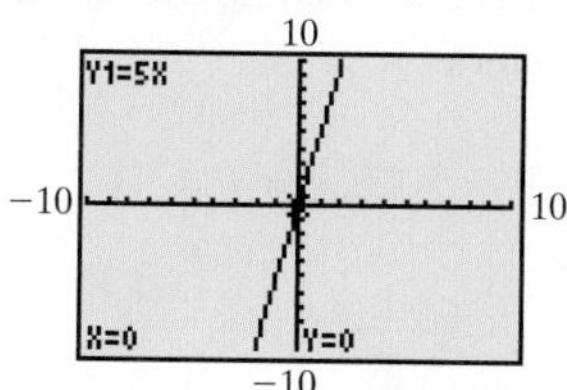

A.

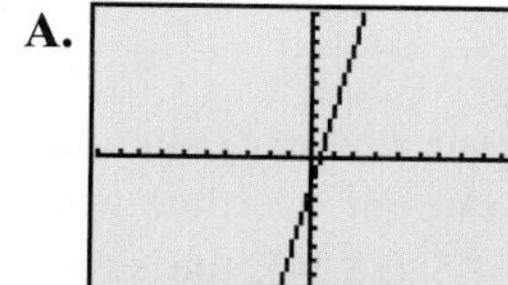

B.

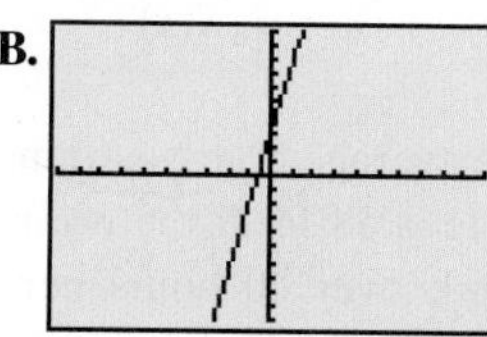

C.

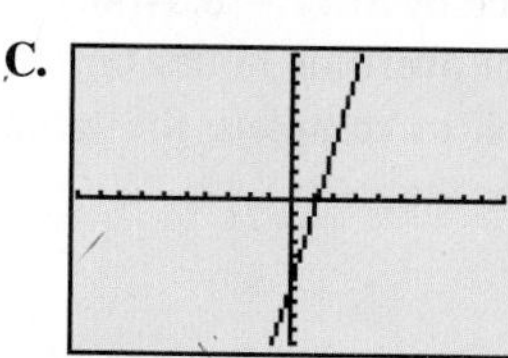

D.

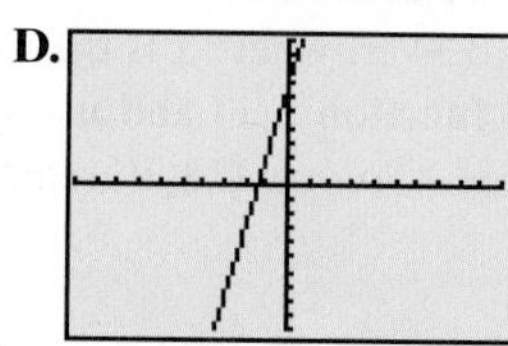

9. $f(x) = 5x - 6$

10. $f(x) = 5x - 2$

11. $f(x) = 5x + 7$

12. $f(x) = 5x + 3$

Graph each linear function by finding x- and y-intercepts. Then write each equation using function notation. See Examples 4 and 5.

13. $x - y = 3$

14. $x - y = -4$

15. $x = 5y$

16. $2x = y$

17. $-x + 2y = 6$

18. $x - 2y = -8$

19. $2x - 4y = 8$

20. $2x + 3y = 6$

21. In your own words, explain how to find x- and y-intercepts.

22. Explain why it is a good idea to use three points to graph a linear equation.

Graph each linear equation. See Examples 6 and 7.

23. $x = -1$

24. $y = 5$

25. $y = 0$

26. $x = 0$

27. $y + 7 = 0$

28. $x - 3 = 0$

Match each equation below with its graph.

A

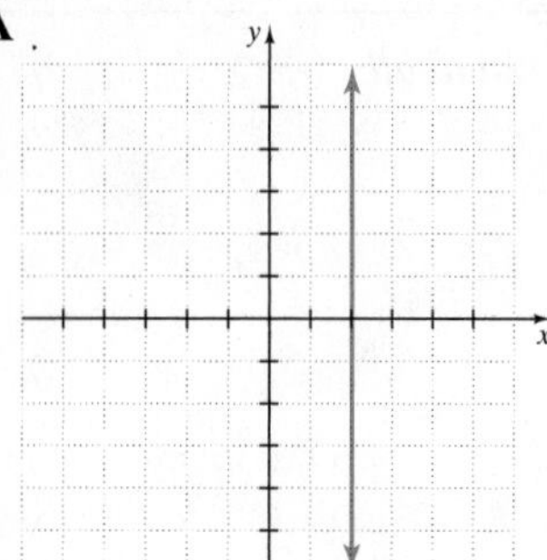

B

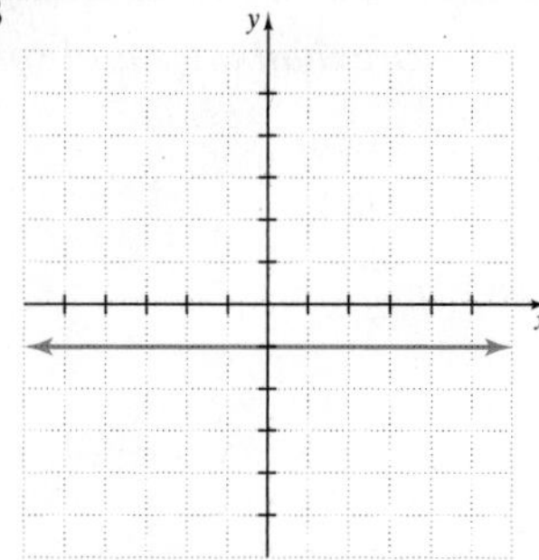

C

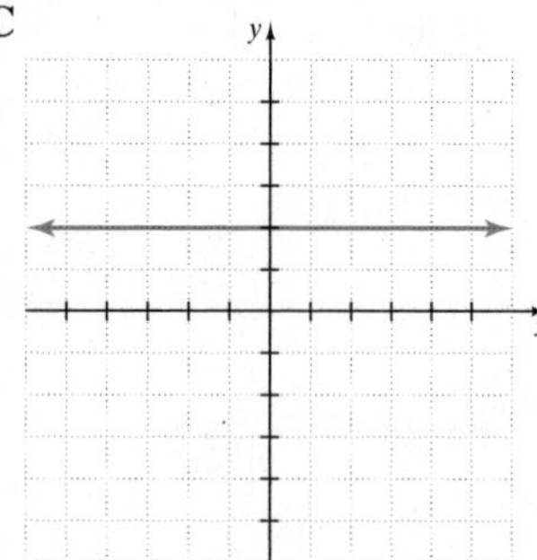

D

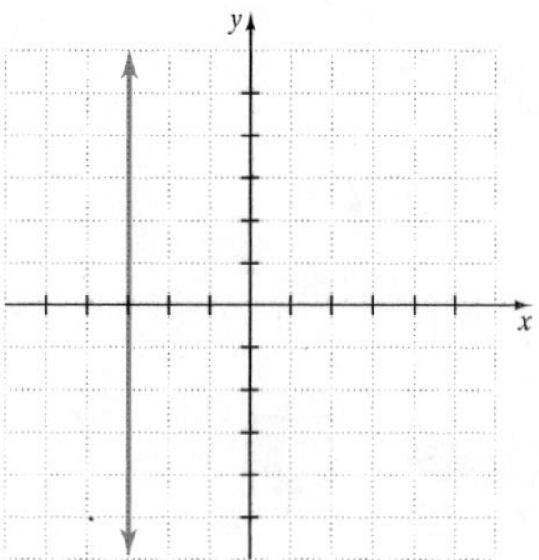

29. $y = 2$

30. $x = -3$

31. $x - 2 = 0$

32. $y + 1 = 0$

33. Discuss whether a vertical line ever has a y-intercept.

34. Discuss whether a horizontal line ever has an x-intercept.

MIXED PRACTICE

Graph each linear equation. See Examples 1 through 7.

35. $x + 2y = 8$

36. $x - 3y = 3$

37. $3x + 5y = 7$

38. $3x - 2y = 5$

39. $x + 8y = 8$

40. $x - 3y = 9$

41. $5 = 6x - y$

42. $4 = x - 3y$

43. $-x + 10y = 11$

44. $-x + 9 = -y$

45. $y = \frac{3}{2}$

46. $x = \frac{3}{2}$

47. $2x + 3y = 6$

48. $4x + y = 5$

49. $x + 3 = 0$

50. $y - 6 = 0$

51. $f(x) = \frac{3}{4}x + 2$

52. $f(x) = \frac{4}{3}x + 2$

53. $f(x) = x$

54. $f(x) = -x$

55. $f(x) = \frac{1}{2}x$

56. $f(x) = -2x$

57. $f(x) = 4x - \frac{1}{3}$

58. $f(x) = -3x + \frac{3}{4}$

59. $x = -3$

60. $f(x) = 3$

61. Given the graph of $f(x)$, which of the following statements are true?

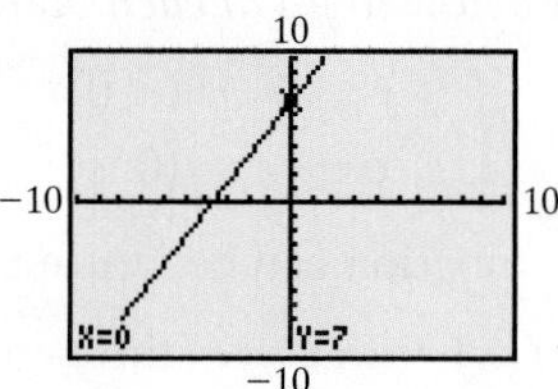

a. $f(7) = 0$
b. $f(0) = 7$
c. The x-intercept is $(7, 0)$.
d. The y-intercept is $(0, 7)$.

62. Given the graph of $g(x)$, which of the following statements are true?

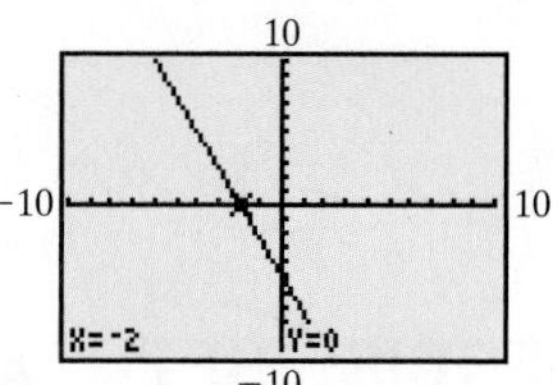

a. $g(-2) = 0$
b. $g(0) = -2$
c. The x-intercept is $(-2, 0)$.
d. The y-intercept is $(0, -2)$.

Solve. See Example 9.

63. Kevin Elliott works in the Human Resource department at a rate of $15.75 per hour for a 40-hour work week. He makes time and a half for overtime. His salary, before any deductions, can be represented by the function $S(x) = 15.75(40) + 1.5(15.75)x$, where x is the number of overtime hours. Graph the function and use it to complete the table below for the salary $S(x)$ in dollars.

No. of Overtime Hours	x	2	3.25	7.5	9.75
Salary in Dollars	$S(x)$				

64. The average hourly earnings of someone who works in retail trade is $8.34. If the normal hourly rate for overtime work (work over 40 hours per week) is 1.5 ($8.34), the salary, before deductions, can be represented by $S(x) = 8.34(40) + 1.5(8.34)x$, where x is the number of overtime hours. Graph the function $S(x)$ and use the graph to complete the table below. (*Source:* U.S. Bureau of Labor Statistics)

No. of Overtime Hours	2	10	12.5	15.75
Salary in Dollars				

REVIEW AND PREVIEW

Simplify.

65. $\dfrac{-6 - 3}{2 - 8}$

66. $\dfrac{4 - 5}{-1 - 0}$

67. $\dfrac{-8 - (-2)}{-3 - (-2)}$

68. $\dfrac{12 - 3}{10 - 9}$

69. $\dfrac{0 - 6}{5 - 0}$

70. $\dfrac{2 - 2}{3 - 5}$

CONCEPT EXTENSIONS

Solve.

71. Broyhill Furniture found that it takes 2 hours to manufacture each table for one of its special dining room sets. Each chair takes 3 hours to manufacture. A total of 1500 hours is available to produce tables and chairs of this style. The linear equation that models this situation is $2x + 3y = 1500$, where x represents the number of tables produced and y the number of chairs produced.
   a. Complete the ordered pair solution (0,) of this equation. Describe the manufacturing situation this solution corresponds to.
   b. Complete the ordered pair solution (, 0) for this equation. Describe the manufacturing situation this solution corresponds to.
   c. If 50 tables are produced, find the greatest number of chairs the company can make.

72. While manufacturing two different camera models, Kodak found that the basic model costs \$55 to produce, whereas the deluxe model costs \$75. The weekly budget for these two models is limited to \$33,000 in production costs. The linear equation that models this situation is $55x + 75y = 33{,}000$, where x represents the number of basic models and y the number of deluxe models.
   a. Complete the ordered pair solution (0,) of this equation. Describe the manufacturing situation this solution corresponds to.
   b. Complete the ordered pair solution (,0) of this equation. Describe the manufacturing situation this solution corresponds to.
   c. If 350 deluxe models are produced, find the greatest number of basic models that can be made in one week.

73. The cost of renting a car for a day is given by the linear function $C(x) = 0.2x + 24$, where $C(x)$ is in dollars and x is the number of miles driven.
   a. Find the cost of driving the car 200 miles.
   b. Graph $C(x) = 0.2x + 24$.
   c. How can you tell from the graph of $C(x)$ that as the number of miles driven increases, the total cost increases also?

74. The cost of renting a piece of machinery is given by the linear function $C(x) = 4x + 10$, where $C(x)$ is in dollars and x is given in hours.
   a. Find the cost of renting the piece of machinery for 8 hours.
   b. Graph $C(x) = 4x + 10$.
   c. How can you tell from the graph of $C(x)$ that as the number of hours increases, the total cost increases also?

75. The yearly cost of tuition (in-state) and required fees for attending a public two-year college full time can be estimated by the linear function $f(x) = 107.3x + 1245.62$, where x is the number of years after 2000 and $f(x)$ is the total cost. (*Source:* U.S. National Center for Education Statistics)
   a. Use this function to approximate the yearly cost of attending a two-year college in the year 2015. [*Hint:* Find $f(15)$.]
   b. Use the given function to predict in what year the yearly cost of tuition and required fees will exceed \$2500. [*Hint:* Let $f(x) = 2500$, solve for x, then round your solution up to the next whole year.]
   c. Use this function to approximate the yearly cost of attending a two-year college in the present year. If you attend a two-year college, is this amount greater than or less than the amount that is currently charged by the college you attend?

76. The yearly cost of tuition (in-state) and required fees for attending a public four-year college full time can be estimated by the linear function $f(x) = 291.5x + 2944.05$, where x is the number of years after 2000 and $f(x)$ is the total cost in dollars. (*Source:* U.S. National Center for Education Statistics)
   a. Use this function to approximate the yearly cost of attending a four-year college in the year 2015. [*Hint:* Find $f(15)$.]
   b. Use the given function to predict in what year the yearly cost of tuition and required fees will exceed \$6000. [*Hint:* Let $f(x) = 6000$, solve for x, then round your solution up to the next whole year.]
   c. Use this function to approximate the yearly cost of attending a four-year college in the present year. If you attend a four-year college, is this amount greater than or less than the amount that is currently charged by the college you attend?

77. The graph of $f(x)$ or $y = -4x$ is given below. Without actually graphing, describe the shape and location of
   a. $y = -4x + 2$
   b. $y = -4x - 5$

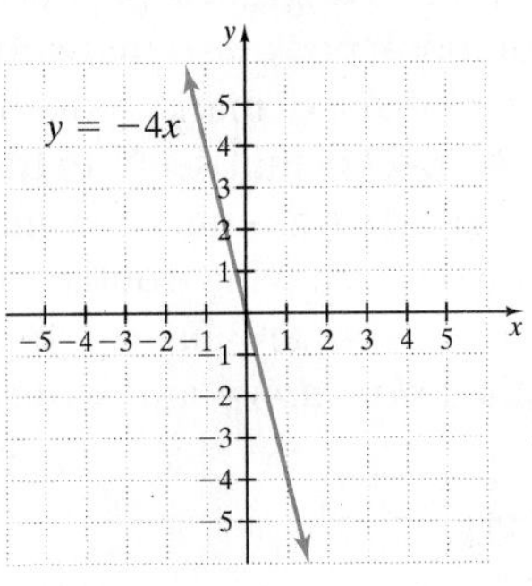

It is true that for any function $f(x)$, the graph of $f(x) + K$ is the same as the graph of $f(x)$ shifted K units up if K is positive and $|K|$ units down if K is negative.

The graph of $y = |x|$ is

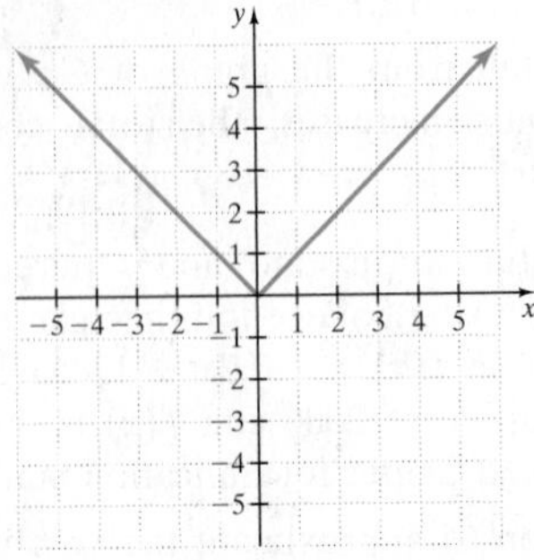

Without actually graphing, match each equation with its graph.

a. $y = |x| - 1$ **b.** $y = |x| + 1$

c. $y = |x| - 3$ **d.** $y = |x| + 3$

78.

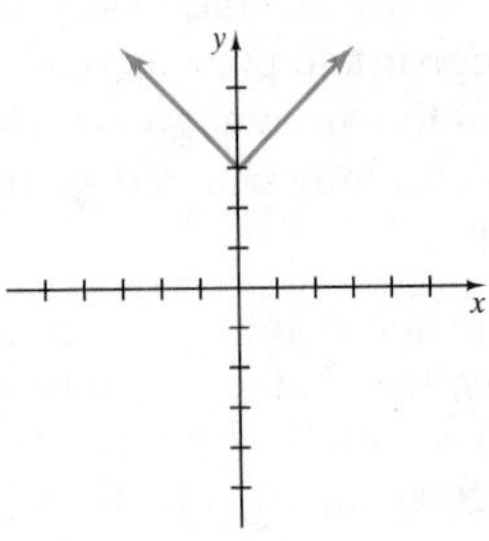

79.

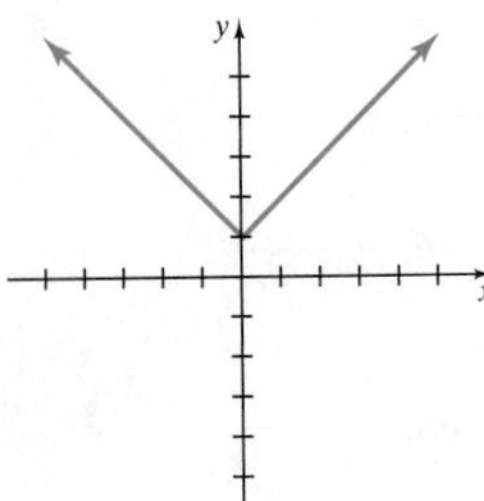

80.

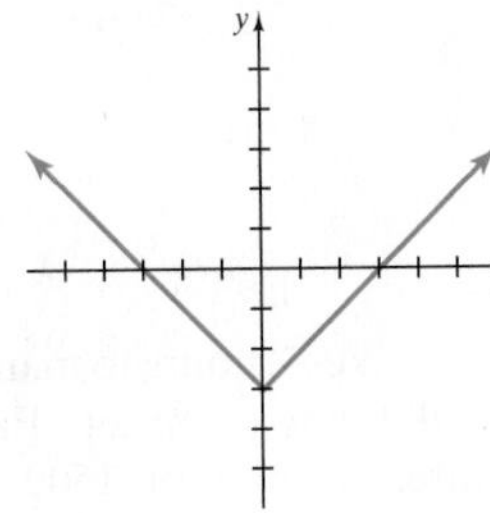

81.

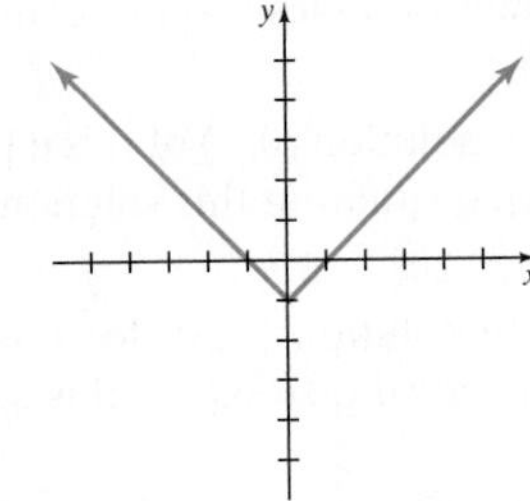

STUDY SKILLS BUILDER

Are You Organized?

When it's time to study for a test, are your notes neat and organized? Have you ever had trouble reading your own mathematics handwriting? (Be honest—I have.)

When any of these things happen, it's time to get organized. Here are a few suggestions:

Write your notes and complete your homework assignment in a notebook with pockets (spiral or ring binder). When you receive graded papers or handouts, place them in the notebook pocket so that you will not lose them.

Remember to mark (possibly with an exclamation point) any note(s) that seem extra important to you. Also mark (possibly with a question mark) any notes or homework that you are having trouble with.

Also, if you are having trouble reading your own handwriting, *slow down* and write your mathematics work clearly!

Exercises

1. Have you been completing your assignments on time?
2. Have you been correcting any exercises you may be having difficulty with?
3. If you are having trouble with a mathematical concept or correcting any homework exercises, have you visited your instructor, a tutor, or your campus math lab?
4. Are you taking lecture notes in your mathematics course? (By the way, these notes should include all worked-out examples solved by your instructor.)
5. Is your mathematics course material (handouts, graded papers, lecture notes) organized?
6. If your answer to Exercise 5 is no, take a moment and review your course material. List at least two ways that you might better organize it..

STUDY SKILLS BUILDER

Tips for Studying for an Exam

To prepare for an exam, try the following study techniques:

- Start the study process days before your exam.
- Make sure that you are up-to-date on your assignments.
- If there is a topic that you are unsure of, use one of the many resources that are available to you. For example,

  See your instructor.

  Visit a learning resource center on campus.

  Read the textbook material and examples on the topic.

  View a video on the topic.
- Reread your notes and carefully review the Chapter Highlights at the end of any chapter.
- Work the review exercises at the end of the chapter. Check your answers and correct any mistakes. If you have trouble, use a resource listed above.
- Find a quiet place to take the Chapter Test found at the end of the chapter. Do not use any resources when taking this sample test. This way, you will have a clear indication of how prepared you are for your exam. Check your answers and make sure that you correct any missed exercises.
- Get lots of rest the night before the exam. It's hard to show how well you know the material if your brain is foggy from lack of sleep.

Good luck and keep a positive attitude.

Let's see how you did on your last exam.

1. How many days before your last exam did you start studying for that exam?
2. Were you up-to-date on your assignments at that time or did you need to catch up on assignments?
3. List the most helpful text supplement (if you used one).
4. List the most helpful campus supplement (if you used one).
5. List your process for preparing for a mathematics test.
6. Was this process helpful? In other words, were you satisfied with your performance on your exam?
7. If not, what changes can you make in your process that will make it more helpful to you?

CHAPTER 15 GROUP ACTIVITY

Modeling Real Data

The number of children who live with only one parent has been steadily increasing in the United States since the 1960s. According to the U.S. Bureau of the Census, the percent of children living with both parents is declining. The following table shows the percent of children (under age 18) living with *both* parents during selected years from 1980 to 2005. In this project, you will have the opportunity to use the data in the table to find a linear function $f(x)$ that represents the data, reflecting the change in living arrangements for children. This project may be completed by working in groups or individually.

Percent of U.S. Children Who Live with Both Parents

Year	***1980***	***1985***	***1990***	***1995***	***2000***	***2005***
x	0	5	10	15	20	25
Percent, y	77	74	73	69	67	68

Source: U.S. Bureau of the Census

1. Plot the data given in the table as ordered pairs.
2. Use a straight edge to draw on your graph what appears to be the line that "best fits" the data you plotted.
3. Estimate the coordinates of two points that fall on your best fitting line. Use these points to find a linear function $f(x)$ for the line.
4. What is the slope of your line? Interpret its meaning. Does it make sense in the context of this situation?
5. Find the value of $f(50)$. Write a sentence interpreting its meaning in context.
6. Compare your linear function with that of another student or group. Are they different? If so, explain why.
7. Enter the data from the table into a graphing calculator. Use the linear regression feature of the calculator to find a linear function for the data. Compare this function to the one you found in Question 3. How are they alike or different? Find the value of $f(50)$ using the model you found with the graphing calculator. Compare it to the value of $f(50)$ you found in Question 5.

CHAPTER 15 VOCABULARY CHECK

Fill in each blank with one of the words or phrases listed below.

relation	standard	slope-intercept	range	point-slope
line	slope	x	parallel	perpendicular
function	domain	y	linear function	

1. A ________ is a set of ordered pairs.
2. The graph of every linear equation in two variables is a ________.
3. The equation $y - 8 = -5(x + 1)$ is written in ____________ form.
4. ________ form of a linear equation in two variables is $Ax + By = C$.
5. The ________ of a relation is the set of all second components of the ordered pairs of the relation.
6. ________ lines have the same slope and different y-intercepts.
7. ____________ form of a linear equation in two variables is $y = mx + b$.
8. A ________ is a relation in which each first component in the ordered pairs corresponds to exactly one second component.
9. In the equation $y = 4x - 2$, the coefficient of x is the ________ of its corresponding graph.
10. Two lines are ____________ if the product of their slopes is -1.
11. To find the x-intercept of a linear equation, let _____ = 0 and solve for the other variable.
12. The ________ of a relation is the set of all first components of the ordered pairs of the relation.
13. A ____________ is a function that can be written in the form $f(x) = mx + b$.
14. To find the y-intercept of a linear equation, let _____ = 0 and solve for the other variable.

Helpful Hint

Are you preparing for your test? Don't forget to take the Chapter 15 Test on page 1003. Then check your answers at the back of the text and use the Chapter Test Prep Video CD to see the fully worked-out solutions to any of the exercises you want to review.

CHAPTER 15 HIGHLIGHTS

DEFINITIONS AND CONCEPTS	EXAMPLES
SECTION 15.1 INTRODUCTION TO FUNCTIONS	
A **relation** is a set of ordered pairs. The **domain** of the relation is the set of all first components of the ordered pairs. The **range** of the relation is the set of all second components of the ordered pairs.	*Relation* 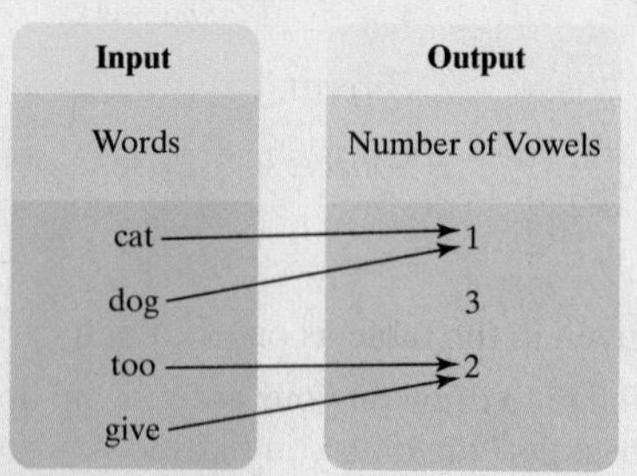 Domain: {cat, dog, too, give} Range: {1, 2}
A **function** is a relation in which each element of the first set corresponds to exactly one element of the second set.	The previous relation is a function. Each word contains exactly one number of vowels.

DEFINITIONS AND CONCEPTS	EXAMPLES

SECTION 15.1 INTRODUCTION TO FUNCTIONS (continued)

Vertical Line Test

If no vertical line can be drawn so that it intersects a graph more than once, the graph is the graph of a function.

Find the domain and the range of the relation. Also determine whether the relation is a function.

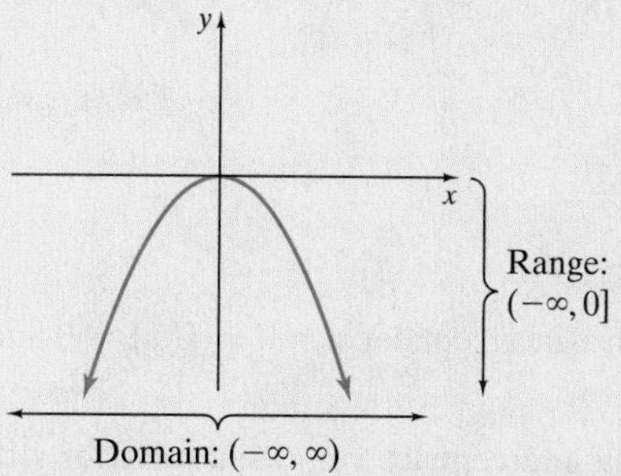

By the vertical line test, this graph is the graph of a function.

The symbol $f(x)$ means **function of *x*** and is called **function notation.**

If $f(x) = 2x^2 - 5$, find $f(-3)$.

$$f(-3) = 2(-3)^2 - 5 = 2(9) - 5 = 13$$

SECTION 15.2 GRAPHING LINEAR FUNCTIONS

A **linear function** is a function that can be written in the form $f(x) = mx + b$.

To graph a linear function, find three ordered pair solutions. (Use the third ordered pair to check.) Graph the solutions and draw a line through the plotted points.

Linear Functions

$$f(x) = -3, g(x) = 5x, h(x) = -\frac{1}{3}x - 7$$

Graph $f(x) = -2x$.

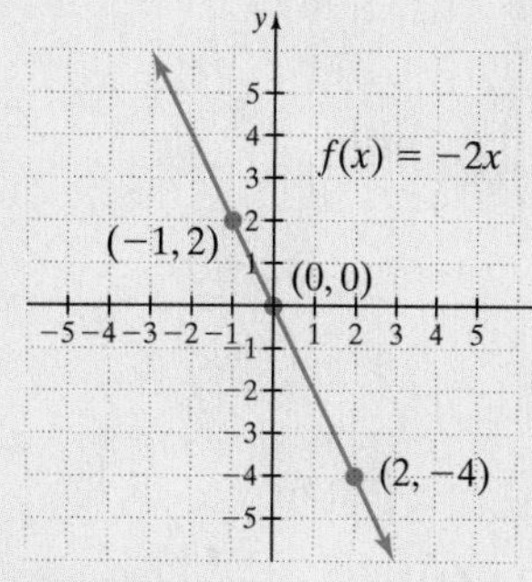

x	y or $f(x)$
−1	2
0	0
2	−4

The graph of $y = mx + b$ is the same as the graph of $y = mx$, but shifted b units up if b is positive and b units down if b is negative.

Graph $g(x) = -2x + 3$.

This is the same as the graph of $f(x) = -2x$ shifted 3 units up.

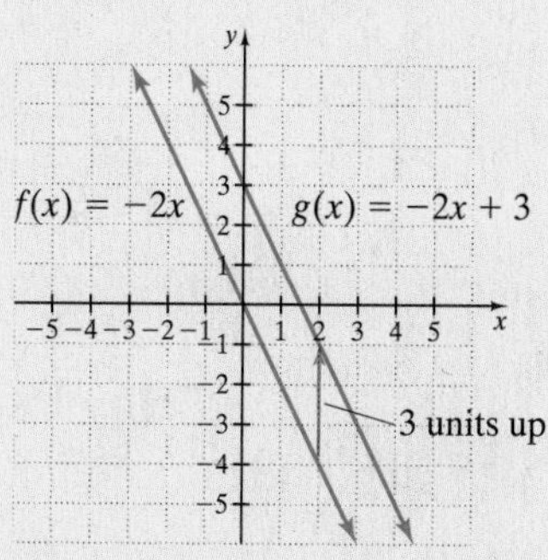

(continued)

DEFINITIONS AND CONCEPTS	EXAMPLES

SECTION 15.2 GRAPHING LINEAR FUNCTIONS (continued)

The x-coordinate of a point where a graph crosses the x-axis is called an ***x*-intercept.** The y-coordinate of a point where a graph crosses the y-axis is called a ***y*-intercept.**

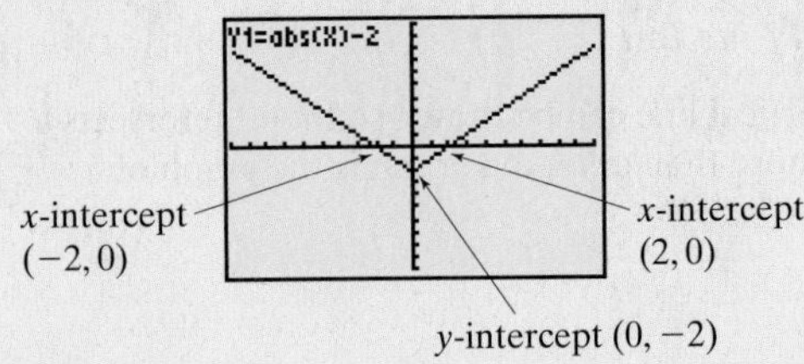

The x-intercepts of the graph are -2 and 2. The y-intercept is -2.

To find an x-intercept, let $y = 0$ or $f(x) = 0$ and solve for x.

To find a y-intercept, let $x = 0$ and solve for y.

Graph $5x - y = -5$ by finding intercepts.

If $x = 0$, then	If $y = 0$, then
$5x - y = -5$	$5x - y = -5$
$5 \cdot 0 - y = -5$	$5x - 0 = -5$
$-y = -5$	$5x = -5$
$y = 5$	$x = -1$
$(0, 5)$	$(-1, 0)$

Ordered pairs are $(0, 5)$ and $(-1, 0)$.

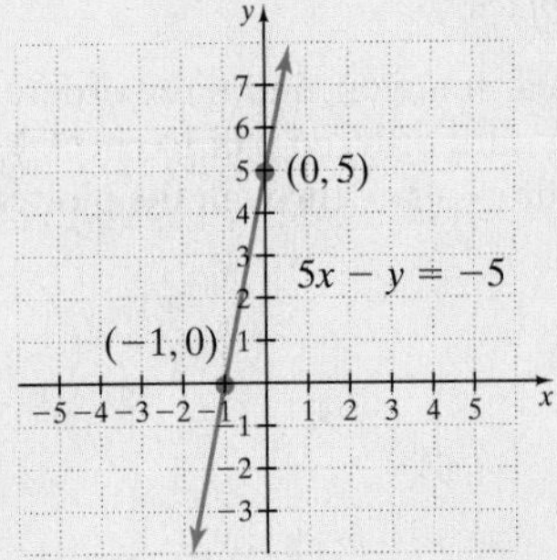

The graph of $x = c$ is a vertical line with x-intercept $(c, 0)$.

The graph of $y = c$ is a horizontal line with y-intercept $(0, c)$.

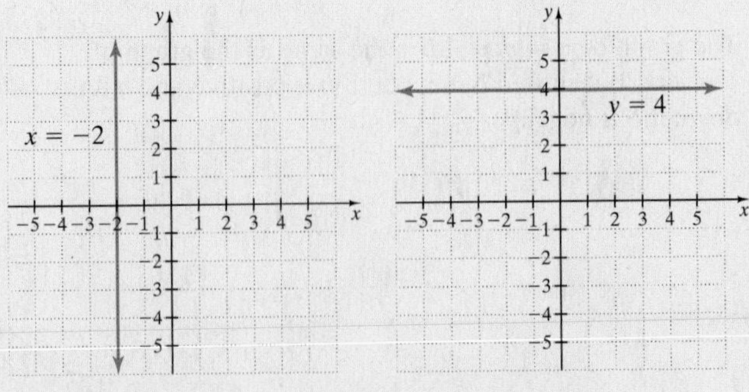

STUDY SKILLS BUILDER

Are You Prepared for a Test on Chapter 15?

Below I have listed some common trouble areas for students in Chapter 15. After studying for your test—but before taking your test—read these.

- Don't forget that the graph of an ordered pair is a *single* point in the rectangular coordinate plane.
- Remember that the slope of a horizontal line is 0 while a vertical line has undefined slope or no slope.
- For a linear equation such as $2y = 3x - 6$, the slope is not the coefficient of x unless the equation is solved for y. Solving this equation for y, we have $y = \frac{3}{2}x - 3$. The slope is $\frac{3}{2}$ and the y-intercept is $(0, -3)$.

Slope	*Parallel line*	*Perpendicular line*
$m = 6$	$m = 6$	$m = -\frac{1}{6}$
$m = -\frac{2}{3}$	$m = -\frac{2}{3}$	$m = \frac{3}{2}$

- Parallel lines have the same slope while perpendicular lines have negative reciprocal slopes.
- Don't forget that the statement $f(2) = 3$ corresponds to the ordered pair $(2, 3)$.

Remember: This is simply a checklist of common trouble areas. For a review of Chapter 15, see the Highlights and Chapter Review at the end of this chapter.

CHAPTER 15 REVIEW

(15.1) *Find the domain and range of each relation. Also determine whether the relation is a function.*

1. $\left\{\left(-\frac{1}{2}, \frac{3}{4}\right), (6, 0.75), (0, -12), (25, 25)\right\}$

2. $\left\{\left(\frac{3}{4}, -\frac{1}{2}\right), (0.75, 6), (-12, 0), (25, 25)\right\}$

3.

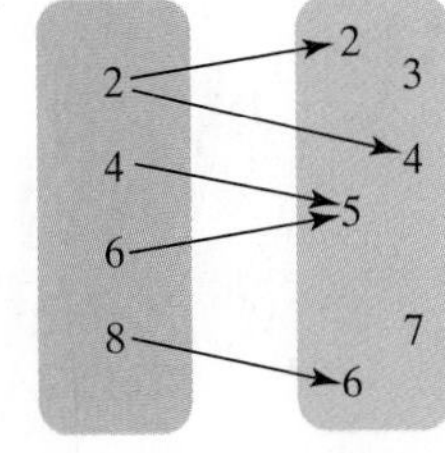

4.

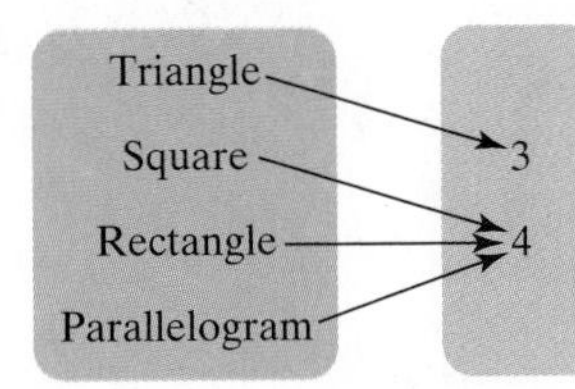

5.

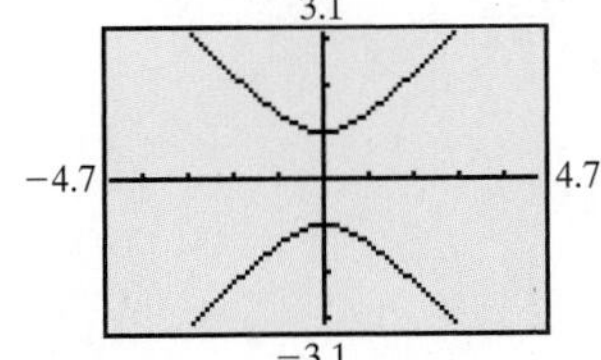

6.

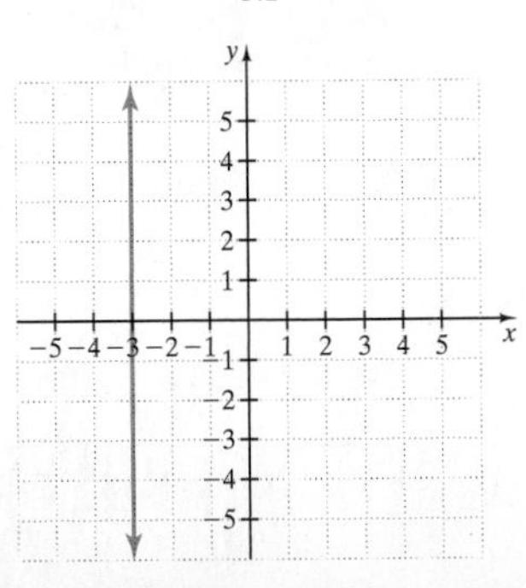

7.

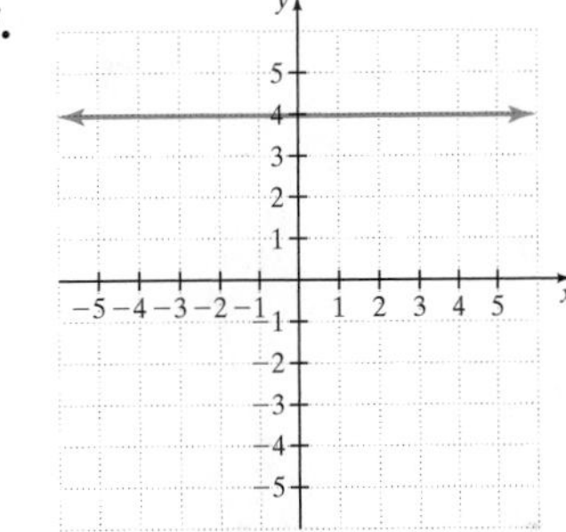

8.

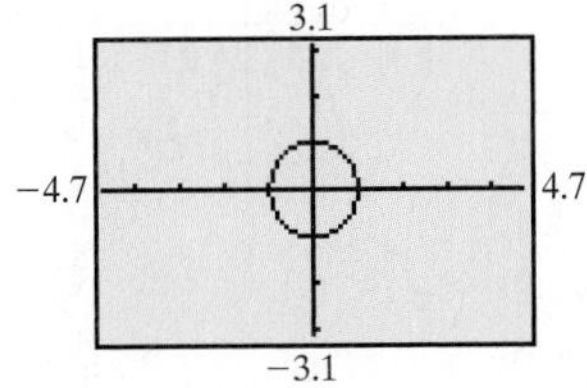

If $f(x) = x - 5$, $g(x) = -3x$, *and* $h(x) = 2x^2 - 6x + 1$, *find the following.*

9. $f(2)$ **10.** $g(0)$ **11.** $g(-6)$

12. $h(-1)$ **13.** $h(1)$ **14.** $f(5)$

Use the graph of the function below to answer Exercises 35 through 38.

15. Find $f(-1)$.

16. Find $f(1)$.

17. Find all values of x such that $f(x) = 1$.

18. Find all values of x such that $f(x) = -1$.

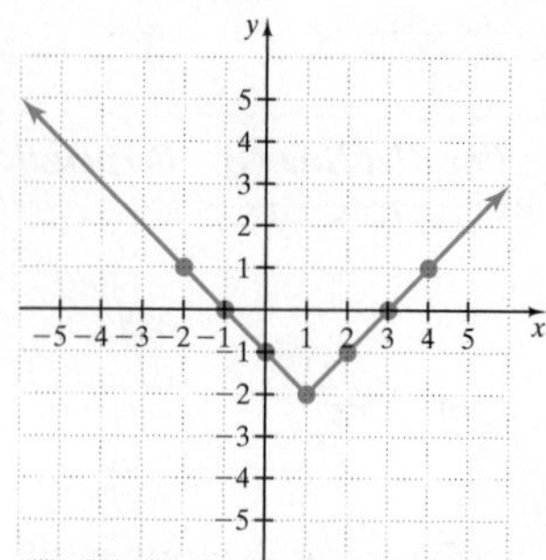

(15.2) *Graph each linear function.*

19. $f(x) = x$ **20.** $f(x) = -\frac{1}{3}x$ **21.** $g(x) = 4x - 1$

The graph of $f(x) = 3x$ is sketched below. Use this graph to match each linear function with its graph.

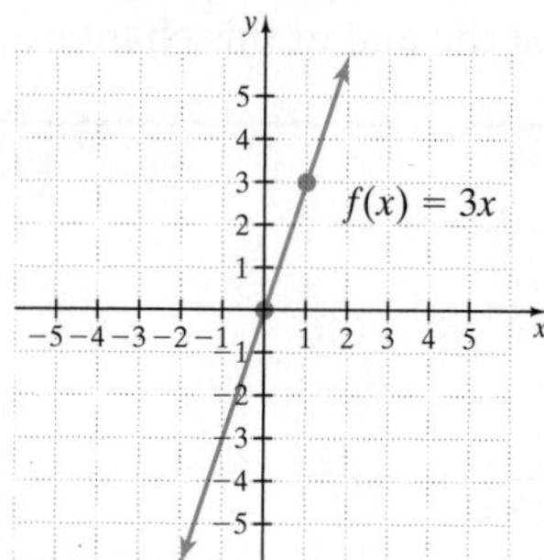

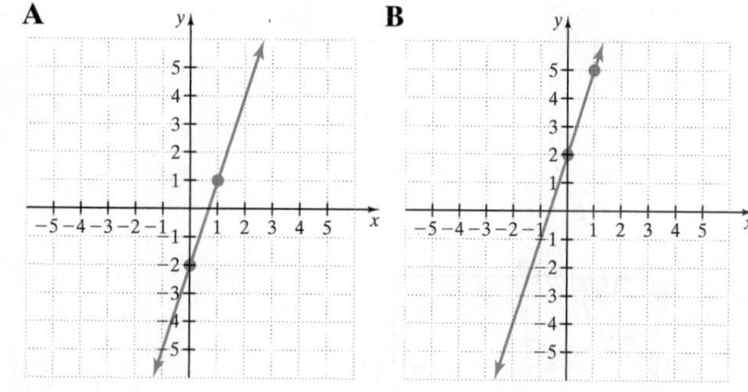

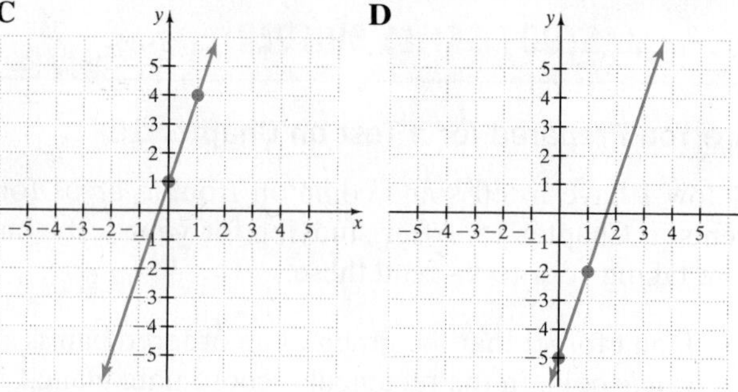

22. $f(x) = 3x + 1$

23. $f(x) = 3x - 2$

24. $f(x) = 3x + 2$

25 $f(x) = 3x - 5$

Graph each linear equation by finding intercepts if possible.

26. $4x + 5y = 20$

27. $3x - 2y = -9$

28. $4x - y = 3$

29. $2x + 6y = 9$

30. $y = 5$

31 $x = -2$

Graph each linear equation.

32 $x - 2 = 0$

33. $y + 3 = 0$

34. The cost C, in dollars, of renting a minivan for a day is given by the linear function $C(x) = 0.3x + 42$, where x is number of miles driven.

a. Find the cost of renting the minivan for a day and driving it 150 miles.

b. Graph $C(x) = 0.3x + 42$.

CHAPTER 15 TEST

Remember to use the Chapter Test Prep Video CD to see the fully worked-out solutions to any of the exercises you want to review.

1. Plot the points, and name the quadrant or axis in which each is located: $A(6, -2)$, $B(4, 0)$, $C(-1, 6)$.

Graph each line.

2. $2x - 3y = -6$
3. $4x + 6y = 7$
4. $f(x) = \frac{2}{3}x$
5. $y = -3$
6. Find the slope of the line that passes through $(5, -8)$ and $(-7, 10)$.
7. Find the slope and the y-intercept of the line $3x + 12y = 8$.

Find an equation of each line satisfying the given conditions. Write Exercises 8–12 in standard form. Write Exercises 13–15 using function notation.

8. Horizontal; through $(2, -8)$
9. Vertical; through $(-4, -3)$
10. Perpendicular to $x = 5$; through $(3, -2)$
11. Through $(4, -1)$; slope -3
12. Through $(0, -2)$; slope 5
13. Through $(4, -2)$ and $(6, -3)$
14. Through $(-1, 2)$; perpendicular to $3x - y = 4$
15. Parallel to $2y + x = 3$; through $(3, -2)$
16. Line L_1 has the equation $2x - 5y = 8$. Line L_2 passes through the points $(1, 4)$ and $(-1, -1)$. Determine whether these lines are parallel lines, perpendicular lines, or neither.

Match each graph with its equation.

17.

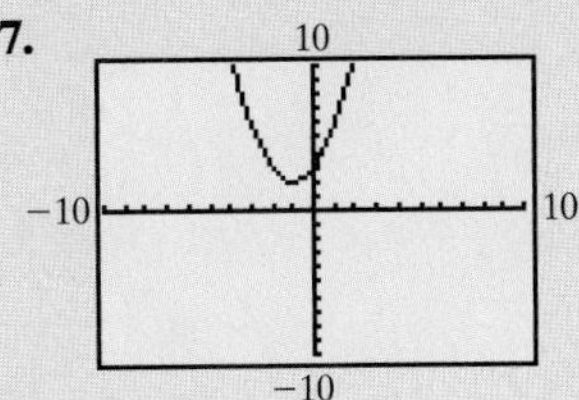

18.

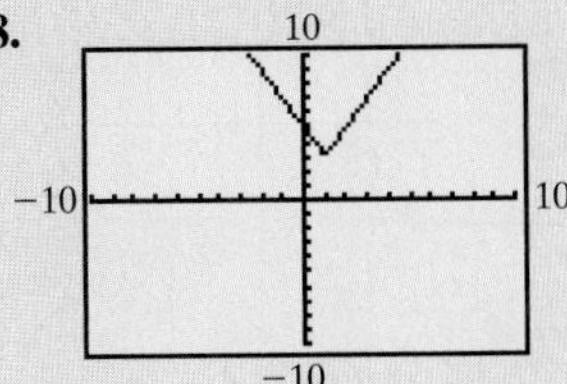

19.

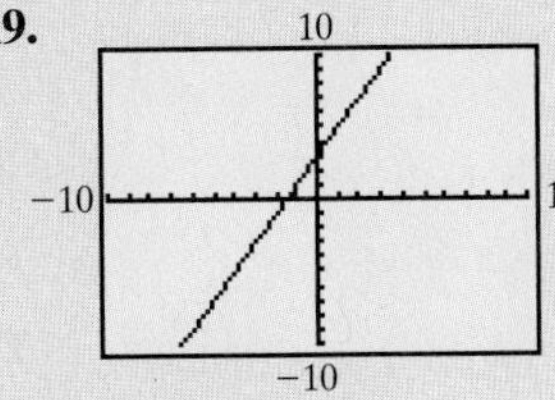

20.

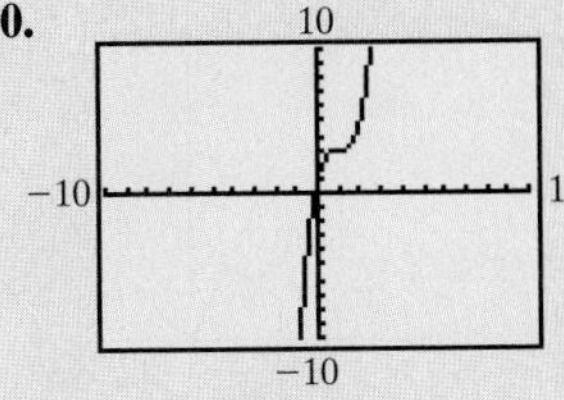

a. $y = 2|x - 1| + 3$
b. $y = x^2 + 2x + 3$
c. $y = 2(x - 1)^3 + 3$
d. $y = 2x + 3$

Find the domain and range of each relation. Also determine whether the relation is a function.

21.

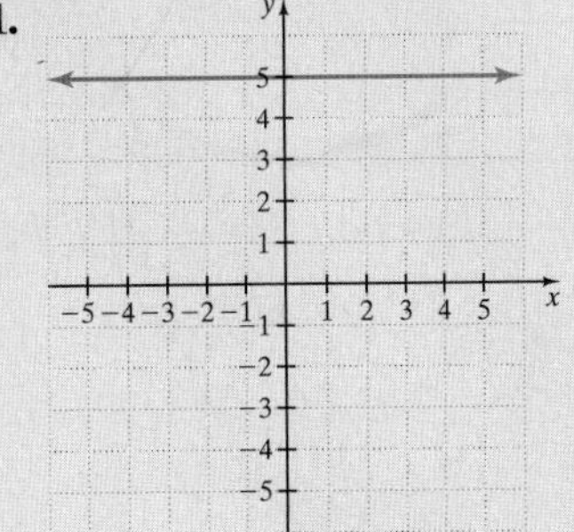

22.

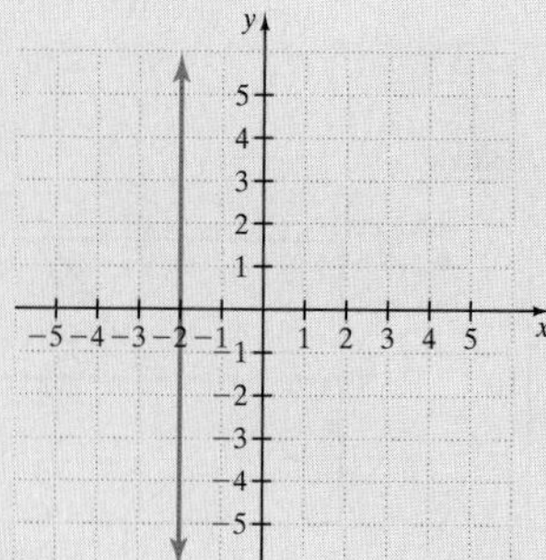

23

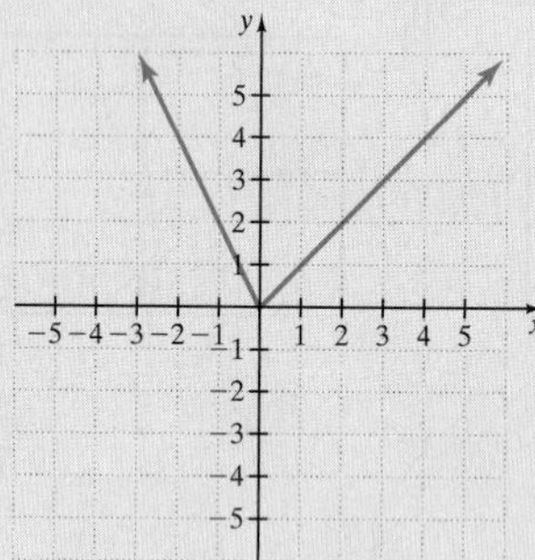

24

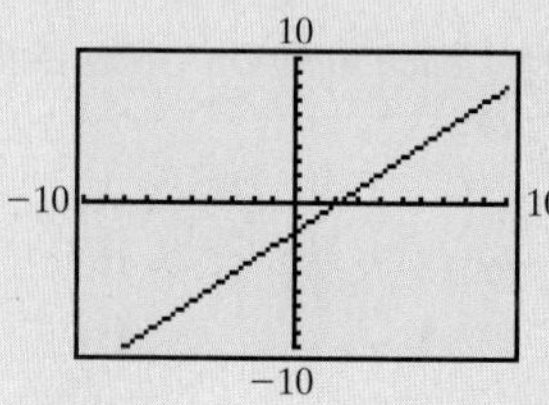

25. The average yearly earnings for high school graduates age 18 and older is given by the linear function

$$f(x) = 1031x + 25{,}193$$

where x is the number of years since 2000 that a person graduated. (*Source:* U.S. Census Bureau)

a. Find the average earnings in 2000 for high school graduates.

b. Find the average earnings for high school graduates in the year 2007.

c. Predict the first whole year that the average earnings for high school graduates will be greater than $40,000.

d. Find and interpret the slope of this equation.

e. Find and interpret the y-intercept of this equation.

Equations and Inequalities 16

Mathematics is a tool for solving problems in such diverse fields as transportation, engineering, economics, medicine, business, and biology. We solve problems using mathematics by modeling real-world phenomena with mathematical equations or inequalities. Our ability to solve problems using mathematics, then, depends in part on our ability to solve equations and inequalities. In this chapter, we solve linear equations and inequalities and graph their solutions.

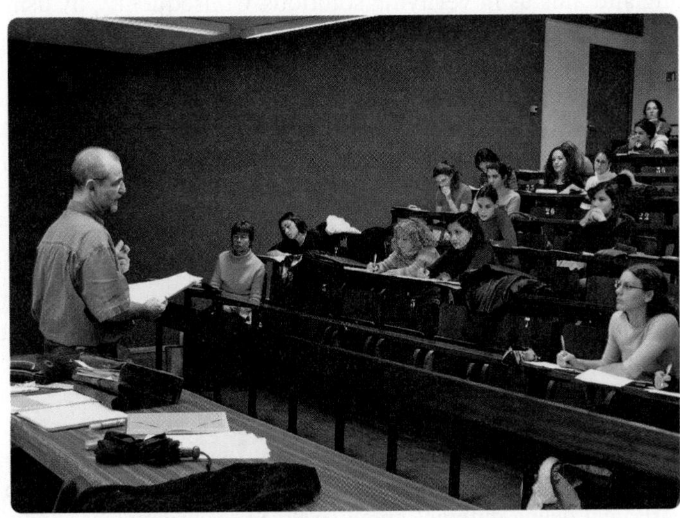

The federal Bureau of Labor Statistics (BLS) issued its projections for job growth in the United States for the Civilian Labor Force. The table and graph below show the rise in the civilian labor force between the years 1998 and 2008. In Exercise Set 16.2, Exercise 80, you will use the equation calculated below to predict future civilian labor force. (*Source*: Bureau of Labor Statistics)

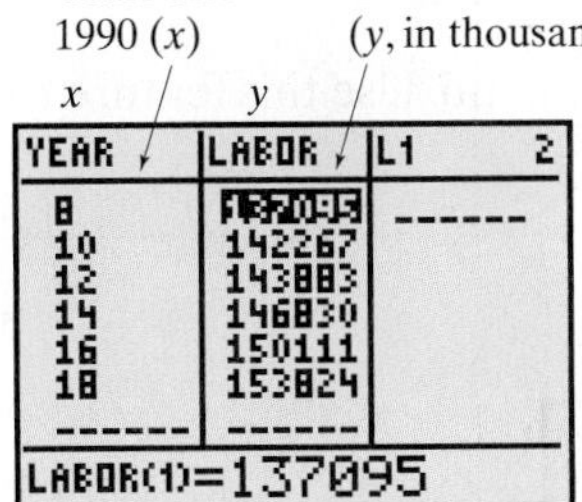

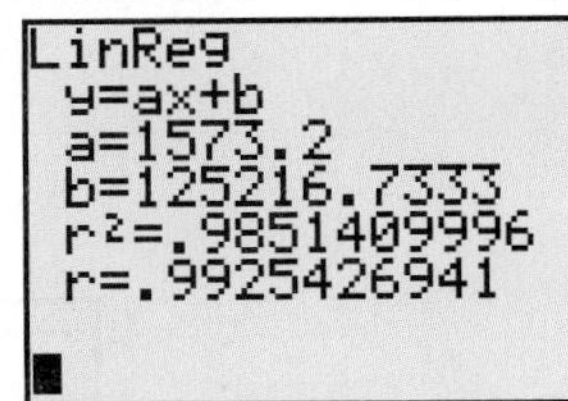

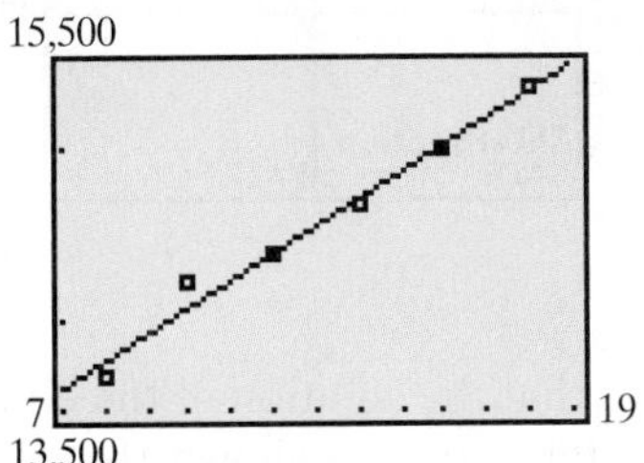

16.1 SOLVING LINEAR EQUATIONS GRAPHICALLY

OBJECTIVES

1. Solve linear equations using the intersection-of-graphs method.
2. Solve problems using graphing methods.
3. Solve an identity or a contradiction.
4. Solve linear equations using the x-intercept method.

In Chapter 15, we solved linear equations algebraically and checked the solution numerically with a calculator. Recall that a solution of an equation is a value for the variable that makes the equation a true statement. In this section we solve equations algebraically and graphically. Then we use various methods to check the solution. We need to stress the importance of the check. Technology allows us to reduce the time spent on solving and aids us in verifying solutions. Consequently, by using technology we can increase the accuracy of our work.

OBJECTIVE 1 ▶ Solving equations using the intersection-of-graphs method. There are two methods we will use to graphically obtain a solution of an equation. The first method we refer to as the **intersection-of-graphs method.** For this method, we graph

$$y_1 = \text{left side of equation and}$$
$$y_2 = \text{right side of equation.}$$

Recall that when a solution is substituted for a variable in an equation, the left side of the equation is equal to the right side of the equation. This means that graphically a solution occurs when $y_1 = y_2$ or where the graphs of y_1 and y_2 intersect.

TECHNOLOGY NOTE

Most graphing utilities have the ability to select and deselect graphs, graph equations simultaneously, and define different graph styles. See your graphing utility manual to check its capabilities. Also, find the instructions for using the intersection and root, or zero, features.

DISCOVER THE CONCEPT

Consider the equation $2x - 5 = 27$ and graph $y_1 = 2x - 5$ and $y_2 = 27$ in an integer window.

a. Use the trace feature to estimate the point of intersection of the two graphs.

b. Solve the equation algebraically and compare the x-coordinate of the point of intersection found in part **a** to the algebraic solution of the equation.

c. Locate the intersect feature on your graphing utility, sometimes found on the calculate menu. Use this feature to find the point of intersection of the two graphs.

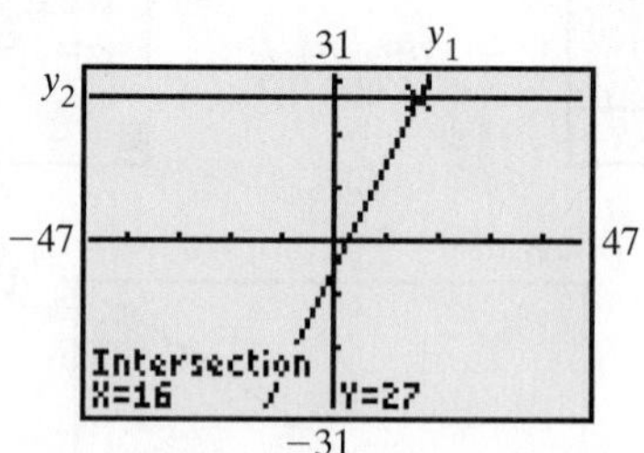

The above discovery indicates that the solution of the equation $2x - 5 = 27$ is 16, the x-coordinate of the point of intersection, as shown above.

To check this solution, we may replace x with 16 in the original equation.

$$2x - 5 = 27$$
$$2 \cdot 16 - 5 = 27 \quad \text{Let } x = 16.$$
$$32 - 5 = 27$$
$$27 = 27 \quad \text{True}$$

Recall that 27 is the y-coordinate of the point of intersection. Why? Because it is the value of both the left side and the right side of the equation when x is replaced with the solution.

The steps below may be used to solve an equation by the intersection-of-graphs method.

Intersection-of-Graphs Method for Solving an Equation

STEP 1. Graph y_1 = left side of the equation and y_2 = right side of the equation.

STEP 2. Find the point(s) of intersection of the two graphs.

STEP 3. The x-coordinate of a point of intersection is a solution to the equation.

STEP 4. The y-coordinate of the point of intersection is the value of both the left side and the right side of the original equation when x is replaced with the solution.

EXAMPLE 1 Solve the equation $5(x - 2) + 15 = 20$.

Algebraic Solution:

$5(x - 2) + 15 = 20$

$5x - 10 + 15 = 20$ Use the distributive property.

$5x + 5 = 20$ Combine like terms.

$5x = 15$ Subtract 5 from both sides.

$x = 3$ Divide both sides by 5.

To check, we replace x with 3 and see that a true statement results.

$5(x - 2) + 15 = 20$

$5(3 - 2) + 15 = 20$

$5(1) + 15 = 20$

$20 = 20$ True

The solution is 3.

Graphical Solution:

Graph $y_1 = 5(x - 2) + 15$ Left side of equation

$y_2 = 20$ Right side of equation

Since the graph of the equation $y = 20$ is a horizontal line with y-intercept 20, use the window $[-25, 25, 5]$ by $[-25, 25, 5]$.

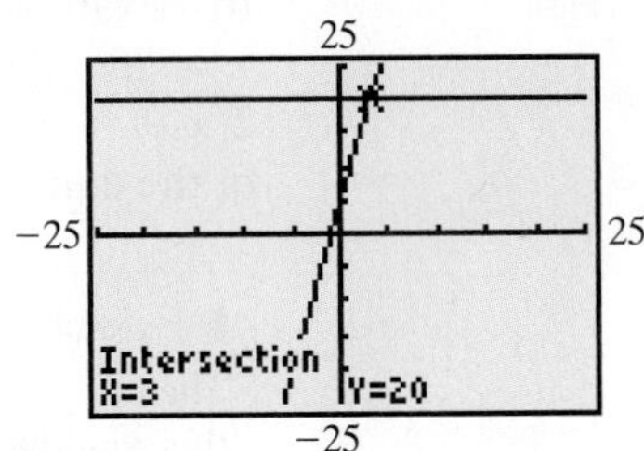

The x-coordinate of the point of intersection is 3. Thus, the solution is 3.

We can also use a table feature to check the solution. If $y_1 = 5(x - 2) + 15$ and $y_2 = 20$, scroll to $x = 3$ and see that y_1 and y_2 are both 20. □

PRACTICE 1 Solve the equation $2(x - 1) + 6 = 8$.

When solving equations graphically, we often have no indication where the intersection lies before looking at the graphs of the two equations. The zoom feature of your graphing utility may be used to quickly look for an appropriate window. If the graphs are present but the intersection point is missing, you can assess the situation and decide which component to adjust on the window setting. You will quickly get used to this assessment process as you solve more equations.

EXAMPLE 2 Graphically solve the equation

$$2(x - 30) + 6(x - 10) - 70 = 35 - x.$$

Solution Graph $y_1 = 2(x - 30) + 6(x - 10) - 70$ and $y_2 = 35 - x$ in an integer window.

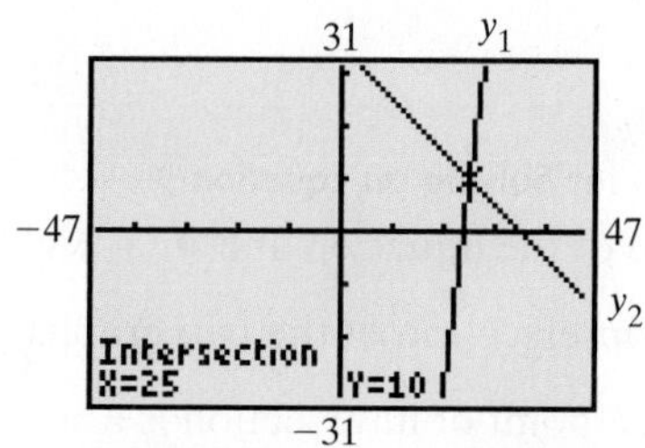

The point of intersection (25, 10) indicates that the solution is 25. To check numerically with a calculator, see the screen below.

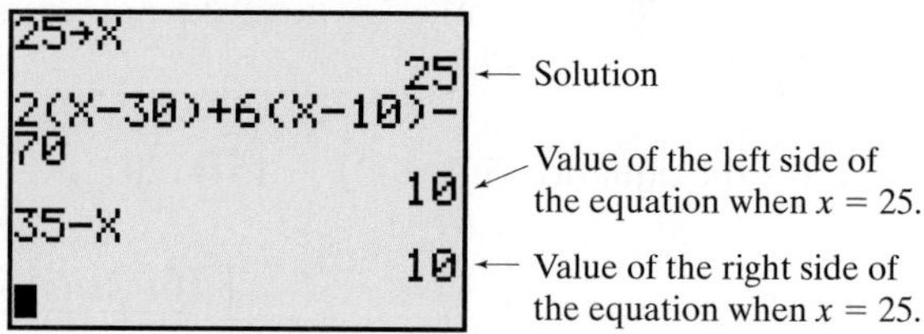

□

PRACTICE 2 Solve graphically: $3(x - 10) + 5(x + 2) - 25 = 9 - x$.

In Example 2, recall that the intersection point (25, 10) indicates that if $x = 25$, then the value of the expression on the left side of the equation $2(x - 30) + 6(x - 10) - 70$ is 10, and the value of the expression on the right side of the equation, $35 - x$, is also 10.

> **Helpful Hint**
> The integer window allows the cursor to move along a graph with integer x-values only. Using this window does *not* mean that the calculator will give only integer values when calculating a point of intersection.

> **Helpful Hint**
> In general, when using the intersection method, the x-coordinate of the point of intersection is a solution of the equation, and the y-coordinate of the point of intersection is the value of each side of the original equation when the variable is replaced with the solution.

EXAMPLE 3 Solve the equation using the intersection-of-graphs method.

$$5.1x + 3.78 = x + 4.7$$

Solution Define $y_1 = 5.1x + 3.78$ and $y_2 = x + 4.7$ and graph in a standard window. The screen below shows the intersection point.

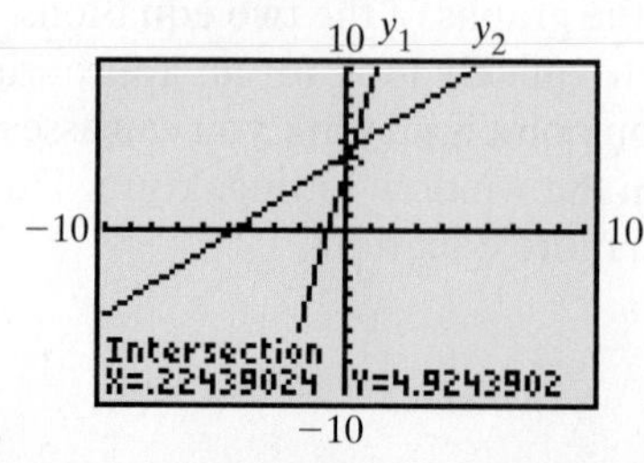

Notice the coordinates of the intersection point. When this happens, we will approximate the solution. For this example, the solution rounded to four decimal places is 0.2244.

To check when the solution is an approximation, note that the value of the left side of the equation and the value of the right side may differ slightly because of rounding. In the screen below we see a check of the equation for $x \approx 0.2244$.

```
.2244→X
                .2244
5.1X+3.78
              4.92444
X+4.7
               4.9244
```

The solution is approximately ($\approx$) 0.2244. □

TECHNOLOGY NOTE

The point of intersection shown suggests that either the exact solution of the equation is a fraction with decimal equivalence greater than or equal to 8 decimal places, or the solution is an irrational number. To see if it is a fraction, you may want to see if your graphing utility can convert to fractions.

PRACTICE

3 Solve the equation using the intersection-of-graphs method. Round the solution to 3 decimal places. $3.51x + 5.728 = x - 3.41$

OBJECTIVE 2 ▶ Solving applications using graphing methods. Next, we use the intersection-of-graphs method to solve a problem.

EXAMPLE 4 **Purchasing a Refrigerator**

The McDonalds are purchasing a new refrigerator. They find two models that fit their needs. Model 1 sells for \$575 and costs \$0.07 per hour to run. Model 2 is the energy efficient model that sells for \$825, but only costs \$0.04 per hour to run. If x represents number of hours, then the costs to purchase and run the refrigerators are modeled by the equations

$$C_1(x) = 575 + 0.07x \quad \text{Cost to buy and run Model 1}$$
$$C_2(x) = 825 + 0.04x \quad \text{Cost to buy and run Model 2}$$

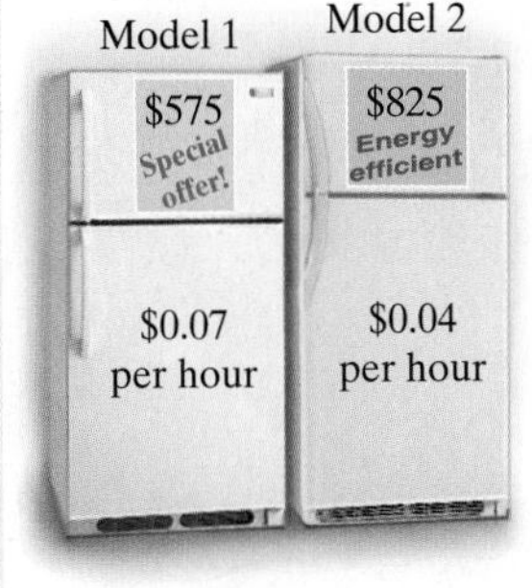

a. If the McDonalds buy Model 2, how many hours must it run before they save money?

b. How many days must it run before they save money?

Solution Graph $y_1 = 575 + 0.07x$ and $y_2 = 825 + 0.04x$. Here, the ordered pairs represent (x, y).
hours ↗ ↖ cost

a. Find the point of intersection of the graphs.

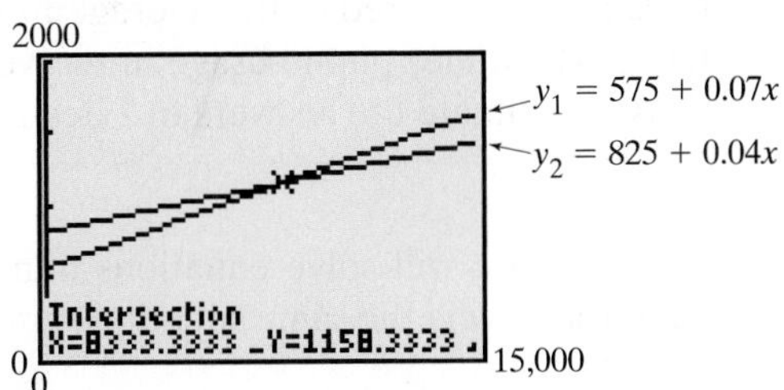

The point of intersection is $(8333.\overline{3}, 1158.\overline{3})$. This means that in approximately 8333.33 hours, both machines cost a total of approximately \$1158.33 to buy and run. Before that point of intersection, the graph of y_1 is below the graph of y_2. This means that the cost of Model 1 is less than the cost of Model 2. Likewise, after the point of intersection, the graph of y_2 is below the graph of y_1. This means that the cost of Model 2 is less than the cost of Model 1. Thus, in approximately 8333.33 hours, the McDonalds start saving money.

b. To find the approximate number of days, find

$$\frac{8333.33}{24} \approx 347.22 \text{ days.}$$

□

PRACTICE

4 Using the data from Example 4, find how much more its costs (original purchase price and use) for the \$575 refrigerator at the end of 2 years than the \$825 model.

EXAMPLE 5 **Cell Phone Usage vs. Residential Phone Usage**

The annual expenditure for cell phone usage can be modeled using the equation $C(x) = 60.429x + 151.333$. The annual expenditure for residential (landline) phone usage can be modeled by the equation $R(x) = -27.457x + 704.6$. In both cases $x =$ the number of years since 2000. Using these models, find what year we can expect the amount of money spent for cell phone usage to equal the amount spent for residential (landline) usage, or find when $C(x) = R(x)$.

Solution Graph

$$y_1 = 60.429x + 151.333 \text{ and}$$
$$y_2 = -27.457x + 704.6$$

where the ordered pairs (x, y) represent (years, cost). Find the point of intersection of the two graphs. Let's first find an appropriate window. We'll start by looking at the years between 2000 and 2015 (x-values) and considering annual costs from \$0 to \$1000 (y-values). In other words, we'll start with the window $[0, 15, 1]$ by $[0, 1000, 100]$.

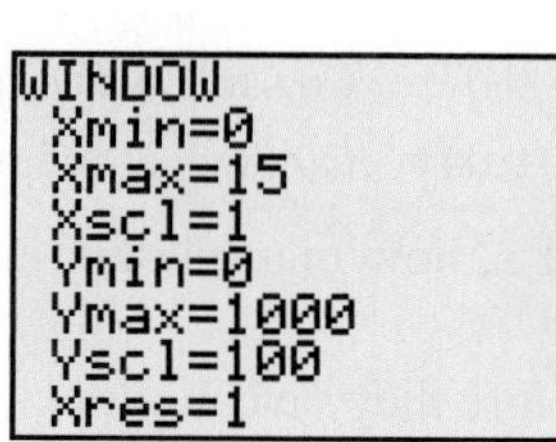

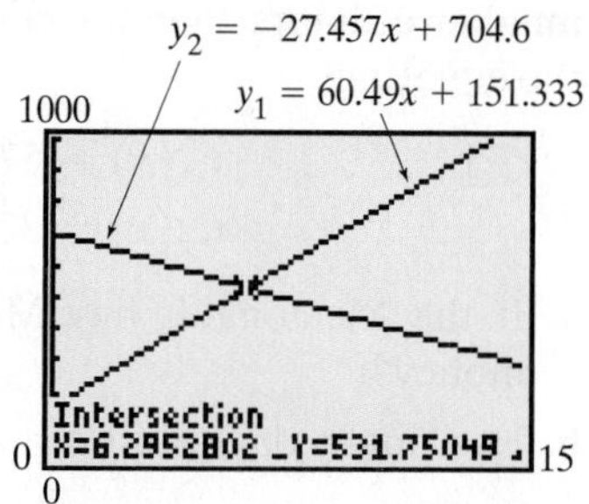

The point of intersection is approximately (6.295, 531.750). This means that during the year 2006 (2000 + 6) the annual usage cost per unit for cell phones equaled the cost per unit for residential (landline) phones and that average cost was about \$531.75. □

PRACTICE

5 Use the graphs in Example 5 to predict the average annual expenditure for cell phone usage and residential (landline) phone usage in the year 2012 (if the trend continues at the same rates.) Approximate the answers to 2 decimal places.

In the Exercise set for this section, we will solve equations numerically using tables. Now we look at another option for solving the same situations graphically.

OBJECTIVE 3 ▶ Solving an identity or a contradiction. An equation in one variable that has no solution is called a contradiction and an equation in one variable that has every number (for which the equation is defined) as a solution is called an identity. We now look at these two special types of equations graphically.

EXAMPLE 6 Solve: $4(x + 6) - 2(x - 3) = 2x + 30$

Algebraic Solution:

$$4(x + 6) - 2(x - 3) = 2x + 30$$
$$4x + 24 - 2x + 6 = 2x + 30 \quad \text{Multiply.}$$
$$2x + 30 = 2x + 30 \quad \text{Simplify.}$$

Since both sides are the same, we see that replacing x with any real number will result in a true statement. This equation is an identity and all real numbers are solutions. Using set notation, the solution set is $\{x|x \text{ is a real number}\}$.

Graphical Solution:

Graph $y_1 = 4(x + 6) - 2(x - 3)$ and
$y_2 = 2x + 30$

The graphs shown below appear to be the same since there appears to be a single line only. When we trace along y_1, we have the same ordered pairs as when we trace along y_2. (If 2 points of y_1 are the same as 2 points of y_2, we know the lines are identical because 2 points uniquely determine a line.)

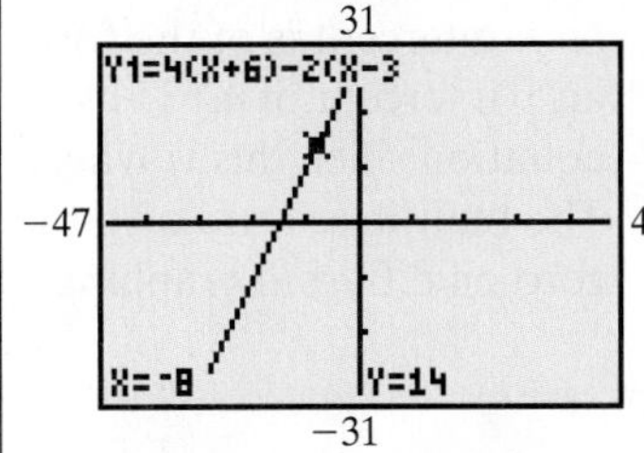

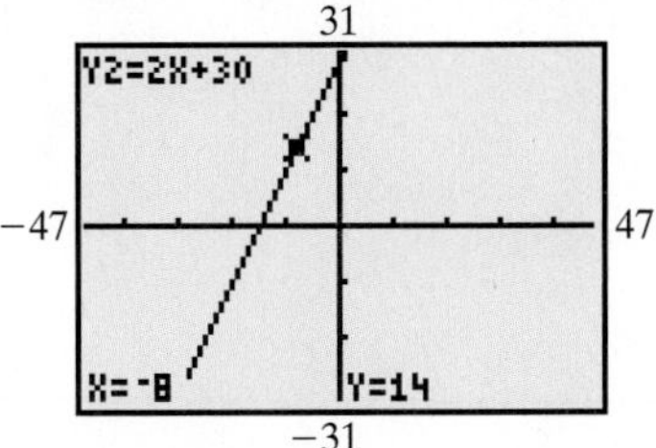

Thus, this equation is an identity. All real numbers are solutions, or the solution set is $\{x|x \text{ is a real number}\}$.

Once again, both solutions show that the equation is an identity and the solution set is the set of real numbers or $\{x|x \text{ is a real number}\}$. □

PRACTICE 6 Solve: $5(x - 1) - 3(x + 7) = 2x - 26$.

EXAMPLE 7 Solve: $3x - 8 = 5(x - 1) - 2(x + 6)$.

Algebraic Solution:

$$3x - 8 = 5(x - 1) - 2(x + 6)$$
$$3x - 8 = 5x - 5 - 2x - 12 \quad \text{Multiply.}$$
$$3x - 8 = 3x - 17 \quad \text{Simplify.}$$
$$3x - 8 - 3x = 3x - 17 - 3x \quad \text{Subtract } 3x.$$
$$-8 = -17$$

This equation is a false statement no matter what value the variable x might have. The equation has no solution and is a contradiction. The solution set is $\{\ \}$ or $\varnothing$.

Graphical Solution:

Graph $y_1 = 3x - 8$ and
$y_2 = 5(x - 1) - 2(x + 6)$

The graph to the right shows that the lines appear to be parallel and, therefore, will never intersect.

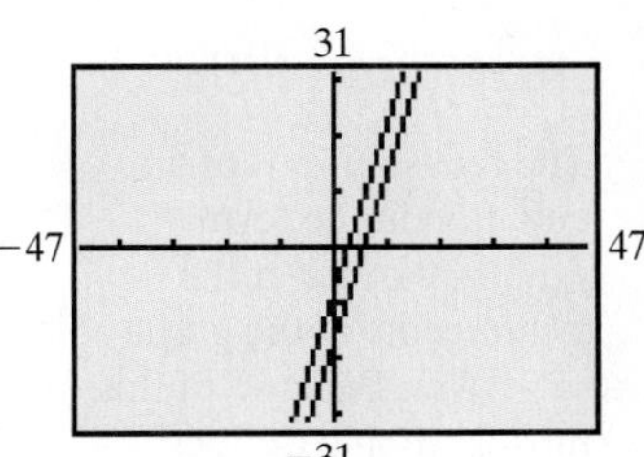

To be sure, check the slope of each graph.

$$y_1 = 3x - 8 \qquad y_2 = 5(x - 1) - 2(x + 6)$$
$$y_2 = 3x - 17$$

The lines have the same slope, 3, and their graphs are distinct, so they are indeed parallel. Since the lines do not intersect, there is no solution. The equation is a contradiction and the solution set is $\{\ \}$ or $\varnothing$.

Both solutions show that the equation is a contradiction and the solution set is { } or ∅. □

PRACTICE

7 Solve: $2x - 7 = 7(x + 1) - 5(x - 2)$.

OBJECTIVE 4 ▶ Solving equations using the *x*-intercept method. We now look at another method for solving equations graphically, called the ***x*-intercept method.** It is actually a form of the intersection-of-graphs method, but for this method we write an equivalent equation with one side of the equation 0. Since $y = 0$ is the x-axis, we look for points where the graph intersects the x-axis or x-intercepts. Recall that an x-intercept is of the form $(x, 0)$. (An x-intercept of $(a, 0)$ is sometimes simply called an x-intercept of a.) Thus, the solutions that lie on the x-axis are called the **zeros** of the equation since this is where $y = 0$. They are also referred to as **roots** of the equation. The built-in feature on graphing utilities to find these solutions is referred to as root or zero on different graphing utilities.

***x*-Intercept Method (or Zeros Method) for Solving an Equation**

STEP 1. Write the equation so that one side is 0.

STEP 2. Graph y_1 = the nonzero side of the equation.

STEP 3. Find an x-intercept or zero of the graph.

STEP 4. The x-coordinate of an x-intercept is a solution of the equation.

▶ **Helpful Hint**

Don't forget: One way to check a solution is to substitute it back into the *original equation* and see that a true statement results.

EXAMPLE 8 Solve the following equation using the x-intercept method.

$$-3.1(x + 1) + 8.3 = -x + 12.4$$

Solution We begin by writing the equation so that one side equals 0 by adding x to both sides and subtracting 12.4 from both sides.

$$-3.1(x + 1) + 8.3 = -x + 12.4$$
$$-3.1(x + 1) + 8.3 + x - 12.4 = 0$$

TECHNOLOGY NOTE

The real solutions of an equation in the form $f(x) = 0$ occur at the x-intercepts of the graph $y = f(x)$. Because of this, most graphing utilities have a root or zero feature to find the x-intercepts.

Define $y_1 = -3.1(x + 1) + 8.3 + x - 12.4$ and graph in a standard window. Choose the root, or zero, feature to solve. You will be prompted to indicate a left bound—an x-value less than the x-intercept and a right bound—an x-value greater than the x-intercept. The guess portion of the prompting asks you to move the cursor close to the x-intercept.

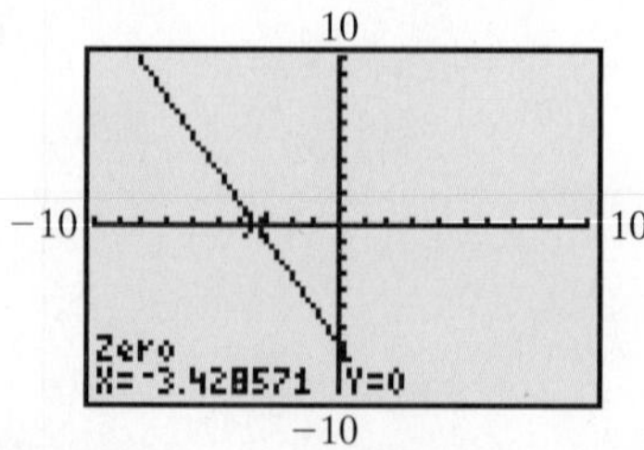

The x-intercept is approximately $(-3.428571, 0)$, which means that the solution to the equation is approximately -3.428571.

To check, replace x with -3.428571 and see that the left side of the equation is approximately the right side. Rounded to two decimal places, $x \approx -3.43$, or the solution is approximately -3.43. □

PRACTICE 8 Solve the equation using the x-intercept method.

$$2.5(x - 1) + 3.4 = 2x - 1$$

VOCABULARY & READINESS CHECK

Fill in each blank using the choices below.

x-intercept x zero intersection-of-graphs y root

1. To solve an equation by the ____________________ method, graph the left-hand side of the equation in y_1, the right-hand side of the equation in y_2, and find the intersection point of the two graphs.
2. To solve an equation by the ____________ method, first write the equation as an equivalent equation with one side 0.
3. For the intersection-of-graphs method, the _-coordinate of the point of intersection is the solution of the equation.
4. For the intersection-of-graphs method, the _-coordinate of the point of intersection is the value of each side of the equation when the solution is substituted into the equation.
5. List two other terms for the solution of an equation: _______, _______.

Mentally solve the following equations.

6. $4x = 24$
7. $6x = -12$
8. $2x + 10 = 20$
9. $5x + 25 = 30$
10. $-3x = 0$
11. $-2x = -14$
12. $2x + 3 = 2x - 1$
13. $2(x - 5) = 2x - 10$

16.1 EXERCISE SET

MyMathLab

PRACTICE

WATCH

DOWNLOAD

READ

REVIEW

Solve each equation algebraically and graphically. See Examples 1 through 3 and 8.

1. $5x + 2 = 3x + 6$
2. $2x + 9 = 3x + 7$

3. $9 - x = 2x + 12$
4. $3 - 4x = 2 - 3x$
5. $8 - (2x - 1) = 13$
6. $3(2 - x) + 4 = 2x + 3$

For each given screen, write an equation in x and its solution.

7.

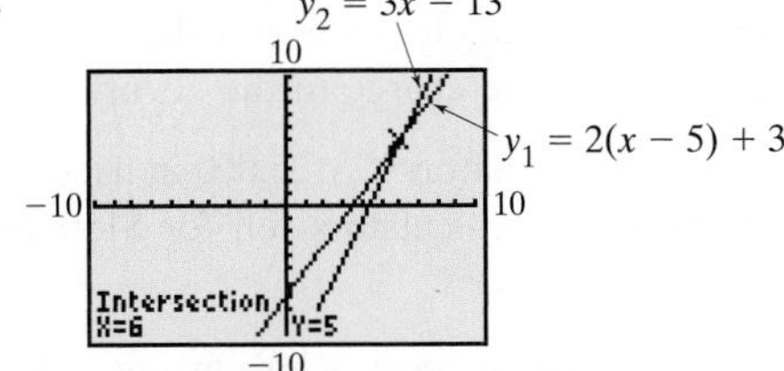

8.

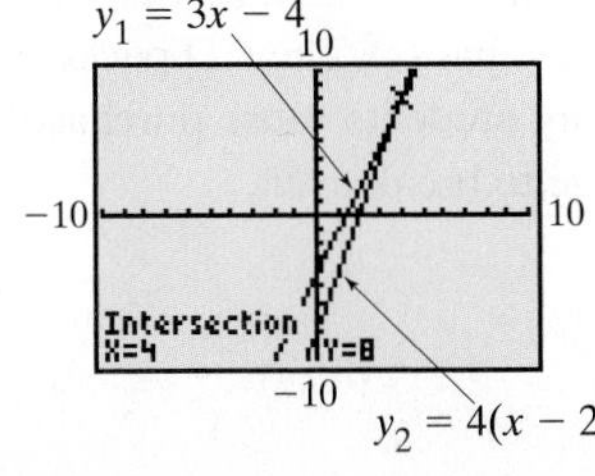

9.

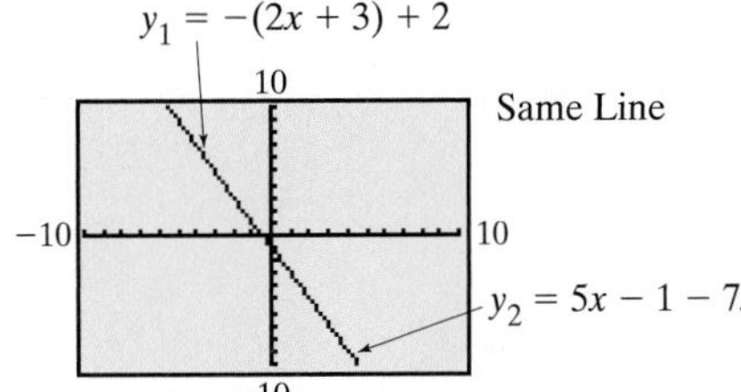

10.

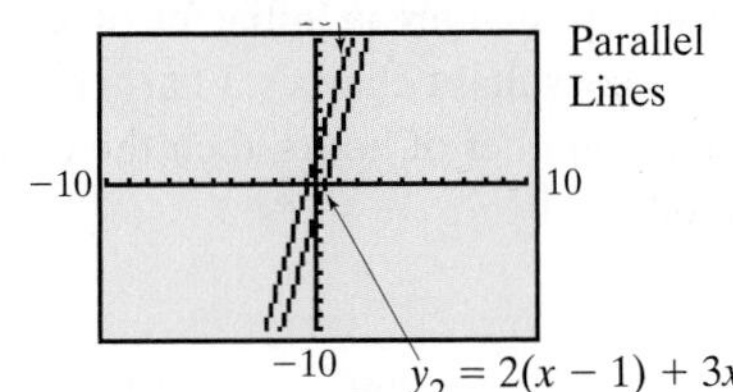

Solve each equation algebraically and graphically. See Examples 6 and 7.

11. $7(x - 6) = 5(x + 2) + 2x$
12. $6x - 9 = 6(x - 3)$

13. $3x - (6x + 2) = -(3x + 2)$
14. $8x - (2x + 3) = 6(x + 5)$
15. $5(x + 1) - 3(x - 7) = 2(x + 4) - 3$
16. $(5x + 8) - 2(x + 3) = (7x - 4) - (4x + 6)$
17. $3(x + 2) - 6(x - 5) = 36 - 3x$
18. $2(x + 3) - 7 = 4 + 2x$

MIXED PRACTICE

Solve each equation. If necessary, round solutions to two decimal places.

19. $(x + 2.1) - (0.5x + 3) = 12$
20. $2(x + 1.3) - 4(5 - x) = 15$
21. $5(a - 12) + 2(a + 15) = a - 9$
22. $8(b + 2) - 4(b - 5) = b + 12$
23. $8(p - 4) - 5(2p + 3) = 3.5(2p - 5)$
24. $3(x + 2) - 5(x - 7) = x + 3$
25. $5(x - 2) + 2x = 7(x + 4)$
26. $3x + 2(x + 4) = 5(x + 1) + 3$
27. $y + 0.2 = 0.6(y + 3)$
28. $-(w + 0.2) = 0.3(4 - w)$
29. $2y + 5(y - 4) = 4y - 2(y - 10)$
30. $9c - 3(6 - 5c) = c - 2(3c + 9)$
31. $2(x - 8) + x = 3(x - 6) + 2$
32. $4(x + 5) = 3(x - 4) + x$
33. $\frac{5x - 1}{6} - 3x = \frac{1}{3} + \frac{4x + 3}{9}$
34. $\frac{2r - 5}{3} - \frac{r}{5} = 4 - \frac{r + 8}{10}$
35. $-2(b - 4) - (3b - 1) = 5b + 3$
36. $4(t - 3) - 3(t - 2) = 2t + 8$
37. $1.5(4 - x) = 1.3(2 - x)$
38. $2.4(2x + 3) = -0.1(2x + 3)$
39. $\frac{1}{4}(a + 2) = \frac{1}{6}(5 - a)$
40. $\frac{1}{3}(8 + 2c) = \frac{1}{5}(3c - 5)$

Use a graphing method to solve. See Examples 4 and 5.

41. Acme Mortgage Company wants to hire a student computer consultant. A first consultant charges an initial fee of \$30 plus \$20 per hour. A second consultant charges a flat fee of \$25 per hour. If x represents number of hours, then the costs of the consultants are modeled by

$C_1(x) = 30 + 20x$ First consultant's total cost
$C_2(x) = 25x$ Second consultant's total cost

a. Find which consultant's cost is lower if the job takes 2 hours.
b. Find which consultant's cost is lower if the job takes 8 hours.
c. When is the cost of hiring each consultant the same?

42. Rod Pasch needs to hire a graphic artist. A first graphic artist charges \$50 plus \$35 per hour. A second one charges \$50 per hour. If x represents number of hours, then the costs of the graphic artists can be modeled by

$G_1(x) = 50 + 35x$ First graphic artist's total cost
$G_2(x) = 50x$ Second graphic artist's total cost

a. Which graphic artist costs less if the job takes 3 hours?
b. Which graphic artist costs less if the job takes 5 hours?
c. When is the cost of hiring each artist the same?

43. One car rental agency charges \$25 a day plus \$0.30 a mile. A second car rental agency charges \$28 a day plus \$0.25 a mile. If x represents the number of miles driven, then the costs of the car rental agencies for a 1-day rental can be modeled by

$R_1(x) = 25 + 0.30x$ First agency's cost
$R_2(x) = 28 + 0.25x$ Second agency's cost

a. Which agency's cost is lower if 50 miles are driven?
b. Which agency's cost is lower if 100 miles are driven?
c. When is the cost of using each agency the same?

44. Copycat Printing charges \$18 plus \$0.03 per page for making black and white copies. Duplicate, Inc. charges \$0.05 per black and white page copied. If x represents the number of pages copied, then the charges for the companies can be modeled by

$C_1(x) = 18 + 0.03x$ Copycat
$C_2(x) = 0.05x$ Duplicate, Inc.

a. For 500 copies, which company charges less?
b. For 1000 copies, which company charges less?
c. When is the cost of using each company the same?

45. Tara Outzen is considering a job in pharmaceutical sales. She is offered a monthly salary of \$1000 plus 4% commission with one company or an 8% commission-only position. How much must she sell per month, in order that the two plans give her the same gross pay?

46. Cheryl Brooks is a Certified Public Accountant and has clients who she charges a flat \$500 fee for doing tax returns and others she charges an initial consultation fee of \$150 and then \$125 per hour. How many hours would she work that both plans would be the same charge to the client?

47. The cost of producing x calculators is \$125,000 in fixed costs and \$75 per calculator. The calculators sell for \$150 each. Find the break-even point.

48. The local college finds that the cost of producing CDs for their distance learning program is \$550 and \$2 per CD and there are 10 CDs in each course packet. The CD packet sells for \$45 each. Find how many students must purchase the packet in order for the college to break even.

REVIEW AND PREVIEW

Determine which numbers in the set $\{-3, -2, -1, 0, 1, 2, 3\}$ are solutions of each inequality.

49. $x < 0$ **50.** $x > 1$

51. $x + 5 \leq 6$ **52.** $x - 3 \geq -7$

53. In your own words, explain what real numbers are solutions of $x < 0$.

54. In your own words, explain what real numbers are solutions of $x > 1$.

CONCEPT EXTENSIONS

The given screen shows the graphs of y_1 and y_2 and their intersection. Use this screen to answer the questions below.

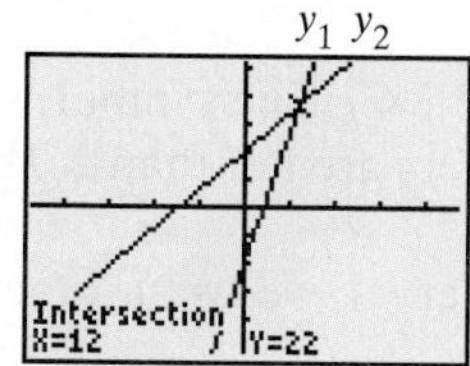

55. Complete the ordered pair for the graphs of both y_1 and y_2: (12,).

56. If x is less than 12, is y_1 less than, greater than, or equal to y_2?

57. If x is greater than 12, is y_1 less than, greater than, or equal to y_2?

58. True or false? If x is 45, $y_1 < y_2$.

Solve each equation graphically and check by a method of your choice. Round solutions to the nearest hundredth.

59. $1.75x - 2.5 = 0$ **60.** $3.1x + 5.6 = 0$

61. $2.5x + 3 = 7.8x - 5$ **62.** $4.8x - 2.3 = 6.8x + 2.7$

63. $3x + \sqrt{5} = 7x - \sqrt{2}$ **64.** $0.9x + \sqrt{3} = 2.5x - \sqrt{5}$

65. $2\pi x - 5.6 = 7(x - \pi)$ **66.** $-\pi x + 1.2 = 0.3(x - 5)$

67. If the intersection-of-graphs method leads to parallel lines, explain what this means in terms of the solution of the original equation.

68. If the intersection-of-graphs method leads to the same line, explain what this means in terms of the solution of the original equation.

16.2 LINEAR INEQUALITIES AND PROBLEM SOLVING

OBJECTIVES

1. Use interval notation.
2. Solve linear inequalities using the addition property of inequality.
3. Solve linear inequalities using the multiplication and the addition properties of inequality.
4. Solve problems that can be modeled by linear inequalities.

Relationships among measurable quantities are not always described by equations. For example, suppose that a salesperson earns a base of \$600 per month plus a commission of 20% of sales. Suppose we want to find the minimum amount of sales needed to receive a total income of *at least* \$1500 per month. Here, the phrase "at least" implies that an income of \$1500 *or more* is acceptable. In symbols, we can write

$$\text{income} \geq 1500$$

This is an example of an inequality, and we will solve this problem in Example 8.

A **linear inequality** is similar to a linear equation except that the equality symbol is replaced with an inequality symbol, such as $<, >, \leq$, or $\geq$.

Linear Inequalities in One Variable

$3x + 5 \geq 4$	$2y < 0$	$3(x - 4) > 5x$	$\frac{x}{3} \leq 5$
↑	↑	↑	↑
is greater than or equal to	is less than	is greater than	is less than or equal to

Linear Inequality in One Variable

A linear inequality in one variable is an inequality that can be written in the form

$$ax + b < c$$

where a, b, and c are real numbers and $a \neq 0$.

In this section, when we make definitions, state properties, or list steps about an inequality containing the symbol $<$, we mean that the definition, property, or steps apply to inequalities containing the symbols $>, \leq$, and $\geq$ also.

OBJECTIVE 1 ▶ Using interval notation. A **solution** of an inequality is a value of the variable that makes the inequality a true statement. The **solution set** of an inequality is the set of all solutions. Notice that the solution set of the inequality $x > 2$, for example, contains all numbers greater than 2. Its graph is an interval on the number line since an infinite number of values satisfy the variable. If we use open/closed-circle notation, the graph of $\{x|x > 2\}$ looks like the following.

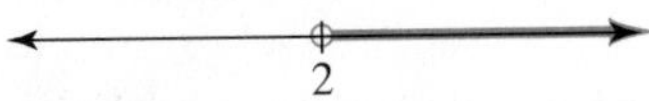

In this text **interval notation** will be used to write solution sets of inequalities. To help us understand this notation, a different graphing notation will be used. Instead of an open circle, we use a parenthesis. With this new notation, the graph of $\{x|x > 2\}$ now looks like

and can be represented in interval notation as $(2, \infty)$. The symbol ∞ is read "infinity" and indicates that the interval includes *all* numbers greater than 2. The left parenthesis indicates that 2 *is not* included in the interval.

In the case where 2 *is* included in the interval, we use a bracket. The graph of $\{x|x \geq 2\}$ is below

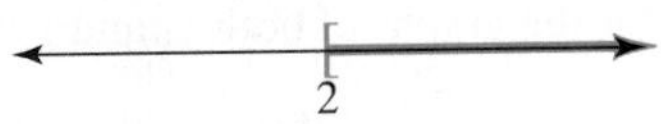

and can be represented as $[2, \infty)$.

The following table shows three equivalent ways to describe an interval: in set notation, as a graph, and in interval notation.

Set Notation	*Graph*	*Interval Notation*
$\{x\|x < a\}$	a	$(-\infty, a)$
$\{x\|x > a\}$	a	(a, ∞)
$\{x\|x \leq a\}$	a	$(-\infty, a]$
$\{x\|x \geq a\}$	a	$[a, \infty)$
$\{x\|a < x < b\}$	a b	(a, b)
$\{x\|a \leq x \leq b\}$	a b	$[a, b]$
$\{x\|a < x \leq b\}$	a b	$(a, b]$
$\{x\|a \leq x < b\}$	a b	$[a, b)$
$\{x\|x$ is a real number$\}$		$(-\infty, \infty)$

Helpful Hint
Notice that a parenthesis is always used to enclose ∞ and $-\infty$.

Concept Check ✓
Explain what is wrong with writing the interval $(5, \infty]$.

Answer to Concept Check:
should be $(5, \infty)$ since a parenthesis is always used to enclose ∞

EXAMPLE 1 Graph each set on a number line and then write in interval notation.

a. $\{x|x \geq 2\}$ **b.** $\{x|x < -1\}$ **c.** $\{x|0.5 < x \leq 3\}$

Solution

a. 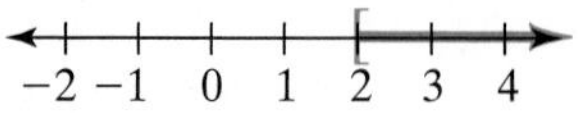 −2 −1 0 1 2 3 4 $[2, \infty)$

b. 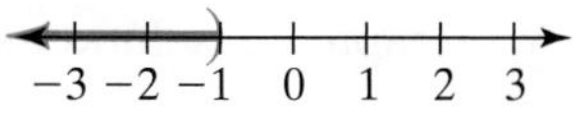 −3 −2 −1 0 1 2 3 $(-\infty, -1)$

c. 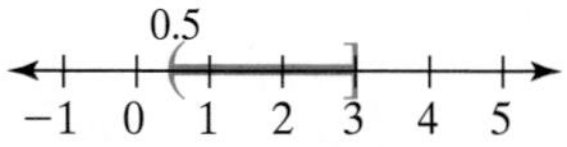 0.5 −1 0 1 2 3 4 5 $(0.5, 3]$

□

PRACTICE

1 Graph each set on a number line and then write in interval notation.

a. $\{x|x < 3.5\}$

b. $\{x|x \geq -3\}$

c. $\{x|-1 \leq x < 4\}$

OBJECTIVE 2 ▶ Solving linear inequalities using the addition property. We will use interval notation to write solutions of linear inequalities. To solve a linear inequality, we use a process similar to the one used to solve a linear equation. We use properties of inequalities to write equivalent inequalities until the variable is isolated.

Addition Property of Inequality

If a, b, and c are real numbers, then

$$a < b \quad \text{and} \quad a + c < b + c$$

are equivalent inequalities.

In other words, we may add the same real number to both sides of an inequality and the resulting inequality will have the same solution set. This property also allows us to subtract the same real number from both sides.

EXAMPLE 2 Solve algebraically: $x - 2 < 5$. Graph the solution set on a number line and write it in interval notation.

Solution

$$x - 2 < 5$$

$$x - 2 + 2 < 5 + 2 \quad \text{Add 2 to both sides.}$$

$$x < 7 \quad \text{Simplify.}$$

The solution set is $\{x|x < 7\}$, which in interval notation is $(-\infty, 7)$. The number-line graph of the solution set is

4 5 6 7 8 9 10

□

PRACTICE

2 Solve: $x + 5 > 9$. Graph the solution set on a number line and write it in interval notation.

Helpful Hint

In Example 2, the solution set is $\{x|x < 7\}$. This means that *all* numbers less than 7 are solutions. For example, 6.9, 0, $-\pi$, 1, and -56.7 are solutions, just to name a few. To see this, replace x in $x - 2 < 5$ with each of these numbers and see that the result is a true inequality.

EXAMPLE 3 Solve algebraically: $3x + 4 \geq 2x - 6$. Graph the solution set on a number line and write it in interval notation.

Solution

$3x + 4 \geq 2x - 6$

$3x + 4 - 2x \geq 2x - 6 - 2x$ Subtract $2x$ from both sides.

$x + 4 \geq -6$ Combine like terms.

$x + 4 - 4 \geq -6 - 4$ Subtract 4 from both sides.

$x \geq -10$ Simplify.

The solution set is $\{x|x \geq -10\}$, which in interval notation is $[-10, \infty)$. The number-line graph of the solution set is

−11 −10 −9 −8 −7 −6

PRACTICE 3 Solve: $8x + 21 \leq 2x - 3$. Graph the solution set on a number line and write it in interval notation.

DISCOVER THE CONCEPT

Let's use a graphing utility to check the solution of $3x + 4 \geq 2x - 6$ from Example 3. Let $y_1 = 3x + 4$ and $y_2 = 2x - 6$ and we can now think of the inequality as $y_1 \geq y_2$.

a. Graph y_1 and y_2 using the window $[-15, 20, 5]$ by $[-40, 30, 10]$.

b. Find the point of intersection of the graphs. What does this point represent?

c. Determine where the graph of y_1 is above the graph of y_2.

d. Now find the x-values for which $y_1 \geq y_2$.

e. Write the solution set of the inequality $y_1 \geq y_2$.

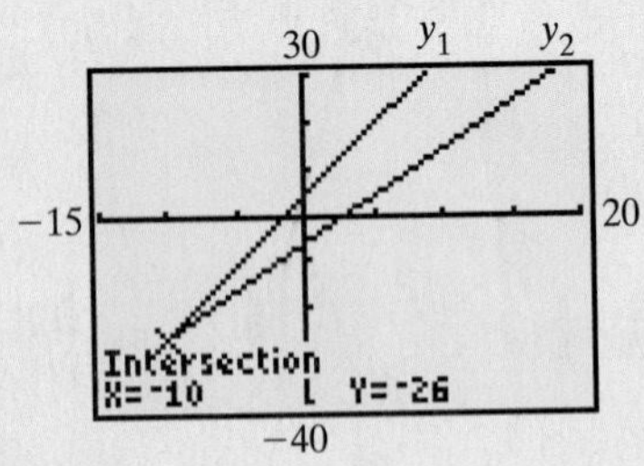

The graphs of y_1 and y_2 are shown to the left. From the above discovery, we find that

b. The point of intersection is $(-10, -26)$. This means that the solution of the equation $y_1 = y_2$ is -10.

c. The graph of y_1 is above the graph of y_2 to the right of the point of intersection, $(-10, -26)$.

d. The x-values for which $y_1 \geq y_2$ are -10 and those x-values to the right of -10 on the x-axis.

e. The solution set is $[-10, \infty)$.

Since there are an infinite number of solutions, checking solution after solution by hand is impossible. Here, the ability to check by graphing is a huge advantage.

OBJECTIVE 3 ▶ Solving linear inequalities using the multiplication and addition properties. Next, we introduce and use the multiplication property of inequality to solve linear inequalities. To understand this property, let's start with the true statement $-3 < 7$ and multiply both sides by 2.

$$-3 < 7$$
$$-3(2) < 7(2) \quad \text{Multiply by 2.}$$
$$-6 < 14 \quad \text{True}$$

The statement remains true.

Notice what happens if both sides of $-3 < 7$ are multiplied by -2.

$$-3 < 7$$
$$-3(-2) < 7(-2) \quad \text{Multiply by } -2.$$
$$6 < -14 \quad \text{False}$$

The inequality $6 < -14$ is a false statement. However, **if the direction of the inequality sign is reversed,** the result is true.

$$6 > -14 \quad \text{True}$$

These examples suggest the following property.

Multiplication Property of Inequality

If a, b, and c are real numbers and c is **positive**, then

$$a < b \quad \text{and} \quad ac < bc$$

are equivalent inequalities.

If a, b, and c are real numbers and c is **negative**, then

$$a < b \quad \text{and} \quad ac > bc$$

are equivalent inequalities.

In other words, we may multiply both sides of an inequality by the same positive real number and the result is an equivalent inequality.

We may also multiply both sides of an inequality by the same **negative number** and **reverse the direction of the inequality symbol**, and the result is an equivalent inequality. The multiplication property holds for division also, since division is defined in terms of multiplication.

Helpful Hint

Whenever both sides of an inequality are multiplied or divided by a negative number, the direction of the inequality symbol **must be** reversed to form an equivalent inequality.

EXAMPLE 4 Solve algebraically and graph the solution set on a number line. Write the solution set in interval notation.

a. $\frac{1}{4}x \le \frac{3}{8}$ **b.** $-2.3x < 6.9$

Solution

a.

$$\frac{1}{4}x \le \frac{3}{8}$$
$$4 \cdot \frac{1}{4}x \le 4 \cdot \frac{3}{8} \quad \text{Multiply both sides by 4.}$$
$$x \le \frac{3}{2} \quad \text{Simplify.}$$

Helpful Hint

The inequality symbol is the same since we are multiplying by a *positive* number.

The solution set is $\left\{x \middle| x \leq \frac{3}{2}\right\}$, which in interval notation is $\left(-\infty, \frac{3}{2}\right]$. The number-line graph of the solution set is

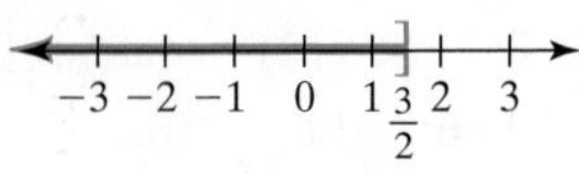

b. $-2.3x < 6.9$

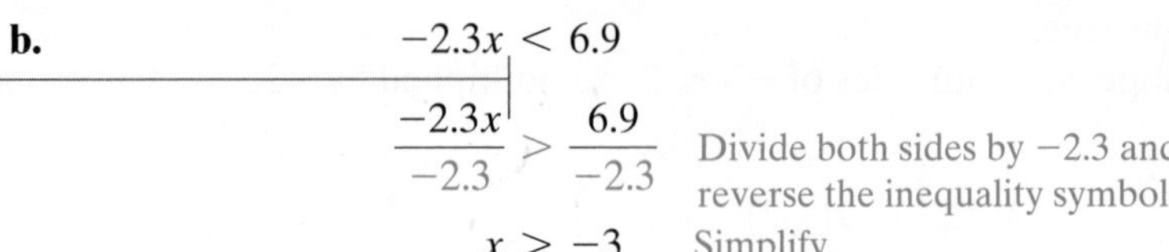

$$\frac{-2.3x}{-2.3} > \frac{6.9}{-2.3}$$ Divide both sides by −2.3 and reverse the inequality symbol.

$$x > -3$$ Simplify.

> **Helpful Hint**
> The inequality symbol is *reversed* since we divided by a *negative* number.

The solution set is $\{x | x > -3\}$, which is $(-3, \infty)$ in interval notation. The number-line graph of the solution set is

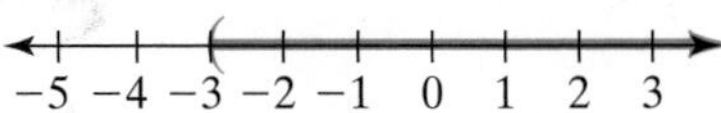

□

PRACTICE 4 Solve and graph the solution set on a number line. Write the solution set in interval notation.

a. $\frac{2}{5}x \geq \frac{4}{15}$

b. $-2.4x < 9.6$

Concept Check ✓

In which of the following inequalities must the inequality symbol be reversed during the solution process?

a. $-2x > 7$

b. $2x - 3 > 10$

c. $-x + 4 + 3x < 7$

d. $-x + 4 < 5$

To solve linear inequalities in general, we follow steps similar to those for solving linear equations.

Solving a Linear Inequality in One Variable

STEP 1. Clear the inequality of fractions by multiplying both sides of the inequality by the least common denominator (LCD) of all fractions in the inequality.

STEP 2. Use the distributive property to remove grouping symbols such as parentheses.

STEP 3. Combine like terms on each side of the inequality.

STEP 4. Use the addition property of inequality to write the inequality as an equivalent inequality with variable terms on one side and numbers on the other side.

STEP 5. Use the multiplication property of inequality to isolate the variable.

EXAMPLE 5 Solve algebraically: $-(x - 3) + 2 \leq 3(2x - 5) + x$ and check graphically.

Solution

$$-(x - 3) + 2 \leq 3(2x - 5) + x$$

$$-x + 3 + 2 \leq 6x - 15 + x$$ Apply the distributive property.

$$5 - x \leq 7x - 15$$ Combine like terms.

$$5 - x + x \leq 7x - 15 + x$$ Add x to both sides.

$$5 \leq 8x - 15$$ Combine like terms.

Answer to Concept Check:
a, d

$$5 + 15 \le 8x - 15 + 15 \quad \text{Add 15 to both sides.}$$
$$20 \le 8x \quad \text{Combine like terms.}$$
$$\frac{20}{8} \le \frac{8x}{8} \quad \text{Divide both sides by 8.}$$
$$\frac{5}{2} \le x, \quad \text{or} \quad x \ge \frac{5}{2} \quad \text{Simplify.}$$

> **Helpful Hint**
>
> Don't forget that $\frac{5}{2} \le x$ means the same as $x \ge \frac{5}{2}$.

The solution set written in interval notation is $\left[\frac{5}{2}, \infty\right)$.

To check, graph $y_1 = -(x - 3) + 2$ and $y_2 = 3(2x - 5) + x$ and find x-values such that $y_1 \le y_2$.

The point of intersection is (2.5, 2.5). The graph of y_1 is equal to or below the graph of y_2 for all x-values equal to or greater than 2.5, or for the interval $\left[\frac{5}{2}, \infty\right)$.

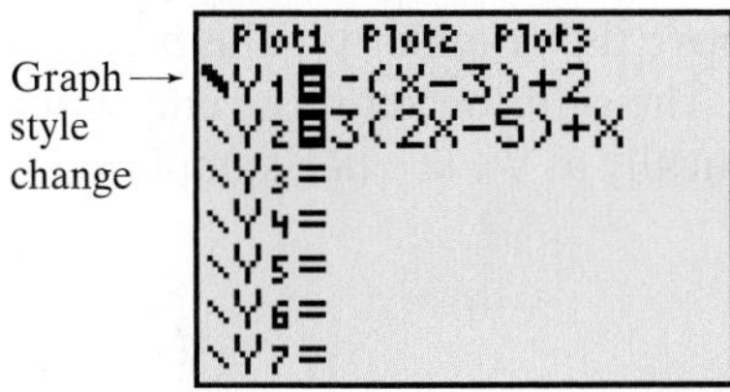

To change the graph style, go to the icon in front of the Y= and press Enter until you get the desired style.

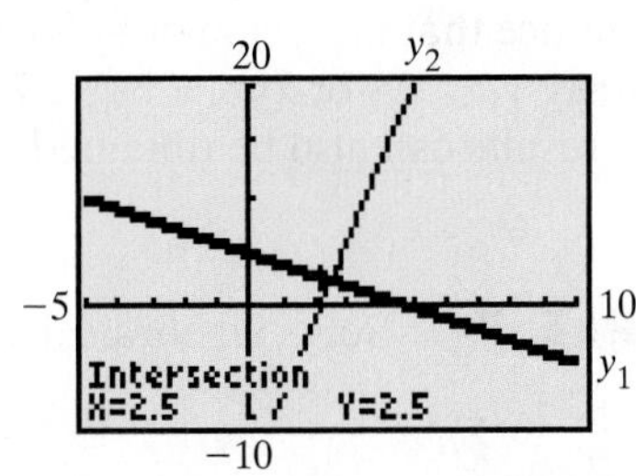

A calculator check of Example 5.

PRACTICE 5 Solve: $-(4x + 6) \le 2(5x + 9) + 2x$. Check graphically and write the solution set in interval notation.

EXAMPLE 6 Solve algebraically: $\frac{2}{5}(x - 6) \ge x - 1$ and check graphically.

Solution

$$\frac{2}{5}(x - 6) \ge x - 1$$
$$5\left[\frac{2}{5}(x - 6)\right] \ge 5(x - 1) \quad \text{Multiply both sides by 5 to eliminate fractions.}$$
$$2(x - 6) \ge 5(x - 1)$$
$$2x - 12 \ge 5x - 5 \quad \text{Apply the distributive property.}$$
$$-3x - 12 \ge -5 \quad \text{Subtract } 5x \text{ from both sides.}$$
$$-3x \ge 7 \quad \text{Add 12 to both sides.}$$
$$\frac{-3x}{-3} \le \frac{7}{-3} \quad \text{Divide both sides by } -3 \text{ and reverse the inequality symbol.}$$
$$x \le -\frac{7}{3} \quad \text{Simplify.}$$

The solution set written in interval notation is $\left(-\infty, -\frac{7}{3}\right]$. The graphing utility check is shown in the margin.

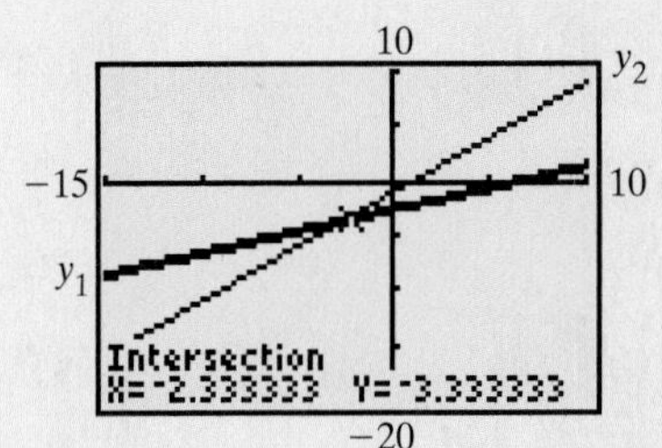

The intersection of y_1 and y_2 is the point $\left(-\frac{7}{3}, -\frac{10}{3}\right)$. $y_1 \ge y_2$ for all x-values in the interval $\left(-\infty, -\frac{7}{3}\right]$ since this is where y_1 is equal to or above y_2.

PRACTICE 6 Solve: $\frac{3}{5}(x - 3) \ge x - 7$. Check graphically and write the solution set in interval notation.

Recall that when the graph of the left side and the right side of an equation do not intersect, the equation has no solution. Let's see what a similar situation means for inequalities.

DISCOVER THE CONCEPT

a. Use a graphing utility to solve $2(x + 3) > 2x + 1$. To do so, graph $y_1 = 2(x + 3)$ and $y_2 = 2x + 1$ and find the x-values for which the graph of y_1 is above the graph of y_2.

b. Next, solve $2(x + 3) < 2x + 1$. Notice that the graphs of y_1 and y_2 found in part **a** can be used. Find the x-values for which the graph of y_1 is below the graph of y_2.

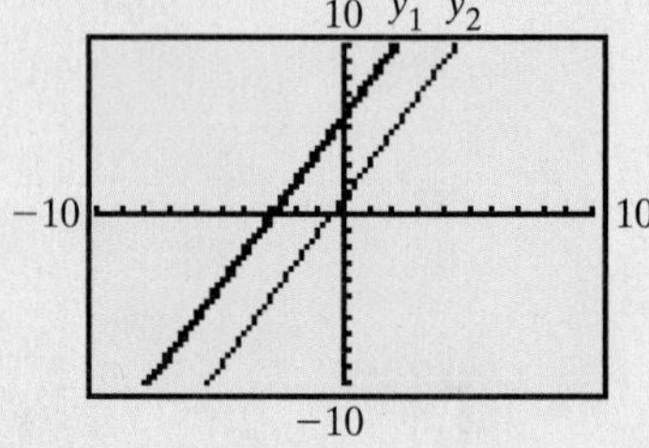

The graphs of parallel lines y_1 and y_2 from the discovery above are shown at the left. Since the graph of y_1 is *always* above the graph of y_2, all x-values satisfy the inequality $y_1 > y_2$ or $2(x + 3) > 2x + 1$. The solution set is all real numbers or $(-\infty, \infty)$.

Also, notice that the graph of y_2 is *never* above the graph of y_1. This means that no x-values satisfy $y_1 < y_2$ or $2(x + 3) < 2x + 1$. The solution set is the empty set or $\varnothing$.

These results can also be obtained algebraically as we see in Example 7.

EXAMPLE 7 Solve algebraically:

a. $2(x + 3) > 2x + 1$ **b.** $2(x + 3) < 2x + 1$

Solution

a.

$$2(x + 3) > 2x + 1$$

$$2x + 6 > 2x + 1 \quad \text{Distribute on the left side.}$$

$$2x + 6 - 2x > 2x + 1 - 2x \quad \text{Subtract } 2x \text{ from both sides.}$$

$$6 > 1 \quad \text{Simplify.}$$

$6 > 1$ is a true statement for all values of x, so this inequality and the original inequality are true for all numbers. The solution set is $\{x|x \text{ is a real number}\}$, or $(-\infty, \infty)$ in interval notation.

b. Solving $2(x + 3) < 2x + 1$ in a similar fashion leads us to the statement $6 < 1$. This statement, as well as the original inequality, is false for all values of x. This means that the solution set is the empty set, or $\varnothing$. □

PRACTICE 7 Solve algebraically: **a.** $4(x - 2) < 4x + 5$ **b.** $4(x - 2) > 4x + 5$. Write the solution set in interval notation.

OBJECTIVE 4 ▶ Solving problems modeled by linear inequalities. Application problems containing words such as "at least," "at most," "between," "no more than," and "no less than" usually indicate that an inequality be solved instead of an equation. In solving applications involving linear inequalities, we use the same procedure as when we solved applications involving linear equations.

EXAMPLE 8 **Calculating Income with Commission**

A salesperson earns \$600 per month plus a commission of 20% of sales. Find the minimum amount of sales needed to receive a total income of at least \$1500 per month.

Solution

1. UNDERSTAND. Read and reread the problem. Let x = amount of sales.
2. TRANSLATE. As stated in the beginning of this section, we want the income to be at least, or greater than or equal to, \$1500. To write an inequality, notice that the salesperson's income consists of \$600 plus a commission (20% of sales).

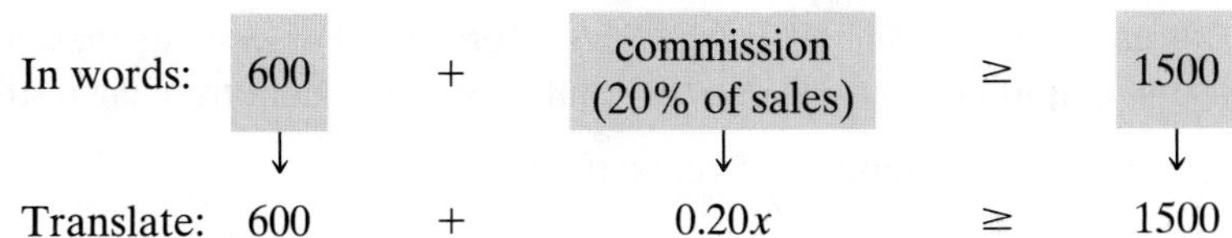

3. SOLVE the inequality for x.

First, let's decide on a window.

For sales of \$2000, gross pay = \$600 + 20%(\$2000) = \$1000. Similarly, for sales of \$5000, gross pay is \$1600. This means that a sales amount between \$2000 and \$5000 will give a gross pay of \$1500. Although many windows are acceptable, for this example, we graph $y_1 = 600 + 0.20x$ and $y_2 = 1500$ on a [2000, 5000, 1000] by [1000, 2000, 100] window.

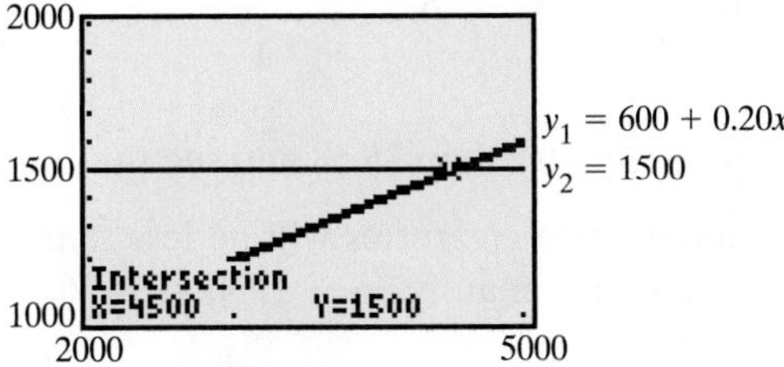

From the graph we see that $y_1 \geq y_2$ for x-values greater than or equal to 4500, or for x-values in the interval $[4500, \infty)$.

4. INTERPRET.

Check: The income for sales of \$4500 is

$$600 + 0.20(4500), \text{ or } 1500.$$

Thus, if sales are greater than or equal to \$4500, income is greater than or equal to \$1500.

State: The minimum amount of sales needed for the salesperson to earn at least \$1500 per month is \$4500 per month. □

PRACTICE

8 A salesperson earns \$900 a month plus a commission of 15% of sales. Find the minimum amount of sales needed to receive a total income of at least \$2400 per month.

EXAMPLE 9 Finding the Annual Consumption

In the United States, the annual consumption of cigarettes is declining. The consumption c in billions of cigarettes per year since the year 1990 can be approximated by the formula

$$c = -9.2t + 527.33$$

where t is the number of years after 1990. Use this formula to predict the years that the consumption of cigarettes will be less than 200 billion per year.

Solution

1. UNDERSTAND. Read and reread the problem. To become familiar with the given formula, let's find the cigarette consumption after 20 years, which would be the year 1990 + 20, or 2010. To do so, we substitute 20 for t in the given formula.

$$c = -9.2(20) + 527.33 = 343.33$$

Thus, in 2010, we predict cigarette consumption to be about 343.3 billion.

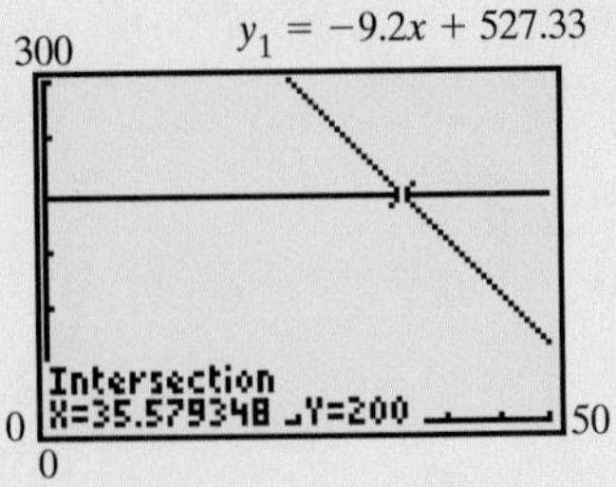

Variables have already been assigned in the given formula. For review, they are $c =$ the annual consumption of cigarettes in the United States in billions of cigarettes

$t =$ the number of years after 1990

2. TRANSLATE. We are looking for the years that the consumption of cigarettes c is less than 200. Since we are finding years t, we substitute the expression in the formula given for c, or

$$-9.2t + 527.33 < 200$$

300 $y_1 = -9.2x + 527.33$

Intersection X=35.579348 Y=200

0 50 0

A calculator solution for Example 9.

3. SOLVE the inequality.

$$-9.2t + 527.33 < 200$$
$$-9.2t < -327.33$$
$$t > \text{approximately } 35.58$$

4. INTERPRET.

Check: Substitute a number greater than 35.58 and see that c is less than 200.

State: The annual consumption of cigarettes will be less than 200 billion more than 35.58 years after 1990, or in approximately $36 + 1990 = 2026$. □

PRACTICE
9 Use the formula given in Example 9 to predict when the consumption of cigarettes will be less than 250 billion per year.

VOCABULARY & READINESS CHECK

Match each graph with the interval notation that describes it.

1.

a. $(-5, \infty)$ b. $(-5, -\infty)$
c. $(\infty, -5)$ d. $(-\infty, -5)$

2.

a. $(-\infty, -11]$ b. $(-11, \infty)$
c. $[-11, \infty)$ d. $(-\infty, -11)$

3.

a. $\left[\frac{7}{4}, -2.5\right)$ b. $\left(-2.5, \frac{7}{4}\right]$
c. $\left[-2.5, \frac{7}{4}\right)$ d. $\left(\frac{7}{4}, -2.5\right)$

4.

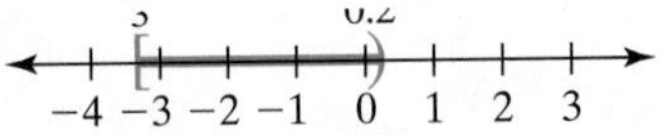

−4 −3 −2 −1 0 1 2 3

a. $\left[-\frac{10}{3}, 0.2\right)$ b. $\left(0.2, -\frac{10}{3}\right]$
c. $\left(-\frac{10}{3}, 0.2\right]$ d. $\left[0.2, -\frac{10}{3}\right)$

Use the choices below to fill in each blank.

$(-\infty, -0.4)$ $(-\infty, -0.4]$ $[-0.4, \infty)$ $(-0.4, \infty)$ $(\infty, -0.4]$

5. The set $\{x \mid x \geq -0.4\}$ written in interval notation is ____________.
6. The set $\{x \mid x < -0.4\}$ written in interval notation is ____________.
7. The set $\{x \mid x \leq -0.4\}$ written in interval notation is ____________.
8. The set $\{x \mid x > -0.4\}$ written in interval notation is ____________.

Each inequality below is solved by dividing both sides by the coefficient of x. In which inequality will the inequality symbol be reversed during this solution process?

9. $3x > -14$ **10.** $-3x \leq 14$ **11.** $-3x < -14$ **12.** $-x \geq 23$

16.2 EXERCISE SET

Graph the solution set of each inequality on a number line and write it in interval notation. See Example 1.

1. $\{x|x < -3\}$
2. $\{x|x > 5\}$
3. $\{x|x \geq 0.3\}$
4. $\{x|x < -0.2\}$
5. $\{x|-2 < x < 5\}$
6. $\{x|-5 \leq x \leq -1\}$
7. $\{x|5 \geq x > -1\}$
8. $\{x|-3 > x \geq -7\}$

Solve. Graph the solution set on a number line and write it in interval notation. See Examples 2 through 4.

9. $x - 7 \geq -9$
10. $x + 2 \leq -1$
11. $8x - 7 \leq 7x - 5$
12. $7x - 1 \geq 6x - 1$
13. $\frac{3}{4}x \geq 6$
14. $\frac{5}{6}x \geq 5$
15. $-5x > 23.5$
16. $-4x < 11.2$

Use the given screen to solve each inequality. Write the solution in interval notation.

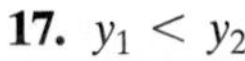

17. $y_1 < y_2$

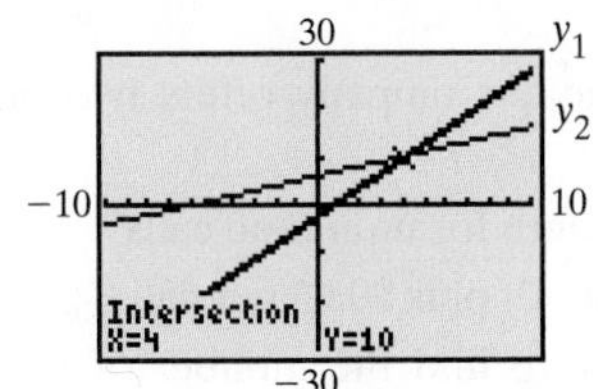

18. $y_1 \geq 0$

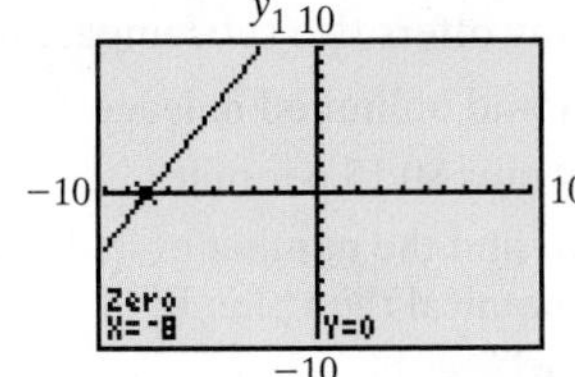

19. $y_1 \geq y_2$

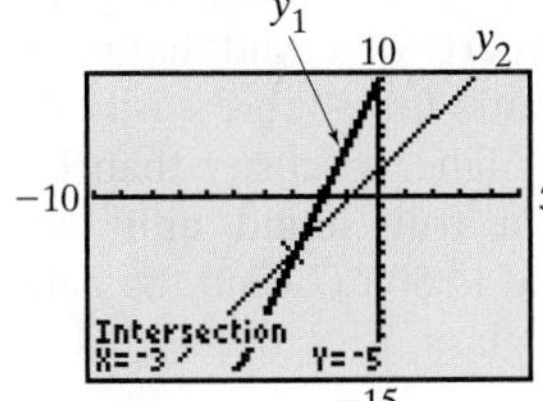

20. $y_1 > y_2$

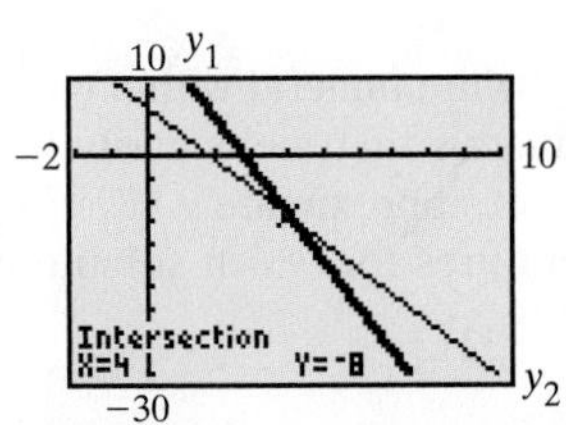

Use the graph of parallel lines y_1 and y_2 to solve each inequality. Write the solution in interval notation.

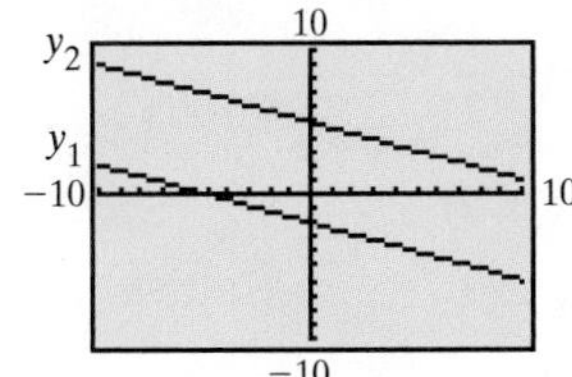

21. $y_1 > y_2$
22. $y_1 < y_2$

Solve. Write the solution set using interval notation. See Examples 5 through 7.

23. $-2x + 7 \geq 9$
24. $8 - 5x \leq 23$
25. $15 + 2x \geq 4x - 7$
26. $20 + x < 6x - 15$
27. $4(2x + 1) > 4$
28. $6(2 - 3x) \geq 12$
29. $3(x - 5) < 2(2x - 1)$
30. $5(x + 4) \leq 4(2x + 3)$
31. $\frac{5x + 1}{7} - \frac{2x - 6}{4} \geq -4$
32. $\frac{1 - 2x}{3} + \frac{3x + 7}{7} > 1$
33. $-3(2x - 1) < -4[2 + 3(x + 2)]$
34. $-2(4x + 2) > -5[1 + 2(x - 1)]$

MIXED PRACTICE

Solve. Write the solution set using interval notation. See Examples 1 through 7. Check solutions graphically.

35. $x + 9 < 3$
36. $x - 9 < -12$
37. $-x < -4$
38. $-x > -2$
39. $-7x \leq 3.5$
40. $-6x \leq 4.2$
41. $\frac{1}{2} + \frac{2}{3} \geq \frac{x}{6}$
42. $\frac{3}{4} - \frac{2}{3} \geq \frac{x}{6}$
43. $-5x + 4 \leq -4(x - 1)$
44. $-6x + 2 < -3(x + 4)$
45. $\frac{3}{4}(x - 7) \geq x + 2$
46. $\frac{4}{5}(x + 1) \leq x + 1$
47. $0.8x + 0.6x \geq 4.2$
48. $0.7x - x > 0.45$
49. $4(x - 6) + 2x - 4 \geq 3(x - 7) + 10x$
50. $7(2x + 3) + 4x \leq 7 + 5(3x - 4) + x$
51. $14 - (5x - 6) \geq -6(x + 1) - 5$
52. $13y - (9y + 2) \leq 5(y - 6) + 10$
53. $\frac{1}{2}(3x - 4) \leq \frac{3}{4}(x - 6) + 1$
54. $\frac{2}{3}(x + 3) < \frac{1}{6}(2x - 8) + 2$
55. $\frac{-x + 2}{2} - \frac{1 - 5x}{8} < -1$
56. $\frac{3 - 4x}{6} - \frac{1 - 2x}{12} \leq -2$

57. $\frac{x+5}{5} - \frac{3+x}{8} \geq -\frac{3}{10}$

58. $\frac{x-4}{2} - \frac{x-2}{3} > \frac{5}{6}$

59. $\frac{x+3}{12} + \frac{x-5}{15} < \frac{2}{3}$

60. $\frac{3x+2}{18} - \frac{1+2x}{6} \leq -\frac{1}{2}$

61. $0.4(4x - 3) < 1.2(x + 2)$

62. $0.2(8x - 2) < 1.2(x - 3)$

63. $\frac{2}{5}x - \frac{1}{4} \leq \frac{3}{10}x - \frac{4}{5}$

64. $\frac{7}{12}x - \frac{1}{3} \leq \frac{3}{8}x - \frac{5}{6}$

65. $4(x - 1) \geq 4x - 8$

66. $3x + 1 < 3(x - 2)$

67. $7x < 7(x - 2)$

68. $8(x + 3) \leq 7(x + 5) + x$

Solve. See Examples 8 and 9. For Exercises 69 through 76, ***a.*** *answer with an inequality, and* ***b.*** *in your own words, explain the meaning of your answer to part* ***a.***

69. Shureka Washburn has scores of 72, 67, 82, and 79 on her algebra tests.

a. Use an inequality to find the scores she must make on the final exam to pass the course with an average of 77 or higher, given that the final exam counts as two tests.

b. In your own words explain the meaning of your answer to part **a.**

70. In a Winter Olympics 5000-meter speed-skating event, Hans Holden scored times of 6.85, 7.04, and 6.92 minutes on his first three trials.

a. Use an inequality to find the times he can score on his last trial so that his average time is under 7.0 minutes.

b. In your own words, explain the meaning of your answer to part **a.**

71. A small plane's maximum takeoff weight is 2000 pounds or less. Six passengers weigh an average of 160 pounds each. Use an inequality to find the luggage and cargo weights the plane can carry.

72. A shopping mall parking garage charges $1 for the first half-hour and 60 cents for each additional half-hour. Use an inequality to find how long you can park if you have only $4.00 in cash.

73. A clerk must use the elevator to move boxes of paper. The elevator's maximum weight limit is 1500 pounds. If each box of paper weighs 66 pounds and the clerk weighs 147 pounds, use an inequality to find the number of whole boxes she can move on the elevator at one time.

74. As of May 2008, the cost to mail an envelope first class is 42 cents for the first ounce and 17 cents per ounce for each additional ounce. Use an inequality to find the number of whole ounces that can be mailed for no more than $2.50.

75. Northeast Telephone Company offers two billing plans for local calls.

Plan 1: $25 per month for unlimited calls

Plan 2: $13 per month plus $0.06 per call

Use an inequality to find the number of monthly calls for which plan 1 is more economical than plan 2.

76. A car rental company offers two subcompact rental plans.

Plan A: $36 per day and unlimited mileage

Plan B: $24 per day plus $0.15 per mile

Use an inequality to find the number of daily miles for which plan A is more economical than plan B.

77. At room temperature, glass used in windows actually has some properties of a liquid. It has a very slow, viscous flow. (Viscosity is the property of a fluid that resists internal flow. For example, lemonade flows more easily than fudge syrup. Fudge syrup has a higher viscosity than lemonade.) Glass does not become a true liquid until temperatures are greater than or equal to 500°C. Find the Fahrenheit temperatures for which glass is a liquid. (Use the formula $F = \frac{9}{5}C + 32$.)

78. Stibnite is a silvery white mineral with a metallic luster. It is one of the few minerals that melts easily in a match flame or at temperatures of approximately 977°F or greater. Find the Celsius temperatures for which stibnite melts. [Use the formula $C = \frac{5}{9}(F - 32)$.]

79. Although beginning salaries vary greatly according to your field of study, the equation

$$s = 651.2t + 28{,}472$$

can be used to approximate and to predict average beginning salaries for candidates with bachelor's degrees. The variable s is the starting salary and t is the number of years after 1990.

a. Approximate when beginning salaries for candidates will be greater than $42,000.

b. Determine the year you plan to graduate from college. Use this year to find the corresponding value of t and approximate your beginning salary.

80. The equation $y = 1573x + 125{,}217$ can be used to approximate the civilian labor force. Here, x is the number of years after 1990 and y is the civilian labor force (in thousands). (See Chapter 16 opener.)

a. Assume this trend continues and predict the year when the civilian labor force will be greater than 160,000 thousand. Round up to the nearest year.

b. Determine the year you plan to graduate from college. Use this year to predict the corresponding civilian labor force.

The average consumption per person per year of whole milk w in gallons can be approximated by the equation

$$y = -0.19t + 7.6$$

where t is the number of years after 2000. The average consumption of nonfat milk s per person per year can be approximated by the equation

$$y = -0.07t + 3.5$$

where t is the number of years after 2000. The consumption of whole milk is shown on the graph in red and the consumption of nonfat milk is shown on the graph in blue. Use this information to answer Exercises 81–88.

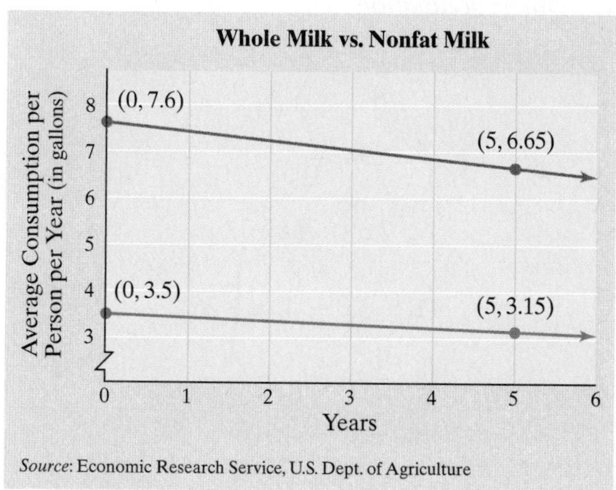

81. Is the consumption of whole milk increasing or decreasing over time? Explain how you arrived at your answer.

82. Is the consumption of nonfat milk increasing or decreasing over time? Explain how you arrived at your answer.

83. Predict the consumption of whole milk in the year 2010. (*Hint:* Find the value of t that corresponds to the year 2010.)

84. Predict the consumption of nonfat milk in the year 2010. (*Hint:* Find the value of t that corresponds to the year 2010.)

85. Determine when the consumption of whole milk was first less than 6 gallons per person per year.

86. Determine when the consumption of nonfat milk was first less than 3 gallons per person per year.

87. For 2000 through 2005 the consumption of whole milk was greater than the consumption of nonfat milk. Explain how this can be determined from the graph.

88. How will the two lines in the graph appear if the consumption of whole milk is the same as the consumption of nonfat milk?

REVIEW AND PREVIEW

List or describe the integers that make both inequalities true.

89. $x < 5$ and $x > 1$

90. $x \geq 0$ and $x \leq 7$

91. $x \geq -2$ and $x \geq 2$

92. $x < 6$ and $x < -5$

Solve each equation for x. See Section 1.5.

93. $2x - 6 = 4$

94. $3x - 12 = 3$

95. $-x + 7 = 5x - 6$

96. $-5x - 4 = -x - 4$

CONCEPT EXTENSIONS

Each row of the table shows three equivalent ways of describing an interval. Complete this table by filling in the equivalent descriptions. The first row has been completed for you.

	Set Notation	Graph	Interval Notation
	$\{x \mid x < -3\}$	-3	$(-\infty, -3)$
97.		2	
98.		-4	
99.	$\{x \mid x < 0\}$		
100.	$\{x \mid x \leq 5\}$		
101.			$(-2, 1.5]$
102.			$[-3.7, 4)$

103. Solve: $2x - 3 = 5$.

104. Solve: $2x - 3 < 5$.

105. Solve: $2x - 3 > 5$.

106. Read the equations and inequalities for Exercises 103, 104, and 105 and their solutions. In your own words, write down your thoughts.

107. When graphing the solution set of an inequality, explain how you know whether to use a parenthesis or a bracket.

108. Explain what is wrong with the interval notation $(-6, -\infty)$.

109. Explain how solving a linear inequality is similar to solving a linear equation.

110. Explain how solving a linear inequality is different from solving a linear equation.

111. Write an inequality whose solution set is $\{x \mid x \leq 2\}$.

THE BIGGER PICTURE SOLVING EQUATIONS AND INEQUALITIES

Although suggestions will be given, this outline should be in your own words. Once you complete this new portion, try the exercises below.

Solving Equations and Inequalities

I. Equations

A. Linear equations: Power on variable is 1 and there are no variables in denominator. (Section 16.1)

II. Inequalities

A. Linear Inequalities: Inequality sign and power on x is 1 and there are no variables in denominator. (Section 16.2)

$-3(x+2) \geq 6$	Linear inequality
$-3x - 6 \geq 6$	Multiply.
$-3x \geq 12$	Add 6 to both sides.
$\dfrac{-3x}{-3} \leq \dfrac{12}{-3}$	Divide both sides by -3, and *change* the direction of the inequality sign.
$x \leq -4$ or $(-\infty, -4]$	

Solve. Write inequality solutions in interval notation.

1. $7x - 2 = 5(2x + 1) + 3$

2. $5 + 9x = 5(x + 1)$

3. $\dfrac{x+3}{2} > 1$

4. $\dfrac{x+2}{2} + \dfrac{x+4}{3} = \dfrac{29}{6}$

5. $\dfrac{7}{5} - \dfrac{y}{10} = 2$

6. $5 + 9x = 9(x + 1)$

7. $4(x - 2) + 3x \geq 9(x - 1) - 2$

8. $8(x + 1) - 2 = 8x + 6$

INTEGRATED REVIEW LINEAR EQUATIONS AND INEQUALITIES

Sections 16.1–16.2

Solve each equation or inequality. For inequalities, write the solution set in interval notation.

1. $-4x = 20$

2. $-4x < 20$

3. $\dfrac{3x}{4} \geq 2$

4. $5x + 3 \geq 2 + 4x$

5. $6(y - 4) = 3(y - 8)$

6. $-4x \leq \dfrac{2}{5}$

7. $-3x \geq \dfrac{1}{2}$

8. $5(y + 4) = 4(y + 5)$

9. $7x < 7(x - 2)$

10. $\dfrac{-5x + 11}{2} \leq 7$

11. $-5x + 1.5 = -19.5$

12. $-5x + 4 = -26$

13. $5 + 2x - x = -x + 3 - 14$

14. $12x + 14 < 11x - 2$

15. $\dfrac{x}{5} - \dfrac{x}{4} = \dfrac{x-2}{2}$

16. $12x - 12 = 8(x - 1)$

17. $2(x - 3) > 70$

18. $-3x - 4.7 = 11.8$

19. $-2(b - 4) - (3b - 1) = 5b + 3$

20. $8(x + 3) < 7(x + 5) + x$

21. $\dfrac{3t+1}{8} = \dfrac{5+2t}{7} + 2$

22. $4(x - 6) - x = 8(x - 3) - 5x$

23. $\dfrac{x}{6} + \dfrac{3x-2}{2} < \dfrac{2}{3}$

24. $\dfrac{y}{3} + \dfrac{y}{5} = \dfrac{y+3}{10}$

25. $5(x - 6) + 2x > 3(2x - 1) - 4$

26. $14(x - 1) - 7x \leq 2(3x - 6) + 4$

27. $\dfrac{1}{4}(3x + 2) - x \geq \dfrac{3}{8}(x - 5) + 2$

28. $\dfrac{1}{3}(x - 10) - 4x > \dfrac{5}{6}(2x + 1) - 1$

16.3 COMPOUND INEQUALITIES

OBJECTIVES

1. Find the intersection of two sets.
2. Solve compound inequalities containing **and.**
3. Find the union of two sets.
4. Solve compound inequalities containing **or.**

Two inequalities joined by the words **and** or **or** are called **compound inequalities.**

Compound Inequalities

$$x + 3 < 8 \quad \text{and} \quad x > 2$$

$$\frac{2x}{3} \geq 5 \quad \text{or} \quad -x + 10 < 7$$

OBJECTIVE 1 ▶ Finding the intersection of two sets. The solution set of a compound inequality formed by the word **and** is the **intersection** of the solution sets of the two inequalities. We use the symbol $\cap$ to represent "intersection."

Intersection of Two Sets

The intersection of two sets, A and B, is the set of all elements common to both sets. A intersect B is denoted by

$A \cap B$

A B

EXAMPLE 1 If $A = \{x|x \text{ is an even number greater than 0 and less than 10}\}$ and $B = \{3, 4, 5, 6\}$, find $A \cap B$.

Solution Let's list the elements in set A.

$$A = \{2, 4, 6, 8\}$$

The numbers 4 and 6 are in sets A and B. The intersection is $\{4, 6\}$. □

PRACTICE

1 If $A = \{x|x \text{ is an odd number greater than 0 and less than 10}\}$ and $B = \{1, 2, 3, 4\}$, find $A \cap B$.

OBJECTIVE 2 ▶ Solving compound inequalities containing "and." A value is a solution of a compound inequality formed by the word **and** if it is a solution of *both* inequalities. For example, the solution set of the compound inequality $x \leq 5$ and $x \geq 3$ contains all values of x that make the inequality $x \leq 5$ a true statement **and** the inequality $x \geq 3$ a true statement. The first graph shown below is the graph of $x \leq 5$, the second graph is the graph of $x \geq 3$, and the third graph shows the intersection of the two graphs. The third graph is the graph of $x \leq 5$ **and** $x \geq 3$.

Set	Graph	Interval
$\{x\|x \leq 5\}$	−1 0 1 2 3 4 5 6	$(-\infty, 5]$
$\{x\|x \geq 3\}$	−1 0 1 2 3 4 5 6	$[3, \infty)$
$\{x\|x \leq 5 \text{ and } x \geq 3\}$ also $\{x\|3 \leq x \leq 5\}$ (see below)	−1 0 1 2 3 4 5 6	$[3, 5]$

Since $x \geq 3$ is the same as $3 \leq x$, the compound inequality $3 \leq x$ and $x \leq 5$ can be written in a more compact form as $3 \leq x \leq 5$. The solution set $\{x|3 \leq x \leq 5\}$ includes all numbers that are greater than or equal to 3 and at the same time less than or equal to 5.

In interval notation, the set $\{x|x \leq 5 \text{ and } x \geq 3\}$ or $\{x|3 \leq x \leq 5\}$ is written as $[3, 5]$.

Helpful Hint

Don't forget that some compound inequalities containing "and" can be written in a more compact form.

Compound Inequality	*Compact Form*	*Interval Notation*
$2 \le x$ *and* $x \le 6$	$2 \le x \le 6$	$[2, 6]$
Graph:	 0 1 2 3 4 5 6 7	

EXAMPLE 2 Solve: $x - 7 < 2$ *and* $2x + 1 < 9$

Solution First we solve each inequality separately.

$$\begin{aligned} x - 7 < 2 \quad &\textit{and} \quad 2x + 1 < 9 \\ x < 9 \quad &\textit{and} \quad 2x < 8 \\ x < 9 \quad &\textit{and} \quad x < 4 \end{aligned}$$

Now we can graph the two intervals on two number lines and find their intersection. Their intersection is shown on the third number line.

$\{x \mid x < 9\}$ 3 4 5 6 7 8 9 10 $(-\infty, 9)$

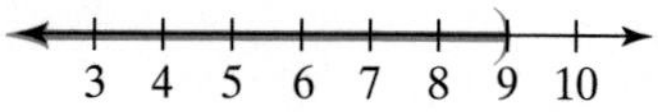

$\{x \mid x < 4\}$ 3 4 5 6 7 8 9 10 $(-\infty, 4)$

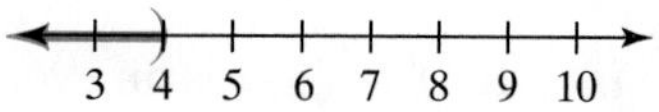

$\{x \mid x < 9 \text{ and } x < 4\} = \{x \mid x < 4\}$ 3 4 5 6 7 8 9 10 $(-\infty, 4)$

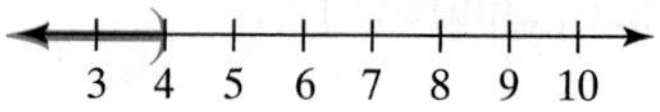

The solution set is $(-\infty, 4)$. □

PRACTICE
2 Solve: $x + 3 < 8$ *and* $2x - 1 < 3$. Write the solution set in interval notation.

EXAMPLE 3 Solve: $2x \ge 0$ *and* $4x - 1 \le -9$.

Solution First we solve each inequality separately.

$$\begin{aligned} 2x \ge 0 \quad &\textit{and} \quad 4x - 1 \le -9 \\ x \ge 0 \quad &\textit{and} \quad 4x \le -8 \\ x \ge 0 \quad &\textit{and} \quad x \le -2 \end{aligned}$$

Now we can graph the two intervals on number lines and find their intersection.

$\{x \mid x \ge 0\}$ −3 −2 −1 0 1 2 3 4 $[0, \infty)$

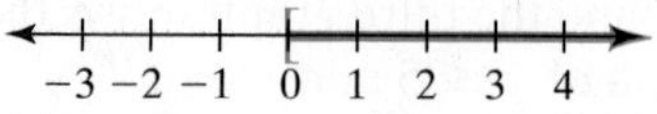

$\{x \mid x \le -2\}$ −3 −2 −1 0 1 2 3 4 $(-\infty, -2]$

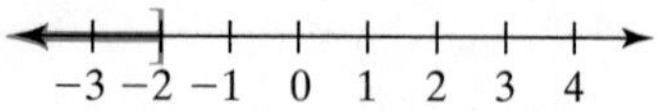

$\{x \mid x \ge 0 \text{ and } x \le -2\} = \varnothing$  $\varnothing$

There is no number that is greater than or equal to 0 *and* less than or equal to −2. The solution set is $\varnothing$. □

PRACTICE
3 Solve: $4x \le 0$ *and* $3x + 2 > 8$. Write the solution set in interval notation.

Helpful Hint

Example 3 shows that some compound inequalities have no solution. Also, some have all real numbers as solutions.

To solve a compound inequality written in a compact form, such as $2 < 4 - x < 7$, we get x alone in the "middle part." Since a compound inequality is really two inequalities in one statement, we must perform the same operations on all three parts of the inequality.

EXAMPLE 4 Solve: $2 < 4 - x < 7$

Solution To get x alone, we first subtract 4 from all three parts.

$$2 < 4 - x < 7$$

$$2 - 4 < 4 - x - 4 < 7 - 4 \quad \text{Subtract 4 from all three parts.}$$

$$-2 < -x < 3 \quad \text{Simplify.}$$

$$\frac{-2}{-1} > \frac{-x}{-1} > \frac{3}{-1} \quad \text{Divide all three parts by } -1 \text{ and reverse the inequality symbols.}$$

$$2 > x > -3$$

Helpful Hint
Don't forget to reverse both inequality symbols.

This is equivalent to $-3 < x < 2$.

The solution set in interval notation is $(-3, 2)$, and its number-line graph is shown.

−4 −3 −2 −1 0 1 2 3

□

PRACTICE 4 Solve: $3 < 5 - x < 9$. Write the solution set in interval notation.

DISCOVER THE CONCEPT

For the compound inequality $2 < 4 - x < 7$, in Example 4, graph $y_1 = 2$, $y_2 = 4 - x$, and $y_3 = 7$. With this notation, we can think of our inequality as $y_1 < y_2 < y_3$.

a. Find the point of intersection of y_1 and y_2.

b. Find the point of intersection of y_2 and y_3.

c. Determine where the graph of y_2 is between the graphs of y_1 and y_3.

d. Find the x-values for which $y_1 < y_2 < y_3$.

e. Write the solution set of $y_1 < y_2 < y_3$.

In the discovery above, we find the points of intersection as shown.

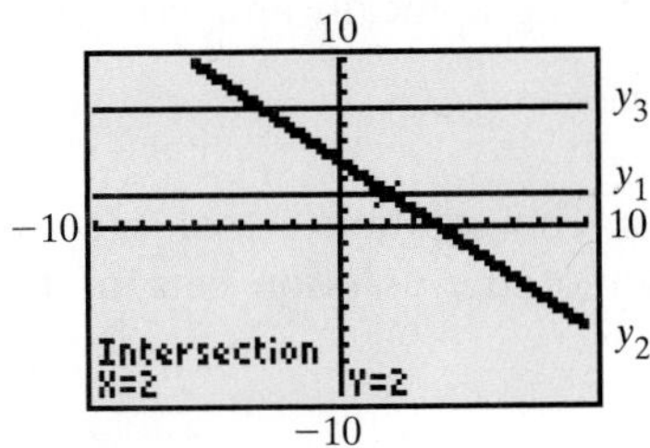

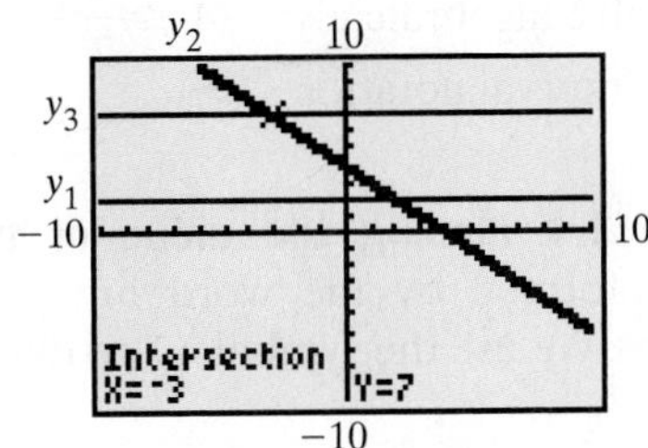

The solution of $y_1 < y_2 < y_3$, or $2 < 4 - x < 7$ contains the x-values where the graph of $y_2 = 4 - x$ is between $y_1 = 2$ and $y_3 = 7$. These x-values in interval notation are $(-3, 2)$. (Parentheses are used because of the inequality symbols $<$.)

EXAMPLE 5 Solve algebraically: $-1 \le \frac{2x}{3} + 5 \le 2$. Check graphically.

Solution First, clear the inequality of fractions by multiplying all three parts by the LCD of 3.

$$-1 \le \frac{2x}{3} + 5 \le 2$$

$$3(-1) \le 3\left(\frac{2x}{3} + 5\right) \le 3(2) \quad \text{Multiply all three parts by the LCD of 3.}$$

$$-3 \le 2x + 15 \le 6 \quad \text{Use the distributive property and multiply.}$$

$$-3 - 15 \le 2x + 15 - 15 \le 6 - 15 \quad \text{Subtract 15 from all three parts.}$$

$$-18 \le 2x \le -9 \quad \text{Simplify.}$$

$$\frac{-18}{2} \le \frac{2x}{2} \le \frac{-9}{2} \quad \text{Divide all three parts by 2.}$$

$$-9 \le x \le -\frac{9}{2} \quad \text{Simplify.}$$

The number-line graph of the solution is shown.

$-\frac{9}{2}$

−10 −9 −8 −7 −6 −5 −4 −3

The solution set in interval notation is $\left[-9, -\frac{9}{2}\right]$.

To check, graph $y_1 = -1$, $y_2 = \frac{2x}{3} + 5$, and $y_3 = 2$ in a $[-15, 5, 3]$ by $[-5, 5, 1]$ window and solve $y_1 \le y_2 \le y_3$.

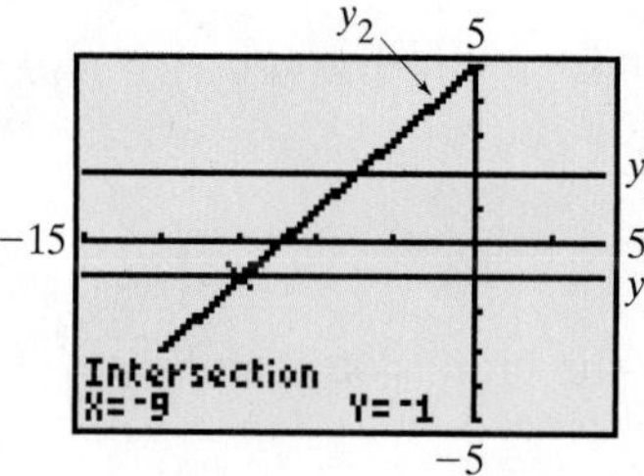

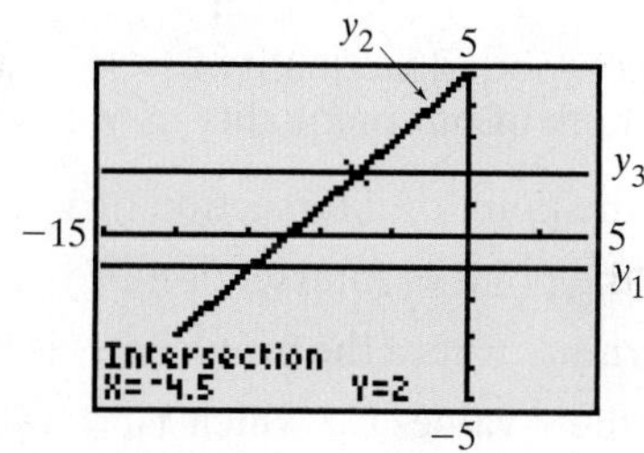

The solution of $y_1 \le y_2 \le y_3$ consists of the x-values where the graph of y_2 is between or equal to the graphs of y_1 and y_3. The solution set in interval notation is $[-9, -4.5]$ or $\left[-9, -\frac{9}{2}\right]$. □

PRACTICE 5 Solve algebraically: $-4 \le \frac{x}{2} - 1 \le 3$. Check graphically and write the solution set in interval notation.

OBJECTIVE 3 ▶ Finding the union of two sets. The solution set of a compound inequality formed by the word **or** is the **union** of the solution sets of the two inequalities. We use the symbol ∪ to denote "union."

▶ Helpful Hint

The word "either" in this definition means "one or the other or both."

Union of Two Sets

The **union** of two sets, A and B, is the set of elements that belong to *either* of the sets. A union B is denoted by

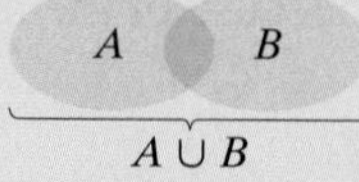

EXAMPLE 6 If $A = \{x|x \text{ is an even number greater than 0 and less than 10}\}$ and $B = \{3, 4, 5, 6\}$, find $A \cup B$.

Solution Recall from Example 1 that $A = \{2, 4, 6, 8\}$. The numbers that are in either set or both sets are $\{2, 3, 4, 5, 6, 8\}$. This set is the union. □

PRACTICE 6 If $A = \{x|x \text{ is an odd number greater than 0 and less than 10}\}$ and $B = \{2, 3, 4, 5, 6\}$. Find $A \cup B$.

OBJECTIVE 4 ▶ Solving compound inequalities containing "or." A value is a solution of a compound inequality formed by the word **or** if it is a solution of **either** inequality. For example, the solution set of the compound inequality $x \le 1$ **or** $x \ge 3$ contains all numbers that make the inequality $x \le 1$ a true statement **or** the inequality $x \ge 3$ a true statement.

Set	Number line	Interval
$\{x \mid x \le 1\}$	−1 0 1 2 3 4 5 6	$(-\infty, 1]$
$\{x \mid x \ge 3\}$	−1 0 1 2 3 4 5 6	$[3, \infty)$
$\{x \mid x \le 1 \text{ or } x \ge 3\}$	−1 0 1 2 3 4 5 6	$(-\infty, 1] \cup [3, \infty)$

In interval notation, the set $\{x \mid x \le 1 \text{ or } x \ge 3\}$ is written as $(-\infty, 1] \cup [3, \infty)$.

EXAMPLE 7 Solve: $5x - 3 \le 10$ *or* $x + 1 \ge 5$.

Solution First we solve each inequality separately.

$$\begin{aligned} 5x - 3 \le 10 \quad &or \quad x + 1 \ge 5 \\ 5x \le 13 \quad &or \quad x \ge 4 \\ x \le \frac{13}{5} \quad &or \quad x \ge 4 \end{aligned}$$

Now we can graph each interval on a number line and find their union.

Set	Number line	Interval
$\left\{x \mid x \le \frac{13}{5}\right\}$	$\frac{13}{5}$; −1 0 1 2 3 4 5 6	$\left(-\infty, \frac{13}{5}\right]$
$\{x \mid x \ge 4\}$	−1 0 1 2 3 4 5 6	$[4, \infty)$
$\left\{x \mid x \le \frac{13}{5} \text{ or } x \ge 4\right\}$	$\frac{13}{5}$; −1 0 1 2 3 4 5 6	$\left(-\infty, \frac{13}{5}\right] \cup [4, \infty)$

The solution set is $\left(-\infty, \frac{13}{5}\right] \cup [4, \infty)$. □

PRACTICE 7 Solve: $8x + 5 \le 8$ or $x - 1 \ge 2$. Write the solution set in interval notation.

EXAMPLE 8 Solve: $-2x - 5 < -3$ *or* $6x < 0$.

Solution First we solve each inequality separately.

$$\begin{aligned} -2x - 5 < -3 \quad &or \quad 6x < 0 \\ -2x < 2 \quad &or \quad x < 0 \\ x > -1 \quad &or \quad x < 0 \end{aligned}$$

Now we can graph each interval on a number line and find their union.

$\{x|x > -1\}$ — number line from -4 to 3 — $(-1, \infty)$

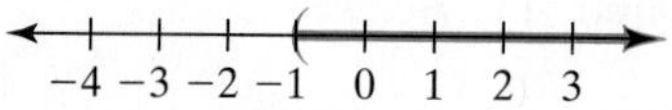

$\{x|x < 0\}$ — number line from -4 to 3 — $(-\infty, 0)$

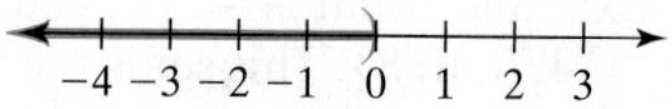

$\{x|x > -1 \text{ or } x < 0\}$ = all real numbers — number line from -4 to 3 — $(-\infty, \infty)$

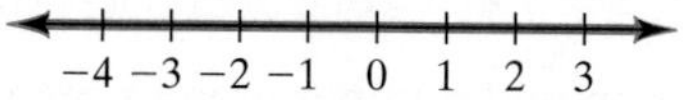

The solution set is $(-\infty, \infty)$. □

PRACTICE

8 Solve: $-3x - 2 > -8$ *or* $5x > 0$. Write the solution set in interval notation.

Concept Check ✓

Which of the following is *not* a correct way to represent the set of all numbers between -3 and 5?

a. $\{x| -3 < x < 5\}$ **b.** $-3 < x$ or $x < 5$

c. $(-3, 5)$ **d.** $x > -3$ and $x < 5$

Answer to Concept Check:
b is not correct

VOCABULARY & READINESS CHECK

Use the choices below to fill in each blank. Some choices may be used more than once.

or	∪	∅
and	∩	compound

1. Two inequalities joined by the words "and" or "or" are called ________ inequalities.
2. The word ______ means intersection.
3. The word ______ means union.
4. The symbol ______ represents intersection.
5. The symbol ______ represents union.
6. The symbol ______ is the empty set.
7. The inequality $-2 \le x < 1$ means $-2 \le x$ ______ $x < 1$.
8. $\{x|x < 0 \text{ and } x > 0\} =$ ____

16.3 EXERCISE SET

MIXED PRACTICE

If $A = \{x|x \text{ is an even integer}\}$, $B = \{x|x \text{ is an odd integer}\}$, $C = \{2, 3, 4, 5\}$, *and* $D = \{4, 5, 6, 7\}$, *list the elements of each set. See Examples 1 and 6.*

1. $C \cup D$
2. $C \cap D$
3. $A \cap D$
4. $A \cup D$
5. $A \cup B$
6. $A \cap B$
7. $B \cap D$
8. $B \cup D$
9. $B \cup C$
10. $B \cap C$
11. $A \cap C$
12. $A \cup C$

Solve each compound inequality. Graph the solution set on a number line and write it in interval notation. See Examples 2 and 3.

13. $x < 1$ and $x > -3$
14. $x \le 0$ and $x \ge -2$
15. $x \le -3$ and $x \ge -2$
16. $x < 2$ and $x > 4$
17. $x < -1$ and $x < 1$
18. $x \ge -4$ and $x > 1$

Solve each compound inequality. Write solutions in interval notation. See Examples 2 and 3.

19. $x + 1 \ge 7$ and $3x - 1 \ge 5$
20. $x + 2 \ge 3$ and $5x - 1 \ge 9$
21. $4x + 2 \le -10$ and $2x \le 0$
22. $2x + 4 > 0$ and $4x > 0$

23. $-2x < -8$ and $x - 5 < 5$
24. $-7x \leq -21$ and $x - 20 \leq -15$

Solve each compound inequality. See Examples 4 and 5.

25. $5 < x - 6 < 11$
26. $-2 \leq x + 3 \leq 0$
27. $-2 \leq 3x - 5 \leq 7$
28. $1 < 4 + 2x < 7$
29. $1 \leq \frac{2}{3}x + 3 \leq 4$
30. $-2 < \frac{1}{2}x - 5 < 1$
31. $-5 \leq \frac{-3x + 1}{4} \leq 2$
32. $-4 \leq \frac{-2x + 5}{3} \leq 1$

Solve each compound inequality. Graph the solution set on a number line and write it in interval notation. See Examples 7 and 8.

33. $x < 4$ *or* $x < 5$
34. $x \geq -2$ *or* $x \leq 2$
35. $x \leq -4$ *or* $x \geq 1$
36. $x < 0$ *or* $x < 1$
37. $x > 0$ *or* $x < 3$
38. $x \geq -3$ *or* $x \leq -4$

Solve each compound inequality. Write solutions in interval notation. See Examples 7 and 8.

39. $-2x \leq -4$ or $5x - 20 \geq 5$
40. $-5x \leq 10$ or $3x - 5 \geq 1$
41. $x + 4 < 0$ or $6x > -12$
42. $x + 9 < 0$ or $4x > -12$
43. $3(x - 1) < 12$ or $x + 7 > 10$
44. $5(x - 1) \geq -5$ or $5 - x \leq 11$

MIXED PRACTICE

Solve each compound inequality. Write solutions in interval notation. See Examples 1 through 8.

45. $x < \frac{2}{3}$ and $x > -\frac{1}{2}$
46. $x < \frac{5}{7}$ and $x < 1$
47. $x < \frac{2}{3}$ or $x > -\frac{1}{2}$
48. $x < \frac{5}{7}$ or $x < 1$
49. $0 \leq 2x - 3 \leq 9$
50. $3 < 5x + 1 < 11$
51. $\frac{1}{2} < x - \frac{3}{4} < 2$
52. $\frac{2}{3} < x + \frac{1}{2} < 4$
53. $x + 3 \geq 3$ and $x + 3 \leq 2$
54. $2x - 1 \geq 3$ and $-x > 2$
55. $3x \geq 5$ or $-\frac{5}{8}x - 6 > 1$
56. $\frac{3}{8}x + 1 \leq 0$ or $-2x < -4$
57. $0 < \frac{5 - 2x}{3} < 5$
58. $-2 < \frac{-2x - 1}{3} < 2$
59. $-6 < 3(x - 2) \leq 8$
60. $-5 < 2(x + 4) < 8$
61. $-x + 5 > 6$ and $1 + 2x \leq -5$
62. $5x \leq 0$ and $-x + 5 < 8$
63. $3x + 2 \leq 5$ or $7x > 29$
64. $-x < 7$ or $3x + 1 < -20$
65. $5 - x > 7$ and $2x + 3 \geq 13$
66. $-2x < -6$ or $1 - x > -2$
67. $-\frac{1}{2} \leq \frac{4x - 1}{6} < \frac{5}{6}$
68. $-\frac{1}{2} \leq \frac{3x - 1}{10} < \frac{1}{2}$
69. $\frac{1}{15} < \frac{8 - 3x}{15} < \frac{4}{5}$
70. $-\frac{1}{4} < \frac{6 - x}{12} < -\frac{1}{6}$
71. $0.3 < 0.2x - 0.9 < 1.5$
72. $-0.7 \leq 0.4x + 0.8 < 0.5$

Solve each compound inequality using the graphing utility screens.

73. **a.** $y_1 < y_2 < y_3$
b. $y_2 < y_1$ or $y_2 > y_3$

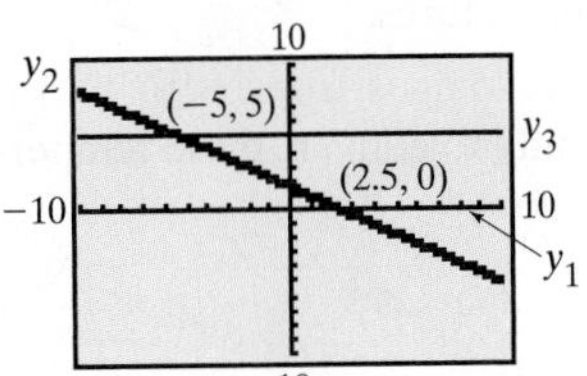

74. **a.** $y_1 < y_2 < y_3$
b. $y_2 < y_1$ or $y_2 > y_3$

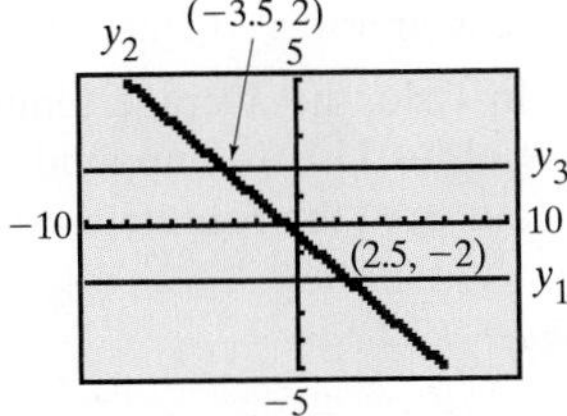

75. **a.** $y_1 \leq y_2 \leq y_3$
b. $y_2 \leq y_1$ or $y_2 \geq y_3$

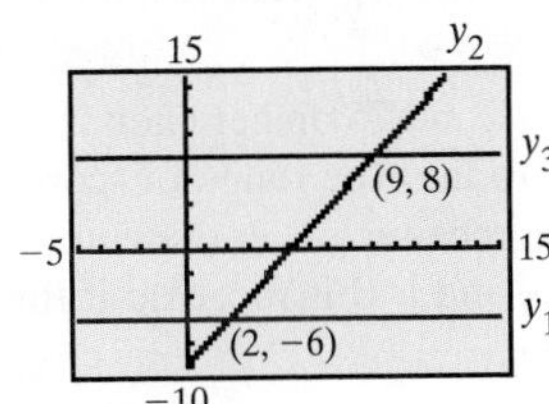

76. **a.** $y_1 \leq y_2 \leq y_3$
b. $y_2 \leq y_1$ or $y_2 \geq y_3$

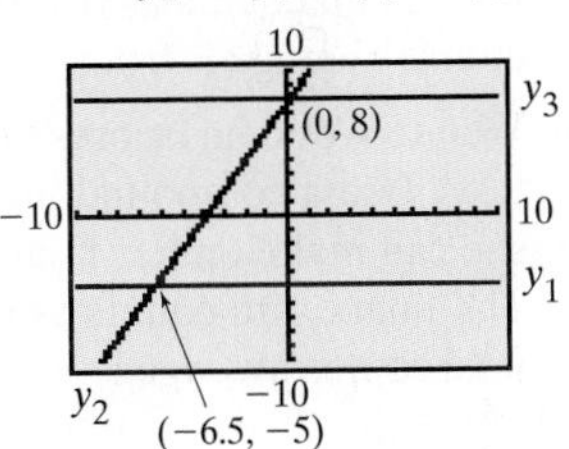

REVIEW AND PREVIEW

Evaluate the following.

77. $|-7| - |19|$
78. $|-7 - 19|$
79. $-(-6) - |-10|$
80. $|-4| - (-4) + |-20|$

Find by inspection all values for x that make each equation true.

81. $|x| = 7$
82. $|x| = 5$
83. $|x| = 0$
84. $|x| = -2$

CONCEPT EXTENSIONS

Use the graph to answer Exercises 85 and 86.

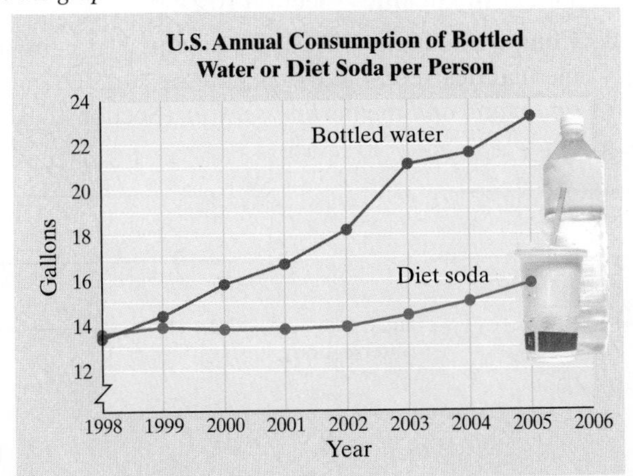

85. For what years was the consumption of bottled water greater than 20 gallons per person *and* the consumption of diet soda greater than 14 gallons per person?

86. For what years was the consumption of bottled water less than 15 gallons per person *or* the consumption of diet soda greater than 14 gallons per person?

The formula for converting Fahrenheit temperatures to Celsius temperatures is $C = \frac{5}{9}(F - 32)$. *Use this formula for Exercises 87 and 88.*

87. During a recent year, the temperatures in Chicago ranged from $-29°$ to $35°C$. Use a compound inequality to convert these temperatures to Fahrenheit temperatures.

88. In Oslo, the average temperature ranges from $-10°$ to $18°$ Celsius. Use a compound inequality to convert these temperatures to the Fahrenheit scale.

Solve.

89. Christian D'Angelo has scores of 68, 65, 75, and 78 on his algebra tests. Use a compound inequality to find the scores he can make on his final exam to receive a C in the course. The final exam counts as two tests, and a C is received if the final course average is from 70 to 79.

90. Wendy Wood has scores of 80, 90, 82, and 75 on her chemistry tests. Use a compound inequality to find the range of scores she can make on her final exam to receive a B in the course. The final exam counts as two tests, and a B is received if the final course average is from 80 to 89.

Solve each compound inequality for x. See the example below. To solve $x - 6 < 3x < 2x + 5$, *notice that this inequality contains a variable not only in the middle, but also on the left and the right. When this occurs, we solve by rewriting the inequality using the word* ***and.***

$$x - 6 < 3x \quad \text{and} \quad 3x < 2x + 5$$
$$-6 < 2x \quad \text{and} \quad x < 5$$
$$-3 < x$$
$$x > -3 \quad \text{and} \quad x < 5$$

−4 −3 −2 −1 0 1 2 3 4 5 6

$x > -3$

−4 −3 −2 −1 0 1 2 3 4 5 6

$x < 5$

−4 −3 −2 −1 0 1 2 3 4 5 6

$-3 < x < 5$, or $(-3, 5)$

91. $2x - 3 < 3x + 1 < 4x - 5$

92. $x + 3 < 2x + 1 < 4x + 6$

93. $-3(x - 2) \le 3 - 2x \le 10 - 3x$

94. $7x - 1 \le 7 + 5x \le 3(1 + 2x)$

95. $5x - 8 < 2(2 + x) < -2(1 + 2x)$

96. $1 + 2x < 3(2 + x) < 1 + 4x$

THE BIGGER PICTURE SOLVING EQUATIONS AND INEQUALITIES

We now continue the outline from Section 16.2. Although suggestions will be given, this outline should be in your own words. Once you complete this new portion, try the exercises below.

Solving Equations and Inequalities

I. Equations

 A. Linear equations (Section 16.1)

II. Inequalities

 A. Linear Inequalities (Section 16.2)

 B. Compound Inequalities: Two inequality signs or 2 inequalities separated by "and" or "or." *Or* means *union* and *and* means *intersection*. (Section 16.3)

$x \le 3$ *and* $x < -7$ $\qquad$ $x \le 3$ *or* $x < -7$

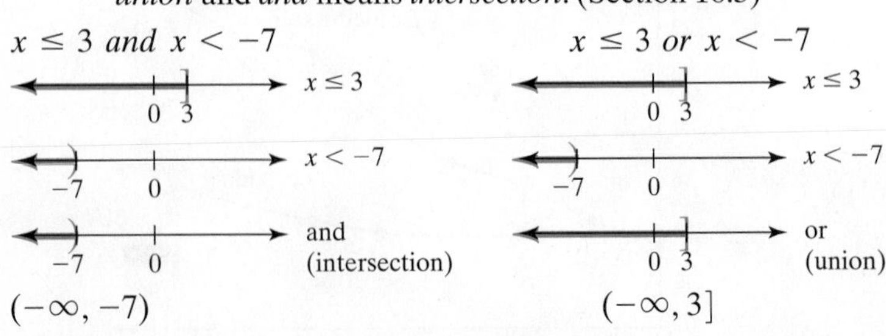

Solve. Write inequality solutions in interval notation.

1. $x - 2 \le 1$ and $3x - 1 \ge -4$

2. $-2 < x - 1 < 5$

3. $-2x + 2.5 = -7.7$

4. $-5x > 20$

5. $x \le -3$ or $x \le -5$

6. $5x < -10$ or $3x - 4 > 2$

7. $\frac{5t}{2} - \frac{3t}{4} = 7$

8. $5(x - 3) + x + 2 \ge 3(x + 2) + 2x$

16.4 ABSOLUTE VALUE EQUATIONS

OBJECTIVE 1 ▶ Solving absolute equations. In Chapter 15, we defined the absolute value of a number as its distance from 0 on a number line.

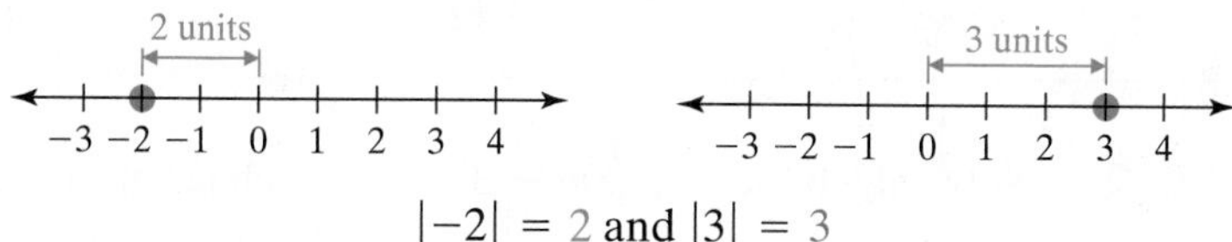

$$|-2| = 2 \text{ and } |3| = 3$$

In this section, we concentrate on solving equations containing the absolute value of a variable or a variable expression. Examples of absolute value equations are

$$|x| = 3 \qquad -5 = |2y + 7| \qquad |z - 6.7| = |3z + 1.2|$$

Since distance and absolute value are so closely related, absolute value equations and inequalities (see Section 16.5) are extremely useful in solving distance-type problems, such as calculating the possible error in a measurement.

For the absolute value equation $|x| = 3$, its solution set will contain all numbers whose distance from 0 is 3 units. Two numbers are 3 units away from 0 on the number line: 3 and -3.

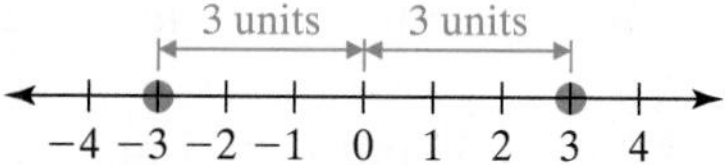

Thus, the solution set of the equation $|x| = 3$ is $\{3, -3\}$. This suggests the following:

OBJECTIVE

1 Solve absolute value equations.

TECHNOLOGY NOTE

Remember, absolute value can be found under the Math Num menu or under Catolog. Check your graphing calculator manual to find the location on your calculator.

Solving Equations of the Form $|X| = a$

If a is a positive number, then $|X| = a$ is equivalent to $X = a$ or $X = -a$.

EXAMPLE 1 Solve: $|p| = 2$.

Solution Since 2 is positive, $|p| = 2$ is equivalent to $p = 2$ or $p = -2$.

To check, let $p = 2$ and then $p = -2$ in the original equation.

$\|p\| = 2$	Original equation	$\|p\| = 2$	Original equation
$\|2\| = 2$	Let $p = 2$.	$\|-2\| = 2$	Let $p = -2$.
$2 = 2$	True	$2 = 2$	True

The solutions are 2 and -2 or the solution set is $\{2, -2\}$.

To visualize the solution, we solve $|x| = 2$ by the intersection-of-graphs method. Graph $y_1 = |x|$ and $y_2 = 2$.

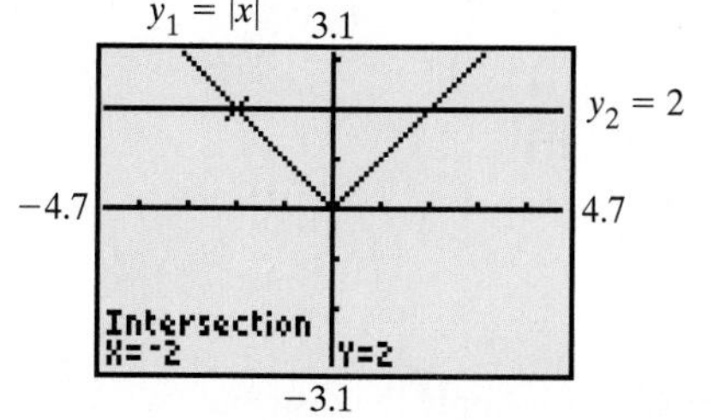

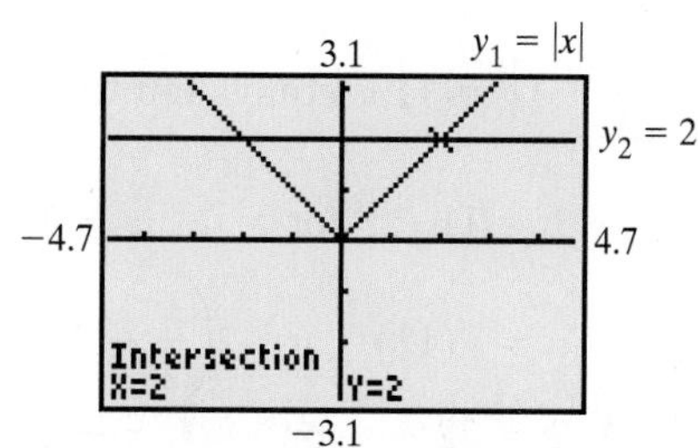

The graphs of $y_1 = |x|$ and $y_2 = 2$ intersect at $(-2, 2)$ and $(2, 2)$. The solutions are thus the x-values -2 and 2. □

PRACTICE 1 Solve: $|q| = 7$.

If the expression inside the absolute value bars is more complicated than a single variable, we can still apply the absolute value property.

> **Helpful Hint**
> For the equation $|X| = a$ in the box above, X can be a single variable or a variable expression.

EXAMPLE 2 Solve algebraically: $|5w + 3| = 7$ and check graphically.

Solution Here the expression inside the absolute value bars is $5w + 3$. If we think of the expression $5w + 3$ as X in the absolute value property, we see that $|X| = 7$ is equivalent to

$$X = 7 \quad \text{or} \quad X = -7$$

Then substitute $5w + 3$ for X, and we have

$$5w + 3 = 7 \quad \text{or} \quad 5w + 3 = -7$$

Solve these two equations for w.

$$\begin{aligned} 5w + 3 &= 7 & \text{or} \quad 5w + 3 &= -7 \\ 5w &= 4 & \text{or} \quad 5w &= -10 \\ w &= \frac{4}{5} & \text{or} \quad w &= -2 \end{aligned}$$

Check: To check, graph $y_1 = |5x + 3|$ and $y_2 = 7$ in a standard window as shown.

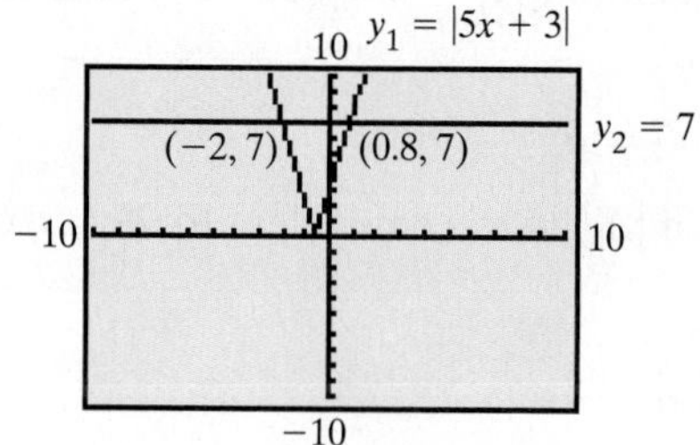

The intersections of the two graphs are the points $(-2, 7)$ and $(0.8, 7)$. Therefore, the solutions to the equation $|5x + 3| = 7$ are -2 and 0.8, or $\frac{4}{5}$.

Both solutions check, and the solutions are -2 and $\frac{4}{5}$ or the solution set is $\left\{-2, \frac{4}{5}\right\}$. □

PRACTICE 2 Solve algebraically: $|2x - 3| = 5$ and check graphically.

EXAMPLE 3 Solve: $\left|\frac{x}{2} - 1\right| = 11$.

Solution $\left|\frac{x}{2} - 1\right| = 11$ is equivalent to

$$\begin{aligned} \frac{x}{2} - 1 &= 11 & \text{or} \quad \frac{x}{2} - 1 &= -11 & \\ 2\left(\frac{x}{2} - 1\right) &= 2(11) & \text{or} \quad 2\left(\frac{x}{2} - 1\right) &= 2(-11) & \text{Clear fractions.} \\ x - 2 &= 22 & \text{or} \quad x - 2 &= -22 & \text{Apply the distributive property.} \\ x &= 24 & \text{or} \quad x &= -20 & \end{aligned}$$

The solutions are 24 and -20. □

PRACTICE 3 Solve: $\left|\frac{x}{5} + 1\right| = 15$.

To apply the absolute value rule, first make sure that the absolute value expression is isolated.

> **Helpful Hint**
> If the equation has a single absolute value expression containing variables, isolate the absolute value expression first.

EXAMPLE 4 Solve: $|2x| + 5 = 7$.

Solution We want the absolute value expression alone on one side of the equation, so begin by subtracting 5 from both sides. Then apply the absolute value property.

$$|2x| + 5 = 7$$

$$|2x| = 2 \qquad \text{Subtract 5 from both sides.}$$

$$2x = 2 \quad \text{or} \quad 2x = -2$$

$$x = 1 \quad \text{or} \quad x = -1$$

The solutions are -1 and 1. □

PRACTICE 4 Solve: $|3x| + 8 = 14$.

EXAMPLE 5 Solve: $|y| = 0$.

Solution We are looking for all numbers whose distance from 0 is zero units. The only number is 0. The solution is 0. □

PRACTICE 5 Solve: $|z| = 0$.

The next two examples illustrate a special case for absolute value equations. This special case occurs when an isolated absolute value is equal to a negative number.

EXAMPLE 6 Solve $2|x| + 25 = 23$ algebraically and graphically.

Algebraic Solution:

First, isolate the absolute value.

$$2|x| + 25 = 23$$

$$2|x| = -2 \qquad \text{Subtract 25 from both sides.}$$

$$|x| = -1 \qquad \text{Divide both sides by 2.}$$

The absolute value of a number is never negative, so this equation has no solution.

Graphical Solution:

Graph $y_1 = 2|x| + 25$ and $y_2 = 23$ in a $[-47, 47, 10]$ by $[-30, 50, 10]$ window.

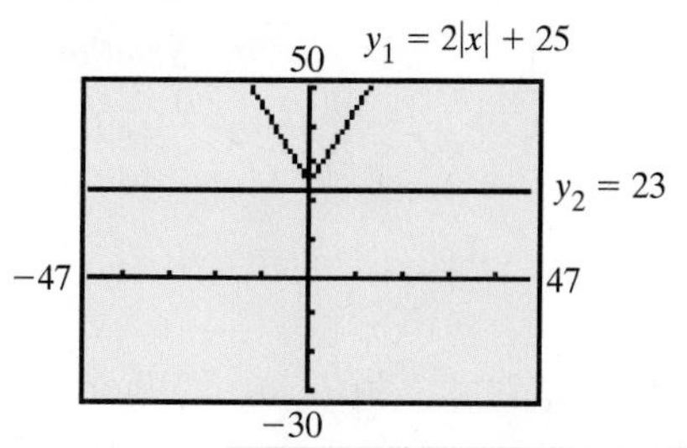

Since there is no point of intersection, there is no solution.

The solution set is { } or ∅. □

PRACTICE 6 Solve $3|z| + 9 = 7$ algebraically and graphically.

EXAMPLE 7 Solve: $\left|\dfrac{3x + 1}{2}\right| = -2.$

Solution Again, the absolute value of any expression is never negative, so no solution exists. The solution set is $\{\ \}$ or $\varnothing$. □

PRACTICE 7 Solve: $\left|\dfrac{5x + 3}{4}\right| = -8.$

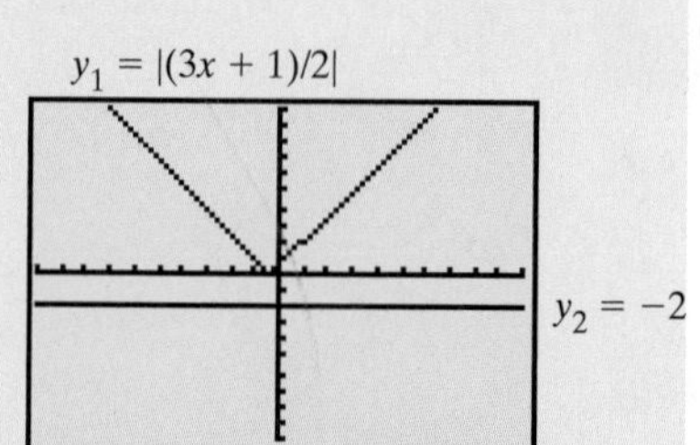
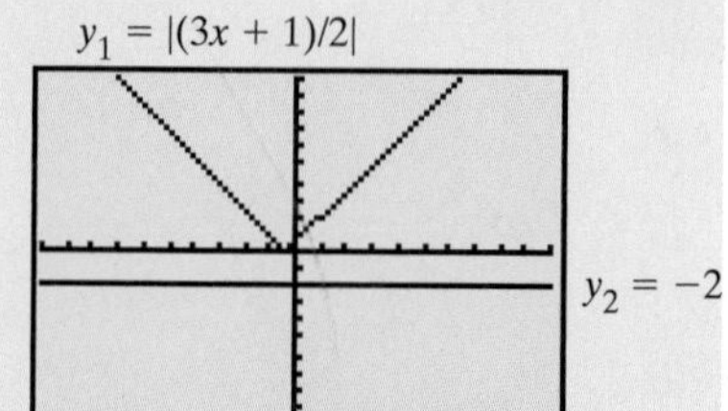

A calculator check for Example 7.

Given two absolute value expressions, we might ask, when are the absolute values of two expressions equal? To see the answer, notice that

$$|2| = |2|, \quad |-2| = |-2|, \quad |-2| = |2|, \quad \text{and} \quad |2| = |-2|$$

same same opposites opposites

Two absolute value expressions are equal when the expressions inside the absolute value bars are equal to or are opposites of each other.

EXAMPLE 8 Solve $|3x + 2| = |5x - 8|$ algebraically and check graphically.

Solution This equation is true if the expressions inside the absolute value bars are equal to or are opposites of each other.

$$3x + 2 = 5x - 8 \quad \text{or} \quad 3x + 2 = -(5x - 8)$$

Next, solve each equation.

$$\begin{aligned} 3x + 2 &= 5x - 8 & \text{or} \quad 3x + 2 &= -5x + 8 \\ -2x + 2 &= -8 & \text{or} \quad 8x + 2 &= 8 \\ -2x &= -10 & \text{or} \quad 8x &= 6 \\ x &= 5 & \text{or} \quad x &= \frac{3}{4} \end{aligned}$$

Using the x-intercept method to check, rewrite the equation as

$$|3x + 2| - |5x - 8| = 0$$

and graph $y_1 = |3x + 2| - |5x - 8|$. The x-intercepts are $x = 0.75$ and $x = 5$ as shown in the margin. The solutions are $\frac{3}{4}$ and 5. □

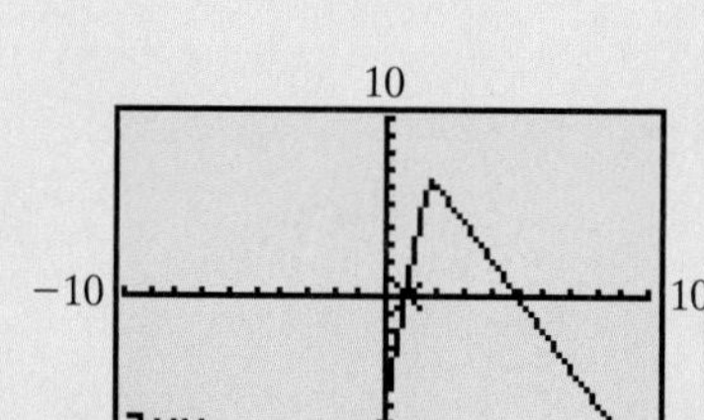

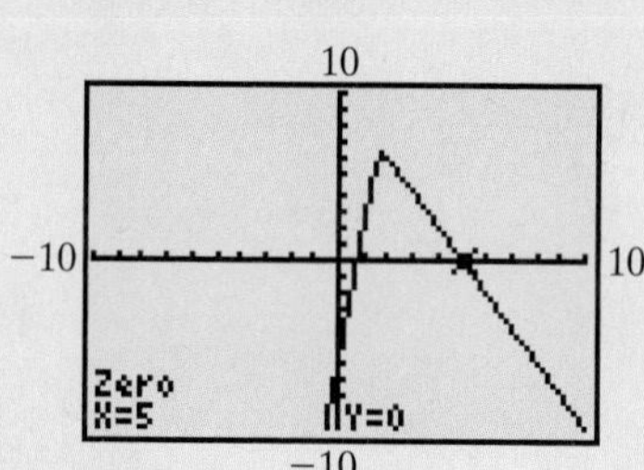

PRACTICE 8 Solve $|2x + 4| = |3x - 1|$ algebraically and check graphically.

EXAMPLE 9 Solve: $|x - 3| = |5 - x|$.

Solution

$$\begin{aligned} x - 3 &= 5 - x & \text{or} \quad x - 3 &= -(5 - x) \\ 2x - 3 &= 5 & \text{or} \quad x - 3 &= -5 + x \\ 2x &= 8 & \text{or} \quad x - 3 - x &= -5 + x - x \\ x &= 4 & \text{or} \quad -3 &= -5 \quad \text{False} \end{aligned}$$

When an equation simplifies to a false statement, the equation has no solution. Thus, the only solution for the original absolute value equation is 4. □

PRACTICE 9 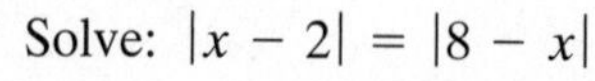 Solve: $|x - 2| = |8 - x|$.

Concept Check ✓

True or false? Absolute value equations always have two solutions. Explain your answer.

Answer to Concept Check:
false; answers may vary

The following box summarizes the methods shown for solving absolute value equations.

Absolute Value Equations

$|X| = a$ $\begin{cases} \text{If } a \text{ is positive, then solve } X = a \text{ or } X = -a. \\ \text{If } a \text{ is } 0 \text{, solve } X = 0. \\ \text{If } a \text{ is negative, the equation } |X| = a \text{ has no solution.} \end{cases}$

$|X| = |Y|$ Solve $X = Y$ or $X = -Y$.

VOCABULARY & READINESS CHECK

Match each absolute value equation with an equivalent statement.

1. $|x - 2| = 5$
2. $|x - 2| = 0$
3. $|x - 2| = |x + 3|$
4. $|x + 3| = 5$
5. $|x + 3| = -5$

A. $x - 2 = 0$
B. $x - 2 = x + 3$ or $x - 2 = -(x + 3)$
C. $x - 2 = 5$ or $x - 2 = -5$
D. $\varnothing$
E. $x + 3 = 5$ or $x + 3 = -5$

16.4 EXERCISE SET

Solve each absolute value equation. See Examples 1 through 7.

1. $|x| = 7$
2. $|y| = 15$
3. $|3x| = 12.6$
4. $|6n| = 12.6$
5. $|2x - 5| = 9$
6. $|6 + 2n| = 4$
7. $\left|\frac{x}{2} - 3\right| = 1$
8. $\left|\frac{n}{3} + 2\right| = 4$
9. $|z| + 4 = 9$
10. $|x| + 1 = 3$
11. $|3x| + 5 = 14$
12. $|2x| - 6 = 4$
13. $|2x| = 0$
14. $|7z| = 0$
15. $|4n + 1| + 10 = 4$
16. $|3z - 2| + 8 = 1$
17. $|5x - 1| = 0$
18. $|3y + 2| = 0$

19. Write an absolute value equation representing all numbers x whose distance from 0 is 5 units.

20. Write an absolute value equation representing all numbers x whose distance from 0 is 2 units.

Solve. See Examples 8 and 9.

21. $|5x - 7| = |3x + 11|$
22. $|9y + 1| = |6y + 4|$
23. $|z + 8| = |z - 3|$
24. $|2x - 5| = |2x + 5|$

25. Describe how solving an absolute value equation such as $|2x - 1| = 3$ is similar to solving an absolute value equation such as $|2x - 1| = |x - 5|$.

26. Describe how solving an absolute value equation such as $|2x - 1| = 3$ is different from solving an absolute value equation such as $|2x - 1| = |x - 5|$.

Use the given graphing utility screens to solve the equations shown. Write the solution set of the equation.

27. $|2x - 3| = 5$, where $y_1 = |2x - 3|$ and $y_2 = 5$

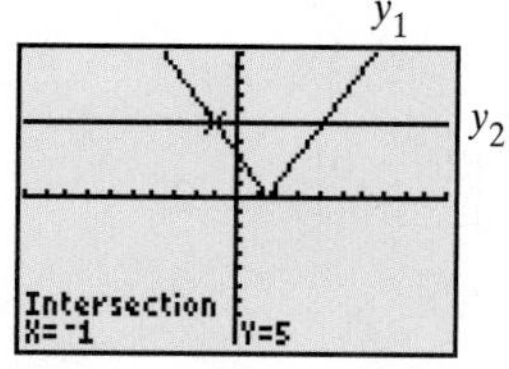

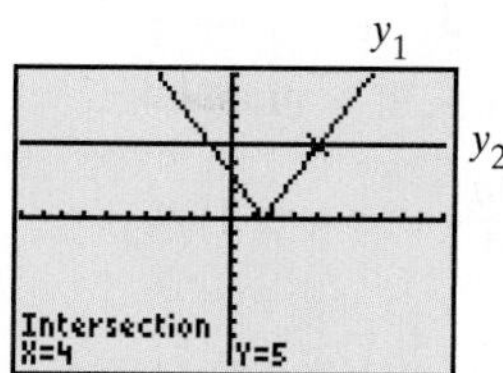

28. $|3x - 4| = 14$, where $y_1 = |3x - 4|$ and $y_2 = 14$

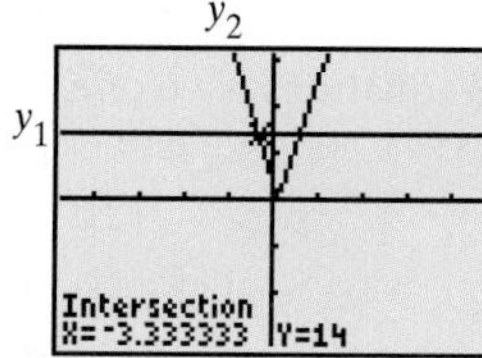

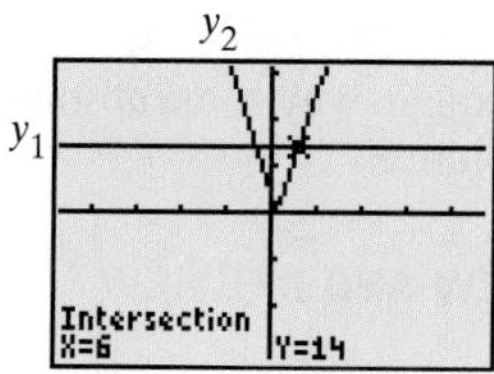

29. $|x - 4| = |1 - x|$, where $y_1 = |x - 4|$ and $y_2 = |1 - x|$

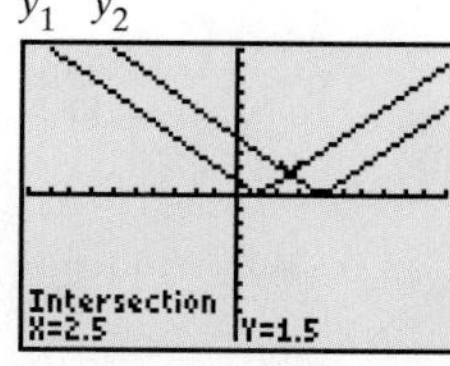

30. $|x + 2| = |3 - x|$, where $y_1 = |x + 2|$ and $y_2 = |3 - x|$

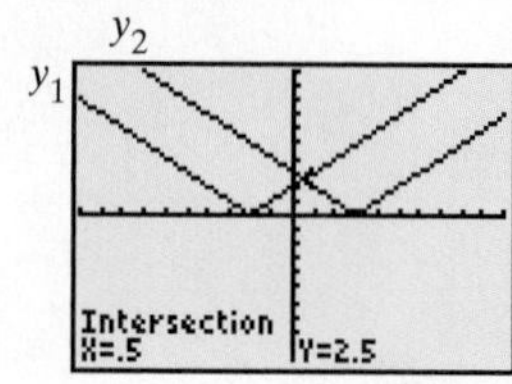

MIXED PRACTICE

Solve each absolute value equation. See Examples 1 through 9.

31. $|x| = 4$
32. $|x| = 1$
33. $|z| = -2$
34. $|y| = -9$
35. $|7 - 3x| = 7$
36. $|4m + 5| = 5$
37. $|6x| - 1 = 11$
38. $|7z| + 1 = 22$
39. $|x - 3| + 3 = 7$
40. $|x + 4| - 4 = 1$
41. $\left|\frac{z}{4} + 5\right| = -7$
42. $\left|\frac{c}{5} - 1\right| = -2$
43. $|9v - 3| = -8$
44. $|1 - 3b| = -7$
45. $|8n + 1| = 0$
46. $|5x - 2| = 0$
47. $|1 + 6c| - 7 = -3$
48. $|2 + 3m| - 9 = -7$
49. $|5x + 1| = 11$
50. $|8 - 6c| = 1$
51. $|4x - 2| = |-10|$
52. $|3x + 5| = |-4|$
53. $|5x + 1| = |4x - 7|$
54. $|3 + 6n| = |4n + 11|$
55. $|6 + 2x| = -|-7|$
56. $|4 - 5y| = -|-3|$
57. $|2x - 6| = |10 - 2x|$
58. $|4n + 5| = |4n + 3|$
59. $\left|\frac{2x - 5}{3}\right| = 7$
60. $\left|\frac{1 + 3n}{4}\right| = 4$
61. $2 + |5n| = 17$
62. $8 + |4m| = 24$
63. $\left|\frac{2x - 1}{3}\right| = |-5|$
64. $\left|\frac{5x + 2}{2}\right| = |-6|$
65. $|2y - 3| = |9 - 4y|$
66. $|5z - 1| = |7 - z|$
67. $\left|\frac{3n + 2}{8}\right| = |-1|$
68. $\left|\frac{2r - 6}{5}\right| = |-2|$
69. $|x + 4| = |7 - x|$
70. $|8 - y| = |y + 2|$
71. $\left|\frac{8c - 7}{3}\right| = -|-5|$
72. $\left|\frac{5d + 1}{6}\right| = -|-9|$
73. Explain why some absolute value equations have two solutions.
74. Explain why some absolute value equations have one solution.

REVIEW AND PREVIEW

The circle graph shows the U.S. cheese consumption for 2001. Use this graph to answer Exercises 75–77.

U.S. Cheese Consumption

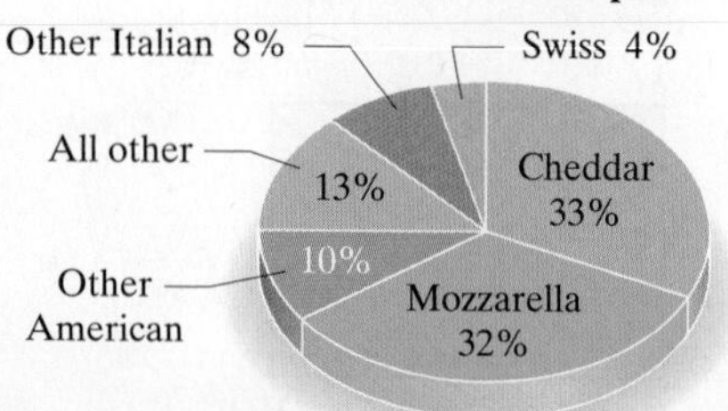

75. What percent of cheese consumption came from cheddar cheese?
76. A circle contains 360°. Find the number of degrees in the 4% sector for swiss cheese.
77. If a family consumed 120 pounds of cheese in 2001, find the amount of mozzarella we might expect they consumed.

List five integer solutions of each inequality.

78. $|x| \le 3$
79. $|x| \ge -2$
80. $|y| > -10$
81. $|y| < 0$

CONCEPT EXTENSIONS

82. Write an absolute value equation representing all numbers x whose distance from 1 is 5 units.
83. Write an absolute value equation representing all numbers x whose distance from 3 is 2 units.

Write each as an equivalent absolute value.

84. $x = 6$ or $x = -6$
85. $2x - 1 = 4$ or $2x - 1 = -4$
86. $x - 2 = 3x - 4$ or $x - 2 = -(3x - 4)$
87. For what value(s) of c will an absolute value equation of the form $|ax + b| = c$ have
    a. one solution?
    b. no solution?
    c. two solutions?

Use a graphical approach to approximate the solutions of each equation. Round the solutions to two decimal places.

88. $|2.3x - 1.5| = 5$
89. $|-7.6x + 2.6| = 1.9$
90. $3.6 - |4.1x - 2.6| = |x - 1.4|$
91. $-1.2 + |5x + 12.1| = -|x + 7.3| + 10$

16.5 ABSOLUTE VALUE INEQUALITIES

OBJECTIVES

1 Solve absolute value inequalities of the form $|x| < a$.

2 Solve absolute value inequalities of the form $|x| > a$.

OBJECTIVE 1 ▶ Solving absolute value inequalities of the form $|x| < a$. The solution set of an absolute value inequality such as $|x| < 2$ contains all numbers whose distance from 0 is less than 2 units, as shown below.

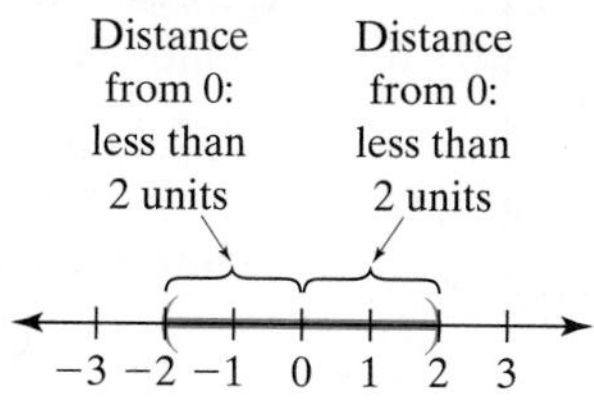

The solution set is $\{x|-2 < x < 2\}$, or $(-2, 2)$ in interval notation.

EXAMPLE 1 Solve: $|x| \le 3$.

Solution The solution set of this inequality contains all numbers whose distance from 0 is less than or equal to 3. Thus 3, −3, and all numbers between 3 and −3 are in the solution set.

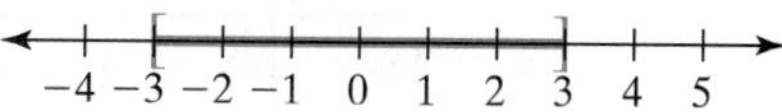

The solution set is $[-3, 3]$. □

PRACTICE 1 Solve: $|x| < 2$ and graph the solution set on a number line.

In general, we have the following.

Solving Absolute Value Inequalities of the Form $|X| < a$

If a is a positive number, then $|X| < a$ is equivalent to $-a < X < a$.

This property also holds true for the inequality symbol $\le$.

DISCOVER THE CONCEPT

a. Solve the equation $|x| = 7$ by graphing $y_1 = |x|$, $y_2 = 7$, and finding the point(s) of intersection.
b. Move the trace cursor along y_1 from the left-hand point of intersection of the two graphs to the right-hand point of intersection. Observe the y-values of the points as you move the cursor.
c. Find the x-values for which $|x| < 7$ (or $y_1 < y_2$).
d. Write the solution set of $|x| < 7$ (or $y_1 < y_2$).

In the discovery above, we see that the solutions of $|x| = 7$ are 7 and −7, the x-values of the points of intersection of y_1 and y_2. The solutions of $|x| < 7$ consist of all x-values for which $y_1 < y_2$ or for which the graph of y_1 is below the graph of y_2. These x-values are between −7 and 7, or $(-7, 7)$.

Also notice that the solutions of $|x| > 7$ consist of all x-values for which $y_1 > y_2$ or for which the graph of y_1 is above the graph of y_2. These x-values are less than -7 or greater than 7, or $(-\infty, -7) \cup (7, \infty)$.

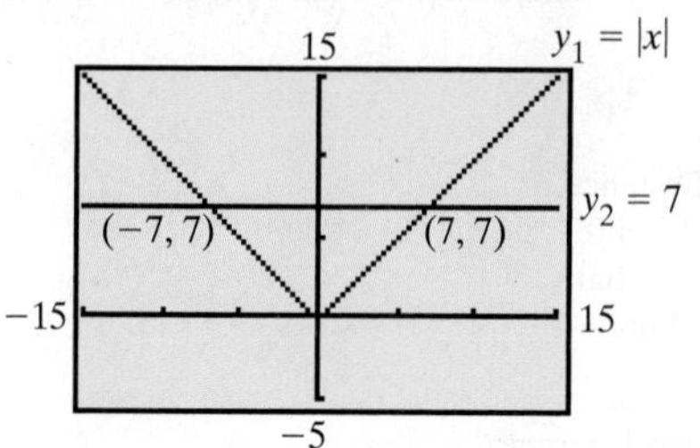

The solution set of the inequality $|x| < 7$ consists of the x-values where $y_1 < y_2$, or in interval notation $(-7, 7)$.

The solution set of the inequality $|x| > 7$ consists of the x-values where $y_1 > y_2$, or in interval notation $(-\infty, -7) \cup (7, \infty)$.

EXAMPLE 2

Solve algebraically and graphically for m: $|m - 6| < 2$.

Algebraic Solution:

From the preceding property, we see that

$$|m - 6| < 2 \text{ is equivalent to } -2 < m - 6 < 2$$

Solve this compound inequality for m by adding 6 to all three sides.

$$-2 < m - 6 < 2$$

$$-2 + 6 < m - 6 + 6 < 2 + 6 \quad \text{Add 6 to all three sides.}$$

$$4 < m < 8 \quad \text{Simplify.}$$

The solution set is $(4, 8)$.

Graphical Solution:

In the inequality $|m - 6| < 2$, replace m with x and proceed as usual. Graph $y_1 = |x - 6|$, $y_2 = 2$, and find x-values for which $y_1 < y_2$.

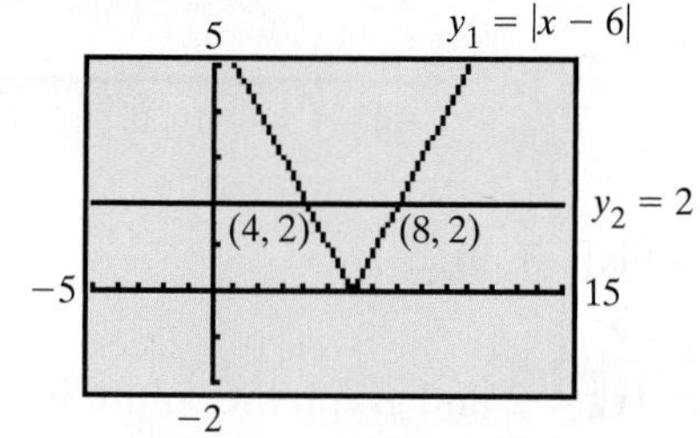

y_1 is below y_2 for x-values between 4 and 8. Thus, the solution set of $|x - 6| < 2$ in interval notation is $(4, 8)$.

The solution set is $(4, 8)$, and its number-line graph is shown.

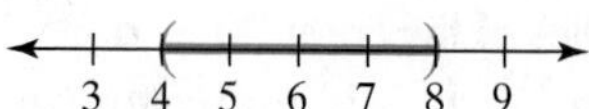

□

PRACTICE 2 Solve algebraically and graphically for b: $|b + 1| < 3$. Graph the solution set on a number line.

> **Helpful Hint**
> Before using an absolute value inequality property, isolate the absolute value expression on one side of the inequality.

EXAMPLE 3 Solve algebraically for x: $|5x + 1| + 1 \le 10$.

Solution First, isolate the absolute value expression by subtracting 1 from both sides.

$$|5x + 1| + 1 \le 10$$

$$|5x + 1| \le 10 - 1 \quad \text{Subtract 1 from both sides.}$$

$$|5x + 1| \le 9 \quad \text{Simplify.}$$

Since 9 is positive, we apply the absolute value property for $|X| \le a$.

$$-9 \le 5x + 1 \le 9$$

$$-9 - 1 \le 5x + 1 - 1 \le 9 - 1 \quad \text{Subtract 1 from all three parts.}$$

$$-10 \le 5x \le 8 \quad \text{Simplify.}$$

$$-2 \le x \le \frac{8}{5} \quad \text{Divide all three parts by 5.}$$

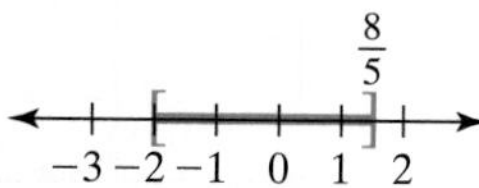

The solution set is $\left[-2, \frac{8}{5}\right]$, and the number-line graph is shown above. □

PRACTICE 3 Solve for x: $|3x - 2| + 5 \le 9$. Graph the solution set on a number line.

EXAMPLE 4 Solve for x: $\left|2x - \frac{1}{10}\right| < -13$. Check graphically.

Solution The absolute value of a number is always nonnegative and can never be less than -13. Thus this absolute value inequality has no solution. The solution set is { } or $\varnothing$. □

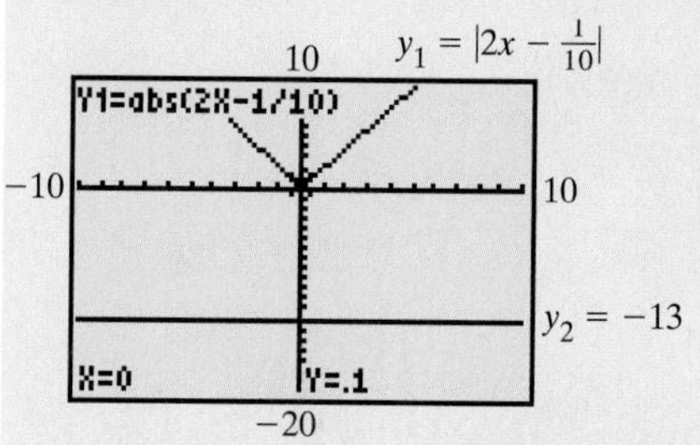

A calculator check for Example 4. Here, the absolute value graph is always above or greater than the horizontal line $y = -13$ so the solution set is { } or $\varnothing$.

PRACTICE 4 Solve for x: $\left|3x + \frac{5}{8}\right| < -4$. Check graphically.

OBJECTIVE 2 ▶ Solving absolute value inequalities of the form $|x| > a$. Let us now solve an absolute value inequality of the form $|X| > a$, such as $|x| \ge 3$. The solution set contains all numbers whose distance from 0 is 3 or more units. Thus the graph of the solution set contains 3 and all points to the right of 3 on the number line or -3 and all points to the left of -3 on the number line.

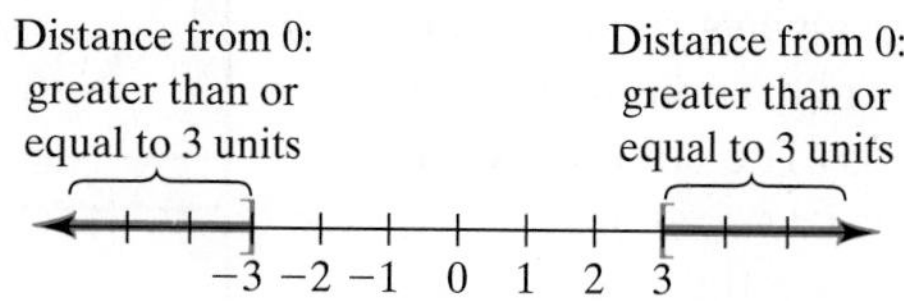

This solution set is written as $\{x \mid x \le -3 \text{ or } x \ge 3\}$. In interval notation, the solution is $(-\infty, -3] \cup [3, \infty)$, since "or" means "union." In general, we have the following.

Solving Absolute Value Inequalities of the Form $|X| > a$

If a is a positive number, then $|X| > a$ is equivalent to $X < -a$ or $X > a$.

This property also holds true for the inequality symbol $\ge$.

EXAMPLE 5 Solve algebraically and graphically for x: $|x - 3| \geq 7$.

Algebraic Solution:

Since 7 is positive,

$$|x - 3| \geq 7 \text{ is equivalent to}$$
$$x - 3 \leq -7 \text{ or } x - 3 \geq 7$$

Next, solve the compound inequality.

$$x - 3 \leq -7 \quad \text{or} \quad x - 3 \geq 7$$
$$x - 3 + 3 \leq -7 + 3 \quad \text{or} \quad x - 3 + 3 \geq 7 + 3$$
$$x \leq -4 \quad \text{or} \quad x \geq 10$$

The solution set is $(-\infty, -4] \cup [10, \infty)$, and its number-line graph is shown.

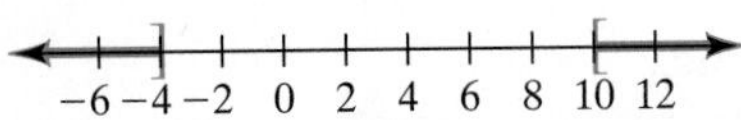

Graphical Solution:

Graph $y_1 = |x - 3|$ and $y_2 = 7$. Find the x-values for which $y_1 \geq y_2$.

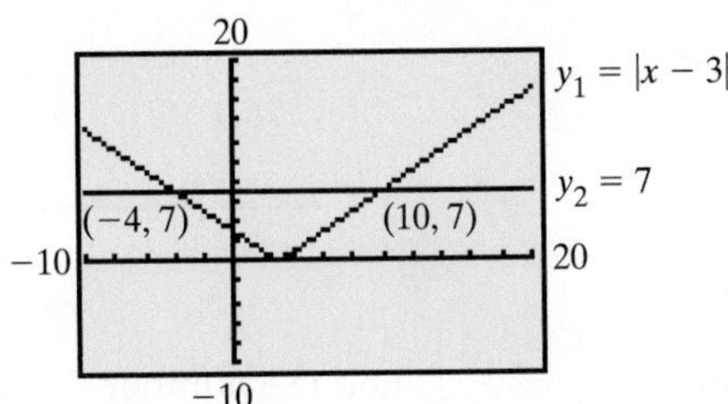

y_1 intersects or is above y_2 for x-values less than or equal to -4 and also x-values greater than or equal to 10, or $(-\infty, -4] \cup [10, \infty)$. □

PRACTICE 5 Solve algebraically and graphically for y: $|y + 4| \geq 6$. Graph the solution set on a number line.

Examples 6 and 8 illustrate special cases of absolute value inequalities. These special cases occur when an isolated absolute value expression is less than, less than or equal to, greater than, or greater than or equal to a negative number or 0.

EXAMPLE 6 Solve $|2x + 9| + 5 > 3$ algebraically and check graphically.

Solution First isolate the absolute value expression by subtracting 5 from both sides.

$$|2x + 9| + 5 > 3$$
$$|2x + 9| + 5 - 5 > 3 - 5 \quad \text{Subtract 5 from both sides.}$$
$$|2x + 9| > -2 \quad \text{Simplify.}$$

The absolute value of any number is always nonnegative and thus is always greater than -2. This inequality and the original inequality are true for all values of x. The solution set is $\{x | x \text{ is a real number}\}$ or $(-\infty, \infty)$.

To check graphically, see the screen to the left. Notice that $y_1 > y_2$ or $|2x + 9| + 5 > 3$ for all real numbers.

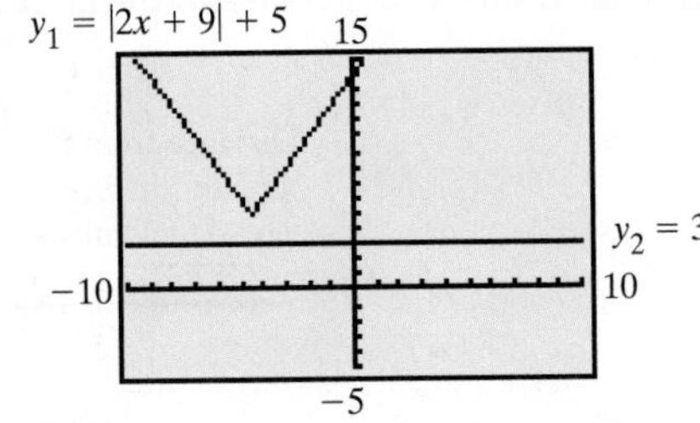

□

PRACTICE 6 Solve $|4x + 3| + 5 > 3$ algebraically and check graphically.

Concept Check ✓

Without taking any solution steps, how do you know that the absolute value inequality $|3x - 2| > -9$ has a solution? What is its solution?

Answer to Concept Check:
$(-\infty, \infty)$ since the absolute value is always nonnegative

EXAMPLE 7 Use a graphical approach to solve $\left|\frac{x}{3} - 1\right| - 2 \geq 0$.

Solution Graph $y_1 = \left|\frac{x}{3} - 1\right| - 2$ and use the graph of y_1 to solve $y_1 \geq 0$. Find x-values where the graph of y_1 is above the x-axis.

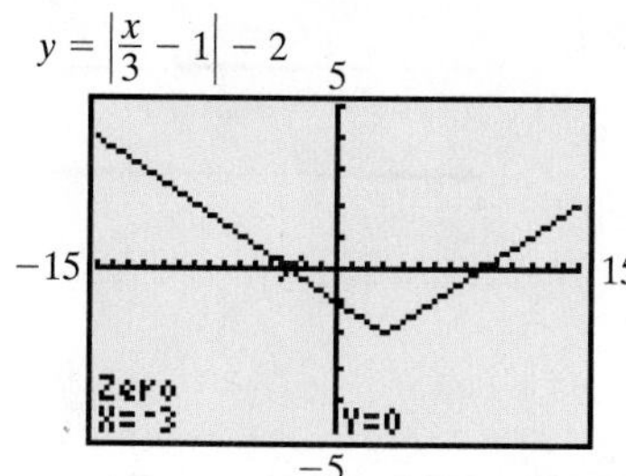

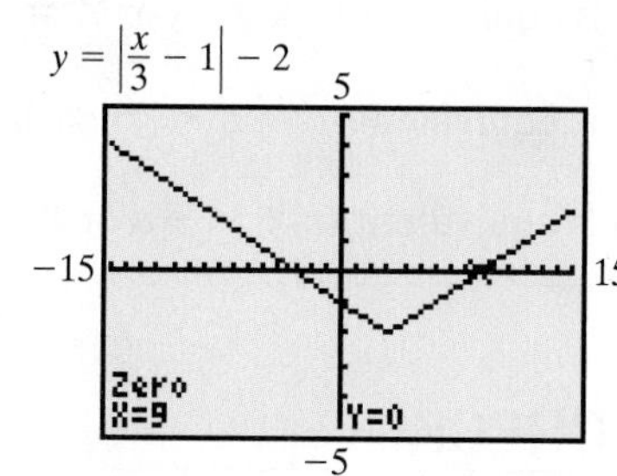

The graph of $y = \left|\frac{x}{3} - 1\right| - 2$ is above or on the x-axis for x-values less than or equal to -3 or greater than or equal to 9.

The solution set is $(-\infty, -3] \cup [9, \infty)$. □

PRACTICE 7 Use a graphical approach to solve $\left|\frac{x}{2} - 3\right| - 3 > 0$.

EXAMPLE 8 Solve for x: $\left|\frac{2(x+1)}{3}\right| \leq 0$.

Solution Recall that "≤" means "less than or equal to." The absolute value of any expression will never be less than 0, but it may be equal to 0. Thus, to solve $\left|\frac{2(x+1)}{3}\right| \leq 0$ we solve $\left|\frac{2(x+1)}{3}\right| = 0$

$$\frac{2(x+1)}{3} = 0$$

$$3\left[\frac{2(x+1)}{3}\right] = 3(0) \quad \text{Clear the equation of fractions.}$$

$$2x + 2 = 0 \quad \text{Apply the distributive property.}$$

$$2x = -2 \quad \text{Subtract 2 from both sides.}$$

$$x = -1 \quad \text{Divide both sides by 2.}$$

The solution set is $\{-1\}$. See the screen to the left to check this solution set graphically. □

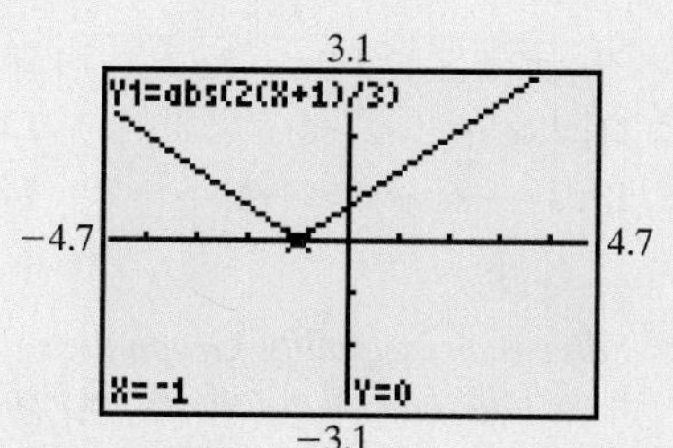

The graph touches the x-axis at $x = -1$ and is never below the x-axis. Therefore, the only point that satisfies the inequality has x-value -1.

PRACTICE 8 Solve for x: $\left|\frac{3(x-2)}{5}\right| \leq 0$.

The following box summarizes the types of absolute value equations and inequalities.

Solving Absolute Value Equations and Inequalities with $a > 0$

Algebraic Solution

$|X| = a$ is equivalent to $X = a$ or $X = -a$.

$|X| < a$ is equivalent to $-a < X < a$.

$|X| > a$ is equivalent to $X < -a$ or $X > a$.

Solution Graph

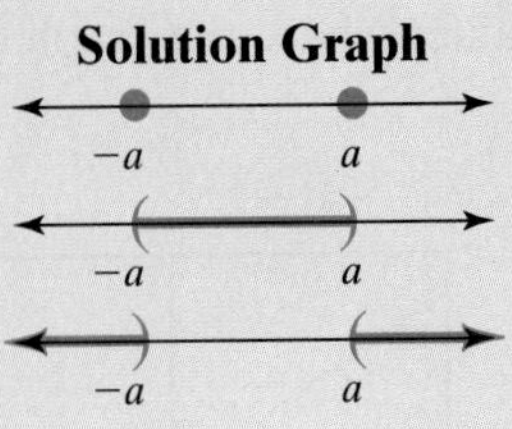

VOCABULARY & READINESS CHECK

Match each absolute value statement with an equivalent statement.

1. $|2x + 1| = 3$
2. $|2x + 1| \leq 3$
3. $|2x + 1| < 3$
4. $|2x + 1| \geq 3$
5. $|2x + 1| > 3$

A. $2x + 1 > 3$ or $2x + 1 < -3$
B. $2x + 1 \geq 3$ or $2x + 1 \leq -3$
C. $-3 < 2x + 1 < 3$
D. $2x + 1 = 3$ or $2x + 1 = -3$
E. $-3 \leq 2x + 1 \leq 3$

16.5 EXERCISE SET

Powered by CourseCompass and MathXL MyMathLab

Solve each inequality. Then graph the solution set on a number line and write it in interval notation. See Examples 1 through 4.

1. $|x| \leq 4$
2. $|x| < 6$
3. $|x - 3| < 2$
4. $|y - 7| \leq 5$
5. $|x + 3| < 2$
6. $|x + 4| < 6$
7. $|2x + 7| \leq 13$
8. $|5x - 3| \leq 18$
9. $|x| + 7 \leq 12$
10. $|x| + 6 \leq 7$
11. $|3x - 1| < -5$
12. $|8x - 3| < -2$
13. $|x - 6| - 7 \leq -1$
14. $|z + 2| - 7 < -3$

Solve each inequality. Graph the solution set on a number line and write it in interval notation. See Examples 5 through 7.

15. $|x| > 3$
16. $|y| \geq 4$
17. $|x + 10| \geq 14$
18. $|x - 9| \geq 2$
19. $|x| + 2 > 6$
20. $|x| - 1 > 3$
21. $|5x| > -4$
22. $|4x - 11| > -1$
23. $|6x - 8| + 3 > 7$
24. $|10 + 3x| + 1 > 2$

Solve each inequality. Graph the solution set on a number line and write it in interval notation. See Example 8.

25. $|x| \leq 0$
26. $|x| \geq 0$
27. $|8x + 3| > 0$
28. $|5x - 6| < 0$

MIXED PRACTICE

Solve each inequality. Graph the solution set on a number line and write it in interval notation. See Examples 1 through 8.

29. $|x| \leq 2$
30. $|z| < 8$
31. $|y| > 1$
32. $|x| \geq 10$
33. $|x - 3| < 8$
34. $|-3 + x| \leq 10$
35. $|0.6x - 3| > 0.6$
36. $|1 + 0.3x| \geq 0.1$
37. $5 + |x| \leq 2$
38. $8 + |x| < 1$
39. $|x| > -4$
40. $|x| \leq -7$
41. $|2x - 7| \leq 11$
42. $|5x + 2| < 8$
43. $|x + 5| + 2 \geq 8$
44. $|-1 + x| - 6 > 2$
45. $|x| > 0$
46. $|x| < 0$
47. $9 + |x| > 7$
48. $5 + |x| \geq 4$
49. $6 + |4x - 1| \leq 9$
50. $-3 + |5x - 2| \leq 4$
51. $\left|\frac{2}{3}x + 1\right| > 1$
52. $\left|\frac{3}{4}x - 1\right| \geq 2$
53. $|5x + 3| < -6$
54. $|4 + 9x| \geq -6$
55. $\left|\frac{8x - 3}{4}\right| \leq 0$
56. $\left|\frac{5x + 6}{2}\right| \leq 0$
57. $|1 + 3x| + 4 < 5$
58. $|7x - 3| - 1 \leq 10$
59. $\left|\frac{x + 6}{3}\right| > 2$
60. $\left|\frac{7 + x}{2}\right| \geq 4$
61. $-15 + |2x - 7| \leq -6$

62. $-9 + |3 + 4x| < -4$

63. $\left|2x + \frac{3}{4}\right| - 7 \le -2$

64. $\left|\frac{3}{5} + 4x\right| - 6 < -1$

MIXED PRACTICE

Solve each equation or inequality for x. (See Sections 16.4 and 16.5.)

65. $|2x - 3| < 7$
66. $|2x - 3| > 7$
67. $|2x - 3| = 7$
68. $|5 - 6x| = 29$
69. $|x - 5| \ge 12$
70. $|x + 4| \ge 20$
71. $|9 + 4x| = 0$
72. $|9 + 4x| \ge 0$
73. $|2x + 1| + 4 < 7$
74. $8 + |5x - 3| \ge 11$
75. $|3x - 5| + 4 = 5$
76. $|5x - 3| + 2 = 4$
77. $|x + 11| = -1$
78. $|4x - 4| = -3$
79. $\left|\frac{2x - 1}{3}\right| = 6$
80. $\left|\frac{6 - x}{4}\right| = 5$
81. $\left|\frac{3x - 5}{6}\right| > 5$
82. $\left|\frac{4x - 7}{5}\right| < 2$

Use the given graphing utility screen to solve each equation or inequality.

83. **a.** $|x - 3| - 2 = 6$
b. $|x - 3| - 2 < 6$
c. $|x - 3| - 2 \ge 6$

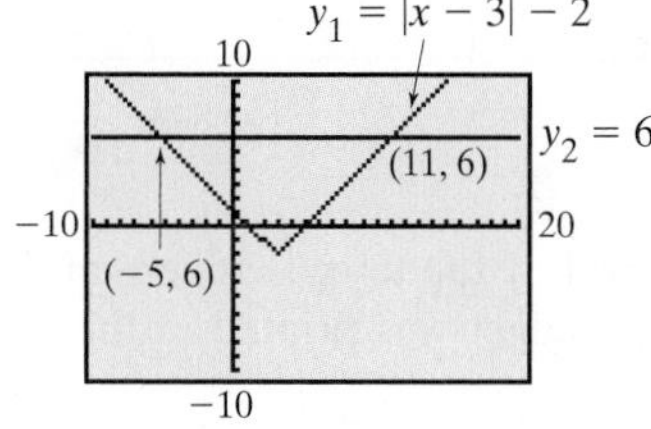

84. **a.** $|x + 5| - 4 = 3$
b. $|x + 5| - 4 \le 3$
c. $|x + 5| - 4 > 3$

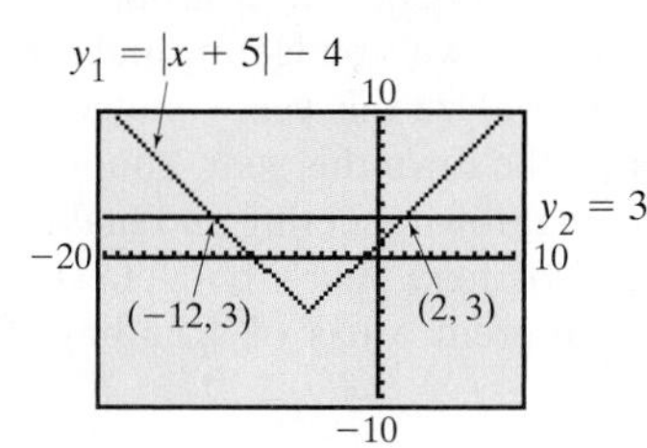

85. **a.** $|x + 2| - 10 = -4$
b. $|x + 2| - 10 \le -4$
c. $|x + 2| - 10 > -4$

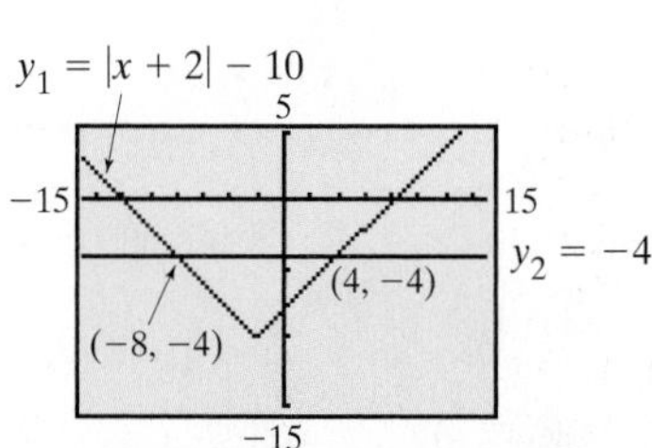

86. **a.** $|x + 2| + 1 = -5$
b. $|x + 2| + 1 < -5$
c. $|x + 2| + 1 > -5$

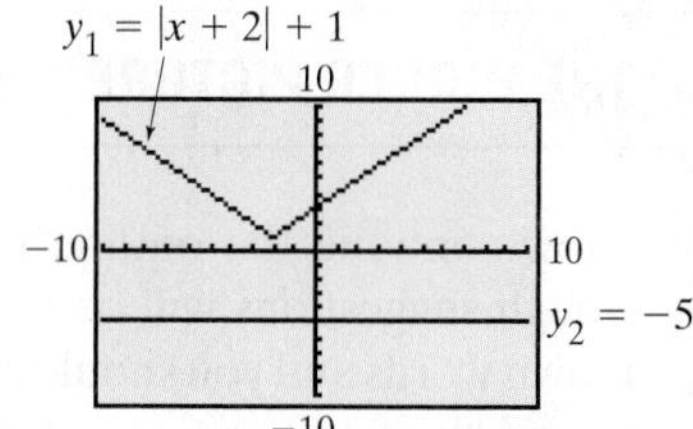

REVIEW AND PREVIEW

Recall the formula:

$$\textit{Probability of an event} = \frac{\textit{number of ways that the event can occur}}{\textit{number of possible outcomes}}$$

Find the probability of rolling each number on a single toss of a die. (Recall that a die is a cube with each of its six sides containing 1, 2, 3, 4, 5, and 6 black dots, respectively.)

87. P(rolling a 2)
88. P(rolling a 5)
89. P(rolling a 7)
90. P(rolling a 0)
91. P(rolling a 1 or 3)
92. P(rolling a 1, 2, 3, 4, 5, or 6)

Consider the equation $3x - 4y = 12$. For each value of x or y given, find the corresponding value of the other variable that makes the statement true.

93. If $x = 2$, find y
94. If $y = -1$, find x
95. If $y = -3$, find x
96. If $x = 4$, find y

CONCEPT EXTENSIONS

97. Write an absolute value inequality representing all numbers x whose distance from 0 is less than 7 units.
98. Write an absolute value inequality representing all numbers x whose distance from 0 is greater than 4 units.
99. Write $-5 \le x \le 5$ as an equivalent inequality containing an absolute value.
100. Write $x > 1$ or $x < -1$ as an equivalent inequality containing an absolute value.
101. Describe how solving $|x - 3| = 5$ is different from solving $|x - 3| < 5$.
102. Describe how solving $|x + 4| = 0$ is similar to solving $|x + 4| \le 0$.

The expression $|x_T - x|$ is defined to be the absolute error in x, where x_T is the true value of a quantity and x is the measured value or value as stored in a computer.

103. If the true value of a quantity is 3.5 and the absolute error must be less than 0.05, find the acceptable measured values.
104. If the true value of a quantity is 0.2 and the approximate value stored in a computer is $\frac{51}{256}$, find the absolute error.

THE BIGGER PICTURE SOLVING EQUATIONS AND INEQUALITIES

We now continue the outline from Sections 16.2, and 16.3. Although suggestions will be given, this outline should be in your own words and you should include at least "how to recognize" and "how to begin to solve" under each letter heading.

For example:

Solving Equations and Inequalities

I. Equations

A. Linear equations (Section 16.1)

B. Absolute Value Equations: Equation contains the absolute value of a variable expression. (Section 16.4)

$|3x - 1| - 12 = -4$ Absolute value equation.

$|3x - 1| = 8$ Isolate absolute value.

$3x - 1 = 8$ or $3x - 1 = -8$

$3x = 9$ or $3x = -7$

$x = 3$ or $x = -\frac{7}{3}$

$|x - 5| = |x + 1|$ Absolute value equation.

$x - 5 = x + 1$ or $x - 5 = -(x + 1)$

$-5 = 1$ or $x - 5 = -x - 1$

No solution or $2x = 4$

$x = 2$

II. Inequalities

A. Linear Inequalities (Section 16.2)

B. Compound Inequalities (Section 16.3)

C. Absolute Value Inequalities: Inequality with absolute value bars about variable expression. (Section 16.5)

$\lvert x - 5\rvert - 8 < -2$	$\lvert 2x + 1\rvert \geq 17$
$\lvert x - 5\rvert < 6$	$2x + 1 \geq 17$ or $2x + 1 \leq -17$
$-6 < x - 5 < 6$	$2x \geq 16$ or $2x \leq -18$
$-1 < x < 11$	$x \geq 8$ or $x \leq -9$
$(-1, 11)$	$(-\infty, -9] \cup [8, \infty)$

Solve. If an inequality, write your solutions in interval notation.

1. $9x - 14 = 11x + 2$
2. $|x - 4| = 17$
3. $x - 1 \leq 5$ or $3x - 2 \leq 10$
4. $-x < 7$ and $4x \leq 20$
5. $|x - 2| = |x + 15|$
6. $9y - 6y + 1 = 4y + 10 - y + 3$
7. $1.5x - 3 = 1.2x - 18$
8. $\frac{7x + 1}{8} - 3 = x + \frac{2x + 1}{4}$
9. $|5x + 2| - 10 \leq -3$
10. $|x + 11| > 2$
11. $|9x + 2| - 1 = 24$
12. $\left|\frac{3x - 1}{2}\right| = |2x + 5|$

CHAPTER 16 GROUP ACTIVITY

Analyzing Municipal Budgets

Nearly all cities, towns, and villages operate with an annual budget. Budget items might include expenses for fire and police protection as well as for street maintenance and parks. No matter how big or small the budget, city officials need to know if municipal spending is over or under budget. In this project, you will have the opportunity to analyze a municipal budget and make budgetary recommendations. This project may be completed by working in groups or individually.

Suppose that each year your town creates a municipal budget. The next year's annual municipal budget is submitted for approval by the town's citizens at the annual town meeting. This year's budget was printed in the town newspaper earlier in the year.

You have joined a group of citizens who are concerned about your town's budgeting and spending processes. Your group plans to analyze this year's budget along with what was actually spent by the town this year. You hope to present your findings at the annual town meeting and make some budgetary recommendations for next year's budget. The municipal budget contains many different areas of spending. To help focus your group's analysis, you have decided to research spending habits only for categories in which the actual expenses differ from the budgeted amount by more than 12% of the budgeted amount.

1. For each category in the budget, write a specific absolute value inequality that describes the condition that must be met before your group will research spending habits for that category. In each case, let the variable x represent the actual expense for a budget category.
2. For each category in the budget, write an equivalent compound inequality for the condition described in Question 1. Again, let the variable x represent the actual expense for a budget category.
3. Below is a listing of the actual expenditures made this year for each budget category. Use the inequalities from either Question 1 or Question 2 to complete the Budget Worksheet given at the end of this project. (The first category has been filled in.) From the Budget Worksheet, decide which categories must be researched.
4. Can you think of possible reasons why spending in the categories that must be researched were over or under budget?
5. Based on this year's municipal budget and actual expenses, what recommendations would you make for next year's budget? Explain your reasoning.
6. (Optional) Research the annual budget used by your own town or your college or university. Conduct a similar analysis of the budget with respect to actual expenses. What can you conclude?

	Department/Program	*Actual Expenditure*
I.	**Board of Health**	
	Immunization Programs	$14,800
	Inspections	$41,900
II.	**Fire Department**	
	Equipment	$375,000
	Salaries	$268,500
III.	**Libraries**	
	Book/Periodical Purchases	$107,300
	Equipment	$29,000
	Salaries	$118,400
IV.	**Parks and Recreation**	
	Maintenance	$82,500
	Playground Equipment	$45,000
	Salaries	$118,000
	Summer Programs	$96,200
V.	**Police Department**	
	Equipment	$328,000
	Salaries	$405,000
VI.	**Public Works**	
	Recycling	$48,100
	Sewage	$92,500
	Snow Removal & Road Salt	$268,300
	Street Maintenance	$284,000
	Water Treatment	$94,100
	TOTAL	$2,816,600

THE TOWN CRIER

Annual Budget Set at Town Meeting

ANYTOWN, USA (MG)—This year's annual budget is as follows:

	Amount Budgeted
BOARD OF HEALTH	
Immunization Programs	$15,000
Inspections	$50,000
FIRE DEPARTMENT	
Equipment	$450,000
Salaries	$275,000
LIBRARIES	
Book/Periodical Purchases	$90,000
Equipment	$30,000
Salaries	$120,000
PARKS AND RECREATION	
Maintenance	$70,000
Playground Equipment	$50,000
Salaries	$140,000
Summer Programs	$80,000
POLICE DEPARTMENT	
Equipment	$300,000
Salaries	$400,000
PUBLIC WORKS	
Recycling	$50,000
Sewage	$100,000
Snow Removal & Road Salt	$200,000
Street Maintenance	$250,000
Water Treatment	$100,000
TOTAL	**$2,770,000**

BUDGET WORKSHEET

Budget category	Budgeted amount	Minimum allowed	Actual expense	Maximum allowed	Within budget?	Amt over/ under budget
Immunization Programs	$15,000	$13,200	$14,800	$16,800	Yes	Under $200

STUDY SKILLS BUILDER

Are You Preparing for a Test on Chapter 16?

Below are listed some common trouble areas for students in Chapter 16. After studying for your test—but before taking your test—read these.

- Remember to solve equations both algebraically and graphically to ensure accuracy.
- Remember to reverse the direction of the inequality symbol when multiplying or dividing both sides of an inequality by a negative number.

$$-11x < 33 \quad \text{Direction of arrow is reversed.}$$
$$\frac{-11x}{-11} > \frac{33}{-11}$$
$$x > -3$$

- Remember the differences when solving absolute value equations and inequalities.

$\lvert x+1\rvert = 3$	$\lvert x+1\rvert < 3$	$\lvert x+1\rvert > 3$
$x + 1 = 3$ or $x + 1 = -3$	$-3 < x + 1 < 3$	$x + 1 < -3$ or $x + 1 > 3$
$x = 2$ or $x = -4$	$-3 - 1 < x < 3 - 1$	$x < -4$ or $x > 2$
$\{2, -4\}$	$-4 < x < 2$	$(-\infty, -4) \cup (2, \infty)$
	$(-4, 2)$	

- Remember that an equation is not solved for a specified variable unless the variable is alone on one side of an equation *and* the other side contains *no* specified variables.

$y = 10x + 6 - y$ Equation is not solved for y.

$2y = 10x + 6$ Add y to both sides.

$y = 5x + 3$ Divide both sides by 2.

Remember: This is simply a checklist of common trouble areas. For a review of Chapter 16, see the Highlights and Chapter Review at the end of this chapter.

CHAPTER 16 VOCABULARY CHECK

Fill in each blank with one of the words or phrases listed below.

contradiction	absolute value	linear inequality in one variable
linear equation in one variable	compound inequality	identity
intersection	solution	union

1. Two inequalities joined by the words "and" or "or" is called a(n) ________________.
2. An equation in one variable that has no solution is called a(n) ___________.
3. The ___________ of two sets is the set of all elements common to both sets.
4. The _____ of two sets is the set of all elements that belong to either of the sets.
5. An equation in one variable that has every number (for which the equation is defined) as a solution is called a(n) _______.
6. A number's distance from 0 is called its ____________.
7. When a variable in an equation is replaced by a number and the resulting equation is true, then that number is called a(n) _______ of the equation.
8. The statement $5x - 0.2 < 7$ is an example of a(n) ________________________.
9. The statement $5x - 0.2 = 7$ is an example of a(n) ________________________.

Helpful Hint

Are you preparing for your test? Don't forget to take the Chapter 16 Test on page 1057. Then check your answers at the back of the text and use the Chapter Test Prep Video CD to see the fully worked-out solutions to any of the exercises you want to review.

CHAPTER 16 HIGHLIGHTS

DEFINITIONS AND CONCEPTS	EXAMPLES

SECTION 16.1 SOLVING LINEAR EQUATIONS GRAPHICALLY

To solve an equation graphically by the **intersection-of-graphs method:**

- Graph the left side of the equation as y_1.
- Graph the right side of the equation as y_2.
- Find any points of intersection, or where $y_1 = y_2$.
- The x-coordinate of an intersection point is a solution.
- The y-coordinate of an intersection point is the value of each side of the original equation when the variable is replaced with the solution.

Solve $5(x - 2) + 1 = 2(x - 1) + 2$

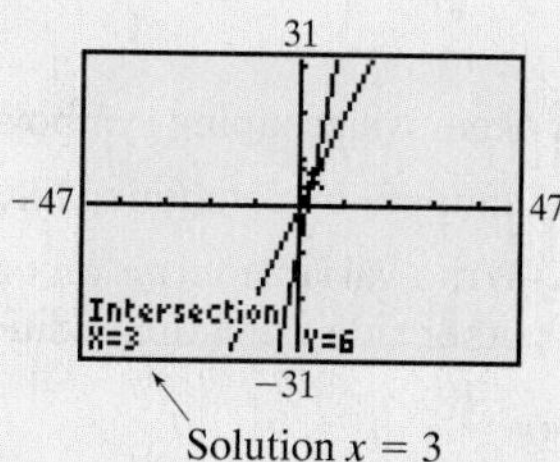

Solution $x = 3$

To solve an equation using the **x-intercept method:**

- Write the equation so that one side is 0.
- For the equation $y_1 = 0$, graph y_1.
- The x-intercepts of the graph are solutions of $y_1 = 0$.

Solve $5(x - 2) + 1 = 2(x - 1) + 2$

$5(x - 2) + 1 - 2(x - 1) - 2 = 0$

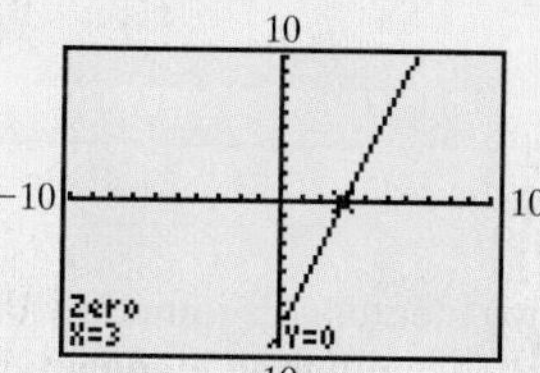

SECTION 16.2 LINEAR INEQUALITIES AND PROBLEM SOLVING

A **linear inequality in one variable** is an inequality that can be written in the form $ax + b < c$, where a, b, and c are real numbers and $a \neq 0$. (The inequality symbols $\leq$, $>$, and $\geq$ also apply here.)

Linear inequalities:

$$5x - 2 \leq -7 \qquad 3y > 1 \qquad \frac{z}{7} < -9(z - 3)$$

The **addition property of inequality** guarantees that the same number may be added to (or subtracted from) both sides of an inequality, and the resulting inequality will have the same solution set.

$$x - 9 \leq -16$$
$$x - 9 + 9 \leq -16 + 9 \quad \text{Add 9.}$$
$$x \leq -7$$

The **multiplication property of inequality** guarantees that both sides of an inequality may be multiplied by (or divided by) the same **positive** number, and the resulting inequality will have the same solution set. We may also multiply (or divide) both sides of an inequality by the same **negative** number and **reverse the direction of the inequality symbol,** and the result is an inequality with the same solution set.

Solve.

$$6x < -66$$
$$\frac{6x}{6} < \frac{-66}{6} \quad \text{Divide by 6. Do not reverse direction of inequality symbol.}$$
$$x < -11$$

Solve.

$$-6x < -66$$
$$\frac{-6x}{-6} > \frac{-66}{-6} \quad \text{Divide by }-6\text{. Reverse direction of inequality symbol.}$$
$$x > 11$$

(continued)

DEFINITIONS AND CONCEPTS	EXAMPLES
SECTION 16.2 LINEAR INEQUALITIES AND PROBLEM SOLVING (continued)	
To solve a linear inequality in one variable:	Solve for x: $\frac{3}{7}(x-4) \geq x+2$
1. Clear the equation of fractions.	**1.** $7\left[\frac{3}{7}(x-4)\right] \geq 7(x+2)$ Multiply by 7. $3(x-4) \geq 7(x+2)$
2. Remove grouping symbols such as parentheses. **3.** Simplify by combining like terms. **4.** Write variable terms on one side and numbers on the other side using the addition property of inequality.	**2.** $3x - 12 \geq 7x + 14$ Apply the distributive property. **4.** $-4x - 12 \geq 14$ Subtract $7x$. $-4x \geq 26$ Add 12. $\frac{-4x}{-4} \leq \frac{26}{-4}$ Divide by -4. Reverse direction of inequality symbol.
5. Isolate the variable using the multiplication property of inequality.	$x \leq -\frac{13}{2}$
SECTION 16.3 COMPOUND INEQUALITIES	
Two inequalities joined by the words **and** or **or** are called **compound inequalities.**	Compound inequalities: $x - 7 \leq 4$ and $x \geq -21$ $2x + 7 > x - 3$ or $5x + 2 > -3$
The solution set of a compound inequality formed by the word **and** is the **intersection** $\cap$ of the solution sets of the two inequalities.	Solve for x: $x < 5$ and $x < 3$ $\{x \mid x < 5\}$ −1 0 1 2 3 4 5 6 $(-\infty, 5)$ $\{x \mid x < 3\}$ −1 0 1 2 3 4 5 6 $(-\infty, 3)$ $\{x \mid x < 3$ and $x < 5\}$ −1 0 1 2 3 4 5 6 $(-\infty, 3)$
The solution set of a compound inequality formed by the word **or** is the **union,** $\cup$, of the solution sets of the two inequalities.	Solve for x: $x - 2 \geq -3$ or $2x \leq -4$ $x \geq -1$ or $x \leq -2$ $\{x \mid x \geq -1\}$ −4 −3 −2 −1 0 1 2 3 $[-1, \infty)$ $\{x \mid x \leq -2\}$ −4 −3 −2 −1 0 1 2 3 $(-\infty, -2]$ $\{x \mid x \leq -2$ or $x \geq -1\}$ −4 −3 −2 −1 0 1 2 3 $(-\infty, -2] \cup [-1, \infty)$

DEFINITIONS AND CONCEPTS	EXAMPLES

SECTION 16.3 COMPOUND INEQUALITIES (continued)

To solve a compound inequality $y_1 < y_2 < y_3$ graphically,

1. Graph separately each of the three parts y_1, y_2, and y_3, respectively, in an appropriate window.
2. Observe where the graph of y_2 is between the graphs of y_1 and y_3.
3. Find the x-coordinates of the points of intersection and determine the appropriate interval of the solution.

Solve for x: $-13 < 3x - 4 \le 8$

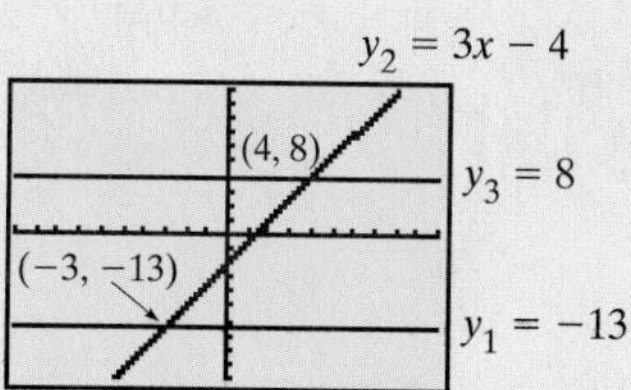

The solution in interval notation is $(-3, 4]$.

SECTION 16.4 ABSOLUTE VALUE EQUATIONS

If a is a positive number, then $|x| = a$ is equivalent to $x = a$ or $x = -a$.

Solve for y:

$$|5y - 1| - 7 = 4$$

$$|5y - 1| = 11$$

$$5y - 1 = 11 \quad \text{or} \quad 5y - 1 = -11 \quad \text{Add 7.}$$

$$5y = 12 \quad \text{or} \quad 5y = -10 \quad \text{Add 1.}$$

$$y = \frac{12}{5} \quad \text{or} \quad y = -2 \quad \text{Divide by 5.}$$

The solutions are -2 and $\frac{12}{5}$.

If a is negative, then $|x| = a$ has no solution.

Solve for x:

$$\left|\frac{x}{2} - 7\right| = -1$$

The solution set is { } or $\varnothing$.

If an absolute value equation is of the form $|x| = |y|$, solve $x = y$ or $x = -y$.

Solve for x:

$$|x - 7| = |2x + 1|$$

$$x - 7 = 2x + 1 \quad \text{or} \quad x - 7 = -(2x + 1)$$

$$x = 2x + 8 \qquad x - 7 = -2x - 1$$

$$-x = 8 \qquad x = -2x + 6$$

$$x = -8 \quad \text{or} \quad 3x = 6$$

$$x = 2$$

The solutions are -8 and 2.

SECTION 16.5 ABSOLUTE VALUE INEQUALITIES

If a is a positive number, then $|x| < a$ is equivalent to $-a < x < a$.

Solve for y:

$$|y - 5| \le 3$$

$$-3 \le y - 5 \le 3$$

$$-3 + 5 \le y - 5 + 5 \le 3 + 5 \quad \text{Add 5.}$$

$$2 \le y \le 8$$

The solution set is $[2, 8]$.

(continued)

DEFINITIONS AND CONCEPTS	EXAMPLES
SECTION 16.5 ABSOLUTE VALUE INEQUALITIES (continued)	
If a is a positive number, then $\|x\| > a$ is equivalent to $x < -a$ or $x > a$.	Solve for x: $\left\|\frac{x}{2} - 3\right\| > 7$ $\frac{x}{2} - 3 < -7$ or $\frac{x}{2} - 3 > 7$ $x - 6 < -14$ or $x - 6 > 14$ Multiply by 2. $x < -8$ or $x > 20$ Add 6. The solution set is $(-\infty, -8) \cup (20, \infty)$.

CHAPTER 16 REVIEW

(16.1) *Solve each equation algebraically and graphically.*

1. $4(x - 6) + 3 = 27$

2. $15(x + 2) - 6 = 18$

3. $5x + 15 = 3(x + 2) + 2(x - 3)$

4. $2x - 5 + 3(x - 4) = 5(x + 2) - 27$

5. $14 - 2(x + 3) = 3(x - 9) + 18$

6. $16 + 2(5 - x) = 19 - 3(x + 2)$

Solve each equation graphically. Round solutions to the nearest hundredth.

7. $0.4(x - 6) = \pi x + \sqrt{3}$

8. $1.7x + \sqrt{7} = -0.4x - \sqrt{6}$

(16.2) *Solve each linear inequality. Write your answers in interval notation.*

9. $3(x - 5) > -(x + 3)$

10. $-2(x + 7) \geq 3(x + 2)$

11. $4x - (5 + 2x) < 3x - 1$

12. $3(x - 8) < 7x + 2(5 - x)$

13. $24 \geq 6x - 2(3x - 5) + 2x$

14. $\frac{x}{3} + \frac{1}{2} > \frac{2}{3}$

15. $x + \frac{3}{4} < -\frac{x}{2} + \frac{9}{4}$

16. $\frac{x - 5}{2} \leq \frac{3}{8}(2x + 6)$

Solve.

17. George Boros can pay his housekeeper \$15 per week to do his laundry, or he can have the laundromat do it at a cost of 50 cents per pound for the first 10 pounds and 40 cents for each additional pound. Use an inequality to find the weight at which it is more economical to use the housekeeper than the laundromat.

18. Ceramic firing temperatures usually range from 500° to 1000° Fahrenheit. Use a compound inequality to convert this range to the Celsius scale. Round to the nearest degree. $\left(\text{Use } F = \frac{9C + 160}{5}\right)$

19. In the Olympic gymnastics competition, Nana must average a score of 9.65 to win the silver medal. Seven of the eight judges have reported scores of 9.5, 9.7, 9.9, 9.7, 9.7, 9.6, and 9.5. Use an inequality to find the minimum score that Nana must receive from the last judge to win the silver medal.

20. Carol would like to pay cash for a car when she graduates from college and estimates that she can afford a car that costs between \$4000 and \$8000. She has saved \$500 so far and plans to earn the rest of the money by working the next two summers. If Carol plans to save the same amount each summer, use a compound inequality to find the range of money she must save each summer to buy the car.

(16.3) *Solve each inequality. Write your answers in interval notation.*

21. $1 \leq 4x - 7 \leq 3$

22. $-2 \leq 8 + 5x < -1$

23. $-3 < 4(2x - 1) < 12$

24. $-6 < x - (3 - 4x) < -3$

25. $\frac{1}{6} < \frac{4x - 3}{3} \leq \frac{4}{5}$

26. $x \leq 2$ and $x > -5$

27. $3x - 5 > 6$ or $-x < -5$

(16.4) *Solve each absolute value equation.*

28. $|x - 7| = 9$

29. $|8 - x| = 3$

30. $|2x + 9| = 9$

31. $|-3x + 4| = 7$

32. $|3x - 2| + 6 = 10$

33. $5 + |6x + 1| = 5$

34. $-5 = |4x - 3|$

35. $|5 - 6x| + 8 = 3$

36. $-8 = |x - 3| - 10$

37. $\left|\frac{3x - 7}{4}\right| = 2$

38. $|6x + 1| = |15 + 4x|$

(16.5) Solve each absolute value inequality. Graph the solution set and write it in interval notation.

39. $|5x - 1| < 9$

40. $|6 + 4x| \geq 10$

41. $|3x| - 8 > 1$

42. $9 + |5x| < 24$

43. $|6x - 5| \leq -1$

44. $\left|3x + \frac{2}{5}\right| \geq 4$

45. $\left|\frac{x}{3} + 6\right| - 8 > -5$

46. $\left|\frac{4(x - 1)}{7}\right| + 10 < 2$

MIXED REVIEW

Solve.

47. $\frac{x - 2}{5} + \frac{x + 2}{2} = \frac{x + 4}{3}$

48. $\frac{2z - 3}{4} - \frac{4 - z}{2} = \frac{z + 1}{3}$

Solve. If an inequality, write your solutions in interval notation.

49. $\frac{3(x - 2)}{5} > \frac{-5(x - 2)}{3}$

50. $0 \leq \frac{2(3x + 4)}{5} \leq 3$

51. $x \leq 2$ or $x > -5$

52. $-2x \leq 6$ and $-2x + 3 < -7$

53. $|7x| - 26 = -5$

54. $\left|\frac{9 - 2x}{5}\right| = -3$

55. $|x - 3| = |7 + 2x|$

56. $|6x - 5| \geq -1$

57. $\left|\frac{4x - 3}{5}\right| < 1$

58. $48 + x \geq 5(2x + 4) - 2x$

CHAPTER 16 TEST

Remember to use your Chapter Test Prep Video CD to help you study and view solutions to the test questions you need help with.

1. Solve $15x + 26 = -2(x + 1) - 1$ algebraically and graphically.

2. Solve $-3x - \sqrt{5} = \pi(x - 1)$ graphically. Round the solution to the nearest hundredth.

Solve. Write inequality solutions in interval notation.

3. $|6x - 5| - 3 = -2$

4. $|8 - 2t| = -6$

5. $3(2x - 7) - 4x > -(x + 6)$

6. $8 - \frac{x}{2} \geq 7$

7. $-3 < 2(x - 3) \leq 4$

8. $|3x + 1| > 5$

9. $x \leq -2$ and $x \leq -5$

10. $x \leq -2$ or $x \leq -5$

11. $-x > 1$ and $3x + 3 \geq x - 3$

12. $6x + 1 > 5x + 4$ or $1 - x > -4$

13. $|x - 5| - 4 < -2$

14. $\left|\frac{5x - 7}{2}\right| = 4$

15. $\left|17x - \frac{1}{5}\right| > -2$

16. $|x - 5| = |x + 2|$

Graph each inequality.

17. $x \leq -4$

18. $2x - y > 5$

Use the given screen to solve each inequality. Write the solution in interval notation.

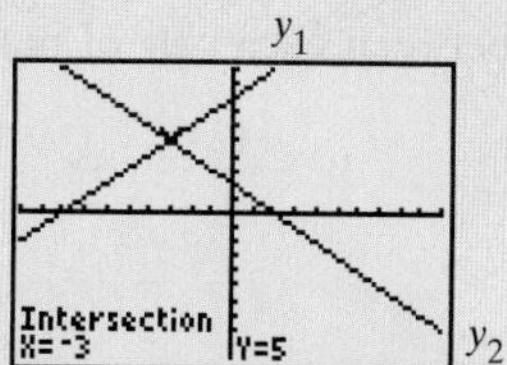

19. $y_1 < y_2$

20. $y_1 > y_2$

21. The company that makes Photoray sunglasses figures that the cost C to make x number of sunglasses weekly is given by $C = 3910 + 2.8x$, and the weekly revenue R is given by $R = 7.4x$. Use an inequality to find the number of sunglasses that must be made and sold to make a profit. (Revenue must exceed cost in order to make a profit.)

CHAPTER 16 CUMULATIVE REVIEW

List the elements in each set.

1. a. $\{x|x \text{ is a natural number greater than } 100\}$
b. $\{x|x \text{ is a whole number between 1 and 6}\}$

2. a. $\{x|x \text{ is an integer between } -3 \text{ and } 5\}$
b. $\{x|x \text{ is a whole number between 3 and 5}\}$

3. Find each value.
a. $|3|$ **b.** $\left|-\frac{1}{7}\right|$ **c.** $-|2.7|$
d. $-|-8|$ **e.** $|0|$

4. Find the opposite of each number.
a. $\frac{2}{3}$ **b.** -9 **c.** 1.5

5. Add.
a. $-3 + (-11)$ **b.** $3 + (-7)$ **c.** $-10 + 15$
d. $-8.3 + (-1.9)$ **e.** $-\frac{2}{3} + \frac{3}{7}$

6. Subtract.
a. $-2 - (-10)$ **b.** $1.7 - 8.9$
c. $-\frac{1}{2} - \frac{1}{4}$

7. Find the square roots.
a. $\sqrt{9}$ **b.** $\sqrt{25}$ **c.** $\sqrt{\frac{1}{4}}$
d. $-\sqrt{36}$ **e.** $\sqrt{-36}$

8. Multiply or divide.
a. $-3(-2)$ **b.** $-\frac{3}{4}\left(-\frac{4}{7}\right)$
c. $\frac{0}{-2}$ **d.** $\frac{-20}{-2}$

9. Evaluate each algebraic expression when $x = 2$, $y = -1$, and $z = -3$.
a. $z - y$ **b.** $-2z^2$ **c.** $\frac{2x + y}{z}$ **d.** $-x^2 - 4x$

10. Find the roots.
a. $\sqrt[4]{1}$ **b.** $\sqrt[3]{8}$ **c.** $\sqrt[4]{81}$

11. Write each sentence using mathematical symbols.
a. The sum of x and 5 is 20.
b. Two times the sum of 3 and y amounts to 4.
c. Subtract 8 from x, and the difference is the same as the product of 2 and x.
d. The quotient of z and 9 amounts to 9 plus z.

12. Insert $<, >,$ or $=$ between each pair of numbers to form a true statement.
a. $-3 \quad -5$ **b.** $\frac{-12}{-4} \quad 3$
c. $0 \quad -2$

Solve for x.

13. $2x + 5 = 9$

14. $11.2 = 1.2 - 5x$

15. $6x - 4 = 2 + 6(x - 1)$

16. $2x + 1.5 = -0.2 + 1.6x$

17. Write the following as algebraic expressions. Then simplify.
a. The sum of three consecutive integers, if x is the first consecutive integer.
b. The perimeter of the triangle with sides of length x, $5x$, and $6x - 3$.

18. Write the following as algebraic expressions. Then simplify.
a. The sum of three consecutive odd integers if x is the first consecutive integers.
b. The perimeter of a square with side length $3x + 1$.

19. Find three numbers such that the second number is 3 more than twice the first number and the third number is four times the first number. The sum of the three numbers is 164.

20. Find two numbers such that the second number is 2 more than three times the first number and the difference of the two numbers is 24.

21. Solve $3y - 2x = 7$ for y.

22. Solve $7x - 4y = 10$ for x.

23. Solve $A = \frac{1}{2}(B + b)h$ for b.

24. Solve $P = 2l + 2w$ for l.

25. Write each in interval notation.
a. $\{x|x \geq 2\}$ **b.** $\{x|x < -1\}$
c. $\{x|0.5 < x \leq 3\}$

26. Write each in interval notation.
a. $\{x|x \leq -3\}$
b. $\{x|-2 \leq x < 0.1\}$

Solve.

27. $-(x - 3) + 2 \leq 3(2x - 5) + x$

28. $2(7x - 1) - 5x > -(-7x) + 4$

29. a. $2(x + 3) > 2x + 1$
b. $2(x + 3) < 2x + 1$

30. $4(x + 1) - 3 < 4x + 1$

31. If $A = \{x|x \text{ is an even number greater than 0 and less than } 10\}$ and $B = \{3, 4, 5, 6\}$, find $A \cap B$.

32. Find the union: $\{-2, 0, 2, 4\} \cup \{-1, 1, 3, 5\}$

33. Solve: $x - 7 < 2$ and $2x + 1 < 9$

34. Solve: $x + 3 \leq 1$ or $3x - 1 < 8$

35. If $A = \{x|x \text{ is an even number greater than 0 and less than } 10\}$ and $B = \{3, 4, 5, 6\}$, find $A \cup B$.

36. Find the intersection: $\{-2, 0, 2, 4\} \cap \{-1, 1, 3, 5\}$

37. Solve: $-2x - 5 < -3$ or $6x < 0$

38. Solve: $-2x - 5 < -3$ and $6x < 0$

Solve.

39. $|p| = 2$

40. $|x| = 5$

41. $\left|\frac{x}{2} - 1\right| = 11$

42. $\left|\frac{y}{3} + 2\right| = 10$

43. $|x - 3| = |5 - x|$

44. $|x + 3| = |7 - x|$

45. $|x| \leq 3$

46. $|x| > 1$

47. $|2x + 9| + 5 > 3$

48. $|3x + 1| + 9 < 1$

Systems of Linear Equations and Inequalities

17

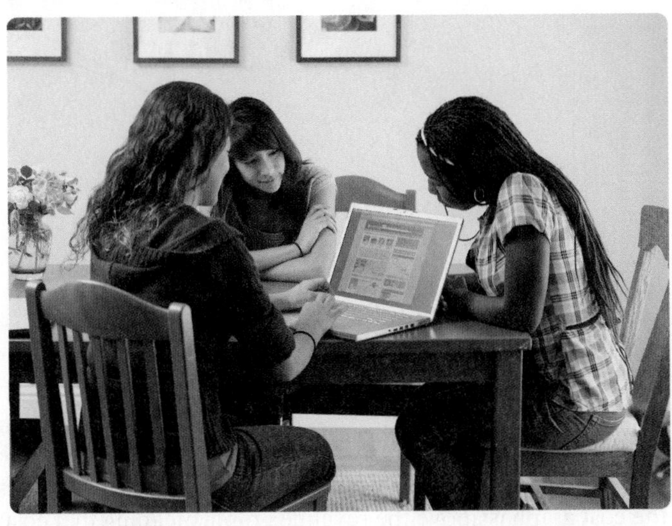

MySpace and Facebook are both popular social networking Web sites offering interactive, user-submitted networks of friends, personal profiles, blogs, groups, music, videos, and photos.>

MySpace is currently the world's sixth most popular Web site in any language and the third most popular Web site in the United States. Facebook was launched in early 2004 and is currently the seventh most visited Web site.

We will form and use the functions graphed below to solve the system of equations.

In this chapter, two or more equations in two or more variables are solved simultaneously. Such a collection of equations is called a **system of equations.** Systems of equations are good mathematical models for many real-world problems because these problems may involve several related patterns.

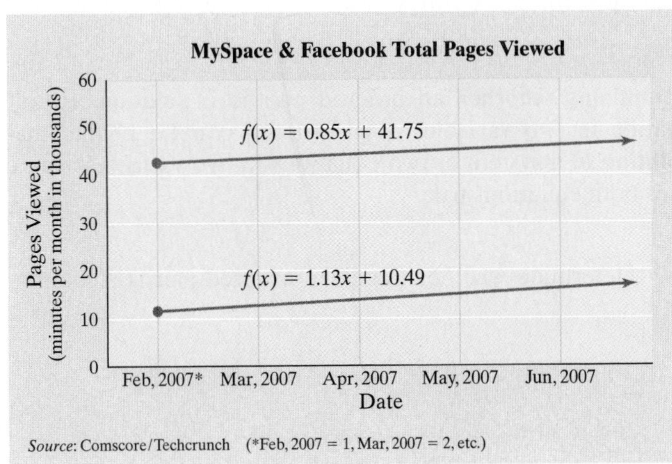

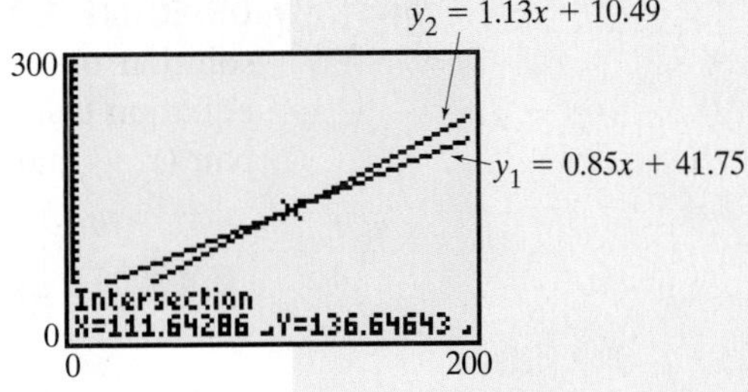

17.1 SOLVING SYSTEMS OF LINEAR EQUATIONS IN TWO VARIABLES

OBJECTIVES

1. Determine whether an ordered pair is a solution of a system of two linear equations.
2. Solve a system by graphing.
3. Solve a system by substitution.
4. Solve a system by elimination.

An important problem that often occurs in the fields of business and economics concerns the concepts of revenue and cost. For example, suppose that a small manufacturing company begins to manufacture and sell compact disc storage units. The revenue of a company is the company's income from selling these units, and the cost is the amount of money that a company spends to manufacture these units. The following coordinate system shows the graphs of revenue and cost for the storage units.

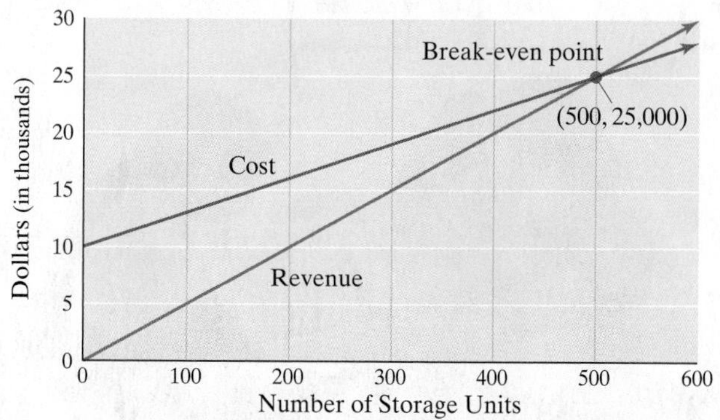

These lines intersect at the point (500, 25,000). This means that when 500 storage units are manufactured and sold, both cost and revenue are \$25,000. In business, this point of intersection is called the **break-even point.** Notice that for x-values (units sold) less than 500, the cost graph is above the revenue graph, meaning that cost of manufacturing is greater than revenue, and so the company is losing money. For x-values (units sold) greater than 500, the revenue graph is above the cost graph, meaning that revenue is greater than cost, and so the company is making money.

Recall from Chapter 15 that each line is a graph of some linear equation in two variables. Both equations together form a **system of equations.** The common point of intersection is called the **solution of the system.** Some examples of systems of linear equations in two variables are

Systems of Linear Equations in Two Variables

$$\begin{cases} x - 2y = -7 \\ 3x + y = 0 \end{cases} \qquad \begin{cases} x = 5 \\ x + \dfrac{y}{2} = 9 \end{cases} \qquad \begin{cases} x - 3 = 2y + 6 \\ y = 1 \end{cases}$$

OBJECTIVE 1 ▶ Determining whether an ordered pair is a solution. Recall that a solution of an equation in two variables is an ordered pair (x, y) that makes the equation true. A **solution of a system** of two equations in two variables is an ordered pair (x, y) that makes both equations true.

EXAMPLE 1 Determine whether the given ordered pair is a solution of the system.

a. $\begin{cases} -x + y = 2 \\ 2x - y = -3 \end{cases}$ $(-1, 1)$ **b.** $\begin{cases} 5x + 3y = -1 \\ x - y = 1 \end{cases}$ $(-2, 3)$

Solution

a. We replace x with -1 and y with 1 in each equation.

$-x + y = 2$	First equation	$2x - y = -3$	Second equation
$-(-1) + (1) \stackrel{?}{=} 2$	Let $x = -1$ and $y = 1$.	$2(-1) - (1) \stackrel{?}{=} -3$	Let $x = -1$ and $y = 1$.
$1 + 1 \stackrel{?}{=} 2$		$-2 - 1 \stackrel{?}{=} -3$	
$2 = 2$	True	$-3 = -3$	True

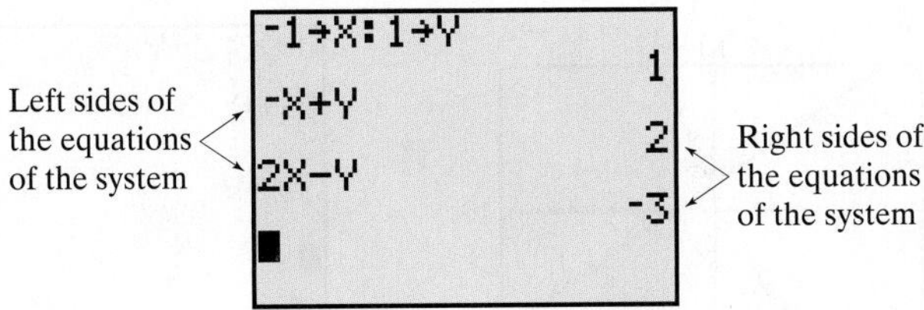

A calculator check for Example 1a.

Since $(-1, 1)$ makes *both* equations true, it is a solution. Using set notation, the solution set is $\{(-1, 1)\}$.

b. We replace x with -2 and y with 3 in each equation.

$$\begin{aligned} 5x + 3y &= -1 && \text{First equation} \\ 5(-2) + 3(3) &\stackrel{?}{=} -1 && \text{Let } x = -2 \text{ and } y = 3. \\ -10 + 9 &\stackrel{?}{=} -1 \\ -1 &= -1 && \text{True} \end{aligned}$$

$$\begin{aligned} x - y &= 1 && \text{Second equation} \\ (-2) - (3) &\stackrel{?}{=} 1 && \text{Let } x = -2 \text{ and } y = 3. \\ -5 &= 1 && \text{False} \end{aligned}$$

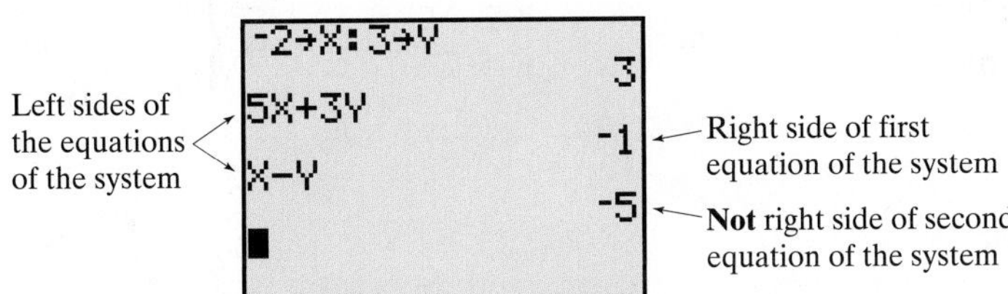

A calculator check for Example 1b.

Since the ordered pair $(-2, 3)$ does not make *both* equations true, it is not a solution of the system. □

PRACTICE 1 Determine whether the given ordered pair is a solution of the system.

a. $\begin{cases} -x - 4y = 1 \\ 2x + y = 5 \end{cases}$ $(3, -1)$

b. $\begin{cases} 4x + y = -4 \\ -x + 3y = 8 \end{cases}$ $(-2, 4)$

Example 1 above shows how to determine that an ordered pair is a solution of a system of equations, but how do we find such a solution? Actually, there are various methods to find the solution. We will investigate several in this chapter: graphing, substitution, elimination, matrices, and determinants.

OBJECTIVE 2 ▶ Solving a system by graphing. To solve by graphing, we graph each equation in an appropriate window and find the coordinates of any points of intersection.

EXAMPLE 2 Solve the system by graphing.

$$\begin{cases} x + y = 2 \\ 3x - y = -2 \end{cases}$$

Solution Since the graph of a linear equation in two variables is a line, graphing two such equations yields two lines in a plane. To use a graphing utility, solve each equation for y.

$$\begin{cases} y = -x + 2 & \text{First equation} \\ y = 3x + 2 & \text{Second equation} \end{cases}$$

Graph $y_1 = -x + 2$ and $y_2 = 3x + 2$ and find the point of intersection.

TECHNOLOGY NOTE

When solving a system of equations by graphing, try the standard or integer window first and see if the intersection appears. If it does not appear in one of these windows, you may be able to see enough of the graph to estimate where the intersection will occur and adjust the window setting accordingly.

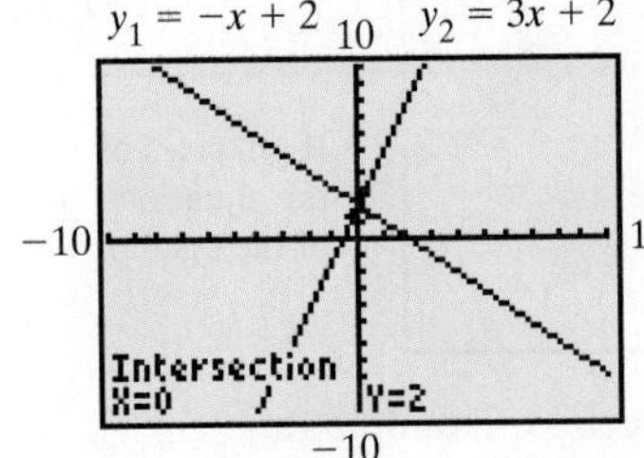

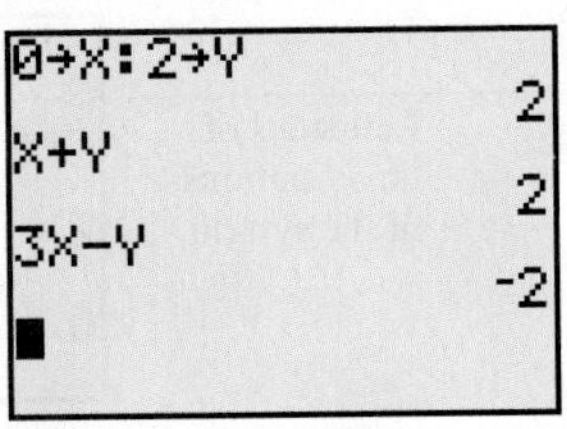

A check of the solution: (0, 2).

Verify the ordered pair solution (0, 2) by replacing x with 0 and y with 2 in both original equations and seeing that true statements result each time. The screen on the right above shows that the ordered pair (0, 2) does satisfy both equations. We conclude therefore that (0, 2) is the solution of the system. A system that has at least one solution, such as this one, is said to be **consistent.** □

PRACTICE 2 Solve each system by graphing. If the system has just one solution, find the solution.

a. $\begin{cases} 3x - 2y = 4 \\ -9x + 6y = -12 \end{cases}$ **b.** $\begin{cases} y = 5x \\ 2x + y = 7 \end{cases}$ **c.** $\begin{cases} y = \frac{3}{4}x + 1 \\ 3x - 4y = 12 \end{cases}$

DISCOVER THE CONCEPT

Use your graphing utility to solve the system

$$\begin{cases} x - 2y = 4 \\ x = 2y \end{cases}$$

In the discovery above, we see that solving each equation for y produces the following:

$x - 2y = 4$	First equation	$x = 2y$	Second equation
$-2y = -x + 4$	Subtract x from both sides.	$\frac{1}{2}x = y$	Divide both sides by 2.
$y = \frac{1}{2}x - 2$	Divide both sides by −2.	$y = \frac{1}{2}x$	

10
$y_2 = \frac{1}{2}x$
−10
10
−10
$y_1 = \frac{1}{2}x - 2$

Notice that each equation is now in the form $y = mx + b$. From this form, we see that both lines have the same slope, $\frac{1}{2}$, but different y-intercepts, so they are parallel as shown to the left. Therefore, the system has no solution since the equations have no common solution (there are no intersection points). A system that has no solution is said to be **inconsistent.**

DISCOVER THE CONCEPT

Use your graphing utility to solve the system

$$\begin{cases} 2x + 4y = 10 \\ x + 2y = 5 \end{cases}$$

In the discovery above, we see that solving each equation for y produces the following:

$2x + 4y = 10$	First equation	$x + 2y = 5$	Second equation
$y = -\frac{1}{2}x + \frac{5}{2}$		$y = -\frac{1}{2}x + \frac{5}{2}$	

Notice that both lines have the same slope, $-\frac{1}{2}$, and the same y-intercept, $\frac{5}{2}$. This means that the graph of each equation is the same line.

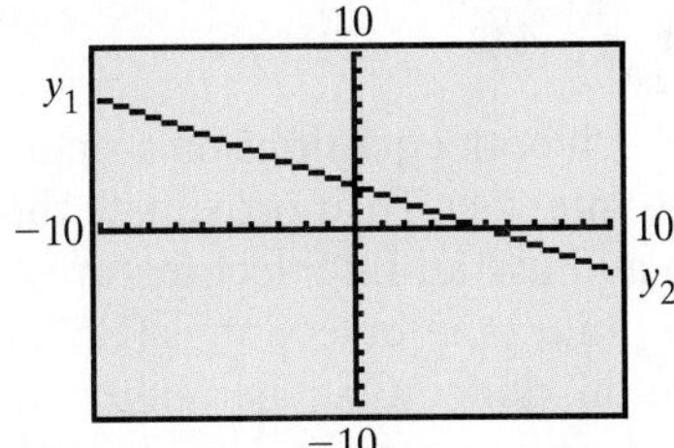

X	Y1	Y2
-3	4	4
-2	3.5	3.5
-1	3	3
0	2.5	2.5
1	2	2
2	1.5	1.5
3	1	1

Y1=(-2X+10)/4

> **Helpful Hint**
> - If a system of equations has *at least one solution,* the system is *consistent.*
> - If a system of equations has *no solution,* the system is *inconsistent.*

To confirm this, notice that the entries for y_1 and y_2 are the same in the table shown on the right above. The equations have identical solutions and any ordered pair solution of one equation satisfies the other equation also. Thus, these equations are said to be **dependent equations.** The solution set of the system is $\{(x, y)|x + 2y = 5\}$ or, equivalently, $\{(x, y)|2x + 4y = 10\}$ since the equations describe identical ordered pairs. Written this way, the solution set is read "the set of all ordered pairs (x, y), such that $2x + 4y = 10$." There are therefore an infinite number of solutions to the system.

> **Helpful Hint**
> - If the graphs of two equations *differ,* they are *independent* equations.
> - If the graphs of two equations are the *same,* they *are dependent* equations.

Concept Check ✓

The equations in the system are dependent and the system has an infinite number of solutions. Which ordered pairs below are solutions?

$$\begin{cases} -x + 3y = 4 \\ 2x + 8 = 6y \end{cases}$$

a. $(4, 0)$ **b.** $(-4, 0)$ **c.** $(-1, 1)$

We can summarize the information discovered in Example 2 as follows.

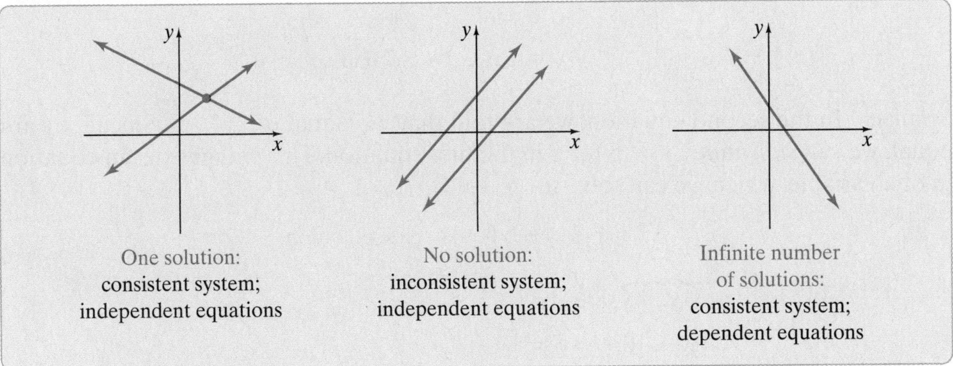

One solution: consistent system; independent equations

No solution: inconsistent system; independent equations

Infinite number of solutions: consistent system; dependent equations

Concept Check ✓

How can you tell just by looking at the following system that it has no solution?

$$\begin{cases} y = 3x + 5 \\ y = 3x - 7 \end{cases}$$

How can you tell just by looking at the following system that it has infinitely many solutions?

$$\begin{cases} x + y = 5 \\ 2x + 2y = 10 \end{cases}$$

A graphing calculator is a very useful tool for approximating solutions to a system of equations in two variables. See the next example.

Answer to Concept Check: b, c; answers may vary

EXAMPLE 3 Solve the system by graphing. Approximate the solution to two decimal places.

$$\begin{cases} y + 2.6x = 5.6 \\ y - 4.3x = -4.9 \end{cases}$$

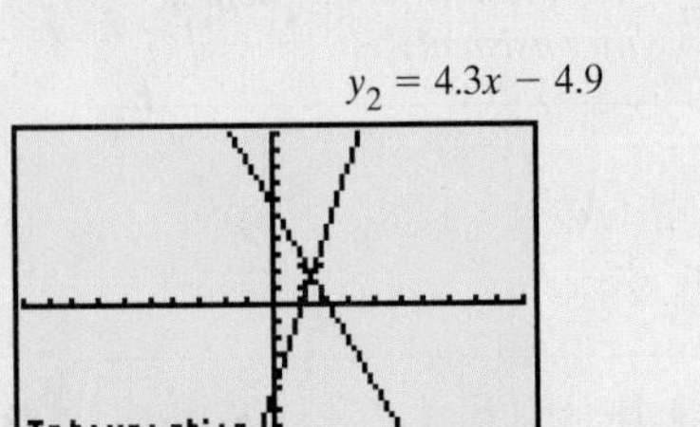

Solving graphically. x- and y-values are automatically stored to 14 decimal places.

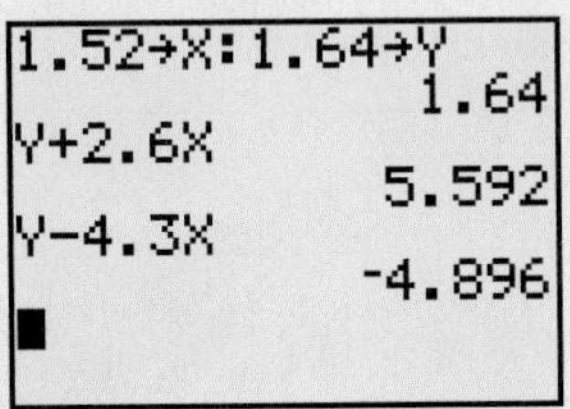

The numerical check with decimal approximations.

Solution First use a standard window and graph both equations on a single screen. The screen in the margin shows that the two lines intersect. To approximate the point of intersection, trace to the point of intersection and use an Intersect feature of the graphing calculator. We find that the approximate point of intersection is (1.52, 1.64).

Because the solution is an approximation, notice that the numerical check with these approximations does not show equivalent expressions. For example, instead of $y + 2.6x = 5.6$, we have $y + 2.6x = 5.592$. The number 5.592 is close to 5.6, but not equal to 5.6. Keep this in mind when checking approximations. □

PRACTICE

3 Solve by graphing. Approximate the solution to two decimal places.

$$\begin{cases} y - 0.25x = 1.6 \\ y + 1.03x = -5.1 \end{cases}$$

OBJECTIVE 3 ▶ Solving a system by substitution. Graphing the equations of a system by hand is often a good method of finding approximate solutions of a system, but it is not a reliable method of finding exact solutions of a system. We turn instead to two algebraic methods of solving systems. We use the first method, the **substitution method,** to solve the system

$$\begin{cases} 2x + 4y = -6 & \text{First equation} \\ x = 2y - 5 & \text{Second equation} \end{cases}$$

EXAMPLE 4 Use the substitution method to solve the system.

$$\begin{cases} 2x + 4y = -6 & \text{First equation} \\ x = 2y - 5 & \text{Second equation} \end{cases}$$

Solution In the second equation, we are told that x is equal to $2y - 5$. Since they are equal, we can *substitute* $2y - 5$ for x in the first equation. This will give us an equation in one variable, which we can solve for y.

$$2x + 4y = -6 \quad \text{First equation}$$
$$2(2y - 5) + 4y = -6 \quad \text{Substitute } 2y - 5 \text{ for } x.$$
$$4y - 10 + 4y = -6$$
$$8y = 4$$
$$y = \frac{4}{8} = \frac{1}{2} \quad \text{Solve for } y.$$

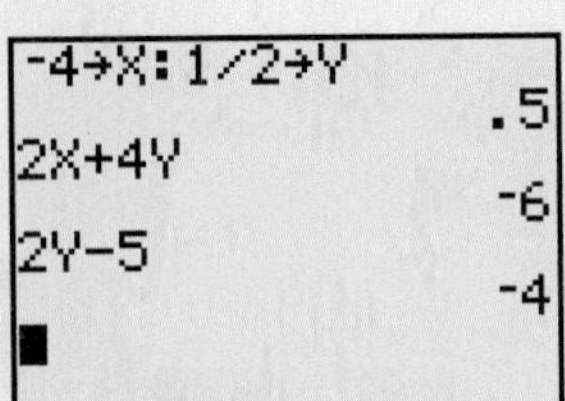

A numeric check of the solution $\left(-4, \frac{1}{2}\right)$ for Example 4.

The y-coordinate of the solution is $\frac{1}{2}$. To find the x-coordinate, we replace y with $\frac{1}{2}$ in the second equation,

$$x = 2y - 5.$$
$$x = 2y - 5$$
$$x = 2\left(\frac{1}{2}\right) - 5 = 1 - 5 = -4$$

The ordered pair solution is $\left(-4, \frac{1}{2}\right)$. Check to see that $\left(-4, \frac{1}{2}\right)$ satisfies both equations of the system. □

PRACTICE 4 Use the substitution method to solve the system.

$$\begin{cases} y = 4x + 7 \\ 2x + y = 4 \end{cases}$$

The steps below summarize the substitution method.

Solving a System of Two Equations Using the Substitution Method

STEP 1. Solve one of the equations for one of its variables.

STEP 2. Substitute the expression for the variable found in Step 1 into the other equation.

STEP 3. Find the value of one variable by solving the equation from Step 2.

STEP 4. Find the value of the other variable by substituting the value found in Step 3 into the equation from Step 1.

STEP 5. Check the ordered pair solution in *both* original equations.

Helpful Hint

If a system of equations contains equations with fractions, first clear the equations of fractions.

EXAMPLE 5 Use the substitution method to solve the system.

$$\begin{cases} -\frac{x}{6} + \frac{y}{2} = \frac{1}{2} \\ \frac{x}{3} - \frac{y}{6} = -\frac{3}{4} \end{cases}$$

Solution First we multiply each equation by its least common denominator to clear the system of fractions. We multiply the first equation by 6 and the second equation by 12.

$$\begin{cases} 6\left(-\frac{x}{6} + \frac{y}{2}\right) = 6\left(\frac{1}{2}\right) \\ 12\left(\frac{x}{3} - \frac{y}{6}\right) = 12\left(-\frac{3}{4}\right) \end{cases} \quad \text{simplifies to} \quad \begin{cases} -x + 3y = 3 & \text{First equation} \\ 4x - 2y = -9 & \text{Second equation} \end{cases}$$

To use the substitution method, we now solve the first equation for x.

Helpful Hint

To avoid tedious fractions, solve for a variable whose coefficient is 1 or -1, if possible.

$$-x + 3y = 3 \quad \text{First equation}$$
$$3y - 3 = x \quad \text{Solve for } x.$$

Next we replace x with $3y - 3$ in the second equation.

$$4x - 2y = -9 \quad \text{Second equation}$$
$$4(3y - 3) - 2y = -9$$
$$12y - 12 - 2y = -9$$
$$10y = 3$$
$$y = \frac{3}{10} \quad \text{Solve for } y.$$

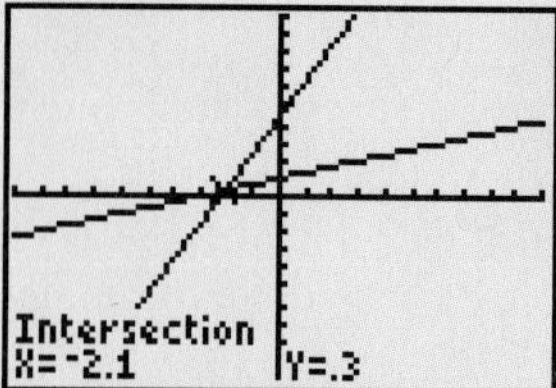

To find the corresponding x-coordinate, we replace y with $\frac{3}{10}$ in the equation $x = 3y - 3$. Then

$$x = 3\left(\frac{3}{10}\right) - 3 = \frac{9}{10} - 3 = \frac{9}{10} - \frac{30}{10} = -\frac{21}{10}$$

The ordered pair solution is $\left(-\frac{21}{10}, \frac{3}{10}\right)$ or equivalently $(-2.1, 0.3)$. We check this solution graphically to the left. □

PRACTICE 5 Use the substitution method to solve the system.

$$\begin{cases} -\frac{x}{3} + \frac{y}{4} = \frac{1}{2} \\ \frac{x}{4} - \frac{y}{2} = -\frac{1}{4} \end{cases}$$

OBJECTIVE 4 ▶ Solving a system by elimination. The **elimination method,** or **addition method,** is a second algebraic technique for solving systems of equations. For this method, we rely on a version of the addition property of equality, which states that "equals added to equals are equal."

> If $A = B$ and $C = D$ then $A + C = B + D$.

EXAMPLE 6 Use the elimination method to solve the system.

$$\begin{cases} x - 5y = -12 & \text{First equation} \\ -x + y = 4 & \text{Second equation} \end{cases}$$

Solution Since the left side of each equation is equal to the right side, we add equal quantities by adding the left sides of the equations and the right sides of the equations. This sum gives us an equation in one variable, y, which we can solve for y.

$$\begin{aligned} x - 5y &= -12 && \text{First equation} \\ -x + y &= 4 && \text{Second equation} \\ \hline -4y &= -8 && \text{Add.} \\ y &= 2 && \text{Solve for } y. \end{aligned}$$

The y-coordinate of the solution is 2. To find the corresponding x-coordinate, we replace y with 2 in either original equation of the system. Let's use the second equation.

$$\begin{aligned} -x + y &= 4 && \text{Second equation} \\ -x + 2 &= 4 && \text{Let } y = 2. \\ -x &= 2 \\ x &= -2 \end{aligned}$$

The ordered pair solution is $(-2, 2)$. We check numerically (to the left) to see that $(-2, 2)$ satisfies both equations of the system. □

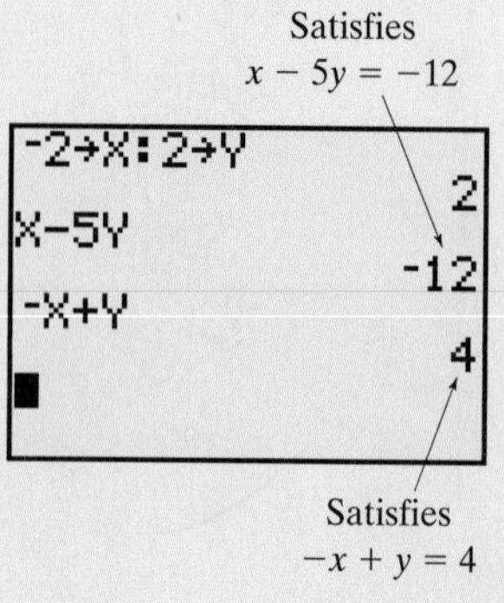

PRACTICE 6 Use the elimination method to solve the system.

$$\begin{cases} 3x - y = 5 \\ 5x + y = 11 \end{cases}$$

The steps below summarize the elimination method.

Solving a System of Two Linear Equations Using the Elimination Method

STEP 1. Rewrite each equation in standard form, $Ax + By = C$.

STEP 2. If necessary, multiply one or both equations by some nonzero number so that the coefficients of a variable are opposites of each other.

STEP 3. Add the equations.

STEP 4. Find the value of one variable by solving the equation from Step 3.

STEP 5. Find the value of the second variable by substituting the value found in Step 4 into either original equation.

STEP 6. Check the proposed ordered pair solution in *both* original equations.

EXAMPLE 7 Use the elimination method to solve the system.

$$\begin{cases} 3x - 2y = 10 \\ 4x - 3y = 15 \end{cases}$$

Solution If we add the two equations, the sum will still be an equation in two variables. Notice, however, that we can eliminate y when the equations are added if we multiply both sides of the first equation by 3 and both sides of the second equation by -2. Then

$$\begin{cases} 3(3x - 2y) = 3(10) \\ -2(4x - 3y) = -2(15) \end{cases} \quad \text{simplifies to} \quad \begin{cases} 9x - 6y = 30 \\ -8x + 6y = -30 \end{cases}$$

Next we add the left sides and add the right sides.

$$\begin{array}{r} 9x - 6y = 30 \\ -8x + 6y = -30 \\ \hline x \qquad = 0 \end{array}$$

To find y, we let $x = 0$ in either equation of the system.

$$\begin{aligned} 3x - 2y &= 10 && \text{First equation} \\ 3(0) - 2y &= 10 && \text{Let } x = 0. \\ -2y &= 10 \\ y &= -5 \end{aligned}$$

The ordered pair solution is $(0, -5)$. Check to see that $(0, -5)$ satisfies both equations of the system. □

PRACTICE 7 Use the elimination method to solve the system.

$$\begin{cases} 3x - 2y = -6 \\ 4x + 5y = -8 \end{cases}$$

EXAMPLE 8 Use the elimination method to solve the system.

$$\begin{cases} 3x + \dfrac{y}{2} = 2 \\ 6x + y = 5 \end{cases}$$

Solution If we multiply both sides of the first equation by -2, the coefficients of x in the two equations will be opposites. Then

$$\begin{cases} -2\left(3x + \dfrac{y}{2}\right) = -2(2) \\ 6x + y = 5 \end{cases} \quad \text{simplifies to} \quad \begin{cases} -6x - y = -4 \\ 6x + y = 5 \end{cases}$$

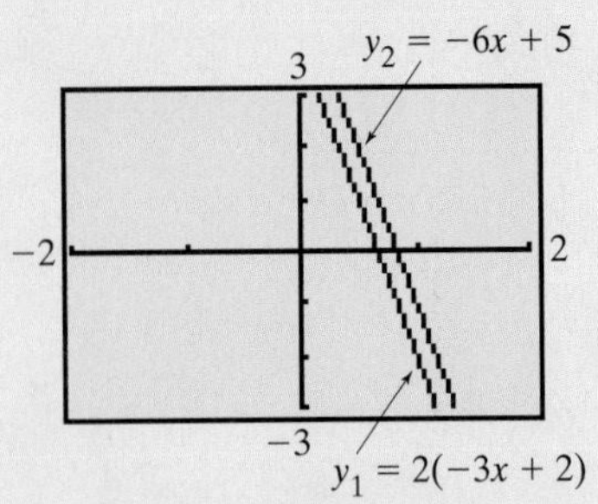

The two graphs appear to be parallel lines, supporting no solution to the system of Example 8.

Now we can add the left sides and add the right sides.

$$\begin{array}{r} -6x - y = -4 \\ 6x + y = 5 \\ \hline 0 = 1 \end{array} \quad \text{False}$$

The resulting equation, $0 = 1$, is false for all values of y or x. Thus, the system has no solution. The solution set is { } or ∅. This system is inconsistent, and the graphs of the equations are parallel lines. □

PRACTICE 8 Use the elimination method to solve the system.

$$\begin{cases} 8x + y = 6 \\ 2x + \dfrac{y}{4} = -2 \end{cases}$$

EXAMPLE 9 Use the elimination method to solve the system.

$$\begin{cases} -5x - 3y = 9 \\ 10x + 6y = -18 \end{cases}$$

Solution To eliminate x when the equations are added, we multiply both sides of the first equation by 2. Then

$$\begin{cases} 2(-5x - 3y) = 2(9) \\ 10x + 6y = -18 \end{cases} \quad \text{simplifies to} \quad \begin{cases} -10x - 6y = 18 \\ 10x + 6y = -18 \end{cases}$$

Next we add the equations.

$$\begin{array}{r} -10x - 6y = 18 \\ 10x + 6y = -18 \\ \hline 0 = 0 \end{array}$$

The resulting equation, $0 = 0$, is true for all possible values of y or x. Notice in the original system that if both sides of the first equation are multiplied by -2, the result is the second equation. This means that the two equations are equivalent. They have the same solution set and there are an infinite number of solutions. Thus, the equations of this system are dependent, and the solution set of the system is

$$\{(x, y) \mid -5x - 3y = 9\} \quad \text{or, equivalently,} \quad \{(x, y) \mid 10x + 6y = -18\}. \quad □$$

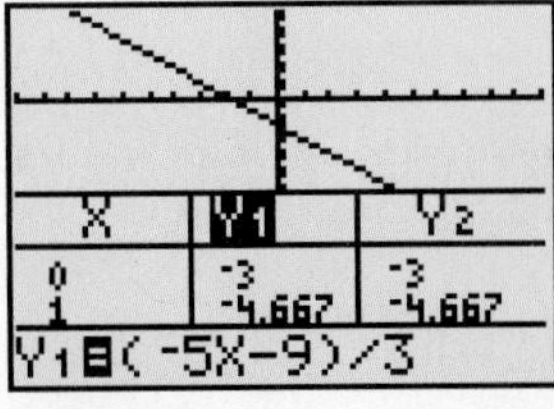

The graph (shown on a standard window) and table indicate that the graph of both equations is the same line. This supports the solution above for Example 9.

PRACTICE
9 Use the elimination method to solve the system.

$$\begin{cases} -3x + 2y = -1 \\ 9x - 6y = 3 \end{cases}$$

Helpful Hint

Remember that not all ordered pairs are solutions of the system in Example 9, only the infinite number of ordered pairs that satisfy $-5x - 3y = 9$ or equivalently $10x + 6y = -18$.

EXAMPLE 10 Finding the Break-Even Point

A small manufacturing company manufactures and sells compact disc storage units. The revenue equation for these units is

$$y = 50x$$

where x is the number of units sold and y is the revenue, or income, in dollars for selling x units. The cost equation for these units is

$$y = 30x + 10{,}000$$

where x is the number of units manufactured and y is the total cost in dollars for manufacturing x units. Use these equations to find the number of units to be sold for the company to break even.

Solution The break-even point is found by solving the system

$$\begin{cases} y = 50x & \text{First equation} \\ y = 30x + 10{,}000 & \text{Second equation} \end{cases}$$

To solve the system, graph $y_1 = 50x$ and $y_2 = 30x + 10{,}000$ and find the point of intersection, the break-even point.

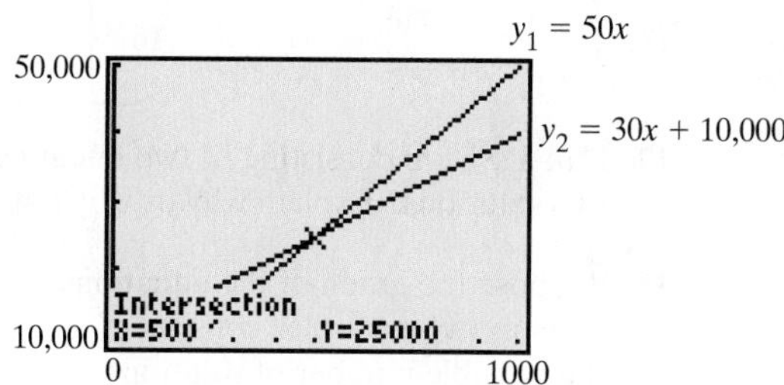

The ordered pair solution is (500, 25,000). This means that the business must sell 500 compact disc storage units to break even. A hand-drawn graph of the equations in this system can be found at the beginning of this section. □

PRACTICE
10 The revenue equation for a certain product is $y = 17x$, where x is the number of units sold and y is the revenue in dollars. The cost equation for the product is $y = 6x + 8030$, where x is the number of units manufactured and y is the cost in dollars for manufacturing x units. Find the number of units for the company to break even.

VOCABULARY & READINESS CHECK

Match each graph with the solution of the corresponding system.

A

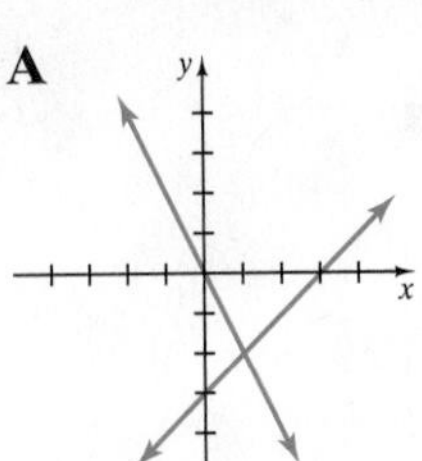

B

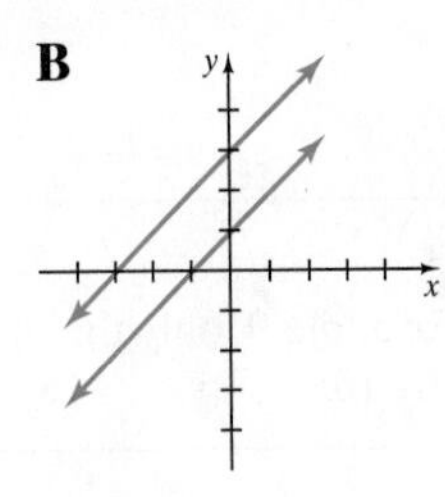

C

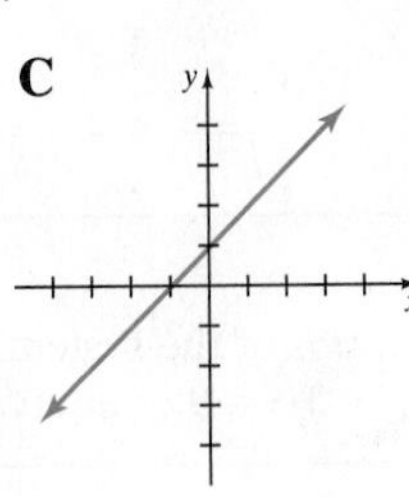

D

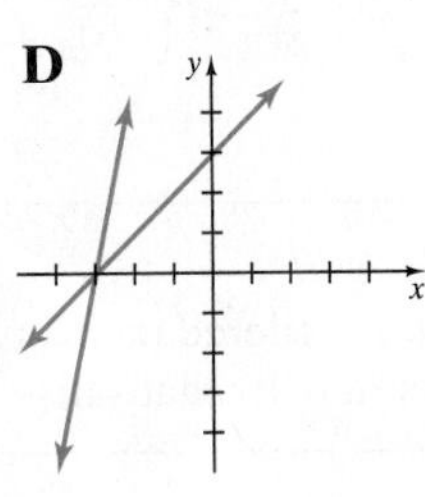

1. no solution **2.** Infinite number of solutions **3.** $(1, -2)$ **4.** $(-3, 0)$

17.1 EXERCISE SET

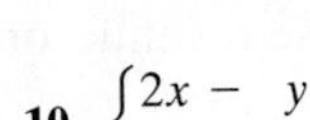

Determine whether each given ordered pair is a solution of each system. See Example 1.

1. $\begin{cases} x - y = 3 \\ 2x - 4y = 8 \end{cases}$ $(2, -1)$

2. $\begin{cases} x - y = -4 \\ 2x + 10y = 4 \end{cases}$ $(-3, 1)$

3. $\begin{cases} 2x - 3y = -9 \\ 4x + 2y = -2 \end{cases}$ $(3, 5)$

4. $\begin{cases} 2x - 5y = -2 \\ 3x + 4y = 4 \end{cases}$ $(4, 2)$

5. $\begin{cases} 3x + 7y = -19 \\ -6x = 5y + 8 \end{cases}$ $\left(\frac{2}{3}, -3\right)$

6. $\begin{cases} 4x + 5y = -7 \\ -8x = 3y - 1 \end{cases}$ $\left(\frac{3}{4}, -2\right)$

A system of equations and the graph of each equation of the system is given below. Find the solution of the system and verify that it is the solution. See Example 1.

7. $\begin{cases} 2x + 5y = 8 \\ 6x + y = 10 \end{cases}$

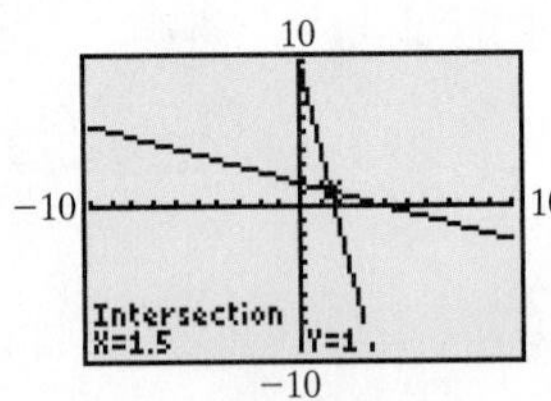

8. $\begin{cases} x + y = 1 \\ x - 2y = 4 \end{cases}$

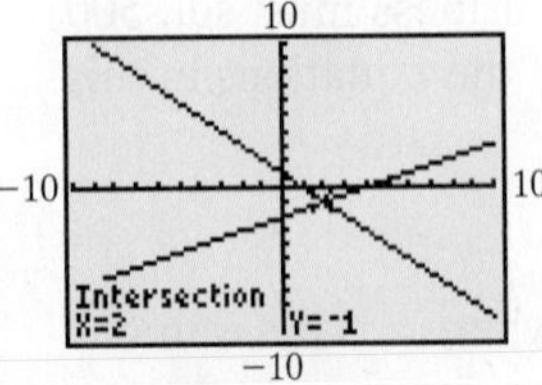

9. $\begin{cases} x - 4y = -5 \\ -3x - 8y = 0 \end{cases}$

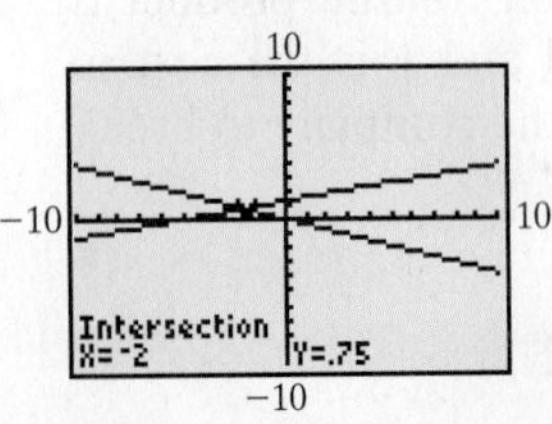

10. $\begin{cases} 2x - y = 8 \\ x - 3y = 11 \end{cases}$

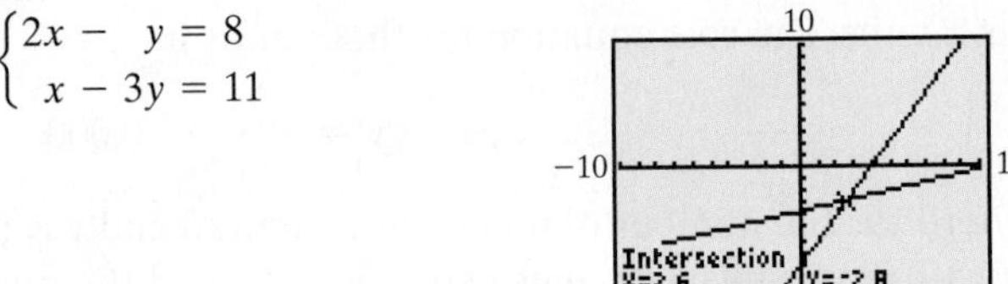

Solve each system by graphing. See Examples 2 and 3.

11. $\begin{cases} x + y = 1 \\ x - 2y = 4 \end{cases}$

12. $\begin{cases} 2x - y = 8 \\ x + 3y = 11 \end{cases}$

13. $\begin{cases} 2y - 4x = 0 \\ x + 2y = 5 \end{cases}$

14. $\begin{cases} 4x - y = 6 \\ x - y = 0 \end{cases}$

15. $\begin{cases} 3x - y = 4 \\ 6x - 2y = 4 \end{cases}$

16. $\begin{cases} -x + 3y = 6 \\ 3x - 9y = 9 \end{cases}$

17. Can a system consisting of two linear equations have exactly two solutions? Explain why or why not.

18. Suppose the graph of the equations in a system of two equations in two variables consists of a circle and a line. Discuss the possible number of solutions for this system.

Solve each system of equations by the substitution method. See Examples 4 and 5.

19. $\begin{cases} x + y = 10 \\ y = 4x \end{cases}$

20. $\begin{cases} 5x + 2y = -17 \\ x = 3y \end{cases}$

21. $\begin{cases} 4x - y = 9 \\ 2x + 3y = -27 \end{cases}$

22. $\begin{cases} 3x - y = 6 \\ -4x + 2y = -8 \end{cases}$

23. $\begin{cases} \frac{1}{2}x + \frac{3}{4}y = -\frac{1}{4} \\ \frac{3}{4}x - \frac{1}{4}y = 1 \end{cases}$

24. $\begin{cases} \frac{2}{5}x + \frac{1}{5}y = -1 \\ x + \frac{2}{5}y = -\frac{8}{5} \end{cases}$

25. $\begin{cases} \dfrac{x}{3} + y = \dfrac{4}{3} \\ -x + 2y = 11 \end{cases}$

26. $\begin{cases} \dfrac{x}{8} - \dfrac{y}{2} = 1 \\ \dfrac{x}{3} - y = 2 \end{cases}$

Solve each system of equations by the elimination method. See Examples 6 through 9.

27. $\begin{cases} -x + 2y = 0 \\ x + 2y = 5 \end{cases}$

28. $\begin{cases} -2x + 3y = 0 \\ 2x + 6y = 3 \end{cases}$

29. $\begin{cases} 5x + 2y = 1 \\ x - 3y = 7 \end{cases}$

30. $\begin{cases} 6x - y = -5 \\ 4x - 2y = 6 \end{cases}$

31. $\begin{cases} \dfrac{3}{4}x + \dfrac{5}{2}y = 11 \\ \dfrac{1}{16}x - \dfrac{3}{4}y = -1 \end{cases}$

32. $\begin{cases} \dfrac{2}{3}x + \dfrac{1}{4}y = -\dfrac{3}{2} \\ \dfrac{1}{2}x - \dfrac{1}{4}y = -2 \end{cases}$

33. $\begin{cases} 3x - 5y = 11 \\ 2x - 6y = 2 \end{cases}$

34. $\begin{cases} 6x - 3y = -3 \\ 4x + 5y = -9 \end{cases}$

35. $\begin{cases} x - 2y = 4 \\ 2x - 4y = 4 \end{cases}$

36. $\begin{cases} -x + 3y = 6 \\ 3x - 9y = 9 \end{cases}$

37. $\begin{cases} 3x + y = 1 \\ 2y = 2 - 6x \end{cases}$

38. $\begin{cases} y = 2x - 5 \\ 8x - 4y = 20 \end{cases}$

MIXED PRACTICE

Solve each system of equations.

39. $\begin{cases} 2x + 5y = 8 \\ 6x + y = 10 \end{cases}$

40. $\begin{cases} x - 4y = -5 \\ -3x - 8y = 0 \end{cases}$

41. $\begin{cases} x + y = 1 \\ x - 2y = 4 \end{cases}$

42. $\begin{cases} 2x - y = 8 \\ x + 3y = 11 \end{cases}$

43. $\begin{cases} \dfrac{1}{3}x + y = \dfrac{4}{3} \\ -\dfrac{1}{4}x - \dfrac{1}{2}y = -\dfrac{1}{4} \end{cases}$

44. $\begin{cases} \dfrac{3}{4}x - \dfrac{1}{2}y = -\dfrac{1}{2} \\ x + y = -\dfrac{3}{2} \end{cases}$

45. $\begin{cases} 2x + 6y = 8 \\ 3x + 9y = 12 \end{cases}$

46. $\begin{cases} x = 3y - 1 \\ 2x - 6y = -2 \end{cases}$

47. $\begin{cases} 4x + 2y = 5 \\ 2x + y = -1 \end{cases}$

48. $\begin{cases} 3x + 6y = 15 \\ 2x + 4y = 3 \end{cases}$

49. $\begin{cases} 10y - 2x = 1 \\ 5y = 4 - 6x \end{cases}$

50. $\begin{cases} 3x + 4y = 0 \\ 7x = 3y \end{cases}$

51. $\begin{cases} 5x - 2y = 27 \\ -3x + 5y = 18 \end{cases}$

52. $\begin{cases} 3x + 4y = 2 \\ 2x + 5y = -1 \end{cases}$

53. $\begin{cases} x = 3y + 2 \\ 5x - 15y = 10 \end{cases}$

54. $\begin{cases} y = \dfrac{1}{7}x + 3 \\ x - 7y = -21 \end{cases}$

55. $\begin{cases} 2x - y = -1 \\ y = -2x \end{cases}$

56. $\begin{cases} x = \dfrac{1}{5}y \\ x - y = -4 \end{cases}$

57. $\begin{cases} 2x = 6 \\ y = 5 - x \end{cases}$

58. $\begin{cases} x = 3y + 4 \\ -y = 5 \end{cases}$

59. $\begin{cases} \dfrac{x + 5}{2} = \dfrac{6 - 4y}{3} \\ \dfrac{3x}{5} = \dfrac{21 - 7y}{10} \end{cases}$

60. $\begin{cases} \dfrac{y}{5} = \dfrac{8 - x}{2} \\ x = \dfrac{2y - 8}{3} \end{cases}$

61. $\begin{cases} 4x - 7y = 7 \\ 12x - 21y = 24 \end{cases}$

62. $\begin{cases} 2x - 5y = 12 \\ -4x + 10y = 20 \end{cases}$

63. $\begin{cases} \dfrac{2}{3}x - \dfrac{3}{4}y = -1 \\ -\dfrac{1}{6}x + \dfrac{3}{8}y = 1 \end{cases}$

64. $\begin{cases} \dfrac{1}{2}x - \dfrac{1}{3}y = -3 \\ \dfrac{1}{8}x + \dfrac{1}{6}y = 0 \end{cases}$

65. $\begin{cases} 0.7x - 0.2y = -1.6 \\ 0.2x - y = -1.4 \end{cases}$

66. $\begin{cases} -0.7x + 0.6y = 1.3 \\ 0.5x - 0.3y = -0.8 \end{cases}$

67. $\begin{cases} 4x - 1.5y = 10.2 \\ 2x + 7.8y = -25.68 \end{cases}$

68. $\begin{cases} x - 3y = -5.3 \\ 6.3x + 6y = 3.96 \end{cases}$

REVIEW AND PREVIEW

Determine whether the given replacement values make each equation true or false.

69. $3x - 4y + 2z = 5; x = 1, y = 2$, and $z = 5$

70. $x + 2y - z = 7; x = 2, y = -3$, and $z = 3$

71. $-x - 5y + 3z = 15; x = 0, y = -1$, and $z = 5$

72. $-4x + y - 8z = 4; x = 1, y = 0$, and $z = -1$

Add the equations. See Section 17.1.

73. $3x + 2y - 5z = 10$
$-3x + 4y + z = 15$

74. $x + 4y - 5z = 20$
$2x - 4y - 2z = -17$

75. $10x + 5y + 6z = 14$
$-9x + 5y - 6z = -12$

76. $-9x - 8y - z = 31$
$9x + 4y - z = 12$

CONCEPT EXTENSIONS

The concept of supply and demand is used often in business. In general, as the unit price of a commodity increases, the demand for that commodity decreases. Also, as a commodity's unit price increases, the manufacturer normally increases the supply. The point where supply is equal to demand is called the equilibrium point. The following shows the graph of a demand equation and the graph of a supply equation for previously rented DVDs. The x-axis represents the number of DVDs in thousands, and the y-axis represents the cost of a DVD. Use this graph to answer Exercises 77 through 80. See Example 10.

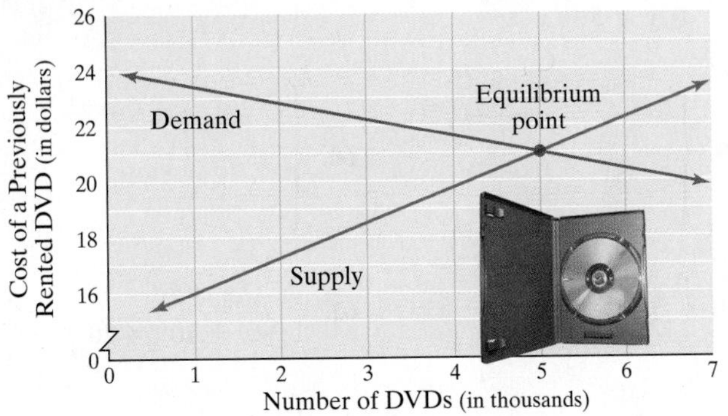

77. Find the number of DVDs and the price per DVD when supply equals demand.

78. When x is between 3 and 4, is supply greater than demand or is demand greater than supply?

79. When x is greater than 7, is supply greater than demand or is demand greater than supply?

80. For what x-values are the y-values corresponding to the supply equation greater than the y-values corresponding to the demand equation?

The revenue equation for a certain brand of toothpaste is $y = 2.5x$, where x is the number of tubes of toothpaste sold and y is the total income for selling x tubes. The cost equation is $y = 0.9x + 3000$, where x is the number of tubes of toothpaste manufactured and y is the cost of producing x tubes. The following set of axes shows the graph of the cost and revenue equations. Use this graph for Exercises 81 through 86. See Example 10.

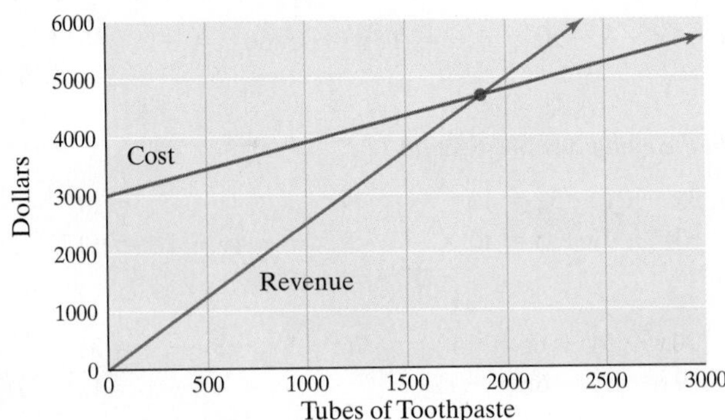

81. Find the coordinates of the point of intersection, or break-even point, by solving the system

$$\begin{cases} y = 2.5x \\ y = 0.9x + 3000 \end{cases}$$

82. Explain the meaning of the ordered pair point of intersection.

83. If the company sells 2000 tubes of toothpaste, does the company make money or lose money?

84. If the company sells 1000 tubes of toothpaste, does the company make money or lose money?

85. For what x-values will the company make a profit? (*Hint:* For what x-values is the revenue graph "higher" than the cost graph?)

86. For what x-values will the company lose money? (*Hint:* For what x-values is the revenue graph "lower" than the cost graph?)

87. Write a system of two linear equations in x and y that has the ordered pair solution $(2, 5)$.

88. Which method would you use to solve the system?

$$\begin{cases} 5x - 2y = 6 \\ 2x + 3y = 5 \end{cases}$$

Explain your choice.

89. The amount y of red meat consumed per person in the United States (in pounds) in the year x can be modeled by the linear equation $y = -0.3x + 113$. The amount y of all poultry consumed per person in the United States (in pounds) in the year x can be modeled by the linear equation $y = x + 68$. In both models, $x = 0$ represents the year 2000. (*Source:* Based on data and forecasts from the Economic Research Service, U.S. Department of Agriculture)

a. What does the slope of each equation tell you about the patterns of red meat and poultry consumption in the United States?

b. Solve this system of equations. (Round your final results to the nearest whole numbers.)

c. Explain the meaning of your answer to part **b.**

90. The number of books (in thousands) in the University of Texas libraries y for the years 2002 through 2005 can be modeled by the linear equation $y = 230x + 8146$. For the same time period, the number of books (in thousands) in the Columbia University libraries can be modeled by $y = 611x + 7378$, where x is the number of years since 2002. (*Source:* Association of Research Libraries)

a. What does the slope of each equation tell you about the pattern of books in these two university libraries?

b. Solve this system of equations. (Round your results to the nearest whole number.)

c. Explain the meaning of your answer to part **b.**

STUDY SKILLS BUILDER

Are You Familiar with Your Textbook Supplements?

There are many student supplements available for additional study. Below, I have listed some of these. See the preface of this text or your instructor for further information.

- *Chapter Test Prep Video CD*. This material is found in your textbook and is fully explained. The CD contains video clip solutions to the Chapter Test exercises in this text and are excellent help when studying for chapter tests.
- *Lecture Video CDs*. These video segments are keyed to each section of the text. The material is presented by me, Elayn Martin-Gay, and I have placed a video icon by each exercise in the text that I have worked on the video.
- *The Student Solutions Manual*. This contains worked-out solutions to odd-numbered exercises as well as every exercise in the Integrated Reviews, Chapter Reviews, Chapter Tests, and Cumulative Reviews.
- *Prentice Hall Tutor Center*. Mathematics questions may be phoned, faxed, or e-mailed to this center.
- *MyMathLab, MathXL, and Interact Math*. These are computer and Internet tutorials. This supplement may already be available to you somewhere on campus, for example at your local learning resource lab. Take a moment and find the name and location of any such lab on campus.

As usual, your instructor is your best source of information.

Let's see how you are doing with textbook supplements:

1. Name one way the Chapter Test Prep Video can help you prepare for a chapter test.
2. List any textbook supplements that you have found useful.
3. Have you located and visited a learning resource lab located on your campus?
4. List the textbook supplements that are currently housed in your campus' learning resource lab.

17.2 SYSTEMS OF LINEAR EQUATIONS AND PROBLEM SOLVING

OBJECTIVES

1 Solve problems that can be modeled by a system of two linear equations.

2 Solve problems with cost and revenue functions.

3 Solve problems that can be modeled by a system of three linear equations.

OBJECTIVE 1 ▶ Solving problems modeled by systems of two equations. Thus far, we have solved problems by writing one-variable equations and solving for the variable. Some of these problems can be solved, perhaps more easily, by writing a system of equations, as illustrated in this section.

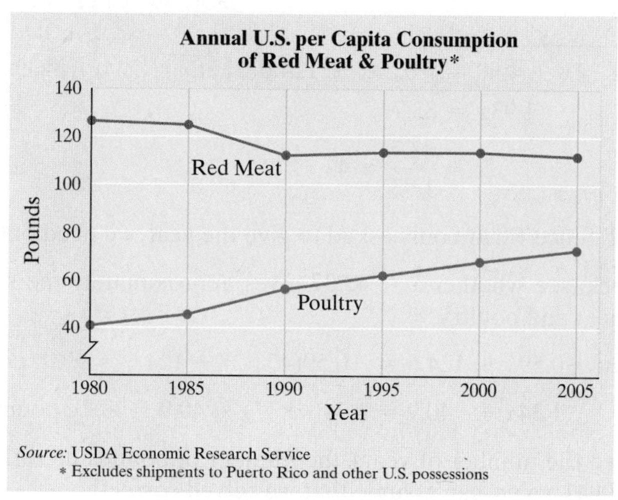

EXAMPLE 1 **Predicting Equal Consumption of Red Meat and Poultry**

America's consumption of red meat has decreased most years since 1980 while consumption of poultry has increased. The function $y = -0.59x + 124.6$ approximates the annual pounds of red meat consumed per capita, where x is the number of years since 1980. The function $y = 1.34x + 40.9$ approximates the annual pounds of poultry consumed per capita, where x is also the number of years since 1980. If this trend continues, determine the year in which the annual consumption of red meat and poultry is equal. (*Source:* Based on data from Economic Research Service, U.S. Dept. of Agriculture)

Solution

1. UNDERSTAND. Read and reread the problem and guess a year. Let's guess the year 2020. This year is 40 years since 1980, so $x = 40$. Now let $x = 40$ in each given function.

$$\text{Red meat:}\quad y = -0.59x + 124.6 = -0.59(40) + 124.6 = 101 \text{ pounds}$$
$$\text{Poultry:}\quad y = 1.34x + 40.9 = 1.34(40) + 40.9 = 94.5 \text{ pounds}$$

Since the projected pounds in 2020 for red meat and poultry are not the same, we guessed incorrectly, but we do have a better understanding of the problem. We also know that the year will be later than 2020 since projected consumption of red meat is still greater than poultry that year.

2. TRANSLATE. We are already given the system of equations.

3. SOLVE. We want to know the year x in which pounds y are the same, so we solve the system:

$$\begin{cases} y = -0.59x + 124.6 \\ y = 1.34x + 40.9 \end{cases}$$

$y_1 = -0.59x + 124.6$
$y_2 = 1.34x + 40.9$
200
Intersection
X=43.367876 Y=99.012953
0
0
100

A calculator check for Example 1.

We solve by paper and pencil below, and a calculator check is shown in the margin. Since both equations are solved for y, one way to solve is to use the substitution method.

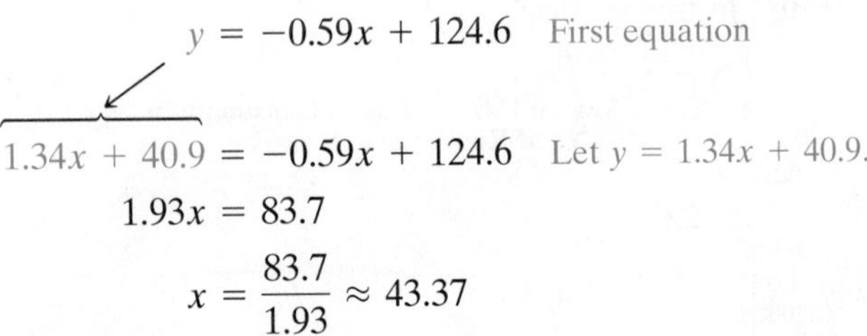

$$y = -0.59x + 124.6 \quad \text{First equation}$$
$$1.34x + 40.9 = -0.59x + 124.6 \quad \text{Let } y = 1.34x + 40.9.$$
$$1.93x = 83.7$$
$$x = \frac{83.7}{1.93} \approx 43.37$$

4. INTERPRET. Since we are only asked to give the year, we need only solve for x.

Check: To check, see whether $x \approx 43.37$ gives approximately the same number of pounds of red meat and poultry.

$$\text{Red meat:}\quad -0.59x + 124.6 = -0.59(43.37) + 124.6 = 99.01 \text{ pounds}$$
$$\text{Poultry:}\quad 1.34x + 40.9 = 1.34(43.37) + 40.9 = 99.02 \text{ pounds}$$

Since we rounded the number of years, the number of pounds do differ slightly. They differ only by 0.0041, so we can assume that we solved correctly.

State: The consumption of red meat and poultry will be the same about 43.37 years after 1980, or 2023.37. Thus, in the year 2023, we predict the consumption will be the same, about 99.01 pounds. □

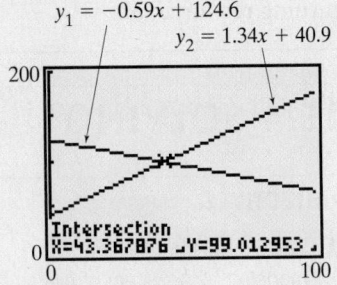

PRACTICE 1 Read Example 1. If we use the years 1995, 2000, and 2005 only to write functions approximating the consumption of red meat and poultry, we have the following:

$$\text{Red meat:}\quad y = -0.16x + 113.9$$
$$\text{Poultry:}\quad y = 1.06x + 62.3$$

where x is the years since 1995 and y is pounds per year consumed.

a. Assuming this trend continues, predict the year in which the consumption of red meat and poultry will be the same.

b. Does your answer differ from the example? Why or why not?

Note: A similar exercise is found in Section 17.1, Exercise 89. In the example above, the data years used to generate the equations are 1980–2005. In Section 17.1, the data years used are 2000–2005. Note all the differing equations and answers.

EXAMPLE 2 Finding Unknown Numbers

A first number is 4 less than a second number. Four times the first number is 6 more than twice the second. Find the numbers.

Solution

1. UNDERSTAND. Read and reread the problem and guess a solution. If a first number is 10 and this is 4 less than a second number, the second number is 14. Four times the first number is 4(10), or 40. This is not equal to 6 more than twice the second number, which is $2(14) + 6$ or 34. Although we guessed incorrectly, we now have a better understanding of the problem.

Since we are looking for two numbers, we will let

$$x = \text{first number}$$
$$y = \text{second number}$$

2. TRANSLATE. Since we have assigned two variables to this problem, we will translate the given facts into two equations. For the first statement we have

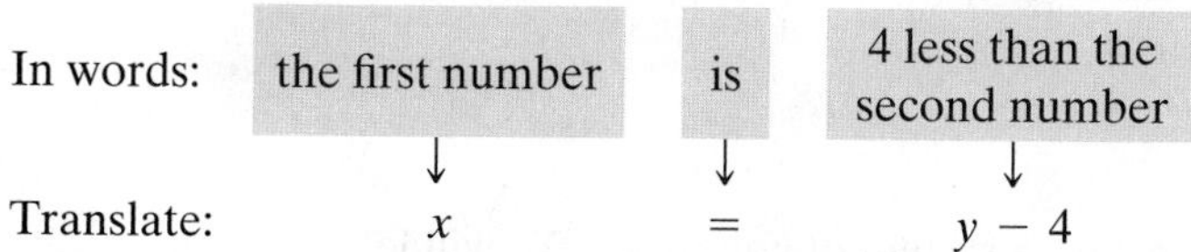

Next we translate the second statement into an equation.

In words:	four times the first number	is	6 more than twice the second number
	↓	↓	↓
Translate:	$4x$	$=$	$2y + 6$

3. SOLVE. Here we solve the system

$$\begin{cases} x = y - 4 \\ 4x = 2y + 6 \end{cases}$$

Since the first equation expresses x in terms of y, we will use substitution. We substitute $y - 4$ for x in the second equation and solve for y.

$$4x = 2y + 6 \quad \text{Second equation}$$

$$\begin{aligned} 4(y - 4) &= 2y + 6 \\ 4y - 16 &= 2y + 6 \quad \text{Let } x = y - 4. \\ 2y &= 22 \\ y &= 11 \end{aligned}$$

Now we replace y with 11 in the equation $x = y - 4$ and solve for x. Then $x = y - 4$ becomes $x = 11 - 4 = 7$. The ordered pair solution of the system is $(7, 11)$.

4. INTERPRET. Since the solution of the system is (7, 11), then the first number we are looking for is 7 and the second number is 11.

Check: Notice that 7 *is* 4 less than 11, and 4 times 7 *is* 6 more than twice 11. The proposed numbers, 7 and 11, are correct.

State: The numbers are 7 and 11. □

PRACTICE 2 A first number is 5 more than a second number. Twice the first number is 2 less than 3 times the second number. Find the numbers.

EXAMPLE 3 Finding the Rate of Speed

Two cars leave Indianapolis, one traveling east and the other west. After 3 hours they are 297 miles apart. If one car is traveling 5 mph faster than the other, what is the speed of each?

Solution

1. UNDERSTAND. Read and reread the problem. Let's guess a solution and use the formula $d = rt$ (distance = rate · time) to check. Suppose that one car is traveling at a rate of 55 miles per hour. This means that the other car is traveling at a rate of 50 miles per hour since we are told that one car is traveling 5 mph faster than the other. To find the distance apart after 3 hours, we will first find the distance traveled by each car. One car's distance is rate · time = 55(3) = 165 miles. The other car's distance is rate · time = 50(3) = 150 miles. Since one car is traveling east and the other west, their distance apart is the sum of their distances, or 165 miles + 150 miles = 315 miles. Although this distance apart is not the required distance of 297 miles, we now have a better understanding of the problem.

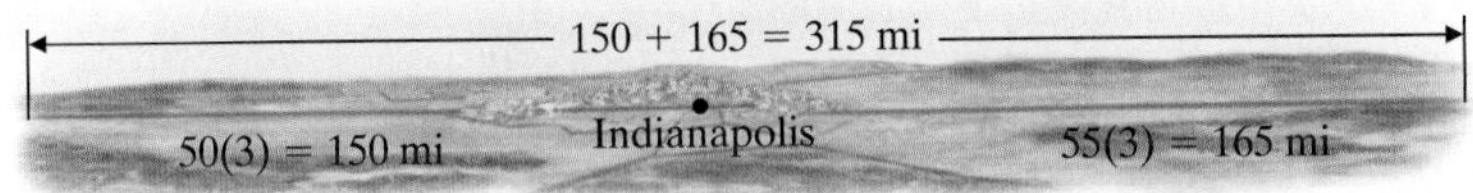

Let's model the problem with a system of equations. We will let

x = speed of one car

y = speed of the other car

We summarize the information on the following chart. Both cars have traveled 3 hours. Since distance = rate · time, their distances are $3x$ and $3y$ miles, respectively.

	Rate	•	*Time*	=	*Distance*
One Car	x		3		$3x$
Other Car	y		3		$3y$

2. TRANSLATE. We can now translate the stated conditions into two equations.

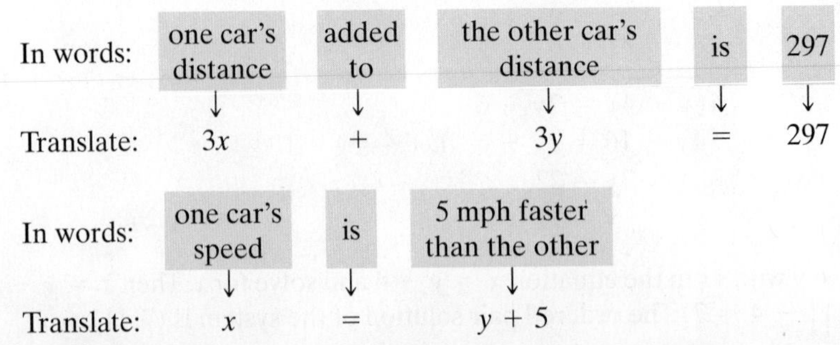

In words:	one car's distance	added to	the other car's distance	is	297
	↓	↓	↓	↓	↓
Translate:	$3x$	+	$3y$	=	297

In words:	one car's speed	is	5 mph faster than the other
	↓	↓	↓
Translate:	x	=	$y + 5$

3. SOLVE. Here we solve the system

$$\begin{cases} 3x + 3y = 297 \\ x = y + 5 \end{cases}$$

Again, the substitution method is appropriate. We replace x with $y + 5$ in the first equation and solve for y.

$$3x + 3y = 297 \quad \text{First equation}$$

$$3(y + 5) + 3y = 297 \quad \text{Let } x = y + 5.$$

$$3y + 15 + 3y = 297$$

$$6y = 282$$

$$y = 47$$

To find x, we replace y with 47 in the equation $x = y + 5$. Then $x = 47 + 5 = 52$. The ordered pair solution of the system is (52, 47). A graphical solution is shown in the margin.

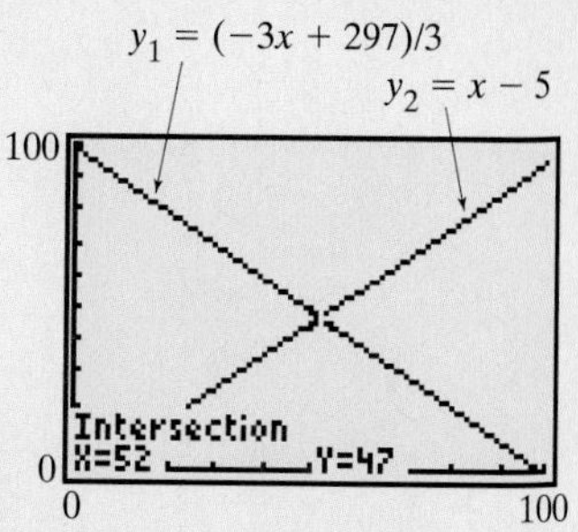

A graphical solution. We choose the window [0, 100, 10] for the x and y windows, which indicates that the speed is between 0 and 100 mph.

4. INTERPRET. The solution (52, 47) means that the cars are traveling at 52 mph and 47 mph, respectively.

Check: Notice that one car is traveling 5 mph faster than the other. Also, if one car travels 52 mph for 3 hours, the distance is $3(52) = 156$ miles. The other car traveling for 3 hours at 47 mph travels a distance of $3(47) = 141$ miles. The sum of the distances $156 + 141$ is 297 miles, the required distance.

State: The cars are traveling at 52 mph and 47 mph. □

Helpful Hint

Don't forget to attach units, if appropriate.

PRACTICE

3 In 2007, the French train TGV V150 became the fastest conventional rail train in the world. It broke the 1990 record of the next fastest conventional rail train, the French TGV Atlantique. Assume the V150 and the Atlantique left the same station in Paris, with one heading west and one heading east. After 2 hours, they were 2150 kilometers apart. If the V150 is 75 kph faster than the Atlantique, what is the speed of each?

EXAMPLE 4 Mixing Solutions

Lynn Pike, a pharmacist, needs 70 liters of a 50% alcohol solution. She has available a 30% alcohol solution and an 80% alcohol solution. How many liters of each solution should she mix to obtain 70 liters of a 50% alcohol solution?

Solution

1. UNDERSTAND. Read and reread the problem. Next, guess the solution. Suppose that we need 20 liters of the 30% solution. Then we need $70 - 20 = 50$ liters of the 80% solution. To see if this gives us 70 liters of a 50% alcohol solution, let's find the amount of pure alcohol in each solution.

number of liters	×	alcohol strength	=	amount of pure alcohol
↓		↓		↓
20 liters	×	0.30	=	6 liters
50 liters	×	0.80	=	40 liters
70 liters	×	0.50	=	35 liters

Since 6 liters + 40 liters = 46 liters and not 35 liters, our guess is incorrect, but we have gained some insight as to how to model and check this problem.

We will let

$$x = \text{amount of 30\% solution, in liters}$$
$$y = \text{amount of 80\% solution, in liters}$$

and use a table to organize the given data.

	Number of Liters	*Alcohol Strength*	*Amount of Pure Alcohol*
30% Solution	x	30%	$0.30x$
80% Solution	y	80%	$0.80y$
50% Solution Needed	70	50%	$(0.50)(70)$

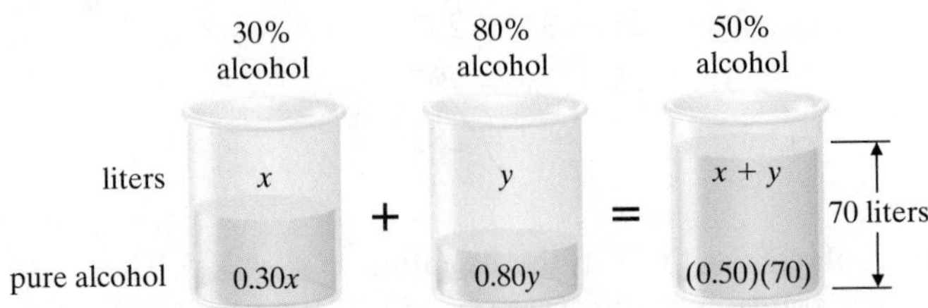

2. TRANSLATE. We translate the stated conditions into two equations.

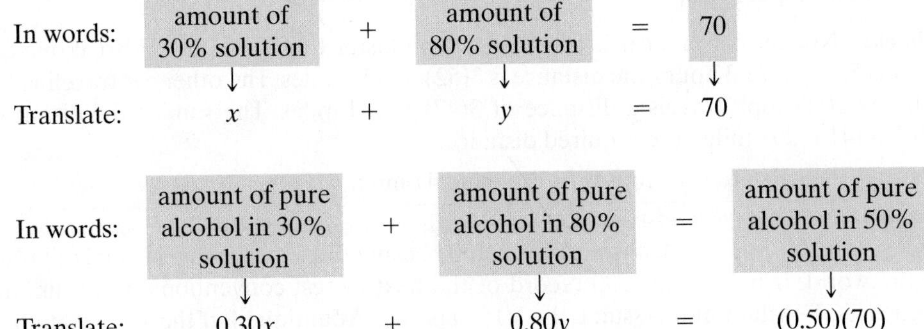

In words: amount of 30% solution + amount of 80% solution = 70
Translate: x + y = 70
In words: amount of pure alcohol in 30% solution + amount of pure alcohol in 80% solution = amount of pure alcohol in 50% solution
Translate: 0.30x + 0.80y = (0.50)(70)

3. SOLVE. Here we solve the system

$$\begin{cases} x + y = 70 \\ 0.30x + 0.80y = (0.50)(70) \end{cases}$$

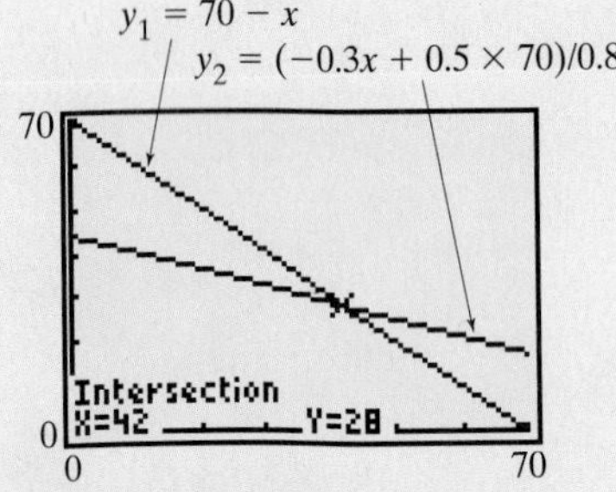

A graphical solution. The x and y windows are both [0, 70, 10] since the total amount is 70 liters.

To solve this system, we use the elimination method. We multiply both sides of the first equation by -3 and both sides of the second equation by 10. Then

$$\begin{cases} -3(x + y) = -3(70) \\ 10(0.30x + 0.80y) = 10(0.50)(70) \end{cases} \quad \text{simplifies to} \quad \begin{cases} -3x - 3y = -210 \\ 3x + 8y = 350 \end{cases}$$

$$5y = 140$$

$$y = 28$$

Now we replace y with 28 in the equation $x + y = 70$ and find that $x + 28 = 70$, or $x = 42$.

The ordered pair solution of the system is (42, 28).

4. INTERPRET.

Check: Check the solution in the same way that we checked our guess.

State: The pharmacist needs to mix 42 liters of 30% solution and 28 liters of 80% solution to obtain 70 liters of 50% solution. □

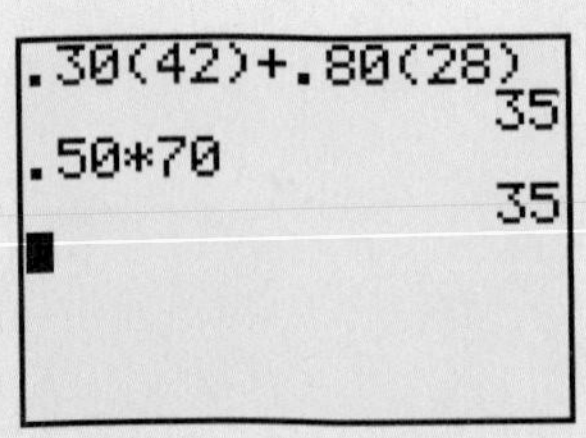

A calculator check for Example 4. (We already see by inspection that $42 + 28 = 70$, as needed.)

PRACTICE 4 Keith Robinson is a chemistry teacher who needs 1 liter of a solution of 5% hydrochloric acid to carry out an experiment. If he only has a stock solution of 99% hydrochloric acid, how much water (0% acid) and how much stock solution (99%) of HCL must he mix to get 1 liter of 5% solution? Round answers to the nearest hundredth of a liter.

Concept Check ✓

Suppose you mix an amount of 25% acid solution with an amount of 60% acid solution. You then calculate the acid strength of the resulting acid mixture. For which of the following results should you suspect an error in your calculation? Why?

a. 14% **b.** 32% **c.** 55%

OBJECTIVE 2 ▶ Solving problems with cost and revenue functions. Recall that businesses are often computing cost and revenue functions or equations to predict sales, to determine whether prices need to be adjusted, and to see whether the company is making or losing money. Recall also that the value at which revenue equals cost is called the break-even point. When revenue is less than cost, the company is losing money; when revenue is greater than cost, the company is making money.

EXAMPLE 5 **Finding a Break-Even Point**

A manufacturing company recently purchased $3000 worth of new equipment to offer new personalized stationery to its customers. The cost of producing a package of personalized stationery is $3.00, and it is sold for $5.50. Find the number of packages that must be sold for the company to break even.

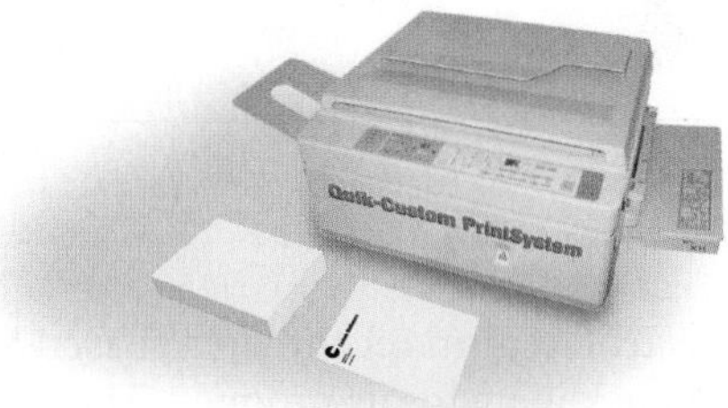

Solution

1. UNDERSTAND. Read and reread the problem. Notice that the cost to the company will include a one-time cost of $3000 for the equipment and then $3.00 per package produced. The revenue will be $5.50 per package sold.

To model this problem, we will let

x = number of packages of personalized stationery
$C(x)$ = total cost for producing x packages of stationery
$R(x)$ = total revenue for selling x packages of stationery

2. TRANSLATE. The revenue equation is

In words:	revenue for selling x packages of stationery	=	price per package	·	number of packages
	↓		↓		↓
Translate:	$R(x)$	=	5.5	·	x

The cost equation is

In words:	cost for producing x packages of stationery	=	cost per package	·	number of packages	+	cost for equipment
	↓		↓		↓	↓	
Translate:	$C(x)$	=	3	·	x	+	3000

Since the break-even point is when $R(x) = C(x)$, we solve the equation

$$5.5x = 3x + 3000$$

Answer to Concept Check:
a; answers may vary

3. SOLVE.

$$5.5x = 3x + 3000$$
$$2.5x = 3000 \quad \text{Subtract } 3x \text{ from both sides.}$$
$$x = 1200 \quad \text{Divide both sides by 2.5.}$$

4. INTERPRET.

Check: To see whether the break-even point occurs when 1200 packages are produced and sold, see if revenue equals cost when $x = 1200$. When $x = 1200$, $R(x) = 5.5x = 5.5(1200) = 6600$ and $C(x) = 3x + 3000 = 3(1200) + 3000 = 6600$. Since $R(1200) = C(1200) = 6600$, the break-even point is 1200.

State: The company must sell 1200 packages of stationery to break even. The graph of this system is shown.

$y_2 = 3x + 3000$

$y_1 = 5.5x$

Intersection X=1200 Y=6600

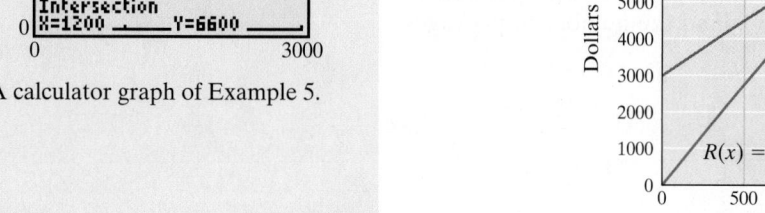

A calculator graph of Example 5.

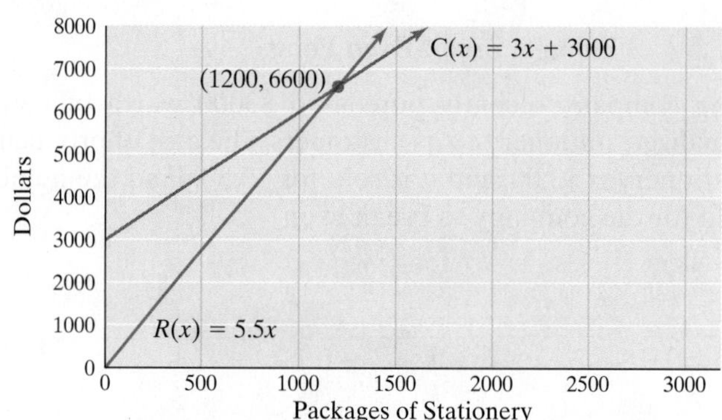

PRACTICE 5 An online-only electronics firm recently purchased \$3000 worth of new equipment to create shock-proof packaging for its products. The cost of producing one shock-proof package is \$2.50, and the firm charges the customer \$4.50 for the packaging. Find the number of packages that must be sold for the company to break even.

OBJECTIVE 3 ▶ Solving problems modeled by systems of three equations. To introduce problem solving by writing a system of three linear equations in three variables, we solve a problem about triangles.

17.2 EXERCISE SET

PRACTICE

WATCH

DOWNLOAD

READ

REVIEW

MIXED PRACTICE

Solve. See Examples 1 through 4.

1. One number is two more than a second number. Twice the first is 4 less than 3 times the second. Find the numbers.

2. Three times one number minus a second is 8, and the sum of the numbers is 12. Find the numbers.

3. The United States has the world's only "large deck" aircraft carriers which can hold up to 72 aircraft. The Enterprise class carrier is longest in length while the Nimitz class carrier is the second longest. The total length of these two carriers is 2193 feet while the difference of their lengths is only 9 feet. (*Source: U.S.A. Today*)

a. Find the length of each class carrier.

b. If a football field has a length of 100 yards, determine the length of the Enterprise class carrier in terms of number of football fields.

4. The rate of growth of participation (age 7 and older) in sports featured in the X-Games has slowed in recent years, but still surpasses that for some older sports such as football. The most popular X-Game sport is inline roller skating, followed by skateboarding. In 2005, the total number of participants in both sports was 25.1 million. If the number of participants in skateboarding was 14.2 million less than twice the number of participants in inline skating, find the number of participants in each sport. (*Source:* National Sporting Goods Association)

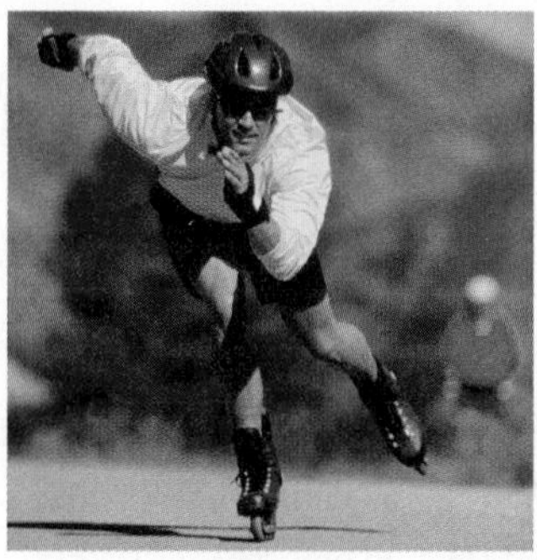

5. A B747 aircraft flew 6 hours with the wind. The return trip took 7 hours against the wind. If the speed of the plane in still air is 13 times the speed of the wind, find the wind speed and the speed of the plane in still air.

6. During a multi-day camping trip, Terry Watkins rowed 17 hours downstream. It took 26.5 hours rowing upstream to travel the same distance. If the speed of the current is 6.8 kilometers per hour less than his rowing speed in still water, find his rowing speed and the speed of the current.

7. Find how many quarts of 4% butterfat milk and 1% butterfat milk should be mixed to yield 60 quarts of 2% butterfat milk.

8. A pharmacist needs 500 milliliters of a 20% phenobarbital solution but has only 5% and 25% phenobarbital solutions available. Find how many milliliters of each he should mix to get the desired solution.

9. In 2005, the United Kingdom was the most popular host country in which U.S. students traveling abroad studied. Italy was the second most popular destination. A total of 56,929 students visited one of the two countries. If 7213 more U.S. students studied in the United Kingdom than in Italy, find how many students studied abroad in each country. (*Source:* Institute of International Education, *Open Doors 2006*)

10. Harvard University and Cornell University are each known for their excellent libraries, and each is participating with Google to put their collections into Google's searchable database. In 2005, Harvard libraries contained 266,791 more printed volumes than twice the number of printed volumes in the libraries of Cornell. Together, these two great libraries house 23,199,904 printed volumes. Find the number of printed volumes in each library. (*Source:* Association of Research Libraries)

11. Karen Karlin bought some large frames for \$15 each and some small frames for \$8 each at a closeout sale. If she bought 22 frames for \$239, find how many of each type she bought.

12. Hilton University Drama Club sold 311 tickets for a play. Student tickets cost 50 cents each; nonstudent tickets cost \$1.50. If total receipts were \$385.50, find how many tickets of each type were sold.

13. One number is two less than a second number. Twice the first is 4 more than 3 times the second. Find the numbers.

14. Twice a first number plus a second number is 42, and the first number minus the second number is -6. Find the numbers.

15. In the United States, the percent of women using the Internet is increasing faster than the percent of men. The function $y = 5.3x + 39.5$ can be used to estimate the percent of females using the Internet, while the function $y = 4.5x + 45.5$ can be used to estimate the percent of males. For both functions, x is the number of years since 2000. Use these functions to give the year in which the percent of females using the Internet equals the percent of males. (*Source:* Pew Internet & American Life Project)

16. The percent of car vehicle sales has been decreasing over a ten-year period while the percent of light truck (pickups, sport-utility vans, and minivans) vehicles has been increasing. For the years 2000–2006, the function $y = -x + 54.2$ can be used to estimate the percent of new car vehicle sales in the United States, while the function $y = x + 45.8$ can be used to estimate the percent of light truck vehicle sales. For both functions, x is the number of years since 2000. (*Source: USA Today,* Environmental Protection Agency, "Light-Duty Automotive Technology and Fuel Economy Trends: 1975–2006")

a. Calculate the year in which the percent of new car sales equaled the percent of light truck sales.

b. Before the actual 2001 vehicle sales data was published, *USA Today* predicted that light truck sales would likely be greater than car sales in the year 2001. Does your finding in part **a** agree with this statement?

17. An office supply store in San Diego sells 7 writing tablets and 4 pens for \$6.40. Also, 2 tablets and 19 pens cost \$5.40. Find the price of each.

18. A Candy Barrel shop manager mixes M&M's worth \$2.00 per pound with trail mix worth \$1.50 per pound. Find how many pounds of each she should use to get 50 pounds of a party mix worth \$1.80 per pound.

19. A Piper airplane and a B737 aircraft cross each other (at different altitudes) traveling in opposite directions. The B737 travels 5 times the speed of the Piper. If in 4 hours, they are 2160 miles apart, find the speed of each aircraft.

20. Two cyclists start at the same point and travel in opposite directions. One travels 4 mph faster than the other. In 4 hours they are 112 miles apart. Find how fast each is traveling.

21. While it is said that trains opened up the American West to settlement, U.S. railroad miles have been on the decline for decades. On the other hand, the miles of roads in the U.S. highway system have been increasing. The function $y = -1379.4x + 150{,}604$ represents the U.S. railroad miles, while the function $y = 478.4x + 157{,}838$ models the number of U.S. highway miles. For each function, x is the number of years after 1995. (*Source:* Association of American Railroads, Federal Highway Administration)

a. Explain how the decrease in railroad miles can be verified by their given function while the increase in highway miles can be verified by their given function.

b. Find the year in which it is estimated that the number of U.S. railroad miles and the number of U.S. highway miles were the same.

22. The annual U.S. per capita consumption of whole milk has decreased since 1980, while the per capita consumption of lower fat milk has increased. For the years 1980–2005, the function $y = -0.40x + 15.9$ approximates the annual U.S. per capita consumption of whole milk in gallons, and the function $y = 0.14x + 11.9$ approximates the annual U.S. per capita consumption of lower fat milk in gallons. Determine the year in which the per capita consumption of whole milk equaled the per capita consumption of lower fat milk. (*Source:* Economic Research Service: U.S.D.A.)

△ **23.** The perimeter of a triangle is 93 centimeters. If two sides are equally long and the third side is 9 centimeters longer than the others, find the lengths of the three sides.

24. Jack Reinholt, a car salesman, has a choice of two pay arrangements: a weekly salary of \$200 plus 5% commission on sales, or a straight 15% commission. Find the amount of weekly sales for which Jack's earnings are the same regardless of the pay arrangement.

25. Hertz car rental agency charges \$25 daily plus 10 cents per mile. Budget charges \$20 daily plus 25 cents per mile. Find the daily mileage for which the Budget charge for the day is twice that of the Hertz charge for the day.

26. Carroll Blakemore, a drafting student, bought three templates and a pencil one day for \$6.45. Another day he bought two pads of paper and four pencils for \$7.50. If the price of a pad of paper is three times the price of a pencil, find the price of each type of item.

△ **27.** In the figure, line l and line m are parallel lines cut by transversal t. Find the values of x and y.

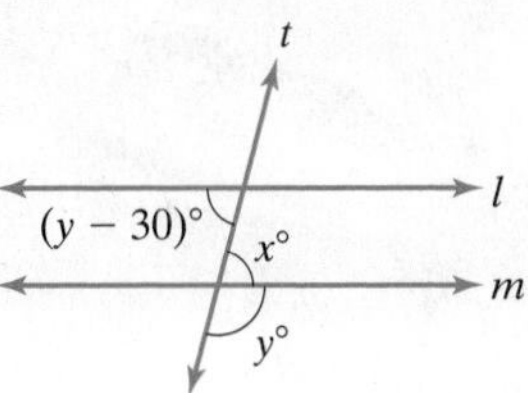

△ **28.** Find the values of x and y in the following isosceles triangle.

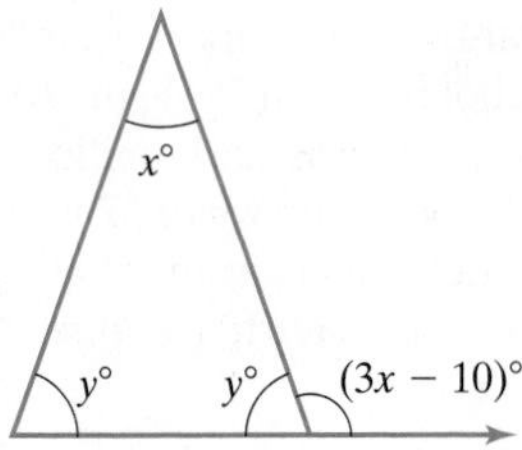

Given the cost function $C(x)$ and the revenue function $R(x)$, find the number of units x that must be sold to break even. See Example 5.

29. $C(x) = 30x + 10{,}000$; $R(x) = 46x$

30. $C(x) = 12x + 15{,}000$; $R(x) = 32x$

31. $C(x) = 1.2x + 1500$; $R(x) = 1.7x$

32. $C(x) = 0.8x + 900$; $R(x) = 2x$

33. $C(x) = 75x + 160{,}000$; $R(x) = 200x$

34. $C(x) = 105x + 70{,}000$; $R(x) = 245x$

35. The planning department of Abstract Office Supplies has been asked to determine whether the company should introduce a new computer desk next year. The department estimates that \$6000 of new manufacturing equipment will need to be purchased and that the cost of constructing each desk will be \$200. The department also estimates that the revenue from each desk will be \$450.

a. Determine the revenue function $R(x)$ from the sale of x desks.

b. Determine the cost function $C(x)$ for manufacturing x desks.

c. Find the break-even point.

36. Baskets, Inc., is planning to introduce a new woven basket. The company estimates that \$500 worth of new equipment will be needed to manufacture this new type of basket and that it will cost \$15 per basket to manufacture. The company also estimates that the revenue from each basket will be \$31.

a. Determine the revenue function $R(x)$ from the sale of x baskets.

b. Determine the cost function $C(x)$ for manufacturing x baskets.

c. Find the break-even point.

INTEGRATED REVIEW SYSTEMS OF LINEAR EQUATIONS

Sections 17.1–17.2

The graphs of various systems of equations are shown. Match each graph with the solution of its corresponding system.

A

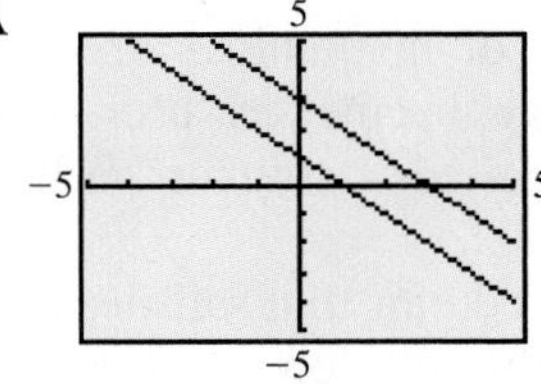

B

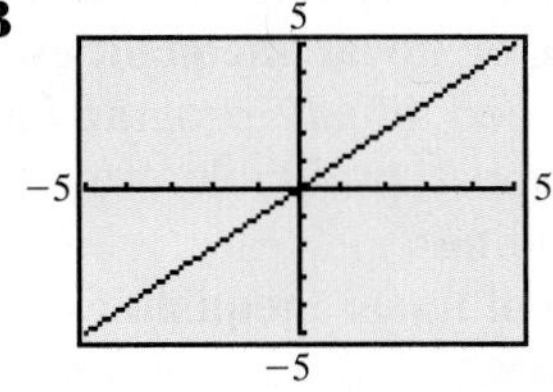

C

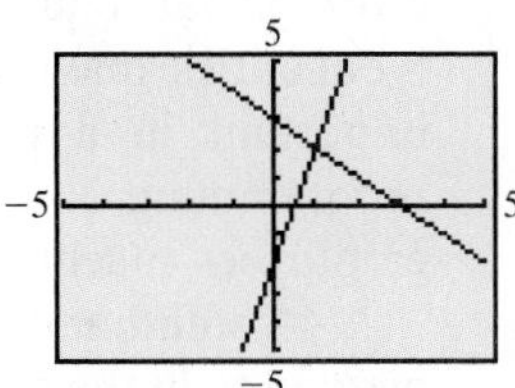

D

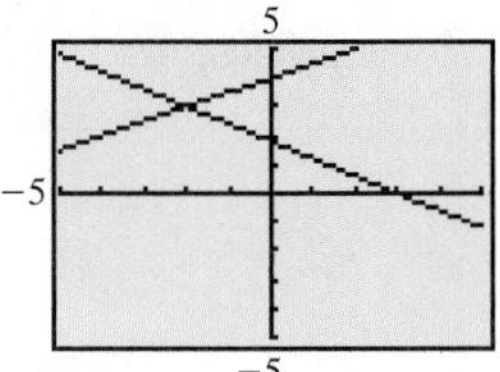

1. Solution: $(1, 2)$

2. Solution: $(-2, 3)$

3. No solution

4. Infinite number of solutions

Solve each system by elimination or substitution.

5. $\begin{cases} x + y = 4 \\ y = 3x \end{cases}$

6. $\begin{cases} x - y = -4 \\ y = 4x \end{cases}$

7. $\begin{cases} x + y = 1 \\ x - 2y = 4 \end{cases}$

8. $\begin{cases} 2x - y = 8 \\ x + 3y = 11 \end{cases}$

9. $\begin{cases} 2x + 5y = 8 \\ 6x + y = 10 \end{cases}$

10. $\begin{cases} \frac{1}{8}x - \frac{1}{2}y = -\frac{5}{8} \\ -3x - 8y = 0 \end{cases}$

11. $\begin{cases} 4x - 7y = 7 \\ 12x - 21y = 24 \end{cases}$

12. $\begin{cases} 2x - 5y = 3 \\ -4x + 10y = -6 \end{cases}$

13. $\begin{cases} y = \frac{1}{3}x \\ 5x - 3y = 4 \end{cases}$

14. $\begin{cases} y = \frac{1}{4}x \\ 2x - 4y = 3 \end{cases}$

15. A first number is 8 less than a second number. Twice the first number is 11 more than the second number. Find the numbers.

STUDY SKILLS BUILDER

Are You Satisfied with Your Performance on a Particular Quiz or Exam?

If not, don't forget to analyze your quiz or exam and look for common errors. Were most of your errors a result of:

- *Carelessness?* Did you turn in your quiz or exam before the allotted time expired? If so, resolve next time to use the entire time allotted. Any extra time can be spent checking your work.
- *Running out of time?* If so, make a point to better manage your time on your next quiz or exam. Try completing any questions that you are unsure of last and delay checking your work until all questions have been answered.
- *Not understanding a concept?* If so, review that concept and correct your work. Try to understand how this happened so that you make sure it doesn't happen before the next quiz or exam.
- *Test conditions?* When studying for a quiz or exam, make sure you place yourself in conditions similar to test conditions. For example, before your next quiz or exam, use a few sheets of blank paper and take a sample test without the aid of your notes or text.

(See your instructor or use the Chapter Test at the end of each chapter.)

Exercises

1. Have you corrected all your previous quizzes and exams?

2. List any errors you have found common to two or more of your graded papers.

3. Is one of your common errors not understanding a concept? If so, are you making sure you understand all the concepts for the next quiz or exam?

4. Is one of your common errors making careless mistakes? If so, are you now taking all the time allotted to check over your work so that you can minimize the number of careless mistakes?

5. Are you satisfied with your grades thus far on quizzes and tests?

6. If your answer to Exercise 5 is no, are there any more suggestions you can make to your instructor or yourself to help? If so, list them here and share these with your instructor.

17.3 SYSTEMS OF LINEAR INEQUALITIES

OBJECTIVE

1 Graph a system of linear inequalities.

OBJECTIVE 1 ▶ Graphing systems of linear inequalities. In Section 16.7 we solved linear inequalities in two variables as well as their union and intersection. Just as two or more linear equations make a system of linear equations, two or more linear inequalities make a **system of linear inequalities.** Systems of inequalities are very important in a process called linear programming. Many businesses use linear programming to find the most profitable way to use limited resources such as employees, machines, or buildings.

A **solution of a system of linear inequalities** is an ordered pair that satisfies each inequality in the system. The set of all such ordered pairs is the solution set of the system. Graphing this set gives us a picture of the solution set. We can graph a system of inequalities by graphing each inequality in the system and identifying the region of overlap.

Graphing the Solutions of a System of Linear Inequalities

STEP 1. Graph each inequality in the system on the same set of axes.

STEP 2. The solutions of the system are the points common to the graphs of all the inequalities in the system.

EXAMPLE 1 Graph the solutions of the system: $\begin{cases} 3x \geq y \\ x + 2y \leq 8 \end{cases}$

Solution We begin by graphing each inequality on the *same* set of axes. The graph of the solutions of the system is the region contained in the graphs of both inequalities. In other words, it is their intersection.

First let's graph $3x \geq y$. The boundary line is the graph of $3x = y$. We sketch a solid boundary line since the inequality $3x \geq y$ means $3x > y$ or $3x = y$. The test point (1, 0) satisfies the inequality, so we shade the half-plane that includes (1, 0).

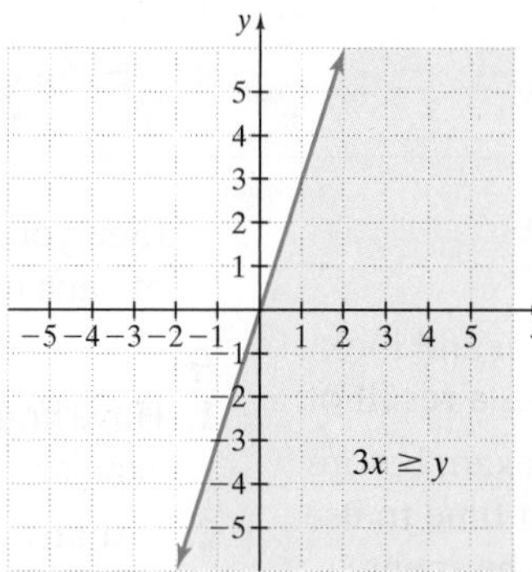

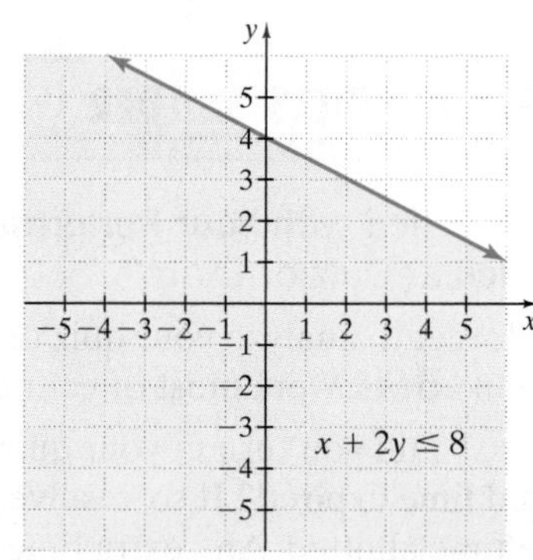

Next we sketch a solid boundary line $x + 2y = 8$ on the same set of axes. The test point (0, 0) satisfies the inequality $x + 2y \leq 8$, so we shade the half-plane that includes (0, 0). (For clarity, the graph of $x + 2y \leq 8$ is shown here on a separate set of axes.) An ordered pair solution of the system must satisfy both inequalities. These solutions are points that lie in both shaded regions. The solution of the system is the darkest shaded region. This solution includes parts of both boundary lines.

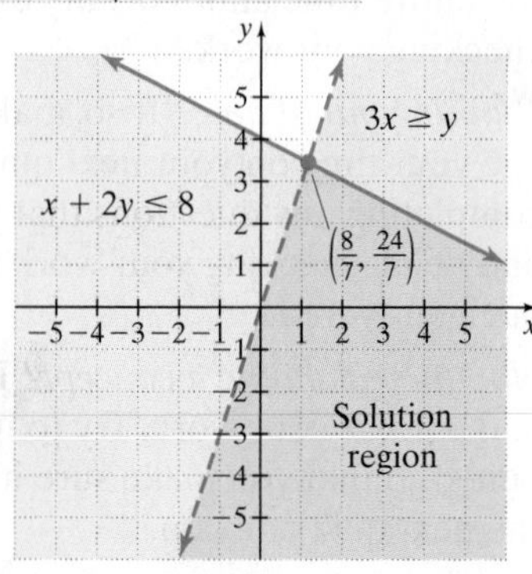

□

PRACTICE 1 Graph the solutions of the system: $\begin{cases} 4x \geq y \\ x + 3y \geq 6 \end{cases}$.

TECHNOLOGY NOTE

When solving systems of inequalities as in Example 1, some graphing utilities have APPS (installed or downloadable applications) that make it easier to see the shaded portion of the intersection of the graphs. One such App is Inequalz.

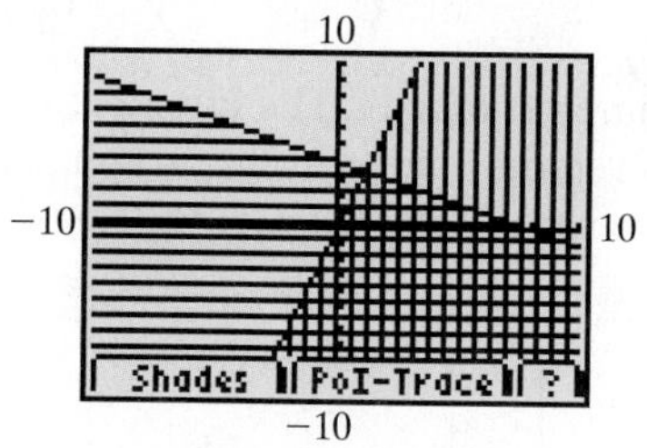

Example 1 using the Inequalz App.

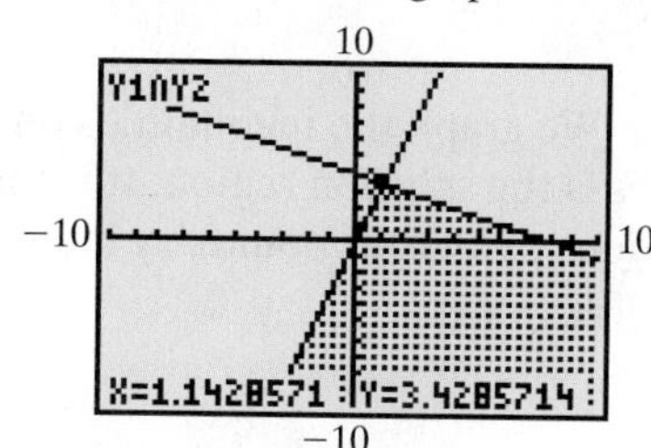

Finding the Point of Intersection (PoI).

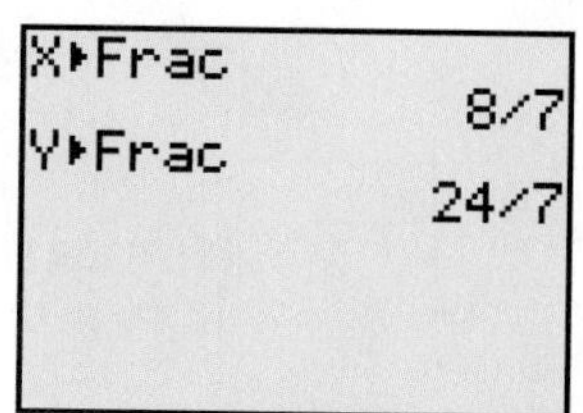

Point of Intersection Coordinates.

In linear programming, it is sometimes necessary to find the coordinates of the **corner point:** the point at which the two boundary lines intersect. To find the corner point for the system of Example 1, we solve the related linear system

$$\begin{cases} 3x = y \\ x + 2y = 8 \end{cases}$$

using either the substitution or the elimination method. The lines intersect at $\left(\frac{8}{7}, \frac{24}{7}\right)$, the corner point of the graph.

EXAMPLE 2 Graph the solutions of the system: $\begin{cases} x - y < 2 \\ x + 2y > -1 \\ y < 2 \end{cases}$

Solution First we graph all three inequalities on the same set of axes. All boundary lines are dashed lines since the inequality symbols are < and >. The solution of the system is the region shown by the darkest shading. In this example, the boundary lines are *not* a part of the solution.

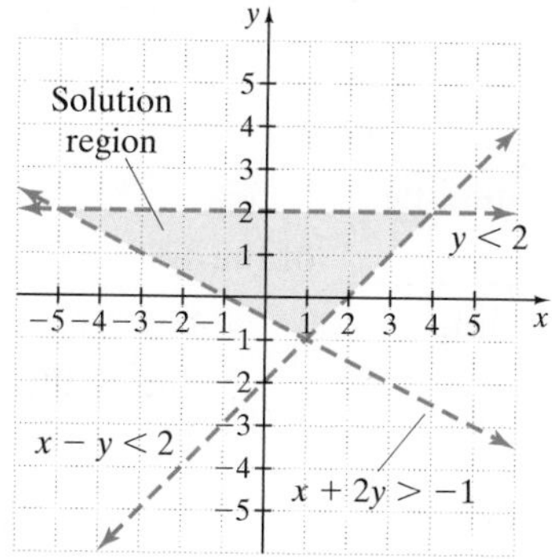

□

PRACTICE 2 Graph the solutions of the system: $\begin{cases} x - y < 1 \\ y < 4 \\ 3x + y > -3 \end{cases}$.

Concept Check ☑

Describe the solution of the system of inequalities: $\begin{cases} x \leq 2 \\ x \geq 2 \end{cases}$

EXAMPLE 3 Graph the solutions of the system: $\begin{cases} -3x + 4y \leq 12 \\ x \leq 3 \\ x \geq 0 \\ y \geq 0 \end{cases}$

Solution We graph the inequalities on the same set of axes. The intersection of the inequalities is the solution region. It is the only region shaded in this graph and includes the portions of all four boundary lines that border the shaded region.

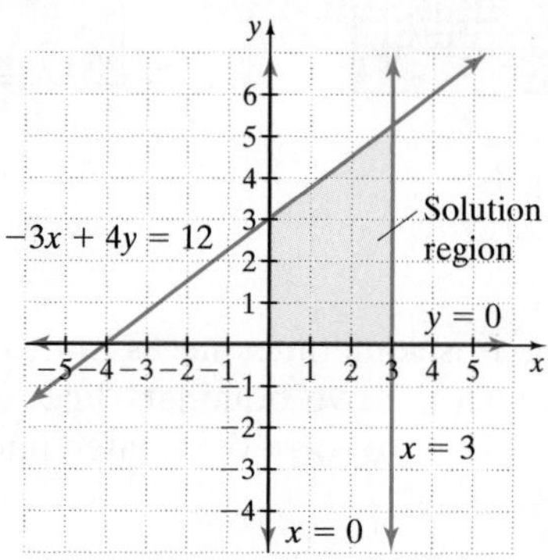

□

PRACTICE 3 Graph the solutions of the system: $\begin{cases} -2x + 5y \leq 10 \\ x \leq 4 \\ x \geq 0 \\ y \geq 0 \end{cases}$.

Answer to Concept Check:
the line $x = 2$

VOCABULARY & READINESS CHECK

Use the choices below to fill in each blank. Not all choices will be used.

solution	union	system
corner	intersection	

1. Two or more linear inequalities form a __________ of linear inequalities.
2. An ordered pair that satisfies each inequality in a system is a __________ of the system.
3. The point where two boundary lines intersect is a __________ point.
4. The solution region of a system of inequalities consists of the __________ of the solution regions of the inequalities in the system.

17.3 EXERCISE SET

PRACTICE

WATCH

DOWNLOAD

READ

REVIEW

MIXED PRACTICE

Graph the solutions of each system of linear inequalities. See Examples 1 through 3.

1. $\begin{cases} y \geq x + 1 \\ y \geq 3 - x \end{cases}$
2. $\begin{cases} y \geq x - 3 \\ y \geq -1 - x \end{cases}$
3. $\begin{cases} y < 3x - 4 \\ y \leq x + 2 \end{cases}$
4. $\begin{cases} y \leq 2x + 1 \\ y > x + 2 \end{cases}$
5. $\begin{cases} y < -2x - 2 \\ y > x + 4 \end{cases}$
6. $\begin{cases} y \leq 2x + 4 \\ y \geq -x - 5 \end{cases}$
7. $\begin{cases} y \geq -x + 2 \\ y \leq 2x + 5 \end{cases}$
8. $\begin{cases} y \geq x - 5 \\ y \leq -3x + 3 \end{cases}$
9. $\begin{cases} x \geq 3y \\ x + 3y \leq 6 \end{cases}$
10. $\begin{cases} -2x < y \\ x + 2y < 3 \end{cases}$

11. $\begin{cases} x \le 2 \\ y \ge -3 \end{cases}$

12. $\begin{cases} x \ge -3 \\ y \ge -2 \end{cases}$

13. $\begin{cases} y \ge 1 \\ x < -3 \end{cases}$

14. $\begin{cases} y > 2 \\ x \ge -1 \end{cases}$

15. $\begin{cases} y + 2x \ge 0 \\ 5x - 3y \le 12 \\ y \le 2 \end{cases}$

16. $\begin{cases} y + 2x \le 0 \\ 5x + 3y \ge -2 \\ y \le 4 \end{cases}$

17. $\begin{cases} 3x - 4y \ge -6 \\ 2x + y \le 7 \\ y \ge -3 \end{cases}$

18. $\begin{cases} 4x - y \ge -2 \\ 2x + 3y \le -8 \\ y \ge -5 \end{cases}$

19. $\begin{cases} 2x + y \le 5 \\ x \le 3 \\ x \ge 0 \\ y \ge 0 \end{cases}$

20. $\begin{cases} 3x + y \le 4 \\ x \le 4 \\ x \ge 0 \\ y \ge 0 \end{cases}$

Match each system of inequalities to the corresponding graph.

A

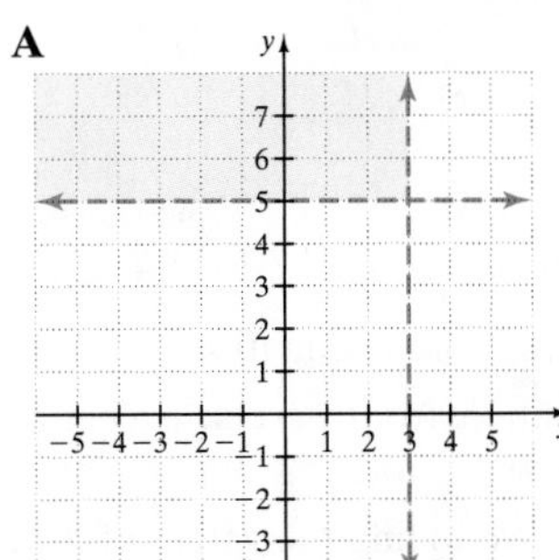

B

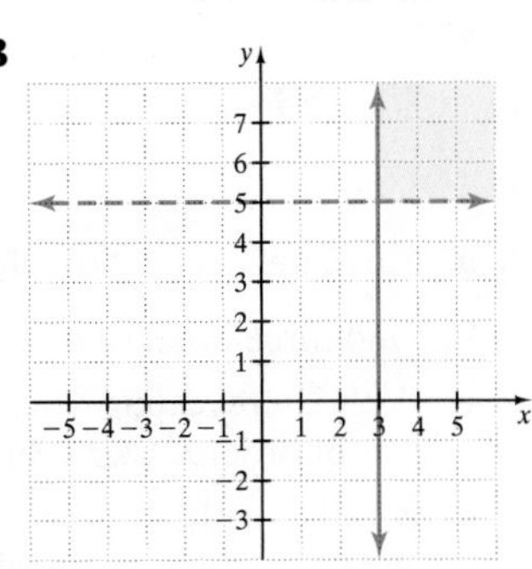

C

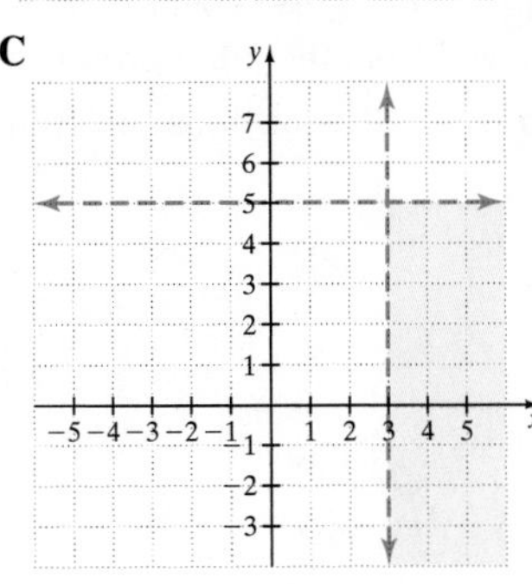

D

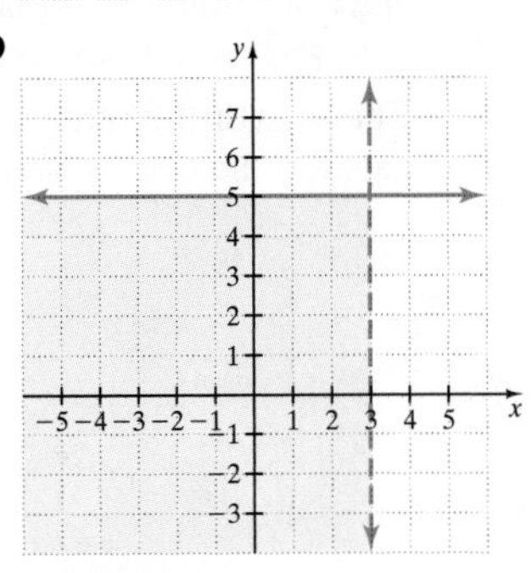

21. $\begin{cases} y < 5 \\ x > 3 \end{cases}$

22. $\begin{cases} y > 5 \\ x < 3 \end{cases}$

23. $\begin{cases} y \le 5 \\ x < 3 \end{cases}$

24. $\begin{cases} y > 5 \\ x \ge 3 \end{cases}$

REVIEW

Evaluate each expression.

25. $(-3)^2$

26. $(-5)^3$

27. $\left(\frac{2}{3}\right)^2$

28. $\left(\frac{3}{4}\right)^3$

Perform each indicated operation.

29. $(-2)^2 - (-3) + 2(-1)$

30. $5^2 - 11 + 3(-5)$

31. $8^2 + (-13) - 4(-2)$

32. $(-12)^2 + (-1)(2) - 6$

CONCEPT EXTENSIONS

Solve. See the Concept Check in this section.

33. Describe the solution of the system: $\begin{cases} y \le 3 \\ y \ge 3 \end{cases}$.

34. Describe the solution of the system: $\begin{cases} x \le 5 \\ x \le 3 \end{cases}$.

35. Explain how to decide which region to shade to show the solution region of the following system.

$$\begin{cases} x \ge 3 \\ y \ge -2 \end{cases}$$

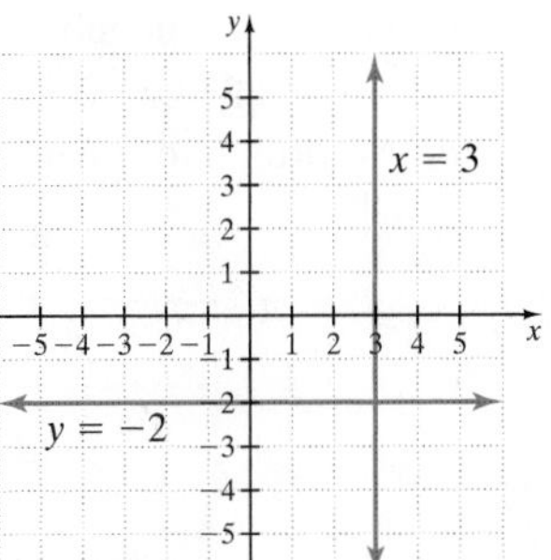

36. Tony Noellert budgets his time at work today. Part of the day he can write bills; the rest of the day he can use to write purchase orders. The total time available is at most 8 hours. Less than 3 hours is to be spent writing bills.

a. Write a system of inequalities to describe the situation. (Let x = hours available for writing bills and y = hours available for writing purchase orders.)

b. Graph the solutions of the system.

CHAPTER 17 GROUP ACTIVITY

Another Mathematical Model

Sometimes mathematical models other than linear models are appropriate for data. Suppose that an equation of the form $y = ax^2 + bx + c$ is an appropriate model for the ordered pairs (x_1, y_1), (x_2, y_2), and (x_3, y_3). Then it is necessary to find the values of a, b, and c such that the given ordered pairs are solutions of the equation $y = ax^2 + bx + c$. To do so, substitute each ordered pair into the equation. Each time, the result is an equation in three unknowns: a, b, and c. Solving the resulting system of three linear equations in three unknowns will give the required values of a, b, and c.

1. The table gives the total beef supply (in billions of pounds) in the United States in each of the years listed.

a. Write the data as ordered pairs of the form (x, y), where y is the beef supply (in billions of pounds) in the year x ($x = 0$ represents 2000).

b. Find the values of a, b, and c such that the equation $y = ax^2 + bx + c$ models this data.

c. Verify that the model you found in part **b** gives each of the ordered pair solutions from part **a.**

d. According to the model, what was the U.S. beef supply in 2005?

Total U.S. Beef Supply	
Year	***Beef Supply (Billions of Pounds)***
2002	27
2004	24.6
2006	25

(*Source:* Economic Research Service, U.S. Department of Agriculture)

2. The table gives Toyota Hybrid sales figures for each of the years listed.

a. Write the data as ordered pairs of the form (x, y), where y is sales in the year x ($x = 0$ represents 2000).

b. Find the values of a, b, and c such that the equation $y = ax^2 + bx + c$ models this data.

c. According to the model, what were the total sales in 2005?

Total Toyota Hybrid Sales	
Year	***Sales in Thousands***
2002	41
2004	135
2006	313

(*Source:* Toyota Motor Corporation)

3. a. Make up an equation of the form $y = ax^2 + bx + c$.

b. Find three ordered pair solutions of the equation.

c. Without revealing your equation from part **a,** exchange lists of ordered pair solutions with another group.

d. Use the method described above to find the values of a, b, and c such that the equation $y = ax^2 + bx + c$ has the ordered pair solutions you received from the other group.

e. Check with the other group to see if your equation from part **d** is the correct one.

CHAPTER 17 VOCABULARY CHECK

Fill in each blank with one of the words or phrases listed below.

consistent	system of equations
solution	inconsistent

1. Two or more linear equations in two variables form a ______________.

2. A __________ of a system of two equations in two variables is an ordered pair that makes both equations true.

3. A(n) __________ system of equations has at least one solution.

4. A(n) __________ system of equations has no solution.

Helpful Hint

Are you preparing for your test? Don't forget to take the Chapter 17 Test on page 1093. Then check your answers at the back of the text and use the Chapter Test Prep Video CD to see the fully worked-out solutions to any of the exercises you want to review.

CHAPTER 17 HIGHLIGHTS

DEFINITIONS AND CONCEPTS	EXAMPLES

SECTION 17.1 SOLVING SYSTEMS OF LINEAR EQUATIONS IN TWO VARIABLES

A **system of linear equations** consists of two or more linear equations.

$$\begin{cases} x - 3y = 6 \\ y = \frac{1}{2}x \end{cases} \qquad \begin{cases} x + 2y - z = 1 \\ 3x - y + 4z = 0 \\ 5y + z = 6 \end{cases}$$

A **solution** of a system of two equations in two variables is an ordered pair (x, y) that makes both equations true.

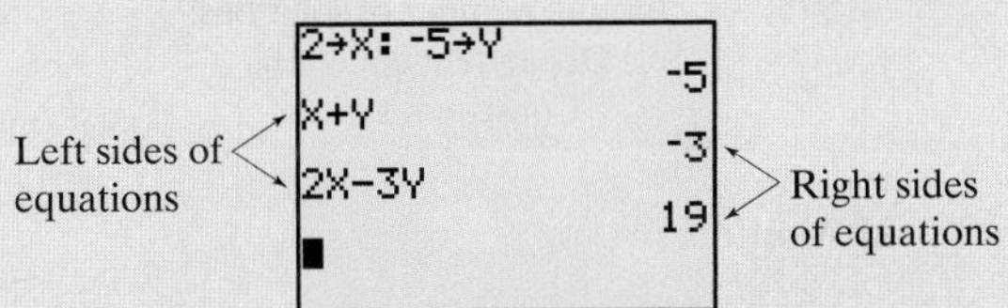

A numerical check that $(2, -5)$ is the solution of the system to the right.

Determine whether $(2, -5)$ is a solution of the system.

$$\begin{cases} x + y = -3 \\ 2x - 3y = 19 \end{cases}$$

Replace x with 2 and y with -5 in both equations.

$$x + y = -3 \qquad 2x - 3y = 19$$
$$2 + (-5) \stackrel{?}{=} -3 \qquad 2(2) - 3(-5) \stackrel{?}{=} 19$$
$$-3 = -3 \quad \text{True} \qquad 4 + 15 \stackrel{?}{=} 19$$
$$19 = 19 \quad \text{True}$$

$(2, -5)$ is a solution of the system.

Geometrically, a solution of a system in two variables is a point of intersection of the graphs of the equations.

Solve by graphing: $\begin{cases} y = 2x - 1 \\ x + 2y = 13 \end{cases}$

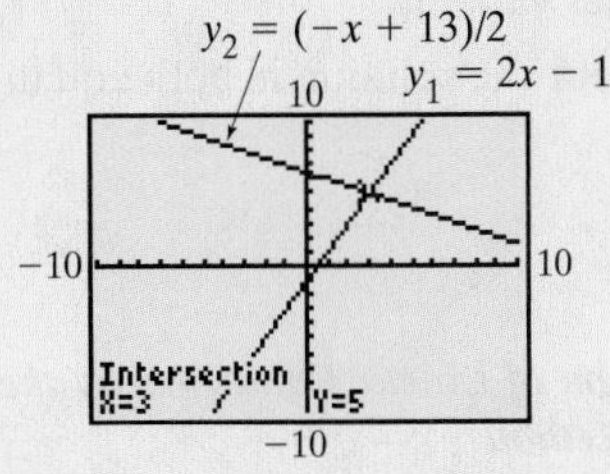

The solution is $(3, 5)$.

DEFINITIONS AND CONCEPTS	EXAMPLES

SECTION 17.1 SOLVING SYSTEMS OF LINEAR EQUATIONS IN TWO VARIABLES (continued)

A system of equations with at least one solution is a **consistent system.** A system that has no solution is an **inconsistent system.**

If the graphs of two linear equations are identical, the equations are **dependent.**

If their graphs are different, the equations are **independent.**

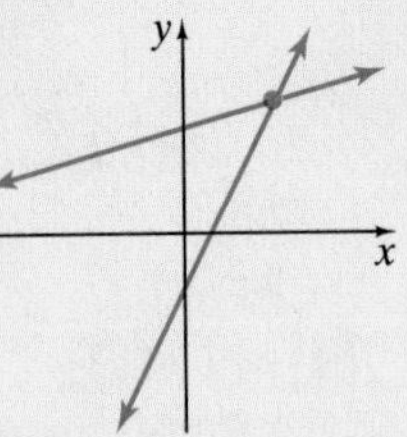

One solution:
Independent equations
Consistent system

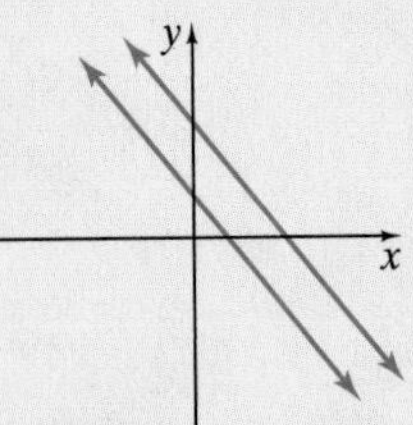

No solution:
Independent equations
Inconsistent system

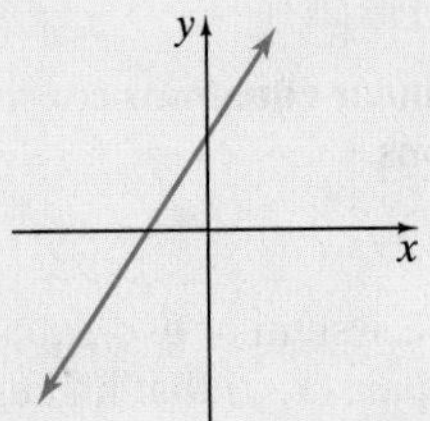

Infinite number of solutions:
Dependent equations
Consistent system

Solving a System of Linear Equations by the Substitution Method

Step 1. Solve one equation for a variable.

Step 2. Substitute the expression for the variable into the other equation.

Step 3. Solve the equation from Step 2 to find the value of one variable.

Step 4. Substitute the value from Step 3 in either original equation to find the value of the other variable.

Step 5. Check the solution in both equations.

Solve by substitution:

$$\begin{cases} y = x + 2 \\ 3x - 2y = -5 \end{cases}$$

Since the first equation is solved for y, substitute $x + 2$ for y in the second equation.

$$\begin{aligned} 3x - 2y &= -5 && \text{Second equation} \\ 3x - 2(x + 2) &= -5 && \text{Let } y = x + 2. \\ 3x - 2x - 4 &= -5 \\ x - 4 &= -5 && \text{Simplify.} \\ x &= -1 && \text{Add 4.} \end{aligned}$$

To find y, let $x = -1$ in $y = x + 2$, so $y = -1 + 2 = 1$. The solution $(-1, 1)$ checks.

Solving a System of Linear Equations by the Elimination Method

Step 1. Rewrite each equation in standard form, $Ax + By = C$.

Step 2. Multiply one or both equations by a nonzero number so that the coefficients of a variable are opposites.

Step 3. Add the equations.

Step 4. Find the value of the remaining variable by solving the resulting equation.

Step 5. Substitute the value from Step 4 into either original equation to find the value of the other variable.

Step 6. Check the solution in both equations.

Solve by elimination:

$$\begin{cases} x - 3y = -3 \\ -2x + y = 6 \end{cases}$$

Multiply both sides of the first equation by 2.

$$\begin{aligned} 2x - 6y &= -6 \\ -2x + y &= 6 \\ \hline -5y &= 0 && \text{Add.} \\ y &= 0 && \text{Divide by } -5. \end{aligned}$$

To find x, let $y = 0$ in an original equation.

$$\begin{aligned} x - 3y &= -3 \\ x - 3 \cdot 0 &= -3 \\ x &= -3 \end{aligned}$$

The solution $(-3, 0)$ checks.

DEFINITIONS AND CONCEPTS	EXAMPLES

SECTION 17.2 SYSTEMS OF LINEAR EQUATIONS AND PROBLEM SOLVING

Two numbers have a sum of 11. Twice one number is 3 less than 3 times the other. Find the numbers.

1. UNDERSTAND the problem.

1. Read and reread.

$x =$ one number

$y =$ other number

2. TRANSLATE.

2. In words: sum of numbers / is / 11

Translate: $x + y = 11$

In words: twice one number / is / 3 less than 3 times the other number

Translate: $2x = 3y - 3$

3. SOLVE.

3. Solve the system: $\begin{cases} x + y = 11 \\ 2x = 3y - 3 \end{cases}$

In the first equation, $x = 11 - y$. Substitute into the other equation.

$$2x = 3y - 3$$
$$2(11 - y) = 3y - 3$$
$$22 - 2y = 3y - 3$$
$$-5y = -25$$
$$y = 5$$

Replace y with 5 in the equation $x = 11 - y$. Then $x = 11 - 5 = 6$. The solution is $(6, 5)$.

4. INTERPRET.

4. *Check:* See that $6 + 5 = 11$ is the required sum and that twice 6 is 3 times 5 less 3. *State:* The numbers are 6 and 5.

SECTION 17.3 SYSTEMS OF LINEAR INEQUALITIES

A **system of linear inequalities** consists of two or more linear inequalities.

To graph a system of inequalities, graph each inequality in the system. The overlapping region is the solution of the system.

$$\begin{cases} x - y \geq 3 \\ y \leq -2x \end{cases}$$

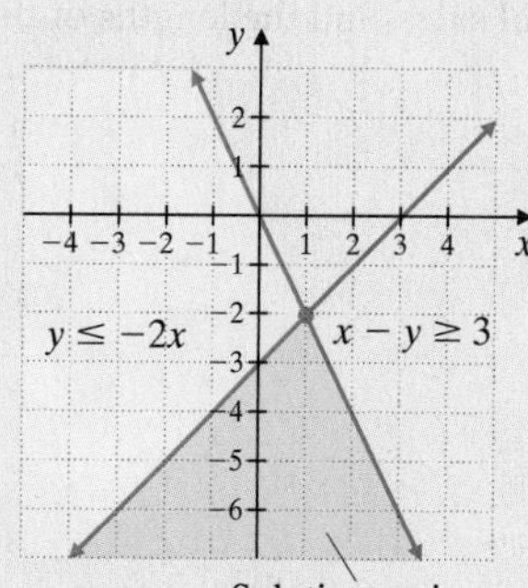

Solution region

CHAPTER 17 REVIEW

(17.1) *Solve each system of equations in two variables by each method: (a) graphing, (b) substitution, and (c) elimination.*

1. $\begin{cases} 3x + 10y = 1 \\ x + 2y = -1 \end{cases}$

2. $\begin{cases} y = \frac{1}{2}x + \frac{2}{3} \\ 4x + 6y = 4 \end{cases}$

3. $\begin{cases} 2x - 4y = 22 \\ 5x - 10y = 15 \end{cases}$

4. $\begin{cases} 3x - 6y = 12 \\ 2y = x - 4 \end{cases}$

5. $\begin{cases} \frac{1}{2}x - \frac{3}{4}y = -\frac{1}{2} \\ \frac{1}{8}x + \frac{3}{4}y = \frac{19}{8} \end{cases}$

6. The revenue equation for a certain style of backpack is $y = 32x$, where x is the number of backpacks sold and y is the income in dollars for selling x backpacks. The cost equation for these units is $y = 15x + 25{,}500$, where x is the number of backpacks manufactured and y is the cost in dollars for manufacturing x backpacks. Find the number of units to be sold for the company to break even. (*Hint:* Solve the system of equations formed by the two given equations.)

(17.2) *Use systems of equations to solve.*

7. One number is three times a second number, and twice the sum of the numbers is 168. Find the numbers.

8. Two cars leave Chicago, one traveling east and the other west. After 4 hours they are 492 miles apart. If one car is traveling 7 mph faster than the other, find the speed of each.

9. The foundation for a rectangular Hardware Warehouse has a length three times the width and is 296 feet around. Find the dimensions of the building.

10. James Callahan has available a 10% alcohol solution and a 60% alcohol solution. Find how many liters of each solution he should mix to make 50 liters of a 40% alcohol solution.

11. If \$10,000 and \$4000 are invested such that \$1250 in interest is earned in one year, and if the rate of interest on the larger investment is 2% more than that on the smaller investment, find the rates of interest.

12. The perimeter of an isosceles (two sides equal) triangle is 73 centimeters. If the unequal side is 7 centimeters longer than the two equal sides, find the lengths of the three sides.

(17.3) *Graph the solution of each system of linear inequalities.*

13. $\begin{cases} y \ge 2x - 3 \\ y \le -2x + 1 \end{cases}$

14. $\begin{cases} y \le -3x - 3 \\ y \le 2x + 7 \end{cases}$

15. $\begin{cases} x + 2y > 0 \\ x - y \le 6 \end{cases}$

16. $\begin{cases} x - 2y \ge 7 \\ x + y \le -5 \end{cases}$

17. $\begin{cases} 3x - 2y \le 4 \\ 2x + y \ge 5 \\ y \le 4 \end{cases}$

18. $\begin{cases} 4x - y \le 0 \\ 3x - 2y \ge -5 \\ y \ge -4 \end{cases}$

19. $\begin{cases} x + 2y \le 5 \\ x \le 2 \\ x \ge 0 \\ y \ge 0 \end{cases}$

20. $\begin{cases} x + 3y \le 7 \\ y \le 5 \\ x \ge 0 \\ y \ge 0 \end{cases}$

MIXED REVIEW

Solve each system.

21. $\begin{cases} y = x - 5 \\ y = -2x + 2 \end{cases}$

22. $\begin{cases} \frac{2}{5}x + \frac{3}{4}y = 1 \\ x + 3y = -2 \end{cases}$

23. $\begin{cases} 5x - 2y = 10 \\ x = \frac{2}{5}y + 2 \end{cases}$

24. $\begin{cases} x - 4y = 4 \\ \frac{1}{8}x - \frac{1}{2}y = 3 \end{cases}$

25. One number is five less than three times a second number. If the sum of the numbers is 127, find the numbers.

26. Graph the solution of the system: $\begin{cases} y \le 3x - \frac{1}{2} \\ 3x + 4y \ge 6 \end{cases}$.

27. In the United States, the consumer spending on VCR decks is decreasing while the spending on DVD players is increasing. For the years 1998–2003, the function $y = -443x + 2584$ estimates the millions of dollars spent on purchasing VCR decks while the function $y = 500x + 551$ estimates the millions of dollars spent on purchasing DVD players. For both functions, x is the number of years since 1998. Use these equations to determine the year in which the amount of money spent on VCR decks equals the amount of money spent on DVD players. (*Source:* Consumer Electronics Association)

CHAPTER 17 TEST

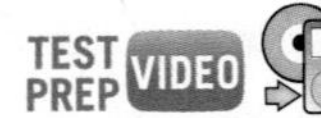

Remember to use the Chapter Test Prep Video CD to see the fully worked-out solutions to any of the exercises you want to review.

Solve each system of equations graphically and then solve by the elimination method or the substitution method.

1. $\begin{cases} 2x - y = -1 \\ 5x + 4y = 17 \end{cases}$

2. $\begin{cases} 7x - 14y = 5 \\ x = 2y \end{cases}$

Solve each system.

3. $\begin{cases} 4x - 7y = 29 \\ 2x + 5y = -11 \end{cases}$

4. $\begin{cases} 15x + 6y = 15 \\ 10x + 4y = 10 \end{cases}$

5. $\begin{cases} \dfrac{x}{2} + \dfrac{y}{4} = -\dfrac{3}{4} \\ x + \dfrac{3}{4}y = -4 \end{cases}$

6. $\begin{cases} x - y = -2 \\ 3x - 3y = -6 \end{cases}$

7. $\begin{cases} x + 2y = -1 \\ 2x + 5y = -5 \end{cases}$

8. A motel in New Orleans charges $90 per day for double occupancy and $80 per day for single occupancy. If 80 rooms are occupied for a total of $6930, how many rooms of each kind are occupied?

9. The research department of a company that manufactures children's fruit drinks is experimenting with a new flavor. A 17.5% fructose solution is needed, but only 10% and 20% solutions are available. How many gallons of a 10% fructose solution should be mixed with a 20% fructose solution to obtain 20 gallons of a 17.5% fructose solution?

10. A company that manufactures boxes recently purchased $2000 worth of new equipment to offer gift boxes to its customers. The cost of producing a package of gift boxes is $1.50 and it is sold for $4.00. Find the number of packages that must be sold for the company to break even.

Graph the solutions of the system of linear inequalities.

11. $\begin{cases} 2y - x \geq 1 \\ x + y \geq -4 \\ y \leq 2 \end{cases}$

CHAPTER 17 CUMULATIVE REVIEW

1. Determine whether each statement is true or false.

a. $3 \in \{x \mid x \text{ is a natural number}\}$

b. $7 \notin \{1, 2, 3\}$

2. Determine whether each statement is true or false.

a. $\{0, 7\} \subseteq \{0, 2, 4, 6, 8\}$

b. $\{1, 3, 5\} \subseteq \{1, 3, 5, 7\}$

3. Simplify the following expressions.

a. $11 + 2 - 7$

b. $-5 - 4 + 2$

4. Subtract.

a. $-7 - (-2)$

b. $14 - 38$

5. Write the additive inverse, or opposite, of each.

a. 4

b. $\dfrac{3}{7}$

c. -11.2

6. Write the reciprocal of each.

a. 5

b. $-\dfrac{2}{3}$

7. Use the distributive property to multiply.

a. $3(2x + y)$

b. $-(3x - 1)$

c. $0.7a(b - 2)$

8. Multiply.

a. $7(3x - 2y + 4)$

b. $-(-2s - 3t)$

9. Use the distributive property to simplify each expression.

a. $3x - 5x + 4$

b. $7yz + yz$

c. $4z + 6.1$

10. Simplify.

a. $5y^2 - 1 + 2(y^2 + 2)$

b. $(7.8x - 1.2) - (5.6x - 2.4)$

Solve.

11. $-4x - 1 + 5x = 9x + 3 - 7x$

12. $8y - 14 = 6y - 14$

13. $0.3x + 0.1 = 0.27x - 0.02$

14. $2(m - 6) - m = 4(m - 3) - 3m$

15. A pennant in the shape of an isosceles triangle is to be constructed for the Slidell High School Athletic Club and sold at a fund-raiser. The company manufacturing the pennant charges according to perimeter, and the athletic club has determined that a perimeter of 149 centimeters should make a nice profit. If each equal side of the triangle is twice the length of the third side, increased by 12 centimeters, find the lengths of the sides of the triangular pennant.

16. A quadrilateral has 4 angles whose sum is 360°. In a particular quadrilateral, two angles have the same measure. A third angle is 10° more than the measure of one of the equal angles, and the fourth angle is half the measure of one of the equal angles. Find the measures of the angles.

17. Solve: $3x + 4 \geq 2x - 6$. Graph the solution set.

18. Solve: $5(2x - 1) > -5$

19. Solve: $2 < 4 - x < 7$

20. Solve: $-1 < \dfrac{-2x - 1}{3} < 1$

21. Solve: $|2x| + 5 = 7$

22. Solve: $|x - 5| = 4$

23. Solve for m: $|m - 6| < 2$

24. $|2x + 1| > 5$

25. Plot each ordered pair on a Cartesian coordinate system and name the quadrant or axis in which the point is located.

a. $(2, -1)$ **b.** $(0, 5)$ **c.** $(-3, 5)$

d. $(-2, 0)$ **e.** $\left(-\frac{1}{2}, -4\right)$ **f.** $(1.5, 1.5)$

26. Name the quadrant or axis in which each point is located.

a. $(-1, -5)$

b. $(4, -2)$

c. $(0, 2)$

27. Is the relation $x = y^2$ also a function?

28. Graph: $-2x + \frac{1}{2}y = -2$

29. If $f(x) = 7x^2 - 3x + 1, g(x) = 3x - 2$, and $h(x) = x^2$, find the following.

a. $f(1)$ **b.** $g(3)$

c. $h(-2)$

30. If $f(x) = 3x^2$, find the following.

a. $f(5)$ **b.** $f(-2)$

31. Graph $g(x) = 2x + 1$. Compare this graph with the graph of $f(x) = 2x$.

32. Find the slope of the line containing $(-2, 6)$ and $(0, 9)$.

33. Find the slope and the y-intercept of the line $3x - 4y = 4$.

34. Find the slope and y-intercept of the line defined by $y = 2$.

35. Are the following pairs of lines parallel, perpendicular, or neither?

a. $3x + 7y = 21$
$6x + 14y = 7$

b. $-x + 3y = 2$
$2x + 6y = 5$

c. $2x - 3y = 12$
$6x + 4y = 16$

36. Find an equation of the line through $(0, -9)$ with slope $\frac{1}{5}$.

37. Find an equation of the line through points (4, 0) and $(-4, -5)$. Write the equation using function notation.

38. Find an equation of the line through $(-2, 6)$ perpendicular to $f(x) = \frac{1}{2}x - \frac{1}{3}$.

39. Graph $3x \geq y$.

40. Graph: $x \geq 1$.

41. Determine whether the given ordered pair is a solution of the system.

a. $\begin{cases} -x + y = 2 \\ 2x - y = -3 \end{cases}$ $(-1, 1)$

b. $\begin{cases} 5x + 3y = -1 \\ x - y = 1 \end{cases}$ $(-2, 3)$

42. Solve the system:

$$\begin{cases} 5x + y = -2 \\ 4x - 2y = -10 \end{cases}$$

43. Solve the system:

$$\begin{cases} -6x + 8y = 0 \\ 9x - 12y = 2 \end{cases}$$

$$\begin{cases} x + 3y = 5 \\ 2x - y = -4 \end{cases}$$

Rational Expressions

18

Movies still attract more people (1,448 million annually) than either theme parks (341 million) or major professional league sports (137 million) combined. U.S. theater admissions grew 3.3% in 2006 and movie advertising is changing, with advertising on TV or in the newspaper decreasing and online advertising increasing.

The graph below shows yearly rating changes for top grossing films.

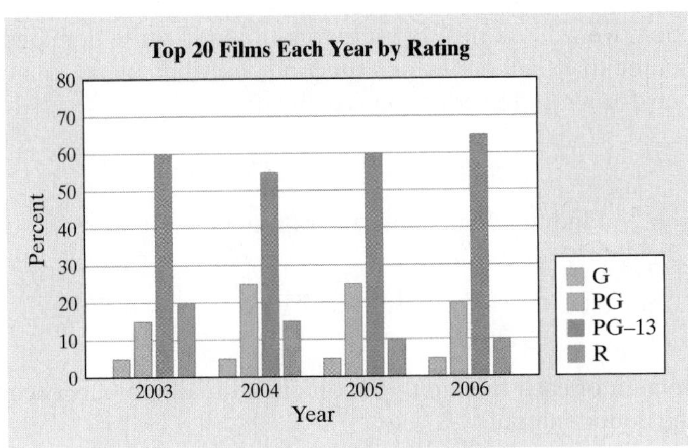

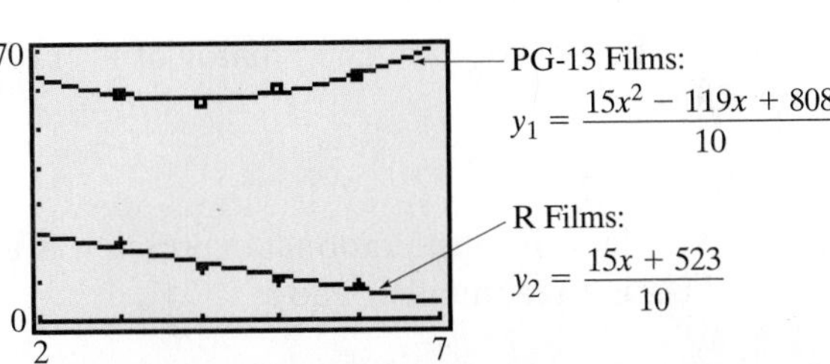

The calculator screen shows function models for the percent changes of R and PG-13 top grossing films for years 2003–2006.

Polynomials are to algebra what integers are to arithmetic. We have added, subtracted, multiplied, and raised polynomials to powers, each operation yielding another polynomial, just as these operations on integers yield another integer. But when we divide one integer by another, the result may or may not be another integer. Likewise, when we divide one polynomial by another, we may or may not get a polynomial in return. The quotient $x \div (x + 1)$ is not a polynomial; it is a *rational expression* that can be written as $\dfrac{x}{x + 1}$.

In this chapter, we study these new algebraic forms known as rational expressions and the *rational functions* they generate.

18.1 RATIONAL FUNCTIONS AND MULTIPLYING AND DIVIDING RATIONAL EXPRESSIONS

OBJECTIVES

1 Find the domain of a rational expression.

2 Simplify rational expressions.

3 Multiply rational expressions.

4 Divide rational expressions.

5 Use rational functions in applications.

Recall that a *rational number,* or *fraction,* is a number that can be written as the quotient $\frac{p}{q}$ of two integers p and q as long as q is not 0. A **rational expression** is an expression that can be written as the quotient $\frac{P}{Q}$ of two polynomials P and Q as long as Q is not 0.

Examples of Rational Expressions

$$\frac{3x+7}{2} \qquad \frac{5x^2-3}{x-1} \qquad \frac{7x-2}{2x^2+7x+6}$$

Rational expressions are sometimes used to describe functions. For example, we call the function $f(x) = \frac{x^2+2}{x-3}$ a **rational function** since $\frac{x^2+2}{x-3}$ is a rational expression.

OBJECTIVE 1 ▶ Finding the domain of a rational expression. As with fractions, a rational expression is **undefined** if the denominator is 0. If a variable in a rational expression is replaced with a number that makes the denominator 0, we say that the rational expression is **undefined** for this value of the variable. For example, the rational expression $\frac{x^2+2}{x-3}$ is undefined when x is 3, because replacing x with 3 results in a denominator of 0. For this reason, we must exclude 3 from the domain of the function $f(x) = \frac{x^2+2}{x-3}$.

The domain of f is then

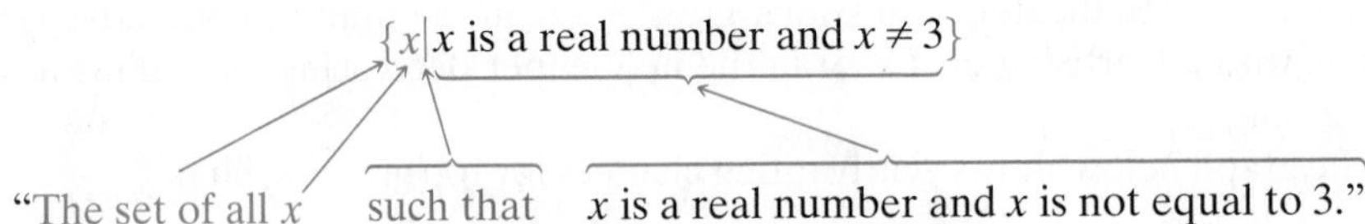
{x|x is a real number and x ≠ 3}
"The set of all x
such that
x is a real number and x is not equal to 3."

In this section, we will use this set builder notation to write domains. Unless told otherwise, we assume that the domain of a function described by an equation is the set of all real numbers for which the equation is defined.

EXAMPLE 1 Find the domain of each rational function.

a. $f(x) = \frac{8x^3+7x^2+20}{2}$ **b.** $g(x) = \frac{7x+2}{x-3}$ **c.** $f(x) = \frac{9x-13}{x^2-2x-15}$

Solution The domain of each function will contain all real numbers except those values that make the denominator 0.

a. No matter what the value of x, the denominator of $f(x) = \frac{8x^3+7x^2+20}{2}$ is never 0, so the domain of f is $\{x|x \text{ is a real number}\}$.

b. To find the values of x that make the denominator of $g(x)$ equal to 0, we solve the equation "denominator = 0":

$$x - 3 = 0, \quad \text{or} \quad x = 3$$

The domain must exclude 3 since the rational expression is undefined when x is 3. The domain of g is $\{x|x \text{ is a real number and } x \neq 3\}$.

c. We find the domain by setting the denominator equal to 0.

$$x^2 - 2x - 15 = 0 \quad \text{Set the denominator equal to 0 and solve.}$$
$$(x - 5)(x + 3) = 0$$
$$x - 5 = 0 \quad \text{or} \quad x + 3 = 0$$
$$x = 5 \quad \text{or} \quad x = -3$$

If x is replaced with 5 or with -3, the rational expression is undefined.

The domain of f is $\{x|x \text{ is a real number and } x \neq 5, x \neq -3\}$. □

PRACTICE 1 Find the domain of each rational function.

a. $f(x) = \dfrac{4x^5 - 3x^2 + 2}{-6}$ **b.** $g(x) = \dfrac{6x^2 + 1}{x + 3}$ **c.** $h(x) = \dfrac{8x - 3}{x^2 - 5x + 6}$

Let's use a graphing utility to confirm the domain of the function in Example 1b, $g(x) = \dfrac{7x + 2}{x - 3}$.

To confirm this domain, graph $y_1 = \dfrac{7x + 2}{x - 3}$. The domain of $g(x)$ does not include 3, so the graph of $g(x)$ does not exist at $x = 3$. If we graph $g(x)$ in dot mode, the graph shows that the function is undefined at $x = 3$ and no ordered pair solutions exist with an x-value of 3. See the graph in the margin.

The graph of $g(x) = \dfrac{7x + 2}{x - 3}$ confirms that the domain is $\{x|x \text{ is a real number and } x \neq 3\}$.

TECHNOLOGY NOTE

Most graphing utilities have a dot mode. When graphing a function in dot mode only the calculated points of the function are plotted. Consult your owner's manual for specific instructions on using this feature.

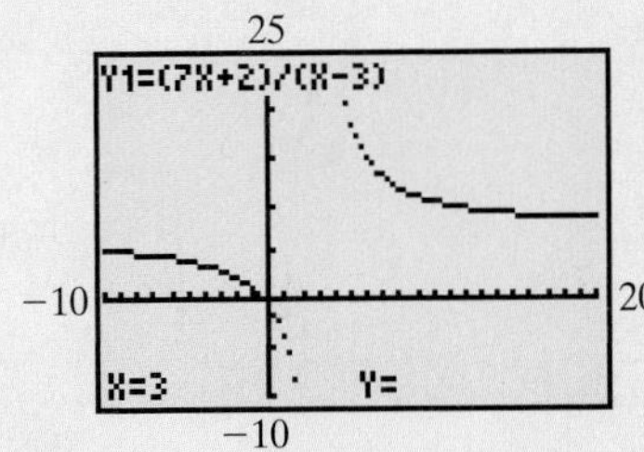

In dot mode the graphing utility plots only the ordered pairs that make the equation true. Notice y_1 is undefined when $x = 3$ and thus a point does not exist on the graph of the function.

TECHNOLOGY NOTE

Use care when interpreting the graph of a rational expression on a graphing utility. For example, if we graph $g(x) = \dfrac{7x + 2}{x - 3}$ in *connected* mode, the graphing utility *connects* the last point plotted before $x = 3$ with the next point plotted after $x = 3$. The result of this appears as a vertical line on the graph.

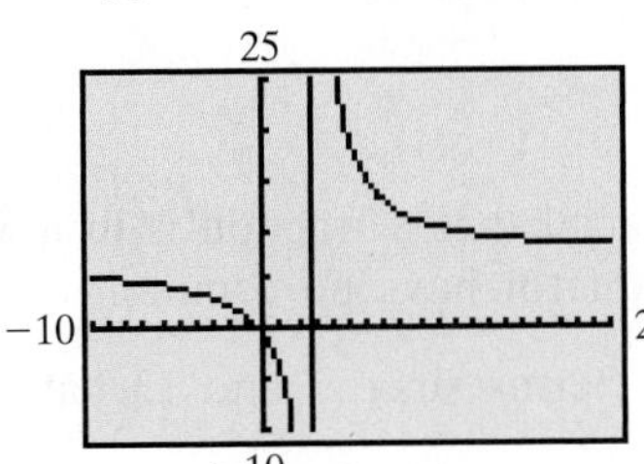

We know that this vertical line is not part of the graph because the function is undefined at $x = 3$. We also know that this vertical line is not part of the graph since the graph of this function would then not pass the vertical line test.

The graph of $y = \dfrac{7x + 2}{x - 3}$ is undefined at $x = 3$.

EXAMPLE 2 Find the domain of each rational function. Then graph each rational function and use the graph to confirm the domain.

a. $f(x) = \dfrac{x + 1}{x^2 - 4}$ **b.** $h(x) = \dfrac{x^2}{2x^2 + 7x - 4}$

Solution **a.** To find the domain of $f(x) = \dfrac{x + 1}{x^2 - 4}$, find the values that make the denominator 0.

$$x^2 - 4 = 0$$
$$(x - 2)(x + 2) = 0$$
$$x - 2 = 0 \text{ or } x + 2 = 0$$
$$x = 2 \text{ or } x = -2$$

This means that both 2 and -2 make $f(x)$ undefined. Thus the domain is $\{x|x$ is a real number and $x \neq \pm 2\}$. The graph below to the left shows that the function is undefined for $x = -2$ and $x = 2$.

b. To find the domain, solve "denominator = 0."

$$2x^2 + 7x - 4 = 0$$
$$(2x - 1)(x + 4) = 0$$
$$2x - 1 = 0 \text{ or } x + 4 = 0$$
$$x = \frac{1}{2} \text{ or } x = -4$$

Thus, the domain is $\{x|x$ is a real number and $x \neq \frac{1}{2}, x \neq -4\}$. The graph below to the right shows the function undefined at $x = -4$ and $x = \frac{1}{2}$.

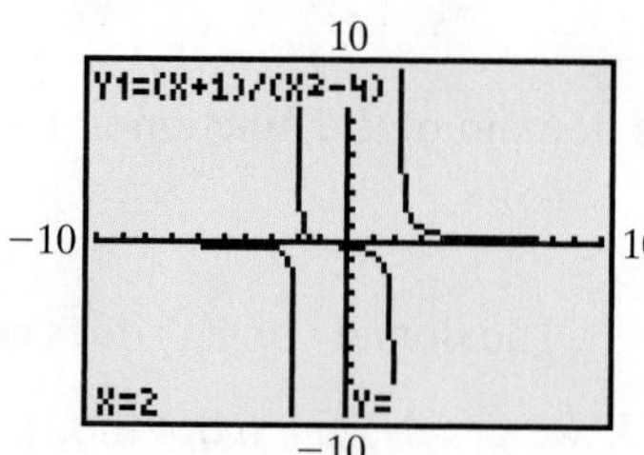

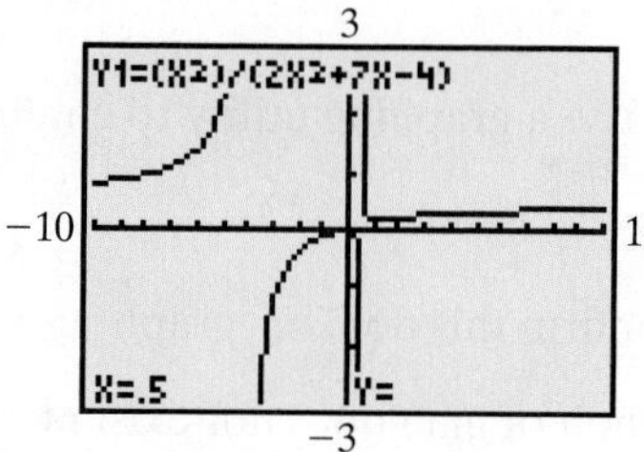

□

PRACTICE 2 Find the domain of each rational function. Then graph each rational function and use the graph to confirm the domain.

a. $f(x) = \dfrac{9x - 14}{x + 3}$ **b.** $g(x) = \dfrac{5x}{3x^2 - 8x + 5}$

Concept Check ✓

For which of these values (if any) is the rational expression $\dfrac{x - 3}{x^2 + 2}$ undefined?

a. 2 **b.** 3 **c.** -2 **d.** 0 **e.** None of these

OBJECTIVE 2 ▸ Simplifying rational expressions. Recall that a fraction is in lowest terms or simplest form if the numerator and denominator have no common factors other than 1 (or -1). For example, $\frac{3}{13}$ is in lowest terms since 3 and 13 have no common factors other than 1 (or -1).

To **simplify** a rational expression, or to write it in lowest terms, we use a method similar to simplifying a fraction.

Recall that to simplify a fraction, we essentially "remove factors of 1." Our ability to do this comes from these facts:

- If $c \neq 0$, then $\frac{c}{c} = 1$. For example, $\frac{7}{7} = 1$ and $\frac{-8.65}{-8.65} = 1$.
- $n \cdot 1 = n$. For example, $-5 \cdot 1 = -5$, $126.8 \cdot 1 = 126.8$, and $\frac{a}{b} \cdot 1 = \frac{a}{b}$, $b \neq 0$.

In other words, we have the following:

$$\frac{a \cdot c}{b \cdot c} = \frac{a}{b} \cdot \frac{c}{c} = \frac{a}{b}$$

Since $\frac{a}{b} \cdot 1 = \frac{a}{b}$

Answer to Concept Check: e

Let's practice simplifying a fraction by simplifying $\frac{15}{65}$.

$$\frac{15}{65} = \frac{3 \cdot 5}{13 \cdot 5} = \frac{3}{13} \cdot \frac{5}{5} = \frac{3}{13} \cdot 1 = \frac{3}{13}$$

Let's use the same technique and simplify the rational expression $\frac{(x+2)^2}{x^2-4}$.

$$\frac{(x+2)^2}{x^2-4} = \frac{(x+2)(x+2)}{(x-2)(x+2)}$$

$$= \frac{(x+2)}{(x-2)} \cdot \frac{x+2}{x+2}$$

$$= \frac{x+2}{x-2} \cdot 1$$

$$= \frac{x+2}{x-2}$$

This means that the rational expression $\frac{(x+2)^2}{x^2-4}$ has the same value as the rational expression $\frac{x+2}{x-2}$ for all values of x except 2 and -2. (Remember that when x is 2, the denominators of both rational expressions are 0 and that when x is -2, the original rational expression has a denominator of 0.)

As we simplify rational expressions, we will assume that the simplified rational expression is equivalent to the original rational expression for all real numbers except those for which either denominator is 0.

Just as for numerical fractions, we can use a shortcut notation. Remember that as long as exact factors in both the numerator and denominator are divided out, we are "removing a factor of 1." We can use the following notation:

$$\frac{(x+2)^2}{x^2-4} = \frac{(x+2)(x+2)}{(x-2)(x+2)}$$ A factor of 1 is identified by the shading.

$$= \frac{x+2}{x-2}$$ "Remove" the factor of 1.

This "removing a factor of 1" is stated in the principle below:

X	Y1	Y2
-3	.2	.2
-2	ERROR	0
-1	-.3333	-.3333
0	-1	-1
1	-3	-3
2	ERROR	ERROR
3	5	5

Y1■(X+2)²/(X²-4)

In this table, $y_1 = \frac{(x+2)^2}{x^2-4}$ and $y_2 = \frac{x+2}{x-2}$. Notice that both expressions are undefined at $x = 2$ (and an error message is given), and when $x = -2$, y_1 is not defined.

Fundamental Principle of Rational Expressions

For any rational expression $\frac{P}{Q}$ and any polynomial R, where $R \neq 0$,

$$\frac{PR}{QR} = \frac{P}{Q} \cdot \frac{R}{R} = \frac{P}{Q} \cdot 1 = \frac{P}{Q}$$

or, simply,

$$\frac{PR}{QR} = \frac{P}{Q}$$

In general, the following steps may be used to simplify rational expressions or to write a rational expression in lowest terms.

Simplifying or Writing a Rational Expression in Lowest Terms

STEP 1. Completely factor the numerator and denominator of the rational expression.

STEP 2. Divide out factors common to the numerator and denominator. (This is the same as "removing a factor of 1.")

For now, we assume that variables in a rational expression do not represent values that make the denominator 0.

EXAMPLE 3 Simplify each rational expression.

a. $\dfrac{2x^2}{10x^3 - 2x^2}$ **b.** $\dfrac{9x^2 + 13x + 4}{8x^2 + x - 7}$

Solution

a. $\dfrac{2x^2}{10x^3 - 2x^2} = \dfrac{2x^2 \cdot 1}{2x^2(5x - 1)} = 1 \cdot \dfrac{1}{5x - 1} = \dfrac{1}{5x - 1}$

b. $\dfrac{9x^2 + 13x + 4}{8x^2 + x - 7} = \dfrac{(9x + 4)(x + 1)}{(8x - 7)(x + 1)}$ Factor the numerator and denominator.

$= \dfrac{9x + 4}{8x - 7} \cdot 1$ Since $\dfrac{x + 1}{x + 1} = 1$

$= \dfrac{9x + 4}{8x - 7}$ Simplest form □

PRACTICE 3 Simplify each rational expression.

a. $\dfrac{5z^4}{10z^5 - 5z^4}$ **b.** $\dfrac{5x^2 + 13x + 6}{6x^2 + 7x - 10}$

EXAMPLE 4 Simplify each rational expression.

a. $\dfrac{2 + x}{x + 2}$ **b.** $\dfrac{2 - x}{x - 2}$

Solution

a. $\dfrac{2 + x}{x + 2} = \dfrac{x + 2}{x + 2} = 1$ By the commutative property of addition, $2 + x = x + 2$.

b. $\dfrac{2 - x}{x - 2}$

The terms in the numerator of $\dfrac{2 - x}{x - 2}$ differ by sign from the terms of the denominator, so the polynomials are opposites of each other and the expression simplifies to -1. To see this, we factor out -1 from the numerator or the denominator. If -1 is factored from the numerator, then

$$\frac{2 - x}{x - 2} = \frac{-1(-2 + x)}{x - 2} = \frac{-1(x - 2)}{x - 2} = \frac{-1}{1} = -1$$

If −1 is factored from the denominator, the result is the same.

$$\frac{2-x}{x-2} = \frac{2-x}{-1(-x+2)} = \frac{2-x}{-1(2-x)} = \frac{1}{-1} = -1$$ □

Helpful Hint

When the numerator and the denominator of a rational expression are opposites of each other, the expression simplifies to −1.

PRACTICE 4 Simplify each rational expression.

a. $\frac{x+3}{3+x}$ **b.** $\frac{3-x}{x-3}$

DISCOVER THE CONCEPT

a. Consider the expression $\frac{2x^2-18}{x^2-2x-3}$. Graph the numerator as $y_1 = 2x^2 - 18$ and the denominator as $y_2 = x^2 - 2x - 3$ in the same window.

b. Completely factor the numerator and the denominator of the original expression.

c. What do you notice about the common factor in the expression and the point of intersection of the graphs of the numerator and denominator?

In the above discovery, we notice that both graphs intersect the x-axis at $x = 3$. In part **b**, we find that $(x - 3)$ is a common factor of the numerator and denominator.

$$\frac{2x^2-18}{x^2-2x-3} = \frac{2(x^2-9)}{x^2-2x-3} = \frac{2(x+3)(x-3)}{(x+1)(x-3)}$$

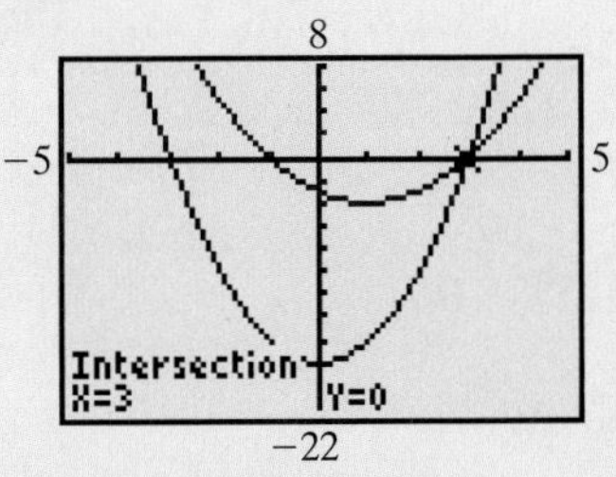

Graphs of $y_1 = 2x^2 - 18$ and $y_2 = x^2 - 2x - 3$ both intersect the x-axis at $x = 3$.

In general, if the graphs of the numerator and denominator of a rational expression share an x-intercept c, then $(x - c)$ is a common factor of the numerator and denominator of the rational expression.

EXAMPLE 5 Simplify $\frac{18-2x^2}{x^2-2x-3}$.

Solution

$$\frac{18-2x^2}{x^2-2x-3} = \frac{2(9-x^2)}{(x+1)(x-3)}$$ Factor.

$$= \frac{2(3+x)(3-x)}{(x+1)(x-3)}$$ Factor completely.

$$= \frac{2(3+x)\cdot -1(x-3)}{(x+1)(x-3)}$$ Notice the opposites $3 - x$ and $x - 3$. Write $3 - x$ as $-1(x - 3)$ and simplify.

$$= -\frac{2(3+x)}{x+1}$$ □

PRACTICE 5 Simplify $\frac{20-5x^2}{x^2+x-6}$.

Helpful Hint

Recall that for a fraction $\frac{a}{b}$,

$$\frac{a}{-b} = \frac{-a}{b} = -\frac{a}{b}$$

For example

$$\frac{-(x+1)}{(x+2)} = \frac{(x+1)}{-(x+2)} = -\frac{x+1}{x+2}$$

Concept Check ✓

Which of the following expressions are equivalent to $\frac{x}{8-x}$?

a. $\frac{-x}{x-8}$ **b.** $\frac{-x}{8-x}$ **c.** $\frac{x}{x-8}$ **d.** $\frac{-x}{-8+x}$

EXAMPLE 6 Simplify each rational expression. Check graphically.

a. $\frac{x^3+8}{2+x}$ **b.** $\frac{2y^2+2}{y^3-5y^2+y-5}$

Solution

a. $\frac{x^3+8}{2+x} = \frac{(x+2)(x^2-2x+4)}{x+2}$ Factor the sum of the two cubes.

$= x^2 - 2x + 4$ Divide out common factors.

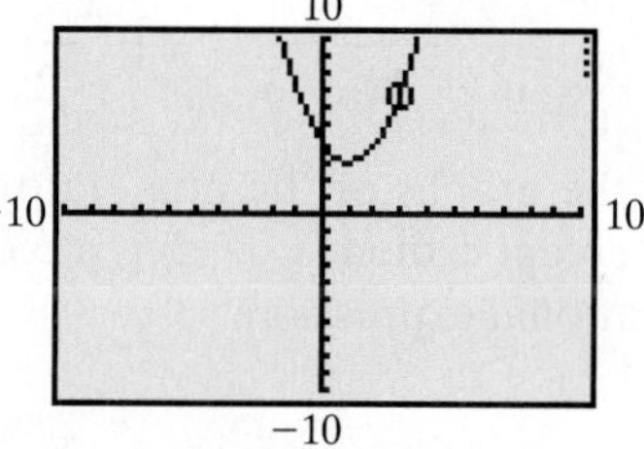

Notice in y_2 that the graph style was changed to visualize that y_1 and y_2 have the same graph.

b. $\frac{2y^2+2}{y^3-5y^2+y-5} = \frac{2(y^2+1)}{(y^3-5y^2)+(y-5)}$ Factor the numerator.

$= \frac{2(y^2+1)}{y^2(y-5)+1(y-5)}$ Factor the denominator by grouping.

$= \frac{2(y^2+1)}{(y-5)(y^2+1)}$

$= \frac{2}{y-5}$ Divide out common factors. □

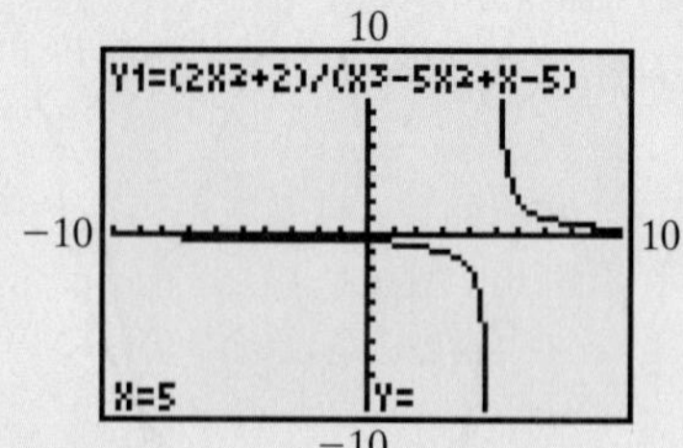

Here, $y_1 = \frac{2x^2+2}{x^3-5x^2+x-5}$ and $y_2 = \frac{2}{y-5}$. Notice that both graphs are undefined when x is 5.

PRACTICE 6 Simplify each rational expression.

a. $\frac{x^3+64}{4+x}$ **b.** $\frac{5z^2+10}{z^3-3z^2+2z-6}$

Concept Check ✓

Does $\frac{n}{n+2}$ simplify to $\frac{1}{2}$? Why or why not?

Answers to Concept Check:
a and d
no; answers may vary

OBJECTIVE 3 ▶ Multiplying rational expressions. Arithmetic operations on rational expressions are performed in the same way as they are on rational numbers.

Multiplying Rational Expressions

The rule for multiplying rational expressions is

$$\frac{P}{Q}\cdot\frac{R}{S}=\frac{PR}{QS} \quad \text{as long as } Q \neq 0 \text{ and } S \neq 0.$$

To multiply rational expressions, you may use these steps:

STEP 1. Completely factor each numerator and denominator.

STEP 2. Use the rule above and multiply the numerators and the denominators.

STEP 3. Simplify the product by dividing the numerator and denominator by their common factors.

When we multiply rational expressions, notice that we factor each numerator and denominator first. This helps when we apply the fundamental principle to write the product in simplest form.

EXAMPLE 7 Multiply.

a. $\frac{1+3n}{2n}\cdot\frac{2n-4}{3n^2-2n-1}$ **b.** $\frac{x^3-1}{-3x+3}\cdot\frac{15x^2}{x^2+x+1}$

Solution

a. $\frac{1+3n}{2n}\cdot\frac{2n-4}{3n^2-2n-1}=\frac{1+3n}{2n}\cdot\frac{2(n-2)}{(3n+1)(n-1)}$ Factor.

$=\frac{(1+3n)\cdot 2(n-2)}{2n(3n+1)(n-1)}$ Multiply.

$=\frac{n-2}{n(n-1)}$ Divide out common factors.

b. $\frac{x^3-1}{-3x+3}\cdot\frac{15x^2}{x^2+x+1}=\frac{(x-1)(x^2+x+1)}{-3(x-1)}\cdot\frac{15x^2}{x^2+x+1}$ Factor.

$=\frac{(x-1)(x^2+x+1)\cdot 3\cdot 5x^2}{-1\cdot 3(x-1)(x^2+x+1)}$ Factor.

$=\frac{5x^2}{-1}=-5x^2$ Simplest form □

PRACTICE

7 Multiply.

a. $\frac{2+5n}{3n}\cdot\frac{6n+3}{5n^2-3n-2}$ **b.** $\frac{x^3-8}{-6x+12}\cdot\frac{6x^2}{x^2+2x+4}$

OBJECTIVE 4 ▶ Dividing rational expressions. Recall that two numbers are reciprocals of each other if their product is 1. Similarly, if $\frac{P}{Q}$ is a rational expression, then $\frac{Q}{P}$ is its **reciprocal,** since

$$\frac{P}{Q}\cdot\frac{Q}{P}=\frac{P\cdot Q}{Q\cdot P}=1$$

The following are examples of expressions and their reciprocals.

Expression	***Reciprocal***
$\frac{3}{x}$	$\frac{x}{3}$
$\frac{2 + x^2}{4x - 3}$	$\frac{4x - 3}{2 + x^2}$
x^3	$\frac{1}{x^3}$
0	no reciprocal

Dividing Rational Expressions

The rule for dividing rational expressions is

$$\frac{P}{Q} \div \frac{R}{S} = \frac{P}{Q} \cdot \frac{S}{R} = \frac{PS}{QR} \quad \text{as long as } Q \neq 0, S \neq 0, \text{ and } R \neq 0.$$

To divide by a rational expression, use the rule above and multiply by its reciprocal. Then simplify if possible.

Notice that division of rational expressions is the same as for rational numbers.

EXAMPLE 8 Divide.

a. $\frac{8m^2}{3m^2 - 12} \div \frac{40}{2 - m}$ **b.** $\frac{18y^2 + 9y - 2}{24y^2 - 10y + 1} \div \frac{3y^2 + 17y + 10}{8y^2 + 18y - 5}$

Solution

a. $\frac{8m^2}{3m^2 - 12} \div \frac{40}{2 - m} = \frac{8m^2}{3m^2 - 12} \cdot \frac{2 - m}{40}$ Multiply by the reciprocal of the divisor.

$= \frac{8m^2(2 - m)}{3(m + 2)(m - 2) \cdot 40}$ Factor and multiply.

$= \frac{8m^2 \cdot -1(m - 2)}{3(m + 2)(m - 2) \cdot 8 \cdot 5}$ Write $(2 - m)$ as $-1(m - 2)$.

$= -\frac{m^2}{15(m + 2)}$ Simplify.

b. $\frac{18y^2 + 9y - 2}{24y^2 - 10y + 1} \div \frac{3y^2 + 17y + 10}{8y^2 + 18y - 5}$

$= \frac{18y^2 + 9y - 2}{24y^2 - 10y + 1} \cdot \frac{8y^2 + 18y - 5}{3y^2 + 17y + 10}$ Multiply by the reciprocal.

$= \frac{(6y - 1)(3y + 2)}{(6y - 1)(4y - 1)} \cdot \frac{(4y - 1)(2y + 5)}{(3y + 2)(y + 5)}$ Factor.

$= \frac{2y + 5}{y + 5}$ Simplest form □

PRACTICE 8 Divide.

a. $\frac{6y^3}{3y^2 - 27} \div \frac{42}{3 - y}$ **b.** $\frac{10x^2 + 23x - 5}{5x^2 - 51x + 10} \div \frac{2x^2 + 9x + 10}{7x^2 - 68x - 20}$

Helpful Hint

When dividing rational expressions, do not divide out common factors until the division problem is rewritten as a multiplication problem.

EXAMPLE 9 Perform each indicated operation.

$$\frac{x^2-25}{(x+5)^2}\cdot\frac{3x+15}{4x}\div\frac{x^2-3x-10}{x}$$

Solution

$$\frac{x^2-25}{(x+5)^2}\cdot\frac{3x+15}{4x}\div\frac{x^2-3x-10}{x}$$

$$=\frac{x^2-25}{(x+5)^2}\cdot\frac{3x+15}{4x}\cdot\frac{x}{x^2-3x-10}$$ To divide, multiply by the reciprocal

$$=\frac{(x+5)(x-5)}{(x+5)(x+5)}\cdot\frac{3(x+5)}{4x}\cdot\frac{x}{(x-5)(x+2)}$$

$$=\frac{3}{4(x+2)}$$ □

PRACTICE 9 Perform each indicated operation.

$$\frac{x^2-16}{(x-4)^2}\cdot\frac{5x-20}{3x}\div\frac{x^2+x-12}{x}$$

OBJECTIVE 5 ▶ Using rational functions in applications. Rational functions occur often in real-life situations.

EXAMPLE 10 **Cost for Pressing Compact Discs**

For the ICL Production Company, the rational function $C(x)=\frac{2.6x+10{,}000}{x}$ describes the company's cost per disc of pressing x compact discs. Find the cost per disc for pressing:

a. 100 compact discs

b. 1000 compact discs

Solution

a. $C(100)=\frac{2.6(100)+10{,}000}{100}=\frac{10{,}260}{100}=102.6$

The cost per disc for pressing 100 compact discs is \$102.60.

b. $C(1000)=\frac{2.6(1000)+10{,}000}{1000}=\frac{12{,}600}{1000}=12.6$

The cost per disc for pressing 1000 compact discs is \$12.60. Notice that as more compact discs are produced, the cost per disc decreases. □

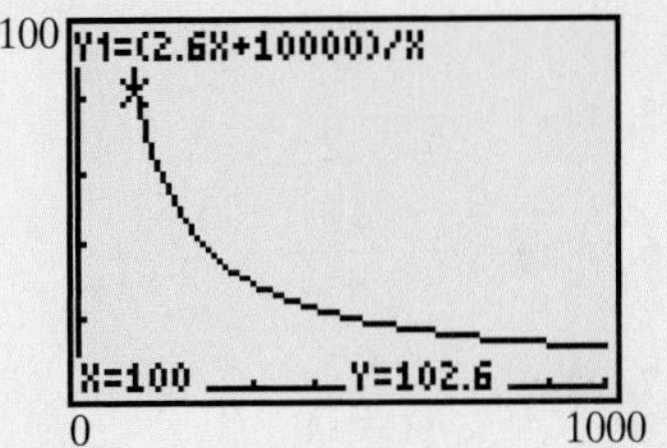

PRACTICE 10 A company's cost per T-shirt for silk screening x T-shirts is given by the rational function $C(x)=\frac{3.2x+400}{x}$. Find the cost per T-shirt for printing:

a. 100 T-shirts **b.** 1000 T-shirts

VOCABULARY & READINESS CHECK

Use the choices below to fill in each blank. Some choices may not be used.

1	true	rational	simplified	$\frac{-a}{-b}$	$\frac{-a}{b}$	$\frac{a}{-b}$
−1	false	domain	0			

1. A __________ expression is an expression that can be written as the quotient $\frac{P}{Q}$ of two polynomials P and Q as long as $Q \neq 0$.

2. A rational expression is undefined if the denominator is _____.

3. The __________ of the rational function $f(x) = \frac{2}{x}$ is $\{x|x$ is a real number and $x \neq 0\}$.

4. A rational expression is __________ if the numerator and denominator have no common factors other than 1 or −1.

5. The expression $\frac{x^2+2}{2+x^2}$ simplifies to _______.

6. The expression $\frac{y-z}{z-y}$ simplifies to ________.

7. For a rational expression, $-\frac{a}{b} =$ _____ $=$ _____.

8. True or false: $\frac{a-6}{a+2} = \frac{-(a-6)}{-(a+2)} = \frac{-a+6}{-a-2}$. _______

Multiply.

9. $\frac{x}{5} \cdot \frac{y}{2}$ **10.** $\frac{y}{6} \cdot \frac{z}{5}$ **11.** $\frac{2}{x} \cdot \frac{y}{3}$ **12.** $\frac{a}{5} \cdot \frac{7}{b}$ **13.** $\frac{m}{6} \cdot \frac{m}{6}$ **14.** $\frac{9}{x} \cdot \frac{8}{x}$

18.1 EXERCISE SET

MyMathLab

Find the domain of each rational function, then graph the function and use the graph to confirm the domain. See Examples 1 and 2.

1. $f(x) = \frac{5x-7}{4}$

2. $g(x) = \frac{4-3x}{2}$

3. $s(t) = \frac{t^2+1}{2t}$

4. $v(t) = -\frac{5t+t^2}{3t}$

5. $f(x) = \frac{3x}{7-x}$

6. $f(x) = \frac{-4x}{-2+x}$

7. $f(x) = \frac{x}{3x-1}$

8. $g(x) = \frac{-2}{2x+5}$

9. $R(x) = \frac{3+2x}{x^3+x^2-2x}$

10. $h(x) = \frac{5-3x}{2x^2-14x+20}$

11. $C(x) = \frac{x+3}{x^2-4}$

12. $R(x) = \frac{5}{x^2-7x}$

Simplify each rational expression. See Examples 3 through 6.

13. $\frac{8x-16x^2}{8x}$

14. $\frac{3x-6x^2}{3x}$

15. $\frac{x^2-9}{3+x}$

16. $\frac{x^2-25}{5+x}$

17. $\frac{9y-18}{7y-14}$

18. $\frac{6y-18}{2y-6}$

19. $\frac{x^2+6x-40}{x+10}$

20. $\frac{x^2-8x+16}{x-4}$

21. $\frac{x-9}{9-x}$

22. $\frac{x-4}{4-x}$

23. $\frac{x^2-49}{7-x}$

24. $\frac{x^2-y^2}{y-x}$

25. $\frac{2x^2-7x-4}{x^2-5x+4}$

26. $\frac{3x^2-11x+10}{x^2-7x+10}$

27. $\frac{x^3-125}{2x-10}$

28. $\frac{4x+4}{x^3+1}$

29. $\frac{3x^2-5x-2}{6x^3+2x^2+3x+1}$

30. $\frac{2x^2-x-3}{2x^3-3x^2+2x-3}$

31. $\dfrac{9x^2 - 15x + 25}{27x^3 + 125}$

32. $\dfrac{8x^3 - 27}{4x^2 + 6x + 9}$

Multiply and simplify. See Example 7.

33. $\dfrac{2x - 4}{15} \cdot \dfrac{6}{2 - x}$

34. $\dfrac{10 - 2x}{7} \cdot \dfrac{14}{5x - 25}$

35. $\dfrac{18a - 12a^2}{4a^2 + 4a + 1} \cdot \dfrac{4a^2 + 8a + 3}{4a^2 - 9}$

36. $\dfrac{a - 5b}{a^2 + ab} \cdot \dfrac{b^2 - a^2}{10b - 2a}$

37. $\dfrac{9x + 9}{4x + 8} \cdot \dfrac{2x + 4}{3x^2 - 3}$

38. $\dfrac{2x^2 - 2}{10x + 30} \cdot \dfrac{12x + 36}{3x - 3}$

39. $\dfrac{2x^3 - 16}{6x^2 + 6x - 36} \cdot \dfrac{9x + 18}{3x^2 + 6x + 12}$

40. $\dfrac{x^2 - 3x + 9}{5x^2 - 20x - 105} \cdot \dfrac{x^2 - 49}{x^3 + 27}$

41. $\dfrac{a^3 + a^2b + a + b}{5a^3 + 5a} \cdot \dfrac{6a^2}{2a^2 - 2b^2}$

42. $\dfrac{4a^2 - 8a}{ab - 2b + 3a - 6} \cdot \dfrac{8b + 24}{3a + 6}$

43. $\dfrac{x^2 - 6x - 16}{2x^2 - 128} \cdot \dfrac{x^2 + 16x + 64}{3x^2 + 30x + 48}$

44. $\dfrac{2x^2 + 12x - 32}{x^2 + 16x + 64} \cdot \dfrac{x^2 + 10x + 16}{x^2 - 3x - 10}$

Divide and simplify. See Example 8.

45. $\dfrac{2x}{5} \div \dfrac{6x + 12}{5x + 10}$

46. $\dfrac{7}{3x} \div \dfrac{14 - 7x}{18 - 9x}$

47. $\dfrac{a + b}{ab} \div \dfrac{a^2 - b^2}{4a^3b}$

48. $\dfrac{6a^2b^2}{a^2 - 4} \div \dfrac{3ab^2}{a - 2}$

49. $\dfrac{x^2 - 6x + 9}{x^2 - x - 6} \div \dfrac{x^2 - 9}{4}$

50. $\dfrac{x^2 - 4}{3x + 6} \div \dfrac{2x^2 - 8x + 8}{x^2 + 4x + 4}$

51. $\dfrac{x^2 - 6x - 16}{2x^2 - 128} \div \dfrac{x^2 + 10x + 16}{x^2 + 16x + 64}$

52. $\dfrac{a^2 - a - 6}{a^2 - 81} \div \dfrac{a^2 - 7a - 18}{4a + 36}$

53. $\dfrac{3x - x^2}{x^3 - 27} \div \dfrac{x}{x^2 + 3x + 9}$

54. $\dfrac{x^2 - 3x}{x^3 - 27} \div \dfrac{2x}{2x^2 + 6x + 18}$

55. $\dfrac{8b + 24}{3a + 6} \div \dfrac{ab - 2b + 3a - 6}{a^2 - 4a + 4}$

56. $\dfrac{2a^2 - 2b^2}{a^3 + a^2b + a + b} \div \dfrac{6a^2}{a^3 + a}$

MIXED PRACTICE

Perform each indicated operation. See Examples 3 through 9.

57. $\dfrac{x^2 - 9}{4} \cdot \dfrac{x^2 - x - 6}{x^2 - 6x + 9}$

58. $\dfrac{x^2 - 4}{9} \cdot \dfrac{x^2 - 6x + 9}{x^2 - 5x + 6}$

59. $\dfrac{2x^2 - 4x - 30}{5x^2 - 40x - 75} \div \dfrac{x^2 - 8x + 15}{x^2 - 6x + 9}$

60. $\dfrac{4a + 36}{a^2 - 7a - 18} \div \dfrac{a^2 - a - 6}{a^2 - 81}$

61. Simplify: $\dfrac{r^3 + s^3}{r + s}$

62. Simplify: $\dfrac{m^3 - n^3}{m - n}$

63. $\dfrac{4}{x} \div \dfrac{3xy}{x^2} \cdot \dfrac{6x^2}{x^4}$

64. $\dfrac{4}{x} \cdot \dfrac{3xy}{x^2} \div \dfrac{6x^2}{x^4}$

65. $\dfrac{3x^2 - 5x - 2}{y^2 + y - 2} \cdot \dfrac{y^2 + 4y - 5}{12x^2 + 7x + 1} \div \dfrac{5x^2 - 9x - 2}{8x^2 - 2x - 1}$

66. $\dfrac{x^2 + x - 2}{3y^2 - 5y - 2} \cdot \dfrac{12y^2 + y - 1}{x^2 + 4x - 5} \div \dfrac{8y^2 - 6y + 1}{5y^2 - 9y - 2}$

67. $\dfrac{5a^2 - 20}{3a^2 - 12a} \div \dfrac{a^3 + 2a^2}{2a^2 - 8a} \cdot \dfrac{9a^3 + 6a^2}{2a^2 - 4a}$

68. $\dfrac{5a^2 - 20}{3a^2 - 12a} \div \left(\dfrac{a^3 + 2a^2}{2a^2 - 8a} \cdot \dfrac{9a^3 + 6a^2}{2a^2 - 4a}\right)$

69. $\dfrac{5x^4 + 3x^2 - 2}{x - 1} \cdot \dfrac{x + 1}{x^4 - 1}$

70. $\dfrac{3x^4 - 10x^2 - 8}{x - 2} \cdot \dfrac{3x + 6}{15x^2 + 10}$

Find each function value. See Example 10.

71. If $f(x) = \dfrac{x + 8}{2x - 1}$, find $f(2)$, $f(0)$, and $f(-1)$.

72. If $f(x) = \dfrac{x - 2}{-5 + x}$, find $f(-5)$, $f(0)$, and $f(10)$.

73. If $g(x) = \dfrac{x^2 + 8}{x^3 - 25x}$, find $g(3)$, $g(-2)$, and $g(1)$.

74. If $s(t) = \dfrac{t^3 + 1}{t^2 + 1}$, find $s(-1)$, $s(1)$, and $s(2)$.

75. The total revenue from the sale of a popular book is approximated by the rational function $R(x) = \dfrac{1000x^2}{x^2 + 4}$, where x is the number of years since publication and $R(x)$ is the total revenue in millions of dollars.

a. Find the total revenue at the end of the first year.

b. Find the total revenue at the end of the second year.

c. Find the revenue during the second year only.

d. Find the domain of function R.

76. The function $f(x) = \dfrac{100{,}000x}{100 - x}$ models the cost in dollars for removing x percent of the pollutants from a bayou in which a nearby company dumped creosol.

a. Find the cost of removing 20% of the pollutants from the bayou. [*Hint:* Find $f(20)$.]

b. Find the cost of removing 60% of the pollutants and then 80% of the pollutants.

c. Find $f(90)$, then $f(95)$, and then $f(99)$. What happens to the cost as x approaches 100%?

d. Find the domain of function f.

REVIEW AND PREVIEW

Perform each indicated operation.

77. $\dfrac{4}{5} + \dfrac{3}{5}$

78. $\dfrac{4}{10} - \dfrac{7}{10}$

79. $\dfrac{5}{28} - \dfrac{2}{21}$

80. $\dfrac{5}{13} + \dfrac{2}{7}$

81. $\dfrac{3}{8} + \dfrac{1}{2} - \dfrac{3}{16}$

82. $\dfrac{2}{9} - \dfrac{1}{6} + \dfrac{2}{3}$

CONCEPT EXTENSIONS

Solve. For Exercises 83 and 84, see the first Concept Check in this section; for Exercises 85 and 86, see the second Concept Check.

83. Which of the expressions are equivalent to $\dfrac{x}{5 - x}$?

a. $\dfrac{-x}{5 - x}$

b. $\dfrac{-x}{-5 + x}$

c. $\dfrac{x}{x - 5}$

d. $\dfrac{-x}{x - 5}$

84. Which of the expressions are equivalent to $\dfrac{-2 + x}{x}$?

a. $\dfrac{2 - x}{-x}$

b. $-\dfrac{2 - x}{x}$

c. $\dfrac{x - 2}{x}$

d. $\dfrac{x - 2}{-x}$

85. Does $\dfrac{x}{x + 5}$ simplify to $\dfrac{1}{5}$? Why or why not?

86. Does $\dfrac{x + 7}{x}$ simplify to 7? Why or why not?

△ **87.** Find the area of the rectangle.

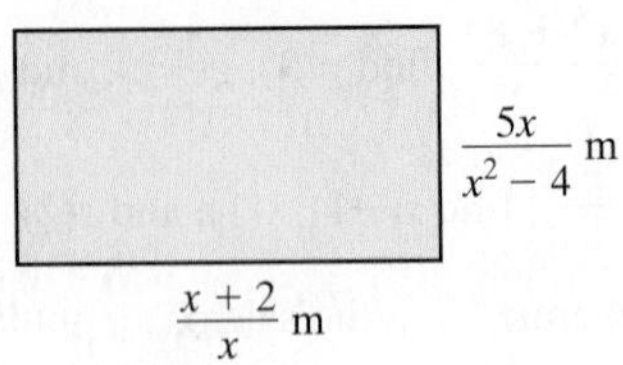

△ **88.** Find the area of the triangle.

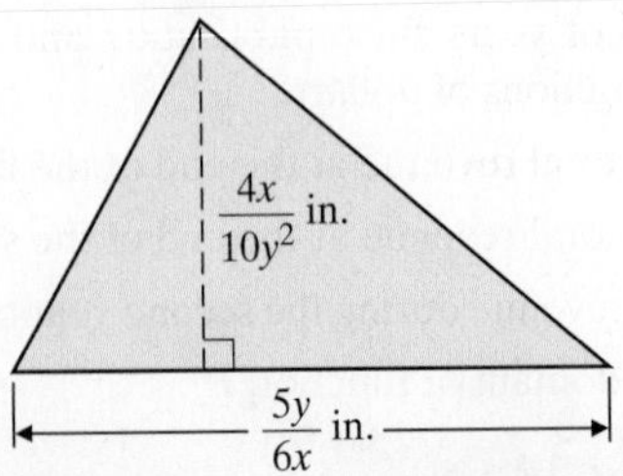

△ **89.** A parallelogram has an area of $\dfrac{x^2 + x - 2}{x^3}$ square feet and a height of $\dfrac{x^2}{x - 1}$ feet. Express the length of its base as a rational expression in x. (*Hint:* Since $A = b \cdot h$, then $b = \dfrac{A}{h}$ or $b = A \div h$.)

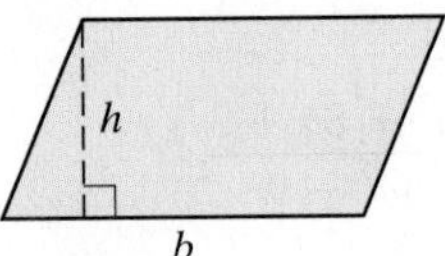

90. A lottery prize of $\dfrac{15x^3}{y^2}$ dollars is to be divided among $5x$ people. Express the amount of money each person is to receive as a rational expression in x and y.

91. In your own words explain how to simplify a rational expression.

92. In your own words, explain the difference between multiplying rational expressions and dividing rational expressions.

93. Decide whether each rational expression equals 1, −1, or neither.

a. $\dfrac{x + 5}{5 + x}$

b. $\dfrac{x - 5}{5 - x}$

c. $\dfrac{x + 5}{x - 5}$

d. $\dfrac{-x - 5}{x + 5}$

e. $\dfrac{x - 5}{-x + 5}$

f. $\dfrac{-5 + x}{x - 5}$

94. In our definition of division for

$$\frac{P}{Q} \div \frac{R}{S}$$

we stated that $Q \neq 0$, $S \neq 0$, and $R \neq 0$. Explain why R cannot equal 0.

95. Find the polynomial in the second numerator such that the following statement is true.

$$\frac{x^2 - 4}{x^2 - 7x + 10} \cdot \frac{?}{2x^2 + 11x + 14} = 1$$

96. In your own words, explain how to find the domain of a rational function.

97. Graph a portion of the function $f(x) = \dfrac{20x}{100 - x}$. To do so, complete the given table, plot the points, and then connect the plotted points with a smooth curve.

x	0	10	30	50	70	90	95	99
y or f(x)								

98. The domain of the function $f(x) = \dfrac{1}{x}$ is all real numbers except 0. This means that the graph of this function will be in two pieces: one piece corresponding to x-values less than 0 and one piece corresponding to x-values greater than 0. Graph the function by completing the following tables, separately plotting the points, and connecting each set of plotted points with a smooth curve.

x	$\frac{1}{4}$	$\frac{1}{2}$	1	2	4
y or $f(x)$					

x	-4	-2	-1	$-\frac{1}{2}$	$-\frac{1}{4}$
y or $f(x)$					

Perform the indicated operation. Write all answers in lowest terms.

99. $\dfrac{x^{2n}-4}{7x}\cdot\dfrac{14x^3}{x^n-2}$

100. $\dfrac{x^{2n}+4x^n+4}{4x-3}\cdot\dfrac{8x^2-6x}{x^n+2}$

101. $\dfrac{y^{2n}+9}{10y}\cdot\dfrac{y^n-3}{y^{4n}-81}$

102. $\dfrac{y^{4n}-16}{y^{2n}+4}\cdot\dfrac{6y}{y^n+2}$

103. $\dfrac{y^{2n}-y^n-2}{2y^n-4}\div\dfrac{y^{2n}-1}{1+y^n}$

104. $\dfrac{y^{2n}+7y^n+10}{10}\div\dfrac{y^{2n}+4y^n+4}{5y^n+25}$

STUDY SKILLS BUILDER

Are You Satisfied with Your Performance in this Course thus Far?

To see if there is room for improvement, answer these questions:

1. Am I attending all classes and arriving on time?
2. Am I working and checking my homework assignments on time?
3. Am I getting help (from my instructor or a campus learning resource lab) when I need it?
4. In addition to my instructor, am I using the text supplements that might help me?
5. Am I satisfied with my performance on quizzes and exams?

18.2 ADDING AND SUBTRACTING RATIONAL EXPRESSIONS

OBJECTIVES

1. Add or subtract rational expressions with common denominators.
2. Identify the least common denominator of two or more rational expressions.
3. Add or subtract rational expressions with unlike denominators.

OBJECTIVE 1 ▶ Adding or subtracting rational expressions with common denominators. Rational expressions, like rational numbers, can be added or subtracted. We add or subtract rational expressions in the same way that we add or subtract rational numbers (fractions).

Adding or Subtracting Rational Expressions with Common Denominators

If $\dfrac{P}{Q}$ and $\dfrac{R}{Q}$ are rational expressions, then

$$\frac{P}{Q}+\frac{R}{Q}=\frac{P+R}{Q} \quad \text{and} \quad \frac{P}{Q}-\frac{R}{Q}=\frac{P-R}{Q}$$

To add or subtract rational expressions with common denominators, add or subtract the numerators and write the sum or difference over the common denominator.

EXAMPLE 1 Add or subtract.

a. $\frac{x}{4} + \frac{5x}{4}$ **b.** $\frac{5}{7z^2} + \frac{x}{7z^2}$ **c.** $\frac{x^2}{x+7} - \frac{49}{x+7}$ **d.** $\frac{x}{3y^2} - \frac{x+1}{3y^2}$

Solution The rational expressions have common denominators, so add or subtract their numerators and place the sum or difference over their common denominator.

a. $\frac{x}{4} + \frac{5x}{4} = \frac{x+5x}{4} = \frac{6x}{4} = \frac{3x}{2}$ Add the numerators and write the result over the common denominator.

b. $\frac{5}{7z^2} + \frac{x}{7z^2} = \frac{5+x}{7z^2}$

c. $\frac{x^2}{x+7} - \frac{49}{x+7} = \frac{x^2-49}{x+7}$ Subtract the numerators and write the result over the common denominator.

$= \frac{(x+7)(x-7)}{x+7}$ Factor the numerator.

$= x - 7$ Simplify.

d. $\frac{x}{3y^2} - \frac{x+1}{3y^2} = \frac{x-(x+1)}{3y^2}$ Subtract the numerators.

$= \frac{x-x-1}{3y^2}$ Use the distributive property.

$= -\frac{1}{3y^2}$ Simplify. □

Helpful Hint

Very Important: Be sure to insert parentheses here so that the entire numerator is subtracted.

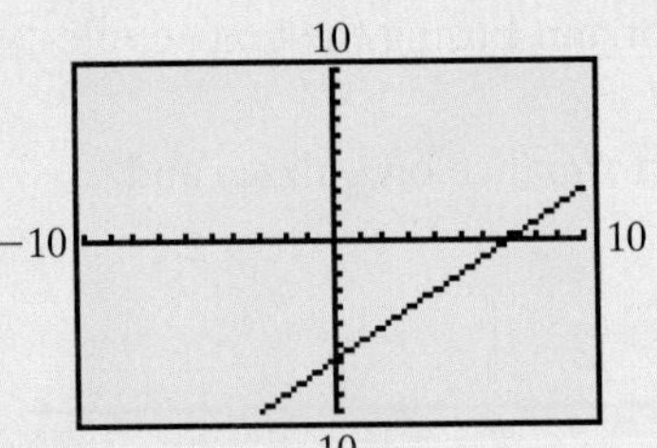

A graphing utility can be used to provide partial support of the result of operations on rational expressions. For example, the graphs of $y_1 = \frac{x^2}{x+7} - \frac{49}{x+7}$ and $y_2 = x - 7$ appear to coincide. This provides partial support for the algebraic solution in part c of Example 1. The trace feature can be used to verify that the two graphs coincide (except when x is −7).

PRACTICE 1 Add or subtract.

a. $\frac{9}{11z^2} + \frac{x}{11z^2}$ **b.** $\frac{x}{8} + \frac{5x}{8}$ **c.** $\frac{x^2}{x+4} - \frac{16}{x+4}$ **d.** $\frac{z}{2a^2} - \frac{z+3}{2a^2}$

Concept Check ✓

Find and correct the error.

$$\frac{3+2y}{y^2-1} - \frac{y+3}{y^2-1} = \frac{3+2y-y+3}{y^2-1}$$
$$= \frac{y+6}{y^2-1}$$

OBJECTIVE 2 ▸ Identifying the least common denominator of rational expressions. To add or subtract rational expressions with unlike denominators, first write the rational expressions as equivalent rational expressions with common denominators.

The **least common denominator (LCD)** is usually the easiest common denominator to work with. The LCD of a list of rational expressions is a polynomial of least degree whose factors include the denominator factors in the list.

Use the following steps to find the LCD.

Finding the Least Common Denominator (LCD)

STEP 1. Factor each denominator completely.

STEP 2. The LCD is the product of all unique factors each raised to a power equal to the greatest number of times that the factor appears in any factored denominator.

Answer to Concept Check:

$$\frac{3+2y}{y^2-1} - \frac{y+3}{y^2-1} = \frac{3+2y-y-3}{y^2-1} = \frac{y}{y^2-1}$$

EXAMPLE 2 Find the LCD of the rational expressions in each list.

a. $\frac{2}{3x^5y^2}, \frac{3z}{5xy^3}$

b. $\frac{7}{z+1}, \frac{z}{z-1}$

c. $\frac{m-1}{m^2-25}, \frac{2m}{2m^2-9m-5}, \frac{7}{m^2-10m+25}$

d. $\frac{x}{x^2-4}, \frac{11}{6-3x}$

Solution

a. First we factor each denominator.

$$3x^5y^2 = 3 \cdot x^5 \cdot y^2$$
$$5xy^3 = 5 \cdot x \cdot y^3$$
$$\text{LCD} = 3 \cdot 5 \cdot x^5 \cdot y^3 = 15x^5y^3$$

Helpful Hint
The greatest power of x is 5, so we have a factor of x^5. The greatest power of y is 3, so we have a factor of y^3.

b. The denominators $z + 1$ and $z - 1$ do not factor further. Thus,

$$\text{LCD} = (z+1)(z-1)$$

c. We first factor each denominator.

$$m^2 - 25 = (m+5)(m-5)$$
$$2m^2 - 9m - 5 = (2m+1)(m-5)$$
$$m^2 - 10m + 25 = (m-5)(m-5)$$
$$\text{LCD} = (m+5)(2m+1)(m-5)^2$$

d. Factor each denominator.

$$x^2 - 4 = (x+2)(x-2)$$
$$6 - 3x = 3(2-x) = 3(-1)(x-2)$$
$$\text{LCD} = 3(-1)(x+2)(x-2)$$
$$= -3(x+2)(x-2)$$

□

Helpful Hint
$(x - 2)$ and $(2 - x)$ are opposite factors. Notice that -1 was factored from $(2 - x)$ so that the factors are identical.

Helpful Hint
If opposite factors occur, do not use both in the LCD. Instead, factor -1 from one of the opposite factors so that the factors are then identical.

PRACTICE
2 Find the LCD of the rational expression in each list.

a. $\frac{7}{6x^3y^5}, \frac{2}{9x^2y^4}$

b. $\frac{11}{x-2}, \frac{x}{x+3}$

c. $\frac{b+2}{b^2-16}, \frac{8}{b^2-8b+16}, \frac{5b}{2b^2-5b-12}$

d. $\frac{y}{y^2-9}, \frac{3}{12-4y}$

OBJECTIVE 3 ▶ Adding or subtracting rational expressions with unlike denominators.
To add or subtract rational expressions with unlike denominators, we write each rational expression as an equivalent rational expression so that their denominators are alike.

Adding or Subtracting Rational Expressions with Unlike Denominators

STEP 1. Find the LCD of the rational expressions.

STEP 2. Write each rational expression as an equivalent rational expression whose denominator is the LCD found in Step 1.

STEP 3. Add or subtract numerators, and write the result over the common denominator.

STEP 4. Simplify the resulting rational expression.

EXAMPLE 3 Perform the indicated operation.

a. $\frac{2}{x^2y} + \frac{5}{3x^3y}$ **b.** $\frac{3x}{x+2} + \frac{2x}{x-2}$ **c.** $\frac{2x-6}{x-1} - \frac{4}{1-x}$

Solution

a. The LCD is $3x^3y$. Write each fraction as an equivalent fraction with denominator $3x^3y$. To do this, we multiply both the numerator and denominator of each fraction by the factors needed to obtain the LCD as denominator.

The first fraction is multiplied by $\frac{3x}{3x}$ so that the new denominator is the LCD.

$$\frac{2}{x^2y} + \frac{5}{3x^3y} = \frac{2\cdot 3x}{x^2y\cdot 3x} + \frac{5}{3x^3y}$$ The second expression already has a denominator of $3x^3y$.

$$= \frac{6x}{3x^3y} + \frac{5}{3x^3y}$$

$$= \frac{6x+5}{3x^3y}$$ Add the numerators.

X	Y_1	Y_2
-3	10.2	10.2
-2	ERROR	ERROR
-1	-2.333	-2.333
0	0	0
1	-1	-1
2	ERROR	ERROR
3	7.8	7.8

Y1■3X/(X+2)+2X/...

This table of $y_1 = \frac{3x}{x+2} + \frac{2x}{x-2}$ and $y_2 = \frac{5x^2-2x}{(x+2)(x-2)}$ provides partial support for the result of part b in Example 3. Notice that both -2 and 2 give error messages indicating each would make the denominator zero.

b. The LCD is the product of the two denominators: $(x+2)(x-2)$.

$$\frac{3x}{x+2} + \frac{2x}{x-2} = \frac{3x\cdot(x-2)}{(x+2)\cdot(x-2)} + \frac{2x\cdot(x+2)}{(x-2)\cdot(x+2)}$$ Write equivalent rational expressions.

$$= \frac{3x^2-6x}{(x+2)(x-2)} + \frac{2x^2+4x}{(x+2)(x-2)}$$ Multiply in the numerators.

$$= \frac{3x^2-6x+2x^2+4x}{(x+2)(x-2)}$$ Add the numerators.

$$= \frac{5x^2-2x}{(x+2)(x-2)}$$ Simplify the numerator.

c. The LCD is either $x-1$ or $1-x$. To get a common denominator of $x-1$, we factor -1 from the denominator of the second rational expression.

$$\frac{2x-6}{x-1} - \frac{4}{1-x} = \frac{2x-6}{x-1} - \frac{4}{-1(x-1)}$$ Write $1-x$ as $-1(x-1)$.

$$= \frac{2x-6}{x-1} - \frac{-1\cdot 4}{x-1}$$ Write $\frac{4}{-1(x-1)}$ as $\frac{-1\cdot 4}{x-1}$.

$$= \frac{2x-6-(-4)}{x-1}$$ Combine the numerators.

$$= \frac{2x-6+4}{x-1}$$ Simplify.

$$= \frac{2x-2}{x-1}$$

$$= \frac{2(x-1)}{x-1}$$ Factor.

$$= 2$$ Simplest form □

PRACTICE 3 Perform the indicated operation.

a. $\frac{4}{p^3q} + \frac{3}{5p^4q}$ **b.** $\frac{4}{y+3} + \frac{5y}{y-3}$ **c.** $\frac{3z-18}{z-5} - \frac{3}{5-z}$

EXAMPLE 4 Subtract $\frac{5k}{k^2-4} - \frac{2}{k^2+k-2}$.

Solution $\frac{5k}{k^2-4} - \frac{2}{k^2+k-2} = \frac{5k}{(k+2)(k-2)} - \frac{2}{(k+2)(k-1)}$ Factor each denominator to find the LCD.

The LCD is $(k+2)(k-2)(k-1)$. We write equivalent rational expressions with the LCD as denominators.

$$\frac{5k}{(k+2)(k-2)} - \frac{2}{(k+2)(k-1)}$$

$$= \frac{5k\cdot(k-1)}{(k+2)(k-2)\cdot(k-1)} - \frac{2\cdot(k-2)}{(k+2)(k-1)\cdot(k-2)}$$ Write equivalent rational expressions.

$$= \frac{5k^2-5k}{(k+2)(k-2)(k-1)} - \frac{2k-4}{(k+2)(k-2)(k-1)}$$ Multiply in the numerators.

$$= \frac{5k^2-5k-2k+4}{(k+2)(k-2)(k-1)}$$ Subtract the numerators.

$$= \frac{5k^2-7k+4}{(k+2)(k-2)(k-1)}$$ Simplify. □

Helpful Hint

Very Important: Because we are subtracting; notice the sign change on 4.

PRACTICE 4 Subtract $\frac{t}{t^2-25} - \frac{3}{t^2-3t-10}$.

EXAMPLE 5 Add $\frac{2x-1}{2x^2-9x-5} + \frac{x+3}{6x^2-x-2}$.

Solution

$$\frac{2x-1}{2x^2-9x-5} + \frac{x+3}{6x^2-x-2} = \frac{2x-1}{(2x+1)(x-5)} + \frac{x+3}{(2x+1)(3x-2)}$$ Factor the denominators.

The LCD is $(2x+1)(x-5)(3x-2)$.

$$= \frac{(2x-1)\cdot(3x-2)}{(2x+1)(x-5)\cdot(3x-2)} + \frac{(x+3)\cdot(x-5)}{(2x+1)(3x-2)\cdot(x-5)}$$

$$= \frac{6x^2-7x+2}{(2x+1)(x-5)(3x-2)} + \frac{x^2-2x-15}{(2x+1)(x-5)(3x-2)}$$ Multiply in the numerators.

$$= \frac{6x^2-7x+2+x^2-2x-15}{(2x+1)(x-5)(3x-2)}$$ Add the numerators.

$$= \frac{7x^2-9x-13}{(2x+1)(x-5)(3x-2)}$$ Simplify. □

PRACTICE 5 Add $\frac{2x + 3}{3x^2 - 5x - 2} + \frac{x - 6}{6x^2 - 13x - 5}$.

EXAMPLE 6 Perform each indicated operation.

$$\frac{7}{x - 1} + \frac{10x}{x^2 - 1} - \frac{5}{x + 1}$$

Solution $\frac{7}{x-1} + \frac{10x}{x^2-1} - \frac{5}{x+1} = \frac{7}{x-1} + \frac{10x}{(x-1)(x+1)} - \frac{5}{x+1}$ Factor the denominators.

The LCD is $(x - 1)(x + 1)$.

$$= \frac{7 \cdot (x + 1)}{(x - 1) \cdot (x + 1)} + \frac{10x}{(x - 1)(x + 1)} - \frac{5 \cdot (x - 1)}{(x + 1) \cdot (x - 1)}$$

$$= \frac{7x + 7}{(x - 1)(x + 1)} + \frac{10x}{(x - 1)(x + 1)} - \frac{5x - 5}{(x + 1)(x - 1)}$$ Multiply in the numerators.

$$= \frac{7x + 7 + 10x - 5x + 5}{(x - 1)(x + 1)}$$ Add and subtract the numerators.

$$= \frac{12x + 12}{(x - 1)(x + 1)}$$ Simplify.

$$= \frac{12(x + 1)}{(x - 1)(x + 1)}$$ Factor the numerator.

$$= \frac{12}{x - 1}$$ Divide out common factors. □

PRACTICE 6 Perform each indicated operation.

$$\frac{2}{x - 2} + \frac{3x}{x^2 - x - 2} - \frac{1}{x + 1}$$

VOCABULARY & READINESS CHECK

Name the operation(s) below that make each statement true.

a. Addition **b.** Subtraction **c.** Multiplication **d.** Division

1. The denominators must be the same before performing the operation.____

2. To perform this operation, you multiply the first rational expression by the reciprocal of the second rational expression.____

3. Numerator times numerator all over denominator times denominator.____

4. These operations are commutative (order doesn't matter.)____

For the rational expressions $\frac{5}{y}$ and $\frac{7}{y}$, perform each operation mentally.

5. Addition ____ **6.** Subtraction ____ **7.** Multiplication ____ **8.** Division ____

Be careful when subtracting! For example, $\dfrac{8}{x+1} - \dfrac{x+5}{x+1} = \dfrac{8-(x+5)}{x+1} = \dfrac{3-x}{x+1}$ or $\dfrac{-x+3}{x+1}$.

Use this example to help you perform the subtractions.

9. $\dfrac{5}{2x} - \dfrac{x+1}{2x} =$ ______ **10.** $\dfrac{9}{5x} - \dfrac{6-x}{5x} =$ ______ **11.** $\dfrac{y+11}{y-2} - \dfrac{y-5}{y-2} =$ ______ **12.** $\dfrac{z-1}{z+6} - \dfrac{z+4}{z+6} =$ ______

18.2 EXERCISE SET

MyMathLab

PRACTICE

WATCH

DOWNLOAD

READ

REVIEW

Add or subtract as indicated. Simplify each answer. See Example 1.

1. $\dfrac{2}{xz^2} - \dfrac{5}{xz^2}$ **2.** $\dfrac{4}{x^2y} - \dfrac{2}{x^2y}$

3. $\dfrac{2}{x-2} + \dfrac{x}{x-2}$ **4.** $\dfrac{x}{5-x} + \dfrac{7}{5-x}$

5. $\dfrac{x^2}{x+2} - \dfrac{4}{x+2}$ **6.** $\dfrac{x^2}{x+6} - \dfrac{36}{x+6}$

7. $\dfrac{2x-6}{x^2+x-6} + \dfrac{3-3x}{x^2+x-6}$ **8.** $\dfrac{5x+2}{x^2+2x-8} + \dfrac{2-4x}{x^2+2x-8}$

9. $\dfrac{x-5}{2x} - \dfrac{x+5}{2x}$ **10.** $\dfrac{x+4}{4x} - \dfrac{x-4}{4x}$

Find the LCD of the rational expressions in each list. See Example 2.

11. $\dfrac{2}{7}, \dfrac{3}{5x}$ **12.** $\dfrac{4}{5y}, \dfrac{3}{4y^2}$

13. $\dfrac{3}{x}, \dfrac{2}{x+1}$ **14.** $\dfrac{5}{2x}, \dfrac{7}{2+x}$

15. $\dfrac{12}{x+7}, \dfrac{8}{x-7}$ **16.** $\dfrac{1}{2x-1}, \dfrac{8}{2x+1}$

17. $\dfrac{5}{3x+6}, \dfrac{2x}{2x-4}$ **18.** $\dfrac{2}{3a+9}, \dfrac{5}{5a-15}$

19. $\dfrac{2a}{a^2-b^2}, \dfrac{1}{a^2-2ab+b^2}$ **20.** $\dfrac{2a}{a^2+8a+16}, \dfrac{7a}{a^2+a-12}$

21. $\dfrac{x}{x^2-9}, \dfrac{5}{x}, \dfrac{7}{12-4x}$ **22.** $\dfrac{9}{x^2-25}, \dfrac{1}{50-10x}, \dfrac{6}{x}$

Add or subtract as indicated. Simplify each answer. See Examples 3a and 3b.

23. $\dfrac{4}{3x} + \dfrac{3}{2x}$ **24.** $\dfrac{10}{7x} + \dfrac{5}{2x}$

25. $\dfrac{5}{2y^2} - \dfrac{2}{7y}$ **26.** $\dfrac{4}{11x^4} - \dfrac{1}{4x^2}$

27. $\dfrac{x-3}{x+4} - \dfrac{x+2}{x-4}$ **28.** $\dfrac{x-1}{x-5} - \dfrac{x+2}{x+5}$

29. $\dfrac{1}{x-5} - \dfrac{19-2x}{(x-5)(x+4)}$ **30.** $\dfrac{4x-2}{(x-5)(x+4)} - \dfrac{2}{x+4}$

Perform the indicated operation. If possible, simplify your answer. See Example 3c.

31. $\dfrac{1}{a-b} + \dfrac{1}{b-a}$ **32.** $\dfrac{1}{a-3} - \dfrac{1}{3-a}$

33. $\dfrac{x+1}{1-x} + \dfrac{1}{x-1}$ **34.** $\dfrac{5}{1-x} - \dfrac{1}{x-1}$

35. $\dfrac{5}{x-2} + \dfrac{x+4}{2-x}$ **36.** $\dfrac{3}{5-x} + \dfrac{x+2}{x-5}$

Perform each indicated operation. If possible, simplify your answer. See Examples 4 through 6.

37. $\dfrac{y+1}{y^2-6y+8} - \dfrac{3}{y^2-16}$

38. $\dfrac{x+2}{x^2-36} - \dfrac{x}{x^2+9x+18}$

39. $\dfrac{x+4}{3x^2+11x+6} + \dfrac{x}{2x^2+x-15}$

40. $\dfrac{x+3}{5x^2+12x+4} + \dfrac{6}{x^2-x-6}$

41. $\dfrac{7}{x^2-x-2} - \dfrac{x-1}{x^2+4x+3}$

42. $\dfrac{a}{a^2+10a+25} - \dfrac{4-a}{a^2+6a+5}$

43. $\dfrac{x}{x^2-8x+7} - \dfrac{x+2}{2x^2-9x-35}$

44. $\dfrac{x}{x^2-7x+6} - \dfrac{x+4}{3x^2-2x-1}$

45. $\dfrac{2}{a^2+2a+1} + \dfrac{3}{a^2-1}$

46. $\dfrac{9x+2}{3x^2-2x-8} + \dfrac{7}{3x^2+x-4}$

MIXED PRACTICE

Add or subtract as indicated. If possible, simplify your answer. See Examples 1 through 6.

47. $\frac{4}{3x^2y^3} + \frac{5}{3x^2y^3}$

48. $\frac{7}{2xy^4} + \frac{1}{2xy^4}$

49. $\frac{13x - 5}{2x} - \frac{13x + 5}{2x}$

50. $\frac{17x + 4}{4x} - \frac{17x - 4}{4x}$

51. $\frac{3}{2x + 10} + \frac{8}{3x + 15}$

52. $\frac{10}{3x - 3} + \frac{1}{7x - 7}$

53. $\frac{-2}{x^2 - 3x} - \frac{1}{x^3 - 3x^2}$

54. $\frac{-3}{2a + 8} - \frac{8}{a^2 + 4a}$

55. $\frac{ab}{a^2 - b^2} + \frac{b}{a + b}$

56. $\frac{x}{25 - x^2} + \frac{2}{3x - 15}$

57. $\frac{5}{x^2 - 4} - \frac{3}{x^2 + 4x + 4}$

58. $\frac{3z}{z^2 - 9} - \frac{2}{3 - z}$

59. $\frac{3x}{2x^2 - 11x + 5} + \frac{7}{x^2 - 2x - 15}$

60. $\frac{2x}{3x^2 - 13x + 4} + \frac{5}{x^2 - 2x - 8}$

61. $\frac{2}{x + 1} - \frac{3x}{3x + 3} + \frac{1}{2x + 2}$

62. $\frac{5}{3x - 6} - \frac{x}{x - 2} + \frac{3 + 2x}{5x - 10}$

63. $\frac{3}{x + 3} + \frac{5}{x^2 + 6x + 9} - \frac{x}{x^2 - 9}$

64. $\frac{x + 2}{x^2 - 2x - 3} + \frac{x}{x - 3} - \frac{x}{x + 1}$

65. $\frac{x}{x^2 - 9} + \frac{3}{x^2 - 6x + 9} - \frac{1}{x + 3}$

66. $\frac{3}{x^2 - 9} - \frac{x}{x^2 - 6x + 9} + \frac{1}{x + 3}$

67. $\left(\frac{1}{x} + \frac{2}{3}\right) - \left(\frac{1}{x} - \frac{2}{3}\right)$

68. $\left(\frac{1}{2} + \frac{2}{x}\right) - \left(\frac{1}{2} - \frac{1}{x}\right)$

Perform the indicated operation. If possible, simplify your answer.

69. $\left(\frac{2}{3} - \frac{1}{x}\right) \cdot \left(\frac{3}{x} + \frac{1}{2}\right)$

70. $\left(\frac{2}{3} - \frac{1}{x}\right) \div \left(\frac{3}{x} + \frac{1}{2}\right)$

71. $\left(\frac{2a}{3}\right)^2 \div \left(\frac{a^2}{a + 1} - \frac{1}{a + 1}\right)$

72. $\left(\frac{x + 2}{2x} - \frac{x - 2}{2x}\right) \cdot \left(\frac{5x}{4}\right)^2$

73. $\left(\frac{2x}{3}\right)^2 \div \left(\frac{x}{3}\right)^2$

74. $\left(\frac{2x}{3}\right)^2 \cdot \left(\frac{3}{x}\right)^2$

75. $\left(\frac{x}{x + 1} - \frac{x}{x - 1}\right) \div \frac{x}{2x + 2}$

76. $\frac{x}{2x + 2} \div \left(\frac{x}{x + 1} + \frac{x}{x - 1}\right)$

77. $\frac{4}{x} \cdot \left(\frac{2}{x + 2} - \frac{2}{x - 2}\right)$

78. $\frac{1}{x + 1} \cdot \left(\frac{5}{x} + \frac{2}{x - 3}\right)$

REVIEW AND PREVIEW

Use the distributive property to multiply the following.

79. $12\left(\frac{2}{3} + \frac{1}{6}\right)$

80. $14\left(\frac{1}{7} + \frac{3}{14}\right)$

81. $x^2\left(\frac{4}{x^2} + 1\right)$

82. $5y^2\left(\frac{1}{y^2} - \frac{1}{5}\right)$

Find each root.

83. $\sqrt{100}$

84. $\sqrt{25}$

85. $\sqrt[3]{8}$

86. $\sqrt[3]{27}$

87. $\sqrt[4]{81}$

88. $\sqrt[4]{16}$

Use the Pythagorean theorem to find each unknown length of a right triangle.

△ 89.

3 meters

4 meters

△ 90.

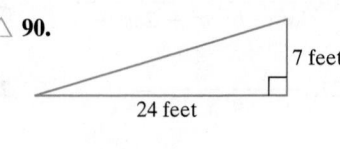

7 feet

24 feet

CONCEPT EXTENSIONS

Find and correct each error. See the Concept Check in this section.

91. $\frac{2x - 3}{x^2 + 1} - \frac{x - 6}{x^2 + 1} = \frac{2x - 3 - x - 6}{x^2 + 1}$

$= \frac{x - 9}{x^2 + 1}$

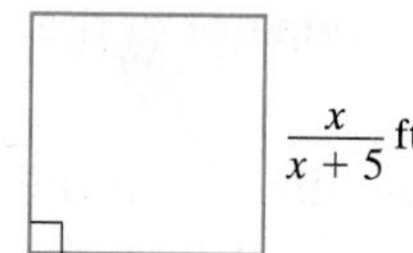

92. $\frac{7}{x+7} - \frac{x+3}{x+7} = \frac{7-x-3}{(x+7)^2} = \frac{-x+4}{(x+7)^2}$

△ **93.** Find the perimeter and the area of the square.

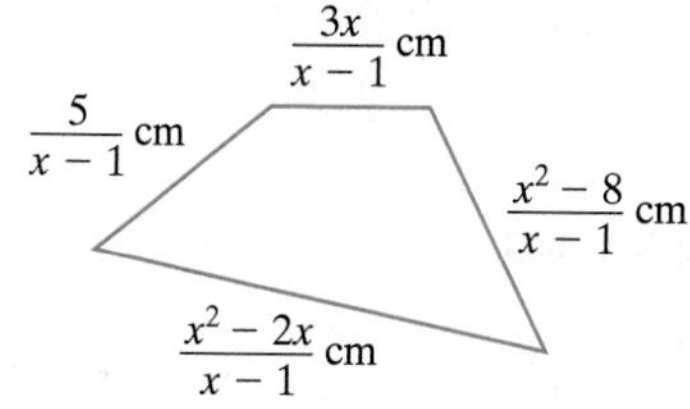

△ **94.** Find the perimeter of the quadrilateral.

Square side: $\frac{x}{x+5}$ ft

Quadrilateral sides: $\frac{3x}{x-1}$ cm, $\frac{5}{x-1}$ cm, $\frac{x^2-8}{x-1}$ cm, $\frac{x^2-2x}{x-1}$ cm

95. When is the LCD of two rational expressions equal to the product of their denominators? $\left(\textit{Hint:}\text{ What is the LCD of } \frac{1}{x} \text{ and } \frac{7}{x+5}?\right)$

96. When is the LCD of two rational expressions with different denominators equal to one of the denominators? $\left(\textit{Hint:}\text{ What is the LCD of } \frac{3x}{x+2} \text{ and } \frac{7x+1}{(x+2)^3}?\right)$

97. In your own words, explain how to add rational expressions with different denominators.

98. In your own words, explain how to multiply rational expressions.

99. In your own words, explain how to divide rational expressions.

100. In your own words, explain how to subtract rational expressions with different denominators.

Perform each indicated operation. (Hint: First write each expression with positive exponents.)

101. $x^{-1} + (2x)^{-1}$

102. $y^{-1} + (4y)^{-1}$

103. $4x^{-2} - 3x^{-1}$

104. $(4x)^{-2} - (3x)^{-1}$

Use a graphing calculator to support the results of each exercise.

105. Exercise 3

106. Exercise 4

18.3 SIMPLIFYING COMPLEX FRACTIONS

OBJECTIVES

1. Simplify complex fractions by simplifying the numerator and denominator and then dividing.
2. Simplify complex fractions by multiplying by a common denominator.
3. Simplify expressions with negative exponents.

OBJECTIVE 1 ▶ Simplifying complex fractions: Method 1. A rational expression whose numerator, denominator, or both contain one or more rational expressions is called a **complex rational expression** or a **complex fraction.**

Complex Fractions

$$\frac{\frac{1}{a}}{\frac{b}{2}} \qquad \frac{\frac{x}{2y^2}}{\frac{6x-2}{9y}} \qquad \frac{x+\frac{1}{y}}{y+1}$$

The parts of a complex fraction are

$$\frac{\left.\frac{x}{y+2}\right\}}{\left.7+\frac{1}{y}\right\}}$$

; Numerator of complex fraction

; Main fraction bar

; Denominator of complex fraction

Our goal in this section is to simplify complex fractions. A complex fraction is simplified when it is in the form $\frac{P}{Q}$, where P and Q are polynomials that have no common factors. Two methods of simplifying complex fractions are introduced. The first method evolves from the definition of a fraction as a quotient.

Simplifying a Complex Fraction: Method 1

STEP 1. Simplify the numerator and the denominator of the complex fraction so that each is a single fraction.

STEP 2. Perform the indicated division by multiplying the numerator of the complex fraction by the reciprocal of the denominator of the complex fraction.

STEP 3. Simplify if possible.

EXAMPLE 1 Simplify each complex fraction.

a. $\dfrac{\frac{2x}{27y^2}}{\frac{6x^2}{9}}$ **b.** $\dfrac{\frac{5x}{x+2}}{\frac{10}{x-2}}$ **c.** $\dfrac{\frac{x}{y^2}+\frac{1}{y}}{\frac{y}{x^2}+\frac{1}{x}}$

Solution

a. The numerator of the complex fraction is already a single fraction, and so is the denominator. Perform the indicated division by multiplying the numerator, $\frac{2x}{27y^2}$, by the reciprocal of the denominator, $\frac{6x^2}{9}$. Then simplify.

$$\frac{\frac{2x}{27y^2}}{\frac{6x^2}{9}} = \frac{2x}{27y^2} \div \frac{6x^2}{9}$$

$$= \frac{2x}{27y^2} \cdot \frac{9}{6x^2} \quad \text{Multiply by the reciprocal of } \frac{6x^2}{9}.$$

$$= \frac{2x \cdot 9}{27y^2 \cdot 6x^2}$$

$$= \frac{1}{9xy^2}$$

Helpful Hint

Both the numerator and denominator are single fractions, so we perform the indicated division.

b. $$\frac{\frac{5x}{x+2}}{\frac{10}{x-2}} = \frac{5x}{x+2} \div \frac{10}{x-2} = \frac{5x}{x+2} \cdot \frac{x-2}{10} \quad \text{Multiply by the reciprocal of } \frac{10}{x-2}.$$

$$= \frac{5x(x-2)}{2 \cdot 5(x+2)}$$

$$= \frac{x(x-2)}{2(x+2)} \quad \text{Simplify.}$$

c. First simplify the numerator and the denominator of the complex fraction separately so that each is a single fraction. Then perform the indicated division.

$$\frac{\frac{x}{y^2}+\frac{1}{y}}{\frac{y}{x^2}+\frac{1}{x}} = \frac{\frac{x}{y^2}+\frac{1\cdot y}{y\cdot y}}{\frac{y}{x^2}+\frac{1\cdot x}{x\cdot x}}$$ Simplify the numerator. The LCD is y^2. Simplify the denominator. The LCD is x^2.

$$= \frac{\frac{x+y}{y^2}}{\frac{y+x}{x^2}}$$ Add.

$$= \frac{x+y}{y^2}\cdot\frac{x^2}{y+x}$$ Multiply by the reciprocal of $\frac{y+x}{x^2}$.

$$= \frac{x^2(x+y)}{y^2(y+x)}$$

$$= \frac{x^2}{y^2}$$ Simplify. □

PRACTICE 1 Simplify each complex fraction.

a. $\dfrac{\frac{5k}{36m}}{\frac{15k}{9}}$ **b.** $\dfrac{\frac{8x}{x-4}}{\frac{3}{x+4}}$ **c.** $\dfrac{\frac{5}{a}+\frac{b}{a^2}}{\frac{5a}{b^2}+\frac{1}{b}}$

Concept Check ✓

Which of the following are equivalent to $\dfrac{\frac{1}{x}}{\frac{3}{y}}$?

a. $\frac{1}{x} \div \frac{3}{y}$ **b.** $\frac{1}{x}\cdot\frac{y}{3}$ **c.** $\frac{1}{x} \div \frac{y}{3}$

OBJECTIVE 2 ▶ Simplifying complex fractions: Method 2. Next we look at another method of simplifying complex fractions. With this method we multiply the numerator and the denominator of the complex fraction by the LCD of all fractions in the complex fraction.

Simplifying a Complex Fraction: Method 2

STEP 1. Multiply the numerator and the denominator of the complex fraction by the LCD of the fractions in both the numerator and the denominator.

STEP 2. Simplify.

Answer to Concept Check:
a and b

EXAMPLE 2 Simplify each complex fraction.

a. $\dfrac{\dfrac{5x}{x+2}}{\dfrac{10}{x-2}}$ **b.** $\dfrac{\dfrac{x}{y^2}+\dfrac{1}{y}}{\dfrac{y}{x^2}+\dfrac{1}{x}}$

Solution

a. The least common denominator of $\dfrac{5x}{x+2}$ and $\dfrac{10}{x-2}$ is $(x+2)(x-2)$. Multiply both the numerator, $\dfrac{5x}{x+2}$, and the denominator, $\dfrac{10}{x-2}$, by the LCD.

$$\frac{\dfrac{5x}{x+2}}{\dfrac{10}{x-2}} = \frac{\left(\dfrac{5x}{x+2}\right)\cdot(x+2)(x-2)}{\left(\dfrac{10}{x-2}\right)\cdot(x+2)(x-2)}$$ Multiply numerator and denominator by the LCD.

$$= \frac{5x\cdot(x-2)}{2\cdot 5\cdot(x+2)}$$ Simplify.

$$= \frac{x(x-2)}{2(x+2)}$$ Simplify.

b. The least common denominator of $\dfrac{x}{y^2}, \dfrac{1}{y}, \dfrac{y}{x^2}$, and $\dfrac{1}{x}$ is x^2y^2.

$$\frac{\dfrac{x}{y^2}+\dfrac{1}{y}}{\dfrac{y}{x^2}+\dfrac{1}{x}} = \frac{\left(\dfrac{x}{y^2}+\dfrac{1}{y}\right)\cdot x^2y^2}{\left(\dfrac{y}{x^2}+\dfrac{1}{x}\right)\cdot x^2y^2}$$ Multiply the numerator and denominator by the LCD.

$$= \frac{\dfrac{x}{y^2}\cdot x^2y^2 + \dfrac{1}{y}\cdot x^2y^2}{\dfrac{y}{x^2}\cdot x^2y^2 + \dfrac{1}{x}\cdot x^2y^2}$$ Use the distributive property.

$$= \frac{x^3 + x^2y}{y^3 + xy^2}$$ Simplify.

$$= \frac{x^2(x+y)}{y^2(y+x)}$$ Factor.

$$= \frac{x^2}{y^2}$$ Simplify. □

PRACTICE 2 Use Method 2 to simplify:

a. $\dfrac{\dfrac{8x}{x-4}}{\dfrac{3}{x+4}}$ **b.** $\dfrac{\dfrac{b}{a^2}+\dfrac{1}{a}}{\dfrac{a}{b^2}+\dfrac{1}{b}}$

OBJECTIVE 3 ▶ Simplifying expressions with negative exponents. If an expression contains negative exponents, write the expression as an equivalent expression with positive exponents.

EXAMPLE 3 Simplify.

$$\frac{x^{-1} + 2xy^{-1}}{x^{-2} - x^{-2}y^{-1}}$$

Solution This fraction does not appear to be a complex fraction. If we write it by using only positive exponents, however, we see that it is a complex fraction.

$$\frac{x^{-1} + 2xy^{-1}}{x^{-2} - x^{-2}y^{-1}} = \frac{\frac{1}{x} + \frac{2x}{y}}{\frac{1}{x^2} - \frac{1}{x^2y}}$$

The LCD of $\frac{1}{x}, \frac{2x}{y}, \frac{1}{x^2}$, and $\frac{1}{x^2y}$ is x^2y. Multiply both the numerator and denominator by x^2y.

$$= \frac{\left(\frac{1}{x} + \frac{2x}{y}\right) \cdot x^2y}{\left(\frac{1}{x^2} - \frac{1}{x^2y}\right) \cdot x^2y}$$

$$= \frac{\frac{1}{x} \cdot x^2y + \frac{2x}{y} \cdot x^2y}{\frac{1}{x^2} \cdot x^2y - \frac{1}{x^2y} \cdot x^2y} \quad \text{Apply the distributive property.}$$

$$= \frac{xy + 2x^3}{y - 1} \text{ or } \frac{x(y + 2x^2)}{y - 1} \quad \text{Simplify.}$$

□

PRACTICE 3 Simplify: $\frac{3x^{-1} + x^{-2}y^{-1}}{y^{-2} + xy^{-1}}$.

EXAMPLE 4 Simplify: $\frac{(2x)^{-1} + 1}{2x^{-1} - 1}$

Solution

$$\frac{(2x)^{-1} + 1}{2x^{-1} - 1} = \frac{\frac{1}{2x} + 1}{\frac{2}{x} - 1} \quad \text{Write using positive exponents.}$$

$$= \frac{\left(\frac{1}{2x} + 1\right) \cdot 2x}{\left(\frac{2}{x} - 1\right) \cdot 2x} \quad \text{The LCD of } \frac{1}{2x} \text{ and } \frac{2}{x} \text{ is } 2x.$$

$$= \frac{\frac{1}{2x} \cdot 2x + 1 \cdot 2x}{\frac{2}{x} \cdot 2x - 1 \cdot 2x} \quad \text{Use the distributive property.}$$

$$= \frac{1 + 2x}{4 - 2x} \text{ or } \frac{1 + 2x}{2(2 - x)} \quad \text{Simplify.}$$

□

Helpful Hint

Don't forget that $(2x)^{-1} = \frac{1}{2x}$, but $2x^{-1} = 2 \cdot \frac{1}{x} = \frac{2}{x}$.

PRACTICE 4 Simplify: $\frac{(3x)^{-1} - 2}{5x^{-1} + 2}$.

VOCABULARY & READINESS CHECK

Complete the steps by writing the simplified complex fraction.

1. $\dfrac{\frac{7}{x}}{\frac{1}{x}+\frac{z}{x}} = \dfrac{x\left(\frac{7}{x}\right)}{x\left(\frac{1}{x}\right)+x\left(\frac{z}{x}\right)} =$ ______

2. $\dfrac{\frac{x}{4}}{\frac{x^2}{2}+\frac{1}{4}} = \dfrac{4\left(\frac{x}{4}\right)}{4\left(\frac{x^2}{2}\right)+4\left(\frac{1}{4}\right)} =$ ______

Write each with positive exponents.

3. $x^{-2} =$ ______
4. $y^{-3} =$ ______
5. $2x^{-1} =$ ______
6. $(2x)^{-1} =$ ______
7. $(9y)^{-1} =$ ______
8. $9y^{-2} =$ ______

18.3 EXERCISE SET

MyMathLab

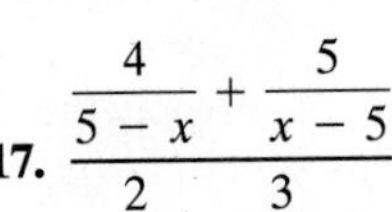

Simplify each complex fraction. See Examples 1 and 2.

1. $\dfrac{\frac{10}{3x}}{\frac{5}{6x}}$

2. $\dfrac{\frac{15}{2x}}{\frac{5}{6x}}$

3. $\dfrac{1+\frac{2}{5}}{2+\frac{3}{5}}$

4. $\dfrac{2+\frac{1}{7}}{3-\frac{4}{7}}$

5. $\dfrac{\frac{4}{x-1}}{\frac{x}{x-1}}$

6. $\dfrac{\frac{x}{x+2}}{\frac{2}{x+2}}$

7. $\dfrac{1-\frac{2}{x}}{x+\frac{4}{9x}}$

8. $\dfrac{5-\frac{3}{x}}{x+\frac{2}{3x}}$

9. $\dfrac{\frac{4x^2-y^2}{xy}}{\frac{2}{y}-\frac{1}{x}}$

10. $\dfrac{\frac{x^2-9y^2}{xy}}{\frac{1}{y}-\frac{3}{x}}$

11. $\dfrac{\frac{x+1}{3}}{\frac{2x-1}{6}}$

12. $\dfrac{\frac{x+3}{12}}{\frac{4x-5}{15}}$

13. $\dfrac{\frac{2}{x}+\frac{3}{x^2}}{\frac{4}{x^2}-\frac{9}{x}}$

14. $\dfrac{\frac{2}{x^2}+\frac{1}{x}}{\frac{4}{x^2}-\frac{1}{x}}$

15. $\dfrac{\frac{1}{x}+\frac{2}{x^2}}{x+\frac{8}{x^2}}$

16. $\dfrac{\frac{1}{y}+\frac{3}{y^2}}{y+\frac{27}{y^2}}$

17. $\dfrac{\frac{4}{5-x}+\frac{5}{x-5}}{\frac{2}{x}+\frac{3}{x-5}}$

18. $\dfrac{\frac{3}{x-4}-\frac{2}{4-x}}{\frac{2}{x-4}-\frac{2}{x}}$

19. $\dfrac{\frac{x+2}{x}-\frac{2}{x-1}}{\frac{x+1}{x}+\frac{x+1}{x-1}}$

20. $\dfrac{\frac{5}{a+2}-\frac{1}{a-2}}{\frac{3}{2+a}+\frac{6}{2-a}}$

21. $\dfrac{\frac{2}{x}+3}{\frac{4}{x^2}-9}$

22. $\dfrac{2+\frac{1}{x}}{4x-\frac{1}{x}}$

23. $\dfrac{1-\frac{x}{y}}{\frac{x^2}{y^2}-1}$

24. $\dfrac{1-\frac{2}{x}}{x-\frac{4}{x}}$

25. $\dfrac{\frac{-2x}{x-y}}{\frac{y}{x^2}}$

26. $\dfrac{\frac{7y}{x^2+xy}}{\frac{y^2}{x^2}}$

27. $\dfrac{\frac{2}{x}+\frac{1}{x^2}}{\frac{y}{x^2}}$

28. $\dfrac{\frac{5}{x^2}-\frac{2}{x}}{\frac{1}{x}+2}$

29. $\dfrac{\frac{x}{9}-\frac{1}{x}}{1+\frac{3}{x}}$

30. $\dfrac{\frac{x}{4}-\frac{4}{x}}{1-\frac{4}{x}}$

31. $\dfrac{\frac{x-1}{x^2-4}}{1+\frac{1}{x-2}}$

32. $\dfrac{\frac{x+3}{x^2-9}}{1+\frac{1}{x-3}}$

33. $\dfrac{\dfrac{2}{x+5}+\dfrac{4}{x+3}}{\dfrac{3x+13}{x^2+8x+15}}$

34. $\dfrac{\dfrac{2}{x+2}+\dfrac{6}{x+7}}{\dfrac{4x+13}{x^2+9x+14}}$

Simplify. See Examples 3 and 4.

35. $\dfrac{x^{-1}}{x^{-2}+y^{-2}}$

36. $\dfrac{a^{-3}+b^{-1}}{a^{-2}}$

37. $\dfrac{2a^{-1}+3b^{-2}}{a^{-1}-b^{-1}}$

38. $\dfrac{x^{-1}+y^{-1}}{3x^{-2}+5y^{-2}}$

39. $\dfrac{1}{x-x^{-1}}$

40. $\dfrac{x^{-2}}{x+3x^{-1}}$

41. $\dfrac{a^{-1}+1}{a^{-1}-1}$

42. $\dfrac{a^{-1}-4}{4+a^{-1}}$

43. $\dfrac{3x^{-1}+(2y)^{-1}}{x^{-2}}$

44. $\dfrac{5x^{-2}-3y^{-1}}{x^{-1}+y^{-1}}$

45. $\dfrac{2a^{-1}+(2a)^{-1}}{a^{-1}+2a^{-2}}$

46. $\dfrac{a^{-1}+2a^{-2}}{2a^{-1}+(2a)^{-1}}$

47. $\dfrac{5x^{-1}+2y^{-1}}{x^{-2}y^{-2}}$

48. $\dfrac{x^{-2}y^{-2}}{5x^{-1}+2y^{-1}}$

49. $\dfrac{5x^{-1}-2y^{-1}}{25x^{-2}-4y^{-2}}$

50. $\dfrac{3x^{-1}+3y^{-1}}{4x^{-2}-9y^{-2}}$

REVIEW AND PREVIEW

Simplify.

51. $\dfrac{3x^3y^2}{12x}$

52. $\dfrac{-36xb^3}{9xb^2}$

53. $\dfrac{144x^5y^5}{-16x^2y}$

54. $\dfrac{48x^3y^2}{-4xy}$

Solve the following. See Section 16.4.

55. $|x-5|=9$

56. $|2y+1|=1$

CONCEPT EXTENSIONS

Solve. See the Concept Check in this section.

57. Which of the following are equivalent to $\dfrac{\dfrac{x+1}{9}}{\dfrac{y-2}{5}}$?

a. $\dfrac{x+1}{9}\div\dfrac{y-2}{5}$ **b.** $\dfrac{x+1}{9}\cdot\dfrac{y-2}{5}$ **c.** $\dfrac{x+1}{9}\cdot\dfrac{5}{y-2}$

58. Which of the following are equivalent to $\dfrac{\dfrac{a}{7}}{\dfrac{b}{13}}$?

a. $\dfrac{a}{7}\cdot\dfrac{b}{13}$ **b.** $\dfrac{a}{7}\div\dfrac{b}{13}$ **c.** $\dfrac{a}{7}\div\dfrac{13}{b}$ **d.** $\dfrac{a}{7}\cdot\dfrac{13}{b}$

59. When the source of a sound is traveling toward a listener, the pitch that the listener hears due to the Doppler effect is given by the complex rational compression $\dfrac{a}{1-\dfrac{s}{770}}$, where a is the actual pitch of the sound and s is the speed of the sound source. Simplify this expression.

60. In baseball, the earned run average (ERA) statistic gives the average number of earned runs scored on a pitcher per game. It is computed with the following expression: $\dfrac{E}{\dfrac{I}{9}}$, where E is the number of earned runs scored on a pitcher and I is the total number of innings pitched by the pitcher. Simplify this expression.

61. Which of the following are equivalent to $\dfrac{\dfrac{1}{x}}{\dfrac{3}{y}}$?

a. $\dfrac{1}{x}\div\dfrac{3}{y}$ **b.** $\dfrac{1}{x}\cdot\dfrac{y}{3}$ **c.** $\dfrac{1}{x}\div\dfrac{y}{3}$

62. In your own words, explain one method for simplifying a complex fraction.

Simplify.

63. $\dfrac{1}{1+(1+x)^{-1}}$

64. $\dfrac{(x+2)^{-1}+(x-2)^{-1}}{(x^2-4)^{-1}}$

65. $\dfrac{x}{1-\dfrac{1}{1+\dfrac{1}{x}}}$

66. $\dfrac{x}{1-\dfrac{1}{1-\dfrac{1}{x}}}$

67. $\dfrac{\dfrac{2}{y^2}-\dfrac{5}{xy}-\dfrac{3}{x^2}}{\dfrac{2}{y^2}+\dfrac{7}{xy}+\dfrac{3}{x^2}}$

68. $\dfrac{\dfrac{2}{x^2}-\dfrac{1}{xy}-\dfrac{1}{y^2}}{\dfrac{1}{x^2}-\dfrac{3}{xy}+\dfrac{2}{y^2}}$

69. $\dfrac{3(a+1)^{-1}+4a^{-2}}{(a^3+a^2)^{-1}}$

70. $\dfrac{9x^{-1}-5(x-y)^{-1}}{4(x-y)^{-1}}$

In the study of calculus, the difference quotient $\dfrac{f(a+h)-f(a)}{h}$ *is often found and simplified. Find and simplify this quotient for each function f(x) by following steps* **a** *through* **d.**

a. *Find* $(a+h)$.

b. *Find* $f(a)$.

c. *Use steps* **a** *and* **b** *to find* $\dfrac{f(a+h)-f(a)}{h}$.

d. *Simplify the result of step* **c.**

71. $f(x)=\dfrac{1}{x}$

72. $f(x)=\dfrac{5}{x}$

73. $\dfrac{3}{x+1}$

74. $\dfrac{2}{x^2}$

STUDY SKILLS BUILDER

How Are You Doing?

If you haven't done so yet, take a few moments and think about how you are doing in this course. Are you working toward your goal of successfully completing this course? Is your performance on homework, quizzes, and tests satisfactory? If not, you might want to see your instructor to see if he/she has any suggestions on how you can improve your performance.

Answer the following.

1. List any textbook supplements you are using to help you through this course.
2. List any campus resources you are using to help you through this course.
3. Write a short paragraph describing how you are doing in your mathematics course.
4. If improvement is needed, list ways that you can work toward improving your situation as described in Exercise 3.

18.4 SOLVING EQUATIONS CONTAINING RATIONAL EXPRESSIONS

OBJECTIVE

1 Solve equations containing rational expressions.

OBJECTIVE 1 ▶ Solving equations containing rational expressions. In this section, we solve equations containing rational expressions. Before beginning this section, make sure that you understand the difference between an *equation* and an *expression*. An **equation** contains an equal sign and an **expression** does not.

Equation	***Expression***
$\dfrac{x}{2}+\dfrac{x}{6}=\dfrac{2}{3}$	$\dfrac{x}{2}+\dfrac{x}{6}$

▶ Helpful Hint

The method described here is for equations only. It may *not* be used for performing operations on expressions.

Solving Equations Containing Rational Expressions

To solve *equations* containing rational expressions, first clear the equation of fractions by multiplying both sides of the equation by the LCD of all rational expressions. Then solve as usual.

Concept Check ✓

True or false? Clearing fractions is valid when solving an equation and when simplifying rational expressions. Explain.

EXAMPLE 1 Solve $\frac{4x}{5} + \frac{3}{2} = \frac{3x}{10}$ algebraically and check graphically.

Solution The LCD of $\frac{4x}{5}, \frac{3}{2}$, and $\frac{3x}{10}$ is 10. We multiply both sides of the equation by 10.

$$\frac{4x}{5} + \frac{3}{2} = \frac{3x}{10}$$

$$10\left(\frac{4x}{5} + \frac{3}{2}\right) = 10\left(\frac{3x}{10}\right) \quad \text{Multiply both sides by the LCD.}$$

$$10 \cdot \frac{4x}{5} + 10 \cdot \frac{3}{2} = 10 \cdot \frac{3x}{10} \quad \text{Use the distributive property.}$$

$$8x + 15 = 3x \quad \text{Simplify.}$$

$$15 = -5x \quad \text{Subtract } 8x \text{ from both sides.}$$

$$-3 = x \quad \text{Solve.}$$

Check: To check this solution graphically, we use the intersection-of-graphs method shown below.

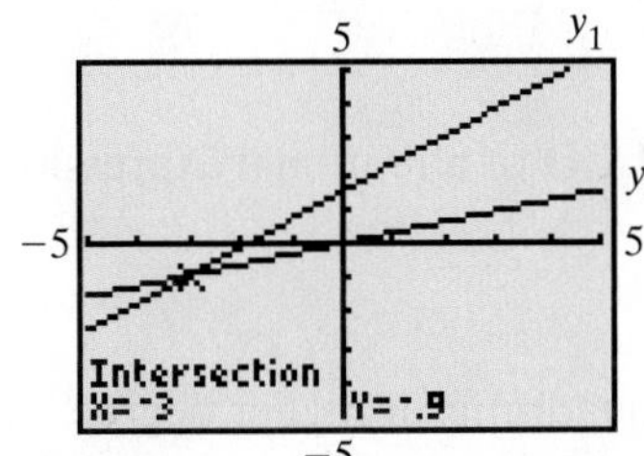

The point of intersection of $y_1 = \frac{4x}{5} + \frac{3}{2}$ and $y_2 = \frac{3x}{10}$ is $(-3, -0.9)$. Thus, the solution of the equation $\frac{4x}{5} + \frac{3}{2} = \frac{3x}{10}$ is $x = -3$.

The solution is −3 or the solution set is $\{-3\}$. □

PRACTICE 1 Solve: $\frac{5x}{4} - \frac{3}{2} = \frac{7x}{8}$.

Answer to Concept Check: false; answers may vary

The important difference of the equations in this section is that the denominator of a rational expression may contain a variable. Recall that a rational expression is undefined for values of the variable that make the denominator 0. If a proposed solution makes the denominator 0, then it must be rejected as a solution of the original equation. Such proposed solutions are called **extraneous solutions.**

EXAMPLE 2 Solve $\frac{3}{x} - \frac{x + 21}{3x} = \frac{5}{3}$ algebraically and check graphically.

Solution The LCD of the denominators x, $3x$, and 3 is $3x$. We multiply both sides by $3x$.

$$\frac{3}{x} - \frac{x + 21}{3x} = \frac{5}{3}$$

$$3x\left(\frac{3}{x} - \frac{x + 21}{3x}\right) = 3x\left(\frac{5}{3}\right) \quad \text{Multiply both sides by the LCD.}$$

$$3x \cdot \frac{3}{x} - 3x \cdot \frac{x + 21}{3x} = 3x \cdot \frac{5}{3} \quad \text{Use the distributive property.}$$

$$9 - (x + 21) = 5x \quad \text{Simplify.}$$

$$9 - x - 21 = 5x$$

$$-12 = 6x$$

$$-2 = x \quad \text{Solve.}$$

The proposed solution is −2.

Check: A check using a graphing utility is shown below.

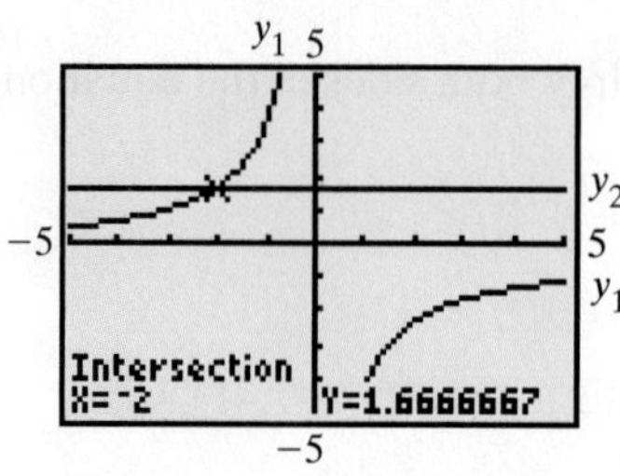

The intersection of $y_1 = \frac{3}{x} - \frac{x+21}{3x}$ and $y_2 = \frac{5}{3}$ verifies that the solution of the equation $\frac{3}{x} - \frac{x+21}{3x} = \frac{5}{3}$ is $x = -2$.

The solution is -2 or the solution set is $\{-2\}$. □

PRACTICE 2 Solve: $\frac{6}{x} - \frac{x+9}{5x} = \frac{2}{5}$.

The following steps may be used to solve equations containing rational expressions.

Solving an Equation Containing Rational Expressions

STEP 1. Multiply both sides of the equation by the LCD of all rational expressions in the equation.

STEP 2. Simplify both sides.

STEP 3. Determine whether the equation is linear, quadratic, or higher degree and solve accordingly.

STEP 4. Check the solution in the original equation.

EXAMPLE 3 Solve: $\frac{x+6}{x-2} = \frac{2(x+2)}{x-2}$.

Solution First we multiply both sides of the equation by the LCD, $x - 2$. (Remember, we can only do this if $x \neq 2$ so that we are not multiplying by 0.)

$$\frac{x+6}{x-2} = \frac{2(x+2)}{x-2}$$

$$(x-2)\cdot\frac{x+6}{x-2} = (x-2)\cdot\frac{2(x+2)}{x-2} \quad \text{Multiply both sides by } x-2.$$

$$x + 6 = 2(x+2) \quad \text{Simplify.}$$

$$x + 6 = 2x + 4 \quad \text{Use the distributive property.}$$

$$2 = x \quad \text{Solve.}$$

TECHNOLOGY NOTE

Recall that when replacing the variable with a number that results in a zero denominator, a graphing utility will give an error message. In Example 3, store 2 in x, evaluate $\frac{(x+6)}{(x-2)}$, and see the results.

From above, we assumed that $x \neq 2$, so this equation has no solution. This will also show as we attempt to check this proposed solution.

Check: The proposed solution is 2. Notice that 2 makes a denominator 0 in the original equation. This can also be seen in a check. Check the proposed solution 2 in the original equation.

$$\frac{x+6}{x-2} = \frac{2(x+2)}{x-2}$$

$$\frac{2+6}{2-2} = \frac{2(2+2)}{2-2}$$

$$\frac{8}{0} = \frac{2(4)}{0}$$

The denominators are 0, so 2 is not a solution of the original equation. The solution is { } or ∅. □

PRACTICE 3 Solve: $\frac{x-5}{x+3} = \frac{2(x-1)}{x+3}$.

EXAMPLE 4 Solve: $\frac{2x}{2x-1} + \frac{1}{x} = \frac{1}{2x-1}$.

Solution The LCD is $x(2x-1)$. Multiply both sides by $x(2x-1)$. By the distributive property, this is the same as multiplying each term by $x(2x-1)$.

$$x(2x-1)\cdot\frac{2x}{2x-1} + x(2x-1)\cdot\frac{1}{x} = x(2x-1)\cdot\frac{1}{2x-1}$$

$$x(2x) + (2x-1) = x \quad \text{Simplify.}$$

$$2x^2 + 2x - 1 - x = 0$$

$$2x^2 + x - 1 = 0$$

$$(x+1)(2x-1) = 0$$

$$x + 1 = 0 \quad \text{or} \quad 2x - 1 = 0$$

$$x = -1 \qquad x = \frac{1}{2}$$

The number $\frac{1}{2}$ makes the denominator $2x - 1$ equal 0, so it is not a solution. The solution is -1.

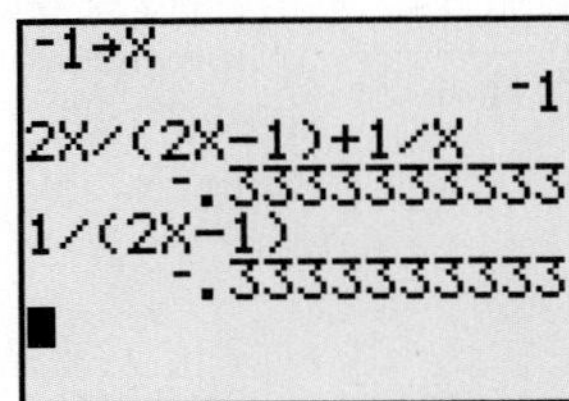

A numerical check that -1 is the solution to the equation in Example 4.

ERR:DIVIDE BY 0
1:Quit
2:Goto

The error message that results when $\frac{1}{2}$ is checked as a proposed solution in Example 4. □

PRACTICE 4 Solve: $\frac{5x}{5x-1} + \frac{1}{x} = \frac{1}{5x-1}$.

EXAMPLE 5 Solve: $\frac{2x}{x-3} + \frac{6-2x}{x^2-9} = \frac{x}{x+3}$.

Solution We factor the second denominator to find that the LCD is $(x+3)(x-3)$. We multiply both sides of the equation by $(x+3)(x-3)$. By the distributive property, this is the same as multiplying each term by $(x+3)(x-3)$.

$$\frac{2x}{x-3} + \frac{6-2x}{x^2-9} = \frac{x}{x+3}$$

$$(x+3)(x-3)\cdot\frac{2x}{x-3} + (x+3)(x-3)\cdot\frac{6-2x}{(x+3)(x-3)}$$

$$= (x+3)(x-3)\left(\frac{x}{x+3}\right)$$

$$2x(x+3) + (6-2x) = x(x-3) \quad \text{Simplify.}$$

$$2x^2 + 6x + 6 - 2x = x^2 - 3x \quad \text{Use the distributive property.}$$

Next we solve this quadratic equation by the factoring method. To do so, we first write the equation so that one side is 0.

$$x^2 + 7x + 6 = 0$$
$$(x + 6)(x + 1) = 0 \quad \text{Factor.}$$
$$x = -6 \text{ or } x = -1 \quad \text{Set each factor equal to 0.}$$

Neither -6 nor -1 makes any denominator 0 so they are both solutions. The solutions are -6 and -1. □

PRACTICE 5 Solve: $\frac{2}{x-2} - \frac{5+2x}{x^2-4} = \frac{x}{x+2}$.

EXAMPLE 6 Solve: $\frac{z}{2z^2 + 3z - 2} - \frac{1}{2z} = \frac{3}{z^2 + 2z}$.

Solution Factor the denominators to find that the LCD is $2z(z + 2)(2z - 1)$. Multiply both sides by the LCD. Remember, by using the distributive property, this is the same as multiplying each term by $2z(z + 2)(2z - 1)$.

$$\frac{z}{2z^2 + 3z - 2} - \frac{1}{2z} = \frac{3}{z^2 + 2z}$$
$$\frac{z}{(2z - 1)(z + 2)} - \frac{1}{2z} = \frac{3}{z(z + 2)}$$
$$2z(z + 2)(2z - 1)\cdot\frac{z}{(2z - 1)(z + 2)} - 2z(z + 2)(2z - 1)\cdot\frac{1}{2z}$$
$$= 2z(z + 2)(2z - 1)\cdot\frac{3}{z(z + 2)} \quad \text{Apply the distributive property.}$$
$$2z(z) - (z + 2)(2z - 1) = 3\cdot 2(2z - 1) \quad \text{Simplify.}$$
$$2z^2 - (2z^2 + 3z - 2) = 12z - 6$$
$$2z^2 - 2z^2 - 3z + 2 = 12z - 6$$
$$-3z + 2 = 12z - 6$$
$$-15z = -8$$
$$z = \frac{8}{15} \quad \text{Solve.}$$

A numerical check for Example 6. The solution is $z = \frac{8}{15}$.

The proposed solution $\frac{8}{15}$ does not make any denominator 0; the solution is $\frac{8}{15}$. □

PRACTICE 6 Solve: $\frac{z}{2z^2 - z - 6} - \frac{1}{3z} = \frac{2}{z^2 - 2z}$.

VOCABULARY & READINESS CHECK

Choose the least common denominator (LCD) for the rational expressions in each equation. Do not solve.

1. $\frac{x}{7} - \frac{x}{2} = \frac{1}{2}$; LCD = ______

a. 7 **b.** 2 **c.** 14 **d.** 28

2. $\frac{9}{x+1} + \frac{5}{(x+1)^2} = \frac{x}{x+1}$; LCD = ______

a. $x + 1$ **b.** $(x + 1)^2$ **c.** $(x + 1)^3$

3. $\frac{7}{x-4} = \frac{x}{x^2-16} + \frac{1}{x+4}$; LCD = ________

a. $(x+4)(x-4)$ **b.** $x-4$ **c.** $x+4$ **d.** $(x^2-16)(x-4)(x+4)$

4. $3 = \frac{1}{x-5} - \frac{2}{x^2-5x}$; LCD = ________

a. $x-5$ **b.** $3(x-5)$ **c.** $3x(x-5)$ **d.** $x(x-5)$

18.4 EXERCISE SET

MyMathLab

PRACTICE

WATCH

DOWNLOAD

READ

REVIEW

Solve each equation. See Examples 1 and 2.

1. $\frac{x}{2} - \frac{x}{3} = 12$

2. $x = \frac{x}{2} - 4$

3. $\frac{x}{3} = \frac{1}{6} + \frac{x}{4}$

4. $\frac{x}{2} = \frac{21}{10} - \frac{x}{5}$

5. $\frac{2}{x} + \frac{1}{2} = \frac{5}{x}$

6. $\frac{5}{3x} + 1 = \frac{7}{6}$

7. $\frac{x^2+1}{x} = \frac{5}{x}$

8. $\frac{x^2-14}{2x} = -\frac{5}{2x}$

Solve each equation. See Examples 3 through 6.

9. $\frac{x+5}{x+3} = \frac{2}{x+3}$

10. $\frac{x-7}{x-1} = \frac{11}{x-1}$

11. $\frac{5}{x-2} - \frac{2}{x+4} = -\frac{4}{x^2+2x-8}$

12. $\frac{1}{x-1} + \frac{1}{x+1} = \frac{2}{x^2-1}$

13. $\frac{1}{x-1} = \frac{2}{x+1}$

14. $\frac{6}{x+3} = \frac{4}{x-3}$

15. $\frac{x^2-23}{2x^2-5x-3} + \frac{2}{x-3} = \frac{-1}{2x+1}$

16. $\frac{4x^2-24x}{3x^2-x-2} + \frac{3}{3x+2} = \frac{-4}{x-1}$

17. $\frac{1}{x-4} - \frac{3x}{x^2-16} = \frac{2}{x+4}$

18. $\frac{3}{2x+3} - \frac{1}{2x-3} = \frac{4}{4x^2-9}$

19. $\frac{1}{x-4} = \frac{8}{x^2-16}$

20. $\frac{2}{x^2-4} = \frac{1}{2x-4}$

21. $\frac{1}{x-2} - \frac{2}{x^2-2x} = 1$

22. $\frac{12}{3x^2+12x} = 1 - \frac{1}{x+4}$

MIXED PRACTICE

Solve each equation. See Examples 1 through 6.

23. $\frac{5}{x} = \frac{20}{12}$

24. $\frac{2}{x} = \frac{10}{5}$

25. $1 - \frac{4}{a} = 5$

26. $7 + \frac{6}{a} = 5$

27. $\frac{x^2+5}{x} - 1 = \frac{5(x+1)}{x}$

28. $\frac{x^2+6}{x} + 5 = \frac{2(x+3)}{x}$

29. $\frac{1}{2x} - \frac{1}{x+1} = \frac{1}{3x^2+3x}$

30. $\frac{2}{x-5} + \frac{1}{2x} = \frac{5}{3x^2-15x}$

31. $\frac{1}{x} - \frac{x}{25} = 0$

32. $\frac{x}{4} + \frac{5}{x} = 3$

33. $5 - \frac{2}{2y-5} = \frac{3}{2y-5}$

34. $1 - \frac{5}{y+7} = \frac{4}{y+7}$

35. $\frac{x-1}{x+2} = \frac{2}{3}$

36. $\frac{6x+7}{2x+9} = \frac{5}{3}$

37. $\frac{x+3}{x+2} = \frac{1}{x+2}$

38. $\frac{2x+1}{4-x} = \frac{9}{4-x}$

39. $\frac{1}{a-3} + \frac{2}{a+3} = \frac{1}{a^2-9}$

40. $\frac{12}{9-a^2} + \frac{3}{3+a} = \frac{2}{3-a}$

41. $\frac{64}{x^2-16} + 1 = \frac{2x}{x-4}$

42. $2 + \frac{3}{x} = \frac{2x}{x+3}$

43. $\frac{-15}{4y+1} + 4 = y$

44. $\frac{36}{x^2-9} + 1 = \frac{2x}{x+3}$

45. $\frac{28}{x^2-9} + \frac{2x}{x-3} + \frac{6}{x+3} = 0$

46. $\frac{x^2-20}{x^2-7x+12} = \frac{3}{x-3} + \frac{5}{x-4}$

47. $\frac{x+2}{x^2+7x+10} = \frac{1}{3x+6} - \frac{1}{x+5}$

48. $\frac{3}{2x-5} + \frac{2}{2x+3} = 0$

REVIEW AND PREVIEW

Write each sentence as an equation and solve.

49. Four more than 3 times a number is 19.

50. The sum of two consecutive integers is 147.

51. The length of a rectangle is 5 inches more than the width. Its perimeter is 50 inches. Find the length and width.

52. The sum of a number and its reciprocal is $\frac{5}{2}$.

The following graph is from statistics gathered for the National Health and Nutrition Examination Survey. Use this histogram to answer Exercises 53 through 57. (*Source*: Economic Research Service: USDA)

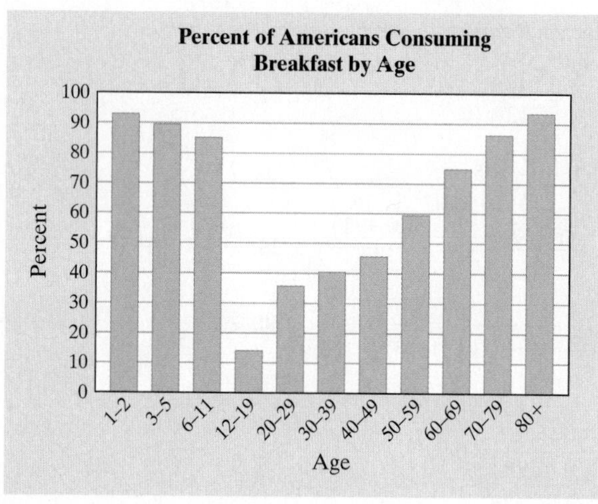

53. What percent of Americans ages 20–29 eat breakfast regularly?

54. What percent of Americans over age 80 eat breakfast regularly?

55. What age category shows the smallest percentage of Americans who eat breakfast regularly?

56. What percent of Americans ages 40–49 eat breakfast regularly?

57. According to the New York City Department of Education, there were about 284,000 high schools students at the end of 2006. Approximately how many of these students would you expect to have eaten breakfast regularly? Round to the nearest ten thousand.

CONCEPT EXTENSIONS

58. In your own words, explain the differences between equations and expressions.

59. In your own words, explain why it is necessary to check solutions to equations containing rational expressions.

60. The average cost of producing x game disks for a computer is given by the function $f(x) = 3.3 + \frac{5400}{x}$. Find the number of game disks that must be produced for the average cost to be \$5.10.

61. The average cost of producing x electric pencil sharpeners is given by the function $f(x) = 20 + \frac{4000}{x}$. Find the number of electric pencil sharpeners that must be produced for the average cost to be \$25.

Solve each equation. Begin by writing each equation with positive exponents only.

62. $x^{-2} - 19x^{-1} + 48 = 0$

63. $x^{-2} - 5x^{-1} - 36 = 0$

64. $p^{-2} + 4p^{-1} - 5 = 0$

65. $6p^{-2} - 5p^{-1} + 1 = 0$

Solve each equation. Round solutions to two decimal places.

66. $\frac{1.4}{x - 2.6} = \frac{-3.5}{x + 7.1}$

67. $\frac{-8.5}{x + 1.9} = \frac{5.7}{x - 3.6}$

68. $\frac{10.6}{y} - 14.7 = \frac{9.92}{3.2} + 7.6$

69. $\frac{12.2}{x} + 17.3 = \frac{9.6}{x} - 14.7$

Solve each equation by substitution.

For example, to solve Exercise 70, first let $u = x - 1$. After substituting, we have $u^2 + 3u + 2 = 0$. Solve for u and then substitute back to solve for x.

70. $(x - 1)^2 + 3(x - 1) + 2 = 0$

71. $(4 - x)^2 - 5(4 - x) + 6 = 0$

72. $\left(\frac{3}{x - 1}\right)^2 + 2\left(\frac{3}{x - 1}\right) + 1 = 0$

73. $\left(\frac{5}{2 + x}\right)^2 + \left(\frac{5}{2 + x}\right) - 20 = 0$

Use a graphing calculator to verify the solution of each given exercise.

74. Exercise 23

75. Exercise 24

76. Exercise 35

77. Exercise 36

18.5 VARIATION AND PROBLEM SOLVING

OBJECTIVES

1 Solve problems involving direct variation.

2 Solve problems involving inverse variation.

3 Solve problems involving joint variation.

4 Solve problems involving combined variation.

OBJECTIVE 1 ▶ Solving problems involving direct variation. A very familiar example of direct variation is the relationship of the circumference C of a circle to its radius r. The formula $C = 2\pi r$ expresses that the circumference is always 2π times the radius. In other words, C is always a constant multiple (2π) of r. Because it is, we say that **C varies directly as r,** that **C varies directly with r,** or that **C is directly proportional to r.**

Direct Variation

***y* varies directly as *x*,** or ***y* is directly proportional to *x*,** if there is a nonzero constant k such that

$$y = kx$$

The number k is called the **constant of variation** or the **constant of proportionality.**

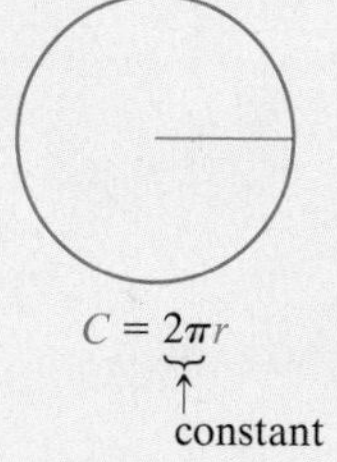

In the above definition, the relationship described between x and y is a linear one. In other words, the graph of $y = kx$ is a line. The slope of the line is k, and the line passes through the origin.

For example, the graph of the direct variation equation $C = 2\pi r$ is shown. The horizontal axis represents the radius r, and the vertical axis is the circumference C. From the graph we can read that when the radius is 6 units, the circumference is approximately 38 units. Also, when the circumference is 45 units, the radius is between 7 and 8 units. Notice that as the radius increases, the circumference increases.

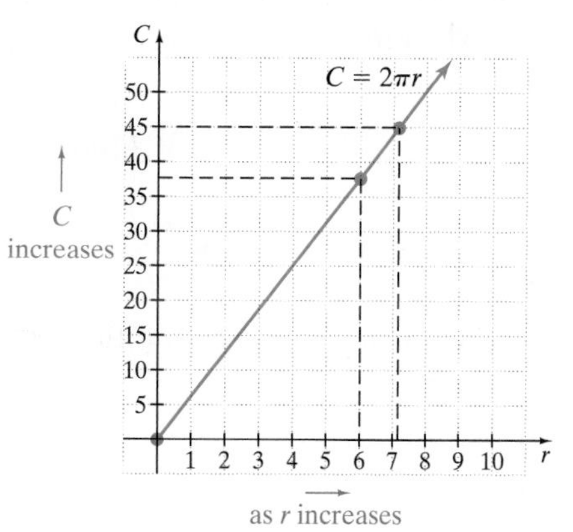

EXAMPLE 1 Suppose that y varies directly as x. If y is 5 when x is 30, find the constant of variation and the direct variation equation.

Solution Since y varies directly as x, we write $y = kx$. If $y = 5$ when $x = 30$, we have that

$$y = kx$$
$$5 = k(30) \quad \text{Replace } y \text{ with 5 and } x \text{ with 30.}$$
$$\frac{1}{6} = k \quad \text{Solve for } k.$$

The constant of variation is $\frac{1}{6}$.

After finding the constant of variation k, the direct variation equation can be written as $y = \frac{1}{6}x$. □

PRACTICE

1 Suppose that y varies directly as x. If y is 20 when x is 15, find the constant of variation and the direct variation equation.

EXAMPLE 2 **Using Direct Variation and Hooke's Law**

Hooke's law states that the distance a spring stretches is directly proportional to the weight attached to the spring. If a 40-pound weight attached to a spring stretches the spring 5 inches, find the distance that a 65-pound weight attached to a spring stretches the spring.

Solution

1. UNDERSTAND. Read and reread the problem. Notice that we are given that the distance a spring stretches is **directly proportional** to the weight attached. We let

$d =$ the distance stretched
$w =$ the weight attached

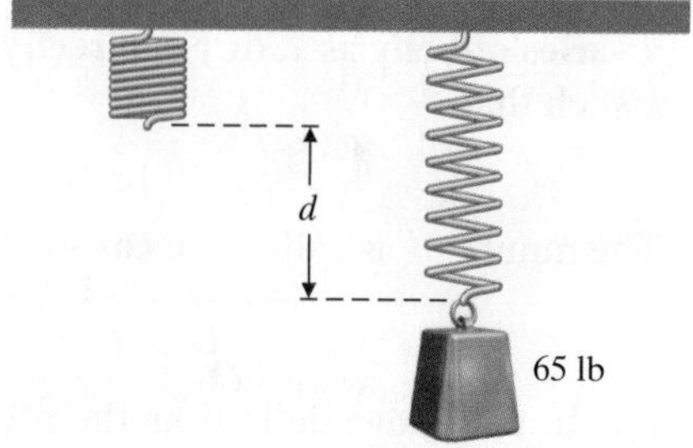

The constant of variation is represented by k.

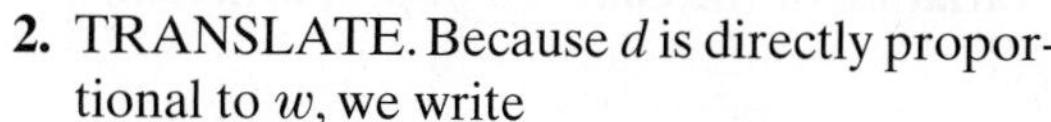

2. TRANSLATE. Because d is directly proportional to w, we write

$$d = kw$$

3. SOLVE. When a weight of 40 pounds is attached, the spring stretches 5 inches. That is, when $w = 40$, $d = 5$.

$$d = kw$$
$$5 = k(40) \quad \text{Replace } d \text{ with 5 and } w \text{ with 40.}$$
$$\frac{1}{8} = k \quad \text{Solve for } k.$$

Now when we replace k with $\frac{1}{8}$ in the equation

$$d = kw, \text{ we have}$$
$$d = \frac{1}{8}w$$

To find the stretch when a weight of 65 pounds is attached, we replace w with 65 to find d.

$$d = \frac{1}{8}(65)$$
$$= \frac{65}{8} = 8\frac{1}{8} \quad \text{or} \quad 8.125$$

4. INTERPRET.

Check: Check the proposed solution of 8.125 inches in the original problem.

State: The spring stetches 8.125 inches when a 65-pound weight is attached. □

PRACTICE 2 Use Hooke's law as stated in Example 2. If a 36-pound weight attached to a spring stretches the spring 9 inches, find the distance that a 75-pound weight attached to the spring stretches the spring.

OBJECTIVE 2 ▶ Solving problems involving inverse variation. When y is proportional to the **reciprocal** of another variable x, we say that **y varies inversely as x,** or that **y is inversely proportional to x.** An example of the inverse variation relationship is the relationship between the pressure that a gas exerts and the volume of its container. As the volume of a container decreases, the pressure of the gas it contains increases.

Inverse Variation

***y* varies inversely as *x*,** or ***y* is inversely proportional to *x*,** if there is a nonzero constant k such that

$$y = \frac{k}{x}$$

The number k is called the **constant of variation** or the **constant of proportionality.**

Notice that $y = \frac{k}{x}$ is a rational equation. Its graph for $k > 0$ and $x > 0$ is shown. From the graph, we can see that as x increases, y decreases.

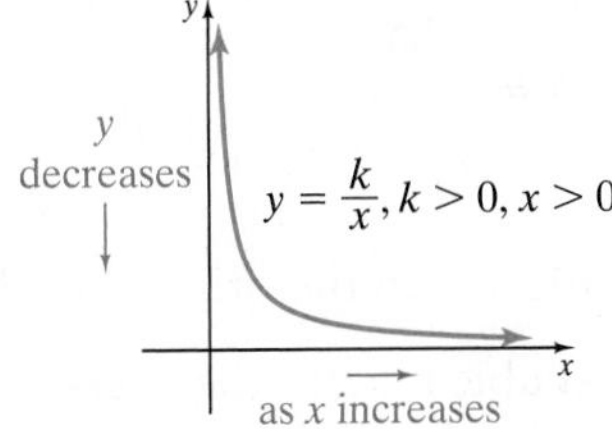

EXAMPLE 3 Suppose that u varies inversely as w. If u is 3 when w is 5, find the constant of variation and the inverse variation equation.

Solution Since u varies inversely as w, we have $u = \frac{k}{w}$. We let $u = 3$ and $w = 5$, and we solve for k.

$$u = \frac{k}{w}$$

$$3 = \frac{k}{5} \quad \text{Let } u = 3 \text{ and } w = 5.$$

$$15 = k \quad \text{Multiply both sides by 5.}$$

The constant of variation k is 15. This gives the inverse variation equation

$$u = \frac{15}{w}$$

□

PRACTICE

3 Suppose that b varies inversely as a. If b is 5 when a is 9, find the constant of variation and the inverse variation equation.

EXAMPLE 4 **Using Inverse Variation and Boyle's Law**

Boyle's law says that if the temperature stays the same, the pressure P of a gas is inversely proportional to the volume V. If a cylinder in a steam engine has a pressure of 960 kilopascals when the volume is 1.4 cubic meters, find the pressure when the volume increases to 2.5 cubic meters.

Solution

1. UNDERSTAND. Read and reread the problem. Notice that we are given that the pressure of a gas is *inversely proportional* to the volume. We will let P = the pressure and V = the volume. The constant of variation is represented by k.
2. TRANSLATE. Because P is inversely proportional to V, we write

$$P = \frac{k}{V}$$

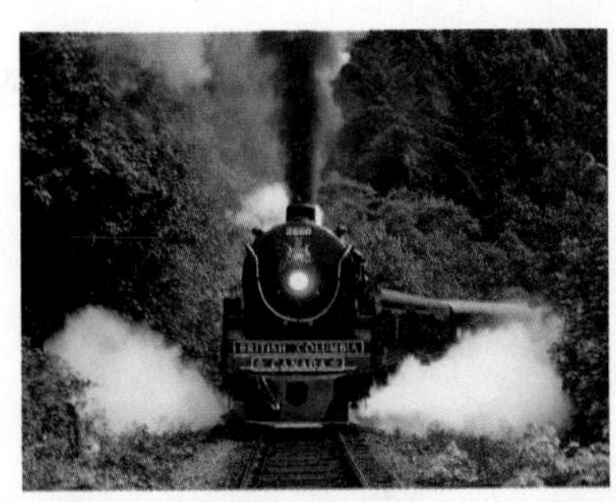

When $P = 960$ kilopascals, the volume $V = 1.4$ cubic meters. We use this information to find k.

$$960 = \frac{k}{1.4} \quad \text{Let } P = 960 \text{ and } V = 1.4.$$
$$1344 = k \quad \text{Multiply both sides by 1.4.}$$

Thus, the value of k is 1344. Replacing k with 1344 in the variation equation, we have

$$P = \frac{1344}{V}$$

Next we find P when V is 2.5 cubic meters.

3. SOLVE.

$$P = \frac{1344}{2.5} \quad \text{Let } V = 2.5.$$
$$= 537.6$$

4. INTERPRET.

Check: Check the proposed solution in the original problem.

State: When the volume is 2.5 cubic meters, the pressure is 537.6 kilopascals. □

PRACTICE 4 Use Boyle's law as stated in Example 4. When $P = 350$ kilopascals and $V = 2.8$ cubic meters, find the pressure when the volume decreases to 1.5 cubic meters.

OBJECTIVE 3 ▶ Solving problems involving joint variation. Sometimes the ratio of a variable to the product of many other variables is constant. For example, the ratio of distance traveled to the product of speed and time traveled is always 1.

$$\frac{d}{rt} = 1 \quad \text{or} \quad d = rt$$

Such a relationship is called **joint variation.**

Joint Variation

If the ratio of a variable y to the product of two or more variables is constant, then y **varies jointly as,** or **is jointly proportional to,** the other variables. If

$$y = kxz$$

then the number k is the **constant of variation** or the **constant of proportionality.**

Concept Check ☑

Which type of variation is represented by the equation $xy = 8$? Explain.

a. Direct variation **b.** Inverse variation **c.** Joint variation

EXAMPLE 5 Expressing Surface Area

The lateral surface area of a cylinder varies jointly as its radius and height. Express this surface area S in terms of radius r and height h.

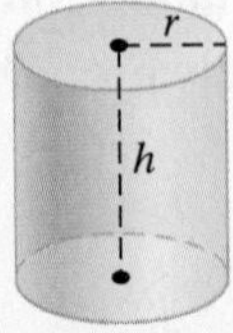

Answer to Concept Check:
b; answers may vary

Solution Because the surface area varies jointly as the radius r and the height h, we equate S to a constant multiple of r and h.

$$S = krh$$

In the equation $S = krh$, it can be determined that the constant k is 2π, and we then have the formula $S = 2\pi rh$. (The lateral surface area formula does not include the areas of the two circular bases.) □

PRACTICE

5 The area of a regular polygon varies jointly as its apothem and its perimeter. Express the area in terms of the apothem a and the perimeter p.

OBJECTIVE 4 ▶ Solving problems involving combined variation. Some examples of variation involve combinations of direct, inverse, and joint variation. We will call these variations **combined variation.**

EXAMPLE 6 Suppose that y varies directly as the square of x. If y is 24 when x is 2, find the constant of variation and the variation equation.

Solution Since y varies directly as the square of x, we have

$$y = kx^2$$

Now let $y = 24$ and $x = 2$ and solve for k.

$$y = kx^2$$
$$24 = k \cdot 2^2$$
$$24 = 4k$$
$$6 = k$$

The constant of variation is 6, so the variation equation is

$$y = 6x^2$$ □

PRACTICE

6 Suppose that y varies inversely as the cube of x. If y is $\frac{1}{2}$ when x is 2, find the constant of variation and the variation equation.

EXAMPLE 7 **Finding Column Weight**

The maximum weight that a circular column can support is directly proportional to the fourth power of its diameter and is inversely proportional to the square of its height. A 2-meter-diameter column that is 8 meters in height can support 1 ton. Find the weight that a 1-meter-diameter column that is 4 meters in height can support.

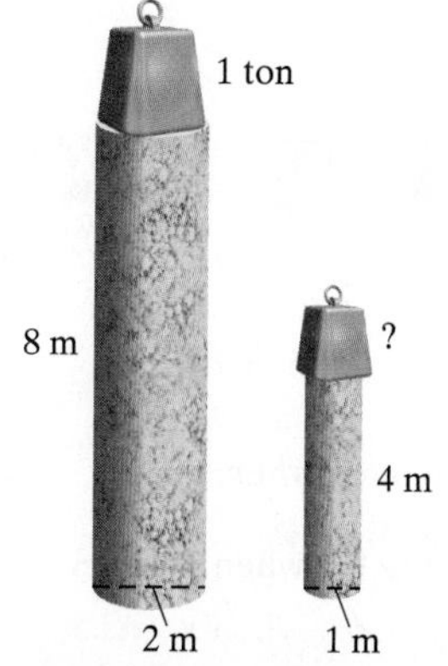

Solution

1. UNDERSTAND. Read and reread the problem. Let w = weight, d = diameter, h = height, and k = the constant of variation.
2. TRANSLATE. Since w is directly proportional to d^4 and inversely proportional to h^2, we have

$$w = \frac{kd^4}{h^2}$$

3. SOLVE. To find k, we are given that a 2-meter-diameter column that is 8 meters in height can support 1 ton. That is, $w = 1$ when $d = 2$ and $h = 8$, or

$$1 = \frac{k \cdot 2^4}{8^2} \quad \text{Let } w = 1, d = 2, \text{ and } h = 8.$$

$$1 = \frac{k \cdot 16}{64}$$

$$4 = k \quad \text{Solve for } k.$$

Now replace k with 4 in the equation $w = \frac{kd^4}{h^2}$ and we have

$$w = \frac{4d^4}{h^2}$$

To find weight w for a 1-meter-diameter column that is 4 meters in height, let $d = 1$ and $h = 4$.

$$w = \frac{4 \cdot 1^4}{4^2}$$

$$w = \frac{4}{16} = \frac{1}{4}$$

4. INTERPRET.

Check: Check the proposed solution in the original problem.

State: The 1-meter-diameter column that is 4 meters in height can hold $\frac{1}{4}$ ton of weight. □

PRACTICE 7 Suppose that y varies directly as z and inversely as the cube of x. If y is 15 when $z = 5$ and $x = 3$, find the constant of variation and the variation equation.

VOCABULARY & READINESS CHECK

State whether each equation represents direct, inverse, or joint variation.

1. $y = 5x$
2. $y = \frac{700}{x}$
3. $y = 5xz$
4. $y = \frac{1}{2}abc$
5. $y = \frac{9.1}{x}$
6. $y = 2.3x$
7. $y = \frac{2}{3}x$
8. $y = 3.1\,st$

18.5 EXERCISE SET

PRACTICE

WATCH

DOWNLOAD

READ

REVIEW

If y varies directly as x, find the constant of variation and the direct variation equation for each situation. See Example 1.

1. $y = 4$ when $x = 20$
2. $y = 5$ when $x = 30$
3. $y = 6$ when $x = 4$
4. $y = 12$ when $x = 8$
5. $y = 7$ when $x = \frac{1}{2}$
6. $y = 11$ when $x = \frac{1}{3}$
7. $y = 0.2$ when $x = 0.8$
8. $y = 0.4$ when $x = 2.5$

Solve. See Example 2.

9. The weight of a synthetic ball varies directly with the cube of its radius. A ball with a radius of 2 inches weighs 1.20 pounds. Find the weight of a ball of the same material with a 3-inch radius.

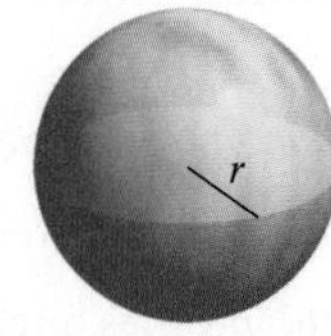

10. At sea, the distance to the horizon is directly proportional to the square root of the elevation of the observer. If a person who is 36 feet above the water can see 7.4 miles, find how far a person 64 feet above the water can see. Round to the nearest tenth of a mile.

11. The amount P of pollution varies directly with the population N of people. Kansas City has a population of 442,000 and produces 260,000 tons of pollutants. Find how many tons of pollution we should expect St. Louis to produce, if we know that its population is 348,000. Round to the nearest whole ton. (*Population Source: The World Almanac*, 2005)

12. Charles's law states that if the pressure P stays the same, the volume V of a gas is directly proportional to its temperature T. If a balloon is filled with 20 cubic meters of a gas at a temperature of 300 K, find the new volume if the temperature rises 360 K while the pressure stays the same.

If y varies inversely as x, find the constant of variation and the inverse variation equation for each situation. See Example 3.

13. $y = 6$ when $x = 5$
14. $y = 20$ when $x = 9$
15. $y = 100$ when $x = 7$
16. $y = 63$ when $x = 3$
17. $y = \frac{1}{8}$ when $x = 16$
18. $y = \frac{1}{10}$ when $x = 40$
19. $y = 0.2$ when $x = 0.7$
20. $y = 0.6$ when $x = 0.3$

Solve. See Example 4.

21. Pairs of markings a set distance apart are made on highways so that police can detect drivers exceeding the speed limit. Over a fixed distance, the speed R varies inversely with the time T. In one particular pair of markings, R is 45 mph when T is 6 seconds. Find the speed of a car that travels the given distance in 5 seconds.

22. The weight of an object on or above the surface of Earth varies inversely as the square of the distance between the object and Earth's center. If a person weighs 160 pounds on Earth's surface, find the individual's weight if he moves 200 miles above Earth. Round to the nearest whole pound. (Assume that Earth's radius is 4000 miles.)

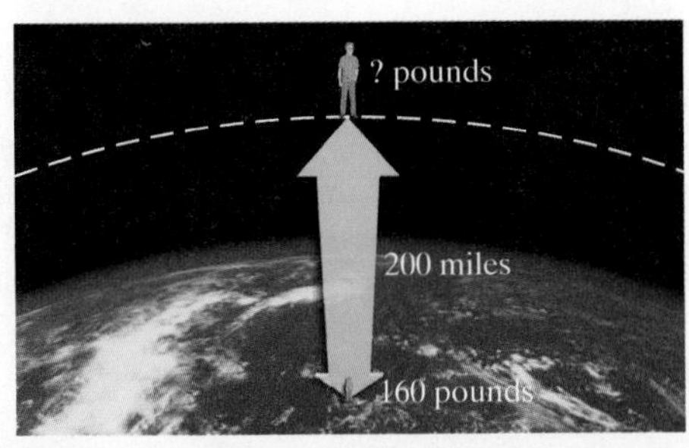

23. If the voltage V in an electric circuit is held constant, the current I is inversely proportional to the resistance R. If the current is 40 amperes when the resistance is 270 ohms, find the current when the resistance is 150 ohms.

24. Because it is more efficient to produce larger numbers of items, the cost of producing Dysan computer disks is inversely proportional to the number produced. If 4000 can be produced at a cost of \$1.20 each, find the cost per disk when 6000 are produced.

25. The intensity I of light varies inversely as the square of the distance d from the light source. If the distance from the light source is doubled (see the figure), determine what happens to the intensity of light at the new location.

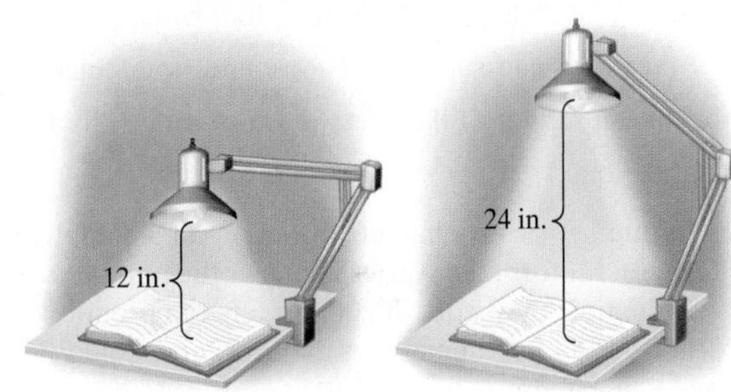

26. The maximum weight that a circular column can hold is inversely proportional to the square of its height. If an 8-foot column can hold 2 tons, find how much weight a 10-foot column can hold.

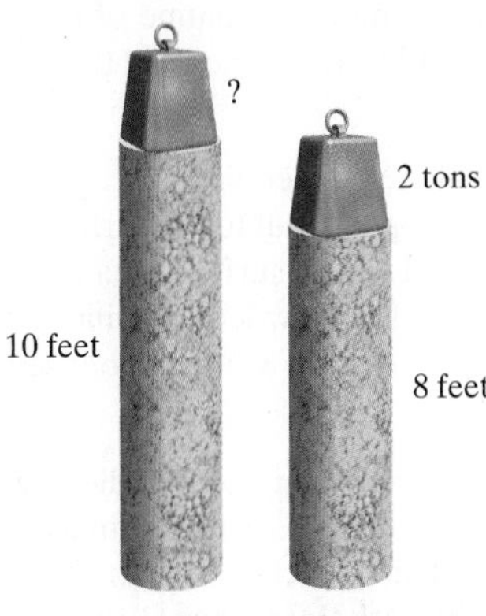

MIXED PRACTICE

Write each statement as an equation. Use k as the constant of variation. See Example 5.

27. x varies jointly as y and z.
28. P varies jointly as R and the square of S.

29. r varies jointly as s and the cube of t.

30. a varies jointly as b and c.

For each statement, find the constant of variation and the variation equation. See Examples 5 and 6.

31. y varies directly as the cube of x; $y = 9$ when $x = 3$

32. y varies directly as the cube of x; $y = 32$ when $x = 4$

33. y varies directly as the square root of x; $y = 0.4$ when $x = 4$

34. y varies directly as the square root of x; $y = 2.1$ when $x = 9$

35. y varies inversely as the square of x; $y = 0.052$ when $x = 5$

36. y varies inversely as the square of x; $y = 0.011$ when $x = 10$

37. y varies jointly as x and the cube of z; $y = 120$ when $x = 5$ and $z = 2$

38. y varies jointly as x and the square of z; $y = 360$ when $x = 4$ and $z = 3$

Solve. See Example 7.

△ **39.** The maximum weight that a rectangular beam can support varies jointly as its width and the square of its height and inversely as its length. If a beam $\frac{1}{2}$ foot wide, $\frac{1}{3}$ foot high, and 10 feet long can support 12 tons, find how much a similar beam can support if the beam is $\frac{2}{3}$ foot wide, $\frac{1}{2}$ foot high, and 16 feet long.

40. The number of cars manufactured on an assembly line at a General Motors plant varies jointly as the number of workers and the time they work. If 200 workers can produce 60 cars in 2 hours, find how many cars 240 workers should be able to make in 3 hours.

△ **41.** The volume of a cone varies jointly as its height and the square of its radius. If the volume of a cone is 32π cubic inches when the radius is 4 inches and the height is 6 inches, find the volume of a cone when the radius is 3 inches and the height is 5 inches.

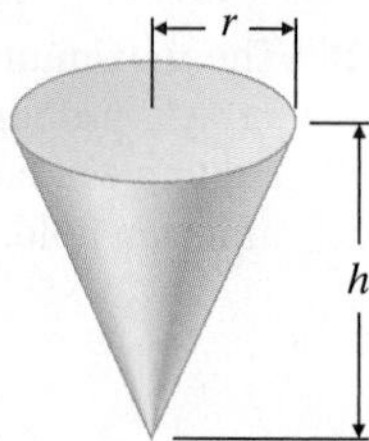

△ **42.** When a wind blows perpendicularly against a flat surface, its force is jointly proportional to the surface area and the speed of the wind. A sail whose surface area is 12 square feet experiences a 20-pound force when the wind speed is 10 miles per hour. Find the force on an 8-square-foot sail if the wind speed is 12 miles per hour.

43. The intensity of light (in foot-candles) varies inversely as the square of x, the distance in feet from the light source. The intensity of light 2 feet from the source is 80 foot-candles. How far away is the source if the intensity of light is 5 foot-candles?

44. The horsepower that can be safely transmitted to a shaft varies jointly as the shaft's angular speed of rotation (in revolutions per minute) and the cube of its diameter. A 2-inch shaft making 120 revolutions per minute safely transmits 40 horsepower. Find how much horsepower can be safely transmitted by a 3-inch shaft making 80 revolutions per minute.

MIXED PRACTICE

Write an equation to describe each variation. Use k for the constant of proportionality. See Examples 1 through 7.

45. y varies directly as x

46. p varies directly as q

47. a varies inversely as b

48. y varies inversely as x

49. y varies jointly as x and z

50. y varies jointly as q, r, and t

51. y varies inversely as x^3

52. y varies inversely as a^4

53. y varies directly as x and inversely as p^2

54. y varies directly as a^5 and inversely as b

REVIEW AND PREVIEW

Find the exact circumference and area of each circle. See the inside cover for a list of geometric formulas.

△ **55.** △ **56.**

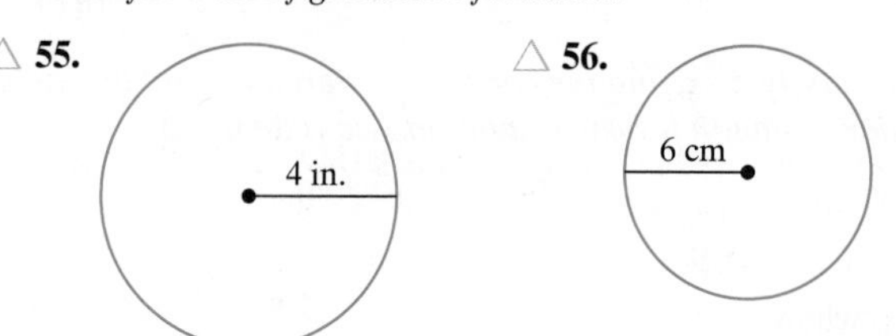

△ **57.** △ **58.**

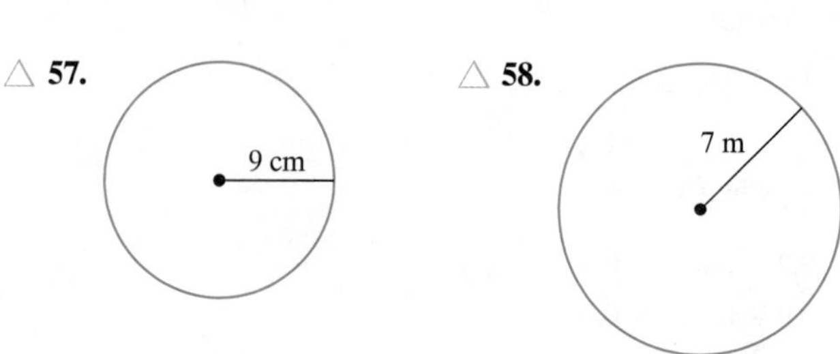

Find each square root. See Section 1.3.

59. $\sqrt{81}$

60. $\sqrt{36}$

61. $\sqrt{1}$

62. $\sqrt{4}$

63. $\sqrt{\frac{1}{4}}$

64. $\sqrt{\frac{1}{25}}$

65. $\sqrt{\frac{4}{9}}$

66. $\sqrt{\frac{25}{121}}$

CONCEPT EXTENSIONS

Solve. See the Concept Check in this section. Choose the type of variation that each equation represents. **a.** *Direct variation* **b.** *Inverse variation* **c.** *Joint variation*

67. $y = \frac{2}{3}x$

68. $y = \frac{0.6}{x}$

69. $y = 9ab$

70. $xy = \frac{2}{11}$

71. The horsepower to drive a boat varies directly as the cube of the speed of the boat. If the speed of the boat is to double, determine the corresponding increase in horsepower required.

72. The volume of a cylinder varies jointly as the height and the square of the radius. If the height is halved and the radius is doubled, determine what happens to the volume.

73. Suppose that y varies directly as x. If x is doubled, what is the effect on y?

74. Suppose that y varies directly as x^2. If x is doubled, what is the effect on y?

Complete the following table for the inverse variation $y = \frac{k}{x}$ over each given value of k. Plot the points on a rectangular coordinate system.

x	$\frac{1}{4}$	$\frac{1}{2}$	1	2	4
$y = \frac{k}{x}$					

75. $k = 3$ **76.** $k = 1$ **77.** $k = \frac{1}{2}$ **78.** $k = 5$

THE BIGGER PICTURE SOLVING EQUATIONS AND INEQUALITIES

Continue the outline from Sections 16.2, 16.3, and 16.5. Write how to recognize and how to solve equations with rational expressions in your own words. For example:

Solving Equations and Inequalities

I. Equations

A. Linear equations (Sec. 16.1)

B. Absolute value equations (Sec. 16.4)

C. Quadratic equations

D. Equations with rational expressions: Equation contains rational expressions.

$$\frac{7}{x-1} + \frac{3}{x+1} = \frac{x+3}{x^2-1} \qquad \text{Equation with rational expressions.}$$

$$\cancel{(x-1)}(x+1)\cdot\frac{7}{\cancel{x-1}} + (x-1)\cancel{(x+1)}\cdot\frac{3}{\cancel{x+1}} = \cancel{(x-1)(x+1)}\cdot\frac{x+3}{\cancel{(x-1)(x+1)}} \qquad \text{Multiply by the LCD.}$$

$$7(x+1) + 3(x-1) = x + 3 \qquad \text{Simplify.}$$

$$7x + 7 + 3x - 3 = x + 3$$

$$9x = -1$$

$$x = -\frac{1}{9} \qquad \text{Solve.}$$

II. Inequalities
  A. Linear inequalities (Sec. 16.2)
  B. Compound inequalities (Sec. 16.3)
  C. Absolute value inequalities (Sec. 16.5)

Solve. Write solutions to inequalities using interval notation.

1. $|-7x + 1| < 15$
2. $|-7x + 1| = 15$
3. $x^2 - 121 = 0$
4. $\frac{8}{x + 2} - \frac{3}{x - 1} = \frac{x + 6}{x^2 + x - 2}$
5. $9x + 6 = 4x - 2$
6. $3x \le 6$ or $-x \ge 5$
7. $3x \le 6$ and $-x \ge 5$
8. $-9 \le -3x + 21 < 0$
9. $\left|\frac{2x - 1}{5}\right| > 7$
10. $15x^3 - 16x^2 = 7x$

INTEGRATED REVIEW EXPRESSIONS AND EQUATIONS CONTAINING RATIONAL EXPRESSIONS

Sections 18.1–18.4

It is very important that you understand the difference between an expression and an equation containing rational expressions. An equation contains an equal sign; an expression does not.

Expression to be Simplified

$$\frac{x}{2} + \frac{x}{6}$$

Write both rational expressions with the LCD, 6, as the denominator.

$$\frac{x}{2} + \frac{x}{6} = \frac{x \cdot 3}{2 \cdot 3} + \frac{x}{6}$$
$$= \frac{3x}{6} + \frac{x}{6}$$
$$= \frac{4x}{6} = \frac{2x}{3}$$

Equation to be Solved

$$\frac{x}{2} + \frac{x}{6} = \frac{2}{3}$$

Multiply both sides by the LCD, 6.

$$6\left(\frac{1}{2} + \frac{x}{6}\right) = 6\left(\frac{2}{3}\right)$$
$$3 + x = 4$$
$$x = 1$$

Check to see that the solution set is 1.

Helpful Hint
Remember: Equations can be cleared of fractions; expressions cannot.

Perform each indicated operation and simplify, or solve the equation for the variable.

1. $\frac{x}{2} = \frac{1}{8} + \frac{x}{4}$

2. $\frac{x}{4} = \frac{3}{2} + \frac{x}{10}$

3. $\frac{1}{8} + \frac{x}{4}$

4. $\frac{3}{2} + \frac{x}{10}$

5. $\frac{4}{x + 2} - \frac{2}{x - 1}$

6. $\frac{5}{x - 2} - \frac{10}{x + 4}$

7. $\frac{4}{x+2} = \frac{2}{x-1}$

8. $\frac{5}{x-2} = \frac{10}{x+4}$

9. $\frac{2}{x^2-4} = \frac{1}{x+2} - \frac{3}{x-2}$

10. $\frac{3}{x^2-25} = \frac{1}{x+5} + \frac{2}{x-5}$

11. $\frac{5}{x^2-3x} + \frac{4}{2x-6}$

12. $\frac{5}{x^2-3x} \div \frac{4}{2x-6}$

13. $\frac{x-1}{x+1} + \frac{x+7}{x-1} = \frac{4}{x^2-1}$

14. $\left(1 - \frac{y}{x}\right) \div \left(1 - \frac{x}{y}\right)$

15. $\frac{a^2-9}{a-6} \cdot \frac{a^2-5a-6}{a^2-a-6}$

16. $\frac{2}{a-6} + \frac{3a}{a^2-5a-6} - \frac{a}{5a+5}$

17. $\frac{2x+3}{3x-2} = \frac{4x+1}{6x+1}$

18. $\frac{5x-3}{2x} = \frac{10x+3}{4x+1}$

19. $\frac{a}{9a^2-1} + \frac{2}{6a-2}$

20. $\frac{3}{4a-8} - \frac{a+2}{a^2-2a}$

21. $-\frac{3}{x^2} - \frac{1}{x} + 2 = 0$

22. $\frac{x}{2x+6} + \frac{5}{x^2-9}$

23. $\frac{x-8}{x^2-x-2} + \frac{2}{x-2}$

24. $\frac{x-8}{x^2-x-2} + \frac{2}{x-2} = \frac{3}{x+1}$

25. $\frac{3}{a} - 5 = \frac{7}{a} - 1$

26. $\frac{7}{3z-9} + \frac{5}{z}$

Use $\frac{x}{5} - \frac{x}{4} = \frac{1}{10}$ *and* $\frac{x}{5} - \frac{x}{4} + \frac{1}{10}$ *for Exercises 27 and 28.*

27. a. Which one above is an expression?

b. Describe the first step to simplify this expression.

c. Simplify the expression.

28. a. Which one above is an equation?

b. Describe the first step to solve this equation.

c. Solve the equation.

For each exercise, choose the correct statement. Each figure represents a real number and no denominators are 0.*

29. a. $\frac{\triangle + \square}{\triangle} = \square$ **b.** $\frac{\triangle + \square}{\triangle} = 1 + \frac{\square}{\triangle}$ **c.** $\frac{\triangle + \square}{\triangle} = \frac{\square}{\triangle}$ **d.** $\frac{\triangle + \square}{\triangle} = 1 + \square$ **e.** $\frac{\triangle + \square}{\triangle - \square} = -1$

30. a. $\frac{\triangle}{\square} + \frac{\square}{\triangle} = \frac{\triangle + \square}{\square + \triangle} = 1$ **b.** $\frac{\triangle}{\square} + \frac{\square}{\triangle} = \frac{\triangle + \square}{\triangle\square}$ **c.** $\frac{\triangle}{\square} + \frac{\square}{\triangle} = \triangle\triangle + \square\square$

d. $\frac{\triangle}{\square} + \frac{\square}{\triangle} = \frac{\triangle\triangle + \square\square}{\square\triangle}$ **e.** $\frac{\triangle}{\square} + \frac{\square}{\triangle} = \frac{\triangle\square}{\square\triangle} = 1$

*My thanks to Kelly Champagne for permission to use her Exercises for 29 and 30.

STUDY SKILLS BUILDER

Are You Preparing for a Test on Chapter 18?

Below I have listed some common trouble areas for students in Chapter 18. After studying for your test—but before taking your test—read these.

- Make sure you know the difference in the following:

Simplify: $\dfrac{\frac{3}{x}}{\frac{1}{x}-\frac{5}{y}}$

Multiply numerator and denominator by the LCD.

$$\frac{\frac{3}{x}\cdot xy}{\frac{1}{x}\cdot xy-\frac{5}{y}\cdot xy}=\frac{3y}{y-5x}$$

Solve: $\dfrac{5x}{6}-\dfrac{1}{2}=\dfrac{5x}{12}$

Multiply both sides by the LCD.

$$12\cdot\frac{5x}{6}-12\cdot\frac{1}{2}=12\cdot\frac{5x}{12}$$
$$2\cdot 5x-6=5x$$
$$10x-6=5x$$
$$5x=6$$
$$x=\frac{6}{5}$$

Subtract: $\dfrac{1}{2x}-\dfrac{7}{x-3}$

Write each expression as an equivalent expression with the LCD.

$$\frac{1\cdot(x-3)}{2x\cdot(x-3)}-\frac{7\cdot 2x}{(x-3)\cdot 2x}$$
$$=\frac{x-3}{2x(x-3)}-\frac{14x}{2x(x-3)}$$
$$=\frac{-13x-3}{2x(x-3)}$$

Remember: This is simply a checklist of common trouble areas. For a review of Chapter 18, see the Highlights and Chapter Review at the end of this chapter.

CHAPTER 18 VOCABULARY CHECK

Fill in each blank with one of the words or phrases listed below.

rational expression	equation	complex fraction	jointly	inversely
least common denominator	expression	opposites	directly	

1. A rational expression whose numerator, denominator, or both contain one or more rational expressions is called a _______________.
2. In the equation $y = kx$, y varies ________ as x.
3. In the equation $y = \frac{k}{x}$, y varies _________ as x.
4. The _____________________ of a list of rational expressions is a polynomial of least degree whose factors include the denominator factors in the list.
5. In the equation $y = kxz$, y varies _______ as x and z.
6. The expressions $(x - 5)$ and $(5 - x)$ are called _________.
7. A _______________ is an expression that can be written as the quotient $\frac{P}{Q}$ of two polynomials P and Q as long as Q is not 0.
8. Which is an expression and which is an equation? An example of an _________ is $\frac{2}{x}+\frac{2}{x^2}=7$ and an example of an _________ is $\frac{2}{x}+\frac{5}{x^2}$.

Helpful Hint

Are you preparing for your test? Don't forget to take the Chapter 18 Test on page 1147. Then check your answers at the back of the text and use the Chapter Test Prep Video CD to see the fully worked-out solutions to any of the exercises you want to review.

CHAPTER 18 HIGHLIGHTS

DEFINITIONS AND CONCEPTS	EXAMPLES
SECTION 18.1 RATIONAL FUNCTIONS AND MULTIPLYING AND DIVIDING RATIONAL EXPRESSIONS	
A **rational expression** is the quotient $\frac{P}{Q}$ of two polynomials P and Q, as long as Q is not 0.	$\frac{2x-6}{7}, \quad \frac{t^2-3t+5}{t-1}$
To Simplify a Rational Expression **Step 1.** Completely factor the numerator and the denominator. **Step 2.** Apply the fundamental principle of rational expressions.	Simplify. $\frac{2x^2+9x-5}{x^2-25} = \frac{(2x-1)(x+5)}{(x-5)(x+5)} = \frac{2x-1}{x-5}$
To Multiply Rational Expressions **Step 1.** Completely factor numerators and denominators. **Step 2.** Multiply the numerators and multiply the denominators. **Step 3.** Apply the fundamental principle of rational expressions.	Multiply $\frac{x^3+8}{12x-18} \cdot \frac{14x^2-21x}{x^2+2x}$. $= \frac{(x+2)(x^2-2x+4)}{6(2x-3)} \cdot \frac{7x(2x-3)}{x(x+2)}$ $= \frac{7(x^2-2x+4)}{6}$
To Divide Rational Expressions Multiply the first rational expression by the reciprocal of the second rational expression.	Divide $\frac{x^2+6x+9}{5xy-5y} \div \frac{x+3}{10y}$. $= \frac{(x+3)(x+3)}{5y(x-1)} \cdot \frac{2 \cdot 5y}{x+3}$ $= \frac{2(x+3)}{x-1}$
A **rational function** is a function described by a rational expression.	$f(x) = \frac{2x-6}{7}, \quad h(t) = \frac{t^2-3t+5}{t-1}$
SECTION 18.2 ADDING AND SUBTRACTING RATIONAL EXPRESSIONS	
To Add or Subtract Rational Expressions **Step 1.** Find the LCD. **Step 2.** Write each rational expression as an equivalent rational expression whose denominator is the LCD. **Step 3.** Add or subtract numerators and write the result over the common denominator. **Step 4.** Simplify the resulting rational expression.	Subtract $\frac{3}{x+2} - \frac{x+1}{x-3}$. $= \frac{3 \cdot (x-3)}{(x+2) \cdot (x-3)} - \frac{(x+1) \cdot (x+2)}{(x-3) \cdot (x+2)}$ $= \frac{3(x-3)-(x+1)(x+2)}{(x+2)(x-3)}$ $= \frac{3x-9-(x^2+3x+2)}{(x+2)(x-3)}$ $= \frac{3x-9-x^2-3x-2}{(x+2)(x-3)}$ $= \frac{-x^2-11}{(x+2)(x-3)}$

(continued)

DEFINITIONS AND CONCEPTS	EXAMPLES

SECTION 18.3 SIMPLIFYING COMPLEX FRACTIONS

Method 1: Simplify the numerator and the denominator so that each is a single fraction. Then perform the indicated division and simplify if possible.

Simplify $\dfrac{\dfrac{x+2}{x}}{x-\dfrac{4}{x}}$.

Method 1: $\dfrac{\dfrac{x+2}{x}}{\dfrac{x\cdot x}{1\cdot x}-\dfrac{4}{x}} = \dfrac{\dfrac{x+2}{x}}{\dfrac{x^2-4}{x}}$

$= \dfrac{x+2}{x}\cdot\dfrac{x}{(x+2)(x-2)} = \dfrac{1}{x-2}$

Method 2: Multiply the numerator and the denominator of the complex fraction by the LCD of the fractions in both the numerator and the denominator. Then simplify if possible.

Method 2: $\dfrac{\left(\dfrac{x+2}{x}\right)\cdot x}{\left(x-\dfrac{4}{x}\right)\cdot x} = \dfrac{x+2}{x\cdot x-\dfrac{4}{x}\cdot x}$

$= \dfrac{x+2}{x^2-4} = \dfrac{x+2}{(x+2)(x-2)} = \dfrac{1}{x-2}$

SECTION 18.4 SOLVING EQUATIONS CONTAINING RATIONAL EXPRESSIONS

To solve an equation containing rational expressions: Multiply both sides of the equation by the LCD of all rational expressions. Then apply the distributive property and simplify. Solve the resulting equation and then check each proposed solution to see whether it makes the denominator 0. If so, it is an **extraneous solution.**

Solve $x-\dfrac{3}{x}=\dfrac{1}{2}$.

$2x\left(x-\dfrac{3}{x}\right)=2x\left(\dfrac{1}{2}\right)$ The LCD is $2x$.

$2x\cdot x-2x\left(\dfrac{3}{x}\right)=2x\left(\dfrac{1}{2}\right)$ Distribute.

$2x^2-6=x$

$2x^2-x-6=0$ Subtract x.

$(2x+3)(x-2)=0$ Factor.

$x=-\dfrac{3}{2}$ or $x=2$ Solve.

Both $-\dfrac{3}{2}$ and 2 check. The solutions are 2 and $-\dfrac{3}{2}$.

SECTION 18.5 VARIATION AND PROBLEM SOLVING

y **varies directly as** *x*, or *y* is **directly proportional to** *x*, if there is a nonzero constant *k* such that

$$y = kx$$

The circumference of a circle *C* varies directly as its radius *r*.

$$C = \underbrace{2\pi}_{k} r$$

y **varies inversely as** *x*, or *y* is **inversely proportional to** *x*, if there is a nonzero constant *k* such that

$$y = \frac{k}{x}$$

Pressure *P* varies inversely with volume *V*.

$$P = \frac{k}{V}$$

y **varies jointly as** *x* and *z*, or *y* is **jointly proportional to** *x* and *z*, if there is a nonzero constant *k* such that

$$y = kxz$$

The lateral surface area *S* of a cylinder varies jointly as its radius *r* and height *h*.

$$S = \underbrace{2\pi}_{k} rh$$

CHAPTER 18 REVIEW

(18.1) Find the domain for each rational function.

1. $f(x) = \dfrac{3 - 5x}{7}$

2. $g(x) = \dfrac{2x + 4}{11}$

3. $F(x) = \dfrac{-3x^2}{x - 5}$

4. $h(x) = \dfrac{4x}{3x - 12}$

5. $f(x) = \dfrac{x^3 + 2}{x^2 + 8x}$

6. $G(x) = \dfrac{20}{3x^2 - 48}$

Write each rational expression in lowest terms.

7. $\dfrac{x - 12}{12 - x}$

8. $\dfrac{5x - 15}{25x - 75}$

9. $\dfrac{2x}{2x^2 - 2x}$

10. $\dfrac{x + 7}{x^2 - 49}$

11. $\dfrac{2x^2 + 4x - 30}{x^2 + x - 20}$

12. The average cost (per bookcase) of manufacturing x bookcases is given by the rational function.

$$C(x) = \frac{35x + 4200}{x}$$

a. Find the average cost per bookcase of manufacturing 50 bookcases.

b. Find the average cost per bookcase of manufacturing 100 bookcases.

c. As the number of bookcases increases, does the average cost per bookcase increase or decrease? (See parts **a** and **b**.)

Perform each indicated operation. Write your answers in lowest terms.

13. $\dfrac{4 - x}{5} \cdot \dfrac{15}{2x - 8}$

14. $\dfrac{x^2 - 6x + 9}{2x^2 - 18} \cdot \dfrac{4x + 12}{5x - 15}$

15. $\dfrac{a - 4b}{a^2 + ab} \cdot \dfrac{b^2 - a^2}{8b - 2a}$

16. $\dfrac{x^2 - x - 12}{2x^2 - 32} \cdot \dfrac{x^2 + 8x + 16}{3x^2 + 21x + 36}$

17. $\dfrac{4x + 8y}{3} \div \dfrac{5x + 10y}{9}$

18. $\dfrac{x^2 - 25}{3} \div \dfrac{x^2 - 10x + 25}{x^2 - x - 20}$

19. $\dfrac{a - 4b}{a^2 + ab} \div \dfrac{20b - 5a}{b^2 - a^2}$

20. $\dfrac{3x + 3}{x - 1} \div \dfrac{x^2 - 6x - 7}{x^2 - 1}$

21. $\dfrac{2x - x^2}{x^3 - 8} \div \dfrac{x^2}{x^2 + 2x + 4}$

22. $\dfrac{5x - 15}{3 - x} \cdot \dfrac{x + 2}{10x + 20} \cdot \dfrac{x^2 - 9}{x^2 - x - 6}$

(18.2) Find the LCD of the rational expressions in each list.

23. $\dfrac{5}{4x^2y^5}, \dfrac{3}{10x^2y^4}, \dfrac{x}{6y^4}$

24. $\dfrac{5}{2x}, \dfrac{7}{x - 2}$

25. $\dfrac{3}{5x}, \dfrac{2}{x - 5}$

26. $\dfrac{1}{5x^3}, \dfrac{4}{x^2 + 3x - 28}, \dfrac{11}{10x^2 - 30x}$

Perform each indicated operation. Write your answers in lowest terms.

27. $\dfrac{4}{x - 4} + \dfrac{x}{x - 4}$

28. $\dfrac{4}{3x^2} + \dfrac{2}{3x^2}$

29. $\dfrac{1}{x - 2} - \dfrac{1}{4 - 2x}$

30. $\dfrac{1}{10 - x} + \dfrac{x - 1}{x - 10}$

31. $\dfrac{x}{9 - x^2} - \dfrac{2}{5x - 15}$

32. $2x + 1 - \dfrac{1}{x - 3}$

33. $\dfrac{2}{a^2 - 2a + 1} + \dfrac{3}{a^2 - 1}$

34. $\dfrac{x}{9x^2 + 12x + 16} - \dfrac{3x + 4}{27x^3 - 64}$

Perform each indicated operation. Write your answers in lowest terms.

35. $\dfrac{2}{x - 1} - \dfrac{3x}{3x - 3} + \dfrac{1}{2x - 2}$

36. Find the perimeter of the heptagon (a polygon with seven sides).

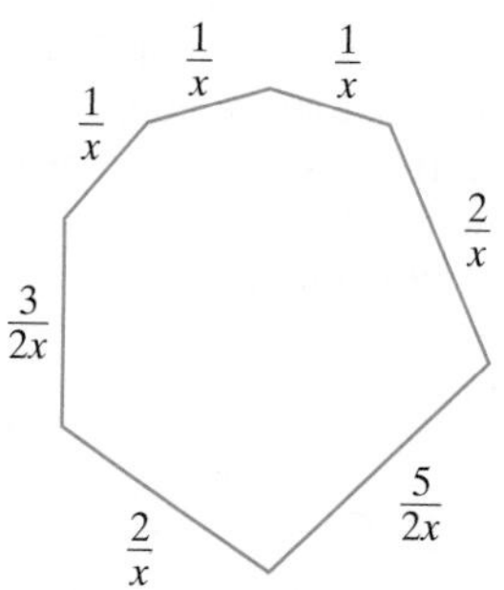

(18.3) Simplify each complex fraction.

37. $\dfrac{1 - \dfrac{3x}{4}}{2 + \dfrac{x}{4}}$

38. $\dfrac{\dfrac{x^2}{15}}{\dfrac{x + 1}{5x}}$

39. $\dfrac{2 - \dfrac{3}{2x}}{x - \dfrac{2}{5x}}$

40. $\dfrac{1 + \dfrac{x}{y}}{\dfrac{x^2}{y^2} - 1}$

41. $\dfrac{\dfrac{5}{x} + \dfrac{1}{xy}}{\dfrac{3}{x^2}}$

42. $\dfrac{\dfrac{x}{3} - \dfrac{3}{x}}{1 + \dfrac{3}{x}}$

43. $\dfrac{\dfrac{1}{x - 1} + 1}{\dfrac{1}{x + 1} - 1}$

44. $\dfrac{\dfrac{x - 3}{x + 3} + \dfrac{x + 3}{x - 3}}{\dfrac{x - 3}{x + 3} - \dfrac{x + 3}{x - 3}}$

If $f(x) = \dfrac{3}{x}$, $x \neq 0$, find each of the following.

45. $f(a + h)$

46. $f(a)$

47. Use Exercises 45 and 46 to find $\dfrac{f(a + h) - f(a)}{h}$.

48. Simplify the results of Exercise 47.

(18.4) Solve each equation.

49. $\dfrac{3}{x} + \dfrac{1}{3} = \dfrac{5}{x}$

50. $\dfrac{2x + 3}{5x - 9} = \dfrac{3}{2}$

51. $\dfrac{1}{x - 2} - \dfrac{3x}{x^2 - 4} = \dfrac{2}{x + 2}$

52. $\dfrac{7}{x} - \dfrac{x}{7} = 0$

Solve each equation or perform each indicated operation. Simplify.

53. $\dfrac{5}{x^2 - 7x} + \dfrac{4}{2x - 14}$

54. $3 - \dfrac{5}{x} - \dfrac{2}{x^2} = 0$

55. $\dfrac{4}{3 - x} - \dfrac{7}{2x - 6} + \dfrac{5}{x}$

(18.5) Solve each variation problem.

56. A is directly proportional to B. If $A = 6$ when $B = 14$, find A when $B = 21$.

57. According to Boyle's law, the pressure exerted by a gas is inversely proportional to the volume, as long as the temperature stays the same. If a gas exerts a pressure of 1250 kilopascals when the volume is 2 cubic meters, find the volume when the pressure is 800 kilopascals.

MIXED REVIEW

For expressions, perform the indicated operation and/or simplify. For equations, solve the equation for the unknown variable.

58. $\dfrac{22x + 8}{11x + 4}$

59. $\dfrac{xy - 3x + 2y - 6}{x^2 + 4x + 4}$

60. $\dfrac{2}{5x} \div \dfrac{4 - 18x}{6 - 27x}$

61. $\dfrac{7x + 28}{2x + 4} \div \dfrac{x^2 + 2x - 8}{x^2 - 2x - 8}$

62. $\dfrac{5a^2 - 20}{a^3 + 2a^2 + a + 2} \div \dfrac{7a}{a^3 + a}$

63. $\dfrac{4a + 8}{5a^2 - 20} \cdot \dfrac{3a^2 - 6a}{a + 3} \div \dfrac{2a^2}{5a + 15}$

64. $\dfrac{7}{2x} + \dfrac{5}{6x}$

65. $\dfrac{x - 2}{x + 1} - \dfrac{x - 3}{x - 1}$

66. $\dfrac{2x + 1}{x^2 + x - 6} + \dfrac{2 - x}{x^2 + x - 6}$

67. $\dfrac{2}{x^2 - 16} - \dfrac{3x}{x^2 + 8x + 16} + \dfrac{3}{x + 4}$

68. $\dfrac{\dfrac{1}{x} - \dfrac{2}{3x}}{\dfrac{5}{2x} - \dfrac{1}{3}}$

69. $\dfrac{2}{1 - \dfrac{2}{x}}$

70. $\dfrac{\dfrac{x^2 + 5x - 6}{4x + 3}}{\dfrac{(x + 6)^2}{8x + 6}}$

71. $\dfrac{\dfrac{3}{x - 1} - \dfrac{2}{1 - x}}{\dfrac{2}{x - 1} - \dfrac{2}{x}}$

72. $4 + \dfrac{8}{x} = 8$

73. $\dfrac{x - 2}{x^2 - 7x + 10} = \dfrac{1}{5x - 10} - \dfrac{1}{x - 5}$

74. C is inversely proportional to D. If $C = 12$ when $D = 8$, find C when $D = 24$.

75. The surface area of a sphere varies directly as the square of its radius. If the surface area is 36π square inches when the radius is 3 inches, find the surface area when the radius is 4 inches.

CHAPTER 18 TEST

Remember to use the Chapter Test Prep Video CD to see the fully worked-out solutions to any of the exercises you want to review.

Find the domain of each rational function.

1. $f(x) = \dfrac{5x^2}{1 - x}$

2. $g(x) = \dfrac{9x^2 - 9}{x^2 + 4x + 3}$

Write each rational expression in lowest terms.

3. $\dfrac{7x - 21}{24 - 8x}$

4. $\dfrac{x^2 - 4x}{x^2 + 5x - 36}$

5. $\dfrac{x^3 - 8}{x - 2}$

Perform the indicated operation. If possible, simplify your answer.

6. $\dfrac{2x^3 + 16}{6x^2 + 12x} \cdot \dfrac{5}{x^2 - 2x + 4}$

7. $\dfrac{5}{4x^3} + \dfrac{7}{4x^3}$

8. $\dfrac{3x^2 - 12}{x^2 + 2x - 8} \div \dfrac{6x + 18}{x + 4}$

9. $\dfrac{4x - 12}{2x - 9} \div \dfrac{3 - x}{4x^2 - 81} \cdot \dfrac{x + 3}{5x + 15}$

10. $\dfrac{3 + 2x}{10 - x} + \dfrac{13 + x}{x - 10}$

11. $\dfrac{2x^2 + 7}{2x^4 - 18x^2} - \dfrac{6x + 7}{2x^4 - 18x^2}$

12. $\dfrac{3}{x^2 - x - 6} + \dfrac{2}{x^2 - 5x + 6}$

13. $\dfrac{5}{x - 7} - \dfrac{2x}{3x - 21} + \dfrac{x}{2x - 14}$

14. $\dfrac{3x}{5} \cdot \left(\dfrac{5}{x} - \dfrac{5}{2x}\right)$

Simplify each complex fraction.

15. $\dfrac{\dfrac{5}{x} - \dfrac{7}{3x}}{\dfrac{9}{8x} - \dfrac{1}{x}}$

16. $\dfrac{\dfrac{x^2 - 5x + 6}{x + 3}}{\dfrac{x^2 - 4x + 4}{x^2 - 9}}$

Divide.

17. $(4x^2y + 9x + 3xz) \div 3xz$

18. $(4x^3 - 5x) \div (2x + 1)$

Solve each equation for x.

19. $\dfrac{x}{x - 4} = 3 - \dfrac{4}{x - 4}$

20. $\dfrac{3}{x + 2} - \dfrac{1}{5x} = \dfrac{2}{5x^2 + 10x}$

21. $\dfrac{x^2 + 8}{x} - 1 = \dfrac{2(x + 4)}{x}$

22. Solve for x: $\dfrac{x + b}{a} = \dfrac{4x - 7a}{b}$

23. Suppose that W is inversely proportional to V. If $W = 20$ when $V = 12$, find W when $V = 15$.

24. Suppose that Q is jointly proportional to R and the square of S. If $Q = 24$ when $R = 3$ and $S = 4$, find Q when $R = 2$ and $S = 3$.

25. When an anvil is dropped into a gorge, the speed with which it strikes the ground is directly proportional to the square root of the distance it falls. An anvil that falls 400 feet hits the ground at a speed of 160 feet per second. Find the height of a cliff over the gorge if a dropped anvil hits the ground at a speed of 128 feet per second.

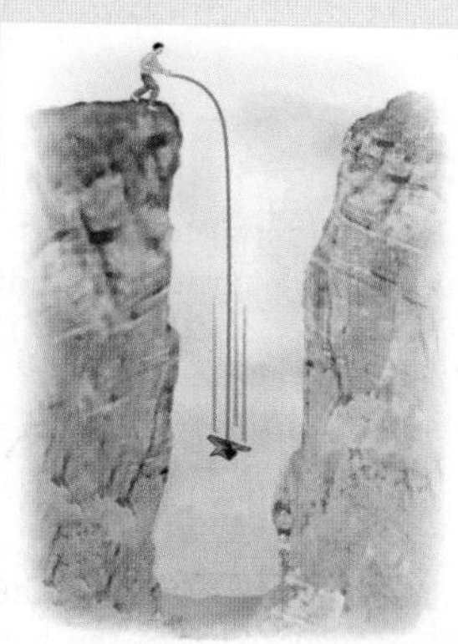

CHAPTER 18 CUMULATIVE REVIEW

1. Translate each phrase to an algebraic expression. Use the variable x to represent each unknown number.
   a. Eight times a number
   b. Three more than eight times a number
   c. The quotient of a number and -7
   d. One and six-tenths subtracted from twice a number
   e. Six less than a number
   f. Twice the sum of four and a number

2. Translate each phrase to an algebraic expression. Use the variable x to represent each unknown number.
   a. One third subtracted from a number
   b. Six less than five times a number
   c. Three more than eight times a number
   d. The quotient of seven and the difference of two and a number.

3. Solve for y: $\frac{y}{3} - \frac{y}{4} = \frac{1}{6}$

4. Solve $\frac{x}{7} + \frac{x}{5} = \frac{12}{5}$

5. The formula $C = \frac{5}{9}(F - 32)$ converts degrees Fahrenheit to degrees Celsius. Use this formula and the table feature of your calculator to complete the table. If necessary, round values to the nearest hundredth.

Fahrenheit	-4	10	32	70	100
Celsius					

6. Olivia has scores of 78, 65, 82, and 79 on her algebra tests. Use an inequality to find the minimum score she can make on her final exam to pass the course with a 78 average or higher, given that the final exam counts as two tests.

7. Solve: $\left|\frac{3x + 1}{2}\right| = -2$

8. Solve: $\left|\frac{2x - 1}{3}\right| + 6 = 3$

9. Solve for x: $\left|\frac{2(x + 1)}{3}\right| \le 0$

10. Solve for x: $\left|\frac{3(x - 1)}{4}\right| \ge 2$

11. Graph the equation $y = -2x + 3$.

12. Graph the equation $y = -x + 3$.

13. Which of the following relations are also functions?
   a. $\{(-2, 5), (2, 7), (-3, 5), (9, 9)\}$
   b.

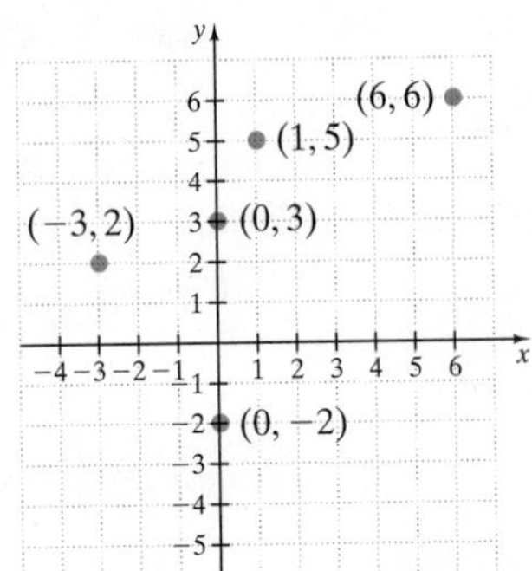

   c.

Input	Correspondence	Output
People in a certain city	Each person's age	The set of nonnegative integers

14. If $f(x) = -x^2 + 3x - 2$, find
   a. f(0) b. $f(-3)$ c. $f\left(\frac{1}{3}\right)$

15. Graph $x - 3y = 6$ by plotting intercept points.

16. Graph $3x - y = 6$ by plotting x- and y-intercepts.

17. Find an equation of the line with slope -3 containing the point $(1, -5)$. Write the equation in slope-intercept form $y = mx + b$.

18. Find an equation of the line with slope $\frac{1}{2}$ containing the point $(-1, 3)$. Use function notation to write the equation.

19. Graph the intersection of $x \ge 1$ and $y \ge 2x - 1$.

20. Graph the union of $2x + y \le 4$ or $y > 2$.

21. Use the elimination method to solve the system.
$$\begin{cases} 3x - 2y = 10 \\ 4x - 3y = 15 \end{cases}$$

22. Use the substitution method to solve the system.
$$\begin{cases} -2x + 3y = 6 \\ 3x - y = 5 \end{cases}$$

23. The measure of the largest angle of a triangle is 80° more than the measure of the smallest angle, and the measure of the remaining angle is 10° more than the measure of the smallest angle. Find the measure of each angle.

24. Kernersville office supply sold three reams of paper and two boxes of manila folders for \$21.90. Also, five reams of paper and one box of manila folders cost \$24.25. Find the price of a ream of paper and a box of manila folders.

25. Evaluate the following.

a. 7^0 **b.** -7^0

c. $(2x + 5)^0$ **d.** $2x^0$

26. Simplify the following. Write answers with positive exponents.

a. $2^{-2} + 3^{-1}$ **b.** $-6a^0$ **c.** $\dfrac{x^{-5}}{x^{-2}}$

27. Simplify each. Assume that a and b are integers and that x and y are not 0.

a. $x^{-b}(2x^b)^2$ **b.** $\dfrac{(y^{3a})^2}{y^{a-6}}$

28. Simplify each. Assume that a and b are integers and that x and y are not 0.

a. $3x^{4a}(4x^{-a})^2$ **b.** $\dfrac{(y^{4b})^3}{y^{2b-3}}$

29. Find the degree of each term.

a. $3x^2$ **b.** -2^3x^5 **c.** y

d. $12x^2yz^3$ **e.** 5.27

30. Subtract $(2x - 7)$ from $2x^2 + 8x - 3$.

31. Multiply $[3 + (2a + b)]^2$.

32. Multiply $[4 + (3x - y)]^2$.

33. Factor $ab - 6a + 2b - 12$.

34. Factor $xy + 2x - 5y - 10$.

35. Factor $2n^2 - 38n + 80$.

36. Factor $6x^2 - x - 35$.

37. Factor $x^2 + 4x + 4 - y^2$.

38. Factor $4x^2 - 4x + 1 - 9y^2$.

39. Solve $(x + 2)(x - 6) = 0$.

40. Solve $2x(3x + 1)(x - 3) = 0$.

41. Simplify:

a. $\dfrac{2x^2}{10x^3 - 2x^2}$

b. $\dfrac{9x^2 + 13x + 4}{8x^2 + x - 7}$

42. For the graph of $f(x)$, answer the following:

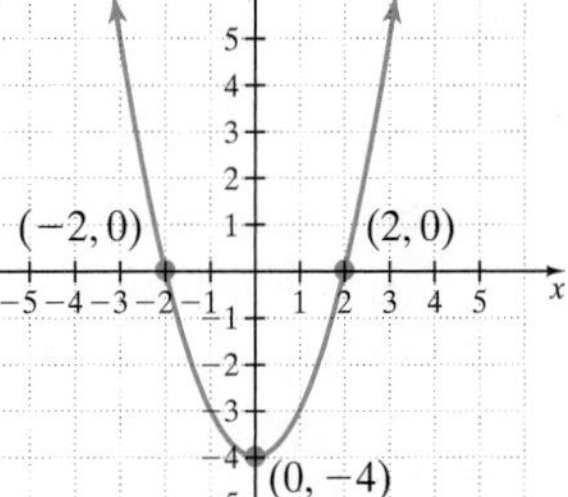

a. Find the domain and range.

b. List the x- and y-intercepts.

c. Find the coordinates of the point with the greatest y-value.

d. Find the coordinates of the point with the least y-value.

e. List the x-values whose y-values are equal to 0.

f. List the x-values whose y-values are less than 0.

g. Find the solutions of $f(x) = 0$.

43. Subtract $\dfrac{5k}{k^2 - 4} - \dfrac{2}{k^2 + k - 2}$.

44. Subtract $\dfrac{5a}{a^2 - 4} - \dfrac{3}{2 - a}$.

45. Solve: $\dfrac{3}{x} - \dfrac{x + 21}{3x} = \dfrac{5}{3}$.

46. Solve: $\dfrac{3x - 4}{2x} = -\dfrac{8}{x}$.

19 Rational Exponents, Radicals, and Complex Numbers

In this chapter, radical notation is reviewed, and then rational exponents are introduced. As the name implies, rational exponents are exponents that are rational numbers. We present an interpretation of rational exponents that is consistent with the meaning and rules already established for integer exponents, and we present two forms of notation for roots: radical and exponent. We conclude this chapter with complex numbers, a natural extension of the real number system.

What is a zorb? Simply put, a zorb is a large inflated ball within a ball, and zorbing is a recreational activity which may involve rolling down a hill while strapped in a zorb. Zorbing started in New Zealand (as well as bungee jumping) and was invented by Andrew Akers and Dwane van der Sluis. The first site was set up in New Zealand's North Island. This downhill course has a length of about 490 feet, and you can reach speeds of up to 20 mph.

An example of a course is shown in the diagram below, and you can see the mathematics involved. In Section 19.3, Exercise 115, page 1184, you will calculate the outer radius of a zorb, which would certainly be closely associated with the cost of production.

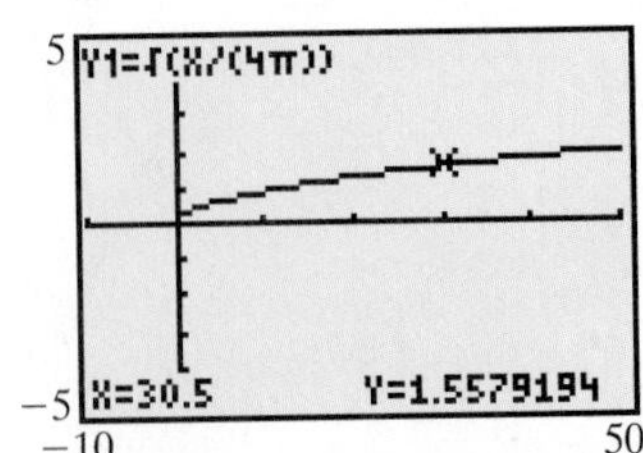

Surface area (A) vs. radius (r) of a sphere

The radius of a sphere with surface area A is calculated using the formula $r = \sqrt{\dfrac{A}{4\pi}}$. In this chapter, we learn that this can also be written as $r = \dfrac{1}{\sqrt{4\pi}} \cdot \sqrt{A}$. This means that r, radius, varies directly as the square root of A. The graph illustrates that as the surface area increases, so does the radius of a sphere.

19.1 RADICALS AND RADICAL FUNCTIONS

OBJECTIVES

1 Find square roots.

2 Approximate roots.

3 Find cube roots.

4 Find *n*th roots.

5 Find $\sqrt[n]{a^n}$ where *a* is a real number.

6 Graph square and cube root functions.

OBJECTIVE 1 ▶ Finding square roots. To find a **square root** of a number *a*, we find a number that was squared to get *a*.

Thus, because

$$5^2 = 25 \quad \text{and} \quad (-5)^2 = 25, \text{ then}$$

both 5 and −5 are square roots of 25.

Recall that we denote the **nonnegative, or principal, square root** with the **radical sign.**

$$\sqrt{25} = 5$$

We denote the **negative square root** with the **negative radical sign.**

$$-\sqrt{25} = -5$$

An expression containing a radical sign is called a **radical expression.** An expression within, or "under," a radical sign is called a **radicand.**

radical expression: 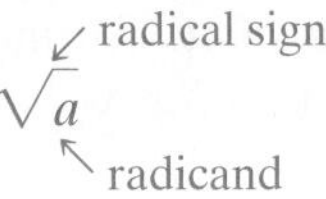

Principal and Negative Square Roots

If *a* is a nonnegative number, then

$\sqrt{a}$ is the **principal, or nonnegative, square root** of *a*

$-\sqrt{a}$ is the **negative square root** of *a*

EXAMPLE 1 Simplify. Assume that all variables represent positive numbers.

a. $\sqrt{36}$ **b.** $\sqrt{0}$ **c.** $\sqrt{\frac{4}{49}}$ **d.** $\sqrt{0.25}$

e. $\sqrt{x^6}$ **f.** $\sqrt{9x^{12}}$ **g.** $-\sqrt{81}$ **h.** $\sqrt{-81}$

Solution

a. $\sqrt{36} = 6$ because $6^2 = 36$ and 6 is not negative.

b. $\sqrt{0} = 0$ because $0^2 = 0$ and 0 is not negative.

c. $\sqrt{\frac{4}{49}} = \frac{2}{7}$ because $\left(\frac{2}{7}\right)^2 = \frac{4}{49}$ and $\frac{2}{7}$ is not negative.

d. $\sqrt{0.25} = 0.5$ because $(0.5)^2 = 0.25$.

e. $\sqrt{x^6} = x^3$ because $(x^3)^2 = x^6$.

f. $\sqrt{9x^{12}} = 3x^6$ because $(3x^6)^2 = 9x^{12}$.

g. $-\sqrt{81} = -9$. The negative in front of the radical indicates the negative square root of 81.

h. $\sqrt{-81}$ is not a real number. □

TECHNOLOGY NOTE

Most graphing utilities will give a message such as the one below when taking the square root of a negative number when you are in real mode.

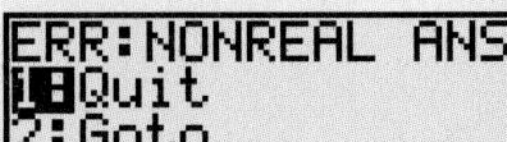

PRACTICE 1 Simplify. Assume that all variables represent positive numbers.

a. $\sqrt{49}$ **b.** $\sqrt{\frac{0}{1}}$ **c.** $\sqrt{\frac{16}{81}}$ **d.** $\sqrt{0.64}$

e. $\sqrt{z^8}$ **f.** $\sqrt{16b^4}$ **g.** $-\sqrt{36}$ **h.** $\sqrt{-36}$

Recall our discussion of the square root of a negative number. For example, can we simplify $\sqrt{-4}$? That is, can we find a real number whose square is -4? No, there is no real number whose square is -4, and we say that $\sqrt{-4}$ is not a real number. In general:

The square root of a negative number is not a real number. (See the first Technology Note in this section.)

> **Helpful Hint**
> - Remember: $\sqrt{0} = 0$
> - Don't forget, the square root of a negative number, such as $\sqrt{-9}$, is not a real number. In Section 19.7, we will see what kind of a number $\sqrt{-9}$ is.

OBJECTIVE 2 ▶ Approximating roots. Recall that numbers such as 1, 4, 9, and 25 are called **perfect squares,** since $1 = 1^2, 4 = 2^2, 9 = 3^2$, and $25 = 5^2$. Square roots of perfect square radicands simplify to rational numbers. What happens when we try to simplify a root such as $\sqrt{3}$? Since there is no rational number whose square is 3, then $\sqrt{3}$ is not a rational number. It is called an **irrational number,** and we can find a decimal **approximation** of it. To find decimal approximations, use a calculator. For example, an approximation for $\sqrt{3}$ is

$$\sqrt{3} \approx 1.732$$

↑
approximation symbol

To see if the approximation is reasonable, notice that since

$$1 < 3 < 4, \text{ then}$$
$$\sqrt{1} < \sqrt{3} < \sqrt{4}, \text{ or}$$
$$1 < \sqrt{3} < 2.$$

We found $\sqrt{3} \approx 1.732$, a number between 1 and 2, so our result is reasonable.

EXAMPLE 2 Use a calculator to approximate $\sqrt{20}$. Round the approximation to 3 decimal places and check to see that your approximation is reasonable.

$\sqrt{20} \approx 4.472$ A calculator screen is shown in the margin.

Solution Is this reasonable? Since $16 < 20 < 25$, then $\sqrt{16} < \sqrt{20} < \sqrt{25}$, or $4 < \sqrt{20} < 5$. The approximation is between 4 and 5 and thus is reasonable. □

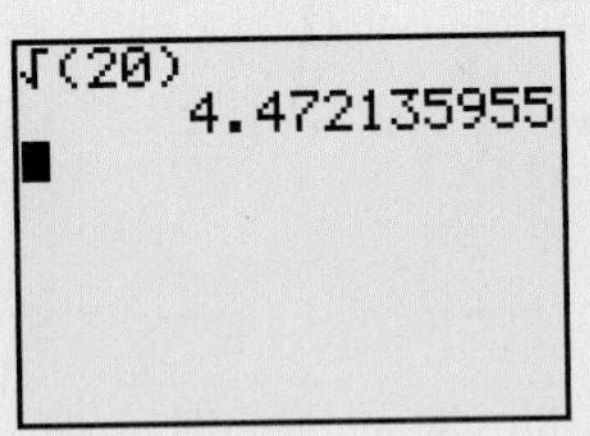

A calculator solution for Example 2.

PRACTICE 2 Use a calculator to approximate $\sqrt{45}$. Round the approximation to three decimal places and check to see that your approximation is reasonable.

OBJECTIVE 3 ▶ Finding cube roots. Finding roots can be extended to other roots such as cube roots. For example, since $2^3 = 8$, we call 2 the **cube root** of 8. In symbols, we write

$$\sqrt[3]{8} = 2$$

> **Cube Root**
>
> The **cube root** of a real number a is written as $\sqrt[3]{a}$, and
>
> $$\sqrt[3]{a} = b \text{ only if } b^3 = a$$

From this definition, we have

$$\sqrt[3]{64} = 4 \text{ since } 4^3 = 64$$
$$\sqrt[3]{-27} = -3 \text{ since } (-3)^3 = -27$$
$$\sqrt[3]{x^3} = x \text{ since } x^3 = x^3$$

Notice that, unlike with square roots, *it is possible to have a negative radicand when finding a cube root*. This is so because the *cube* of a negative number is a negative number. Therefore, the *cube root* of a negative number is a negative number.

EXAMPLE 3 Find the cube roots.

a. $\sqrt[3]{1}$ **b.** $\sqrt[3]{-64}$ **c.** $\sqrt[3]{\frac{8}{125}}$ **d.** $\sqrt[3]{x^6}$ **e.** $\sqrt[3]{-27x^9}$

Solution

a. $\sqrt[3]{1} = 1$ because $1^3 = 1$.

b. $\sqrt[3]{-64} = -4$ because $(-4)^3 = -64$.

c. $\sqrt[3]{\frac{8}{125}} = \frac{2}{5}$ because $\left(\frac{2}{5}\right)^3 = \frac{8}{125}$.

d. $\sqrt[3]{x^6} = x^2$ because $(x^2)^3 = x^6$.

e. $\sqrt[3]{-27x^9} = -3x^3$ because $(-3x^3)^3 = -27x^9$. □

A calculator check for Example 3b and c.

PRACTICE 3 Find the cube roots.

a. $\sqrt[3]{-1}$ **b.** $\sqrt[3]{27}$ **c.** $\sqrt[3]{\frac{27}{64}}$ **d.** $\sqrt[3]{x^{12}}$ **e.** $\sqrt[3]{-8x^3}$

OBJECTIVE 4 ▸ Finding *n*th roots. Just as we can raise a real number to powers other than 2 or 3, we can find roots other than square roots and cube roots. In fact, we can find the ***n*th root** of a number, where n is any natural number. In symbols, the nth root of a is written as $\sqrt[n]{a}$, where n is called the **index.** The index 2 is usually omitted for square roots.

> **Helpful Hint**
>
> If the index is even, such as $\sqrt{\ }$, $\sqrt[4]{\ }$, $\sqrt[6]{\ }$, and so on, the radicand must be nonnegative for the root to be a real number. For example,
>
> $\sqrt[4]{16} = 2$, but $\sqrt[4]{-16}$ is not a real number.
>
> $\sqrt[6]{64} = 2$, but $\sqrt[6]{-64}$ is not a real number.
>
> If the index is odd, such as $\sqrt[3]{\ }$, $\sqrt[5]{\ }$, and so on, the radicand may be any real number. For example,
>
> $\sqrt[3]{64} = 4$ and $\sqrt[3]{-64} = -4$
>
> $\sqrt[5]{32} = 2$ and $\sqrt[5]{-32} = -2$

Concept Check ☑

Which one is not a real number?

a. $\sqrt[3]{-15}$ **b.** $\sqrt[4]{-15}$ **c.** $\sqrt[5]{-15}$ **d.** $\sqrt{(-15)^2}$

EXAMPLE 4 Simplify the following expressions.

a. $\sqrt[4]{81}$ **b.** $\sqrt[5]{-243}$ **c.** $-\sqrt{25}$ **d.** $\sqrt[4]{-81}$ **e.** $\sqrt[3]{64x^3}$

Solution

a. $\sqrt[4]{81} = 3$ because $3^4 = 81$ and 3 is positive.

b. $\sqrt[5]{-243} = -3$ because $(-3)^5 = -243$.

c. $-\sqrt{25} = -5$ because -5 is the opposite of $\sqrt{25}$.

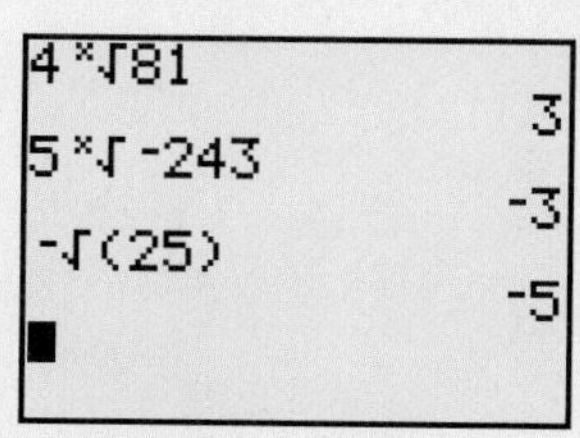

A calculator check for Example 4a, b, c.

Answer to Concept Check: b

d. $\sqrt[4]{-81}$ is not a real number. There is no real number that, when raised to the fourth power, is -81.

e. $\sqrt[3]{64x^3} = 4x$ because $(4x)^3 = 64x^3$. □

PRACTICE 4 Simplify the following expressions.

a. $\sqrt[4]{10000}$ **b.** $\sqrt[5]{-1}$ **c.** $-\sqrt{81}$ **d.** $\sqrt[4]{-625}$ **e.** $\sqrt[3]{27x^9}$

OBJECTIVE 5 ▶ Finding $\sqrt[n]{a^n}$ where a is a real number. Recall that the notation $\sqrt{a^2}$ indicates the positive square root of a^2 only. For example,

$$\sqrt{(-5)^2} = \sqrt{25} = 5$$

When variables are present in the radicand and it is unclear whether the variable represents a positive number or a negative number, absolute value bars are sometimes needed to ensure that the result is a positive number. For example,

$$\sqrt{x^2} = |x|$$

This ensures that the result is positive. This same situation may occur when the index is any *even* positive integer. When the index is any *odd* positive integer, absolute value bars are not necessary.

Finding $\sqrt[n]{a^n}$

If n is an *even* positive integer, then $\sqrt[n]{a^n} = |a|$.

If n is an *odd* positive integer, then $\sqrt[n]{a^n} = a$.

EXAMPLE 5 Simplify.

a. $\sqrt{(-3)^2}$ **b.** $\sqrt{x^2}$ **c.** $\sqrt[4]{(x-2)^4}$ **d.** $\sqrt[3]{(-5)^3}$

e. $\sqrt[5]{(2x-7)^5}$ **f.** $\sqrt{25x^2}$ **g.** $\sqrt{x^2+2x+1}$

Solution

a. $\sqrt{(-3)^2} = |-3| = 3$ When the index is even, the absolute value bars ensure us that our result is not negative.

b. $\sqrt{x^2} = |x|$

c. $\sqrt[4]{(x-2)^4} = |x-2|$

d. $\sqrt[3]{(-5)^3} = -5$

e. $\sqrt[5]{(2x-7)^5} = 2x-7$ Absolute value bars are not needed when the index is odd.

f. $\sqrt{25x^2} = 5|x|$

g. $\sqrt{x^2+2x+1} = \sqrt{(x+1)^2} = |x+1|$ □

PRACTICE 5 Simplify.

a. $\sqrt{(-4)^2}$ **b.** $\sqrt{x^{14}}$ **c.** $\sqrt[4]{(x+7)^4}$ **d.** $\sqrt[3]{(-7)^3}$

e. $\sqrt[5]{(3x-5)^5}$ **f.** $\sqrt{49x^2}$ **g.** $\sqrt{x^2+4x+4}$

OBJECTIVE 6 ▶ Graphing square and cube root functions. Recall that an equation in x and y describes a function if each x-value is paired with exactly one y-value. With this in mind, does the equation

$$y = \sqrt{x}$$

describe a function? First, notice that replacement values for x must be nonnegative real numbers, since $\sqrt{x}$ is not a real number if $x < 0$. The notation $\sqrt{x}$ denotes the principal square root of x, so for every nonnegative number x, there is exactly one number, $\sqrt{x}$. Therefore, $y = \sqrt{x}$ describes a function, and we may write it as

$$f(x) = \sqrt{x}$$

In general, radical functions are functions of the form

$$f(x) = \sqrt[n]{x}.$$

Recall that the domain of a function in x is the set of all possible replacement values of x. This means that if n is even, the domain is the set of all nonnegative numbers, $\{x|x \geq 0\}$ or $[0, \infty)$ in interval notation. If n is odd, the domain is the set of all real numbers or $(-\infty, \infty)$. Keep this in mind as we find function values.

EXAMPLE 6 If $f(x) = \sqrt{x - 4}$ and $g(x) = \sqrt[3]{x + 2}$, find each function value.

a. $f(8)$ **b.** $f(6)$ **c.** $g(-1)$ **d.** $g(1)$

Solution

a. $f(8) = \sqrt{8 - 4} = \sqrt{4} = 2$

b. $f(6) = \sqrt{6 - 4} = \sqrt{2}$

c. $g(-1) = \sqrt[3]{-1 + 2} = \sqrt[3]{1} = 1$

d. $g(1) = \sqrt[3]{1 + 2} = \sqrt[3]{3}$ □

PRACTICE 6 If $f(x) = \sqrt{x + 5}$ and $g(x) = \sqrt[3]{x - 3}$, find each function value.

a. $f(11)$ **b.** $f(-1)$ **c.** $g(11)$ **d.** $g(-5)$

Helpful Hint

Notice that for the function $f(x) = \sqrt{x - 4}$, the domain includes all real numbers that make the radicand ≥ 0. To see what numbers these are, solve $x - 4 \geq 0$ and find that $x \geq 4$. The domain is $\{x|x \geq 4\}$ or $[4, \infty)$ in interval notation.

The domain of the cube root function $g(x) = \sqrt[3]{x + 2}$ is the set of real numbers, or $(-\infty, \infty)$.

EXAMPLE 7 Identify the domain of the square root function $f(x) = \sqrt{x}$ and then graph the function.

Solution Recall that we graphed this function in Section 15.7. To become familiar with this function again, we find function values for $f(x)$. For example,

$$f(0) = \sqrt{0} = 0$$
$$f(1) = \sqrt{1} = 1$$
$$f(4) = \sqrt{4} = 2$$
$$f(9) = \sqrt{9} = 3$$

Choosing perfect squares for x ensures us that $f(x)$ is a rational number, but it is important to stress that $f(x) = \sqrt{x}$ is defined for all nonnegative real numbers. For example,

$$f(3) = \sqrt{3} \approx 1.732$$

The domain of this function is the set of all nonnegative numbers, $\{x|x \geq 0\}$ or $[0, \infty)$. On the next page, we graph $y_1 = \sqrt{x}$ in a $[-3, 10, 1]$ by $[-2, 10, 1]$ window. The table on the next page shows that a negative x-value gives an error message since $\sqrt{x}$ is not a real number when x is negative.

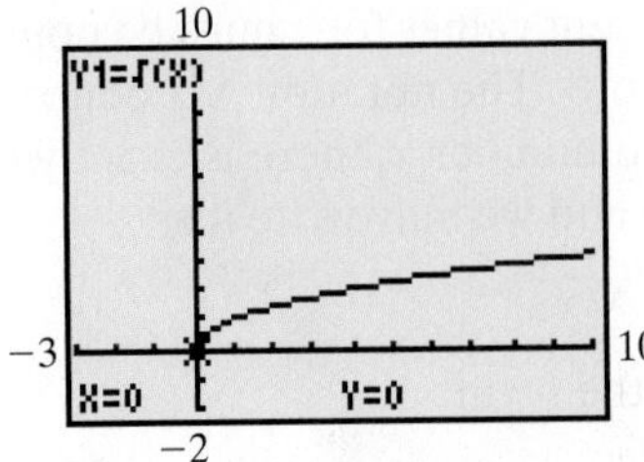

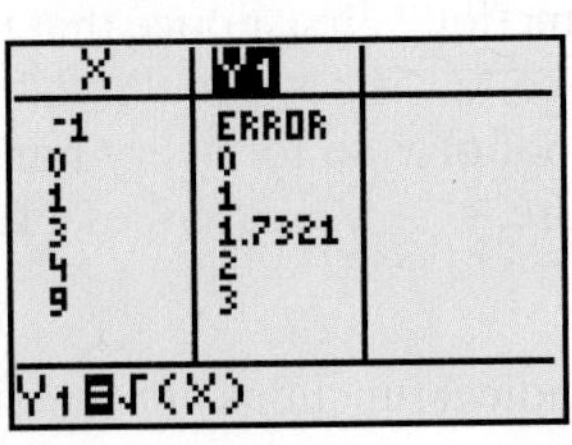

Notice that the graph of this function passes the vertical line test, as expected. □

PRACTICE 7 Graph the square root function $h(x) = \sqrt{x+2}$.

Recall from Sections 15.1 and 15.2 that the equation $f(x) = \sqrt[3]{x}$ also describes a function. Here x may be any real number, so the domain of this function is the set of all real numbers, or $(-\infty, \infty)$. A few function values are given next.

$$f(0) = \sqrt[3]{0} = 0$$
$$f(1) = \sqrt[3]{1} = 1$$
$$f(-1) = \sqrt[3]{-1} = -1$$
$$f(6) = \sqrt[3]{6}$$
$$f(-6) = \sqrt[3]{-6}$$

Here, there is no rational number whose cube is 6. Thus, the radicals do not simplify to rational numbers.

$$f(8) = \sqrt[3]{8} = 2$$
$$f(-8) = \sqrt[3]{-8} = -2$$

EXAMPLE 8 Identify the domain of the function $f(x) = \sqrt[3]{x}$ and then graph the function.

Solution The domain of this function is the set of all real numbers. Below, we graph $y_1 = \sqrt[3]{x}$ in a $[-10, 10, 1]$ by $[-5, 5, 1]$ window.

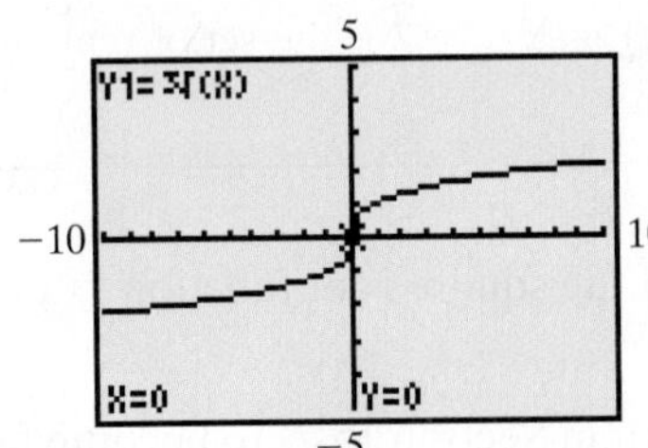

X	Y1
0	0
1	1
-1	-1
6	1.8171
-6	-1.817
8	2
-8	-2

Y1■3√(X)

The graph of this function passes the vertical line test, as expected. □

PRACTICE 8 Graph the function $f(x) = \sqrt[3]{x} - 4$.

VOCABULARY & READINESS CHECK

Use the choices below to fill in each blank. Not all choices will be used.

is	cubes	$-\sqrt{a}$	radical sign	index
is not	squares	$\sqrt{-a}$	radicand	

1. In the expression $\sqrt[n]{a}$, the n is called the ________, the $\sqrt{}$ is called the ________, and a is called the ________.
2. If $\sqrt{a}$ is the positive square root of a, $a \neq 0$, then ________ is the negative square root of a.
3. The square root of a negative number ________ a real number.
4. Numbers such as 1, 4, 9, and 25 are called perfect ________ whereas numbers such as 1, 8, 27, and 125 are called perfect ________.

Fill in the blank.

5. The domain of the function $f(x) = \sqrt{x}$ is ______.

6. The domain of the function $f(x) = \sqrt[3]{x}$ is ________.

7. If $f(16) = 4$, the corresponding ordered pair is _______.

8. If $g(-8) = -2$, the corresponding ordered pair is ________.

Choose the correct letter or letters. No pencil is needed, just think your way through these.

9. Which radical is not a real number?
a. $\sqrt{3}$ **b.** $-\sqrt{11}$ **c.** $\sqrt[3]{-10}$ **d.** $\sqrt{-10}$

10. Which radical(s) simplify to 3?
a. $\sqrt{9}$ **b.** $\sqrt{-9}$ **c.** $\sqrt[3]{27}$ **d.** $\sqrt[3]{-27}$

11. Which radical(s) simplify to -3?
a. $\sqrt{9}$ **b.** $\sqrt{-9}$ **c.** $\sqrt[3]{27}$ **d.** $\sqrt[3]{-27}$

12. Which radical does not simplify to a whole number?
a. $\sqrt{64}$ **b.** $\sqrt[3]{64}$ **c.** $\sqrt{8}$ **d.** $\sqrt[3]{8}$

19.1 EXERCISE SET

MyMathLab

PRACTICE

WATCH

DOWNLOAD

READ

REVIEW

Simplify. Assume that variables represent positive real numbers. See Example 1.

1. $\sqrt{100}$ **2.** $\sqrt{400}$

3. $\sqrt{\frac{1}{4}}$ **4.** $\sqrt{\frac{9}{25}}$

5. $\sqrt{0.0001}$ **6.** $\sqrt{0.04}$

7. $-\sqrt{36}$ **8.** $-\sqrt{9}$

9. $\sqrt{x^{10}}$ **10.** $\sqrt{x^{16}}$

11. $\sqrt{16y^6}$ **12.** $\sqrt{64y^{20}}$

Use a calculator to approximate each square root to 3 decimal places. Check to see that each approximation is reasonable. See Example 2.

13. $\sqrt{7}$ **14.** $\sqrt{11}$

15. $\sqrt{38}$ **16.** $\sqrt{56}$

17. $\sqrt{200}$ **18.** $\sqrt{300}$

Find each cube root. See Example 3.

19. $\sqrt[3]{64}$ **20.** $\sqrt[3]{27}$

21. $\sqrt[3]{\frac{1}{8}}$ **22.** $\sqrt[3]{\frac{27}{64}}$

23. $\sqrt[3]{-1}$ **24.** $\sqrt[3]{-125}$

25. $\sqrt[3]{x^{12}}$ **26.** $\sqrt[3]{x^{15}}$

27. $\sqrt[3]{-27x^9}$ **28.** $\sqrt[3]{-64x^6}$

Find each root. Assume that all variables represent nonnegative real numbers. See Example 4.

29. $-\sqrt[4]{16}$ **30.** $\sqrt[5]{-243}$

31. $\sqrt[4]{-16}$ **32.** $\sqrt{-16}$

33. $\sqrt[5]{-32}$ **34.** $\sqrt[5]{-1}$

35. $\sqrt[5]{x^{20}}$ **36.** $\sqrt[4]{x^{20}}$

37. $\sqrt[6]{64x^{12}}$ **38.** $\sqrt[5]{-32x^{15}}$

39. $\sqrt{81x^4}$ **40.** $\sqrt[4]{81x^4}$

41. $\sqrt[4]{256x^8}$ **42.** $\sqrt{256x^8}$

Simplify. Assume that the variables represent any real number. See Example 5.

43. $\sqrt{(-8)^2}$ **44.** $\sqrt{(-7)^2}$

45. $\sqrt[3]{(-8)^3}$ **46.** $\sqrt[5]{(-7)^5}$

47. $\sqrt{4x^2}$ **48.** $\sqrt[4]{16x^4}$

49. $\sqrt[3]{x^3}$ **50.** $\sqrt[5]{x^5}$

51. $\sqrt{(x-5)^2}$ **52.** $\sqrt{(y-6)^2}$

53. $\sqrt{x^2+4x+4}$
(*Hint:* Factor the polynomial first.)

54. $\sqrt{x^2-8x+16}$
(*Hint:* Factor the polynomial first.)

MIXED PRACTICE

Simplify each radical. Assume that all variables represent positive real numbers.

55. $-\sqrt{121}$ **56.** $-\sqrt[3]{125}$

57. $\sqrt[3]{8x^3}$ **58.** $\sqrt{16x^8}$

59. $\sqrt{y^{12}}$ **60.** $\sqrt[3]{y^{12}}$

61. $\sqrt{25a^2b^{20}}$ **62.** $\sqrt{9x^4y^6}$

63. $\sqrt[3]{-27x^{12}y^9}$ **64.** $\sqrt[3]{-8a^{21}b^6}$

65. $\sqrt[4]{a^{16}b^4}$ **66.** $\sqrt[4]{x^8y^{12}}$

67. $\sqrt[5]{-32x^{10}y^5}$ **68.** $\sqrt[5]{-243z^{15}}$

69. $\sqrt{\frac{25}{49}}$ **70.** $\sqrt{\frac{4}{81}}$

71. $\sqrt{\frac{x^2}{4y^2}}$ **72.** $\sqrt{\frac{y^{10}}{9x^6}}$

73. $-\sqrt[3]{\frac{z^{21}}{27x^3}}$ **74.** $-\sqrt[3]{\frac{64a^3}{b^9}}$

75. $\sqrt[4]{\frac{x^4}{16}}$ **76.** $\sqrt[4]{\frac{y^4}{81x^4}}$

If $f(x) = \sqrt{2x+3}$ and $g(x) = \sqrt[3]{x-8}$, find the following function values. See Example 6.

77. $f(0)$ **78.** $g(0)$

79. $g(7)$ **80.** $f(-1)$

81. $g(-19)$ **82.** $f(3)$

83. $f(2)$ **84.** $g(1)$

For Exercises 85 through 88, match the graph with its equation. All graphs are in a $[-10, 10, 1]$ by $[-5, 5, 5]$ window. Also give the domain of each equation in interval notation. See Example 7.

A.

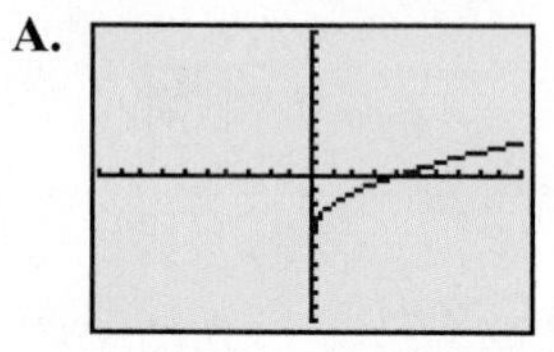

B.

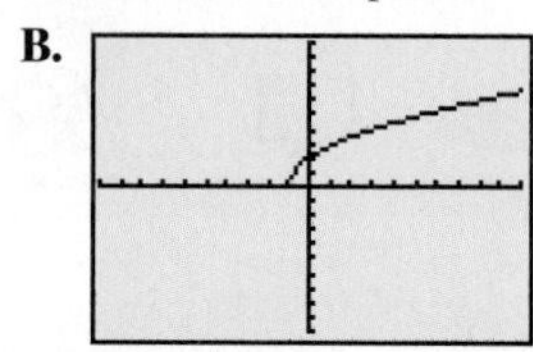

C.

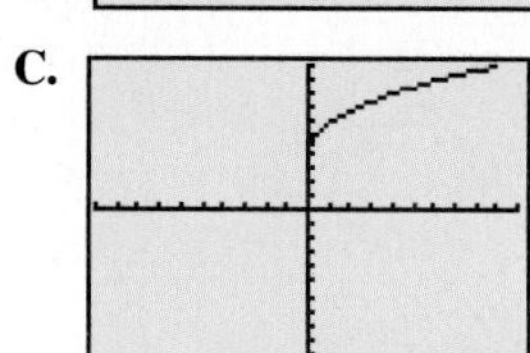

D.

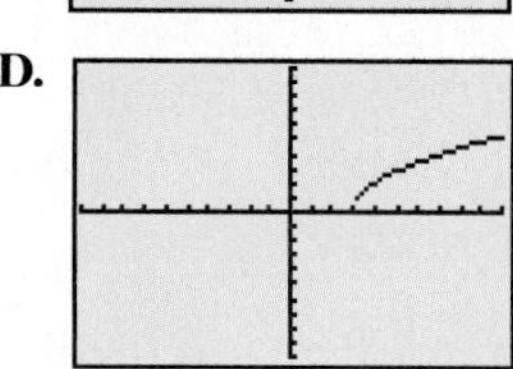

85. $f(x) = \sqrt{x} + 2$ **86.** $f(x) = \sqrt{x} - 2$

87. $f(x) = \sqrt{x-3}$ **88.** $f(x) = \sqrt{x+1}$

For Exercises 89 through 92, match the graph with its equation. All graphs are in a $[-4.7, 4.7, 1]$ by $[-5, 5, 1]$ window. Also give the domain of each function in interval notation. See Example 8.

A.

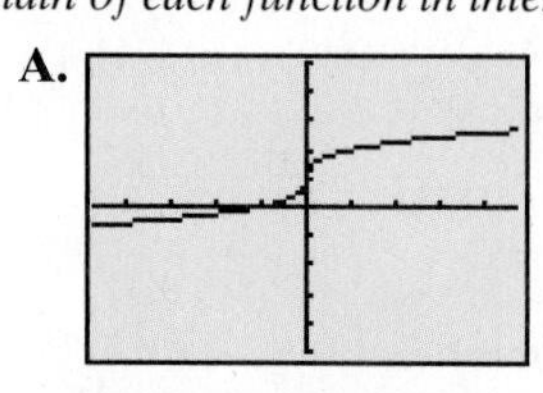

B.

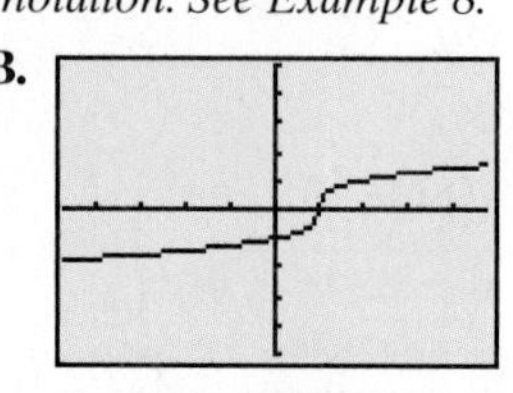

C.

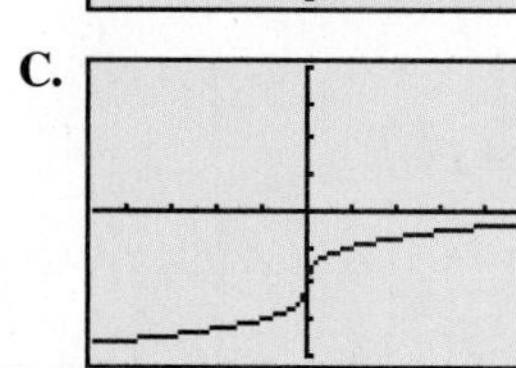

D.

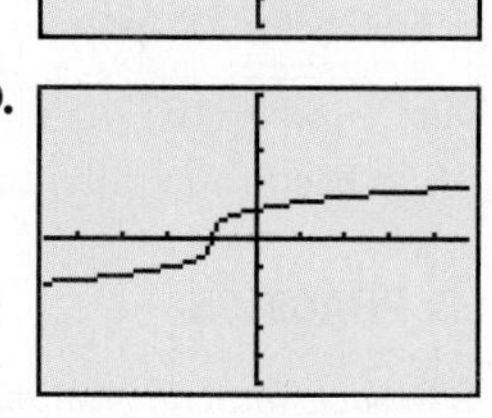

89. $f(x) = \sqrt[3]{x} + 1$ **90.** $f(x) = \sqrt[3]{x} - 2$

91. $g(x) = \sqrt[3]{x-1}$ **92.** $g(x) = \sqrt[3]{x+1}$

REVIEW AND PREVIEW

Simplify each exponential expression.

93. $(-2x^3y^2)^5$ **94.** $(4y^6z^7)^3$

95. $(-3x^2y^3z^5)(20x^5y^7)$ **96.** $(-14a^5bc^2)(2abc^4)$

97. $\frac{7x^{-1}y}{14(x^5y^2)^{-2}}$ **98.** $\frac{(2a^{-1}b^2)^3}{(8a^2b)^{-2}}$

CONCEPT EXTENSIONS

Which of the following are not real numbers? See the Concept Check in this section.

99. $\sqrt{-17}$ **100.** $\sqrt[3]{-17}$

101. $\sqrt[10]{-17}$ **102.** $\sqrt[15]{-17}$

103. Explain why $\sqrt{-64}$ is not a real number.

104. Explain why $\sqrt[3]{-64}$ is a real number.

For Exercises 105 through 108, do not use a calculator.

105. $\sqrt{160}$ is closest to

a. 10 **b.** 13 **c.** 20 **d.** 40

106. $\sqrt{1000}$ is closest to

a. 10 **b.** 30 **c.** 100 **d.** 500

107. The perimeter of the triangle is closest to

a. 12 **b.** 18

c. 66 **d.** 132

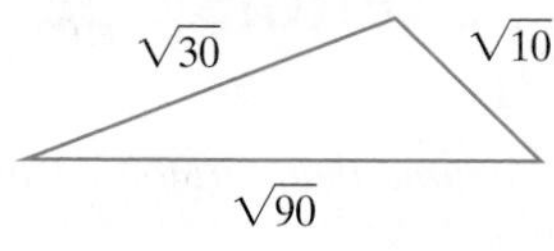

108. The length of the bent wire is closest to

a. 5 **b.** $\sqrt{28}$

c. 7 **d.** 14

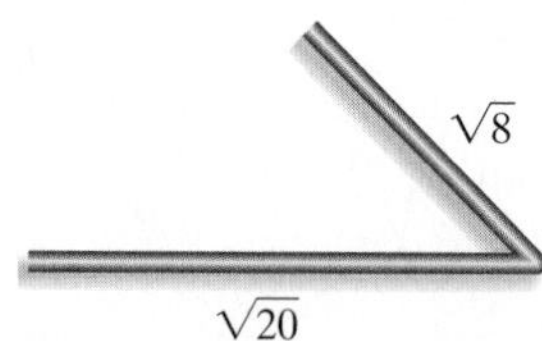

The Mosteller formula for calculating adult body surface area is $B = \sqrt{\frac{hw}{3131}}$, where B is an individual's body surface area in square meters, h is the individual's height in inches, and w is the individual's weight in pounds. Use this information to answer Exercises 109 and 110. Round answers to 2 decimal places.

109. Find the body surface area of an individual who is 66 inches tall and who weighs 135 pounds.

110. Find the body surface area of an individual who is 74 inches tall and who weighs 225 pounds.

111. Suppose that a friend tells you that $\sqrt{13} \approx 5.7$. Without a calculator, how can you convince your friend that he or she must have made an error?

112. Escape velocity is the minimum speed that an object must reach to escape a planet's pull of gravity. Escape velocity v is given by the equation $v = \sqrt{\frac{2Gm}{r}}$, where m is the mass of the planet, r is its radius, and G is the universal gravitational constant, which has a value of $G = 6.67 \times 10^{-11}$ m^3/kg · sec^2. The mass of Earth is 5.97×10^{24} kg and its radius is 6.37×10^6 m. Use this information to find the escape velocity for Earth. Round to the nearest whole number. (*Source:* National Space Science Data Center)

STUDY SKILLS BUILDER

How Are Your Homework Assignments Going?

Remember that it is important to keep up with homework. Why? Many concepts in mathematics build on each other. Often, your understanding of a day's lecture depends on an understanding of the previous day's material.

To complete a homework assignment, remember these four things:

- Attempt all of it.
- Check it.
- Correct it.
- If needed, ask questions about it.

Take a moment and review your completed homework assignments. Answer the exercises below based on this review.

1. Approximate the fraction of your homework you have attempted.
2. Approximate the fraction of your homework you have checked (if possible).
3. If you are able to check your homework, have you corrected it when errors have been found?
4. What do you do if you do not understand a concept while working on homework?

19.2 RATIONAL EXPONENTS

OBJECTIVES

1 Understand the meaning of $a^{1/n}$.

2 Understand the meaning of $a^{m/n}$.

3 Understand the meaning of $a^{-m/n}$.

4 Use rules for exponents to simplify expressions that contain rational exponents.

5 Use rational exponents to simplify radical expressions.

OBJECTIVE 1 ▶ Understanding the meaning of $a^{1/n}$. So far in this text, we have not defined expressions with rational exponents such as $3^{1/2}$, $x^{2/3}$, and $-9^{-1/4}$. We will define these expressions so that the rules for exponents will apply to these rational exponents as well.

Suppose that $x = 5^{1/3}$. Then

$$x^3 = (5^{1/3})^3 = 5^{1/3 \cdot 3} = 5^1 \text{ or } 5$$

(using rules for exponents)

Since $x^3 = 5$, then x is the number whose cube is 5, or $x = \sqrt[3]{5}$. Notice that we also know that $x = 5^{1/3}$. This means

$$5^{1/3} = \sqrt[3]{5}$$

Definition of $a^{1/n}$

If n is a positive integer greater than 1 and $\sqrt[n]{a}$ is a real number, then

$$a^{1/n} = \sqrt[n]{a}$$

Notice that the denominator of the rational exponent corresponds to the index of the radical.

EXAMPLE 1 Use radical notation to write the following. Simplify if possible.

a. $4^{1/2}$ **b.** $64^{1/3}$ **c.** $x^{1/4}$ **d.** $0^{1/6}$ **e.** $-9^{1/2}$ **f.** $(81x^8)^{1/4}$ **g.** $(5y)^{1/3}$

Solution

a. $4^{1/2} = \sqrt{4} = 2$

b. $64^{1/3} = \sqrt[3]{64} = 4$

c. $x^{1/4} = \sqrt[4]{x}$

d. $0^{1/6} = \sqrt[6]{0} = 0$

e. $-9^{1/2} = -\sqrt{9} = -3$

f. $(81x^8)^{1/4} = \sqrt[4]{81x^8} = 3x^2$

g. $(5y)^{1/3} = \sqrt[3]{5y}$ □

PRACTICE 1 Use radical notation to write the following. Simplify if possible.

a. $36^{1/2}$ **b.** $1000^{1/3}$ **c.** $x^{1/5}$ **d.** $1^{1/4}$ **e.** $-64^{1/2}$
f. $(125x^9)^{1/3}$ **g.** $(3x)^{1/4}$

OBJECTIVE 2 ▶ Understanding the meaning of $a^{m/n}$. As we expand our use of exponents to include $\frac{m}{n}$, we define their meaning so that rules for exponents still hold true. For example, by properties of exponents,

$$8^{2/3} = (8^{1/3})^2 = (\sqrt[3]{8})^2 \quad \text{or}$$
$$8^{2/3} = (8^2)^{1/3} = \sqrt[3]{8^2}$$

Definition of $a^{m/n}$

If m and n are positive integers greater than 1 with $\frac{m}{n}$ in lowest terms, then

$$a^{m/n} = \sqrt[n]{a^m} = \left(\sqrt[n]{a}\right)^m$$

as long as $\sqrt[n]{a}$ is a real number.

Notice that the denominator n of the rational exponent corresponds to the index of the radical. The numerator m of the rational exponent indicates that the base is to be raised to the mth power. This means

$$8^{2/3} = \sqrt[3]{8^2} = \sqrt[3]{64} = 4 \quad \text{or}$$
$$8^{2/3} = \left(\sqrt[3]{8}\right)^2 = 2^2 = 4$$

From simplifying $8^{2/3}$, can you see that it doesn't matter whether you raise to a power first and then take the nth root or you take the nth root first and then raise to a power?

▶ Helpful Hint
Most of the time, $\left(\sqrt[n]{a}\right)^m$ will be easier to calculate than $\sqrt[n]{a^m}$.

EXAMPLE 2 Use radical notation to write the following. Then simplify if possible.

a. $4^{3/2}$ **b.** $-16^{3/4}$ **c.** $(-27)^{2/3}$
d. $\left(\frac{1}{9}\right)^{3/2}$ **e.** $(4x - 1)^{3/5}$

Solution

a. $4^{3/2} = \left(\sqrt{4}\right)^3 = 2^3 = 8$

b. $-16^{3/4} = -\left(\sqrt[4]{16}\right)^3 = -(2)^3 = -8$

c. $(-27)^{2/3} = \left(\sqrt[3]{-27}\right)^2 = (-3)^2 = 9$

d. $\left(\frac{1}{9}\right)^{3/2} = \left(\sqrt{\frac{1}{9}}\right)^3 = \left(\frac{1}{3}\right)^3 = \frac{1}{27}$

e. $(4x - 1)^{3/5} = \sqrt[5]{(4x - 1)^3}$ □

PRACTICE 2 Use radical notation to write the following. Simplify if possible.

a. $16^{3/2}$ **b.** $-1^{3/5}$ **c.** $-(81)^{3/4}$
d. $\left(\frac{1}{25}\right)^{3/2}$ **e.** $(3x + 2)^{5/9}$

Helpful Hint

The *denominator* of a rational exponent is the index of the corresponding radical. For example, $x^{1/5} = \sqrt[5]{x}$ and $z^{2/3} = \sqrt[3]{z^2}$, or $z^{2/3} = (\sqrt[3]{z})^2$.

OBJECTIVE 3 ▶ Understanding the meaning of $a^{-m/n}$. The rational exponents we have given meaning to exclude negative rational numbers. To complete the set of definitions, we define $a^{-m/n}$.

Definition of $a^{-m/n}$

$$a^{-m/n} = \frac{1}{a^{m/n}}$$

as long as $a^{m/n}$ is a nonzero real number.

EXAMPLE 3 Write each expression with a positive exponent, and then simplify.

a. $16^{-3/4}$ **b.** $(-27)^{-2/3}$

Solution

a. $16^{-3/4} = \frac{1}{16^{3/4}} = \frac{1}{(\sqrt[4]{16})^3} = \frac{1}{2^3} = \frac{1}{8}$

b. $(-27)^{-2/3} = \frac{1}{(-27)^{2/3}} = \frac{1}{(\sqrt[3]{-27})^2} = \frac{1}{(-3)^2} = \frac{1}{9}$ □

A calculator check for Example 3.

PRACTICE 3 Write each expression with a positive exponent; then simplify.

a. $9^{-3/2}$ **b.** $(-64)^{-2/3}$

Helpful Hint

If an expression contains a negative rational exponent, such as $9^{-3/2}$, you may want to first write the expression with a positive exponent and then interpret the rational exponent. Notice that the sign of the base is not affected by the sign of its exponent. For example,

$$9^{-3/2} = \frac{1}{9^{3/2}} = \frac{1}{(\sqrt{9})^3} = \frac{1}{27}$$

Also,

$$(-27)^{-1/3} = \frac{1}{(-27)^{1/3}} = -\frac{1}{3}$$

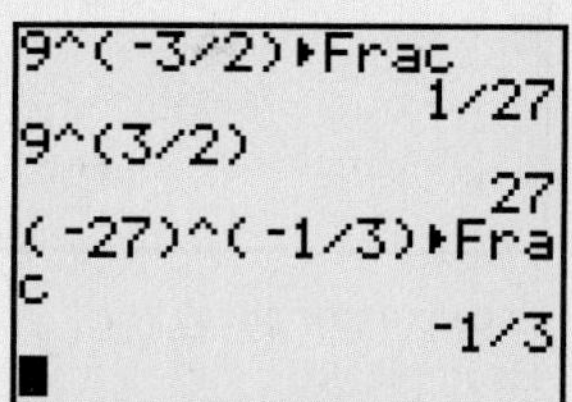

A calculator check for the Helpful Hint.

Concept Check ☑

Which one is correct?

a. $-8^{2/3} = \frac{1}{4}$ **b.** $8^{-2/3} = -\frac{1}{4}$ **c.** $8^{-2/3} = -4$ **d.** $-8^{-2/3} = -\frac{1}{4}$

OBJECTIVE 4 ▶ Using rules for exponents to simplify expressions. It can be shown that the properties of integer exponents hold for rational exponents. By using these properties and definitions, we can now simplify expressions that contain rational exponents.

These rules are repeated here for review.

Note: For the remainder of this chapter, we will assume that variables represent positive real numbers. Since this is so, we need not insert absolute value bars when we simplify even roots.

Answer to Concept Check: d

Summary of Exponent Rules

If m and n are rational numbers, and a, b, and c are numbers for which the expressions below exist, then

Product rule for exponents: $a^m \cdot a^n = a^{m+n}$

Power rule for exponents: $(a^m)^n = a^{m \cdot n}$

Power rules for products and quotients: $(ab)^n = a^n b^n$ and $\left(\frac{a}{c}\right)^n = \frac{a^n}{c^n}, c \neq 0$

Quotient rule for exponents: $\frac{a^m}{a^n} = a^{m-n}, a \neq 0$

Zero exponent: $a^0 = 1, a \neq 0$

Negative exponent: $a^{-n} = \frac{1}{a^n}, a \neq 0$

EXAMPLE 4 Use properties of exponents to simplify. Write results with only positive exponents.

a. $b^{1/3} \cdot b^{5/3}$ **b.** $x^{1/2}x^{1/3}$ **c.** $\frac{7^{1/3}}{7^{4/3}}$

d. $y^{-4/7} \cdot y^{6/7}$ **e.** $\frac{(2x^{2/5}y^{-1/3})^5}{x^2y}$

Solution

a. $b^{1/3} \cdot b^{5/3} = b^{(1/3+5/3)} = b^{6/3} = b^2$

b. $x^{1/2}x^{1/3} = x^{(1/2+1/3)} = x^{3/6+2/6} = x^{5/6}$ Use the product rule.

c. $\frac{7^{1/3}}{7^{4/3}} = 7^{1/3-4/3} = 7^{-3/3} = 7^{-1} = \frac{1}{7}$ Use the quotient rule.

A calculator check for Example 4c.

d. $y^{-4/7} \cdot y^{6/7} = y^{-4/7+6/7} = y^{2/7}$ Use the product rule.

e. We begin by using the power rule $(ab)^m = a^m b^m$ to simplify the numerator.

$$\frac{(2x^{2/5}y^{-1/3})^5}{x^2y} = \frac{2^5(x^{2/5})^5(y^{-1/3})^5}{x^2y} = \frac{32x^2y^{-5/3}}{x^2y}$$ Use the power rule and simplify.

$$= 32x^{2-2}y^{-5/3-3/3}$$ Apply the quotient rule.

$$= 32x^0y^{-8/3}$$

$$= \frac{32}{y^{8/3}}$$ □

PRACTICE 4 Use properties of exponents to simplify.

a. $y^{2/3} \cdot y^{8/3}$ **b.** $x^{3/5} \cdot x^{1/4}$ **c.** $\frac{9^{2/7}}{9^{9/7}}$

d. $b^{4/9} \cdot b^{-2/9}$ **e.** $\frac{\left(3x^{1/4}y^{-2/3}\right)^4}{x^4y}$

EXAMPLE 5 Multiply.

a. $z^{2/3}(z^{1/3} - z^5)$ **b.** $(x^{1/3} - 5)(x^{1/3} + 2)$

Solution

a. $z^{2/3}(z^{1/3} - z^5) = z^{2/3}z^{1/3} - z^{2/3}z^5$ Apply the distributive property.

$= z^{(2/3+1/3)} - z^{(2/3+5)}$ Use the product rule.

$= z^{3/3} - z^{(2/3+15/3)}$

$= z - z^{17/3}$

b. $(x^{1/3} - 5)(x^{1/3} + 2) = x^{2/3} + 2x^{1/3} - 5x^{1/3} - 10$ Think of $(x^{1/3} - 5)$ and $(x^{1/3} + 2)$ as 2 binomials, and FOIL.

$= x^{2/3} - 3x^{1/3} - 10$

□

PRACTICE 5 Multiply.

a. $x^{3/5}(x^{1/3} - x^2)$ **b.** $(x^{1/2} + 6)(x^{1/2} - 2)$

EXAMPLE 6 Factor $x^{-1/2}$ from the expression $3x^{-1/2} - 7x^{5/2}$. Assume that all variables represent positive numbers.

Solution

$$3x^{-1/2} - 7x^{5/2} = (x^{-1/2})(3) - (x^{-1/2})(7x^{6/2})$$
$$= x^{-1/2}(3 - 7x^3)$$

To check, multiply $x^{-1/2}(3 - 7x^3)$ to see that the product is $3x^{-1/2} - 7x^{5/2}$. □

PRACTICE 6 Factor $x^{-1/5}$ from the expression $2x^{-1/5} - 7x^{4/5}$.

OBJECTIVE 5 ▶ Using rational exponents to simplify radical expressions. Some radical expressions are easier to simplify when we first write them with rational exponents. We can simplify some radical expressions by first writing the expression with rational exponents. Use properties of exponents to simplify, and then convert back to radical notation.

EXAMPLE 7 Use rational exponents to simplify. Assume that variables represent positive numbers.

a. $\sqrt[8]{x^4}$ **b.** $\sqrt[6]{25}$ **c.** $\sqrt[4]{r^2s^6}$

Solution

a. $\sqrt[8]{x^4} = x^{4/8} = x^{1/2} = \sqrt{x}$

b. $\sqrt[6]{25} = 25^{1/6} = (5^2)^{1/6} = 5^{2/6} = 5^{1/3} = \sqrt[3]{5}$

c. $\sqrt[4]{r^2s^6} = (r^2s^6)^{1/4} = r^{2/4}s^{6/4} = r^{1/2}s^{3/2} = (rs^3)^{1/2} = \sqrt{rs^3}$ □

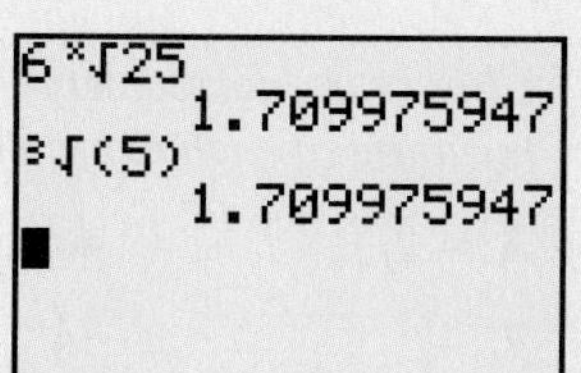

A calculator check for Example 7b.

PRACTICE 7 Use rational exponents to simplify. Assume that the variables represent positive numbers.

a. $\sqrt[9]{x^3}$ **b.** $\sqrt[4]{36}$ **c.** $\sqrt[8]{a^4b^2}$

EXAMPLE 8 Use rational exponents to write as a single radical.

a. $\sqrt{x} \cdot \sqrt[4]{x}$ **b.** $\dfrac{\sqrt{x}}{\sqrt[3]{x}}$ **c.** $\sqrt[3]{3} \cdot \sqrt{2}$

Solution

a. $\sqrt{x} \cdot \sqrt[4]{x} = x^{1/2} \cdot x^{1/4} = x^{1/2+1/4}$
$= x^{3/4} = \sqrt[4]{x^3}$

b. $\dfrac{\sqrt{x}}{\sqrt[3]{x}} = \dfrac{x^{1/2}}{x^{1/3}} = x^{1/2-1/3} = x^{3/6-2/6}$
$= x^{1/6} = \sqrt[6]{x}$

A calculator check for Example 8c.

c. $\sqrt[3]{3} \cdot \sqrt{2} = 3^{1/3} \cdot 2^{1/2}$ Write with rational exponents.
$= 3^{2/6} \cdot 2^{3/6}$ Write the exponents so that they have the same denominator.
$= (3^2 \cdot 2^3)^{1/6}$ Use $a^n b^n = (ab)^n$.
$= \sqrt[6]{3^2 \cdot 2^3}$ Write with radical notation.
$= \sqrt[6]{72}$ Multiply $3^2 \cdot 2^3$. □

PRACTICE
8 Use rational expressions to write each of the following as a single radical.

a. $\sqrt[3]{x} \cdot \sqrt[4]{x}$ **b.** $\dfrac{\sqrt[3]{y}}{\sqrt[5]{y}}$ **c.** $\sqrt[3]{5} \cdot \sqrt{3}$

VOCABULARY & READINESS CHECK

Answer each true or false.

1. $9^{-1/2}$ is a positive number. _____

2. $9^{-1/2}$ is a whole number. _____

3. $\dfrac{1}{a^{-m/n}} = a^{m/n}$ (where $a^{m/n}$ is a nonzero real number). _____

Fill in the blank with the correct choice.

4. To simplify $x^{2/3} \cdot x^{1/5}$, _____ the exponents.
a. add **b.** subtract **c.** multiply **d.** divide

5. To simplify $(x^{2/3})^{1/5}$, ________ the exponents.
a. add **b.** subtract **c.** multiply **d.** divide

6. To simplify $\dfrac{x^{2/3}}{x^{1/5}}$, ________ the exponents.
a. add **b.** subtract **c.** multiply **d.** divide

Choose the correct letter for each exercise. Letters will be used more than once. No pencil is needed. Just think about the meaning of each expression.

A = 2, B = −2, C = not a real number

7. $4^{1/2}$ ___ **8.** $-4^{1/2}$ ___ **9.** $(-4)^{1/2}$ ___ **10.** $8^{1/3}$ ___ **11.** $-8^{1/3}$ ___ **12.** $(-8)^{1/3}$ ___

19.2 EXERCISE SET

Use radical notation to write each expression. Simplify if possible. See Example 1.

1. $49^{1/2}$
2. $64^{1/3}$
3. $27^{1/3}$
4. $8^{1/3}$
5. $\left(\dfrac{1}{16}\right)^{1/4}$
6. $\left(\dfrac{1}{64}\right)^{1/2}$
7. $169^{1/2}$
8. $81^{1/4}$
9. $2m^{1/3}$
10. $(2m)^{1/3}$

11. $(9x^4)^{1/2}$ **12.** $(16x^8)^{1/2}$
13. $(-27)^{1/3}$ **14.** $-64^{1/2}$
15. $-16^{1/4}$ **16.** $(-32)^{1/5}$

Use radical notation to write each expression. Simplify if possible. See Example 2.

17. $16^{3/4}$ **18.** $4^{5/2}$
19. $(-64)^{2/3}$ **20.** $(-8)^{4/3}$
21. $(-16)^{3/4}$ **22.** $(-9)^{3/2}$
23. $(2x)^{3/5}$ **24.** $2x^{3/5}$
25. $(7x+2)^{2/3}$ **26.** $(x-4)^{3/4}$
27. $\left(\frac{16}{9}\right)^{3/2}$ **28.** $\left(\frac{49}{25}\right)^{3/2}$

Write with positive exponents. Simplify if possible. See Example 3.

29. $8^{-4/3}$ **30.** $64^{-2/3}$
31. $(-64)^{-2/3}$ **32.** $(-8)^{-4/3}$
33. $(-4)^{-3/2}$ **34.** $(-16)^{-5/4}$
35. $x^{-1/4}$ **36.** $y^{-1/6}$
37. $\frac{1}{a^{-2/3}}$ **38.** $\frac{1}{n^{-8/9}}$
39. $\frac{5}{7x^{-3/4}}$ **40.** $\frac{2}{3y^{-5/7}}$

Use the properties of exponents to simplify each expression. Write with positive exponents. See Example 4.

41. $a^{2/3}a^{5/3}$ **42.** $b^{9/5}b^{8/5}$
43. $x^{-2/5} \cdot x^{7/5}$ **44.** $y^{4/3} \cdot y^{-1/3}$
45. $3^{1/4} \cdot 3^{3/8}$ **46.** $5^{1/2} \cdot 5^{1/6}$
47. $\frac{y^{1/3}}{y^{1/6}}$ **48.** $\frac{x^{3/4}}{x^{1/8}}$
49. $(4u^2)^{3/2}$ **50.** $(32^{1/5}x^{2/3})^3$
51. $\frac{b^{1/2}b^{3/4}}{-b^{1/4}}$ **52.** $\frac{a^{1/4}a^{-1/2}}{a^{2/3}}$
53. $\frac{(x^3)^{1/2}}{x^{7/2}}$ **54.** $\frac{y^{11/3}}{(y^5)^{1/3}}$
55. $\frac{(3x^{1/4})^3}{x^{1/12}}$ **56.** $\frac{(2x^{1/5})^4}{x^{3/10}}$
57. $\frac{(y^3z)^{1/6}}{y^{-1/2}z^{1/3}}$ **58.** $\frac{(m^2n)^{1/4}}{m^{-1/2}n^{5/8}}$
59. $\frac{(x^3y^2)^{1/4}}{(x^{-5}y^{-1})^{-1/2}}$ **60.** $\frac{(a^{-2}b^3)^{1/8}}{(a^{-3}b)^{-1/4}}$

Multiply. See Example 5.

61. $y^{1/2}(y^{1/2} - y^{2/3})$
62. $x^{1/2}(x^{1/2} + x^{3/2})$
63. $x^{2/3}(x-2)$
64. $3x^{1/2}(x+y)$
65. $(2x^{1/3}+3)(2x^{1/3}-3)$
66. $(y^{1/2}+5)(y^{1/2}+5)$

Factor the common factor from the given expression. See Example 6.

67. $x^{8/3}$; $x^{8/3} + x^{10/3}$
68. $x^{3/2}$; $x^{5/2} - x^{3/2}$
69. $x^{1/5}$; $x^{2/5} - 3x^{1/5}$
70. $x^{2/7}$; $x^{3/7} - 2x^{2/7}$
71. $x^{-1/3}$; $5x^{-1/3} + x^{2/3}$
72. $x^{-3/4}$; $x^{-3/4} + 3x^{1/4}$

Use rational exponents to simplify each radical. Assume that all variables represent positive numbers. See Example 7.

73. $\sqrt[6]{x^3}$ **74.** $\sqrt[9]{a^3}$
75. $\sqrt[6]{4}$ **76.** $\sqrt[4]{36}$
77. $\sqrt[4]{16x^2}$ **78.** $\sqrt[8]{4y^2}$
79. $\sqrt[8]{x^4y^4}$ **80.** $\sqrt[9]{y^6z^3}$
81. $\sqrt[12]{a^8b^4}$ **82.** $\sqrt[10]{a^5b^5}$
83. $\sqrt[4]{(x+3)^2}$ **84.** $\sqrt[8]{(y+1)^4}$

Use rational expressions to write as a single radical expression. See Example 8.

85. $\sqrt[3]{y} \cdot \sqrt[5]{y^2}$ **86.** $\sqrt[3]{y^2} \cdot \sqrt[6]{y}$
87. $\frac{\sqrt[3]{b^2}}{\sqrt[4]{b}}$ **88.** $\frac{\sqrt[4]{a}}{\sqrt[5]{a}}$
89. $\sqrt[3]{x} \cdot \sqrt[4]{x} \cdot \sqrt[8]{x^3}$ **90.** $\sqrt[6]{y} \cdot \sqrt[3]{y} \cdot \sqrt[5]{y^2}$
91. $\frac{\sqrt[3]{a^2}}{\sqrt[6]{a}}$ **92.** $\frac{\sqrt[5]{b^2}}{\sqrt[10]{b^3}}$
93. $\sqrt{3} \cdot \sqrt[3]{4}$ **94.** $\sqrt[3]{5} \cdot \sqrt{2}$
95. $\sqrt[5]{7} \cdot \sqrt[3]{y}$ **96.** $\sqrt[4]{5} \cdot \sqrt[3]{x}$
97. $\sqrt{5r} \cdot \sqrt[3]{s}$ **98.** $\sqrt[3]{b} \cdot \sqrt[5]{4a}$

REVIEW AND PREVIEW

Write each integer as a product of two integers such that one of the factors is a perfect square. For example, write 18 as $9 \cdot 2$, because 9 is a perfect square.

99. 75 **100.** 20
101. 48 **102.** 45

Write each integer as a product of two integers such that one of the factors is a perfect cube. For example, write 24 as $8 \cdot 3$, because 8 is a perfect cube.

103. 16 **104.** 56
105. 54 **106.** 80

CONCEPT EXTENSIONS

Basal metabolic rate (BMR) is the number of calories per day a person needs to maintain life. A person's basal metabolic rate $B(w)$ in calories per day can be estimated with the function $B(w) = 70w^{3/4}$, where w is the person's weight in kilograms. Use this information to answer Exercises 107 and 108.

107. Estimate the BMR for a person who weighs 60 kilograms. Round to the nearest calorie. (*Note:* 60 kilograms is approximately 132 pounds.)

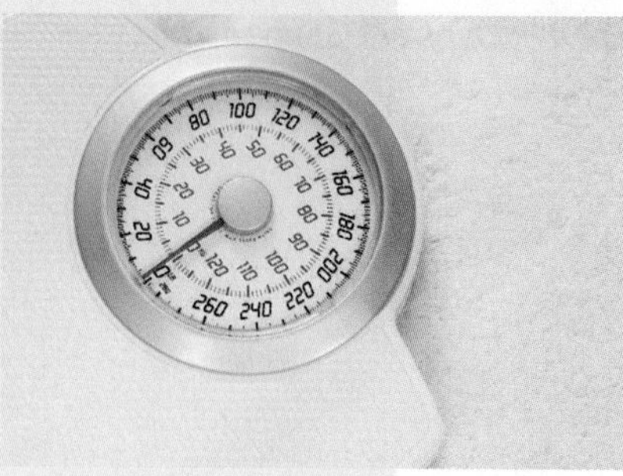

108. Estimate the BMR for a person who weighs 90 kilograms. Round to the nearest calorie. (*Note:* 90 kilograms is approximately 198 pounds.)

The number of cellular telephone subscriptions in the United States from 1996 through 2006 can be modeled by the function $f(x) = 33.3x^{4/5}$, where y is the number of cellular telephone subscriptions in millions, x years after 1996. (Source: Based on data from the Cellular Telecommunications & Internet Association, 1994–2000). Use this information to answer Exercises 109 and 110.

109. Use this model to estimate the number of cellular telephone subscriptions in the United States in 2006. Round to the nearest tenth of a million.

110. Predict the number of cellular telephone subscriptions in the United States in 2010. Round to the nearest tenth of a million.

Fill in each box with the correct expression.

111. $\square \cdot a^{2/3} = a^{3/3}$, or a

112. $\square \cdot x^{1/8} = x^{4/8}$, or $x^{1/2}$

113. $\dfrac{\square}{x^{-2/5}} = x^{3/5}$

114. $\dfrac{\square}{y^{-3/4}} = y^{4/4}$, or y

Use a calculator to write a four-decimal-place approximation of each number.

115. $8^{1/4}$

116. $20^{1/5}$

117. $18^{3/5}$

118. $76^{5/7}$

119. In physics, the speed of a wave traveling over a stretched string with tension t and density u is given by the expression $\dfrac{\sqrt{t}}{\sqrt{u}}$. Write this expression with rational exponents.

120. In electronics, the angular frequency of oscillations in a certain type of circuit is given by the expression $(LC)^{-1/2}$. Use radical notation to write this expression.

19.3 SIMPLIFYING RADICAL EXPRESSIONS

OBJECTIVES

1. Use the product rule for radicals.
2. Use the quotient rule for radicals.
3. Simplify radicals.
4. Use the distance and midpoint formulas.

OBJECTIVE 1 ▶ Using the product rule. It is possible to simplify some radicals that do not evaluate to rational numbers. To do so, we use a product rule and a quotient rule for radicals. To discover the product rule, notice the following pattern.

$$\sqrt{9} \cdot \sqrt{4} = 3 \cdot 2 = 6$$
$$\sqrt{9 \cdot 4} = \sqrt{36} = 6$$

Since both expressions simplify to 6, it is true that

$$\sqrt{9} \cdot \sqrt{4} = \sqrt{9 \cdot 4}$$

This pattern suggests the following product rule for radicals.

Product Rule for Radicals

If $\sqrt[n]{a}$ and $\sqrt[n]{b}$ are real numbers, then

$$\sqrt[n]{a} \cdot \sqrt[n]{b} = \sqrt[n]{ab}$$

Notice that the product rule is the relationship $a^{1/n} \cdot b^{1/n} = (ab)^{1/n}$ stated in radical notation.

EXAMPLE 1 Multiply.

a. $\sqrt{3} \cdot \sqrt{5}$ b. $\sqrt{21} \cdot \sqrt{x}$ c. $\sqrt[3]{4} \cdot \sqrt[3]{2}$

d. $\sqrt[4]{5y^2} \cdot \sqrt[4]{2x^3}$ e. $\sqrt{\frac{2}{a}} \cdot \sqrt{\frac{b}{3}}$

Solution

a. $\sqrt{3} \cdot \sqrt{5} = \sqrt{3 \cdot 5} = \sqrt{15}$

b. $\sqrt{21} \cdot \sqrt{x} = \sqrt{21x}$

c. $\sqrt[3]{4} \cdot \sqrt[3]{2} = \sqrt[3]{4 \cdot 2} = \sqrt[3]{8} = 2$

d. $\sqrt[4]{5y^2} \cdot \sqrt[4]{2x^3} = \sqrt[4]{5y^2 \cdot 2x^3} = \sqrt[4]{10y^2x^3}$

e. $\sqrt{\frac{2}{a}} \cdot \sqrt{\frac{b}{3}} = \sqrt{\frac{2}{a} \cdot \frac{b}{3}} = \sqrt{\frac{2b}{3a}}$ □

PRACTICE
1 Multiply.

a. $\sqrt{5} \cdot \sqrt{7}$ b. $\sqrt{13} \cdot \sqrt{z}$ c. $\sqrt[4]{125} \cdot \sqrt[4]{5}$

d. $\sqrt[3]{5y} \cdot \sqrt[3]{3x^2}$ e. $\sqrt{\frac{5}{m}} \cdot \sqrt{\frac{t}{2}}$

OBJECTIVE 2 ▶ Using the quotient rule. To discover a quotient rule for radicals, notice the following pattern.

$$\sqrt{\frac{4}{9}} = \frac{2}{3}$$

$$\frac{\sqrt{4}}{\sqrt{9}} = \frac{2}{3}$$

Since both expressions simplify to $\frac{2}{3}$, it is true that

$$\sqrt{\frac{4}{9}} = \frac{\sqrt{4}}{\sqrt{9}}$$

This pattern suggests the following quotient rule for radicals.

Quotient Rule for Radicals

If $\sqrt[n]{a}$ and $\sqrt[n]{b}$ are real numbers and $\sqrt[n]{b}$ is not zero, then

$$\sqrt[n]{\frac{a}{b}} = \frac{\sqrt[n]{a}}{\sqrt[n]{b}}$$

Notice that the quotient rule is the relationship $\left(\frac{a}{b}\right)^{1/n} = \frac{a^{1/n}}{b^{1/n}}$ stated in radical notation. We can use the quotient rule to simplify radical expressions by reading the rule from left to right, or to divide radicals by reading the rule from right to left.

For example,

$$\sqrt{\frac{x}{16}} = \frac{\sqrt{x}}{\sqrt{16}} = \frac{\sqrt{x}}{4} \qquad \text{Using } \sqrt[n]{\frac{a}{b}} = \frac{\sqrt[n]{a}}{\sqrt[n]{b}}$$

$$\frac{\sqrt{75}}{\sqrt{3}} = \sqrt{\frac{75}{3}} = \sqrt{25} = 5 \qquad \text{Using } \frac{\sqrt[n]{a}}{\sqrt[n]{b}} = \sqrt[n]{\frac{a}{b}}$$

Note: *Recall that from Section 19.2 on, we assume that variables represent positive real numbers. Since this is so, we need not insert absolute value bars when we simplify even roots.*

EXAMPLE 2 Use the quotient rule to simplify.

a. $\sqrt{\frac{25}{49}}$ **b.** $\sqrt{\frac{x}{9}}$ **c.** $\sqrt[3]{\frac{8}{27}}$ **d.** $\sqrt[4]{\frac{3}{16y^4}}$

Solution

a. $\sqrt{\frac{25}{49}} = \frac{\sqrt{25}}{\sqrt{49}} = \frac{5}{7}$

b. $\sqrt{\frac{x}{9}} = \frac{\sqrt{x}}{\sqrt{9}} = \frac{\sqrt{x}}{3}$

c. $\sqrt[3]{\frac{8}{27}} = \frac{\sqrt[3]{8}}{\sqrt[3]{27}} = \frac{2}{3}$

d. $\sqrt[4]{\frac{3}{16y^4}} = \frac{\sqrt[4]{3}}{\sqrt[4]{16y^4}} = \frac{\sqrt[4]{3}}{2y}$ □

```
√(25)/√(49)▸Frac
                5/7
³√(8/27)▸Frac
                2/3
```

A calculator check for Example 2a and c.

PRACTICE 2 Use the quotient rule to simplify.

a. $\sqrt{\frac{36}{49}}$ **b.** $\sqrt{\frac{z}{16}}$ **c.** $\sqrt[3]{\frac{125}{8}}$ **d.** $\sqrt[4]{\frac{5}{81x^8}}$

OBJECTIVE 3 ▸ Simplifying radicals. Both the product and quotient rules can be used to simplify a radical. If the product rule is read from right to left, we have that

$$\sqrt[n]{ab} = \sqrt[n]{a} \cdot \sqrt[n]{b}.$$

This is used to simplify the following radicals.

EXAMPLE 3 Simplify the following.

a. $\sqrt{50}$ **b.** $\sqrt[3]{24}$ **c.** $\sqrt{26}$ **d.** $\sqrt[4]{32}$

Solution

a. Factor 50 such that one factor is the largest perfect square that divides 50. The largest perfect square factor of 50 is 25, so we write 50 as $25 \cdot 2$ and use the product rule for radicals to simplify.

$$\sqrt{50} = \sqrt{25 \cdot 2} = \sqrt{25} \cdot \sqrt{2} = 5\sqrt{2}$$

The largest perfect square factor of 50

▸ Helpful Hint
Don't forget that, for example, $5\sqrt{2}$ means $5 \cdot \sqrt{2}$.

```
√(50)
        7.071067812
5√(2)
        7.071067812
```

A calculator check for Example 3a.

b. $\sqrt[3]{24} = \sqrt[3]{8 \cdot 3} = \sqrt[3]{8} \cdot \sqrt[3]{3} = 2\sqrt[3]{3}$

The largest perfect cube factor of 24

c. $\sqrt{26}$ The largest perfect square factor of 26 is 1, so $\sqrt{26}$ cannot be simplified further.

d. $\sqrt[4]{32} = \sqrt[4]{16 \cdot 2} = \sqrt[4]{16} \cdot \sqrt[4]{2} = 2\sqrt[4]{2}$

The largest fourth power factor of 32 (points to 16) □

PRACTICE 3 Simplify the following.

a. $\sqrt{98}$ **b.** $\sqrt[3]{54}$ **c.** $\sqrt{35}$ **d.** $\sqrt[4]{243}$

After simplifying a radical such as a square root, always check the radicand to see that it contains no other perfect square factors. It may, if the largest perfect square factor of the radicand was not originally recognized. For example,

$$\sqrt{200} = \sqrt{4 \cdot 50} = \sqrt{4} \cdot \sqrt{50} = 2\sqrt{50}$$

Notice that the radicand 50 still contains the perfect square factor 25. This is because 4 is not the largest perfect square factor of 200. We continue as follows.

$$2\sqrt{50} = 2\sqrt{25 \cdot 2} = 2 \cdot \sqrt{25} \cdot \sqrt{2} = 2 \cdot 5 \cdot \sqrt{2} = 10\sqrt{2}$$

The radical is now simplified since 2 contains no perfect square factors (other than 1).

Helpful Hint

To help you recognize largest perfect power factors of a radicand, it will help if you are familiar with some perfect powers. A few are listed below.

Perfect Squares	1,	4,	9,	16,	25,	36,	49,	64,	81,	100,	121,	144
	1^2	2^2	3^2	4^2	5^2	6^2	7^2	8^2	9^2	10^2	11^2	12^2
Perfect Cubes	1,	8,	27,	64,	125							
	1^3	2^3	3^3	4^3	5^3							
Perfect Fourth Powers	1,	16,	81,	256								
	1^4	2^4	3^4	4^4								

In general, we say that a radicand of the form $\sqrt[n]{a}$ is simplified when the radicand a contains no factors that are perfect nth powers (other than 1 or −1).

EXAMPLE 4 Use the product rule to simplify.

a. $\sqrt{25x^3}$ **b.** $\sqrt[3]{54x^6y^8}$ **c.** $\sqrt[4]{81z^{11}}$

Solution

a. $\sqrt{25x^3} = \sqrt{25x^2 \cdot x}$ Find the largest perfect square factor.

$= \sqrt{25x^2} \cdot \sqrt{x}$ Apply the product rule.

$= 5x\sqrt{x}$ Simplify.

b. $\sqrt[3]{54x^6y^8} = \sqrt[3]{27 \cdot 2 \cdot x^6 \cdot y^6 \cdot y^2}$ Factor the radicand and identify perfect cube factors.

$= \sqrt[3]{27x^6y^6 \cdot 2y^2}$

$= \sqrt[3]{27x^6y^6} \cdot \sqrt[3]{2y^2}$ Apply the product rule.

$= 3x^2y^2\sqrt[3]{2y^2}$ Simplify.

c. $\sqrt[4]{81z^{11}} = \sqrt[4]{81 \cdot z^8 \cdot z^3}$ Factor the radicand and identify perfect fourth power factors.

$= \sqrt[4]{81z^8} \cdot \sqrt[4]{z^3}$ Apply the product rule.

$= 3z^2\sqrt[4]{z^3}$ Simplify. □

PRACTICE 4 Use the product rule to simplify.

a. $\sqrt{36z^7}$ **b.** $\sqrt[3]{32p^4q^7}$ **c.** $\sqrt[4]{16x^{15}}$

EXAMPLE 5 Use the quotient rule to divide, and simplify if possible.

a. $\dfrac{\sqrt{20}}{\sqrt{5}}$ **b.** $\dfrac{\sqrt{50x}}{2\sqrt{2}}$ **c.** $\dfrac{7\sqrt[3]{48x^4y^8}}{\sqrt[3]{6y^2}}$ **d.** $\dfrac{2\sqrt[4]{32a^8b^6}}{\sqrt[4]{a^{-1}b^2}}$

Solution

a. $\dfrac{\sqrt{20}}{\sqrt{5}} = \sqrt{\dfrac{20}{5}}$ Apply the quotient rule.

$= \sqrt{4}$ Simplify.

$= 2$ Simplify.

b. $\dfrac{\sqrt{50x}}{2\sqrt{2}} = \dfrac{1}{2}\cdot\sqrt{\dfrac{50x}{2}}$ Apply the quotient rule.

$= \dfrac{1}{2}\cdot\sqrt{25x}$ Simplify.

$= \dfrac{1}{2}\cdot\sqrt{25}\cdot\sqrt{x}$ Factor 25x.

$= \dfrac{1}{2}\cdot 5\cdot\sqrt{x}$ Simplify.

$= \dfrac{5}{2}\sqrt{x}$

c. $\dfrac{7\sqrt[3]{48x^4y^8}}{\sqrt[3]{6y^2}} = 7\cdot\sqrt[3]{\dfrac{48x^4y^8}{6y^2}}$ Apply the quotient rule.

$= 7\cdot\sqrt[3]{8x^4y^6}$ Simplify.

$= 7\sqrt[3]{8x^3y^6\cdot x}$ Factor.

$= 7\cdot\sqrt[3]{8x^3y^6}\cdot\sqrt[3]{x}$ Apply the product rule.

$= 7\cdot 2xy^2\cdot\sqrt[3]{x}$ Simplify.

$= 14xy^2\sqrt[3]{x}$

d. $\dfrac{2\sqrt[4]{32a^8b^6}}{\sqrt[4]{a^{-1}b^2}} = 2\sqrt[4]{\dfrac{32a^8b^6}{a^{-1}b^2}} = 2\sqrt[4]{32a^9b^4} = 2\sqrt[4]{16\cdot a^8\cdot b^4\cdot 2\cdot a}$

$= 2\sqrt[4]{16a^8b^4}\cdot\sqrt[4]{2a} = 2\cdot 2a^2b\cdot\sqrt[4]{2a} = 4a^2b\sqrt[4]{2a}$ □

PRACTICE

5 Use the quotient rule to divide and simplify.

a. $\dfrac{\sqrt{80}}{\sqrt{5}}$ **b.** $\dfrac{\sqrt{98z}}{3\sqrt{2}}$ **c.** $\dfrac{5\sqrt[3]{40x^5y^7}}{\sqrt[3]{5y}}$ **d.** $\dfrac{3\sqrt[5]{64x^9y^8}}{\sqrt[5]{x^{-1}y^2}}$

Concept Check ☑

Find and correct the error:

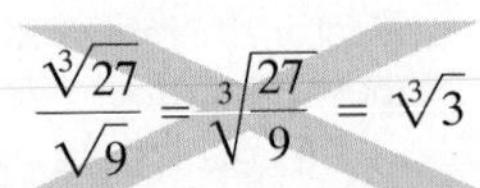

Answer to Concept Check:

$\dfrac{\sqrt[3]{27}}{\sqrt{9}} = \dfrac{3}{3} = 1$

OBJECTIVE 4 ▶ Using the distance and midpoint formulas. Now that we know how to simplify radicals, we can derive and use the distance formula. The midpoint formula is often confused with the distance formula, so to clarify both, we will also review the midpoint formula.

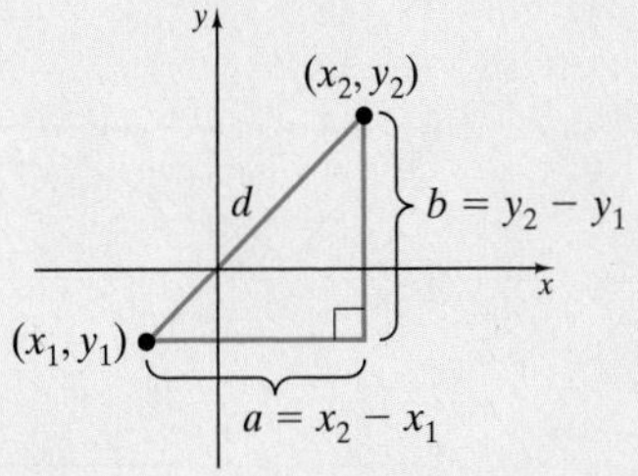

The Cartesian coordinate system helps us visualize a distance between points. To find the distance between two points, we use the distance formula, which is derived from the Pythagorean theorem.

To find the distance d between two points (x_1, y_1) and (x_2, y_2) as shown to the left, notice that the length of leg a is $x_2 - x_1$ and that the length of leg b is $y_2 - y_1$.

Thus, the Pythagorean theorem tells us that

$$d^2 = a^2 + b^2$$

or

$$d^2 = (x_2 - x_1)^2 + (y_2 - y_1)^2$$

or

$$d = \sqrt{(x_2 - x_1)^2 + (y_2 - y_1)^2}$$

This formula gives us the distance between any two points on the real plane.

Distance Formula

The distance d between two points (x_1, y_1) and (x_2, y_2) is given by

$$d = \sqrt{(x_2 - x_1)^2 + (y_2 - y_1)^2}$$

EXAMPLE 6 Find the distance between $(2, -5)$ and $(1, -4)$. Give an exact distance and a three-decimal-place approximation.

Solution To use the distance formula, it makes no difference which point we call (x_1, y_1) and which point we call (x_2, y_2). We will let $(x_1, y_1) = (2, -5)$ and $(x_2, y_2) = (1, -4)$.

$$\begin{aligned} d &= \sqrt{(x_2 - x_1)^2 + (y_2 - y_1)^2} \\ &= \sqrt{(1 - 2)^2 + [-4 - (-5)]^2} \\ &= \sqrt{(-1)^2 + (1)^2} \\ &= \sqrt{1 + 1} \\ &= \sqrt{2} \approx 1.414 \end{aligned}$$

The distance between the two points is exactly $\sqrt{2}$ units, or approximately 1.414 units. □

PRACTICE

6 Find the distance between $P(-3,7)$ and $Q(-2,3)$. Give an exact distance and a three-decimal-place approximation.

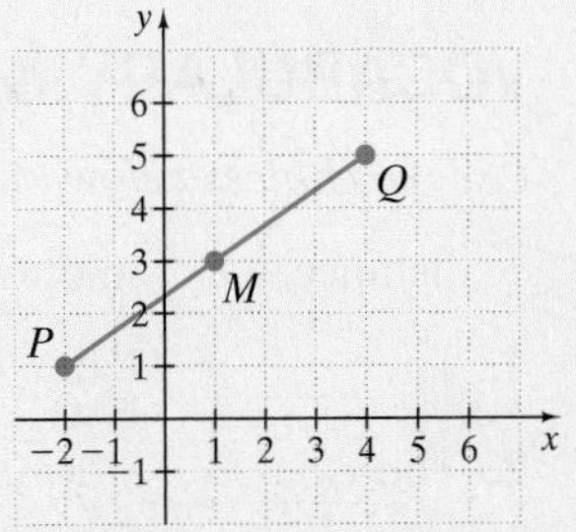

The **midpoint** of a line segment is the **point** located exactly halfway between the two end points of the line segment. On the graph to the left, the point M is the midpoint of line segment PQ. Thus, the distance between M and P equals the distance between M and Q.

Note: We usually need no knowledge of roots to calculate the midpoint of a line segment. We review midpoint here only because it is often confused with the distance between two points.

The x-coordinate of M is at half the distance between the x-coordinates of P and Q, and the y-coordinate of M is at half the distance between the y-coordinates of P and Q. That is, the x-coordinate of M is the average of the x-coordinates of P and Q; the y-coordinate of M is the average of the y-coordinates of P and Q.

Midpoint Formula

The midpoint of the line segment whose end points are (x_1, y_1) and (x_2, y_2) is the point with coordinates

$$\left(\frac{x_1 + x_2}{2}, \frac{y_1 + y_2}{2}\right)$$

EXAMPLE 7 Find the midpoint of the line segment that joins points $P(-3, 3)$ and $Q(1, 0)$.

Solution Use the midpoint formula. It makes no difference which point we call (x_1, y_1) or which point we call (x_2, y_2). Let $(x_1, y_1) = (-3, 3)$ and $(x_2, y_2) = (1, 0)$.

$$\begin{aligned} \text{midpoint} &= \left(\frac{x_1 + x_2}{2}, \frac{y_1 + y_2}{2}\right) \\ &= \left(\frac{-3 + 1}{2}, \frac{3 + 0}{2}\right) \\ &= \left(\frac{-2}{2}, \frac{3}{2}\right) \\ &= \left(-1, \frac{3}{2}\right) \end{aligned}$$

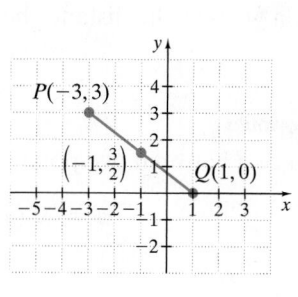

The midpoint of the segment is $\left(-1, \frac{3}{2}\right)$. □

PRACTICE

7 Find the midpoint of the line segment that joins points $P(5, -2)$ and $Q(8, -6)$.

Helpful Hint

The distance between two points is a distance. The midpoint of a line segment is the point halfway between the end points of the segment.

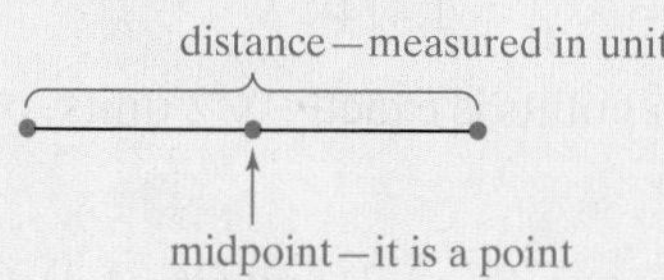

VOCABULARY & READINESS CHECK

Use the choices below to fill in each blank. Some choices may be used more than once.

distance midpoint point

1. The __________ of a line segment is a ______ exactly halfway between the two end points of the line segment.

2. The _________ formula is $d = \sqrt{(x_2 - x_1)^2 + (y_2 - y_1)^2}$.

3. The __________ formula is $\left(\frac{x_1 + x_2}{2}, \frac{y_1 + y_2}{2}\right)$.

Answer true or false. Assume all radicals represent nonzero real numbers.

4. $\sqrt[n]{a}\cdot\sqrt[n]{b}=\sqrt[n]{ab}$ _____

5. $\sqrt[3]{7}\cdot\sqrt[3]{11}=\sqrt[3]{18}$ _____

6. $\sqrt[3]{7}\cdot\sqrt{11}=\sqrt{77}$ _____

7. $\sqrt{x^7y^8}=\sqrt{x^7}\cdot\sqrt{y^8}$ _____

8. $\dfrac{\sqrt[n]{a}}{\sqrt[n]{b}}=\sqrt[n]{\dfrac{a}{b}}$ _____

9. $\dfrac{\sqrt[3]{12}}{\sqrt[3]{4}}=\sqrt[3]{8}$ _____

10. $\dfrac{\sqrt[n]{x^7}}{\sqrt[n]{x}}=\sqrt[n]{x^6}$ _____

19.3 EXERCISE SET

MyMathLab

PRACTICE

WATCH

DOWNLOAD

READ

REVIEW

Use the product rule to multiply. See Example 1.

1. $\sqrt{7}\cdot\sqrt{2}$

2. $\sqrt{11}\cdot\sqrt{10}$

3. $\sqrt[4]{8}\cdot\sqrt[4]{2}$

4. $\sqrt[4]{27}\cdot\sqrt[4]{3}$

5. $\sqrt[3]{4}\cdot\sqrt[3]{9}$

6. $\sqrt[3]{10}\cdot\sqrt[3]{5}$

7. $\sqrt{2}\cdot\sqrt{3x}$

8. $\sqrt{3y}\cdot\sqrt{5x}$

9. $\sqrt{\dfrac{7}{x}}\cdot\sqrt{\dfrac{2}{y}}$

10. $\sqrt{\dfrac{6}{m}}\cdot\sqrt{\dfrac{n}{5}}$

11. $\sqrt[4]{4x^3}\cdot\sqrt[4]{5}$

12. $\sqrt[4]{ab^2}\cdot\sqrt[4]{27ab}$

Use the quotient rule to simplify. See Examples 2 and 3.

13. $\sqrt{\dfrac{6}{49}}$

14. $\sqrt{\dfrac{8}{81}}$

15. $\sqrt{\dfrac{2}{49}}$

16. $\sqrt{\dfrac{5}{121}}$

17. $\sqrt[4]{\dfrac{x^3}{16}}$

18. $\sqrt[4]{\dfrac{y}{81x^4}}$

19. $\sqrt[3]{\dfrac{4}{27}}$

20. $\sqrt[3]{\dfrac{3}{64}}$

21. $\sqrt[4]{\dfrac{8}{x^8}}$

22. $\sqrt[4]{\dfrac{a^3}{81}}$

23. $\sqrt[3]{\dfrac{2x}{81y^{12}}}$

24. $\sqrt[3]{\dfrac{3}{8x^6}}$

25. $\sqrt{\dfrac{x^2y}{100}}$

26. $\sqrt{\dfrac{y^2z}{36}}$

27. $\sqrt{\dfrac{5x^2}{4y^2}}$

28. $\sqrt{\dfrac{y^{10}}{9x^6}}$

29. $-\sqrt[3]{\dfrac{z^7}{27x^3}}$

30. $-\sqrt[3]{\dfrac{64a}{b^9}}$

Simplify. See Examples 3 and 4.

31. $\sqrt{32}$

32. $\sqrt{27}$

33. $\sqrt[3]{192}$

34. $\sqrt[3]{108}$

35. $5\sqrt{75}$

36. $3\sqrt{8}$

37. $\sqrt{24}$

38. $\sqrt{20}$

39. $\sqrt{100x^5}$

40. $\sqrt{64y^9}$

41. $\sqrt[3]{16y^7}$

42. $\sqrt[3]{64y^9}$

43. $\sqrt[4]{a^8b^7}$

44. $\sqrt[5]{32z^{12}}$

45. $\sqrt{y^5}$

46. $\sqrt[3]{y^5}$

47. $\sqrt{25a^2b^3}$

48. $\sqrt{9x^5y^7}$

49. $\sqrt[5]{-32x^{10}y}$

50. $\sqrt[5]{-243z^9}$

51. $\sqrt[3]{50x^{14}}$

52. $\sqrt[3]{40y^{10}}$

53. $-\sqrt{32a^8b^7}$

54. $-\sqrt{20ab^6}$

55. $\sqrt{9x^7y^9}$

56. $\sqrt{12r^9s^{12}}$

57. $\sqrt[3]{125r^9s^{12}}$

58. $\sqrt[3]{8a^6b^9}$

Use the quotient rule to divide. Then simplify if possible. See Example 5.

59. $\dfrac{\sqrt{14}}{\sqrt{7}}$

60. $\dfrac{\sqrt{45}}{\sqrt{9}}$

61. $\dfrac{\sqrt[3]{24}}{\sqrt[3]{3}}$

62. $\dfrac{\sqrt[3]{10}}{\sqrt[3]{2}}$

63. $\dfrac{5\sqrt[4]{48}}{\sqrt[4]{3}}$

64. $\dfrac{7\sqrt[4]{162}}{\sqrt[4]{2}}$

65. $\dfrac{\sqrt{x^5y^3}}{\sqrt{xy}}$

66. $\dfrac{\sqrt{a^7b^6}}{\sqrt{a^3b^2}}$

67. $\dfrac{8\sqrt[3]{54m^7}}{\sqrt[3]{2m}}$

68. $\dfrac{\sqrt[3]{128x^3}}{-3\sqrt[3]{2x}}$

69. $\dfrac{3\sqrt{100x^2}}{2\sqrt{2x^{-1}}}$

70. $\dfrac{\sqrt{270y^2}}{5\sqrt{3y^{-4}}}$

71. $\dfrac{\sqrt[4]{96a^{10}b^3}}{\sqrt[4]{3a^2b^3}}$

72. $\dfrac{\sqrt[5]{64x^{10}y^3}}{\sqrt[5]{2x^3y^{-7}}}$

Find the distance between each pair of points. Give an exact distance and a three-decimal-place approximation. See Example 6.

73. $(5,1)$ and $(8,5)$

74. $(2,3)$ and $(14,8)$

75. $(-3, 2)$ and $(1, -3)$

76. $(3, -2)$ and $(-4, 1)$

77. $(-9, 4)$ and $(-8, 1)$

78. $(-5, -2)$ and $(-6, -6)$

79. $(0, -\sqrt{2})$ and $(\sqrt{3}, 0)$

80. $(-\sqrt{5}, 0)$ and $(0, \sqrt{7})$

81. $(1.7, -3.6)$ and $(-8.6, 5.7)$

82. $(9.6, 2.5)$ and $(-1.9, -3.7)$

Find the midpoint of the line segment whose end points are given. See Example 7.

83. $(6, -8), (2, 4)$

84. $(3, 9), (7, 11)$

85. $(-2, -1), (-8, 6)$

86. $(-3, -4), (6, -8)$

87. $(7, 3), (-1, -3)$

88. $(-2, 5), (-1, 6)$

89. $\left(\frac{1}{2}, \frac{3}{8}\right), \left(-\frac{3}{2}, \frac{5}{8}\right)$

90. $\left(-\frac{2}{5}, \frac{7}{15}\right), \left(-\frac{2}{5}, -\frac{4}{15}\right)$

91. $(\sqrt{2}, 3\sqrt{5}), (\sqrt{2}, -2\sqrt{5})$

92. $(\sqrt{8}, -\sqrt{12}), (3\sqrt{2}, 7\sqrt{3})$

93. $(4.6, -3.5), (7.8, -9.8)$

94. $(-4.6, 2.1), (-6.7, 1.9)$

REVIEW AND PREVIEW

Perform each indicated operation.

95. $6x + 8x$

96. $(6x)(8x)$

97. $(2x + 3)(x - 5)$

98. $(2x + 3) + (x - 5)$

99. $9y^2 - 8y^2$

100. $(9y^2)(-8y^2)$

101. $-3(x + 5)$

102. $-3 + x + 5$

103. $(x - 4)^2$

104. $(2x + 1)^2$

CONCEPT EXTENSIONS

Find and correct the error. See the Concept Check in this section.

105. $\frac{\sqrt[3]{64}}{\sqrt{64}} = \sqrt[3]{\frac{64}{64}} = \sqrt[3]{1} = 1$

106. $\frac{\sqrt[4]{16}}{\sqrt{4}} = \sqrt[4]{\frac{16}{4}} = \sqrt[4]{4}$

Simplify. See the Concept Check in this section. Assume variables represent positive numbers.

107. $\sqrt[5]{x^{35}}$

108. $\sqrt[6]{y^{48}}$

109. $\sqrt[4]{a^{12}b^4c^{20}}$

110. $\sqrt[3]{a^9b^{21}c^3}$

111. $\sqrt[3]{z^{32}}$

112. $\sqrt[5]{x^{49}}$

113. $\sqrt[7]{q^{17}r^{40}s^7}$

114. $\sqrt[4]{p^{11}q^4r^{45}}$

115. The formula for the radius r of a sphere with surface area A is given by $r = \sqrt{\frac{A}{4\pi}}$. Calculate the radius of a standard zorb whose outside surface area is 32.17 sq m. Round to the nearest tenth. (See the chapter opener, page 1160. *Source:* Zorb, Ltd.)

△ 116. The formula for the surface area A of a cone with height h and radius r is given by

$$A = \pi r\sqrt{r^2 + h^2}$$

a. Find the surface area of a cone whose height is 3 centimeters and whose radius is 4 centimeters.

b. Approximate to two decimal places the surface area of a cone whose height is 7.2 feet and whose radius is 6.8 feet.

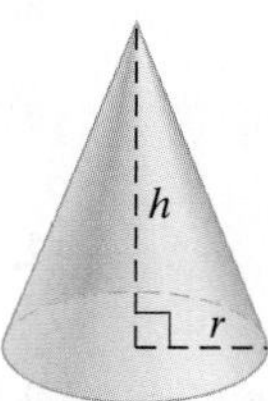

117. The owner of Knightime Video has determined that the demand equation for renting older releases is given by the equation $F(x) = 0.6\sqrt{49 - x^2}$, where x is the price in dollars per two-day rental and $F(x)$ is the number of times the video is demanded per week.

a. Approximate to one decimal place the demand per week of an older release if the rental price is \$3 per two-day rental.

b. Approximate to one decimal place the demand per week of an older release if the rental price is \$5 per two-day rental.

c. Explain how the owner of the video store can use this equation to predict the number of copies of each tape that should be in stock.

△ 118. Before Mount Vesuvius, a volcano in Italy, erupted violently in 79 A.D., its height was 4190 feet. Vesuvius was roughly cone-shaped, and its base had a radius of approximately 25,200 feet. Use the formula for the surface area of a cone, given in Exercise 116, to approximate the surface area this volcano had before it erupted. (*Source:* Global Volcanism Network)

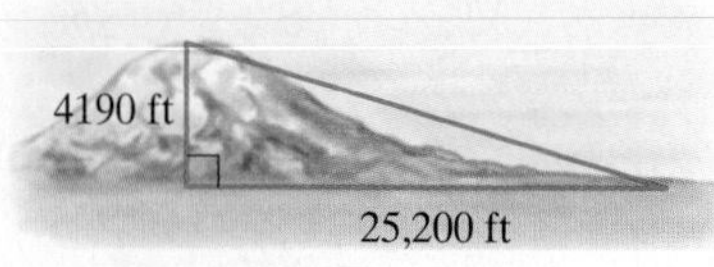

19.4 ADDING, SUBTRACTING, AND MULTIPLYING RADICAL EXPRESSIONS

OBJECTIVES

1 Add or subtract radical expressions.

2 Multiply radical expressions.

OBJECTIVE 1 ▶ Adding or subtracting radical expressions. We have learned that sums or differences of like terms can be simplified. To simplify these sums or differences, we use the distributive property. For example,

$$2x + 3x = (2 + 3)x = 5x \quad \text{and} \quad 7x^2y - 4x^2y = (7 - 4)x^2y = 3x^2y$$

The distributive property can also be used to add **like radicals.**

Like Radicals

Radicals with the same index and the same radicand are like radicals.

For example, $2\sqrt{7} + 3\sqrt{7} = (2 + 3)\sqrt{7} = 5\sqrt{7}$. Also,

Like radicals

$$5\sqrt{3x} - 7\sqrt{3x} = (5 - 7)\sqrt{3x} = -2\sqrt{3x}$$

The expression $2\sqrt{7} + 2\sqrt[3]{7}$ cannot be simplified further since $2\sqrt{7}$ and $2\sqrt[3]{7}$ are not like radicals.

Unlike radicals

EXAMPLE 1 Add or subtract as indicated. Assume all variables represent positive real numbers.

a. $4\sqrt{11} + 8\sqrt{11}$ **b.** $5\sqrt[3]{3x} - 7\sqrt[3]{3x}$ **c.** $2\sqrt{7} + 2\sqrt[3]{7}$

Solution

a. $4\sqrt{11} + 8\sqrt{11} = (4 + 8)\sqrt{11} = 12\sqrt{11}$

b. $5\sqrt[3]{3x} - 7\sqrt[3]{3x} = (5 - 7)\sqrt[3]{3x} = -2\sqrt[3]{3x}$

c. $2\sqrt{7} + 2\sqrt[3]{7}$

This expression cannot be simplified since $2\sqrt{7}$ and $2\sqrt[3]{7}$ do not contain like radicals. □

PRACTICE 1 Add or subtract as indicated.

a. $3\sqrt{17} + 5\sqrt{17}$ **b.** $7\sqrt[3]{5z} - 12\sqrt[3]{5z}$ **c.** $3\sqrt{2} + 5\sqrt[3]{2}$

When adding or subtracting radicals, always check first to see whether any radicals can be simplified.

Concept Check ☑

True or false?

$$\sqrt{a} + \sqrt{b} = \sqrt{a + b}$$

Explain.

Answer to Concept Check: false; answers may vary

EXAMPLE 2 Add or subtract. Assume that variables represent positive real numbers.

a. $\sqrt{20} + 2\sqrt{45}$ **b.** $\sqrt[3]{54} - 5\sqrt[3]{16} + \sqrt[3]{2}$ **c.** $\sqrt{27x} - 2\sqrt{9x} + \sqrt{72x}$
d. $\sqrt[3]{98} + \sqrt{98}$ **e.** $\sqrt[3]{48y^4} + \sqrt[3]{6y^4}$

Solution First, simplify each radical. Then add or subtract any like radicals.

a.
$$\begin{aligned}\sqrt{20} + 2\sqrt{45} &= \sqrt{4\cdot 5} + 2\sqrt{9\cdot 5} && \text{Factor 20 and 45.}\\ &= \sqrt{4}\cdot\sqrt{5} + 2\cdot\sqrt{9}\cdot\sqrt{5} && \text{Use the product rule.}\\ &= 2\cdot\sqrt{5} + 2\cdot 3\cdot\sqrt{5} && \text{Simplify } \sqrt{4} \text{ and } \sqrt{9}.\\ &= 2\sqrt{5} + 6\sqrt{5} && \text{Add like radicals.}\\ &= 8\sqrt{5}\end{aligned}$$

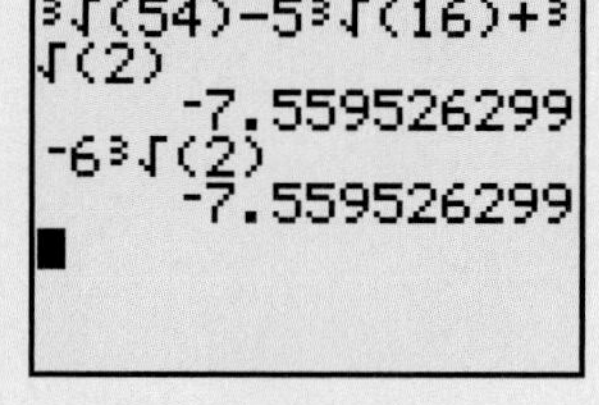

A calculator check for Example 2b.

b. $\sqrt[3]{54} - 5\sqrt[3]{16} + \sqrt[3]{2}$
$$\begin{aligned}&= \sqrt[3]{27}\cdot\sqrt[3]{2} - 5\cdot\sqrt[3]{8}\cdot\sqrt[3]{2} + \sqrt[3]{2} && \text{Factor and use the product rule.}\\ &= 3\cdot\sqrt[3]{2} - 5\cdot 2\cdot\sqrt[3]{2} + \sqrt[3]{2} && \text{Simplify } \sqrt[3]{27} \text{ and } \sqrt[3]{8}.\\ &= 3\sqrt[3]{2} - 10\sqrt[3]{2} + \sqrt[3]{2} && \text{Write } 5\cdot 2 \text{ as 10.}\\ &= -6\sqrt[3]{2} && \text{Combine like radicals.}\end{aligned}$$

c. $\sqrt{27x} - 2\sqrt{9x} + \sqrt{72x}$
$$\begin{aligned}&= \sqrt{9}\cdot\sqrt{3x} - 2\cdot\sqrt{9}\cdot\sqrt{x} + \sqrt{36}\cdot\sqrt{2x} && \text{Factor and use the product rule.}\\ &= 3\cdot\sqrt{3x} - 2\cdot 3\cdot\sqrt{x} + 6\cdot\sqrt{2x} && \text{Simplify } \sqrt{9} \text{ and } \sqrt{36}.\\ &= 3\sqrt{3x} - 6\sqrt{x} + 6\sqrt{2x} && \text{Write } 2\cdot 3 \text{ as 6.}\end{aligned}$$

Helpful Hint
None of these terms contain like radicals. We can simplify no further.

d.
$$\begin{aligned}\sqrt[3]{98} + \sqrt{98} &= \sqrt[3]{98} + \sqrt{49}\cdot\sqrt{2} && \text{Factor and use the product rule.}\\ &= \sqrt[3]{98} + 7\sqrt{2} && \text{No further simplification is possible.}\end{aligned}$$

e.
$$\begin{aligned}\sqrt[3]{48y^4} + \sqrt[3]{6y^4} &= \sqrt[3]{8y^3}\cdot\sqrt[3]{6y} + \sqrt[3]{y^3}\cdot\sqrt[3]{6y} && \text{Factor and use the product rule.}\\ &= 2y\sqrt[3]{6y} + y\sqrt[3]{6y} && \text{Simplify } \sqrt[3]{8y^3} \text{ and } \sqrt[3]{y^3}.\\ &= 3y\sqrt[3]{6y} && \text{Combine like radicals.}\end{aligned}$$
□

PRACTICE
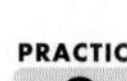
2 Add or subtract.

a. $\sqrt{24} + 3\sqrt{54}$ **b.** $\sqrt[3]{24} - 4\sqrt[3]{81} + \sqrt[3]{3}$ **c.** $\sqrt{75x} - 3\sqrt{27x} + \sqrt{12x}$
d. $\sqrt{40} + \sqrt[3]{40}$ **e.** $\sqrt[3]{81x^4} + \sqrt[3]{3x^4}$

Let's continue to assume that variables represent positive real numbers.

EXAMPLE 3 Add or subtract as indicated.

a. $\dfrac{\sqrt{45}}{4} - \dfrac{\sqrt{5}}{3}$ **b.** $\sqrt[3]{\dfrac{7x}{8}} + 2\sqrt[3]{7x}$

Solution

a.
$$\begin{aligned}\frac{\sqrt{45}}{4} - \frac{\sqrt{5}}{3} &= \frac{3\sqrt{5}}{4} - \frac{\sqrt{5}}{3} && \text{To subtract, notice that the LCD is 12.}\\ &= \frac{3\sqrt{5}\cdot 3}{4\cdot 3} - \frac{\sqrt{5}\cdot 4}{3\cdot 4} && \text{Write each expression as an equivalent expression with a denominator of 12.}\\ &= \frac{9\sqrt{5}}{12} - \frac{4\sqrt{5}}{12} && \text{Multiply factors in the numerator and the denominator.}\\ &= \frac{5\sqrt{5}}{12} && \text{Subtract.}\end{aligned}$$

b. $\sqrt[3]{\frac{7x}{8}} + 2\sqrt[3]{7x} = \frac{\sqrt[3]{7x}}{\sqrt[3]{8}} + 2\sqrt[3]{7x}$ Apply the quotient rule for radicals.

$= \frac{\sqrt[3]{7x}}{2} + 2\sqrt[3]{7x}$ Simplify.

$= \frac{\sqrt[3]{7x}}{2} + \frac{2\sqrt[3]{7x}\cdot 2}{2}$ Write each expression as an equivalent expression with a denominator of 2.

$= \frac{\sqrt[3]{7x}}{2} + \frac{4\sqrt[3]{7x}}{2}$

$= \frac{5\sqrt[3]{7x}}{2}$ Add. □

PRACTICE 3 Add or subtract as indicated.

a. $\frac{\sqrt{28}}{3} - \frac{\sqrt{7}}{4}$ **b.** $\sqrt[3]{\frac{6y}{64}} + 3\sqrt[3]{6y}$

OBJECTIVE 2 ▶ Multiplying radical expressions. We can multiply radical expressions by using many of the same properties used to multiply polynomial expressions. For instance, to multiply $\sqrt{2}(\sqrt{6} - 3\sqrt{2})$, we use the distributive property and multiply $\sqrt{2}$ by each term inside the parentheses.

$\sqrt{2}(\sqrt{6} - 3\sqrt{2}) = \sqrt{2}(\sqrt{6}) - \sqrt{2}(3\sqrt{2})$ Use the distributive property.

$= \sqrt{2\cdot 6} - 3\sqrt{2\cdot 2}$

$= \sqrt{2\cdot 2\cdot 3} - 3\cdot 2$ Use the product rule for radicals.

$= 2\sqrt{3} - 6$

EXAMPLE 4 Multiply.

a. $\sqrt{3}(5 + \sqrt{30})$ **b.** $(\sqrt{5} - \sqrt{6})(\sqrt{7} + 1)$ **c.** $(7\sqrt{x} + 5)(3\sqrt{x} - \sqrt{5})$

d. $(4\sqrt{3} - 1)^2$ **e.** $(\sqrt{2x} - 5)(\sqrt{2x} + 5)$ **f.** $(\sqrt{x - 3} + 5)^2$

Solution

a. $\sqrt{3}(5 + \sqrt{30}) = \sqrt{3}(5) + \sqrt{3}(\sqrt{30})$

$= 5\sqrt{3} + \sqrt{3\cdot 30}$

$= 5\sqrt{3} + \sqrt{3\cdot 3\cdot 10}$

$= 5\sqrt{3} + 3\sqrt{10}$

b. To multiply, we can use the FOIL method.

First Outer Inner Last

$(\sqrt{5} - \sqrt{6})(\sqrt{7} + 1) = \sqrt{5}\cdot\sqrt{7} + \sqrt{5}\cdot 1 - \sqrt{6}\cdot\sqrt{7} - \sqrt{6}\cdot 1$

$= \sqrt{35} + \sqrt{5} - \sqrt{42} - \sqrt{6}$

c. $(7\sqrt{x} + 5)(3\sqrt{x} - \sqrt{5}) = 7\sqrt{x}(3\sqrt{x}) - 7\sqrt{x}(\sqrt{5}) + 5(3\sqrt{x}) - 5(\sqrt{5})$

$= 21x - 7\sqrt{5x} + 15\sqrt{x} - 5\sqrt{5}$

d. $(4\sqrt{3} - 1)^2 = (4\sqrt{3} - 1)(4\sqrt{3} - 1)$

$= 4\sqrt{3}(4\sqrt{3}) - 4\sqrt{3}(1) - 1(4\sqrt{3}) - 1(-1)$

$= 16\cdot 3 - 4\sqrt{3} - 4\sqrt{3} + 1$

$= 48 - 8\sqrt{3} + 1$

$= 49 - 8\sqrt{3}$

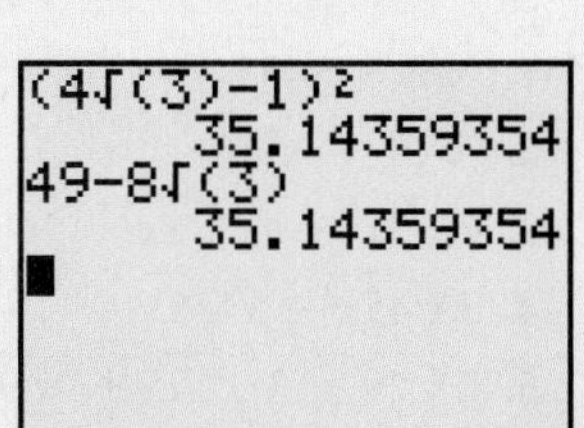

A calculator check for Example 4d.

e. $\left(\sqrt{2x}-5\right)\left(\sqrt{2x}+5\right) = \sqrt{2x}\cdot\sqrt{2x} + 5\sqrt{2x} - 5\sqrt{2x} - 5\cdot 5$
$= 2x - 25$

f. $(\underbrace{\sqrt{x-3}}_{a} + \underbrace{5}_{b})^2 = (\underbrace{\sqrt{x-3}}_{a^2})^2 + \underbrace{2\cdot}_{+2\cdot}\underbrace{\sqrt{x-3}}_{a}\cdot\underbrace{5}_{\cdot b} + \underbrace{5^2}_{+b^2}$

$= x - 3 + 10\sqrt{x-3} + 25$ Simplify.

$= x + 22 + 10\sqrt{x-3}$ Combine like terms. □

PRACTICE

4 Multiply.

a. $\sqrt{5}\left(2+\sqrt{15}\right)$

b. $\left(\sqrt{2}-\sqrt{5}\right)\left(\sqrt{6}+2\right)$

c. $\left(3\sqrt{z}-4\right)\left(2\sqrt{z}+3\right)$

d. $\left(\sqrt{6}-3\right)^2$

e. $\left(\sqrt{5x}+3\right)\left(\sqrt{5x}-3\right)$

f. $\left(\sqrt{x+2}+3\right)^2$

VOCABULARY & READINESS CHECK

Complete the table with "Like" or "Unlike."

	Terms	*Like or Unlike Radical Terms?*
1.	$\sqrt{7}, \sqrt[3]{7}$	
2.	$\sqrt[3]{x^2y}, \sqrt[3]{yx^2}$	
3.	$\sqrt[3]{abc}, \sqrt[3]{cba}$	
4.	$2x\sqrt{5}, 2x\sqrt{10}$	

Simplify. Assume that all variables represent positive real numbers.

5. $2\sqrt{3} + 4\sqrt{3} =$ ______
6. $5\sqrt{7} + 3\sqrt{7} =$ ______
7. $8\sqrt{x} - \sqrt{x} =$ ______
8. $3\sqrt{y} - \sqrt{y} =$ ______
9. $7\sqrt[3]{x} + \sqrt[3]{x} =$ ______
10. $8\sqrt[3]{z} + \sqrt[3]{z} =$ ______

Add or subtract if possible.

11. $\sqrt{11} + \sqrt[3]{11} =$ ______
12. $9\sqrt{13} - \sqrt[4]{13} =$ ______
13. $8\sqrt[3]{2x} + 3\sqrt[3]{2x} - \sqrt[3]{2x} =$ ______
14. $8\sqrt[3]{2x} + 3\sqrt[3]{2x^2} - \sqrt[3]{2x} =$ ______

19.4 EXERCISE SET

MyMathLab

PRACTICE

WATCH

DOWNLOAD

READ

REVIEW

Add or subtract. See Examples 1 through 3.

1. $\sqrt{8} - \sqrt{32}$
2. $\sqrt{27} - \sqrt{75}$
3. $2\sqrt{2x^3} + 4x\sqrt{8x}$
4. $3\sqrt{45x^3} + x\sqrt{5x}$
5. $2\sqrt{50} - 3\sqrt{125} + \sqrt{98}$
6. $4\sqrt{32} - \sqrt{18} + 2\sqrt{128}$
7. $\sqrt[3]{16x} - \sqrt[3]{54x}$
8. $2\sqrt[3]{3a^4} - 3a\sqrt[3]{81a}$
9. $\sqrt{9b^3} - \sqrt{25b^3} + \sqrt{49b^3}$
10. $\sqrt{4x^7} + 9x^2\sqrt{x^3} - 5x\sqrt{x^5}$
11. $\frac{5\sqrt{2}}{3} + \frac{2\sqrt{2}}{5}$
12. $\frac{\sqrt{3}}{2} + \frac{4\sqrt{3}}{3}$
13. $\sqrt[3]{\frac{11}{8}} - \frac{\sqrt[3]{11}}{6}$
14. $\frac{2\sqrt[3]{4}}{7} - \frac{\sqrt[3]{4}}{14}$
15. $\frac{\sqrt{20x}}{9} + \sqrt{\frac{5x}{9}}$

16. $\frac{3x\sqrt{7}}{5} + \sqrt{\frac{7x^2}{100}}$

17. $7\sqrt{9} - 7 + \sqrt{3}$

18. $\sqrt{16} - 5\sqrt{10} + 7$

19. $2 + 3\sqrt{y^2} - 6\sqrt{y^2} + 5$

20. $3\sqrt{7} - \sqrt[3]{x} + 4\sqrt{7} - 3\sqrt[3]{x}$

21. $3\sqrt{108} - 2\sqrt{18} - 3\sqrt{48}$

22. $-\sqrt{75} + \sqrt{12} - 3\sqrt{3}$

23. $-5\sqrt[3]{625} + \sqrt[3]{40}$

24. $-2\sqrt[3]{108} - \sqrt[3]{32}$

25. $\sqrt{9b^3} - \sqrt{25b^3} + \sqrt{16b^3}$

26. $\sqrt{4x^7y^5} + 9x^2\sqrt{x^3y^5} - 5xy\sqrt{x^5y^3}$

27. $5y\sqrt{8y} + 2\sqrt{50y^3}$

28. $3\sqrt{8x^2y^3} - 2x\sqrt{32y^3}$

29. $\sqrt[3]{54xy^3} - 5\sqrt[3]{2xy^3} + y\sqrt[3]{128x}$

30. $2\sqrt[3]{24x^3y^4} + 4x\sqrt[3]{81y^4}$

31. $6\sqrt[3]{11} + 8\sqrt{11} - 12\sqrt{11}$

32. $3\sqrt[3]{5} + 4\sqrt{5}$

33. $-2\sqrt[4]{x^7} + 3\sqrt[4]{16x^7}$

34. $6\sqrt[3]{24x^3} - 2\sqrt[3]{81x^3} - x\sqrt[3]{3}$

35. $\frac{4\sqrt{3}}{3} - \frac{\sqrt{12}}{3}$

36. $\frac{\sqrt{45}}{10} + \frac{7\sqrt{5}}{10}$

37. $\frac{\sqrt[3]{8x^4}}{7} + \frac{3x\sqrt[3]{x}}{7}$

38. $\frac{\sqrt[4]{48}}{5x} - \frac{2\sqrt[4]{3}}{10x}$

39. $\sqrt{\frac{28}{x^2}} + \sqrt{\frac{7}{4x^2}}$

40. $\frac{\sqrt{99}}{5x} - \sqrt{\frac{44}{x^2}}$

41. $\sqrt[3]{\frac{16}{27}} - \frac{\sqrt[3]{54}}{6}$

42. $\frac{\sqrt[3]{3}}{10} + \sqrt[3]{\frac{24}{125}}$

43. $-\frac{\sqrt[3]{2x^4}}{9} + \sqrt[3]{\frac{250x^4}{27}}$

44. $\frac{\sqrt[3]{y^5}}{8} + \frac{5y\sqrt[3]{y^2}}{4}$

△ 45. Find the perimeter of the trapezoid.

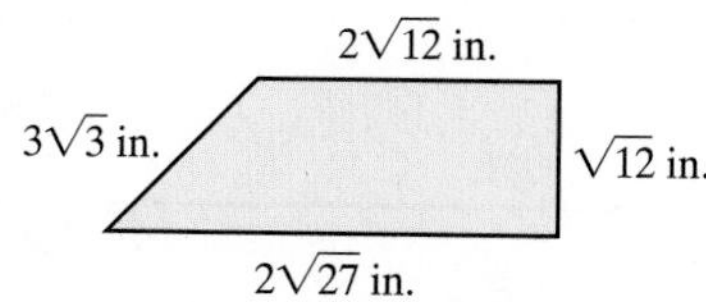

△ 46. Find the perimeter of the triangle.

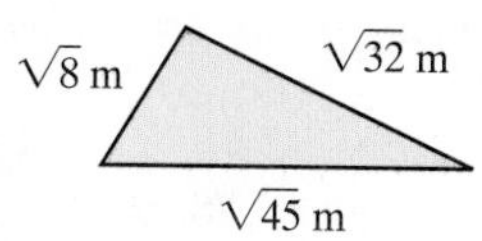

Multiply, and then simplify if possible. See Example 4.

47. $\sqrt{7}(\sqrt{5} + \sqrt{3})$

48. $\sqrt{5}(\sqrt{15} - \sqrt{35})$

49. $(\sqrt{5} - \sqrt{2})^2$

50. $(3x - \sqrt{2})(3x - \sqrt{2})$

51. $\sqrt{3x}(\sqrt{3} - \sqrt{x})$

52. $\sqrt{5y}(\sqrt{y} + \sqrt{5})$

53. $(2\sqrt{x} - 5)(3\sqrt{x} + 1)$

54. $(8\sqrt{y} + z)(4\sqrt{y} - 1)$

55. $(\sqrt[3]{a} - 4)(\sqrt[3]{a} + 5)$

56. $(\sqrt[3]{a} + 2)(\sqrt[3]{a} + 7)$

57. $6(\sqrt{2} - 2)$

58. $\sqrt{5}(6 - \sqrt{5})$

59. $\sqrt{2}(\sqrt{2} + x\sqrt{6})$

60. $\sqrt{3}(\sqrt{3} - 2\sqrt{5x})$

61. $(2\sqrt{7} + 3\sqrt{5})(\sqrt{7} - 2\sqrt{5})$

62. $(\sqrt{6} - 4\sqrt{2})(3\sqrt{6} + \sqrt{2})$

63. $(\sqrt{x} - y)(\sqrt{x} + y)$

64. $(\sqrt{3x} + 2)(\sqrt{3x} - 2)$

65. $(\sqrt{3} + x)^2$

66. $(\sqrt{y} - 3x)^2$

67. $(\sqrt{5x} - 2\sqrt{3x})(\sqrt{5x} - 3\sqrt{3x})$

68. $(5\sqrt{7x} - \sqrt{2x})(4\sqrt{7x} + 6\sqrt{2x})$

69. $(\sqrt[3]{4} + 2)(\sqrt[3]{2} - 1)$

70. $(\sqrt[3]{3} + \sqrt[3]{2})(\sqrt[3]{9} - \sqrt[3]{4})$

71. $(\sqrt[3]{x} + 1)(\sqrt[3]{x^2} - \sqrt[3]{x} + 1)$

72. $(\sqrt[3]{3x} + 2)(\sqrt[3]{9x^2} - 2\sqrt[3]{3x} + 4)$

73. $(\sqrt{x - 1} + 5)^2$

74. $(\sqrt{3x + 1} + 2)^2$

75. $(\sqrt{2x + 5} - 1)^2$

76. $(\sqrt{x - 6} - 7)^2$

REVIEW AND PREVIEW

Factor each numerator and denominator. Then simplify if possible. See Section 18.1.

77. $\frac{2x - 14}{2}$

78. $\frac{8x - 24y}{4}$

79. $\frac{7x - 7y}{x^2 - y^2}$

80. $\frac{x^3 - 8}{4x - 8}$

81. $\frac{6a^2b - 9ab}{3ab}$

82. $\frac{14r - 28r^2s^2}{7rs}$

83. $\frac{-4 + 2\sqrt{3}}{6}$

84. $\frac{-5 + 10\sqrt{7}}{5}$

CONCEPT EXTENSIONS

△ **85.** Find the perimeter and area of the rectangle.

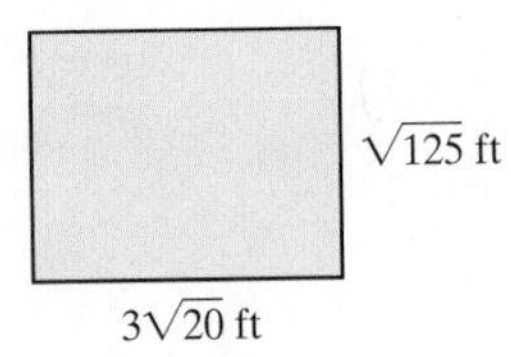

△ **86.** Find the area and perimeter of the trapezoid. (*Hint:* The area of a trapezoid is the product of half the height $6\sqrt{3}$ meters and the sum of the bases $2\sqrt{63}$ and $7\sqrt{7}$ meters.)

$2\sqrt{63}$ m

$2\sqrt{27}$ m

$6\sqrt{3}$ m

$7\sqrt{7}$ m

87. **a.** Add: $\sqrt{3} + \sqrt{3}$.

b. Multiply: $\sqrt{3} \cdot \sqrt{3}$.

c. Describe the differences in parts **a** and **b**.

88. Multiply: $(\sqrt{2} + \sqrt{3} - 1)^2$.

89. Explain how simplifying $2x + 3x$ is similar to simplifying $2\sqrt{x} + 3\sqrt{x}$.

90. Explain how multiplying $(x - 2)(x + 3)$ is similar to multiplying $(\sqrt{x} - \sqrt{2})(\sqrt{x} + 3)$.

STUDY SKILLS BUILDER

Have You Decided to Successfully Complete This Course?

Hopefully by now, one of your current goals is to successfully complete this course.

If it is not a goal of yours, ask yourself why? One common reason is fear of failure. Amazingly enough, fear of failure alone can be strong enough to keep many of us from doing our best in any endeavor. Another common reason is that you simply haven't taken the time to make successfully completing this course one of your goals.

Anytime you are registered for a course, successfully completing that course should probably be a goal. How do you do this? Start by writing this goal in your mathematics notebook. Then list steps you will take to ensure success. A great first step is to make a commitment to try the suggestions in this section.

Good luck, and don't forget that a positive attitude will make a big difference.

Let's see how you are doing.

1. Have you made the decision to make "successfully completing this course" a goal of yours? If not, please list reasons that this has not happened. Study your list and talk to your instructor about this.
2. If your answer to Exercise 1 is yes, take a moment and list, in your notebook, further specific goals that will help you achieve this major goal of successfully completing this course. (For example, "My goal this semester is not to miss any of my mathematics classes.")
3. Rate your commitment to this course with a number between 1 and 5. Use the diagram below to help.

High Commitment		Average Commitment		Not Committed at All
5	4	3	2	1

4. If you have rated your personal commitment level (from the exercise above) as a 1, 2, or 3, list the reasons why this is so. Then determine whether it is possible to increase your commitment level to a 4 or 5.

19.5 RATIONALIZING DENOMINATORS AND NUMERATORS OF RADICAL EXPRESSIONS

OBJECTIVES

1. Rationalize denominators.
2. Rationalize denominators having two terms.
3. Rationalize numerators.

OBJECTIVE 1 ▶ Rationalizing denominators of radical expressions. Often in mathematics, it is helpful to write a radical expression such as $\frac{\sqrt{3}}{\sqrt{2}}$ either without a radical in the denominator or without a radical in the numerator. The process of writing this expression as an equivalent expression but without a radical in the denominator is called **rationalizing the denominator.** To rationalize the denominator of $\frac{\sqrt{3}}{\sqrt{2}}$, we use the fundamental principle of fractions and multiply the numerator and the denominator by $\sqrt{2}$. Recall that this is the same as multiplying by $\frac{\sqrt{2}}{\sqrt{2}}$, which simplifies to 1.

$$\frac{\sqrt{3}}{\sqrt{2}} = \frac{\sqrt{3} \cdot \sqrt{2}}{\sqrt{2} \cdot \sqrt{2}} = \frac{\sqrt{6}}{\sqrt{4}} = \frac{\sqrt{6}}{2}$$

In this section, we continue to assume that variables represent positive real numbers.

EXAMPLE 1 Rationalize the denominator of each expression.

a. $\frac{2}{\sqrt{5}}$ **b.** $\frac{2\sqrt{16}}{\sqrt{9x}}$ **c.** $\sqrt[3]{\frac{1}{2}}$

Solution

a. To rationalize the denominator, we multiply the numerator and denominator by a factor that makes the radicand in the denominator a perfect square.

$$\frac{2}{\sqrt{5}} = \frac{2 \cdot \sqrt{5}}{\sqrt{5} \cdot \sqrt{5}} = \frac{2\sqrt{5}}{5} \quad \text{The denominator is now rationalized.}$$

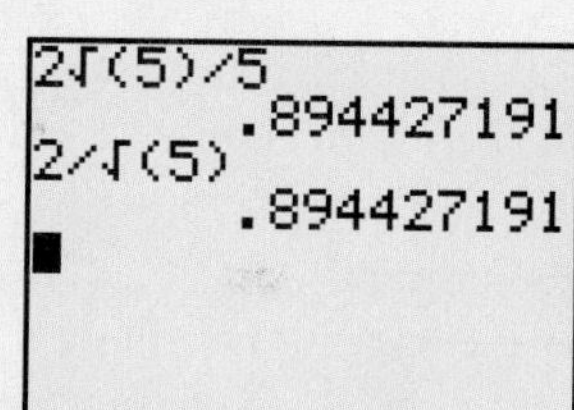

A calculator check for Example 1a.

b. First, we simplify the radicals and then rationalize the denominator.

$$\frac{2\sqrt{16}}{\sqrt{9x}} = \frac{2(4)}{3\sqrt{x}} = \frac{8}{3\sqrt{x}}$$

To rationalize the denominator, multiply the numerator and denominator by $\sqrt{x}$. Then

$$\frac{8}{3\sqrt{x}} = \frac{8 \cdot \sqrt{x}}{3\sqrt{x} \cdot \sqrt{x}} = \frac{8\sqrt{x}}{3x}$$

c. $\sqrt[3]{\frac{1}{2}} = \frac{\sqrt[3]{1}}{\sqrt[3]{2}} = \frac{1}{\sqrt[3]{2}}$. Now we rationalize the denominator. Since $\sqrt[3]{2}$ is a cube root, we want to multiply by a value that will make the radicand 2 a perfect cube. If we multiply $\sqrt[3]{2}$ by $\sqrt[3]{2^2}$, we get $\sqrt[3]{2^3} = \sqrt[3]{8} = 2$.

$$\frac{1 \cdot \sqrt[3]{2^2}}{\sqrt[3]{2} \cdot \sqrt[3]{2^2}} = \frac{\sqrt[3]{4}}{\sqrt[3]{2^3}} = \frac{\sqrt[3]{4}}{2} \quad \text{Multiply the numerator and denominator by } \sqrt[3]{2^2} \text{ and then simplify.}$$

□

PRACTICE 1 Rationalize the denominator of each expression.

a. $\frac{5}{\sqrt{3}}$ **b.** $\frac{3\sqrt{25}}{\sqrt{4x}}$ **c.** $\sqrt[3]{\frac{2}{9}}$

Concept Check ☑

Determine by which number both the numerator and denominator can be multiplied to rationalize the denominator of the radical expression.

a. $\frac{1}{\sqrt[3]{7}}$ **b.** $\frac{1}{\sqrt[4]{8}}$

EXAMPLE 2 Rationalize the denominator of $\sqrt{\frac{7x}{3y}}$.

Solution $\sqrt{\frac{7x}{3y}} = \frac{\sqrt{7x}}{\sqrt{3y}}$ Use the quotient rule. No radical may be simplified further.

$= \frac{\sqrt{7x}\cdot\sqrt{3y}}{\sqrt{3y}\cdot\sqrt{3y}}$ Multiply numerator and denominator by $\sqrt{3y}$ so that the radicand in the denominator is a perfect square.

$= \frac{\sqrt{21xy}}{3y}$ Use the product rule in the numerator and denominator. Remember that $\sqrt{3y}\cdot\sqrt{3y} = 3y$. □

PRACTICE 2 Rationalize the denominator of $\sqrt{\frac{3z}{5y}}$.

EXAMPLE 3 Rationalize the denominator of $\frac{\sqrt[4]{x}}{\sqrt[4]{81y^5}}$.

Solution First, simplify each radical if possible.

$\frac{\sqrt[4]{x}}{\sqrt[4]{81y^5}} = \frac{\sqrt[4]{x}}{\sqrt[4]{81y^4}\cdot\sqrt[4]{y}}$ Use the product rule in the denominator.

$= \frac{\sqrt[4]{x}}{3y\sqrt[4]{y}}$ Write $\sqrt[4]{81y^4}$ as $3y$.

$= \frac{\sqrt[4]{x}\cdot\sqrt[4]{y^3}}{3y\sqrt[4]{y}\cdot\sqrt[4]{y^3}}$ Multiply numerator and denominator by $\sqrt[4]{y^3}$ so that the radicand in the denominator is a perfect fourth power.

$= \frac{\sqrt[4]{xy^3}}{3y\sqrt[4]{y^4}}$ Use the product rule in the numerator and denominator.

$= \frac{\sqrt[4]{xy^3}}{3y^2}$ In the denominator, $\sqrt[4]{y^4} = y$ and $3y\cdot y = 3y^2$. □

PRACTICE 3 Rationalize the denominator of $\frac{\sqrt[3]{z^2}}{\sqrt[3]{27x^4}}$.

OBJECTIVE 2 ▶ Rationalizing denominators having two terms. Remember the product of the sum and difference of two terms?

$$(a + b)(a - b) = a^2 - b^2$$

↖ ↗

These two expressions are called **conjugates** of each other.

Answer to Concept Check:
a. $\sqrt[3]{7^2}$ or $\sqrt[3]{49}$ **b.** $\sqrt[4]{2}$

To rationalize a numerator or denominator that is a sum or difference of two terms, we use conjugates. To see how and why this works, let's rationalize the denominator of the expression $\frac{5}{\sqrt{3}-2}$. To do so, we multiply both the numerator and the denominator by $\sqrt{3}+2$, the **conjugate** of the denominator $\sqrt{3}-2$, and see what happens.

$$\frac{5}{\sqrt{3}-2} = \frac{5(\sqrt{3}+2)}{(\sqrt{3}-2)(\sqrt{3}+2)}$$

$$= \frac{5(\sqrt{3}+2)}{(\sqrt{3})^2 - 2^2}$$ Multiply the sum and difference of two terms: $(a+b)(a-b) = a^2 - b^2$.

$$= \frac{5(\sqrt{3}+2)}{3-4}$$

$$= \frac{5(\sqrt{3}+2)}{-1}$$

$$= -5(\sqrt{3}+2) \quad \text{or} \quad -5\sqrt{3}-10$$

Notice in the denominator that the product of $(\sqrt{3}-2)$ and its conjugate, $(\sqrt{3}+2)$, is -1. In general, the product of an expression and its conjugate will contain no radical terms. This is why, when rationalizing a denominator or a numerator containing two terms, we multiply by its conjugate. Examples of conjugates are

$$\sqrt{a}-\sqrt{b} \quad \text{and} \quad \sqrt{a}+\sqrt{b}$$
$$x+\sqrt{y} \quad \text{and} \quad x-\sqrt{y}$$

EXAMPLE 4 Rationalize each denominator.

a. $\frac{2}{3\sqrt{2}+4}$ **b.** $\frac{\sqrt{6}+2}{\sqrt{5}-\sqrt{3}}$ **c.** $\frac{2\sqrt{m}}{3\sqrt{x}+\sqrt{m}}$

Solution

a. Multiply the numerator and denominator by the conjugate of the denominator, $3\sqrt{2}+4$.

$$\frac{2}{3\sqrt{2}+4} = \frac{2(3\sqrt{2}-4)}{(3\sqrt{2}+4)(3\sqrt{2}-4)}$$

$$= \frac{2(3\sqrt{2}-4)}{(3\sqrt{2})^2 - 4^2}$$

$$= \frac{2(3\sqrt{2}-4)}{18-16}$$

$$= \frac{2(3\sqrt{2}-4)}{2}, \quad \text{or} \quad 3\sqrt{2}-4$$

It is often useful to leave a numerator in factored form to help determine whether the expression can be simplified.

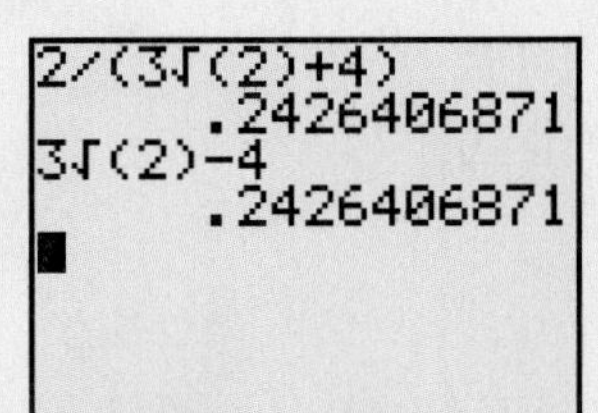

A calculator check for Example 4a. Notice the use of parentheses in the first expression.

A calculator check for Example 4b. Notice the use of parentheses in the numerators and the denominator containing more than one term.

b. Multiply the numerator and denominator by the conjugate of $\sqrt{5} - \sqrt{3}$.

$$\frac{\sqrt{6}+2}{\sqrt{5}-\sqrt{3}} = \frac{(\sqrt{6}+2)(\sqrt{5}+\sqrt{3})}{(\sqrt{5}-\sqrt{3})(\sqrt{5}+\sqrt{3})}$$

$$= \frac{\sqrt{6}\sqrt{5}+\sqrt{6}\sqrt{3}+2\sqrt{5}+2\sqrt{3}}{(\sqrt{5})^2-(\sqrt{3})^2}$$

$$= \frac{\sqrt{30}+\sqrt{18}+2\sqrt{5}+2\sqrt{3}}{5-3}$$

$$= \frac{\sqrt{30}+3\sqrt{2}+2\sqrt{5}+2\sqrt{3}}{2}$$

c. Multiply by the conjugate of $3\sqrt{x} + \sqrt{m}$ to eliminate the radicals from the denominator.

$$\frac{2\sqrt{m}}{3\sqrt{x}+\sqrt{m}} = \frac{2\sqrt{m}(3\sqrt{x}-\sqrt{m})}{(3\sqrt{x}+\sqrt{m})(3\sqrt{x}-\sqrt{m})} = \frac{6\sqrt{mx}-2m}{(3\sqrt{x})^2-(\sqrt{m})^2}$$

$$= \frac{6\sqrt{mx}-2m}{9x-m}$$

□

PRACTICE 4 Rationalize the denominator.

a. $\frac{5}{3\sqrt{5}+2}$ **b.** $\frac{\sqrt{2}+5}{\sqrt{3}-\sqrt{5}}$ **c.** $\frac{3\sqrt{x}}{2\sqrt{x}+\sqrt{y}}$

OBJECTIVE 3 ▶ Rationalizing numerators. As mentioned earlier, it is also often helpful to write an expression such as $\frac{\sqrt{3}}{\sqrt{2}}$ as an equivalent expression without a radical in the numerator. This process is called **rationalizing the numerator.** To rationalize the numerator of $\frac{\sqrt{3}}{\sqrt{2}}$, we multiply the numerator and the denominator by $\sqrt{3}$.

$$\frac{\sqrt{3}}{\sqrt{2}} = \frac{\sqrt{3}\cdot\sqrt{3}}{\sqrt{2}\cdot\sqrt{3}} = \frac{\sqrt{9}}{\sqrt{6}} = \frac{3}{\sqrt{6}}$$

EXAMPLE 5 Rationalize the numerator of $\frac{\sqrt{7}}{\sqrt{45}}$.

Solution First we simplify $\sqrt{45}$.

$$\frac{\sqrt{7}}{\sqrt{45}} = \frac{\sqrt{7}}{\sqrt{9\cdot5}} = \frac{\sqrt{7}}{3\sqrt{5}}$$

Next we rationalize the numerator by multiplying the numerator and the denominator by $\sqrt{7}$.

$$\frac{\sqrt{7}}{3\sqrt{5}} = \frac{\sqrt{7}\cdot\sqrt{7}}{3\sqrt{5}\cdot\sqrt{7}} = \frac{7}{3\sqrt{5\cdot7}} = \frac{7}{3\sqrt{35}}$$

□

PRACTICE 5 Rationalize the numerator of $\frac{\sqrt{32}}{\sqrt{80}}$.

EXAMPLE 6 Rationalize the numerator of $\frac{\sqrt[3]{2x^2}}{\sqrt[3]{5y}}$.

Solution The numerator and the denominator of this expression are already simplified. To rationalize the numerator, $\sqrt[3]{2x^2}$, we multiply the numerator and denominator by a factor that will make the radicand a perfect cube. If we multiply $\sqrt[3]{2x^2}$ by $\sqrt[3]{4x}$, we get $\sqrt[3]{8x^3} = 2x$.

$$\frac{\sqrt[3]{2x^2}}{\sqrt[3]{5y}} = \frac{\sqrt[3]{2x^2} \cdot \sqrt[3]{4x}}{\sqrt[3]{5y} \cdot \sqrt[3]{4x}} = \frac{\sqrt[3]{8x^3}}{\sqrt[3]{20xy}} = \frac{2x}{\sqrt[3]{20xy}}$$ □

PRACTICE 6 Rationalize the numerator of $\frac{\sqrt[3]{5b}}{\sqrt[3]{2a}}$.

EXAMPLE 7 Rationalize the numerator of $\frac{\sqrt{x} + 2}{5}$.

Solution We multiply the numerator and the denominator by the conjugate of the numerator, $\sqrt{x} + 2$.

$$\frac{\sqrt{x} + 2}{5} = \frac{(\sqrt{x} + 2)(\sqrt{x} - 2)}{5(\sqrt{x} - 2)}$$ Multiply by $\sqrt{x} - 2$, the conjugate of $\sqrt{x} + 2$.

$$= \frac{(\sqrt{x})^2 - 2^2}{5(\sqrt{x} - 2)}$$ $(a + b)(a - b) = a^2 - b^2$

$$= \frac{x - 4}{5(\sqrt{x} - 2)}$$ □

PRACTICE 7 Rationalize the numerator of $\frac{\sqrt{x} - 3}{4}$.

VOCABULARY & READINESS CHECK

Use the choices below to fill in each blank. Not all choices will be used.

rationalizing the numerator	conjugate	$\frac{\sqrt{3}}{\sqrt{3}}$
rationalizing the denominator	$\frac{5}{5}$	

1. The __________ of $a + b$ is $a - b$.
2. The process of writing an equivalent expression, but without a radical in the denominator, is called ____________________.
3. The process of writing an equivalent expression, but without a radical in the numerator, is called ____________________.
4. To rationalize the denominator of $\frac{5}{\sqrt{3}}$, we multiply by __________.

Find the conjugate of each expression.

5. $\sqrt{2} + x$
6. $\sqrt{3} + y$
7. $5 - \sqrt{a}$
8. $6 - \sqrt{b}$
9. $-7\sqrt{5} + 8\sqrt{x}$
10. $-9\sqrt{2} - 6\sqrt{y}$

19.5 EXERCISE SET

MyMathLab

PRACTICE

WATCH

DOWNLOAD

READ

REVIEW

Rationalize each denominator. See Examples 1 through 3.

1. $\frac{\sqrt{2}}{\sqrt{7}}$
2. $\frac{\sqrt{3}}{\sqrt{2}}$
3. $\sqrt{\frac{1}{5}}$
4. $\sqrt{\frac{1}{2}}$
5. $\sqrt{\frac{4}{x}}$
6. $\sqrt{\frac{25}{y}}$
7. $\frac{4}{\sqrt[3]{3}}$
8. $\frac{6}{\sqrt[3]{9}}$
9. $\frac{3}{\sqrt{8x}}$
10. $\frac{5}{\sqrt{27a}}$
11. $\frac{3}{\sqrt[3]{4x^2}}$
12. $\frac{5}{\sqrt[3]{3y}}$
13. $\frac{9}{\sqrt{3a}}$
14. $\frac{x}{\sqrt{5}}$
15. $\frac{3}{\sqrt[3]{2}}$
16. $\frac{5}{\sqrt[3]{9}}$
17. $\frac{2\sqrt{3}}{\sqrt{7}}$
18. $\frac{-5\sqrt{2}}{\sqrt{11}}$
19. $\sqrt{\frac{2x}{5y}}$
20. $\sqrt{\frac{13a}{2b}}$
21. $\sqrt[3]{\frac{3}{5}}$
22. $\sqrt[3]{\frac{7}{10}}$
23. $\sqrt{\frac{3x}{50}}$
24. $\sqrt{\frac{11y}{45}}$
25. $\frac{1}{\sqrt{12z}}$
26. $\frac{1}{\sqrt{32x}}$
27. $\frac{\sqrt[3]{2y^2}}{\sqrt[3]{9x^2}}$
28. $\frac{\sqrt[3]{3x}}{\sqrt[3]{4y^4}}$
29. $\sqrt[4]{\frac{81}{8}}$
30. $\sqrt[4]{\frac{1}{9}}$
31. $\sqrt[4]{\frac{16}{9x^7}}$
32. $\sqrt[5]{\frac{32}{m^6n^{13}}}$
33. $\frac{5a}{\sqrt[5]{8a^9b^{11}}}$
34. $\frac{9y}{\sqrt[4]{4y^9}}$

Rationalize each denominator. See Example 4.

35. $\frac{6}{2-\sqrt{7}}$
36. $\frac{3}{\sqrt{7}-4}$
37. $\frac{-7}{\sqrt{x}-3}$
38. $\frac{-8}{\sqrt{y}+4}$
39. $\frac{\sqrt{2}-\sqrt{3}}{\sqrt{2}+\sqrt{3}}$
40. $\frac{\sqrt{3}+\sqrt{4}}{\sqrt{2}-\sqrt{3}}$
41. $\frac{\sqrt{a}+1}{2\sqrt{a}-\sqrt{b}}$
42. $\frac{2\sqrt{a}-3}{2\sqrt{a}+\sqrt{b}}$
43. $\frac{8}{1+\sqrt{10}}$
44. $\frac{-3}{\sqrt{6}-2}$
45. $\frac{\sqrt{x}}{\sqrt{x}+\sqrt{y}}$
46. $\frac{2\sqrt{a}}{2\sqrt{x}-\sqrt{y}}$
47. $\frac{2\sqrt{3}+\sqrt{6}}{4\sqrt{3}-\sqrt{6}}$
48. $\frac{4\sqrt{5}+\sqrt{2}}{2\sqrt{5}-\sqrt{2}}$

Rationalize each numerator. See Examples 5 and 6.

49. $\sqrt{\frac{5}{3}}$
50. $\sqrt{\frac{3}{2}}$
51. $\sqrt{\frac{18}{5}}$
52. $\sqrt{\frac{12}{7}}$
53. $\frac{\sqrt{4x}}{7}$
54. $\frac{\sqrt{3x^5}}{6}$
55. $\frac{\sqrt[3]{5y^2}}{\sqrt[3]{4x}}$
56. $\frac{\sqrt[3]{4x}}{\sqrt[3]{z^4}}$
57. $\sqrt{\frac{2}{5}}$
58. $\sqrt{\frac{3}{7}}$
59. $\frac{\sqrt{2x}}{11}$
60. $\frac{\sqrt{y}}{7}$
61. $\sqrt[3]{\frac{7}{8}}$
62. $\sqrt[3]{\frac{25}{2}}$
63. $\frac{\sqrt[3]{3x^5}}{10}$
64. $\sqrt[3]{\frac{9y}{7}}$
65. $\sqrt{\frac{18x^4y^6}{3z}}$
66. $\sqrt{\frac{8x^5y}{2z}}$

67. When rationalizing the denominator of $\frac{\sqrt{5}}{\sqrt{7}}$, explain why both the numerator and the denominator must be multiplied by $\sqrt{7}$.

68. When rationalizing the numerator of $\frac{\sqrt{5}}{\sqrt{7}}$, explain why both the numerator and the denominator must be multiplied by $\sqrt{5}$.

Rationalize each numerator. See Example 7.

69. $\frac{2-\sqrt{11}}{6}$
70. $\frac{\sqrt{15}+1}{2}$
71. $\frac{2-\sqrt{7}}{-5}$
72. $\frac{\sqrt{5}+2}{\sqrt{2}}$
73. $\frac{\sqrt{x}+3}{\sqrt{x}}$
74. $\frac{5+\sqrt{2}}{\sqrt{2x}}$
75. $\frac{\sqrt{2}-1}{\sqrt{2}+1}$
76. $\frac{\sqrt{8}-\sqrt{3}}{\sqrt{2}+\sqrt{3}}$
77. $\frac{\sqrt{x}+1}{\sqrt{x}-1}$
78. $\frac{\sqrt{x}+\sqrt{y}}{\sqrt{x}-\sqrt{y}}$

REVIEW AND PREVIEW

Solve each equation.

79. $2x - 7 = 3(x - 4)$

80. $9x - 4 = 7(x - 2)$

81. $(x - 6)(2x + 1) = 0$

82. $(y + 2)(5y + 4) = 0$

83. $x^2 - 8x = -12$

84. $x^3 = x$

CONCEPTS EXTENSIONS

Determine the smallest number both the numerator and denominator should be multiplied by to rationalize the denominator of the radical expression. See the Concept Check in this section.

85. $\frac{9}{\sqrt[3]{5}}$

86. $\frac{5}{\sqrt{27}}$

△ **87.** The formula of the radius r of a sphere with surface area A is

$$r = \sqrt{\frac{A}{4\pi}}$$

Rationalize the denominator of the radical expression in this formula.

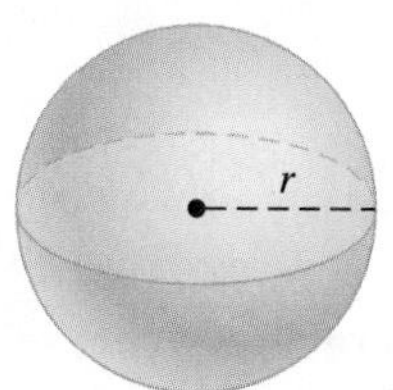

△ **88.** The formula for the radius r of a cone with height 7 centimeters and volume V is

$$r = \sqrt{\frac{3V}{7\pi}}$$

Rationalize the numerator of the radical expression in this formula.

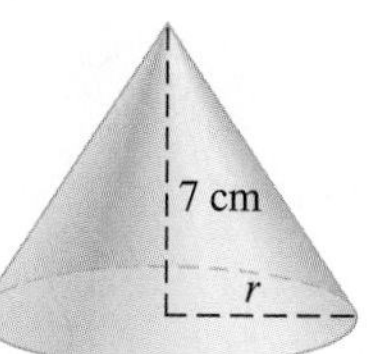

89. Explain why rationalizing the denominator does not change the value of the original expression.

90. Explain why rationalizing the numerator does not change the value of the original expression.

INTEGRATED REVIEW RADICALS AND RATIONAL EXPONENTS

Sections 19.1–19.5

Find each root. Throughout this review, assume that all variables represent positive real numbers.

1. $\sqrt{81}$

2. $\sqrt[3]{-8}$

3. $\sqrt[4]{\frac{1}{16}}$

4. $\sqrt{x^6}$

5. $\sqrt[3]{y^9}$

6. $\sqrt{4y^{10}}$

7. $\sqrt[5]{-32y^5}$

8. $\sqrt[4]{81b^{12}}$

Use radical notation to rewrite each expression. Simplify if possible.

9. $36^{1/2}$

10. $(3y)^{1/4}$

11. $64^{-2/3}$

12. $(x + 1)^{3/5}$

Use the properties of exponents to simplify each expression. Write with positive exponents.

13. $y^{-1/6} \cdot y^{7/6}$

14. $\frac{(2x^{1/3})^4}{x^{5/6}}$

15. $\frac{x^{1/4}x^{3/4}}{x^{-1/4}}$

16. $4^{1/3} \cdot 4^{2/5}$

Use rational exponents to simplify each radical.

17. $\sqrt[3]{8x^6}$

18. $\sqrt[12]{a^9b^6}$

Use rational exponents to write each as a single radical expression.

19. $\sqrt[4]{x} \cdot \sqrt{x}$

20. $\sqrt{5} \cdot \sqrt[3]{2}$

Simplify.

21. $\sqrt{40}$

22. $\sqrt[4]{16x^7y^{10}}$

23. $\sqrt[3]{54x^4}$

24. $\sqrt[5]{-64b^{10}}$

Multiply or divide. Then simplify if possible.

25. $\sqrt{5}\cdot\sqrt{x}$ **26.** $\sqrt[3]{8x}\cdot\sqrt[3]{8x^2}$ **27.** $\dfrac{\sqrt{98y^6}}{\sqrt{2y}}$ **28.** $\dfrac{\sqrt[4]{48a^9b^3}}{\sqrt[4]{ab^3}}$

Perform each indicated operation.

29. $\sqrt{20}-\sqrt{75}+5\sqrt{7}$ **30.** $\sqrt[3]{54y^4}-y\sqrt[3]{16y}$ **31.** $\sqrt{3}(\sqrt{5}-\sqrt{2})$

32. $(\sqrt{7}+\sqrt{3})^2$ **33.** $(2x-\sqrt{5})(2x+\sqrt{5})$ **34.** $(\sqrt{x+1}-1)^2$

Rationalize each denominator.

35. $\sqrt{\dfrac{7}{3}}$ **36.** $\dfrac{5}{\sqrt[3]{2x^2}}$ **37.** $\dfrac{\sqrt{3}-\sqrt{7}}{2\sqrt{3}+\sqrt{7}}$

Rationalize each numerator.

38. $\sqrt{\dfrac{7}{3}}$ **39.** $\sqrt[3]{\dfrac{9y}{11}}$ **40.** $\dfrac{\sqrt{x}-2}{\sqrt{x}}$

19.6 RADICAL EQUATIONS AND PROBLEM SOLVING

OBJECTIVES

1 Solve equations that contain radical expressions.

2 Use the Pythagorean theorem to model problems.

OBJECTIVE 1 ▶ Solving equations that contain radical expressions. In this section, we present techniques to solve equations containing radical expressions such as

$$\sqrt{2x-3}=9$$

We use the power rule to help us solve these radical equations.

Power Rule

If both sides of an equation are raised to the same power, **all** solutions of the original equation are **among** the solutions of the new equation.

This property *does not* say that raising both sides of an equation to a power yields an equivalent equation. A solution of the new equation *may or may not* be a solution of the original equation. For example, $(-2)^2 = 2^2$, but $-2 \neq 2$. Thus, *each solution of the new equation must be checked* to make sure it is a solution of the original equation. Recall that a proposed solution that is not a solution of the original equation is called an **extraneous solution.**

EXAMPLE 1 Solve: $\sqrt{2x-3}=9$. Use a graphing utility to check.

Solution We use the power rule to square both sides of the equation to eliminate the radical.

$$\begin{aligned}\sqrt{2x-3}&=9\\(\sqrt{2x-3})^2&=9^2\\2x-3&=81\\2x&=84\\x&=42\end{aligned}$$

Now check the solution using a graphing utility. To check using the intersection-of-graphs method, graph $y_1 = \sqrt{2x - 3}$ and $y_2 = 9$ in a $[0, 95, 10]$ by $[-5, 15, 1]$ window. The intersection has x-value 42, the solution, as shown.

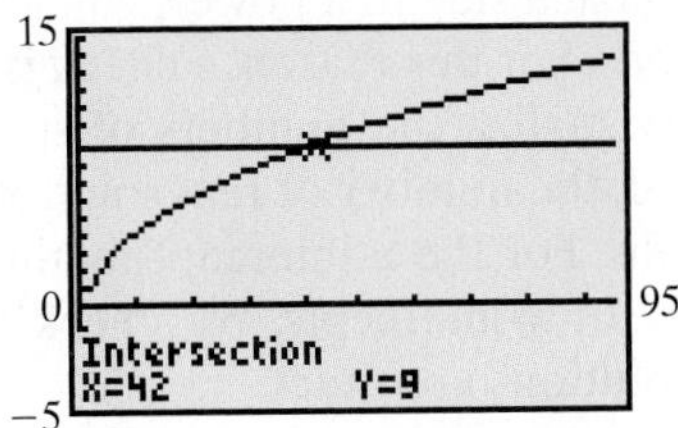

The solution checks, so we conclude that the solution is 42 or the solution set is $\{42\}$. □

PRACTICE 1 Solve: $\sqrt{3x - 5} = 7$.

In the next example, we choose to solve the equation graphically, using the x-intercept method, since the equation is written so that one side is 0.

EXAMPLE 2 Solve: $\sqrt{-10x - 1} + 3x = 0$.

Solution Graph $y_1 = \sqrt{-10x - 1} + 3x$ in a decimal window.

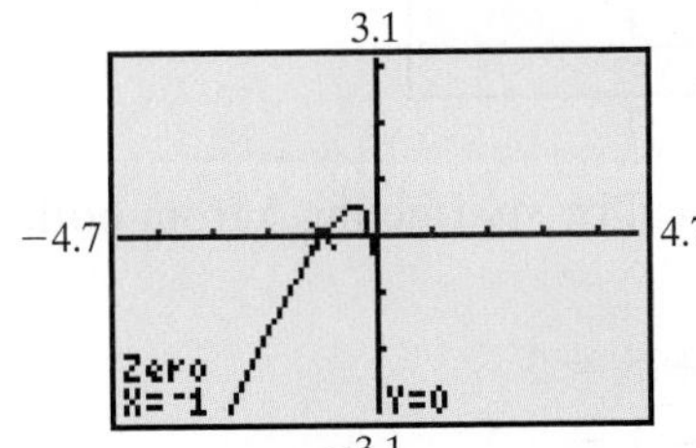

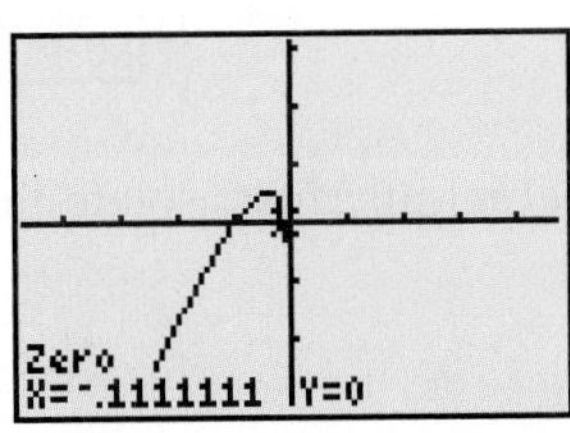

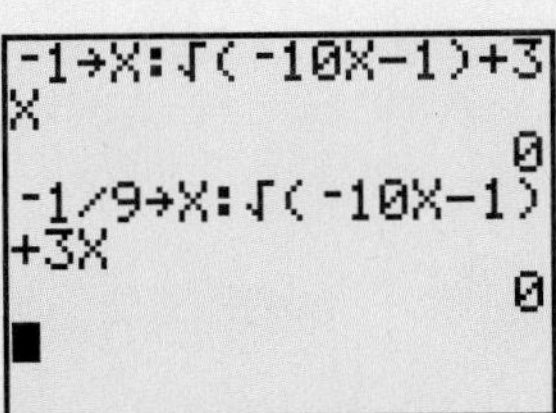

A numerical check showing -1 and $-\frac{1}{9}$ are both solutions of the equation in Example 2.

The equation has two solutions since there are two x-intercepts. The x-intercepts are $x = -1$ and $x = -0.11111\ldots$, a repeating decimal. Use the fraction command to write $-0.\overline{1}$ as the equivalent fraction $-\frac{1}{9}$.

Check the solutions numerically as in the screen to the left.

Both solutions check. The solutions are $-\frac{1}{9}$ and -1 or the solution set is $\left\{-\frac{1}{9}, -1\right\}$. □

PRACTICE 2 Solve: $\sqrt{3 - 2x} - 4x = 0$.

The following steps may be used to solve a radical equation.

Solving a Radical Equation Algebraically

STEP 1. Isolate one radical on one side of the equation.

STEP 2. Raise each side of the equation to a power equal to the index of the radical and simplify.

STEP 3. If the equation still contains a radical term, repeat Steps 1 and 2. If not, solve the equation.

STEP 4. Check all proposed solutions in the original equation.

Helpful Hint
To solve a radical equation graphically, use the intersection-of-graphs method or the x-intercept method.

When do we solve a radical equation algebraically and when do we solve it graphically? If given a choice, it depends on the complexity of the equation itself. An equation that contains only one radical may be a good candidate for the algebraic process. Recall that by raising each side to a power, you are introducing the possibility of extraneous roots or solutions. For this reason, a check is mandatory. However, when solving graphically, you can visualize the numbers of solutions immediately. For the intersection-of-graphs method, the number of real solutions is equal to the number of intersections of the two graphs. For the x-intercept method, the number of real solutions is equal to the number of x-intercepts. We check after solving by a graphing method to confirm that the solutions are exact.

In Example 3, we choose to solve graphically by the intersection-of-graphs method and we confirm the solution algebraically.

EXAMPLE 3 Solve $\sqrt[3]{x+1} + 5 = 3$ graphically and check algebraically.

Solution Graph $y_1 = \sqrt[3]{x+1} + 5$ and $y_2 = 3$. The intersection of the two graphs has an x-value of -9, the solution of the equation.

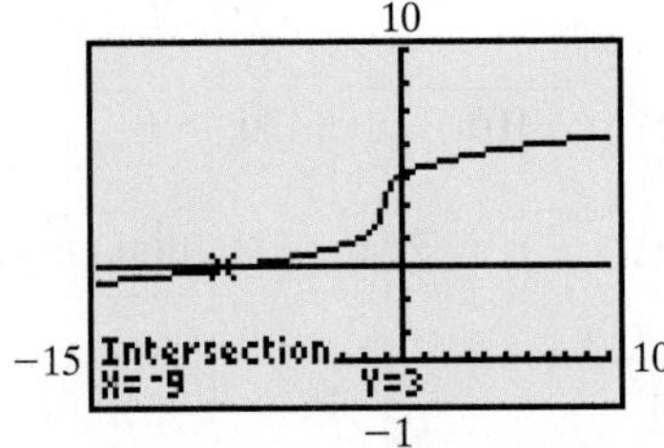

To check algebraically, first, isolate the radical by subtracting 5 from both sides of the equation.

$$\sqrt[3]{x+1} + 5 = 3$$
$$\sqrt[3]{x+1} = -2$$

Next we raise both sides of the equation to the third power to eliminate the radical.

$$\left(\sqrt[3]{x+1}\right)^3 = (-2)^3$$
$$x + 1 = -8$$
$$x = -9$$

The solution checks in the original equation, so the solution is -9. □

PRACTICE 3 Solve: $\sqrt[3]{x-2} + 1 = 3$.

In Example 4, we solve algebraically and check graphically. Notice that in solving algebraically, an extraneous solution is introduced. However, graphically we see that there is only one solution because there is only one point of intersection for the two graphs.

EXAMPLE 4 Solve algebraically: $\sqrt{4-x} = x - 2$. Then check algebraically and graphically.

Solution

$$\sqrt{4-x} = x - 2$$
$$\left(\sqrt{4-x}\right)^2 = (x-2)^2$$
$$4 - x = x^2 - 4x + 4$$
$$x^2 - 3x = 0 \quad \text{Write the quadratic equation in standard form.}$$
$$x(x-3) = 0 \quad \text{Factor.}$$
$$x = 0 \quad \text{or} \quad x - 3 = 0 \quad \text{Set each factor equal to 0.}$$
$$x = 3$$

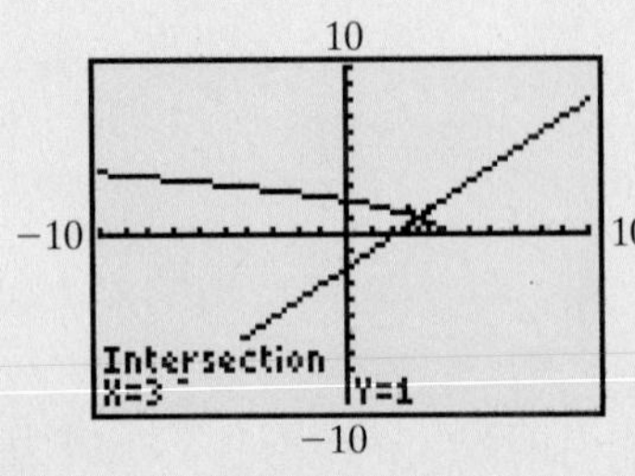

To check the results of Example 4, graph $y_1 = \sqrt{4-x}$ and $y_2 = x - 2$. The x-value of the point of intersection is 3, as expected.

Check: $\sqrt{4-x} = x - 2$ $\qquad$ $\sqrt{4-x} = x - 2$

$\sqrt{4-0} \stackrel{?}{=} 0 - 2$ Let $x = 0$. $\qquad$ $\sqrt{4-3} \stackrel{?}{=} 3 - 2$ Let $x = 3$.

$2 = -2$ False $\qquad$ $1 = 1$ True

The proposed solution 3 checks, but 0 does not. Since 0 is an extraneous solution, the only solution is 3. A graphical check is shown in the margin of the previous page. □

PRACTICE

4 Solve: $\sqrt{16 + x} = x - 4$.

> **Helpful Hint**
> In Example 4, notice that $(x-2)^2 = x^2 - 4x + 4$. Make sure binomials are squared correctly.

Concept Check ☑

How can you immediately tell that the equation $\sqrt{2y+3} = -4$ has no real solution?

In Example 5 we solve graphically. Use the intersection of graphs method and confirm the solution algebraically.

EXAMPLE 5 Solve: $\sqrt{2x+5} + \sqrt{2x} = 3$.

Solution Graph $y_1 = \sqrt{2x+5} + \sqrt{2x}$ and $y_2 = 3$ in a $[-10, 10, 1]$ by $[-1, 10, 1]$ window. The intersection of the two graphs is $x = 0.22222\ldots$, a repeating decimal. Convert the value of x to fraction form using the fraction command. The solution is $\frac{2}{9}$.

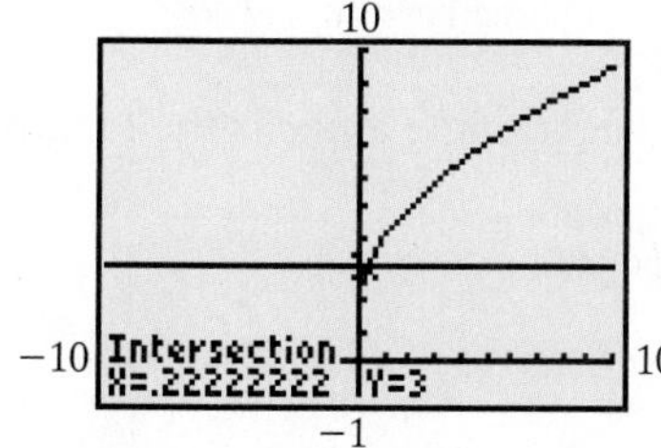

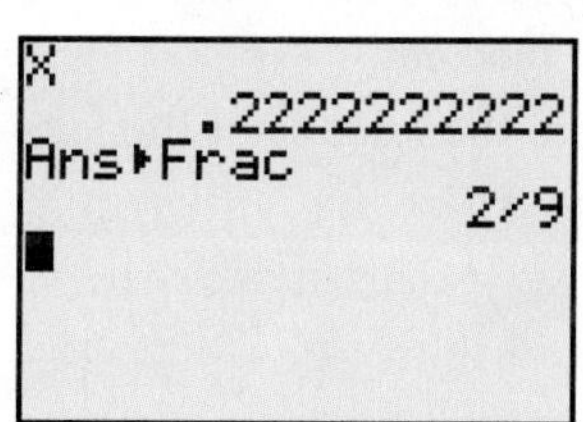

To check, we confirm the solution algebraically.

We get one radical alone by subtracting $\sqrt{2x}$ from both sides.

$$\sqrt{2x+5} + \sqrt{2x} = 3$$
$$\sqrt{2x+5} = 3 - \sqrt{2x}$$

Now we use the power rule to begin eliminating the radicals. First we square both sides.

$$\left(\sqrt{2x+5}\right)^2 = \left(3 - \sqrt{2x}\right)^2$$
$$2x + 5 = 9 - 6\sqrt{2x} + 2x \quad \text{Multiply } \left(3 - \sqrt{2x}\right)\left(3 - \sqrt{2x}\right).$$

There is still a radical in the equation, so we get a radical alone again. Then we square both sides.

$2x + 5 = 9 - 6\sqrt{2x} + 2x$ Get the radical alone.

$6\sqrt{2x} = 4$

$36(2x) = 16$ Square both sides of the equation to eliminate the radical.

$72x = 16$ Multiply.

$x = \frac{16}{72}$ Solve.

$x = \frac{2}{9}$ Simplify.

The proposed solution, $\frac{2}{9}$, checks in the original equation. The solution is $\frac{2}{9}$. □

PRACTICE

5 Solve: $\sqrt{8x+1} + \sqrt{3x} = 2$.

Answers to Concept Check:
answers may vary

Helpful Hint

Make sure expressions are squared correctly. In Example 5, we squared $(3 - \sqrt{2x})$ as

$$\begin{aligned}(3 - \sqrt{2x})^2 &= (3 - \sqrt{2x})(3 - \sqrt{2x})\\ &= 3\cdot 3 - 3\sqrt{2x} - 3\sqrt{2x} + \sqrt{2x}\cdot\sqrt{2x}\\ &= 9 - 6\sqrt{2x} + 2x\end{aligned}$$

Concept Check ✓

What is wrong with the following solution?

$$\begin{aligned}\sqrt{2x+5} + \sqrt{4-x} &= 8\\ (\sqrt{2x+5} + \sqrt{4-x})^2 &= 8^2\\ (2x+5) + (4-x) &= 64\\ x + 9 &= 64\\ x &= 55\end{aligned}$$

OBJECTIVE 2 ▶ Using the Pythagorean theorem. Recall that the Pythagorean theorem states that in a right triangle, the length of the hypotenuse squared equals the sum of the lengths of each of the legs squared.

Pythagorean Theorem

If a and b are the lengths of the legs of a right triangle and c is the length of the hypotenuse, then $a^2 + b^2 = c^2$.

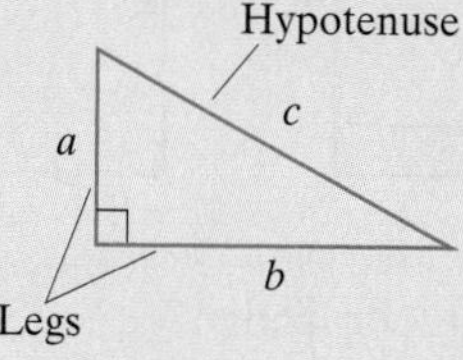

EXAMPLE 6 Find the length of the unknown leg of the right triangle.

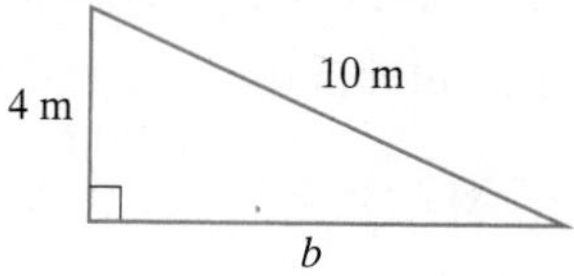

Solution In the formula $a^2 + b^2 = c^2$, c is the hypotenuse. Here, $c = 10$, the length of the hypotenuse, and $a = 4$. We solve for b. Then $a^2 + b^2 = c^2$ becomes

$$\begin{aligned}4^2 + b^2 &= 10^2\\ 16 + b^2 &= 100\\ b^2 &= 84 \quad \text{Subtract 16 from both sides.}\\ b &= \pm\sqrt{84} = \pm\sqrt{4\cdot 21} = \pm 2\sqrt{21}\end{aligned}$$

Since b is a length and thus is positive, we will use the positive value only. The unknown leg of the triangle is $2\sqrt{21}$ meters long. □

PRACTICE 6 Find the length of the unknown leg of the right triangle.

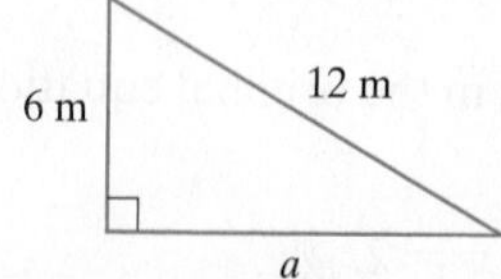

Answers to Concept Check:
$(\sqrt{2x+5} + \sqrt{4-x})^2$ is not $(2x+5) + (4-x)$.

EXAMPLE 7 Calculating Placement of a Wire

A 50-foot supporting wire is to be attached to a 75-foot antenna. Because of surrounding buildings, sidewalks, and roadways, the wire must be anchored exactly 20 feet from the base of the antenna.

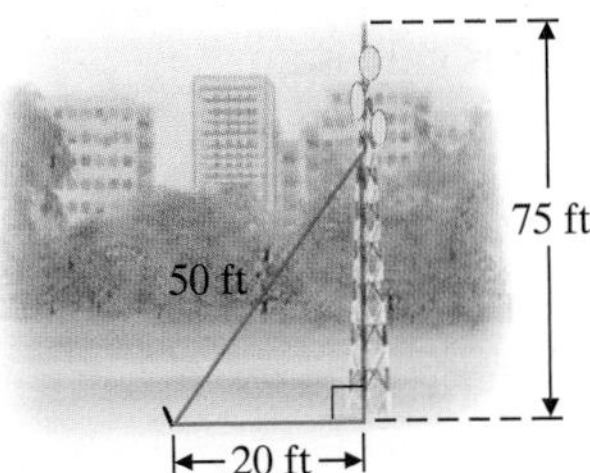

a. How high from the base of the antenna is the wire attached?

b. Local regulations require that a supporting wire be attached at a height no less than $\frac{3}{5}$ of the total height of the antenna. From part **a,** have local regulations been met?

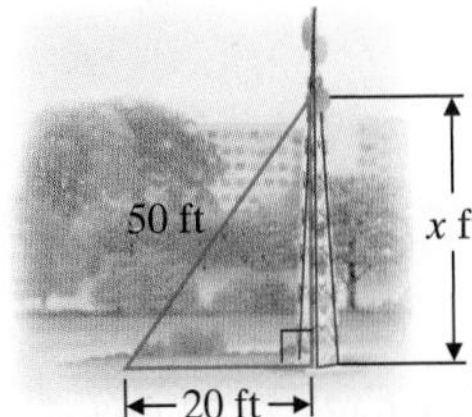

Solution

1. UNDERSTAND. Read and reread the problem. From the diagram we notice that a right triangle is formed with hypotenuse 50 feet and one leg 20 feet. Let x be the height from the base of the antenna to the attached wire.
2. TRANSLATE. Use the Pythagorean theorem.

$$a^2 + b^2 = c^2$$
$$20^2 + x^2 = 50^2 \quad a = 20, c = 50$$

3. SOLVE.

$$\begin{aligned} 20^2 + x^2 &= 50^2 \\ 400 + x^2 &= 2500 \\ x^2 &= 2100 \quad \text{Subtract 400 from both sides.} \\ x &= \pm\sqrt{2100} \\ &= \pm 10\sqrt{21} \end{aligned}$$

4. INTERPRET. *Check* the work and *state* the solution.

Check: We will use only the positive value, $x = 10\sqrt{21}$, because x represents length. The wire is attached exactly $10\sqrt{21}$ feet from the base of the pole, or approximately 45.8 feet.

State: The supporting wire must be attached at a height no less than $\frac{3}{5}$ of the total height of the antenna. This height is $\frac{3}{5}(75 \text{ feet})$, or 45 feet. Since we know from part **a** that the wire is to be attached at a height of approximately 45.8 feet, local regulations have been met. □

PRACTICE

7 Keith Robinson bought two Siamese fighting fish, but when he got home he found he only had one rectangular tank that was 12 in. long, 7 in. wide, and 5 in. deep. Since the fish must be kept separated, he needs to insert a plastic divider in the diagonal of the tank. He already has a piece that is 5 in. in one dimension, but how long must it be to fit corner to corner in the tank?

VOCABULARY & READINESS CHECK

Use the choices below to fill in each blank. Not all choices will be used.

hypotenuse	right	$x^2 + 25$	$16 - 8\sqrt{7x} + 7x$
extraneous solution	legs	$x^2 - 10x + 25$	$16 + 7x$

1. A proposed solution that is not a solution of the original equation is called an ______________.

2. The Pythagorean theorem states that $a^2 + b^2 = c^2$ where a and b are the lengths of the ________ of a ________ triangle and c is the length of the ____________.

3. The square of $x - 5$, or $(x - 5)^2 =$ ______________.

4. The square of $4 - \sqrt{7x}$, or $(4 - \sqrt{7x})^2 =$ ______________.

19.6 EXERCISE SET

Solve. See Examples 1 and 2.

1. $\sqrt{2x} = 4$

2. $\sqrt{3x} = 3$

3. $\sqrt{x - 3} = 2$

4. $\sqrt{x + 1} = 5$

5. $\sqrt{2x} = -4$

6. $\sqrt{5x} = -5$

7. $\sqrt{4x - 3} - 5 = 0$

8. $\sqrt{x - 3} - 1 = 0$

9. $\sqrt{2x - 3} - 2 = 1$

10. $\sqrt{3x + 3} - 4 = 8$

Solve. See Example 3.

11. $\sqrt[3]{6x} = -3$

12. $\sqrt[3]{4x} = -2$

13. $\sqrt[3]{x - 2} - 3 = 0$

14. $\sqrt[3]{2x - 6} - 4 = 0$

Solve. See Examples 4 and 5.

15. $\sqrt{13 - x} = x - 1$

16. $\sqrt{2x - 3} = 3 - x$

17. $x - \sqrt{4 - 3x} = -8$

18. $2x + \sqrt{x + 1} = 8$

19. $\sqrt{y + 5} = 2 - \sqrt{y - 4}$

20. $\sqrt{x + 3} + \sqrt{x - 5} = 3$

21. $\sqrt{x - 3} + \sqrt{x + 2} = 5$

22. $\sqrt{2x - 4} - \sqrt{3x + 4} = -2$

MIXED PRACTICE

Solve. See Examples 1 through 5.

23. $\sqrt{3x - 2} = 5$

24. $\sqrt{5x - 4} = 9$

25. $-\sqrt{2x} + 4 = -6$

26. $-\sqrt{3x + 9} = -12$

27. $\sqrt{3x + 1} + 2 = 0$

28. $\sqrt{3x + 1} - 2 = 0$

29. $\sqrt[4]{4x + 1} - 2 = 0$

30. $\sqrt[4]{2x - 9} - 3 = 0$

31. $\sqrt{4x - 3} = 7$

32. $\sqrt{3x + 9} = 6$

33. $\sqrt[3]{6x - 3} - 3 = 0$

34. $\sqrt[3]{3x + 4} = 7$

35. $\sqrt[3]{2x - 3} - 2 = -5$

36. $\sqrt[3]{x - 4} - 5 = -7$

37. $\sqrt{x + 4} = \sqrt{2x - 5}$

38. $\sqrt{3y + 6} = \sqrt{7y - 6}$

39. $x - \sqrt{1 - x} = -5$

40. $x - \sqrt{x - 2} = 4$

41. $\sqrt[3]{-6x - 1} = \sqrt[3]{-2x - 5}$

42. $\sqrt[3]{-4x - 3} = \sqrt[3]{-x - 15}$

43. $\sqrt{5x - 1} - \sqrt{x} + 2 = 3$

44. $\sqrt{2x - 1} - 4 = -\sqrt{x - 4}$

45. $\sqrt{2x - 1} = \sqrt{1 - 2x}$

46. $\sqrt{7x - 4} = \sqrt{4 - 7x}$

47. $\sqrt{3x + 4} - 1 = \sqrt{2x + 1}$

48. $\sqrt{x - 2} + 3 = \sqrt{4x + 1}$

49. $\sqrt{y + 3} - \sqrt{y - 3} = 1$

50. $\sqrt{x + 1} - \sqrt{x - 1} = 2$

Find the length of the unknown side of each triangle. See Example 6.

51.

6 ft
3 ft

52.

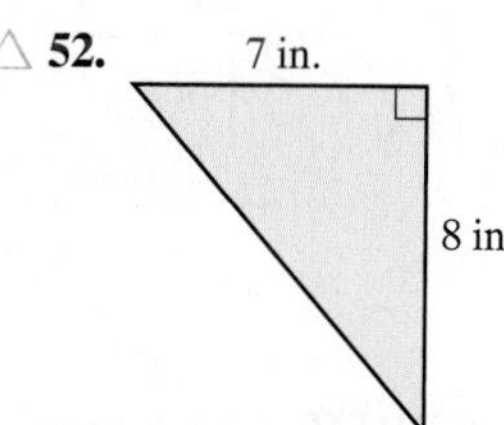

53. **54.**

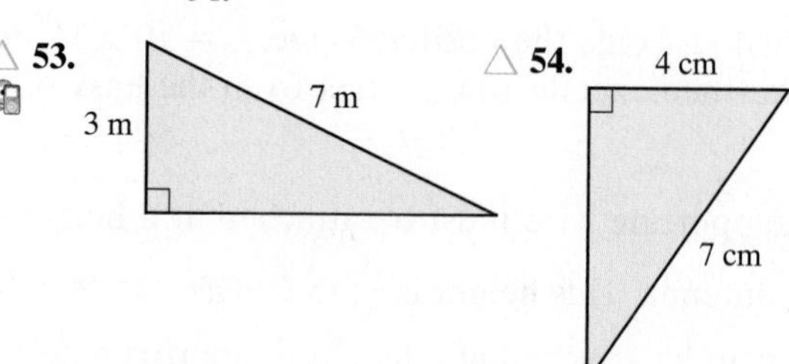

Find the length of the unknown side of each triangle. Give the exact length and a one-decimal-place approximation. See Example 6.

55.

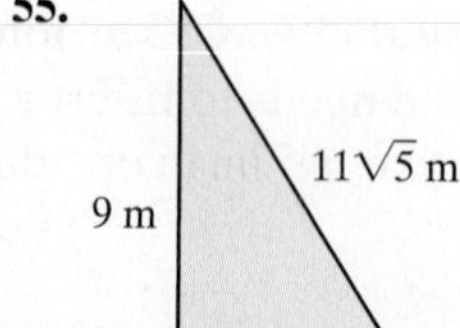

56.

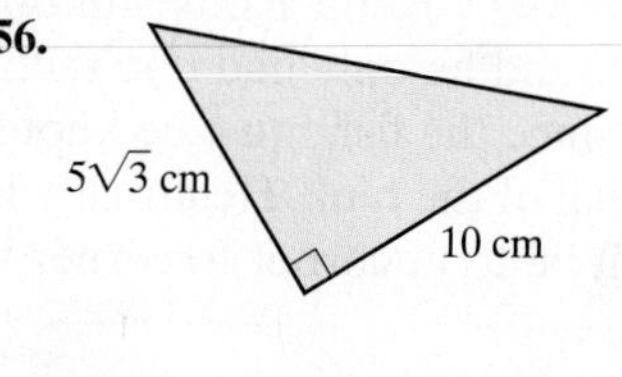

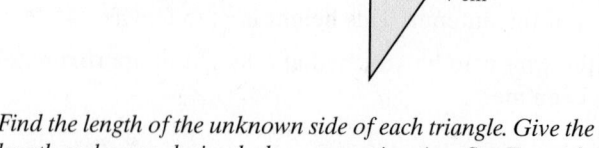

△ **57.**

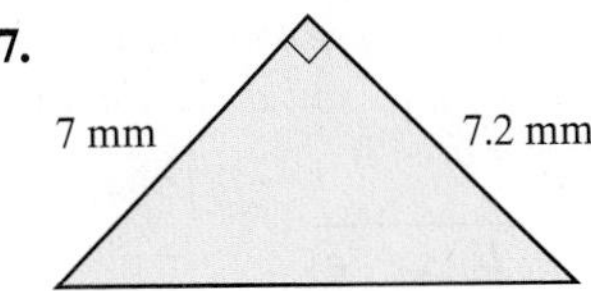

△ **58.**

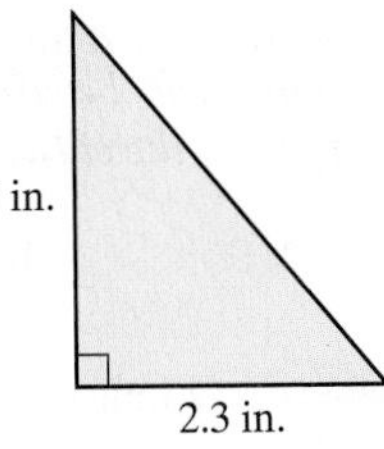

Solve. See Example 7. Give exact answers and two-decimal-place approximations where appropriate.

△ **59.** A wire is needed to support a vertical pole 15 feet high. The cable will be anchored to a stake 8 feet from the base of the pole. How much cable is needed?

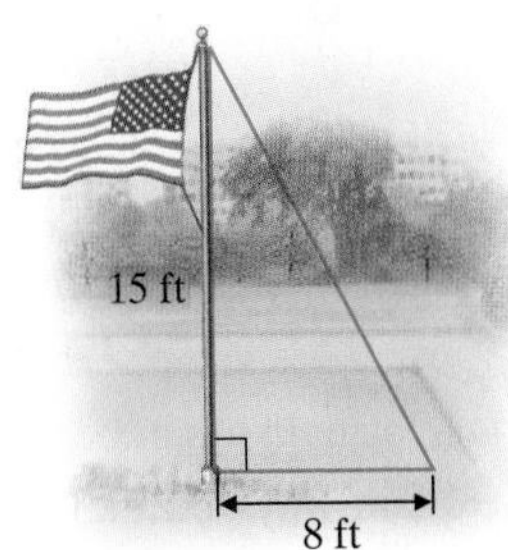

△ **60.** The tallest structure in the United States is a TV tower in Blanchard, North Dakota. Its height is 2063 feet. A 2382-foot length of wire is to be used as a guy wire attached to the top of the tower. Approximate to the nearest foot how far from the base of the tower the guy wire must be anchored. (*Source:* U.S. Geological Survey)

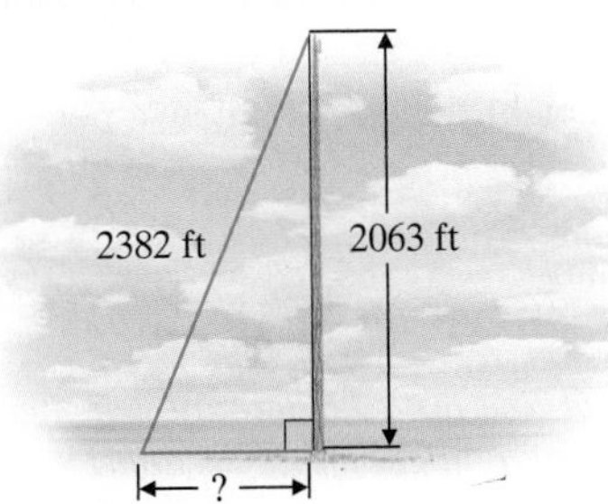

△ **61.** A spotlight is mounted on the eaves of a house 12 feet above the ground. A flower bed runs between the house and the sidewalk, so the closest the ladder can be placed to the house is 5 feet. How long a ladder is needed so that an electrician can reach the place where the light is mounted?

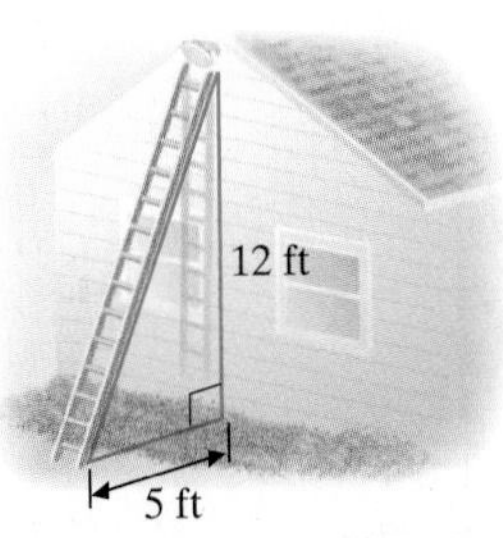

△ **62.** A wire is to be attached to support a telephone pole. Because of surrounding buildings, sidewalks, and roadways, the wire must be anchored exactly 15 feet from the base of the pole. Telephone company workers have only 30 feet of cable, and 2 feet of that must be used to attach the cable to the pole and to the stake on the ground. How high from the base of the pole can the wire be attached?

△ **63.** The radius of the Moon is 1080 miles. Use the formula for the radius r of a sphere given its surface area A,

$$r = \sqrt{\frac{A}{4\pi}}$$

to find the surface area of the Moon. Round to the nearest square mile. (*Source:* National Space Science Data Center)

64. Police departments find it very useful to be able to approximate the speed of a car when they are given the distance that the car skidded before it came to a stop. If the road surface is wet concrete, the function $S(x) = \sqrt{10.5x}$ is used, where $S(x)$ is the speed of the car in miles per hour and x is the distance skidded in feet. Find how fast a car was moving if it skidded 280 feet on wet concrete.

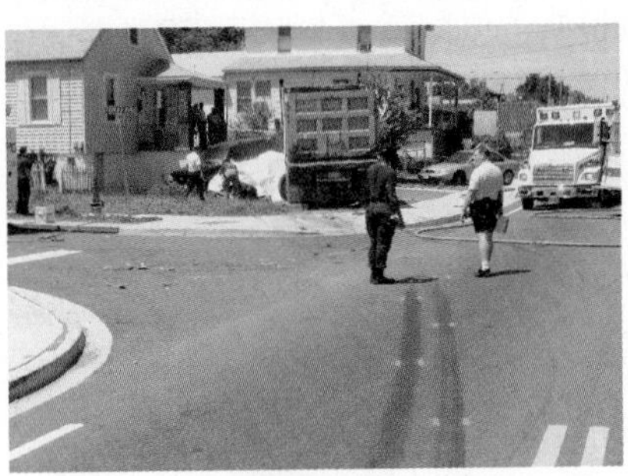

65. The formula $v = \sqrt{2gh}$ gives the velocity v, in feet per second, of an object when it falls h feet accelerated by gravity g, in feet per second squared. If g is approximately 32 feet per second squared, find how far an object has fallen if its velocity is 80 feet per second.

66. Two tractors are pulling a tree stump from a field. If two forces A and B pull at right angles (90°) to each other, the size of the resulting force R is given by the formula $R = \sqrt{A^2 + B^2}$. If tractor A is exerting 600 pounds of force and the resulting force is 850 pounds, find how much force tractor B is exerting.

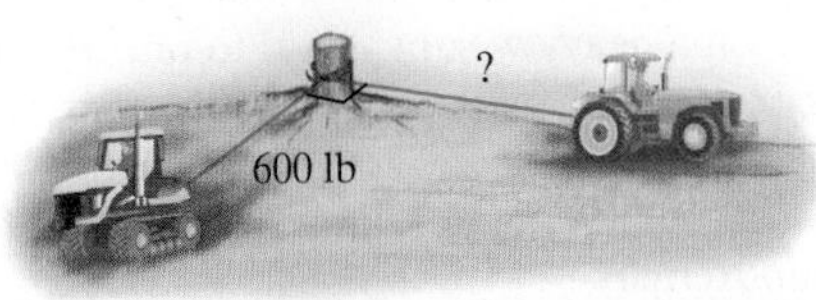

In psychology, it has been suggested that the number S of nonsense syllables that a person can repeat consecutively depends on his or her IQ score I according to the equation $S = 2\sqrt{I} - 9$.

67. Use this relationship to estimate the IQ of a person who can repeat 11 nonsense syllables consecutively.

68. Use this relationship to estimate the IQ of a person who can repeat 15 nonsense syllables consecutively.

The ***period*** *of a pendulum is the time it takes for the pendulum to make one full back-and-forth swing. The period of a pendulum depends on the length of the pendulum. The formula for the period P, in seconds, is* $P = 2\pi\sqrt{\frac{l}{32}}$, *where l is the length of the pendulum in feet. Use this formula for Exercises 69 through 74.*

69. Find the period of a pendulum whose length is 2 feet. Give an exact answer and a two-decimal-place approximation.

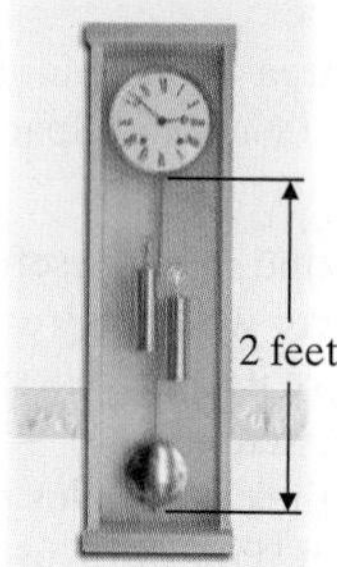

70. Klockit sells a 43-inch lyre pendulum. Find the period of this pendulum. Round your answer to 2 decimal places. (*Hint:* First convert inches to feet.)

71. Find the length of a pendulum whose period is 4 seconds. Round your answer to 2 decimal places.

72. Find the length of a pendulum whose period is 3 seconds. Round your answer to 2 decimal places.

73. Study the relationship between period and pendulum length in Exercises 69 through 72 and make a conjecture about this relationship.

74. Galileo experimented with pendulums. He supposedly made conjectures about pendulums of equal length with different bob weights. Try this experiment. Make two pendulums 3 feet long. Attach a heavy weight (lead) to one and a light weight (a cork) to the other. Pull both pendulums back the same angle measure and release. Make a conjecture from your observations. (There is more about pendulums in the Chapter 19 Group Activity.)

If the three lengths of the sides of a triangle are known, Heron's formula can be used to find its area. If a, b, and c are the three lengths of the sides, Heron's formula for area is

$$A = \sqrt{s(s-a)(s-b)(s-c)}$$

where s is half the perimeter of the triangle, or $s = \frac{1}{2}(a+b+c)$.

Use this formula to find the area of each triangle. Give an exact answer and then a two-decimal place approximation.

△ **75.**

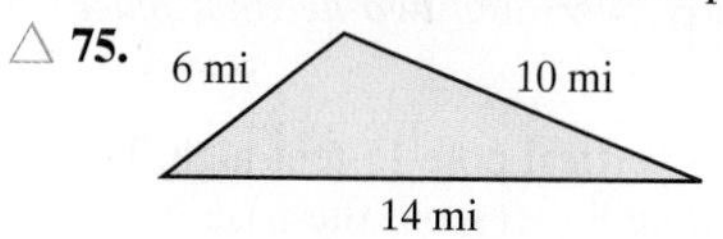

△ **76.**

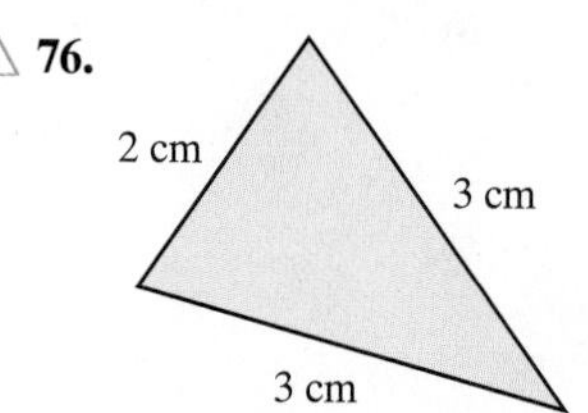

77. Describe when Heron's formula might be useful.

78. In your own words, explain why you think s in Heron's formula is called the *semiperimeter*.

The maximum distance D(h) in kilometers that a person can see from a height h kilometers above the ground is given by the function $D(h) = 111.7\sqrt{h}$. *Use this function for Exercises 79 and 80. Round your answers to two decimal places.*

79. Find the height that would allow a person to see 80 kilometers.

80. Find the height that would allow a person to see 40 kilometers.

REVIEW AND PREVIEW

Use the vertical line test to determine whether each graph represents the graph of a function. See Section 15.2.

81. **82.**

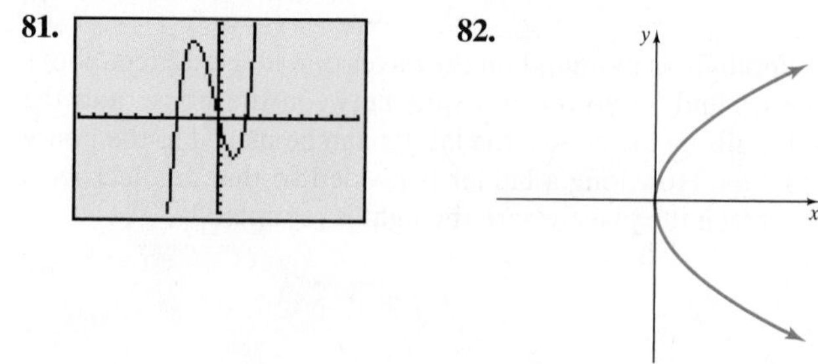

83. **84.**

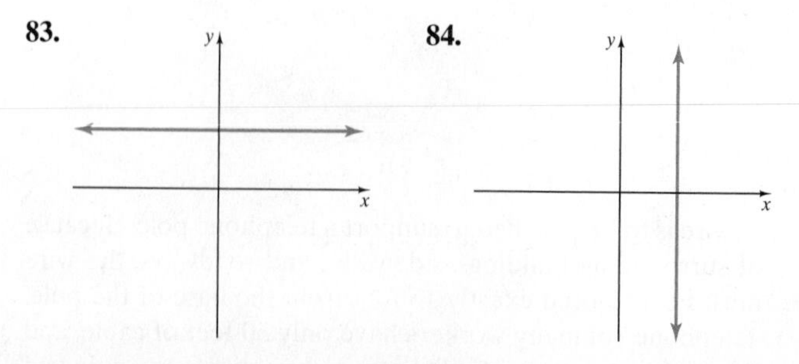

85.

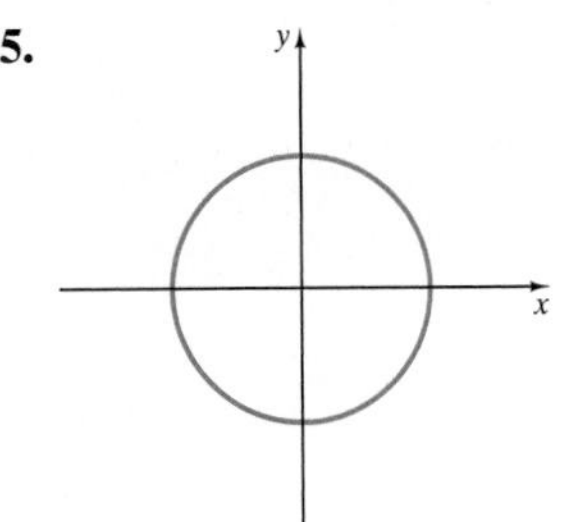

86.

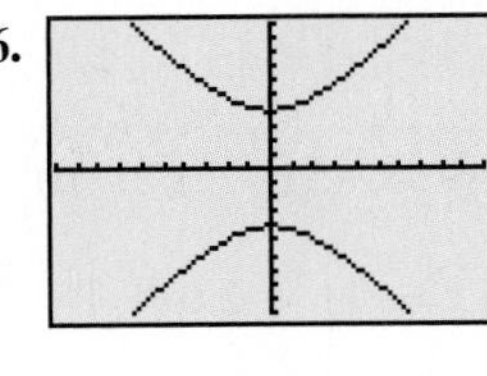

Simplify. See Section 18.3.

87. $\dfrac{\frac{x}{6}}{\frac{2x}{3}+\frac{1}{2}}$

88. $\dfrac{\frac{1}{y}+\frac{4}{5}}{\frac{-3}{20}}$

89. $\dfrac{\frac{z}{5}+\frac{1}{10}}{\frac{z}{20}-\frac{z}{5}}$

90. $\dfrac{\frac{1}{y}+\frac{1}{x}}{\frac{1}{y}-\frac{1}{x}}$

CONCEPT EXTENSIONS

91. Find the error in the following solution and correct. See the second Concept Check in this section.

$$\sqrt{5x-1}+4=7$$
$$(\sqrt{5x-1}+4)^2=7^2$$
$$5x-1+16=49$$
$$5x=34$$
$$x=\frac{34}{5}$$

92. Explain why proposed solutions of radical equations must be checked.

93. Solve: $\sqrt{\sqrt{x+3}+\sqrt{x}}=\sqrt{3}$

94. The cost $C(x)$ in dollars per day to operate a small delivery service is given by $C(x)=80\sqrt[3]{x}+500$, where x is the number of deliveries per day. In July, the manager decides that it is necessary to keep delivery costs below \$1620.00. Find the greatest number of deliveries this company can make per day and still keep overhead below \$1620.00.

95. Consider the equations $\sqrt{2x}=4$ and $\sqrt[3]{2x}=4$.

a. Explain the difference in solving these equations.

b. Explain the similarity in solving these equations.

Example

For Exercises 96 through 99, see the example below.
Solve $(t^2-3t)-2\sqrt{t^2-3t}=0$.

Solution

Substitution can be used to make this problem somewhat simpler. Since t^2-3t occurs more than once, let $x=t^2-3t$.

$$(t^2-3t)-2\sqrt{t^2-3t}=0$$
$$x-2\sqrt{x}=0$$
$$x=2\sqrt{x}$$
$$x^2=(2\sqrt{x})^2$$
$$x^2=4x$$
$$x^2-4x=0$$
$$x(x-4)=0$$
$$x=0 \quad\text{or}\quad x-4=0$$
$$x=4$$

Now we "undo" the substitution.
$x=0$ Replace x with t^2-3t.

$$t^2-3t=0$$
$$t(t-3)=0$$
$$t=0 \quad\text{or}\quad t-3=0$$
$$t=3$$

$x=4$ Replace x with t^2-3t.

$$t^2-3t=4$$
$$t^2-3t-4=0$$
$$(t-4)(t+1)=0$$
$$t-4=0 \quad\text{or}\quad t+1=0$$
$$t=4 \qquad t=-1$$

In this problem, we have four possible solutions: 0, 3, 4, and −1. All four solutions check in the original equation, so the solutions are −1, 0, 3, 4.

Solve. See the preceding example.

96. $3\sqrt{x^2-8x}=x^2-8x$

97. $\sqrt{(x^2-x)+7}=2(x^2-x)-1$

98. $7-(x^2-3x)=\sqrt{(x^2-3x)+5}$

99. $x^2+6x=4\sqrt{x^2+6x}$

THE BIGGER PICTURE SOLVING EQUATIONS AND INEQUALITIES

Continue your outline from Sections 16.2, 16.3, 16.5, and 18.5. Write how to recognize and how to solve equations with radicals in your own words. For example:

Solving Equations and Inequalities

I. Equations
 A. Linear equations (Sec. 1.5 and 16.1)
 B. Absolute value equations (Sec. 16.4)
 C. Quadratic and higher degree equations
 D. Equations with rational expressions (Sec. 18.5)
 E. Equations with radicals: Equation contains at least one root of a variable expression.

$\sqrt{5x+10}-2=x$	Radical equation
$\sqrt{5x+10}=x+2$	Isolate the radical.
$(\sqrt{5x+10})^2=(x+2)^2$	Square both sides.

$5x + 10 = x^2 + 4x + 4$	Simplify.
$0 = x^2 - x - 6$	Write in standard form.
$0 = (x - 3)(x + 2)$	Factor.
$x - 3 = 0$ or $x + 2 = 0$	Set each factor equal to 0.
$x = 3$ or $x = -2$	Solve.

Both solutions check.

II. Inequalities
  A. Linear inequalities (Sec. 16.2)
  B. Compound inequalities (Sec. 16.3)
  C. Absolute value inequalities (Sec. 16.5)

Solve. Write inequality solutions in interval notation.

1. $\frac{x}{4} + \frac{x + 18}{20} = \frac{x - 5}{5}$
2. $|3x - 5| = 10$
3. $2x^2 - x = 45$
4. $-6 \leq -5x - 1 \leq 10$
5. $4(x - 1) + 3x > 1 + 2(x - 6)$
6. $\sqrt{x} + 14 = x - 6$
7. $x \geq 10$ or $-x < 5$
8. $\sqrt{3x - 1} + 4 = 1$
9. $|x - 2| > 15$
10. $5x - 4[x - 2(3x + 1)] = 25$

19.7 COMPLEX NUMBERS

OBJECTIVES

1 Write square roots of negative numbers in the form *bi*.

2 Add or subtract complex numbers.

3 Multiply complex numbers.

4 Divide complex numbers.

5 Raise *i* to powers.

OBJECTIVE 1 ▶ Writing numbers in the form *bi*. Our work with radical expressions has excluded expressions such as $\sqrt{-16}$ because $\sqrt{-16}$ is not a real number; there is no real number whose square is -16. In this section, we discuss a number system that includes roots of negative numbers. This number system is the **complex number system,** and it includes the set of real numbers as a subset. The complex number system allows us to solve equations such as $x^2 + 1 = 0$ that have no real number solutions. The set of complex numbers includes the **imaginary unit.**

Imaginary Unit

The imaginary unit, written i, is the number whose square is -1. That is,

$$i^2 = -1 \quad \text{and} \quad i = \sqrt{-1}$$

To write the square root of a negative number in terms of i, use the property that if a is a positive number, then

$$\sqrt{-a} = \sqrt{-1} \cdot \sqrt{a}$$
$$= i \cdot \sqrt{a}$$

Using i, we can write $\sqrt{-16}$ as

$$\sqrt{-16} = \sqrt{-1 \cdot 16} = \sqrt{-1} \cdot \sqrt{16} = i \cdot 4, \text{ or } 4i$$

TECHNOLOGY NOTE

Many graphing utilities have a complex mode. Check your manual, and if yours has it, set your graphing utility to this mode for this chapter. Recall that a real number is a complex number, so in complex mode the graphing utility will display real numbers and imaginary numbers.

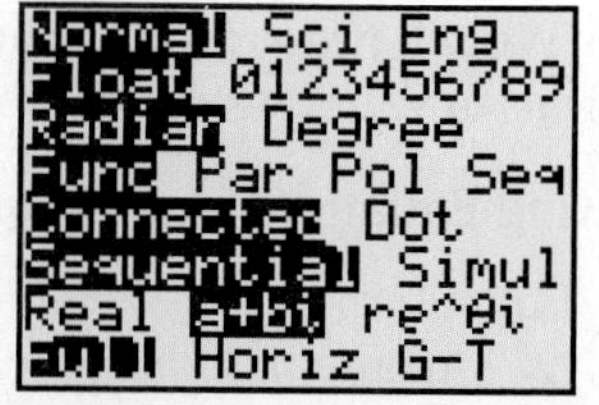

EXAMPLE 1 Write with i notation.

a. $\sqrt{-36}$ **b.** $\sqrt{-5}$ **c.** $-\sqrt{-20}$

Solution

a. $\sqrt{-36} = \sqrt{-1 \cdot 36} = \sqrt{-1} \cdot \sqrt{36} = i \cdot 6$, or $6i$

b. $\sqrt{-5} = \sqrt{-1(5)} = \sqrt{-1} \cdot \sqrt{5} = i\sqrt{5}$.

c. $-\sqrt{-20} = -\sqrt{-1 \cdot 20} = -\sqrt{-1} \cdot \sqrt{4 \cdot 5} = -i \cdot 2\sqrt{5} = -2i\sqrt{5}$ □

Helpful Hint

Since $\sqrt{5}i$ can easily be confused with $\sqrt{5i}$, we write $\sqrt{5}i$ as $i\sqrt{5}$.

This is an approximate answer, whereas $i\sqrt{5}$ is an exact answer.

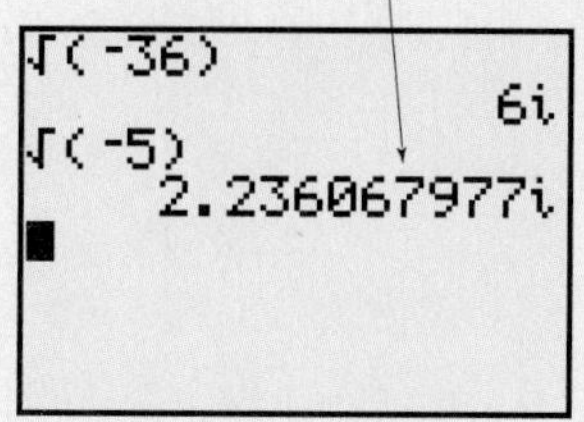

A calculator check of Example 1a and b.

PRACTICE 1 Write with i notation.

a. $\sqrt{-4}$ **b.** $\sqrt{-7}$ **c.** $-\sqrt{-18}$

The product rule for radicals does not necessarily hold true for imaginary numbers. *To multiply square roots of negative numbers, first we write each number in terms of the imaginary unit i.* For example, to multiply $\sqrt{-4}$ and $\sqrt{-9}$, we first write each number in the form bi.

$$\sqrt{-4}\sqrt{-9} = 2i(3i) = 6i^2 = 6(-1) = -6 \quad \text{Correct}$$

We will also use this method to simplify quotients of square roots of negative numbers. Why? The product rule does not work for this example. In other words,

$$\sqrt{-4} \cdot \sqrt{-9} = \sqrt{(-4)(-9)} = \sqrt{36} = 6 \quad \text{Incorrect}$$

EXAMPLE 2 Multiply or divide as indicated.

a. $\sqrt{-3} \cdot \sqrt{-5}$ **b.** $\sqrt{-36} \cdot \sqrt{-1}$ **c.** $\sqrt{8} \cdot \sqrt{-2}$ **d.** $\frac{\sqrt{-125}}{\sqrt{5}}$

Solution

a. $\sqrt{-3} \cdot \sqrt{-5} = i\sqrt{3}(i\sqrt{5}) = i^2\sqrt{15} = -1\sqrt{15} = -\sqrt{15}$

b. $\sqrt{-36} \cdot \sqrt{-1} = 6i(i) = 6i^2 = 6(-1) = -6$

c. $\sqrt{8} \cdot \sqrt{-2} = 2\sqrt{2}(i\sqrt{2}) = 2i(\sqrt{2}\sqrt{2}) = 2i(2) = 4i$

d. $\frac{\sqrt{-125}}{\sqrt{5}} = \frac{i\sqrt{125}}{\sqrt{5}} = i\sqrt{25} = 5i$ □

PRACTICE 2 Multiply or divide as indicated.

a. $\sqrt{-5} \cdot \sqrt{-6}$ **b.** $\sqrt{-9} \cdot \sqrt{-1}$ **c.** $\sqrt{125} \cdot \sqrt{-5}$ **d.** $\frac{\sqrt{-27}}{\sqrt{3}}$

Now that we have practiced working with the imaginary unit, we define complex numbers.

Complex Numbers

A **complex number** is a number that can be written in the form $a + bi$, where a and b are real numbers.

Notice that the set of real numbers is a subset of the complex numbers since any real number can be written in the form of a complex number. For example,

$$16 = 16 + 0i$$

In general, a complex number $a + bi$ is a real number if $b = 0$. Also, a complex number is called a **pure imaginary number** if $a = 0$ and $b \neq 0$. For example,

$$3i = 0 + 3i \quad \text{and} \quad i\sqrt{7} = 0 + i\sqrt{7}$$

are pure imaginary numbers.

The following diagram shows the relationship between complex numbers and their subsets.

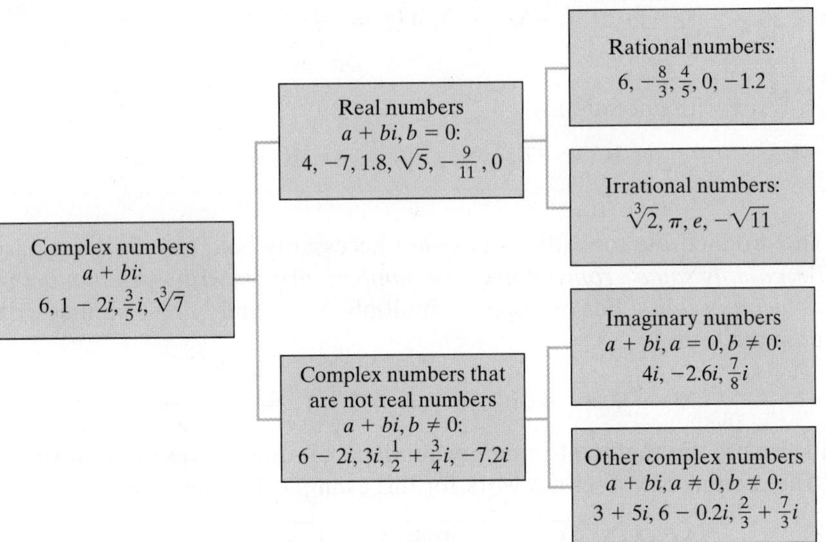

Concept Check ☑

True or false? Every complex number is also a real number.

OBJECTIVE 2 ▶ Adding or subtracting complex numbers. Two complex numbers $a + bi$ and $c + di$ are equal if and only if $a = c$ and $b = d$. Complex numbers can be added or subtracted by adding or subtracting their real parts and then adding or subtracting their imaginary parts.

Sum or Difference of Complex Numbers

If $a + bi$ and $c + di$ are complex numbers, then their sum is

$$(a + bi) + (c + di) = (a + c) + (b + d)i$$

Their difference is

$$(a + bi) - (c + di) = a + bi - c - di = (a - c) + (b - d)i$$

```
(2+3i)+(-3+2i)
           -1+5i
5i-(1-i)
           -1+6i
(-3-7i)-(-6)
            3-7i
```

A calculator check for Example 3.

Answer to Concept Check: false

EXAMPLE 3 Add or subtract the complex numbers. Write the sum or difference in the form $a + bi$.

a. $(2 + 3i) + (-3 + 2i)$ **b.** $5i - (1 - i)$ **c.** $(-3 - 7i) - (-6)$

Solution

a. $(2 + 3i) + (-3 + 2i) = (2 - 3) + (3 + 2)i = -1 + 5i$

b. $5i - (1 - i) = 5i - 1 + i$

$= -1 + (5 + 1)i$

$= -1 + 6i$

c. $(-3 - 7i) - (-6) = -3 - 7i + 6$
$= (-3 + 6) - 7i$
$= 3 - 7i$ □

PRACTICE
3 Add or subtract the complex numbers. Write the sum or difference in the form $a + bi$.

a. $(3 - 5i) + (-4 + i)$ **b.** $4i - (3 - i)$ **c.** $(-5 - 2i) - (-8)$

OBJECTIVE 3 ▶ Multiplying complex numbers. To multiply two complex numbers of the form $a + bi$, we multiply as though they are binomials. Then we use the relationship $i^2 = -1$ to simplify.

EXAMPLE 4 Multiply the complex numbers. Write the product in the form $a + bi$.

a. $-7i \cdot 3i$ **b.** $3i(2 - i)$ **c.** $(2 - 5i)(4 + i)$
d. $(2 - i)^2$ **e.** $(7 + 3i)(7 - 3i)$

Solution

a. $-7i \cdot 3i = -21i^2$
$= -21(-1)$ Replace i^2 with -1.
$= 21$

b. $3i(2 - i) = 3i \cdot 2 - 3i \cdot i$ Use the distributive property.
$= 6i - 3i^2$ Multiply.
$= 6i - 3(-1)$ Replace i^2 with -1.
$= 6i + 3$
$= 3 + 6i$

Use the FOIL order below. (First, Outer, Inner, Last)

c. $(2 - 5i)(4 + i) = 2(4) + 2(i) - 5i(4) - 5i(i)$
F O I L
$= 8 + 2i - 20i - 5i^2$
$= 8 - 18i - 5(-1)$ $i^2 = -1$
$= 8 - 18i + 5$
$= 13 - 18i$

d. $(2 - i)^2 = (2 - i)(2 - i)$
$= 2(2) - 2(i) - 2(i) + i^2$
$= 4 - 4i + (-1)$ $i^2 = -1$
$= 3 - 4i$

e. $(7 + 3i)(7 - 3i) = 7(7) - 7(3i) + 3i(7) - 3i(3i)$
$= 49 - 21i + 21i - 9i^2$
$= 49 - 9(-1)$ $i^2 = -1$
$= 49 + 9$
$= 58$ □

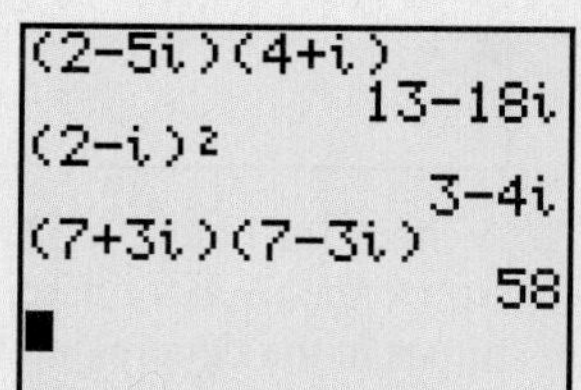

A calculator check for Example 4c, d, and e.

PRACTICE
4 Multiply the complex numbers. Write the product in the form $a + bi$.

a. $-4i \cdot 5i$ **b.** $5i(2 + i)$ **c.** $(2 + 3i)(6 - i)$
d. $(3 - i)^2$ **e.** $(9 + 2i)(9 - 2i)$

Notice that if you add, subtract, or multiply two complex numbers, just like real numbers, the result is a complex number.

OBJECTIVE 4 ▶ Dividing complex numbers. From Example 4e, notice that the product of $7 + 3i$ and $7 - 3i$ is a real number. These two complex numbers are called **complex conjugates** of one another. In general, we have the following definition.

> **Complex Conjugates**
> The complex numbers $(a + bi)$ and $(a - bi)$ are called **complex conjugates** of each other, and $(a + bi)(a - bi) = a^2 + b^2$.

To see that the product of a complex number $a + bi$ and its conjugate $a - bi$ is the real number $a^2 + b^2$, we multiply.

$$\begin{aligned}(a + bi)(a - bi) &= a^2 - abi + abi - b^2i^2 \\ &= a^2 - b^2(-1) \\ &= a^2 + b^2\end{aligned}$$

We use complex conjugates to divide by a complex number.

EXAMPLE 5 Divide. Write in the form $a + bi$.

a. $\dfrac{2 + i}{1 - i}$ **b.** $\dfrac{7}{3i}$

Solution

a. Multiply the numerator and denominator by the complex conjugate of $1 - i$ to eliminate the imaginary number in the denominator.

$$\begin{aligned}\frac{2 + i}{1 - i} &= \frac{(2 + i)(1 + i)}{(1 - i)(1 + i)} \\ &= \frac{2(1) + 2(i) + 1(i) + i^2}{1^2 - i^2} \\ &= \frac{2 + 3i - 1}{1 + 1} \qquad \text{Here, } i^2 = -1. \\ &= \frac{1 + 3i}{2} \quad \text{or} \quad \frac{1}{2} + \frac{3}{2}i\end{aligned}$$

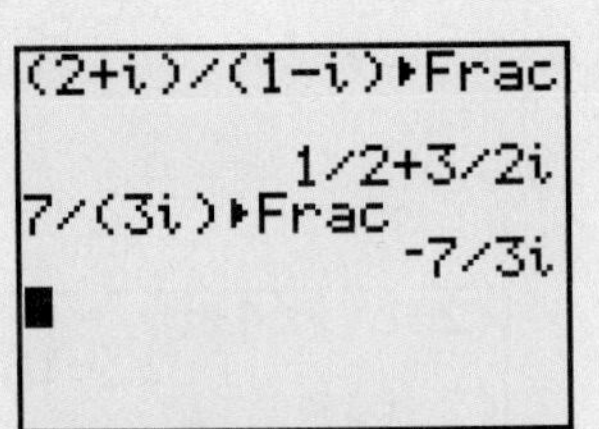

A check for Example 5. Notice the need for parentheses in the denominator when simplifying part b.

b. Multiply the numerator and denominator by the conjugate of $3i$. Note that $3i = 0 + 3i$, so its conjugate is $0 - 3i$ or $-3i$.

$$\frac{7}{3i} = \frac{7(-3i)}{(3i)(-3i)} = \frac{-21i}{-9i^2} = \frac{-21i}{-9(-1)} = \frac{-21i}{9} = \frac{-7i}{3} \quad \text{or} \quad 0 - \frac{7}{3}i$$ □

PRACTICE 5 Divide. Write in the form $a + bi$.

a. $\dfrac{4 - i}{3 + i}$ **b.** $\dfrac{5}{2i}$

> **▶ Helpful Hint**
> Recall that division can be checked by multiplication.
> To check that $\dfrac{2 + i}{1 - i} = \dfrac{1}{2} + \dfrac{3}{2}i$, in Example 5a, multiply $\left(\dfrac{1}{2} + \dfrac{3}{2}i\right)(1 - i)$ to verify that the product is $2 + i$.

OBJECTIVE 5 ▶ Finding powers of *i*. We can use the fact that $i^2 = -1$ to find higher powers of i. To find i^3, we rewrite it as the product of i^2 and i.

$$i^3 = i^2 \cdot i = (-1)i = -i$$
$$i^4 = i^2 \cdot i^2 = (-1)\cdot(-1) = 1$$

We continue this process and use the fact that $i^4 = 1$ and $i^2 = -1$ to simplify i^5 and i^6.

$$i^5 = i^4 \cdot i = 1 \cdot i = i$$
$$i^6 = i^4 \cdot i^2 = 1\cdot(-1) = -1$$

If we continue finding powers of i, we generate the following pattern. Notice that the values i, -1, $-i$, and 1 repeat as i is raised to higher and higher powers.

$i^1 = i$	$i^5 = i$	$i^9 = i$
$i^2 = -1$	$i^6 = -1$	$i^{10} = -1$
$i^3 = -i$	$i^7 = -i$	$i^{11} = -i$
$i^4 = 1$	$i^8 = 1$	$i^{12} = 1$

This pattern allows us to find other powers of i. To do so, we will use the fact that $i^4 = 1$ and rewrite a power of i in terms of i^4. For example,

$$i^{22} = i^{20} \cdot i^2 = (i^4)^5 \cdot i^2 = 1^5 \cdot (-1) = 1\cdot(-1) = -1.$$

EXAMPLE 6 Find the following powers of i.

a. i^7 **b.** i^{20} **c.** i^{46} **d.** i^{-12}

Solution

a. $i^7 = i^4 \cdot i^3 = 1(-i) = -i$

b. $i^{20} = (i^4)^5 = 1^5 = 1$

c. $i^{46} = i^{44} \cdot i^2 = (i^4)^{11} \cdot i^2 = 1^{11}(-1) = -1$

d. $i^{-12} = \dfrac{1}{i^{12}} = \dfrac{1}{(i^4)^3} = \dfrac{1}{(1)^3} = \dfrac{1}{1} = 1$ □

PRACTICE 6 Find the following powers of i.

a. i^9 **b.** i^{16} **c.** i^{34} **d.** i^{-24}

VOCABULARY & READINESS CHECK

Use the choices below to fill in each blank. Not all choices will be used.

-1	$\sqrt{-1}$	real	imaginary unit
1	$\sqrt{1}$	complex	pure imaginary

1. A ________ number is one that can be written in the form $a + bi$, where a and b are real numbers.
2. In the complex number system, i denotes the ____________.
3. $i^2 =$ ________
4. $i =$ ________
5. A complex number, $a + bi$, is a ________ number if $b = 0$.
6. A complex number, $a + bi$, is a ____________ number if $a = 0$ and $b \neq 0$.

Simplify. See Example 1.

7. $\sqrt{-81}$
8. $\sqrt{-49}$
9. $\sqrt{-7}$
10. $\sqrt{-3}$
11. $-\sqrt{16}$
12. $-\sqrt{4}$
13. $\sqrt{-64}$
14. $\sqrt{-100}$

19.7 EXERCISE SET

Write in terms of i. See Example 1.

1. $\sqrt{-24}$
2. $\sqrt{-32}$
3. $-\sqrt{-36}$
4. $-\sqrt{-121}$
5. $8\sqrt{-63}$
6. $4\sqrt{-20}$
7. $-\sqrt{54}$
8. $\sqrt{-63}$

Multiply or divide. See Example 2.

9. $\sqrt{-2}\cdot\sqrt{-7}$
10. $\sqrt{-11}\cdot\sqrt{-3}$
11. $\sqrt{-5}\cdot\sqrt{-10}$
12. $\sqrt{-2}\cdot\sqrt{-6}$
13. $\sqrt{16}\cdot\sqrt{-1}$
14. $\sqrt{3}\cdot\sqrt{-27}$
15. $\dfrac{\sqrt{-9}}{\sqrt{3}}$
16. $\dfrac{\sqrt{49}}{\sqrt{-10}}$
17. $\dfrac{\sqrt{-80}}{\sqrt{-10}}$
18. $\dfrac{\sqrt{-40}}{\sqrt{-8}}$

Add or subtract. Write the sum or difference in the form a + bi. See Example 3.

19. $(4-7i)+(2+3i)$
20. $(2-4i)-(2-i)$
21. $(6+5i)-(8-i)$
22. $(8-3i)+(-8+3i)$
23. $6-(8+4i)$
24. $(9-4i)-9$

Multiply. Write the product in the form a + bi. See Example 4.

25. $-10i\cdot -4i$
26. $-2i\cdot -11i$
27. $6i(2-3i)$
28. $5i(4-7i)$
29. $(\sqrt{3}+2i)(\sqrt{3}-2i)$
30. $(\sqrt{5}-5i)(\sqrt{5}+5i)$
31. $(4-2i)^2$
32. $(6-3i)^2$

Write each quotient in the form a + bi. See Example 5.

33. $\dfrac{4}{i}$
34. $\dfrac{5}{6i}$
35. $\dfrac{7}{4+3i}$
36. $\dfrac{9}{1-2i}$
37. $\dfrac{3+5i}{1+i}$
38. $\dfrac{6+2i}{4-3i}$
39. $\dfrac{5-i}{3-2i}$
40. $\dfrac{6-i}{2+i}$

MIXED PRACTICE

Perform each indicated operation. Write the result in the form a + bi.

41. $(7i)(-9i)$
42. $(-6i)(-4i)$
43. $(6-3i)-(4-2i)$
44. $(-2-4i)-(6-8i)$
45. $-3i(-1+9i)$
46. $-5i(-2+i)$
47. $\dfrac{4-5i}{2i}$
48. $\dfrac{6+8i}{3i}$
49. $(4+i)(5+2i)$
50. $(3+i)(2+4i)$
51. $(6-2i)(3+i)$
52. $(2-4i)(2-i)$
53. $(8-3i)+(2+3i)$
54. $(7+4i)+(4-4i)$
55. $(1-i)(1+i)$
56. $(6+2i)(6-2i)$
57. $\dfrac{16+15i}{-3i}$
58. $\dfrac{2-3i}{-7i}$
59. $(9+8i)^2$
60. $(4-7i)^2$
61. $\dfrac{2}{3+i}$
62. $\dfrac{5}{3-2i}$
63. $(5-6i)-4i$
64. $(6-2i)+7i$
65. $\dfrac{2-3i}{2+i}$
66. $\dfrac{6+5i}{6-5i}$
67. $(2+4i)+(6-5i)$
68. $(5-3i)+(7-8i)$
69. $(\sqrt{3}+2i)(\sqrt{3}-2i)$
70. $(\sqrt{5}-5i)(\sqrt{5}+5i)$
71. $(4-2i)^2$
72. $(6-3i)^2$

Find each power of i. See Example 6.

73. i^8
74. i^{10}
75. i^{21}
76. i^{15}
77. i^{11}
78. i^{40}
79. i^{-6}
80. i^{-9}
81. $(2i)^6$
82. $(5i)^4$
83. $(-3i)^5$
84. $(-2i)^7$

REVIEW AND PREVIEW

Recall that the sum of the measures of the angles of a triangle is 180°. Find the unknown angle in each triangle.

85.

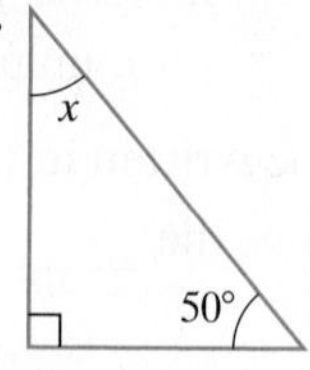

86.

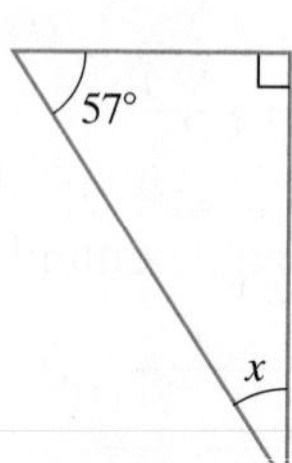

Use synthetic division to divide the following. See Section 18.4.

87. $(x^3-6x^2+3x-4)\div(x-1)$
88. $(5x^4-3x^2+2)\div(x+2)$

Thirty people were recently polled about their average monthly balance in their checking accounts. The results of this poll are shown in the following histogram. Use this graph to answer Exercises 89 through 94.

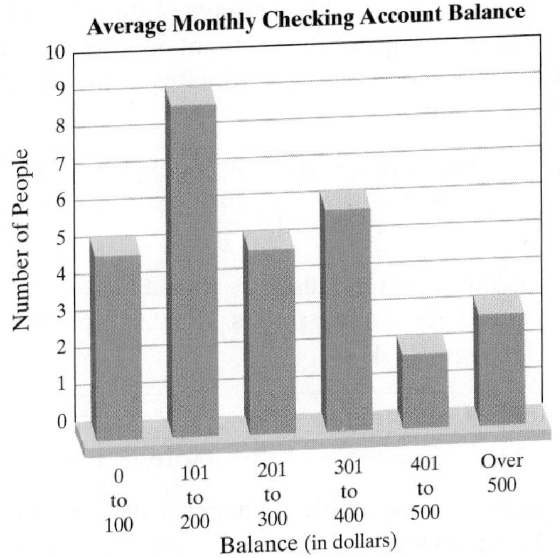

89. How many people polled reported an average checking balance of \$201 to \$300?

90. How many people polled reported an average checking balance of \$0 to \$100?

91. How many people polled reported an average checking balance of \$200 or less?

92. How many people polled reported an average checking balance of \$301 or more?

93. What percent of people polled reported an average checking balance of \$201 to \$300?

94. What percent of people polled reported an average checking balance of \$0 to \$100?

CONCEPT EXTENSIONS

Write in the form $a + bi$.

95. $i^3 - i^4$

96. $i^8 - i^7$

97. $i^6 + i^8$

98. $i^4 + i^{12}$

99. $2 + \sqrt{-9}$

100. $5 - \sqrt{-16}$

101. $\dfrac{6 + \sqrt{-18}}{3}$

102. $\dfrac{4 - \sqrt{-8}}{2}$

103. $\dfrac{5 - \sqrt{-75}}{10}$

104. Describe how to find the conjugate of a complex number.

105. Explain why the product of a complex number and its complex conjugate is a real number.

Simplify.

106. $(8 - \sqrt{-3}) - (2 + \sqrt{-12})$

107. $(8 - \sqrt{-4}) - (2 + \sqrt{-16})$

108. Determine whether $2i$ is a solution of $x^2 + 4 = 0$.

109. Determine whether $-1 + i$ is a solution of $x^2 + 2x = -2$.

CHAPTER 19 GROUP ACTIVITY

Heron of Alexandria

Heron (also Hero) was a Greek mathematician and engineer. He lived and worked in Alexandria, Egypt, around 75 A.D. During his prolific work life, Heron developed a rotary steam engine called an aeolipile, a surveying tool called a dioptra, as well as a wind organ and a fire engine. As an engineer, he must have had the need to approximate square roots because he described an iterative method for doing so in his work *Metrica*. Heron's method for approximating a square root can be summarized as follows:

> Suppose that x is not a perfect square and a^2 is the nearest perfect square to x. For a rough estimate of the value of $\sqrt{x}$, find the value of $y_1 = \frac{1}{2}\left(a + \frac{x}{a}\right)$. This estimate can be improved by calculating a second estimate using the first estimate y_1 in place of a: $y_2 = \frac{1}{2}\left(y_1 + \frac{x}{y_1}\right)$.
>
> Repeating this process several times will give more and more accurate estimates of $\sqrt{x}$.

Critical Thinking

1. a. Which perfect square is closest to 80?

b. Use Heron's method for approximating square roots to calculate the first estimate of the square root of 80. Give an exact decimal answer.

c. Use the first estimate of the square root of 80 to find a more refined second estimate. Round this second estimate to 6 decimal places.

d. Use a calculator to find the actual value of the square root of 80. List all digits shown on your calculator's display.

e. Compare the actual value from part **d** to the values of the first and second estimates. What do you notice?

f. How many iterations of this process are necessary to get an estimate that differs no more than one digit from the actual value recorded in part **d**?

2. Repeat Question 1 for finding an estimate of the square root of 30.

3. Repeat Question 1 for finding an estimate of the square root of 4572.

4. Why would this iterative method have been important to people of Heron's era? Would you say that this method is as important today? Why or why not?

STUDY SKILLS BUILDER

Are You Prepared for a Test on Chapter 19?

Below I have listed some common trouble areas for students in Chapter 19. After studying for your test, but before taking your test, read these.

- Remember how to convert an expression with rational expressions to one with radicals and one with radicals to one with rational expressions.

$$7^{2/3} = \sqrt[3]{7^2} \text{ or } (\sqrt[3]{7})^2$$
$$\sqrt[5]{4^3} = 4^{3/5}$$

- Remember the difference between $\sqrt{x} + \sqrt{x}$ and $\sqrt{x} \cdot \sqrt{x}, x > 0$.

$$\sqrt{x} + \sqrt{x} = 2\sqrt{x}$$
$$\sqrt{x} \cdot \sqrt{x} = x$$

- Don't forget the difference between rationalizing the denominator of $\sqrt{\frac{2}{x}}$ and rationalizing the denominator of $\frac{\sqrt{2}}{\sqrt{x} + 1}, x > 0$.

$$\sqrt{\frac{2}{x}} = \frac{\sqrt{2}}{\sqrt{x}} = \frac{\sqrt{2} \cdot \sqrt{x}}{\sqrt{x} \cdot \sqrt{x}} = \frac{\sqrt{2x}}{x}$$
$$\frac{\sqrt{2}}{\sqrt{x} + 1} = \frac{\sqrt{2}(\sqrt{x} - 1)}{(\sqrt{x} + 1)(\sqrt{x} - 1)} = \frac{\sqrt{2}(\sqrt{x} - 1)}{x - 1}$$

- Remember that the midpoint of a segment is a *point*. The x-coordinate is the average of the x-coordinates of the end points of the segment and the y-coordinate is the average of the y-coordinates of the end points of the segment.

  The midpoint of the segment joining $(-1, 5)$ and $(3, 4)$ is $\left(\frac{-1 + 3}{2}, \frac{5 + 4}{2}\right)$ or $\left(1, \frac{9}{2}\right)$.

- Remember that the distance formula gives the *distance* between two points. The distance between $(-1, 5)$ and $(3, 4)$ is

$$\sqrt{(3 - (-1))^2 + (4 - 5)^2} = \sqrt{4^2 + (-1)^2}$$
$$= \sqrt{16 + 1} = \sqrt{17} \text{ units}$$

Remember: This is simply a checklist of common trouble areas. For a review of Chapter 19, see the Highlights and Chapter Review at the end of this chapter.

CHAPTER 19 VOCABULARY CHECK

Fill in each blank with one of the words or phrases listed below.

index	rationalizing	conjugate	principal square root	cube root	midpoint
complex number	like radicals	radicand	imaginary unit	distance	

1. The __________ of $\sqrt{3} + 2$ is $\sqrt{3} - 2$.
2. The __________ of a nonnegative number a is written as $\sqrt{a}$.
3. The process of writing a radical expression as an equivalent expression but without a radical in the denominator is called __________ the denominator.
4. The __________, written i, is the number whose square is -1.
5. The __________ of a number is written as $\sqrt[3]{a}$.
6. In the notation $\sqrt[n]{a}$, n is called the __________ and a is called the __________.
7. Radicals with the same index and the same radicand are called __________.
8. A __________ is a number that can be written in the form $a + bi$, where a and b are real numbers.
9. The __________ formula is $d = \sqrt{(x_2 - x_1)^2 + (y_2 - y_1)^2}$.
10. The __________ formula is $\left(\frac{x_1 + x_2}{2}, \frac{y_1 + y_2}{2}\right)$.

Helpful Hint

Are you preparing for your test? Don't forget to take the Chapter 19 Test on page 1213. Then check your answers at the back of the text and use the Chapter Test Prep Video CD to see the fully worked-out solutions to any of the exercises you want to review.

CHAPTER 19 HIGHLIGHTS

DEFINITIONS AND CONCEPTS	EXAMPLES
SECTION 19.1 RADICALS AND RADICAL FUNCTIONS	
The **positive, or principal, square root** of a nonnegative number a is written as $\sqrt{a}$. $\sqrt{a} = b$ only if $b^2 = a$ and $b \geq 0$ The **negative square root** of a is written as $-\sqrt{a}$. The **cube root** of a real number a is written as $\sqrt[3]{a}$. $\sqrt[3]{a} = b$ only if $b^3 = a$ If n is an even positive integer, then $\sqrt[n]{a^n} = \lvert a \rvert$. If n is an odd positive integer, then $\sqrt[n]{a^n} = a$.	$\sqrt{36} = 6$ $\quad \sqrt{\frac{9}{100}} = \frac{3}{10}$ $-\sqrt{36} = -6$ $\quad \sqrt{0.04} = 0.2$ $\sqrt[3]{27} = 3$ $\quad \sqrt[3]{-\frac{1}{8}} = -\frac{1}{2}$ $\sqrt[3]{y^6} = y^2$ $\quad \sqrt[3]{64x^9} = 4x^3$ $\sqrt{(-3)^2} = \lvert -3 \rvert = 3$ $\sqrt[3]{(-7)^3} = -7$
A **radical function** in x is a function defined by an expression containing a root of x.	If $f(x) = \sqrt{x} + 2$, $f(1) = \sqrt{(1)} + 2 = 1 + 2 = 3$ $f(3) = \sqrt{(3)} + 2 \approx 3.73$
SECTION 19.2 RATIONAL EXPONENTS	
$a^{1/n} = \sqrt[n]{a}$ if $\sqrt[n]{a}$ is a real number.	$81^{1/2} = \sqrt{81} = 9$ $(-8x^3)^{1/3} = \sqrt[3]{-8x^3} = -2x$
If m and n are positive integers greater than 1 with $\frac{m}{n}$ in lowest terms and $\sqrt[n]{a}$ is a real number, then $a^{m/n} = (a^{1/n})^m = (\sqrt[n]{a})^m$	$4^{5/2} = (\sqrt{4})^5 = 2^5 = 32$ $27^{2/3} = (\sqrt[3]{27})^2 = 3^2 = 9$ $16^{-3/4} = \frac{1}{16^{3/4}} = \frac{1}{(\sqrt[4]{16})^3} = \frac{1}{2^3} = \frac{1}{8}$
$a^{-m/n} = \frac{1}{a^{m/n}}$ as long as $a^{m/n}$ is a nonzero number. **Exponent rules** are true for rational exponents.	$x^{2/3} \cdot x^{-5/6} = x^{2/3-5/6} = x^{-1/6} = \frac{1}{x^{1/6}}$ $(8^4)^{1/2} = 8^2 = 64$ $\frac{a^{4/5}}{a^{-2/5}} = a^{4/5-(-2/5)} = a^{6/5}$

(*continued*)

DEFINITIONS AND CONCEPTS	EXAMPLES
SECTION 19.3 SIMPLIFYING RADICAL EXPRESSIONS	
Product and Quotient Rules If $\sqrt[n]{a}$ and $\sqrt[n]{b}$ are real numbers, $\sqrt[n]{a}\cdot\sqrt[n]{b} = \sqrt[n]{a\cdot b}$ $\frac{\sqrt[n]{a}}{\sqrt[n]{b}} = \sqrt[n]{\frac{a}{b}}$, provided $\sqrt[n]{b} \neq 0$	Multiply or divide as indicated: $\sqrt{11}\cdot\sqrt{3} = \sqrt{33}$ $\frac{\sqrt[3]{40x}}{\sqrt[3]{5x}} = \sqrt[3]{8} = 2$
A radical of the form $\sqrt[n]{a}$ is **simplified** when a contains no factors that are perfect nth powers.	$\sqrt{40} = \sqrt{4\cdot 10} = 2\sqrt{10}$ $\sqrt{36x^5} = \sqrt{36x^4\cdot x} = 6x^2\sqrt{x}$ $\sqrt[3]{24x^7y^3} = \sqrt[3]{8x^6y^3\cdot 3x} = 2x^2y\sqrt[3]{3x}$ $\sqrt{36x^4\cdot x} = 6x^2\sqrt{x}$
Distance Formula The distance d between two points (x_1, y_1) and (x_2, y_2) is given by $d = \sqrt{(x_2 - x_1)^2 + (y_2 - y_1)^2}$	Find the distance between points $(-1, 6)$ and $(-2, -4)$. Let $(x_1, y_1) = (-1, 6)$ and $(x_2, y_2) = (-2, -4)$. $d = \sqrt{(x_2 - x_1)^2 + (y_2 - y_1)^2}$ $= \sqrt{(-2-(-1))^2 + (-4-6)^2}$ $= \sqrt{1 + 100} = \sqrt{101}$
Midpoint Formula The midpoint of the line segment whose end points are (x_1, y_1) and (x_2, y_2) is the point with coordinates $\left(\frac{x_1 + x_2}{2}, \frac{y_1 + y_2}{2}\right)$	Find the midpoint of the line segment whose end points are $(-1, 6)$ and $(-2, -4)$. $\left(\frac{-1+(-2)}{2}, \frac{6+(-4)}{2}\right)$ The midpoint is $\left(-\frac{3}{2}, 1\right)$.
SECTION 19.4 ADDING, SUBTRACTING, AND MULTIPLYING RADICAL EXPRESSIONS	
Radicals with the same index and the same radicand are **like radicals.** The distributive property can be used to add like radicals.	$5\sqrt{6} + 2\sqrt{6} = (5+2)\sqrt{6} = 7\sqrt{6}$ $= \sqrt[3]{3x} - 10\sqrt[3]{3x} + 3\sqrt[3]{10x}$ $= (-1-10)\sqrt[3]{3x} + 3\sqrt[3]{10x}$ $= -11\sqrt[3]{3x} + 3\sqrt[3]{10x}$
Radical expressions are multiplied by using many of the same properties used to multiply polynomials.	Multiply: $(\sqrt{5} - \sqrt{2x})(\sqrt{2} + \sqrt{2x})$ $= \sqrt{10} + \sqrt{10x} - \sqrt{4x} - 2x$ $= \sqrt{10} + \sqrt{10x} - 2\sqrt{x} - 2x$ $(2\sqrt{3} - \sqrt{8x})(2\sqrt{3} + \sqrt{8x})$ $= 4(3) - 8x = 12 - 8x$

DEFINITIONS AND CONCEPTS	EXAMPLES

SECTION 19.5 RATIONALIZING DENOMINATORS AND NUMERATORS OF RADICAL EXPRESSIONS

The **conjugate** of $a + b$ is $a - b$.

The conjugate of $\sqrt{7} + \sqrt{3}$ is $\sqrt{7} - \sqrt{3}$.

The process of writing the denominator of a radical expression without a radical is called **rationalizing the denominator.**

Rationalize each denominator.

$$\frac{\sqrt{5}}{\sqrt{3}} = \frac{\sqrt{5}\cdot\sqrt{3}}{\sqrt{3}\cdot\sqrt{3}} = \frac{\sqrt{15}}{3}$$

$$\frac{6}{\sqrt{7}+\sqrt{3}} = \frac{6(\sqrt{7}-\sqrt{3})}{(\sqrt{7}+\sqrt{3})(\sqrt{7}-\sqrt{3})}$$

$$= \frac{6(\sqrt{7}-\sqrt{3})}{7-3}$$

$$= \frac{6(\sqrt{7}-\sqrt{3})}{4} = \frac{3(\sqrt{7}-\sqrt{3})}{2}$$

The process of writing the numerator of a radical expression without a radical is called **rationalizing the numerator.**

Rationalize each numerator:

$$\frac{\sqrt[3]{9}}{\sqrt[3]{5}} = \frac{\sqrt[3]{9}\cdot\sqrt[3]{3}}{\sqrt[3]{5}\cdot\sqrt[3]{3}} = \frac{\sqrt[3]{27}}{\sqrt[3]{15}} = \frac{3}{\sqrt[3]{15}}$$

$$\frac{\sqrt{9}+\sqrt{3x}}{12} = \frac{(\sqrt{9}+\sqrt{3x})(\sqrt{9}-\sqrt{3x})}{12(\sqrt{9}-\sqrt{3x})}$$

$$= \frac{9-3x}{12(\sqrt{9}-\sqrt{3x})}$$

$$= \frac{3(3-x)}{3\cdot 4(3-\sqrt{3x})} = \frac{3-x}{4(3-\sqrt{3x})}$$

SECTION 19.6 RADICAL EQUATIONS AND PROBLEM SOLVING

To Solve a Radical Equation

Solve: $x = \sqrt{4x+9} + 3$.

Step 1. Write the equation so that one radical is by itself on one side of the equation.

1. $x - 3 = \sqrt{4x+9}$

Step 2. Raise each side of the equation to a power equal to the index of the radical and simplify.

2. $(x-3)^2 = (\sqrt{4x+9})^2$

$x^2 - 6x + 9 = 4x + 9$

Step 3. If the equation still contains a radical, repeat Steps 1 and 2. If not, solve the equation.

3. $x^2 - 10x = 0$

$x(x-10) = 0$

$x = 0$ or $x = 10$

Step 4. Check all proposed solutions in the original equation.

4. The proposed solution 10 checks, but 0 does not. The solution is 10.

(continued)

DEFINITIONS AND CONCEPTS	EXAMPLES

SECTION 19.6 RADICAL EQUATIONS AND PROBLEM SOLVING (continued)

To Solve a Radical Equation Graphically

Use the intersection-of-graphs method or the x-intercept method.

Solve $x = \sqrt{4x + 9} + 3$ using the intersection-of-graphs method.

Graph $y_1 = x$ and $y_2 = \sqrt{4x + 9} + 3$ in a $[-5, 20, 5]$ by $[-10, 15, 5]$ window.

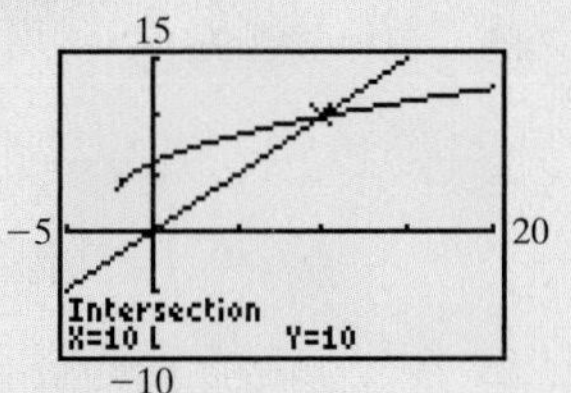

The intersection of the two graphs is at $x = 10$. The solution of the equation is 10.

See the algebraic solution for a check.

SECTION 19.7 COMPLEX NUMBERS

$i^2 = -1$ and $i = \sqrt{-1}$

A **complex number** is a number that can be written in the form $a + bi$, where a and b are real numbers.

Simplify: $\sqrt{-9}$.

$$\sqrt{-9} = \sqrt{-1 \cdot 9} = \sqrt{-1} \cdot \sqrt{9} = i \cdot 3 \text{ or } 3i$$

Complex Numbers	***Written in Form a + bi***
12	$12 + 0i$
$-5i$	$0 + (-5)i$
$-2 - 3i$	$-2 + (-3)i$

Multiply,

$$\begin{aligned} \sqrt{-3} \cdot \sqrt{-7} &= i\sqrt{3} \cdot i\sqrt{7} \\ &= i^2\sqrt{21} \\ &= -\sqrt{21} \end{aligned}$$

To add or subtract complex numbers, add or subtract their real parts and then add or subtract their imaginary parts.

Perform each indicated operation.

$$\begin{aligned} (-3 + 2i) - (7 - 4i) &= -3 + 2i - 7 + 4i \\ &= -10 + 6i \end{aligned}$$

To multiply complex numbers, multiply as though they are binomials.

$$\begin{aligned} (-7 - 2i)(6 + i) &= -42 - 7i - 12i - 2i^2 \\ &= -42 - 19i - 2(-1) \\ &= -42 - 19i + 2 \\ &= -40 - 19i \end{aligned}$$

The complex numbers $(a + bi)$ and $(a - bi)$ are called **complex conjugates.**

The complex conjugate of

$(3 + 6i)$ is $(3 - 6i)$.

Their product is a real number:

$$\begin{aligned} (3 - 6i)(3 + 6i) &= 9 - 36i^2 \\ &= 9 - 36(-1) = 9 + 36 = 45 \end{aligned}$$

To divide complex numbers, multiply the numerator and the denominator by the conjugate of the denominator.

Divide.

$$\begin{aligned} \frac{4}{2 - i} &= \frac{4(2 + i)}{(2 - i)(2 + i)} \\ &= \frac{4(2 + i)}{4 - i^2} \\ &= \frac{4(2 + i)}{5} \\ &= \frac{8 + 4i}{5} = \frac{8}{5} + \frac{4}{5}i \end{aligned}$$

CHAPTER 19 REVIEW

(19.1) *Find the root. Assume that all variables represent positive numbers.*

1. $\sqrt{81}$
2. $\sqrt[4]{81}$
3. $\sqrt[3]{-8}$
4. $\sqrt[4]{-16}$
5. $-\sqrt{\frac{1}{49}}$
6. $\sqrt{x^{64}}$
7. $-\sqrt{36}$
8. $\sqrt[3]{64}$
9. $\sqrt[3]{-a^6b^9}$
10. $\sqrt{16a^4b^{12}}$
11. $\sqrt[5]{32a^5b^{10}}$
12. $\sqrt[5]{-32x^{15}y^{20}}$
13. $\sqrt{\frac{x^{12}}{36y^2}}$
14. $\sqrt[3]{\frac{27y^3}{z^{12}}}$

Simplify. Use absolute value bars when necessary.

15. $\sqrt{(-x)^2}$
16. $\sqrt[4]{(x^2-4)^4}$
17. $\sqrt[3]{(-27)^3}$
18. $\sqrt[5]{(-5)^5}$
19. $-\sqrt[5]{x^5}$
20. $\sqrt[4]{16(2y+z)^{12}}$
21. $\sqrt{25(x-y)^{10}}$
22. $\sqrt[5]{-y^5}$
23. $\sqrt[9]{-x^9}$

Identify the domain and then graph each function.

24. $f(x) = \sqrt{x} + 3$
25. $g(x) = \sqrt[3]{x} - 3$; use the accompanying table.

x	-5	2	3	4	11
$g(x)$					

(19.2) *Evaluate the following.*

26. $\left(\frac{1}{81}\right)^{1/4}$
27. $\left(-\frac{1}{27}\right)^{1/3}$
28. $(-27)^{-1/3}$
29. $(-64)^{-1/3}$
30. $-9^{3/2}$
31. $64^{-1/3}$
32. $(-25)^{5/2}$
33. $\left(\frac{25}{49}\right)^{-3/2}$
34. $\left(\frac{8}{27}\right)^{-2/3}$
35. $\left(-\frac{1}{36}\right)^{-1/4}$

Write with rational exponents.

36. $\sqrt[3]{x^2}$
37. $\sqrt[5]{5x^2y^3}$

Write with radical notation.

38. $y^{4/5}$
39. $5(xy^2z^5)^{1/3}$
40. $(x+2y)^{-1/2}$

Simplify each expression. Assume that all variables represent positive numbers. Write with only positive exponents.

41. $a^{1/3}a^{4/3}a^{1/2}$
42. $\frac{b^{1/3}}{b^{4/3}}$
43. $(a^{1/2}a^{-2})^3$
44. $(x^{-3}y^6)^{1/3}$
45. $\left(\frac{b^{3/4}}{a^{-1/2}}\right)^8$
46. $\frac{x^{1/4}x^{-1/2}}{x^{2/3}}$
47. $\left(\frac{49c^{5/3}}{a^{-1/4}b^{5/6}}\right)^{-1}$
48. $a^{-1/4}(a^{5/4} - a^{9/4})$

Use a calculator and write a three-decimal-place approximation.

49. $\sqrt{20}$
50. $\sqrt[3]{-39}$
51. $\sqrt[4]{726}$
52. $56^{1/3}$
53. $-78^{3/4}$
54. $105^{-2/3}$

Use rational exponents to write each radical with the same index. Then multiply.

55. $\sqrt[3]{2}\cdot\sqrt{7}$
56. $\sqrt[3]{3}\cdot\sqrt[4]{x}$

(19.3) *Perform the indicated operations and then simplify if possible. For the remainder of this review, assume that variables represent positive numbers only.*

57. $\sqrt{3}\cdot\sqrt{8}$
58. $\sqrt[3]{7y}\cdot\sqrt[3]{x^2z}$
59. $\frac{\sqrt{44x^3}}{\sqrt{11x}}$
60. $\frac{\sqrt[4]{a^6b^{13}}}{\sqrt[4]{a^2b}}$

Simplify.

61. $\sqrt{60}$
62. $-\sqrt{75}$
63. $\sqrt[3]{162}$
64. $\sqrt[3]{-32}$
65. $\sqrt{36x^7}$
66. $\sqrt[3]{24a^5b^7}$
67. $\sqrt{\frac{p^{17}}{121}}$
68. $\sqrt[3]{\frac{y^5}{27x^6}}$
69. $\sqrt[4]{\frac{xy^6}{81}}$
70. $\sqrt{\frac{2x^3}{49y^4}}$

△ 71. The formula for the radius r of a circle of area A is

$$r = \sqrt{\frac{A}{\pi}}$$

a. Find the exact radius of a circle whose area is 25 square meters.

b. Approximate to two decimal places the radius of a circle whose area is 104 square inches.

Find the distance between each pair of points. Give an exact value and a three-decimal-place approximation.

72. $(-6, 3)$ and $(8, 4)$
73. $(-4, -6)$ and $(-1, 5)$

74. $(-1, 5)$ and $(2, -3)$

75. $(-\sqrt{2}, 0)$ and $(0, -4\sqrt{6})$

76. $(-\sqrt{5}, -\sqrt{11})$ and $(-\sqrt{5}, -3\sqrt{11})$

77. $(7.4, -8.6)$ and $(-1.2, 5.6)$

Find the midpoint of each line segment whose end points are given.

78. $(2, 6); (-12, 4)$

79. $(-6, -5); (-9, 7)$

80. $(4, -6); (-15, 2)$

81. $\left(0, -\frac{3}{8}\right); \left(\frac{1}{10}, 0\right)$

82. $\left(\frac{3}{4}, -\frac{1}{7}\right); \left(-\frac{1}{4}, -\frac{3}{7}\right)$

83. $(\sqrt{3}, -2\sqrt{6})$ and $(\sqrt{3}, -4\sqrt{6})$

(19.4) *Perform the indicated operation.*

84. $2\sqrt{50} - 3\sqrt{125} + \sqrt{98}$

85. $x\sqrt{75xy} - \sqrt{27x^3y}$

86. $\sqrt[3]{128} + \sqrt[3]{250}$

87. $3\sqrt[4]{32a^5} - a\sqrt[4]{162a}$

88. $\frac{5}{\sqrt{4}} + \frac{\sqrt{3}}{3}$

89. $\sqrt{\frac{8}{x^2}} - \sqrt{\frac{50}{16x^2}}$

90. $2\sqrt{32x^2y^3} - xy\sqrt{98y}$

91. $2a\sqrt[4]{32b^5} - 3b\sqrt[4]{162a^4b} + \sqrt[4]{2a^4b^5}$

Multiply and then simplify if possible.

92. $\sqrt{3}(\sqrt{27} - \sqrt{3})$

93. $(\sqrt{x} - 3)^2$

94. $(\sqrt{5} - 5)(2\sqrt{5} + 2)$

95. $(2\sqrt{x} - 3\sqrt{y})(2\sqrt{x} + 3\sqrt{y})$

96. $(\sqrt{a} + 3)(\sqrt{a} - 3)$

97. $(\sqrt[3]{a} + 2)^2$

98. $(\sqrt[3]{5x} + 9)(\sqrt[3]{5x} - 9)$

99. $(\sqrt[3]{a} + 4)(\sqrt[3]{a^2} - 4\sqrt[3]{a} + 16)$

(19.5) *Rationalize each denominator.*

100. $\frac{3}{\sqrt{7}}$

101. $\sqrt{\frac{x}{12}}$

102. $\frac{5}{\sqrt[3]{4}}$

103. $\sqrt{\frac{24x^5}{3y^2}}$

104. $\sqrt[3]{\frac{15x^6y^7}{z^2}}$

105. $\frac{5}{2 - \sqrt{7}}$

106. $\frac{3}{\sqrt{y} - 2}$

107. $\frac{\sqrt{2} - \sqrt{3}}{\sqrt{2} + \sqrt{3}}$

Rationalize each numerator.

108. $\frac{\sqrt{11}}{3}$

109. $\sqrt{\frac{18}{y}}$

110. $\frac{\sqrt[3]{9}}{7}$

111. $\sqrt{\frac{24x^5}{3y^2}}$

112. $\sqrt[3]{\frac{xy^2}{10z}}$

113. $\frac{\sqrt{x} + 5}{-3}$

(19.6) *Solve each equation for the variable.*

114. $\sqrt{y - 7} = 5$

115. $\sqrt{2x} + 10 = 4$

116. $\sqrt[3]{2x - 6} = 4$

117. $\sqrt{x + 6} = \sqrt{x + 2}$

118. $2x - 5\sqrt{x} = 3$

119. $\sqrt{x + 9} = 2 + \sqrt{x - 7}$

Find each unknown length.

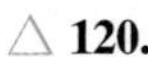 **120.**

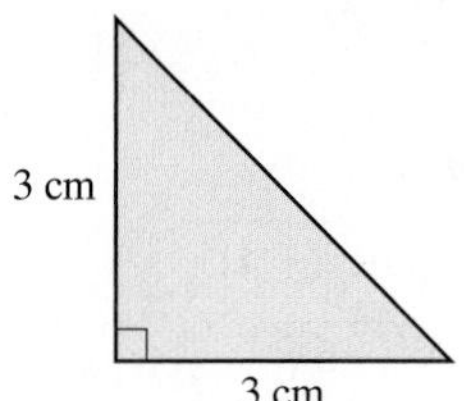

△ **121.**

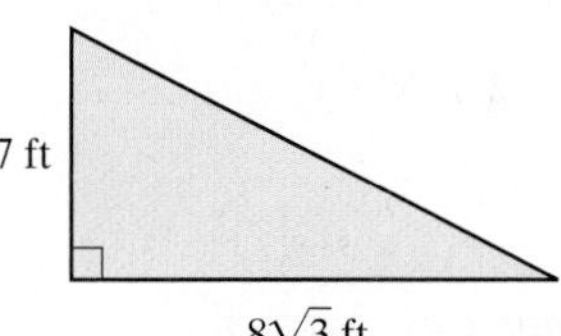

122. Beverly Hillis wants to determine the distance x across a pond on her property. She is able to measure the distances shown on the following diagram. Find how wide the lake is at the crossing point, indicated by the triangle, to the nearest tenth of a foot.

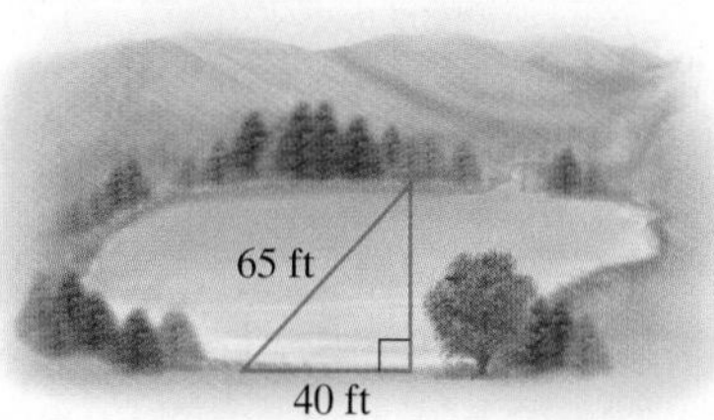

△ **123.** A pipe fitter needs to connect two underground pipelines that are offset by 3 feet, as pictured in the diagram. Neglecting the joints needed to join the pipes, find the length of the shortest possible connecting pipe rounded to the nearest hundredth of a foot.

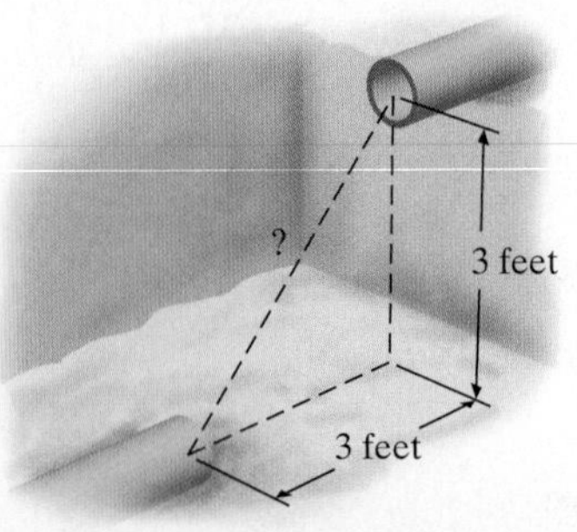

(19.7) Perform the indicated operation and simplify. Write the result in the form $a + bi$.

124. $\sqrt{-8}$ **125.** $-\sqrt{-6}$

126. $\sqrt{-4} + \sqrt{-16}$ **127.** $\sqrt{-2} \cdot \sqrt{-5}$

128. $(12 - 6i) + (3 + 2i)$ **129.** $(-8 - 7i) - (5 - 4i)$

130. $(2i)^6$ **131.** $-3i(6 - 4i)$

132. $(3 + 2i)(1 + i)$ **133.** $(2 - 3i)^2$

134. $(\sqrt{6} - 9i)(\sqrt{6} + 9i)$ **135.** $\dfrac{2 + 3i}{2i}$

136. $\dfrac{1 + i}{-3i}$

MIXED REVIEW

Simplify. Use absolute value bars when necessary.

137. $\sqrt[3]{x^3}$ **138.** $\sqrt{(x + 2)^2}$

Simplify. Assume that all variables represent positive real numbers. If necessary, write answers with positive exponents only.

139. $-\sqrt{100}$ **140.** $\sqrt[3]{-x^{12}y^3}$

141. $\sqrt[4]{\dfrac{y^{20}}{16x^{12}}}$ **142.** $9^{1/2}$

143. $64^{-1/2}$ **144.** $\left(\dfrac{27}{64}\right)^{-2/3}$

145. $\dfrac{(x^{2/3}x^{-3})^3}{x^{-1/2}}$ **146.** $\sqrt{200x^9}$

147. $\sqrt{\dfrac{3n^3}{121m^{10}}}$ **148.** $3\sqrt{20} - 7x\sqrt[3]{40} + 3\sqrt[3]{5x^3}$

149. $(2\sqrt{x} - 5)^2$

150. Find the distance between $(-3, 5)$ and $(-8, 9)$.

151. Find the midpoint of the line segment joining $(-3, 8)$ and $(11, 24)$.

Rationalize each denominator.

152. $\dfrac{7}{\sqrt{13}}$ **153.** $\dfrac{2}{\sqrt{x} + 3}$

Solve.

154. $\sqrt{x} + 2 = x$

CHAPTER 19 TEST

Remember to use the Chapter Test Prep Video CD to see the fully worked-out solutions to any of the exercises you want to review.

Raise to the power or find the root. Assume that all variables represent positive numbers. Write with only positive exponents.

1. $\sqrt{216}$ **2.** $-\sqrt[4]{x^{64}}$

3. $\left(\dfrac{1}{125}\right)^{1/3}$ **4.** $\left(\dfrac{1}{125}\right)^{-1/3}$

5. $\left(\dfrac{8x^3}{27}\right)^{2/3}$ **6.** $\sqrt[3]{-a^{18}b^9}$

7. $\left(\dfrac{64c^{4/3}}{a^{-2/3}b^{5/6}}\right)^{1/2}$ **8.** $a^{-2/3}(a^{5/4} - a^3)$

Find the root. Use absolute value bars when necessary.

9. $\sqrt[4]{(4xy)^4}$ **10.** $\sqrt[3]{(-27)^3}$

Rationalize the denominator. Assume that all variables represent positive numbers.

11. $\sqrt{\dfrac{9}{y}}$ **12.** $\dfrac{4 - \sqrt{x}}{4 + 2\sqrt{x}}$

13. $\dfrac{\sqrt[3]{ab}}{\sqrt[3]{ab^2}}$

14. Rationalize the numerator of $\dfrac{\sqrt{6} + x}{8}$ and simplify.

Perform the indicated operations. Assume that all variables represent positive numbers.

15. $\sqrt{125x^3} - 3\sqrt{20x^3}$

16. $\sqrt{3}(\sqrt{16} - \sqrt{2})$

17. $(\sqrt{x} + 1)^2$

18. $(\sqrt{2} - 4)(\sqrt{3} + 1)$

19. $(\sqrt{5} + 5)(\sqrt{5} - 5)$

Use a calculator to approximate each to three decimal places.

20. $\sqrt{561}$ **21.** $386^{-2/3}$

Solve.

22. $x = \sqrt{x - 2} + 2$ **23.** $\sqrt{x^2 - 7} + 3 = 0$

24. $\sqrt[3]{x + 5} = \sqrt[3]{2x - 1}$

Perform the indicated operation and simplify. Write the result in the form $a + bi$.

25. $\sqrt{-2}$ **26.** $-\sqrt{-8}$

27. $(12 - 6i) - (12 - 3i)$ **28.** $(6 - 2i)(6 + 2i)$

29. $(4 + 3i)^2$ **30.** $\dfrac{1 + 4i}{1 - i}$

△ **31.** Find x.

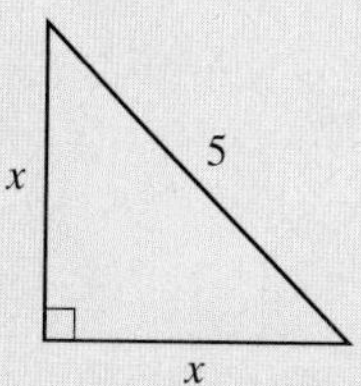

32. Identify the domain of $g(x)$. Then complete the accompanying table and graph $g(x)$.

$$g(x) = \sqrt{x + 2}$$

x	-2	-1	2	7
$g(x)$				

33. Find the distance between the points $(-6, 3)$ and $(-8, -7)$.

34. Find the distance between the points $(-2\sqrt{5}, \sqrt{10})$ and $(-\sqrt{5}, 4\sqrt{10})$.

35. Find the midpoint of the line segment whose end points are $(-2, -5)$ and $(-6, 12)$.

36. Find the midpoint of the line segment whose end points are $\left(-\frac{2}{3}, -\frac{1}{5}\right)$ and $\left(-\frac{1}{3}, \frac{4}{5}\right)$.

Solve.

37. The function $V(r) = \sqrt{2.5r}$ can be used to estimate the maximum safe velocity V in miles per hour at which a car can travel if it is driven along a curved road with a *radius of curvature* r in feet. To the nearest whole number, find the maximum safe speed if a cloverleaf exit on an expressway has a radius of curvature of 300 feet.

38. Use the formula from Exercise 37 to find the radius of curvature if the safe velocity is 30 mph.

CHAPTER 19 CUMULATIVE REVIEW

1. Simplify each expression.

a. $3xy - 2xy + 5 - 7 + xy$

b. $7x^2 + 3 - 5(x^2 - 4)$

c. $(2.1x - 5.6) - (-x - 5.3)$

d. $\frac{1}{2}(4a - 6b) - \frac{1}{3}(9a + 12b - 1) + \frac{1}{4}$

2. Simplify each expression.

a. $2(x - 3) + (5x + 3)$

b. $4(3x + 2) - 3(5x - 1)$

c. $7x + 2(x - 7) - 3x$

3. Solve for x: $\frac{x + 5}{2} + \frac{1}{2} = 2x - \frac{x - 3}{8}$

4. Solve: $\frac{a - 1}{2} + a = 2 - \frac{2a + 7}{8}$

5. A part-time salesperson earns \$600 per month plus a commission of 20% of sales. Find the minimum amount of sales needed to receive a total income of at least \$1500 per month.

6. The Smith family owns a lake house 121.5 miles from home. If it takes them $4\frac{1}{2}$ hours round-trip to drive from their house to their lake house, find their average speed.

7. Solve: $2|x| + 25 = 23$

8. Solve: $|3x - 2| + 5 = 5$

9. Solve: $\left|\frac{x}{3} - 1\right| - 2 \geq 0$

10. Solve: $\left|\frac{x}{2} - 1\right| \leq 0$

11. Graph the equation $y = |x|$.

12. Graph $y = |x - 2|$.

13. Determine the domain and range of each relation.

a. $\{(2, 3), (2, 4), (0, -1), (3, -1)\}$

b.

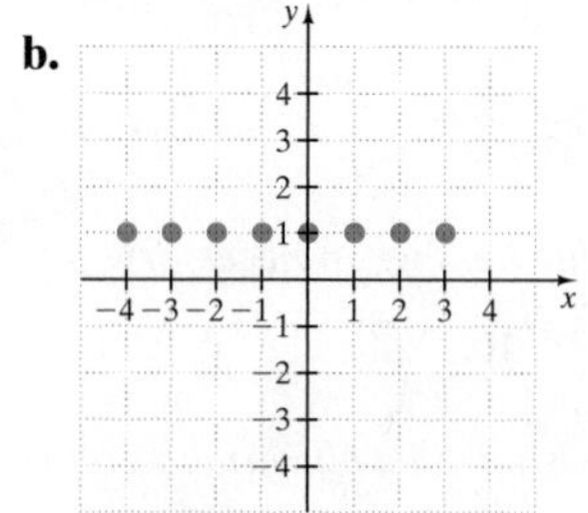

c.

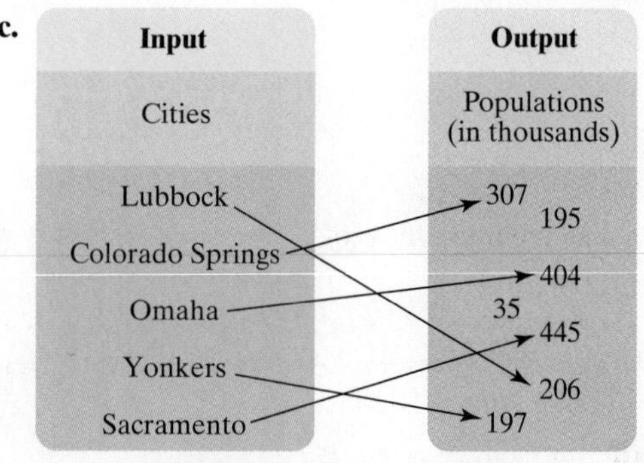

14. Find the domain and the range of each relation. Use the vertical line test to determine whether each graph is the graph of a function.

a.

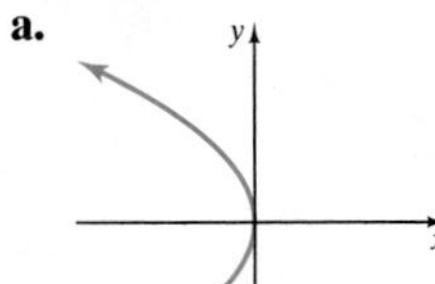

b.

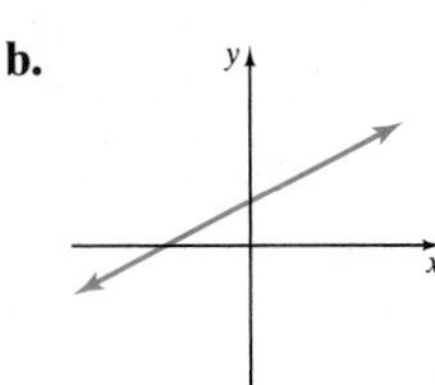

c.

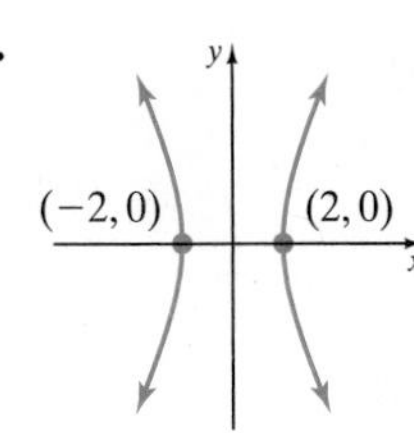

15. Graph $y = -3$.

16. Graph $f(x) = -2$.

17. Find the slope of the line $x = -5$.

18. Find the slope of $y = -3$.

19. Use the substitution method to solve the system.

$$\begin{cases} -\frac{x}{6} + \frac{y}{2} = \frac{1}{2} \\ \frac{x}{3} - \frac{y}{6} = -\frac{3}{4} \end{cases}$$

20. Use the substitution method to solve the system.

$$\begin{cases} \frac{x}{6} - \frac{y}{2} = 1 \\ \frac{x}{3} - \frac{y}{4} = 2 \end{cases}$$

21. Use the product rule to simplify.

a. $2^2 \cdot 2^5$

b. x^7x^3

c. $y \cdot y^2 \cdot y^4$

22. At a seasonal clearance sale, Nana Long spent \$33.75. She paid \$3.50 for T-shirts and \$4.25 for shorts. If she bought 9 items, how many of each item did she buy?

23. Use scientific notation to simplify $\frac{2000 \times 0.000021}{700}$.

24. Use scientific notation to simplify and write the answer in scientific notation $\frac{0.0000035 \times 4000}{0.28}$.

25. If $P(x) = 3x^2 - 2x - 5$, find the following.

a. $P(1)$

b. $P(-2)$

26. Subtract $(2x - 5)$ from the sum of $(5x^2 - 3x + 6)$ and $(4x^2 + 5x - 3)$.

27. Multiply and simplify the product if possible.

a. $(x + 3)(2x + 5)$

b. $(2x - 3)(5x^2 - 6x + 7)$

28. Multiply and simplify the product if possible.

a. $(y - 2)(3y + 4)$

b. $(3y - 1)(2y^2 + 3y - 1)$

29. Find the GCF of $20x^3y$, $10x^2y^2$, and $35x^3$.

30. Factor $x^3 - x^2 + 4x - 4$.

31. Simplify each rational expression.

a. $\frac{x^3 + 8}{2 + x}$

b. $\frac{2y^2 + 2}{y^3 - 5y^2 + y - 5}$

32. Simplify each rational expression.

a. $\frac{a^3 - 8}{2 - a}$

b. $\frac{3a^2 - 3}{a^3 + 5a^2 - a - 5}$

33. Perform the indicated operation.

a. $\frac{2}{x^2y} + \frac{5}{3x^3y}$

b. $\frac{3x}{x + 2} + \frac{2x}{x - 2}$

c. $\frac{2x - 6}{x - 1} - \frac{4}{1 - x}$

34. Perform the indicated operations.

a. $\frac{3}{xy^2} - \frac{2}{3x^2y}$

b. $\frac{5x}{x + 3} - \frac{2x}{x - 3}$

c. $\frac{x}{x - 2} - \frac{5}{2 - x}$

35. Simplify each complex fraction.

a. $\frac{\frac{5x}{x + 2}}{\frac{10}{x - 2}}$

b. $\frac{\frac{x}{y^2} + \frac{1}{y}}{\frac{y}{x^2} + \frac{1}{x}}$

36. Simplify each complex fraction.

a. $\frac{\frac{y - 2}{16}}{\frac{2y + 3}{12}}$

b. $\frac{\frac{x}{16} - \frac{1}{x}}{1 - \frac{4}{x}}$

37. Solve: $\dfrac{x+6}{x-2} = \dfrac{2(x+2)}{x-2}$.

38. Solve: $\dfrac{28}{9-a^2} = \dfrac{2a}{a-3} + \dfrac{6}{a+3}$.

39. Solve: $\dfrac{1}{x} + \dfrac{1}{y} = \dfrac{1}{z}$ for x.

40. Solve: $A = \dfrac{h(a+b)}{2}$ for a.

41. Suppose that u varies inversely as w. If u is 3 when w is 5, find the constant of variation and the inverse variation equation.

42. Suppose that y varies directly as x. If $y = 0.51$ when $x = 3$, find the constant of variation and the direct variation equation.

43. Write each expression with a positive exponent, and then simplify.

a. $16^{-3/4}$

b. $(-27)^{-2/3}$

44. Write each expression with a positive exponent, and then simplify.

a. $(81)^{-3/4}$

b. $(-125)^{-2/3}$

45. Rationalize the numerator of $\dfrac{\sqrt{x}+2}{5}$.

46. Add or subtract.

a. $\sqrt{36a^3} - \sqrt{144a^3} + \sqrt{4a^3}$

b. $\sqrt[3]{128ab^3} - 3\sqrt[3]{2ab^3} + b\sqrt[3]{16a}$

c. $\dfrac{\sqrt[3]{81}}{10} + \sqrt[3]{\dfrac{192}{125}}$

Quadratic Equations and Functions

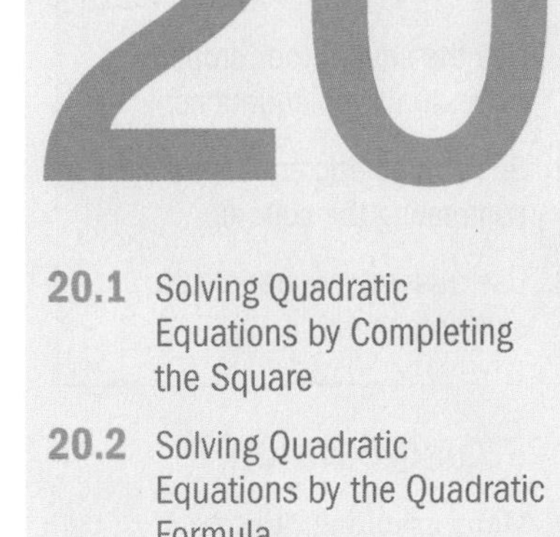

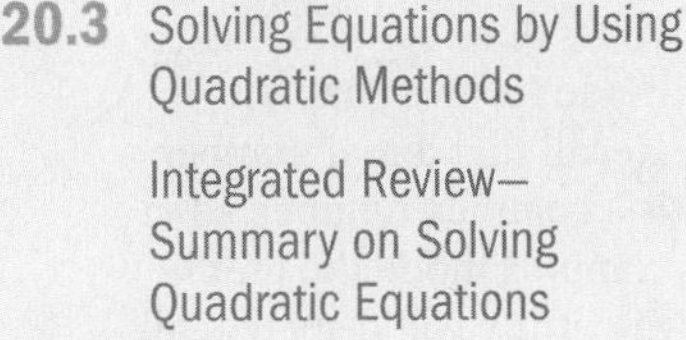

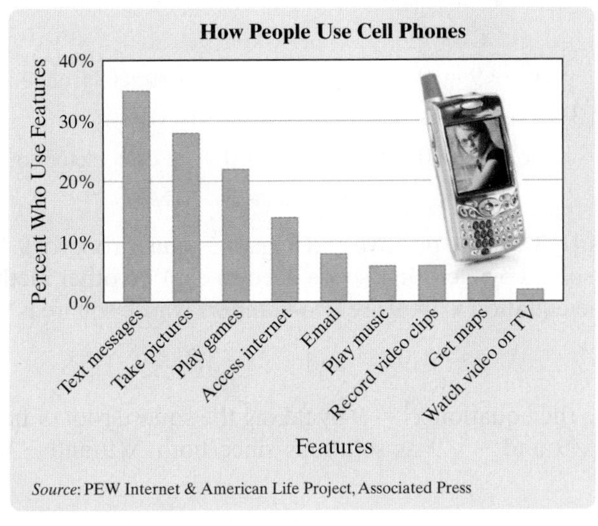

Source: PEW Internet & American Life Project, Associated Press

The growth of cell phones, shown below, can be approximated by a quadratic function. More interesting information is probably given on the graph above. As shown, the cell phone is certainly no longer just a phone.

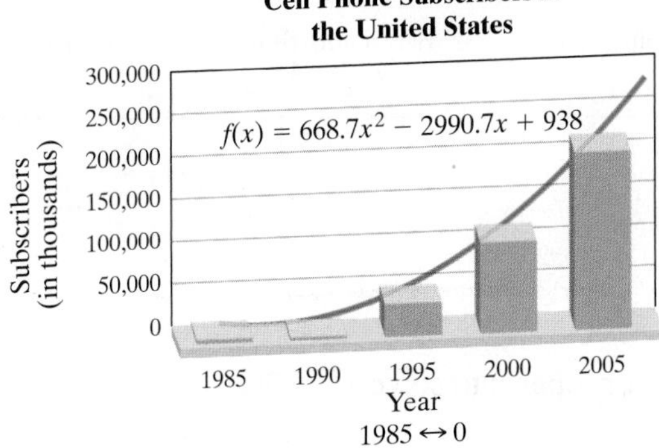

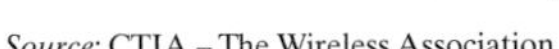

Source: CTIA – The Wireless Association

300,000 Y1=668.7X²-2990.7X+938

−50,000 X=20 Y=208604

0 25

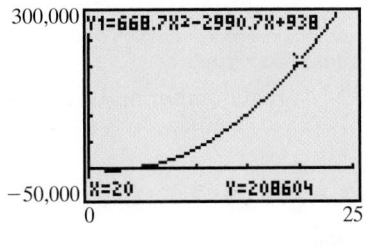

An important part of the study of algebra is learning to model and solve problems. Often, the model of a problem is a quadratic equation or a function containing a second-degree polynomial. In this chapter, we continue the work begun when we solved polynomial equations in one variable by factoring. Two additional methods of solving quadratic equations are analyzed, as well as methods of solving nonlinear inequalities in one variable.

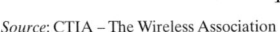

20.1 SOLVING QUADRATIC EQUATIONS BY COMPLETING THE SQUARE

OBJECTIVES

1. Use the square root property to solve quadratic equations.
2. Solve quadratic equations by completing the square.
3. Use quadratic equations to solve problems.

TECHNOLOGY NOTE

Many graphing utilities have a complex mode. If yours does, set it to this mode for this chapter. Recall that a real number is a complex number, so in complex mode the graphing utility will display real numbers as well as complex numbers that are not real numbers.

OBJECTIVE 1 ▶ Using the square root property. Recall that a **quadratic,** or **second-degree, equation** is an equation that can be written in the form $ax^2 + bx + c = 0$, where a, b, and c are real numbers and a is not 0. To solve a quadratic equation such as $x^2 = 9$ by factoring, we use the zero-factor theorem. To use the zero-factor theorem, the equation must first be written in standard form, $ax^2 + bx + c = 0$.

$$x^2 = 9$$
$$x^2 - 9 = 0 \quad \text{Subtract 9 from both sides.}$$
$$(x + 3)(x - 3) = 0 \quad \text{Factor.}$$
$$x + 3 = 0 \quad \text{or} \quad x - 3 = 0 \quad \text{Set each factor equal to 0.}$$
$$x = -3 \qquad x = 3 \quad \text{Solve.}$$

The solution set is $\{-3, 3\}$, the positive and negative square roots of 9. Not all quadratic equations can be solved by factoring, so we need to explore other methods. Notice that the solutions of the equation $x^2 = 9$ are two numbers whose square is 9.

$$3^2 = 9 \quad \text{and} \quad (-3)^2 = 9$$

Thus, we can solve the equation $x^2 = 9$ by taking the square root of both sides. Be sure to include both $\sqrt{9}$ and $-\sqrt{9}$ as solutions since both $\sqrt{9}$ and $-\sqrt{9}$ are numbers whose square is 9.

$$x^2 = 9$$
$$\sqrt{x^2} = \pm\sqrt{9}$$
$$x = \pm 3$$

The notation $\pm\sqrt{9}$ (read as "plus or minus $\sqrt{9}$") indicates the pair of numbers $+\sqrt{9}$ and $-\sqrt{9}$.

This illustrates the square root property.

▶ Helpful Hint

The notation ± 3, for example, is read as "plus or minus 3." It is a shorthand notation for the pair of numbers $+3$ and -3.

Square Root Property

If b is a real number and if $a^2 = b$, then $a = \pm\sqrt{b}$.

EXAMPLE 1 Use the square root property to solve $x^2 = 50$.

Solution

$$x^2 = 50$$
$$x = \pm\sqrt{50} \quad \text{Use the square root property.}$$
$$x = \pm 5\sqrt{2} \quad \text{Simplify the radical.}$$

Check:

Let $x = 5\sqrt{2}$.
$$x^2 = 50$$
$$(5\sqrt{2})^2 \stackrel{?}{=} 50$$
$$25 \cdot 2 \stackrel{?}{=} 50$$
$$50 = 50 \quad \text{True}$$

Let $x = -5\sqrt{2}$.
$$x^2 = 50$$
$$(-5\sqrt{2})^2 \stackrel{?}{=} 50$$
$$25 \cdot 2 \stackrel{?}{=} 50$$
$$50 = 50 \quad \text{True}$$

```
5√(2)→X:X²
                50
-5√(2)→X:X²
                50
```

A calculator check of both solutions for Example 1.

The solutions are $5\sqrt{2}$ and $-5\sqrt{2}$, or the solution set is $\{-5\sqrt{2}, 5\sqrt{2}\}$. □

PRACTICE 1 Use the square root property to solve $x^2 = 18$.

EXAMPLE 2 Use the square root property to solve $2x^2 - 14 = 0$.

Solution First we get the squared variable alone on one side of the equation.

$$2x^2 - 14 = 0$$
$$2x^2 = 14 \quad \text{Add 14 to both sides.}$$
$$x^2 = 7 \quad \text{Divide both sides by 2.}$$
$$x = \pm\sqrt{7} \quad \text{Use the square root property.}$$

Check to see that the solutions are $\sqrt{7}$ and $-\sqrt{7}$, or the solution set is $\{-\sqrt{7}, \sqrt{7}\}$. □

PRACTICE 2 Use the square root property to solve $3x^2 - 30 = 0$.

EXAMPLE 3 Use the square root property to solve $(x + 1)^2 = 12$. Use a graphing utility to check.

Solution

$$(x + 1)^2 = 12$$
$$x + 1 = \pm\sqrt{12} \quad \text{Use the square root property.}$$
$$x + 1 = \pm 2\sqrt{3} \quad \text{Simplify the radical.}$$
$$x = -1 \pm 2\sqrt{3} \quad \text{Subtract 1 from both sides.}$$

Check: Below is a check for $-1 + 2\sqrt{3}$. The check for $-1 - 2\sqrt{3}$ is almost the same and is left for you to do on your own.

$$(x + 1)^2 = 12$$
$$\left(-1 + 2\sqrt{3} + 1\right)^2 \stackrel{?}{=} 12$$
$$\left(2\sqrt{3}\right)^2 \stackrel{?}{=} 12$$
$$4 \cdot 3 \stackrel{?}{=} 12$$
$$12 = 12 \quad \text{True}$$

The solutions are $-1 + 2\sqrt{3}$ and $-1 - 2\sqrt{3}$.

To check graphically, we use the intersection-of-graphs method and graph

$$y_1 = (x + 1)^2 \quad \text{and} \quad y_2 = 12$$

The approximate points of intersection are shown below in the first two screens.

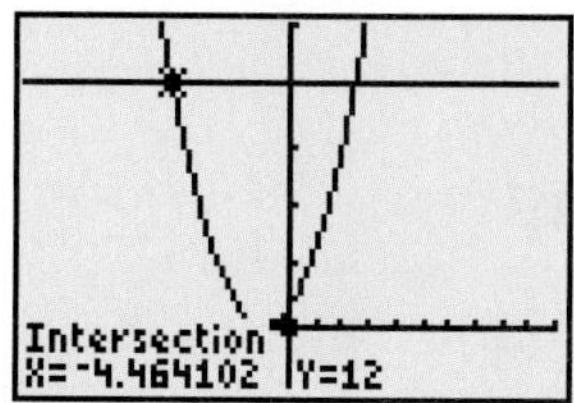

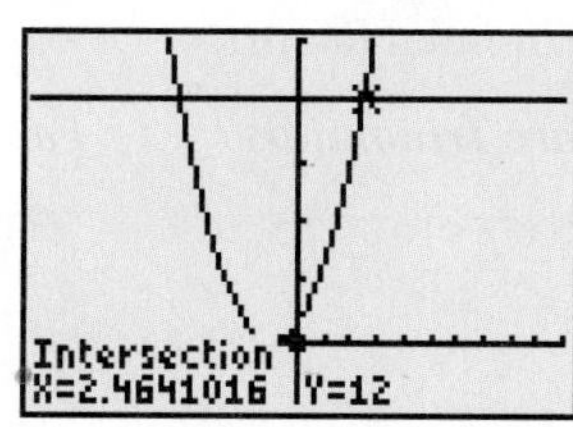

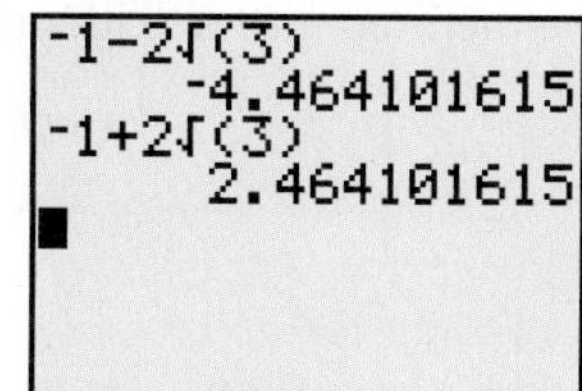

Notice that this graphical check gives approximate solutions only since $-1 + 2\sqrt{3}$ and $-1 - 2\sqrt{3}$ are irrational. The approximate solutions are $x \approx -4.464$ and $x \approx 2.464$. The exact solutions are $x = -1 + 2\sqrt{3}$ and $x = -1 - 2\sqrt{3}$.

Next, see that the x-values of the points of intersection approximate the exact solutions. The screen above and to the right confirms this. □

PRACTICE 3 Use the square root property to solve $(x + 3)^2 = 20$.

EXAMPLE 4 Use the square root property to solve $(2x - 5)^2 = -16$.

Solution

$$(2x - 5)^2 = -16$$

$$2x - 5 = \pm\sqrt{-16} \quad \text{Use the square root property.}$$

$$2x - 5 = \pm 4i \quad \text{Simplify the radical.}$$

$$2x = 5 \pm 4i \quad \text{Add 5 to both sides.}$$

$$x = \frac{5 \pm 4i}{2} \quad \text{Divide both sides by 2.}$$

The solutions are $\frac{5 + 4i}{2}$ and $\frac{5 - 4i}{2}$. □

PRACTICE 4 Use the square root property to solve $(5x - 2)^2 = -9$.

Concept Check ✓

How do you know just by looking that $(x - 2)^2 = -4$ has complex, but not real, solutions?

DISCOVER THE CONCEPT

From the previous Example 4, we know that the equation $(2x - 5)^2 = -16$ has two complex, but not real, solutions. Use the intersection-of-graphs method to check.

a. Graph $y_1 = (2x - 5)^2$ and $y_2 = -16$.

b. Locate any points of intersection of the graphs.

c. Summarize the results of parts **a** and **b**, and what you think occurred.

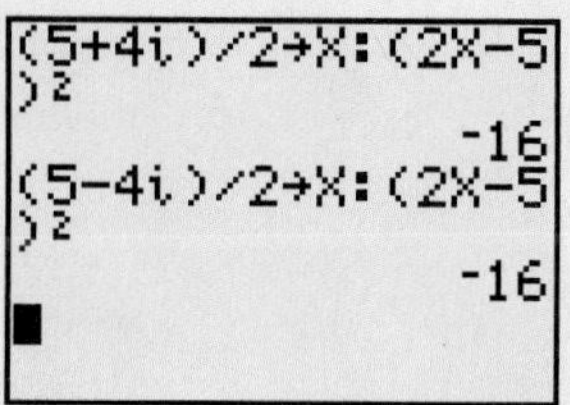

The x-axis and the y-axis of the rectangular coordinate system include real numbers only. Thus, coordinates of points of the associated plane are real numbers only. This means that the intersection-of-graphs method on the rectangular coordinate system gives real number solutions of a related equation only. Since the graphs above do not intersect, the equation has no real number solutions.

To check Example 4 numerically, see the screen to the left.

OBJECTIVE 2 ▶ Solving by completing the square. Notice from Examples 3 and 4 that, if we write a quadratic equation so that one side is the square of a binomial, we can solve by using the square root property. To write the square of a binomial, we write perfect square trinomials. Recall that a perfect square trinomial is a trinomial that can be factored into two identical binomial factors.

Perfect Square Trinomials	***Factored Form***
$x^2 + 8x + 16$	$(x + 4)^2$
$x^2 - 6x + 9$	$(x - 3)^2$
$x^2 + 3x + \frac{9}{4}$	$\left(x + \frac{3}{2}\right)^2$

Notice that for each perfect square trinomial, **the constant term of the trinomial is the square of half the coefficient of the x-term.** For example,

$$x^2 + 8x + 16 \qquad x^2 - 6x + 9$$

$$\frac{1}{2}(8) = 4 \text{ and } 4^2 = 16 \qquad \frac{1}{2}(-6) = -3 \text{ and } (-3)^2 = 9$$

The process of writing a quadratic equation so that one side is a perfect square trinomial is called **completing the square.**

Answer to Concept Check: answers may vary

EXAMPLE 5 Solve $p^2 + 2p = 4$ by completing the square.

Solution First, add the square of half the coefficient of p to both sides so that the resulting trinomial will be a perfect square trinomial. The coefficient of p is 2.

$$\frac{1}{2}(2) = 1 \quad \text{and} \quad 1^2 = 1$$

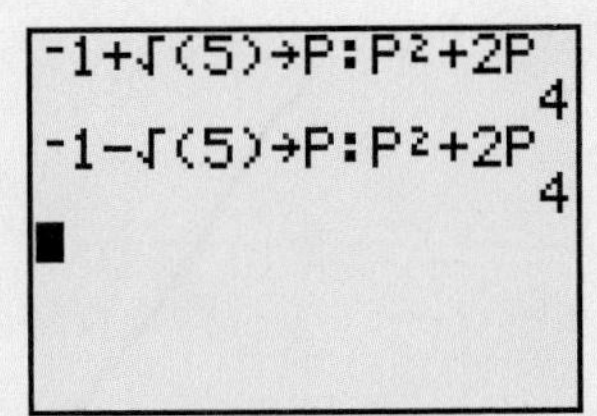

Add 1 to both sides of the original equation.

$$p^2 + 2p = 4$$

$$p^2 + 2p + 1 = 4 + 1 \quad \text{Add 1 to both sides.}$$

$$(p + 1)^2 = 5 \quad \text{Factor the trinomial; simplify the right side.}$$

We may now use the square root property and solve for p.

$$p + 1 = \pm\sqrt{5} \quad \text{Use the square root property.}$$

$$p = -1 \pm \sqrt{5} \quad \text{Subtract 1 from both sides.}$$

Notice that there are two solutions: $-1 + \sqrt{5}$ and $-1 - \sqrt{5}$. A numerical check is shown to the left. □

PRACTICE 5 Solve $b^2 + 4b = 3$ by completing the square.

EXAMPLE 6 Solve $m^2 - 7m - 1 = 0$ for m.

Algebraic Solution:

To solve by completing the square, we first add 1 to both sides of the equation so that the left side has no constant term.

$$m^2 - 7m - 1 = 0$$

$$m^2 - 7m = 1$$

Now find the constant term that makes the left side a perfect square trinomial by squaring half the coefficient of m. Add this constant to both sides of the equation.

$$\frac{1}{2}(-7) = -\frac{7}{2}$$

and

$$\left(-\frac{7}{2}\right)^2 = \frac{49}{4}$$

$$m^2 - 7m + \frac{49}{4} = 1 + \frac{49}{4} \quad \text{Add } \frac{49}{4} \text{ to both sides of the equation.}$$

$$\left(m - \frac{7}{2}\right)^2 = \frac{53}{4} \quad \text{Factor the perfect square trinomial and simplify the right side.}$$

$$m - \frac{7}{2} = \pm\sqrt{\frac{53}{4}} \quad \text{Apply the square root property.}$$

$$m = \frac{7}{2} \pm \frac{\sqrt{53}}{2} \quad \text{Add } \frac{7}{2} \text{ to both sides and simplify } \sqrt{\frac{53}{4}}.$$

$$m = \frac{7 \pm \sqrt{53}}{2} \quad \text{Simplify.}$$

Graphical Solution:

Enter $y_1 = x^2 - 7x - 1$ and find the x-intercepts of the graph, or the zeros by using the zero option on the Calc menu.

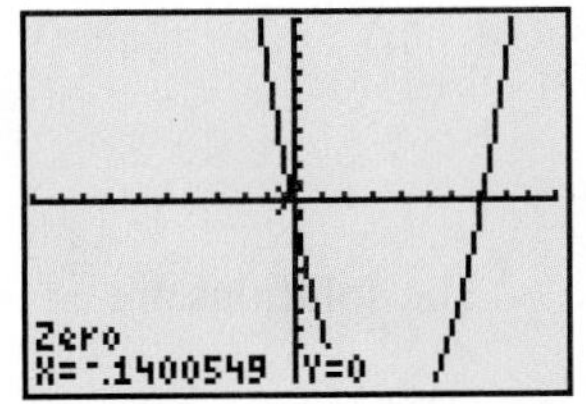

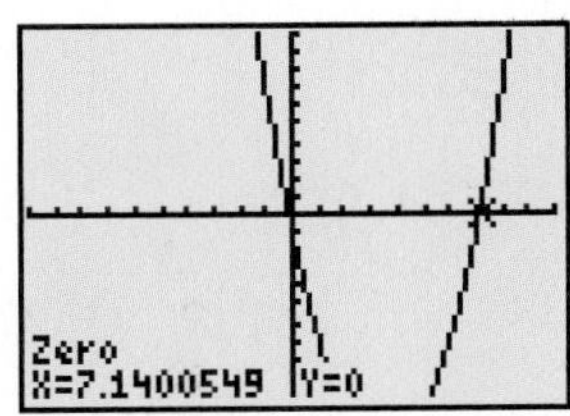

Rounded to the nearest hundredth we have x (or m) ≈ -0.14 and x (or m) ≈ 7.14. These are approximations of the exact solutions as shown below.

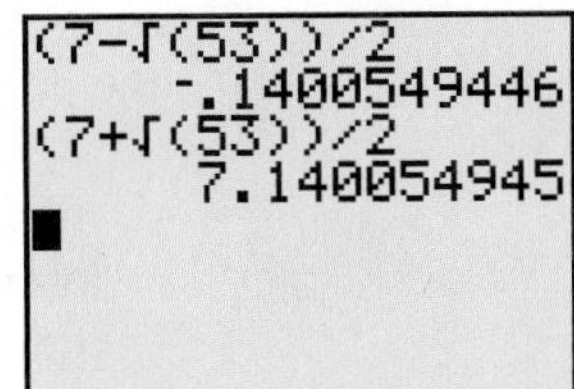

The solutions are $\frac{7 + \sqrt{53}}{2}$ and $\frac{7 - \sqrt{53}}{2}$. □

PRACTICE 6 Solve $p^2 - 3p + 1 = 0$ by completing the square.

EXAMPLE 7 Solve: $2x^2 - 8x + 3 = 0$.

Solution Our procedure for finding the constant term to complete the square works only if the coefficient of the squared variable term is 1. Therefore, to solve this equation, the first step is to divide both sides by 2, the coefficient of x^2.

$$2x^2 - 8x + 3 = 0$$

$$x^2 - 4x + \frac{3}{2} = 0 \quad \text{Divide both sides by 2.}$$

$$x^2 - 4x = -\frac{3}{2} \quad \text{Subtract } \frac{3}{2} \text{ from both sides.}$$

Next find the square of half of -4.

$$\frac{1}{2}(-4) = -2 \quad \text{and} \quad (-2)^2 = 4$$

Add 4 to both sides of the equation to complete the square.

$$x^2 - 4x + 4 = -\frac{3}{2} + 4$$

$$(x - 2)^2 = \frac{5}{2} \quad \text{Factor the perfect square and simplify the right side.}$$

$$x - 2 = \pm\sqrt{\frac{5}{2}} \quad \text{Apply the square root property.}$$

$$x - 2 = \pm\frac{\sqrt{10}}{2} \quad \text{Rationalize the denominator.}$$

$$x = 2 \pm \frac{\sqrt{10}}{2} \quad \text{Add 2 to both sides.}$$

$$= \frac{4}{2} \pm \frac{\sqrt{10}}{2} \quad \text{Find the common denominator.}$$

$$= \frac{4 \pm \sqrt{10}}{2} \quad \text{Simplify.}$$

The solutions are $\frac{4 + \sqrt{10}}{2}$ and $\frac{4 - \sqrt{10}}{2}$. □

PRACTICE 7 Solve: $3x^2 - 12x + 1 = 0$.

The following steps may be used to solve a quadratic equation such as $ax^2 + bx + c = 0$ by completing the square. This method may be used whether or not the polynomial $ax^2 + bx + c$ is factorable.

Solving a Quadratic Equation in x by Completing the Square

STEP 1. If the coefficient of x^2 is 1, go to Step 2. Otherwise, divide both sides of the equation by the coefficient of x^2.

STEP 2. Isolate all variable terms on one side of the equation.

STEP 3. Complete the square for the resulting binomial by adding the square of half of the coefficient of x to both sides of the equation.

STEP 4. Factor the resulting perfect square trinomial and write it as the square of a binomial.

STEP 5. Use the square root property to solve for x.

EXAMPLE 8 Solve $3x^2 - 9x + 8 = 0$ by completing the square.

Solution $3x^2 - 9x + 8 = 0$

STEP 1. $x^2 - 3x + \frac{8}{3} = 0$ Divide both sides of the equation by 3.

STEP 2. $x^2 - 3x = -\frac{8}{3}$ Subtract $\frac{8}{3}$ from both sides.

Since $\frac{1}{2}(-3) = -\frac{3}{2}$ and $\left(-\frac{3}{2}\right)^2 = \frac{9}{4}$, we add $\frac{9}{4}$ to both sides of the equation.

STEP 3. $x^2 - 3x + \frac{9}{4} = -\frac{8}{3} + \frac{9}{4}$

STEP 4. $\left(x - \frac{3}{2}\right)^2 = -\frac{5}{12}$ Factor the perfect square trinomial.

STEP 5. $x - \frac{3}{2} = \pm\sqrt{-\frac{5}{12}}$ Apply the square root property.

$x - \frac{3}{2} = \pm\frac{i\sqrt{5}}{2\sqrt{3}}$ Simplify the radical.

$x - \frac{3}{2} = \pm\frac{i\sqrt{15}}{6}$ Rationalize the denominator.

$x = \frac{3}{2} \pm \frac{i\sqrt{15}}{6}$ Add $\frac{3}{2}$ to both sides.

$= \frac{9}{6} \pm \frac{i\sqrt{15}}{6}$ Find a common denominator.

$= \frac{9 \pm i\sqrt{15}}{6}$ Simplify.

The solutions are $\frac{9 + i\sqrt{15}}{6}$ and $\frac{9 - i\sqrt{15}}{6}$. □

PRACTICE 8 Solve $2x^2 - 5x + 7 = 0$ by completing the square.

OBJECTIVE 3 ▶ Solving problems modeled by quadratic equations. Recall the **simple interest** formula $I = Prt$, where I is the interest earned, P is the principal, r is the rate of interest, and t is time in years. If \$100 is invested at a simple interest rate of 5% annually, at the end of 3 years the total interest I earned is

$$I = P \cdot r \cdot t$$

or

$$I = 100 \cdot 0.05 \cdot 3 = \$15$$

and the new principal is

$$\$100 + \$15 = \$115$$

Most of the time, the interest computed on money borrowed or money deposited is **compound interest.** Compound interest, unlike simple interest, is computed on original principal *and* on interest already earned. To see the difference between simple interest and compound interest, suppose that \$100 is invested at a rate of 5% compounded annually. To find the total amount of money at the end of 3 years, we calculate as follows.

$$I = P \cdot r \cdot t$$

First year: Interest = \$100 · 0.05 · 1 = \$5.00
New principal = \$100.00 + \$5.00 = \$105.00

Second year: Interest = $105.00 · 0.05 · 1 = $5.25
New principal = $105.00 + $5.25 = $110.25

Third year: Interest = $110.25 · 0.05 · 1 ≈ $5.51
New principal = $110.25 + $5.51 = $115.76

At the end of the third year, the total compound interest earned is $15.76, whereas the total simple interest earned is $15.

It is tedious to calculate compound interest as we did above, so we use a compound interest formula. The formula for calculating the total amount of money when interest is compounded annually is

$$A = P(1 + r)^t$$

where P is the original investment, r is the interest rate per compounding period, and t is the number of periods. For example, the amount of money A at the end of 3 years if $100 is invested at 5% compounded annually is

$$A = \$100(1 + 0.05)^3 \approx \$100(1.1576) = \$115.76$$

as we previously calculated.

EXAMPLE 9 **Finding Interest Rates**

Use the formula $A = P(1 + r)^t$ to find the interest rate r if $2000 compounded annually grows to $2420 in 2 years.

Solution

1. UNDERSTAND the problem. Since the $2000 is compounded annually, we use the compound interest formula. For this example, make sure that you understand the formula for compounding interest annually.
2. TRANSLATE. We substitute the given values into the formula.

$$A = P(1 + r)^t$$
$$2420 = 2000(1 + r)^2 \qquad \text{Let } A = 2420,\ P = 2000, \text{ and } t = 2.$$

3. SOLVE. Solve the equation for r. We will solve algebraically and graphically.

Algebraic Solution:

$2420 = 2000(1 + r)^2$

$\frac{2420}{2000} = (1 + r)^2$ Divide both sides by 2000.

$\frac{121}{100} = (1 + r)^2$ Simplify the fraction.

$\pm\sqrt{\frac{121}{100}} = 1 + r$ Use the square root property.

$\pm\frac{11}{10} = 1 + r$ Simplify.

$-1 \pm \frac{11}{10} = r$

$-\frac{10}{10} \pm \frac{11}{10} = r$

$\frac{1}{10} = r$ or $-\frac{21}{10} = r$

Graphical Solution:

Enter $y_1 = 2000(1 + x)^2$ and $y_2 = 2420$. You may need to experiment a little before you find an appropriate window, but keep the following in mind. Since $y_2 = 2420$, use a window for the y-axis that includes this number. Since x represents the rate, use a much smaller window for the x-axis. The viewing window for the graph below is $[-2.5, 1, 0.1]$ for x and $[2000, 3000, 200]$ for y.

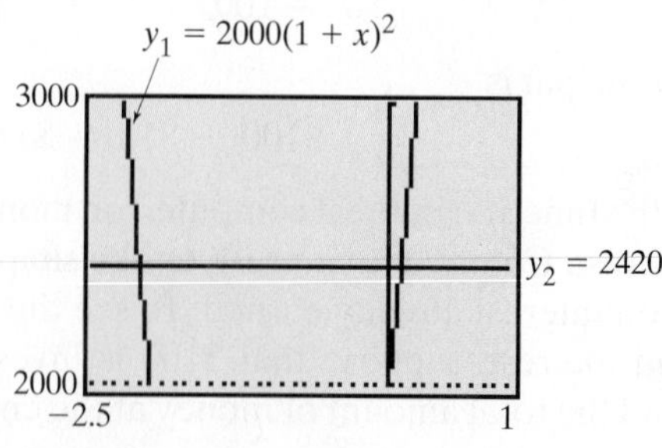

The two points of intersection have x-coordinates of -2.1 and 0.1.

4. INTERPRET. The rate cannot be negative, so we reject $-\frac{21}{10}$.

Check: $\frac{1}{10} = 0.10 = 10\%$ per year. If we invest \$2000 at 10% compounded annually, in 2 years the amount in the account would be $2000(1 + 0.10)^2 = 2420$ dollars, the desired amount.

State: The interest rate is 10% compounded annually. □

PRACTICE 9 Use the formula from Example 9 to find the interest rate r if \$5000 compounded annually grows to \$5618 in 2 years.

VOCABULARY & READINESS CHECK

Use the choices below to fill in each blank. Not all choices will be used.

binomial	$\sqrt{b}$	$\pm\sqrt{b}$	b^2	9	25	completing the square
quadratic	$-\sqrt{b}$	$\frac{b}{2}$	$\left(\frac{b}{2}\right)^2$	3	5	

1. By the square root property, if b is a real number, and $a^2 = b$, then $a =$ ________.

2. A ____________ equation can be written in the form $ax^2 + bx + c = 0, a \neq 0$.

3. The process of writing a quadratic equation so that one side is a perfect square trinomial is called ________________.

4. A perfect square trinomial is one that can be factored as a ____________ squared.

5. To solve $x^2 + 6x = 10$ by completing the square, add _____ to both sides.

6. To solve $x^2 + bx = c$ by completing the square, add _________ to both sides.

Fill in the blank with the number needed to make the expression a perfect square trinomial.

7. $m^2 + 2m +$ ______

8. $m^2 - 2m +$ ______

9. $y^2 - 14y +$ ______

10. $z^2 + z +$ ______

20.1 EXERCISE SET

Powered by CourseCompass and MathXL **MyMathLab**

PRACTICE

WATCH

DOWNLOAD

READ

REVIEW

Use the square root property to solve each equation. These equations have real number solutions. See Examples 1 through 3.

1. $x^2 = 16$

2. $x^2 = 49$

3. $x^2 - 7 = 0$

4. $x^2 - 11 = 0$

5. $x^2 = 18$

6. $y^2 = 20$

7. $3z^2 - 30 = 0$

8. $2x^2 - 4 = 0$

9. $(x + 5)^2 = 9$

10. $(y - 3)^2 = 4$

11. $(z - 6)^2 = 18$

12. $(y + 4)^2 = 27$

13. $(2x - 3)^2 = 8$

14. $(4x + 9)^2 = 6$

Use the square root property to solve each equation. See Examples 1 through 4.

15. $x^2 + 9 = 0$

16. $x^2 + 4 = 0$

17. $x^2 - 6 = 0$

18. $y^2 - 10 = 0$

19. $2z^2 + 16 = 0$

20. $3p^2 + 36 = 0$

21. $(x - 1)^2 = -16$

22. $(y + 2)^2 = -25$

23. $(z + 7)^2 = 5$

24. $(x + 10)^2 = 11$

25. $(x + 3)^2 = -8$

26. $(y - 4)^2 = -18$

Add the proper constant to each binomial so that the resulting trinomial is a perfect square trinomial. Then factor the trinomial.

27. $x^2 + 16x +$ __________

28. $y^2 + 2y +$ __________

29. $z^2 - 12z +$ __________

30. $x^2 - 8x +$ __________

31. $p^2 + 9p +$ ________

32. $n^2 + 5n +$ ________

33. $x^2 + x +$ ________

34. $y^2 - y +$ ________

MIXED PRACTICE

Solve each equation by completing the square. These equations have real number solutions. See Examples 5 through 7.

35. $x^2 + 8x = -15$

36. $y^2 + 6y = -8$

37. $x^2 + 6x + 2 = 0$

38. $x^2 - 2x - 2 = 0$

39. $x^2 + x - 1 = 0$

40. $x^2 + 3x - 2 = 0$

41. $x^2 + 2x - 5 = 0$

42. $y^2 + y - 7 = 0$

43. $3p^2 - 12p + 2 = 0$

44. $2x^2 + 14x - 1 = 0$

45. $4y^2 - 12y - 2 = 0$

46. $6x^2 - 3 = 6x$

47. $2x^2 + 7x = 4$

48. $3x^2 - 4x = 4$

49. $x^2 - 4x - 5 = 0$

50. $y^2 + 6y - 8 = 0$

51. $x^2 + 8x + 1 = 0$

52. $x^2 - 10x + 2 = 0$

53. $3y^2 + 6y - 4 = 0$

54. $2y^2 + 12y + 3 = 0$

55. $2x^2 - 3x - 5 = 0$

56. $5x^2 + 3x - 2 = 0$

Solve each equation by completing the square. See Examples 5 through 8.

57. $y^2 + 2y + 2 = 0$

58. $x^2 + 4x + 6 = 0$

59. $x^2 - 6x + 3 = 0$

60. $x^2 - 7x - 1 = 0$

61. $2a^2 + 8a = -12$

62. $3x^2 + 12x = -14$

63. $x^2 + 10x + 28 = 0$

64. $y^2 + 8y + 18 = 0$

65. $z^2 + 3z - 4 = 0$

66. $y^2 + y - 2 = 0$

67. $2x^2 - 4x = -3$

68. $9x^2 - 36x = -40$

69. $3x^2 + 3x = 5$

70. $5y^2 - 15y = 1$

Use the graph to determine how many real number solutions exist for each equation.

71. $2x^2 - 3x - 5 = 0$
$y = 2x^2 - 3x - 5$

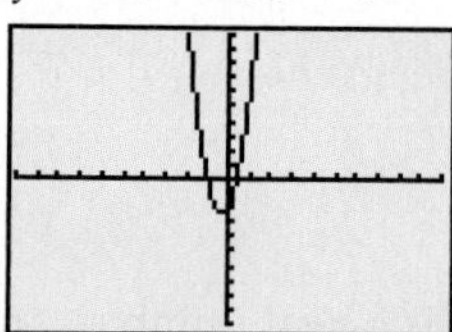

72. $5x^2 + 3x - 2 = 0$
$y = 5x^2 + 3x - 2$

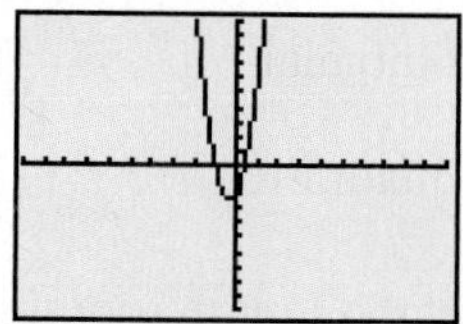

73. $x^2 + 2x + 2 = 0$
$y = x^2 + 2x + 2$

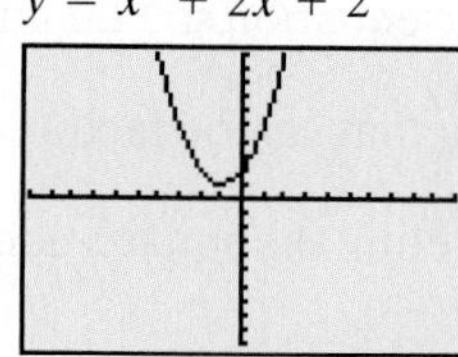

74. $x^2 + 4x + 6 = 0$
$y = x^2 + 4x + 6$

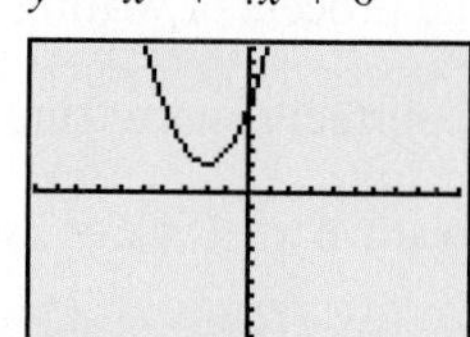

Use the formula $A = P(1 + r)^t$ to solve Exercises 75 through 78. See Example 9.

75. Find the rate r at which \$3000 compounded annually grows to \$4320 in 2 years.

76. Find the rate r at which \$800 compounded annually grows to \$882 in 2 years.

77. Find the rate at which \$15,000 compounded annually grows to \$16,224 in 2 years.

78. Find the rate at which \$2000 compounded annually grows to \$2880 in 2 years.

79. In your own words, what is the difference between simple interest and compound interest?

Neglecting air resistance, the distance $s(t)$ in feet traveled by a freely falling object is given by the function $s(t) = 16t^2$, where t is time in seconds. Use this formula to solve Exercises 80 through 83. Round answers to two decimal places.

80. The Petronas Towers in Kuala Lumpur, built in 1997, are the tallest buildings in Malaysia. Each tower is 1483 feet tall. How long would it take an object to fall to the ground from the top of one of the towers? (*Source:* Council on Tall Buildings and Urban Habitat, Lehigh University)

81. The height of the Chicago Beach Tower Hotel, built in 1998 in Dubai, United Arab Emirates, is 1053 feet. How long would it take an object to fall to the ground from the top of the building? (*Source:* Council on Tall Buildings and Urban Habitat, Lehigh University)

82. The height of the Nurek Dam in Tajikistan (part of the former USSR that borders Afghanistan) is 984 feet. How long would it take an object to fall from the top to the base of the dam? (*Source:* U.S. Committee on Large Dams of the International Commission on Large Dams)

83. The Hoover Dam, located on the Colorado River on the border of Nevada and Arizona near Las Vegas, is 725 feet tall. How long would it take an object to fall from the top to the base of the dam? (*Source:* U.S. Committee on Large Dams of the International Commission on Large Dams)

84. If you are depositing money in an account that pays 4%, would you prefer the interest to be simple or compound? Explain why.

85. If you are borrowing money at a rate of 10%, would you prefer the interest to be simple or compound? Explain why.

REVIEW AND PREVIEW

Simplify each expression. See Section 19.1.

86. $\frac{3}{4} - \sqrt{\frac{25}{16}}$ **87.** $\frac{3}{5} + \sqrt{\frac{16}{25}}$

88. $\frac{1}{2} - \sqrt{\frac{9}{4}}$ **89.** $\frac{9}{10} - \sqrt{\frac{49}{100}}$

Simplify each expression. See Section 18.1.

90. $\frac{6 + 4\sqrt{5}}{2}$ **91.** $\frac{10 - 20\sqrt{3}}{2}$

92. $\frac{3 - 9\sqrt{2}}{6}$ **93.** $\frac{12 - 8\sqrt{7}}{16}$

Evaluate $\sqrt{b^2 - 4ac}$ for each set of values. See Section 19.1.

94. $a = 2, b = 4, c = -1$ **95.** $a = 1, b = 6, c = 2$

96. $a = 3, b = -1, c = -2$ **97.** $a = 1, b = -3, c = -1$

CONCEPT EXTENSIONS

Without solving, determine whether the solutions of each equation are real numbers or complex, but not real, numbers. See the Concept Check in this section.

98. $(x + 1)^2 = -1$

99. $(y - 5)^2 = -9$

100. $3z^2 = 10$

101. $4x^2 = 17$

102. $(2y - 5)^2 + 7 = 3$

103. $(3m + 2)^2 + 4 = 1$

Find two possible missing terms so that each is a perfect square trinomial.

104. $x^2 + \quad + 16$ **105.** $y^2 + \quad + 9$

106. $z^2 + \quad + \frac{25}{4}$ **107.** $x^2 + \quad + \frac{1}{4}$

Solve.

△ **108.** The area of a square room is 225 square feet. Find the dimensions of the room.

△ **109.** The area of a circle is 36π square inches. Find the radius of the circle.

△ **110.** An isosceles right triangle has legs of equal length. If the hypotenuse is 20 centimeters long, find the length of each leg.

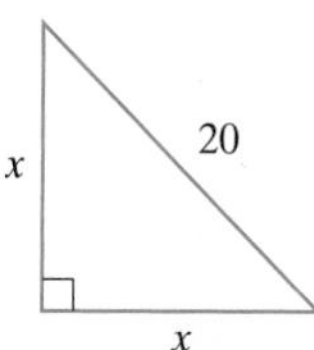

△ **111.** A 27-inch TV is advertised in the *Daily Sentry* newspaper. If 27 inches is the measure of the diagonal of the picture tube, find the measure of each side of the picture tube.

A common equation used in business is a demand equation. It expresses the relationship between the unit price of some commodity and the quantity demanded. For Exercises 112 and 113, p represents the unit price and x represents the quantity demanded in thousands.

112. A manufacturing company has found that the demand equation for a certain type of scissors is given by the equation $p = -x^2 + 47$. Find the demand for the scissors if the price is \$11 per pair.

113. Acme, Inc., sells desk lamps and has found that the demand equation for a certain style of desk lamp is given by the equation $p = -x^2 + 15$. Find the demand for the desk lamp if the price is \$7 per lamp.

20.2 SOLVING QUADRATIC EQUATIONS BY THE QUADRATIC FORMULA

OBJECTIVES

1. Solve quadratic equations by using the quadratic formula.
2. Determine the number and type of solutions of a quadratic equation by using the discriminant.
3. Solve geometric problems modeled by quadratic equations.

OBJECTIVE 1 ▶ Solving quadratic equations by using the quadratic formula. Any quadratic equation can be solved by completing the square. Since the same sequence of steps is repeated each time we complete the square, let's complete the square for a general quadratic equation, $ax^2 + bx + c = 0, a \neq 0$. By doing so, we find a pattern for the solutions of a quadratic equation known as the **quadratic formula.**

Recall that to complete the square for an equation such as $ax^2 + bx + c = 0$, we first divide both sides by the coefficient of x^2.

$$ax^2 + bx + c = 0$$

$$x^2 + \frac{b}{a}x + \frac{c}{a} = 0 \quad \text{Divide both sides by } a\text{, the coefficient of } x^2.$$

$$x^2 + \frac{b}{a}x = -\frac{c}{a} \quad \text{Subtract the constant } \frac{c}{a} \text{ from both sides.}$$

Next, find the square of half $\frac{b}{a}$, the coefficient of x.

$$\frac{1}{2}\left(\frac{b}{a}\right) = \frac{b}{2a} \quad \text{and} \quad \left(\frac{b}{2a}\right)^2 = \frac{b^2}{4a^2}$$

Add this result to both sides of the equation.

$$x^2 + \frac{b}{a}x + \frac{b^2}{4a^2} = -\frac{c}{a} + \frac{b^2}{4a^2} \quad \text{Add } \frac{b^2}{4a^2} \text{ to both sides.}$$

$$x^2 + \frac{b}{a}x + \frac{b^2}{4a^2} = \frac{-c \cdot 4a}{a \cdot 4a} + \frac{b^2}{4a^2} \quad \text{Find a common denominator on the right side.}$$

$$x^2 + \frac{b}{a}x + \frac{b^2}{4a^2} = \frac{b^2 - 4ac}{4a^2} \quad \text{Simplify the right side.}$$

$$\left(x + \frac{b}{2a}\right)^2 = \frac{b^2 - 4ac}{4a^2} \quad \text{Factor the perfect square trinomial on the left side.}$$

$$x + \frac{b}{2a} = \pm\sqrt{\frac{b^2 - 4ac}{4a^2}} \quad \text{Apply the square root property.}$$

$$x + \frac{b}{2a} = \pm\frac{\sqrt{b^2 - 4ac}}{2a} \quad \text{Simplify the radical.}$$

$$x = -\frac{b}{2a} \pm \frac{\sqrt{b^2 - 4ac}}{2a} \quad \text{Subtract } \frac{b}{2a} \text{ from both sides.}$$

$$x = \frac{-b \pm \sqrt{b^2 - 4ac}}{2a} \quad \text{Simplify.}$$

TECHNOLOGY NOTE

When evaluating the quadratic formula using a calculator, it is sometimes more convenient to evaluate the radicand separately. This prevents incorrect placement of parentheses.

This equation identifies the solutions of the general quadratic equation in standard form and is called the quadratic formula. It can be used to solve any equation written in standard form, $ax^2 + bx + c = 0$, as long as a is not 0.

Quadratic Formula

A quadratic equation written in the form $ax^2 + bx + c = 0$ has the solutions

$$x = \frac{-b \pm \sqrt{b^2 - 4ac}}{2a}$$

EXAMPLE 1 Solve $3x^2 + 16x + 5 = 0$ for x.

Solution This equation is in standard form, so $a = 3$, $b = 16$, and $c = 5$. Substitute these values into the quadratic formula.

$$x = \frac{-b \pm \sqrt{b^2 - 4ac}}{2a} \quad \text{Quadratic formula}$$

$$= \frac{-16 \pm \sqrt{16^2 - 4(3)(5)}}{2 \cdot 3} \quad \text{Use } a = 3, b = 16, \text{ and } c = 5.$$

$$= \frac{-16 \pm \sqrt{256 - 60}}{6}$$

$$= \frac{-16 \pm \sqrt{196}}{6} = \frac{-16 \pm 14}{6}$$

$$x = \frac{-16 + 14}{6} = -\frac{1}{3} \quad \text{or} \quad x = \frac{-16 - 14}{6} = -\frac{30}{6} = -5$$

The solutions are $-\frac{1}{3}$ and -5, or the solution set is $\left\{-\frac{1}{3}, -5\right\}$. A numerical check is shown to the left. Notice the correct placement of parentheses. □

Checking Example 1 numerically by evaluating the formula using a calculator.

PRACTICE 1 Solve $3x^2 - 5x - 2 = 0$ for x.

As usual, another way to check the solution of an equation is to use a graphical method such as the intersection-of-graphs method. Remember that this graphical method shows real number solutions only.

EXAMPLE 2 Solve: $2x^2 - 4x = 3$.

Solution First write the equation in standard form by subtracting 3 from both sides.

$$2x^2 - 4x - 3 = 0$$

Helpful Hint
To replace a, b, and c correctly in the quadratic formula, write the quadratic equation in standard form, $ax^2 + bx + c = 0$.

Now $a = 2$, $b = -4$, and $c = -3$. Substitute these values into the quadratic formula.

$$x = \frac{-b \pm \sqrt{b^2 - 4ac}}{2a}$$

$$= \frac{-(-4) \pm \sqrt{(-4)^2 - 4(2)(-3)}}{2 \cdot 2}$$

$$= \frac{4 \pm \sqrt{16 + 24}}{4}$$

$$= \frac{4 \pm \sqrt{40}}{4} = \frac{4 \pm 2\sqrt{10}}{4}$$

$$= \frac{2(2 \pm \sqrt{10})}{2 \cdot 2} = \frac{2 \pm \sqrt{10}}{2}$$

The solutions are $\frac{2 + \sqrt{10}}{2}$ and $\frac{2 - \sqrt{10}}{2}$, or the solution set is $\left\{\frac{2 - \sqrt{10}}{2}, \frac{2 + \sqrt{10}}{2}\right\}$.

Since the solutions are real numbers, let's check using the intersection-of-graphs method. To do so, graph $y_1 = 2x^2 - 4x$ and $y_2 = 3$. Find the approximate points of intersection as shown next, and see that the exact solutions have the same approximations.

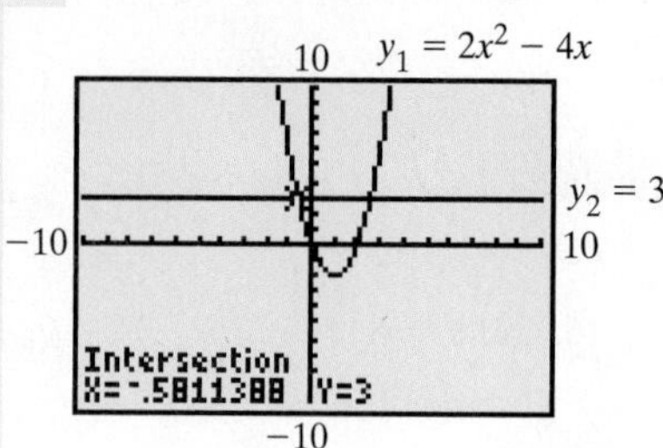

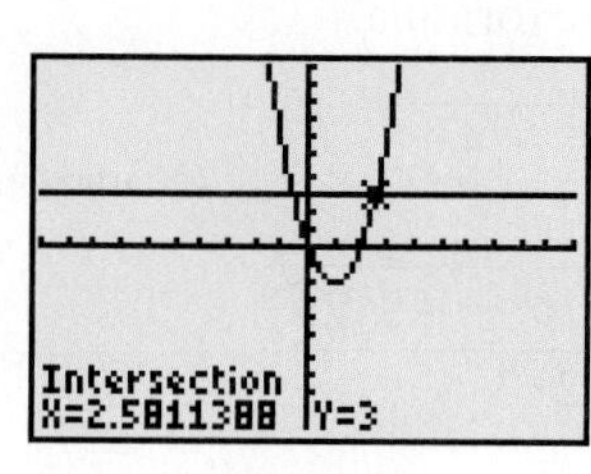

The screen to the right above shows that the exact solutions using the quadratic formula have the same approximations as those found by the intersection-of-graphs method. □

PRACTICE 2 Solve: $3x^2 - 8x = 2$.

Helpful Hint

To simplify the expression $\frac{4 \pm 2\sqrt{10}}{4}$ in the preceding example, note that 2 is factored out of both terms of the numerator *before* simplifying.

$$\frac{4 \pm 2\sqrt{10}}{4} = \frac{2(2 \pm \sqrt{10})}{2 \cdot 2} = \frac{2 \pm \sqrt{10}}{2}$$

Concept Check ✓

For the quadratic equation $x^2 = 7$, which substitution is correct?

a. $a = 1, b = 0$, and $c = -7$

b. $a = 1, b = 0$, and $c = 7$

c. $a = 0, b = 0$, and $c = 7$

d. $a = 1, b = 1$, and $c = -7$

EXAMPLE 3 Solve: $\frac{1}{4}m^2 - m + \frac{1}{2} = 0$.

Solution We could use the quadratic formula with $a = \frac{1}{4}$, $b = -1$, and $c = \frac{1}{2}$. Instead, we find a simpler, equivalent standard form equation whose coefficients are not fractions.

Multiply both sides of the equation by the LCD, 4, to clear fractions.

$$4\left(\frac{1}{4}m^2 - m + \frac{1}{2}\right) = 4 \cdot 0$$

$$m^2 - 4m + 2 = 0 \quad \text{Simplify.}$$

Substitute $a = 1, b = -4$, and $c = 2$ into the quadratic formula and simplify.

$$m = \frac{-(-4) \pm \sqrt{(-4)^2 - 4(1)(2)}}{2 \cdot 1} = \frac{4 \pm \sqrt{16 - 8}}{2}$$

$$= \frac{4 \pm \sqrt{8}}{2} = \frac{4 \pm 2\sqrt{2}}{2} = \frac{2(2 \pm \sqrt{2})}{2}$$

$$= 2 \pm \sqrt{2}$$

The solutions are $2 + \sqrt{2}$ and $2 - \sqrt{2}$. □

PRACTICE 3 Solve: $\frac{1}{8}x^2 - \frac{1}{4}x - 2 = 0$.

Answer to Concept Check: a

EXAMPLE 4 Solve: $x = -3x^2 - 3$.

Solution The equation in standard form is $3x^2 + x + 3 = 0$. Thus, let $a = 3, b = 1$, and $c = 3$ in the quadratic formula.

$$x = \frac{-1 \pm \sqrt{1^2 - 4(3)(3)}}{2 \cdot 3} = \frac{-1 \pm \sqrt{1 - 36}}{6} = \frac{-1 \pm \sqrt{-35}}{6} = \frac{-1 \pm i\sqrt{35}}{6}$$

The solutions are $\frac{-1 + i\sqrt{35}}{6}$ and $\frac{-1 - i\sqrt{35}}{6}$.

Since the solutions are not real numbers, we check numerically as shown below.

```
(-1+i√(35))/6→P:
3P²+P+3
                0
(-1-i√(35))/6→P:
3P²+P+3
                0
```

□

PRACTICE 4 Solve: $x = -2x^2 - 2$.

Concept Check ✓

What is the first step in solving $-3x^2 = 5x - 4$ using the quadratic formula?

In Example 1, the equation $3x^2 + 16x + 5 = 0$ had 2 real roots, $-\frac{1}{3}$ and -5. In Example 4, the equation $3x^2 + x + 3 = 0$ (written in standard form) had no real roots. How do their related graphs compare? Recall that the x-intercepts of $f(x) = 3x^2 + 16x + 5$ occur where $f(x) = 0$ or where $3x^2 + 16x + 5 = 0$. Since this equation has 2 real roots, the graph has 2 x-intercepts. Similarly, since the equation $3x^2 + x + 3 = 0$ has no real roots, the graph of $f(x) = 3x^2 + x + 3$ has no x-intercepts.

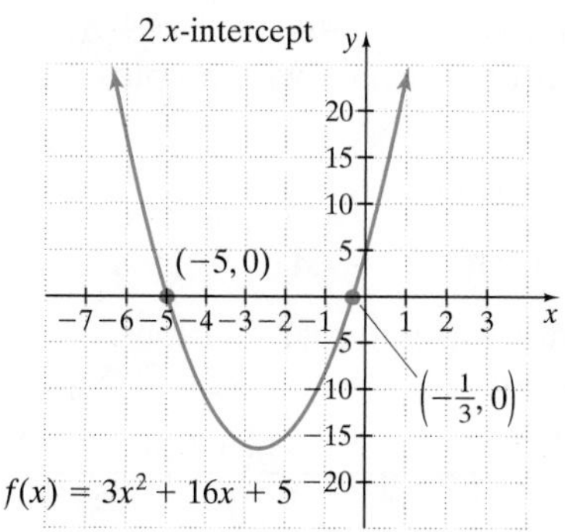

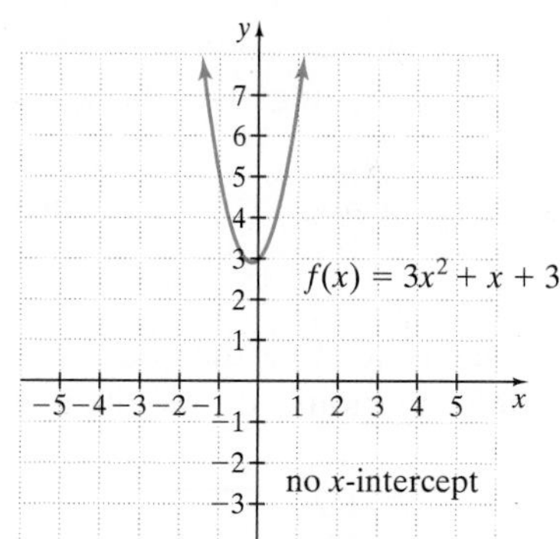

OBJECTIVE 2 ▶ Using the discriminant. In the quadratic formula, $x = \frac{-b \pm \sqrt{b^2 - 4ac}}{2a}$, the radicand $b^2 - 4ac$ is called the **discriminant** because, by knowing its value, we can **discriminate** among the possible number and type of solutions of a quadratic equation. Possible values of the discriminant and their meanings are summarized next.

Answer to Concept Check:
Write the equation in standard form.

Discriminant

The following table corresponds the discriminant $b^2 - 4ac$ of a quadratic equation of the form $ax^2 + bx + c = 0$ with the number and type of solutions of the equation.

$b^2 - 4ac$	*Number and Type of Solutions*
Positive	Two real solutions
Zero	One real solution
Negative	Two complex but not real solutions

To see the results of the discriminant graphically, study the screens below showing examples of graphs of $y = ax^2 + bx + c$.

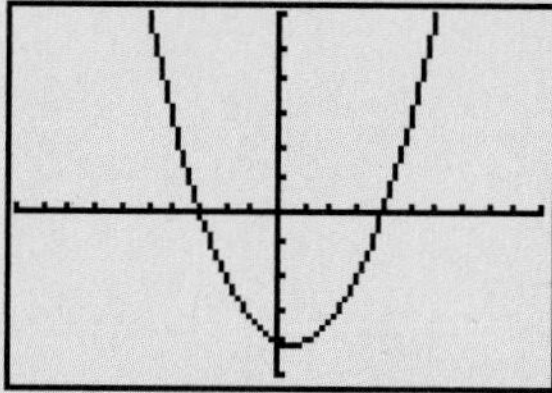

$b^2 - 4ac$ is positive
Two x-intercepts
Two real solutions

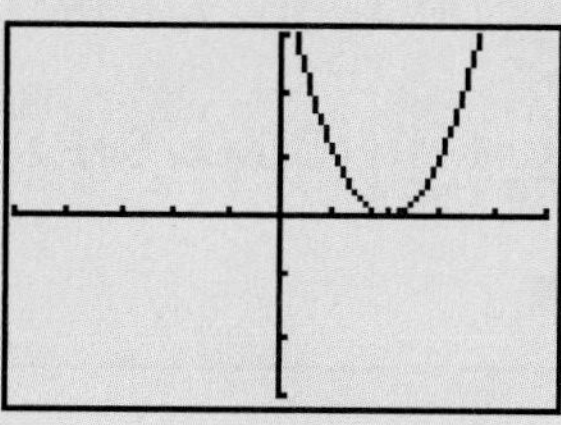

$b^2 - 4ac = 0$
One x-intercept
One real solution
(double root)

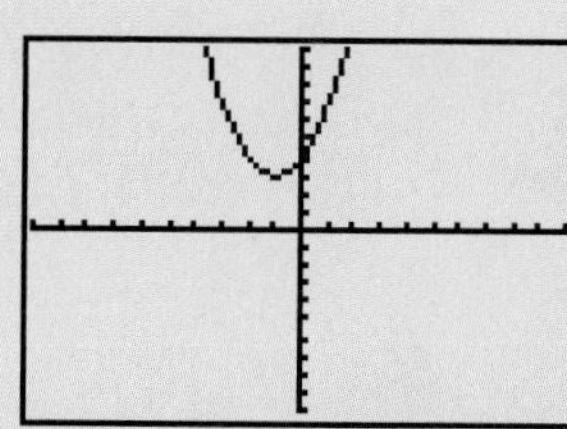

$b^2 - 4ac$ is negative
No x-intercept
Two complex, but not real, solutions

EXAMPLE 5 Use the discriminant to determine the number and type of solutions of each quadratic equation.

a. $x^2 + 2x + 1 = 0$ **b.** $3x^2 + 2 = 0$ **c.** $2x^2 - 7x - 4 = 0$

Solution

a. In $x^2 + 2x + 1 = 0$, $a = 1$, $b = 2$, and $c = 1$. Thus,

$$b^2 - 4ac = 2^2 - 4(1)(1) = 0$$

Since $b^2 - 4ac = 0$, this quadratic equation has one real solution.

b. In this equation, $a = 3, b = 0$, and $c = 2$. Then $b^2 - 4ac = 0 - 4(3)(2) = -24$. Since $b^2 - 4ac$ is negative, the quadratic equation has two complex but not real solutions.

c. In this equation, $a = 2, b = -7$, and $c = -4$. Then

$$b^2 - 4ac = (-7)^2 - 4(2)(-4) = 81$$

Since $b^2 - 4ac$ is positive, the quadratic equation has two real solutions.

To confirm graphically, see the results below.

a.

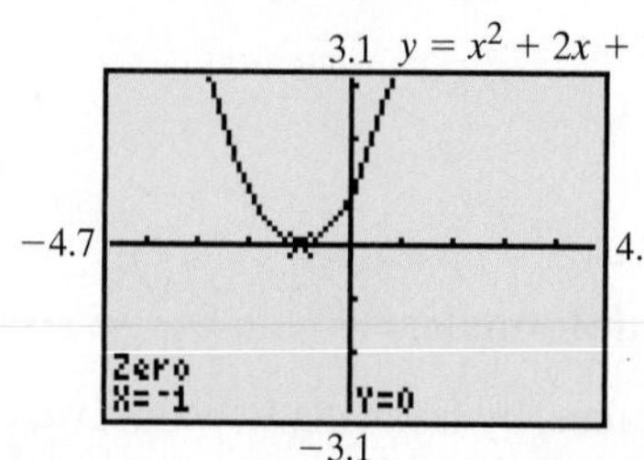

One x-intercept indicates one real solution.

b.

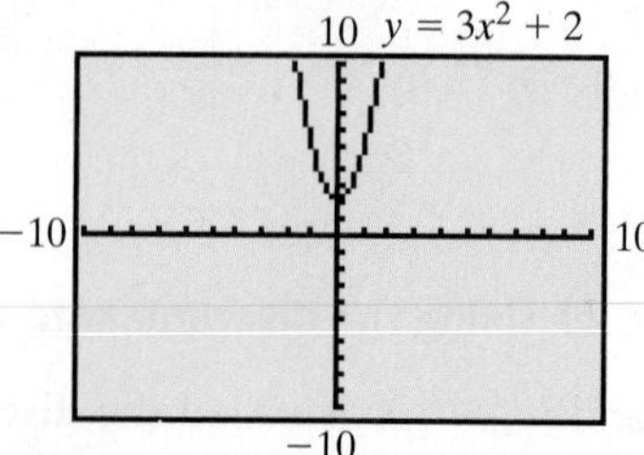

No x-intercepts indicates no real solutions, but two complex, not real, solutions.

c. 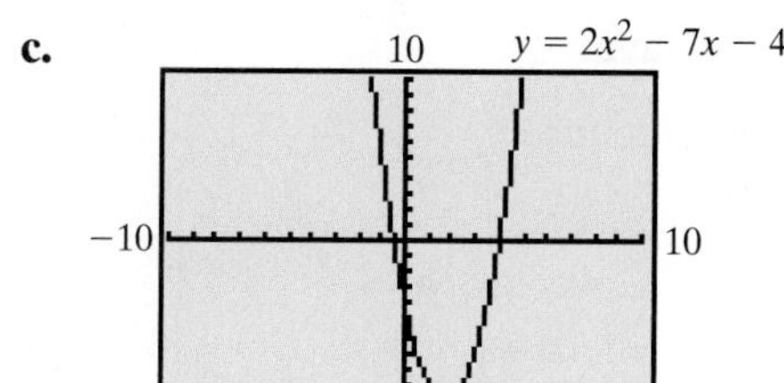

Two x-intercepts indicate two real solutions.

PRACTICE 5 Use the discriminant to determine the number and type of solutions of each quadratic equation.

a. $x^2 - 6x + 9 = 0$ **b.** $x^2 - 3x - 1 = 0$ **c.** $7x^2 + 11 = 0$

The discriminant helps us determine the number and type of solutions of a quadratic equation, $ax^2 + bx + c = 0$. Recall that the solutions of this equation are the same as the x-intercepts of its related graph, $f(x) = ax^2 + bx + c$. This means that the discriminant of $ax^2 + bx + c = 0$ also tells us the number of x-intercepts for the graph of $f(x) = ax^2 + bx + c$, or equivalently $y = ax^2 + bx + c$.

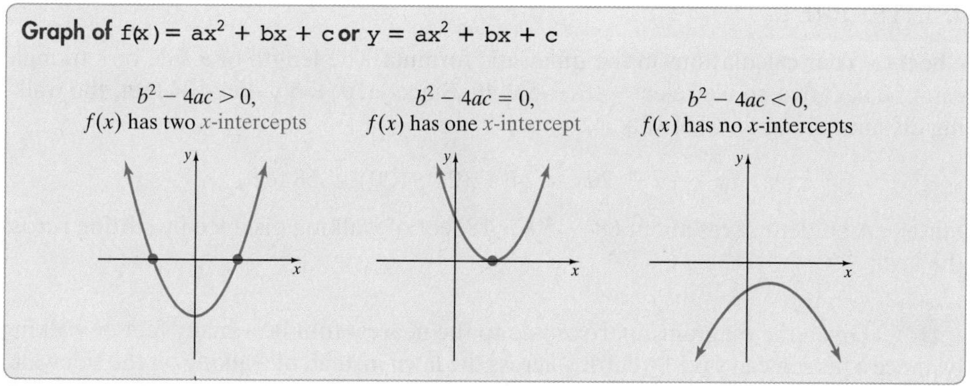

OBJECTIVE 3 ▶ Solving problems modeled by quadratic equations. The quadratic formula is useful in solving problems that are modeled by quadratic equations.

EXAMPLE 6 Calculating Distance Saved

At a local university, students often leave the sidewalk and cut across the lawn to save walking distance. Given the diagram of a favorite place to cut across the lawn, approximate how many feet of walking distance a student saves by cutting across the lawn instead of walking on the sidewalk.

Solution

1. UNDERSTAND. Read and reread the problem. In the diagram, notice that a triangle is formed. Since the corner of the block forms a right angle, we use the Pythagorean theorem for right triangles. You may want to review this theorem.

2. TRANSLATE. By the Pythagorean theorem, we have

In words: $(\text{leg})^2 + (\text{leg})^2 = (\text{hypotenuse})^2$
Translate: $x^2 + (x + 20)^2 = 50^2$

3. SOLVE.

Algebraic Solution:

$$x^2 + x^2 + 40x + 400 = 2500 \quad \text{Square } (x + 20) \text{ and } 50.$$
$$2x^2 + 40x - 2100 = 0 \quad \text{Set the equation equal to 0.}$$
$$x^2 + 20x - 1050 = 0 \quad \text{Divide by 2.}$$

Here, $a = 1, b = 20, c = -1050$. By the quadratic formula,

$$x = \frac{-20 \pm \sqrt{20^2 - 4(1)(-1050)}}{2 \cdot 1}$$
$$= \frac{-20 \pm \sqrt{400 + 4200}}{2} = \frac{-20 \pm \sqrt{4600}}{2}$$
$$= \frac{-20 \pm \sqrt{100 \cdot 46}}{2} = \frac{-20 \pm 10\sqrt{46}}{2}$$
$$= -10 \pm 5\sqrt{46} \quad \text{Simplify.}$$

Graphical Solution:

Let $y_1 = x^2 + (x + 20)^2$ and $y_2 = 50^2$. Since x represents feet, we are interested in positive solutions only. We also estimate the length labeled x to be less than 50, so we choose the x-window to be [0, 50, 10]. The y-window is chosen to be [2000, 3000, 100] so it contains 2500. Find $x \approx -44$ and $x \approx 24$.

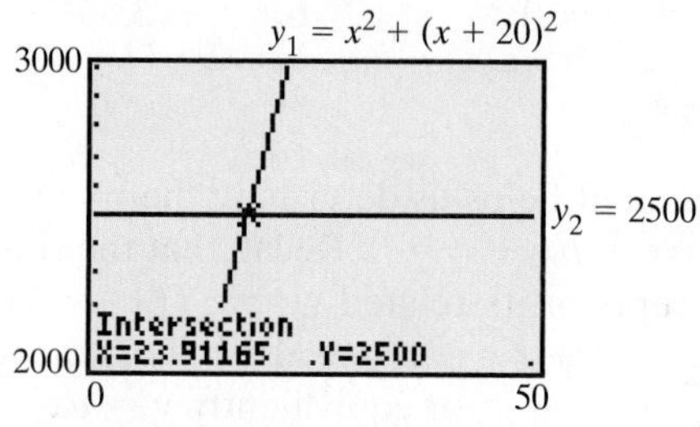

The positive solution is approximately 24.

4. INTERPRET.

Check: Your calculations in the quadratic formula. The length of a side of a triangle can't be negative, so we reject $-10 - 5\sqrt{46}$. Since $-10 + 5\sqrt{46} \approx 24$ feet, the walking distance along the sidewalk is

$$x + (x + 20) \approx 24 + (24 + 20) = 68 \text{ feet.}$$

State: A student saves about 68 − 50 or 18 feet of walking distance by cutting across the lawn. □

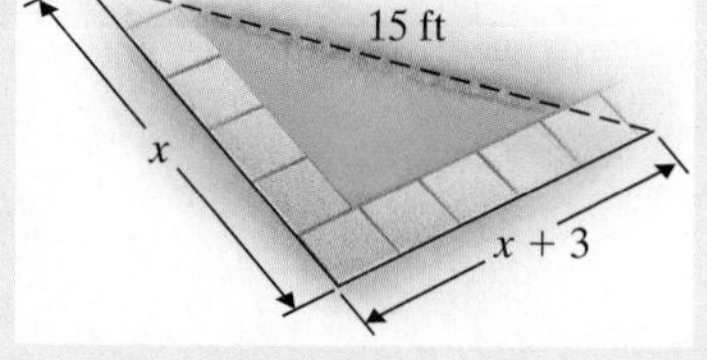

PRACTICE
6 Given the diagram, approximate to the nearest foot how many feet of walking distance a person can save by cutting across the lawn instead of walking on the sidewalk.

EXAMPLE 7 Calculating Landing Time

An object is thrown upward from the top of a 200-foot cliff with a velocity of 12 feet per second. The height h in feet of the object after t seconds is

$$h = -16t^2 + 12t + 200$$

How long after the object is thrown will it strike the ground? Round to the nearest tenth of a second.

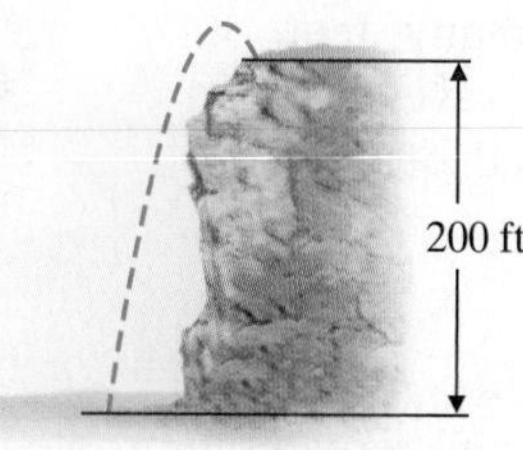

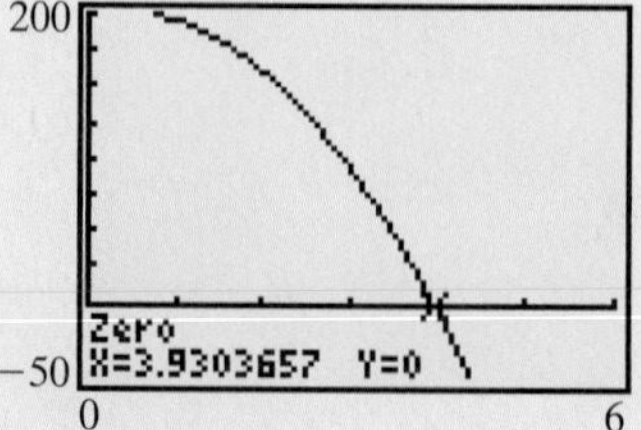

A graphical solution or check for Example 7. The graph of $y_1 = -16x^2 + 12x + 200$ is shown. The solution is the x-value of the x-intercept, as shown.

Solution

1. UNDERSTAND. Read and reread the problem.
2. TRANSLATE. Since we want to know when the object strikes the ground, we want to know when the height $h = 0$, or

$$0 = -16t^2 + 12t + 200$$

3. SOLVE. First we divide both sides of the equation by -4.

$$0 = 4t^2 - 3t - 50 \quad \text{Divide both sides by } -4.$$

Here, $a = 4$, $b = -3$, and $c = -50$. By the quadratic formula,

$$t = \frac{-(-3) \pm \sqrt{(-3)^2 - 4(4)(-50)}}{2 \cdot 4}$$

$$= \frac{3 \pm \sqrt{9 + 800}}{8}$$

$$= \frac{3 \pm \sqrt{809}}{8}$$

4. INTERPRET.

Check: We check our calculations from the quadratic formula. Since the time won't be negative, we reject the proposed solution

$$\frac{3 - \sqrt{809}}{8}.$$

State: The time it takes for the object to strike the ground is exactly

$$\frac{3 + \sqrt{809}}{8} \text{ seconds} \approx 3.9 \text{ seconds}.$$

□

PRACTICE
7 A toy rocket is shot upward at the edge of a building, 45 feet high, with an initial velocity of 20 feet per second. The height h in feet of the rocket after t seconds is

$$h = -16t^2 + 20t + 45$$

How long after the rocket is launched will it strike the ground? Round to the nearest tenth of a second.

VOCABULARY & READINESS CHECK

Fill in each blank.

1. The quadratic formula is ______________________.
2. For $2x^2 + x + 1 = 0$, if $a = 2$, then $b =$ _____ and $c =$ _____.
3. For $5x^2 - 5x - 7 = 0$, if $a = 5$, then $b =$ _____ and $c =$ _____.
4. For $7x^2 - 4 = 0$, if $a = 7$, then $b =$ _____ and $c =$ _____.
5. For $x^2 + 9 = 0$, if $c = 9$, then $a =$ _____ and $b =$ _____.
6. The correct simplified form of $\frac{5 \pm 10\sqrt{2}}{5}$ is ___________.

a. $1 \pm 10\sqrt{2}$ **b.** $2\sqrt{2}$ **c.** $1 \pm 2\sqrt{2}$ **d.** $\pm 5\sqrt{2}$

20.2 EXERCISE SET

Use the quadratic formula to solve each equation. These equations have real number solutions only. See Examples 1 through 3.

1. $m^2 + 5m - 6 = 0$
2. $p^2 + 11p - 12 = 0$
3. $2y = 5y^2 - 3$
4. $5x^2 - 3 = 14x$
5. $x^2 - 6x + 9 = 0$
6. $y^2 + 10y + 25 = 0$
7. $x^2 + 7x + 4 = 0$
8. $y^2 + 5y + 3 = 0$
9. $8m^2 - 2m = 7$
10. $11n^2 - 9n = 1$
11. $3m^2 - 7m = 3$
12. $x^2 - 13 = 5x$
13. $\frac{1}{2}x^2 - x - 1 = 0$
14. $\frac{1}{6}x^2 + x + \frac{1}{3} = 0$
15. $\frac{2}{5}y^2 + \frac{1}{5}y = \frac{3}{5}$
16. $\frac{1}{8}x^2 + x = \frac{5}{2}$
17. $\frac{1}{3}y^2 = y + \frac{1}{6}$
18. $\frac{1}{2}y^2 = y + \frac{1}{2}$
19. $x^2 + 5x = -2$
20. $y^2 - 8 = 4y$
21. $(m + 2)(2m - 6) = 5(m - 1) - 12$
22. $7p(p - 2) + 2(p + 4) = 3$

MIXED PRACTICE

Use the quadratic formula to solve each equation. These equations have real solutions and complex, but not real, solutions. See Examples 1 through 4.

23. $x^2 + 6x + 13 = 0$
24. $x^2 + 2x + 2 = 0$
25. $(x + 5)(x - 1) = 2$
26. $x(x + 6) = 2$
27. $6 = -4x^2 + 3x$
28. $2 = -9x^2 - x$
29. $\frac{x^2}{3} - x = \frac{5}{3}$
30. $\frac{x^2}{2} - 3 = -\frac{9}{2}x$
31. $10y^2 + 10y + 3 = 0$
32. $3y^2 + 6y + 5 = 0$
33. $x(6x + 2) = 3$
34. $x(7x + 1) = 2$
35. $\frac{2}{5}y^2 + \frac{1}{5}y + \frac{3}{5} = 0$
36. $\frac{1}{8}x^2 + x + \frac{5}{2} = 0$
37. $\frac{1}{2}y^2 = y - \frac{1}{2}$
38. $\frac{2}{3}x^2 - \frac{20}{3}x = -\frac{100}{6}$
39. $(n - 2)^2 = 2n$
40. $\left(p - \frac{1}{2}\right)^2 = \frac{p}{2}$

Use the discriminant to determine the number and types of solutions of each equation. See Example 5.

41. $x^2 - 5 = 0$
42. $x^2 - 7 = 0$
43. $4x^2 + 12x = -9$
44. $9x^2 + 1 = 6x$
45. $3x = -2x^2 + 7$
46. $3x^2 = 5 - 7x$
47. $6 = 4x - 5x^2$
48. $5 - 4x + 12x^2 = 0$

Given the following graphs of quadratic equations of the form $y = f(x)$, find the number of real number solutions of the related equation $f(x) = 0$.

49. a. 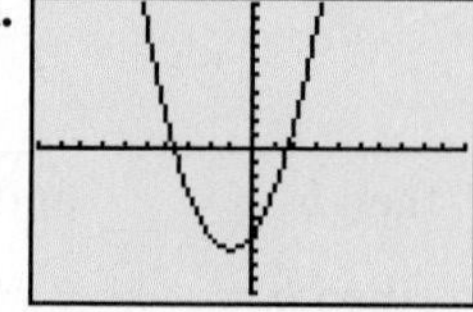 b. 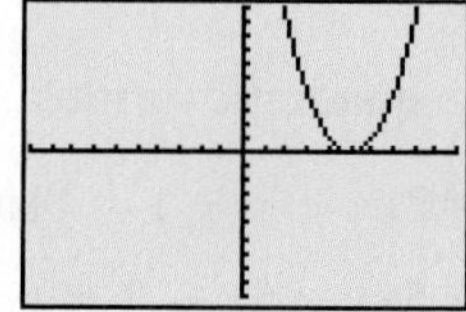

50. a. 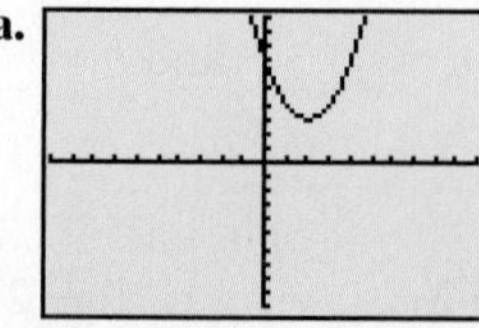 b. 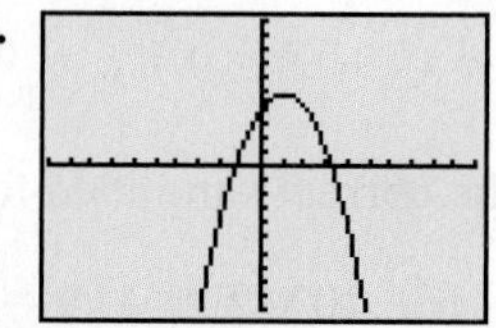

Solve. See Examples 6 and 7.

△ **51.** Nancy, Thelma, and John Varner live on a corner lot. Often, neighborhood children cut across their lot to save walking distance. Given the diagram below, approximate to the nearest foot how many feet of walking distance is saved by cutting across their property instead of walking around the lot.

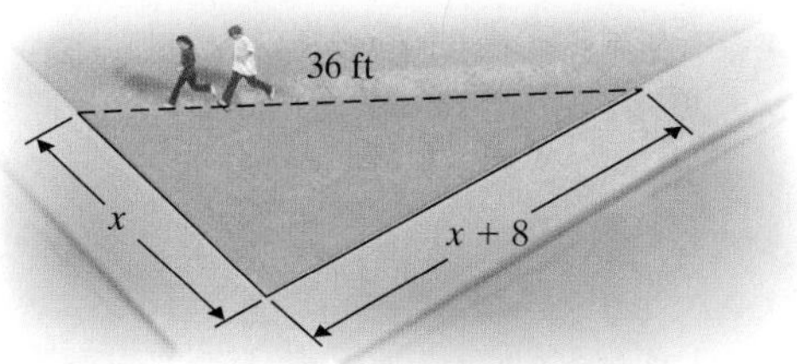

△ **52.** Given the diagram below, approximate to the nearest foot how many feet of walking distance a person saves by cutting across the lawn instead of walking on the sidewalk.

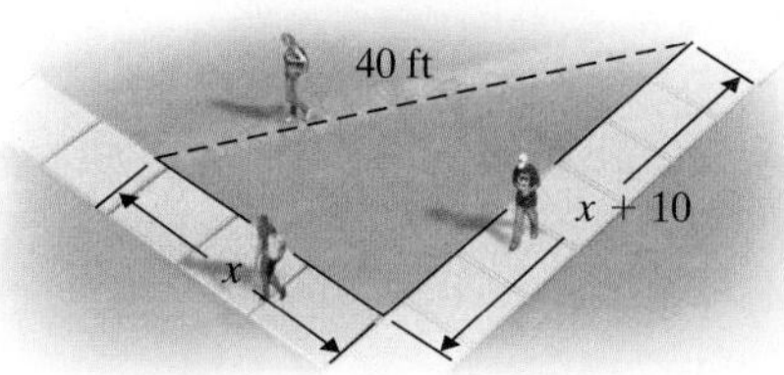

△ **53.** The hypotenuse of an isosceles right triangle is 2 centimeters longer than either of its legs. Find the exact length of each side. (*Hint:* An isosceles right triangle is a right triangle whose legs are the same length.)

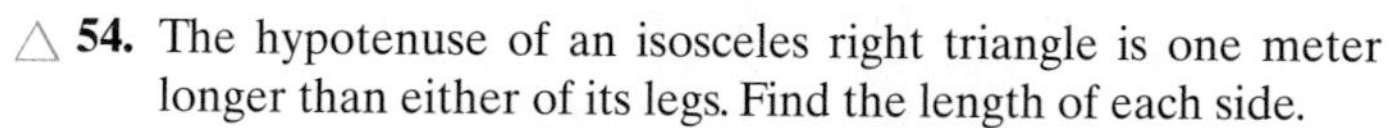

△ **54.** The hypotenuse of an isosceles right triangle is one meter longer than either of its legs. Find the length of each side.

△ **55.** Bailey's rectangular dog pen for his Irish setter must have an area of 400 square feet. Also, the length must be 10 feet longer than the width. Find the dimensions of the pen.

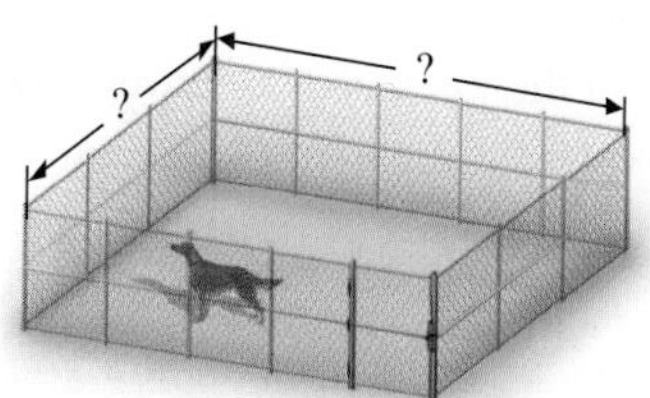

△ **56.** An entry in the Peach Festival Poster Contest must be rectangular and have an area of 1200 square inches. Furthermore, its length must be 20 inches longer than its width. Find the dimensions each entry must have.

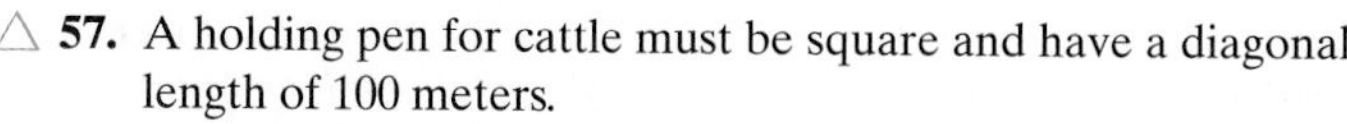

△ **57.** A holding pen for cattle must be square and have a diagonal length of 100 meters.

a. Find the length of a side of the pen.

b. Find the area of the pen.

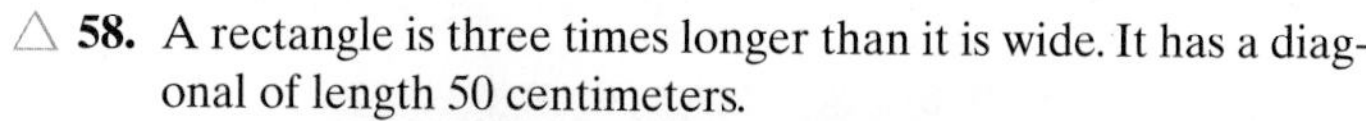

△ **58.** A rectangle is three times longer than it is wide. It has a diagonal of length 50 centimeters.

a. Find the dimensions of the rectangle.

b. Find the perimeter of the rectangle.

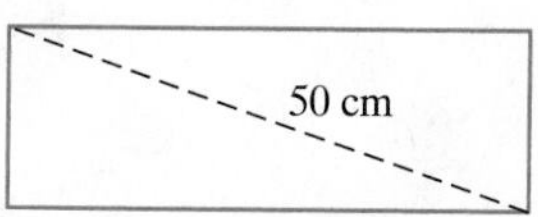

△ **59.** The heaviest reported door in the world is the 708.6 ton radiation shield door in the National Institute for Fusion Science at Toki, Japan. If the height of the door is 1.1 feet longer than its width, and its front area (neglecting depth) is 1439.9 square feet, find its width and height [Interesting note: the door is 6.6 feet thick.] (*Source: Guinness World Records*)

△ **60.** Christi and Robbie Wegmann are constructing a rectangular stained glass window whose length is 7.3 inches longer than its width. If the area of the window is 569.9 square inches, find its width and length.

△ **61.** The base of a triangle is four more than twice its height. If the area of the triangle is 42 square centimeters, find its base and height.

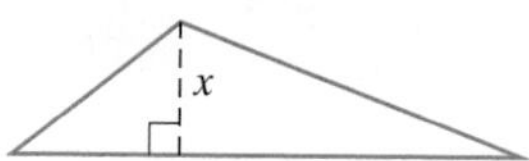

62. If a point B divides a line segment such that the smaller portion is to the larger portion as the larger is to the whole, the whole is the length of the *golden ratio.*

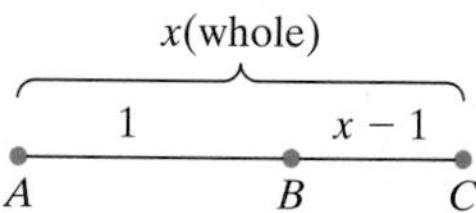

The golden ratio was thought by the Greeks to be the most pleasing to the eye, and many of their buildings contained numerous examples of the golden ratio. The value of the golden ratio is the positive solution of

$$\begin{matrix}\text{(smaller)} \\ \text{(larger)}\end{matrix} \quad \frac{x-1}{1} = \frac{1}{x} \quad \begin{matrix}\text{(larger)} \\ \text{(whole)}\end{matrix}$$

Find this value.

The Wollomombi Falls in Australia have a height of 1100 feet. A pebble is thrown upward from the top of the falls with an initial velocity of 20 feet per second. The height of the pebble h after t seconds is given by the equation $h = -16t^2 + 20t + 1100$. Use this equation for Exercises 63 and 64.

63. How long after the pebble is thrown will it hit the ground? Round to the nearest tenth of a second.

64. How long after the pebble is thrown will it be 550 feet from the ground? Round to the nearest tenth of a second.

A ball is thrown downward from the top of a 180-foot building with an initial velocity of 20 feet per second. The height of the ball h after t seconds is given by the equation $h = -16t^2 - 20t + 180$. Use this equation to answer Exercises 65 and 66.

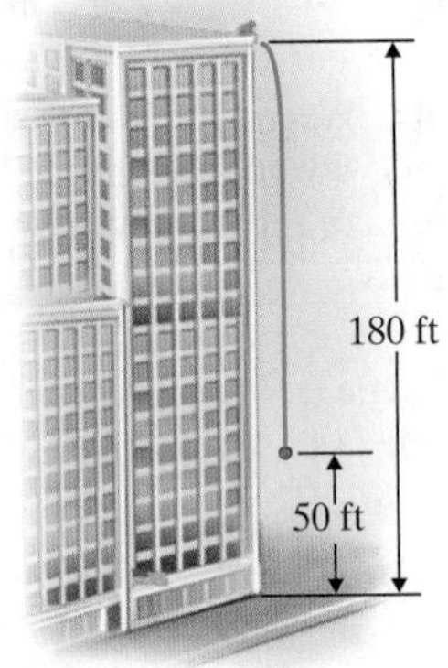

65. How long after the ball is thrown will it strike the ground? Round the result to the nearest tenth of a second.

66. How long after the ball is thrown will it be 50 feet from the ground? Round the result to the nearest tenth of a second.

REVIEW AND PREVIEW

Solve each equation. See Sections 18.5 and 19.6.

67. $\sqrt{5x - 2} = 3$

68. $\sqrt{y + 2} + 7 = 12$

69. $\frac{1}{x} + \frac{2}{5} = \frac{7}{x}$

70. $\frac{10}{z} = \frac{5}{z} - \frac{1}{3}$

Factor.

71. $x^4 + x^2 - 20$

72. $2y^4 + 11y^2 - 6$

73. $z^4 - 13z^2 + 36$

74. $x^4 - 1$

CONCEPT EXTENSIONS

For each quadratic equation, choose the correct substitution for a, b, and c in the standard form $ax^2 + bx + c = 0$.

75. $x^2 = -10$

a. $a = 1, b = 0, c = -10$
b. $a = 1, b = 0, c = 10$
c. $a = 0, b = 1, c = -10$
d. $a = 1, b = 1, c = 10$

76. $x^2 + 5 = -x$

a. $a = 1, b = 5, c = -1$
b. $a = 1, b = -1, c = 5$
c. $a = 1, b = 5, c = 1$
d. $a = 1, b = 1, c = 5$

77. Solve Exercise 1 by factoring. Explain the result.

78. Solve Exercise 2 by factoring. Explain the result.

Use the quadratic formula and a calculator to approximate each solution to the nearest tenth.

79. $2x^2 - 6x + 3 = 0$

80. $3.6x^2 + 1.8x - 4.3 = 0$

The accompanying graph shows the daily low temperatures for one week in New Orleans, Louisiana.

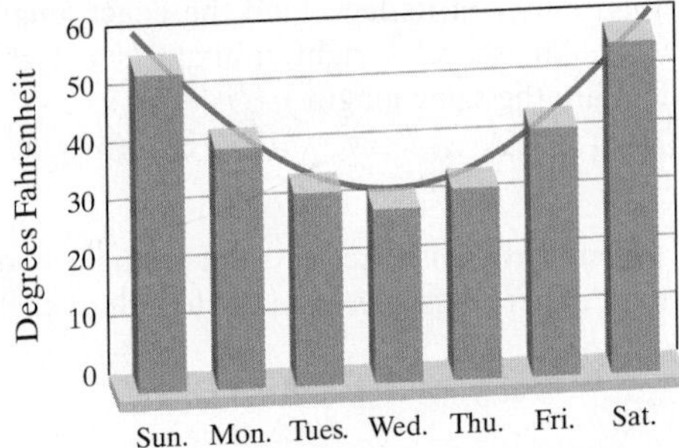

81. Which day of the week shows the greatest decrease in low temperature?

82. Which day of the week shows the greatest increase in low temperature?

83. Which day of the week had the lowest low temperature?

84. Use the graph to estimate the low temperature on Thursday.

Notice that the shape of the temperature graph is similar to the curve drawn. In fact, this graph can be modeled by the quadratic function $f(x) = 3x^2 - 18x + 56$, where $f(x)$ is the temperature in degrees Fahrenheit and x is the number of days from Sunday. (This graph is shown in blue.) Use this function to answer Exercises 85 and 86.

85. Use the quadratic function given to approximate the temperature on Thursday. Does your answer agree with the graph?

86. Use the function given and the quadratic formula to find when the temperature was 35° F. [*Hint:* Let $f(x) = 35$ and solve for x.] Round your answer to one decimal place and interpret your result. Does your answer agree with the graph?

87. The number of Starbucks stores can be modeled by the quadratic function $f(x) = 115x^2 + 711x + 3946$, where $f(x)$ is the number of Starbucks and x is the number of years after 2000. (*Source: Starbuck's Annual Report 2006*)

a. Find the number of Starbucks in 2004.

b. If the trend described by the model continues, predict the year after 2000 in which the number of Starbucks will be 25,000. Round to the nearest whole year.

88. The number of visitors to U.S. theme parks can be modeled by the quadratic equation $v(x) = 0.25x^2 + 2.6x + 315.6$, where $v(x)$ is the number of visitors (in millions) and x is the number of years after 2000. (*Source:* Price Waterhouse Coopers)

a. Find the number of visitors to U.S. theme parks in 2005. Round to the nearest million.

b. Find the projected number of visitors to U.S. theme parks in 2010. Round to the nearest million.

The solutions of the quadratic equation $ax^2 + bx + c = 0$ are $\dfrac{-b + \sqrt{b^2 - 4ac}}{2a}$ *and* $\dfrac{-b - \sqrt{b^2 - 4ac}}{2a}$.

89. Show that the sum of these solutions is $\dfrac{-b}{a}$.

90. Show that the product of these solutions is $\dfrac{c}{a}$.

Use the quadratic formula to solve each quadratic equation.

91. $3x^2 - \sqrt{12}x + 1 = 0$
(*Hint:* $a = 3, b = -\sqrt{12}, c = 1$)

92. $5x^2 + \sqrt{20}x + 1 = 0$

93. $x^2 + \sqrt{2}x + 1 = 0$

94. $x^2 - \sqrt{2}x + 1 = 0$

95. $2x^2 - \sqrt{3}x - 1 = 0$

96. $7x^2 + \sqrt{7}x - 2 = 0$

STUDY SKILLS BUILDER

How Well Do You Know Your Textbook?

Let's check to see whether you are familiar with your textbook yet.

1. What does the icon mean?
2. What does the icon mean?
3. What does the icon mean?
4. Where can you find a review for each chapter? What answers to this review can be found in the back of your text?
5. Each chapter contains an overview of the chapter along with examples. What is this feature called?
6. Each chapter contains a review of vocabulary. What is this feature called?
7. There are free CDs in your text. What content is contained on these CDs?
8. What is the location of the section that is entirely devoted to study skills?
9. There are Practice Problems that are contained in the margin of the text. What are they and how can they be used?

20.3 SOLVING EQUATIONS BY USING QUADRATIC METHODS

OBJECTIVES

1 Solve various equations that are quadratic in form.

2 Solve problems that lead to quadratic equations.

OBJECTIVE 1 ▶ Solving equations that are quadratic in form. In this section, we discuss various types of equations that can be solved in part by using the methods for solving quadratic equations.

Once each equation is simplified, you may want to use these steps when deciding what method to use to solve the quadratic equation.

Solving a Quadratic Equation

STEP 1. If the equation is in the form $(ax + b)^2 = c$, use the square root property and solve. If not, go to Step 2.

STEP 2. Write the equation in standard form: $ax^2 + bx + c = 0$.

STEP 3. Try to solve the equation by the factoring method. If not possible, go to Step 4.

STEP 4. Solve the equation by the quadratic formula.

The first example is a radical equation that becomes a quadratic equation once we square both sides.

EXAMPLE 1 Solve: $x - \sqrt{x} - 6 = 0$.

Solution Recall that to solve a radical equation, first get the radical alone on one side of the equation. Then square both sides.

$$x - 6 = \sqrt{x} \quad \text{Add } \sqrt{x} \text{ to both sides.}$$
$$(x - 6)^2 = \left(\sqrt{x}\right)^2 \quad \text{Square both sides.}$$
$$x^2 - 12x + 36 = x$$
$$x^2 - 13x + 36 = 0 \quad \text{Set the equation equal to 0.}$$
$$(x - 9)(x - 4) = 0$$
$$x - 9 = 0 \quad \text{or} \quad x - 4 = 0$$
$$x = 9 \qquad\qquad x = 4$$

A graphical check for Example 1 shows that there is only one solution to the equation.

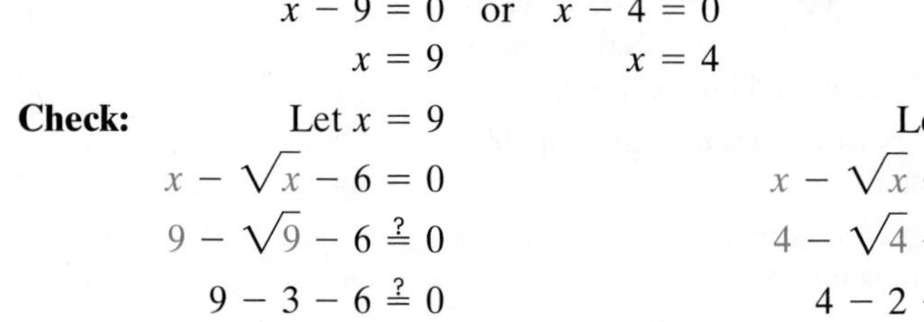

Check:

Let $x = 9$		Let $x = 4$	
$x - \sqrt{x} - 6 = 0$		$x - \sqrt{x} - 6 = 0$	
$9 - \sqrt{9} - 6 \stackrel{?}{=} 0$		$4 - \sqrt{4} - 6 \stackrel{?}{=} 0$	
$9 - 3 - 6 \stackrel{?}{=} 0$		$4 - 2 - 6 \stackrel{?}{=} 0$	
$0 = 0$	True	$-4 = 0$	False

The solution is 9 or the solution set is {9}. □

PRACTICE 1 Solve: $x - \sqrt{x + 1} - 5 = 0$.

EXAMPLE 2 Solve: $\dfrac{3x}{x - 2} - \dfrac{x + 1}{x} = \dfrac{6}{x(x - 2)}$.

Solution In this equation, x cannot be either 2 or 0, because these values cause denominators to equal zero. To solve for x, we first multiply both sides of the equation by $x(x - 2)$ to clear the fractions. By the distributive property, this means that we multiply each term by $x(x - 2)$.

$$x(x - 2)\left(\frac{3x}{x - 2}\right) - x(x - 2)\left(\frac{x + 1}{x}\right) = x(x - 2)\left[\frac{6}{x(x - 2)}\right]$$
$$3x^2 - (x - 2)(x + 1) = 6 \quad \text{Simplify.}$$
$$3x^2 - (x^2 - x - 2) = 6 \quad \text{Multiply.}$$
$$3x^2 - x^2 + x + 2 = 6$$
$$2x^2 + x - 4 = 0 \quad \text{Simplify.}$$

This equation cannot be factored using integers, so we solve by the quadratic formula.

$$x = \frac{-1 \pm \sqrt{1^2 - 4(2)(-4)}}{2 \cdot 2} \quad \text{Use } a = 2, b = 1, \text{ and } c = -4 \text{ in the quadratic formula.}$$
$$= \frac{-1 \pm \sqrt{1 + 32}}{4} \quad \text{Simplify.}$$
$$= \frac{-1 \pm \sqrt{33}}{4}$$

Neither proposed solution will make the denominators 0.

The solutions are $\dfrac{-1 + \sqrt{33}}{4}$ and $\dfrac{-1 - \sqrt{33}}{4}$ or the solution set is $\left\{\dfrac{-1 + \sqrt{33}}{4}, \dfrac{-1 - \sqrt{33}}{4}\right\}$.

To check, we evaluate the left and right sides of the equation with the proposed solutions and see that a true statement results. Careful placement of parentheses is important, as shown below.

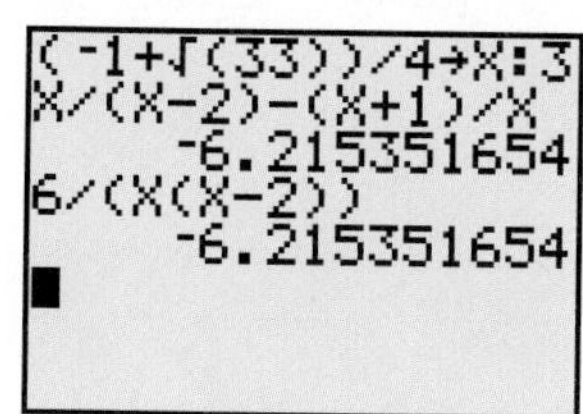

□

PRACTICE 2 Solve: $\frac{5x}{x+1} - \frac{x+4}{x} = \frac{3}{x(x+1)}$.

EXAMPLE 3 Solve: $p^4 - 3p^2 - 4 = 0$.

Solution First we factor the trinomial.

$$p^4 - 3p^2 - 4 = 0$$

$$(p^2 - 4)(p^2 + 1) = 0 \quad \text{Factor.}$$

$$(p - 2)(p + 2)(p^2 + 1) = 0 \quad \text{Factor further.}$$

$$p - 2 = 0 \quad \text{or} \quad p + 2 = 0 \quad \text{or} \quad p^2 + 1 = 0 \quad \text{Set each factor equal to 0 and solve.}$$

$$p = 2 \qquad p = -2 \qquad p^2 = -1$$

$$p = \pm\sqrt{-1} = \pm i$$

The solutions are 2, −2, i, and $-i$. □

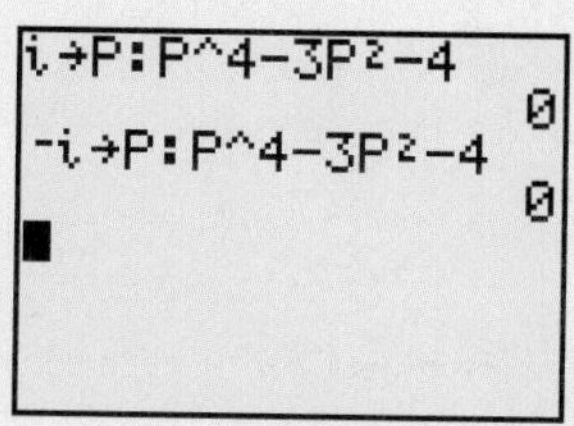

Example 3 numerical check for the imaginary solutions.

PRACTICE 3 Solve: $p^4 - 7p^2 - 144 = 0$.

Helpful Hint

Example 3 can be solved using substitution also. Think of $p^4 - 3p^2 - 4 = 0$ as

$$(p^2)^2 - 3p^2 - 4 = 0 \quad \text{Then let } x = p^2\text{, and solve and substitute back.}$$
$$x^2 - 3x - 4 = 0 \quad \text{The solutions will be the same.}$$

Concept Check ✓

a. True or false? The maximum number of solutions that a quadratic equation can have is 2.

b. True or false? The maximum number of solutions that an equation in quadratic form can have is 2.

EXAMPLE 4 Solve: $(x - 3)^2 - 3(x - 3) - 4 = 0$.

Solution Notice that the quantity $(x - 3)$ is repeated in this equation. Sometimes it is helpful to substitute a variable (in this case other than x) for the repeated quantity. We will let $y = x - 3$. Then

$$(x - 3)^2 - 3(x - 3) - 4 = 0$$

becomes

$$y^2 - 3y - 4 = 0 \quad \text{Let } x - 3 = y.$$

$$(y - 4)(y + 1) = 0 \quad \text{Factor.}$$

To solve, we use the zero-factor property.

$$y - 4 = 0 \quad \text{or} \quad y + 1 = 0 \quad \text{Set each factor equal to 0.}$$

$$y = 4 \qquad y = -1 \quad \text{Solve.}$$

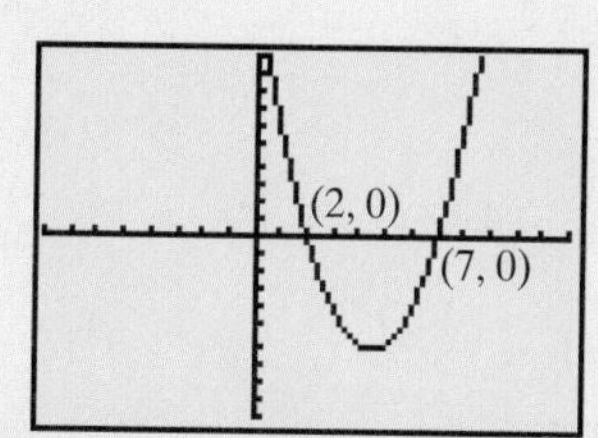

A graphical check for Example 4. The solutions are found from the x-intercepts of the graph of $y_1 = (x - 3)^2 - 3(x - 3) - 4$.

Answer to Concept Check:
a. true **b.** false

> **Helpful Hint**
> When using substitution, don't forget to substitute back to the original variable.

To find values of x, we substitute back. That is, we substitute $x - 3$ for y.

$$x - 3 = 4 \quad \text{or} \quad x - 3 = -1$$
$$x = 7 \qquad\qquad x = 2$$

Both 2 and 7 check. The solutions are 2 and 7. □

PRACTICE 4 Solve: $(x + 2)^2 - 2(x + 2) - 3 = 0$.

EXAMPLE 5 Solve: $x^{2/3} - 5x^{1/3} + 6 = 0$.

Solution The key to solving this equation is recognizing that $x^{2/3} = (x^{1/3})^2$. We replace $x^{1/3}$ with m so that

$$(x^{1/3})^2 - 5x^{1/3} + 6 = 0$$

becomes

$$m^2 - 5m + 6 = 0$$

Now we solve by factoring.

$$m^2 - 5m + 6 = 0$$
$$(m - 3)(m - 2) = 0 \qquad \text{Factor.}$$
$$m - 3 = 0 \quad \text{or} \quad m - 2 = 0 \qquad \text{Set each factor equal to 0.}$$
$$m = 3 \qquad\qquad m = 2$$

Since $m = x^{1/3}$, we have

$$x^{1/3} = 3 \quad \text{or} \quad x^{1/3} = 2$$
$$x = 3^3 = 27 \quad \text{or} \quad x = 2^3 = 8$$

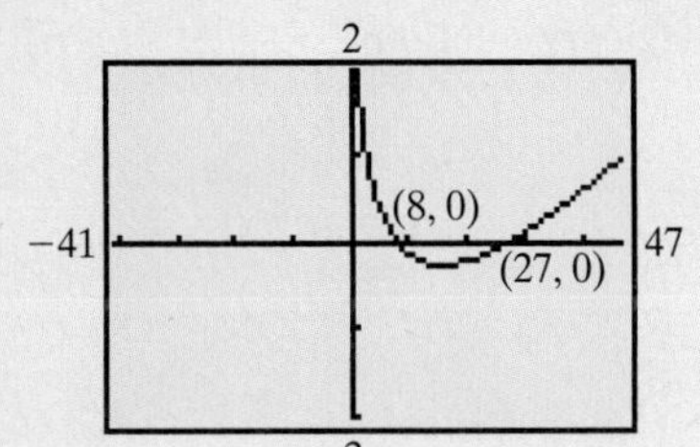

Both 8 and 27 check. The solutions are 8 and 27.

To visualize these solutions, graph $y_1 = x^{2/3} - 5x^{1/3} + 6$ and find the x-intercepts of the graph.

The x-intercepts are (8, 0) and (27, 0), so the solutions 8 and 27 check. □

PRACTICE 5 Solve: $x^{2/3} - 5x^{1/3} + 4 = 0$.

OBJECTIVE 2 ▸ Solving problems that lead to quadratic equations. The next example is a work problem. This problem is modeled by a rational equation that simplifies to a quadratic equation.

EXAMPLE 6 **Finding Work Time**

Together, an experienced word processor and an apprentice word processor can create a word document in 6 hours. Alone, the experienced word processor can create the document 2 hours faster than the apprentice word processor can. Find the time in which each person can create the word document alone.

Solution

1. UNDERSTAND. Read and reread the problem. The key idea here is the relationship between the *time* (hours) it takes to complete the job and the *part of the job* completed in one unit of time (hour). For example, because they can complete the job together in 6 hours, the *part of the job* they can complete in 1 hour is $\frac{1}{6}$.

   Let

   x = the *time* in hours it takes the apprentice word processor to complete the job alone

   $x - 2$ = the *time* in hours it takes the experienced word processor to complete the job alone

We can summarize in a chart the information discussed

	Total Hours to Complete Job	*Part of Job Completed in 1 Hour*
Apprentice Word Processor	x	$\frac{1}{x}$
Experienced Word Processor	$x - 2$	$\frac{1}{x-2}$
Together	6	$\frac{1}{6}$

2. TRANSLATE.

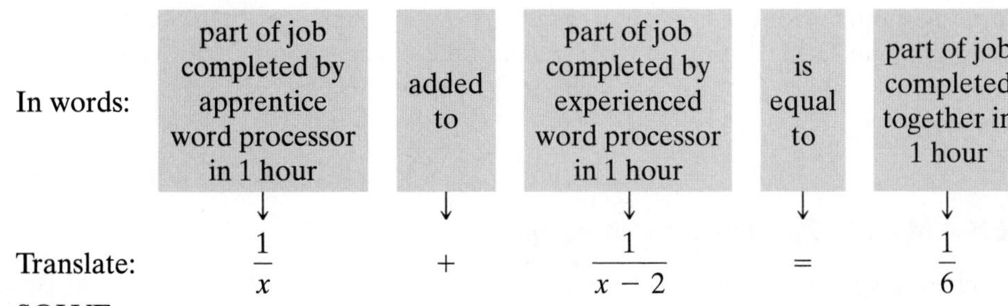

Translate: $\frac{1}{x} \quad + \quad \frac{1}{x-2} \quad = \quad \frac{1}{6}$

3. SOLVE.

Algebraic Solution:

$$\frac{1}{x} + \frac{1}{x-2} = \frac{1}{6}$$

$$6x(x-2)\left(\frac{1}{x} + \frac{1}{x-2}\right) = 6x(x-2) \cdot \frac{1}{6}$$ Multiply both sides by the LCD $6x(x-2)$.

$$6x(x-2) \cdot \frac{1}{x} + 6x(x-2) \cdot \frac{1}{x-2} = 6x(x-2) \cdot \frac{1}{6}$$ Use the distributive property.

$$6(x-2) + 6x = x(x-2)$$
$$6x - 12 + 6x = x^2 - 2x$$
$$0 = x^2 - 14x + 12$$

Now we can substitute $a = 1$, $b = -14$, and $c = 12$ into the quadratic formula and simplify.

$$x = \frac{-(-14) \pm \sqrt{(-14)^2 - 4(1)(12)}}{2 \cdot 1} = \frac{14 \pm \sqrt{148}}{2}$$

$$x \approx \frac{14 + 12.2}{2} = 13.1 \quad \text{or} \quad x \approx \frac{14 - 12.2}{2} = 0.9$$

Graphical Solution:

Graph $y_1 = \frac{1}{x} + \frac{1}{x-2}$ and $y_2 = \frac{1}{6}$ in a 0, 20, 5] by [−1, 1, 1] window. The approximate intersections are $x \approx 0.9$ and $x \approx 13.1$. A hand sketch is shown below followed by graphing utility screens.

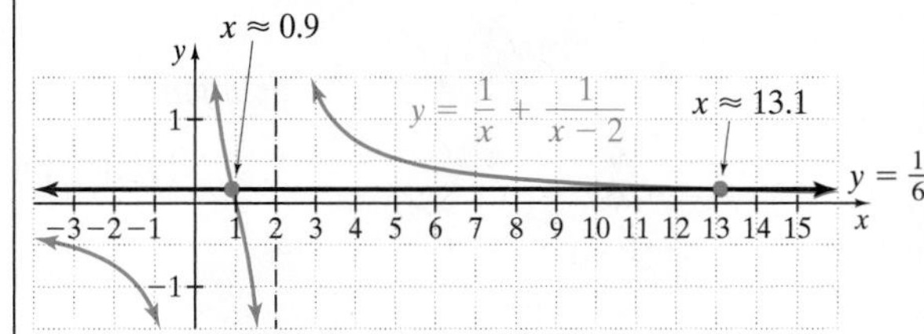

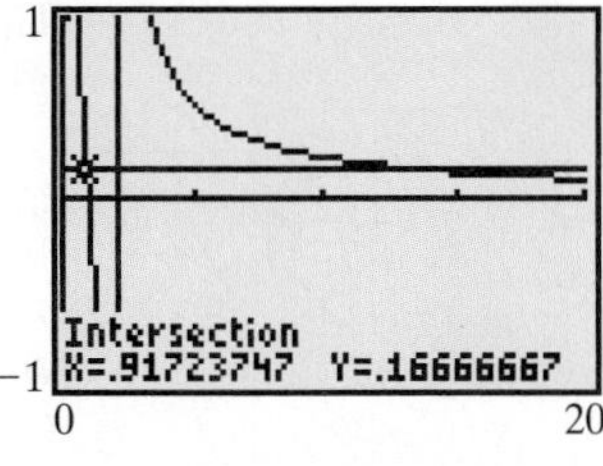

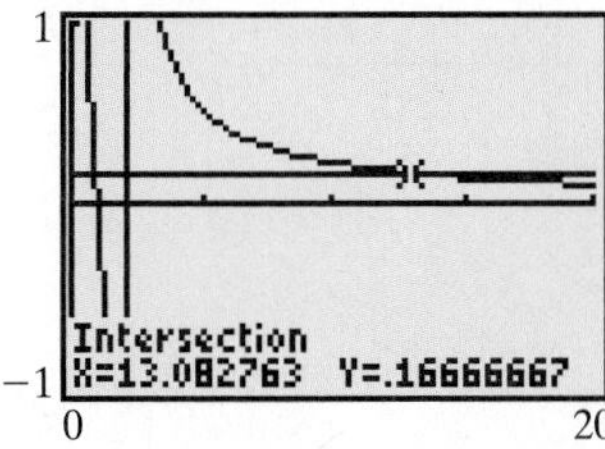

Since x represents time, we show the first-quadrant portion of the graph only.

4. INTERPRET.

Check: If the apprentice word processor completes the job alone in 0.9 hours, the experienced word processor completes the job alone in $x - 2 = 0.9 - 2 = -1.1$ hours. Since this is not possible, we reject the solution of 0.9. The approximate solution thus is 13.1 hours.

State: The apprentice word processor can complete the job alone in approximately 13.1 hours, and the experienced word processor can complete the job alone in approximately

$$x - 2 = 13.1 - 2 = 11.1 \text{ hours.}$$

□

PRACTICE 6 Together, Katy and Steve can groom all the dogs at the Barkin' Doggie Day Care in 4 hours. Alone, Katy can groom the dogs 1 hour faster than Steve can groom the dogs alone. Find the time in which each of them can groom the dogs alone.

EXAMPLE 7 Finding Driving Speeds

Beach and Fargo are about 400 miles apart. A salesperson travels from Fargo to Beach one day at a certain speed. She returns to Fargo the next day and drives 10 mph faster. Her total travel time was $14\frac{2}{3}$ hours. Find her speed to Beach and the return speed to Fargo.

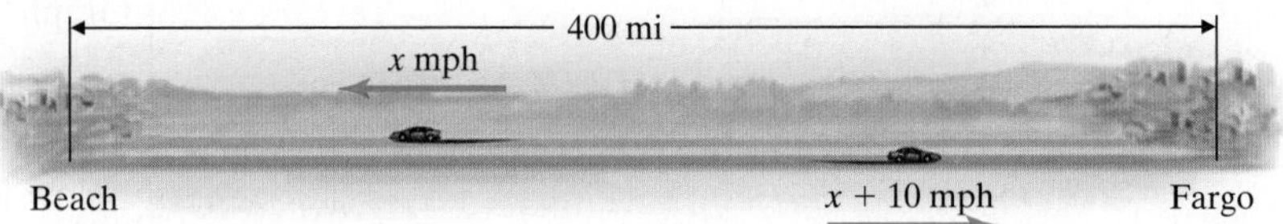

Solution

1. UNDERSTAND. Read and reread the problem. Let

$$x = \text{the speed to Beach, so}$$
$$x + 10 = \text{the return speed to Fargo.}$$

Then organize the given information in a table.

Helpful Hint

Since $d = rt$, then $t = \frac{d}{r}$. The time column was completed using $\frac{d}{r}$.

	distance	=	*rate*	·	*time*
To Beach	400		x		$\frac{400}{x}$; distance ; rate
Return to Fargo	400		$x + 10$		$\frac{400}{x+10}$; distance ; rate

2. TRANSLATE.

In words: time to Beach + return time to Fargo = $14\frac{2}{3}$ hours

Translate:
$$\frac{400}{x} + \frac{400}{x+10} = \frac{44}{3}$$

3. SOLVE.

$$\frac{400}{x} + \frac{400}{x+10} = \frac{44}{3}$$

$$\frac{100}{x} + \frac{100}{x+10} = \frac{11}{3} \quad \text{Divide both sides by 4.}$$

$$3x(x+10)\left(\frac{100}{x} + \frac{100}{x+10}\right) = 3x(x+10)\cdot\frac{11}{3} \quad \text{Multiply both sides by the LCD, } 3x(x+10).$$

$$3x(x+10)\cdot\frac{100}{x} + 3x(x+10)\cdot\frac{100}{x+10} = 3x(x+10)\cdot\frac{11}{3} \quad \text{Use the distributive property.}$$

$$3(x+10)\cdot 100 + 3x\cdot 100 = x(x+10)\cdot 11$$

$$300x + 3000 + 300x = 11x^2 + 110x$$

$$0 = 11x^2 - 490x - 3000 \quad \text{Set equation equal to 0.}$$

$$0 = (11x+60)(x-50) \quad \text{Factor.}$$

$$11x + 60 = 0 \quad \text{or} \quad x - 50 = 0 \quad \text{Set each factor equal to 0.}$$

$$x = -\frac{60}{11} \text{ or } -5\frac{5}{11}; \quad x = 50$$

```
WINDOW
 Xmin=0
 Xmax=65
 Xscl=10
 Ymin=0
 Ymax=20
 Yscl=2
 Xres=1
```

Below is a graphical solution for Example 7. Since x represents mph, we choose [0, 65, 10]. Since the y-window should include $\frac{44}{3}$, we choose [0, 20, 2].

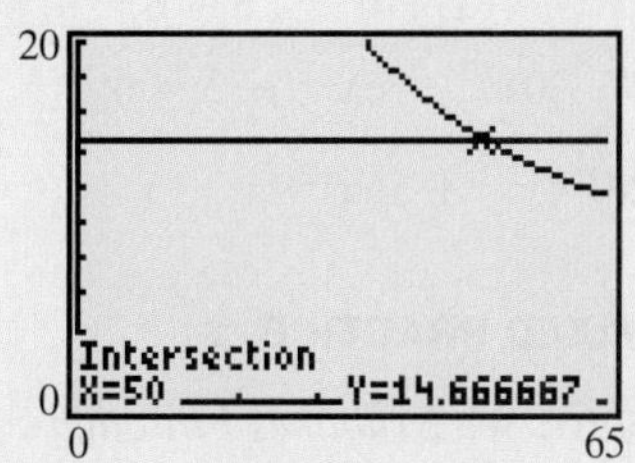

Here $x = 50$ indicates the speed.

4. INTERPRET.

Check: The speed is not negative, so it's not $-5\frac{5}{11}$. The number 50 does check.

State: The speed to Beach was 50 mph and her return speed to Fargo was 60 mph. □

PRACTICE 7 The 36-km S-shaped Hangzhou Bay Bridge is the longest cross-sea bridge in the world, linking Ningbo and Shanghai, China. A merchant drives over the bridge one morning from Ningbo to Shanghai in very heavy traffic and returns home that night driving 50 km per hour faster. The total travel time was 1.3 hours. Find the speed to Shanghai and the return speed to Ningbo.

20.3 EXERCISE SET

PRACTICE WATCH DOWNLOAD READ REVIEW

Solve. See Example 1.

1. $2x = \sqrt{10 + 3x}$

2. $3x = \sqrt{8x + 1}$

3. $x - 2\sqrt{x} = 8$

4. $x - \sqrt{2x} = 4$

5. $\sqrt{9x} = x + 2$

6. $\sqrt{16x} = x + 3$

Solve. See Example 2.

7. $\frac{2}{x} + \frac{3}{x-1} = 1$

8. $\frac{6}{x^2} = \frac{3}{x+1}$

9. $\frac{3}{x} + \frac{4}{x+2} = 2$

10. $\frac{5}{x-2} + \frac{4}{x+2} = 1$

11. $\frac{7}{x^2 - 5x + 6} = \frac{2x}{x-3} - \frac{x}{x-2}$

12. $\frac{11}{2x^2 + x - 15} = \frac{5}{2x-5} - \frac{x}{x+3}$

Solve. See Example 3.

13. $p^4 - 16 = 0$

14. $x^4 + 2x^2 - 3 = 0$

15. $4x^4 + 11x^2 = 3$

16. $z^4 = 81$

17. $z^4 - 13z^2 + 36 = 0$

18. $9x^4 + 5x^2 - 4 = 0$

Solve. See Examples 4 and 5.

19. $x^{2/3} - 3x^{1/3} - 10 = 0$

20. $x^{2/3} + 2x^{1/3} + 1 = 0$

21. $(5n + 1)^2 + 2(5n + 1) - 3 = 0$

22. $(m - 6)^2 + 5(m - 6) + 4 = 0$

23. $2x^{2/3} - 5x^{1/3} = 3$

24. $3x^{2/3} + 11x^{1/3} = 4$

25. $1 + \frac{2}{3t - 2} = \frac{8}{(3t - 2)^2}$

26. $2 - \frac{7}{x + 6} = \frac{15}{(x + 6)^2}$

27. $20x^{2/3} - 6x^{1/3} - 2 = 0$

28. $4x^{2/3} + 16x^{1/3} = -15$

MIXED PRACTICE

Solve. See Examples 1 through 5.

29. $a^4 - 5a^2 + 6 = 0$

30. $x^4 - 12x^2 + 11 = 0$

31. $\frac{2x}{x - 2} + \frac{x}{x + 3} = -\frac{5}{x + 3}$

32. $\frac{5}{x - 3} + \frac{x}{x + 3} = \frac{19}{x^2 - 9}$

33. $(p + 2)^2 = 9(p + 2) - 20$

34. $2(4m - 3)^2 - 9(4m - 3) = 5$

35. $2x = \sqrt{11x + 3}$

36. $4x = \sqrt{2x + 3}$

37. $x^{2/3} - 8x^{1/3} + 15 = 0$

38. $x^{2/3} - 2x^{1/3} - 8 = 0$

39. $y^3 + 9y - y^2 - 9 = 0$

40. $x^3 + x - 3x^2 - 3 = 0$

41. $2x^{2/3} + 3x^{1/3} - 2 = 0$

42. $6x^{2/3} - 25x^{1/3} - 25 = 0$

43. $x^{-2} - x^{-1} - 6 = 0$

44. $y^{-2} - 8y^{-1} + 7 = 0$

45. $x - \sqrt{x} = 2$

46. $x - \sqrt{3x} = 6$

47. $\frac{x}{x - 1} + \frac{1}{x + 1} = \frac{2}{x^2 - 1}$

48. $\frac{x}{x - 5} + \frac{5}{x + 5} = -\frac{1}{x^2 - 25}$

49. $p^4 - p^2 - 20 = 0$

50. $x^4 - 10x^2 + 9 = 0$

51. $(x + 3)(x^2 - 3x + 9) = 0$

52. $(x - 6)(x^2 + 6x + 36) = 0$

53. $1 = \frac{4}{x - 7} + \frac{5}{(x - 7)^2}$

54. $3 + \frac{1}{2p + 4} = \frac{10}{(2p + 4)^2}$

55. $27y^4 + 15y^2 = 2$

56. $8z^4 + 14z^2 = -5$

Solve. See Examples 6 and 7.

57. A jogger ran 3 miles, decreased her speed by 1 mile per hour, and then ran another 4 miles. If her total time jogging was $1\frac{3}{5}$ hours, find her speed for each part of her run.

58. Mark Keaton's workout consists of jogging for 3 miles, and then riding his bike for 5 miles at a speed 4 miles per hour faster than he jogs. If his total workout time is 1 hour, find his jogging speed and his biking speed.

59. A Chinese restaurant in Mandeville, Louisiana, has a large goldfish pond around the restaurant. Suppose that an inlet pipe and a hose together can fill the pond in 8 hours. The inlet pipe alone can complete the job in one hour less time than the hose alone. Find the time that the hose can complete the job alone and the time that the inlet pipe can complete the job alone. Round each to the nearest tenth of an hour.

60. A water tank on a farm in Flatonia, Texas, can be filled with a large inlet pipe and a small inlet pipe in 3 hours. The large inlet pipe alone can fill the tank in 2 hours less time than the small inlet pipe alone. Find the time to the nearest tenth of an hour each pipe can fill the tank alone.

61. Roma Sherry drove 330 miles from her hometown to Tucson. During her return trip, she was able to increase her speed by 11 mph. If her return trip took 1 hour less time, find her original speed and her speed returning home.

62. A salesperson drove to Portland, a distance of 300 miles. During the last 80 miles of his trip, heavy rainfall forced him to decrease his speed by 15 mph. If his total driving time was 6 hours, find his original speed and his speed during the rainfall.

63. Bill Shaughnessy and his son Billy can clean the house together in 4 hours. When the son works alone, it takes him an hour longer to clean than it takes his dad alone. Find how long to the nearest tenth of an hour it takes the son to clean alone.

64. Together, Noodles and Freckles eat a 50-pound bag of dog food in 30 days. Noodles by himself eats a 50-pound bag in 2 weeks less time than Freckles does by himself. How many days to the nearest whole day would a 50-pound bag of dog food last Freckles?

65. The product of a number and 4 less than the number is 96. Find the number.

66. A whole number increased by its square is two more than twice itself. Find the number.

△ **67.** Suppose that an open box is to be made from a square sheet of cardboard by cutting out squares from each corner as shown and then folding along the dotted lines. If the box is to have a volume of 300 cubic centimeters, find the original dimensions of the sheet of cardboard.

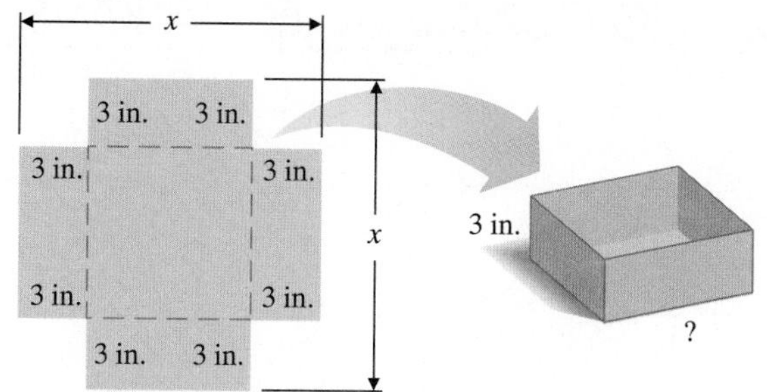

a. The ? in the drawing above will be the length (and also the width) of the box as shown. Represent this length in terms of x.

b. Use the formula for volume of a box, $V = l \cdot w \cdot h$, to write an equation in x.

c. Solve the equation for x and give the dimensions of the sheet of cardboard. Check your solution.

△ **68.** Suppose that an open box is to be made from a square sheet of cardboard by cutting out squares from each corner as shown and then folding along the dotted lines. If the box is to have a volume of 128 cubic inches, find the original dimensions of the sheet of cardboard.

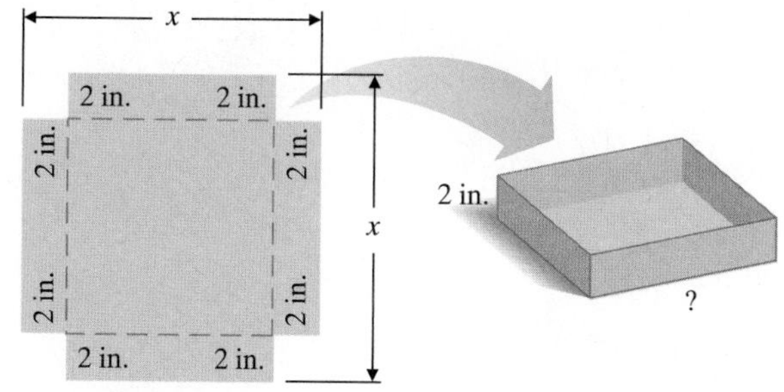

a. The ? in the drawing above will be the length (and also the width) of the box as shown. Represent this length in terms of x.

b. Use the formula for volume of a box, $V = l \cdot w \cdot h$, to write an equation in x.

c. Solve the equation for x and give the dimensions of the sheet of cardboard. Check your solution.

△ **69.** A sprinkler that sprays water in a circular motion is to be used to water a square garden. If the area of the garden is 920 square feet, find the smallest whole number *radius* that the sprinkler can be adjusted to so that the entire garden is watered.

△ **70.** Suppose that a square field has an area of 6270 square feet. See Exercise 69 and find a new sprinkler radius.

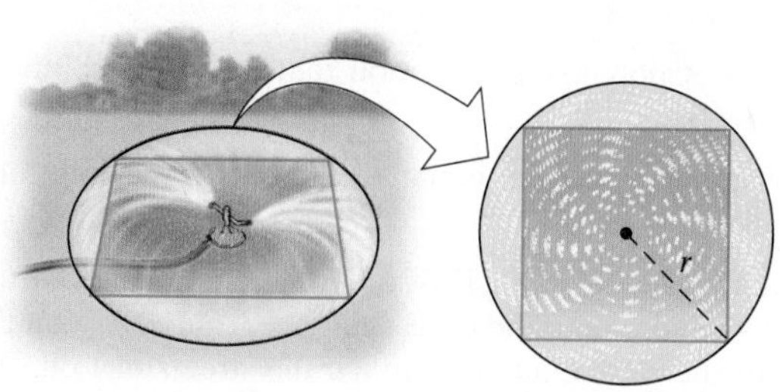

REVIEW AND PREVIEW

Solve each inequality. See Section 16.2.

71. $\frac{5x}{3} + 2 \leq 7$

72. $\frac{2x}{3} + \frac{1}{6} \geq 2$

73. $\frac{y - 1}{15} > -\frac{2}{5}$

74. $\frac{z - 2}{12} < \frac{1}{4}$

Find the domain and range of each graphed relation. Decide which relations are also functions. See Section 15.2.

75.

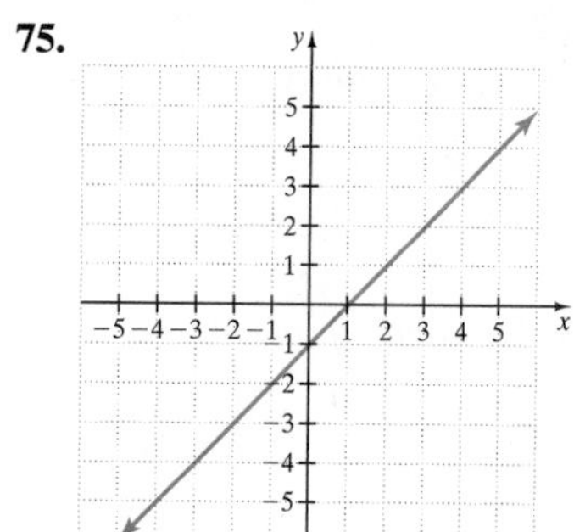

76. **77.**

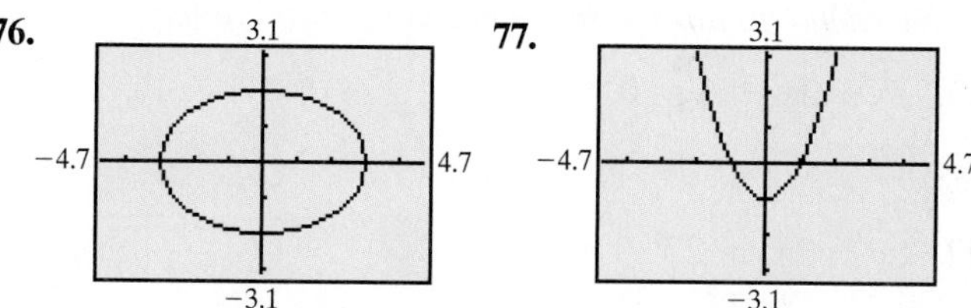

78.

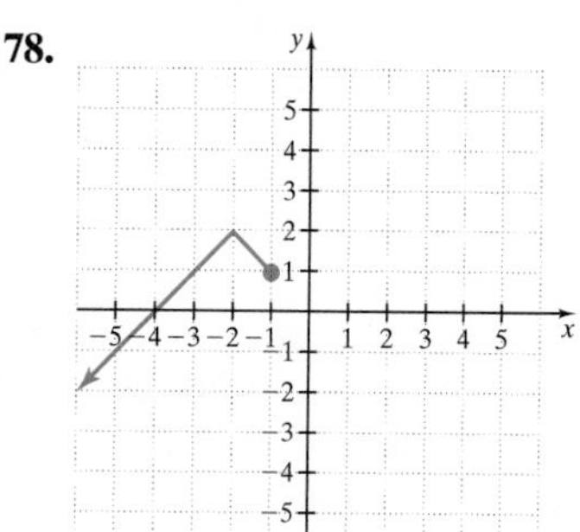

CONCEPT EXTENSIONS

Solve.

79. $y^3 + 9y - y^2 - 9 = 0$

80. $x^3 + x - 3x^2 - 3 = 0$

81. $x^{-2} - x^{-1} - 6 = 0$

82. $y^{-2} - 8y^{-1} + 7 = 0$

83. $2x^3 = -54$

84. $y^3 - 216 = 0$

85. Write a polynomial equation that has three solutions: 2, 5, and -7.

86. Write a polynomial equation that has three solutions: 0, $2i$, and $-2i$.

87. At the 2007 Grand Prix of Long Beach auto race, Simon Pagenaud posted the fastest lap speed, but Sebastian Bourdais won the race. One lap through the streets of Long Beach is 10,391 feet (1.968 miles) long. Pagenaud's fastest lap speed was 0.55 foot per second faster than Bourdais's fastest lap speed. Traveling at these fastest speeds, Bourdais would have taken 0.25 second longer than Pagenaud to complete a lap. (*Source:* Championship Auto Racing Teams, Inc.)

a. Find Sebastian Bourdais's fastest lap speed during the race. Round to two decimal places.

b. Find Simon Pagenaud's fastest lap speed during the race. Round to two decimal places.

c. Convert each speed to miles per hour. Round to one decimal place.

88. Use a graphing calculator to solve Exercise 29. Compare the solution with the solution from Exercise 29. Explain any differences.

INTEGRATED REVIEW SUMMARY ON SOLVING QUADRATIC EQUATIONS

Sections 20.1–20.3

Use the square root property to solve each equation.

1. $x^2 - 10 = 0$

2. $x^2 - 14 = 0$

3. $(x - 1)^2 = 8$

4. $(x + 5)^2 = 12$

Solve each equation by completing the square.

5. $x^2 + 2x - 12 = 0$

6. $x^2 - 12x + 11 = 0$

7. $3x^2 + 3x = 5$

8. $16y^2 + 16y = 1$

Use the quadratic formula to solve each equation.

9. $2x^2 - 4x + 1 = 0$

10. $\frac{1}{2}x^2 + 3x + 2 = 0$

11. $x^2 + 4x = -7$

12. $x^2 + x = -3$

Solve each equation. Use a method of your choice.

13. $x^2 + 3x + 6 = 0$

14. $2x^2 + 18 = 0$

15. $x^2 + 17x = 0$

16. $4x^2 - 2x - 3 = 0$

17. $(x - 2)^2 = 27$

18. $\frac{1}{2}x^2 - 2x + \frac{1}{2} = 0$

19. $3x^2 + 2x = 8$

20. $2x^2 = -5x - 1$

21. $x(x - 2) = 5$

22. $x^2 - 31 = 0$

23. $5x^2 - 55 = 0$

24. $5x^2 + 55 = 0$

25. $x(x + 5) = 66$

26. $5x^2 + 6x - 2 = 0$

27. $2x^2 + 3x = 1$

△ 28. The diagonal of a square room measures 20 feet. Find the exact length of a side of the room. Then approximate the length to the nearest tenth of a foot.

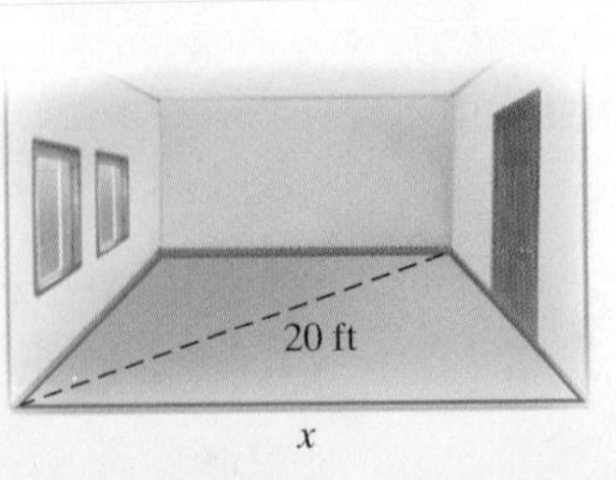

29. Together, Jack and Lucy Hoag can prepare a crawfish boil for a large party in 4 hours. Lucy alone can complete the job in 2 hours less time than Jack alone. Find the time that each person can prepare the crawfish boil alone. Round each time to the nearest tenth of an hour.

30. Diane Gray exercises at Total Body Gym. On the treadmill, she runs 5 miles, then increases her speed by 1 mile per hour and runs an additional 2 miles. If her total time on the tread mill is $1\frac{1}{3}$ hours, find her speed during each part of her run.

STUDY SKILLS BUILDER

Are You Preparing for a Test on Chapter 20?

Below I have listed some common trouble areas for students in Chapter 20. After studying for your test—but before taking your test—read these.

- Don't forget that to solve a quadratic equation such as $x^2 + 6x = 1$ by completing the square, add the square of half of 6 to both sides.

$$x^2 + 6x = 1$$

$$x^2 + 6x + 9 = 1 + 9 \qquad \text{Add 9 to both sides } \left(\frac{1}{2}(6) = 3 \text{ and } 3^2 = 9\right).$$

$$(x + 3)^2 = 10$$

$$x + 3 = \pm\sqrt{10}$$

$$x = -3 \pm \sqrt{10}$$

- Remember to write a quadratic equation in standard form, $(ax^2 + bx + c = 0)$, before using the quadratic formula to solve.

$$x(4x - 1) = 1$$

$$4x^2 - x - 1 = 0 \qquad \text{Write in standard form.}$$

$$x = \frac{-(-1) \pm \sqrt{(-1)^2 - 4(4)(-1)}}{2 \cdot 4} \qquad \text{Use the quadratic formula with } a = 4, b = -1, \text{ and } c = -1.$$

$$x = \frac{1 \pm \sqrt{17}}{8} \qquad \text{Simplify.}$$

- Review the steps for solving a quadratic equation in general.

Remember: This is simply a checklist of common trouble areas. For a review of Chapter 20, see the Highlights and Chapter Review at the end of this chapter.

CHAPTER 20 VOCABULARY CHECK

Fill in each blank with one of the words or phrases listed below.

quadratic formula	quadratic	$\pm\sqrt{b}$
completing the square	discriminant	

1. The ____________ helps us find the number and type of solutions of a quadratic equation.

2. If $a^2 = b$, then $a =$ ________.

3. The process of writing a quadratic equation so that one side is a perfect square trinomial is called ________________.

4. The formula $x = \dfrac{-b \pm \sqrt{b^2 - 4ac}}{2a}$ is called the ______________.

5. A ___________ equation is one that can be written in the form $ax^2 + bx + c = 0$, where a, b, and c are real numbers and a is not 0.

Helpful Hint

Are you preparing for your test? Don't forget to take the Chapter 20 Test on page 1252. Then check your answers at the back of the text and use the Chapter Test Prep Video CD to see the fully worked-out solutions to any of the exercises you want to review.

CHAPTER 20 HIGHLIGHTS

DEFINITIONS AND CONCEPTS	EXAMPLES
SECTION 20.1 SOLVING QUADRATIC EQUATIONS BY COMPLETING THE SQUARE	
Square root property If b is a real number and if $a^2 = b$, then $a = \pm\sqrt{b}$.	Solve: $(x + 3)^2 = 14$. $x + 3 = \pm\sqrt{14}$ $x = -3 \pm \sqrt{14}$
To solve a quadratic equation in x by completing the square	Solve: $3x^2 - 12x - 18 = 0$.
Step 1. If the coefficient of x^2 is not 1, divide both sides of the equation by the coefficient of x^2.	**1.** $x^2 - 4x - 6 = 0$
Step 2. Isolate the variable terms.	**2.** $x^2 - 4x = 6$

DEFINITIONS AND CONCEPTS	EXAMPLES
SECTION 20.1 SOLVING QUADRATIC EQUATIONS BY COMPLETING THE SQUARE (CONTINUED)	
Step 3. Complete the square by adding the square of half of the coefficient of x to both sides.	**3.** $\frac{1}{2}(-4) = -2$ and $(-2)^2 = 4$ $x^2 - 4x + 4 = 6 + 4$
Step 4. Write the resulting trinomial as the square of a binomial.	**4.** $(x - 2)^2 = 10$
Step 5. Apply the square root property and solve for x.	**5.** $x - 2 = \pm\sqrt{10}$ $x = 2 \pm \sqrt{10}$
SECTION 20.2 SOLVING QUADRATIC EQUATIONS BY THE QUADRATIC FORMULA	
A quadratic equation written in the form $ax^2 + bx + c = 0$ has solutions $x = \frac{-b \pm \sqrt{b^2 - 4ac}}{2a}$	Solve: $x^2 - x - 3 = 0$. $a = 1, b = -1, c = -3$ $x = \frac{-(-1) \pm \sqrt{(-1)^2 - 4(1)(-3)}}{2 \cdot 1}$ $x = \frac{1 \pm \sqrt{13}}{2}$
SECTION 20.3 SOLVING EQUATIONS BY USING QUADRATIC METHODS	
Substitution is often helpful in solving an equation that contains a repeated variable expression.	Solve: $(2x + 1)^2 - 5(2x + 1) + 6 = 0$. Let $m = 2x + 1$. Then $m^2 - 5m + 6 = 0$ Let $m = 2x + 1$. $(m - 3)(m - 2) = 0$ $m = 3$ or $m = 2$ $2x + 1 = 3$ or $2x + 1 = 2$ Substitute back. $x = 1$ or $x = \frac{1}{2}$

CHAPTER 20 REVIEW

(20.1) *Solve by factoring.*

1. $x^2 - 15x + 14 = 0$

2. $7a^2 = 29a + 30$

Solve by using the square root property.

3. $4m^2 = 196$

4. $(5x - 2)^2 = 2$

Solve by completing the square.

5. $z^2 + 3z + 1 = 0$

6. $(2x + 1)^2 = x$

7. If P dollars are originally invested, the formula $A = P(1 + r)^2$ gives the amount A in an account paying interest rate r compounded annually after 2 years. Find the interest rate r such that \$2500 increases to \$2717 in 2 years. Round the result to the nearest hundredth of a percent.

△ **8.** Two ships leave a port at the same time and travel at the same speed. One ship is traveling due north and the other due east. In a few hours, the ships are 150 miles apart. How many miles has each ship traveled? Give an exact answer and a one-decimal-place approximation.

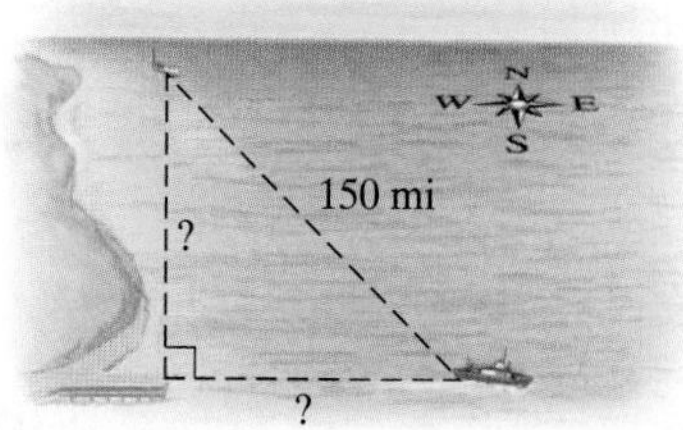

(20.2) If the discriminant of a quadratic equation has the given value, determine the number and type of solutions of the equation.

9. -8 **10.** 48

11. 100 **12.** 0

Solve by using the quadratic formula.

13. $x^2 - 16x + 64 = 0$ **14.** $x^2 + 5x = 0$

15. $2x^2 + 3x = 5$ **16.** $9a^2 + 4 = 2a$

17. $6x^2 + 7 = 5x$ **18.** $(2x - 3)^2 = x$

19. Cadets graduating from military school usually toss their hats high into the air at the end of the ceremony. One cadet threw his hat so that its distance $d(t)$ in feet above the ground t seconds after it was thrown was $d(t) = -16t^2 + 30t + 6$.

a. Find the distance above the ground of the hat 1 second after it was thrown.

b. Find the time it took the hat to hit the ground. Give an exact time and a one-decimal-place approximation.

△ **20.** The hypotenuse of an isosceles right triangle is 6 centimeters longer than either of the legs. Find the length of the legs.

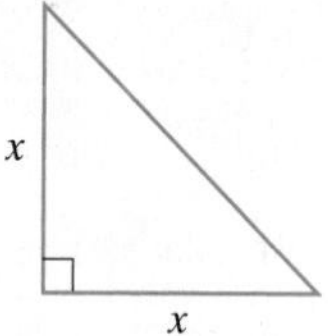

(20.3) Solve each equation for the variable.

21. $x^3 = 27$

22. $y^3 = -64$

23. $\frac{5}{x} + \frac{6}{x - 2} = 3$

24. $x^4 - 21x^2 - 100 = 0$

25. $x^{2/3} - 6x^{1/3} + 5 = 0$

26. $5(x + 3)^2 - 19(x + 3) = 4$

27. $a^6 - a^2 = a^4 - 1$

28. $y^{-2} + y^{-1} = 20$

29. Two postal workers, Jerome Grant and Tim Bozik, can sort a stack of mail in 5 hours. Working alone, Tim can sort the mail in 1 hour less time than Jerome can. Find the time that each postal worker can sort the mail alone. Round the result to one decimal place.

30. A negative number decreased by its reciprocal is $-\frac{24}{5}$. Find the number.

MIXED REVIEW

Solve each equation.

31. $x^2 - x - 30 = 0$

32. $(9n + 1)^2 = 9$

33. $x^2 + x + 7 = 0$

34. $(3x - 4)^2 = 10x$

35. $x^2 + 11 = 0$

36. $(5a - 2)^2 - a = 0$

37. $\frac{7}{8} = \frac{8}{x^2}$

38. $x^{2/3} - 6x^{1/3} = -8$

CHAPTER 20 TEST

TEST PREP VIDEO  Remember to use the Chapter Test Prep Video CD to see the fully worked-out solutions to any of the exercises you want to review.

Solve each equation for the variable.

1. $5x^2 - 2x = 7$

2. $(x + 1)^2 = 10$

3. $m^2 - m + 8 = 0$

4. $u^2 - 6u + 2 = 0$

5. $7x^2 + 8x + 1 = 0$

6. $y^2 - 3y = 5$

7. $\frac{4}{x + 2} + \frac{2x}{x - 2} = \frac{6}{x^2 - 4}$

8. $x^5 + 3x^4 = x + 3$

9. $x^6 + 1 = x^4 + x^2$

10. $(x + 1)^2 - 15(x + 1) + 56 = 0$

Solve the equation for the variable by completing the square.

11. $x^2 - 6x = -2$

12. $2a^2 + 5 = 4a$

CHAPTER 20 CUMULATIVE REVIEW

1. Write each sentence using mathematical symbols.
a. The sum of 5 and y is greater than or equal to 7.
b. 11 is not equal to z.
c. 20 is less than the difference of 5 and twice x.

2. Solve $|3x - 2| = -5$.

3. Find the slope of the line containing the points (0, 3) and (2, 5). Graph the line.

4. Use the elimination method to solve the system.
$$\begin{cases} -6x + y = 5 \\ 4x - 2y = 6 \end{cases}$$

5. Use the elimination method to solve the system.
$$\begin{cases} x - 5y = -12 \\ -x + y = 4 \end{cases}$$

6. Simplify. Use positive exponents to write each answer.
a. $(a^{-2}bc^3)^{-3}$
b. $\left(\frac{a^{-4}b^2}{c^3}\right)^{-2}$ **c.** $\left(\frac{3a^8b^2}{12a^5b^5}\right)^{-2}$

7. Multiply.
a. $(2x - 7)(3x - 4)$
b. $(3x^2 + y)(5x^2 - 2y)$

8. Multiply.
a. $(4a - 3)(7a - 2)$
b. $(2a + b)(3a - 5b)$

9. Factor.
a. $8x^2 + 4$
b. $5y - 2z^4$
c. $6x^2 - 3x^3 + 12x^4$

10. Factor.
a. $9x^3 + 27x^2 - 15x$
b. $2x(3y - 2) - 5(3y - 2)$
c. $2xy + 6x - y - 3$

Factor the polynomials in Exercises 11 through 14.

11. $x^2 - 12x + 35$

12. $x^2 - 2x - 48$

13. $3a^2x - 12abx + 12b^2x$

14. Factor. $2ax^2 - 12axy + 18ay^2$

15. Solve $3(x^2 + 4) + 5 = -6(x^2 + 2x) + 13$.

16. Solve $2(a^2 + 2) - 8 = -2a(a - 2) - 5$.

17. Solve $x^3 = 4x$.

18. Simplify $\frac{2x^2}{10x^3 - 2x^2}$.

19. Simplify $\frac{x^2 - 4x + 4}{2 - x}$.

20. Add $\frac{2x - 1}{2x^2 - 9x - 5} + \frac{x + 3}{6x^2 - x - 2}$.

21. Subtract $\frac{a + 1}{a^2 - 6a + 8} - \frac{3}{16 - a^2}$.

22. Simplify $\frac{x^{-1} + 2xy^{-1}}{x^{-2} - x^{-2}y^{-1}}$.

23. Simplify $\frac{(2a)^{-1} + b^{-1}}{a^{-1} + (2b)^{-1}}$.

24. Divide $\frac{3x^5y^2 - 15x^3y - x^2y - 6x}{x^2y}$.

25. Solve $\frac{4x}{5} + \frac{3}{2} = \frac{3x}{10}$.

26. Solve $\frac{x + 3}{x^2 + 5x + 6} = \frac{3}{2x + 4} - \frac{1}{x + 3}$.

27. Mr. Briley can roof his house in 24 hours. His son can roof the same house in 40 hours. If they work together, how long will it take to roof the house?

28. Suppose that y varies directly as x. If y is 5 when x is 30, find the constant of variation and the direct variation equation.

29. Suppose that y varies inversely as x. If y is 8 when x is 14, find the constant of variation and the inverse variation equation.

30. Simplify.
a. $\sqrt{(-3)^2}$ **b.** $\sqrt{x^2}$
c. $\sqrt[4]{(x - 2)^4}$ **d.** $\sqrt[3]{(-5)^3}$
e. $\sqrt[5]{(2x - 7)^5}$ **f.** $\sqrt{25x^2}$
g. $\sqrt{x^2 + 2x + 1}$

31. Simplify. Assume that the variables represent any real number.
a. $\sqrt{(-2)^2}$ **b.** $\sqrt{y^2}$
c. $\sqrt[4]{(a - 3)^4}$ **d.** $\sqrt[3]{(-6)^3}$
e. $\sqrt[5]{(3x - 1)^5}$

32. Use rational exponents to simplify. Assume that variables represent positive numbers.
a. $\sqrt[8]{x^4}$ **b.** $\sqrt[6]{25}$
c. $\sqrt[4]{r^2s^6}$

33. Use rational exponents to simplify. Assume that variables represent positive numbers.
a. $\sqrt[4]{5^2}$ **b.** $\sqrt[12]{x^3}$
c. $\sqrt[6]{x^2y^4}$

34. Use the product rule to simplify.
a. $\sqrt{25x^3}$ **b.** $\sqrt[3]{54x^6y^8}$
c. $\sqrt[4]{81z^{11}}$

35. Use the product rule to simplify. Assume that variables represent positive numbers.

a. $\sqrt{64a^5}$ **b.** $\sqrt[3]{24a^7b^9}$

c. $\sqrt[4]{48x^9}$

36. Rationalize the denominator of each expression.

a. $\frac{2}{\sqrt{5}}$ **b.** $\frac{2\sqrt{16}}{\sqrt{9x}}$

c. $\sqrt[3]{\frac{1}{2}}$

37. Multiply. Simplify if possible.

a. $(\sqrt{3}-4)(2\sqrt{3}+2)$

b. $(\sqrt{5}-x)^2$

c. $(\sqrt{a}+b)(\sqrt{a}-b)$

38. Solve $\sqrt{2x+5}+\sqrt{2x}=3$.

39. Solve $\sqrt{x-2}=\sqrt{4x+1}-3$.

40. Divide. Write in the form $a+bi$.

a. $\frac{2+i}{1-i}$ **b.** $\frac{7}{3i}$

41. Write each product in the form of $a+bi$.

a. $3i(5-2i)$

b. $(6-5i)^2$

c. $(\sqrt{3}+2i)(\sqrt{3}-2i)$

42. Use the square root property to solve $(x+1)^2=12$.

43. Use the square root property to solve $(y-1)^2=24$.

44. Solve $x-\sqrt{x}-6=0$.

45. Use the quadratic formula to solve $m^2=4m+8$.

Answers to Selected Exercises

Chapter 1 The Whole Numbers

Section 1.2

Vocabulary and Readiness Check **1.** whole **3.** words **5.** period

Exercise Set 1.2 **1.** tens **3.** thousands **5.** hundred-thousands **7.** millions **9.** three hundred fifty-four **11.** eight thousand, two hundred seventy-nine **13.** twenty-six thousand, nine hundred ninety **15.** two million, three hundred eighty-eight thousand **17.** twenty-four million, three hundred fifty thousand, one hundred eighty-five **19.** three hundred four thousand, three hundred sixty-seven **21.** two thousand, six hundred **23.** fifteen million, eight hundred thousand **25.** fourteen thousand, four hundred thirty-three **27.** thirteen million **29.** 6587 **31.** 59,800 **33.** 13,601,011 **35.** 7,000,017 **37.** 260,997 **39.** 395 **41.** 16,732 **43.** $72,704,000 **45.** 1317 **47.** 400 + 6 **49.** 3000 + 400 + 70 **51.** 80,000 + 700 + 70 + 4 **53.** 60,000 + 6000 + 40 + 9 **55.** 30,000,000 + 9,000,000 + 600,000 + 80,000 **57.** 5532; five thousand, five hundred thirty-two **59.** 5000 + 400 + 90 + 2 **61.** Mt. Washington **63.** Boxer **65.** Labrador retriever; one hundred twenty-three thousand, seven hundred sixty **67.** 25 pounds **69.** 9861 **71.** no; one hundred five **73.** answers may vary **75.** 1,000,000,000,000,000 **77.** Canton

Section 1.3

Calculator Explorations **1.** 134 **3.** 340 **5.** 2834

Vocabulary and Readiness Check **1.** number **3.** sum; addend **5.** grouping; associative

Exercise Set 1.3 **1.** 36 **3.** 292 **5.** 49 **7.** 5399 **9.** 117 **11.** 512 **13.** 209,078 **15.** 25 **17.** 62 **19.** 212 **21.** 94 **23.** 910 **25.** 8273 **27.** 11,926 **29.** 1884 **31.** 16,717 **33.** 1110 **35.** 8999 **37.** 35,901 **39.** 632,389 **41.** 42 in. **43.** 25 ft **45.** 24 in. **47.** 8 yd **49.** 29 in. **51.** 44 m **53.** 2093 **55.** 266 **57.** 544 **59.** 3452 **61.** 22,478 thousand **63.** 6684 ft **65.** 340 ft **67.** 2425 ft **69.** 313,769 motorcycles **71.** 85,446 automobiles **73.** 124 ft **75.** 3170 **77.** California **79.** 506 stores **81.** Florida and Georgia **83.** 5894 mi **85.** answers may vary **87.** answers may vary **89.** 1,044,473,765 **91.** correct **93.** incorrect: 530

Section 1.4

Calculator Explorations **1.** 770 **3.** 109 **5.** 8978

Vocabulary and Readiness Check **1.** 0 **3.** minuend; subtrahend **5.** 0 **7.** 600

Exercise Set 1.4 **1.** 44 **3.** 265 **5.** 135 **7.** 2254 **9.** 5545 **11.** 600 **13.** 25 **15.** 45 **17.** 146 **19.** 288 **21.** 168 **23.** 106 **25.** 447 **27.** 5723 **29.** 504 **31.** 89 **33.** 79 **35.** 39,914 **37.** 32,711 **39.** 5041 **41.** 31,213 **43.** 4 **45.** 20 **47.** 7 **49.** 72 **51.** 88 **53.** 264 pages **55.** 3 million sq km **57.** 264,000 sq mi **59.** 283,000 sq mi **61.** 6065 ft **63.** 28 ft **65.** 358 mi **67.** $619 **69.** 452 thousand **71.** 100 dB **73.** 58 dB **75.** 320 **77.** 5920 sq ft **79.** Hartsfield Atlanta International **81.** 26 million **83.** Jo; by 271 votes **85.** 1034 **87.** 9 **89.** 8518 **91.** 22,876 **93.** minuend: 48; subtrahend: 1 **95.** minuend: 70; subtrahend: 7 **97.** incorrect: 685 **99.** correct **101.** 5269 − 2385 = 2884 **103.** no; answers may vary **105.** no: 1089 more pages

Section 1.5

Vocabulary and Readiness Check **1.** graph **3.** 70; 60

Exercise Set 1.5 **1.** 420 **3.** 640 **5.** 2800 **7.** 500 **9.** 21,000 **11.** 34,000 **13.** 328,500 **15.** 36,000 **17.** 39,990 **19.** 30,000,000 **21.** 5280; 5300; 5000 **23.** 9440; 9400; 9000 **25.** 14,880; 14,900; 15,000 **27.** 84,000 members **29.** 38,000 points **31.** $43,000,000,000 **33.** $4,100,000 **35.** US: 263,000,000; India: 297,000,000 **37.** 130 **39.** 80 **41.** 5700 **43.** 300 **45.** 11,400 **47.** incorrect **49.** correct **51.** correct **53.** $3400 **55.** 900 mi **57.** 6000 ft **59.** Joliet is larger by approximately 60,000. **61.** The increase was 2000. **63.** 391,000,000; 390,000,000; 400,000,000 **65.** 349,000,000; 350,000,000; 300,000,000 **67.** 5723, for example **69. a.** 8550 **b.** 8649 **71.** answers may vary **73.** 140 m

Section 1.6

Calculator Explorations **1.** 3456 **3.** 15,322 **5.** 272,291

Vocabulary and Readiness Check **1.** 0 **3.** product; factor **5.** grouping; associative **7.** length

Exercise Set 1.6 **1.** 24 **3.** 0 **5.** 0 **7.** 87 **9.** $6 \cdot 3 + 6 \cdot 8$ **11.** $4 \cdot 3 + 4 \cdot 9$ **13.** $20 \cdot 14 + 20 \cdot 6$ **15.** 512 **17.** 3678 **19.** 1662 **21.** 6444 **23.** 1157 **25.** 24,418 **27.** 24,786 **29.** 15,600 **31.** 0 **33.** 6400 **35.** 48,126 **37.** 142,506 **39.** 2,369,826 **41.** 64,790 **43.** 3,949,935 **45.** 800 **47.** 11,000 **49.** 74,060 **51.** 24,000 **53.** 45,000 **55.** 3,280,000 **57.** area: 63 sq m; perimeter: 32 m **59.** area: 680 sq ft; perimeter: 114 ft **61.** 240,000 **63.** 300,000 **65.** c **67.** c **69.** 880 **71.** 4200 **73.** 4480 **75.** 375 cal **77.** $3290 **79. a.** 20 **b.** 100 **c.** 2000 lb **81.** 8800 sq ft **83.** 56,000 sq ft **85.** 5828 pixels **87.** 2100 characters **89.** 1280 cal **91.** $10, $60; $10, $200; $12, $36; $12, $36; total cost: $372 **93.** 1,440,000 tea bags **95.** 135 **97.** 2144 **99.** 23 **101.** 15 **103.** $5 \cdot 6$ or $6 \cdot 5$ **105. a.** 5 + 5 + 5 or 3 + 3 + 3 + 3 + 3 **b.** answers may vary **107.** $\begin{array}{r} 203 \\ \times\ 14 \\ \hline 812 \\ 2030 \\ \hline 2842 \end{array}$ **109.** $\begin{array}{r} 42 \\ \times 93 \\ \hline \end{array}$ **111.** answers may vary **113.** 506 windows

Section 1.7

Calculator Explorations **1.** 53 **3.** 62 **5.** 261 **7.** 0

Vocabulary and Readiness Check **1.** quotient; dividend; divisor **3.** 1 **5.** undefined

Exercise Set 1.7 **1.** 6 **3.** 12 **5.** 0 **7.** 31 **9.** 1 **11.** 8 **13.** undefined **15.** 1 **17.** 0 **19.** 9 **21.** 29 **23.** 74 **25.** 338 **27.** undefined **29.** 9 **31.** 25 **33.** 68 R 3 **35.** 236 R 5 **37.** 38 R 1 **39.** 326 R 4 **41.** 13 **43.** 49 **45.** 97 R 8 **47.** 209 R 11 **49.** 506 **51.** 202 R 7 **53.** 54 **55.** 99 R 100 **57.** 202 R 15 **59.** 579 R 72 **61.** 17 **63.** 511 R 3 **65.** 2132 R 32 **67.** 6080 **69.** 23 R 2 **71.** 5 R 25 **73.** 20 R 2 **75.** 33 students

77. 165 lb **79.** 310 yd **81.** 89 bridges **83.** 11 light poles **85.** 5 mi **87.** 1760 yd **89.** 20 **91.** 387 **93.** 79 **95.** 74° **97.** 9278 **99.** 15,288 **101.** 679 **103.** undefined **105.** 9 R 12 **107.** c **109.** b **111.** 120 **113.** increase; answers may vary **115.** no; answers may vary **117.** 12 ft **119.** answers may vary **121.** 5 R 1

Integrated Review **1.** 148 **2.** 6555 **3.** 1620 **4.** 562 **5.** 79 **6.** undefined **7.** 9 **8.** 1 **9.** 0 **10.** 0 **11.** 0 **12.** 3 **13.** 2433 **14.** 9826 **15.** 213 R 3 **16.** 79,317 **17.** 27 **18.** 9 **19.** 138 **20.** 276 **21.** 1099 R 2 **22.** 111 R 1 **23.** 663 R 6 **24.** 1076 R 60 **25.** 1024 **26.** 9899 **27.** 30,603 **28.** 47,500 **29.** 65 **30.** 456 **31.** 6 R 8 **32.** 53 **33.** 183 **34.** 231 **35.** 9740; 9700; 10,000 **36.** 1430; 1400; 1000 **37.** 20,800; 20,800; 21,000 **38.** 432,200; 432,200; 432,000 **39.** perimeter: 24 ft; area: 36 sq ft **40.** perimeter: 42 in.; area: 98 sq in. **41.** 28 mi **42.** 26 m **43.** 24 **44.** 124 **45.** Lake Pontchartrain Bridge; 2175 ft **46.** 730 qt

Section 1.8

Exercise Set 1.8 **1.** 49 **3.** 237 **5.** 42 **7.** 600 **9. a.** 400 ft **b.** 9600 sq ft **11.** $15,500 **13.** 168 hr **15.** 3500 ft **17.** 129 yr **19.** 312 billion bricks **21.** 719 towns **23.** $27 **25.** 55 cal **27.** 23 hot dogs **29.** $30,956,764 **31.** 155,300 **33.** 3987 mi **35.** 13 paychecks **37.** $239 **39.** $1045 **41.** b will be cheaper by $3 **43.** Asia **45.** 559 million **47.** 109 million **49.** 404 million **51.** $14,754 **53.** 16,800 mg **55. a.** 3750 sq ft **b.** 375 sq ft **c.** 3375 sq ft **57.** $171 **59.** answers may vary

Section 1.9

Calculator Explorations **1.** 4096 **3.** 3125 **5.** 2048 **7.** 2526 **9.** 4295 **11.** 8

Vocabulary and Readiness Check **1.** base; exponent **3.** addition **5.** division

Exercise Set 1.9 **1.** 4^3 **3.** 7^6 **5.** 12^3 **7.** $6^2 \cdot 5^3$ **9.** $9 \cdot 8^2$ **11.** $3 \cdot 2^4$ **13.** $3 \cdot 2^4 \cdot 5^5$ **15.** 64 **17.** 125 **19.** 32 **21.** 1 **23.** 7 **25.** 128 **27.** 256 **29.** 256 **31.** 729 **33.** 144 **35.** 100 **37.** 20 **39.** 729 **41.** 192 **43.** 162 **45.** 3 **47.** 8 **49.** 12 **51.** 4 **53.** 21 **55.** 7 **57.** 5 **59.** 16 **61.** 46 **63.** 8 **65.** 64 **67.** 83 **69.** 2 **71.** 48 **73.** 4 **75.** undefined **77.** 59 **79.** 52 **81.** 44 **83.** 12 **85.** 21 **87.** 24 **89.** 28 **91.** 3 **93.** 25 **95.** 23 **97.** 13 **99.** area: 49 sq m; perimeter: 28 m **101.** area: 529 sq mi; perimeter: 92 mi **103.** true **105.** false **107.** $(2+3) \cdot 6 - 2$ **109.** $24 \div (3 \cdot 2) + 2 \cdot 5$ **111.** 1260 ft **113.** 6,384,814 **115.** answers may vary; $(20 - 10) \cdot 5 \div 25 + 3$

Chapter 1 Vocabulary Check **1.** whole numbers **2.** perimeter **3.** place value **4.** exponent **5.** area **6.** square root **7.** digits **8.** average **9.** divisor **10.** dividend **11.** quotient **12.** factor **13.** product **14.** minuend **15.** subtrahend **16.** difference **17.** addend **18.** sum

Chapter 1 Review **1.** tens **2.** ten-millions **3.** seven thousand, six hundred forty **4.** forty-six million, two hundred thousand, one hundred twenty **5.** 3000 + 100 + 50 + 8 **6.** 400,000,000 + 3,000,000 + 200,000 + 20,000 + 5000 **7.** 81,900 **8.** 6,304,000,000 **9.** 384,633,765 **10.** 11,805,500 **11.** Middle East **12.** Asia **13.** 63 **14.** 67 **15.** 48 **16.** 77 **17.** 956 **18.** 840 **19.** 7950 **20.** 7250 **21.** 4211 **22.** 1967 **23.** 1326 **24.** 886 **25.** 27,346 **26.** 39,300 **27.** 8032 mi **28.** $197,699 **29.** 276 ft **30.** 66 km **31.** 14 **32.** 34 **33.** 65 **34.** 304 **35.** 3914 **36.** 7908 **37.** 17,897 **38.** 34,658 **39.** 184,338 **40.** 25,738 **41.** 397 pages **42.** $25,626 **43.** May **44.** August **45.** $110 **46.** $240 **47.** 90 **48.** 50 **49.** 470 **50.** 500 **51.** 4800 **52.** 58,000 **53.** 50,000,000 **54.** 800,000 **55.** 65,000,000 **56.** 93,000 **57.** 7400 **58.** 4100 **59.** 2500 mi **60.** 900,000 **61.** 1911 **62.** 1396 **63.** 1410 **64.** 2898 **65.** 800 **66.** 900 **67.** 3696 **68.** 1694 **69.** 0 **70.** 0 **71.** 16,994 **72.** 8954 **73.** 113,634 **74.** 44,763 **75.** 411,426 **76.** 636,314 **77.** 375,000 **78.** 108,000 **79.** 12,000 **80.** 35,000 **81.** 5,100,000 **82.** 7,600,000 **83.** 1150 **84.** 4920 **85.** 108 **86.** 112 **87.** 24 g **88.** $122,240 **89.** 60 sq mi **90.** 500 sq cm **91.** 3 **92.** 4 **93.** 6 **94.** 7 **95.** 5 R 2 **96.** 4 R 2 **97.** undefined **98.** 0 **99.** 1 **100.** 10 **101.** 0 **102.** undefined **103.** 33 R 2 **104.** 19 R 7 **105.** 24 R 2 **106.** 35 R 15 **107.** 506 R 10 **108.** 907 R 40 **109.** 2793 R 140 **110.** 2012 R 60 **111.** 18 R 2 **112.** 21 R 2 **113.** 458 ft **114.** 13 mi **115.** 51 **116.** 59 **117.** 27 boxes **118.** $192 **119.** 7 billion **120.** 75¢ **121.** $898 **122.** 23,150 sq ft **123.** 49 **124.** 125 **125.** 45 **126.** 400 **127.** 13 **128.** 10 **129.** 15 **130.** 7 **131.** 12 **132.** 9 **133.** 42 **134.** 33 **135.** 9 **136.** 2 **137.** 1 **138.** 0 **139.** 6 **140.** 29 **141.** 40 **142.** 72 **143.** 5 **144.** 7 **145.** 49 sq m **146.** 9 sq in. **147.** 307 **148.** 682 **149.** 2169 **150.** 2516 **151.** 901 **152.** 1411 **153.** 458 R 8 **154.** 237 R 1 **155.** 70,848 **156.** 95,832 **157.** 1644 **158.** 8481 **159.** 740 **160.** 258,000 **161.** 2000 **162.** 40,000 **163.** thirty-six thousand, nine hundred eleven **164.** one hundred fifty-four thousand, eight hundred sixty-three **165.** 70,943 **166.** 43,401 **167.** 64 **168.** 125 **169.** 12 **170.** 10 **171.** 12 **172.** 1 **173.** 2 **174.** 6 **175.** 4 **176.** 24 **177.** 24 **178.** 14 **179.** $513,000 **180.** $4,488,000 **181.** 53 full boxes with 18 left over **182.** $86

Chapter 1 Test **1.** eighty-two thousand, four hundred twenty-six **2.** 402,550 **3.** 141 **4.** 113 **5.** 14,880 **6.** 766 R 42 **7.** 200 **8.** 10 **9.** 0 **10.** undefined **11.** 33 **12.** 21 **13.** 8 **14.** 36 **15.** 5,698,000 **16.** 11,200,000 **17.** 52,000 **18.** 13,700 **19.** 1600 **20.** 92 **21.** 122 **22.** 1605 **23.** 7 R 2 **24.** $17 **25.** $126 **26.** 360 cal **27.** $7905 **28.** 20 cm; 25 sq cm **29.** 60 yd; 200 sq yd

Chapter 2 Multiplying and Dividing Fractions

Section 2.1

Vocabulary and Readiness Check **1.** fraction; denominator; numerator **3.** improper; proper; mixed number

Exercise Set 2.1 **1.** numerator: 1; denominator: 2; proper **3.** numerator: 10; denominator: 3; improper **5.** numerator: 15; denominator: 15; improper **7.** 1 **9.** undefined **11.** 13 **13.** 0 **15.** undefined **17.** 16 **19.** $\frac{5}{6}$ **21.** $\frac{7}{12}$ **23.** $\frac{3}{7}$ **25.** $\frac{4}{9}$ **27.** $\frac{1}{6}$ **29.** $\frac{5}{8}$ **31.**

33.

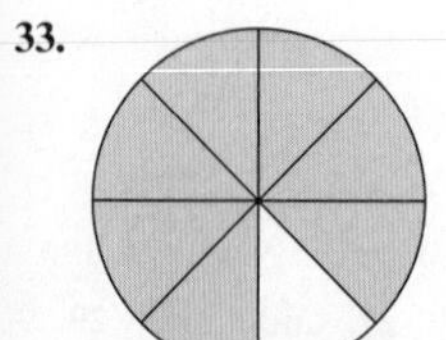

35. **37.**

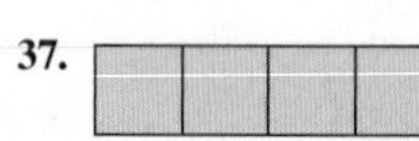

39. $\frac{42}{131}$ **41. a.** 89 **b.** $\frac{89}{131}$ **43.** $\frac{7}{44}$

45. $\frac{15}{28}$ of the tropical storms **47.** $\frac{11}{31}$ of the month **49.** $\frac{10}{31}$ of the class **51. a.** $\frac{33}{50}$ of the states **b.** 17 states **c.** $\frac{17}{50}$ of the states

53. a. $\frac{21}{50}$ **b.** 29 **c.** $\frac{29}{50}$ **55. a.** $\frac{11}{4}$ **b.** $2\frac{3}{4}$ **57. a.** $\frac{23}{6}$ **b.** $3\frac{5}{6}$ **59. a.** $\frac{4}{3}$ **b.** $1\frac{1}{3}$ **61. a.** $\frac{11}{2}$ **b.** $5\frac{1}{2}$ **63.** $\frac{7}{3}$ **65.** $\frac{18}{5}$ **67.** $\frac{53}{8}$ **69.** $\frac{41}{15}$ **71.** $\frac{83}{7}$ **73.** $\frac{84}{13}$ **75.** $\frac{109}{24}$ **77.** $\frac{211}{12}$ **79.** $\frac{187}{20}$ **81.** $\frac{265}{107}$ **83.** $\frac{500}{3}$ **85.** $3\frac{2}{5}$ **87.** $4\frac{5}{8}$ **89.** $3\frac{2}{15}$ **91.** $2\frac{4}{21}$ **93.** 33 **95.** 15 **97.** $66\frac{2}{3}$ **99.** $10\frac{17}{23}$ **101.** $17\frac{13}{18}$ **103.** $1\frac{7}{175}$ **105.** $6\frac{65}{112}$ **107.** 9 **109.** 125 **111.** 7^5 **113.** $2^3 \cdot 3$ **115.** answers may vary **117.** $\frac{2}{3}$ **119.** ● ● ● ● ○ ○ ○ ○ ○ **121.** $\frac{576}{3167}$ of the stores **123.** $\frac{1700}{2250}$ of the affiliates

Section 2.2

Vocabulary and Readiness Check **1.** prime factorization **3.** prime **5.** factors

Exercise Set 2.2 **1.** 1, 2, 4, 8 **3.** 1, 5, 25 **5.** 1, 2, 4 **7.** 1, 2, 3, 6, 9, 18 **9.** 1, 29 **11.** 1, 2, 4, 5, 8, 10, 16, 20, 40, 80 **13.** 1, 2, 3, 4, 6, 12 **15.** 1, 2, 17, 34 **17.** prime **19.** composite **21.** prime **23.** composite **25.** prime **27.** composite **29.** prime **31.** composite **33.** composite **35.** 2^5 **37.** $3 \cdot 5$ **39.** $2^3 \cdot 5$ **41.** $2^2 \cdot 3^2$ **43.** $3 \cdot 13$ **45.** $2^2 \cdot 3 \cdot 5$ **47.** $2 \cdot 5 \cdot 11$ **49.** $5 \cdot 17$ **51.** 2^7 **53.** $2 \cdot 7 \cdot 11$**55.** $2^2 \cdot 3 \cdot 5^2$ **57.** $2^4 \cdot 3 \cdot 5$ **59.** $2^2 \cdot 3^2 \cdot 23$ **61.** $2 \cdot 3^2 \cdot 7^2$ **63.** $7^2 \cdot 13$ **65.** $3 \cdot 11$ **67.** $2 \cdot 7^2$ **69.** prime **71.** $3^3 \cdot 17$ **73.** prime **75.** $2^2 \cdot 5^2 \cdot 7$ **77.** 4300 **79.** 7,660,000 **81.** 20,000 **83.** 159 **85.** $\frac{27}{159}$ **87.** $2^2 \cdot 3^5 \cdot 5 \cdot 7$ **89.** answers may vary **91.** answers may vary

Section 2.3

Calculator Explorations **1.** $\frac{4}{7}$ **3.** $\frac{20}{27}$ **5.** $\frac{15}{8}$ **7.** $\frac{9}{2}$

Vocabulary and Readiness Check **1.** simplest form **3.** cross products **5.** 0

Exercise Set 2.3 **1.** $\frac{1}{4}$ **3.** $\frac{2}{21}$ **5.** $\frac{7}{8}$ **7.** $\frac{2}{3}$ **9.** $\frac{7}{10}$ **11.** $\frac{7}{9}$ **13.** $\frac{3}{5}$ **15.** $\frac{27}{64}$ **17.** $\frac{5}{8}$ **19.** $\frac{5}{8}$ **21.** $\frac{14}{17}$ **23.** $\frac{3}{2}$ or $1\frac{1}{2}$ **25.** $\frac{3}{4}$ **27.** $\frac{5}{14}$ **29.** $\frac{3}{14}$ **31.** $\frac{11}{17}$ **33.** $\frac{3}{14}$ **35.** $\frac{7}{8}$ **37.** $\frac{3}{5}$ **39.** 14 **41.** equivalent **43.** not equivalent **45.** equivalent **47.** equivalent **49.** not equivalent **51.** not equivalent **53.** $\frac{1}{4}$ of a shift **55.** $\frac{1}{2}$ mi **57. a.** $\frac{8}{25}$ **b.** 34 states **c.** $\frac{17}{25}$ **59.** $\frac{5}{12}$ of the wall **61. a.** 18 **b.** $\frac{9}{25}$ **63.** $\frac{11}{160}$ of U.S. astronauts **65.** 364 **67.** 2322 **69.** 2520 **71.** answers may vary **73.** $\frac{3}{5}$ **75.** $\frac{9}{25}$ **77.** $\frac{1}{25}$ **79.** $\frac{1}{10}$ **81.** answers may vary **83.** $\frac{2}{25}$ **85.** answers may vary **87.** 786, 222, 900, 1470 **89.** 6; answers may vary

Integrated Review **1.** $\frac{3}{6}$ (or $\frac{1}{2}$ simplified) **2.** $\frac{7}{4}$ or $1\frac{3}{4}$ **3.** $\frac{73}{85}$ **4.** **5.** 1 **6.** 17 **7.** 0 **8.** undefined **9.** $\frac{25}{8}$ **10.** $\frac{28}{5}$ **11.** $\frac{69}{7}$ **12.** $\frac{141}{7}$ **13.** $2\frac{6}{7}$ **14.** 5 **15.** $4\frac{7}{8}$ **16.** $8\frac{10}{11}$ **17.** 1, 5, 7, 35 **18.** 1, 2, 4, 5, 8, 10, 20, 40 **19.** composite **20.** prime **21.** $5 \cdot 13$ **22.** $2 \cdot 5 \cdot 7$ **23.** $2^5 \cdot 3$ **24.** $2^2 \cdot 3 \cdot 11$ **25.** $2^2 \cdot 3^2 \cdot 7$ **26.** prime **27.** $3^2 \cdot 5 \cdot 7$ **28.** $3^2 \cdot 7^2$ **29.** $2 \cdot 11 \cdot 13$ **30.** prime **31.** $\frac{1}{7}$ **32.** $\frac{6}{5}$ or $1\frac{1}{5}$ **33.** $\frac{9}{19}$ **34.** $\frac{21}{55}$ **35.** $\frac{14}{15}$ **36.** $\frac{9}{10}$ **37.** $\frac{2}{5}$ **38.** $\frac{3}{8}$ **39.** $\frac{11}{14}$ **40.** $\frac{7}{11}$ **41.** not equivalent **42.** equivalent **43. a.** $\frac{1}{25}$ **b.** 48 **c.** $\frac{24}{25}$ **44. a.** $\frac{33}{95}$ **b.** 310 **c.** $\frac{62}{95}$

Section 2.4

Vocabulary and Readiness Check **1.** $\frac{a \cdot c}{b \cdot d}$ **3.** multiplication

Exercise Set 2.4 **1.** $\frac{2}{15}$ **3.** $\frac{6}{35}$ **5.** $\frac{9}{80}$ **7.** $\frac{5}{28}$ **9.** $\frac{12}{5}$ or $2\frac{2}{5}$ **11.** $\frac{1}{70}$ **13.** 0 **15.** $\frac{1}{110}$ **17.** $\frac{18}{55}$ **19.** $\frac{27}{80}$ **21.** $\frac{1}{56}$ **23.** $\frac{2}{105}$ **25.** 0 **27.** $\frac{1}{90}$ **29.** 8 **31.** 6 **33.** 20 **35.** 3 **37.** $\frac{5}{2}$ or $2\frac{1}{2}$ **39.** $\frac{1}{5}$ **41.** $\frac{5}{3}$ or $1\frac{2}{3}$ **43.** $\frac{2}{3}$ **45.** Exact: $\frac{77}{10}$ or $7\frac{7}{10}$; Estimate: 8 **47.** Exact: $\frac{836}{35}$ or $23\frac{31}{35}$; Estimate: 24 **49.** $\frac{25}{2}$ or $21\frac{1}{2}$ **51.** 15 **53.** 6 **55.** $\frac{45}{4}$ or $11\frac{1}{4}$ **57.** $\frac{49}{3}$ or $16\frac{1}{3}$ **59.** $\frac{1}{30}$ **61.** 0 **63.** $\frac{16}{5}$ or $3\frac{1}{5}$ **65.** $\frac{7}{2}$ or $3\frac{1}{2}$ **67.** $\frac{1}{8}$ **69.** $\frac{1}{56}$ **71.** $\frac{55}{3}$ or $18\frac{1}{3}$ **73.** 0 **75.** $\frac{208}{7}$ or $29\frac{5}{7}$ **77.** 50 **79.** 20 **81.** 128 **83.** 49 million **85.** 868 mi **87.** $\frac{3}{16}$ in. **89.** 30 gal **91.** $\frac{17}{2}$ or $8\frac{1}{2}$ in. **93.** $\frac{39}{2}$ or $19\frac{1}{2}$ in. **95.** $\frac{2242}{625}$ or $3\frac{367}{625}$ sq in. **97.** $\frac{1}{14}$ sq ft **99.** $\frac{7}{2}$ or $3\frac{1}{2}$ sq yd **101.** 3840 mi **103.** 2400 mi **105.** 206 **107.** 56 R 12 **109.** answers may vary **111.** $3\frac{2}{3} \cdot 1\frac{1}{7} = \frac{11}{3} \cdot \frac{8}{7} = \frac{11 \cdot 8}{3 \cdot 7} = \frac{88}{21}$ or $4\frac{4}{21}$ **113.** b **115.** a **117.** 37 **119.** $87\frac{3}{5}$ million households

Section 2.5

Vocabulary and Readiness Check **1.** reciprocals **3.** $\frac{a \cdot d}{b \cdot c}$

Exercise Set 2.5 **1.** $\frac{7}{4}$ **3.** 11 **5.** $\frac{1}{15}$ **7.** $\frac{7}{12}$ **9.** $\frac{4}{5}$ **11.** $\frac{16}{9}$ or $1\frac{7}{9}$ **13.** $\frac{18}{35}$ **15.** $\frac{3}{4}$ **17.** $\frac{1}{100}$ **19.** $\frac{1}{3}$ **21.** $\frac{5}{3}$ or $1\frac{2}{3}$ **23.** $\frac{35}{36}$ **25.** $\frac{14}{37}$ **27.** $\frac{8}{45}$ **29.** 1 **31.** undefined **33.** 0 **35.** $\frac{7}{10}$ **37.** $\frac{1}{6}$ **39.** $\frac{40}{3}$ or $13\frac{1}{3}$ **41.** 5 **43.** $\frac{5}{28}$ **45.** $\frac{36}{35}$ or $1\frac{1}{35}$ **47.** $\frac{26}{51}$ **49.** 0 **51.** $\frac{17}{13}$ or $1\frac{4}{13}$ **53.** $\frac{35}{18}$ or $1\frac{17}{18}$ **55.** $\frac{19}{30}$

57. $\frac{1}{6}$ **59.** $\frac{121}{60}$ or $2\frac{1}{60}$ **61.** 96 **63.** $\frac{3}{4}$ **65.** undefined **67.** $\frac{11}{119}$ **69.** $\frac{35}{11}$ or $3\frac{2}{11}$ **71.** $\frac{9}{5}$ or $1\frac{4}{5}$ **73.** $3\frac{3}{16}$ miles **75.** $\frac{5}{6}$ Tbsp **77.** $\frac{19}{30}$ in. **79.** 14 lb **81.** $4\frac{2}{3}$ m **83.** $\frac{8}{35}$ **85.** $\frac{128}{51}$ or $2\frac{26}{51}$ **87.** $\frac{16}{15}$ or $1\frac{1}{15}$ **89.** $\frac{121}{400}$ **91.** 201 **93.** 196 **95.** 1569 **97.** $20\frac{2}{3} \div 10\frac{1}{2} = \frac{62}{3} \div \frac{21}{2} = \frac{62}{3} \cdot \frac{2}{21} = \frac{124}{63}$ or $1\frac{61}{63}$ **99.** c **101.** d **103.** 5 **105.** 654 aircraft **107.** answers may vary

Chapter 2 Vocabulary Check **1.** reciprocals **2.** composite number **3.** equivalent **4.** improper fraction **5.** prime number **6.** simplest form **7.** proper fraction **8.** mixed number **9.** numerator; denominator **10.** prime factorization **11.** undefined **12.** 0 **13.** cross products

Chapter 2 Review **1.** proper **2.** improper **3.** proper **4.** mixed number **5.** $\frac{2}{6}$ **6.** $\frac{4}{7}$ **7.** $\frac{7}{3}$ **8.** $\frac{13}{4}$ **9.** $\frac{11}{12}$ **10.** **a.** 108 **b.** $\frac{108}{131}$ **11.** $3\frac{3}{4}$ **12.** $45\frac{5}{6}$ **13.** 3 **14.** 5 **15.** $\frac{6}{5}$ **16.** $\frac{22}{21}$ **17.** $\frac{26}{9}$ **18.** $\frac{47}{12}$ **19.** composite **20.** prime **21.** 1, 2, 3, 6, 7, 14, 21, 42 **22.** 1, 2, 4, 5, 10, 20 **23.** $2^2 \cdot 17$ **24.** $2 \cdot 3^2 \cdot 5$ **25.** $5 \cdot 157$ **26.** $3 \cdot 5 \cdot 17$ **27.** $\frac{3}{7}$ **28.** $\frac{5}{9}$ **29.** $\frac{1}{3}$ **30.** $\frac{1}{2}$ **31.** $\frac{29}{32}$ **32.** $\frac{18}{23}$ **33.** 8 **34.** 6 **35.** $\frac{2}{3}$ of a foot **36.** $\frac{3}{5}$ of the cars **37.** no **38.** yes **39.** $\frac{3}{10}$ **40.** $\frac{5}{14}$ **41.** 9 **42.** $\frac{1}{2}$ **43.** $\frac{35}{8}$ or $4\frac{3}{8}$ **44.** $\frac{5}{2}$ or $2\frac{1}{2}$ **45.** $\frac{5}{3}$ or $1\frac{2}{3}$ **46.** $\frac{49}{3}$ or $16\frac{1}{3}$ **47.** Exact: $\frac{26}{5}$ or $5\frac{1}{5}$; Estimate: 6 **48.** Exact: $\frac{60}{11}$ or $5\frac{5}{11}$; Estimate: 8 **49.** $\frac{99}{4}$ or $24\frac{3}{4}$ **50.** $\frac{1}{6}$ **51.** $\frac{110}{3}$ or $36\frac{2}{3}$ g **52.** $\frac{135}{4}$ or $33\frac{3}{4}$ in. **53.** $\frac{119}{80}$ or $1\frac{39}{80}$ sq in. **54.** $\frac{275}{8}$ or $34\frac{3}{8}$ sq m **55.** $\frac{1}{7}$ **56.** 8 **57.** $\frac{23}{14}$ **58.** $\frac{5}{17}$ **59.** 2 **60.** $\frac{15}{4}$ or $3\frac{3}{4}$ **61.** $\frac{5}{6}$ **62.** $\frac{8}{3}$ or $2\frac{2}{3}$ **63.** $\frac{21}{4}$ or $5\frac{1}{4}$ **64.** $\frac{121}{46}$ or $2\frac{29}{46}$ **65.** 22 mi **66.** $\frac{21}{20}$ or $1\frac{1}{20}$ mi **67.** proper **68.** improper **69.** mixed number **70.** improper **71.** $31\frac{1}{4}$ **72.** 6 **73.** $\frac{95}{17}$ **74.** $\frac{47}{6}$ **75.** composite **76.** prime **77.** $2^2 \cdot 3^2 \cdot 5$ **78.** $2 \cdot 7^2$ **79.** $\frac{9}{10}$ **80.** $\frac{5}{7}$ **81.** $\frac{14}{15}$ **82.** $\frac{3}{5}$ **83.** $\frac{7}{12}$ **84.** $\frac{1}{4}$ **85.** 9 **86.** $\frac{27}{2}$ or $13\frac{1}{2}$ **87.** Exact: 10; Estimate: 8 **88.** Exact: $\frac{51}{4}$ or $12\frac{3}{4}$; Estimate: 12 **89.** $\frac{7}{3}$ or $2\frac{1}{3}$ **90.** $\frac{32}{5}$ or $6\frac{2}{5}$ **91.** $\frac{81}{2}$ or $40\frac{1}{2}$ sq ft **92.** $\frac{47}{61}$ in.

Chapter 2 Test **1.** $\frac{7}{16}$ **2.** $\frac{13}{5}$ **3.** $\frac{23}{3}$ **4.** $\frac{39}{11}$ **5.** $4\frac{3}{5}$ **6.** $18\frac{3}{4}$ **7.** $\frac{4}{35}$ **8.** $\frac{3}{5}$ **9.** not equivalent **10.** equivalent **11.** $2^2 \cdot 3 \cdot 7$ **12.** $3^2 \cdot 5 \cdot 11$ **13.** $\frac{4}{3}$ or $1\frac{1}{3}$ **14.** $\frac{4}{3}$ or $1\frac{1}{3}$ **15.** $\frac{1}{4}$ **16.** $\frac{16}{45}$ **17.** 16 **18.** $\frac{9}{2}$ or $4\frac{1}{2}$ **19.** $\frac{4}{11}$ **20.** 9 **21.** $\frac{64}{3}$ or $21\frac{1}{3}$ **22.** $\frac{45}{2}$ or $22\frac{1}{2}$ **23.** $\frac{18}{5}$ or $3\frac{3}{5}$ **24.** $\frac{20}{3}$ or $6\frac{2}{3}$ **25.** $\frac{34}{27}$ or $1\frac{7}{27}$ sq mi **26.** 24 mi **27.** $\frac{16{,}000}{3}$ or $5333\frac{1}{3}$ sq yd **28.** $90 per share

Cumulative Review **1.** hundred-thousands (Sec. 1.2, Ex. 1) **2.** two thousand, thirty-six **3.** 805 (Sec. 1.2, Ex. 9) **4.** 31 **5.** 184,046 (Sec. 1.3, Ex. 2) **6.** 39 **7.** 13 in. (Sec. 1.3, Ex. 5) **8.** 17 **9.** 98,638 (Sec. 1.3, Ex. 7) **10.** 5 **11.** 7321 (Sec. 1.4, Ex. 2) **12.** 64 **13.** **a.** Indonesia **b.** 236 (Sec. 1.3, Ex. 8) **14.** 25 R 5 **15.** 570 (Sec. 1.5, Ex. 1) **16.** 2400 **17.** 1800 (Sec. 1.5, Ex. 5) **18.** 300 **19.** **a.** 6 **b.** 0 **c.** 45 **d.** 0 (Sec. 1.6, Ex. 1) **20.** 20 **21.** **a.** $3 \cdot 4 + 3 \cdot 5$ **b.** $10 \cdot 6 + 10 \cdot 8$ **c.** $2 \cdot 7 + 2 \cdot 3$ (Sec. 1.6, Ex. 2) **22.** 180 **23.** **a.** 0 **b.** 0 **c.** 0 **d.** undefined (Sec. 1.7, Ex. 3) **24.** 154 sq mi **25.** 208 (Sec. 1.7, Ex. 5) **26.** 4014 **27.** 12 cards; 10 cards left over (Sec. 1.7, Ex. 11) **28.** 63 **29.** 40 ft (Sec. 1.8, Ex. 5) **30.** 16 **31.** 7^3 (Sec. 1.9, Ex. 1) **32.** 7^4 **33.** $3^4 \cdot 17^3$ (Sec. 1.9, Ex. 4) **34.** $2^2 \cdot 3^4$ **35.** 7 (Sec. 1.9, Ex. 12) **36.** 0 **37.** $\frac{2}{5}$ (Sec. 2.1, Ex. 7) **38.** $2^2 \cdot 3 \cdot 13$ **39.** **a.** $\frac{38}{9}$ **b.** $\frac{19}{11}$ (Sec. 2.1, Ex. 17) **40.** $\frac{39}{5}$ **41.** 1, 2, 4, 5, 10, 20 (Sec. 2.2, Ex. 1) **42.** yes **43.** $\frac{7}{11}$ (Sec. 2.3, Ex. 2) **44.** $\frac{2}{3}$ **45.** $\frac{35}{12}$ or $2\frac{11}{12}$ (Sec. 2.4, Ex. 8) **46.** $\frac{8}{3}$ or $2\frac{2}{3}$ **47.** $\frac{3}{1}$ or 3 (Sec. 2.5, Ex. 3) **48.** $\frac{1}{9}$ **49.** $\frac{5}{12}$ (Sec. 2.5, Ex. 6) **50.** $\frac{11}{56}$

Chapter 3 Adding and Subtracting Fractions

Section 3.1

Vocabulary and Readiness Check **1.** like; unlike **3.** **5.** unlike **7.** like **9.** like **11.** unlike

Exercise Set 3.1 **1.** $\frac{3}{7}$ **3.** $\frac{1}{5}$ **5.** $\frac{2}{3}$ **7.** $\frac{7}{20}$ **9.** $\frac{1}{2}$ **11.** $\frac{13}{11}$ or $1\frac{2}{11}$ **13.** $\frac{7}{13}$ **15.** $\frac{2}{3}$ **17.** $\frac{6}{11}$ **19.** $\frac{3}{5}$ **21.** 1 **23.** $\frac{3}{4}$ **25.** $\frac{5}{6}$ **27.** $\frac{4}{5}$ **29.** $\frac{1}{90}$ **31.** $\frac{19}{33}$ **33.** $\frac{13}{21}$ **35.** $\frac{9}{10}$ **37.** 0 **39.** $\frac{3}{4}$ **41.** 1 in. **43.** 2 m **45.** $\frac{7}{10}$ mi **47.** $\frac{3}{2}$ or $1\frac{1}{2}$ h **49.** $\frac{9}{24} = \frac{3}{8}$ **51.** $\frac{2}{24} = \frac{1}{12}$ **53.** $\frac{13}{100}$ **55.** $\frac{2}{5}$ **57.** $\frac{7}{25}$ **59.** $\frac{1}{50}$ **61.** $\frac{1}{4}$ **63.** $2 \cdot 5$ **65.** 2^3 **67.** $5 \cdot 11$ **69.** $\frac{5}{8}$ **71.** $\frac{8}{11}$ **73.** $\frac{2}{7} + \frac{9}{7} = \frac{11}{7}$ or $1\frac{4}{7}$ **75.** answers may vary **77.** 1; answers may vary **79.** $\frac{1}{4}$ of a mi

Section 3.2

Vocabulary and Readiness Check **1.** equivalent **3.** multiple

Exercise Set 3.2 **1.** 12 **3.** 45 **5.** 36 **7.** 72 **9.** 126 **11.** 75 **13.** 24 **15.** 42 **17.** 216 **19.** 150 **21.** 68 **23.** 588 **25.** 900 **27.** 1800 **29.** 363 **31.** 60 **33.** $\frac{20}{35}$ **35.** $\frac{14}{21}$ **37.** $\frac{15}{3}$ **39.** $\frac{15}{30}$ **41.** $\frac{30}{21}$ **43.** $\frac{21}{28}$ **45.** $\frac{30}{45}$ **47.** $\frac{36}{81}$ **49.** $\frac{90}{78}$ **51.** $\frac{56}{68}$ **53.** $\frac{54}{100}; \frac{50}{100}; \frac{46}{100}; \frac{50}{100}; \frac{15}{100}; \frac{65}{100}; \frac{45}{100}; \frac{52}{100}; \frac{60}{100}; \frac{61}{100}; \frac{48}{100}; \frac{50}{100}$ **55.** drugs, health and beauty aids **57.** $\frac{1}{2}$ **59.** $\frac{2}{5}$ **61.** $\frac{4}{9}$ **63.** 1 **65.** $\frac{814}{3630}$ **67.** answers may vary **69.** a, b, and d

Section 3.3

Calculator Explorations **1.** $\frac{37}{80}$ **3.** $\frac{95}{72}$ **5.** $\frac{394}{323}$

Vocabulary and Readiness Check **1.** equivalent; least common denominator

Exercise Set 3.3 **1.** $\frac{5}{6}$ **3.** $\frac{5}{6}$ **5.** $\frac{8}{33}$ **7.** $\frac{9}{14}$ **9.** $\frac{3}{5}$ **11.** $\frac{13}{25}$ **13.** $\frac{53}{60}$ **15.** $\frac{1}{6}$ **17.** $\frac{67}{99}$ **19.** $\frac{98}{143}$ **21.** $\frac{13}{27}$ **23.** $\frac{75}{56}$ or $1\frac{19}{56}$ **25.** $\frac{19}{18}$ or $1\frac{1}{18}$ **27.** $\frac{19}{12}$ or $1\frac{7}{12}$ **29.** $\frac{11}{16}$ **31.** $\frac{17}{42}$ **33.** $\frac{33}{56}$ **35.** $\frac{37}{99}$ **37.** $\frac{1}{35}$ **39.** $\frac{11}{36}$ **41.** $\frac{1}{20}$ **43.** $\frac{1}{84}$ **45.** $\frac{9}{1000}$ **47.** $\frac{17}{99}$ **49.** $\frac{19}{36}$ **51.** $\frac{1}{5}$ **53.** $\frac{69}{280}$ **55.** $\frac{14}{9}$ or $1\frac{5}{9}$ **57.** $\frac{34}{15}$ or $2\frac{4}{15}$ cm **59.** $\frac{17}{10}$ or $1\frac{7}{10}$ m **61.** $\frac{7}{100}$ mph **63.** $\frac{5}{8}$ in. **65.** $\frac{31}{32}$ in. **67.** $\frac{19}{100}$ of Girl Scout cookies **69.** $\frac{19}{25}$ **71.** $\frac{1}{25}$ **73.** $\frac{79}{100}$ **75.** 5 **77.** $\frac{16}{29}$ **79.** $\frac{19}{3}$ or $6\frac{1}{3}$ **81.** $\frac{3}{5} + \frac{4}{5} = \frac{7}{5}$ or $1\frac{2}{5}$ **83.** $\frac{223}{540}$ **85.** $\frac{49}{44}$ or $1\frac{5}{44}$ **87.** answers may vary

Integrated Review **1.** 30 **2.** 21 **3.** 14 **4.** 25 **5.** 100 **6.** 90 **7.** $\frac{9}{24}$ **8.** $\frac{28}{36}$ **9.** $\frac{10}{40}$ **10.** $\frac{12}{30}$ **11.** $\frac{55}{75}$ **12.** $\frac{40}{48}$ **13.** $\frac{1}{2}$ **14.** $\frac{2}{5}$ **15.** $\frac{7}{12}$ **16.** $\frac{13}{15}$ **17.** $\frac{3}{4}$ **18.** $\frac{2}{15}$ **19.** $\frac{17}{45}$ **20.** $\frac{19}{50}$ **21.** $\frac{37}{40}$ **22.** $\frac{11}{36}$ **23.** 0 **24.** $\frac{1}{17}$ **25.** $\frac{5}{33}$ **26.** $\frac{1}{42}$ **27.** $\frac{5}{18}$ **28.** $\frac{5}{13}$ **29.** $\frac{11}{18}$ **30.** $\frac{37}{50}$ **31.** $\frac{47}{30}$ or $1\frac{17}{30}$ **32.** $\frac{7}{30}$ **33.** $\frac{3}{5}$ **34.** $\frac{27}{20}$ or $1\frac{7}{20}$ **35.** $\frac{279}{350}$ **36.** $\frac{309}{350}$ **37.** $\frac{98}{5}$ or $19\frac{3}{5}$ **38.** $\frac{9}{250}$ **39.** $\frac{31}{3}$ or $10\frac{1}{3}$ **40.** $\frac{93}{64}$ or $1\frac{29}{64}$ **41.** $\frac{49}{54}$ **42.** $\frac{83}{48}$ or $1\frac{35}{48}$ **43.** $\frac{390}{101}$ or $3\frac{87}{101}$ **44.** $\frac{116}{5}$ or $23\frac{1}{5}$ **45.** $\frac{106}{135}$ **46.** $\frac{67}{224}$

Section 3.4

Vocabulary and Readiness Check **1.** mixed number **3.** round **5.** a **7.** c

Exercise Set 3.4 **1.** Exact: $6\frac{4}{5}$; Estimate: 7 **3.** Exact: $13\frac{11}{14}$; Estimate: 14 **5.** $17\frac{7}{25}$ **7.** $7\frac{5}{8}$ **9.** $7\frac{5}{24}$ **11.** $20\frac{1}{15}$ **13.** 19 **15.** $56\frac{53}{270}$ **17.** $13\frac{13}{24}$ **19.** $47\frac{53}{84}$ **21.** Exact: $2\frac{3}{5}$; Estimate: 3 **23.** Exact: $7\frac{5}{14}$; Estimate: 7 **25.** $\frac{24}{25}$ **27.** $2\frac{7}{15}$ **29.** $5\frac{11}{14}$ **31.** $23\frac{31}{72}$ **33.** $1\frac{4}{5}$ **35.** $1\frac{13}{15}$ **37.** $3\frac{5}{9}$ **39.** $15\frac{3}{4}$ **41.** $28\frac{7}{12}$ **43.** $15\frac{7}{8}$ **45.** 8 **47.** $17\frac{11}{12}$ **49.** $\frac{1}{16}$ in. **51.** no; she will be $\frac{1}{12}$ of a foot short **53.** $7\frac{13}{20}$ in. **55.** $10\frac{1}{4}$ hr **57.** $2\frac{3}{8}$ hr **59.** $92\frac{99}{100}$ m **61.** $352\frac{1}{3}$ yd **63.** $9\frac{13}{30}$ min **65.** $1\frac{4}{5}$ min **67.** 7 mi **69.** $21\frac{5}{24}$ m **71.** 8 **73.** 25 **75.** 4 **77.** 167 **79.** 4 **81.** $9\frac{5}{8}$ **83.** a, b, c **85.** answers may vary **87.** Supreme is heavier by $\frac{1}{8}$ lb

Section 3.5

Exercise Set 3.5 **1.** > **3.** < **5.** < **7.** > **9.** > **11.** < **13.** > **15.** < **17.** $\frac{1}{16}$ **19.** $\frac{8}{125}$ **21.** $\frac{64}{343}$ **23.** $\frac{4}{81}$ **25.** $\frac{1}{6}$ **27.** $\frac{18}{125}$ **29.** $\frac{11}{15}$ **31.** $\frac{3}{35}$ **33.** $\frac{5}{9}$ **35.** $10\frac{4}{99}$ **37.** $\frac{1}{12}$ **39.** $\frac{9}{11}$ **41.** 0 **43.** 0 **45.** $\frac{2}{5}$ **47.** $\frac{2}{77}$ **49.** $\frac{17}{60}$ **51.** $\frac{5}{8}$ **53.** $\frac{1}{2}$ **55.** $\frac{29}{10}$ or $2\frac{9}{10}$ **57.** $\frac{27}{32}$ **59.** $\frac{1}{81}$ **61.** $\frac{5}{6}$ **63.** $\frac{3}{5}$ **65.** $\frac{1}{2}$ **67.** $\frac{19}{7}$ or $2\frac{5}{7}$ **69.** $\frac{9}{64}$ **71.** $\frac{3}{4}$ **73.** $\frac{13}{60}$ **75.** $\frac{13}{25}$ **77.** A **79.** M **81.** S **83.** D **85.** M **87.** A **89.** no; answers may vary **91.** subtraction, multiplication, addition, division **93.** division, multiplication, subtraction, addition **95.** standard mail **97.** New York

Section 3.6

Exercise Set 3.6 **1.** $\frac{1}{2} + \frac{1}{3}$ **3.** $20 \div 6\frac{2}{5}$ **5.** $\frac{15}{16} - \frac{5}{8}$ **7.** $\frac{21}{68} + \frac{7}{34}$ **9.** $8\frac{1}{3} \cdot \frac{7}{9}$ **11.** $3\frac{1}{3}$ c **13.** $12\frac{1}{2}$ in. **15.** $21\frac{1}{2}$ mi per gal **17.** $1\frac{1}{2}$ yr **19.** $9\frac{2}{5}$ in. **21.** no; $\frac{1}{4}$ yd **23.** 5 pieces **25.** $\frac{9}{8}$ or $1\frac{1}{8}$ in. **27.** $3\frac{3}{4}$ c **29.** $11\frac{1}{4}$ sq in. **31.** $1\frac{3}{10}$ min **33.** $5\frac{11}{25}$ cu in. **35.** 67 sheets **37. a.** yes **b.** 1 ft left over **39.** $2\frac{15}{16}$ lb **41.** area: $\frac{9}{128}$ sq in.; perimeter: $1\frac{1}{8}$ in. **43.** area: $\frac{25}{81}$ sq m; perimeter: $2\frac{2}{9}$ m **45.** $4\frac{3}{4}$ ft **47.** $\frac{5}{26}$ ft **49.** 3 **51.** 81 **53.** 4 **55.** 30 **57.** 35 **59.** no; no; answers may vary **61.** $36\frac{44}{81}$ sq ft **63.** 68 customers **65.** 22 hr

Chapter 3 Vocabulary Check **1.** like **2.** least common multiple **3.** equivalent **4.** mixed number **5.** > **6.** < **7.** least common denominator **8.** unlike **9.** exponent

Chapter 3 Review **1.** $\frac{10}{11}$ **2.** $\frac{3}{25}$ **3.** $\frac{2}{3}$ **4.** $\frac{1}{7}$ **5.** $\frac{3}{5}$ **6.** $\frac{3}{5}$ **7.** 1 **8.** 1 **9.** $\frac{19}{25}$ **10.** $\frac{16}{21}$ **11.** $\frac{3}{4}$ of his homework **12.** $\frac{3}{2}$ or $1\frac{1}{2}$ mi **13.** 55 **14.** 60 **15.** 120 **16.** 80 **17.** 252 **18.** 72 **19.** $\frac{56}{64}$ **20.** $\frac{20}{30}$ **21.** $\frac{21}{33}$ **22.** $\frac{20}{26}$ **23.** $\frac{16}{60}$ **24.** $\frac{25}{60}$ **25.** $\frac{11}{18}$ **26.** $\frac{7}{15}$ **27.** $\frac{7}{26}$ **28.** $\frac{17}{36}$ **29.** $\frac{41}{42}$ **30.** $\frac{43}{72}$ **31.** $\frac{13}{45}$ **32.** $\frac{39}{70}$ **33.** $\frac{19}{9}$ or $2\frac{1}{9}$ m **34.** $\frac{3}{2}$ or $1\frac{1}{2}$ ft **35.** $\frac{1}{4}$ of a yd **36.** $\frac{7}{10}$ has been cleaned **37.** $45\frac{16}{21}$ **38.** 60 **39.** $32\frac{13}{22}$ **40.** $3\frac{19}{60}$ **41.** $111\frac{5}{18}$ **42.** $20\frac{7}{24}$ **43.** $5\frac{16}{35}$ **44.** $3\frac{4}{55}$ **45.** $7\frac{4}{5}$ in. **46.** $11\frac{1}{6}$ ft **47.** 5 ft **48.** $\frac{1}{40}$ oz **49.** < **50.** > **51.** < **52.** > **53.** >

54. > **55.** $\frac{9}{49}$ **56.** $\frac{64}{125}$ **57.** $\frac{9}{400}$ **58.** $\frac{9}{100}$ **59.** $\frac{8}{13}$ **60.** 2 **61.** $\frac{81}{196}$ **62.** $\frac{1}{7}$ **63.** $\frac{13}{18}$ **64.** $\frac{11}{15}$ **65.** $\frac{1}{7}$ **66.** $\frac{18}{5}$ or $3\frac{3}{5}$ **67.** $\frac{45}{28}$ or $1\frac{17}{28}$ **68.** $\frac{5}{6}$ **69.** $\frac{99}{56}$ or $1\frac{43}{56}$ **70.** $\frac{29}{110}$ **71.** $\frac{29}{54}$ **72.** $\frac{37}{60}$ **73.** 21 moons **74.** $15\frac{5}{8}$ acres **75.** each measurement is $4\frac{1}{4}$ in. **76.** $\frac{7}{10}$ yd **77.** perimeter: $1\frac{6}{11}$ mi; area: $\frac{3}{22}$ sq mi **78.** perimeter: $2\frac{1}{3}$ m; area: $\frac{5}{16}$ sq m **79.** 90 **80.** 60 **81.** $\frac{40}{48}$ **82.** $\frac{63}{72}$ **83.** $\frac{1}{6}$ **84.** $\frac{1}{5}$ **85.** $\frac{11}{12}$ **86.** $\frac{27}{55}$ **87.** $13\frac{5}{12}$ **88.** $12\frac{3}{8}$ **89.** $3\frac{16}{35}$ **90.** $8\frac{1}{21}$ **91.** $\frac{11}{25}$ **92.** $\frac{1}{8}$ **93.** $\frac{1}{144}$ **94.** $\frac{64}{27}$ or $2\frac{10}{27}$ **95.** $\frac{5}{17}$ **96.** $\frac{1}{12}$ **97.** < **98.** > **99.** $\frac{1}{2}$ hr **100.** $6\frac{7}{20}$ lb **101.** $44\frac{1}{2}$ yd **102.** $2\frac{2}{15}$ ft **103.** $7\frac{1}{2}$ tablespoons **104.** $\frac{3}{8}$ gal

Chapter 3 Test **1.** 60 **2.** 72 **3.** < **4.** < **5.** $\frac{8}{9}$ **6.** $\frac{2}{5}$ **7.** $\frac{13}{10}$ or $1\frac{3}{10}$ **8.** $\frac{8}{21}$ **9.** $\frac{13}{24}$ **10.** $\frac{2}{3}$ **11.** $\frac{67}{60}$ or $1\frac{7}{60}$ **12.** $\frac{7}{50}$ **13.** $\frac{3}{2}$ or $1\frac{1}{2}$ **14.** $14\frac{1}{40}$ **15.** $30\frac{13}{45}$ **16.** $1\frac{7}{24}$ **17.** $16\frac{8}{11}$ **18.** $\frac{5}{3}$ or $1\frac{2}{3}$ **19.** $\frac{16}{81}$ **20.** $\frac{9}{16}$ **21.** $\frac{153}{200}$ **22.** $\frac{3}{8}$ **23.** $\frac{11}{12}$ **24.** $3\frac{3}{4}$ ft **25.** $7\frac{5}{6}$ gal **26.** $\frac{23}{50}$ **27.** $\frac{13}{50}$ **28.** \$2820 **29.** perimeter: $3\frac{1}{3}$ ft; area: $\frac{2}{3}$ sq ft **30.** $1\frac{2}{3}$ in.

Cumulative Review **1.** eighty-five (Sec. 1.2, Ex. 4) **2.** one hundred seven **3.** one hundred twenty-six (Sec. 1.2, Ex. 5) **4.** five thousand, twenty-six **5.** 159 (Sec. 1.3, Ex. 1) **6.** 19 in. **7.** 514 (Sec. 1.4, Ex. 3) **8.** 121 R 1 **9.** 278,000 (Sec. 1.5, Ex. 2) **10.** 1, 2, 3, 5, 6, 10, 15, 30 **11.** 20, 296 (Sec. 1.6, Ex. 4) **12.** 0 **13. a.** 7 **b.** 12 **c.** 1 **d.** 1 **e.** 20 **f.** 1 (Sec. 1.7, Ex. 2) **14.** 25 **15.** 1038 mi (Sec. 1.8, Ex. 1) **16.** 11 **17.** 81 (Sec. 1.9, Ex. 5) **18.** 125 **19.** 81 (Sec. 1.9, Ex. 7) **20.** 1000 **21.** $\frac{4}{3}$ or $1\frac{1}{3}$ (Sec. 2.1, Ex. 15) **22.** $\frac{11}{4}$ or $2\frac{3}{4}$ **23.** $\frac{5}{2}$ or $2\frac{1}{2}$ (Sec. 2.1, Ex. 16) **24.** $\frac{14}{3}$ or $4\frac{2}{3}$ **25.** 3, 11, 17 are prime; 9, 26 are composite; (Sec. 2.2, Ex. 2) **26.** 5 **27.** $2^2 \cdot 3^2 \cdot 5$ (Sec. 2.2, Ex. 4) **28.** 62 **29.** $\frac{36}{13}$ or $2\frac{10}{13}$ (Sec. 2.3, Ex. 5)

Chapter 4 Decimals

Section 4.1

Vocabulary and Readiness Check **1.** words; standard form **3.** and **5.** tens **7.** tenths

Exercise Set 4.1 **1.** six and fifty-two hundredths **3.** sixteen and twenty-three hundredths **5.** two hundred five thousandths **7.** one hundred sixty-seven and nine thousandths **9.** two hundred and five thousandths **11.** one hundred five and six tenths **13.** two and forty-three hundredths **15.** eighty-seven and ninety-seven hundredths **17.** one hundred fourteen and five tenths **19.** R. W. Financial; 321.42; Three hundred twenty-one and 42/100 **21.** Bell South; 59.68; Fifty-nine and 68/100 **23.** 6.5 **25.** 9.08 **27.** 705.625 **29.** 0.0046 **31.** 32.52 **33.** 1.3 **35.** $\frac{3}{10}$ **37.** $\frac{27}{100}$ **39.** $\frac{4}{5}$ **41.** $\frac{3}{20}$ **43.** $5\frac{47}{100}$ **45.** $\frac{6}{125}$ **47.** $7\frac{1}{125}$ **49.** $15\frac{401}{500}$ **51.** $\frac{601}{2000}$ **53.** $487\frac{8}{25}$ **55.** 0.6 **57.** 0.45 **59.** 3.7 **61.** 0.268 **63.** 0.09 **65.** 4.026 **67.** 0.028 **69.** 56.3 **71.** 0.43; forty-three hundredths **73.** 0.8; $\frac{8}{10}$ or $\frac{4}{5}$ **75.** seventy-seven thousandths; $\frac{77}{1000}$ **77.** 47,260 **79.** 47,000 **81.** answers may vary **83.** twenty-six million, eight hundred forty-nine thousand, five hundred seventy-six hundred-billionths **85.** 17.268

Section 4.2

Vocabulary and Readiness Check **1.** circumference **3.** after

Exercise Set 4.2 **1.** < **3.** > **5.** < **7.** = **9.** < **11.** > **13.** 0.006, 0.0061, 0.06 **15.** 0.03, 0.042, 0.36 **17.** 1.01, 1.09, 1.1, 1.16 **19.** 20.905, 21.001, 21.03, 21.12 **21.** 0.6 **23.** 0.23 **25.** 0.594 **27.** 98,210 **29.** 12.3 **31.** 17.67 **33.** 0.5 **35.** 0.130 **37.** 3830 **39.** \$0.07 **41.** \$42,650 **43.** \$27 **45.** \$0.20 **47.** 0.4 cm **49.** 1.56 hr **51.** \$48 **53.** 1.74 min **55.** 24.623 hr **57.** 2.8 min **59.** 5766 **61.** 71 **63.** 243 **65.** b **67.** a **69.** 41.654; $41\frac{327}{500}$; Lance Armstrong **71.** 40.789, 40.788, 40.413, 39.233 **73.** answers may vary **75.** answers may vary **77.** 0.26499, 0.25786 **79.** 0.10299, 0.1037, 0.1038, 0.9 **81.** \$3100 million

Section 4.3

Calculator Explorations **1.** 328.742 **3.** 5.2414 **5.** 865.392

Vocabulary and Readiness Check **1.** 37.0 **3.** difference; minuend; subtrahend **5.** false

Exercise Set 4.3 **1.** 3.5 **3.** 6.83 **5.** 0.094 **7.** 622.012 **9.** 583.09 **11.** Exact: 465.56; Estimate: $\begin{array}{r} 230 \\ +\ 230 \\ \hline 460 \end{array}$ **13.** Exact: 115.123; Estimate: $\begin{array}{r} 100 \\ 6 \\ +\ \ 9 \\ \hline 115 \end{array}$ **15.** 27.0578 **17.** 56.432 **19.** 6.5 **21.** 15.3 **23.** 598.23 **25.** Exact: 1.83; Estimate: 6 − 4 = 2 **27.** 861.6 **29.** 376.89 **31.** Exact: 876.6; Estimate: $\begin{array}{r} 1000 \\ -\ 100 \\ \hline 900 \end{array}$ **33.** 194.4 **35.** 2.9988 **37.** 16.3 **39.** 88.028 **41.** 84.072 **43.** 243.17 **45.** 56.83 **47.** 3.16 **49.** \$7.52 **51.** \$454.71 **53.** \$0.14 **55.** 28.56 m **57.** 10.2 in. **59.** 2.23 degrees Fahrenheit **61.** 285.8 mph **63.** 763.035 mph **65.** 13.8 in. **67.** \$0.32 **69.** 12.4 million (12,400,000)

71. 240.8 in. **73.** 67.44 ft **75.** \$1.475 **77.** 715.05 hr **79.** Switzerland **81.** 4.43 lb **83.**

Country	Pounds of Chocolate per Person
Switzerland	22.36
Austria	20.13
Ireland	19.47
Germany	18.04
Norway	17.93

85. 46 **87.** 3870 **89.** $\frac{4}{9}$ **91.** incorrect; $\begin{array}{r} 9.200 \\ 8.630 \\ +\,4.005 \\ \hline 21.835 \end{array}$ **93.** 6.08 in. **95.** \$1.20 **97.** 1 nickel, 1 dime, and 2 pennies; 3 nickels and 2 pennies; 1 dime and 7 pennies; 2 nickels and 7 pennies

99. answers may vary **101.** answers may vary

Section 4.4

Vocabulary and Readiness Check **1.** sum **3.** right; zeros **5.** circumference **7.** 3 **9.** 4 **11.** 8

Exercise Set 4.4 **1.** 0.12 **3.** 0.6 **5.** 1.3 **7.** Exact: 22.26; Estimate: $5 \times 4 = 20$ **9.** 0.4032 **11.** Exact: 8.23854; Estimate: $\begin{array}{r} 1 \\ \times\,8 \\ \hline 8 \end{array}$ **13.** 11.2746

15. 84.97593 **17.** 65 **19.** 0.65 **21.** 0.072 **23.** 709.3 **25.** 6046 **27.** 0.03762 **29.** 0.0492 **31.** 12.3 **33.** 1.29 **35.** 0.096 **37.** 0.5623 **39.** 43.274 **41.** 5,500,000,000 **43.** 49,800,000 **45.** 314,000 **47.** $8\pi \approx 25.12$ m **49.** $10\pi \approx 31.4$ cm **51.** $18.2\pi \approx 57.148$ yd **53.** \$715.20 **55.** \$4725 **57.** 24.8 g **59.** 10.8 sq in. **61.** 250π ft ≈ 785 ft **63.** 135π m ≈ 423.9 m **65.** 64.9605 in. **67. a.** 62.8 m and 125.6 m **b.** yes **69.** 5.4 sq in. **71.** 26 **73.** 36 **75.** 8 **77.** 9 **79.** 3.64 **81.** 3.56 **83.** 0.1105 **85.** 3,831,600 mi **87.** answers may vary **89.** answers may vary

Integrated Review **1.** 2.57 **2.** 4.05 **3.** 8.9 **4.** 3.5 **5.** 0.16 **6.** 0.24 **7.** 11.06 **8.** 9.72 **9.** 4.8 **10.** 6.09 **11.** 75.56 **12.** 289.12 **13.** 25.026 **14.** 44.125 **15.** 82.7 **16.** 273.9 **17.** 280 **18.** 1600 **19.** 224.938 **20.** 145.079 **21.** 6 **22.** 6.2 **23.** 27.6092 **24.** 145.6312 **25.** 5.4 **26.** 17.74 **27.** 414.44 **28.** 1295.03 **29.** 116.81 **30.** 18.79 **31.** 156.2 **32.** 25.62 **33.** 5.62 **34.** 304.876 **35.** 114.66 **36.** 119.86 **37.** 0.000432 **38.** 0.000075 **39.** 0.0672 **40.** 0.0275 **41.** 862 **42.** 0.0293 **43.** 200 mi

Section 4.5

Calculator Explorations **1.** not reasonable **3.** reasonable

Vocabulary and Readiness Check **1.** quotient; divisor; dividend **3.** left; zeros **5.** 5.9 **7.** 0 **9.** 1 **11.** undefined

Exercise Set 4.5 **1.** 4.6 **3.** 0.094 **5.** 300 **7.** 5.8 **9.** Exact: 6.6; Estimate: $6\overline{)36}$ with quotient 6 **11.** 0.413 **13.** 0.045 **15.** 7 **17.** 4.8 **19.** 2100 **21.** 30 **23.** 7000 **25.** Exact: 9.8; Estimate: $7\overline{)70}$ with quotient 10 **27.** 9.6 **29.** 45 **31.** 54.592 **33.** 0.0055 **35.** 179 **37.** 23.87 **39.** 113.1 **41.** 0.54982 **43.** 2.687 **45.** 0.0129 **47.** 12.6 **49.** 1.31 **51.** 12.225 **53.** 0.045625 **55.** 11 qt **57.** 202.1 lb **59.** 5.1 m **61.** 11.4 boxes **63.** 24 tsp **65.** 8 days **67.** 248.1 mi **69.** 134.6 mph **71.** 18.48 points per game **73.** 2.45 **75.** 0.66 **77.** 80.52 **79.** 14.7 **81.** 930.7 **83.** 571 **85.** 92.06 **87.** 144.4 **89.** $\frac{9}{10}$ **91.** $\frac{1}{20}$ **93.** 4.26 **95.** 1.578 **97.** 26.66 **99.** 904.29 **101.** c **103.** b **105.** 85.5 **107.** 8.6 ft **109.** answers may vary **111.** 65.2–82.6 knots **113.** 319.64 m

Section 4.6

Vocabulary and Readiness Check **1.** false **3.** true

Exercise Set 4.6 **1.** 0.2 **3.** 0.68 **5.** 0.75 **7.** 0.08 **9.** 1.2 **11.** $0.91\overline{6}$ **13.** 0.425 **15.** 0.45 **17.** $0.\overline{3}$ **19.** 0.4375 **21.** $0.\overline{63}$ **23.** 5.85 **25.** 0.624 **27.** 0.33 **29.** 0.44 **31.** 0.6 **33.** 0.62 **35.** 0.73 **37.** 0.02 **39.** $<$ **41.** $=$ **43.** $<$ **45.** $<$ **47.** $<$ **49.** $>$ **51.** $<$ **53.** $<$ **55.** 0.32, 0.34, 0.35 **57.** 0.49, 0.491, 0.498 **59.** 0.73, $\frac{3}{4}$, 0.78 **61.** 0.412, 0.453, $\frac{4}{7}$ **63.** 5.23, $\frac{42}{8}$, 5.34 **65.** $\frac{17}{8}$, 2.37, $\frac{12}{5}$ **67.** 25.65 sq in. **69.** 9.36 sq cm **71.** 0.248 sq yd **73.** 8 **75.** 72 **77.** $\frac{1}{81}$ **79.** $\frac{9}{25}$ **81.** $\frac{5}{2}$ **83.** $=1$ **85.** >1 **87.** <1 **89.** 0.154 **91.** 6100 stations **93.** answers may vary **95.** answers may vary **97.** 47.25 **99.** 3.37 **101.** 0.45

Chapter 4 Vocabulary Check **1.** decimal **2.** numerator; denominator **3.** vertically **4.** and **5.** sum **6.** circumference **7.** standard form **8.** circumference; diameter **9.** difference **10.** quotient **11.** product **12.** sum

Chapter 4 Review **1.** tenths **2.** hundred-thousandths **3.** forty-five hundredths **4.** three hundred forty-five hundred-thousandths **5.** one hundred nine and twenty-three hundredths **6.** forty-six and seven thousandths **7.** 2.15 **8.** 503.102 **9.** $\frac{4}{25}$ **10.** $12\frac{23}{1000}$ **11.** $1\frac{9}{2000}$ **12.** $25\frac{1}{4}$ **13.** 0.9 **14.** 0.25 **15.** 0.045 **16.** 26.1 **17.** $>$ **18.** $=$ **19.** 0.92, 8.09, 8.6 **20.** 0.09, 0.091, 0.1 **21.** 0.6 **22.** 0.94 **23.** \$0.26 **24.** \$12.46 **25.** \$31,304 **26.** $10\frac{3}{4}$ **27.** 9.52 **28.** 2.7 **29.** 7.28 **30.** 26.007 **31.** 459.7 **32.** 100.278 **33.** 65.02 **34.** 189.98 **35.** 52.6 mi **36.** \$2.44 **37.** 22.2 in. **38.** 38.9 ft **39.** 18.5 **40.** 54.6 **41.** 72 **42.** 9345 **43.** 9.246 **44.** 3406.446 **45.** 14π m, 43.96 m **46.** 63.8 mi **47.** 887,000,000 **48.** 600,000 **49.** 0.0877 **50.** 15.825 **51.** 70 **52.** 0.21 **53.** 8.059 **54.** 30.4 **55.** 0.0267 **56.** 9.3 **57.** 7.3 m **58.** 45 mo **59.** 16.94 **60.** 3.89 **61.** 129 **62.** 55

63. 0.81 **64.** 7.26 **65.** 0.8 **66.** 0.923 **67.** $2.\overline{3}$ or 2.333 **68.** $0.21\overline{6}$ or 0.217 **69.** = **70.** = **71.** < **72.** < **73.** 0.837, 0.839, $\frac{17}{20}$ **74.** $\frac{19}{12}$, 1.63, $\frac{18}{11}$
75. 6.9 sq ft **76.** 5.46 sq in. **77.** two hundred and thirty-two ten-thousandths **78.** 16,025.014 **79.** $\frac{231}{100{,}000}$ **80.** 0.75, $\frac{6}{7}$, $\frac{8}{9}$ **81.** 0.07 **82.** 0.1125
83. 51.057 **84.** > **85.** < **86.** < **87.** 42.90 **88.** 16.349 **89.** \$123 **90.** \$3646 **91.** 1.7 **92.** 2.49 **93.** 320.312 **94.** 148.74236 **95.** 8.128
96. 7.245 **97.** 4900 **98.** 23.904 **99.** 9600 sq ft **100.** yes **101.** 0.1024 **102.** 3.6

Chapter 4 Test **1.** forty-five and ninety-two thousandths **2.** 3000.059 **3.** 34.9 **4.** 0.862 **5.** < **6.** $\frac{4}{9}$, 0.445, 0.454 **7.** $\frac{69}{200}$ **8.** $24\frac{73}{100}$ **9.** 0.65
10. $5.\overline{8}$ or 5.889 **11.** 0.941 **12.** 17.583 **13.** 11.4 **14.** 43.86 **15.** 56 **16.** 0.07755 **17.** 6.673 **18.** 12,690 **19.** 4.73 **20.** 0.363 **21.** 6.2
22. 4,583,000,000 **23.** 2.31 sq mi **24.** 18π mi, 56.52 mi **25. a.** 9904 sq ft **b.** 198.08 oz **26.** 54 mi

Cumulative Review **1.** one hundred six million, fifty-two thousand, four hundred forty-seven (Sec. 1.2, Ex. 7) **2.** 276,004 **3.** 98,638 (Sec 1.3, Ex. 7)
4. 288 **5.** 726 (Sec. 1.4, Ex. 4) **6.** 200 **7.** 2300 (Sec. 1.5, Ex. 4) **8.** 84 **9.** 57,600 megabytes (Sec. 1.6, Ex. 11) **10.** perimeter: 28 ft; area: 49 sq ft
11. 401 R 2 (Sec. 1.7, Ex. 8) **12.** $\frac{21}{8}$ **13.** 47 (Sec. 1.9, Ex. 15) **14.** $12\frac{4}{5}$ **15.** numerator: 3; denominator: 7 (Sec. 2.1, Ex. 1) **16.** 9
17. $\frac{1}{10}$ (Sec. 2.3, Ex. 6) **18.** 17 **19.** $\frac{15}{1}$ or 15 (Sec. 2.4, Ex. 9) **20.** 13 **21.** $\frac{63}{16}$ (Sec. 2.5, Ex. 5) **22.** 128 **23.** $\frac{15}{4}$ or $3\frac{3}{4}$ (Sec. 2.4, Ex. 10) **24.** \$9
25. $\frac{3}{20}$ (Sec. 2.5, Ex. 8) **26.** $\frac{27}{20}$ or $1\frac{7}{20}$ **27.** $\frac{7}{9}$ (Sec. 3.1, Ex. 4) **28.** $\frac{2}{5}$ **29.** $\frac{1}{4}$ (Sec. 3.1, Ex. 5) **30.** $\frac{2}{5}$ **31.** $\frac{15}{20}$ (Sec. 3.2, Ex. 8) **32.** $\frac{35}{45}$
33. $\frac{13}{30}$ (Sec. 3.3, Ex. 2) **34.** $\frac{1}{90}$ **35.** $4\frac{7}{40}$ lb (Sec. 3.4, Ex. 7) **36.** $27\frac{3}{4}$ lb **37.** $\frac{1}{16}$ (Sec. 3.5, Ex. 3) **38.** $\frac{49}{121}$ **39.** $\frac{3}{256}$ (Sec. 3.5, Ex. 5) **40.** $\frac{2}{81}$
41. $\frac{43}{100}$ (Sec. 4.1, Ex. 8) **42.** 0.75 **43.** > (Sec. 4.2, Ex. 1) **44.** 5.06 **45.** 11.568 (Sec. 4.3, Ex. 4) **46.** 75.329 **47.** 2370.2 (Sec. 4.4, Ex. 6)
48. 0.119 **49.** 768.05 (Sec. 4.4, Ex. 9) **50.** 8.9

Chapter 5 Ratio and Proportion

Section 5.1

Vocabulary and Readiness Check **1.** true **3.** false **5.** true **7.** true

Exercise Set 5.1 **1.** $\frac{11}{4}$ **3.** $\frac{23}{10}$ **5.** $\frac{151}{201}$ **7.** $\frac{2.8}{7.6}$ **9.** $\frac{5}{7\frac{1}{2}}$ **11.** $\frac{3\frac{3}{4}}{1\frac{2}{3}}$ **13.** $\frac{2}{3}$ **15.** $\frac{77}{100}$ **17.** $\frac{463}{821}$ **19.** $\frac{3}{4}$ **21.** $\frac{5}{12}$ **23.** $\frac{8}{25}$ **25.** $\frac{12}{7}$ **27.** $\frac{16}{23}$ **29.** $\frac{2}{5}$
31. $\frac{2}{7}$ **33.** $\frac{4}{1}$ **35.** $\frac{10}{29}$ **37.** $\frac{16}{51}$ **39.** $\frac{25}{144}$ **41.** $\frac{5}{4}$ **43.** $\frac{15}{1}$ **45.** $\frac{17}{40}$ **47.** $\frac{10}{279}$ **49.** $\frac{1}{3}$ **51.** $\frac{7}{151}$ **53.** $\frac{1}{49}$ **55.** 2.3 **57.** 0.15 **59.** the ratio of seven to nine **61.** the ratio of thirty to one **63.** no; answers may vary **65.** no; $\frac{3}{2}$ **67.** no; $\frac{2}{5}$ **69.** no; $\frac{9}{2}$ **71.** no, the shipment should not be refused
73. a. $\frac{3}{5}$ **b.** $\frac{3}{2}$ **c.** no; answers may vary

Section 5.2

Vocabulary and Readiness Check **1.** unit **3.** division **5.** numerator; denominator

Exercise Set 5.2 **1.** $\frac{\text{1 shrub}}{\text{3 ft}}$ **3.** $\frac{\text{3 returns}}{\text{20 sales}}$ **5.** $\frac{\text{3 laser printers}}{\text{14 computers}}$ **7.** $\frac{\text{9 gal}}{\text{2 acres}}$ **9.** $\frac{\text{3 flight attendants}}{\text{100 passengers}}$ **11.** $\frac{\text{71 cal}}{\text{2 fl oz}}$ **13.** 110 cal/oz **15.** 75 riders/car
17. 90 wingbeats/sec **19.** \$50,000/yr **21.** 225,250 voters/senator **23.** 300 good/defective **25.** \$4,390,000/player **27.** 66 crayons/day
29. \$0.14/mile **31.** \$59,800/house **33.** 6.2 tornadoes/hr **35. a.** 31.25 computer boards/hr **b.** 33.5 computer boards/hr **c.** Suellen
37. a. ≈ 27.6 miles/gal **b.** ≈ 29.2 miles/gal **c.** the truck **39.** \$11.50 per DVD **41.** \$0.17 per banana **43.** 8 oz: \$0.149 per oz; 12 oz: \$0.133 per oz; 12 oz **45.** 16 oz: \$0.106 per oz; 6 oz: \$0.115 per oz; 16 oz **47.** 12 oz: \$0.191 per oz; 8 oz: \$0.186 per oz; 8 oz
49. 100: \$0.006 per napkin; 180: \$0.005 per napkin; 180 napkins **51.** 10.2 **53.** 4.44 **55.** 1.9 **57.** 257; 19.2 **59.** 347; 21.6 **61.** 1.5 steps/ft
63. answers may vary **65.** no; answers may vary

Integrated Review **1.** $\frac{9}{10}$ **2.** $\frac{9}{25}$ **3.** $\frac{43}{50}$ **4.** $\frac{8}{23}$ **5.** $\frac{173}{139}$ **6.** $\frac{6}{7}$ **7.** $\frac{7}{26}$ **8.** $\frac{20}{33}$ **9.** $\frac{2}{3}$ **10.** $\frac{1}{8}$ **11.** $\frac{1087}{761}$ **12.** $\frac{1}{4}$ **13. a.** 13 **b.** $\frac{1}{3}$
14. $\frac{2}{3}$ **15.** $\frac{\text{1 office}}{\text{4 graduate assistants}}$ **16.** $\frac{\text{2 lights}}{\text{5 ft}}$ **17.** $\frac{\text{2 senators}}{\text{1 state}}$ **18.** $\frac{\text{1 teacher}}{\text{28 students}}$ **19.** $\frac{\text{16 computers}}{\text{25 households}}$ **20.** $\frac{\text{9 students}}{\text{2 computers}}$ **21.** 55 mi/hr
22. 140 ft/sec **23.** 21 employees/fax line **24.** 17 phone calls/teenager **25.** 23 mi/gal **26.** 16 teachers/computer **27.** 6 books/student
28. 154 lb/adult **29.** 8 lb: \$0.27 per lb; 18 lb: \$0.28 per lb; 8 lb **30.** 100: \$0.020 per plate; 500: \$0.018 per plate; 500 paper plates
31. 3 packs: \$0.80 per pack; 8 packs: \$0.75 per pack; 8 packs **32.** 4: \$0.92 per battery; 10: \$0.99 per battery; 4 batteries

Section 5.3

Vocabulary and Readiness Check **1.** proportion; ratio **3.** true **5.** true **7.** false **9.** true

Exercise Set 5.3 **1.** $\frac{\text{10 diamonds}}{\text{6 opals}} = \frac{\text{5 diamonds}}{\text{3 opals}}$ **3.** $\frac{\text{3 printers}}{\text{12 computers}} = \frac{\text{1 printer}}{\text{4 computers}}$ **5.** $\frac{\text{6 eagles}}{\text{58 sparrows}} = \frac{\text{3 eagles}}{\text{29 sparrows}}$

7. $\dfrac{2\frac{1}{4}\text{ cups flour}}{24\text{ cookies}} = \dfrac{6\frac{3}{4}\text{ cups flour}}{72\text{ cookies}}$ **9.** $\dfrac{22\text{ vanilla wafers}}{1\text{ cup cookie crumbs}} = \dfrac{55\text{ vanilla wafers}}{2.5\text{ cups cookie crumbs}}$ **11.** true **13.** false **15.** true **17.** true **19.** false **21.** false **23.** true **25.** false **27.** true **29.** $\frac{8}{12} = \frac{4}{6}$; true **31.** $\frac{5}{2} = \frac{13}{5}$; false **33.** $\frac{1.8}{2} = \frac{4.5}{5}$; true **35.** $\dfrac{\frac{2}{3}}{\frac{1}{5}} = \dfrac{\frac{2}{5}}{\frac{1}{9}}$; false **37.** 3 **39.** 9 **41.** 4 **43.** 3.2 **45.** 38.4 **47.** 25 **49.** 0.0025 **51.** 1 **53.** $\frac{9}{20}$ **55.** 12 **57.** $\frac{3}{4}$ **59.** $\frac{35}{18}$ **61.** < **63.** > **65.** < **67.** $\frac{9}{3} = \frac{15}{5}$; $\frac{5}{15} = \frac{3}{9}$; $\frac{15}{9} = \frac{5}{3}$ **69.** $\frac{6}{1} = \frac{18}{3}$; $\frac{3}{18} = \frac{1}{6}$; $\frac{18}{6} = \frac{3}{1}$ **71.** $\frac{d}{b} = \frac{c}{a}$; $\frac{a}{c} = \frac{b}{d}$; $\frac{b}{a} = \frac{d}{c}$ **73.** answers may vary **75.** 14.9 **77.** 0.07 **79.** 3.163 **81.** 0 **83.** 1400 **85.** 252.5

Section 5.4

Exercise Set 5.4 **1.** 360 baskets **3.** 165 min **5.** 630 applications **7.** 23 ft **9.** 270 sq ft **11.** 25 gal **13.** 450 km **15.** 16 bags **17.** 15 hits **19.** 27 people **21.** 18 applications **23.** 5 weeks **25.** $10\frac{2}{3}$ servings **27.** 37.5 sec **29. a.** 18 tsp **b.** 6 tbsp **31.** 6 people **33.** 112 ft; 11-in. difference **35.** 102.9 mg **37.** 1248 feet; coincidentally, this is the actual height of the Empire State Building **39.** 434 emergency room visits **41.** 28 workers **43.** 2.4 c **45. a.** 0.1 gal **b.** 13 fl oz **47. a.** 2062.5 mg **b.** no **49.** $3 \cdot 5$ **51.** $2^2 \cdot 5$ **53.** $2^3 \cdot 5^2$ **55.** 2^5 **57.** 0.8 ml **59.** 1.25 ml **61.** $11 \approx 12$ or 1 dozen; $1.5 \times 8 = 12$; 12 cups of milk **63.** $4\frac{2}{3}$ ft **65.** answers may vary

Chapter 5 Vocabulary Check **1.** ratio **2.** proportion **3.** unit rate **4.** unit price **5.** rate **6.** cross products **7.** equal **8.** not equal

Chapter 5 Review **1.** $\frac{23}{37}$ **2.** $\frac{14}{51}$ **3.** $\frac{5}{4}$ **4.** $\frac{11}{13}$ **5.** $\frac{7}{15}$ **6.** $\frac{17}{35}$ **7.** $\frac{18}{35}$ **8.** $\frac{35}{27}$ **9. a.** 9 **b.** $\frac{9}{25}$ **10. a.** 3 **b.** $\frac{3}{25}$ **11.** $\frac{1\text{ stillborn birth}}{125\text{ live births}}$ **12.** $\frac{3\text{ professors}}{10\text{ assistants}}$ **13.** $\frac{5\text{ pages}}{2\text{ min}}$ **14.** $\frac{4\text{ computers}}{3\text{ hr}}$ **15.** 52 mi/hr **16.** 15 ft/sec **17.** \$6.96/CD **18.** $1\frac{1}{3}$ gal/acre **19.** \$46.80/course **20.** 13 bushels/tree **21.** 8 oz: \$0.124 per oz; 12 oz: \$0.141 per oz; 8-oz size **22.** 18 oz: \$0.083; 28 oz: \$0.085; 18-oz size **23.** 16 oz: \$0.037; 64 oz: \$0.026; 128 oz: \$0.018; 1-gal size **24.** 12 oz: \$0.049; 16 oz: \$0.049; 32 oz: \$0.037; 32-oz size **25.** $\frac{20\text{ men}}{14\text{ women}} = \frac{10\text{ men}}{7\text{ women}}$ **26.** $\frac{50\text{ tries}}{4\text{ successes}} = \frac{25\text{ tries}}{2\text{ successes}}$ **27.** $\frac{16\text{ sandwiches}}{8\text{ players}} = \frac{2\text{ sandwiches}}{1\text{ player}}$ **28.** $\frac{12\text{ tires}}{3\text{ cars}} = \frac{4\text{ tires}}{1\text{ car}}$ **29.** no **30.** yes **31.** yes **32.** no **33.** 5 **34.** 15 **35.** 32.5 **36.** 5.625 **37.** 32 **38.** $6\frac{3}{4}$ **39.** 60 **40.** $7\frac{1}{5}$ **41.** 0.94 **42.** 0.36 **43.** $1\frac{1}{8}$ **44.** $1\frac{3}{7}$ **45.** 14 passes **46.** 35 attempts **47.** 8 bags **48.** 16 bags **49.** no **50.** 79 gal **51.** \$54,600 **52.** \$1023.50 **53.** $40\frac{1}{2}$ ft **54.** $8\frac{1}{4}$ in. **55.** $\frac{3}{5}$ **56.** $\frac{4}{9}$ **57.** $\frac{1}{2}$ **58.** $\frac{5}{12}$ **59.** $\frac{1}{27}$ **60.** $\frac{1}{8}$ **61.** $\frac{1\text{ teacher}}{9\text{ students}}$ **62.** $\frac{1\text{ nurse}}{4\text{ patients}}$ **63.** 4 cups/person **64.** 6 toys/child **65.** 34 miles/hour **66.** 2 gallons/cow **67.** 4 oz: \$1.235; 8 oz: \$1.248; 4-oz size **68.** 12 oz: \$0.054; 64 oz: \$0.047; 64-oz size **69.** $\frac{2\text{ cups cookie dough}}{30\text{ cookies}} = \frac{4\text{ cups cookie dough}}{60\text{ cookies}}$ **70.** $\frac{5\text{ nickels}}{3\text{ dollars}} = \frac{20\text{ nickels}}{12\text{ dollars}}$ **71.** yes **72.** no **73.** 1.6 **74.** 4.8 **75.** 84 **76.** 25 **77.** \$609.50 **78.** \$477 **79.** \$171 **80.** \$95

Chapter 5 Test **1.** $\frac{15}{2}$ **2.** $\frac{9}{13}$ **3.** $\frac{7\text{ men}}{1\text{ woman}}$ **4.** $\frac{13\text{ in.}}{10\text{ days}}$ **5.** $\frac{43}{50}$ **6.** $\frac{47}{78}$ **7.** $\frac{76}{31}$ **8.** 81.25 km/hr **9.** $\frac{2}{3}$ in./hr **10.** 28 students/teacher **11.** 9 inches/sec **12.** 8-oz size **13.** 16-oz size **14.** true **15.** false **16.** $\frac{25\text{ computers}}{600\text{ students}} = \frac{1\text{ computer}}{24\text{ students}}$ **17.** 5 **18.** $4\frac{4}{11}$ **19.** $\frac{7}{3}$ **20.** 8 **21.** $\frac{7}{8}$ **22.** $49\frac{1}{2}$ ft **23.** $3\frac{3}{4}$ hr **24.** $53\frac{1}{3}$ g **25.** $114\frac{2}{3}$ cartons **26.** 4266 adults

Cumulative Review **1. a.** 3 **b.** 15 **c.** 0 **d.** 70 (Sec. 1.4, Ex. 1) **2. a.** 0 **b.** 20 **c.** 0 **d.** 20 **3.** 249,000 (Sec. 1.5, Ex. 3) **4.** 249,000 **5. a.** 200 **b.** 1230 (Sec. 1.6, Ex. 3) **6.** 373 R 24 **7.** \$6171 (Sec. 1.8, Ex. 3) **8.** 16,591 feet **9.** $3 \cdot 3 \cdot 5$ or $3^2 \cdot 5$ (Sec. 2.2, Ex. 3) **10.** 8 **11.** $\frac{3}{5}$ (Sec. 2.3, Ex. 1) **12.** 243 **13.** $\frac{6}{5}$ (Sec. 2.4, Ex. 5) **14.** $\frac{123}{8}$ or $15\frac{3}{8}$ **15.** $\frac{2}{5}$ (Sec. 2.4, Ex. 6) **16.** $\frac{5}{54}$ **17.** $\frac{5}{7}$ (Sec. 3.1, Ex. 1) **18.** $\frac{19}{30}$ **19.** $\frac{16}{13}$ or $1\frac{3}{13}$ (Sec. 3.1, Ex. 3) **20.** $\frac{4}{5}$ **21.** 36 (Sec. 3.2, Ex. 2) **22.** $\frac{49}{50}$ **23.** $\frac{12}{24}$ (Sec. 3.2, Ex. 9) **24.** yes **25.** $\frac{8}{33}$ (Sec. 3.3, Ex. 6) **26.** $7\frac{47}{72}$ **27.** $\frac{1}{6}$ of an hour (Sec. 3.3, Ex. 9) **28.** 27 **29.** $7\frac{17}{24}$ (Sec. 3.4, Ex. 1) **30.** $\frac{16}{27}$ **31.** > (Sec. 3.5, Ex. 1) **32.** 14,000,000 **33.** one and three tenths (Sec. 4.1, Ex. 1) **34.** 0.075 **35.** 736.2 (Sec. 4.2, Ex. 5) **36.** 736.236 **37.** 25.454 (Sec. 4.3, Ex. 1) **38.** 681.24 **39.** 0.0849 (Sec. 4.4, Ex. 2) **40.** 0.375 **41.** 0.125 (Sec. 4.5, Ex. 3) **42.** $\frac{79}{10}$ **43.** 3.7 (Sec. 4.5, Ex. 12) **44.** 3 **45.** $\frac{4}{9}$, $\frac{9}{20}$, 0.456 (Sec. 4.6, Ex. 9) **46.** 140 m/sec **47.** $\frac{2.6}{3.1}$ (Sec. 5.1, Ex. 2) **48.** $\frac{1}{3}$ **49.** $\dfrac{1\frac{1}{2}}{7\frac{3}{4}}$ (Sec. 5.1, Ex. 3) **50.** $\frac{1}{10}$

Chapter 6 Percent

Section 6.1

Vocabulary and Readiness Check **1.** Percent **3.** percent **5.** 0.01

Exercise Set 6.1 **1.** 96% **3. a.** 75% **b.** 25% **5.** football; 37% **7.** 50% **9.** 0.41 **11.** 0.06 **13.** 1.00 or 1 **15.** 0.736 **17.** 0.028 **19.** 0.006 **21.** 3.00 or 3 **23.** 0.3258 **25.** 0.38 **27.** 0.202 **29.** 0.465 **31.** 98% **33.** 310% **35.** 2900% **37.** 0.3% **39.** 22% **41.** 530% **43.** 5.6% **45.** 33.28% **47.** 300% **49.** 70% **51.** 68% **53.** 3.9% **55.** 9.3% **57.** 0.25 **59.** 0.65 **61.** 0.9 **63.** b, d **65.** 4% **67.** network systems and data communication analysts **69.** 0.35 **71.** answers may vary

Section 6.2

Vocabulary and Readiness Check **1.** Percent **3.** 100% **5.** 13% **7.** 87% **9.** 1%

Exercise Set 6.2 **1.** $\frac{3}{25}$ **3.** $\frac{1}{25}$ **5.** $\frac{9}{200}$ **7.** $\frac{7}{4}$ or $1\frac{3}{4}$ **9.** $\frac{73}{100}$ **11.** $\frac{1}{8}$ **13.** $\frac{1}{16}$ **15.** $\frac{3}{50}$ **17.** $\frac{31}{300}$ **19.** $\frac{179}{800}$ **21.** 75% **23.** 70% **25.** 40% **27.** 59% **29.** 34% **31.** $37\frac{1}{2}\%$ **33.** $31\frac{1}{4}\%$ **35.** 160% **37.** $77\frac{7}{9}\%$ **39.** 65% **41.** 250% **43.** 190% **45.** 63.64% **47.** 26.67% **49.** 14.29% **51.** 91.67% **53.** $0.35, \frac{7}{20}$; 20%, 0.2; 50%, $\frac{1}{2}$; 0.7, $\frac{7}{10}$; 37.5%, 0.375 **55.** 0.4, $\frac{2}{5}$; $23\frac{1}{2}\%$, $\frac{47}{200}$; 80%, 0.8; $0.333\overline{3}$, $\frac{1}{3}$; 87.5%, 0.875; 0.075, $\frac{3}{40}$ **57.** 2, 2; 280%, $2\frac{4}{5}$; 7.05, $7\frac{1}{20}$; 454%, 4.54 **59.** 0.262; $\frac{131}{500}$ **61.** 0.23; $\frac{23}{100}$ **63.** 48.3% **65.** 0.0875 **67.** 25% **69.** 0.005; $\frac{1}{200}$ **71.** 0.142; $\frac{71}{500}$ **73.** 0.079; $\frac{79}{1000}$ **75.** $n = 15$ **77.** $n = 10$ **79.** $n = 12$ **81. a.** 52.9% **b.** 52.86% **83.** 107.8% **85.** 65.79% **87.** 77% **89.** 75% **91.** 80% **93.** greater **95.** answers may vary **97.** 0.266; 26.6% **99.** 1.155; 115.5%

Section 6.3

Vocabulary and Readiness Check **1.** is **3.** amount; base; percent **5.** greater **7.** percent: 42%; base: 50; amount: 21 **9.** percent: 125%; base: 86; amount: 107.5

Exercise Set 6.3 **1.** $18\% \cdot 81 = n$ **3.** $20\% \cdot n = 105$ **5.** $0.6 = 40\% \cdot n$ **7.** $n \cdot 80 = 3.8$ **9.** $n = 9\% \cdot 43$ **11.** $n \cdot 250 = 150$ **13.** 3.5 **15.** 28.7 **17.** 10 **19.** 600 **21.** 110% **23.** 34% **25.** 1 **27.** 645 **29.** 500 **31.** 5.16% **33.** 25.2 **35.** 35% **37.** 35 **39.** 0.624 **41.** 0.5% **43.** 145 **45.** 63% **47.** 4% **49.** $n = 30$ **51.** $n = 3\frac{7}{11}$ **53.** $\frac{17}{12} = \frac{n}{20}$ **55.** $\frac{8}{9} = \frac{14}{n}$ **57.** c **59.** b **61.** Twenty percent of some number is eighteen and six tenths. **63.** b **65.** c **67.** c **69.** a **71.** a **73.** answers may vary **75.** 686.625 **77.** 12,285

Section 6.4

Vocabulary and Readiness Check **1.** amount; base; percent **3.** amount **5.** amount: 12.6; base: 42; percent: 30 **7.** amount: 102; base: 510; percent: 20

Exercise Set 6.4 **1.** $\frac{a}{45} = \frac{98}{100}$ **3.** $\frac{a}{150} = \frac{4}{100}$ **5.** $\frac{14.3}{b} = \frac{26}{100}$ **7.** $\frac{84}{b} = \frac{35}{100}$ **9.** $\frac{70}{400} = \frac{p}{100}$ **11.** $\frac{8.2}{82} = \frac{p}{100}$ **13.** 26 **15.** 18.9 **17.** 600 **19.** 10 **21.** 120% **23.** 28% **25.** 37 **27.** 1.68 **29.** 1000 **31.** 210% **33.** 55.18 **33.** 45% **37.** 75 **39.** 0.864 **41.** 0.5% **43.** 140 **45.** 9.6 **47.** 113% **49.** $\frac{7}{8}$ **51.** $3\frac{2}{15}$ **53.** 0.7 **55.** 2.19 **57.** answers may vary **59.** no; $a = 16$ **61.** yes **63.** answers may vary **65.** 12,011.2 **67.** 7270.6

Integrated Review **1.** 12% **2.** 68% **3.** 12.5% **4.** 250% **5.** 520% **6.** 800% **7.** 6% **8.** 44% **9.** 750% **10.** 325% **11.** 3% **12.** 5% **13.** 0.65 **14.** 0.31 **15.** 0.08 **16.** 0.07 **17.** 1.42 **18.** 4 **19.** 0.029 **20.** 0.066 **21.** 0.03; $\frac{3}{100}$ **22.** 0.05; $\frac{1}{20}$ **23.** 0.0525; $\frac{21}{400}$ **24.** 0.1275; $\frac{51}{400}$ **25.** 0.38; $\frac{19}{50}$ **26.** 0.45; $\frac{9}{20}$ **27.** 0.123; $\frac{37}{300}$ **28.** $0.1\overline{6}$; $\frac{1}{6}$ **29.** 8.4 **30.** 100 **31.** 250 **32.** 120% **33.** 28% **34.** 76 **35.** 11 **36.** 130% **37.** 86% **38.** 37.8 **39.** 150 **40.** 62

Section 6.5

Exercise Set 6.5 **1.** 1600 bolts **3.** 8.8 lb **5.** 14% **7.** 232 **9.** 17% **11.** 496 chairs; 5704 chairs **13.** 83,820 physician assistants **15.** 636.864 thousand or approximately 637 thousand **17.** 30% **19.** 50% **21.** 12.5% **23.** 29.2% **25.** $175.000 **27.** 31.2 hr **29.** $867.87; $20,153.87 **31.** 35 ft **33.** increase: $3918; tuition in 2009–2010: $8679 **35.** increase: 41,667 associate degrees; 2017–2018: 772,667 associate degrees **37.** 30; 60% **39.** 52; 80% **41.** 2; 25% **43.** 120; 75% **45.** 44% **47.** 1.3% **49.** 158.0% **51.** 30.8% **53.** 5.6% **55.** 19.7% **57.** 29.0% **59.** 38.8% **61.** 4.56 **63.** 11.18 **65.** 58.54 **67.** The increased number is double the original number. **69.** percent increase $= \frac{30}{150} = 20\%$ **71.** False; the percents are different.

Section 6.6

Vocabulary and Readiness Check **1.** sales tax **3.** commission **5.** sale price

Exercise Set 6.6 **1.** $7.50 **3.** $858.93 **5.** 7% **7. a.** $120 **b.** $130.20 **9.** $117; $1917 **11.** $485 **13.** 6% **15.** $16.10; $246.10 **17.** $53,176.04 **19.** 14% **21.** $4888.50 **23.** $185,500 **25.** $8.90; $80.10 **27.** $98.25; $98.25 **29.** $143.50; $266.50 **31.** $3255; $18,445 **33.** $45; $255 **35.** $27.45; $332.45 **37.** $3.08; $59.08 **39.** $7074 **41.** 8% **43.** 1200 **45.** 132 **47.** 16 **49.** d **51.** $4.00; $6.00; $8.00 **53.** $7.20; $10.80; $14.40 **55.** a discount of 60% is better; answers may vary **57.** $26,838.45

Section 6.7

Calculator Explorations **1.** 1.56051 **3.** 8.06231 **5.** $634.49

Vocabulary and Readiness Check **1.** simple **3.** Compound **5.** Total amount

Exercise Set 6.7 **1.** $32 **3.** $73.60 **5.** $750 **7.** $33.75 **9.** $700 **11.** $101,562.50; $264,062.50 **13.** $5562.50 **15.** $14,280 **17.** $46,815.37 **19.** $2327.14 **21.** $58,163.65 **23.** 2915.75 **25.** $2938.66 **27.** $2971.89 **29.** $260.31 **31.** $637.26 **33.** 32 yd **35.** 35 m **37.** answers may vary **39.** answers may vary

Chapter 6 Vocabulary Check **1.** of **2.** is **3.** Percent **4.** Compound interest **5.** $\frac{\text{amount}}{\text{base}}$ **6.** 100% **7.** 0.01 **8.** $\frac{1}{100}$ **9.** base; amount **10.** Percent of decrease **11.** Percent of increase **12.** Sales tax **13.** Total price **14.** Commission **15.** Amount of discount **16.** Sale price

Chapter 6 Review **1.** 37% **2.** 77% **3.** 0.83 **4.** 0.75 **5.** 0.735 **6.** 0.015 **7.** 1.25 **8.** 1.45 **9.** 0.005 **10.** 0.007 **11.** 2.00 or 2 **12.** 4.00 or 4 **13.** 0.2625 **14.** 0.8534 **15.** 260% **16.** 102% **17.** 35% **18.** 5.5% **19.** 72.5% **20.** 25.2% **21.** 7.6% **22.** 8.5% **23.** 71% **24.** 65% **25.** 400% **26.** 900% **27.** $\frac{1}{100}$ **28.** $\frac{1}{10}$ **29.** $\frac{1}{4}$ **30.** $\frac{17}{200}$ **31.** $\frac{51}{500}$ **32.** $\frac{1}{6}$ **33.** $\frac{1}{3}$ **34.** $1\frac{1}{10}$ **35.** 20% **36.** 70% **37.** $83\frac{1}{3}\%$ **38.** 60% **39.** 125% **40.** $166\frac{2}{3}\%$ **41.** 6.25% **42.** 62.5% **43.** 100,000 **44.** 8000 **45.** 23% **46.** 114.5 **47.** 3000 **48.** 150% **49.** 418 **50.** 300 **51.** 64.8 **52.** 180% **53.** 110% **54.** 165 **55.** 66% **56.** 16% **57.** 20.9% **58.** 106.25% **59.** $206,400 **60.** $13.23 **61.** $263.75 **62.** $1.15 **63.** $5000 **64.** $300.38 **65.** discount: $900; sale price: $2100 **66.** discount: $9; sale price: $81 **67.** $160 **68.** $325 **69.** $30,104.61 **70.** $17,506.54 **71.** $80.61 **72.** $32,830.10 **73.** 0.038 **74.** 0.245 **75.** 0.009 **76.** 54% **77.** 9520% **78.** 30% **79.** $\frac{47}{100}$ **80.** $\frac{8}{125}$ **81.** $\frac{7}{125}$ **82.** $37\frac{1}{2}\%$ **83.** $15\frac{5}{13}\%$ **84.** 120% **85.** 268.75 **86.** 110% **87.** 708.48 **88.** 134% **89.** 300% **90.** 38.4 **91.** 560 **92.** 325% **93.** 26% **94.** $6786.50 **95.** $617.70 **96.** $3.45 **97.** 12.5% **98.** $1491 **99.** $17,951.01 **100.** $11,687.50

Chapter 6 Test **1.** 0.85 **2.** 5 **3.** 0.008 **4.** 5.6% **5.** 610% **6.** 39% **7.** $\frac{6}{5}$ **8.** $\frac{77}{200}$ **9.** $\frac{1}{500}$ **10.** 55% **11.** 37.5% **12.** $155\frac{5}{9}\%$ **13.** 33.6 **14.** 1250 **15.** 75% **16.** 38.4 lb **17.** $56,750 **18.** $358.43 **19.** 5% **20.** discount: $18; sale price: $102 **21.** $395 **22.** 1% **23.** $647.50 **24.** $2005.63 **25.** $427

Cumulative Review **1.** 206 cases; 12 cans; yes (Sec. 1.8, Ex. 2) **2.** 31,084 **3. a.** $4\frac{2}{7}$ **b.** $1\frac{1}{15}$ **c.** 14 (Sec. 2.1, Ex. 18) **4. a.** $\frac{19}{7}$ **b.** $\frac{101}{10}$ **c.** $\frac{43}{8}$ **5.** $2 \cdot 2 \cdot 2 \cdot 2 \cdot 5$ or $2^4 \cdot 5$ (Sec. 2.2, Ex. 7) **6.** 119 sq mi **7.** $\frac{10}{27}$ (Sec. 2.3, Ex. 3) **8.** 44 **9.** $\frac{23}{56}$ (Sec. 2.4, Ex. 4) **10.** 76,500 **11.** $\frac{8}{11}$ (Sec. 2.5, Ex. 2) **12.** $\frac{15}{4}$ or $3\frac{3}{4}$ **13.** $\frac{4}{5}$ in. (Sec. 3.1, Ex. 6) **14.** 50 **15.** 60 (Sec. 3.2, Ex. 4) **16.** $\frac{1}{3}$ **17.** $\frac{2}{3}$ (Sec. 3.3, Ex. 1) **18.** 340 **19.** $3\frac{5}{14}$ (Sec. 3.4, Ex. 5) **20.** 33 **21.** $\frac{7}{16}$ (Sec. 3.5, Ex. 6) **22.** $33\frac{27}{40}$ **23.** $\frac{2}{33}$ (Sec. 3.5, Ex. 8) **24.** $6\frac{3}{8}$ **25.** 0.8 (Sec. 4.1, Ex. 13) **26.** 0.09 **27.** 8.7 (Sec. 4.1, Ex. 14) **28.** 0.0048 **29.** $3.18 (Sec. 4.2, Ex. 7) **30.** 27.94 **31.** 829.6561 (Sec. 4.3, Ex. 2) **32.** 1248.3 **33.** 18.408 (Sec. 4.4, Ex. 1) **34.** 76,300 **35.** 0.7861 (Sec. 4.5, Ex. 8) **36.** 1.276 **37.** 0.012 (Sec. 4.5, Ex. 9) **38.** 50.65 **39.** 7.236 (Sec. 4.5, Ex. 11) **40.** 0.191 **41.** 0.25 (Sec. 4.6, Ex. 1) **42.** $0.\overline{5} \approx 0.556$ **43.** $\frac{5\text{ nails}}{3\text{ ft}}$ (Sec. 5.2, Ex. 1) **44.** 23 miles/gal **45.** no (Sec. 5.3, Ex. 3) **46.** 18: 0.052 per tortilla; 24: 0.058 per tortilla; 18 tortilla pkg is better buy. **47.** $17\frac{1}{2}$ mi (Sec. 5.4, Ex. 1) **48. a.** 0.07 **b.** 2 **c.** 0.005 **49.** $n = 25\% \cdot 0.008$ (Sec. 6.3, Ex. 3) **50.** 37.5% or $37\frac{1}{2}\%$

Chapter 7 Measurement

Section 7.1

Vocabulary and Readiness Check **1.** meter **3.** yard **5.** feet **7.** feet

Exercise Set 7.1 **1.** 5 ft **3.** 36 ft **5.** 8 mi **7.** 102 in. **9.** $3\frac{1}{3}$ yd **11.** 33,792 ft **13.** 4.5 yd **15.** 0.25 ft **17.** 13 yd 1 ft **19.** 7 ft 1 in. **21.** 1 mi 4720 ft **23.** 62 in. **25.** 26 ft **27.** 84 in. **29.** 11 ft 2 in. **31.** 22 yd 1 ft **33.** 6 ft 5 in. **35.** 7 ft 6 in. **37.** 14 ft 4 in. **39.** 83 yd 1 ft **41.** 6000 cm **43.** 4 cm **45.** 0.5 km **47.** 1.7 m **49.** 15 m **51.** 42,000 cm **53.** 7000 m **55.** 83 mm **57.** 0.201 dm **59.** 40 mm **61.** 8.94 m **63.** 2.94 m or 2940 mm **65.** 1.29 cm or 12.9 mm **67.** 12.64 km or 12,640 m **69.** 54.9 m **71.** 1.55 km **73.** $348\frac{2}{3}$; 12,552 **75.** $11\frac{2}{3}$; 420 **77.** 5000; 0.005; 500 **79.** 0.065; 65; 0.000065 **81.** 342,000; 342,000,000; 34,200,000 **83. a.** $213\frac{2}{3}$ yd **b.** 7692 in. **85.** 10 ft 6 in. **87.** 5100 ft **89.** 4.8 times **91.** 13 ft 11 in. **93.** 26.7 mm **95.** 15 ft 9 in. **97.** 3 ft 1 in. **99.** 41.25 m or 4125 cm **101.** 3.35 m **103.** 2.13 m **105.** $121\frac{1}{3}$ yd **107.** 15 tiles **109.** $\frac{21}{100}$ **111.** 0.13 **113.** 0.25 **115.** no **117.** yes **119.** no **121.** Estimate: 13 yd **123.** answers may vary; for example, $1\frac{1}{3}$ yd or 48 in. **125.** answers may vary **127.** 334.89 sq m

Section 7.2

Vocabulary and Readiness Check **1.** mass **3.** gram **5.** 2000 **7.** 2 lb **9.** 2 tons

Exercise Set 7.2 **1.** 32 oz **3.** 10,000 lb **5.** 9 tons **7.** $3\frac{3}{4}$ lb **9.** $1\frac{3}{4}$ tons **11.** 204 oz **13.** 9800 lb **15.** 76 oz **17.** 1.5 tons **19.** $\frac{1}{20}$ lb **21.** 92 oz **23.** 161 oz **25.** 5 lb 9 oz **27.** 53 lb 10 oz **29.** 8 tons 750 lb **31.** 3 tons 175 lb **33.** 8 lb 11 oz **35.** 31 lb 2 oz **37.** 1 ton 700 lb **39.** 0.5 kg **41.** 4000 mg **43.** 25,000 g **45.** 0.048 g **47.** 0.0063 kg **49.** 15,140 mg **51.** 6250 g **53.** 350,000 cg **55.** 13.5 mg **57.** 5.815 g or 5815 mg **59.** 1850 mg or 1.85 g **61.** 1360 g or 1.36 kg **63.** 13.52 kg **65.** 2.125 kg **67.** 200,000; 3,200,000 **69.** $\frac{269}{400}$ or 0.6725; 21,520 **71.** 0.5; 0.0005; 50

73. 21,000; 21,000,000; 2,100,000 **75.** 8.064 kg **77.** 30 mg **79.** 5 lb 8 oz **81.** 35 lb 14 oz **83.** 6 lb 15.4 oz **85.** 144 mg **87.** 6.12 kg **89.** 130 lb **91.** 211 lb **93.** 0.16 **95.** 0.875 **97.** no **99.** yes **101.** no **103.** answers may vary; for example, 250 mg or 0.25 g **105.** true **107.** answers may vary

Section 7.3

Vocabulary and Readiness Check **1.** capacity **3.** fluid ounces **5.** cups **7.** quarts **9.** 2 pt **11.** 2 gal **13.** 3 qt **15.** 3 c

Exercise Set 7.3 **1.** 4 c **3.** 16 pt **5.** $3\frac{1}{2}$ gal **7.** 5 pt **9.** 8 c **11.** $3\frac{3}{4}$ qt **13.** $10\frac{1}{2}$ qt **15.** 9 c **17.** 23 qt **19.** $\frac{1}{4}$ pt **21.** 14 gal 2 qt **23.** 4 gal 3 qt 1 pt **25.** 22 pt **27.** 13 gal 2 qt **29.** 4 c 4 fl oz **31.** 1 gal 1 qt **33.** 2 gal 3 qt 1 pt **35.** 17 gal **37.** 4 gal 3 qt **39.** 5000 ml **41.** 0.00016 kl **43.** 5.6 L **45.** 320 cl **47.** 0.41 kl **49.** 0.064 L **51.** 160 L **53.** 3600 ml **55.** 19.3 L **57.** 4.5 L or 4500 ml **59.** 8410 ml or 8.41 L **61.** 16,600 ml or 16.6 L **63.** 3840 ml **65.** 162.4 L **67.** 336; 84; 168 **69.** $\frac{1}{4}$; 1; 2 **71.** 1.59 L **73.** 18.954 L **75.** 4.3 fl oz **77.** yes **79.** $0.316 **81.** $\frac{4}{5}$ **83.** $\frac{3}{5}$ **85.** $\frac{9}{10}$ **87.** no **89.** no **91.** less than; answers may vary **93.** answers may vary **95.** 128 fl oz **97.** 1.5 cc **99.** 2.7 cc **101.** 54 u or 0.54 cc **103.** 86 u or 0.86 cc

Integrated Review **1.** 3 ft **2.** 2 mi **3.** $6\frac{2}{3}$ yd **4.** 19 ft **5.** 11,088 ft **6.** 38.4 in. **7.** 3000 cm **8.** 2.4 cm **9.** 2 m **10.** 18 m **11.** 72 mm **12.** 0.6 km **13.** 15,000 lb **14.** 5.5 tons **15.** 136 oz **16.** 4.5 lb **17.** 6.5 lb **18.** 80 oz **19.** 28,000 g **20.** 1.4 g **21.** 0.0056 kg **22.** 6000 g **23.** 0.67 g **24.** 0.0036 kg **25.** 12 pt **26.** 2.5 qt **27.** 3.5 gal **28.** 8.5 pt **29.** 7 c **30.** 6.5 gal **31.** 7000 ml **32.** 0.35 kl **33.** 0.047 L **34.** 970 L **35.** 126 L **36.** 0.075 L **37.** 4 fl oz **38.** 12 c

Section 7.4

Exercise Set 7.4 **1.** 25.57 fl oz **3.** 218.44 cm **5.** 40 oz **7.** 57.66 mi **9.** 3.77 gal **11.** 13.5 kg **13.** 1.5; $1\frac{2}{3}$; 150; 60 **15.** 55; 5500; 180; 2160 **17.** 3.94 in. **19.** 80.5 kph **21.** 0.008 oz **23.** yes **25.** 2790 mi **27.** 90 mm **29.** 112.5 g **31.** 104 mph **33.** 26.24 ft **35.** 3 mi **37.** 8 fl oz **39.** b **41.** b **43.** c **45.** d **47.** d **49.** 29 **51.** 9 **53.** 5 **55.** 36 **57.** 2.13 sq m **59.** 1.19 sq m **61.** 1.69 sq m **63.** 21.3 mg–25.56 mg **65.** 800 sq m or 8606.72 sq ft

Section 7.5

Exercise Set 7.5 **1.** 5°C **3.** 40°C **5.** 140°F **7.** 239°F **9.** 16.7°C **11.** 61.2°C **13.** 197.6°F **15.** 61.3°F **17.** 50°C **19.** 80.6°F **21.** 100°C **23.** 37.9°C **25.** 244.4°F **27.** 462.2°C **29.** 21.1°C **31.** 12 in. **33.** 12 cm **35.** 8 ft 4 in. **37.** false **39.** true **41.** ≈ 520,000,000°C **43.** yes **45.** no **47.** no **49.** yes **51.** answers may vary

Chapter 7 Vocabulary Check **1.** Weight **2.** Mass **3.** meter **4.** unit fractions **5.** gram **6.** Energy **7.** British Thermal Unit **8.** liter **9.** calorie

Chapter 7 Review **1.** 9 ft **2.** 24 yd **3.** 7920 ft **4.** 18 in. **5.** 17 yd 1 ft **6.** 3 ft 10 in. **7.** 4200 cm **8.** 820 mm **9.** 0.01218 m **10.** 0.00231 km **11.** 21 yd 1 ft **12.** 7 ft 5 in. **13.** 41 ft 3 in. **14.** 3 ft 8 in. **15.** 9.5 cm or 95 mm **16.** 2.74 m or 274 cm **17.** 34.48 m **18.** 2.45 km **19.** 169 yd 2 ft **20.** 126 ft 8 in. **21.** 108.5 km **22.** 0.24 sq m **23.** 4.125 lb **24.** 4600 lb **25.** 3 lb 4 oz **26.** 5 tons 300 lb **27.** 0.027 g **28.** 40,000 g **29.** 21 dag **30.** 0.0003 dg **31.** 3 lb 9 oz **32.** 10 tons 800 lb **33.** 2 tons 750 lb **34.** 33 lb 8 oz **35.** 21.5 mg **36.** 0.6 kg or 600 g **37.** 4 lb 4 oz **38.** 9 tons 1075 lb **39.** 7.85 kg **40.** 1.1625 kg **41.** 8 qt **42.** 5 c **43.** 7 pt **44.** 72 c **45.** 4 qt 1 pt **46.** 3 gal 3 qt **47.** 3800 ml **48.** 0.042 dl **49.** 1.4 kl **50.** 3060 cl **51.** 1 gal 1 qt **52.** 7 gal **53.** 736 ml or 0.736 L **54.** 15.5 L or 15,500 ml **55.** 2 gal 3 qt **56.** 6 fl oz **57.** 10.88 L **58.** yes **59.** 22.96 ft **60.** 10.55 m **61.** 4.55 gal **62.** 8.27 qt **63.** 425.25 g **64.** 10.35 kg **65.** 109 yd **66.** 180.4 lb **67.** 3.18 qt **68.** 2.36 in. **69.** 473°F **70.** 320°F **71.** 107.6°F **72.** 34°C **73.** 5.2°C **74.** 26.7°C **75.** 1.7°C **76.** 329°C **77.** 13,200 ft **78.** 75 in. **79.** 4.5 mi **80.** 10.75 ft **81.** 4 tons 200 lb **82.** 2 tons 300 lb **83.** 500 cm **84.** 0.000286 km **85.** 1.4 g **86.** 0.24 g **87.** 27 qt **88.** 21 qt **89.** 17 c **90.** $12\frac{1}{2}$ c **91.** 186.8°F **92.** 59°F **93.** 11°C **94.** 28°C **95.** 9117 m or 9.117 km **96.** 8.353 km or 8353 m **97.** 13.9 L or 13,900 ml **98.** 35.7 L or 35,700 ml **99.** 8.1 g or 8100 mg **100.** 1.6 g or 1600 mg **101.** 50.4 kg **102.** 12.8 kg **103.** 7 gal 3 qt **104.** 8 gal 2 qt **105.** 38 dm or 3800 mm **106.** 58 dm or 5800 mm **107.** 2.25 tons **108.** 2.25 tons

Chapter 7 Test **1.** 23 ft 4 in. **2.** 10 qt **3.** 1.875 lb **4.** 5600 lb **5.** $4\frac{3}{4}$ gal **6.** 0.04 g **7.** 2400 g **8.** 36 mm **9.** 0.43 g **10.** 830 ml **11.** 1 gal 2 qt **12.** 3 lb 13 oz **13.** 8 ft 3 in. **14.** 2 gal 3 qt **15.** 66 mm or 6.6 cm **16.** 2.256 km or 2256 m **17.** 28.9°C **18.** 54.7°F **19.** 5.6 m **20.** 4 gal 3 qt **21.** 91.4 m **22.** 16 ft 6 in. **23.** 493 ft 6 in. **24.** 150.368 m **25.** 57.8°C **26.** 105.8°F **27.** 37,336 pt **28.** 0.2 oz **29.** 3.1 mi **30.** 18.95 L

Cumulative Review **1.** 2010 (Sec. 1.3, Ex. 4) **2.** 1531 **3.** $3 \cdot 3 \cdot 3 \cdot 5 \cdot 7$ or $3^3 \cdot 5 \cdot 7$ (Sec. 2.2, Ex. 5) **4.** 153 sq in. **5.** 33 (Sec. 3.2, Ex. 7) **6.** $\frac{10}{63}$ **7.** $5\frac{1}{15}$ (Sec. 3.4, Ex. 2) **8.** $10\frac{1}{3}$ **9.** $\frac{1}{8}$ (Sec. 4.1, Ex. 10) **10.** $1\frac{1}{5}$ **11.** $105\frac{83}{1000}$ (Sec. 4.1, Ex. 12) **12.** $\frac{8}{27}$ **13.** $<$ (Sec. 4.2, Ex. 2) **14.** 25 **15.** 67.69 (Sec. 4.3, Ex. 6) **16.** 139.231 **17.** 4.21 (Sec. 4.4, Ex. 8) **18.** 186,040 **19.** 0.0092 (Sec. 4.4, Ex. 10) **20.** 5.8 **21.** 0.26 (Sec. 4.5, Ex. 2) **22.** $\frac{21}{20}$ or $1\frac{1}{20}$ **23.** 2.1875 (Sec. 4.6, Ex. 4) **24.** 7.3 **25.** $0.\overline{6}$ (Sec. 4.6, Ex. 2) **26.** 2.16 **27.** $\frac{12}{17}$ (Sec. 5.1, Ex. 1) **28.** $\frac{12}{23}$ **29.** 22.5 mi/gal (Sec. 5.2, Ex. 5) **30.** $\frac{1}{4}$ **31.** $n = \frac{35}{6}$ or $5\frac{5}{6}$ (Sec. 5.3, Ex. 6) **32.** 7.5 cups **33.** 7 bags (Sec. 5.4, Ex. 3) **34.** $\frac{23}{100}$ **35.** 0.23 (Sec. 6.1, Ex. 3) **36.** 87.5% or $87\frac{1}{2}\%$ **37.** 8.33% (Sec. 6.2, Ex. 9) **38.** 24% **39.** 14 (Sec. 6.3, Ex. 7) **40.** 32 pints **41.** $\frac{75}{30} = \frac{p}{100}$ (Sec. 6.4, Ex. 5) **42.** 860 cm **43.** 18% (Sec. 6.5, Ex. 6) **44.** 6.5 tons **45.** discount: $16.25; sale price: $48.75 (Sec. 6.6, Ex. 5) **46.** 52 oz **47.** $120 (Sec. 6.7, Ex. 1) **48.** 15% **49.** $4\frac{1}{2}$ tons (Sec. 7.2, Ex. 1) **50.** 77°F

Chapter 8 Real Numbers and Introduction to Algebra

Section 8.1

Vocabulary and Readiness Check **1.** whole **3.** inequality **5.** real **7.** 0 **9.** absolute value

Exercise Set 8.1 **1.** $<$ **3.** $>$ **5.** $=$ **7.** $<$ **9.** $32 < 212$ **11.** $30 \le 45$ **13.** true **15.** false **17.** true **19.** false **21.** $20 \le 25$ **23.** $6 > 0$ **25.** $-12 < -10$ **27.** $7 < 11$ **29.** $5 \ge 4$ **31.** $15 \ne -2$ **33.** 14,494; −282 **35.** −28,000 **37.** 475; −195 **39.** −4 −3 −2 −1 0 1 2 3 4 5 **41.** $-\frac{1}{4}\ \frac{1}{3}$ −4 −3 −2 −1 0 1 2 3 4 **43.** −4.5 $-\frac{3}{2}$ $\frac{7}{4}$ 3.25 −5 −4 −3 −2 −1 0 1 2 3 4 **45.** whole, integers, rational, real **47.** integers, rational, real **49.** natural, whole, integers, rational, real **51.** rational, real **53.** false **55.** true **57.** false **59.** false **61.** 8.9 **63.** 20 **65.** $\frac{9}{2}$ **67.** $\frac{12}{13}$ **69.** $>$ **71.** $=$ **73.** $<$ **75.** $<$ **77.** 905 thousand $>$ 823 thousand, or $905{,}000 > 823{,}000$ **79.** decreased by 24 or −24 **81.** 49 million $>$ 16 million, or $49{,}000{,}000 > 16{,}000{,}000$ **83.** 38 million pounds less, or −38 million **85.** $-0.04 > -26.7$ **87.** sun **89.** sun **91.** answers may vary

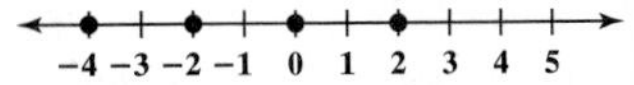

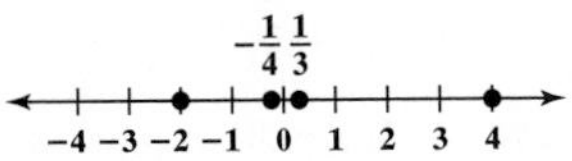

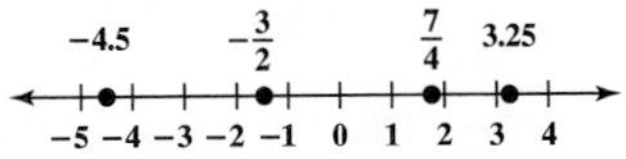

Section 8.2

Calculator Explorations **1.** 125 **3.** 59,049 **5.** 30 **7.** 9857 **9.** 2376

Vocabulary and Readiness Check **1.** base; exponent **3.** multiplication **5.** subtraction **7.** expression **9.** expression; variables **11.** equation

Exercise Set 8.2 **1.** 243 **3.** 27 **5.** 1 **7.** 5 **9.** 49 **11.** $\frac{16}{81}$ **13.** $\frac{1}{125}$ **15.** 1.44 **17.** 0.343 **19.** 5^2 sq m **21.** 17 **23.** 20 **25.** 12 **27.** 21 **29.** 45 **31.** 0 **33.** $\frac{2}{7}$ **35.** 30 **37.** 2 **39.** $\frac{7}{18}$ **41.** $\frac{27}{10}$ **43.** $\frac{7}{5}$ **45.** 32 **47.** $\frac{23}{27}$ **49.** 9 **51.** 1 **53.** 1 **55.** 11 **57.** 8 **59.** 45 **61.** 27 **63.** 132 **65.** $\frac{37}{18}$ **67.** solution **69.** not a solution **71.** not a solution **73.** solution **75.** not a solution **77.** solution **79.** $x + 15$ **81.** $x - 5$ **83.** $\frac{x}{4}$ **85.** $3x + 22$ **87.** $1 + 2 = 9 \div 3$ **89.** $3 \ne 4 \div 2$ **91.** $5 + x = 20$ **93.** $7.6x = 17$ **95.** $13 - 3x = 13$ **97.** no; answers may vary **99. a.** 64 **b.** 43 **c.** 19 **d.** 22 **101.** 14 in., 12 sq in. **103.** 14 in., 9.01 sq in. **105.** Rectangles with the same perimeter can have different areas. **107.** $(20 - 4) \cdot 4 \div 2$ **109. a.** expression **b.** equation **c.** equation **d.** expression **e.** expression **111.** answers may vary **113.** answers may vary, for example, $-2(5) - 1$.

Section 8.3

Vocabulary and Readiness Check **1.** 0 **3.** a

Exercise Set 8.3 **1.** 3 **3.** −14 **5.** 1 **7.** −12 **9.** −5 **11.** −12 **13.** −4 **15.** 7 **17.** −2 **19.** 0 **21.** −19 **23.** 31 **25.** −47 **27.** −2.1 **29.** 38 **31.** −13.1 **33.** $\frac{1}{4}$ **35.** $-\frac{3}{16}$ **37.** $-\frac{13}{10}$ **39.** −8 **41.** −8 **43.** −59 **45.** −9 **47.** 5 **49.** 11 **51.** −18 **53.** 19 **55.** −7 **57.** −26 **59.** −6 **61.** 2 **63.** 0 **65.** −6 **67.** −2 **69.** 7 **71.** 7.9 **73.** $5z$ **75.** $\frac{2}{3}$ **77.** −70 **79.** 3 **81.** 19 **83.** −10 **85.** $0 + (-215) + (-16) = -231$; 231 ft below the surface **87.** 107°F **89.** −95 m **91.** −21 **93.** −\$6.9 million **95.** July **97.** October **99.** 4.7°F **101.** answers may vary **103.** −3 **105.** −22 **107.** true **109.** false **111.** answers may vary

Section 8.4

Vocabulary and Readiness Check **1.** $a + (-b)$; b **3.** $-10 - (-14)$; d

Exercise Set 8.4 **1.** −10 **3.** −5 **5.** 19 **7.** 11 **9.** −8 **11.** −11 **13.** 37 **15.** 5 **17.** −71 **19.** 0 **21.** $\frac{2}{11}$ **23.** −6.4 **25.** 4.1 **27.** $-\frac{1}{6}$ **29.** $-\frac{11}{12}$ **31.** 8.92 **33.** −8.92 **35.** 13 **37.** −5 **39.** −1 **41.** −23 **43.** −26 **45.** −24 **47.** 3 **49.** −45 **51.** −4 **53.** 13 **55.** 6 **57.** 9 **59.** −9 **61.** $\frac{7}{5}$ **63.** −7 **65.** 21 **67.** $\frac{1}{4}$ **69.** not a solution **71.** not a solution **73.** solution **75.** 265°F **77.** 35,653 ft **79.** 30° **81.** −308 ft **83.** 19,852 ft **85.** 130° **87.** $-5 + x$ **89.** $-20 - x$ **91.** −4.4°, 2.6°, 12°, 23.5°, 15.3° **93.** May **95.** answers may vary **97.** 16 **99.** −20 **101.** true; answers may vary **103.** false; answers may vary **105.** negative, −30,387

Integrated Review **1.** negative **2.** negative **3.** positive **4.** 0 **5.** positive **6.** 0 **7.** positive **8.** positive **9.** $-\frac{1}{7}; \frac{1}{7}$ **10.** $\frac{12}{5}; \frac{12}{5}$ **11.** 3; 3 **12.** $-\frac{9}{11}; \frac{9}{11}$ **13.** −42 **14.** 10 **15.** 2 **16.** −18 **17.** −7 **18.** −39 **19.** −2 **20.** −9 **21.** −3.4 **22.** −9.8 **23.** $-\frac{25}{28}$ **24.** $-\frac{5}{24}$ **25.** −4 **26.** −24 **27.** 6 **28.** 20 **29.** 6 **30.** 61 **31.** −6 **32.** −16 **33.** −19 **34.** −13 **35.** −4 **36.** −1 **37.** $\frac{13}{20}$ **38.** $-\frac{29}{40}$ **39.** 4 **40.** 9 **41.** −1 **42.** −3 **43.** 8 **44.** 10 **45.** 47 **46.** $\frac{2}{3}$

Section 8.5

Calculator Explorations **1.** 38 **3.** −441 **5.** 490 **7.** 54,499 **9.** 15,625

Vocabulary and Readiness Check **1.** negative **3.** positive **5.** 0 **7.** 0

Exercise Set 8.5 **1.** -24 **3.** -2 **5.** 50 **7.** -45 **9.** $\frac{3}{10}$ **11.** -7 **13.** -15 **15.** 0 **17.** 16 **19.** -16 **21.** $\frac{9}{16}$ **23.** -0.49 **25.** $\frac{3}{2}$ **27.** $-\frac{1}{14}$ **29.** $-\frac{11}{3}$ **31.** $\frac{1}{0.2}$ **33.** -9 **35.** -4 **37.** 0 **39.** undefined **41.** $-\frac{18}{7}$ **43.** 160 **45.** 64 **47.** $-\frac{8}{27}$ **49.** 3 **51.** -15 **53.** -125 **55.** -0.008 **57.** $\frac{2}{3}$ **59.** $\frac{20}{27}$ **61.** 0.84 **63.** -40 **65.** 81 **67.** -1 **69.** -121 **71.** -1 **73.** -19 **75.** 90 **77.** -84 **79.** -5 **81.** $-\frac{9}{2}$ **83.** 18 **85.** 17 **87.** -20 **89.** 16 **91.** 2 **93.** $-\frac{34}{7}$ **95.** 0 **97.** $\frac{6}{5}$ **99.** $\frac{3}{2}$ **101.** $-\frac{5}{38}$ **103.** 3 **105.** -1 **107.** undefined **109.** $-\frac{22}{9}$ **111.** solution **113.** not a solution **115.** solution **117.** $-71 \cdot x$ or $-71x$ **119.** $-16 - x$ **121.** $-29 + x$ **123.** $\frac{x}{-33}$ or $x \div (-33)$ **125.** $3 \cdot (-4) = -12$; a loss of 12 yd **127.** $5(-20) = -100$; a depth of 100 ft **129.** true **131.** false **133.** $-162°$F **135.** answers may vary **137.** $1, -1$; answers may vary **139.** $\frac{0}{5} - 7 = -7$ **141.** $-8(-5) + (-1) = 39$

Section 8.6

Vocabulary and Readiness Check **1.** commutative property of addition **3.** distributive property **5.** associative property of addition **7.** opposites or additive inverses

Exercise Set 8.6 **1.** $16 + x$ **3.** $y \cdot (-4)$ **5.** yx **7.** $13 + 2x$ **9.** $x \cdot (yz)$ **11.** $(2 + a) + b$ **13.** $(4a) \cdot b$ **15.** $a + (b + c)$ **17.** $17 + b$ **19.** $24y$ **21.** y **23.** $26 + a$ **25.** $-72x$ **27.** s **29.** $-\frac{5}{2}x$ **31.** $4x + 4y$ **33.** $9x - 54$ **35.** $6x + 10$ **37.** $28x - 21$ **39.** $18 + 3x$ **41.** $-2y + 2z$ **43.** $-y - \frac{5}{3}$ **45.** $5x + 20m + 10$ **47.** $8m - 4n$ **49.** $-5x - 2$ **51.** $-r + 3 + 7p$ **53.** $3x + 4$ **55.** $-x + 3y$ **57.** $6r + 8$ **59.** $-36x - 70$ **61.** $-1.6x - 2.5$ **63.** $4(1 + y)$ **65.** $11(x + y)$ **67.** $-1(5 + x)$ **69.** $30(a + b)$ **71.** commutative property of multiplication **73.** associative property of addition **75.** commutative property of addition **77.** associative property of multiplication **79.** identity element for addition **81.** distributive property **83.** multiplicative inverse property **85.** identity element for multiplication **87.** $-8; \frac{1}{8}$ **89.** $-x; \frac{1}{x}$ **91.** $2x; -2x$ **93.** false **95.** no **97.** yes **99.** yes **101.** yes **103. a.** commutative property of addition **b.** commutative property of addition **c.** associative property of addition **105.** answers may vary **107.** answers may vary

Section 8.7

Vocabulary and Readiness Check **1.** expression **3.** combine like term **5.** like; unlike **7.** -7 **9.** 1 **11.** 17 **13.** like **15.** unlike **17.** like

Exercise Set 8.7 **1.** $15y$ **3.** $13w$ **5.** $-7b - 9$ **7.** $-m - 6$ **9.** -8 **11.** $7.2x - 5.2$ **13.** $k - 6$ **15.** $-15x + 18$ **17.** $4x - 3$ **19.** $5x^2$ **21.** -11 **23.** $1.3x + 3.5$ **25.** $5y + 20$ **27.** $-2x - 4$ **29.** $-10x + 15y - 30$ **31.** $-3x + 2y - 1$ **33.** $7d - 11$ **35.** 16 **37.** $x + 5$ **39.** $x + 2$ **41.** $2k + 10$ **43.** $-3x + 5$ **45.** $2x + 14$ **47.** $3y + \frac{5}{6}$ **49.** $-22 + 24x$ **51.** $0.9m + 1$ **53.** $10 - 6x - 9y$ **55.** $-x - 38$ **57.** $5x - 7$ **59.** $10x - 3$ **61.** $-4x - 9$ **63.** $-4m - 3$ **65.** $2x - 4$ **67.** $\frac{3}{4}x + 12$ **69.** $12x - 2$ **71.** $8x + 48$ **73.** $x - 10$ **75.** balanced **77.** balanced **79.** answers may vary **81.** $(18x - 2)$ ft **83.** $(15x + 23)$ in. **85.** answers may vary

Chapter 8 Vocabulary Check **1.** inequality symbols **2.** equation **3.** absolute value **4.** variable **5.** opposites **6.** numerator **7.** solution **8.** reciprocals **9.** base; exponent **10.** numerical coefficient **11.** denominator **12.** grouping symbols **13.** term **14.** like terms **15.** unlike terms

Chapter 8 Review **1.** $<$ **2.** $>$ **3.** $>$ **4.** $>$ **5.** $<$ **6.** $>$ **7.** $=$ **8.** $=$ **9.** $>$ **10.** $<$ **11.** $4 \geq -3$ **12.** $6 \neq 5$ **13.** $0.03 < 0.3$ **14.** $155 < 400$ **15. a.** 1, 3 **b.** 0, 1, 3 **c.** $-6, 0, 1, 3$ **d.** $-6, 0, 1, 1\frac{1}{2}, 3, 9.62$ **e.** π **f.** all numbers in set **16. a.** 2, 5 **b.** 2, 5 **c.** $-3, 2, 5$ **d.** $-3, -1.6, 2, 5, \frac{11}{2}, 15.1$ **e.** $\sqrt{5}, 2\pi$ **f.** all numbers in set **17.** Friday **18.** Wednesday **19.** c **20.** b **21.** 37 **22.** 41 **23.** $\frac{18}{7}$ **24.** 80 **25.** $20 - 12 = 2 \cdot 4$ **26.** $\frac{9}{2} > -5$ **27.** 18 **28.** 108 **29.** 5 **30.** 24 **31.** 63° **32.** 105° **33.** solution **34.** not a solution **35.** 9 **36.** $-\frac{2}{3}$ **37.** -2 **38.** 7 **39.** -11 **40.** -17 **41.** $-\frac{3}{16}$ **42.** -5 **43.** -13.9 **44.** 3.9 **45.** -14 **46.** -11.5 **47.** 5 **48.** -11 **49.** -19 **50.** 4 **51.** a **52.** a **53.** \$51 **54.** \$54 **55.** $-\frac{1}{6}$ **56.** $\frac{5}{3}$ **57.** -48 **58.** 28 **59.** 3 **60.** -14 **61.** -36 **62.** 0 **63.** undefined **64.** $-\frac{1}{2}$ **65.** commutative property of addition **66.** identity element for multiplication **67.** distributive property **68.** additive inverse property **69.** associative property of addition **70.** commutative property of multiplication **71.** distributive property **72.** associative property of multiplication **73.** multiplicative inverse property **74.** identity element for addition **75.** commutative property of addition **76.** distributive property **77.** $6x$ **78.** $-11.8z$ **79.** $4x - 2$ **80.** $2y + 3$ **81.** $3n - 18$ **82.** $4w - 6$ **83.** $-6x + 7$ **84.** $-0.4y + 2.3$ **85.** $3x - 7$ **86.** $5x + 5.6$ **87.** $<$ **88.** $>$ **89.** -15.3 **90.** -6 **91.** -80 **92.** -5 **93.** $-\frac{1}{4}$ **94.** 0.15 **95.** 16 **96.** 16 **97.** -5 **98.** 9 **99.** $-\frac{5}{6}$ **100.** undefined **101.** $16x - 41$ **102.** $18x - 12$

Chapter 8 Test **1.** $|-7| > 5$ **2.** $9 + 5 \geq 4$ **3.** -5 **4.** -11 **5.** -14 **6.** -39 **7.** 12 **8.** -2 **9.** undefined **10.** -8 **11.** $-\frac{1}{3}$ **12.** $4\frac{5}{8}$ **13.** $\frac{51}{40}$ **14.** -32 **15.** -48 **16.** 3 **17.** 0 **18.** $>$ **19.** $>$ **20.** $>$ **21.** $=$ **22. a.** 1, 7 **b.** 0, 1, 7 **c.** $-5, -1, 0, 1, 7$ **d.** $-5, -1, \frac{1}{4}, 0, 1, 7, 11.6$ **e.** $\sqrt{7}, 3\pi$ **f.** $-5, -1, \frac{1}{4}, 0, 1, 7, 11.6, \sqrt{7}, 3\pi$ **23.** 40 **24.** 12 **25.** 22 **26.** -1 **27.** associative property of addition **28.** commutative property of multiplication **29.** distributive property **30.** multiplicative inverse **31.** 9 **32.** -3 **33.** second down **34.** yes **35.** 17° **36.** \$420 **37.** $y - 10$ **38.** $5.9x + 1.2$ **39.** $-2x + 10$ **40.** $-15y + 1$

Chapter 9 Equations, Inequalities, and Problem Solving

Section 9.1

Vocabulary and Readiness Check **1.** expression **3.** equation **5.** expression; equation **7.** Equivalent **9.** 2 **11.** 12 **13.** 17

Exercise Set 9.1 **1.** 3 **3.** −2 **5.** −14 **7.** 0.5 **9.** $\frac{1}{4}$ **11.** $\frac{5}{12}$ **13.** −3 **15.** −9 **17.** −10 **19.** 2 **21.** −7 **23.** −1 **25.** −9 **27.** −12 **29.** $-\frac{1}{2}$ **31.** 11 **33.** 21 **35.** 25 **37.** −3 **39.** −0.7 **41.** 11 **43.** 13 **45.** −30 **47.** −0.4 **49.** −7 **51.** $-\frac{1}{3}$ **53.** −17.9 **55.** $(10 - x)$ ft **57.** $(180 - x)°$ **59.** $n - 28{,}000$ **61.** $7x$ sq mi **63.** $\frac{8}{5}$ **65.** $\frac{1}{2}$ **67.** −9 **69.** x **71.** y **73.** x **75.** answers may vary **77.** 4 **79.** answers may vary **81.** $(173 - 3x)°$ **83.** answers may vary **85.** −145.478

Section 9.2

Vocabulary and Readiness Check **1.** multiplication **3.** equation; expression **5.** Equivalent **7.** 9 **9.** 2 **11.** −5

Exercise Set 9.2 **1.** 4 **3.** 0 **5.** 12 **7.** −12 **9.** 3 **11.** 2 **13.** 0 **15.** 6.3 **17.** 10 **19.** −20 **21.** 0 **23.** −9 **25.** 1 **27.** −30 **29.** 3 **31.** $\frac{10}{9}$ **33.** −1 **35.** −4 **37.** $-\frac{1}{2}$ **39.** 0 **41.** 4 **43.** $-\frac{1}{14}$ **45.** 0.21 **47.** 5 **49.** 6 **51.** −5.5 **53.** −5 **55.** 0 **57.** −3 **59.** $-\frac{9}{28}$ **61.** $\frac{14}{3}$ **63.** −9 **65.** −2 **67.** $\frac{11}{2}$ **69.** $-\frac{1}{4}$ **71.** $\frac{9}{10}$ **73.** $-\frac{17}{20}$ **75.** −16 **77.** $2x + 2$ **79.** $2x + 2$ **81.** $5x + 20$ **83.** $7x - 12$ **85.** $12z + 44$ **87.** 1 **89.** −48 **91.** answers may vary **93.** answers may vary **95.** 2

Section 9.3

Calculator Explorations **1.** solution **3.** not a solution **5.** solution

Vocabulary and Readiness Check **1.** equation **3.** expression **5.** expression **7.** equation

Exercise Set 9.3 **1.** −6 **3.** 3 **5.** 1 **7.** $\frac{3}{2}$ **9.** 0 **11.** −1 **13.** 4 **15.** −4 **17.** −3 **19.** 2 **21.** 50 **23.** 1 **25.** $\frac{7}{3}$ **27.** 0.2 **29.** all real numbers **31.** no solution **33.** no solution **35.** all real numbers **37.** 18 **39.** $\frac{19}{9}$ **41.** $\frac{14}{3}$ **43.** 13 **45.** 4 **47.** all real numbers **49.** $-\frac{3}{5}$ **51.** −5 **53.** 10 **55.** no solution **57.** 3 **59.** −17 **61.** $\frac{7}{5}$ **63.** $-\frac{1}{50}$ **65.** $(6x - 8)$ m **67.** $-8 - x$ **69.** $-3 + 2x$ **71.** $9(x + 20)$ **73. a.** all real numbers **b.** answers may vary **c.** answers may vary **75.** a **77.** b **79.** c **81.** answers may vary **83. a.** $x + x + x + 2x + 2x = 28$ **b.** $x = 4$ **c.** $x = 4$ cm; $2x$ cm $= 8$ cm **85.** answers may vary **87.** 15.3 **89.** −0.2

Integrated Review **1.** 6 **2.** −17 **3.** 12 **4.** −26 **5.** −3 **6.** −1 **7.** $\frac{27}{2}$ **8.** $\frac{25}{2}$ **9.** 8 **10.** −64 **11.** 2 **12.** −3 **13.** 5 **14.** −1 **15.** 2 **16.** 2 **17.** −2 **18.** −2 **19.** $-\frac{5}{6}$ **20.** $\frac{1}{6}$ **21.** 1 **22.** 6 **23.** 4 **24.** 1 **25.** $\frac{9}{5}$ **26.** $-\frac{6}{5}$ **27.** all real numbers **28.** all real numbers **29.** 0 **30.** −1.6 **31.** $\frac{4}{19}$ **32.** $-\frac{5}{19}$ **33.** $\frac{7}{2}$ **34.** $-\frac{1}{4}$ **35.** no solution **36.** no solution **37.** $\frac{7}{6}$ **38.** $\frac{1}{15}$

Section 9.4

Vocabulary and Readiness Check **1.** $2x$; $2x-31$ **3.** $x + 5$; $2(x + 5)$ **5.** $20 - y$; $\frac{20 - y}{3}$ or $(20 - y) \div 3$

Exercise Set 9.4 **1.** $2x + 7 = x + 6$; −1 **3.** $3x - 6 = 2x + 8$; 14 **5.** −25 **7.** $-\frac{3}{4}$ **9.** 3 in.; 6 in.; 16 in. **11.** 1st piece: 5 in.; 2nd piece: 10 in.; 3rd piece: 25 in. **13.** Texas: 30 million pounds; New Mexico: 45 million pounds **15.** 172 mi **17.** 25 mi **19.** 1st angle: 37.5°; 2nd angle: 37.5°; 3rd angle: 105° **21.** A: 60°; B: 120°; C: 120°; D: 60° **23.** $3x + 3$ **25.** $x + 2$; $x + 4$; $2x + 4$ **27.** $x + 1$; $x + 2$; $x + 3$; $4x + 6$ **29.** $x + 2$; $x + 4$; $2x + 6$ **31.** 234, 235 **33.** Belgium: 32; France: 33; Spain: 34 **35.** 5 ft, 12 ft **37.** Maglev: 361 mph; TGV: 357.2 mph **39.** 43°, 137° **41.** 58°, 60°, 62° **43.** 1 **45.** 280 mi **47.** USC: 38; Penn State: 24 **49.** Montana: 56 counties; California: 58 counties **51.** Neptune: 8 moons; Uranus: 21 moons; Saturn: 18 moons **53.** −16 **55.** Sahara: 3,500,000 sq mi; Gobi: 500,000 sq mi **57.** Australia: 6; Germany: 7; Korea: 8 **59.** Chambliss: 1,220,854; Martin: 905,637 **61.** 34.5°; 34.5°; 111° **63.** Eagles: *Their Greatest Hits, 1971–1975* **65.** *Thriller*: $27 million; *The Wall*: $23 million **67.** answers may vary **69.** 34 **71.** 225π **73.** 15 ft by 24 ft **75.** 5400 chirps per hour; 129,600 chirps per day; 47,304,000 chirps per year **77.** answers may vary **79.** answers may vary **81.** c

Section 9.5

Exercise Set 9.5 **1.** $h = 3$ **3.** $h = 3$ **5.** $h = 20$ **7.** $c = 12$ **9.** $r = 2.5$ **11.** $h = \frac{f}{5g}$ **13.** $w = \frac{V}{lh}$ **15.** $y = 7 - 3x$ **17.** $R = \frac{A - P}{PT}$ **19.** $A = \frac{3V}{h}$ **21.** $a = P - b - c$ **23.** $h = \frac{S - 2\pi r^2}{2\pi r}$ **25.** 120 ft **27. a.** area: 480 sq in.; perimeter: 120 in. **b.** frame: perimeter; glass: area **29. a.** area: 103.5 sq ft; perimeter: 41 ft **b.** baseboard: perimeter; carpet: area **31.** −10°C **33.** 6.25 hr **35.** length: 78 ft; width: 52 ft **37.** 18 ft, 36 ft, 48 ft **39.** 137.5 mi **41.** 61.5°F **43.** 60 chirps per minute **45.** increases **47.** 96 piranhas **49.** 2 bags **51.** one 16-in. pizza **53.** 4.65 min **55.** 13 in. **57.** 2.25 hr **59.** 12,090 ft **61.** 50°C **63.** 515,509.5 cu in. **65.** 449 cu in. **67.** 333°F **69.** 0.32 **71.** 2.00 or 2 **73.** 17% **75.** 720% **77.** $V = G(N - R)$ **79.** multiplies the volume by 8; answers may vary **81.** $53\frac{1}{3}$ **83.** ○ = $\frac{\triangle - \square}{▮}$ **85.** 44.3 sec **87.** $P = 3{,}200{,}000$ **89.** $V = 113.1$

Section 9.6

Vocabulary and Readiness Check **1.** no **3.** yes

Exercise Set 9.6 **1.** 11.2 **3.** 55% **5.** 180 **7.** 4% **9.** 9990 **11.** discount: \$1480; new price: \$17,020 **13.** \$46.58 **15.** 50% **17.** 30% **19.** \$104 **21.** \$42,500 **23.** 2 gal **25.** 7 lb **27.** 4.6 **29.** 50 **31.** 30% **33.** 71% **35.** 181,155 **37.** 56%, 7%, 28%, 2% **39.** 75% **41.** \$3900 **43.** 300% **45.** mark-up: \$0.11; new price: \$2.31 **47.** 400 oz **49.** 52.3% **51.** 120 employees **53.** decrease: \$64; sale price: \$192 **55.** 854 thousand Scoville units **57.** 361 college students **59.** 400 oz **61.** $>$ **63.** $=$ **65.** $>$ **67.** no; answers may vary **69.** 9.6% **71.** 26.9%; yes **73.** 17.1%

Section 9.7

Vocabulary and Readiness Check **1.** expression **3.** inequality **5.** equation **7.** -5 **9.** 4.1

Exercise Set 9.7 **1.** **3.** **5.** **7.** **9.** **11.** **13.** $\{x \mid x \geq -5\}$

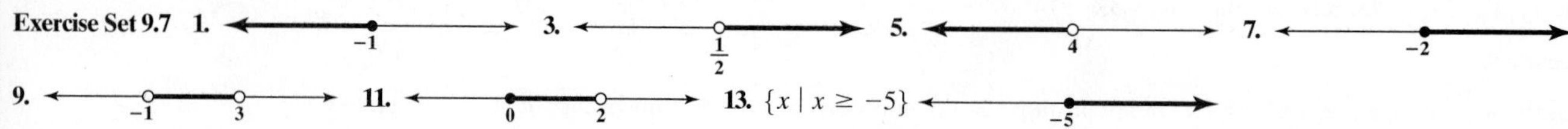

15. $\{y \mid y < 9\}$ **17.** $\{x \mid x > -3\}$ **19.** $\{x \mid x \leq 1\}$ **21.** $\{x \mid x < -3\}$ **23.** $\{x \mid x \geq -2\}$ **25.** $\{x \mid x < 0\}$ **27.** $\left\{y \middle| y \geq -\frac{8}{3}\right\}$ **29.** $\{y \mid y > 3\}$ **31.** $\{x \mid x > -15\}$ **33.** $\{x \mid x \geq -11\}$ **35.** $\left\{x \middle| x > \frac{1}{4}\right\}$ **37.** $\{y \mid y \geq -12\}$ **39.** $\{z \mid z < 0\}$ **41.** $\{x \mid x > -3\}$ **43.** $\left\{x \middle| x \geq -\frac{2}{3}\right\}$ **45.** $\{x \mid x \leq -2\}$ **47.** $\{x \mid x > -13\}$ **49.** $\{x \mid x \leq -8\}$ **51.** $\{x \mid x > 4\}$ **53.** $\left\{x \middle| x \leq \frac{5}{4}\right\}$ **55.** $\left\{x \middle| x > \frac{8}{3}\right\}$ **57.** $\{x \mid x \geq 0\}$ **59.** all numbers greater than -10 **61.** 35 cm **63.** at least 193 **65.** 86 people **67.** 35 min **69.** 81 **71.** 1 **73.** $\frac{49}{64}$ **75.** about 3200 **77.** 2006 and 2007 **79.** 2005 **81.** $>$ **83.** $\geq$ **85.** when multiplying or dividing by a negative number **87.** final exam score ≥ 78.5

Chapter 9 Vocabulary Check **1.** linear equation in one variable **2.** equivalent equations **3.** formula **4.** linear inequality in one variable **5.** all real numbers **6.** no solution **7.** the same **8.** reversed

Chapter 9 Review **1.** 4 **2.** -3 **3.** 6 **4.** -6 **5.** 0 **6.** -9 **7.** -23 **8.** 28 **9.** b **10.** a **11.** b **12.** c **13.** -12 **14.** 4 **15.** 0 **16.** -7 **17.** 0.75 **18.** -3 **19.** -6 **20.** -1 **21.** -1 **22.** $\frac{3}{2}$ **23.** $-\frac{1}{5}$ **24.** 7 **25.** $3x + 3$ **26.** $2x + 6$ **27.** -4 **28.** -4 **29.** 2 **30.** -3 **31.** no solution **32.** no solution **33.** $\frac{3}{4}$ **34.** $-\frac{8}{9}$ **35.** 20 **36.** $-\frac{6}{23}$ **37.** $\frac{23}{7}$ **38.** $-\frac{2}{5}$ **39.** 102 **40.** 0.25 **41.** 6665.5 in. **42.** short piece: 4 ft; long piece: 8 ft **43.** Harvard: 80; Cornell: 39 **44.** $-39, -38, -37$ **45.** 3 **46.** -4 **47.** $w = 9$ **48.** $h = 4$ **49.** $m = \frac{y - b}{x}$ **50.** $s = \frac{r + 5}{vt}$ **51.** $x = \frac{2y - 7}{5}$ **52.** $y = \frac{2 + 3x}{6}$ **53.** $\pi = \frac{C}{D}$ **54.** $\pi = \frac{C}{2r}$ **55.** 15 m **56.** 18 ft by 12 ft **57.** 1 hr and 20 min **58.** 40°C **59.** 20% **60.** 70% **61.** 110 **62.** 1280 **63.** mark-up: \$209; new price: \$2109 **64.** 50,844 **65.** 40% solution: 10 gal; 10% solution: 20 gal **66.** 1.9% increase **67.** 18% **68.** swerving into another lane **69.** 966 customers **70.** no; answers may vary **71.** **72.** **73.** $\{x \mid x \leq 1\}$ **74.** $\{x \mid x > -5\}$ **75.** $\{x \mid x \leq 10\}$ **76.** $\{x \mid x < -4\}$ **77.** $\{x \mid x < -4\}$ **78.** $\{x \mid x \leq 4\}$ **79.** $\{y \mid y > 9\}$ **80.** $\{y \mid y \geq -15\}$ **81.** $\left\{x \middle| x < \frac{7}{4}\right\}$ **82.** $\left\{x \middle| x \leq \frac{19}{3}\right\}$ **83.** \$2500 **84.** score must be less than 83 **85.** 4 **86.** -14 **87.** $-\frac{3}{2}$ **88.** 21 **89.** all real numbers **90.** no solution **91.** -13 **92.** shorter piece: 4 in.; longer piece: 19 in. **93.** $h = \frac{3V}{A}$ **94.** 22.1 **95.** 160 **96.** 20% **97.** $\{x \mid x > 9\}$ **98.** $\{x \mid x > -4\}$ **99.** $\{x \mid x \leq 0\}$

Chapter 9 Test **1.** -5 **2.** 8 **3.** $\frac{7}{10}$ **4.** 0 **5.** 27 **6.** $-\frac{19}{6}$ **7.** 3 **8.** $\frac{3}{11}$ **9.** 0.25 **10.** $\frac{25}{7}$ **11.** no solution **12.** 21 **13.** 7 gal **14.** $x = 6$ **15.** $h = \frac{V}{\pi r^2}$ **16.** $y = \frac{3x - 10}{4}$ **17.** $\{x \mid x \leq -2\}$ **18.** $\{x \mid x < 4\}$ **19.** $\{x \mid x \leq -8\}$ **20.** $\{x \mid x \geq 11\}$ **21.** $\left\{x \middle| x > \frac{2}{5}\right\}$ **22.** 552 **23.** 40% **24.** 401,802 **25.** New York: 754; Georgia: 58

Cumulative Review **1.** True; Sec. 8.1, Ex. 3 **2.** False **3.** True; Sec. 8.1, Ex. 4 **4.** True **5.** False; Sec. 8.1, Ex. 5 **6.** True **7.** True; Sec. 8.1, Ex. 6 **8.** True **9. a.** $<$ **b.** $=$ **c.** $>$ **d.** $<$ **e.** $>$; Sec. 8.1, Ex. 13 **10. a.** 5 **b.** 8 **c.** $\frac{2}{3}$ **11.** $\frac{8}{3}$; Sec. 8.2, Ex. 6 **12.** 33 **13.** -19; Sec. 8.3, Ex. 6 **14.** -10 **15.** 8; Sec. 8.3, Ex. 7 **16.** 10 **17.** -0.3; Sec. 8.3, Ex. 8 **18.** 0 **19. a.** -12 **b.** -3; Sec. 8.4, Ex. 7 **20. a.** 5 **b.** $\frac{2}{3}$ **c.** a **d.** -3 **21. a.** 0 **b.** -24 **c.** 90; Sec. 8.5, Ex. 7 **22. a.** -11.1 **b.** $-\frac{1}{5}$ **c.** $\frac{3}{4}$ **23. a.** -6 **b.** 7 **c.** -5; Sec. 8.5, Ex. 10 **24. a.** -0.36 **b.** $\frac{6}{17}$ **25.** $15 - 10z$; Sec. 8.6, Ex. 8 **26.** $2x^3 - 6x^2 + 8x$ **27.** $3x + 17$; Sec. 8.6, Ex. 12 **28.** $2x + 8$ **29. a.** unlike **b.** like **c.** like **d.** like **e.** like; Sec. 8.7, Ex. 2 **30. a.** -4 **b.** 9 **c.** $\frac{10}{63}$ **31.** $-2x - 1$; Sec. 8.7, Ex. 15 **32.** $-15x - 2$ **33.** 17; Sec. 9.1, Ex. 1 **34.** $-\frac{1}{6}$ **35.** -10; Sec. 9.2, Ex. 7 **36.** 3 **37.** 0; Sec. 9.3, Ex. 4

38. 72 **39.** Republicans: 178; Democrats: 256; Sec. 9.4, Ex. 4 **40.** 5 **41.** 79.2 yr; Sec. 9.5, Ex. 1 **42.** 6 **43.** 87.5%; Sec. 9.6, Ex. 1 **44.** $\frac{C}{2\pi} = r$ **45.** $-\frac{9}{10}$; Sec. 9.2, Ex. 10 **46.** $\{x \mid x > 5\}$ **47.** -1 Sec. 9.7, Ex. 2 **48.** $\{x \mid x \le -10\}$ **49.** $\{x \mid x \ge 1\}$; Sec. 9.7, Ex. 9 **50.** $\{x \mid x \le -3\}$

Chapter 10 Exponents and Polynomials

Section 10.1

Vocabulary and Readiness Check **1.** exponent **3.** add **5.** 1 **7.** exponent: 2; base: 3 **9.** exponent: 2; base: 4 **11.** exponent: 2; base: x

Exercise Set 10.1 **1.** 49 **3.** -5 **5.** -16 **7.** 16 **9.** $\frac{1}{27}$ **11.** 112 **13.** 4 **15.** 135 **17.** 150 **19.** $\frac{32}{5}$ **21.** x^7 **23.** $(-3)^{12}$ **25.** $15y^5$ **27.** $x^{19}y^6$ **29.** $-72m^3n^8$ **31.** $-24z^{20}$ **33.** $20x^5$ sq ft **35.** x^{36} **37.** p^8q^8 **39.** $8a^{15}$ **41.** $x^{10}y^{15}$ **43.** $49a^4b^{10}c^2$ **45.** $\frac{r^9}{s^9}$ **47.** $\frac{m^9p^9}{n^9}$ **49.** $\frac{4x^2z^2}{y^{10}}$ **51.** $64z^{10}$ sq dm **53.** $27y^{12}$ cu ft **55.** x^2 **57.** -64 **59.** p^6q^5 **61.** $\frac{y^3}{2}$ **63.** 1 **65.** 1 **67.** -7 **69.** 2 **71.** -81 **73.** $\frac{1}{64}$ **75.** b^6 **77.** a^9 **79.** $-16x^7$ **81.** $a^{11}b^{20}$ **83.** $26m^9n^7$ **85.** z^{40} **87.** $64a^3b^3$ **89.** $36x^2y^2z^6$ **91.** $3x$ **93.** $81x^2y^2$ **95.** 9 **97.** $\frac{y^{15}}{8x^{12}}$ **99.** $2x^2y$ **101.** 2 **103.** $\frac{x^{18}}{4y^{22}}$ **105.** $-b^5$ **107.** -2 **109.** 5 **111.** -7 **113.** c **115.** e **117.** answers may vary **119.** answers may vary **121.** 343 cu m **123.** volume **125.** answers may vary **127.** answers may vary **129.** x^{9a} **131.** a^{5b} **133.** x^{5a}

Section 10.2

Calculator Explorations **1.** 5.31 EE 3 **3.** 6.6 EE -9 **5.** 1.5×10^{13} **7.** 8.15×10^{19}

Vocabulary and Readiness Check **1.** $\frac{1}{x^3}$ **3.** scientific notation **5.** $\frac{5}{x^2}$ **7.** y^6 **9.** $4y^3$

Exercise Set 10.2 **1.** $\frac{1}{64}$ **3.** $\frac{7}{x^3}$ **5.** -64 **7.** $\frac{5}{6}$ **9.** p^3 **11.** $\frac{q^4}{p^5}$ **13.** $\frac{1}{x^3}$ **15.** z^3 **17.** $\frac{4}{9}$ **19.** $\frac{1}{9}$ **21.** $-p^4$ **23.** -2 **25.** x^4 **27.** p^4 **29.** m^{11} **31.** r^6 **33.** $\frac{1}{x^{15}y^9}$ **35.** $\frac{1}{x^4}$ **37.** $\frac{1}{a^2}$ **39.** $4k^3$ **41.** $3m$ **43.** $-\frac{4a^5}{b}$ **45.** $-\frac{6}{7y^2z^5}$ **47.** $\frac{27a^6}{b^{12}}$ **49.** $\frac{a^{30}}{b^{12}}$ **51.** $\frac{1}{x^{10}y^6}$ **53.** $\frac{z^2}{4}$ **55.** $\frac{x^{11}}{81}$ **57.** $\frac{49a^4}{b^6}$ **59.** $-\frac{3m^7}{n^4}$ **61.** $a^{24}b^8$ **63.** 200 **65.** x^9y^{19} **67.** $-\frac{y^8}{8x^2}$ **69.** $\frac{25b^{33}}{a^{16}}$ **71.** $\frac{27}{z^3x^6}$ cu in. **73.** 7.8×10^4 **75.** 1.67×10^{-6} **77.** 6.35×10^{-3} **79.** 1.16×10^6 **81.** 2.4×10^3 **83.** 0.0000000008673 **85.** 0.033 **87.** 20,320 **89.** 700,000,000 **91.** 1.84×10^{11} **93.** 155,000,000,000 **95.** 35,000 **97.** 0.000036 **99.** 0.0000000000000000028 **101.** 0.0000005 **103.** 200,000 **105.** 2.7×10^9 gal **107.** $-2x + 7$ **109.** $2y - 10$ **111.** $-x - 4$ **113.** 90,000,000; 9×10^7 **115.** 1,000,000,000; 1×10^9 **117.** 440,000,000; 4.4×10^8 **119.** no; answers may vary **121.** $9a^{13}$ **123.** -5 **125.** answers may vary **127. a.** 1.3×10^1 **b.** 4.4×10^7 **c.** 6.1×10^{-2} **129.** answers may vary **131.** $\frac{1}{x^{9s}}$ **133.** a^{4m+5}

Section 10.3

Vocabulary and Readiness Check **1.** binomial **3.** trinomial **5.** constant

Exercise Set 10.3 **1.** 1; $-3x$; 5 **3.** -5; 3.2; 1; -5 **5.** 1; binomial **7.** 3; none of these **9.** 6; trinomial **11.** 4; binomial **13. a.** -6 **b.** -11 **15. a.** -2 **b.** 4 **17. a.** -15 **b.** -10 **19.** 184 ft **21.** 595.84 ft **23.** 164 thousand **25.** 371.95 million wireless subscribers **27.** $-11x$ **29.** $23x^3$ **31.** $16x^2 - 7$ **33.** $12x^2 - 13$ **35.** $7s$ **37.** $-1.1y^2 + 4.8$ **39.** $\frac{5}{6}x^4 - 7x^3 - 19$ **41.** $\frac{3}{20}x^3 + 6x^2 - \frac{13}{20}x - \frac{1}{10}$ **43.** $4x^2 + 7x + x^2 + 5x$; $5x^2 + 12x$ **45.** $5x + 3 + 4x + 3 + 2x + 6 + 3x + 7x$; $21x + 12$ **47.** 2, 1, 1, 0; 2 **49.** 4, 0, 4, 3; 4 **51.** $9ab - 11a$ **53.** $4x^2 - 7xy + 3y^2$ **55.** $-3xy^2 + 4$ **57.** $14y^3 - 19 - 16a^2b^2$ **59.** $7x^2 + 0x + 3$ **61.** $x^3 + 0x^2 + 0x - 64$ **63.** $5y^3 + 0y^2 + 2y - 10$ **65.** $2y^4 + 0y^3 + 0y^2 + 8y + 0y^0$ or $2y^4 + 0y^3 + 0y^2 + 8y + 0$ **67.** $6x^5 + 0x^4 + x^3 + 0x^2 - 3x + 15$ **69.** $10x + 19$ **71.** $-x + 5$ **73.** answers may vary **75.** answers may vary **77.** x^{13} **79.** a^3b^{10} **81.** $2y^{20}$ **83.** answers may vary **85.** answers may vary **87.** $11.1x^2 - 7.97x + 10.76$

Section 10.4

Vocabulary and Readiness Check **1.** $-14y$ **3.** $7x$ **5.** $5m^2 + 2m$

Exercise Set 10.4 **1.** $12x + 12$ **3.** $-3x^2 + 10$ **5.** $-3x^2 + 4$ **7.** $-y^2 - 3y - 1$ **9.** $7.9x^3 + 4.4x^2 - 3.4x - 3$ **11.** $\frac{1}{2}m^2 - \frac{7}{10}m + \frac{13}{16}$ **13.** $8t^2 - 4$ **15.** $15a^3 + a^2 - 3a + 16$ **17.** $-x + 14$ **19.** $5x^2 + 2y^2$ **21.** $-2x + 9$ **23.** $2x^2 + 7x - 16$ **25.** $2x^2 + 11x$ **27.** $-0.2x^2 + 0.2x - 2.2$ **29.** $\frac{2}{5}z^2 - \frac{3}{10}z + \frac{7}{20}$ **31.** $-2z^2 - 16z + 6$ **33.** $2u^5 - 10u^2 + 11u - 9$ **35.** $5x - 9$ **37.** $4x - 3$ **39.** $11y + 7$ **41.** $-2x^2 + 8x - 1$ **43.** $14x + 18$ **45.** $3a^2 - 6a + 11$ **47.** $3x - 3$ **49.** $7x^2 - 4x + 2$ **51.** $7x^2 - 2x + 2$ **53.** $4y^2 + 12y + 19$ **55.** $-15x + 7$ **57.** $-2a - b + 1$ **59.** $3x^2 + 5$ **61.** $6x^2 - 2xy + 19y^2$ **63.** $8r^2s + 16rs - 8 + 7r^2s^2$ **65.** $(x^2 + 7x + 4)$ ft **67.** $\left(\frac{19}{2}x + 3\right)$ units **69.** $(3y^2 + 4y + 11)$ m **71.** $-6.6x^2 - 1.8x - 1.8$ **73.** $6x^2$ **75.** $-12x^8$ **77.** $200x^3y^2$ **79.** 2; 2 **81.** 4; 3; 3; 4 **83.** b **85.** e **87. a.** $4z$ **b.** $3z^2$ **c.** $-4z$ **d.** $3z^2$; answers may vary **89. a.** m^3 **b.** $3m$ **c.** $-m^3$ **d.** $-3m$; answers may vary **91.** $874x^2 + 66x + 25{,}376$

Section 10.5

Vocabulary and Readiness Check **1.** distributive **3.** $(5y-1)(5y-1)$ **5.** x^8 **7.** cannot simplify **9.** x^{14} **11.** $2x^7$ **13.** $99y^4$ **15.** $20y^2$

Exercise Set 10.5 **1.** $24x^3$ **3.** x^4 **5.** $-28n^{10}$ **7.** $-12.4x^{12}$ **9.** $-\frac{2}{15}y^3$ **11.** $-24x^8$ **13.** $6x^2+15x$ **15.** $7x^3+14x^2-7x$ **17.** $-2a^2-8a$ **19.** $6x^3-9x^2+12x$ **21.** $12a^5+45a^2$ **23.** $-6a^4+4a^3-6a^2$ **25.** $6x^5y-3x^4y^3+24x^2y^4$ **27.** $-4x^3y+7x^2y^2-xy^3-3y^4$ **29.** $4x^4-3x^3+\frac{1}{2}x^2$ **31.** $x^2+7x+12$ **33.** $a^2+5a-14$ **35.** $x^2+\frac{1}{3}x-\frac{2}{9}$ **37.** $12x^4+25x^2+7$ **39.** $12x^2-29x+15$ **41.** $1-7a+12a^2$ **43.** $4y^2-16y+16$ **45.** $x^3-5x^2+13x-14$ **47.** $x^4+5x^3-3x^2-11x+20$ **49.** $10a^3-27a^2+26a-12$ **51.** $49x^2y^2-14xy^2+y^2$ **53.** $12x^2-64x-11$ **55.** $2x^3+10x^2+11x-3$ **57.** $2x^4+3x^3-58x^2+4x+63$ **59.** $8.4y^7$ **61.** $-3x^3-6x^2+24x$ **63.** $2x^2+39x+19$ **65.** $x^2-\frac{2}{7}x-\frac{3}{49}$ **67.** $9y^2+30y+25$ **69.** $a^3-2a^2-18a+24$ **71.** $(4x^2-25)$ sq yd **73.** $(6x^2-4x)$ sq in. **75.** $5a+15a=20a$; $5a-15a=-10a$; $5a\cdot 15a=75a^2$; $\frac{5a}{15a}=\frac{1}{3}$ **77.** $-3y^5+9y^4$, cannot be simplified; $-3y^5-9y^4$, cannot be simplified; $-3y^5\cdot 9y^4=-27y^9$; $\frac{-3y^5}{9y^4}=-\frac{y}{3}$ **79. a.** $6x+12$ **b.** $9x^2+36x+35$; answers may vary **81.** $13x-7$ **83.** $30x^2-28x+6$ **85.** $-7x+5$ **87.** x^2+3x **89.** $x+2x^2$; $x(1+2x)$ **91.** $11a$ **93.** $25x^2+4y^2$ **95. a.** a^2-b^2 **b.** $4x^2-9y^2$ **c.** $16x^2-49$ **d.** answers may vary

Section 10.6

Vocabulary and Readiness Check **1.** false **3.** false

Exercise Set 10.6 **1.** $x^2+7x+12$ **3.** $x^2+5x-50$ **5.** $5x^2+4x-12$ **7.** $4y^2-25y+6$ **9.** $6x^2+13x-5$ **11.** $6y^3+4y^2+42y+28$ **13.** $x^2+\frac{1}{3}x-\frac{2}{9}$ **15.** $0.08-2.6a+15a^2$ **17.** $2x^2+9xy-5y^2$ **19.** x^2+4x+4 **21.** $4a^2-12a+9$ **23.** $9a^2-30a+25$ **25.** $x^4+x^2+0.25$ **27.** $y^2-\frac{4}{7}y+\frac{4}{49}$ **29.** $4x^2-4x+1$ **31.** $25x^2+90x+81$ **33.** $9x^2-42xy+49y^2$ **35.** $16m^2+40mn+25n^2$ **37.** $25x^8-30x^4+9$ **39.** a^2-49 **41.** x^2-36 **43.** $9x^2-1$ **45.** x^4-25 **47.** $4y^4-1$ **49.** $16-49x^2$ **51.** $9x^2-\frac{1}{4}$ **53.** $81x^2-y^2$ **55.** $4m^2-25n^2$ **57.** $a^2+9a+20$ **59.** $a^2-14a+49$ **61.** $12a^2-a-1$ **63.** x^2-4 **65.** $9a^2+6a+1$ **67.** $4x^2+3xy-y^2$ **69.** $\frac{1}{9}a^4-49$ **71.** $6b^2-b-35$ **73.** x^4-100 **75.** $16x^2-25$ **77.** $25x^2-60xy+36y^2$ **79.** $4r^2-9s^2$ **81.** $(4x^2+4x+1)$ sq ft **83.** $\frac{5b^5}{7}$ **85.** $-\frac{2a^{10}}{b^5}$ **87.** $\frac{2y^8}{3}$ **89.** c **91.** d **93.** 2 **95.** (x^4-3x^2+1) sq m **97.** $(24x^2-32x+8)$ sq m **99.** answers may vary **101.** answers may vary

Integrated Review **1.** $35x^5$ **2.** $-32y^9$ **3.** -16 **4.** 16 **5.** $2x^2-9x-5$ **6.** $3x^2+13x-10$ **7.** $3x-4$ **8.** $4x+3$ **9.** $7x^6y^2$ **10.** $\frac{10b^6}{7}$ **11.** $144m^{14}n^{12}$ **12.** $64y^{27}z^{30}$ **13.** $16y^2-9$ **14.** $49x^2-1$ **15.** $\frac{y^{45}}{x^{63}}$ **16.** $\frac{1}{64}$ **17.** $\frac{x^{27}}{27}$ **18.** $\frac{r^{58}}{16s^{14}}$ **19.** $2x^2-2x-6$ **20.** $6x^2+13x-11$ **21.** $2.5y^2-6y-0.2$ **22.** $8.4x^2-6.8x-4.2$ **23.** $2y^2-6y-1$ **24.** $6z^2+2z+\frac{11}{2}$ **25.** $x^2+8x+16$ **26.** $y^2-18y+81$ **27.** $2x+8$ **28.** $2y-18$ **29.** $7x^2-10xy+4y^2$ **30.** $-a^2-3ab+6b^2$ **31.** $x^3+2x^2-16x+3$ **32.** x^3-2x^2-5x-2 **33.** $6x^2-x-70$ **34.** $20x^2+21x-5$ **35.** $2x^3-19x^2+44x-7$ **36.** $5x^3+9x^2-17x+3$ **37.** $4x^2-\frac{25}{81}$ **38.** $144y^2-\frac{9}{49}$

Section 10.7

Vocabulary and Readiness Check **1.** dividend; quotient; divisor **3.** a^2 **5.** y

Exercise Set 10.7 **1.** $12x^3+3x$ **3.** $4x^3-6x^2+x+1$ **5.** $5p^2+6p$ **7.** $-\frac{3}{2x}+3$ **9.** $-3x^2+x-\frac{4}{x^3}$ **11.** $-1+\frac{3}{2x}-\frac{7}{4x^4}$ **13.** $x+1$ **15.** $2x+3$ **17.** $2x+1+\frac{7}{x-4}$ **19.** $3a^2-3a+1+\frac{2}{3a+2}$ **21.** $4x+3-\frac{2}{2x+1}$ **23.** $2x^2+6x-5-\frac{2}{x-2}$ **25.** $x+6$ **27.** x^2+3x+9 **29.** $-3x+6-\frac{11}{x+2}$ **31.** $2b-1-\frac{6}{2b-1}$ **33.** $ab-b^2$ **35.** $4x+9$ **37.** $x+4xy-\frac{y}{2}$ **39.** $2b^2+b+2-\frac{12}{b+4}$ **41.** $y^2+5y+10+\frac{24}{y-2}$ **43.** $-6x-12-\frac{19}{x-2}$ **45.** x^3-x^2+x **47.** 3 **49.** -4 **51.** $3x$ **53.** $9x$ **55.** $(3x^3+x-4)$ ft **57.** $(2x+5)$ m **59.** answers may vary **61.** c

Chapter 10 Vocabulary Check **1.** term **2.** FOIL **3.** trinomial **4.** degree of a polynomial **5.** binomial **6.** coefficient **7.** degree of a term **8.** monomial **9.** polynomials **10.** distributive

Chapter 10 Review **1.** base: 3; exponent: 2 **2.** base: -5; exponent: 4 **3.** base: 5; exponent: 4 **4.** base: x; exponent: 6 **5.** 512 **6.** 36 **7.** -36 **8.** -65 **9.** 1 **10.** 1 **11.** y^9 **12.** x^{14} **13.** $-6x^{11}$ **14.** $-20y^7$ **15.** x^8 **16.** y^{15} **17.** $81y^{24}$ **18.** $8x^9$ **19.** x^5 **20.** z^7 **21.** $\frac{x^3y^4}{4}$ **22.** $\frac{x^6y^6}{4}$ **23.** $40a^{19}$ **24.** $36x^3$ **25.** $-a^9$ **26.** $-x^7$ **27.** 3 **28.** 9 **29.** b **30.** c **31.** $\frac{1}{49}$ **32.** $-\frac{1}{49}$ **33.** $\frac{2}{x^4}$ **34.** $\frac{1}{16x^4}$ **35.** 125 **36.** $\frac{9}{4}$ **37.** $\frac{17}{16}$ **38.** $\frac{1}{42}$ **39.** r **40.** y^3 **41.** c^4 **42.** $\frac{x^3}{y^3}$ **43.** $\frac{a^2}{5b^7c^3}$ **44.** $\frac{b^3}{5a^6c^7}$ **45.** $\frac{9}{x^6y^{13}}$ **46.** $\frac{3a^{10}}{b^{10}}$ **47.** 2.7×10^{-4} **48.** 8.868×10^{-1} **49.** 8.08×10^7

50. 8.68×10^5 **51.** 1.27×10^8 **52.** 1.5×10^5 **53.** 867,000 **54.** 0.00386 **55.** 0.00086 **56.** 893,600 **57.** 1,431,280,000,000,000 **58.** 0.0000000001 **59.** 0.016 **60.** 400,000,000,000 **61.** 5 **62.** 2 **63.** 5 **64.** 6 **65.** 4000 ft; 3984 ft; 3856 ft; 3600 ft **66.** 22; 78; 154.02; 400 **67.** $2a^2$ **68.** $-4y$ **69.** $15a^2 + 4a$ **70.** $22x^2 + 3x + 6$ **71.** $-6a^2b - 3b^2 - q^2$ **72.** cannot be combined **73.** $8x^2 + 3x + 6$ **74.** $2x^5 + 3x^4 + 4x^3 + 9x^2 + 7x + 6$ **75.** $-7y^2 - 1$ **76.** $-6m^7 - 3x^4 + 7m^6 - 4m^2$ **77.** $-x^2 - 6xy - 2y^2$ **78.** $x^6 + 4xy + 2y^2$ **79.** $-5x^2 + 5x + 1$ **80.** $-2x^2 - x + 20$ **81.** $6x + 30$ **82.** $9x - 63$ **83.** $8a + 28$ **84.** $54a - 27$ **85.** $-7x^3 - 35x$ **86.** $-32y^3 + 48y$ **87.** $-2x^3 + 18x^2 - 2x$ **88.** $-3a^3b - 3a^2b - 3ab^2$ **89.** $-6a^4 + 8a^2 - 2a$ **90.** $42b^4 - 28b^2 + 14b$ **91.** $2x^2 - 12x - 14$ **92.** $6x^2 - 11x - 10$ **93.** $4a^2 + 27a - 7$ **94.** $42a^2 + 11a - 3$ **95.** $x^4 + 7x^3 + 4x^2 + 23x - 35$ **96.** $x^6 + 2x^5 + x^2 + 3x + 2$ **97.** $x^4 + 4x^3 + 4x^2 - 16$ **98.** $x^6 + 8x^4 + 16x^2 - 16$ **99.** $x^3 + 21x^2 + 147x + 343$ **100.** $8x^3 - 60x^2 + 150x - 125$ **101.** $x^2 + 14x + 49$ **102.** $x^2 - 10x + 25$ **103.** $9x^2 - 42x + 49$ **104.** $16x^2 + 16x + 4$ **105.** $25x^2 - 90x + 81$ **106.** $25x^2 - 1$ **107.** $49x^2 - 16$ **108.** $a^2 - 4b^2$ **109.** $4x^2 - 36$ **110.** $16a^4 - 4b^2$ **111.** $(9x^2 - 6x + 1)$ sq m **112.** $(5x^2 - 3x - 2)$ sq mi **113.** $\frac{1}{7} + \frac{3}{x} + \frac{7}{x^2}$ **114.** $-a^2 + 3b - 4$ **115.** $a + 1 + \frac{6}{a - 2}$ **116.** $4x + \frac{7}{x + 5}$ **117.** $a^2 + 3a + 8 + \frac{22}{a - 2}$ **118.** $3b^2 - 4b - \frac{1}{3b - 2}$ **119.** $2x^3 - x^2 + 2 - \frac{1}{2x - 1}$ **120.** $-x^2 - 16x - 117 - \frac{684}{x - 6}$ **121.** $\left(5x - 1 + \frac{20}{x^2}\right)$ ft **122.** $(7a^3b^6 + a - 1)$ units **123.** 27 **124.** $-\frac{1}{8}$ **125.** $4x^4y^7$ **126.** $\frac{2x^6}{3}$ **127.** $\frac{27a^{12}}{b^6}$ **128.** $\frac{x^{16}}{16y^{12}}$ **129.** $9a^2b^8$ **130.** $2y^2 - 10$ **131.** $11x - 5$ **132.** $5x^2 + 3x - 2$ **133.** $5y^2 - 3y - 1$ **134.** $6x^2 + 11x - 10$ **135.** $28x^3 + 12x$ **136.** $28x^2 - 71x + 18$ **137.** $x^3 + x^2 - 18x + 18$ **138.** $25x^2 + 40x + 16$ **139.** $36x^2 - 9$ **140.** $4a - 1 + \frac{2}{a^2} - \frac{5}{2a^3}$ **141.** $x - 3 + \frac{25}{x + 5}$ **142.** $2x^2 + 7x + 5 + \frac{19}{2x - 3}$

Chapter 10 Test **1.** 32 **2.** 81 **3.** -81 **4.** $\frac{1}{64}$ **5.** $-15x^{11}$ **6.** y^5 **7.** $\frac{1}{r^5}$ **8.** $\frac{16y^{14}}{x^2}$ **9.** $\frac{1}{6xy^8}$ **10.** 5.63×10^5 **11.** 8.63×10^{-5} **12.** 0.0015 **13.** 62,300 **14.** 0.036 **15. a.** 4, 3; 7, 3; 1, 4; −2, 0 **b.** 4 **16.** $-2x^2 + 12x + 11$ **17.** $16x^3 + 7x^2 - 3x - 13$ **18.** $-3x^3 + 5x^2 + 4x + 5$ **19.** $x^3 + 8x^2 + 3x - 5$ **20.** $3x^3 + 22x^2 + 41x + 14$ **21.** $6x^4 - 9x^3 + 21x^2$ **22.** $3x^2 + 16x - 35$ **23.** $9x^2 - \frac{1}{25}$ **24.** $16x^2 - 16x + 4$ **25.** $64x^2 + 48x + 9$ **26.** $x^4 - 81b^2$ **27.** 1001 ft; 985 ft; 857 ft; 601 ft **28.** $(4x^2 - 9)$ sq in. **29.** $\frac{x}{2y} + \frac{1}{4} - \frac{7}{8y}$ **30.** $x + 2$ **31.** $9x^2 - 6x + 4 - \frac{16}{3x + 2}$

Cumulative Review **1. a.** 11, 112 **b.** 0, 11, 112 **c.** −3, −2, 0, 11, 112 **d.** $-3, -2, 0, \frac{1}{4}, 11, 112$ **e.** $\sqrt{2}$ **f.** $-2, 0, \frac{1}{4}, 112, -3, 11, \sqrt{2}$; Sec. 8.1, Ex. 11 **2. a.** 7.2 **b.** 0 **c.** $\frac{1}{2}$ **3. a.** 9 **b.** 125 **c.** 16 **d.** 7 **e.** $\frac{9}{49}$ **f.** 0.36; Sec. 8.2, Ex. 1 **4. a.** $\frac{1}{4}$ **b.** $2\frac{5}{12}$ **5.** $\frac{1}{4}$; Sec. 8.2, Ex. 4 **6.** $\frac{3}{25}$ **7. a.** $x + 3$ **b.** $3x$ **c.** $7.3 \div x$ or $\frac{7.3}{x}$ **d.** $10 - x$ **e.** $5x + 7$; Sec. 8.2, Ex. 9 **8.** 41 **9.** 6.7; Sec. 8.3, Ex. 10 **10.** no **11. a.** $\frac{1}{2}$ **b.** 9; Sec. 8.4, Ex. 8 **12. a.** −33 **b.** 5 **13.** 3; Sec. 8.5, Ex. 11a **14.** −8 **15.** −70; Sec. 8.5, Ex. 11d **16.** 150 **17.** $15x + 10$; Sec. 8.7, Ex. 8 **18.** $-6x + 9$ **19.** $-2y - 0.6z + 2$; Sec. 8.7, Ex. 9 **20.** $-4x^3 + 24x - 4x$ **21.** $-9x - y + 2z - 6$; Sec. 8.7, Ex. 10 **22.** $4xy - 6y + 2$ **23.** $a = 19$; Sec. 9.1, Ex. 6 **24.** $x = -\frac{1}{2}$ **25.** $y = 140$; Sec. 9.2, Ex. 4 **26.** $j = \frac{12}{5}$ **27.** $x = 4$; Sec. 9.3, Ex. 5 **28.** $x = 1$ **29.** 10; Sec. 9.4, Ex. 2 **30.** $(x + 7) - 2x$ or $-x + 7$ **31.** 40 ft; Sec. 9.5, Ex. 2 **32.** undefined **33.** 800; Sec. 9.6, Ex. 2 **34.** 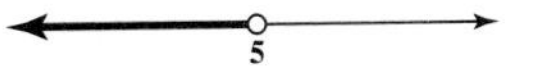

35. 

$\{x \mid x \leq 4\}$; Sec. 9.7, Ex. 7 **36. a.** 25 **b.** −25 **c.** 50 **37. a.** x^{11} **b.** $\frac{t^4}{16}$ **c.** $81y^{10}$; Sec. 10.1, Ex. 33 **38.** z^4 **39.** $\frac{b^3}{27a^6}$; Sec. 10.2, Ex. 10 **40.** $-15x^{16}$ **41.** $\frac{1}{25y^6}$; Sec. 10.2, Ex. 13 **42.** $\frac{1}{9}$ **43.** $10x^3$; Sec. 10.3, Ex. 8 **44.** $4y^2 - 8$ **45.** $5x^2 - 3x - 3$; Sec. 10.3, Ex. 9 **46.** $100x^4 - 9$ **47.** $7x^3 + 14x^2 + 35x$; Sec. 10.5, Ex. 4 **48.** $100x^4 + 60x^2 + 9$ **49.** $3x^3 - 4 + \frac{1}{x}$; Sec. 10.7. Ex. 2

Chapter 11 Factoring Polynomials

Section 11.1

Vocabulary and Readiness Check **1.** factors **3.** least **5.** false **7.** $2 \cdot 7$ **9.** 3 **11.** 5

Exercise Set 11.1 **1.** 4 **3.** 6 **5.** 1 **7.** y^2 **9.** z^7 **11.** xy^2 **13.** 7 **15.** $4y^3$ **17.** $5x^2$ **19.** $3x^3$ **21.** $9x^2y$ **23.** $10a^6b$ **25.** $3(a + 2)$ **27.** $15(2x - 1)$ **29.** $x^2(x + 5)$ **31.** $2y^3(3y + 1)$ **33.** $2x(16y - 9x)$ **35.** $4(x - 2y + 1)$ **37.** $3x(2x^2 - 3x + 4)$ **39.** $a^2b^2(a^5b^4 - a + b^3 - 1)$ **41.** $5xy(x^2 - 3x + 2)$ **43.** $4(2x^5 + 4x^4 - 5x^3 + 3)$ **45.** $\frac{1}{3}x(x^3 + 2x^2 - 4x^4 + 1)$ **47.** $(x^2 + 2)(y + 3)$ **49.** $(y + 4)(z + 3)$ **51.** $(z^2 - 6)(r + 1)$ **53.** $-1(x + 7)$ **55.** $-1(2 - z)$ **57.** $-1(-3a + b - 2)$ **59.** $(x + 2)(x^2 + 5)$ **61.** $(x + 3)(5 + y)$ **63.** $(3x - 2)(2x^2 + 5)$ **65.** $(5m^2 + 6n)(m + 1)$ **67.** $(y - 4)(2 + x)$ **69.** $(2x + 1)(x^2 + 4)$ **71.** not factorable by grouping **73.** $(x - 2y)(4x - 3)$ **75.** $(5q - 4p)(q - 1)$ **77.** $2(2y - 7)(3x^2 - 1)$ **79.** $3(2a + 3b^2)(a + b)$ **81.** $x^2 + 7x + 10$ **83.** $b^2 - 3b - 4$ **85.** 2, 6 **87.** −1, −8 **89.** −2, 5 **91.** −8, 3 **93.** d **95.** factored **97.** not factored **99. a.** 22,752 thousand bales **b.** 18,960 thousand bales **c.** $-1264(x^2 - 4x - 15)$ or $1264(-x^2 + 4x + 15)$ **101.** $4x^2 - \pi x^2$; $x^2(4 - \pi)$ **103.** $(x^3 - 1)$ units **105.** answers may vary **107.** answers may vary

Section 11.2

Vocabulary and Readiness Check **1.** true **3.** false **5.** $+5$ **7.** -3 **9.** $+2$

Exercise Set 11.2 **1.** $(x+6)(x+1)$ **3.** $(y-9)(y-1)$ **5.** $(x-3)(x-3)$ or $(x-3)^2$ **7.** $(x-6)(x+3)$ **9.** $(x+10)(x-7)$ **11.** prime **13.** $(x+5y)(x+3y)$ **15.** $(a^2-5)(a^2+3)$ **17.** $(m+13)(m+1)$ **19.** $(t-2)(t+12)$ **21.** $(a-2b)(a-8b)$ **23.** $2(z+8)(z+2)$ **25.** $2x(x-5)(x-4)$ **27.** $(x-4y)(x+y)$ **29.** $(x+12)(x+3)$ **31.** $(x-2)(x+1)$ **33.** $(r-12)(r-4)$ **35.** $(x+2y)(x-y)$ **37.** $3(x+5)(x-2)$ **39.** $3(x-18)(x-2)$ **41.** $(x-24)(x+6)$ **43.** prime **45.** $(x-5)(x-3)$ **47.** $6x(x+4)(x+5)$ **49.** $4y(x^2+x-3)$ **51.** $(x-7)(x+3)$ **53.** $(x+5y)(x+2y)$ **55.** $2(t+8)(t+4)$ **57.** $x(x-6)(x+4)$ **59.** $2t^3(t-4)(t-3)$ **61.** $5xy(x-8y)(x+3y)$ **63.** $3(m-9)(m-6)$ **65.** $-1(x-11)(x-1)$ **67.** $\frac{1}{2}(y-11)(y+2)$ **69.** $x(xy-4)(xy+5)$ **71.** $2x^2+11x+5$ **73.** $15y^2-17y+4$ **75.** $9a^2+23ab-12b^2$ **77.** $x^2+5x-24$ **79.** answers may vary **81.** $2x^2+28x+66$; $2(x+3)(x+11)$ **83.** $-16(t-5)(t+1)$ **85.** $\left(x+\frac{1}{4}\right)\left(x+\frac{1}{4}\right)$ or $\left(x+\frac{1}{4}\right)^2$ **87.** $(x+1)(z-10)(z+7)$ **89.** 15; 28; 39; 48; 55; 60; 63; 64 **91.** 9; 12; 21 **93.** $(x^n+10)(x^n-2)$

Section 11.3

Vocabulary and Readiness Check **1.** d **3.** c

Exercise Set 11.3 **1.** $x+4$ **3.** $10x-1$ **5.** $4x-3$ **7.** $(2x+3)(x+5)$ **9.** $(y-1)(8y-9)$ **11.** $(2x+1)(x-5)$ **13.** $(4r-1)(5r+8)$ **15.** $(10x+1)(x+3)$ **17.** $(3x-2)(x+1)$ **19.** $(3x-5y)(2x-y)$ **21.** $(3m-5)(5m+3)$ **23.** $(x-4)(x-5)$ **25.** $(2x+11)(x-9)$ **27.** $(7t+1)(t-4)$ **29.** $(3a+b)(a+3b)$ **31.** $(7p+1)(7p-2)$ **33.** $(6x-7)(3x+2)$ **35.** prime **37.** $(8x+3)(3x+4)$ **39.** $x(3x+2)(4x+1)$ **41.** $3(7b+5)(b-3)$ **43.** $(3z+4)(4z-3)$ **45.** $2y^2(3x-10)(x+3)$ **47.** $(2x-7)(2x+3)$ **49.** $3(x^2-14x+21)$ **51.** $(4x+9y)(2x-3y)$ **53.** $-1(x-6)(x+4)$ **55.** $x(4x+3)(x-3)$ **57.** $(4x-9)(6x-1)$ **59.** $b(8a-3)(5a+3)$ **61.** $2x(3x+2)(5x+3)$ **63.** $2y(3y+5)(y-3)$ **65.** $5x^2(2x-y)(x+3y)$ **67.** $-1(2x-5)(7x-2)$ **69.** $p^2(4p-5)(4p-5)$ or $p^2(4p-5)^2$ **71.** $-1(2x+1)(x-5)$ **73.** $-4(12x-1)(x-1)$ **75.** $(2t^2+9)(t^2-3)$ **77.** prime **79.** $a(6a^2+b^2)(a^2+6b^2)$ **81.** x^2-16 **83.** x^2+4x+4 **85.** $4x^2-4x+1$ **87.** no **89.** $4x^2+21x+5$; $(4x+1)(x+5)$ **91.** $\left(2x+\frac{1}{2}\right)\left(2x+\frac{1}{2}\right)$ or $\left(2x+\frac{1}{2}\right)^2$ **93.** $(y-1)^2(4x+5)(x+5)$ **95.** 2; 14 **97.** 2 **99.** answers may vary

Section 11.4

Vocabulary and Readiness Check **1.** a **3.** b

Exercise Set 11.4 **1.** $(x+3)(x+2)$ **3.** $(y+8)(y-2)$ **5.** $(8x-5)(x-3)$ **7.** $(5x^2-3)(x^2+5)$ **9. a.** 9, 2 **b.** $9x+2x$ **c.** $(2x+3)(3x+1)$ **11. a.** $-20, -3$ **b.** $-20x-3x$ **c.** $(3x-4)(5x-1)$ **13.** $(3y+2)(7y+1)$ **15.** $(7x-11)(x+1)$ **17.** $(5x-2)(2x-1)$ **19.** $(2x-5)(x-1)$ **21.** $(2x+3)(2x+3)$ or $(2x+3)^2$ **23.** $(2x+3)(2x-7)$ **25.** $(5x-4)(2x-3)$ **27.** $x(2x+3)(x+5)$ **29.** $2(8y-9)(y-1)$ **31.** $(2x-3)(3x-2)$ **33.** $3(3a+2)(6a-5)$ **35.** $a(4a+1)(5a+8)$ **37.** $3x(4x+3)(x-3)$ **39.** $y(3x+y)(x+y)$ **41.** prime **43.** $6(a+b)(4a-5b)$ **45.** $p^2(15p+q)(p+2q)$ **47.** $(7+x)(5+x)$ or $(x+7)(x+5)$ **49.** $(6-5x)(1-x)$ or $(5x-6)(x-1)$ **51.** x^2-4 **53.** $y^2+8y+16$ **55.** $81z^2-25$ **57.** $16x^2-24x+9$ **59.** $10x^2+45x+45$; $5(2x+3)(x+3)$ **61.** $(x^n+2)(x^n+3)$ **63.** $(3x^n-5)(x^n+7)$ **65.** answers may vary

Section 11.5

Calculator Explorations

	x^2-2x+1	x^2-2x-1	$(x-1)^2$
$x=5$	16	14	16
$x=-3$	16	14	16
$x=2.7$	2.89	0.89	2.89
$x=-12.1$	171.61	169.61	171.61
$x=0$	1	-1	1

Vocabulary and Readiness Check **1.** 1^2 **3.** 9^2 **5.** 3^2 **7.** $(3x)^2$ **9.** $(5a)^2$ **11.** $(6p^2)^2$

Exercise Set 11.5 **1.** yes **3.** no **5.** no **7.** yes **9.** yes **11.** $(x+11)^2$ **13.** $(x-8)^2$ **15.** $(4a-3)^2$ **17.** $3(x-4)^2$ **19.** $(xy-5)^2$ **21.** $m(m+9)^2$ **23.** prime **25.** $(3x-4y)^2$ **27.** $(x^2+2)^2$ **29.** $(x+5)(x-5)$ **31.** $(3+2z)(3-2z)$ **33.** prime **35.** $xy(x+11y)(x-11y)$ **37.** $(y+9)(y-5)$ **39.** $4(4x+5)(4x-5)$ **41.** $2y(3x+1)(3x-1)$ **43.** $(3x+7)(3x-7)$ **45.** $(x^2+9)(x+3)(x-3)$ **47.** $(x+2y+3)(x+2y-3)$ **49.** $(x+8+x^2)(x+8-x^2)$ **51.** $(x-5+y)(x-5-y)$ **53.** $(2x+1+z)(2x+1-z)$ **55.** $(m^2+1)(m+1)(m-1)$ **57.** $(x+3)(x^2-3x+9)$ **59.** $(z-1)(z^2+z+1)$ **61.** $(m+n)(m^2-mn+n^2)$ **63.** $y^2(x-3)(x^2+3x+9)$ **65.** $b(a+2b)(a^2-2ab+4b^2)$ **67.** $(5y-2x)(25y^2+10xy+4x^2)$ **69.** $(x^2-y)(x^4+x^2y+y^2)$ **71.** $(2x+3y)(4x^2-6xy+9y^2)$ **73.** $(x-1)(x^2+x+1)$ **75.** $(x+5)(x^2-5x+25)$ **77.** $3y^2(x^2+3)(x^4-3x^2+9)$ **79.** 5 **81.** $-\frac{1}{3}$ **83.** 0 **85.** 5 **87.** $\left(x-\frac{1}{3}\right)^2$ **89.** $(x+2+y)(x+2-y)$ **91.** $(b-4)(a+4)(a-4)$ **93.** $(x+3+2y)(x+3-2y)$ **95.** $(x^n+10)(x^n-10)$ **97.** 8 **99.** answers may vary **101.** $(x+6)$ **103.** $a^2+2ab+b^2$ **105. a.** 2560 ft **b.** 1920 ft **c.** 13 sec **d.** $16(13-t)(13+t)$ **107. a.** 1456 feet **b.** 816 feet **c.** 10 seconds **d.** $16(10+t)(10-t)$

Integrated Review **1.** $(x-3)(x+4)$ **2.** $(x-8)(x-2)$ **3.** $(x+2)(x-3)$ **4.** $(x+1)^2$ **5.** $(x-3)^2$ **6.** $(x+2)(x-1)$ **7.** $(x+3)(x-2)$ **8.** $(x+3)(x+4)$ **9.** $(x-5)(x-2)$ **10.** $(x-6)(x+5)$ **11.** $2(x+7)(x-7)$ **12.** $3(x+5)(x-5)$ **13.** $(x+3)(x+5)$ **14.** $(y-7)(3+x)$ **15.** $(x+8)(x-2)$ **16.** $(x-7)(x+4)$ **17.** $4x(x+7)(x-2)$ **18.** $6x(x-5)(x+4)$ **19.** $2(3x+4)(2x+3)$ **20.** $(2a-b)(4a+5b)$ **21.** $(2a+b)(2a-b)$ **22.** $(x+5y)(x-5y)$ **23.** $(4-3x)(7+2x)$ **24.** $(5-2x)(4+x)$ **25.** prime **26.** prime **27.** $(3y+5)(2y-3)$ **28.** $(4x-5)(x+1)$ **29.** $9x(2x^2-7x+1)$ **30.** $4a(3a^2-6a+1)$ **31.** $(4a-7)^2$ **32.** $(5p-7)^2$ **33.** $(7-x)(2+x)$ **34.** $(3+x)(1-x)$ **35.** $3x^2y(x+6)(x-4)$ **36.** $2xy(x+5y)(x-y)$ **37.** $3xy(4x^2+81)$ **38.** $2xy^2(3x^2+4)$ **39.** $2xy(1+6x)(1-6x)$ **40.** $2x(x+3)(x-3)$ **41.** $(x+6)(x+2)(x-2)$ **42.** $(x-2)(x+6)(x-6)$ **43.** $2a^2(3a+5)$ **44.** $2n(2n-3)$ **45.** $(3x-1)(x^2+4)$ **46.** $(x-2)(x^2+3)$ **47.** $6(x+2y)(x+y)$ **48.** $2(x+4y)(6x-y)$ **49.** $(x+y)(5+x)$ **50.** $(x-y)(7+y)$ **51.** $(7t-1)(2t-1)$ **52.** prime **53.** $(3x+5)(x-1)$ **54.** $(7x-2)(x+3)$ **55.** $(1-10a)(1+2a)$ **56.** $(1+5a)(1-12a)$ **57.** $(x+3)(x-3)(x+1)(x-1)$ **58.** $(x+3)(x-3)(x+2)(x-2)$ **59.** $(x-15)(x-8)$ **60.** $(y+16)(y+6)$ **61.** prime **62.** $(4a-7b)^2$ **63.** $(5p-7q)^2$ **64.** $(7x+3y)(x+3y)$ **65.** $-1(x-5)(x+6)$ **66.** $-1(x-2)(x-4)$ **67.** $(3r-1)(s+4)$ **68.** $(x-2)(x^2+1)$ **69.** $(x-2y)(4x-3)$ **70.** $(2x-y)(2x+7z)$ **71.** $(x+12y)(x-3y)$ **72.** $(3x-2y)(x+4y)$ **73.** $(x^2+2)(x+4)(x-4)$ **74.** $(x^2+3)(x+5)(x-5)$ **75.** $x(x-1)(x^2+x+1)$ **76.** $x^3(x+1)(x^2-x+1)$ **77.** $(2x+5y)(4x^2-10xy+25y^2)$ **78.** $(3x-4y)(9x^2+12xy+16y^2)$ **79.** answers may vary **80.** yes; $9(x^2+9y^2)$

Section 11.6

Vocabulary and Readiness Check **1.** quadratic **3.** $3, -5$

Exercise Set 11.6 **1.** $2, -1$ **3.** $6, 7$ **5.** $-9, -17$ **7.** $0, -6$ **9.** $0, 8$ **11.** $-\frac{3}{2}, \frac{5}{4}$ **13.** $\frac{7}{2}, -\frac{2}{7}$ **15.** $\frac{1}{2}, -\frac{1}{3}$ **17.** $-0.2, -1.5$ **19.** $9, 4$ **21.** $-4, 2$ **23.** $0, 7$ **25.** $0, -20$ **27.** $4, -4$ **29.** $8, -4$ **31.** $-3, 12$ **33.** $\frac{7}{3}, -2$ **35.** $\frac{8}{3}, -9$ **37.** $0, -\frac{1}{2}, \frac{1}{2}$ **39.** $\frac{17}{2}$ **41.** $\frac{3}{4}$ **43.** $-\frac{1}{2}, \frac{1}{2}$ **45.** $-\frac{3}{2}, -\frac{1}{2}, 3$ **47.** $-5, 3$ **49.** $-\frac{5}{6}, \frac{6}{5}$ **51.** $2, -\frac{4}{5}$ **53.** $-\frac{4}{3}, 5$ **55.** $-4, 3$ **57.** $0, 8, 4$ **59.** -7 **61.** $0, \frac{3}{2}$ **63.** $0, 1, -1$ **65.** $-6, \frac{4}{3}$ **67.** $\frac{6}{7}, 1$ **69.** $\frac{47}{45}$ **71.** $\frac{17}{60}$ **73.** $\frac{7}{10}$ **75.** didn't write equation in standard form; should be $x = 4$ or $x = -2$ **77.** answers may vary, for example, $(x-6)(x+1) = 0$ **79.** answers may vary, for example, $x^2 - 12x + 35 = 0$ **81. a.** 300; 304; 276; 216; 124; 0; −156 **b.** 5 sec **c.** 304 ft **83.** $0, \frac{1}{2}$ **85.** $0, -15$

Section 11.7

Exercise Set 11.7 **1.** width: x; length: $x + 4$ **3.** x and $x + 2$ if x is an odd integer **5.** base: x; height: $4x + 1$ **7.** 11 units **9.** 15 cm, 13 cm, 22 cm, 70 cm **11.** base: 16 mi; height: 6 mi **13.** 5 sec **15.** width: 5 cm; length: 6 cm **17.** 54 diagonals **19.** 10 sides **21.** −12 or 11 **23.** 14, 15 **25.** 13 feet **27.** 5 in. **29.** 12 mm, 16 mm, 20 mm **31.** 10 km **33.** 36 ft **35.** 9.5 sec **37.** 20% **39.** length: 15 mi; width: 8 mi **41.** 105 units **43.** 1.9 million or 1,900,000 **45.** 1.9 million or 1,900,000 **47.** 2003 **49.** answers may vary **51.** 8 m **53.** 10 and 15 **55.** width of pool: 29 m; length of pool: 35 m

Chapter 11 Vocabulary Check **1.** quadratic equation **2.** Factoring **3.** greatest common factor **4.** perfect square trinomial **5.** hypotenuse **6.** leg **7.** hypotenuse

Chapter 11 Review **1.** $2x-5$ **2.** $2x^4+1-5x^3$ **3.** $5(m+6)$ **4.** $4x(5x^2+3x+6)$ **5.** $(2x+3)(3x-5)$ **6.** $(x+1)(5x-1)$ **7.** $(x-1)(3x+2)$ **8.** $(a+3b)(3a+b)$ **9.** $(2a+b)(5a+7b)$ **10.** $(3x+5)(2x-1)$ **11.** $(x+4)(x+2)$ **12.** $(x-8)(x-3)$ **13.** prime **14.** $(x-6)(x+1)$ **15.** $(x+4)(x-2)$ **16.** $(x+6y)(x-2y)$ **17.** $(x+5y)(x+3y)$ **18.** $2(3-x)(12+x)$ **19.** $4(8+3x-x^2)$ **20.** $5y(y-6)(y-4)$ **21.** $-48, 2$ **22.** factor out the GCF, 3 **23.** $(2x+1)(x+6)$ **24.** $(2x+3)(2x-1)$ **25.** $(3x+4y)(2x-y)$ **26.** prime **27.** $(2x+3)(x-13)$ **28.** $(6x+5y)(3x-4y)$ **29.** $5y(2y-3)(y+4)$ **30.** $3y(4y-1)(5y-2)$ **31.** $5x^2-9x-2$; $(5x+1)(x-2)$ **32.** $16x^2-28x+6$; $2(4x-1)(2x-3)$ **33.** $(x+9)(x-9)$ **34.** $(x+6)^2$ **35.** $(2x+3)(2x-3)$ **36.** $(3t+5s)(3t-5s)$ **37.** prime **38.** $(n-9)^2$ **39.** $3(r+6)^2$ **40.** $(3y-7)^2$ **41.** $5m^6(m+1)(m-1)$ **42.** $(2x-7y)^2$ **43.** $3y(x+y)^2$ **44.** $(4x^2+1)(2x+1)(2x-1)$ **45.** $(y+7)(y-3)$ **46.** $(x+1)(x-7)$ **47.** $(2-3y)(4+6y+9y^2)$ **48.** $(1-4y)(1+4y+16y^2)$ **49.** $6xy(x+2)(x^2-2x+4)$ **50.** $2x^2(x+2y)(x^2-2xy+4y^2)$ **51.** $(x-1+y)(x-1-y)$ **52.** $\pi h(R+r)(R-r)$ cu units **53.** $-6, 2$ **54.** $-11, 7$ **55.** $0, -1, \frac{2}{7}$ **56.** $-\frac{1}{5}, -3$ **57.** $-7, -1$ **58.** $-4, 6$ **59.** -5 **60.** $2, 8$ **61.** $\frac{1}{3}$ **62.** $-\frac{2}{7}, \frac{3}{8}$ **63.** $0, 6$ **64.** $5, -5$ **65.** $x^2-9x+20=0$ **66.** $x^2+2x+1=0$ **67.** c **68.** d **69.** 9 units **70.** 8 units, 13 units, 16 units, 10 units **71.** width: 20 in.; length: 25 in. **72.** 36 yd **73.** 19 and 20 **74.** 20 and 22 **75. a.** 17.5 sec and 10 sec; answers may vary **b.** 27.5 sec **76.** 32 cm **77.** $6(x+4)$ **78.** $7(x-9)$ **79.** $(4x-3)(11x-6)$ **80.** $(x-5)(2x-1)$ **81.** $(3x-4)(x^2+2)$ **82.** $(y+2)(x-1)$ **83.** $2(x+4)(x-3)$ **84.** $3x(x-9)(x-1)$ **85.** $(2x+9)(2x-9)$ **86.** $2(x+3)(x-3)$ **87.** $(4x-3)^2$ **88.** $5(x+2)^2$ **89.** $-\frac{7}{2}, 4$ **90.** $-3, 5$ **91.** $0, -7, -4$ **92.** $3, 2$ **93.** $0, 16$ **94.** 19 in.; 8 in.; 21 in. **95.** length: 6 in.; width: 2 in.

Chapter 11 Test **1.** $3x(3x-1)$ **2.** $(x+7)(x+4)$ **3.** $(7+m)(7-m)$ **4.** $(y+11)^2$ **5.** $(x^2+4)(x+2)(x-2)$ **6.** $(a+3)(4-y)$ **7.** prime **8.** $(y-12)(y+4)$ **9.** $(a+b)(3a-7)$ **10.** $(3x-2)(x-1)$ **11.** $5(6+x)(6-x)$ **12.** $3x(3x+1)(x+4)$ **13.** $(6t+5)(t-1)$ **14.** $(x-7)(y-2)(y+2)$ **15.** $x(1+x^2)(1+x)(1-x)$ **16.** $(x+12y)(x+2y)$ **17.** $(x+4)(x^2-4x+16)$ **18.** $3x(3y-z)(9y^2+3yz+z^2)$ **19.** $3, -9$ **20.** $-7, 2$ **21.** $-7, 1$ **22.** $0, \frac{3}{2}, -\frac{4}{3}$ **23.** $-3, 5$ **24.** $0, -4$ **25.** $0, 3, -3$ **26.** $-\frac{2}{3}, 1$ **27.** 17 ft **28.** 7 sec **29.** width: 6 units; length: 9 units **30.** hypotenuse: 25 cm; legs: 15 cm, 20 cm **31.** 8.25 sec

Cumulative Review **1. a.** $9 \le 11$ **b.** $8 > 1$ **c.** $3 \ne 4$; Sec. 8.1, Ex. 7 **2. a.** $>$ **b.** $<$; Sec. 8.1 **3.** solution; Sec. 8.2, Ex. 8 **4.** 102; Sec. 8.2 **5.** −12; Sec. 8.4, Ex. 5a **6.** −102; Sec. 8.5 **7. a.** $\frac{3}{4}$ **b.** −24 **c.** 1; Sec. 8.5, Ex. 16 **8.** −98; Sec. 8.5 **9.** $5x+7$; Sec. 8.7, Ex. 4 **10.** $19-6x$; Sec. 8.7 **11.** $-4a-1$; Sec. 8.7, Ex. 5 **12.** $-13x-21$; Sec. 8.7 **13.** $7.3x-6$; Sec. 8.7, Ex. 7 **14.** 2; Sec. 9.3 **15.** −11; Sec. 9.3, Ex. 3 **16.** 28; Sec. 9.2 **17.** every real number; Sec. 9.3, Ex. 7 **18.** 33; Sec. 9.2 **19.** $l = \frac{V}{wh}$; Sec. 9.5, Ex. 5 **20.** $y = \frac{-3x-7}{2}$ or $y = -\frac{3}{2}x - \frac{7}{2}$; Sec. 9.5

21. 5^{18}; Sec. 12.1, Ex. 16 **22.** 30; Sec. 12.1 **23.** y^{16}; Sec. 12.1, Ex. 17 **24.** y^{10}; Sec. 12.1 **25.** $16x^6$; Sec. 12.2, Ex. 9 **26.** $\frac{1}{9}$; Sec. 12.2 **27.** $\frac{y^{18}}{z^{36}}$; Sec. 5.2, Ex. 11 **28.** x^4; Sec. 12.2 **29.** $\frac{1}{x^{19}}$; Sec. 12.2, Ex. 12 **30.** $25a^9$; Sec. 12.2 **31.** $4x$; Sec. 12.3, Ex. 6 **32.** $\frac{5}{6}x - 77$; Sec. 12.3 **33.** $13x^2 - 2$; Sec. 12.3, Ex. 7 **34.** $-0.5x + 1.2$; Sec. 12.3 **35.** $4x^2 - 4xy + y^2$; Sec. 12.5, Ex. 8 **36.** $9x^2 - 42xy + 49y^2$; Sec. 12.5 **37.** $t^2 + 4t + 4$; Sec. 12.6, Ex. 5 **38.** $x^2 - 26x + 169$; Sec. 12.6 **39.** $x^4 - 14x^2y + 49y^2$; Sec. 12.6, Ex. 8 **40.** $49x^2 + 14xy + y^2$; Sec. 12.6 **41.** $2xy - 4 + \frac{1}{2y}$; Sec. 12.7, Ex. 3 **42.** $(z^2 + 7)(z + 1)$; Sec. 13.1 **43.** $(x + 3)(5 + y)$; Sec. 13.1, Ex. 9 **44.** $2x(x + 7)(x - 6)$; Sec. 13.2 **45.** $(x^2 + 2)(x^2 + 3)$; Sec. 13.2, Ex. 7 **46.** $(-4x + 1)(x + 6)$ or $-1(4x - 1)(x + 6)$; Sec. 13.3 **47.** $2(x - 2)(3x + 5)$; Sec. 13.4, Ex. 2 **48.** $x(3y + 4)(3y - 4)$; Sec. 13.5 **49.** $(-a - 2)(a^2 - 2a + 4)$ **50.** $(x - 6y)(x^2 + 6xy + 36y^2)$ **51.** $(2x + 3)(4x^2 - 6x + 9)$ **52.** 3 sec; Sec. 13.7, Ex. 1 **53.** 9, 4

Chapter 12 Rational Expressions

Section 12.1

Vocabulary and Readiness Check **1.** rational expression **3.** -1 **5.** 2 **7.** $\frac{-a}{b}$; $\frac{a}{-b}$ **9.** yes **11.** no

Exercise Set 12.1 **1.** $\frac{7}{4}$ **3.** $-\frac{8}{3}$ **5.** $-\frac{11}{2}$ **7. a.** \$403 **b.** \$7 **c.** decrease; answers may vary **9.** $x = 0$ **11.** $x = -2$ **13.** $x = \frac{5}{2}$ **15.** $x = 0, x = -2$ **17.** none **19.** $x = 6, x = -1$ **21.** $x = -2, x = -\frac{7}{3}$ **23.** 1 **25.** -1 **27.** $\frac{1}{4(x + 2)}$ **29.** $\frac{1}{x + 2}$ **31.** can't simplify **33.** -5 **35.** $\frac{7}{x}$ **37.** $\frac{1}{x - 9}$ **39.** $5x + 1$ **41.** $\frac{x^2}{x - 2}$ **43.** $7x$ **45.** $\frac{x + 5}{x - 5}$ **47.** $\frac{x + 2}{x + 4}$ **49.** $\frac{x + 2}{2}$ **51.** $-(x + 2)$ **53.** $\frac{x + 1}{x - 1}$ **55.** $x + y$ **57.** $\frac{5 - y}{2}$ **59.** $\frac{2y + 5}{3y + 4}$ **61.** $\frac{-(x - 10)}{x + 8}$; $\frac{-x + 10}{x + 8}$; $\frac{x - 10}{-(x + 8)}$; $\frac{x - 10}{-x - 8}$ **63.** $\frac{-(5y - 3)}{y - 12}$; $\frac{-5y + 3}{y - 12}$; $\frac{5y - 3}{-(y - 12)}$; $\frac{5y - 3}{-y + 12}$ **65.** correct **67.** correct **69.** $\frac{3}{11}$ **71.** $\frac{4}{3}$ **73.** $\frac{117}{40}$ **75.** correct **77.** incorrect; $\frac{1 + 2}{1 + 3} = \frac{3}{4}$ **79.** answers may vary **81.** answers may vary **83.** 400 mg **85.** $C = 78.125$; medium **87.** 65.3%

Section 12.2

Vocabulary and Readiness Check **1.** reciprocals **3.** $\frac{a \cdot d}{b \cdot c}$ **5.** $\frac{6}{7}$

Exercise Set 12.2 **1.** $\frac{21}{4y}$ **3.** x^4 **5.** $-\frac{b^2}{6}$ **7.** $\frac{x^2}{10}$ **9.** $\frac{1}{3}$ **11.** $\frac{m + n}{m - n}$ **13.** $\frac{x + 5}{x}$ **15.** $\frac{(x + 2)(x - 3)}{(x - 4)(x + 4)}$ **17.** $\frac{2x^4}{3}$ **19.** $\frac{12}{y^6}$ **21.** $x(x + 4)$ **23.** $\frac{3(x + 1)}{x^3(x - 1)}$ **25.** $m^2 - n^2$ **27.** $-\frac{x + 2}{x - 3}$ **29.** $\frac{x + 2}{x - 3}$ **31.** $\frac{5}{6}$ **33.** $\frac{3x}{8}$ **35.** $\frac{3}{2}$ **37.** $\frac{3x + 4y}{2(x + 2y)}$ **39.** $\frac{2(x + 2)}{x - 2}$ **41.** $-\frac{y(x + 2)}{4}$ **43.** $\frac{(a + 5)(a + 3)}{(a + 2)(a + 1)}$ **45.** $\frac{5}{x}$ **47.** $\frac{2(n - 8)}{3n - 1}$ **49.** 1440 **51.** 5 **53.** 81 **55.** 73 **57.** 56.7 **59.** 1,201,500 sq ft **61.** 244.9 miles/hour **63.** 1 **65.** $-\frac{10}{9}$ **67.** $-\frac{1}{5}$ **69.** true **71.** false; $\frac{x^2 + 3x}{20}$ **73.** $\frac{2}{9(x - 5)}$ sq ft **75.** $\frac{x}{2}$ **77.** $\frac{5a(2a + b)(3a - 2b)}{b^2(a - b)(a + 2b)}$ **79.** answers may vary **81.** 1510 euros

Chapter 12 Vocabulary Check **1.** rational expression **2.** $\frac{-a}{b}$; $\frac{a}{-b}$ **3.** denominator **4.** simplifying **5.** reciprocals **6.** unit

Chapter 12 Review **1.** $x = 2, x = -2$ **2.** $x = \frac{5}{2}, x = -\frac{3}{2}$ **3.** $\frac{4}{3}$ **4.** $\frac{11}{12}$ **5.** $\frac{2}{x}$ **6.** $\frac{3}{x}$ **7.** $\frac{1}{x - 5}$ **8.** $\frac{1}{x + 1}$ **9.** $\frac{x(x - 2)}{x + 1}$ **10.** $\frac{5(x - 5)}{x - 3}$ **11.** $\frac{x - 3}{x - 5}$ **12.** $\frac{x}{x + 4}$ **13.** $\frac{x + a}{x - c}$ **14.** $\frac{x + 5}{x - 3}$ **15.** $\frac{3x^2}{y}$ **16.** $-\frac{9x^2}{8}$ **17.** $\frac{x - 3}{x + 2}$ **18.** $-\frac{2x(2x + 5)}{(x - 6)^2}$ **19.** $\frac{x + 3}{x - 4}$ **20.** $\frac{4x}{3y}$ **21.** $(x - 6)(x - 3)$ **22.** $\frac{2}{3}$ **23.** $\frac{1}{2}$ **24.** $\frac{3(x + 2)}{3x + y}$ **25.** $\frac{1}{2x}$ **26.** $\frac{x(x - 3)}{x + 7}$ **27.** $\frac{x - 4}{x + 4}$ **28.** $\frac{(x - 9)(x + 8)}{(x + 5)(x + 9)}$

Chapter 12 Test **1.** $x = -1, x = -3$ **2. a.** \$115 **b.** \$103 **3.** $\frac{3}{5}$ **4.** $\frac{1}{x + 6}$ **5.** -1 **6.** $-\frac{1}{x + y}$ **7.** $\frac{2m(m + 2)}{m - 2}$ **8.** $\frac{a + 2}{a + 5}$ **9.** $\frac{(x - 6)(x - 7)}{(x + 7)(x + 2)}$ **10.** 15 **11.** $\frac{y - 2}{4}$

Cumulative Review **1. a.** $\frac{15}{x} = 4$ **b.** $12 - 3 = x$ **c.** $4x + 17 = 21$; Sec. 1.3, Ex. 10 **2. a.** $12 - x = -45$ **b.** $12x = -45$ **c.** $x - 10 = 2x$ **3. a.** -12 **b.** -9; Sec. 8.3, Ex. 12 **4. a.** -8 **b.** -17 **5.** distributive property; Sec. 8.6, Ex. 15 **6.** commutative property of addition **7.** associative property of addition; Sec. 8.6, Ex. 16 **8.** associative property of multiplication **9.** $x = -4$; Sec. 9.1, Ex. 7 **10.** $x = 0$ **11.** shorter piece, 2 ft; longer piece, 8 ft; Sec. 9.4, Ex. 3 **12.** 190, 192 **13.** $\frac{y - b}{m} = x$; Sec. 9.5, Ex. 6 **14.** $x = \frac{2y + 6}{3}$ **15.** $x \leq -10$; 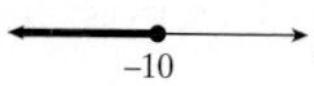

; Sec. 9.7, Ex. 4

16. $\{x \mid x < -1\}$ **17.** x^3; Sec. 10.1, Ex. 24 **18.** 1 **19.** 256; Sec. 10.1, Ex. 25 **20.** $x^{15}y^6$ **21.** -27; Sec. 10.1, Ex. 26 **22.** $x^{18}y^4$ **23.** $2x^4y$; Sec. 10.1, Ex. 27 **24.** $-15a^5b^2$ **25.** $\frac{2}{x^3}$; Sec. 10.2, Ex. 2 **26.** $\frac{1}{49}$ **27.** $\frac{1}{16}$; Sec. 10.2, Ex. 4 **28.** $\frac{5}{z^7}$ **29.** $10x^4 + 30x$; Sec. 10.5, Ex. 5 **30.** $x^2 + 18x + 81$ **31.** $-15x^4 - 18x^3 + 3x^2$; Sec. 10.5, Ex. 6 **32.** $4x^2 - 1$ **33.** $4x^2 - 4x + 6 - \frac{11}{2x+3}$; Sec. 10.7, Ex. 7 **34.** $4x^2 + 16x + 55 + \frac{222}{x-4}$ **35.** $(x + 3)(x + 4)$; Sec. 11.2, Ex. 1 **36.** $-2(a + 1)(a - 6)$ **37.** $(5x + 2y)^2$; Sec. 11.5, Ex. 5 **38.** $(x + 2)(x - 2)$ **39.** $x = 11, x = -2$; Sec. 11.6, Ex. 4 **40.** $-2, \frac{1}{3}$ **41.** $\frac{2}{5}$; Sec. 12.2, Ex. 2 **42.** $\frac{x+5}{2x^3}$ **43.** $(1 - a)(1 + a + a^2)$ **44.** $7x^4(x^2 - x + 1)$ **45.** $(x - 4)(x^2 + 4x + 16)$ **46.** $(2x + 3)^2$ **47.** $x(2x + 1)(4x^2 - 2x + 1)$ **48.** $\frac{30}{x+3}$

Chapter 13 Graphing Equations and Inequalities

Section 13.1

Vocabulary and Readiness Check **1.** x-axis **3.** origin **5.** x-coordinate; y-coordinate **7.** solution

Exercise Set 13.1 **1.** France **3.** France, U.S., Spain, China **5.** 43 million **7.** 71,000 **9.** 2005; 78,100 **11.** 50 **13.** from 1984 to 1986 **15.** 1994 **17.**

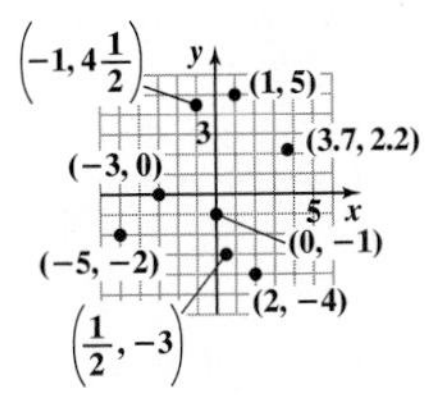

(1, 5) and (3.7, 2.2) are in quadrant I, $\left(-1, 4\frac{1}{2}\right)$ is in quadrant II, $(-5, -2)$ is in quadrant III, $(2, -4)$ and $\left(\frac{1}{2}, -3\right)$ are in quadrant IV, $(-3, 0)$ lies on the x-axis, $(0, -1)$ lies on the y-axis **19.** (0, 0) **21.** (3, 2) **23.** $(-2, -2)$ **25.** $(2, -1)$ **27.** $(0, -3)$ **29.** (1, 3) **31.** $(-3, -1)$ **33. a.** (2003, 9.17), (2004, 9.22), (2005, 8.83), (2006, 9.14), (2007, 9.63), (2008, 9.79) **b.** In the year 2006, the domestic box office was $9.14 billion.

c.

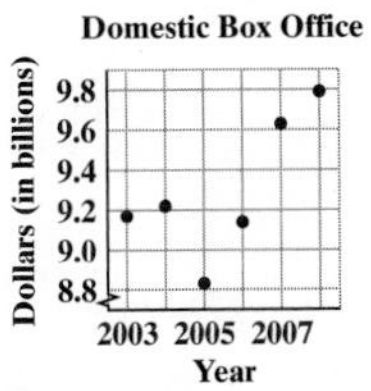

d. answers may vary

35. a. (0.50, 10), (0.75, 12), (1.00, 15), (1.25, 16), (1.50, 18), (1.50, 19), (1.75, 19), (2.00, 20) **b.** When Minh studied 1.25 hours, her quiz score was 16. **c.**

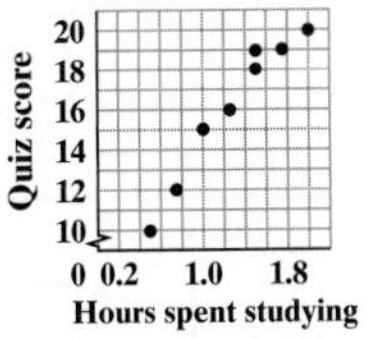

d. answers may vary **37.** $(-4, -2), (4, 0)$ **39.** $(-8, -5), (16, 1)$ **41.** $0; 7; -\frac{2}{7}$ **43.** 2; 2; 5 **45.** $0; -3; 2$ **47.** 2; 6; 3 **49.** $-12; 5; -6$ **51.** $\frac{5}{7}; \frac{5}{2}; -1$ **53.** $0; -5; -2$ **55.** $2; 1; -6$

57. a. 13,000; 21,000; 29,000 **b.** 45 desks **59. a.** 5.59; 5.99; 6.39 **b.** 2005 **c.** 2013 **61.** $y = 5 - x$ **63.** $y = \frac{5 - 2x}{4}$ **65.** $y = -2x$ **67.** false **69.** true **71.** negative; negative **73.** positive; negative **75.** 0; 0 **77.** y **79.** no; answers may vary **81.** answers may vary **83.** answers may vary **85.** $(4, -7)$ **87.** 26 units **89.** $47 billion; $53 billion; $59 billion; $63 billion

Section 13.2

Calculator Explorations **1.**

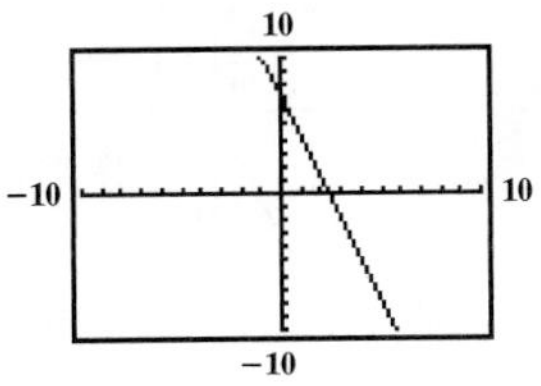

3.

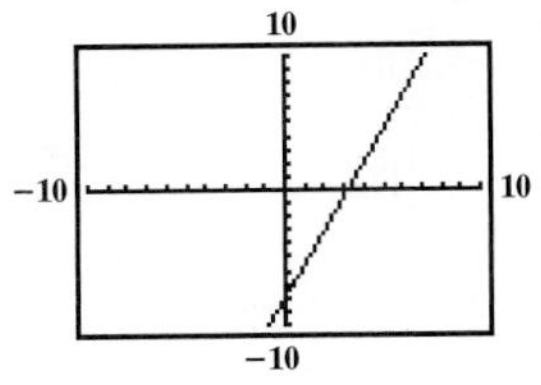

5.

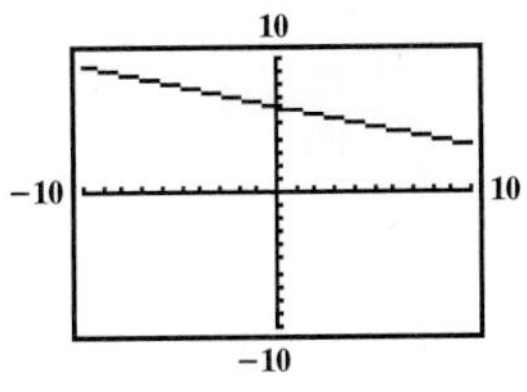

Exercise Set 13.2 **1.** $6; -2; 5$

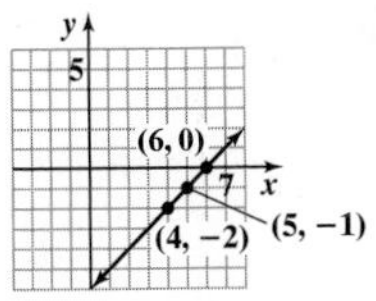

3. $-4; 0; 4$

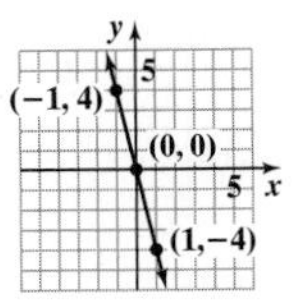

5. $0; 2; -1$

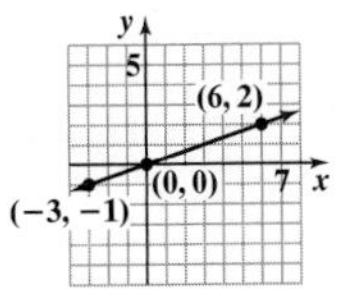

7. $3; -1; -5$

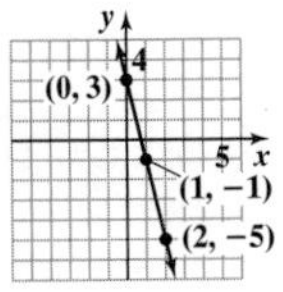

9. 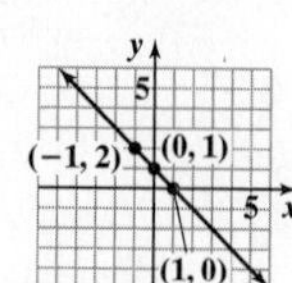

11. 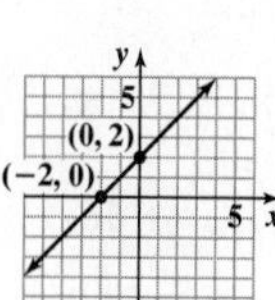

13. 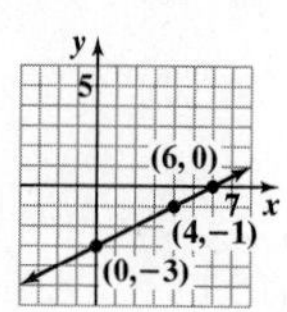

15. 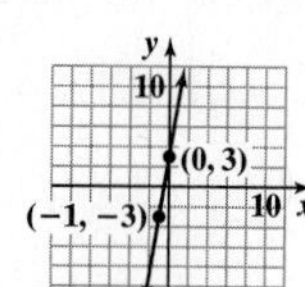

17. 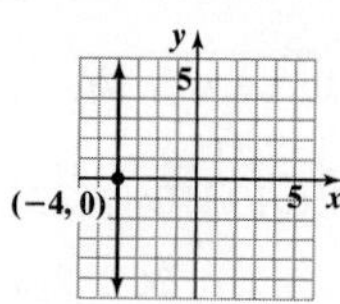

19. 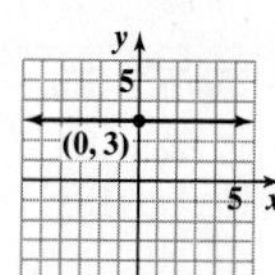

21. 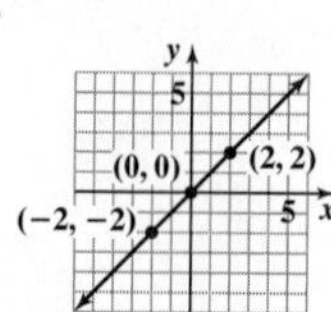

23. 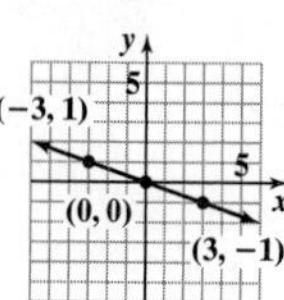

25. 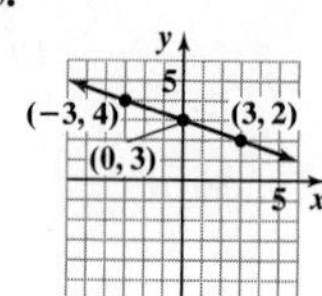

27. 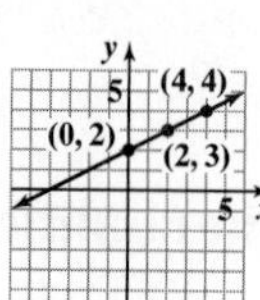

29. 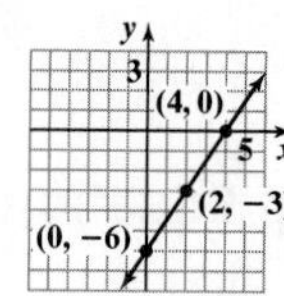

31. 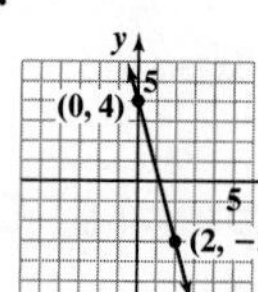

33. a. 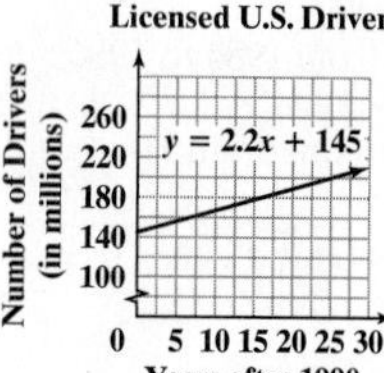

b. yes; answers may vary **35. a.** 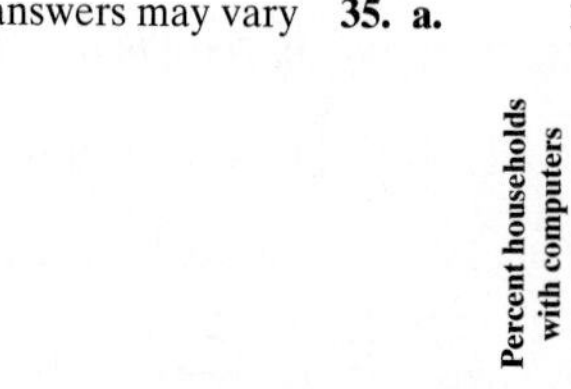

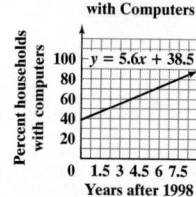

b. $(5, 66.5)$
c. In 2003, 66.5% of American households had at least one computer.

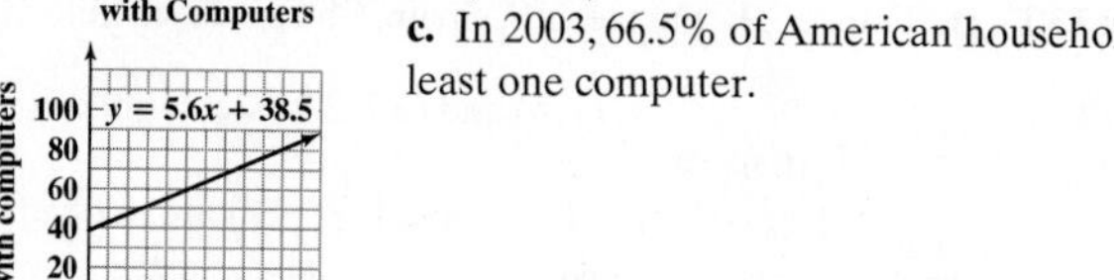

37. $(4, -1)$ **39.** $3; -3$ **41.** $0; 0$ **43.** 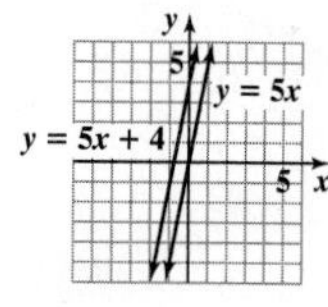

45. 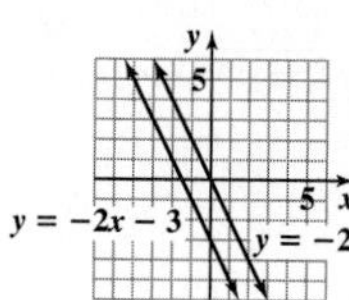

47. $0; 1; 1; 4; 4$ 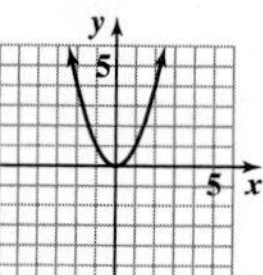

49. $x + y = 12$; 9 cm **51.** yes; answers may vary

Section 13.3

Calculator Explorations **1.** 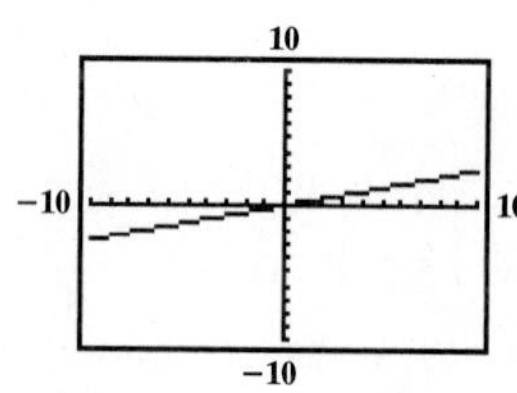 **3.** 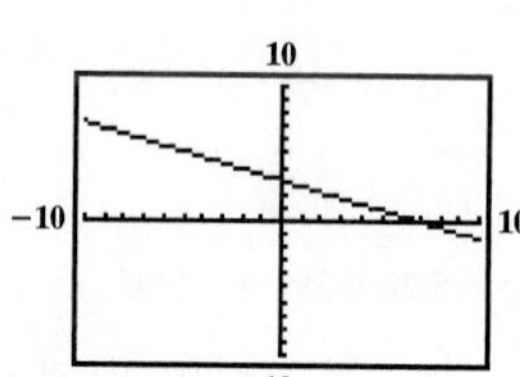 **5.** 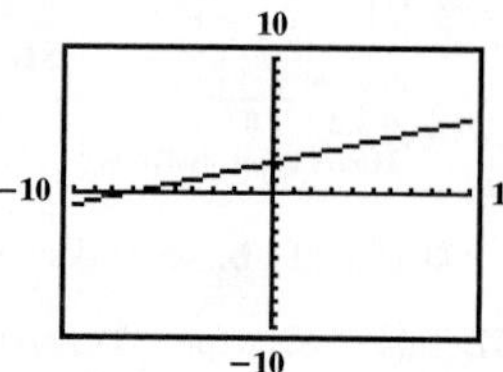

Vocabulary and Readiness Check **1.** linear **3.** horizontal **5.** y-intercept **7.** $y; x$ **9.** false **11.** true

Exercise Set 13.3 **1.** $(-1, 0); (0, 1)$ **3.** $(-2, 0); (2, 0); (0, -2)$ **5.** $(-2, 0); (1, 0); (3, 0); (0, 3)$ **7.** $(-1, 0); (1, 0); (0, 1); (0, -2)$

9. 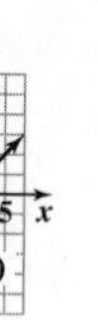

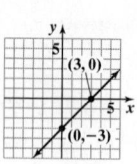

11. 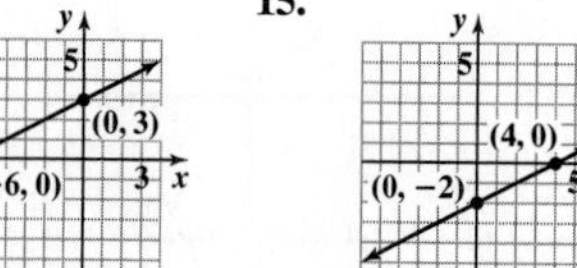

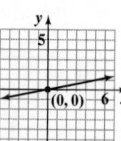

13. 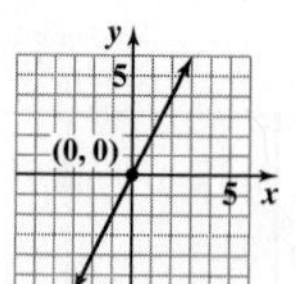

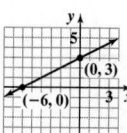

15. 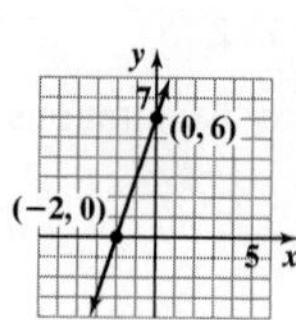

17. (0, 0)
19. (0, 6) (−2, 0)

21. 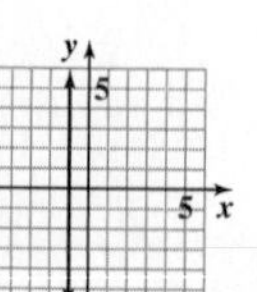
23. 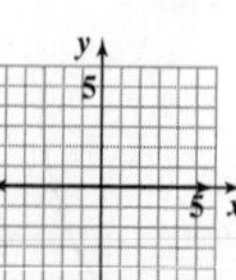
25. 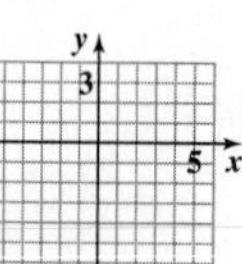
27. 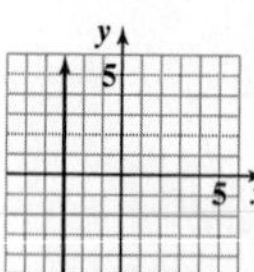
29. 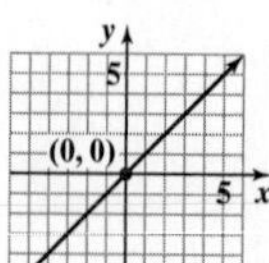

31. 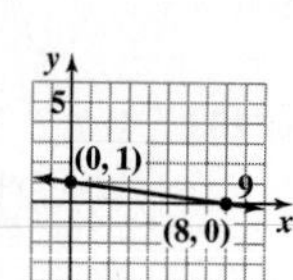

33. 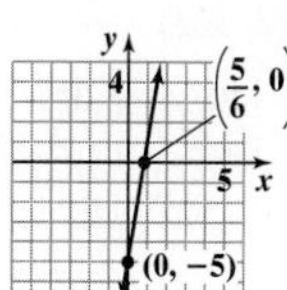

35. 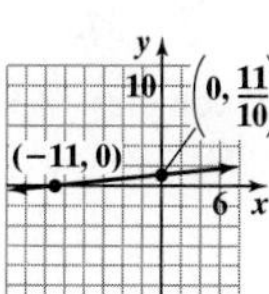

37. 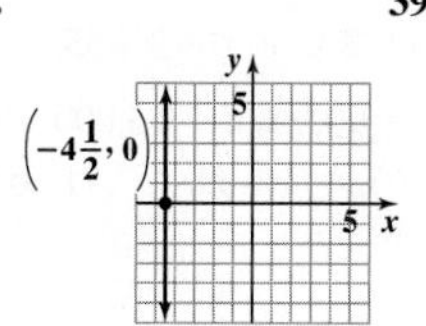

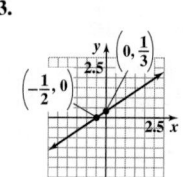

39. $\left(3\frac{1}{4}, 0\right)$

41. 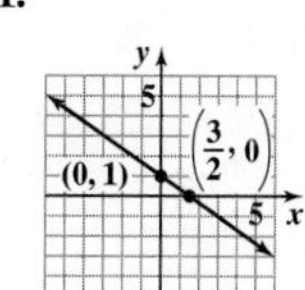

43. $\left(0, \frac{1}{3}\right)$ $\left(-\frac{1}{2}, 0\right)$

45. $\frac{3}{2}$ **47.** 6 **49.** $-\frac{6}{5}$ **51.** c **53.** a **55.** infinite **57.** 0 **59.** answers may vary **61.** (0, 200); no chairs and 200 desks are manufactured. **63.** 300 chairs **65.** $y = -4$ **67. a.** (31.1, 0) **b.** 31.1 years after 2003, there may be no newspaper circulation.

Section 13.4

Calculator Explorations **1.**

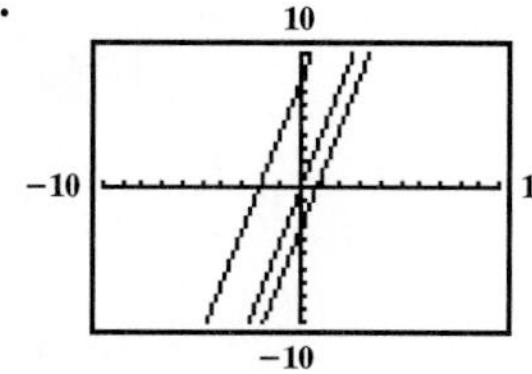

3.

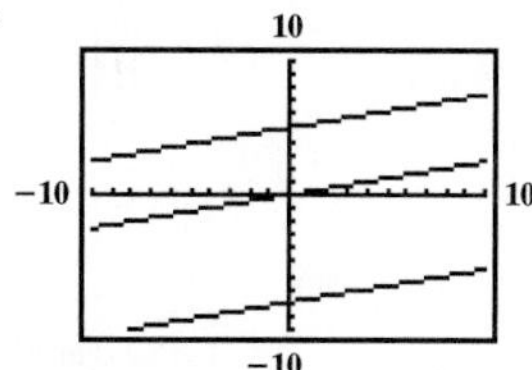

Vocabulary and Readiness Check **1.** slope **3.** 0 **5.** positive **7.** $y; x$ **9.** positive **11.** 0 **13.** downward **15.** vertical

Exercise Set 13.4 **1.** $m = -1$ **3.** $m = -\frac{1}{4}$ **5.** $m = 0$ **7.** undefined slope **9.** $m = -\frac{4}{3}$ **11.** $m = \frac{5}{2}$ **13.** line 1 **15.** line 2 **17.** $m = 5$ **19.** $m = -0.3$ **21.** $m = -2$ **23.** undefined slope **25.** $m = \frac{2}{3}$ **27.** undefined slope **29.** $m = \frac{1}{2}$ **31.** $m = 0$ **33.** $m = -\frac{3}{4}$ **35.** $m = 4$ **37.** neither **39.** neither **41.** parallel **43.** perpendicular **45. a.** 1 **b.** −1 **47. a.** $\frac{9}{11}$ **b.** $-\frac{11}{9}$ **49.** $\frac{3}{5}$ **51.** 12.5% **53.** 40% **55.** 37%; 35% **57.** $m = \frac{5}{4}$; Every 4 years, there are/should be 5 million more U.S. households with televisions. **59.** $m = 0.15$; Every year, the median age of U.S. automobiles increases by 0.15 year. **61.** $y = 2x - 14$ **63.** $y = -6x - 11$ **65.** d **67.** b **69.** e **71.** $m = \frac{1}{2}$ **73.** answers may vary **75.** 29.5 **77.** 1999; 28.3 mi per gal **79.** from 2006 to 2007 **81.** $x = 20$ **83. a.** (2004, 2025), (2007, 2208) **b.** 61 **c.** For the years 2004 through 2007, the number of heart transplants increased at a rate of 61 per year. **85.** Opposite sides are parallel since their slopes are equal, so the figure is a parallelogram. **87.** 2.0625 **89.** −1.6 **91.** The line becomes steeper.

Section 13.5

Calculator Explorations **1.**

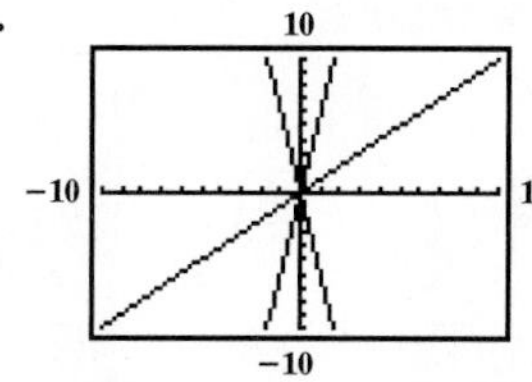

3.

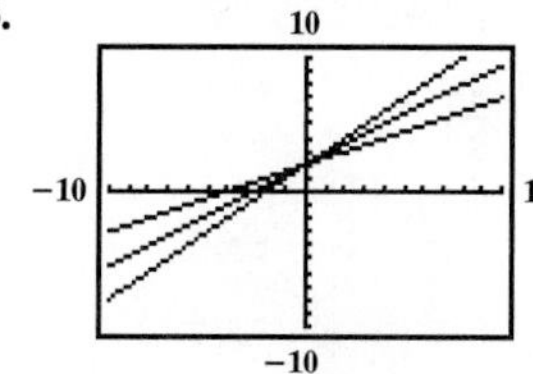

Vocabulary and Readiness Check **1.** slope-intercept; m; b **3.** point-slope **5.** slope- intercept **7.** horizontal

Exercise Set 13.5 **1.** 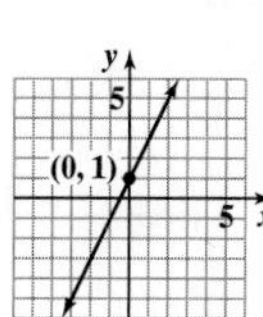

3. **5.** 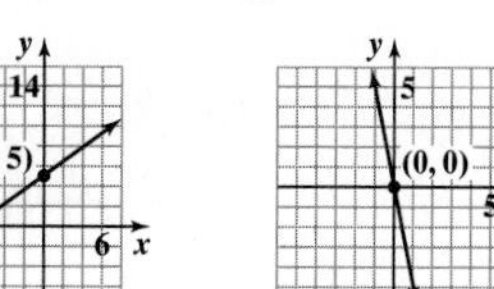

7. 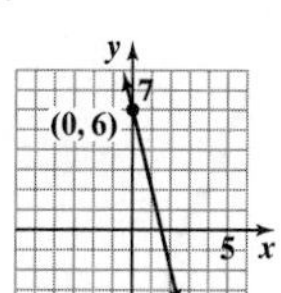

9. (0, 2)

11. 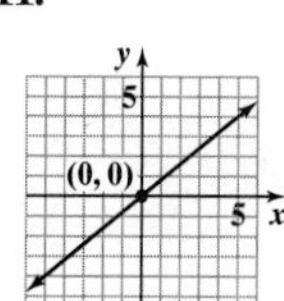

13. $y = 5x + 3$ **15.** $y = -4x - \frac{1}{6}$ **17.** $y = \frac{2}{3}x$ **19.** $y = -8$ **21.** $y = -\frac{1}{5}x + \frac{1}{9}$ **23.** $-6x + y = -10$ **25.** $8x + y = -13$ **27.** $3x - 2y = 27$ **29.** $x + 2y = -3$ **31.** $2x - y = 4$ **33.** $8x - y = -11$ **35.** $4x - 3y = -1$ **37.** $8x + 13y = 0$ **39.** $y = -\frac{1}{2}x + \frac{5}{3}$ **41.** $y = -x + 17$

43. $x = -\frac{3}{4}$ **45.** $y = x + 16$ **47.** $y = -5x + 7$ **49.** $y = 2$ **51.** $y = \frac{3}{2}x$ **53.** $y = -3$ **55.** $y = -\frac{4}{7}x - \frac{18}{7}$ **57. a.** $(0, 302), (4, 322)$ **b.** $y = 5x + 302$ **c.** 312 million **59. a.** $s = 32t$ **b.** 128 ft/sec **61. a.** $y = 90{,}000x + 83{,}000$ **b.** 533,000 vehicles **63. a.** $y = -40x + 5700$ **b.** 5420 cinema sites **65. a.** $S = -1000p + 13{,}000$ **b.** 9500 Fun Noodles **67.** -1 **69.** 5 **71.** b **73.** d **75.** $3x - y = -5$ **77.** $x + 3y = 5$

Integrated Review **1.** $m = 2$ **2.** $m = 0$ **3.** $m = -\frac{2}{3}$ **4.** slope is undefined

5.

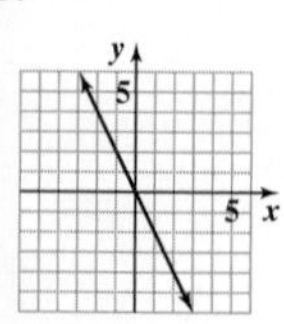

6.

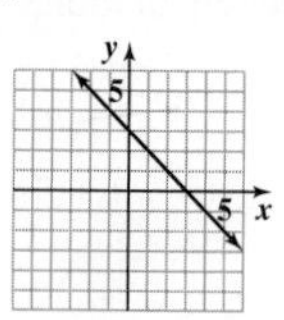

7.

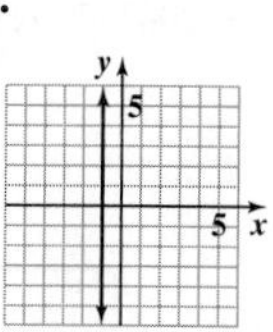

8.

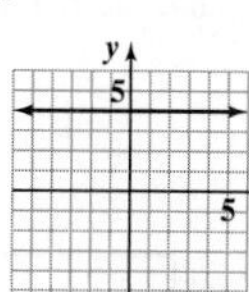

9.

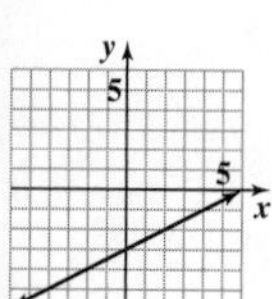

10.

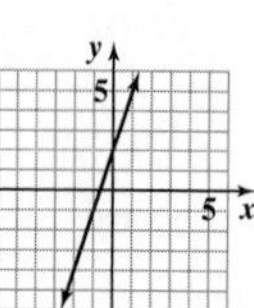

11.

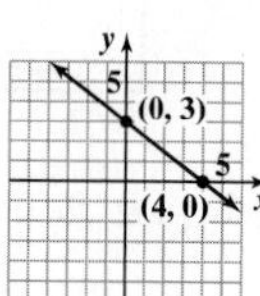

12.

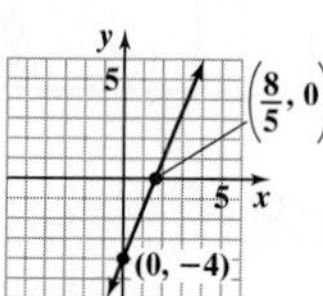

13. $m = 3$ **14.** $m = -6$ **15.** $m = -\frac{7}{2}$ **16.** $m = 2$ **17.** undefined slope **18.** $m = 0$ **19.** $y = 2x - \frac{1}{3}$ **20.** $y = -4x - 1$ **21.** $-x + y = -2$ **22.** neither **23.** perpendicular **24. a.** (2002, 2133); (2007, 3478) **b.** 269 **c.** For the years 2002 through 2007, the amount of yogurt produced increased at a rate of 269 million pounds per year.

Section 13.6

Vocabulary and Readiness Check **1.** linear inequality in two variables **3.** false **5.** true

Exercise Set 13.6 **1.** no; no **3.** yes; no **5.** no; yes **7.**

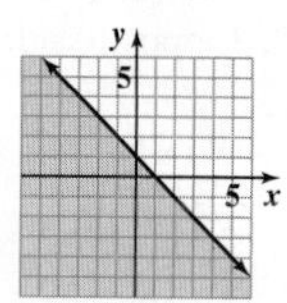

9.

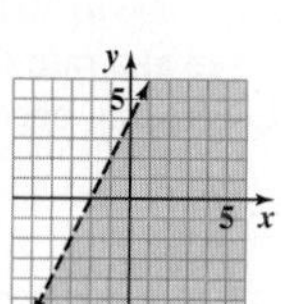

11.

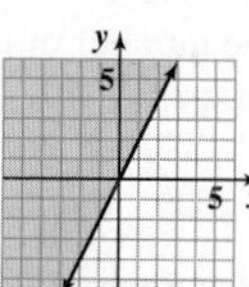

13.

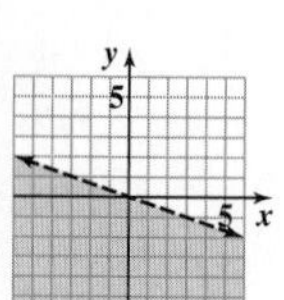

15.

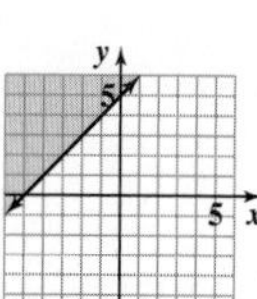

17.

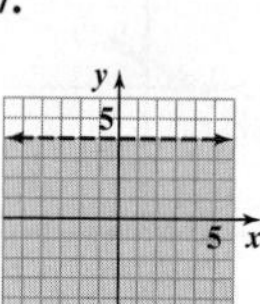

19.

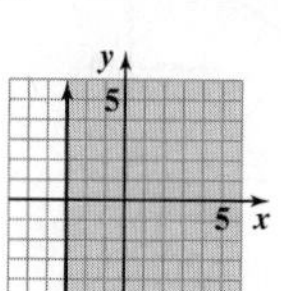

21.

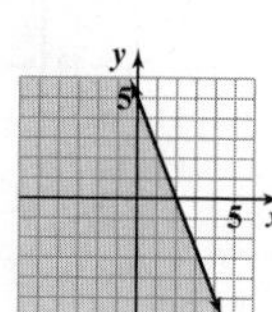

23.

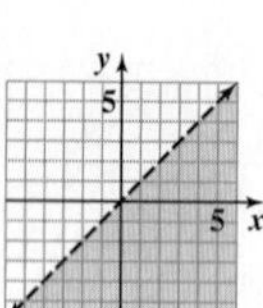

25.

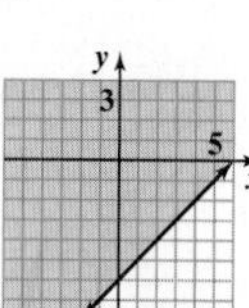

27.

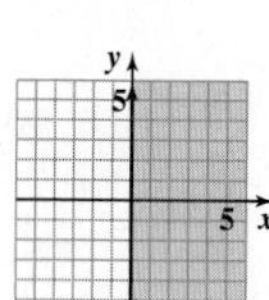

29.

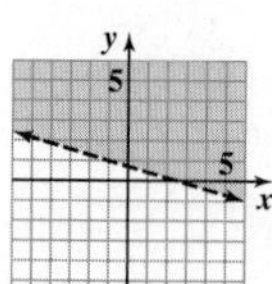

31.

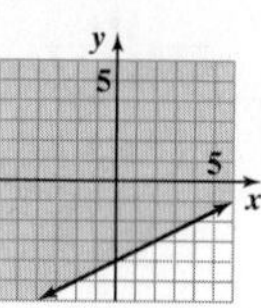

33. $(-2, 1)$ **35.** $(-3, -1)$ **37.** a **39.** b **41.** answers may vary **43.** yes **45.** yes **47. a.** $30x + 0.15y \leq 500$ **b.**

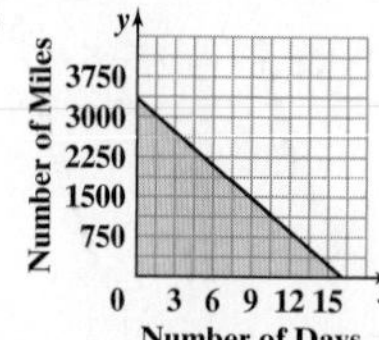
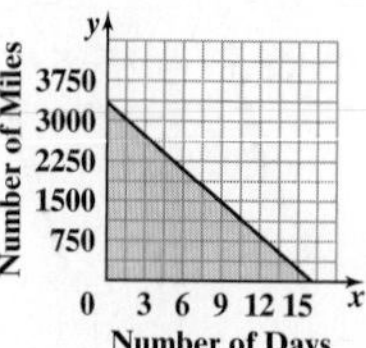

c. answers may vary

Chapter 13 Vocabulary Check **1.** solution **2.** y-axis **3.** linear **4.** x-intercept **5.** standard **6.** y-intercept **7.** slope-intercept **8.** point-slope **9.** y **10.** x-axis **11.** x **12.** slope

Chapter 13 Review **1–6.**

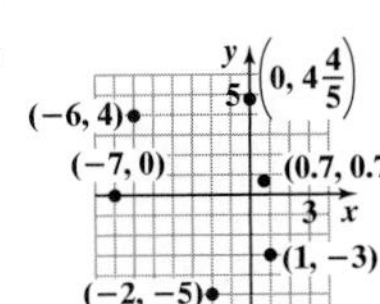

7. (7, 44) **8.** $\left(-\frac{13}{3}, -8\right)$ **9.** −3; 1; 9 **10.** 5; 5; 5 **11.** 0; 10; −10 **12. a.** 2005; 2500; 7000 **b.** 886 compact disc holders

13.

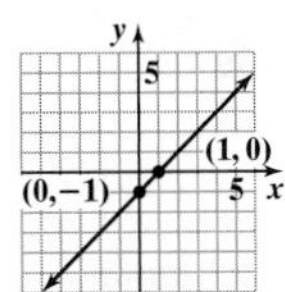

14.

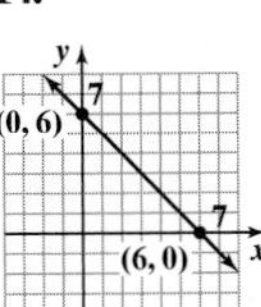

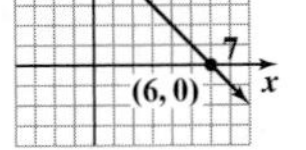

15.

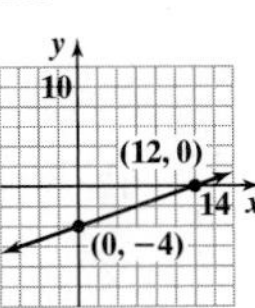

16.

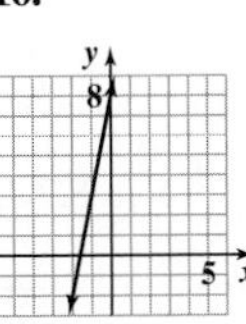

17.

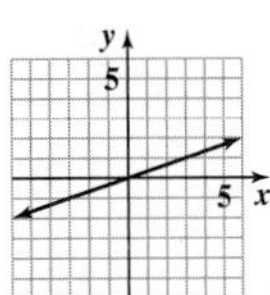

18.

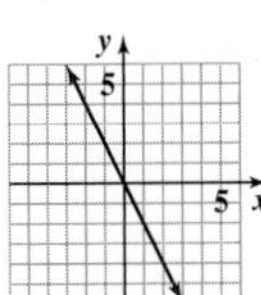

19. (4, 0); (0, −2) **20.** (−2, 0); (2, 0); (0, 2); (0, −2) **21.**

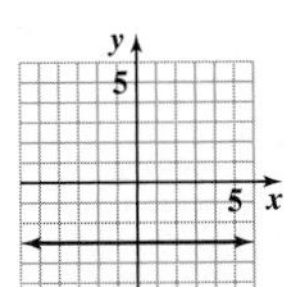

22.

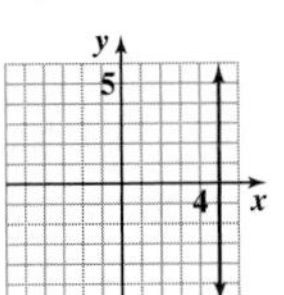

23. (12, 0), (0,−4) **24.** (−2, 0), (0, 8) **25.** $m = -\frac{3}{4}$ **26.** $m = \frac{1}{5}$ **27.** d **28.** b **29.** c **30.** a **31.** $m = \frac{3}{4}$ **32.** $m = \frac{5}{3}$ **33.** $m = 4$ **34.** $m = -1$ **35.** $m = 3$ **36.** $m = \frac{1}{2}$ **37.** $m = 0$ **38.** undefined slope **39.** perpendicular **40.** parallel **41.** neither **42.** perpendicular **43.** $m = 0.025$; Every 1 year, 0.025 million (25,000) more students graduate with a bachelor's degree. **44.** $m = 600$; Every 1 year, 600 more people get a kidney transplant. **45.** $m = \frac{1}{6}$; $\left(0, \frac{1}{6}\right)$ **46.** $m = -3$; (0, 7) **47.** $y = -5x + \frac{1}{2}$ **48.** $y = \frac{2}{3}x + 6$ **49.** d **50.** c **51.** a **52.** b **53.** $-4x + y = -8$ **54.** $3x + y = -5$ **55.** $-3x + 5y = 17$ **56.** $x + 3y = 6$ **57.** $y = -14x + 21$ **58.** $y = -\frac{1}{2}x + 4$

59.

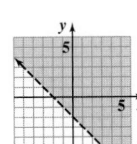

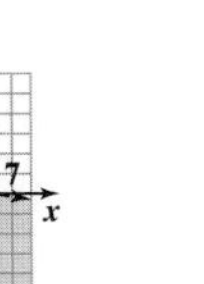

60.

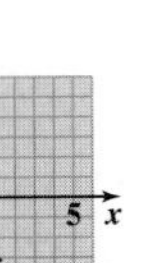

61.

62.

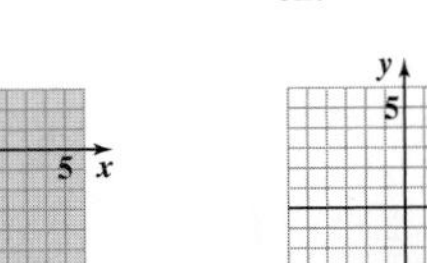

63.

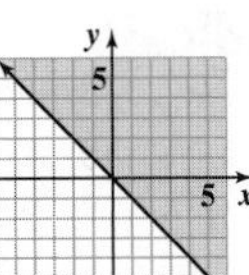

64.

65. 7; −1; −3 **66.** 0; −3; −2 **67.** (3, 0); (0, −2) **68.** (−2, 0); (0, 10) **69.**

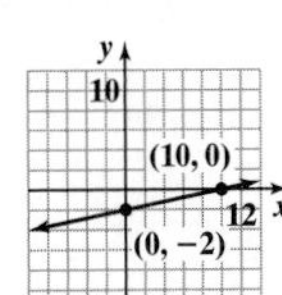

70.

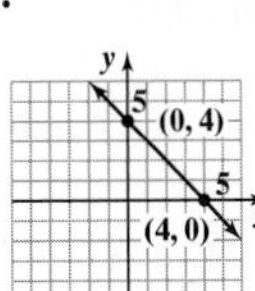

71.

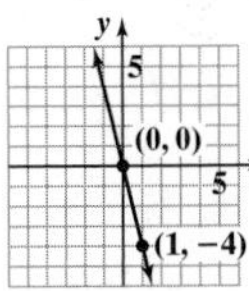

72.

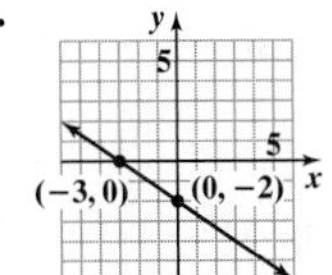

73.

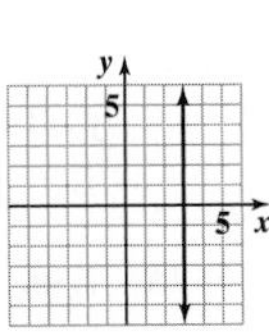

74.

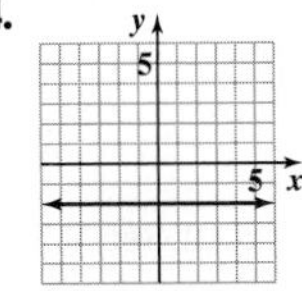

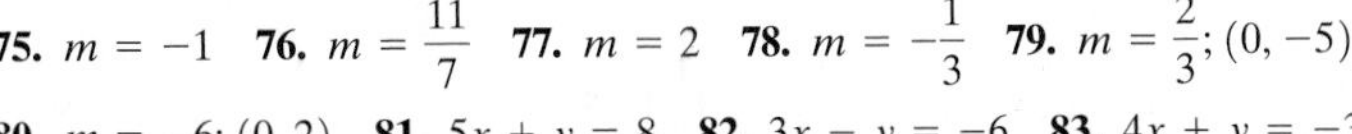

75. $m = -1$ **76.** $m = \frac{11}{7}$ **77.** $m = 2$ **78.** $m = -\frac{1}{3}$ **79.** $m = \frac{2}{3}$; (0, −5) **80.** $m = -6$; (0, 2) **81.** $5x + y = 8$ **82.** $3x - y = -6$ **83.** $4x + y = -3$ **84.** $5x + y = 16$

Chapter 13 Test **1.** (1, 1) **2.** (−4, 17) **3.** $m = \frac{2}{5}$ **4.** $m = 0$ **5.** $m = -1$ **6.** $m = -7$ **7.** $m = 3$ **8.** undefined slope

9.

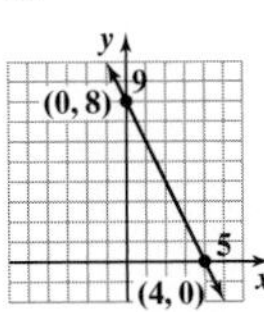

10.

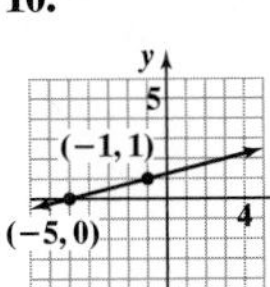

11.

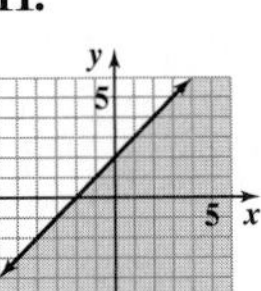

12.

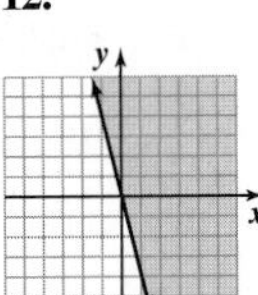

13.

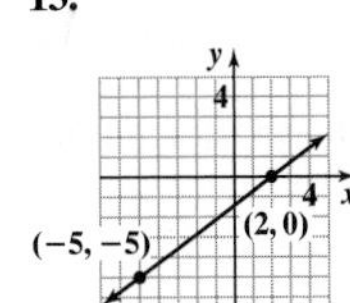

14.

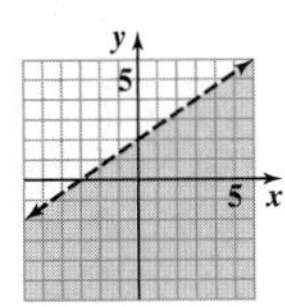

15.

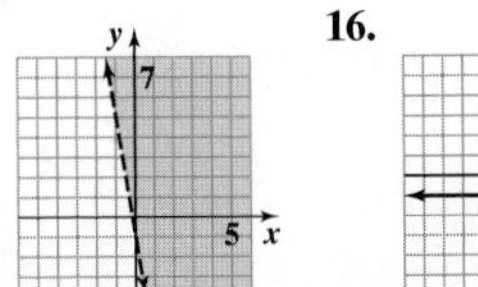

16.

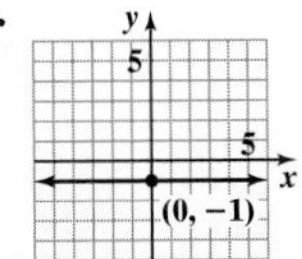

17. neither **18.** $x + 4y = 10$ **19.** $7x + 6y = 0$ **20.** $8x + y = 11$ **21.** $x - 8y = -96$ **22.** $x + 2y = 21$; $x = 5$ m **23. a.** (2003, 66.0); (2004, 65.4); (2005, 65.4); (2006, 65.6); (2007, 64.9); (2008, 63.7); (2009, 62.1)

b. 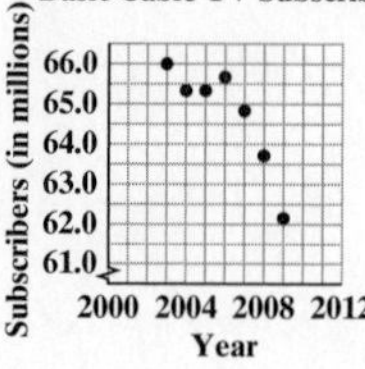

24. $m = -28$; For every 1 year, 28 million fewer movie tickets are sold.

Cumulative Review **1.** 27; Sec. 8.2, Ex. 2 **2.** $\frac{25}{7}$ **3.** 51; Sec. 8.2, Ex. 5 **4.** 23 **5.** 20,602 ft; Sec. 8.4, Ex. 10 **6.** $0.8x - 36$ **7.** $2x + 6$; Sec. 8.7, Ex. 16 **8.** $-15\left(x + \frac{2}{3}\right) = -15x - 10$ **9.** $(x - 4) \div 7$ or $\frac{x-4}{7}$; Sec. 8.7, Ex. 17 **10.** $\frac{-9}{2x}$ **11.** $5 + (x + 1) = 6 + x$; Sec. 8.7, Ex. 18 **12.** $-86 - x$ **13.** 6; Sec. 9.2, Ex. 1 **14.** -24 **15.** (number line, open circle at -2, shaded left) $\{x \mid x < -2\}$; Sec. 9.7, Ex. 6 **16.** $\left\{x \middle| x \le \frac{8}{3}\right\}$ **17. a.** 2; trinomial **b.** 1; binomial **c.** 3; none of these; Sec. 10.3, Ex. 3 **18.** $y = \frac{6-x}{2}$ **19.** $-4x^2 + 6x + 2$; Sec. 10.4, Ex. 2 **20.** $4x - 4$ **21.** $9y^2 + 6y + 1$; Sec. 10.6, Ex. 4 **22.** $x^2 - 24x + 144$ **23.** $3a(-3a^4 + 6a - 1)$; Sec. 11.1, Ex. 5 **24.** $4(x + 3)(x - 3)$ **25.** $(x - 2)(x + 6)$; Sec. 11.2, Ex. 3 **26.** $(3x + y)(x - 7y)$ **27.** $(4x - 1)(2x - 5)$; Sec. 11.3, Ex. 2 **28.** $(18x - 1)(x + 2)$ **29.** $x = 11, x = -2$; Sec. 11.6, Ex. 4 **30.** $x = 0, x = 1$ **31.** 1; Sec. 12.2, Ex. 7 **32.** $\frac{x+5}{2x^3}$ **33.** $\frac{12ab^2}{27a^2b}$; Sec. 12.3, Ex. 9a **34.** $\frac{7x^2}{14x^3}$ **35.** $x = -2, x = \frac{1}{3}$ **36. a.** $(0, 12)$ **b.** $(2, 6)$ **c.** $(-1, 15)$; Sec. 13.1, Ex. 5 **37.** 0; 5; -2 **38.** 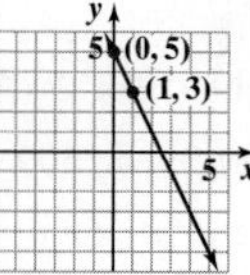

Sec. 13.2, Ex. 1 **39.** $\frac{1}{5}$ **40.** $\frac{2}{3}$; Sec. 13.4, Ex. 3 **41.** undefined slope **42.** $y = -2x + 3$; Sec. 13.5, Ex. 4 **43.** $m = \frac{2}{5}$, y-intercept: $(0, -2)$ **44.** $3x - 2y = 0$

Chapter 14 Roots and Radicals

Section 14.1

Calculator Explorations **1.** 2.449 **3.** 3.317 **5.** 9.055 **7.** 3.420 **9.** 2.115 **11.** 1.783

Vocabulary and Readiness Check **1.** principal **3.** square root **5.** power **7.** false **9.** true

Exercise Set 14.1 **1.** 4 **3.** $\frac{1}{5}$ **5.** -10 **7.** not a real number **9.** -11 **11.** $\frac{3}{5}$ **13.** 30 **15.** 12 **17.** $\frac{1}{10}$ **19.** 0.5 **21.** 5 **23.** -4 **25.** -2 **27.** $\frac{1}{2}$ **29.** -5 **31.** 2 **33.** 9 **35.** not a real number **37.** $-\frac{3}{4}$ **39.** -5 **41.** 1 **43.** 2.646 **45.** 6.083 **47.** 11.662 **49.** $\sqrt{2} \approx 1.41$; 126.90 ft **51.** m **53.** x^2 **55.** $3x^4$ **57.** $9x$ **59.** ab^2 **61.** $4a^3b^2$ **63.** a^2b^6 **65.** $-2xy^9$ **67.** $\frac{x^3}{6}$ **69.** $\frac{5y}{3}$ **71.** $25 \cdot 2$ **73.** $16 \cdot 2$ or $4 \cdot 8$ **75.** $4 \cdot 7$ **77.** $9 \cdot 3$ **79.** a, b **81.** 7 mi **83.** 3.1 in. **85.** 3 **87.** 10 **89.** 4, 5 **91.** 8, 9 **93.** 6.1 sec **95.** answers may vary **97.** 1; 1.7; 2; 3 **99.** $|x|$ **101.** $|x + 2|$ **103.** $(2, 0)$; answers may vary **105.** $(-4, 0)$; answers may vary

Chapter 14 Review **1.** 9 **2.** -7 **3.** 3 **4.** 3 **5.** $-\frac{3}{8}$ **6.** $\frac{2}{3}$ **7.** 2 **8.** -2 **9.** c **10.** a, c **11.** x^6 **12.** x^4 **13.** $3y$ **14.** $5x^2$

Cumulative Review **1.** 28; Sec. 8.5, Ex. 3 **2.** -46.8 **3.** $-\frac{8}{21}$; Sec. 8.5, Ex. 4 **4.** -18 **5.** 2; Sec. 9.3, Ex. 1 **6.** 15 **7. a.** 17% **b.** 21% **c.** 43 American travelers; Sec. 9.6, Ex. 3 **8. a.** $\frac{3}{2}$ **b.** 9 **9. a.** 102,000 **b.** 0.007358 **c.** 84,000,000 **d.** 0.00003007; Sec. 10.2, Ex. 18 **10. a.** 7.2×10^6 **b.** 3.08×10^{-4} **11.** $6x^2 - 11x - 10$; Sec. 10.5; Ex. 7b **12.** $49x^2 + 14x + 1$ **13.** $(y + 2)(x + 3)$; Sec. 11.1; Ex. 10 **14.** $(y^2 + 5)(x - 1)$ **15.** $(3x + 2)(x + 3)$; Sec. 11.3, Ex. 1 **16.** $3(x + 2)(x + 3)$ **17.** $y = -2x + 4$ **18.** $2a^2 + 10a - 5$ **19.** 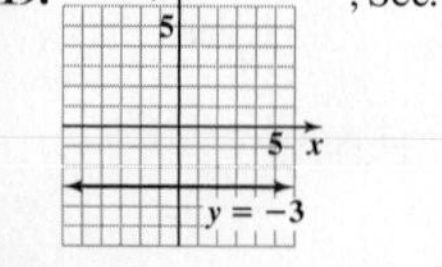

; Sec. 13.3, Ex. 7 **20.** 6; 4; 0 **21.** $y = \frac{1}{4}x - 3$; Sec. 13.5, Ex. 3 **22.** $y = -\frac{1}{2}x + \frac{11}{2}$ **23.** 1; Sec. 14.1, Ex. 6 **24.** 11 **25.** -3; Sec. 14.1, Ex. 7 **26.** $\frac{1}{2}$ **27.** $\frac{1}{5}$; Sec. 14.1, Ex. 8 **28.** $\frac{5}{12}$ **29.** $3\sqrt{6}$; Sec. 14.2, Ex. 1 **30.** $3\sqrt{7}$ **31.** $10\sqrt{2}$; Sec. 14.2, Ex. 3 **32.** $10\sqrt{5}$

Chapter 15 Graphs and Functions

Section 15.1

Practice Exercises

1. a. Domain: {4, 5}; Range: {1, −3, −2, 6} **b.** Domain: {3}; Range: {−4, −3, −2, −1, 0, 1, 2, 3, 4} **c.** Domain: {Administrative Secretary, Game Developer, Engineer, Restaurant Manager, Marketing}; Range: {27, 50, 73, 35} **2. a.** yes, a function **b.** not a function **c.** yes, a function **3.** yes, a function **4.** yes, a function **5. a.** yes, a function **b.** yes, a function **c.** no, not a function **d.** yes, a function **e.** no, not a function **f.** yes, a function **6. a.** Domain: $\{x \mid -1 \le x \le 2\}$; Range: $\{y \mid -2 \le y \le 9\}$; yes, a function **b.** Domain: $\{x \mid -1 \le x \le 1\}$; Range: $\{y \mid -4 \le y \le 4\}$; not a function **c.** Domain: all real numbers; Range: $\{y \mid y \le 4\}$; yes, a function **d.** Domain: all real numbers; Range: all real numbers; yes, a function **7. a.** 1 **b.** 6 **c.** −2 **d.** 15 **8. a.** 6.4 **b.** 37.6 **c.** −4 **d.** −2.726 **9. a.** −3 **b.** −2 **c.** 3 **d.** 1 **e.** −1 and 3 **f.** −3 **10.** \$17.25, \$26.16, \$44.28, \$60.95 **11.** \$35 billion **12.** \$57.224 billion

Vocabulary and Readiness Check 15.1 **1.** origin **3.** x; y **5.** V-shaped **7.** relation **9.** domain **11.** vertical

Exercise Set 15.1 **1.** domain: $\{-1, 0, -2, 5\}$; range: $\{7, 6, 2\}$; function **3.** domain: $\{-2, 6, -7\}$; range: $\{4, -3, -8\}$; not a function **5.** domain: $\{1\}$; range: $\{1, 2, 3, 4\}$; not a function **7.** domain: $\left\{\frac{3}{2}, 0\right\}$; range: $\left\{\frac{1}{2}, -7, \frac{4}{5}\right\}$; not a function **9.** domain: $\{-3, 0, 3\}$; range: $\{-3, 0, 3\}$; function **11.** domain: $\{-1, 1, 2, 3\}$; range: $\{2, 1\}$; function **13.** domain: {Iowa, Alaska, Delaware, Illinois, Connecticut, New York}; range: {5, 1, 19, 29}; function **15.** domain: $\{32°, 104°, 212°, 50°\}$; range: $\{0°, 40°, 10°, 100°\}$; function **17.** domain: $\{0\}$; range: $\{2, -1, 5, 100\}$; not a function **19.** function **21.** not a function **23.** function **25.** not a function **27.** function **29.** function **31.** not a funcion **33.** domain: $\{x \mid x \ge 0\}$; range: all real numbers; not a function **35.** domain: $\{x \mid -1 \le x \le 1\}$; range: all real numbers; not a function **37.** domain: all real numbers; range $\{y \mid y \le -3 \text{ and } y \ge 3\}$; not a function **39.** domain: $\{x \mid 2 \le x \le 7\}$; range: $\{y \mid 1 \le y \le 6\}$; not a function **41.** domain: $\{-2\}$; range: all real numbers; not a function **43.** domain: all real numbers; range: $\{y \mid y \le 3\}$; function **45.** domain: all real numbers; range: all real numbers; function **47.** answers may vary **49.** yes **51.** no **53.** yes **55.** yes **57.** yes **59.** no **61.** 15 **63.** 38 **65.** 7 **67.** 3 **69. a.** 0 **b.** 1 **c.** −1 **71. a.** 246 **b.** 6 **c.** $\frac{9}{2}$ **73. a.** −5 **b.** −5 **c.** −5 **75. a.** 5.1 **b.** 15.5 **c.** 9.533 **77. a.** 23 **b.** 23 **c.** 33 **79.** 7 **81.** (1, −10) **83.** (4, 56) **85.** $f(-1) = -2$ **87.** $g(2) = 0$ **89.** −4, 0 **91.** −4 **93.** infinite number **95.** 55, 90, 125, 160, 195 **97. a.** 36 **b.** 64 **c.** 84 **d.** 96 **e.** 100 **f.** 0 **99. a.** \$17 billion **b.** \$15.592 billion **101.** \$15.54 billion **103.** $f(x) = x + 7$ **105.** 25π sq cm **107.** 2744 cu in. **109.** 166.38 cm **111.** 163.2 mg **113. a.** 106.26; per capita consumption of poultry was 106.26 lb in 2006. **b.** 108.54 lb **115.** 5, −5, 6

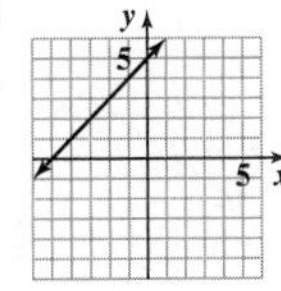

117. $2, \frac{8}{7}, \frac{12}{7}$

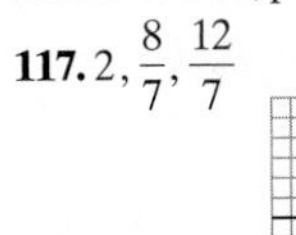

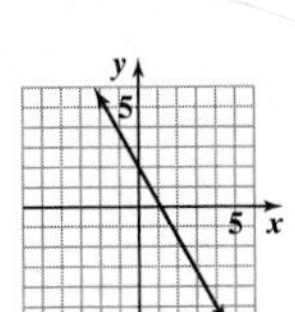

119. 0, 0, −6

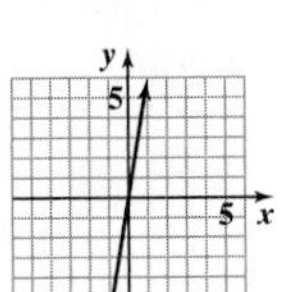

121. yes; 170 m **123.** false **125.** true **127. a.** $-3s + 12$ **b.** $-3r + 12$ **129. a.** 132 **b.** $a^2 - 12$ **131.** answers may vary

Section 15.2

Practice Exercises

1.

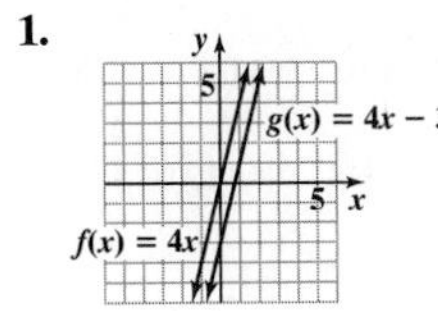

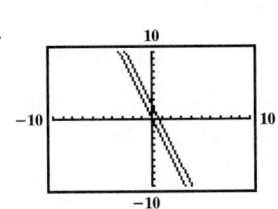

2. ; shifting the graph of $f(x)$ up 2 units **3.** shifting the graph of $y = -x$ down 5 units

4.

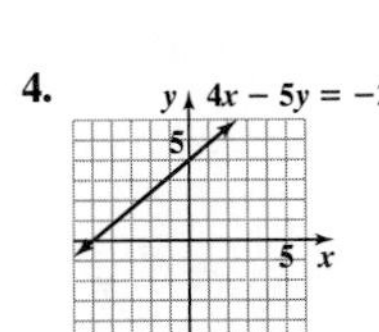

5. a. $\left(0, -\frac{2}{5}\right)$

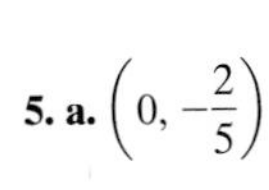

b. (0, 4.1) **6.**

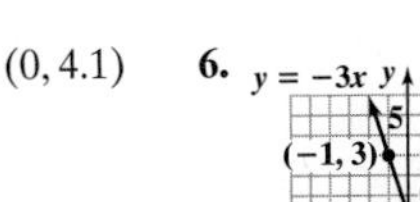

7.

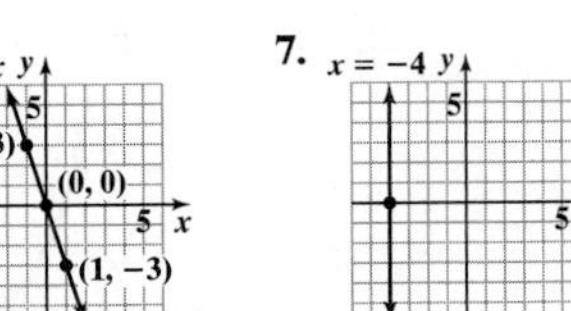

8.

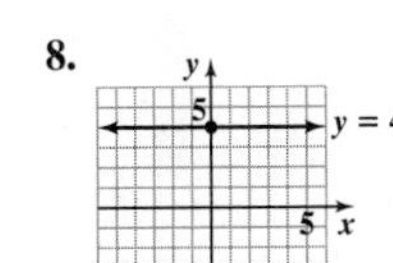

9. 84; 96.50; 100; 124

Vocabulary and Readiness Check 15.2 **1.** linear **3.** vertical; $(c, 0)$ **5.** y; $f(x)$; x

Exercise Set 15.2 **1.**

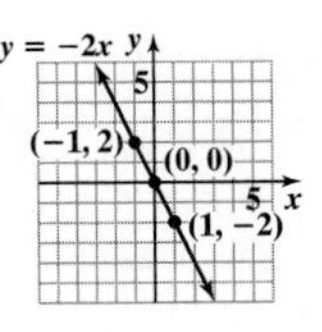

3.

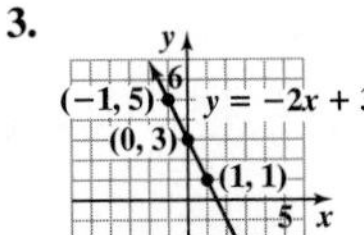

5.

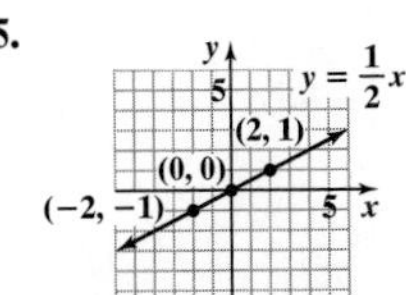

7.

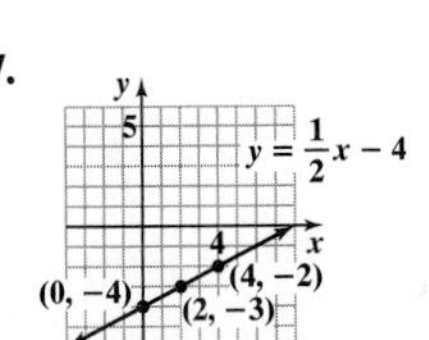

9. C **11.** D

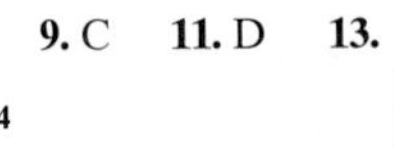

13.

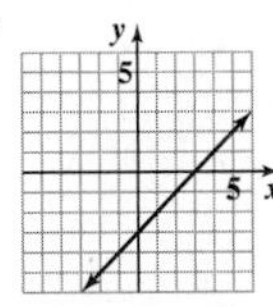

15. **17.** **19.** **21.** answers may vary **23.** **25.**

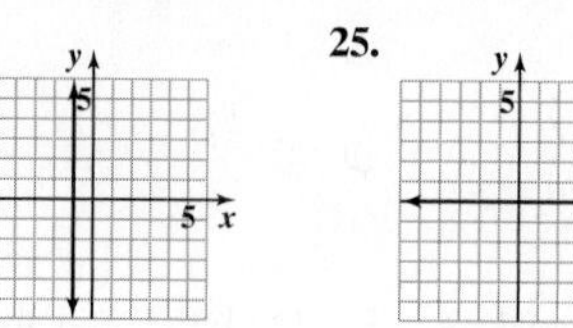

27. **29.** C **31.** A **33.** The vertical line $x = 0$ has y-intercepts. **35.** **37.**

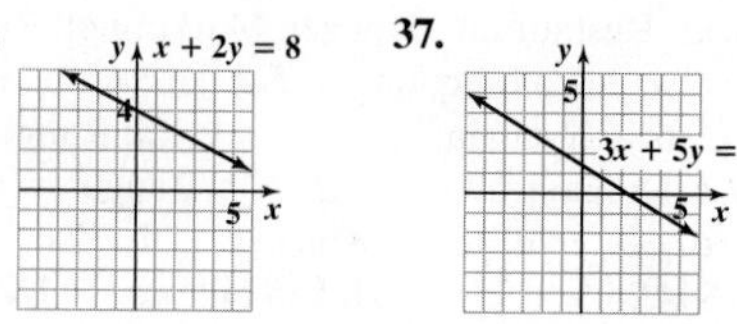

39.

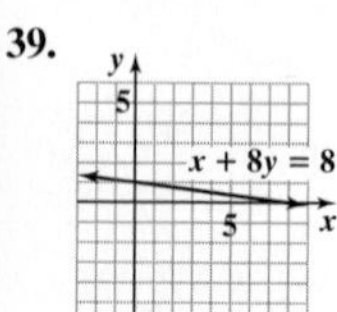

41.

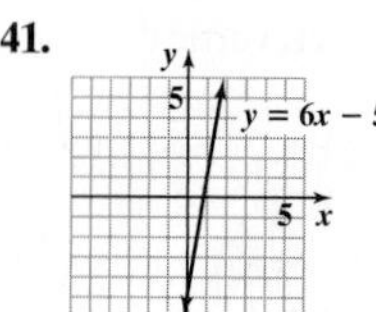

43.

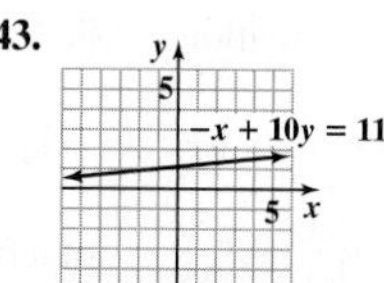

45.

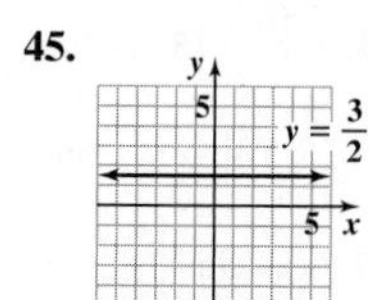

47.

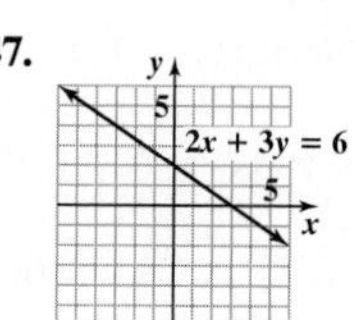

49.

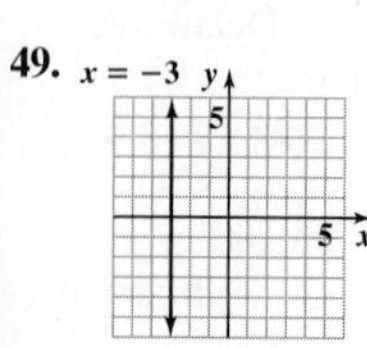

51.

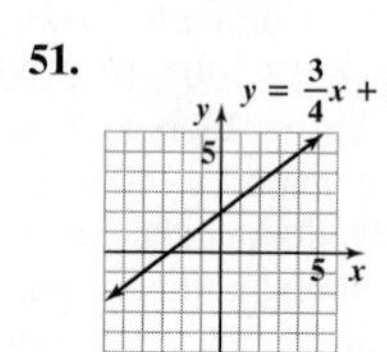

53.

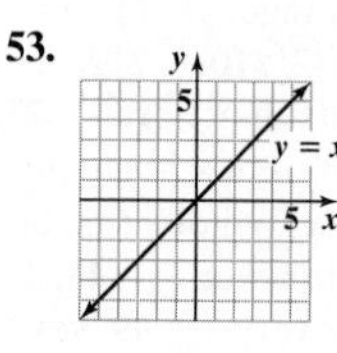

55.

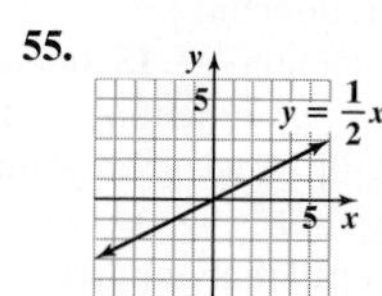

57.

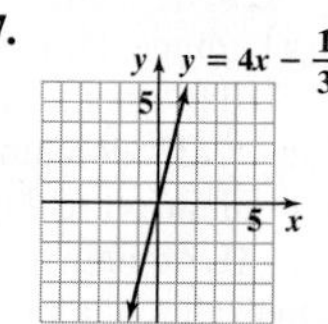

59.

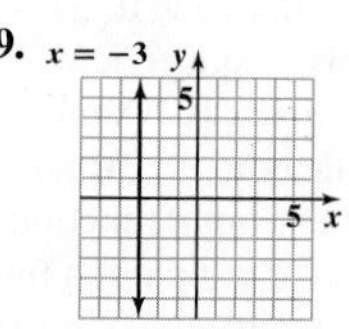

61. b, d **63.** 677.25, 706.78, 807.19, 860.34 **65.** $\frac{3}{2}$ **67.** 6 **69.** $-\frac{6}{5}$

71. a. (0, 500); if no tables are produced, 500 chairs can be produced **b.** (750, 0); if no chairs are produced, 750 tables can be produced **c.** 466 chairs

73. a. \$64 **b.**

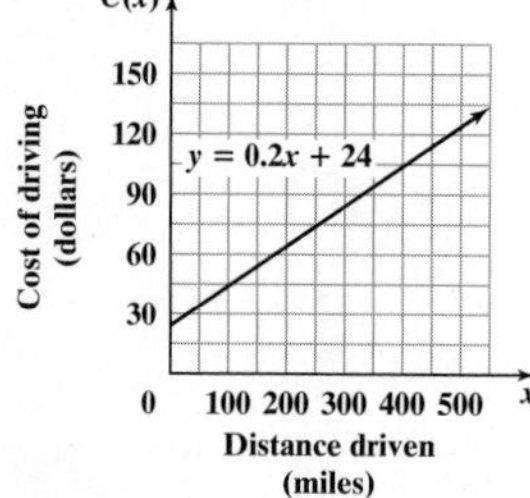

c. The line moves upward from left to right. **75. a.** \$2855.12 **b.** 2012 **c.** answers may vary

77. a. a line parallel to $y = -4x$ but with y-intercept $(0, 2)$ **b.** a line parallel to $y = -4x$ but with y-intercept $(0, -5)$ **79.** B **81.** A

Chapter 15 Review **1.** domain: $\left\{-\frac{1}{2}, 6, 0, 25\right\}$; range: $\left\{\frac{3}{4} \text{ or } 0.75, -12, 25\right\}$; function **3.** domain: $\{2, 4, 6, 8\}$; range: $\{2, 4, 5, 6\}$; not a function **5.** domain: all real numbers; range: $\{y | y \le -1 \text{ or } y \ge 1\}$; not a function **7.** domain: all real numbers; range: $\{4\}$; function **9.** -3 **11.** 18 **13.** -3 **17.** 0 **19.** $-2, 4$ **21.** **23.** **25.** A **27.** D **29.**

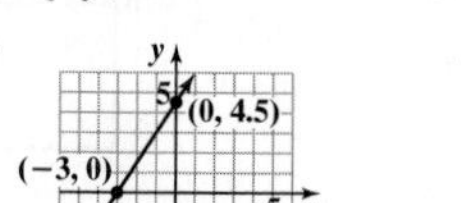

31. **33.**

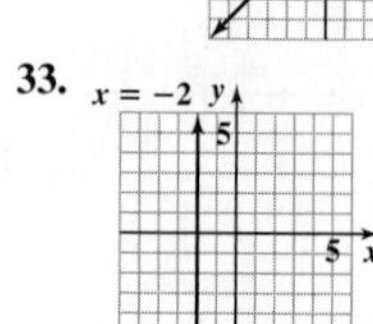

35.

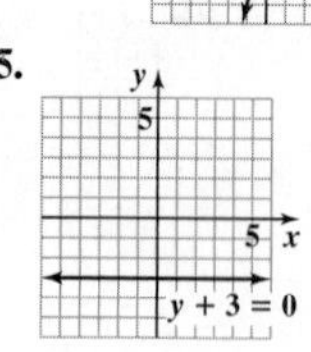

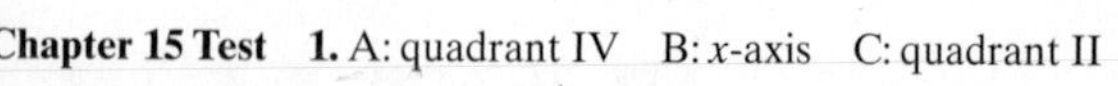

Chapter 15 Test **1.** A: quadrant IV B: x-axis C: quadrant II **2.**

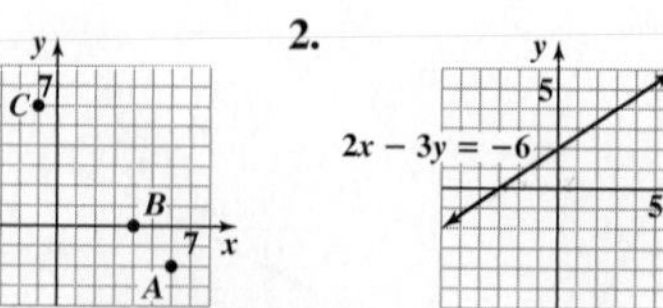

3.

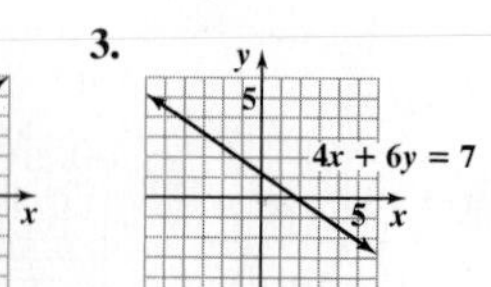

4.

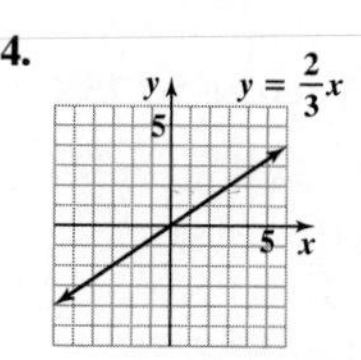

5. 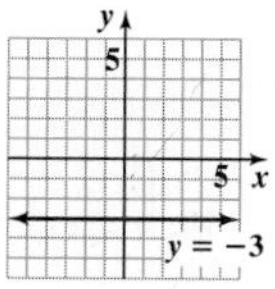

6. $-\frac{3}{2}$ **7.** $m = -\frac{1}{4}, b = \frac{2}{3}$ **8.** $y = -8$ **9.** $x = -4$ **10.** $y = -2$ **11.** $3x + y = 11$ **12.** $5x - y = 2$ **13.** $f(x) = -\frac{1}{2}x$ **14.** $f(x) = -\frac{1}{3}x + \frac{5}{3}$ **15.** $f(x) = -\frac{1}{2}x - \frac{1}{2}$ **16.** neither **17.** B **18.** A **19.** D **20.** C **21.** domain: all real numbers; range: {5}; function **22.** domain: {2}; range: all real numbers; not a function **23.** domain: all real numbers; range: $\{y | y \geq 0\}$; function **24.** domain: all real numbers: range: all real numbers: function **25. a.** $25,193 **b.** $32,410 **c.** 2015 **d.** The average yearly earnings for high school graduates increases $1031 per year. **e.** The average yearly earnings for a high school graduate in 2000 was $25,193.

Chapter 16 Equations and Inequalities

Section 16.1

Practice Exercises

1. 2 **2.** 6 **3.** −3.641 **4.** $275.60 **5.** cell phone: $876.46; residential phone: $375.12 **6.** all real numbers **7.** { } or ∅ **8.** −3.8

Vocabulary and Readiness Check 16.1 **1.** intersection-of-graphs **3.** x **5.** root, zero **7.** −2 **9.** 1 **11.** 7 **13.** all real numbers

Exercise Set 16.1 **1.** 2 **3.** −1 **5.** −2 **7.** $3x - 13 = 2(x - 5) + 3$; 6 **9.** $-(2x + 3) + 2 = 5x - 1 - 7x$; all real numbers **11.** ∅ **13.** all real numbers **15.** ∅ **17.** all real numbers **19.** 25.8 **21.** 3.5 **23.** −3.28 **25.** ∅ **27.** 4 **29.** 8 **31.** all real numbers **33.** −0.32 **35.** 0.6 **37.** 17 **39.** 0.8 **41. a.** second consultant **b.** first consultant **c.** 6-hr job **43. a.** first agency **b.** second agency **c.** 60 mi **45.** $25,000 **47.** If the company produces 1667 calculators, the cost and the revenue will be approximately $250,050. **49.** {−3, −2, −1} **51.** {−3, −2, −1, 0, 1} **53.** answers may vary **55.** 22 **57.** greater than **59.** 1.43 **61.** 1.51 **63.** 0.91 **65.** 22.87 **67.** The equation has no solution.

Section 16.2

Practice Exercises

1. a. 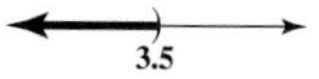 $(-\infty, 3.5)$ **b.** 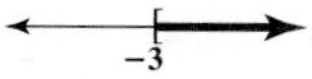 $[-3, \infty)$ **c.**  $[-1, 4)$ **2.**  $(4, \infty)$

3. 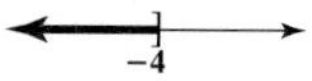 $(-\infty, -4]$ **4. a.** 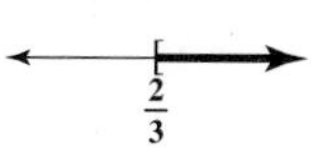 $\left[\frac{2}{3}, \infty\right)$ **b.**  $(-4, \infty)$ **5.** $\left[-\frac{3}{2}, \infty\right)$

6. $(-\infty, 13]$ **7. a.** $(-\infty, \infty)$ **b.** ∅ **8.** $10,000 per month. **9.** the entire year 2021 and after

Vocabulary and Readiness Check 16.2 **1.** d **3.** b **5.** $[-0.4, \infty)$ **7.** $(-\infty, -0.4]$ **9.** no **11.** yes

Exercise Set 16.2 **1.**  $(-\infty, -3)$ **3.** 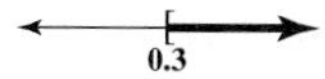 $[0.3, \infty)$ **5.**  $(-2, 5)$ **7.**  $(-1, 5]$ **9.** 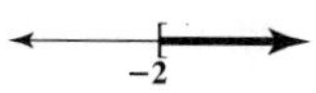 $[-2, \infty)$ **11.** 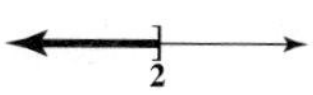 $(-\infty, 2]$ **13.** 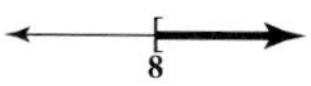 $[8, \infty)$ **15.** 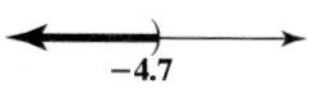 $(-\infty, -4.7)$ **17.** $(-\infty, 4)$ **19.** $[-3, \infty)$ **21.** ∅ **23.** $(-\infty, -1]$ **25.** $(-\infty, 11]$ **27.** $(0, \infty)$ **29.** $(-13, \infty)$ **31.** $\left[-\frac{79}{3}, \infty\right)$ **33.** $\left(-\infty, -\frac{35}{6}\right)$ **35.** $(-\infty, -6)$ **37.** $(4, \infty)$ **39.** $[-0.5, \infty)$ **41.** $(-\infty, 7]$ **43.** $[0, \infty)$ **45.** $(-\infty, -29]$ **47.** $[3, \infty)$ **49.** $(-\infty, -1]$ **51.** $[-31, \infty)$ **53.** $(-\infty, -2]$ **55.** $(-\infty, -15)$ **57.** $\left[-\frac{37}{3}, \infty\right)$ **59.** $(-\infty, 5)$ **61.** $(-\infty, 9)$ **63.** $\left(-\infty, -\frac{11}{2}\right]$ **65.** $(-\infty, \infty)$ **67.** ∅ **69. a.** $\{x | x \geq 81\}$ **b.** A final exam grade of 81 or higher will result in an average of 77 or higher. **71. a.** $\{x | x \leq 1040\}$ **b.** The luggage and cargo must weigh 1040 pounds or less. **73. a.** $\{x | x \leq 20\}$ **b.** She can move at most 20 whole boxes at one time. **75. a.** $\{x | x > 200\}$ **b.** If you make more than 200 calls, plan 1 is more economical. **77.** $\{F | F \geq 932°\}$ **79. a.** 2011 **b.** answers may vary **81.** decreasing; answers may vary **83.** 5.7 gal **85.** during 2008 **87.** answers may vary **89.** 2, 3, 4 **91.** 2, 3, 4, . . . **93.** 5 **95.** $\frac{13}{6}$ **97.** $\{x | x \geq 2\}$; $[2, \infty)$ **99.**  ; $(-\infty, 0)$ **101.** $\{x | -2 < x \leq 1.5\}$;  **103.** {4} **105.** $(4, \infty)$ **107.** answers may vary **109.** answers may vary **111.** answers may vary

The Bigger Picture

1. $-\frac{10}{3}$ **2.** 0 **3.** $(-1, \infty)$ **4.** 3 **5.** -6 **6.** $\varnothing$ **7.** $\left(-\infty, \frac{3}{2}\right]$ **8.** all real numbers or $(-\infty, \infty)$

Integrated Review **1.** -5 **2.** $(-5, \infty)$ **3.** $\left[\frac{8}{3}, \infty\right)$ **4.** $[-1, \infty)$ **5.** 0 **6.** $\left[-\frac{1}{10}, \infty\right)$ **7.** $\left(-\infty, -\frac{1}{6}\right]$ **8.** 0 **9.** $\varnothing$ **10.** $\left[-\frac{3}{5}, \infty\right)$ **11.** 4.2 **12.** 6 **13.** -8 **14.** $(-\infty, -16)$ **15.** $\frac{20}{11}$ **16.** 1 **17.** $(38, \infty)$ **18.** -5.5 **19.** $\frac{3}{5}$ **20.** $(-\infty, \infty)$ **21.** 29 **22.** all real numbers **23.** $(-\infty, 1)$ **24.** $\frac{9}{13}$ **25.** $(23, \infty)$ **26.** $(-\infty, 6]$ **27.** $\left(-\infty, \frac{3}{5}\right]$ **28.** $\left(-\infty, -\frac{19}{32}\right)$

Section 16.3

Practice Exercises

1. $\{1, 3\}$ **2.** $(-\infty, 2)$ **3.** { } or $\varnothing$ **4.** $(-4, 2)$ **5.** $[-6, 8]$ **6.** $\{1, 2, 3, 4, 5, 6, 7, 9\}$ **7.** $\left(-\infty, \frac{3}{8}\right] \cup [3, \infty)$ **8.** $(-\infty, \infty)$

Vocabulary and Readiness Check 16.3 **1.** compound **3.** or **5.** $\cup$ **7.** and

Exercise Set 16.3 **1.** $\{2, 3, 4, 5, 6, 7\}$ **3.** $\{4, 6\}$ **5.** $\{\ldots, -2, -1, 0, 1, \ldots\}$ **7.** $\{5, 7\}$ **9.** $\{x \mid x \text{ is an odd integer or } x = 2 \text{ or } x = 4\}$ **11.** $\{2, 4\}$ **13.** $(-3, 1)$ **15.** $\varnothing$ **17.** $(-\infty, -1)$ **19.** $[6, \infty)$ **21.** $(-\infty, -3]$ **23.** $(4, 10)$ **25.** $(11, 17)$ **27.** $[1, 4]$ **29.** $\left[-3, \frac{3}{2}\right]$ **31.** $\left[-\frac{7}{3}, 7\right]$ **33.** $(-\infty, 5)$ **35.** $(-\infty, -4] \cup [1, \infty)$ **37.** $(-\infty, \infty)$ **39.** $[2, \infty)$ **41.** $(-\infty, -4) \cup (-2, \infty)$ **43.** $(-\infty, \infty)$ **45.** $\left(-\frac{1}{2}, \frac{2}{3}\right)$ **47.** $(-\infty, \infty)$ **49.** $\left[\frac{3}{2}, 6\right]$ **51.** $\left(\frac{5}{4}, \frac{11}{4}\right)$ **53.** $\varnothing$ **55.** $\left(-\infty, -\frac{56}{5}\right) \cup \left[\frac{5}{3}, \infty\right)$ **57.** $\left(-5, \frac{5}{2}\right)$ **59.** $\left(0, \frac{14}{3}\right]$ **61.** $(-\infty, -3]$ **63.** $(-\infty, 1] \cup \left(\frac{29}{7}, \infty\right)$ **65.** $\varnothing$ **67.** $\left[-\frac{1}{2}, \frac{3}{2}\right)$ **69.** $\left(-\frac{4}{3}, \frac{7}{3}\right)$ **71.** $(6, 12)$ **73. a.** $(-5, 2.5)$ **b.** $(-\infty, -5) \cup (2.5, \infty)$ **75. a.** $[2, 9]$ **b.** $(-\infty, 2] \cup [9, \infty)$ **77.** -12 **79.** -4 **81.** $-7, 7$ **83.** 0 **85.** 2003, 2004, 2005 **87.** $-20.2° \le F \le 95°$ **89.** $67 \le$ final score ≤ 94 **91.** $(6, \infty)$ **93.** $[3, 7]$ **95.** $(-\infty, -1)$

The Bigger Picture

1. $[-1, 3]$ **2.** $(-1, 6)$ **3.** 5.1 **4.** $(-\infty, -4)$ **5.** $(-\infty, -3]$ **6.** $(-\infty, -2) \cup (2, \infty)$ **7.** 4 **8.** $[19, \infty)$

Section 16.4

Practice Exercises

1. $-7, 7$ **2.** $-1, 4$ **3.** $-80, 70$ **4.** $-2, 2$ **5.** 0 **6.** { } or $\varnothing$ **7.** { } or $\varnothing$ **8.** $-\frac{3}{5}, 5$ **9.** 5

Vocabulary and Readiness Check 16.4 **1.** C **3.** B **5.** D

Exercise Set 16.4 **1.** $7, -7$ **3.** $4.2, -4.2$ **5.** $7, -2$ **7.** $8, 4$ **9.** $5, -5$ **11.** $3, -3$ **13.** 0 **15.** $\varnothing$ **17.** $\frac{1}{5}$ **19.** $|x| = 5$ **21.** $9, -\frac{1}{2}$ **23.** $-\frac{5}{2}$ **25.** answers may vary **27.** $\{-1, 4\}$ **29.** $\{2.5\}$ **31.** $4, -4$ **33.** $\varnothing$ **35.** $0, \frac{14}{3}$ **37.** $2, -2$ **39.** $7, -1$ **41.** $\varnothing$ **43.** $\varnothing$ **45.** $-\frac{1}{8}$ **47.** $\frac{1}{2}, -\frac{5}{6}$ **49.** $2, -\frac{12}{5}$ **51.** $3, -2$ **53.** $-8, \frac{2}{3}$ **55.** $\varnothing$ **57.** 4 **59.** $13, -8$ **61.** $3, -3$ **63.** $8, -7$ **65.** $2, 3$ **67.** $2, -\frac{10}{3}$ **69.** $\frac{3}{2}$ **71.** $\varnothing$ **73.** answers may vary **75.** 33% **77.** 38.4 lb **79.** answers may vary **81.** no solution **83.** $|x - 3| = 2$ **85.** $|2x - 1| = 4$ **87. a.** $c = 0$ **b.** c is a negative number **c.** c is a positive number **89.** 0.09, 0.59 **91.** $-4, -1.37$

Section 16.5

Practice Exercises

1. $(-2, 2)$ **2.** $(-4, 2)$ **3.** $\left[-\frac{2}{3}, 2\right]$ **4.** { } or $\varnothing$ **5.** $(-\infty, -10] \cup [2, \infty)$ **6.** $(-\infty, \infty)$ **7.** $(-\infty, 0) \cup (12, \infty)$ **8.** 2

Vocabulary and Readiness Check 16.5 **1.** D **3.** C **5.** A

Exercise Set 16.5

1.  ; $[-4, 4]$ **3.** ; $(1, 5)$ **5.**  ; $(-5, -1)$ **7.** ; $[-10, 3]$ **9.** ; $[-5, 5]$

11. 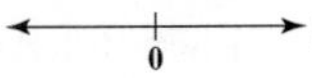 ; $\varnothing$ **13.** ; $[0, 12]$ **15.** 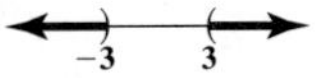 ; $(-\infty, -3) \cup (3, \infty)$ **17.**  ; $(-\infty, -24] \cup [4, \infty)$

19.  ; $(-\infty, -4) \cup (4, \infty)$ **21.**  ; $(-\infty, \infty)$ **23.** 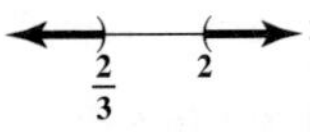 ; $\left(-\infty, \frac{2}{3}\right) \cup (2, \infty)$ **25.**  ; $\{0\}$

27.  ; $\left(-\infty, -\frac{3}{8}\right) \cup \left(-\frac{3}{8}, \infty\right)$ **29.**  ; $[-2, 2]$ **31.** 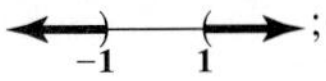 ; $(-\infty, -1) \cup (1, \infty)$

33.  ; $(-5, 11)$ **35.** 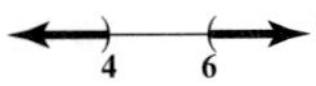 ; $(-\infty, 4) \cup (6, \infty)$ **37.** 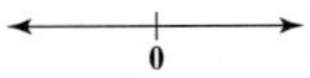 ; $\varnothing$ **39.**  ; $(-\infty, \infty)$

41.  ; $[-2, 9]$ **43.**  ; $(-\infty, -11] \cup [1, \infty)$ **45.** ; $(-\infty, 0) \cup (0, \infty)$ **47.** ; $(-\infty, \infty)$

49. 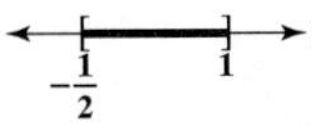 ; $\left[-\frac{1}{2}, 1\right]$ **51.**  ; $(-\infty, -3) \cup (0, \infty)$ **53.** 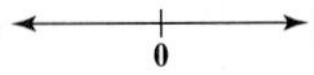 ; $\varnothing$ **55.** 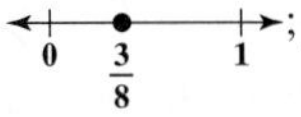 ; $\frac{3}{8}$

57. 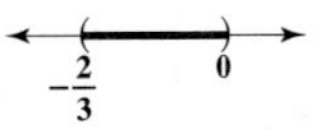 ; $\left(-\frac{2}{3}, 0\right)$ **59.** 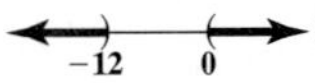 ; $(-\infty, -12) \cup (0, \infty)$ **61.** ; $[-1, 8]$ **63.** 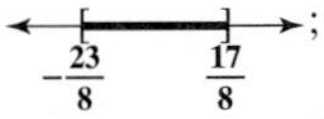 ; $\left[-\frac{23}{8}, \frac{17}{8}\right]$

65. $(-2, 5)$ **67.** $5, -2$ **69.** $(-\infty, -7] \cup [17, \infty)$ **71.** $-\frac{9}{4}$ **73.** $(-2, 1)$ **75.** $2, \frac{4}{3}$ **77.** $\varnothing$ **79.** $\frac{19}{2}, -\frac{17}{2}$ **81.** $\left(-\infty, -\frac{25}{3}\right) \cup \left(\frac{35}{3}, \infty\right)$

83. a. $\{-5, 11\}$ **b.** $(-5, 11)$ **c.** $(-\infty, -5] \cup [11, \infty)$ **85. a.** $\{-8, 4\}$ **b.** $[-8, 4]$ **c.** $(-\infty, -8) \cup (4, \infty)$ **87.** $\frac{1}{6}$ **89.** 0 **91.** $\frac{1}{3}$

93. -1.5 **95.** 0 **97.** $|x| < 7$ **99.** $|x| \le 5$ **101.** answers may vary **103.** $3.45 < x < 3.55$

The Bigger Picture

1. -8 **2.** $-13, 21$ **3.** $(-\infty, 6]$ **4.** $(-7, 5]$ **5.** $-\frac{13}{2}$ **6.** $\varnothing$ **7.** -50 **8.** -5 **9.** $\left[-\frac{9}{5}, 1\right]$ **10.** $(\infty, -13) \cup (-9, \infty)$ **11.** $-3, \frac{23}{9}$ **12.** $-11, -\frac{9}{7}$

Chapter 16 Vocabulary Check **1.** compound inequality **2.** contradiction **3.** intersection **4.** union **5.** identity **6.** absolute value **7.** solution **8.** linear inequality in one variable **9.** linear equation in one variable

Chapter 16 Review **1.** 12 **3.** $\varnothing$ **5.** $\frac{17}{5}$ **7.** -1.51 **9.** $(3, \infty)$ **11.** $(-4, \infty)$ **13.** $(-\infty, 7]$ **15.** $(-\infty, 1)$ **17.** more economical to use housekeeper for more than 35 pounds per week **19.** 9.6 **21.** $\left[2, \frac{5}{2}\right]$ **23.** $\left(\frac{1}{8}, 2\right)$ **25.** $\left(\frac{7}{8}, \frac{27}{20}\right]$ **27.** $\left(\frac{11}{3}, \infty\right)$ **29.** 5, 11 **31.** $-1, \frac{11}{3}$ **33.** $-\frac{1}{6}$ **35.** $\varnothing$ **37.** $5, -\frac{1}{3}$ **39.** 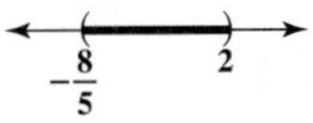 $\left(-\frac{8}{5}, 2\right)$ **41.**  $(-\infty, -3) \cup (3, \infty)$ **43.**  $\varnothing$

45. 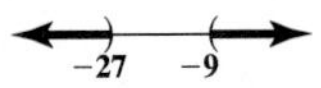 $(-\infty, -27) \cup (-9, \infty)$ **47.** 2 **49.** $(2, \infty)$ **51.** $(-\infty, \infty)$ **53.** $3, -3$ **55.** $-10, -\frac{4}{3}$ **57.** $\left(-\frac{1}{2}, 2\right)$

Chapter 16 Test **1.** $-\frac{29}{17}$ **2.** 0.15 **3.** $1, \frac{2}{3}$ **4.** $\varnothing$ **5.** $(5, \infty)$ **6.** $(-\infty, 2]$ **7.** $\left(\frac{3}{2}, 5\right]$ **8.** $(-\infty, -2) \cup \left(\frac{4}{3}, \infty\right)$ **9.** $(-\infty, -5]$

10. $(-\infty, -2]$ **11.** $[-3, -1)$ **12.** $(-\infty, \infty)$ **13.** $(3, 7)$ **14.** $3, -\frac{1}{5}$ **15.** $(-\infty, \infty)$ **16.** $\frac{3}{2}$ **17.** **18.**

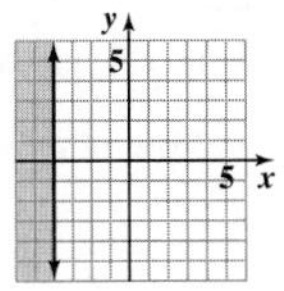

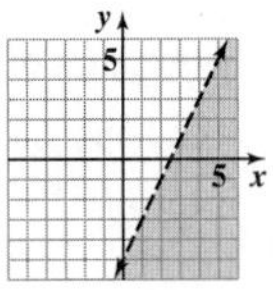

19. $(-\infty, -3)$ **20.** $(-3, \infty)$ **21.** more than 850 sunglasses

Chapter 16 Cumulative Review **1. a.** {101, 102, 103, ...} **b.** {2, 3, 4, 5} **3. a.** 3 **b.** $\frac{1}{7}$ **c.** −2.7 **d.** −8 **e.** 0 **5. a.** −14 **b.** −4 **c.** 5 **d.** −10.2 **e.** $-\frac{5}{21}$ **7. a.** 3 **b.** 5 **c.** $\frac{1}{2}$ **d.** −6 **e.** not a real number **9. a.** −2 **b.** −18 **c.** −1 **d.** −12 **11. a.** $x + 5 = 20$ **b.** $2(3 + y) = 4$ **c.** $x - 8 = 2x$ **d.** $\frac{z}{9} = 9 + z$ **13.** 2 **15.** all real numbers **17. a.** $3x + 3$ **b.** $12x - 3$ **19.** 23, 49, 92 **21.** $y = \frac{2x + 7}{3}$ or $y = \frac{2x}{3} + \frac{7}{3}$ **23.** $b = \frac{2A - Bh}{h}$ **25. a.** $[2, \infty)$ **b.** $(-\infty, -1)$ **c.** (0.5, 3]; Sec. 16.2, Ex. 1 **27.** $\left[\frac{5}{2}, \infty\right)$; Sec. 16.2, Ex. 5 **29. a.** $(-\infty, \infty)$ **b.** ∅; Sec. 16.2, Ex. 7 **31.** {4, 6}; Sec. 16.3, Ex. 1 **33.** $(-\infty, 4)$; Sec. 16.3, Ex. 2 **35.** {2, 3, 4, 5, 6, 8}; Sec. 16.3, Ex. 6 **37.** $(-\infty, \infty)$; Sec. 16.3, Ex. 8 **39.** 2, −2; Sec. 16.4, Ex. 1 **41.** 24, −20; Sec. 16.4, Ex. 3 **43.** 4; Sec. 16.4, Ex. 9 **45.** [−3, 3]; Sec. 16.5, Ex. 1 **47.** $(-\infty, \infty)$; Sec. 16.5, Ex. 6

Chapter 17 Systems of Linear Equations and Inequalities

Section 17.1

Practice Exercises

1. a. yes **b.** no **2. a.** infinite number of solutions of the form $\{(x, y) \mid 3x - 2y = 4\}$ or $\{(x, y) \mid -9x + 6y = -12\}$

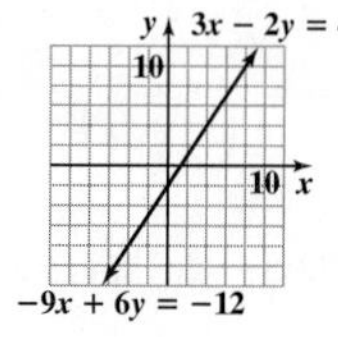

2. b. solution: (1, 5)

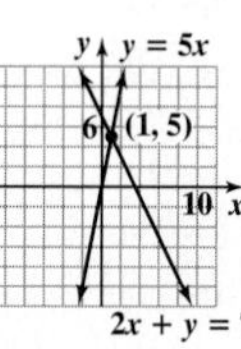

c. no solution

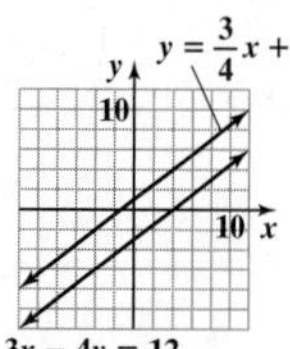

3. (−5.23, 0.29)

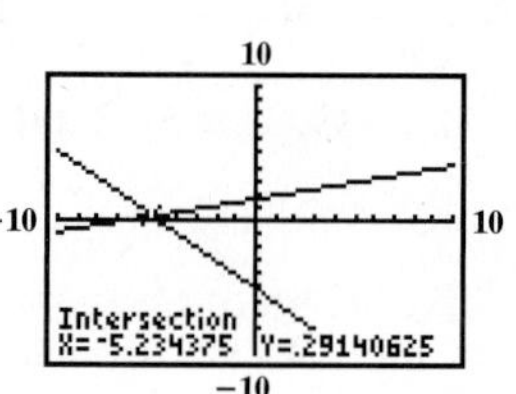

4. $\left(-\frac{1}{2}, 5\right)$ **5.** $\left(-\frac{9}{5}, -\frac{2}{5}\right)$ **6.** (2, 1) **7.** (−2, 0) **8.** ∅ or { } **9.** $\{(x, y) \mid -3x + 2y = -1\}$ or $\{(x, y) \mid 9x - 6y = 3\}$ **10.** 730 units

Vocabulary and Readiness Check 17.1 **1.** B **3.** A

Exercise Set 17.1 **1.** yes **3.** no **5.** no **7.** (1.5, 1) **9.** (−2, 0.75) **11.** (2, −1)

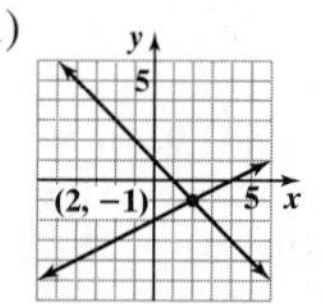

13. (1, 2)

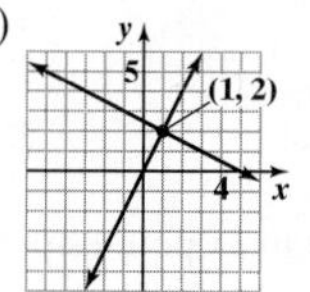

15. ∅

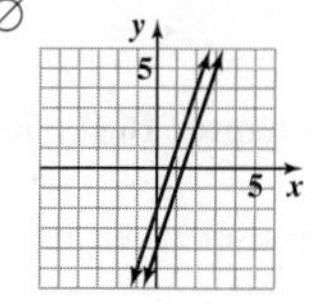

17. No; answers may vary **19.** (2, 8) **21.** (0, −9) **23.** (1, −1) **25.** (−5, 3) **27.** $\left(\frac{5}{2}, \frac{5}{4}\right)$ **29.** (1, −2) **31.** (8, 2) **33.** (7, 2) **35.** ∅ **37.** $\{(x, y) \mid 3x + y = 1\}$ **39.** $\left(\frac{3}{2}, 1\right)$ **41.** (2, −1) **43.** (−5, 3) **45.** $\{(x, y) \mid 3x + 9y = 12\}$ **47.** ∅ **49.** $\left(\frac{1}{2}, \frac{1}{5}\right)$ **51.** (9, 9) **53.** $\{(x, y) \mid x = 3y + 2\}$ **55.** $\left(-\frac{1}{4}, \frac{1}{2}\right)$ **57.** (3, 2) **59.** (7, −3) **61.** ∅ **63.** (3, 4) **65.** (−2, 1) **67.** (1.2, −3.6) **69.** true **71.** false **73.** $6y - 4z = 25$ **75.** $x + 10y = 2$ **77.** 5000 DVDs; $21 **79.** supply greater than demand **81.** (1875, 4687.5) **83.** makes money **85.** for x-values greater than 1875 **87.** answers may vary; One possibility: $\begin{cases} -2x + y = 1 \\ x - 2y = -8 \end{cases}$ **89. a.** Consumption of red meat is decreasing while consumption of poultry is increasing. **b.** (35, 103) **c.** In the year 2035, red meat and poultry consumption will each be about 103 pounds per person.

Section 17.2

Practice Exercises

1. a. 2037 **b.** yes; answers may vary **2.** 12 and 17 **3.** Atlantique: 500 kph; V150: 575 kph **4.** 0.95 liter of water; 0.05 liter of 99% HCL **5.** 1500 packages **6.** 40°, 60°, 80°

Exercise Set 17.2 **1.** 10 and 8 **3. a.** Enterprise class: 1101 ft; Nimitz class: 1092 ft **b.** 3.67 football fields **5.** plane: 520 mph; wind: 40 mph **7.** 20 qt of 4%; 40 qt of 1% **9.** United Kingdom: 32,071 students; Italy: 24,858 students **11.** 9 large frames; 13 small frames **13.** -10 and -8 **15.** 2007 **17.** tablets: \$0.80; pens: \$0.20 **19.** B737: 450 mph; Piper: 90 mph **21. a.** answers may vary but notice the slope of each function **b.** 1991 **23.** 28 cm; 28 cm; 37 cm **25.** 600 mi **27.** $x = 75; y = 105$ **29.** 625 units **31.** 3000 units **33.** 1280 units **35. a.** $R(x) = 450x$ **b.** $C(x) = 200x + 6000$ **c.** 24 desks

Integrated Review **1.** C **2.** D **3.** A **4.** B **5.** $(1, 3)$ **6.** $\left(\frac{4}{3}, \frac{16}{3}\right)$ **7.** $(2, -1)$ **8.** $(5, 2)$ **9.** $\left(\frac{3}{2}, 1\right)$ **10.** $\left(-2, \frac{3}{4}\right)$ **11.** $\varnothing$ **12.** $\{(x, y) \mid 2x - 5y = 3\}$ **13.** $\left(1, \frac{1}{3}\right)$ **14.** $\left(3, \frac{3}{4}\right)$ **15.** 19 and 27

Section 17.3

Practice Exercises

1. Solution Region

2.

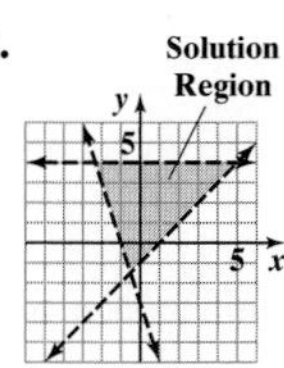

3.

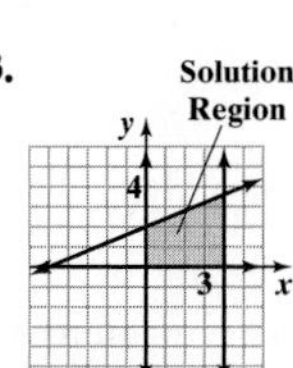

Vocabulary and Readiness Check 17.3 **1.** system **3.** corner

Exercise Set 17.3 **1.**

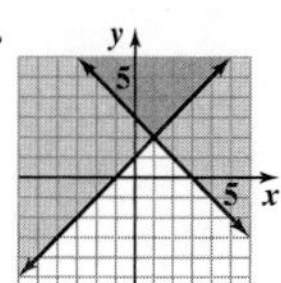

3.

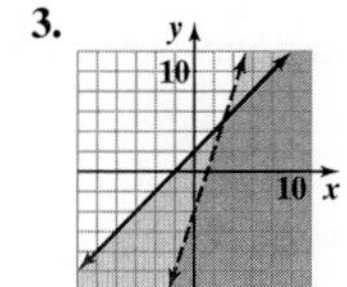

5.

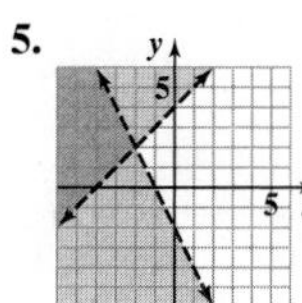

7.

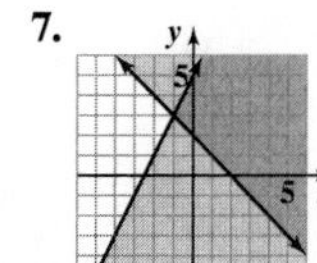

9.

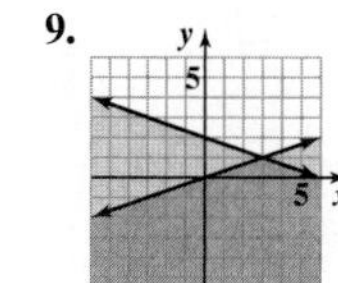

11.

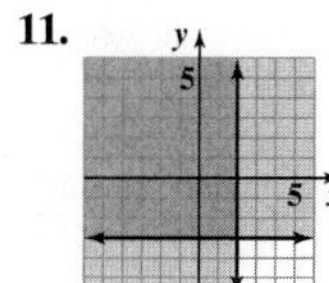

13.

15.

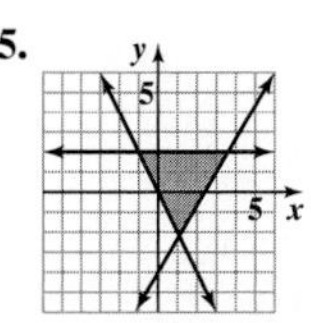

17.

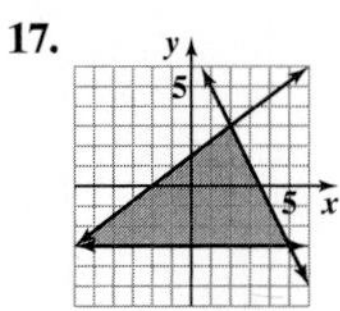

19.

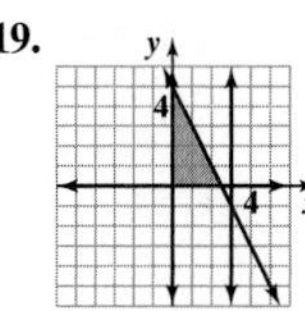

21. C **23.** D **25.** 9 **27.** $\frac{4}{9}$ **29.** 5 **31.** 59 **33.** the line $y = 3$ **35.** answers may vary

Chapter 17 Vocabulary Check **1.** system of equations **2.** solution **3.** consistent **4.** inconsistent

Chapter 17 Review **1.** $(-3, 1)$ **3.** $\varnothing$ **5.** $\left(3, \frac{8}{3}\right)$ **8.** 58 mph; 65 mph **10.** 20 L of 10% solution; 30 L of 60% solution **12.** two sides: 22 cm each; third side; 29 cm **13.**

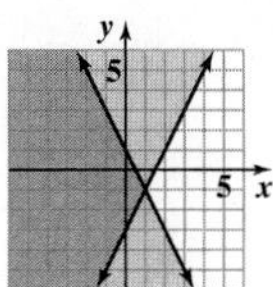

15.

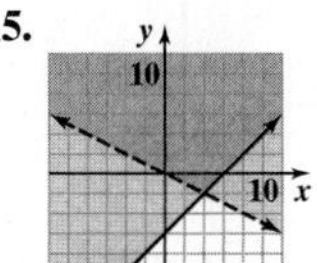

17.

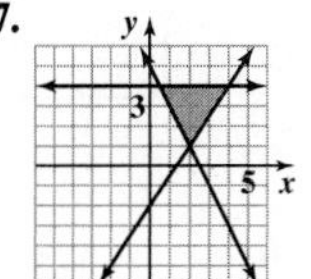

19.

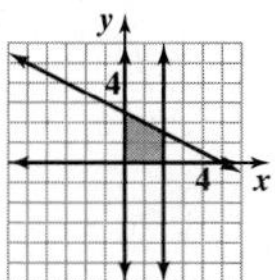

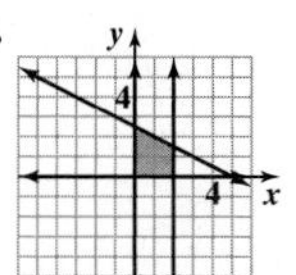

21. $\left(\frac{7}{3}, -\frac{8}{3}\right)$ **23.** $\{(x, y) \mid 5x - 2y = 10\}$ **27.** 2000

Chapter 17 Test **1.** $(1, 3)$

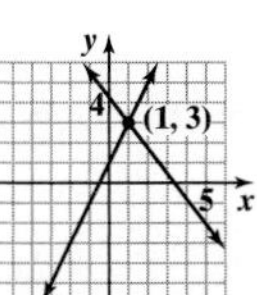

2. $\varnothing$

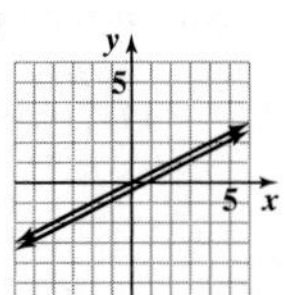

3. $(2, -3)$ **4.** $\{(x, y) \mid 10x + 4y = 10\}$

5. $\left(\frac{7}{2}, -10\right)$ **6.** $\{(x, y) \mid x - y = -2\}$ **7.** $(5, -3)$ **8.** 53 double rooms; 27 single rooms **9.** 5 gal of 10%; 15 gal of 20%

10. 800 packages **11.**

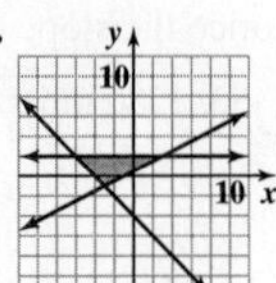

Chapter 17 Cumulative Review **1. a.** true **b.** true **3. a.** 6 **b.** -7 **5. a.** -4 **b.** $-\frac{3}{7}$ **c.** 11.2 **7. a.** $6x + 3y$ **b.** $-3x + 1$ **c.** $0.7ab - 1.4a$ **9. a.** $-2x + 4$ **b.** $8yz$ **c.** $4z + 6.1$ **11.** -4 **13.** -4 **15.** 25 cm, 62 cm, 62 cm

17. $[-10, \infty)$; Sec. 16.2, Ex. 3 **19.** $(-3, 2)$; Sec. 16.3, Ex. 4 **21.** $1, -1$; Sec. 16.4, Ex. 4 **23.** $(4, 8)$; Sec. 16.5, Ex. 2

25. a. IV **b.** y-axis **c.** II **d.** x-axis **e.** III **f.** I; **27.** no; Sec. 15.1, Ex. 4 **29. a.** 5 **b.** 7 **c.** 4 Sec. 15.1, Ex. 7

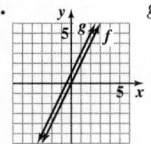

31. $g(x)$ is the same as $f(x)$ shifted up one unit; Sec. 15.2, Ex. 1 **33.** slope: $\frac{3}{4}$; y-intercept: $(0, -1)$ **35. a.** parallel

b. neither **c.** perpendicular **37.** $f(x) = \frac{5}{8}x - \frac{5}{2}$ **39.** **41. a.** yes **b.** no; Sec. 17.1, Ex. 1

43. $(-1, 2)$

Chapter 18 Rational Expressions

Section 18.1

Practice Exercises

1. a. $\{x \mid x \text{ is a real number}\}$ **b.** $\{x \mid x \text{ is a real number and } x \neq -3\}$ **c.** $\{x \mid x \text{ is a real number and } x \neq 2, x \neq 3\}$

2. a. $\{x \mid x \text{ is a real number and } x \neq -3\}$ **b.** $\left\{x \middle| x \text{ is a real number and } x \neq 1, x \neq \frac{5}{3}\right\}$

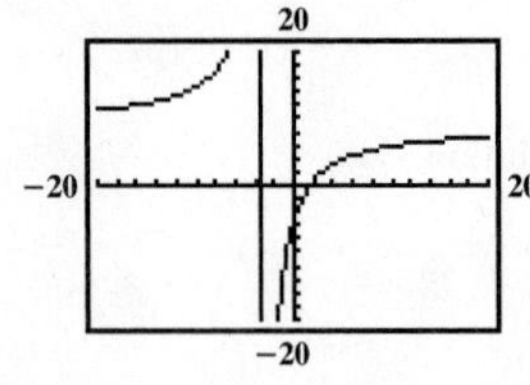

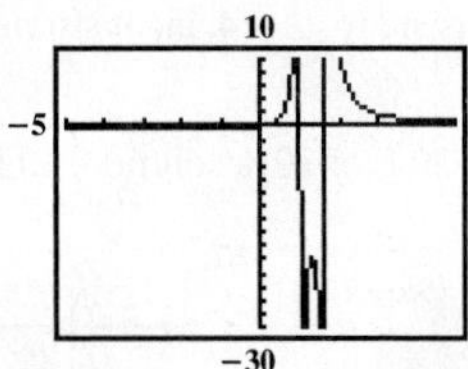

3. a. $\frac{1}{2z - 1}$ **b.** $\frac{5x + 3}{6x - 5}$ **4. a.** 1 **b.** -1 **5.** $-\frac{5(2 + x)}{x + 3}$ **6. a.** $x^2 - 4x + 16$ **b.** $\frac{5}{z - 3}$ **7. a.** $\frac{2n + 1}{n(n - 1)}$ **b.** $-x^2$

8. a. $\frac{-y^3}{21(y + 3)}$ **b.** $\frac{7x + 2}{x + 2}$ **9.** $\frac{5}{3(x - 3)}$ **10. a.** \$7.20 **b.** \$3.60

Vocabulary and Readiness Check 18.1 **1.** rational **3.** domain **5.** 1 **7.** $\frac{-a}{b}; \frac{a}{-b}$ **9.** $\frac{xy}{10}$ **11.** $\frac{2y}{3x}$ **13.** $\frac{m^2}{36}$

Exercise Set 18.1 **1.** $\{x \mid x \text{ is a real number}\}$ **3.** $\{t \mid t \text{ is a real number and } t \neq 0\}$ **5.** $\{x \mid x \text{ is a real number and } x \neq 7\}$

7. $\left\{x \middle| x \text{ is a real number and } x \neq \frac{1}{3}\right\}$ **9.** $\{x \mid x \text{ is a real number and } x \neq -2, x \neq 0, x \neq 1\}$ **11.** $\{x \mid x \text{ is a real number and } x \neq 2, x \neq -2\}$

13. $1 - 2x$ **15.** $x - 3$ **17.** $\frac{9}{7}$ **19.** $x - 4$ **21.** -1 **23.** $-(x + 7)$ **25.** $\frac{2x + 1}{x - 1}$ **27.** $\frac{x^2 + 5x + 25}{2}$ **29.** $\frac{x - 2}{2x^2 + 1}$

31. $\frac{1}{3x + 5}$ **33.** $-\frac{4}{5}$ **35.** $-\frac{6a}{2a + 1}$ **37.** $\frac{3}{2(x - 1)}$ **39.** $\frac{x + 2}{x + 3}$ **41.** $\frac{3a}{5(a - b)}$ **43.** $\frac{1}{6}$ **45.** $\frac{x}{3}$ **47.** $\frac{4a^2}{a - b}$

49. $\frac{4}{(x+2)(x+3)}$ **51.** $\frac{1}{2}$ **53.** -1 **55.** $\frac{8(a-2)}{3(a+2)}$ **57.** $\frac{(x+2)(x+3)}{4}$ **59.** $\frac{2(x+3)(x-3)}{5(x^2-8x-15)}$ **61.** $r^2 - rs + s^2$

63. $\frac{8}{x^2y}$ **65.** $\frac{(y+5)(2x-1)}{(y+2)(5x+1)}$ **67.** $\frac{5(3a+2)}{a}$ **69.** $\frac{5x^2-2}{(x-1)^2}$ **71.** $\frac{10}{3}, -8, -\frac{7}{3}$ **73.** $-\frac{17}{48}, \frac{2}{7}, -\frac{3}{8}$

75. a. \$200 million **b.** \$500 million **c.** \$300 million **d.** $\{x|x$ is a real number$\}$ **77.** $\frac{7}{5}$ **79.** $\frac{1}{12}$ **81.** $\frac{11}{16}$

83. b and d **85.** no; answers may vary **87.** $\frac{5}{x-2}$ sq m **89.** $\frac{(x+2)(x-1)^2}{x^5}$ ft **91.** answers may vary

93. a. 1 **b.** -1 **c.** neither **d.** -1 **e.** -1 **f.** 1 **95.** $(x-5)(2x+7)$ **97.** $0, \frac{20}{9}, \frac{60}{7}, 20, \frac{140}{3}$, 180, 380, 1980;

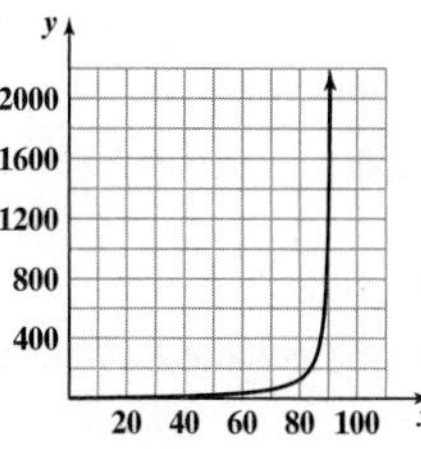

99. $2x^2(x^n + 2)$ **101.** $\frac{1}{10y(y^n+3)}$ **103.** $\frac{y^n+1}{2(y^n-1)}$

Section 18.2

Practice Exercises

1. a. $\frac{9+x}{11z^2}$ **b.** $\frac{3x}{4}$ **c.** $x-4$ **d.** $\frac{-3}{2a^2}$ **2. a.** $18x^3y^5$ **b.** $(x-2)(x+3)$ **c.** $(b-4)^2(b+4)(2b+3)$ **d.** $-4(y-3)(y+3)$

3. a. $\frac{20p+3}{5p^4q}$ **b.** $\frac{5y^2+19y-12}{(y+3)(y-3)}$ **c.** 3 **4.** $\frac{t^2-t-15}{(t+5)(t-5)(t+2)}$ **5.** $\frac{5x^2-12x-3}{(3x+1)(x-2)(2x-5)}$ **6.** $\frac{4}{x-2}$

Vocabulary and Readiness Check 18.2 **1.** a, b **3.** c **5.** $\frac{12}{y}$ **7.** $\frac{35}{y^2}$ **9.** $\frac{-x+4}{2x}$ **11.** $\frac{16}{y-2}$

Exercise Set 18.2 **1.** $-\frac{3}{xz^2}$ **3.** $\frac{x+2}{x-2}$ **5.** $x-2$ **7.** $\frac{-1}{x-2}$ or $\frac{1}{2-x}$ **9.** $-\frac{5}{x}$ **11.** $35x$ **13.** $x(x+1)$ **15.** $(x+7)(x-7)$

17. $6(x+2)(x-2)$ **19.** $(a+b)(a-b)^2$ **21.** $-4x(x+3)(x-3)$ **23.** $\frac{17}{6x}$ **25.** $\frac{35-4y}{14y^2}$ **27.** $\frac{-13x+4}{(x+4)(x-4)}$ **29.** $\frac{3}{x+4}$ **31.** 0

33. $-\frac{x}{x-1}$ **35.** $\frac{-x+1}{x-2}$ **37.** $\frac{y^2+2y+10}{(y+4)(y-4)(y-2)}$ **39.** $\frac{5(x^2+x-4)}{(3x+2)(x+3)(2x-5)}$ **41.** $\frac{-x^2+10x+19}{(x-2)(x+1)(x+3)}$

43. $\frac{x^2+4x+2}{(2x+5)(x-7)(x-1)}$ **45.** $\frac{5a+1}{(a+1)^2(a-1)}$ **47.** $\frac{3}{x^2y^3}$ **49.** $-\frac{5}{x}$ **51.** $\frac{25}{6(x+5)}$ **53.** $\frac{-2x-1}{x^2(x-3)}$ **55.** $\frac{b(2a-b)}{(a+b)(a-b)}$

57. $\frac{2(x+8)}{(x+2)^2(x-2)}$ **59.** $\frac{3x^2+23x-7}{(2x-1)(x-5)(x+3)}$ **61.** $\frac{5-2x}{2(x+1)}$ **63.** $\frac{2(x^2+x-21)}{(x+3)^2(x-3)}$ **65.** $\frac{6x}{(x+3)(x-3)^2}$ **67.** $\frac{4}{3}$

69. $\frac{2x^2+9x-18}{6x^2}$ or $\frac{(x+6)(2x-3)}{6x^2}$ **71.** $\frac{4a^2}{9(a-1)}$ **73.** 4 **75.** $-\frac{4}{x-1}$ **77.** $-\frac{32}{x(x+2)(x-2)}$ **79.** 10 **81.** $4+x^2$ **83.** 10

85. 2 **87.** 3 **89.** 5 m **91.** $\frac{2x-3}{x^2+1} - \frac{x-6}{x^2+1} = \frac{2x-3-x+6}{x^2+1} = \frac{x+3}{x^2+1}$ **93.** $\frac{4x}{x+5}$ ft; $\frac{x^2}{(x+5)^2}$ sq ft **95.** answers may vary

97. answers may vary **99.** answers may vary **101.** $\frac{3}{2x}$ **103.** $\frac{4-3x}{x^2}$ **105.**

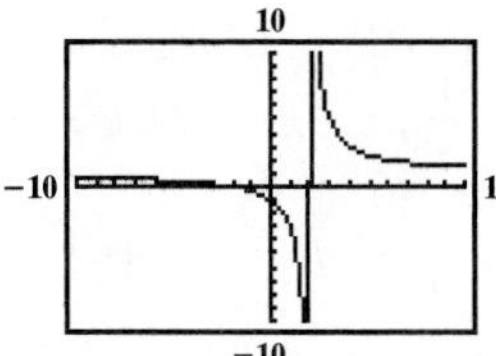

Section 18.3

Practice Exercises

1. a. $\frac{1}{12m}$ **b.** $\frac{8x(x+4)}{3(x-4)}$ **c.** $\frac{b^2}{a^2}$ **2. a.** $\frac{8x(x+4)}{3(x-4)}$ **b.** $\frac{b^2}{a^2}$ **3.** $\frac{y(3xy+1)}{x^2(1+xy)}$ **4.** $\frac{1-6x}{15+6x}$

Vocabulary and Readiness Check 18.3 **1.** $\frac{7}{1+z}$ **3.** $\frac{1}{x^2}$ **5.** $\frac{2}{x}$ **7.** $\frac{1}{9y}$

Exercise Set 18.3 **1.** 4 **3.** $\frac{7}{13}$ **5.** $\frac{4}{x}$ **7.** $\frac{9(x-2)}{9x^2+4}$ **9.** $2x+y$ **11.** $\frac{2(x+1)}{2x-1}$ **13.** $\frac{2x+3}{4-9x}$ **15.** $\frac{1}{x^2-2x+4}$ **17.** $\frac{x}{5(x-2)}$

19. $\frac{x-2}{2x-1}$ **21.** $\frac{x}{2-3x}$ **23.** $-\frac{y}{x+y}$ **25.** $-\frac{2x^3}{y(x-y)}$ **27.** $\frac{2x+1}{y}$ **29.** $\frac{x-3}{9}$ **31.** $\frac{1}{x+2}$ **33.** 2

35. $\frac{xy^2}{x^2+y^2}$ **37.** $\frac{2b^2+3a}{b(b-a)}$ **39.** $\frac{x}{(x+1)(x-1)}$ **41.** $\frac{1+a}{1-a}$ **43.** $\frac{x(x+6y)}{2y}$ **45.** $\frac{5a}{2(a+2)}$ **47.** $xy(5y+2x)$

49. $\frac{xy}{2x+5y}$ **51.** $\frac{x^2y^2}{4}$ **53.** $-9x^3y^4$ **55.** $-4, 14$ **57.** a and c **59.** $\frac{770a}{770-s}$ **61.** a, b **63.** $\frac{1+x}{2+x}$ **65.** $x(x+1)$

67. $\frac{x-3y}{x+3y}$ **69.** $3a^2+4a+4$ **71. a.** $\frac{1}{a+h}$ **b.** $\frac{1}{a}$ **c.** $\frac{\frac{1}{a+h}-\frac{1}{a}}{h}$ **d.** $\frac{-1}{a(a+h)}$ **73. a.** $\frac{3}{a+h+1}$

b. $\frac{3}{a+1}$ **c.** $\frac{\frac{3}{a+h+1}-\frac{3}{a+1}}{h}$ **d.** $\frac{-3}{(a+h+1)(a+1)}$

Section 18.4

Practice Exercises

1. 4 **2.** 7 **3.** { } or $\varnothing$ **4.** -1 **5.** 1 **6.** 12, -1

Vocabulary and Readiness Check 18.4 **1.** c **3.** a

Exercise Set 18.4 **1.** 72 **3.** 2 **5.** 6 **7.** 2, -2 **9.** $\varnothing$ **11.** $-\frac{28}{3}$ **13.** 3 **15.** -8 **17.** 3 **19.** $\varnothing$ **21.** 1 **23.** 3 **25.** -1

27. 6 **29.** $\frac{1}{3}$ **31.** $-5, 5$ **33.** 3 **35.** 7 **37.** $\varnothing$ **39.** $\frac{4}{3}$ **41.** -12 **43.** $1, \frac{11}{4}$ **45.** $-5, -1$ **47.** $-\frac{7}{5}$ **49.** 5

51. length, 15 in.; width, 10 in. **53.** 36% **55.** 12–19 **57.** 40,000 students **59.** answers may vary **61.** 800 pencil sharpeners **63.** $\frac{1}{9}, -\frac{1}{4}$

65. 3, 2 **67.** 1.39 **69.** -0.08 **71.** 1, 2 **73.** $-3, -\frac{3}{4}$ **75.** **77.**

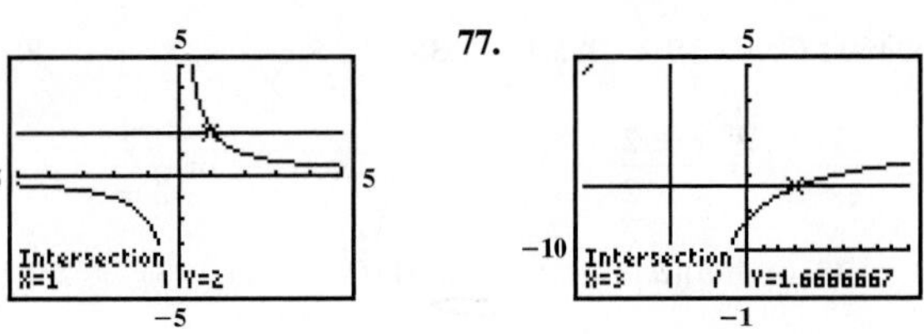

Section 18.5

Practice Exercises

1. $k=\frac{4}{3}; y=\frac{4}{3}x$ **2.** $18\frac{3}{4}$ inches **3.** $k=45; b=\frac{45}{a}$ **4.** $P=653\frac{1}{3}$ kilopascals **5.** $A=kpa$ **6.** $k=4; y=\frac{4}{x^3}$ **7.** $k=81; y=\frac{81z}{x^3}$

Vocabulary and Readiness Check 18.5 **1.** direct **3.** joint **5.** inverse **7.** direct

Exercise Set 18.5 **1.** $k=\frac{1}{5}; y=\frac{1}{5}x$ **3.** $k=\frac{3}{2}; y=\frac{3}{2}x$ **5.** $k=14; y=14x$ **7.** $k=0.25; y=0.25x$ **9.** 4.05 lb **11.** 204,706 tons

13. $k=30; y=\frac{30}{x}$ **15.** $k=700; y=\frac{700}{x}$ **17.** $k=2; y=\frac{2}{x}$ **19.** $k=0.14; y=\frac{0.14}{x}$ **21.** 54 mph **23.** 72 amps **25.** divided by 4

27. $x=kyz$ **29.** $r=kst^3$ **31.** $k=\frac{1}{3}; y=\frac{1}{3}x^3$ **33.** $k=0.2; y=0.2\sqrt{x}$ **35.** $k=1.3; y=\frac{1.3}{x^2}$ **37.** $k=3; y=3xz^3$ **39.** 22.5 tons

41. 15π cu in. **43.** 8 ft **45.** $y=kx$ **47.** $a=\frac{k}{b}$ **49.** $y=kxz$ **51.** $y=\frac{k}{x^3}$ **53.** $y=\frac{kx}{p^2}$ **55.** $C=8\pi$ in.; $A=16\pi$ sq in.

57. $C=18\pi$ cm; $A=81\pi$ sq cm **59.** 9 **61.** 1 **63.** $\frac{1}{2}$ **65.** $\frac{2}{3}$ **67.** a **69.** c **71.** multiplied by 8 **73.** multiplied by 2

75. **77.**

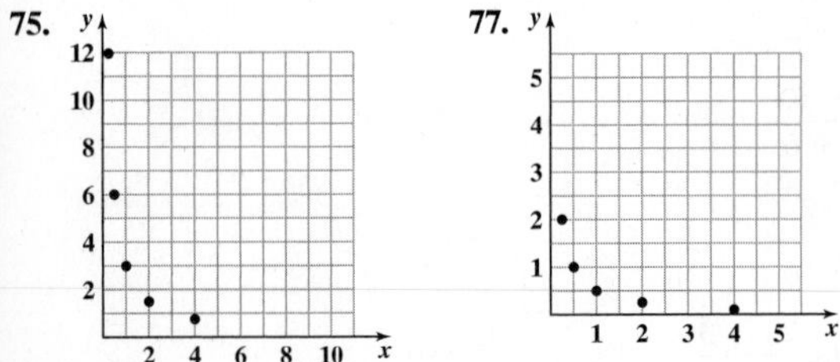

The Bigger Picture

1. $\left(-2, \frac{16}{7}\right)$ **2.** $-2, \frac{16}{7}$ **3.** ± 11 **4.** 5 **5.** $-\frac{8}{5}$ **6.** $(-\infty, 2]$ **7.** $(-\infty, -5]$ **8.** $(7, 10]$ **9.** $(-\infty, -17) \cup (18, \infty)$ **10.** $0, -\frac{1}{3}, \frac{7}{5}$

Integrated Review **1.** $\frac{1}{2}$ **2.** 10 **3.** $\frac{1+2x}{8}$ **4.** $\frac{15+x}{10}$ **5.** $\frac{2(x-4)}{(x+2)(x-1)}$ **6.** $-\frac{5(x-8)}{(x-2)(x+4)}$ **7.** 4 **8.** 8 **9.** -5 **10.** $-\frac{2}{3}$

11. $\frac{2x+5}{x(x-3)}$ **12.** $\frac{5}{2x}$ **13.** -2 **14.** $-\frac{y}{x}$ **15.** $\frac{(a+3)(a+1)}{a+2}$ **16.** $\frac{-a^2+31a+10}{5(a-6)(a+1)}$ **17.** $-\frac{1}{5}$ **18.** $-\frac{3}{13}$ **19.** $\frac{4a+1}{(3a+1)(3a-1)}$

20. $\frac{-a-8}{4a(a-2)}$ or $-\frac{a+8}{4a(a-2)}$ **21.** $-1, \frac{3}{2}$ **22.** $\frac{x^2-3x+10}{2(x+3)(x-3)}$ **23.** $\frac{3}{x+1}$ **24.** $\{x|x$ is a real number and $x \neq 2, x \neq -1\}$ **25.** -1
26. $\frac{22z-45}{3z(z-3)}$ **27. a.** $\frac{x}{5}-\frac{x}{4}+\frac{1}{10}$ **b.** Write each rational expression term so that the denominator is the LCD, 20. **c.** $\frac{-x+2}{20}$

28. a. $\frac{x}{5}-\frac{x}{4}=\frac{1}{10}$ **b.** Clear the equation of fractions by multiplying each term by the LCD, 20. **c.** -2 **29.** b **30.** d **31.** d **32.** a **33.** d

Chapter 18 Vocabulary Check **1.** complex fraction **2.** directly **3.** inversely **4.** least common denominator
5. jointly **6.** opposites **7.** rational expression **8.** equation, expression

Chapter 18 Review **1.** $\{x|x$ is a real number$\}$ **3.** $\{x|x$ is a real number and $x \neq 5\}$ **5.** $\{x|x$ is a real number and $x \neq 0, x \neq -8\}$ **7.** -1
9. $\frac{1}{x-1}$ **11.** $\frac{2(x-3)}{x-4}$ **13.** $-\frac{3}{2}$ **15.** $\frac{a-b}{2a}$ **17.** $\frac{12}{5}$ **19.** $\frac{a-b}{5a}$ **21.** $-\frac{1}{x}$ **23.** $60x^2y^5$ **25.** $5x(x-5)$ **27.** $\frac{4+x}{x-4}$
29. $\frac{3}{2(x-2)}$ **31.** $\frac{-7x-6}{5(x-3)(x+3)}$ **33.** $\frac{5a-1}{(a-1)^2(a+1)}$ **35.** $\frac{5-2x}{2(x-1)}$ **37.** $\frac{4-3x}{8+x}$ **39.** $\frac{5(4x-3)}{2(5x^2-2)}$ **41.** $\frac{x(5y+1)}{3y}$ **43.** $\frac{1+x}{1-x}$
45. $\frac{3}{a+h}$ **47.** $\frac{\frac{3}{a+h}-\frac{3}{a}}{h}$ **49.** 6 **51.** $\frac{3}{2}$ **53.** $\frac{2x+5}{x(x-7)}$ **55.** $\frac{-5(x+6)}{2x(x-3)}$ **56.** 9 **57.** 3.125 cu m **58.** 2 **60.** $\frac{3}{5x}$
62. $\frac{5(a-2)}{7}$ **64.** $\frac{13}{3x}$ **66.** $\frac{1}{x-2}$ **68.** $\frac{2}{15-2x}$ **70.** $\frac{2(x-1)}{x+6}$ **72.** 2

Chapter 18 Test **1.** $\{x|x$ is a real number and $x \neq 1\}$ **2.** $\{x|x$ is a real number and $x \neq -3, x \neq -1\}$ **3.** $-\frac{7}{8}$ **4.** $\frac{x}{x+9}$ **5.** x^2+2x+4
6. $\frac{5}{3x}$ **7.** $\frac{3}{x^3}$ **8.** $\frac{x+2}{2(x+3)}$ **9.** $-\frac{4(2x+9)}{5}$ **10.** -1 **11.** $\frac{1}{x(x+3)}$ **12.** $\frac{5x-2}{(x-3)(x+2)(x-2)}$ **13.** $\frac{-x+30}{6(x-7)}$
14. $\frac{3}{2}$ **15.** $\frac{64}{3}$ **16.** $\frac{(x-3)^2}{x-2}$ **17.** $\frac{4xy}{3z}+\frac{3}{z}+1$ **18.** $2x^2-x-2+\frac{2}{2x+1}$ **19.** 8 **20.** $\frac{2}{7}$ **21.** 3 **22.** $x=\frac{7a^2+b^2}{4a-b}$
23. 16 **24.** 9 **25.** 256 ft

Chapter 18 Cumulative Review

1. a. $8x$ **b.** $8x+3$ **c.** $x \div -7$ or $\frac{x}{-7}$ **d.** $2x-1.6$ **e.** $x-6$ **f.** $2(4+x)$ **3.** 2
5. $-20, -12.22, 0, 21.11, 37.78$; Sec. 1.8, Ex. 6 **7.** $\varnothing$; Sec. 3.4, Ex. 7 **9.** -1; Sec. 3.5, Ex. 8 **11.**

; Sec. 2.1, Ex. 5

13. a. function **b.** not a function **c.** function; Sec. 2.2, Ex. 2 **15.**

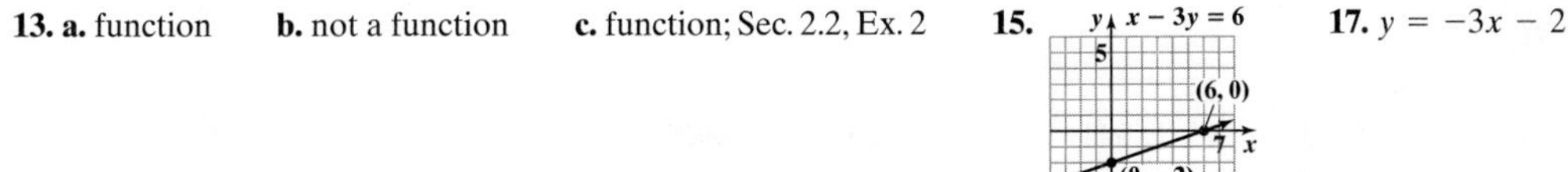

17. $y=-3x-2$;

19.

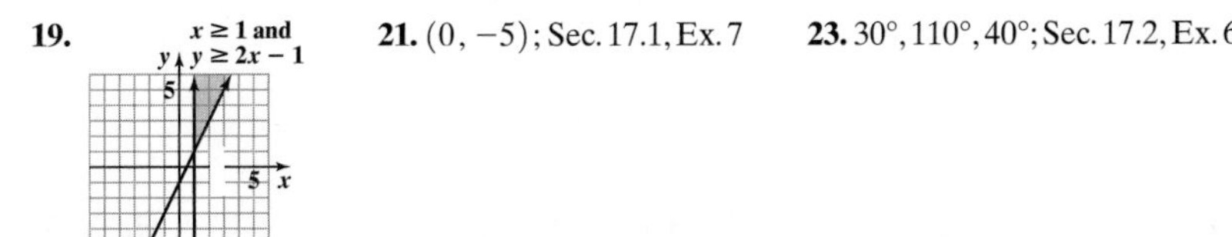

21. $(0, -5)$; Sec. 17.1, Ex. 7 **23.** $30°, 110°, 40°$; Sec. 17.2, Ex. 6

25. a. 1 **b.** -1 **c.** 1 **d.** 2 **26. a.** $4x^b$ **b.** y^{5a+6};
29. a. 2 **b.** 5 **c.** 1 **d.** 6 **e.** 0 **31.** $9+12a+6$ɔ $+4a^2+4ab+b^2$; **33.** $(b-6)(a+2)$;
35. $2(n^2-19n+40)$; **37.** $(x+2+y)(x+2-y)$; **39.** $-2, 6$; **41. a.** $\frac{1}{5x-1}$
b. $\frac{9x+4}{8x-7}$; Sec. 18.1, Ex. 2 **43.** $\frac{5k^2-7k+4}{(k+2)(k-2)(k-1)}$; Sec. 18.2, Ex. 4 **45.** -2; Sec. 18.4, Ex. 2

Answers to Selected Exercises

Chapter 19 Rational Exponents, Radicals, and Complex Numbers

Section 19.1

Practice Exercises

1. a. 7 **b.** 0 **c.** $\frac{4}{9}$ **d.** 0.8 **e.** z^4 **f.** $4b^2$ **g.** -6 **h.** not a real number **2.** 6.708 **3. a.** -1 **b.** 3 **c.** $\frac{3}{4}$ **d.** x^4 **e.** $-2x$
4. a. 10 **b.** -1 **c.** -9 **d.** not a real number **e.** $3x^3$ **5. a.** 4 **b.** $|x^7|$ **c.** $|x + 7|$ **d.** -7 **e.** $3x - 5$ **f.** $7|x|$ **g.** $|x + 2|$
6. a. 4 **b.** 2 **c.** 2 **d.** -2 **7.** **8.**

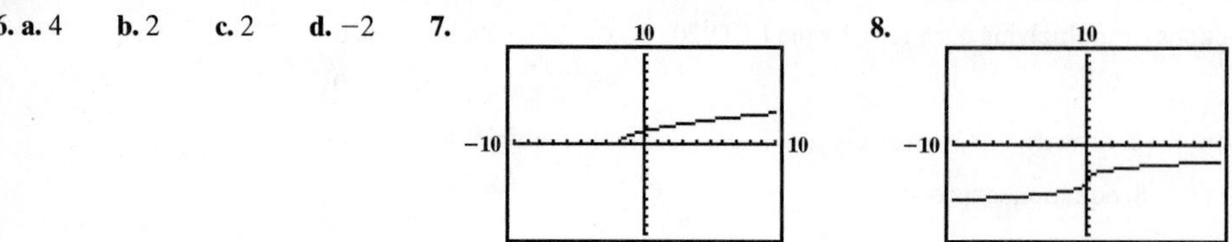

Vocabulary and Readiness Check 19.1
1. index; radical sign; radicand **3.** is not **5.** $[0,\infty)$ **7.** (16, 4) **9.** d **11.** d

Exercise Set 19.1 **1.** 10 **3.** $\frac{1}{2}$ **5.** 0.01 **7.** -6 **9.** x^5 **11.** $4y^3$ **13.** 2.646 **15.** 6.164 **17.** 14.142 **19.** 4 **21.** $\frac{1}{2}$
23. -1 **25.** x^4 **27.** $-3x^3$ **29.** -2 **31.** not a real number **33.** -2 **35.** x^4 **37.** $2x^2$ **39.** $9x^2$ **41.** $4x^2$
43. 8 **45.** -8 **47.** $2|x|$ **49.** x **51.** $|x - 5|$ **53.** $|x + 2|$ **55.** -11 **57.** $2x$ **59.** y^6 **61.** $5ab^{10}$
63. $-3x^4y^3$ **65.** a^4b **67.** $-2x^2y$ **69.** $\frac{5}{7}$ **71.** $\frac{x}{2y}$ **73.** $-\frac{z^7}{3x}$ **75.** $\frac{x}{2}$ **77.** $\sqrt{3}$ **79.** -1 **81.** -3 **83.** $\sqrt{7}$
85. C; $[0,\infty)$ **87.** D; $[3,\infty)$ **89.** A; $(-\infty, \infty)$ **91.** B; $(-\infty, \infty)$ **93.** $-32x^{15}y^{10}$ **95.** $-60x^7y^{10}z^5$ **97.** $\frac{x^9y^5}{2}$ **99.** not a real number
101. not a real number **103.** answers may vary **105.** 13 **107.** 18 **109.** 1.69 sq m **111.** answers may vary

Section 19.2

Practice Exercises

1. a. 6 **b.** 10 **c.** $\sqrt[5]{x}$ **d.** 1 **e.** -8 **f.** $5x^3$ **g.** $\sqrt[4]{3x}$ **2. a.** 64 **b.** -1 **c.** -27 **d.** $\frac{1}{125}$ **e.** $\sqrt[9]{(3x + 2)^5}$
3. a. $\frac{1}{27}$ **b.** $\frac{1}{16}$ **4. a.** $y^{10/3}$ **b.** $x^{17/20}$ **c.** $\frac{1}{9}$ **d.** $b^{2/9}$ **e.** $\frac{81}{x^3y^{11/3}}$ **5. a.** $x^{14/15} - x^{13/5}$ **b.** $x + 4x^{1/2} - 12$ **6.** $x^{-1/5}(2 - 7x)$
7. a. $\sqrt[3]{x}$ **b.** $\sqrt{6}$ **c.** $\sqrt[4]{a^2b}$ **8. a.** $\sqrt[12]{x^7}$ **b.** $\sqrt[15]{y^2}$ **c.** $\sqrt[6]{675}$

Vocabulary and Readiness Check 19.2 **1.** true **3.** true **5.** multiply **7.** A **9.** C **11.** B

Exercise Set 19.2 **1.** 7 **3.** 3 **5.** $\frac{1}{2}$ **7.** 13 **9.** $2\sqrt[3]{m}$ **11.** $3x^2$ **13.** -3 **15.** -2 **17.** 8 **19.** 16 **21.** not a real number
23. $\sqrt[5]{(2x)^3}$ **25.** $\sqrt[3]{(7x + 2)^2}$ **27.** $\frac{64}{27}$ **29.** $\frac{1}{16}$ **31.** $\frac{1}{16}$ **33.** not a real number **35.** $\frac{1}{x^{1/4}}$ **37.** $a^{2/3}$ **39.** $\frac{5x^{3/4}}{7}$ **41.** $a^{7/3}$ **43.** x
45. $3^{5/8}$ **47.** $y^{1/6}$ **49.** $8u^3$ **51.** $-b$ **53.** $\frac{1}{x^2}$ **55.** $27x^{2/3}$ **57.** $\frac{y}{z^{1/6}}$ **59.** $\frac{1}{x^{7/4}}$ **61.** $y - y^{7/6}$ **63.** $x^{5/3} - 2x^{2/3}$ **65.** $4x^{2/3} - 9$
67. $x^{8/3}(1 + x^{2/3})$ **69.** $x^{1/5}(x^{1/5} - 3)$ **71.** $x^{-1/3}(5 + x)$ **73.** $\sqrt{x}$ **75.** $\sqrt[3]{2}$ **77.** $2\sqrt{x}$ **79.** $\sqrt{xy}$ **81.** $\sqrt[3]{a^2b}$ **83.** $\sqrt{x + 3}$
85. $\sqrt[15]{y^{11}}$ **87.** $\sqrt[12]{b^5}$ **89.** $\sqrt[24]{x^{23}}$ **91.** $\sqrt{a}$ **93.** $\sqrt[6]{432}$ **95.** $\sqrt[15]{343y^5}$ **97.** $\sqrt[6]{125r^3s^2}$ **99.** $25 \cdot 3$ **101.** $16 \cdot 3$ or $4 \cdot 12$ **103.** $8 \cdot 2$
105. $27 \cdot 2$ **107.** 1509 calories **109.** 210.1 million **111.** $a^{1/3}$ **113.** $x^{1/5}$ **115.** 1.6818 **117.** 5.6645 **119.** $\frac{t^{1/2}}{u^{1/2}}$

Section 19.3

Practice Exercises

1. a. $\sqrt{35}$ **b.** $\sqrt{13z}$ **c.** 5 **d.** $\sqrt[3]{15x^2y}$ **e.** $\sqrt{\frac{5t}{2m}}$ **2. a.** $\frac{6}{7}$ **b.** $\frac{\sqrt{z}}{4}$ **c.** $\frac{5}{2}$ **d.** $\frac{\sqrt[4]{5}}{3x^2}$ **3. a.** $7\sqrt{2}$ **b.** $3\sqrt[3]{2}$ **c.** $\sqrt{35}$ **d.** $3\sqrt[4]{3}$
4. a. $6z^3\sqrt{z}$ **b.** $2pq^2\sqrt[3]{4pq}$ **c.** $2x^3\sqrt[4]{x^3}$ **5. a.** 4 **b.** $\frac{7}{3}\sqrt{z}$ **c.** $10xy^2\sqrt[3]{x^2}$ **d.** $6x^2y\sqrt[5]{2y}$ **6.** $\sqrt{17} \approx 4.123$ **7.** $\left(\frac{13}{2}, -4\right)$

Vocabulary and Readiness Check 19.3 **1.** midpoint; point **3.** midpoint **5.** false **7.** true **9.** false

Exercise Set 19.3 **1.** $\sqrt{14}$ **3.** 2 **5.** $\sqrt[3]{36}$ **7.** $\sqrt{6x}$ **9.** $\sqrt{\frac{14}{xy}}$ **11.** $\sqrt[4]{20x^3}$ **13.** $\frac{\sqrt{6}}{7}$ **15.** $\frac{\sqrt{2}}{7}$ **17.** $\frac{\sqrt[4]{x^3}}{2}$ **19.** $\frac{\sqrt[3]{4}}{3}$ **21.** $\frac{\sqrt[4]{8}}{x^2}$ **23.** $\frac{\sqrt[3]{2x}}{3y^4\sqrt[3]{3}}$ **25.** $\frac{x\sqrt{y}}{10}$ **27.** $\frac{x\sqrt{5}}{2y}$ **29.** $-\frac{z^2\sqrt[3]{z}}{3x}$ **31.** $4\sqrt{2}$ **33.** $4\sqrt[3]{3}$ **35.** $25\sqrt{3}$ **37.** $2\sqrt{6}$ **39.** $10x^2\sqrt{x}$ **41.** $2y^2\sqrt[3]{2y}$ **43.** $a^2b\sqrt[4]{b^3}$ **45.** $y^2\sqrt{y}$ **47.** $5ab\sqrt{b}$ **49.** $-2x^2\sqrt[5]{y}$ **51.** $x^4\sqrt[3]{50x^2}$ **53.** $-4a^4b^3\sqrt{2b}$ **55.** $3x^3y^4\sqrt{xy}$ **57.** $5r^3s^4$ **59.** $\sqrt{2}$ **61.** 2 **63.** 10 **65.** x^2y **67.** $24m^2$ **69.** $\frac{15x\sqrt{2x}}{2}$ or $\frac{15x}{2}\sqrt{2x}$ **71.** $2a^2\sqrt[4]{2}$ **73.** 5 units **75.** $\sqrt{41}$ units ≈ 6.403 **77.** $\sqrt{10}$ units ≈ 3.162 **79.** $\sqrt{5}$ units ≈ 2.236 **81.** $\sqrt{192.58}$ units ≈ 13.877 **83.** $(4,-2)$ **85.** $\left(-5, \frac{5}{2}\right)$ **87.** $(3, 0)$ **89.** $\left(-\frac{1}{2}, \frac{1}{2}\right)$ **91.** $\left(\sqrt{2}, \frac{\sqrt{5}}{2}\right)$ **93.** $(6.2, -6.65)$ **95.** $14x$ **97.** $2x^2 - 7x - 15$ **99.** y^2 **101.** $-3x - 15$ **103.** $x^2 - 8x + 16$ **105.** $\frac{\sqrt[3]{64}}{\sqrt{64}} = \frac{4}{8} = \frac{1}{2}$ **107.** x^7 **109.** a^3bc^5 **111.** $z^{10}\sqrt[3]{z^2}$ **113.** $q^2r^5s\sqrt[7]{q^3r^5}$ **115.** $r = 1.6$ meters **117. a.** 3.8 times **b.** 2.9 times **c.** answers may vary

Section 19.4

Practice Exercises

1. a. $8\sqrt{17}$ **b.** $-5\sqrt[3]{5z}$ **c.** $3\sqrt{2} + 5\sqrt[3]{2}$ **2. a.** $11\sqrt{6}$ **b.** $-9\sqrt[3]{3}$ **c.** $-2\sqrt{3x}$ **d.** $2\sqrt{10} + 2\sqrt[3]{5}$ **e.** $4x\sqrt[3]{3x}$ **3. a.** $\frac{5\sqrt{7}}{12}$ **b.** $\frac{13\sqrt[3]{6y}}{4}$ **4. a.** $2\sqrt{5} + 5\sqrt{3}$ **b.** $2\sqrt{3} + 2\sqrt{2} - \sqrt{30} - 2\sqrt{5}$ **c.** $6z + \sqrt{z} - 12$ **d.** $-6\sqrt{6} + 15$ **e.** $5x - 9$ **f.** $6\sqrt{x+2} + x + 11$

Vocabulary and Readiness Check 19.4 **1.** Unlike **3.** Like **5.** $6\sqrt{3}$ **7.** $7\sqrt{x}$ **9.** $8\sqrt[3]{x}$ **11.** $\sqrt{11} + \sqrt[3]{11}$ **13.** $10\sqrt[3]{2x}$

Exercise Set 19.4 **1.** $-2\sqrt{2}$ **3.** $10x\sqrt{2x}$ **5.** $17\sqrt{2} - 15\sqrt{5}$ **7.** $-\sqrt[3]{2x}$ **9.** $5b\sqrt{b}$ **11.** $\frac{31\sqrt{2}}{15}$ **13.** $\frac{\sqrt[3]{11}}{3}$ **15.** $\frac{5\sqrt{5x}}{9}$ **17.** $14 + \sqrt{3}$ **19.** $7 - 3y$ **21.** $6\sqrt{3} - 6\sqrt{2}$ **23.** $-23\sqrt[3]{5}$ **25.** $2b\sqrt{b}$ **27.** $20y\sqrt{2y}$ **29.** $2y\sqrt[3]{2x}$ **31.** $6\sqrt[3]{11} - 4\sqrt{11}$ **33.** $4x\sqrt[4]{x^3}$ **35.** $\frac{2\sqrt{3}}{3}$ **37.** $\frac{5x\sqrt[3]{x}}{7}$ **39.** $\frac{5\sqrt{7}}{2x}$ **41.** $\frac{\sqrt[3]{2}}{6}$ **43.** $\frac{14x\sqrt[3]{2x}}{9}$ **45.** $15\sqrt{3}$ in. **47.** $\sqrt{35} + \sqrt{21}$ **49.** $7 - 2\sqrt{10}$ **51.** $3\sqrt{x} - x\sqrt{3}$ **53.** $6x - 13\sqrt{x} - 5$ **55.** $\sqrt[3]{a^2} + \sqrt[3]{a} - 20$ **57.** $6\sqrt{2} - 12$ **59.** $2 + 2x\sqrt{3}$ **61.** $-16 - \sqrt{35}$ **63.** $x - y^2$ **65.** $3 + 2x\sqrt{3} + x^2$ **67.** $23x - 5x\sqrt{15}$ **69.** $2\sqrt[3]{2} - \sqrt[3]{4}$ **71.** $x + 1$ **73.** $x + 24 + 10\sqrt{x-1}$ **75.** $2x + 6 - 2\sqrt{2x+5}$ **77.** $x - 7$ **79.** $\frac{7}{x+y}$ **81.** $2a - 3$ **83.** $\frac{-2+\sqrt{3}}{3}$ **85.** $22\sqrt{5}$ ft; 150 sq ft **87. a.** $2\sqrt{3}$ **b.** 3 **c.** answers may vary **89.** answers may vary

Section 19.5

Practice Exercises

1. a. $\frac{5\sqrt{3}}{3}$ **b.** $\frac{15\sqrt{x}}{2x}$ **c.** $\frac{\sqrt[3]{6}}{3}$ **2.** $\frac{\sqrt{15yz}}{5y}$ **3.** $\frac{\sqrt[3]{z^2x^2}}{3x^2}$ **4. a.** $\frac{5(3\sqrt{5}-2)}{41}$ **b.** $\frac{\sqrt{6}+5\sqrt{3}+\sqrt{10}+5\sqrt{5}}{-2}$ **c.** $\frac{6x-3\sqrt{xy}}{4x-y}$ **5.** $\frac{2}{\sqrt{10}}$ **6.** $\frac{5b}{\sqrt[3]{50ab^2}}$ **7.** $\frac{x-9}{4(\sqrt{x}+3)}$

Vocabulary and Readiness Check 19.5 **1.** conjugate **3.** rationalizing the numerator **5.** $\sqrt{2} - x$ **7.** $5 + \sqrt{a}$ **9.** $-7\sqrt{5} - 8\sqrt{x}$

Exercise Set 19.5 **1.** $\frac{\sqrt{14}}{7}$ **3.** $\frac{\sqrt{5}}{5}$ **5.** $\frac{2\sqrt{x}}{x}$ **7.** $\frac{4\sqrt[3]{9}}{3}$ **9.** $\frac{3\sqrt{2x}}{4x}$ **11.** $\frac{3\sqrt[3]{2x}}{2x}$ **13.** $\frac{3\sqrt{3a}}{a}$ **15.** $\frac{3\sqrt[3]{4}}{2}$ **17.** $\frac{2\sqrt{21}}{7}$ **19.** $\frac{\sqrt{10xy}}{5y}$ **21.** $\frac{\sqrt[3]{75}}{5}$ **23.** $\frac{\sqrt{6x}}{10}$ **25.** $\frac{\sqrt{3z}}{6z}$ **27.** $\frac{\sqrt[3]{6xy^2}}{3x}$ **29.** $\frac{3\sqrt[4]{2}}{2}$ **31.** $\frac{2\sqrt[4]{9x}}{3x^2}$ **33.** $\frac{5a\sqrt[5]{4ab^4}}{2a^2b^3}$ **35.** $-2(2 + \sqrt{7})$ **37.** $\frac{7(3+\sqrt{x})}{9-x}$ **39.** $-5 + 2\sqrt{6}$ **41.** $\frac{2a+2\sqrt{a}+\sqrt{ab}+\sqrt{b}}{4a-b}$ **43.** $-\frac{8(1-\sqrt{10})}{9}$ **45.** $\frac{x-\sqrt{xy}}{x-y}$ **47.** $\frac{5+3\sqrt{2}}{7}$ **49.** $\frac{5}{\sqrt{15}}$ **51.** $\frac{6}{\sqrt{10}}$ **53.** $\frac{2x}{7\sqrt{x}}$ **55.** $\frac{5y}{\sqrt[3]{100xy}}$ **57.** $\frac{2}{\sqrt{10}}$ **59.** $\frac{2x}{11\sqrt{2x}}$ **61.** $\frac{7}{2\sqrt[3]{49}}$ **63.** $\frac{3x^2}{10\sqrt[3]{9x}}$ **65.** $\frac{6x^2y^3}{\sqrt{6z}}$ **67.** answers may vary **69.** $\frac{-7}{12+6\sqrt{11}}$ **71.** $\frac{3}{10+5\sqrt{7}}$ **73.** $\frac{x-9}{x-3\sqrt{x}}$ **75.** $\frac{1}{3+2\sqrt{2}}$ **77.** $\frac{x-1}{x-2\sqrt{x}+1}$ **79.** 5 **81.** $-\frac{1}{2}, 6$ **83.** 2, 6 **85.** $\sqrt[3]{25}$ **87.** $r = \frac{\sqrt{A\pi}}{2\pi}$ **89.** answers may vary

Answers to Selected Exercises

Integrated Review **1.** 9 **2.** −2 **3.** $\frac{1}{2}$ **4.** x^3 **5.** y^3 **6.** $2y^5$ **7.** $-2y$ **8.** $3b^3$ **9.** 6 **10.** $\sqrt[4]{3y}$ **11.** $\frac{1}{16}$ **12.** $\sqrt[5]{(x+1)^3}$ **13.** y **14.** $16x^{1/2}$ **15.** $x^{5/4}$ **16.** $4^{11/15}$ **17.** $2x^2$ **18.** $\sqrt[4]{a^3b^2}$ **19.** $\sqrt[4]{x^3}$ **20.** $\sqrt[6]{500}$ **21.** $2\sqrt{10}$ **22.** $2xy^2\sqrt[4]{x^3y^2}$ **23.** $3x\sqrt[3]{2x}$ **24.** $-2b^2\sqrt[5]{2}$ **25.** $\sqrt{5x}$ **26.** $4x$ **27.** $7y^2\sqrt{y}$ **28.** $2a^2\sqrt[4]{3}$ **29.** $2\sqrt{5}-5\sqrt{3}+5\sqrt{7}$ **30.** $y\sqrt[3]{2y}$ **31.** $\sqrt{15}-\sqrt{6}$ **32.** $10+2\sqrt{21}$ **33.** $4x^2-5$ **34.** $x+2-2\sqrt{x+1}$ **35.** $\frac{\sqrt{21}}{3}$ **36.** $\frac{5\sqrt[3]{4x}}{2x}$ **37.** $\frac{13-3\sqrt{21}}{5}$ **38.** $\frac{7}{\sqrt{21}}$ **39.** $\frac{3y}{\sqrt[3]{33y^2}}$ **40.** $\frac{x-4}{x+2\sqrt{x}}$

Section 19.6

Practice Exercises

1. 18 **2.** $\frac{3}{8}, -\frac{1}{2}$ **3.** 10 **4.** 9 **5.** $\frac{3}{25}$ **6.** $6\sqrt{3}$ meters **7.** $\sqrt{193}$ in. ≈ 13.89

Vocabulary and Readiness Check 19.6 **1.** extraneous solution **3.** $x^2-10x+25$

Exercise Set 19.6 **1.** 8 **3.** 7 **5.** ∅ **7.** 7 **9.** 6 **11.** $-\frac{9}{2}$ **13.** 29 **15.** 4 **17.** −4 **19.** ∅ **21.** 7 **23.** 9 **25.** 50 **27.** ∅ **29.** $\frac{15}{4}$ **31.** 13 **33.** 5 **35.** −12 **37.** 9 **39.** −3 **41.** 1 **43.** 1 **45.** $\frac{1}{2}$ **47.** 0, 4 **49.** $\frac{37}{4}$ **51.** $3\sqrt{5}$ ft **53.** $2\sqrt{10}$ m **55.** $2\sqrt{131}$ m ≈ 22.9 m **57.** $\sqrt{100.84}$ mm ≈ 10.0 mm **59.** 17 ft **61.** 13 ft **63.** 14,657, 415 sq mi **65.** 100 ft **67.** 100 **69.** $\frac{\pi}{2}$ sec ≈ 1.57 sec **71.** 12.97 ft **73.** answers may vary **75.** $15\sqrt{3}$ sq mi ≈ 25.98 sq mi **77.** answers may vary **79.** 0.51 km **81.** function **83.** function **85.** not a function **87.** $\frac{x}{4x+3}$ **89.** $-\frac{4z+2}{3z}$

91.
$$\begin{aligned}\sqrt{5x-1}+4&=7\\ \sqrt{5x-1}&=3\\ \left(\sqrt{5x-1}\right)^2&=3^2\\ 5x-1&=9\\ 5x&=10\\ x&=2\end{aligned}$$

93. 1 **95. a.–b.** answers may vary **97.** −1, 2 **99.** −8, −6, 0, 2

The Bigger Picture

1. −19 **2.** $-\frac{5}{3}, 5$ **3.** $-\frac{9}{2}, 5$ **4.** $\left[\frac{-11}{5}, 1\right]$ **5.** $\left(-\frac{7}{5}, \infty\right)$ **6.** 25 **7.** $(-5, \infty)$ **8.** ∅ **9.** $(-\infty, -13) \cup (17, \infty)$ **10.** $\frac{17}{25}$

Section 19.7

Practice Exercises

1. a. $2i$ **b.** $i\sqrt{7}$ **c.** $-3i\sqrt{2}$ **2. a.** $-\sqrt{30}$ **b.** −3 **c.** $25i$ **d.** $3i$ **3. a.** $-1-4i$ **b.** $-3+5i$ **c.** $3-2i$ **4. a.** 20 **b.** $-5+10i$ **c.** $15+16i$ **d.** $8-6i$ **e.** 85 **5. a.** $\frac{11}{10}-\frac{7i}{10}$ **b.** $0-\frac{5i}{2}$ **6. a.** i **b.** 1 **c.** −1 **d.** 1

Vocabulary and Readiness Check 19.7 **1.** complex **3.** −1 **5.** real **7.** $9i$ **9.** $i\sqrt{7}$ **11.** −4 **13.** $8i$

Exercise Set 19.7 **1.** $2i\sqrt{6}$ **3.** $-6i$ **5.** $24i\sqrt{7}$ **7.** $-3\sqrt{6}$ **9.** $-\sqrt{14}$ **11.** $-5\sqrt{2}$ **13.** $4i$ **15.** $i\sqrt{3}$ **17.** $2\sqrt{2}$ **19.** $6-4i$ **21.** $-2+6i$ **23.** $-2-4i$ **25.** −40 **27.** $18+12i$ **29.** 7 **31.** $12-16i$ **33.** $-4i$ **35.** $\frac{28}{25}-\frac{21}{25}i$ **37.** $4+i$ **39.** $\frac{17}{13}+\frac{7}{13}i$ **41.** 63 **43.** $2-i$ **45.** $27+3i$ **47.** $-\frac{5}{2}-2i$ **49.** $18+13i$ **51.** 20 **53.** 10 **55.** 2 **57.** $-5+\frac{16}{3}i$ **59.** $17+144i$ **61.** $\frac{3}{5}-\frac{1}{5}i$ **63.** $5-10i$ **65.** $\frac{1}{5}-\frac{8}{5}i$ **67.** $8-i$ **69.** 7 **71.** $12-16i$ **73.** 1 **75.** i **77.** $-i$ **79.** −1 **81.** −64 **83.** $-243i$ **85.** 40° **87.** $x^2-5x-2-\frac{6}{x-1}$ **89.** 5 people **91.** 14 people **93.** 16.7% **95.** $-1-i$ **97.** 0 **99.** $2+3i$ **101.** $2+i\sqrt{2}$ **103.** $\frac{1}{2}-\frac{\sqrt{3}}{2}i$ **105.** answers may vary **107.** $6-6i$ **109.** yes

Chapter 19 Vocabulary Check **1.** conjugate **2.** principal square root **3.** rationalizing **4.** imaginary unit **5.** cube root **6.** index, radicand **7.** like radicals **8.** complex number **9.** distance **10.** midpoint

Chapter 19 Review **1.** 9 **3.** -2 **5.** $-\frac{1}{7}$ **7.** -6 **9.** $-a^2b^3$ **11.** $2ab^2$ **13.** $\frac{x^6}{6y}$ **15.** $|-x|$ **17.** -27 **19.** $-x$ **21.** $5|(x-y)^5|$ **23.** $-x$ **25.** $(-\infty,\infty)$; $-2, -1, 0, 1, 2$ **27.** $-\frac{1}{3}$ **29.** $-\frac{1}{4}$ **31.** $\frac{1}{4}$ **33.** $\frac{343}{125}$ **35.** not a real number **37.** $5^{1/5}x^{2/5}y^{3/5}$ **39.** $5\sqrt[3]{xy^2z^5}$

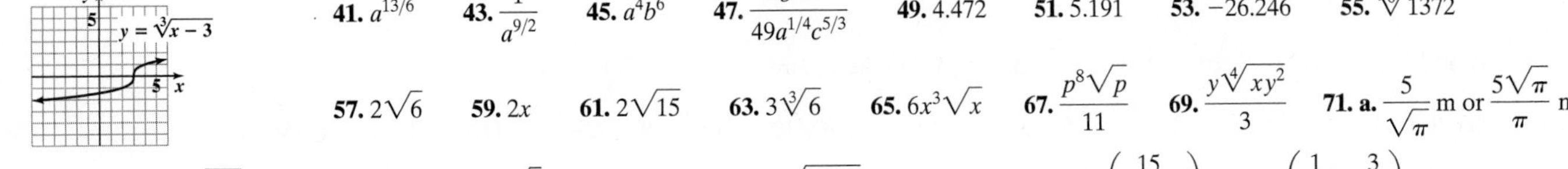

41. $a^{13/6}$ **43.** $\frac{1}{a^{9/2}}$ **45.** a^4b^6 **47.** $\frac{b^{5/6}}{49a^{1/4}c^{5/3}}$ **49.** 4.472 **51.** 5.191 **53.** -26.246 **55.** $\sqrt[6]{1372}$ **57.** $2\sqrt{6}$ **59.** $2x$ **61.** $2\sqrt{15}$ **63.** $3\sqrt[3]{6}$ **65.** $6x^3\sqrt{x}$ **67.** $\frac{p^8\sqrt{p}}{11}$ **69.** $\frac{y\sqrt[4]{xy^2}}{3}$ **71. a.** $\frac{5}{\sqrt{\pi}}$ m or $\frac{5\sqrt{\pi}}{\pi}$ m **b.** 5.75 in. **73.** $\sqrt{130}$ units ≈ 11.402 **75.** $7\sqrt{2}$ units ≈ 9.899 **77.** $\sqrt{275.6}$ units ≈ 16.601 **79.** $\left(-\frac{15}{2}, 1\right)$ **81.** $\left(\frac{1}{20}, -\frac{3}{16}\right)$ **83.** $\left(\sqrt{3}, -3\sqrt{6}\right)$ **85.** $2x\sqrt{3xy}$ **87.** $3a\sqrt[4]{2a}$ **89.** $\frac{3\sqrt{2}}{4x}$ **91.** $-4ab\sqrt[4]{2b}$ **93.** $x - 6\sqrt{x} + 9$ **95.** $4x - 9y$ **97.** $\sqrt[3]{a^2} + 4\sqrt[3]{a} + 4$ **99.** $a + 64$ **101.** $\frac{\sqrt{3x}}{6}$ **103.** $\frac{2x^2\sqrt{2x}}{y}$ **105.** $-\frac{10 + 5\sqrt{7}}{3}$ **107.** $-5 + 2\sqrt{6}$ **109.** $\frac{6}{\sqrt{2y}}$ **111.** $\frac{4x^3}{y\sqrt{2x}}$ **113.** $\frac{x - 25}{-3\sqrt{x} + 15}$ **115.** $\varnothing$ **117.** $\varnothing$ **119.** 16 **121.** $\sqrt{241}$ **123.** 4.24 ft **125.** $-i\sqrt{6}$ **127.** $-\sqrt{10}$ **129.** $-13 - 3i$ **131.** $-12 - 18i$ **133.** $-5 - 12i$ **135.** $\frac{3}{2} - i$ **137.** x **139.** -10 **141.** $\frac{y^5}{2x^3}$ **143.** $\frac{1}{8}$ **145.** $\frac{1}{x^{13/2}}$ **147.** $\frac{n\sqrt{3n}}{11m^5}$ **149.** $4x - 20\sqrt{x} + 25$ **151.** $(4, 16)$ **153.** $\frac{2\sqrt{x} - 6}{x - 9}$

Chapter 19 Test **1.** $6\sqrt{6}$ **2.** $-x^{16}$ **3.** $\frac{1}{5}$ **4.** 5 **5.** $\frac{4x^2}{9}$ **6.** $-a^6b^3$ **7.** $\frac{8a^{1/3}c^{2/3}}{b^{5/12}}$ **8.** $a^{7/12} - a^{7/3}$ **9.** $|4xy|$ or $4|xy|$ **10.** -27 **11.** $\frac{3\sqrt{y}}{y}$ **12.** $\frac{8 - 6\sqrt{x} + x}{8 - 2x}$ **13.** $\frac{\sqrt[3]{b^2}}{b}$ **14.** $\frac{6 - x^2}{8(\sqrt{6} - x)}$ **15.** $-x\sqrt{5x}$ **16.** $4\sqrt{3} - \sqrt{6}$ **17.** $x + 2\sqrt{x} + 1$ **18.** $\sqrt{6} - 4\sqrt{3} + \sqrt{2} - 4$ **19.** -20 **20.** 23.685 **21.** 0.019 **22.** 2, 3 **23.** $\varnothing$ **24.** 6 **25.** $i\sqrt{2}$ **26.** $-2i\sqrt{2}$ **27.** $-3i$ **28.** 40 **29.** $7 + 24i$ **30.** $-\frac{3}{2} + \frac{5}{2}i$ **31.** $\frac{5\sqrt{2}}{2}$ **32.** $[-2, \infty)$; ; 0, 1, 2, 3 **33.** $2\sqrt{26}$ units **34.** $\sqrt{95}$ units **35.** $\left(-4, \frac{7}{2}\right)$ **36.** $\left(-\frac{1}{2}, \frac{3}{10}\right)$ **37.** 27 mph **38.** 360 ft

Chapter 19 Cumulative Review **1. a.** $2xy - 2$ **b.** $2x^2 + 23$ **c.** $3.1x - 0.3$ **d.** $-a - 7b + \frac{7}{12}$; Sec. 1.4, Ex. 16 **3.** $\frac{21}{11}$; Sec. 1.5, Ex. 6 **5.** \$4500 per month; Sec. 3.2, Ex. 8 **7.** $\varnothing$; Sec. 3.4, Ex. 6 **9.** $(-\infty, -3] \cup [9, \infty)$; Sec. 3.5, Ex. 7 **11.** ; Sec. 2.1, Ex. 10 **13. a.** domain: {2, 0, 3}; range: {3, 4, −1} **b.** domain: {−4, −3, −2, −1, 0, 1, 2, 3}; range: {1} **c.** domain: {Lubbock, Colorado Springs, Omaha, Yonkers, Sacramento}; range: {307, 404, 445, 206, 197}; Sec. 15.2, Ex. 1 **15.** ; Sec. 15.3, Ex.8 **17.** undefined; Sec. 15.4, Ex. 5 **19.** $\left(-\frac{21}{10}, \frac{3}{10}\right)$; Sec. 4.1, Ex. 5 **21. a.** 2^7 **b.** x^{10} **c.** y^7; Sec. 5.1, Ex. 1 **23.** 6×10^{-5}; Sec. 5.2, Ex. 7 **25. a.** -4 **b.** 11; Sec. 5.3, Ex. 4 **27. a.** $2x^2 + 11x + 15$ **b.** $10x^3 - 27x^2 + 32x - 21$; Sec. 5.4, Ex. 3 **29.** $5x^2$; Sec. 5.5, Ex. 1 **31. a.** $x^2 - 2x + 4$ **b.** $\frac{2}{y - 5}$; Sec. 18.1, Ex. 6 **33. a.** $\frac{6x + 5}{3x^3y}$ **b.** $\frac{2x^2 + 7x - 6}{(x + 2)(x - 2)}$ **c.** 2; Sec. 18.2, Ex. 3 **35. a.** $\frac{x(x - 2)}{2(x + 2)}$ **b.** $\frac{x^2}{y^2}$; Sec. 18.3, Ex. 2 **37.** $\varnothing$; Sec. 18.5, Ex. 3 **39.** $x = \frac{yz}{y - z}$; Sec. 18.6, Ex. 1 **41.** constant of variation: 15; $u = \frac{15}{w}$; Sec. 18.7, Ex. 3 **43. a.** $\frac{1}{8}$ **b.** $\frac{1}{9}$; Sec. 19.2, Ex. 3 **45.** $\frac{x - 4}{5(\sqrt{x} - 2)}$; Sec. 19.5, Ex. 7

Chapter 20 Quadratic Equations and Functions

Section 20.1

Practice Exercises

1. $-3\sqrt{2}, 3\sqrt{2}$ **2.** $\pm\sqrt{10}$ **3.** $-3 \pm 2\sqrt{5}$ **4.** $\frac{2+3i}{5}, \frac{2-3i}{5}$ **5.** $-2 \pm \sqrt{7}$ **6.** $\frac{3 \pm \sqrt{5}}{2}$ **7.** $\frac{6 \pm \sqrt{33}}{3}$ **8.** $\frac{5 \pm i\sqrt{31}}{4}$ **9.** 6%

Vocabulary and Readiness Check 20.1 **1.** $\pm\sqrt{b}$ **3.** completing the square **5.** 9 **7.** 1 **9.** 49

Exercise Set 20.1 **1.** $-4, 4$ **3.** $-\sqrt{7}, \sqrt{7}$ **5.** $-3\sqrt{2}, 3\sqrt{2}$ **7.** $-\sqrt{10}, \sqrt{10}$ **9.** $-8, -2$ **11.** $6 - 3\sqrt{2}, 6 + 3\sqrt{2}$ **13.** $\frac{3-2\sqrt{2}}{2}, \frac{3+2\sqrt{2}}{2}$ **15.** $-3i, 3i$ **17.** $-\sqrt{6}, \sqrt{6}$ **19.** $-2i\sqrt{2}, 2i\sqrt{2}$ **21.** $1 - 4i, 1 + 4i$ **23.** $-7 - \sqrt{5}, -7 + \sqrt{5}$ **25.** $-3 - 2i\sqrt{2}, -3 + 2i\sqrt{2}$ **27.** $x^2 + 16x + 64 = (x + 8)^2$ **29.** $z^2 - 12z + 36 = (z - 6)^2$ **31.** $p^2 + 9p + \frac{81}{4} = \left(p + \frac{9}{2}\right)^2$ **33.** $x^2 + x + \frac{1}{4} = \left(x + \frac{1}{2}\right)^2$ **35.** $-5, -3$ **37.** $-3 - \sqrt{7}, -3 + \sqrt{7}$ **39.** $\frac{-1-\sqrt{5}}{2}, \frac{-1+\sqrt{5}}{2}$ **41.** $-1 - \sqrt{6}, -1 + \sqrt{6}$ **43.** $\frac{6-\sqrt{30}}{3}, \frac{6+\sqrt{30}}{3}$ **45.** $\frac{3-\sqrt{11}}{2}, \frac{3+\sqrt{11}}{2}$ **47.** $-4, \frac{1}{2}$ **49.** $-1, 5$ **51.** $-4 - \sqrt{15}, -4 + \sqrt{15}$ **53.** $\frac{-3-\sqrt{21}}{3}, \frac{-3+\sqrt{21}}{3}$ **55.** $-1, \frac{5}{2}$ **57.** $-1 - i, -1 + i$ **59.** $3 - \sqrt{6}, 3 + \sqrt{6}$ **61.** $-2 - i\sqrt{2}, -2 + i\sqrt{2}$ **63.** $-5 - i\sqrt{3}, -5 + i\sqrt{3}$ **65.** $-4, 1$ **67.** $\frac{2-i\sqrt{2}}{2}, \frac{2+i\sqrt{2}}{2}$ **69.** $\frac{-3-\sqrt{69}}{6}, \frac{-3+\sqrt{69}}{6}$ **71.** 2 real number solutions **73.** no real number solutions **75.** 20% **77.** 4% **79.** answers may vary **81.** 8.11 sec **83.** 6.73 sec **85.** simple; answers may vary **87.** $\frac{7}{5}$ **89.** $\frac{1}{5}$ **91.** $5 - 10\sqrt{3}$ **93.** $\frac{3-2\sqrt{7}}{4}$ **95.** $2\sqrt{7}$ **97.** $\sqrt{13}$ **99.** complex, but not real numbers **101.** real solutions **103.** complex, but not real numbers **105.** $-6y, 6y$ **107.** $-x, x$ **109.** 6 in. **111.** 16.2 in. × 21.6 in. **113.** 2.828 thousand units or 2828 units

Section 20.2

Practice Exercises

1. $2, -\frac{1}{3}$ **2.** $\frac{4 \pm \sqrt{22}}{3}$ **3.** $1 \pm \sqrt{17}$ **4.** $\frac{-1 \pm i\sqrt{15}}{4}$ **5. a.** one real solution **b.** two real solutions **c.** two complex, but not real solutions **6.** 6 ft **7.** 2.4 sec

Vocabulary and Readiness Check 20.2 **1.** $x = \frac{-b \pm \sqrt{b^2 - 4ac}}{2a}$ **3.** $-5; -7$ **5.** $1; 0$

Exercise Set 20.2 **1.** $-6, 1$ **3.** $-\frac{3}{5}, 1$ **5.** 3 **7.** $\frac{-7-\sqrt{33}}{2}, \frac{-7+\sqrt{33}}{2}$ **9.** $\frac{1-\sqrt{57}}{8}, \frac{1+\sqrt{57}}{8}$ **11.** $\frac{7-\sqrt{85}}{6}, \frac{7+\sqrt{85}}{6}$ **13.** $1 - \sqrt{3}, 1 + \sqrt{3}$ **15.** $-\frac{3}{2}, 1$ **17.** $\frac{3-\sqrt{11}}{2}, \frac{3+\sqrt{11}}{2}$ **19.** $\frac{-5-\sqrt{17}}{2}, \frac{-5+\sqrt{17}}{2}$ **21.** $\frac{5}{2}, 1$ **23.** $-3 - 2i, -3 + 2i$ **25.** $-2 - \sqrt{11}, -2 + \sqrt{11}$ **27.** $\frac{3-i\sqrt{87}}{8}, \frac{3+i\sqrt{87}}{8}$ **29.** $\frac{3-\sqrt{29}}{2}, \frac{3+\sqrt{29}}{2}$ **31.** $\frac{-5-i\sqrt{5}}{10}, \frac{-5+i\sqrt{5}}{10}$ **33.** $\frac{-1-\sqrt{19}}{6}, \frac{-1+\sqrt{19}}{6}$ **35.** $\frac{-1-i\sqrt{23}}{4}, \frac{-1+i\sqrt{23}}{4}$ **37.** 1 **39.** $3 + \sqrt{5}, 3 - \sqrt{5}$ **41.** two real solutions **43.** one real solution **45.** two real solutions **47.** two complex but not real solutions **49. a.** 2 real solutions **b.** There is one x-intercept.; 1 real solution **51.** 14 ft **53.** $2 + 2\sqrt{2}$ cm, $2 + 2\sqrt{2}$ cm, $4 + 2\sqrt{2}$ cm **55.** width: $-5 + 5\sqrt{17}$ ft; length: $5 + 5\sqrt{17}$ ft **57. a.** $50\sqrt{2}$ m **b.** 5000 sq m **59.** 37.4 ft by 38.5 ft **61.** base, $2 + 2\sqrt{43}$ cm; height, $-1 + \sqrt{43}$ cm **63.** 8.9 sec **65.** 2.8 sec **67.** $\frac{11}{5}$ **69.** 15 **71.** $(x^2 + 5)(x + 2)(x - 2)$ **73.** $(z + 3)(z - 3)(z + 2)(z - 2)$ **75.** b **77.** answers may vary **79.** 0.6, 2.4 **81.** Sunday to Monday **83.** Wednesday **85.** 32; yes **87. a.** 8630 stores **b.** 2011 **89.** answers may vary **91.** $\frac{\sqrt{3}}{3}$ **93.** $\frac{-\sqrt{2}-i\sqrt{2}}{2}, \frac{-\sqrt{2}+i\sqrt{2}}{2}$ **95.** $\frac{\sqrt{3}-\sqrt{11}}{4}, \frac{\sqrt{3}+\sqrt{11}}{4}$

Section 20.3

Practice Exercises

1. 8 **2.** $\frac{5 \pm \sqrt{137}}{8}$ **3.** $4, -4, 3i, -3i$ **4.** $1, -3$ **5.** $1, 64$ **6.** Katy: $\frac{7+\sqrt{65}}{2} \approx 7.5$ hr; Steve: $\frac{9+\sqrt{65}}{2} \approx 8.5$ hr **7.** to Shanghai: 40 km/hr; to Ningbo: 90 km/hr

Exercise Set 20.3 **1.** 2 **3.** 16 **5.** 1, 4 **7.** $3-\sqrt{7}, 3+\sqrt{7}$ **9.** $\frac{3-\sqrt{57}}{4}, \frac{3+\sqrt{57}}{4}$ **11.** $\frac{1-\sqrt{29}}{2}, \frac{1+\sqrt{29}}{2}$ **13.** $-2, 2, -2i, 2i$ **15.** $-\frac{1}{2}, \frac{1}{2}, -i\sqrt{3}, i\sqrt{3}$ **17.** $-3, 3, -2, 2$ **19.** $125, -8$ **21.** $-\frac{4}{5}, 0$ **23.** $-\frac{1}{8}, 27$ **25.** $-\frac{2}{3}, \frac{4}{3}$ **27.** $-\frac{1}{125}, \frac{1}{8}$ **29.** $-\sqrt{2}, \sqrt{2}, -\sqrt{3}, \sqrt{3}$ **31.** $\frac{-9-\sqrt{201}}{6}, \frac{-9+\sqrt{201}}{6}$ **33.** 2, 3 **35.** 3 **37.** 27, 125 **39.** $1, -3i, 3i$ **41.** $\frac{1}{8}, -8$ **43.** $-\frac{1}{2}, \frac{1}{3}$ **45.** 4 **47.** -3 **49.** $-\sqrt{5}, \sqrt{5}, -2i, 2i$ **51.** $-3, \frac{3-3i\sqrt{3}}{2}, \frac{3+3i\sqrt{3}}{2}$ **53.** 6, 12 **55.** $-\frac{1}{3}, \frac{1}{3}, -\frac{i\sqrt{6}}{3}, \frac{i\sqrt{6}}{3}$ **57.** 5 mph, then 4 mph **59.** inlet pipe: 15.5 hr; hose: 16.5 hr **61.** 55 mph, 66 mph **63.** 8.5 hr **65.** 12 or -8 **67. a.** $(x-6)$ in. **b.** $300=(x-6)\cdot(x-6)\cdot 3$ **c.** 16 cm by 16 cm **69.** 22 feet **71.** $(-\infty, 3]$ **73.** $(-5, \infty)$ **75.** domain: $(-\infty, \infty)$; range: $(-\infty, \infty)$; function **77.** domain: $(-\infty, \infty)$; range: $[-1, \infty)$; function **79.** $1, -3i, 3i$ **81.** $-\frac{1}{2}, \frac{1}{3}$ **83.** $-3, \frac{3-3i\sqrt{3}}{2}, \frac{3+3i\sqrt{3}}{2}$ **85.** answers may vary **87. a.** 150.94 ft/sec **b.** 151.49 ft/sec **c.** Bourdais: 102.9 mph; Pagenaud: 103.3 mph

Integrated Review **1.** $-\sqrt{10}, \sqrt{10}$ **2.** $-\sqrt{14}, \sqrt{14}$ **3.** $1-2\sqrt{2}, 1+2\sqrt{2}$ **4.** $-5-2\sqrt{3}, -5+2\sqrt{3}$ **5.** $-1-\sqrt{13}, -1+\sqrt{13}$ **6.** 1, 11 **7.** $\frac{-3-\sqrt{69}}{6}, \frac{-3+\sqrt{69}}{6}$ **8.** $\frac{-2-\sqrt{5}}{4}, \frac{-2+\sqrt{5}}{4}$ **9.** $\frac{2-\sqrt{2}}{2}, \frac{2+\sqrt{2}}{2}$ **10.** $-3-\sqrt{5}, -3+\sqrt{5}$ **11.** $-2+i\sqrt{3}, -2-i\sqrt{3}$ **12.** $\frac{-1-i\sqrt{11}}{2}, \frac{-1+i\sqrt{11}}{2}$ **13.** $\frac{-3+i\sqrt{15}}{2}, \frac{-3-i\sqrt{15}}{2}$ **14.** $3i, -3i$ **15.** $0, -17$ **16.** $\frac{1+\sqrt{13}}{4}, \frac{1-\sqrt{13}}{4}$ **17.** $2+3\sqrt{3}, 2-3\sqrt{3}$ **18.** $2+\sqrt{3}, 2-\sqrt{3}$ **19.** $-2, \frac{4}{3}$ **20.** $\frac{-5+\sqrt{17}}{4}, \frac{-5-\sqrt{17}}{4}$ **21.** $1-\sqrt{6}, 1+\sqrt{6}$ **22.** $-\sqrt{31}, \sqrt{31}$ **23.** $-\sqrt{11}, \sqrt{11}$ **24.** $-i\sqrt{11}, i\sqrt{11}$ **25.** $-11, 6$ **26.** $\frac{-3+\sqrt{19}}{5}, \frac{-3-\sqrt{19}}{5}$ **27.** $\frac{-3+\sqrt{17}}{4}, \frac{-3-\sqrt{17}}{4}$ **28.** $10\sqrt{2}$ ft $\approx$ 14.1 ft **29.** Jack: 9.1 hr; Lucy: 7.1 hr **30.** 5 mph during the first part, then 6 mph

Chapter 20 Vocabulary Check **1.** discriminant **2.** $\pm\sqrt{b}$ **3.** completing the square **4.** quadratic formula **5.** quadratic

Chapter 20 Review **1.** 14, 1 **3.** $-7, 7$ **5.** $\frac{-3-\sqrt{5}}{2}, \frac{-3+\sqrt{5}}{2}$ **7.** 4.25% **9.** two complex but not real solutions **11.** two real solutions **13.** 8 **15.** $-\frac{5}{2}, 1$ **17.** $\frac{5-i\sqrt{143}}{12}, \frac{5+i\sqrt{143}}{12}$ **19. a.** 20 ft **b.** $\frac{15+\sqrt{321}}{16}$ sec; 2.1 sec **21.** $3, \frac{-3+3i\sqrt{3}}{2}, \frac{-3-3i\sqrt{3}}{2}$ **23.** $\frac{2}{3}, 5$ **25.** 1, 125 **27.** $-1, 1, -i, i$ **29.** Jerome: 10.5 hr; Tim: 9.5 hr **31.** $-5, 6$ **33.** $\frac{-1-3i\sqrt{3}}{2}, \frac{-1+3i\sqrt{3}}{2}$ **35.** $-i\sqrt{11}, i\sqrt{11}$ **37.** $-\frac{8\sqrt{7}}{7}, \frac{8\sqrt{7}}{7}$

Chapter 20 Test **1.** $\frac{7}{5}, -1$ **2.** $-1-\sqrt{10}, -1+\sqrt{10}$ **3.** $\frac{1+i\sqrt{31}}{2}, \frac{1-i\sqrt{31}}{2}$ **4.** $3-\sqrt{7}, 3+\sqrt{7}$ **5.** $-\frac{1}{7}, -1$ **6.** $\frac{3+\sqrt{29}}{2}, \frac{3-\sqrt{29}}{2}$ **7.** $-2-\sqrt{11}, -2+\sqrt{11}$ **8.** $-1, 1, -i, i, -3$ **9.** $-1, 1, -i, i$ **10.** 6, 7 **11.** $3-\sqrt{7}, 3+\sqrt{7}$ **12.** $\frac{2-i\sqrt{6}}{2}, \frac{2+i\sqrt{6}}{2}$

Chapter 20 Cumulative Review **1. a.** $5+y\geq 7$ **b.** $11\neq z$ **c.** $20<5-2x$ **3.** slope: 1 **5.** $(-2, 2)$; Sec. 17.1, Ex. 6 **7. a.** $6x^2-29x+28$ **b.** $15x^4-x^2y-2y^2$ **9. a.** $4(2x^2+1)$ **b.** prime polynomial **c.** $3x^2(2-x+4x^2)$ **11.** $(x-5)(x-7)$ **13.** $3x(a-2b)^2$ **15.** $-\frac{2}{3}$ **17.** $-2, 0, 2$ **18.** $\frac{1}{5x-1}$; Sec. 18.1, Ex. 3a **20.** $\frac{7x^2-9x-13}{(2x+1)(x-5)(3x-2)}$; Sec. 18.2, Ex. 5 **22.** $\frac{xy+2x^3}{y-1}$; Sec. 18.3, Ex. 3 **24.** $3x^3y-15x-1-\frac{6}{xy}$ **25.** -3; Sec. 18.4, Ex. 1 **28.** $\frac{1}{6}; y=\frac{1}{6}x$ **30. a.** 3 **b.** $|x|$ **c.** $|x-2|$ **d.** -5 **e.** $2x-7$ **f.** $5|x|$ **g.** $|x+1|$; Sec. 19.1, Ex. 5 **32. a.** $\sqrt{x}$ **b.** $\sqrt[3]{5}$ **c.** $\sqrt{rs^3}$; Sec. 19.2, Ex. 7 **34. a.** $5x\sqrt{x}$ **b.** $3x^2y^2\sqrt[3]{2y^2}$ **c.** $3z^2\sqrt[4]{z^3}$; Sec. 19.3, Ex. 4 **36. a.** $\frac{2\sqrt{5}}{5}$ **b.** $\frac{8\sqrt{x}}{3x}$ **c.** $\frac{\sqrt[3]{4}}{2}$; Sec. 19.5, Ex. 1 **38.** $\frac{2}{9}$; Sec. 19.6, Ex. 5 **40. a.** $\frac{1}{2}+\frac{3}{2}i$ **b.** $-\frac{7}{3}i$; Sec. 19.7, Ex. 5 **42.** $-1+2\sqrt{3}, -1-2\sqrt{3}$; Sec. 20.1, Ex. 3 **44.** 9; Sec. 20.3, Ex. 1

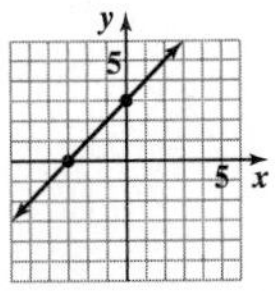

Index

N

O

T

U

V